Still

Still Unwritten

CAROLINE KHOURY

CANELO

First published in the United Kingdom in 2024 by

Canelo
Unit 9, 5th Floor
Cargo Works, 1-2 Hatfields
London SE1 9PG
United Kingdom

A CIP catalogue record for this book is available from the British Library.

Print ISBN 978 1 80436 660 8
Ebook ISBN 978 1 80436 661 5

Cover design by Emily Courdell, Cover illustration by Sophie Melissa

Look for more great books at www.canelo.co

Printed and bound in Great Britain by Clays Ltd, Elcograf S.p.A.

1

To my best friend – Dee

Chapter 1

Passion. You either have it, or you don't. And according to my agent, I don't. *Passione*, they say in Italian, so I couldn't excuse English not being my mother tongue as a reason for not understanding what she was trying to say.

'I don't buy it,' Clara said as she drained the remnants of her iced caramel americano and shoved it to one side of the café table.

63 High Street had its usual buzz of regulars, many keen to extract one more coffee before closing at six; late for a caffeine injection, but not if you needed a boost to get you through a very, very long night of work. A low hum of chatter and clacking of laptop keys drifted through the cool air-conditioned room – a welcome respite from the sticky June afternoon. Green foliage trailed from baskets nailed to hooks on the walls and a schnauzer snoozed next to his owner in the comfy seats at the back. This plant- and dog-friendly coffee shop was my favourite in New Malden – a suburban oasis in southwest London – but also a handy few paces from my studio flat, which was located on the floor above.

'Well, that's what my agent declared on the phone,' I said. 'Right before she concluded that if I didn't show some of this passion in my next audition, it was...' I gave a half-hearted wave.

Clara grabbed my other hand across the white linoleum surface and looked at me with that intense full-eyed stare she always threw during our night shifts at Zara, whenever our manager told us another lorry-load would be arriving when we only had an hour left on the clock.

'You are full of the passion. Look at you.' She wiggled her fingers in front of me. 'Oozing sensuality with your naturally highlighted auburn curls and sexy green eyes, with eyelashes I can only dream of and waste far too much money trying to replicate with falsies.'

I laughed. Need a pick-me-up? Clara was always on hand for a boost.

'Little Miss Francesca "I may be only five foot three, but pack a punch" Cavalieri. Starlet. Of. The. Screen,' she said theatrically, punctuating each word with a hand gesture as if she was imagining my name in lights.

I pulled away from her grasp and gripped my iced hazelnut latte. 'It wasn't in connection to my appearance,' I said, sidestepping the compliments. I was by no means a star. Not even close. 'She was repeating the feedback from my last *failed* audition. Verbatim.' I'd had to google that word after she'd hung up.

Clara wrinkled her nose. 'These parts. They're wrong for you.'

'This one is perfect, though.' My voice rang with hope, though I wished it wouldn't. History had taught me hope only led to disappointment.

Her shoulders danced, head tipping from side to side. 'Tell me more, then.'

I tapped my mobile to life and searched for the email my agent had sent through this morning with the details of the part and the script of the scene. 'They need an actress between five foot two and five foot five.'

'That's you.'

'Latin-style looks.'

'Vague, but I guess your Italian heritage has given you that vibe.'

'No singing or dancing required.'

'*Maravilhoso*,' she said, giving a chef's kiss with her hand.

'And it's for a Netflix series. Drama and romance themes. Ten episodes in the first season and then who knows...' I exited out of the email and tossed my phone on the table. 'I have to audition with a male actor. The scene is where the stars of the show first meet.'

'This could be huge, Fran. Why the long face?' She fiddled with her rings – three rock-shaped ones that she had made on a jewellery course last month.

'The audition is in two days.'

'Ah. *Compreendo.* You only have forty-eight hours to find your passion.'

I popped the lid of my drink and sipped the syrupy remnants, shaking the ice cubes. 'I'm done, Clara. If I don't get this, *this* being probably the biggest chance I will ever have, I am going home.'

She shook her head, her moon-shaped earrings dancing. 'Come on. You came to London for a reason. You can't bail now.'

'I came six years ago. And what have I got to show for that? Nothing more than a walk-on part as a waitress on *EastEnders* and a toothpaste commercial.' I grinned. A double-decker display of teeth. My pearly whites that got me the part and helped pay my rent for three months. But that was over a year ago and there hadn't been anything since. Only countless walk-on 'extra' roles – fleeting moments, mostly of the back of me. Nineteen-pounds-an-hour work, with overtime if shooting ran past the contracted hours. A decent wage. But it wasn't regular enough to rely on.

'That's not your fault. You spent the first four of those years caring for your gran. And maybe if you didn't have the Zara gig and Sunday night at the club, you would've had the time to find this passion.' She cocked her eyebrows. 'You know, more time for S.E.X.'

I leaned in, aware that anyone could be eavesdropping on our conversation as the café was at full capacity. 'Why are you bringing sex into this conversation?' I whispered.

'You told me yourself. This audition. For a romantic scene. They will pair you with a guy, to perform together, no?'

'Yes…' I said, not sure where this conversation was heading.

'Look at you – at the mere mention of sex and standing in front of another man where the very purpose of the scene will be connecting with someone you have never met, you get stressed. Your body is locked.' She leaned over the table and shook my shoulders.

I giggled and batted away her hands. 'Stop! You're making a commotion.' A couple of other café dwellers had now turned in our direction. Even the girl in the corner table buried in her laptop, Beats on, had raised her eyebrows.

Clara clocked headphone girl and tutted. 'This isn't a library, for heaven's sake. We're not going to "put a cork in it".' She smirked. '*Espera.*' She tapped her fingers on her forehead. 'We are not going to "keep a lid on it".'

Clara did two tick signs in the air. It was a game between us. How many English idioms could we drop into conversation? It was a way of keeping on top of our quest for English fluency. When I met Clara on my first Zara night shift two years ago, I had been relieved to discover she was Brazilian. From Paraná in the south, Clara had come to London to work in fashion. She was paying her way through a course at the adult education college in Richmond with her night shifts in Zara and ad hoc waitressing. Our Saturday afternoon rendezvous before our all-night London job were sacred and with English being the only common language between us, it was a perfect opportunity to practise. I had the upper hand, though. Theoretically, I was bilingual. My English mum had seen to that before she left me when I was twelve.

A hard lump formed in my throat at the image of me as a pre-teen sitting on the front steps of the entrance to our apartment block in Sicily, waiting for her to return. But she never had.

The coffee machine hissed and brought me back to the room. Mr Son, the owner of the café, had pressed the switch for the water valve and was wiping down the spout. I lifted my cup for another sip.

'One more drink?' Clara asked. 'Then we can plot your deflowering.'

I choked on an ice cube. 'I am not a virgin.'

'You might as well be. Dickie was how long ago?'

'Richard,' I said in response to the nickname she had given my last boyfriend, which she knew riled me. 'He and I ended six months ago.'

Technically, it wasn't a relationship. We were 'casually dating'. Met on Bumble and had begun seeing each other once or twice a week. But he tired of my night shifts over the weekend, with no opportunity to hook up, and before long stopped replying to my texts. My last message to him on WhatsApp before Christmas had two blue ticks against it but there had been no response since. Ghosted.

'That's not a dry spell,' she said, air-ticking again. 'That's a fucking draught.' She laughed, a snort punctuating her intake of breath.

My shoulders dropped. She was right, as always. 'Three parts to my life. Acting, night shifts and relationships. They don't mix. Without Zara and the club, I can't pay my bills. And night work is the only way I can try and fulfil my acting dream, so I am free during the week to take on any roles. But those shifts mean no weekend socialising. I need this part, desperately.' I sank my head onto the table, lightly tapping it. Sitting up, Clara leaned over and picked something off my forehead.

'That's not a good look,' she said, flicking a crumb from the cinnamon swirl we had shared onto the plate. 'You're not going to attract anyone with that plastered to your face.'

'I don't want to attract anyone. I have Alessandro,' I said, my chin raised.

Clara slapped the table, causing the plate to rattle and the café to go deathly quiet again, as all heads turned in our direction. She pushed our coffee/pastry combo to one side and clutched my wrists, her nostrils flaring.

'I am literally going to chain you to this café. You are not going home to Sicily to work in the hospital and marry Alessandro.' She released my arms dramatically.

'I don't think I am cut out to be an actress. Nursing is an admirable profession and Alessandro is a sweet, kind, caring guy.'

Clara yawned. Not discreetly. A full-on eyes-rolled-so-only-the-whites-were-visible, mouth-open-so-wide-I-could-see-her-tonsils yawn.

'You should be the actress.' I laughed.

She shook her head. 'Fashion is my thing. *You* are the actress. And you would be a bloody good one if you...' She rubbed her fingers together and I knew she was thinking of the right words to express whatever it was she was desperate to tell me.

Clenching her fist, she tapped her mouth. 'What I am trying to say but can't because you don't understand Portuguese and, honestly, I wish sometimes you did because it's so exhausting trying to express myself in this crazy English... You need much more than Alessandro and Dicky and all these other dead-beat guys who you've been with since I've known you. You need someone who will appreciate what they have when they are with you. And more importantly, you need someone who will *satisfy* you.' Her eyebrow arched sharply – like a villain straight from an Agatha Christie movie.

She was never going to let that comment slide – the one I had made over cans of piña colada on Richmond Green one hot Sunday last month after a disastrous second date with a Bumble boy. When I had told her I hadn't ever orgasmed during sex, she had screeched out a rendition of the Rolling Stones' 'Satisfaction' and promised me she would make it her mission to steer me towards guys who knew how to please, having road-tested them. I told her I would not be having her sloppy seconds.

Raising her hand to attract the attention of Mr Son, she clicked her fingers and pointed to my cup and hers. An unspoken command. Rude by all accounts but it was met with a small bow and an accepting smile from the café owner. We were both regulars – the only extravagance I had in my life – and my loyalty card always ensured a free coffee once I had bought nine, our usual drinks (depending on the weather) never needing to be uttered, always known.

The place always had a more serious mood when Mr Son was behind the counter. He was only chatty with fellow Koreans, but his daughter Hana – who surprisingly hadn't made an appearance since we sat down – was always on hand for a conversation. In fact, more than that. Hana always provided me with words of comfort when yet another audition had failed or one of my Bumble dates turned out to be nothing more than a catfish coffee. Having grown up in New Malden, her English was perfect, and she even had a hint of a south London accent, with knowledge of the slang to match. The moment she switched to Korean and spoke to her parents, she took on a different persona – her tone soft and deferential. Her little sister – Sun-hee – only made irregular appearances, usually late morning at the weekend, under a hangover veil.

'Francesca Cavalieri,' Clara said, breaking me away from my thoughts. 'I will not let you return to your old life in Sicily until you give this audition your best shot. And anyway, you can't leave your gran.'

I slumped in my chair. 'She no longer knows who I am.'

She stroked my hand. 'I'm sorry.'

Squeezing my eyes shut, I attempted to block the wave of emotion threatening to engulf me. My English *nonna* had been the reason I had wanted to move to the UK when I turned twenty-two. At least that's what I had told my dad. He would never have let me go if he had known the full truth. I had cherished the time she and I had spent together, the chance to connect after not knowing her for most of my life. But after a few years the onset of dementia had meant I could no longer cope with her on my own and she had moved into a care home.

When I opened my eyes, a strange sensation washed over me. The room darkened as if a blanket of grey clouds had blocked the sunlight streaming through the glass frontage; the IKEA light fittings on the ceiling – clusters of small yellow pinwheels – dimmed. Everyone hushed.

I felt him before I saw him. Stage right. His presence. A movement flickering in the corner of my eye as he neared.

A hand – long fingers holding Clara's iced caramel americano – reached over to place her drink in front of her.

My eyes trailed along the contours of his arm. Smooth skin. A tattoo ran around his bicep – at the edge of his grey T-shirt sleeve – containing a band of numbers plus the degree symbol. Coordinates?

What place have you marked on your unblemished skin? I wondered.

My drink was placed in front of me. Heat. It radiated in the space between us. An unusual sensation, considering I was sitting right by the aircon unit.

I swallowed away my nervous anticipation as my gaze moved along his arm, muscular shoulder, a long, solid neck and settled on his face. Full pink lips. Slightly parted. Deep, dark eyes. Sorrowful.

Are you in pain? Can I help you?

It was a knee-jerk thought – the nurse in me. The need to fix everyone's problems. Because then maybe I wouldn't have to face my own.

He met my eyes only for a second before dipping his gaze, thick dark bangs falling over his forehead. Defined cheekbones sat high on his flawless face. He bowed. A mark of respect, ingrained into his culture.

'Fran?' Clara said.

A beat. My heartbeat, pounding as he came to stand and settled on my eyes again, his boring deep into mine as if he could see it all – my pain, my longing, my needs.

'Iced hazelnut latte,' he stuttered.

Another beat. Thunderous.

'Fran?'

A click of fingers. The spell broken and the room coming to life again in a flash. I blinked rapidly and noticed the guy was no longer standing beside me.

'What happened?' I whispered, my hand over my chest, the rhythm of my heart on double speed.

'*That* happened.' Clara tipped her head to the counter. The mysterious barista guy was stacking a tray full of plates and mugs before wiping down the area. A conversation passed between him and Mr Son, brief nods following their words – back and forth, like a game of tag.

'Who is that?' I asked.

Mr Son ran the coffee shop with his wife. They were also my landlord and landlady, as they owned the whole building. The only other servers were their daughter Hana and a roster of three part-time university students. My regular visits to the café meant I could tell you who was working on any given day.

'No idea,' Clara said. 'But *ele é perfeito*.'

'Nobody's perfect.'

'For you, he is.'

'For me?'

'Yes. Look at you. You're all flushed.' She leaned over the table, cupping my face in both her hands. 'Your pupils are dilated. You have been hit by Cupid's arrow.' She mimicked the drawing of a bow. 'Pow!' She giggled.

'Shh.'

'What? He can't hear me.' She pushed her chair back. 'I'm going to go find out more. Forty-eight hours with *that* guy will give you all the help you need. When time is limited, passion is bound to be in abundance.' She winked.

My hand reached across the table to stop her. 'Don't you dare.'

'Francesca Marie Cavalieri. Do you want this part or not?'

The room closed in. Her words rang in my ears, repeating themselves over and over again. Of course I wanted this part. This part could mean fame. And fame could lead to notoriety.

Then, maybe, *she* would come and find me.

It took me one look

Chapter 2

The sun bore down on me, and I pressed an ice cube on my cheeks to cool them. It wasn't only the emergence of the sun that had inflamed them. Acute embarrassment had already done that. A trickle of water slithered down my neck onto my white vest top, leaving a wet patch in its path. I rattled my cup and placed it on the outdoor table, leaning against the glass window of the café.

A quick glance over my shoulder revealed Clara stretching her arms over the counter, talking animatedly to barista guy. My pleas for her not to approach him had fallen on deaf ears.

Air tick.

She had sashayed over, smoothing out the wrinkles in her home-made patchwork strappy dress as she went, her long black ponytail swishing. A conversation went on between her and Mr Son before he called the guy over from out back, where there was a small kitchenette. As he dipped his head to get through the doorway, I noticed how imposing a figure he struck. He towered over Mr Son and his grey T-shirt fitted his torso like a second skin, revealing nothing but broad shoulders and taut muscles.

When I plucked up the courage to look again, Clara was passing over a piece of paper. I met his gaze again as he held it in his fingers, and I couldn't look away. His eyes were dreamy but doleful. And those long fingers? I idly wondered what it would feel like to have them touch my chin before tracing the outline of my lips.

'*Oddio*,' I had whispered, puffing out my cheeks. What was wrong with me? It was as if I had been injected with a shot of endorphins that were coursing through my veins.

Barista guy had rubbed the back of his neck as he passed the piece of paper to Clara. At that point, I fled.

'Why did you leave?' Clara said the second she came out of the café, the door swinging closed behind her.

'That was mortifying,' I said through clenched teeth.

'Nothing ventured, nothing gained,' she said with a head nod and flick.

'Please stop with the idioms,' I pleaded.

She sat down and slipped her sunglasses off the top of her head, shielding her eyes from the brightness.

I dragged out the chair next to her and parked myself. 'Well…?'

She pursed her lips with a chin tilt. 'No idea.'

'What do you mean "no idea"?'

'He's not exactly chatty.'

'You talk a hundred words a minute; I'm not surprised he didn't get a word in.'

'He's definitely shy. Got more information out of his uncle.' She slurped her coffee.

'Uncle? He's Mr Son's nephew?'

'Yeah. Mrs Son is the sister of Jae-seung's mum.'

'Jae-seung,' I repeated.

'He's visiting for a view days. Lives in Seoul.'

'Oh,' I said, a hint of disappointment in my tone. 'Then what did you say to him?'

She pinched her lips, a sassy smile breaking in the corner of her mouth. 'I said, "You see my hot friend over there, she really, really wants to have messy passionate sex with you."'

I nudged her in the arm. 'You did not?'

She dismissed me with a sweep of her hand. 'Francesca, honey. This is why you need my help. You never seize an opportunity. Approximately six foot two of lushness does not walk into your life on a daily basis. And if he is only here for a few days, he is perfect for your needs.'

'I don't do one-nighters, remember? Tried it. Hated it.'

'But you need help landing this role, no?' She stabbed the ice with her straw.

'I don't need a guy for that. I'm perfectly capable of learning the lines and getting into character myself. I need to practise.'

'With a guy.'

'In front of a mirror,' I clarified.

Clara eye-rolled me. 'I sometimes think I am talking to a child.'

'Charming,' I said.

She grasped my arm. 'This scene. The one for the audition. There's sexual tension, right?'

'I guess. Your point is?'

'Passion. You begin to feel it when you are in the presence of someone you are attracted to. That carnal desire, regardless of whether you actually will connect on a deeper level. And *that* guy.' She cocked her head in the direction of the café door. 'You felt something when you saw him, no?'

I poked my straw further between the ice cubes to reach the liquid below and pictured that moment, wondering what it would have felt like to run my fingers along his arms and breathe him in. 'A flutter,' I concluded, shaking myself from those thoughts.

Clara snort-laughed. 'A flutter. You're a hopeless romantic, aren't you?'

'Nothing wrong with that,' I said, tugging at a thread from my cut-off denim shorts. 'He knocked me back, though. I saw him hand over what you gave him, which I assumed had my number.'

'That was because he doesn't have a mobile. Didn't understand his reason for not having one but...' She rattled her drink. 'I told him you lived above the café.'

My mouth dropped open into an 'o' shape. 'You told him where I live?'

'Don't look so horrified. He's Mr Son's nephew. And he's Korean. I'd say that makes him double security-checked. One of the most respectful cultures in the world.'

That, I knew all too well. New Malden was home to the highest number of Koreans living in the UK. Migration could be traced to the establishment of Samsung's first European headquarters nearby and the site of the first South Korean embassy, so Mr Son had once told me on a slow afternoon in the café. Korean coffee shops, restaurants and bars lined the high street and every Korean I had met since moving here had been nothing but polite and welcoming.

'If he wasn't chatty,' I said, 'what were you talking about?'

'I told him your availability over the next two days: the Zara night shift tonight, that you sleep most of Sunday, work behind the bar at Havana Club in Leicester Square on Sunday night, sleep most of Monday morning and that you had this incredible audition on Monday afternoon that you were hoping he could help with.'

'You basically told him my life story,' I said, peering through the glass. I caught Mr Son's eye and he pointed at his watch, mouthing the words 'ten minutes'. I stuck my thumb up, remembering that he'd said earlier he would be coming over to fix my blocked sink at six.

'I told him enough to pique his interest. But honestly, Fran, I think you need to go in there and ask him out.'

'*No, no, no.*' I waved my hand. 'I am off-the-scale embarrassed now. And like I said, there's little point if he's only here for a few days.'

Her mobile pinged and she tapped it to life. '*Aí sim*,' she said, her face instantly illuminating. 'I gotta go. I'm meeting Philippe in an hour.'

'He's back?' I said, realising my tone was laced with annoyance. 'Sorry, I meant, he's back.' My voice sang with fake cheeriness, which Clara didn't notice as she was too engrossed in the message.

Clara had a causal relationship with a Frenchman she met online a year ago, when he was in 'travel mode'. He lived in Paris but worked in London occasionally. She knew nothing of his home life, and I was convinced he was married – the obvious white mark on his ring finger a bit of a giveaway, but Clara chose to ignore it. She claimed no one was getting hurt with their 'London affair' but I begged to differ. I had lost count of the times she arrived sobbing for one of our Zara shifts because Philippe had cancelled on her last-minute. He was most definitely having his cake and eating it. I mentally did an air tick and groaned. Most of these idioms I had no clue how they had come to be.

'You'll cover for me tonight, right?' Clara said.

My shoulders dipped. 'But that'll be your third sickie in two months.'

'Don't be such a downer. Just because I am going to be having hot sex all night long and you're not, don't be all judgy.'

I bit my tongue. What I wanted to tell her was that Philippe was no good for her. She deserved so much more than he was able to give. 'I'll cover for you,' I said reluctantly.

A thought struck me. Without Clara, it meant the rest of the team and I would have to work even harder to make sure the flagship store was ready for trading by the end of our shift at seven on Sunday morning.

'*Obrigada, obrigada, obrigada*,' she sang, gripping my hand. Tapping out a message on her mobile, a coquettish smirk coated her lips. A reply to Philippe, no doubt. It was the same look she wore whenever they texted.

Once she finished, she stood and slung her bag on her shoulder, before pausing for a second with her finger in the air. 'Don't forget there's rail replacement this weekend. You'll have to take the bus to Waterloo tonight.'

'*Fanculo*.' I swore in Italian. 'Coming home will be a night-mare. It'll take twice as long.' I groaned before standing and tossing our plastic cups in the recycling bin beside the front door.

'I'm sorry your night will suck, and without me too.' She pouted before giving me a couple of air kisses.

'*Ciao, ragazza*,' I said.

She walked away then stopped suddenly. 'Seriously, though. Make a move. It doesn't have to be any more than a casual date. Flirt a bit, find that passion and channel it into your audition prep.'

'I can't ask him out and you know why.' I scuffed my sandal on the pavement, not wanting to recall that one night at Havana Club when I *had* made a move on a guy.

She stepped closer. 'Listen to me,' she said, leaning forward, forcing me to meet her gaze. 'Don't be afraid.'

I opened my mouth to remind her why I was fearful, but she waved her hand to silence me.

'What would Taylor say?' she asked.

'Be fearless,' I recited. The same mantra I always uttered when Clara said that. It was a reference to Taylor Swift's 'Fearless' soliloquy. After seeing her in Hyde Park last summer, we were even bigger Swifties.

'I know why you're afraid to ask him out. You told me the story about when you approached that British guy after your shift, and he knocked you back.'

'He didn't knock me back; he humiliated me.' His words 'she's just a waitress', which he had exclaimed in front of a group of his banking buddies when he thought I was out of earshot, were still ingrained in my mind. It had taught me a valuable lesson, though: never be the first to make a move, no matter how much flirting has flowed.

'But you can't let one bad experience ruin your dating life. And those apps are getting you nowhere. Go ask him out,' Clara repeated. 'It's the twenty-first century, remember. We're in control. Worst case, he says he's busy and you can resort to Plan B, though I don't think following your previous audition prep routine has got you anywhere. And don't for one moment think he's going to suddenly appear climbing the wall of the café to your window like in some nineties romance movie.'

'I'll think about it,' I said with a smile, mainly to silence her, because I had no intention of going into the coffee shop again. The 'I have no mobile' excuse was lame and I had no desire to be humiliated again.

Clara skipped away, leaving behind the aroma of her vanilla body spray, and I pondered her comment about romance. Why wasn't it like that? My English *nonna* – or Gran as she insisted I call her – had an old VCR player and we used to love watching romantic movies from the eighties and nineties together. I used to raid all the charity shops in New Malden where they could be bought for fifty pence each. Curling up on the sofa in her terraced house a ten-minute walk from here was always a comfort. But it soon became impossible to ignore the way she would so easily forget the plots to movies we had only viewed days before. It had been the most difficult decision I had ever had to make – in consultation with our local GP – to move her into a care home. Her house on Darley Drive had been sold to fund her place at Speirs House, a five-minute drive from the high street. Recently, the visits had been harder and harder to bear. Guilt seeped through my pores whenever I knew one of my bi-monthly visits was on the horizon.

Inside my studio flat, I slipped my keys into the home-made plate that one of my half-brothers had created for me in a pottery class a few summers ago – my full name etched in bubble writing along the top. A pang of homesickness washed over me at the thought of the place where I had grown up and an image of my cheeky ten-year-old twin brothers chasing each other down the road to the beach. It had been almost a year since I had last seen them.

On my beside table, I twisted the dial on my sound machine to the tune of ocean waves. Raising the volume to drown out the street noise filtering through the net curtains, I thought of home: summer breezes, waves crashing on the shore of Cala Capreria in the Riserva Naturale Orientata dello Zingaro, less than an hour from my house. A dip there would be welcome right about now, I thought as I tugged at my vest top that was sticking to my skin.

The air in the room was still with a heaviness I knew only the fan could lift. Plugging it into the wall, it came to life for a second before it went dead. 'Just great,' I moaned.

I shuffled over to the kitchen table and grabbed the script for my audition, which I had got the stationer's across the road to print out for me.

'Passion,' I said out loud, tracing the words on the page. Maybe Clara was right. A quick read earlier on had revealed there *was* an unspoken sexual tension between the hero and the heroine. Sparks were flying, banter abounding. How could I express those emotions if I had never encountered them in real life? My dating experience had been limited and, for the most part, a disaster since moving to England.

A knock startled me. I had forgotten that Mr Son was coming round to fix the sink. No one else had the key to the ground-floor entrance, except the sweet old Korean couple who lived in the two-bedroom duplex above me. Their K-dramas were always turned up too high and the smell of kimchi permeated the communal hallway, but I found the sound and smell comforting. Mrs Kim also always made double the amount of beef bulgogi meatballs every Thursday, which meant that had become one of my nights off from cooking.

Turning the door handle, my mouth formed a perfect 'o' again when I saw who was standing behind it.

It took me one look
One look to know

Chapter 3

'*Annyeonghaseyo*,' barista guy said as he bowed, the muscles in his arms flexing from carrying a toolbox in one hand, a wrench in the other.

I repeated the Korean greeting I had heard on many occasions when I entered the café.

'My name is Choi Jae-seung – Son Ji-ho's nephew. I am sorry to bother you, Ms Cavalieri, but my uncle asked me to come and fix your sink.'

'Please call me Fran, or Francesca if you prefer. My dad calls me Cesca.'

A slight flush coated his cheeks. 'I have come to fix your sink… Francesca.' He dipped his eyes.

'So, you're a plumber disguised as a barista?' I said, with a raised eyebrow, before realising that Clara's flirtatiousness had rubbed off on me. 'I mean… you obviously have many hidden talents.' I twirled sections of my hair. OK, now I was making things worse.

Flirting was not my forte, especially when meeting someone organically. Maybe that's why so many of my real-life interactions with dating-app matches had been a disaster. I'd reeled in many guys with a bit of 'witty' online banter, only to follow with 3D me, who was more tongue-tied and awkward. I didn't ooze confidence in the same way Clara did or even all the actresses I would see in waiting rooms at auditions. And my written English was always better than my spoken English, because writing a message meant I could edit it accordingly.

The first hint of a smile broke free in the corner of Jae-seung's mouth. It dropped almost as quickly as it had appeared.

'Plumbing is not my profession, no,' he said. 'But I am trained to do odd jobs.' His tone was so serious, and my attempt at banter was falling flatter than a pancake. *Air tick.* His accent had a slight American inflection and I wondered if maybe he had learned English in the States.

He cleared his throat and tipped his chin. 'Can I?'

'Oh sorry,' I said as I let him step inside.

He slipped off his trainers and lined them neatly by the entrance.

'The sink's… there,' I said, stating the obvious. The studio was a single room with one small bathroom adjoining it. A kitchenette ran along one wall, with a table for two beside it, my double bed large and prominent against the opposite wall, with a two-seater sofa and TV placed to the side. My closet was a rack of clothes stuck in one corner, with boxes of undergarments, socks and nightwear stashed under my bed. Snapshots of Sicilian sunsets and my Italian cat, Marilyn, adorned the walls, as well as ones of me and Clara exploring London. A photo of my family unit – Dad, stepmum and the twins, Federico and Gianluca – sat in a frame on my bedside table.

'I also seem to have blown a fuse when I plugged in my fan, so I am sorry it's so hot in here.'

'That's OK,' he said, clutching the toolbox tighter, the veins in his arms pulsing. 'I can fix that too if you want?'

'Ooh, would you? I'd appreciate that. The tap in the bathroom is dripping too and um…' I scuttled to the second drawer below the kitchen counter, next to the fridge, and tried but failed to open it. 'This seems to be stuck and I have most of my cooking utensils in here.' I wrapped my arms around myself, hoping I wasn't being too demanding. A cut on my finger was proof that I had at least *tried* to fix it myself.

'Of course, no problem.'

He placed his toolbox down on the floor as I stood barely a foot from him. His nearness was making the room feel tighter and perspiration was sticking to the back of my neck. Grabbing a reminder bill from the kitchen table, I fanned myself with it.

He lifted the handle of the tap and let the water run. Within a minute it filled the sink and when he stopped the flow, it didn't drain away.

'I tried Mr Muscle, that scooper thing to unclog it but nothing has worked.'

Jae-seung did not respond but seemed to zone out, chewing on his bottom lip in concentration. Clearing his throat again, he motioned for me to step aside.

'Oh sorry, am I in the way?'

'I will need to lie down on the floor to see what the problem with the sink is.'

'Of course, silly me.' I giggled, a little too high-pitched. Was this why I was failing at securing any romantic leads in my auditions? I needed to rein in the nervous laughter and channel my inner Clara.

'Do you have a bucket?' he asked.

'Yeah, I think there is one in the bathroom.'

Inside, I stole a glimpse of myself in the mirror. My cheeks were bright pink, and my hair had become a frizzy mess – this heat was no good for my curls. I wet my hands and ran my fingers through clumps before splashing my cheeks.

I returned with the bucket and stopped short. 'Oh my,' I whispered.

Jae-seung was lying flat on the floor, head buried in the cupboard, a torch lighting his surroundings. His T-shirt had ridden up and continued to do so every time he moved his arms. I wondered what workout regime he had to warrant that physique. The top of his jeans sat low on his hips, a hint of black Calvins peeking out from the edge of the denim – an unmistakable V-shape curving all the way to his...

'It's hot in here,' I said, louder than I had intended.

A *thwack* resonated from the cupboard as his head met the bottom of the drainpipe.

'Sorry, I didn't mean to startle you.'

He shuffled out and rubbed the top of his head, clenching his teeth. 'It's fine, honestly.'

'Let me see.' I crouched beside him, ignoring his declaration. Sweeping away his hair from his forehead, I saw that he was not fine. He had obviously hit something sharp, and it had pierced his skin, leaving a deep cut that was beginning to ooze with blood. I reached for the box of tissues on the kitchen table and placed a wad of sheets on his forehead. The paper began to soak with his blood, and I sucked in a deep breath.

'*Fanculo*,' I swore as I placed another handful to mop up the flow. 'I think we need to take you to the hospital.'

'No!' he said, clasping my wrist a little forcefully. 'I mean...' He loosened his grip slightly. 'I can't go to the hospital. Sorry, I didn't mean to hurt you.' His eyes bored into mine and that's when I saw it. Fear, singed deep inside the hazelnut irises. 'I am sure it will be fine.'

As I removed the tissues, the blood continued to flow. 'Hmm. I'm not so sure,' I said, placing more sheets on the gash and grasping his hand to hold them in place. 'Let me get you onto my bed and I can inspect it properly.'

Helping him reach my quilt, I plumped one of my lilac cushions behind his head. I held my hand over his, applying some pressure for a couple of minutes. Peeling the paper off, I saw that the blood flow was thankfully beginning to abate.

'Let me get something from my bathroom,' I said, handing him some fresh tissues to hold.

Locating my first-aid kit, I washed my hands before returning to sit beside him on the bed. From within the metal tin, I fished out a sterilised wipe and swept it over his forehead. Leaning in, I saw that the wound was less than half an inch in length and the edges straight.

'I think I can patch this up if you trust me.'

He stared at me, a look of disbelief on his face.

'I'm a trained nurse. Seen worse than this before. I can apply some butterfly stitches, which is what any doctor would do in the hospital.'

He flinched at that last word and his hand rubbed his neck. It was then that I noticed a small scar between his thumb and index finger. A burn?

Is this why you're afraid? I wondered.

'I trust you,' he whispered.

'Close your eyes,' I said, and he did. His jaw pulsed, with nerves no doubt.

I wanted to tell him not to be afraid. This was easy for me. As a former nurse in the accident and emergency department of Azienda Sanitaria Provinciale Di Trapani in Sicily, I had been patching up cuts since I began training in my late teens. Six long years had now passed since those days of twenty-four-hour shifts and constant calf ache from being on my feet all the time. But I knew it was like riding a bike. You never forget.

I patted the area completely dry with a clean cloth before fishing out a pack of Steri-Strips. Using my fingers to gently push the two sides of the wound together, I set about applying the strips with care and precision.

'There,' I said triumphantly, several minutes later. 'All done.'

He let out a long, deep sigh and opened his eyes. His pupils dilated as he focused on my face. That flutter that I'd felt in the coffee shop had returned but the pace of the butterfly wings had increased.

'Hopefully,' I said, my mouth a little dry, 'it should heal up nicely in a few days and you can soak the strips off. But make sure you keep the area dry until then.'

'How can I thank you?' he said.

'You don't need to thank me,' I said, disposing of the blood-stained tissues in the bin. 'It was my fault, after all. I shouldn't have surprised you. Actually, before I forget, are you up to date with your tetanus shots?'

'Yes, I am. It is a requirement… um…' He hesitated. 'For travel.'

'Oh, well, that's a good thing, because you can't be too sure of bacteria having got into that wound.'

I began packing up the first-aid kit.

'You're a nurse turned actress?' His eyebrows raised before he flinched, emitting a guttural groan.

I smiled, remembering how I had greeted him at the door. 'Best to leave any facial movement for a while. But yes, I am, although I wouldn't call myself an actress. A wannabe actress maybe. My friend told you, huh?'

'She said you needed my help, for an audition? She said you needed someone you were attracted to in order for you to get into character.' He said these words with no expression. Of course he didn't. I had told him to remain motionless.

I shook my head rapidly. 'No, you don't have to help me. I'll be fine.' I headed to the bathroom, no longer able to meet his stare. How could Clara have said that to him? I was going to kill her when I saw her next. I placed the first-aid kit under the sink and washed my hands again.

Back in my bedroom, Jae-seung was sitting up, a hint of a smile playing in the corner of his mouth. 'I'm sorry. Did I embarrass you?'

'A little. My friend is… how can I say it? She has no filter when it comes to speaking her mind.'

'She's honest.'

I laughed. 'Brutally.'

He got off my bed and stepped towards me. The sticky air thrummed around us. 'I… should probably get back to fixing the sink.'

'Actually, it's best you rest. In case you hit your head harder than we realised and you need to go to the hospital.'

There it was again – singed in his eyes. Fear. And his hand clasped his neck once more.

Don't be afraid, I thought. *I'm here.*

Reflexively, I held his other hand, and squeezed it. His fingers slowly laced through mine and his touch sent molten waves rippling along my arm, a shot of oxytocin pumping through my veins. Without a second thought, I traced my thumb over his scar, the skin there ridged and pink, and made him a silent promise.

I won't mention the idea of a hospital to you again.

A car horn beeping from the road outside broke the moment.

I dropped my hand and he stepped backwards – an uncomfortable silence filling the space between us, loaded and tense. Neither of us moved, the tick-tock of the kitchen clock the only sound in the room.

He finally grabbed his toolbox. 'I'll return in the morning, then, if it's OK with you?'

'It's a date,' I said, my voice a little too high-pitched.

Jae-seung didn't meet my gaze as he left. Closing the door behind him, I groaned, wishing the ground would open up and swallow me.

Air tick.

Yet again, my flirty banter had failed me. There was no way I was going to land this role.

It took me one look
One look to know
To know I wanted you

Chapter 4

Don't look, Francesca, I thought as I caught a glimpse of Jae-seung on the floor at my feet. His T-shirt had ridden up again as he replaced the U-bend. The muscles in his arms flexed as he swivelled the wrench.

My pulse flickered as I gave him a once-over, grateful that he couldn't see me objectifying him in this way. I could certainly use this unadulterated instant attraction to channel into my audition.

Turning to stir the bubbling pot on the stove, I folded in some cheese, still in shock that Jae-seung was back, barely an hour after he had left. Nothing to do with my charm, I might add. He had received a ticking-off from his uncle for not finishing the job and had returned after cleaning up the café. Brushing aside my concern, he reassured me he would give adequate warning if he was about to pass out. In response to my wide-eyed expression, he had winked and said he was only joking and that he had adequately 'rested' while sweeping the café floor. His initial seriousness had appeared to melt away, a more playful side emerging.

Oh God, I hope it's not concussion, I thought.

Kneeling down, I shuffled close. 'Hey,' I whispered, keen not to startle him again. 'You OK? No dizziness?'

'Only when I close my eyes. There are these odd shapes I see too, like zigzags. That's normal, right?' he said, deadpan, before a broad smile flooded his face.

I swiped him with a tea towel. 'Cut it out. I was being serious.'

He laughed as he twisted the wrench. 'Sorry. I'm fine,' he said, more sincerely. 'Thanks for your concern.'

Returning to the hob, I poured the cheese mixture over large tubes of pasta filled with a meat sauce, before placing the dish in the preheated oven and setting the timer.

Jae-seung appeared by my side and ran the tap. When the water drained away, he punched the air. 'Fixed.' He beamed.

I clapped my hands together as if I was praying. 'Thank you so, so much, you're a star.'

'I got there in the end,' he said, a relieved expression on his face. 'Now for the fan.'

As he rummaged in his toolbox for a screwdriver, I began to clear up the mess from my marathon cooking session.

'That smells amazing,' he said, sniffing the air. 'What is it?'

'Cannelloni. It'll be ready in twenty minutes. Would you like some?' The words tumbled out and I bit my bottom lip, waiting for the let-down.

'I don't want to put you to any trouble if there isn't enough.'

'It's no trouble at all, honest. This will feed ten people.'

'You're expecting guests?'

'Oh no, I don't mean right now.' I laughed. 'And besides, this flat is barely big enough to host one person, let alone ten. I always prepare a big batch on a Saturday and freeze several portions. I never have the energy to cook on Sunday and most weekdays, with my crazy work schedule. I also work a night shift on Wednesday.'

'That's kind of you to offer, then. I'd love some.' He plucked a fuse from his box and set about fixing the fan.

I turned, keen for him not to see the toothy grin that fanned on my face. *Cena per due* was on the menu and all it had taken was a waft of Italian spices to secure it.

A few minutes later, a breeze tickled my arms. Heaven. I turned, not realising Jae-seung was behind me, and careered slap bang into his chest. '*Scusa*,' I mumbled, stepping back and catching the edge of the kitchen table. 'Ow,' I groaned.

'This flat really is a health hazard,' he said. 'You OK?'

'I think I'll live,' I said, rubbing my hip, embarrassed by my clumsiness. My studio wasn't even big enough to swing a cat in. I mentally air-ticked and thought of Clara. Would she be impressed at how this interaction was panning out?

Packing up his toolbox, Jae-seung noticed some papers on the kitchen table. 'Is this for the audition?'

'Yeah,' I said. 'I'm trying to learn the lines.' I pulled out some forks and knives from a drawer under the counter.

'What is your process?'

'My process?' I laid the cutlery on the table, along with a couple of glasses.

'You get into character, right? Before your audition, you take on the person's life, so you can understand how to deliver the lines.'

'You know about acting?' I asked, my interest piqued.

'I did a stage class during my college years in Korea. I know a little.'

'What do you do now, then?'

'I am trying a few things.' He flicked through the pages. 'Music is my passion, though.' Scanning the sheets, he finally came to the end. 'Can I read with you?'

'Um…' I clutched the salt mill to my chest. I had never rehearsed in front of anyone before. It was far easier to portray a different side to me in front of a mirror. 'You don't have to,' I said, setting the grinder down.

'I'd like to,' he said with a look of sincerity. 'Maybe it would help you to have someone read the other part in different ways. Then you would know how to respond when you meet the actor in the audition, and everything hangs on that one moment to impress the director. That way you won't be left with any surprises. I could read the male lead's lines with different emotions, sometimes not giving you a second to think or even breathe.'

I chewed my bottom lip, twisting my fingers in a section of hair. It hadn't occurred to me to even think of it in that way. That sounded like quite an intense methodology. He spoke with authority, as if he knew how to perform, how to portray a different persona.

But had he read the whole way through? If he had, he would know how it ended. My cheeks flushed as my gaze fell on his lips, idly wondering what it would be like to kiss them.

'Sure,' I said, shaking myself from my reverie. 'Why not?'

–

Working with Jae-seung proved to be monumentally helpful. We ran through the lines, and once I got past my initial nerves, it flowed between us. There was an intensity there that I could feel through to my core. Could he feel it too? Or was he only playing the role of the hero?

'I have an idea,' Jae-seung said as we came to the end of the second read-through. 'I will try my part without the script.'

'You've learned the lines already?' I said, leaning back on the kitchen counter.

He lifted one shoulder. 'I kind of have a photographic memory. It comes in handy.'

'I bet. You should consider a career change,' I said, though I still didn't have a grasp of what he did. He had mentioned music being a passion but no further details.

'We can also work through some movement. It will help strengthen your audition.'

Light-bulb moment. Movement. I scanned my body and noticed the tension in my arms, which hung like lead weights by my sides, and my legs seemed stiff.

'Listen to the words,' he said. 'Feel the emotion; the unspoken words are the ones that have the most impact. I will move unexpectedly and see how you respond.'

Jeez, was this guy for real? Hot, handy *and* knew about auditioning.

As we moved through the scene, I was distracted by the way his body appeared in sync with the lines and I surprised myself at how much of my part I could remember without the pages in front of me.

He paused mid-scene. 'Your arms are still locked,' he said, stepping closer. 'Hmm.' He stroked his chin. 'I think there's only one thing that will fix that. Are you ticklish?' he asked, a cheeky grin spreading over his face.

'No,' I lied.

'Really?' he said, traces of doubt in his voice.

I folded my arms, raising an eyebrow. 'Really.'

He stepped even closer, his eye contact intense.

'Are *you*?' I said, beginning to take on the confidence portrayed by the lead role.

'Not even slightly,' he said, putting his hands in the back pockets of his jeans.

I didn't know what came over me, but suddenly I lunged towards him, tickling him on the arms. It didn't take him long to start tickling me back and before I knew it, I was snort-laughing as he found all my sensitive spots and I writhed beneath his fingers, screeching 'stop' periodically. It turned out that he wasn't bluffing at all, as I could not even get one sound from him. He continued torturing me relentlessly until we hit the edge of the bed and fell backwards onto it. The tickling ceased as he propped himself on his arms, his face achingly close to mine. Those lips. Full. Pink. Slightly parted. If he leaned down further...

Ding. Brrrrr. The egg timer vibrated on the kitchen counter and sliced through the moment. Jae-seung pushed himself off the bed and gave me a hand up.

'Dinner's ready,' I said, my voice an octave higher as I tucked my vest top into my denim shorts.

Jae-seung ran a hand through his hair, dropping his gaze to the floor as if he had been caught doodling in class. A smile twitched in the corner of his mouth and an eyebrow arched as he looked up. That pose lightened the intense moment and I smiled.

Over cannelloni and freshly made lemonade, Jae-seung asked me about my life in Sicily and what had brought me to New Malden. I explained I had come to get to know my English grandmother and became her carer when a fall had rendered her not as agile as she was when I first arrived. He listened attentively when I talked about the pain of moving her into a home and empathised when I told him I had found a community in New Malden that made me feel welcome and meant I wanted to stay.

He devoured two plates of food as if it had been days since his last meal, and I smiled as he tore off a hunk of sourdough bread that I had made yesterday and soaked up the sauce on his plate. The only details he shared of his life were the years he spent in New Malden with his aunt and uncle and cousins after his dad had passed when he was thirteen: tales of high-jinks at the local state secondary boys' school, where he was reprimanded on more than one occasion for various misdemeanours, and how close he had become to his cousins, Hana and Sun-hee – like they were the older and younger sisters he never had. I didn't want to press him on why he had left his mum. This town was a second home to him, he said wistfully. He had returned to Seoul when he was seventeen to finish school and go to college but didn't elaborate as to why he left halfway through his A-levels, which seemed like a terrible time to change schools.

The hours slipped by, the ease I felt in his company soothing me into a soporific state. As the room darkened, I lit a couple of tea lights and placed them in glass candle-holders. They sent a flickering glow around the flat, making my dining space feel more intimate.

'This would be good lighting for the scene, I think,' he said.

'Shall we run through it once again?' I asked, beginning to stack our plates. 'Only if you have time. I don't want to put you out.'

'It would be my pleasure. But first.' He laid a hand gently on my wrist. 'Let me clear up.' His touch sent an electric current along my arm.

'You don't have to do that.'

He shook his head. 'It's the least I can do. That was one of the best meals I've ever had.' I beamed. 'Only promise me you won't say that to my aunt.' The corner of his mouth tipped into cheeky territory again, and I giggled.

'I promise. You can come over anytime and have it again.'

'I leave for Seoul on Wednesday.' His shoulders sank and a sad expression took over his face.

'That's a shame. You couldn't get any more days off work?'

He shook his head and moved to the sink and turned the tap. Squirting the dish soap into it, he sloshed the mixture with his hand. I didn't press him, instead filling the silence with more stories about failed auditions and how I thought a leading role in New Malden's amateur dramatic society's version of *Little Women*, with three sold-out shows at the local Catholic church, would've meant instant stardom. I laughed hollowly as I said that. How naïve had I been?

We moved in sync as we chatted: me bringing the dishes over, him washing and then me wiping. The pan needed to be soaked, but I didn't even have to tell him. I added 'domesticated' to his list of attributes. As he dunked his hands beneath the suds and scoured the pan, my eyeline fell on his tattoo. Without a second thought, I reached out and touched it. He flinched and I released my hold.

'Sorry. I was only admiring it. Are they coordinates?'

He turned and traced a wet finger across the numbers, as if he were trying to rub them away. 'Yes, they are.'

He didn't elaborate. I was about to ask him if it was his home in Seoul, or it could even be the coordinates of his girlfriend's house for all I knew, but a ringing sound stopped me before I uttered another word.

Realisation entered my consciousness that it was an alarm on my mobile. *The* alarm. My weekly Saturday 10:30 p.m. alarm to signify it was half an hour until my train that would get me to London Waterloo to make the start of my Zara shift. This thought was swiftly followed by dawning horror as I remembered what Clara had told me right before she said goodbye this afternoon.

'*Merda!*' I cried. Unearthing my phone from my pocket, I crumpled. 'No, no, no.' I had *not* reset the alarm to allow me enough time to get one of the replacement buses into town.

'What's the matter?' Jae-seung asked as he shook off suds from his fingers and dried his hands on a tea towel.

'I'm going to be late,' I said, running in circles. *Ma dai*, I inwardly scolded myself. 'My friend Clara' – I fished a shirt from beneath my bed and sniffed the armpits – 'the one you spoke to in the café. She told me there are no trains running this weekend. I completely forgot to set myself an alarm to give me enough time to grab one of the buses that take forever to get into town, especially as there are roadworks all through Putney still.' I jumped on the spot in frustration. '*And* I promised Clara I would tell our boss before our shift that she was sick, even though she isn't sick – she just wants to have sex all night with her crazy French boyfriend, although I would hardly call him a boyfriend. And what she has failed to remember is that she won't get paid because she's been off too often this month, which honestly is so irresponsible of her—'

'I can take you.'

I stopped moving, holding my shirt in one hand and a pair of jeans in the other. 'You have a car?' I asked.

'No. I have a motorbike. I rented it for my stay. It's the perfect way to get around without…' He cleared his throat and didn't finish his sentence. 'What I mean is, I can take you to work, and maybe step in for your friend…' He clasped his hands with a slight shrug.

I dropped my clothes on my bed. 'You want to take me all the way into London and not get paid for doing a seven-hour shift?' I said in bewilderment. 'Are you feeling all right?' I moved to within inches of his face and reached up, smoothing away his hair. 'Let me inspect this again; you really might have concussion.' I let a smile play about my lips.

He held on to my wrist, gently removing it from his head but not dropping his hold. The pad of his thumb twitched. Back and forth. It was the smallest movement. My pulse throbbed beneath his hold.

'I would like to help you out,' he said.

'Well, it's very thoughtful of you,' I said, pulling my hand away. 'But sadly, you can't cover for her. You're not an employee and insurance wouldn't cover you if something happened, so my boss wouldn't let you. But... I won't say no to that lift.'

'I'll meet you out front, then. Give me five minutes to get my things.'

I grinned, relief washing over me. 'OK, if you're sure.'

He didn't reply but threw me a smile over his shoulder. It was similar to that pose he had struck earlier, as if he had done it many times before. Maybe he was a model. That could be his gig – a way to pay the bills as he waited to be discovered as a musician. With a physique like his, he would be perfect to showcase that pair of Calvins I caught a brief glimpse of earlier.

The door closing snapped me to reality.

Night shift. Zara. Get changed.

Minutes later, I was outside the coffee shop when I caught sight of Jae-seung leaning on a bike, two helmets in his hands.

'Do you have a jacket?' he asked as I approached.

'I have a cardigan in my rucksack,' I said, reaching to pull it off.

'Here,' he said, shrugging off his leather jacket and holding it open for me. 'You'll need something a bit heavier than that. It will get quite chilly when we hit maximum speed.'

I slipped my arms into the sleeves and turned around to face him, the weight of the leather dragging down my shoulders. He took the zip and held the other side. I noticed the veins in his arms snaking his skin as he applied the pressure.

'It's a little tricky to figure out,' he said, tugging it gently.

As he slid the zip, his eyes trailed my body until they locked with mine. I caught a glimpse of his pupils dilating as he settled on my face.

'I haven't ridden before,' I said, clearing my throat as my mind went to an alternate meaning for that statement, which Clara would have clocked. 'A bike, that is.' I was grateful for the semi-darkness so he couldn't see my flushed cheeks. 'Alessandro, my... um... ex, he has a moped and occasionally he used to let me ride it if I was running late to get to the hospital for a shift. But it's about half the size of this.'

'My advice – grip me. Tight. There are handles but if you're not used to riding, I would feel better if you held on to me.'

He handed me the helmet, and I squeezed it on before trying but failing to work the strap. He threaded it through with ease and tightened it, his fingers brushing against my neck, a sensitive spot I had that sent a tremble of pleasure down my collarbone. He then straddled the seat and flicked his head to get me to climb on behind him. I clambered on and lowered the visor. The engine roared beneath me, and a feeling of exhilaration and pure fear gripped my throat. I clung on to him for dear life, not daring to shift my hands.

I tightened my hold as we headed down the busy A-road into town. Across Putney Bridge, we passed the roadworks with ease and Jae-seung rode through green light after green light, as if he knew the exact speed to travel to make each one before it turned red.

As the engine cut, I unclipped my helmet and Jae-seung took off his and steadied the bike. In the distance, I could see my co-workers huddling at the entrance to Zara. We were usually a team of seven and I dreaded telling them that Clara wouldn't be here tonight, inwardly swearing to work twice as hard.

'Thanks,' I said, handing over the helmet to Jae-seung. 'You're a life-saver.' Without thinking, I leaned in and placed a kiss on his cheek. My lips tingled as I met his cool, soft skin and an unexpected thud reverberated deep in my chest.

Jae-seung held his hand over where I had brushed his face with my mouth and smiled. 'It was my pleasure.'

I stepped backwards, feeling like a schoolgirl who had made the first move on her crush. I turned and joined the team to wait for our manager to unlock the doors. When I glanced over my shoulder again, Jae-seung was gone, and I sighed heavily. Guess that was that. Mission accomplished? I would say so. I had rehearsed, got into character and learned my lines, and there was a spark of excitement coursing through me having spent the last few hours with Jae-seung – feelings I could channel into my audition on Monday.

My manager grunted when I explained the Clara sickness sob-story I had prepared on the ride over and the rest of the team threw me death stares during the long hours of the shift. I went through the motions as I lugged heavy boxes from trucks into the store, sorted, folded and placed a wide range of garments in their places. As the hours slipped by, my eyes grew heavier and heavier, and the thought of my journey home to my bed taking double the time filled me with dread.

Making my way outside at seven, I held my hand above my eyes to shield them from the bright morning light and blinked. Was it a mirage? The image ahead of me was Jae-seung sitting on his bike, bathed in sunshine.

With a rushed goodbye to my weary co-workers, I stepped towards him. 'Wh-what are you doing here?'

'You said it was a seven-hour shift.'

'I didn't expect you to come back.'

He rolled his fingers over the handlebars. 'I didn't go back to New Malden. I rode around town for a few hours, stopped off at the main sights. Haven't been to London in so long and it's nice to see it without crowds. Saw the sun rise behind Big Ben around five.'

My eyes widened, surprised that he had been driving around in the dead of night for seven hours when there must be a soft bed waiting for him back at his aunt and uncle's house. 'You must be exhausted.'

'You, too.'

'I'm used to it. I do it twice a week.' I yawned deeply.

'Come on.' He tipped his head to the bike. 'Let's get you home.'

I smiled wearily, touched that he had returned and too knackered to protest any further.

We reached my flat at seven thirty in the morning after a traffic-free ride. I almost drifted off as my head rested on him – lulled into a sleep-inducing state by the thrum of the engine, the way the bike tipped from side to side as Jae-seung weaved it expertly between cars and vans, and the comforting feel of his leather jacket, which I wore again to protect me from the early-morning chill.

There was a stillness to New Malden high street when we arrived. Dawn was long gone but the sun hadn't risen enough for the day to have properly begun. It would be a while before the coffee shops would open and even longer for the supermarkets and regular shops' Sunday trading hours. As he cut the engine, birdsong was the prominent sound, interspersed with the occasional car and the distant rumbling of a train coming into the station.

'Do you want a cup of tea?' I asked as we headed to my flat's main door, the words tumbling out before I had time to second-guess whether it was a good idea to suggest it. 'Herbal. I find it soothing. It's hard to fall asleep when it's so light but you're bone tired. I'm always quite wired after a night shift and find it helps.'

His eyebrows knitted and he traced his fingers over the window of the coffee-shop door. 'My shift begins in an hour so I should probably head to my aunt and uncle's house and get ready.'

Guilt slapped me in the face. 'I had no idea you were working today. But… you haven't slept.'

He leaned on the window. 'Nothing new,' he whispered.

I studied his expression, heart breaking a little at the sadness etched into his face.

'I struggle to sleep, as well,' I said. 'That's why my Sundays and Thursdays tend to be a write-off – I doze on and off most of the day.'

'Do you not work on a Thursday?'

'Sometimes. Depends if my agent gets me booked onto something. But usually, it's nothing more than a walk-on role. Hardly taxing.'

He folded his arms. 'That's why this audition is important to you? Could you give up the night shifts if you got it?'

I nodded. 'It would be life-changing.'

'I hope you get it.'

'Thanks. Anyway, I'd better try and get some sleep,' I said, feeling bad that he wouldn't be able to. 'I've got to work this evening, too.'

'At the club?'

'Yes,' I said, remembering that Clara had told him my every move over the next couple of days.

'I can take you there.'

Affronted, my chin folded into my neck. 'No way. I couldn't let you do that. You haven't slept and you won't get the chance before then. My shift begins at seven.'

'Don't worry about me. I'll catch a nap somehow.' He began to walk away before I could say anything to convince him otherwise. 'See you at six,' he said over his shoulder before putting his helmet on and riding off down the high street.

'Bye,' I said, raising my hand to give him a pointless wave, as he was already out of sight.

Inside my flat, I flipped the switch to the kettle and made a cup of chamomile tea. Having changed into my blue cotton twinset that I liked to lounge in after a shift, I blew the steam rising from my mug and took some soothing sips, moving to curl up on the bed after I had switched on my fan.

My mind turned towards Jae-seung, and I snuggled into my cushions and replayed the last thirteen hours: my fingers on his skin, inspecting his wound, my lips on his cheek as I thanked him for the ride. The way my heart thrummed whenever he stepped close, the look in his eyes that told me he was hurting and sad, which left me aching to know what had caused that pain and melancholy. But there was also a playful side that had emerged as we had tickled each other like a couple of kids.

I finished my tea, placed the mug on my bedside table and turned on my sound machine to the ocean again. Turning up the volume, I slipped under my duvet, stretched out my limbs and closed my eyes, imagining I was on the white sand of Mondello Beach – one of my favourite places in Palermo. Crystal-blue sea, saltwater cooling my sun-kissed arms after a refreshing swim. But I wasn't alone.

I imagined Jae-seung's long fingers stroking my back, applying suncream all over me. The movement gentle and rhythmic. Once the lotion had been absorbed by my skin, he turned me around, those dark eyes still sorrowful, the pain he hadn't yet shared with me making me want to know him more. His hand on my cheek, thumb tracing the outline of my lips.

I groaned as I let the imaginary sensations wash over me, my skin pulsing at the thought of his touch. The tips of his fingers along my jaw, my neck, my collarbone; his lips parted in anticipation.

The swell of the waves from my sound machine cascaded over me and I fell into the sweetest slumber.

It took me one look
One look to know
To know I wanted you
And couldn't let you go

Chapter 5

At six that evening there was a knock on my door. I tugged at the hem of my black miniskirt, tucked in my white shirt tight and grabbed my shoulder bag. Behind the door, Jae-seung stood leaning on the frame, arms folded across his chest – a navy V-neck T-shirt paired with black jeans this time.

'Is it crazy to say,' he said, 'that I would never forgive myself if I let you walk out of my life right now?' His look was smouldering, the colour of his eyes a dark roast coffee bean.

I swallowed hard, completely thrown by his words – a frisson of excitement pulsating through to my core, the heat in my cheeks deepening as I remembered my idle daydreaming this morning. 'I, um—'

'Perfect.' He beamed. 'You've nailed it.'

'What?' I said, blinking in confusion.

'The audition?'

Embarrassment flooded my face when I realised he had delivered a line from the script. 'Oh yeah, I knew that,' I lied, turning to switch off the light, gritting my teeth.

I reminded myself that meet-cutes where the hero and heroine fell for each other instantly and delivered similar lines were only to be found in scripts, not real life. Crushing on him suddenly seemed silly – he hadn't given me any indication that he fancied me. And I reminded myself it was pointless anyway, as he was going home in a couple of days.

As I steadied myself on his motorbike, I resisted the urge to hold on to him again and gripped the handles beside my thighs instead. But without the touch of my hands, I became acutely aware of all other points of contact – how my body was flush against his back, legs tightly bracketing his. Yet again, the ride was smooth and seamless.

At the club, I headed into the staff room where I deposited my bag in a locker and grabbed my Havana Club-logoed apron, wrapping the ties around my waist and into a bow.

Returning to the bar, I was surprised to see Jae-seung still there. 'It's OK if you want to go back to New Malden.'

'No, it's fine. I am excited to watch you work, and I'd love to give you a lift home.'

'I can't let you do that. I'm happy to take the night bus. My shift is five hours, you've barely slept in the last couple of days *and* you will be bored senseless.'

He let a smile play on his lips and I wondered what was amusing him. 'I want to stay,' he said, leaning on the bar, 'and experience this world of yours.' He swept his hand around.

Havana Club was a nightclub with Cuba at the heart of its theme – the décor showcasing portraits of old Chevrolets in bright colours and palm-fringed beaches. One of Clara's old boyfriends was the brother of the owner – Steve – and that's how I got the gig. In my interview, I had wowed him with my *Coyote Ugly*-style cocktail mixing, which I had learned how to do for an audition for the movie's sequel but didn't get. The dance floor was always heaving – the soundtrack an eclectic mix of modern pop, rumba and other Afro-Cuban-influenced music.

Jae-seung was making no sense. Why would anyone in their right mind stay and watch someone serve drinks for several hours?

He took a seat at the bar while I wiped it down. Steve was shifting crates of spirit mixers and placing them in the mini fridge behind us. Having studied the menu, Jae-seung bought a virgin daiquiri cocktail. He sipped it slowly while I served a steady stream of customers – mostly tourists and students. The local bars in New Malden were usually dead on a Sunday night, which was why it was worth the schlep into town for this gig. I made more with tips at Havana Club than I did my regular wage.

Jae-seung's head began nodding to the pulsating beat of the music. When I caught his eye, I leaned in and whispered, 'Why don't you go and dance.'

He took a moment to reply, taking in the scene over his shoulder – the mass of bodies swaying in tight proximity. That cheeky smile began to creep into the corner of his mouth again.

He leaned in further and whispered in my ear. 'Only if you promise to join me later?'

Those hazelnut eyes were pleading for me to say 'yes'.

'I'm a terrible dancer,' I said.

'I'll teach you,' he mouthed. That statement seemed *so* loaded.

I bit my bottom lip before a coy smile escaped. 'Maybe,' I mouthed.

It was as if we were acting out the scene for the audition again – the flirty banter that had eluded me in real life until now.

He drained his drink before heading over to the centre of the dance floor, his shoulders rotating as if he was getting a sense of the beat. He turned, winked and...

Bam. He threw some daring moves, and I spilled the lemonade I was attempting to pour into a double shot of vodka. As I dabbed the liquid with a cloth, I stared hypnotised while his torso dipped and rippled, his hand sliding down his chest before he delivered another sequence that had me spellbound.

'Francesca?' Steve called from behind.

'Hmm?' I said, still staring as Jae-seung began to be surrounded by an audience whooping and cheering as he showcased another more daring dance sequence.

'Any chance your customer could get her order this century?'

Steve clicked his fingers right in front of my face and snapped me to attention.

'Sorry,' I said, finishing the drink and pushing it towards a woman with arms folded over her chest and nostrils flaring.

Over the next couple of hours, I lost sight of Jae-seung as he made his way deeper into the crowd and I carried on with my bar duty. My calves began to ache from standing and the throbbing beat was beginning to give me a headache.

'Why don't you take your break early, Francesca?' Steve said. 'Go and have some fun.'

'Fun?' I questioned. 'I'm gonna flop in the break room and catch forty winks.'

Air tick. Clara.

A cursory glance at my phone showed I had a message from her, as if she had a sixth sense and knew I'd thought of her. She was having a blast with Philippe but wanted to meet at the coffee shop tomorrow after my audition to hear how it had gone.

My stomach tightened at the thought of it. But I had done more prep for this role than any other. All thanks to Jae-seung. This could be it. The realisation of a long-held dream. A 'crazy dream', Alessandro had once called it over dinner with my family, and everyone had laughed in agreement. It had stung. A lot. But now my big break was within reach. My body relaxed, and a smile coated my face, imagining my name on a billboard and what it would mean if everyone knew my name. Like a flower blooming, my heart felt open to possibilities, and I had a new spring in my step – aching calves forgotten – as I served more customers.

-

'He hasn't taken his eyes off you all night,' Steve said a while later as he began pouring several shots of tequila into a cocktail shaker.

Usually, I dreaded the end of my shift, when I would have to slip out of the club without anyone following me. It was a hazard of the job. I never led anyone on and had become more wary since my incident with British banking boy, but I had been serenaded with the opening line from the Human League's 'Don't You Want Me' more times than I could remember. And often when I had replied with: 'No, I don't want you,' quite emphatically, guys had taken that response as an invitation to flirt even more. At the end of most shifts, Steve would insist on me waiting until he had locked up so he could walk me to the bus stop.

'Who hasn't taken his eyes off me?' I asked.

'That guy,' Steve said, tipping his chin in the direction of the dance floor as he hurled a bottle of Cointreau in the air before pouring a shot of it into the shaker. 'The one you came in with.'

I scanned the crowd, and there was Jae-seung. It was as if he was walking in slow motion, other revellers moving out of his way without him even having to change direction. There was a self-assured gait to his walk, as if he was on stage, the lead singer in a band.

'What can I get you?' I asked as he approached the bar.

A slight shake of his head. 'Only a dance. With you.'

A nudge on my shoulder unsteadied me. Steve removed the lemonade hose from my hand, my concentration gone again. 'Will you go and have that break and dance with him for heaven's sake,' he said, 'before we lose any more customers.'

Without breaking eye contact, I wiped my hands on a tea towel. Knowing how sweaty it would be out in the pack of dancers, I began to slowly unbutton my white shirt to reveal a black tank top. As I slipped the shirt off my shoulders, Jae-seung's lips parted and I bit my bottom lip before slowly releasing it. Maybe it was the prospect of tomorrow's audition and the expectation to take on a new persona that caused me to imagine I was the heroine of the Netflix show: sassy and confident, and ready to seduce the leading man.

I took Jae-seung's hand, and he clasped it tightly as he turned to retrace his steps into the crowd. The beat was thunderous, echoing the pounding of my pulse. As he turned to face me, he drew me in, his body flush against mine and I merged into his – a piece of playdough, ready to be moulded by willing hands.

He lifted my arms in the air and slid his hands up and down my skin, his touch igniting sparks that fizzed around my body to the very tips of my toes. As he placed his fingers in mine, he wrapped my arms around his neck.

'Do you trust me?' he said, his lips almost brushing my earlobe.

The truth was, I knew nothing about him, but he had trusted me enough to butterfly-stitch his wound and that made me think I was right to trust *him*.

I nodded and closed my eyes. A feeling of weightlessness, giving in to his touch wholly and unconditionally, flooded my pores. The beat of the music became more thunderous – or was that my heart? His scent invaded me, engulfed me. It was musky yet fresh. Like walking through Parco Naturale Regionale delle Madonie after a summer storm. I was moving, spinning, and when I faced him again, he tugged my hips closer to him, so my pelvis ground deep into his, sending heat spiralling between my legs. He touched me like I had never been touched before, and we moved as I had never moved before.

Time slipped by. *Secondi. Minuti.*

Tick tick boom. An accidental knock in my back from another dancer forced my eyes open. I caught sight of Steve throwing me an *I need you behind the bar* eye shift as he juggled the Coke hose in one hand and a cocktail shaker in the other.

I pushed myself away from Jae-seung's hold and told him I had to get back to work. On my way to the bathroom, I caught a glimpse of my reflection: hair tousled and skirt twisted. Flashes of flushed skin coated my neck, chest and arms too. What had come over me? I needed to take it down a notch, I thought as I straightened my outfit, reminding myself that Jae-seung was only visiting London. This interaction could never lead to anything else.

The rest of my shift went by in a blur. Jae-seung only left the dance floor to down glasses of water. His stamina was incredible. Occasionally, I scanned the room, and once I caught him smiling at me. I threw him a wink, and he laughed.

–

It was one o'clock in the morning when we made it to New Malden – a good hour before I would usually make it home.

I clutched my jacket tightly to my chest and opened and closed my mouth, probably resembling a goldfish. 'Would you like a cup of tea?' I asked, the words tumbling out again, waiting for the second let-down.

Jae-seung stroked the glass of the coffee shop, staring at the dark interior. This time, there was no impending shift.

'Um. Maybe a quick one? Herbal, right?' He smiled and I returned the gesture.

'Yes, herbal,' I said, placing my key in the lock. 'A great way to unwind after being awake for…?'

He shrugged. 'I've lost count now.'

Inside my flat, he placed his trainers at the entrance and unzipped his leather jacket, placing it on one of my kitchen chairs.

Once I flipped the kettle switch, I went over to my sound machine and turned it to the ocean setting. Jae-seung moved to the collage on my wall and stared intently at the pictures.

'Beautiful,' he murmured.

I clambered on my bed to see which snapshot he was studying. 'That's the Riserva Naturale Orientata dello Zingaro in Sicily. I go there every summer with my dad. Complete isolation if you have the strength to hike through it – the edges of the reserve are the only ways in and out, and they're seven kilometres apart. That beach,' I said, pointing to another picture. 'That's my favourite one if you have the stamina to get there from the north entrance – the heat is brutal in the height of summer.'

'Isolation,' he repeated, and his jaw tightened. He took in all the other pictures. 'Do you miss home?'

'Yes, I do. But I get my fill every summer. Haven't booked my next trip yet cos it all depends on this Netflix audition.'

The kettle boiled and I hopped off my bed and prepared the brews. 'Your tea's ready,' I said, and he thanked me. 'I'm going to change. I smell like a distillery.' He nodded, still hypnotised by my photo montage.

Heading to the bathroom with my cotton twinset, I hesitated before changing. Should I go braless and commando like usual? I held my head in my hands. He was only having a cup of tea, I reminded myself. Besides, I thought, letting out a huge yawn, he couldn't have slept more than a couple of hours in the last two days, and I needed my forty winks so I would be fresh for my audition.

And even if he was interested in me, my one-night-stand rule still stood, I mused as I brushed my teeth. Two such encounters I'd had since coming to England had left me feeling empty and lonely and had taught me that sleeping with a guy on a first date never led to more. But did I want more? Right now, my sole focus was landing this role. And if I didn't get it, then maybe it was finally time to consider moving back home, where I could easily slot back into my old life. No regrets, only bitter disappointment. I would've tried to achieve my dream, but it wasn't meant to be.

Returning to my bedroom, I saw Jae-seung stretched out on my bed, his eyes closed. As I tiptoed nearer, I noted the mug of tea half drunk on the nightstand and that he was fast asleep. Long eyelashes fanned out on his face and his lips were slightly parted, rhythmic breathing as his chest lifted and lowered.

He stirred. Lying on his side, he tucked his knees and placed his hand underneath the pillow.

What now? Should I wake him?

I thought about the comment he had made when we returned this morning from my night shift – a hint that sleeping was a problem. No. I couldn't wake him.

Dad had once told me I was a difficult sleeper when I was young and how his heart always sank when he discovered I wasn't in my bed when he came to check on me before he went to sleep. Usually, I was to be found tucked up with Nonna – my Italian grandmother – who had lived with us since I was a little girl. As an adult, my sleeping patterns had been continuously knocked around with night shifts at the hospital and now, with my Zara job, falling asleep had become a problem again.

At the kitchen sink, I filled a glass half full of water and placed it on my bedside table. It was something that my dad had insisted I do ever since I could remember. 'In case you wake thirsty in the night,' he used to say, and it had become routine.

I sat on the other side of the bed, noticing that Jae-seung was hogging two-thirds of it. Lying down, facing away from him, I curled into a tight ball and closed my eyes. The swell of waves from my sound machine and Jae-seung's deep breathing calmed me; warmth radiating from his proximity soothed me. They were heady feelings and I let the sensations wash over me until I drifted off.

–

A touch. It caused me to flinch. The clock on the wall indicated I had only been asleep for an hour.

Jae-seung's fingers touched my shoulder lightly, stroking down my arm, his breath on my neck. He drew me closer, so I was being spooned – the little spoon to his big one. The heat of his body enveloped me, and my breathing became short and ragged. In his arms I lay waiting and wondering if he was going to move again. My body pressed further into him, the fabric of his jeans a little rough against my legs. An ache began to build the longer we lay in that position, a longing for him to move again overtaking my thoughts. I bit my bottom lip in anticipation.

But his breathing became steadier and before long moved in sync with…

The waves. Deep and rhythmic.

I closed my eyes and imagined I was lying on the sand of Mondello Beach again, wrapped in Jae-seung's arms, the sea crashing over us as we embraced, similar to that scene in *From Here to Eternity*. A poster of that clip used to hang in my bedroom in the apartment where I grew up in Sicily.

My version of that movie moment played out in my mind: sand in my hair as his lips met mine for the first time, before breaking from his arms and running away from the shore; me collapsing onto a towel as he towered over me, water dripping from his skin, before he dropped to his knees and kissed me again – our mouths merging, unable to deny the heat, the connection, the chemistry between us anymore.

I shifted in Jae-seung's embrace and reflexively his grip tightened as if he didn't want to let me go. My hand reached for his and I stroked that scar between his fingers again.

What happened, Jae-seung? Tell me what happened to you.

Before long, I fell asleep.

When I saw you that day

Chapter 6

Gone.

He was gone.

There were crowds of tourists thronging around me – the chatter of a group of Italians noticeable among other nationalities – selfie sticks held aloft, turning to get a three-sixty view of Piccadilly Circus. The advertising hoarding flashed with a stream of brands, and pigeons flocked around the fountain until a toddler ran amok, setting them off in a flutter. Everywhere was a blaze of colour and commotion. But Jae-seung was nowhere to be seen.

He'd said he would be standing right here in this spot after my audition. Had I imagined those words?

This morning, butterflies had woken in my stomach at the impending audition. Jae-seung wasn't beside me, and I had no idea at what point in the night he had left my flat. But on the pillow next to mine was a note from him saying he would take me to my audition, and then when we stood here and he wished me luck, he said he would be waiting.

It had gone better than I could ever have dreamed. A swagger. That's what I had when I walked in wearing a sharp light-grey suit with heels, shoulders pinned back, as if I had been born for this role. And when the male actor had appeared stage left, I hadn't been thrown by his good looks or his obvious attempt to flirt, which usually would have flustered me. If I wanted to get the part, I knew that I had to showcase all I had lived and breathed these last two days. I channelled all that suppressed desire, the way Jae-seung had made me glow with pleasure as I lay in his arms. And I think I nailed it.

Pulling out my phone, I checked for messages. *Niente.* Of course there was nothing. He didn't have a mobile and hadn't kept that sheet of paper Clara had attempted to hand over to him in the coffee shop. And I had never asked him why. Maybe it had been a brush-off, as I initially thought, and this was his way of extricating himself from me.

Or... Maybe he'd forgotten he had to do something for his aunt and uncle and didn't have a way of communicating with me while I was in the audition.

I sat on the steps to the fountain and waited. My stomach growled and I realised it had been hours since I had forced myself to munch on a piece of toast and jam. Nerves always rendered me too anxious to eat. I nipped into the Boots behind me for a meal deal, conscious of needing to be in full sight of the spot where Jae-seung had said he would wait for me.

Having devoured a BLT sandwich, packet of salt and vinegar crisps and an orange juice, I headed wearily to the Tube.

–

When I entered 63 High Street an hour later, hope bloomed inside that Jae-seung would be behind the counter, ready with an apology for abandoning me. But that fleeting optimistic thought came crashing down when I saw Hana serving a customer and Mr Son working the coffee machine.

'Hey,' Hana said as I neared. 'The usual?'

'Actually—'

'A different order? Are you feeling all right?' She smiled, that endearing smile she always gave me that made me feel like the coffee shop was a second home.

I tipped my head, gesturing for her to move out of earshot of her dad. She wiped her hands on her apron and popped out through the exit.

'What's up? Why the long face?' Sympathy was etched into her eyes, enlarged by the frames of her round-rimmed glasses. Her black hair was neatly tied in a ballerina bun, her buttoned cream blouse and long black skirt neatly starched and pleated. 'Did the audition not go well?'

'What? No. I think it went great actually.' I glanced over her shoulder to see if Jae-seung was bringing in some drink crates from outside. But the only sights and sounds were the sandwich grill hissing and the microwave pinging.

'That's good, right?' she said. 'I'll keep my fingers crossed for you.'

I smiled. 'Thanks, Hana. It's um… your… cousin?' She didn't immediately register who I was talking about, and I recalled that her dad's brother and sister had also settled in New Malden with five young kids between them. 'Jae-seung,' I clarified. She lowered her head at the mention of his name.

'What about him?' Her tone was guarded.

'Is he here?'

She shook her head. 'No, he isn't.'

OK. So, this was going to be like drawing blood from a stone. *Air tick.* Clara. The clock on the wall showed she would be here soon.

'Why are you so interested in his whereabouts?' she asked, folding her arms.

Before I had a chance to explain, Mr Son called Hana's name and she turned. Their conversation was in Korean and punctuated with the usual head nods. He then returned to making coffee and Hana stared down at her feet.

'Please don't think me out of place saying this, Fran,' she said, her posture rigid.

'Saying what?'

'Forget about him.'

Her words shocked me. What did she know? Had he told her about the time we had spent together?

'I care about you,' she continued. 'We've known each other a while. I've seen guys come and go and I don't know what went on between you and my cousin, but...' She grasped both of my hands. 'Forget about him,' she repeated.

'But why?'

She pursed her lips and scrunched her face. 'Please don't press me for more information. You know I can't lie. He's gone. Don't think about him. He has a lot going on in his life and doesn't need these... complications.'

I prised my hands away from her hold. 'I promise, I am not a complication. He said he would wait for me after my audition, and he wasn't there when I came out. Hell, he was my ride home. It seemed a little out of character.' Was it, though? What did I actually know about him?

'He's gone. Back to Korea. Left a couple of hours ago. I have to get to work.' With a brief bow and an expression that had none of her typical sunny disposition, she returned behind the counter.

Her words were so blunt. And it was clear that pressing her for more information wasn't going to get me anywhere.

'Francesca!' Clara's voice reverberated around the coffee shop. I turned as she floated in, another of her beautiful creations adorning her frame – a red tea dress with white polka dots. I remembered the day she had dragged me to Fabric Land in Kingston, and she had demanded I choose the pattern for her next project. It skimmed her knees and plunged deep, showcasing her full bust. She was beaming and had a strut to her walk. She'd obviously had sex. Lots of it.

She clicked her fingers at Mr Son and pointed between me and her before sliding into the nearest seat.

'Good weekend?' I asked, sitting down opposite her.

She had a faraway look as she propped her elbow on the table and leaned on the palm of her hand. An outpouring of Portuguese floated from her mouth, which had the widest grin.

'OK, so I picked out the words "ten", "hotel" and "sex" from that.'

She chuckled. 'That's a good summary.'

'Did he make it official?' I teased, though bit my tongue after I said it, realising I was becoming all judgy again.

Her smile instantly dropped, and she dipped her head, twisting her ring round her finger. 'He said he was going to leave his… wife. Please.' She raised her hand. 'Don't say anything.'

'I—'

She pressed a finger to my lips, and I swallowed my words.

Closing her eyes, she did a centring pose as if she was about to start a yoga routine – deep, long breaths, in to four beats, out to five. When she opened them, she was herself again. One cocked eyebrow I took as a warning sign not to say what I wanted to say, which would have been along the lines of: *Please don't do this, Clara. You know he will never leave her.* I could only imagine what might have gone on between them. His confession, a heated argument, followed by passionate make-up sex. It was a pattern she had gone through with him before. She claimed it made things exciting between them. But now she knew the truth.

Many questions crowded my mind. Did she want Philippe to leave his wife? Was she going to move to Paris? That thought saddened me. Clara had been my rock since moving Gran to the home, which reminded me that I was due a visit tomorrow. I prayed it would be one where she knew who I was.

'Now, tell me everything,' Clara said. 'What did I miss?'

Hana appeared by our side and handed over Clara's drink. Her eyebrows were knitted, those lines in her forehead even deeper. She paused and then placed mine in front of me. There it was again. A silent warning in her stiff back, reminding me of what she had said – that I had to let Jae-seung go.

'What was that all about?' Clara said when Hana left. 'She has a face like a smacked arse.' She air-ticked.

I filled Clara in on the weekend, from the moment Jae-seung came to fix my sink and cut his head. The fear I saw in his eyes at the mention of the word 'hospital'. Stitching him. That made her smack her hand over her mouth and pretend-heave. Then I told her how he *did* help me with my audition – how he had taught me things that no drama class I had taken since coming to the UK had taught me, the ones that promised the world but were nothing but generic and depressing as they were always attended by fifty-plus hopefuls, making me wonder why I was still chasing this dream. Maybe Alessandro and my dad were right: it was a fantasy. But Jae-seung didn't believe it was. He had helped me.

Jae-seung. At the mere thought of him, I felt a tightening inside my chest. Tracing my fingers down the cold condensation on my cup, an image of his eyes, sad and fearful, formed in my mind. But there had been happy expressions coating his face too: the playfulness of our tickling contest and his gentle teasing when he told me he was dizzy. It was as if there was a battle going on inside him.

Clara held my hand across the table. '*Meu amor.* Tell me, Fran. What happened then?'

'We had an eventful forty-eight hours.' I sighed. 'He was so thoughtful and kind. He even offered to cover your shift at Zara.'

She sat back. 'Seriously?'

I nodded. 'He drove me to Oxford Circus on his motorbike because I had forgotten about the rail replacement and was going to be late. So much more happened…'

Her iced caramel americano fell from her grip. 'You had sex with him?'

The word 'sex' seemed to bounce off the walls of the café. Dwellers turned in our direction, and I couldn't help but notice Hana's jaw drop. *Agh*.

I sank my head into my hands. 'Clara, why don't you have a quiet button?'

She unpicked my hands from my face. '*Desculpa*,' she said softly. 'Did you have sex with him?' she mouthed.

I shook my head. 'No, we didn't but…' I bit my bottom lip as I thought about last night.

'*Você teve um orgasmo?*' she screeched.

I shot her a *for God's sake, woman, keep your voice down* look.

'What?' She tipped her chin defiantly. 'I said it in Portuguese.'

'I didn't have sex with him,' I whispered, 'nor did I have an orgasm.' I folded my arms. 'We... cuddled.'

Lines appeared on her forehead as she raised her eyebrows. 'And...?'

'And what? That's it. He came in for a cup of tea last night after he brought me home from the club and we ended the evening cuddling. Or rather... he fell asleep, I lay down beside him and he reached out to hold me.'

Clara pinched her lips together, trying but failing to hold in her laughter. 'How very PG of you.'

I shot her a stare.

'Sorry. You cuddled and it was obviously a passionate cuddle, judging by your facial expression. Were you the only one conscious?' She sniggered.

I didn't answer that question but turned my shoulders to the side and sucked my coffee through the straw.

'Sorry, sorry. Only teasing. More importantly, the audition was...?'

A wide grin spread across my face. 'Better than I could have ever imagined. I felt so alive, as if I was born to play this role.'

'So, what's the problem? Why the troubled look earlier?'

'I think... I like Jae-seung. I mean, I know I don't know him well, but I thought we had another two days together to spend some time with each other.' I leaned forward across the table, conscious that Hana was still in earshot. 'I think there was a connection, something a little more than physical but... he's gone.'

'Gone where?'

'According to his cousin...' I cocked my head in Hana's direction. 'Home to Korea, no explanation. He said he would be waiting for me after the audition and then suddenly... poof.'

'And you can't contact him?'

'Doesn't have a mobile, remember? And before you came in, I had the strangest conversation with Hana. She told me to forget about him.'

'Now I understand. A red flag to a bull, huh?' Her finger flicked in a tick shape.

'Clara, can we call time on the idioms?'

She narrowed her eyes at me. 'You really are grumpy, aren't you? What I mean to say is, you can't forget about him, can you? And someone telling you to move on will only add fuel to the flames.' She slapped her forehead. 'Shit, I have literally learned English from that idiom book you got me for my birthday.'

My phone buzzing on the table startled me. The name of my agent flashed on the screen. Clara gasped when she saw my reaction and held two fists to her mouth, trying but failing to hold in her squeals.

I held my finger to my pursed lips and answered the call.

'Hi, Jane,' I said, tracing my finger in circles on the table.

'Fran. Great news.'

My eyebrows raised. Clara noticed and began practically levitating off her chair.

'They loved you,' Jane said. 'Thought you oozed confidence, and you enthralled them with your performance.'

'Really?' I said, my voice all high-pitched, unable to show any of that cool, calm attitude I had displayed merely hours ago.

'Yes, you delivered a great audition by the sounds of it. Good to hear you took my pep talk to heart. The *good* news is they want you.'

I took a sharp intake of breath and clamped my hand over my mouth. 'This is happening,' I whispered against my palm. *Finally happening.*

She always said I would be a star. Mum. A memory stirred in my mind – the summer we travelled to Naples to watch her perform with her Cirque du Soleil troupe. It had been one of the happiest of my life. I was nine years old. Mum had let me loose in her dressing room, applied make-up to my face, wrapped me in feather boas and told me I was beautiful. She had taken me out of the tent where several others of the troupe were getting ready and pointed to the sky and told me I would be a star. The scent of candy floss and sweet popcorn had engulfed me as I peered into the dark blue blanket above.

'That one?' I had asked hopefully, my little finger pointing to a shimmer.

She had shaken her head, lifted me in the air, the sequins of her Basque outfit scratching my arms, and turned me around. '*That* one. The biggest and brightest.'

A pinch on my arm brought me back to the present. Clara was waiting for details, but I realised my agent was still on the call.

Wait. A thought popped into my head.

'You said "the good news".' I held my mobile hard against my ear. 'Does that mean there's *bad* news?'

Jane breathed down the phone heavily. 'Here's the thing, Francesca. It's totally their fault, or well, maybe a little bit mine. For the record, this show is going to be huge – one of Netflix's biggest earners, I reckon, when it comes out. But that's why they're not going with unknowns. What I am trying to say is they already cast the lead female role – it's… Ariana Gomez. And you would be her… stand-in.'

My jaw tightened. No sentences formed in my head except a multitude of Italian swear words.

'Please think it through,' she said. 'This could be a great opportunity for you. If you impress the director and the producers, they will definitely see you as a possibility for a future role. Once you are in with Netflix, big things will happen. I know it. It's decent money – shooting begins in a few weeks, and you would need to commit for two months. It's a pretty intense schedule, some weekends too.'

'Stand-in.' I repeated the words and Clara slowly shook her head. 'They want me to be Ariana Gomez's body double?' I said to clarify in case I had completely misunderstood what she had told me.

A beep interrupted my words.

'Listen, Fran. I have another call coming through, but please think about this and let me know. Tomorrow afternoon. That's the deadline.'

She disconnected the call before I had a chance to say goodbye. Or even what I wanted to say: *Che cazzo?* What the hell?

I dropped my mobile onto the table and sank my head into my hands. A reassuring hold was on my shoulders instantly as Clara slid into the seat next to mine, soothing words in Portuguese drifting around me. I didn't understand a word, but the hold was a comfort.

I stared deeply into her almond eyes. 'I got the role as Gomez's double. My body, her acting. It was never going to be the role of my dreams. I'm done,' I said wearily, and Clara didn't contradict me.

She squeezed my arm. 'Please, Fran. Promise me you won't make any rash decisions.'

When I saw you that day
I couldn't silence my heart

Chapter 7

Gravel crunched beneath my feet, and the sweet scent of honeysuckle and roses seeped into my nose as I approached the entrance to Speirs House – Gran's care home. The person at the other end of the intercom recognised my voice and a buzzer sounded, the door clicking open.

Inside, the familiar smell of stewed vegetables engulfed me, and the burgundy carpets with swirling gold patterns stretched out in front of me. During my first visit to the home, I had been lost in these endless corridors, wondering how Gran would adapt to it when she had lived the last fifty years in her home on Darley Drive. Her old street was unrecognisable to the one she'd moved into with my grandad all those years ago, she had once told me. Scaffolding had appeared repeatedly, revealing renovation after renovation as new owners updated the Victorian houses and bungalows that lined the road. It was her beloved home and leaving it had been unbearably hard.

As I passed by the office, I popped my head around the door and saw the manager behind her computer, a stack of files leaning precariously off the edge of the table.

She gave me a kindly smile. 'Hi, Francesca.'

'How is she today?' I asked. Tightening the knot of my white shirt at my waist, I stroked the pleats of my pink skirt. On my last few visits, Gran had passed judgement over my casual clothes so today I had made an effort to dress smart. I knew she didn't mean it. In the four years we had lived together, she had never once passed judgement on my outfits.

'No change, I'm afraid.' That was code for: *she's calm and stable but it is still unlikely she will know who you are.*

My shoulders sank, resigned to the fact that this would be another visit where I had to pretend I was a volunteer with Age UK. If only I could tell her about the call with my agent yesterday and get some advice.

I knocked on her door and opened it, the hinge creaking. Gran was sitting in an armchair, her silvery grey hair cut sharply in a bob at her chin, her blue floral dress hanging long over her knees. She was clutching a letter tightly in her hand, her glasses in the other – the tip of the frame lightly tapping her mouth. She turned and her eyes widened, as if she had seen a ghost.

'Hey…' I said, shifting my weight from one foot to the other, deliberately not saying the word 'Gran' for fear of it upsetting her.

'I knew you would come,' she said, her tone clipped. 'This.' She lifted her chin at the letter before laying it on the side table next to her chair. 'Why would you say these things? Have you come to apologise?'

Oh boy. This was going to be a puzzle. Pulling out the chair by the desk, I sat down and glanced briefly at the envelope. It was addressed to Gran at her old house.

'Well?' she said. 'What have you got to say for yourself, Marie?'

A cool chill spread over my arms, which suddenly hung like dead weights by my side. She thought I was Mum. Glancing at the envelope again, I drew in a sharp breath when I saw the postmark. The date stamp was the year Mum left us. It was a year that had left an indelible mark. This letter had been written in April, two months before she was due home, only she never came back. And no one knew where she had gone. Endless googling had proved fruitless as there was no trace of her beyond her time with the Cirque du Soleil troupe.

On the floor at Gran's feet, I noticed a blue velvet box, opened, letters and postcards littering the inside. A quick glance made my body still. They were similar to the postcards Mum had sent me – the ones from all the countries she had toured – that had been pinned to a noticeboard in my bedroom, until the day I had torn them down in anger, when I had finally accepted she had abandoned me.

'You have nothing to say?' Gran continued. 'You're willing to walk away from your family for *this*?' She held the letter aloft and my heart thundered in anticipation of what had been written. For a fleeting moment, I saw the address. 'You say you found your passion there.' She flapped the paper in my face. 'That you would be willing to turn away from your family in Sicily. Why, Marie? Why would anyone do that? It will crush Davide to know this. Have you told him?' The letter creased in her grasp – the address no longer visible. 'And your little girl. Have you once thought about her?'

'She's all I think about.' I had no clue where those words had risen from, but I suddenly felt the need to play a part. Maybe this was my chance to find out more about Mum's disappearance. 'I would never hurt her. She's only a child.'

'A child?' she barked. 'She's twelve years old. Almost a teenager. This is when she needs her mother more than ever. Her first period. Her first bra purchase. And you're willing to abandon her, to leave her in *his* care.'

'He's a good father,' I said defensively.

'Pah. His mother does everything for him. Have you forgotten my last visit? She was always fussing around, as if I was incapable of being alone with my granddaughter. I don't trust them. Why, Marie? Why did you pursue your foolish dream for stardom? I knew it would end in trouble for you.'

This comment shocked me. Gran had always been supportive of my desire to act. She had sat in the front row of all my performances of *Little Women* at the local church. To know that she wasn't the same with Mum made me feel sad for her, no matter the feelings that I had grappled with for years – the anger, the hurt, the confusion.

'But when you tell him,' she continued, 'he will never want you to see her again. You will lose Francesca.'

Could that have happened? Could Dad have turned her away once she told him she wanted to leave? No. Dad had told me it was *her* decision to leave, and he had never given me any reason to doubt him.

'But I found my… passion?' I said, hoping it might elicit a response that could shed some light.

'Pole dancing? You sound like a glorified hooker. What a waste of your talent.'

Her words stunned me. What on earth had Mum written in that letter? She was a Cirque du Soleil performer – the rings were her speciality. She would swing from them high above the ground.

It had been all she had ever wanted to do but hadn't counted on that summer twenty-nine years ago happening – the one where she had come to Italy to tour. That was the summer she hurt her ankle after an aerial descent went wrong and the doctor on call that night had been Dad, who was working in Rome, where the show had performed for two nights prior. Love at first sight, they called it, and after a passionate summer during which Mum couldn't perform, *I* had been the result. They got married quickly, claiming their affair was for keeps. Growing up with an absent mother had become something I was used to. Calendars on my wall were marked with crosses as I counted the days until she would come home from touring. But then one day I realised those crossed-out days had become endless.

Gran flapped the letter at me, breaking my thoughts, and I shifted my seat forward. This was it. My chance to find out what had happened, why she hadn't ever returned home to Sicily.

But before I could get a finger on the sheet, Gran had drawn her arm and torn the letter in half, then half again, and again until it was nothing more than tiny pieces of a puzzle. Dropping them in the bin on the floor beside her, she threw her head back onto the armchair. Her hand reached for her forehead, and she groaned as she closed her eyes.

'Are you OK?' I said in a panic. 'Can I get you some water?'

When she opened her eyes again, they blinked rapidly. 'Who are *you*?'

I sat back in my chair. 'I'm... your... daughter?'

She gripped the arms of her seat, her nails scratching on the fabric. 'No! You're not. I haven't seen my daughter in fifteen years.'

I raced to do the calculation in my head but was interrupted by more groaning, a deep throaty sound. She was running her hand across her face over and over again. 'Get out! Whoever you are.'

At that moment, a nurse raced in, threw me a sympathetic smile, before crouching beside Gran's chair. 'It's OK, Mrs Lee, you're OK. You're safe, you are being well cared for. This is your granddaughter, Francesca. She came for a quick visit to see how you are. But I think it's time you rested.'

'Granddaughter?' she said, tugging on her ear. 'This isn't my granddaughter. She's only a child and she lives in Sicily. And I haven't seen her in so, so long.' Tears welled in her eyes.

The nurse turned to me and mouthed, 'I'm sorry,' with a nod towards the door. I took that as my cue to leave.

Outside her room, I heard the nurse continue to comfort Gran, reassuring her that everything was fine.

But everything wasn't fine. An overwhelming need to gulp in some fresh air struck me in the chest, and I staggered out of the building.

I leaned on the main door, my fingers grazing the wooden structure, trying to hold my tears. What I wouldn't give for Gran to recognise me again so I could ask what on earth had happened all those years ago.

But it wasn't only the conversation with Gran that had my head in a spin.

No matter how much I tried not to, I couldn't stop thinking of Jae-seung. Flashes of his arms around me on the dance floor, the playfulness of that evening in my flat and his dark, brooding eyes kept invading my mind. But he was gone, home to South Korea, and now I had found out that Mum had found her passion in the very same place he was.

That fleeting glance at the address had shown me that Mum had found her passion in Seoul.

Was she still there?

When I saw you that day
I couldn't silence my heart
And when I held you close

Chapter 8

What are you going to do?

Clara's text message sat unanswered on my mobile along with the woman-shrugging-her-shoulders emoji. I had sent her a rambling voice message, recording it all the way from the care home down into the high street, which she had probably managed to listen to discreetly using her earphones. She was at college today and a proper conversation was out of the question until she finished at five, or possibly during her brief lunch break.

The June heatwave was over, and a downpour had caught me unawares as I approached the coffee shop. Rain battered the glass. A moody gloom sat outside while the atmosphere inside 63 High Street was cosy, with lamps clipped to wire structures on the walls throwing a soft glow over the room. The smell of locally roasted coffee beans invaded my nose and instantly calmed me.

Hana wasn't on the rota today and a part of me was relieved. Our last conversation had left a sour taste in my mouth. She was hiding something from me, and I didn't know why or what she couldn't tell me about her cousin.

Mr Son bowed his head as I approached the counter. 'The sink is good?'

It took me a few seconds to understand what he was referring to. 'Oh yes, I forgot to say thank you so much. I appreciated your nephew's help.'

'He is good boy. Flat white?' he asked, and I nodded. He was a mind reader, knowing that the change in weather warranted my hot choice of coffee.

He typed my order onto his screen, the amount appearing on the card reader. 'That boy makes me very proud.'

I tapped my phone for payment and to collect my loyalty stamp while Mr Son set about making my drink. 'Will Jae-seung be returning to New Malden again?' I asked, leaning over the counter.

He shook his head as he pressed the button for the percolator. 'No, no. He is busy now. Much to do.'

'Oh,' I said, thinking that wasn't in the least bit informative. Did he mean ever?

I puffed out my cheeks. Jae-seung was gone and unlikely to return. That was all the confirmation I needed. There was no point in thinking of what might have been. And what had there been between us anyway? A cuddle. Probably a reflexive sleep-induced stretch at that.

I chewed the inside of my mouth as I watched Mr Son prepare my coffee methodically and meticulously, and I picked apart my time with Jae-seung.

No. It wasn't just how I had fallen asleep in his arms. Jae-seung had been kind, considerate, easy to talk to, and he had taken on the role of my acting guide with such good grace. He had helped me land a role. Only, not the role of my dreams as I had believed it would be.

An ache settled deep in my chest. Today could have been the start of something exciting for me. I had been a body double once before but not for the main star. It involved hours and hours of placement, people prodding me and poking me, getting the right angles, cameras zoomed in. Hot, sweaty rooms crammed with scores of people from lighting to make-up. Continuous cramp when I had been moulded into a shape and wasn't allowed to move. The nudity. It would be my naked body and Ariana's face on the screen. Could I do it? The deadline to confirm loomed large but I needed an injection of caffeine and hoped that maybe Clara could call during her lunch break for some much-needed advice.

Mr Son handed over my coffee. As I turned to get a table, the front door burst open and in strode Sun-hee – his younger daughter. She approached and lambasted her dad in Korean with an increasingly high-pitched voice. She slammed her hand down on the counter, tutting in response to every sentence her dad uttered, before skulking off.

The other customers shifted uncomfortably in their seats, though a couple of mums with toddlers seemed almost relieved that this spot in town was indifferent to a bit of commotion, as their offspring were adding to the din with their whining for more cake and to be allowed to pet every dog in the café.

One of the university students popped their head out from the kitchen, laden with toasted sandwiches and smoothies.

'Tables four and six,' Mr Son announced to him.

'Is everything OK with Sun-hee?' I asked.

His forehead wrinkled. 'She is angry. No longer can she go on her holiday. She needs direction, plan for her future. But she is lost.'

A pang of compassion filled me as I took in his weary face and then turned to Sun-hee, who was slumped in one of the armchairs at the back, sullen and moody. Her black jeans had rips from top to bottom, a plaid shirt hanging loose over a Rolling Stones T-shirt. Pink was the colour of choice today for her pixie haircut.

Hana had often complained that she couldn't relate to her sister. There was an age gap of six years and Sun-hee had dropped out of her college course twice already, while Hana had finished her law degree at Surrey university a few years ago and had a good job at a local solicitor's firm. But she also had her duty to her family, which involved working weekends and the odd weekday shift for her parents, as well as helping do the accounts and tax returns for the café. A part of me wondered whether Hana resented her sister for the carefree way she lived her life.

'Let me talk to her, Mr Son. Maybe I can help?'

He bowed and expressed his thanks. It was the least I could do. Mr and Mrs Son had been the best landlord and landlady, having not raised my rent last year when my initial twelve months was complete. They had also let me paint the walls peach and said they wouldn't need me to Polyfilla any holes on the walls when I ended my lease. And there were a lot of holes. The wall behind my bed was a kaleidoscope of Sicilian memories and movie stars.

'Can I join you?' I asked Sun-hee as I hovered by the green IKEA faux-satin sofa.

'Free country,' she replied.

I braced myself and sat down. She had her AirPods in her ears and was staring at her phone.

'What are you watching?' I asked.

'BTS,' she mumbled, sinking further into the seat.

'That famous boy band?'

She rolled her eyes slowly. 'The biggest K-pop band in the world.'

'Sorry, I don't follow their music. I wouldn't recognise them if they walked into the coffee shop,' I said with a laugh.

She hit pause on her phone. 'Why? Cos all Koreans look the same?'

'God, no. That's not what I meant.' My cheeks flamed. 'I don't follow popular music. I hear songs on the radio but generally I wouldn't recognise most artists if they walked in, regardless of their ethnicity.'

Her lips pinched and she returned to her screen. 'I was meant to see them,' she said in almost a whisper.

'See who?' I asked, noticing a shift in her prickly demeanour. I lifted my cup to my lips and took a sip.

'BTS.'

'In concert?'

'Yeah.' Her bottom lip protruded, and her eyes seemed to water – the moisture shining with the reflection of the mobile screen. 'My friend was meant to fly over with me to Seoul, but some work crisis came up. We had it all planned. Two tickets to see them at the Olympic Stadium. Three nights of freedom in a hotel room with her before beginning my confinement at my aunt's in Dangjin-si.'

'What's that?'

She laughed. 'You mean *where's* that? It's a city about a two-hour bus ride north of Seoul.'

'Why would it be confinement there?'

'Doesn't matter. What's the point in telling you? I'm not going because of my stupid parents.' She threw a dagger stare at her dad, who was greeting a customer with an affable smile. 'They won't let me travel alone. Dumbest thing ever. I'm twenty-two, for heaven's sake. And they don't trust me roaming the streets of Seoul on my own.'

'I'm sorry. That must suck.'

'Tell me about it. I even had backstage passes.'

'Wow, how did you get those?'

'I... um... won a competition. It was going to be the best night of my life. The only way I was allowed to go was if I went with my friend, who my parents approve of, and then I promised them I would agree to spending three weeks with my rels. To "sort myself out".' She did quotation marks with her fingers.

'And that would be bad because... you don't get on?'

'Imagine Hana times one hundred.'

That comment was lost on me. Hana was sweet and kind, but possibly to her sister she was conformist and strait-laced, perhaps?

My mobile buzzed and Clara's name flashed on the screen. 'Sorry, excuse me,' I said, pointing at my phone. 'It's my best friend and I have to take it – she's probably on her lunch break.'

She shrank further into the armchair as if she couldn't care less and pointed at her AirPods as if to confirm that she *really* couldn't care less about my conversation.

'Tell me everything, *meu amor*,' Clara said the second I accepted the call.

'Where do I begin?'

'At the beginning?' There was nothing but sympathy in her tone. Clara's term of endearment that she used to address me always made me smile. We were the nearest each other had to family here in the UK – and Clara wasn't close to hers. I was like the sister she never had, she'd once said as she drained a double Jack and Coke at Havana Club one night when she told me her life story: growing up with an absent father and a mum who worked round the clock and expected Clara to fend for herself.

I relayed the events of the morning to her in a more coherent way than the rambling voice note I had sent: Gran thinking I was my mother, Mum's letter, her passion being found in Seoul. Pole dancing? I shook my head as I said those words. None of it made sense and without the letter to confirm, it could all have been Gran's ramblings – mistaking Mum's classy acrobatics for something a little seedier. From what little conversation Gran and I had had, it appeared she had never been supportive of Mum's career.

'You have to go,' Clara announced when I paused to take a sip of my coffee.

'Go where?'

'Seoul. Go find her.'

I sat back against the sofa at the suggestion. 'But what about the Netflix show?'

'Ugh. I forgot about that.' She paused. 'Fuck it. We aim high, Francesca, or we go home. Not literally go home, I mean we keep pushing ourselves until we get what we deserve. Remember our pact, the one we made in front of Taylor?'

I smiled at the memory. We had been celebrating my *East-Enders* role and Clara getting her first Etsy request for one of her dresses on a night out in Richmond. After a couple of drinks at one of the local pubs, we had bought a bottle of tequila and taken it to Clara's flat share because her three housemates were out, which meant we had the run of the living room. In front of Clara's most prized possession – a framed signed photo of Taylor Swift – we had not only sworn to always 'be fearless' but we had also made a drunken pact: that she wouldn't return to Brazil nor I to Sicily unless we had hit rock bottom. We made a proclamation that we wouldn't settle for less than we deserved – for me to play big roles and for her fashion business to take off. No compromises would be made along the way.

'I remember the pact,' I said.

'This role will *not* further your dream, no matter what your agent says. In fact, it might paint you as someone who settles. And I don't know, Fran, but maybe your mum holds the key to something – the reason why you do all this in the first place or the reason why you don't do it with enough passion.'

Her words threw a chill over me. I had held the real reason for wanting to do all this – the acting, the endless auditions – close to my chest. Clara was a good friend, and obviously an intuitive one too, but I couldn't tell her the reason. I was scared. Scared that if I admitted the truth, I would realise how ridiculous this dream was and how right Alessandro had been to throw water over it that night in front of my family at home in Sicily.

'You should go,' Clara said emphatically.

'Go to South Korea? With what money?'

'Your Sicily fund.'

'But I always go home every summer. Dad and the twins would be devastated if I didn't.'

'Then use your emergency fund, or I will lend you the money.' My heart twisted at the sentiment, knowing full well two of Clara's credit cards were maxed out. 'And before you use it as an excuse, I will cover for any of your shifts at Zara that you miss. Least I can do after you standing in for me so often.'

Thoughts of travelling to a city halfway across the world made my stomach clench. 'I can't do this on my own. And besides, what do I have to go on? Mum *possibly* lived in Seoul, around sixteen years ago. An address I saw fleetingly – the words Mapo-gu the only ones I remember. I googled it. It's a district of Seoul almost twenty-four square metres. And I searched for her name plus that area and all I got was some mention of a jewellery store called Marie. The phrase "looking for a needle in a haystack" springs to mind.'

'I would come at the drop of a hat.' She paused, and I knew she was doing an air tick with her finger. 'But I've got exams next week. I should study. If only the flat were quieter. I'm going to have to camp out in Caffè Nero if that drilling in next door's renovation continues. Have you thought of asking your dad for some information?'

'No. He told me, in no uncertain terms, that he never wanted to talk about her ever again. She abandoned us. Me and him. She shattered his heart. But I still cling on to the fact that her last words to me were: "I'll come back for you."'

Why hadn't she, though? For years and years, I had held on to that statement, even though Dad told me to forget about her. That letter. The one Gran ripped had the answer. Could I risk visiting her again and asking for more information? Or would it upset her too much?

'Francesca, *meu amor.* I will support you in whatever decisions you make. But please, don't let money or your jobs here in England prevent you from going. I gotta go,' she announced.

After saying goodbye, I slumped on the sofa, the buzz of the coffee shop and Clara's words ringing in my ears. Could I do it? Could I really get on a plane to Korea and go and find Mum?

'JK Dance Studio,' Sun-hee declared, breaking through my thoughts.

'Sorry?' A strange expression coated her face. Mischief? Excitement?

She clapped her hands and pulled out her AirPods. 'This is fucking brilliant.'

'What is?'

'You and me. We're going to Seoul. I was totally eavesdropping on your conversation. I searched Mapo-gu and there's only one pole-dancing studio in that area. It's quite famous. Loads of open-call K-pop auditions happen there and it's popular with foreigners. It was established sixteen years ago.'

My mouth was hanging open, a million thoughts crowding my mind – no individual one breaking free.

'Yeah, I know, you think I'm mad and you're worried about cost. Look, the Seoul part of my trip was all expenses paid. It was part of the prize.' She tapped her mobile to life. 'My parents love you, so they'll definitely let me go if you accompany me.' Simpering at her lock screen, she kissed it. 'Nothing gets in the way of a member of the Army seeing her boys.'

Wow. I had heard the devotion of BTS fans was strong, but I didn't realise quite how strong.

Sun-hee rose from her seat and made a fist. 'We're going to Seoul and we're gonna find your mum.'

I dared not let myself get excited by that thought because it was fraught with too many emotions: anger, resentment, hurt. *So* much hurt.

Then another thought broke free. Could this be my chance to see Jae-seung again?

When I saw you that day
I couldn't silence my heart
And when I held you close
I knew we could never be apart

Chapter 9

Pinch me.

Please pinch me. Only so I know this isn't a dream. One of Taylor Swift's iconic lyrics about a nightmare and a daydream sprang to mind, and it made me think of Clara. If only she was here to steady me.

I stared out of the window of our suite on the twenty-second floor of the Grand InterContinental Seoul Parnas. When I say window, I don't mean similar to the four-paned one in my studio in New Malden. This one was floor to ceiling and twenty-four feet wide. The whole room was easily three times the size of my place. The vibrant Teheran-ro in the heart of the Gangnam district was the panorama.

Sung-hee and I had crashed as soon as we had entered our hotel suite a few hours ago – a combination of the night flight and the inability to drift off during it due to a spin cycle of nerves and excitement. It was early evening now, but my body was screaming out that it was still the crack of dawn in England. In the bathroom, I took in my appearance – my travel clothes a wrinkled mess, a whiff of aeroplane food soaked into the fabric.

How did I get here? I thought as I washed my face. Forty-eight hours ago, I was agreeing to have the spare flight ticket to Seoul changed to my name. A multitude of thanks abounded from Mr and Mrs Son for agreeing to be Sun-hee's chaperone. Clara had moved into my studio before I headed to the airport – so she could study for her exams in peace – with a cast-iron guarantee that she would cover for my next two Zara shifts.

The call to my agent had been one of the hardest I had ever made. I turned it down – the 'chance' to be Ariana Gomez's stand-in. I wanted so much more than that.

But I didn't know how to get it.

Maybe Clara was right. Finding Mum could help me make sense of why I wanted stardom so much.

Steve from Havana Club had been rather too enthusiastic about me having Sunday off, especially when I told him Clara was stepping in for me. It made me wonder whether my job there was secure at all. When I mentioned the prospect of seeing that Korean guy who had wowed everyone on the dance floor, he had approved of the lengths I was going to in order to see him again.

But would I see him again? I hadn't plucked up the courage to ask Sun-hee about him. She had been tuned out during the whole twelve-hour flight. Every now and again I had peered over at her mobile screen and seen nothing but image after image of her favourite band – BTS. The routines were phenomenally orchestrated; the way their bodies moved reminded me of an image that was singed in my memory: Jae-seung on the dance floor. He had the same star-quality presence, the abs, the smouldering look when he had glanced over his shoulder at me, as if I was the only person in that room. But he also had that beaming smile that the BTS members showcased in abundance during interviews – a smile that had made me melt as he had tickled me relentlessly.

I wanted to see him again. I wanted to know what pain he was carrying and couldn't let go of.

It's not your job to fix him, a voice inside me said. *Focus on your own pain.* But how could I? I had been running away from it for too long.

I turned away from the window and took in the sweep of the room. Velvet cushions and throws adorned the king-size bed. The bathroom to the left was wall-to-wall marble with a double sink and roll-top bath. It must cost a fortune to stay here and suddenly I felt horribly out of place as I pulled out a simple cotton T-shirt and shorts from my case and slipped them on.

The doors to the other room burst open and Sun-hee strode in dressed in purple short dungarees with a BTS Army T-shirt visible beneath.

'Right,' she announced, flashing her phone at me. 'Street food first and then a trip to Hapjeong-dong. I've registered us for a class this evening at JK Dance Studio.'

'I'm sorry, what?' I said, my head still fuzzy with that post-nap/jet lag confusion. 'I can't dance.'

'We're only going there to check it out, but I thought I should register us in case anyone starts questioning why we are there. After we have sampled the delights of Gangnam, though. I have wanted to come here for so long and we are not going to waste a minute more in this room, even though it's pretty bloody amazing, right?'

As much as I was excited to explore this incredible city, I was also keen to return here later tonight to sink into that bed – the Tempur mattress had sprung back as soon as I had risen, and it had been the sweetest slumber.

But nothing would ever compare to the sleep I had with…

Jae-seung. His arms wrapped around me. Those fingers touching me, stroking me.

But was it destined to be only an innocent moment in time? Two individuals allowing themselves to feel free because there were no expectations. Nothing more than an uncomplicated, brief encounter. One I should forget.

Sun-hee stood in front of me, waving a hand in front of my face. 'You OK?'

'Yes. Sorry. Think the travelling has turned my brain to mush. This place is…' I stretched my arms out. 'I have no words to describe what this is. Not sure how I will ever repay you.'

'You don't need to repay me. It was a gift, and I am happy to share it with you. You're…' She gave me a once-over and I subconsciously tugged at my white T-shirt and smoothed the creases of my green linen shorts. 'I can see why... my parents dig you.'

'That's sweet,' I said, wondering what I had done to warrant the praise. 'Wait. I thought you said this was a prize. Some competition you entered?'

She scuffed the carpet with her boot. 'Yeah, I meant "prize". Anyhow. Let's go.'

The streets of Gangnam were filled with hordes of young, hip Koreans. Couples walked arm in arm at a slow pace. Everyone had an aura of coolness. And everywhere was bright – from shopfront windows to billboards – with script I couldn't fathom, the occasional English word centring me. Cafés mingled with high-end stores. Sun-hee explained that this was one of the main shopping districts.

After exploring the area, we headed on the metro to Gwang-jang Market to sample the delights of its street food. I recognised many of the dishes on offer because I had often been to the many Korean cafés lining the high street in New Malden. Over a couple of *mayak kimbap* – a sushi-like seaweed-wrapped roll stuffed with pickled daikon radish and rice – and *bindaetteok* – a pancake made from ground mung beans with an assortment of vegetables and fried chicken – we hopped on the metro again to the Mapo-gu district.

Bright yellow walls lined the interior of the JK Dance Studio; excited Korean teens and pre-teens waited for a class outside one room. At reception, Sun-hee spoke to the woman behind the desk, and we filled out various forms. I scanned my attire – nowhere near suitable for a dance class but I hoped Sun-hee was right and joining the class was only a way to get some information without arousing suspicion.

I waited as she talked at rapid speed in Korean to someone who the receptionist introduced us to. She was dressed in a Lycra vest and shorts, with a JK Dance Studio-logoed cropped T-shirt slipping off her shoulder, her purple hair in braids. Every now and again Sun-hee pointed at me, and the lady nodded and mumbled, '*Ne.*'

In a whirl of activity, we were ushered into one of the studios, which was full to the brim with young Korean women talking animatedly between themselves, hands held over their mouths as their chatter escalated.

Sun-hee squeezed my arm. 'This is a riot. We're gonna do a K-pop class.'

'Wait, what? I told you I don't dance.'

'We'll skulk at the far end and watch all these wannabes think they're the next member of Blackpink.' She laughed. 'That lady I was talking to said she would meet you here tomorrow afternoon for a chat. She has some information for you.'

The thought that the cold trail of Mum's disappearance was heating up lit a spark inside me.

As the class began, music pounded from speakers tucked in the corners of the ceiling, the beat thunderous and reminiscent of Havana Club's music. I let Sun-hee absorb the atmosphere while I slipped out and had a nose around the place. There was studio after studio with different classes and rhythms reverberating through the windows.

I came across another studio and peered in. The lighting was low, almost burlesque in its feel. Transfixed. There was no other word for it. I was transfixed. Half a dozen women stood holding metal poles dressed mostly in hotpants and Lycra tops, hair loose, wearing heels several inches high. They held the pole and moved around it, as if it was attached to them, in time to a slow beat. They sensually caressed it, their heads periodically tipping, spines curved.

I moved away. It felt voyeuristic standing there and the teacher at the front of the class had spotted me staring.

Along the corridor, I came across the information board with schedules in Korean and English detailing all the classes. That was an intermediate pole-dancing class I had witnessed and the one I had stepped out of was K-pop for beginners.

Another board attracted my attention. It was covered with pictures of dance troupes, dancers of the week and...

My fingers traced over one photo and my heart beat wildly in time to the techno beat pouring out of a nearby studio. *Mum?* It was definitely her – that unmistakable smile revealing one dimple, bright green eyes the same colour as mine, curls cascading from a ponytail pinned high on her head. Her arm was around a Korean woman, who was staring at her with that same look that everyone had when they were in her presence because she was a star. Peering closer, I saw balloons and banners in the background, signalling it was New Year. Eight years ago.

Eight years. Mum had left me and Dad sixteen years ago. The timeline for where she had been all these years had halved. I couldn't believe it. Maybe the meeting tomorrow could make it even smaller. I pulled out the pin and held the picture in my hand, inspecting it more closely.

'Why, Mum?' I whispered. 'Why did you leave me?'

When I saw you that day
I couldn't silence my heart
And when I held you close
I knew we could never be apart
But I can't let you into my world

Chapter 10

The Army. *This* was the BTS Army.

I stood outside the Olympic Stadium with Sun-hee by my side, bopping on the spot uncontrollably. Thousands upon thousands of fans thronged around us, their excited chatter and bursts of singing flowing into the early evening sky. Sixty-nine thousand fans to be exact, as the show was sold out. A fraction of their devoted fan club. According to my host, this concert would be streamed by millions.

The sun was setting on an eventful day in Seoul. My mind was still whirring from the revelation that Mum had lived here for eight years, helping to establish JK Dance Studio with Ara, the lady whose shoulder she was draped over in that picture. Mum was known locally as MJ, short for Marie Jean, her forenames. That explained why it had been so hard to find her online. Then she had moved on to America, the teacher at the studio – Song Yae-lee – had said. Over cans of aloe vera juice, Yae-lee had told me about when she first joined the studio and how Mum had been one of the reasons it had become so successful – drawing in well-known dancers from around the globe to run ad-hoc classes, spawning several K-pop stars in its wake.

All I had now was the name of a place in New York, where Mum had moved on to. A quick Google search had shown it was a pole-dancing studio. Perhaps those words Gran had spoken to me at the care home were true – Mum had found her passion with that form of movement. Maybe I had been too dismissive of it last night at first inspection.

What should I do now? I needed time to digest all the things I'd been told and reminded myself that if Mum had wanted me to find her, she would have found a way to stay in touch and not changed her name. Maybe I could be brave and ask Dad about what he knew.

My thoughts turned to the other person I had wanted to find here. I had casually mentioned his name to Sun-hee during our afternoon sightseeing on the red Seoul City Tour Bus – the best way to see the city if on a tight schedule, Sun-hee had announced – and she had mumbled something about him being hard to reach but that she would try.

Sun-hee was struggling to contain her excitement as we weaved our way through the crowd. Grabbing my hand, she didn't relinquish her grip until we had reached a side entrance where security guards abounded. She produced her mobile, and a guy dressed head to toe in black beeped a scanner over it. She pointed at me and spoke in rapid-fire Korean. Before I knew it, bands were secured on our wrists and backstage passes hung around our necks. Sun-hee grabbed a couple of purple LED wands and glow sticks from the merch table and handed them to me.

I held mine in my hands and stared at the pass in disbelief. We were going to meet BTS? I wished now I had paid more attention to what Sun-hee had told me about the band. I could vaguely remember the name of one of them – Jimin – as there were reminders of him plastered over her outfit, from a T-shirt with his face on it to a necklace with his name in Korean. It didn't seem right that I was going to meet the members when there were thousands around me that would kill to be in my position.

'Come on,' Sun-hee squealed once we made it through the gate. We found our turnstile and flashed our passes, making our way to the interior.

I took in the sight before me. A three-sixty turn revealed an epic arena slowly filling to maximum capacity, the sky above the open roof turning to an inky blue, the stadium ablaze with multicoloured strobe lighting. The stage screens glowed with flashing images of the band and the words *BTS Army* pulsated to a thunderous beat.

Sun-hee jumped on the spot as she absorbed it all. 'I can't believe I am here.' Tears welled in her eyes, and she fanned her face with her hand. 'Thank you, thank you so much for coming with me and making this happen.'

I smiled at her with great affection. 'You're welcome.' Though I knew it should be *me* thanking *her*. So far, she hadn't let me pull out my bank card once, constantly claiming it was an all-expenses-paid trip. It seemed too good to be true.

We took our seats in the front row. Front row? This was insane. At Taylor's concert in Hyde Park, we were so far back that the goddess of pop was a mere speck in the distance.

As darkness enfolded us, fans raised their glow sticks, their chants deafening, the stadium aglow with bursts of red and green moving in rhythm to the beat booming through the loudspeakers.

Sun-hee was soaking up the atmosphere – the broadest grin on her face. Now I could understand why she had been so bereft when she'd thought she couldn't be here. I leaned over and asked her what the fans were screaming.

'They're saying "High JYNKS",' she shouted.

I took in the scene. A clap-clap motion on the word 'High' and then arms outstretched to the word 'JYNKS'. It was mesmerising watching the movement.

'Who's that? Is it someone from BTS?' I said but instantly regretted it at the weary look on Sun-hee's face.

'No,' she said. 'JYNKS is the name of the support band that will come on first. And their fans are known as "High JYNKS".'

'Oh,' I said, grateful for the explanation before I stuck my foot in my mouth any more. *Air tick*, I thought as I nodded and flicked my head. Jeez, it was becoming a nervous affliction. Thinking of Clara made me pull out my phone and do a quick vid to send her of the scene around me, complete with the wide-eyed/shocked emoji.

A countdown appeared on the massive screen behind the stage.

Sixty seconds.

The screams escalated.

Sun-hee nudged me in the arm and chewed her thumbnail. 'OK, so I lied.'

'About what?' I asked.

'I didn't win a competition.'

Fifty seconds.

'So how did you get these tickets?' The thought of a black-market purchase involving maxing out several credit cards that she hadn't told her parents about made my palms feel clammy. 'Please tell me not illegally.'

She gave me the same eye roll she had given me at the coffee shop. 'Why does everyone think the worst of me?' There was a hint of sadness in her tone.

Forty seconds.

'I'm sorry,' I said, touching her elbow. 'Go ahead, tell me your confession.'

'I know the band.'

'BTS?'

'No, stupid, the support band – JYNKS.'

Thirty seconds.

'That's cool. So, they gave you free tickets?'

'They did. I mean, he did. The lead singer. I know him *really* well.'

Twenty seconds.

'JC is his name. And you know him too. He's my cousin.'

The stadium plunged into darkness, and a voice boomed over the loudspeakers counting down the last ten seconds in Korean as her revelation spiralled in my brain.

Set. Dul. Hana. Spotlight.

You, I thought.

I found you.

When I saw you that day
I couldn't silence my heart
And when I held you close
I knew we could never be apart
But I can't let you into my world
Because a love like this…

Chapter 11

Blonde you.

Jae-seung's hair was no longer jet black. A grey tux, with white shirt unbuttoned halfway down, adorned his body; a microphone pressed close to his lips – the kind that had an earpiece and wrapped around the cheek. A voice I had never heard before, so tender. Those lips that had been achingly close to mine as we rehearsed were now singing. Korean words, the melody soaring high. A pitch-perfect note held until...

A blaze of fireworks burst from the middle of the stage on either side of Jae-seung and the rest of the band stepped out from behind him, the music changing into a hard techno/pop beat as they all joined in. A flawless sequence of moves, perfectly in sync. Daring. Brave.

That explains the dancing at the nightclub.

I stood rigid, unmoving while Sun-hee jumped manically beside me. Jae-seung, the guy who had been in my bed only a few days ago was... judging by a quick scan of the crowd... adored by thousands, maybe millions if you counted those streaming online.

Every move was faultless. How they were all able to dance and sing and not be out of breath was truly a sight to behold. Stamina. They had it in abundance and it explained Jae-seung's ability to push through a full night in London, hours at the coffee shop and then witnessing my Havana Club shift all in forty-eight hours. On what? A few hours' sleep at most. I had once read an article in the *Metro* newspaper on my way into

London about the rise in popularity of K-pop bands – the gruelling training sessions, the strict diets.

Is that what you endured to get here? How many hours of practice had it taken to be the support band for the global phenomenon that was BTS?

Another part of the article came to mind. The no-dating rule. A heaviness sat low and deep in my chest at that thought before I shook that feeling away. Had I forgotten how our encounter had ended?

The first song came to a climax and the crowd erupted. Sun-hee beamed like the proud cousin she obviously was.

But there was no time to grill her about how on earth her cousin wasn't in fact the barista/plumber/possible model I had assumed he was, but a K-pop sensation, as the next song came on immediately, seamlessly after.

I couldn't stop staring at Jae-seung – or JC as I guess he was known. His smile was broad and almost too wide. It didn't seem as natural as the one he had shown me that night in my flat, once he had begun to relax in my presence. And he rocked those blonde locks while his bandmates had an assortment of pink and lilac streaks threaded through their hair. They were all handsome, but JC had something special, or was it just that my heart was already his?

Woah. Where had that thought come from? This was ridiculous. I couldn't have fallen for a pop idol. Hana's warning came to mind: 'He doesn't need these… complications.'

In a flash there was a costume change to black jeans and white T-shirt, and more heavily choreographed sequences abounded.

Jae-seung was always at the front or close to the front. Behind them on the big screens, images of the band members flashed. JYNKS stood for JC, Ye-joon, Noodle, Kwang and So. I couldn't help but notice that whenever Jae-seung held the tune alone, the roar was louder. The third song had JC harmonising with Noodle, an interspersion of English words sprinkled among the Korean ones. JC's baritone notes showed strength and that his singing talent was far-reaching.

I closed my eyes.

The memory of his touch as he pulled me into him, and his singing voice, washed over me while I breathed in the humid, fragrant air.

When I opened my eyes, it was as if he had found me in the crowd. He jerked his head a little before resuming his duet, crooning the words 'your love', the microphone pressed tightly against his lips.

A million questions filtered through my mind. Why had he come to New Malden for a few days so near to the start of a tour? Why hadn't he told me who he was? Was he in London only to enjoy some anonymity for a few days? And more importantly, why had he run away? I hadn't dared let myself think of the reasons why, because it was a pain I had suffered before, deeply, and knew how hard it was to heal from. Maybe his sudden departure had nothing to do with me; maybe he had been recognised and fled. But what did that matter now? Jae-seung was a K-pop star and out of my league.

'This is my favourite song off their new album,' Sun-hee announced, breaking through my thoughts as the gentle chords of the next song began. 'It's JC's solo and it's partly in English.'

I stood motionless as Jae-seung pulled off his earpiece and mic and grabbed a handheld microphone from a pillar that had emerged from the side of the stage. He leaped onto the raised platform with ease and began singing. There was so much expression in his face, as if he was feeling every single word. Then there was a look that I had seen before – the one when I suggested we go to the hospital.

'Five minutes,' he sang. 'Five minutes.'

Then something happened – a shift. Was it my imagination or was he missing the beat? The screams from the audience were still deafening. Maybe it was because I was in the front row and my eyes were trained on his lips, but I noticed it.

He tipped his head back, the microphone held flush to his mouth, the notes soaring again. A crack. The slightest break in his voice. The music continued as he held his hand over his eyes, rubbing at them, an emotion obviously too hard to bear engulfing him.

One moment, he was standing tall, then… A thud. He was collapsed on the stage. Had he fallen off the raised platform by accident? Or had he fainted?

Screams abounded. Sun-hee grasped my arm and held her other hand over her mouth. There was a rush on stage of crew and security, and the other band members were immediately placed in front of the commotion – a new song bellowing out, cheery smiles on their faces, even if their eyes kept flicking over to Jae-seung.

'What happened?' I said to Sun-hee.

'I don't know but we have to find out.'

She clutched my hand and pulled me away from our seats as the show continued. I caught a flash of Jae-seung on the ground – an oxygen mask over his mouth. My body tensed. It was a sight I had been used to seeing day in day out at the hospital in Sicily, but this was Jae-seung, and the concern hit deeper.

It seemed too easy to slip unnoticed to the edge of the stage where there were scores of stagehands and other people talking fast in Korean. Our short height meant we could slip around everyone and make our way through to the long winding corridors that formed the backstage. We came to a stop outside one room with the band's name on it. A burly security guard stood in front, arms folded. He grunted at Sun-hee. In return, she flashed her pass and stood on tiptoes to whisper close to his ear. A quick flick of his head and shove of the door with his elbow, and we were allowed inside, where we cowered in the corner.

Jae-seung was lying on the sofa, his face not visible, a dozen or so people around him, a few of them arguing.

'What's going on?' I whispered to Sun-hee.

'That dude,' she said, pointing at a willowy man in a light blue suit and thick-rimmed glasses, 'is the band's agent and he's pissed as anything. Saying something about getting on stage or being dropped, the end of the band, etc. etc. *That* guy' – I followed the line of her finger as it settled on a man with rolled shirtsleeves and black trousers – 'is a doctor I think and he said something about high heart rate and rapid pulse and that JC needs to get to a hospital.'

'No!' I said a little too loudly and all heads turned in my direction.

Oh boy. Busted. So much for keeping in the shadows.

The agent dude pointed at us and barked in Korean. Sun-hee became very reverent and bowed continuously, holding her hand to her chest as she spoke. When she drew me into the conversation, I froze. Then silence.

Her eyes widened and she nudged my arm. 'Tell them who you are,' she said.

I pointed to my chest. 'Me?'

She nodded, shifting from one Dr. Martens boot to the other. 'Before they chuck us out and cart him off to the emergency room.'

Clearing my throat, I stepped forward, awash with the need to play a part – a part I had once auditioned for many months ago for a medical drama. 'I'm Francesca Cavalieri,' I said, my head held high.

The two gentlemen standing in front of Jae-seung parted and I saw him. There was a mask still on his mouth, but slowly he removed it.

'Francesca?' he said, bewildered, his eyes pooling, drawing me in, reminding me of that moment when I offered to stitch his wound.

'I am Jae-seung's – I mean – JC's private nurse, from England. See this.' I pointed to his forehead, where the faint pink line of a scar was visible beneath his foundation. 'I performed an emergency procedure to stitch up this laceration, which has healed nicely,' I declared, my chin raised. I moved closer towards him and kneeled down, reaching for his wrist – his pulse sky high. I felt his forehead – it was hot to the touch and moist. His eyes were hooded, dark, tired.

'He needs rest,' I continued. 'This is exhaustion. You don't need to take him to hospital. I can feel from his pulse that his heart rate is steadying. His blood sugar levels are probably low and that's why he fainted. Someone get him a sugary drink for heaven's sake,' I barked. 'I am sure you don't want to attract any more attention to what happened by taking him to hospital. Some time off and he will be fine. I know it.'

Sun-hee became my interpreter and relayed what I had said to everyone in the room. The response from his agent was that this was impossible because they had one more show tomorrow before the tour resumed in the US in eight days.

Jae-seung found his voice then. He spoke softly in Korean, holding everyone's attention. His presence exuded star quality. The back-and-forth conversation flowed between Jae-seung, the agent and the doctor for a while, at times becoming heated. The agent huffed and tutted repeatedly.

Suddenly, Sun-hee's eyes popped, and she clamped her hands over her mouth.

I caught her attention and raised my eyebrows.

'It's agreed,' she said. 'He's going home. With you.'

'With me?' I asked. 'To New Malden?'

She slowly shook her head. 'To Sicily. To the place he saw in a photograph. A place you told him about. A place of isolation. Where he can't be found.'

When I saw you that day
I couldn't silence my heart
And when I held you close
I knew we could never be apart
But I can't let you into my world
Because a love like this
Will bleed if it unfolds

Chapter 12

A sprained wrist. That's what the agent, doctor and the rest of Jae-seung's entourage had agreed would be the reason why he hadn't finished the concert, even though I hadn't noticed any swelling. Various excuses had been debated but they had decided not to panic fans with the truth; in reality, I reckoned they didn't want any accusations abounding concerning his exhaustion.

As he was bustled into a waiting car outside the venue, camera flashes popping around him, the bandaged appendage plus a makeshift sling were visible.

It was a faulty platform, apparently, that had caused his fall – that was to be the story leaked to the press, with a threat of suing the set design company issued. The need to rest his arm would explain JC's absence from tomorrow's performance, with a cast-iron guarantee to fans that he would continue with the next leg of the tour in seven days. Refunds would be offered but as Sun-hee explained to me, no one would want one when JYNKS were only the support band. Not seeing BTS was not an option for the fans. Correction: the Army.

A member of Jae-seung's entourage had given me instructions regarding the flight and what time to be at the airport, and had poured me into a taxi to take me back to the hotel to pack. I had strict instructions not to make contact with him until we were on the plane.

Now that we had left Incheon International's airspace and Jae-seung was sitting beside me, I could acknowledge his presence. The only noticeable scars from his fall were a bruise on the side of his head and a couple of scratches on his hands. His eyes were closed, and the steady rhythmic movement of his chest confirmed that he had drifted off. The blonde locks were gone, a black cap on his head tilted low, throwing a shadow over his face.

Hushed conversations mingled with the low hum of the aeroplane's engines, the clatter of the drinks cart down the aisle periodically punctuating the din.

I rested my head beside the window and took in the twinkling lights of Seoul becoming smaller and smaller as the plane ascended, my ears popping with the increased altitude. How could I make sense of what had happened over the last couple of hours?

Sun-hee had hugged me goodbye at the concert venue and promised to stay in touch but hadn't accompanied me to the hotel, as there was no way she was missing out on seeing her boys perform and meeting them backstage. I had hesitated before saying goodbye. A promise – I had made a promise to Mr and Mrs Son that I would act as chaperone to their daughter and now I was abandoning her. She had given me a heartfelt guarantee – or rather a pinky promise – that she would behave and send me hourly updates until she was safely in 'confinement'.

A nudge to my elbow startled me. Jae-seung's arm lay flush beside mine on the rest between us, his long limbs pressed against the seat in front. A hazard of economy class when you were over six feet tall. This was all part of the plan to blend in and not draw attention to his celebrity status. So far, we had pulled it off. The absence of the sling and blonde hair helped, as did his casual, scruffy appearance of grey hoodie and faded denim jeans.

Jae-seung's head flopped on my shoulder, the fabric of his cap brushing my cheek. His weight pinned me against my seat and the scent of his shampoo was lush, I noted as I breathed in, notes of cedar and peppermint invading my nose.

A rumble suddenly tore through the aeroplane and our seats shook. The seatbelt sign pinged on, though neither of us had unclasped ours, so I didn't need to move.

Jae-seung jerked his head suddenly and sucked in a gulp of air as he gripped the armrests tight.

'It's OK,' I said soothingly, rubbing his arm as I registered the panicked look on his face. 'Probably a bit of turbulence.' As soon as I uttered those words the plane returned to its steady state.

Jae-seung was holding my hand tightly and I could feel it – his escalated pulse on the underside of his wrist thrumming against my skin. He turned his head to the aisle and stretched his neck to look ahead and behind him before slouching further in his seat. He clocked his hand resting on mine and pulled it away, folding his arms across his chest.

Peering beneath the rim of his cap, he whispered, 'I'm sorry.'

I shook my head. 'You have nothing to be sorry for. Turbulence can be quite unsettling.'

'Not that.' He rubbed the back of his neck. 'This drama. This escape. The way I left you in London.' He clenched his jaw. 'I'm sorry.'

Before I could utter a response, an Italian stewardess had appeared by Jae-seung's side, asking for our drink selection. Bags of mixed nuts and napkins were laid out on our tray tables, along with a couple of Cokes.

The bubbles from the first sip caught in my throat and I coughed, wiping my mouth with the serviette. Jae-seung leaned forward in his seat and cradled the plastic cup.

'One hundred and thirty-nine calories,' he muttered, sloshing the dark liquid around the rim, before inspecting the bag of nuts. 'One hundred and eighty-five.' He set down the packet on the tray table and leaned his head on the headrest.

'Is this what you have to do?' I asked. 'To stay in shape. Count calories?'

He took a slow sip of his drink. 'There is a constant calculation going on in my head. Calories in, calories out. Restrict or burn. There is a choice.'

'That sounds *so* wrong.'

He wiped his serviette over some drops of Coke that had spilled on the table. 'I'm used to it. It's a way of life. It becomes easier to maintain when we tour because the concerts are so intense. There are hours of exercise every day.'

'Is that why you danced in Havana Club all night? Because of the meal we ate together.'

He nodded, slumping further into his seat.

'Soooo,' I said, finally wanting to address the elephant in the room, or rather the plane. 'You're a K-pop idol.'

He laughed. But it was brief and there it was again – that sadness in his downturned mouth and distant stare. 'I am no idol. But yes, I am the lead singer in a band called JYNKS.'

'I gathered,' I said with a smile.

He turned towards me and removed his cap, tucking it in the seat pocket. 'I am sorry I didn't tell you,' he said, running a hand through his hair, shaking it from its flattened state, 'and more importantly for abandoning you in London that day.'

I lifted my shoulder. 'It's fine.'

'No,' he said sharply. 'It is not fine. It was rude and inconsiderate so please, accept my apology.'

He tightened his jaw again and his eyes bored into me pleadingly. I couldn't look away. 'OK, I forgive you,' I said, a sincere smile coating my lips.

'And I am sorry for the dramatic escape. I don't know what happened on that stage. There was this strange sensation spreading through my body from my toes along my limbs.' He rubbed his hands over his thighs, sliding his fingers up and down the denim. 'I think…' He bit his bottom lip, lost in thought. 'I think I stepped forward but didn't realise the size of the plinth. It was a silly accident.'

'Sounds like dizziness. You must've been exhausted. You barely slept during our time together.'

'I did. For the first time in so, so long. I slept. When I was in your…' His Adam's apple bobbed. '…Bed.'

My cheeks flushed as he said that word and I grabbed my drink and took a large sip, wondering if he had been aware of how intimate that time had been. Had he woken embracing me? I hadn't given that thought much consideration as when I had awoken, he was gone, and my mind was solely fixed on the audition.

'That was the most at peace I had felt in a while,' he said. 'I think it was the waves.'

'The waves?'

'Your sound machine. And the tea. You were right, very soothing.'

'I have it down.' I wiggled my eyebrows. 'My sleeping routine, that is. The rest of my life? Pfft. *Non lo so*. Sorry, I mean, I don't know.' I stared out of the window into the darkness, remembering the juncture I had reached in my professional life: no role of my dreams, not even a whiff of one.

'The audition didn't go well?'

I pulled down the shade. 'Oh, no. It went great. I got the part,' I said, a tinge of sarcasm overlaying my words. 'Only, my agent screwed up. It was as the main star's stand-in, which I turned down.'

'Good for you.'

'Is it, though?' I said, unbuckling my seatbelt as the sign above was no longer lit.

'I think so. You deserve so much more than that.'

I smiled at his words. 'That's what my best friend said.'

'And she is right.' He twisted his fingers in his lap as if he was steeling himself to say something. 'This trip to Sicily. Again, I am sorry if it is a big inconvenience for you.'

I held my hand lightly over his arm and squeezed. 'You need to stop apologising. I was planning a trip home anyway.'

'But not with me.'

'No. That is something I could never have pictured. Why did you think of going there?'

He shifted in his seat, turning his body towards me, his knee pressing into my leg a little. 'This is difficult for me to say.'

I curled my hair behind my ears. 'I'm a good listener.'

'And nurse.' He smiled, a hint of humour finally creeping into his expression.

'Listener, nurse, stand-in actress. I'm the full package.' I hoped my attempt at self-deprecation would encourage him to confide in me – to share that pain that he had obviously been carrying for a long time.

The lines by his eyes intensified as he grinned broadly before dropping his head and staring at his hands. He stroked the pink ridges of his scar, and I knew in my heart that all paths led to what had caused it. Was he willing to tell me more?

'I have been struggling the last few weeks,' he said. 'The pressure of the tour has been building and building. The rehearsals have been intense. I thought I would be used to it by now, but I am embarrassed to say… I had begun to let errors creep into my performance. The rest of the band were getting frustrated with me. The more mistakes, the more we have to run through the songs again and again.'

'"Intense" is an understatement, then?'

He traced the rim of the plastic cup with his finger. 'I've been finding it hard to sleep recently and I knew I needed a break. Our management team gave us time off for a few days and so I escaped, told no one where I was going. I missed my family in New Malden, but I realised after that trip I couldn't escape there again.'

'Why not?'

'I never meant to leave you that morning after your audition. I was waiting by my bike and a group of Korean tourists saw me. I obviously understood what they had said. They had seen me with you and were waiting for the opportunity to take pictures of us. I couldn't risk it and of course I couldn't contact you.'

'The no mobile phone rule?'

'Why do you call it that?'

'K-pop mania. There has been a lot of press recently about the lifestyle of Korean pop stars. I had wondered if there was any truth in the gossip,' I said, wondering about one rule in particular.

'Not strictly true. I can have a phone if I want to, but my team have made it clear that there is definitely a detrimental effect to having one. And they are right.' He clutched his cup tightly.

'Why? Did something happen?'

He pursed his lips and fixed his stare at the screen in front of him with the map showing how far we had moved from Incheon airport. The thirteen-and-a-half-hour timer was ticking down – the time it would take to reach Rome. After that it was a short wait for our connecting flight to Palermo.

'Something did happen.' He slowly drained his drink before pushing it to one side. 'Three years ago, not long after we debuted. It was my fault.' He squeezed his eyes shut for a moment, as if the memory was too painful. 'There was a fan who had made a nice comment about one of our songs. I replied to it. She then became quite obsessive and didn't take too kindly to me not responding to everything she messaged after that. She started a hate campaign and began to stalk me.'

'That's terrible. But perhaps very common considering how obsessive fans can get.'

'I guess. The management took it as a reason to prove their point – that I was better off without access to social media.'

'Seems fair. Better off not knowing.'

'And it can become addictive. It can play into your insecurities, constantly wondering if this song or that album has been a success or not and whether we would be able to compete with some of the bigger bands. So now we rely on our management company to feed us the information. Only… I've messed up. Badly. That fall was…' Jae-seung clutched both armrests.

'I promise,' I said, squeezing his hand, 'a spell in Sicily will do wonders for you. I can take care of you.'

He gazed into my eyes. There it was again. That flutter. The one I had felt when I first met him in the coffee shop. That moment that had made the world around me drop away as if it had been only me and him in that room. I focused my attention on his long fingers, which stretched out, and mine slipped easily in between. That's when he locked his and the movement sent pulses along my arm followed by heat, spreading from the tips of my fingers to my toes, nerve endings trembling. My breathing became shallower as he laid his head closer to mine on his headrest.

'You don't have to take care of me,' he said.

'I know. It's a turn of phrase,' I said, embarrassed that I had even uttered those words. I pulled my hand from his hold and fiddled with my hair, smoothing down some flyaway strands. 'What I mean is… a brief break, good food, swimming, lots of sun, and you'll be on that stage in a week, rested and ready to take on what I assume is a crazy schedule?'

He nodded. 'Twenty concerts in ten cities across the world. Then another support band will take over and we'll return to the studio to record another album.'

'Wow,' I mouthed. 'But how on earth did you manage to get your management team to agree to all this?' I swept my hands around the confined space and pointed at the info map on the screen, arcing my finger from Seoul to Sicily.

He stretched out his leg into the aisle and pulled a device from his jeans pocket. It was small and black and had a green light flashing intermittently.

I held it in my hands and turned it over. 'Is this a tracking device?'

'Yup.'

'That's… invasive?'

'It's their way of securing their asset.'

Asset. Jae-seung was thought of as an asset. Not a human with feelings, wants, needs – someone to be tracked. It made me wonder if they trusted him to return.

'Only that?' I asked.

'That was one requirement: to have this' – he put the device in his pocket – 'on me at all times and to call once a day. There was one other condition. Or rather, one warning.'

I shifted in my seat. 'What's that?'

'My contract will cease. All my endorsements will end. I will no longer be the "J" in JYNKS if I don't follow these rules. I will be…' He did a motion with his hand – like a bomb exploding.

'But they can't do that, can they?'

He nodded. 'They can. See how easy it was for them to cover my fall, spread a false story about a sprained wrist.' He twisted his hand to prove there had been no damage. 'I won't have much power if they drop me. It is simple; my contract expects me to perform unless there is a severe medical reason for me not to. So, if I don't appear in New York, it's all over.'

Suddenly, the importance of this trip weighed heavily on my shoulders. Sicily had been a place I had wanted to escape from many times, not to. And going there this time had me wondering what it was going to mean for *me*.

'Does your family know you're going home?' he asked.

I rubbed the back of my neck, the realisation that this plan had no depth to it dawning on me. 'No, I thought I would surprise them. And my dad always insists on picking me up from the airport and I didn't want him asking questions as to why I'm flying in from Rome and not London.'

'I didn't think this through,' he said, clutching his hands tightly in his lap. 'This sounds like so much trouble for you, Francesca. I think it's best if I find a place to stay in Palermo and take a flight straight out to NYC in a couple of days.'

I reached over and held my hand over his, touching gently. 'Don't be silly. I won't hear of it. My dad and stepmum live in a lovely villa close to the sea. She inherited it when her father passed two years ago. More space than they know what to do with. Sometimes they rent out rooms there.'

'So, this isn't where you grew up?'

A flash of my childhood home popped into my mind – wooden shutters opening to the bustling streets of the city, washing hanging off a line secured to the decorative balcony. 'No. I lived in an apartment in the centre of Trapani. When my twin half-brothers came along, it became very crowded and noisy with us all crammed into seven hundred square metres, and no outdoor space.'

'I bet.'

'How about you? Where did you grow up? Did you not think of going home to see your mum?'

Jae-seung's face paled, and his lips twitched. Drawing in a deep breath, he held it tightly in his chest. No words came.

That's when I realised I hadn't removed my hand from earlier. The pads of my fingers were toasty on his skin. I pulled them away and busied myself with zipping my hoodie.

'It's getting a little chilly now,' I said, keen to fill the awkward silence.

He reached behind him. 'Do you want my blanket?'

'Thanks,' I said, ripping open the plastic. 'I can't seem to find mine.'

Jae-seung handed his empty cup to the stewardess as she passed by. He pulled out his cap and placed it on his head. Folding his tray, he tucked the unopened nuts packet into the pocket of the seat in front and grabbed his headphones. He tilted his head to the screen on the headrest and I took the hint that he was about to lose himself in the in-flight entertainment.

It was obvious I had shut down the conversation with my probing of his childhood. He had mentioned his father had passed when he was a teenager and that he had lived in New Malden for a few years before returning to Korea – which I had assumed meant to be with his mum. Perhaps he had a difficult relationship with her and didn't like to speak about it.

I could empathise. Sort of. *My* relationship with my mum had been joyous until she never returned. A void. That's what it had felt like when she had left: a blank space that I had filled with anger and resentment. A huge crater had formed in my heart when I had finally comprehended that she was never returning.

Unearthing the fact that Seoul had been her home, before moving to the States, still had my head in a spin. I needed to confide in Dad. This revelation was too huge to bear on my own. I needed to know whether he thought it was a good idea that I try and find her and reconnect.

As I pulled out my headset and began to flick through the movie options, my mind turned towards home. Dad would be ecstatic to see me, without question. Every summer he hoped this would be the year I returned for good. And he had one major ally in that wish – Alessandro. My high-school sweetheart – my first and only long-term relationship. Our life together had been mapped out right from the start. The plan? Married by twenty-four, then a family, me working in the hospital during the day, with my stepmum caring for our kids while Alessandro worked in his dad's architecture business. There was a plot of land in Trapani he wanted to buy one day, he had once told me, to build our dream home.

But something changed when I was twenty-one. I could no longer dampen my dream to become an actress. When I left Sicily the following year, Alessandro and I had made a promise to each other. If it was meant to be, we would find a way back to each other. And each summer when I returned, we had. It was familiar, easy; it wasn't passionate, instead like Nonna's chicken soup when I was laid low with a cold – comforting.

I shivered and wrapped the blanket over me. Alessandro had come to expect our summer affairs as a given. How would he react to seeing me with Jae-seung in tow?

If this were a love match…

Chapter 13

'*Amoreeeeeeeee*,' Dad bellowed as he stood in the doorway to the living room.

We stepped towards each other, and he enveloped me in a hug so tight, I could hardly breathe. But then I relaxed into his embrace, the scent of fabric conditioner at the collar of his white shirt mixed with a clinical smell reminding me that he had abandoned his patients to rush and greet us when news got to him that I had made a sudden appearance.

'Cesca, *amore mio*, why you did not tell us you were coming home?' Dad said in Italian, stroking my cheek and placing sections of my curls behind my ears as if I was a little girl again.

'I wanted to surprise you,' I said in English.

He pulled me in again and rubbed his hands over my back and rested the side of his face on the top of my head – the bristles from his beard tickling my scalp. A year. It had been a year since I had felt this familial comfort and I had missed it. I had missed him.

When he noticed we were not alone, lines etched his forehead.

'Sorry, Papà. I brought a friend with me…'

Jae-seung stood nervously from the sofa and bowed his head low in greeting.

'This is Jae-seung… from Korea, but he has family in London. In fact, his aunt and uncle own my flat. That's how we connected. I hope it is OK that I said he could stay?'

'OK?' he questioned. 'Of course it is OK.' Dad stepped forward and flung his arms around Jae-seung. Shock registered on his face as Dad slapped him hard on the back. 'Any friend of my Cesca is a friend of ours. Come, come, both sit…' He extended his arm out to the sofa.

'But Papà, your patients.'

He waved away my words. 'I got my next two appointments to be changed. Where is Sandra? Sandraaaaa,' he hollered.

'She went to Oddo's to buy some food, but she made us some *limonata*,' I said, pointing at the tray on the table, which she had brought out the second we had stepped over the threshold to the villa.

Shocked would be understating her reaction when Jae-seung and I turned up on the doorstep. My stepmother spoke hardly any English, so it had been an awkward greeting when I had introduced her to Jae-seung, but she had immediately insisted on calling Dad at the hospital, announcing my arrival.

'*Per favore siediti*.' Dad bustled around, plumping cushions and leading Jae-seung to the sofa while he sat down in the armchair beside it. I poured him a glass of the ice-cold lemonade and he thanked me as he took a sip and smiled.

'*Bella*, Cesca. *Bella, amore mio*. You look well. How long you stay?'

The question caught me off guard. I hadn't given this trip much thought at all. Everything had been last minute. In previous years, I had given my family and Alessandro plenty of notice so they could all take time off work to spend the days with me. And here I was, no warning and not alone.

'I'm not sure, Papà. I… um… I found myself with a gap in my schedule for a few days and Jae-seung…' I nodded towards him. 'He said he had always wanted to visit Sicily. I had told him stories about the *riserva*, how we hike there every summer, and I promised to be his guide for a few days.' I threw Jae-seung a smile and widened my eyes, to which he pursed his lips and didn't utter a response. It wasn't an out-and-out lie – more a stretching of the truth. The tourists' guide on the wall of my New Malden studio had obviously wowed Jae-seung enough to want to escape here. Surely, he could've gone anywhere to recuperate. Yet he had chosen Sicily.

'*Non è possibile*,' Dad said, cutting the air with his hand. 'You have to stay longer than a few days, *amore mio*. I need to give notice to the hospital. Promise me, Cesca.' He reached over to grasp my hands before rubbing my arm. 'Promise me you stay longer than that. Maybe even longer than last year? Maybe... forever?' He gave a slight shrug, his face contorting into an expression that was full of warmth, with a dash of humour but also something else, something I couldn't read.

It was then I noticed the grey flecks in his beard and his hair. The years were rolling by. I was missing out on being with the only parent I had in my life, and on seeing my half-brothers grow up. A recent framed photo of them on the sideboard caught my attention and I smiled.

But the thought of staying in Sicily permanently sent a shiver over my limbs, before I remembered that my dream of stardom currently lay shattered in London. What did I have to go back for? All I needed was to give a month's notice for my flat, and as for my Zara job and the shift at Havana Club, the reality was I could be replaced easily. What else was there waiting for me?

A grandmother who didn't recognise me and...

Clara.

My best friend. My rock. School girlfriends had fallen by the wayside when I had got into a long-term relationship with Alessandro. Our social life centred around each other and meeting with other couples. But then we had become absorbed in our jobs, my nursing schedule never conducive to nights out. Clara had opened my world and I couldn't imagine leaving her behind. Those thoughts made me realise that I hadn't updated her on events since I had sent her the brief video from the concert.

A yawn escaped from my mouth, and I held my hand over it, remembering the long journey here, which I couldn't divulge. 'Maybe I can stretch my trip to ten days,' I said finally, stroking my clammy hands down my jeans, knowing that my words wouldn't appease him enough. I could have plucked any number of days from thin air and it still wouldn't have been what he wanted to hear. 'I would need to arrange a few things in New Malden. But, Papà, my life is in England.'

He leaned forward and squeezed my knee, breaking into Italian. I was conscious that Jae-seung would feel left out of this conversation, but Dad was merely expressing his love, telling me nothing in the world would make him happier than to have me stay forever but if it wasn't possible, then for as long as I was able to.

Guilt. It seeped into my veins whenever he expressed these thoughts. Why did I feel this way? Because I had abandoned my family in pursuit of something so intangible when I had a good, stable life here in Sicily. I knew Dad would ask the inevitable questions once the initial euphoria of my return had worn off: are you still trying to be an actress? What is your plan for your future? Will you rent forever? The grilling always came with a sympathetic tone. An overconcerned father, he always called himself. But there was an undercurrent of expectation that I felt acutely: that I wasn't living the life he had imagined for me – and not once had he told me I could be a star, not like Mum had.

Mum. As I took in the sweep of the room, there were obviously no pictures of her. There were a couple of me as a child – one with Nonna and one with Dad. It was as if she had never existed, but she did exist in the present and I wanted to find out more. This wasn't a conversation to have in front of anyone else. I needed to find a moment to talk to Dad alone.

'So, what is the plan for now?' Dad said, his words interrupting my thoughts. 'The boys will return from football practice at three thirty, so plenty of time to rest. Sandra will get your room ready, *amore mio*, and the blue room is unoccupied,' Dad said, acknowledging Jae-seung's presence.

There was a shift in Dad's tone. I had called Jae-seung my friend, but I knew what he might be thinking – was this more than friendship?

Fiddling with a loose thread on my T-shirt, I thought about our time in London – the teasing playfulness, the sexy dancing at the club and ending up in bed together. The truth was I had no clue what was between us. Shifting on the sofa, I gathered my thoughts. 'The plan is to change,' I said, tugging at my jeans, 'and then I thought we could hire a boat from Pierpaolo if he has any available and go to Favignana, show Jae-seung some of my favourite spots.'

'No need.' A voice filtered through from the kitchen, its tone familiar.

I turned. 'Alessandro?'

He appeared in the doorway dressed in smart black jeans with a pale blue shirt tucked into them, the first three buttons undone, arms outstretched. 'Francesca, *ciao, bella*,' he said.

I lifted myself off the sofa and went to greet him. But when he plumped for a full-on kiss on the mouth, I froze, and for the first time there was no lip-tingling or temperature-raising at the touch.

I pulled back but he held on to my shoulder and squeezed it tight. With his other hand he slapped Dad's palm and held on to it for several beats as if he was part of the family.

'How did you know I was here?' I stared into his greeny-blue eyes, those eyes that my sixteen-year-old self had fallen hard for all those years ago.

'Good news travels fast,' he said in Italian as his eyebrows danced, and he caressed my cheek before cupping my face in his hands and resting his forehead on mine. The gesture was so intimate, and I squirmed within his embrace before gently lifting his hands off my face.

I noticed Jae-seung shift his position on the sofa and I could sense his unease. He had come for isolation, not to be privy to a full-on Cavalieri/Cribiu welcome.

'Alessandro,' I said, trying to loosen myself from his hold. 'This is my friend Jae-seung, from England.'

Jae-seung stood and bowed. Was it my imagination, or could I not only feel Alessandro's grip on my shoulder tighten but he appeared to drag me back a little, too? Alessandro reached his hand out, which Jae-seung took, but it was a brief handshake.

'Who are you?' Alessandro said a little abruptly.

'I am a friend from England. Francesca very kindly offered to show me her home. My family run the coffee shop that is below her flat. That is how we met.' I could sense Jae-seung's unease at the situation, the tone in his voice soft and almost apologetic.

'You work in a coffee shop?' Alessandro said, and there was a note of disdain in his voice.

'His family do,' I clarified. 'Jae-seung is…' I stopped talking when I realised I had been about to blow his cover.

'I work for a music company in Seoul. But I was visiting my family, helping out in the coffee shop, when I met Francesca, and she was very kind to me. I hurt my head and she stitched it,' he said, pulling his hair away from his forehead to reveal the neat scar that was fading by the day.

There was no way to elaborate on this story without telling my family the truth about who Jae-seung was.

A frisson of tension diffused through the air, and I realised it was coming from Alessandro. He was glaring at Jae-seung, who stood at least four inches above him.

'Hmm,' Alessandro murmured as if he could sense there was more to this story. 'So you are only here for a few days?'

Jae-seung nodded.

'And you are staying *here*' – he pointed to the floor – 'and Francesca is your guide?' His squeeze on my shoulder tightened.

I patted Alessandro on the stomach. 'Can we stop with the inquisition? Jae-seung isn't here for long, and I wanted to show him some of Favignana this afternoon, maybe take a picnic, go snorkelling. That's why I thought I would hire a boat from Pierpaolo.'

Alessandro's eyes narrowed. Italian flowed from his mouth, his hands gesticulating wildly. Accusations abounded. The main gist of his consternation was the fact that Pierpaolo would fleece me like other tourists. There had been some incident last month. I wasn't following the story because my head was beginning to throb. I had forgotten how intense Alessandro could be. The lack of sleep was making it hard for me to argue.

I sighed heavily and turned to face Jae-seung, running through my head a shortened version of what had been offered. 'Alessandro has very kindly agreed to be our guide for the afternoon. He has a boat and has insisted we can use it, or rather, be his passengers. He will meet us at the pier in an hour.'

Dad clapped his hands together and seemed wildly excited by this plan.

Jae-seung nodded and thanked Alessandro for his kindness after saying that he didn't want anyone to go to any unnecessary trouble. This sentiment he repeated twice. There was a quiet, calm aura that surrounded him when he spoke, I noticed. But even in crumpled jeans and a T-shirt, Jae-seung's obvious wealth was impossible to ignore, with brand names visible, and I wondered for how long we could keep up the pretence.

Alessandro waved away Jae-seung's reservations, leaned in and kissed me again on the lips before pinching my cheek and making his eyebrows dance again. '*Ciao, ciao*,' he said before giving Dad another handshake/shoulder pat combo farewell.

Dad came over to put his arm around me. '*Va bene allora*, you have a plan. Sandra will get your picnic ready, and we will all have a family dinner tonight. It was nice to meet you…'

'Jae-seung,' I repeated.

'*Sì, sì, scusa*. My… hearing is not what it was.'

I took a step back.

'No, no, Cesca.' He leaned in and attempted to smooth the wrinkles in my forehead. '*Sto bene*. I'm fine. I get old.' With those words, he patted my shoulder and left the room.

I puffed out my cheeks. 'I'm sorry,' I said to Jae-seung. 'I realise we didn't consult you in any of that.'

He shook his head. 'Honestly' – he held his hand over his heart – 'it is such a pleasure to be here, and I am happy to be guided wherever it suits you. Is this what *you* had planned, though?'

'Not really. Alessandro is… how do I say it politely? He is like a bull in a china shop.' The words 'air tick' floated in my mind. I must call Clara. 'Anyway, let me show you to your room and it's best you get changed into some beach clothes. We'll have a chance to swim if you want.'

Jae-seung nodded but could I detect a note of hesitation in his expression?

He had expressed a need for isolation at the concert venue and I was determined to find that for him in some way, even though we had now committed to spending most of the day with Alessandro, followed by an evening with my whole family. And judging by Alessandro's reaction to my unexpected guest, I thought there was an important discussion I needed to have with him.

The only trouble was, I didn't know what I wanted to say. And I didn't need Alessandro's observation that my dream was drifting further and further out of reach and that I should bid it farewell. But I needed to be honest with him. If I did return to Sicily for good, would I want to build a life with him?

If this were a love match
It would never end right

Chapter 14

The spray coated my arms and cooled my sun-kissed skin as Porto di Trapani faded into the distance, the Mediterranean and Tyrrhenian seas embracing ahead. A calmness floated over my weary body as the water lapped against the boat rhythmically and the hum of the engine lulled me. I pulled up the strap of my pale-blue vest top and tightened the drawstring of my black shorts.

Alessandro stood proud in his Hawaiian swim trunks at the helm of his new boat – a gift from his dad for landing a huge client from Dubai in the springtime. His hairy, tanned chest was on full display, the gold chain around his neck glowing in the sun's beams and his arms flexing as he moved the steering wheel. He had told me the full story surrounding its purchase and hadn't paused for breath since we had met at the harbour, where he had swept his arm out to show me his shiny new vessel – *Mio Tesoro*. It was not lost on me that this was the affectionate phrase he greeted me with often.

Jae-seung and I had arrived at the port laden down with a picnic full of cold meats, bruschetta and salads that my stepmum had insisted on preparing for us. Alessandro had taken the baskets from our arms and placed the bottles of water in the mini fridge before lifting me into the boat, ignoring my stretched-out hand. *His* hands had lingered on my waist as he had steadied me.

Another intimate gesture. *Oddio*, I thought. Not only did I need to find the time to talk to Dad, but I also had to be honest and frank with Alessandro. Assuming we would carry on from where we left off last summer was not what I wanted. At least not right now.

Alessandro caught me staring at him and raised his eyebrows.

'*Che cosa?*' he shouted over the engine noise.

I shook my head and mouthed, '*Niente*,' throwing him a smile before turning my face, my hair whipping against my cheeks. Jae-seung was sitting beside me on the bench and had a faraway look on his face, his jaw pulsing. His navy-blue shirt flapped in the breeze and his white vest top was visible beneath, his khaki board shorts revealing muscular thighs. Dad had lent him some sea shoes in case we scaled the rocks down to Cala Rossa later. I knew Alessandro wouldn't want to go there because he didn't like heights and the trek down to the small, enclosed beach was steep. It was also a rocky beach – his favourite being the sandy kind.

Once we moored, Alessandro rented a couple of mopeds and insisted on me hopping on the back of his despite my protestation. He declared that Jae-seung could follow easily if he knew how to operate one, which of course he did. As we sped off, I closed my eyes and smiled at the memory of riding something a lot bigger with him in London.

The day slipped by in a haze of heat. Without much shade, we were fully exposed to the strong sun. We traversed the perimeter of the island, never in one spot longer than an hour. Our picnic was devoured on Lido Burrone, where Alessandro hired some sunbeds.

The combination of food, sun and acute tiredness made me drift off and a post-siesta jolt roused me. I hadn't let on to anyone where we had travelled from and for how long, but it was understandable regardless that I had nodded off. As I shielded my eyes from the sun, I realised I was alone. Well, not literally – the beach was teeming with tourists and locals, kids running in and out of the waves with raucous squeals and impromptu ball games playing out on the sand.

A scan of the shore revealed Jae-seung and Alessandro walking together in the distance. Alessandro was holding forth, his hands gesticulating in all directions. Jae-seung nodded periodically before Alessandro smiled with two rows of teeth on display and slapped him on the shoulder. Had they become best buddies already? I wondered what words had passed between them and how Jae-seung was managing any inquisition about his background.

When they returned to the sunbeds, Alessandro leaned down to mine and stroked my cheek and arched an eyebrow. Before I could question his actions, he had commented that my shoulders were a little red and reached for the suncream. I opened my mouth to tell him I was capable of doing this myself, but he had already begun rubbing the cream into them and my back, sliding the straps of my purple bikini top ever so gently as he worked the lotion into my skin.

As his hands slid lower to my hips, he held them there and leaned in.

'*Mi sei mancata*,' he whispered by my ear.

The words were endearing, and over my shoulder I told him I had missed him, too.

At Cala Azzurra, on the southeast coast of the island, Alessandro challenged Jae-seung to a swim race to the pontoon that lay around three hundred metres away. I told Jae-seung he didn't have to rise to the challenge, but he said he didn't mind. We had done nothing but paddle at this point and a swim had been calling out to us, though I was waiting to reach my favourite beach for that – the one where I knew we could find peace and quiet.

That was the moment Jae-seung peeled off his vest, the hint of abs I had seen in my studio apartment now on full display. I held my hand over my eyes so I could admire him without the bright glare. His appearance wasn't lost on Alessandro either as he gave him a rather obvious once-over. I felt like pulling him to one side to tell him about the regime Jae-seung had to go through to look like that and it made me curse myself for objectifying his physique again. The demands of his K-pop lifestyle were excessive. His appearance was manufactured.

I noticed Alessandro puff his chest before counting to three and charging to the water a fraction ahead of Jae-seung. They both kicked through the waves then dove into the sea.

It occurred to me then that this race was probably not a friendly bit of competition but more a test of strength and endurance. Alessandro didn't need to compete. He had many endearing attributes that meant more to me than whether he could win a swim race (which he knew full well wasn't the way to my heart); being funny and dependable were two such qualities. While Alessandro never told me much about the life he led when he was travelling across Italy with his work, I was in no doubt that he had had several flings and situationships while I was in London. In moments of solitude, when a disastrous date had made me question whether I would ever find love again, I had casually scrolled his Instagram and always noted several new followers each time. Female followers. Yes, I knew that jealousy was an ugly trait.

Alessandro and I had this unspoken promise each time I returned that we wouldn't question what the other had been up to while apart. A postcode relationship. That's what Clara had declared Alessandro and I had when I filled her in on my summer holidays to Sicily. When he and I weren't living in the same postcode, anything was fair game in the world of relationships. But when I was in Sicily, it was us and only us. At what point would that have to end?

When I scanned the water again, I couldn't immediately see either of them. A minute later, both emerged, pulling themselves onto the pontoon, which Alessandro managed to do a fraction ahead of Jae-seung. I could make out their chests lifting and falling rapidly before Alessandro patted Jae-seung on the shoulder and then bent in half, his hands on his hips, trying to catch his breath.

I rolled my eyes. Alessandro wouldn't let that 'false victory' slide and would no doubt mention it repeatedly.

Late afternoon, we arrived at Cala Rossa and steadied the mopeds. Alessandro clapped his hands before spreading them open to me and Jae-seung.

'*Allora*. I have to go.'

I startled; Alessandro hadn't said anything about leaving early. '*Perché?*'

Alessandro ignored my question and put his hand out to Jae-seung, which he shook. 'It was nice to meet you, but now I head to Trapani. I have a dinner to attend with some clients. Francesca, *mio tesoro*.' He leaned in to kiss me on both cheeks. 'Is it OK?' he continued in Italian. 'You can take the public ferry home, no? I am sorry I can't stay longer but I plan to take time off when *he* goes.' He tilted his head in Jae-seung's direction.

'Of course,' I replied in English. 'It's fine, no problem. Thanks so much for being our guide today.'

Jae-seung stepped forward and bowed. 'Thank you so much. It was lovely to experience your island.'

Alessandro clicked his tongue and nodded before putting his shades on. He grabbed the remnants of the picnic, handed me a couple of bottles of water at my request and shoved the empty containers inside the moped's seat. He blew me a kiss before riding off, leaving a cloud of dust in his path.

I placed the bottles in my rucksack and adjusted my vest strap, which had again slipped down my shoulder. 'Now I will show you my favourite spot.' Pulling out my mobile from my shorts, I clocked the time. 'We have about two hours before the last ferry to the mainland. Let me…' I muttered to myself as I googled the Liberty Lines website to book our one-way tickets to Trapani.

'Did you not wish to return with Alessandro?' Jae-seung asked.

I shook my head slowly. 'Jae-seung. I promised you an escape, a bit of respite, and so far, I don't think I have delivered at all. This is my last chance today to show you my favourite spot on the island and enjoy some peace.'

'No. Don't say that. This has been such a pleasure. Meeting your family, your boyfriend—'

'My what?'

'Alessandro.'

I puffed my cheeks before releasing the air trapped in them. 'Did he say something to you?'

'I don't mean to cause trouble,' he said, sweeping his hair from his eyes.

'It's no trouble. Our relationship is… hard to define.'

'He told me when we went for that walk earlier after lunch that you were the love of his life.'

Those words stunned me. Certainly, Alessandro had never said them to me.

'Well…' I delayed my response by focusing on unearthing one of the bottles of water from my bag and held it to my cheeks. But it had lost its chill and did nothing to temper my flushed skin. 'Maybe his words were lost in translation. Alessandro and I are… not currently together. And—'

'There's no need to explain,' he said with a smile. 'I understand. Love can be complicated.'

'*Sì*.' I nodded. '*Complicato*.' That word was not lost in translation. But was it love, or was it friendship? It felt more like following a path I had been pre-destined to – one that would delight my family and Alessandro's. Were they all waiting until I had drawn a line under my dream so I would return and slip into my old life and relationship?

I led Jae-seung down a rocky, steep path. Crickets buzzed in the trees lining it and the distant wash of waves grew louder as we made our way down gingerly; I was grateful for my sea shoes, which had good grips on the soles.

The emergence of the sweep of the beach never failed to take my breath away, and this time was no different. Jae-seung stood beside me and took in the view, the tuff quarries that stood menacingly beside us. The imposing structures lent the beach a distinctly non-family-friendly vibe, which was how I knew there would be few tourists or groups here. The shape of the cove always made me think it was like an amphitheatre.

'How about we set our towels down over there,' I said, pointing to the eastern side of the cove.

Jae-seung agreed and breathed in deeply. 'This is incredible. So peaceful.'

'It's Alessandro's least favourite beach,' I said as I began to trek over rocks, cutting in and out of the shore, 'which is partly why he abandoned us, I think. Flip-flops are definitely not a good option for this terrain. My dad loved bringing me here when I was a teen. We used to swim out and head over to the cave on the other side. It's where I first learned to snorkel. The lack of sand means the water is crystal clear.'

Once we reached a spot that was far away from the scattering of bathers, I dug out the towels from my rucksack and laid them on a flat rock I had chosen as our base. I pulled off my vest top and wriggled out of my shorts, tightening the straps of my bikini while Jae-seung took in the sweep of the cove, before peeling off his T-shirt in one move. Again, I couldn't look away, and his close proximity set off a wave of desire through my body. As his forearm flexed when he bent down to tuck his T-shirt under his towel, I marvelled at his tattoo once more – the dark ink wrapped around his bicep. I clocked the numbers 126 before he turned.

'Do you snorkel?' I asked as I grabbed the face masks and breathing tubes I had packed, deciding not to probe the tattoo's symbolism again for fear of it upsetting him.

'I never have,' he said. 'I can't even remember the last time I came to a beach. My world is a studio or a stage,' he said, drawing the strings of his swim shorts tighter.

'Then how come you're such a good swimmer?'

'My aunt and uncle.' He stepped off the rock into the shallow water and splashed his body with some of it, scooping it with his hands. Droplets glistened on his smooth skin. 'They took me to Saturday swim classes at the New Malden leisure centre. They said it was a necessity – it's what all British kids knew how to do. I remember I was the oldest in the beginners' class, but it turned out I was quite good. I competed in several galas, too. My height made it easy to glide once I mastered the strokes. I used to love the way I could shut out the world when I was underwater.' His eyes twinkled. 'It was fun racing Alessandro.'

I laughed. 'I don't think he's ever met his match.'

'I'm a little out of practice.' He chuckled. 'He was lucky.'

There it was. Finally. A smile – the broadest one I had seen him wear since that time in my studio and instantly I felt my shoulders unlock, relieved that the charm of the island was winning him over.

I dipped a toe in the water and quickly pulled it out, startled by how much cooler the sea was in this cove.

'Do I have to wait all day?' Jae-seung teased, flicking droplets in my direction.

Goose pimples rose where the droplets fell on my skin. 'OK, now you're asking for it,' I said, playfully splashing him back.

But he merely laughed as he rubbed his hands down his chest. 'Already wet.' Dimples formed in his cheeks as he splashed me more until I relented and plunged straight in, yelping dramatically as I re-emerged.

Jae-seung's whole demeanour had changed in a matter of minutes; the playfulness that I had witnessed back in my flat had returned. I had found a way to help him relax. And I had only got started on my tour of my home.

If this were a love match
It would never end right
And it pains me to tell you

Chapter 15

Jae-seung turned out to be a natural at snorkelling. After I had given him some basic instructions and he had practised a few times, we swam further out, heading around the edge of the cove, where we paused inside for a break before diving into the sea again.

Once we got to the shore, he told me the feeling of being underwater had been almost meditative. The silence – it had hit him instantly, the second he felt the cool rush of water against his face. I had taught him a few signals – to help me understand when he needed a break or was struggling – but he hadn't used a single one. Sea bream and gobies had drifted in and around us and once when we skin-dove, we managed to flush out a dusky grouper.

We were both out of breath when we emerged from the sea and rested on our rock, letting the tempered heat of the early evening naturally dry our skin. A quick look at my phone made me realise we would need to hurry along the path to the moped if we were to make it in time for our ferry – the last of the day. Thankfully, we reached the port with a few minutes spare and I bought two granitas for the short crossing.

The engine humming beneath me, I sat on a bench out on deck and put my feet on the one in front, holding my plastic cup with yellow spoon. I had opted for a strawberry-flavoured one while Jae-seung had chosen watermelon. The vessel was relatively full, couples leaning against the barrier watching Favignana disappear from view and snatching kisses, while exhausted kids flopped in parents' arms. Jae-seung sat next to me, tufts of hair peeking through his cap, which he wore backwards. He scooped the syrupy ice into his mouth slowly, and it became a little hypnotic watching him. Sucking each spoonful, he would close his eyes for a second as if he was savouring the flavour.

'I don't know what to say,' Jae-seung said finally as he faced me, catching me staring.

'It's good, right?' I said, licking a scoop of flavoured ice off my spoon – the taste of *fragola* transporting me to childhood summer days with Dad on the beach closest to our apartment, splashing water at each other, with Nonna sitting in a foldaway chair, her face weathered with laughter lines, chuckling away at the unfolding merriment.

Jae-seung smiled. 'Oh, this is heavenly,' he declared, holding his cup aloft. 'But I meant the whole day. I feel…' He took a long, deep breath and lost himself in his thoughts.

'Relaxed? Rejuvenated? Rested?' I offered.

He smiled and slid further down his seat, taking in the view ahead. The island was fading into the distance and the beginnings of a spectacular orange sunset were building on the horizon – the kind where the colour was broken by a blanket of clouds, so it spread far and wide and was all-encompassing.

'All of those things. I've never… stopped. I think I have been afraid of doing so for so long. If I stop, I… I always thought it would be over.'

'Your job is very intense; it's inevitable you would feel drained and exhausted. But "over" seems quite worrying. Is everything OK?'

'Sorry, that was probably a little dramatic. I guess I meant I wouldn't be able to get into the regime of rehearsing and performing again. The only time I usually stop is when I am asleep, but recently that has been harder to do.'

'Hopefully, tonight you'll be able to. We've been awake for a very long time and surely the mix of sun and sea will have you drifting off. And there's no need to start the day early tomorrow; we can take exploring at a slow pace. Today was a lot to pack in.'

'Today was perfect. You have a beautiful soul, Francesca.'

My spoon hovered in the air, ice melting off the edge into the cup. 'What a lovely thing to say.' The rhythm of my heart picked up speed as I studied his face. His eyes seemed lighter, as if the darkness that had encased them was slowly beginning to fade.

'What I mean is…' He licked his lips and they glistened. 'You hardly know me, yet you have taken me into your world. You opened your home to me. And what can I offer you in return?'

I nudged him in the arm. 'Don't be silly; you don't need to offer me anything. I'm happy you're beginning to unwind. And trust me, your family has been nothing but kind to me. They've become good friends. You hear stories about nightmare landlords, but your aunt and uncle have always been there to fix anything and didn't raise my rent when I renewed my lease, and Hana is always on hand for a good chat or advice. And I owe your other cousin a lot, too. Maybe on a subconscious level, this is *my* way of giving back.'

'OK. That makes me feel better. What did Sun-hee do? She is usually better known for causing nothing but concern to her family.'

'I think she's brilliant. Possibly a little misunderstood.' I swirled my spoon in the slush. 'But she helped me unearth some things about my mum and for that I am very grateful. The only thing is, I don't know what to do with this information.'

Jae-seung shifted in his seat, his knee knocking into mine. 'If you want to share, I am happy to listen.'

I took a deep breath. 'My mother left me when I was twelve.' Those words caught in my throat. Every time I uttered them, they had the same effect on me, the pain of her abandonment still deep. 'To this day, I still don't know why. Her mother – my English grandmother, the one that is in a care home in New

Malden – revealed some information about where she has lived all these years. One place was Seoul.'

'Wow. That is why you accompanied Sun-hee?'

I nodded, not willing to confess that that wasn't the only reason.

'My mum founded a dance studio there and Sun-hee helped introduce me to the manager, who told me Mum had moved to New York City about eight years ago.'

'And you think that's where she is now?'

'I have no idea. All I have is another studio name.'

'Then you must go.'

His words stunned me.

'You think it's that easy?' I got up and discarded my sticky cup in the nearest bin, wiping my fingers and mouth with a serviette before returning to sit beside him. 'I can barely make ends meet in London. My career has stalled, or rather, it's never taken off. Buying a ticket to New York is a big expense when I am almost broke. And for what?' My hands gesticulated wildly as I spoke. 'To go and discover if my mum lives there, someone who abandoned me when I was young, who left a gaping hole in my life, someone who clearly doesn't want to be found? And then if I find her, what would I even say to her? And any reason she might feel warranted leaving behind her only child – would that be reason enough to forgive her, to forget what happened?'

It was then I realised that tears had sprung in my eyes and that my lips were trembling. I shook my head to break the intensity. 'God, I'm sorry. No idea where that outburst came from.'

Jae-seung placed his cup on the ground underneath the bench and clasped both my hands in his. They felt cold against mine, unsurprising since he had been clutching his granita for so long. It was like the fire inside me had been moderated in his hold and I found it soothing.

'Those words came from your heart. My opinion, Francesca, for what it's worth, is that you need answers. Go to New York. Find out what happened to her. Don't live your life regretting the decision to do nothing because it might bring you even more pain. I am happy to help get you there. You could come with me – you *are* my private nurse, after all?'

The corner of his mouth twitched upwards. There was that cheeky look again – the one that reminded me of our time in my flat, that made me realise there were so many more layers to this guy.

I lifted one of my hands from underneath his and patted his gently. 'You're sweet. But I can't accept such a generous gift from you.'

'Why? Because we barely know each other? Until now, I've lied to you, let you down and ditched you in the middle of London. I've not exactly left you with a good impression of me, so let's change that. We can get to know each other better tonight.' His eyes sparkled as he said those words. 'Then you will see this as nothing more than someone helping out a good friend,' he added.

He held my gaze, and I couldn't turn away. He considered me a good friend. The sentiment was wholesome, but the lack of romantic attachment did nothing to calm my racing pulse as I fell deeper into his eyes.

'I… I'd love to get to know you more,' I said, pulling my hands away to curl some flyaway strands behind my ears. 'But…' I noticed a handful of passengers gathering their things and beginning to make their way to the exit. 'My guess is when we step off this boat, the welcoming committee will be there. I wouldn't put it past Alessandro to have informed Dad that we were taking the last ferry home. Then it will be dinner. And you have yet to experience an Italian evening meal. It begins late and goes on long into the night.'

'Maybe tomorrow then?' he suggested. 'We could spend some time getting to know each other while sightseeing. Then you might feel more comfortable around me. You might… trust me and accept the flight ticket.'

I let his words linger in the salty air between us. New York City. The Big Apple. So many of my favourite movies had been filmed there; a poster of the film *Manhattan* sat in a box under my bed at the villa, along with others I hadn't yet stuck on the walls. Clara would no doubt remind me of Taylor's own endorsement, that New York was waiting for me.

'It's a deal,' I said finally, stretching out my hand, which he shook as if we had made a pact. A friendly pact. Nothing more, I warned myself. 'But only if you understand it would be a loan. I want to pay you back, one day.' I thought about our plan to get to know each other better tomorrow. 'Hopefully, Alessandro will be too busy at work. It'd be hard to get any conversation in when he's around. And I am assuming you wouldn't want your darkest, deepest secrets being told to him.'

'You think I have dark secrets?' His voice was low and his expression serious.

I tilted my head and took in his face, the hint of the scar still visible beneath the edge of his cap. 'I don't know anything about you, Jae-seung, or JC as perhaps I should call you – international star of the Korean pop world.'

His body sank into itself, his focus on his hands in his lap. 'I'm also just a guy, a simple guy who grew up in the suburbs of Seoul with no desire for this life.' He stroked the pink puckered skin between his thumb and forefinger. The movement wasn't lost on me because I had seen him do it several times.

'Alessandro's a nice guy,' he said suddenly, changing the course of the conversation, staring back out to sea. 'You suit each other. There's an ease between you both.'

'He's a good guy. We've known each other a veeeeery long time. As to whether we suit each other, I'm not so sure. He's never believed in my dream to be an actress.'

Jae-seung straightened. 'Why not?'

I blew out a deep breath, remembering that dinner with my family where he had told me how crazy I was to imagine such a life for myself. 'I've often wondered that, too. Surely if you love someone, if you say they're the love of your life, you would want to encourage that person in whatever they wanted to achieve, even if that support meant having to let them go.'

'You think his lack of encouragement is because he wants to build a life with you here?'

'Maybe.'

'Did he ever consider going with you to England?'

I laughed. 'He would never leave here. This is his home.' I swept my hand around, taking in the view of the mainland growing bigger by the second. 'And he loves the idea of a traditional Italian life, growing old in Sicily.'

'And you?'

The question caught me off guard.

Clara had always encouraged me to shoot for my dream with no compromises and no fixed plan, while my family had always embraced me every summer with a safety net – waiting for me to fall into it, into the bosom of my family and my old life, secretly hoping this would be my last summer spent in Sicily as a holiday destination.

No one until now had asked me what *I* wanted, how I envisaged *my* future. And the truth was… I had never thought beyond becoming famous so Mum would see my name in lights and reconnect with me.

'*Non lo so*,' I whispered, my shoulders dropping, because the truth was, I didn't know.

With that answer hanging in the air, passengers began their departure as the boat had docked.

A thought hit me as we gathered our things to follow the throng, and it hit me hard. I was no longer the girl who'd left this island full of hope six years ago but lacking in experience. While the shine of my aspirations had been tarnished with the recent setback, I had discovered something that day – the day Jae-seung and I had rehearsed in my studio flat. Self-belief. It had buoyed my confidence the next day when I had arrived for that Netflix audition. It was the first time I had thought I could land a role because of my talent and it made me wonder whether this was what I had been destined to do all along. A memory stirred of Clara and I having a Taylor marathon and dancing around her living room. I had just missed out on a role after a second audition and Clara had picked this one song especially: about being strong and life going on. Maybe I shouldn't let that last audition blemish everything. Maybe I should give my dream one more chance and try to find my place in this world.

If this were a love match
It would never end right
And it pains me to tell you
I have no strength for the fight

Chapter 16

'*Não entendo*,' Clara shrieked. 'You're harbouring a fugitive?'

I was sitting on my bed, rubbing aloe vera into my sun-scorched skin, my phone beside me. Wiping my hands on my towel, I switched the mobile from speakerphone to handheld. 'He's not a criminal, for heaven's sake,' I whispered, conscious that someone from my family could walk by and eavesdrop on our conversation.

'*Desculpa*,' Clara said. 'Some of these idioms I have no clue what they mean.'

I was getting ready for bed after a cool shower, my head desperate to hit my pillow and catch forty winks. *Air tick*. But I was thrilled that I had finally got through to Clara, who was taking her break during the shift at Havana Club.

My exhausted state had been pushed over the edge after sharing a carafe of wine at dinner with Dad and my stepmum. Jae-seung had declined a glass of red, which made Dad raise his eyebrows. The twins had been fascinated by our guest and insisted on showing him their entire collection of anime and manga toys. That made me flush with embarrassment that they thought he was Japanese, but Jae-seung was gracious with the misunderstanding when I explained to them that he was from South Korea. Jae-seung had introduced them to Webtoon on the laptop and they had pored over various cartoon strips. He had excused himself as soon as pudding had been devoured – moments after my stepmum had taken the twins to bed.

'But I can't comprehend any of this fantastical tale,' Clara said. 'Nor the fact that Jae-seung and you are shacking up together in your family home in Sicily.'

'There's no cohabiting. We're in separate bedrooms. Not even Alessandro is allowed to sleep in my room when he stays over.'

I heard her slap something, which I assumed was her fore-head. 'I forgot about him. So exciting. A love triangle.'

'It's nothing of the sort,' I said, lying back on my plumped pillows.

'But how did he react to Jae-seung being there?'

I sighed as I thought over our day touring Favignana. 'He challenged Jae-seung to a swim race.'

She snorted down the phone. 'A pissing contest.'

I laughed. 'A modern-day equivalent of a jousting match with me as the prize?'

'Exactly.' Clara giggled.

'Ugh.' A ripple of disgust flowed along my limbs. 'But Jae-seung doesn't see me that way. I think he only agreed to be polite but turns out he's a good swimmer. I have no idea why Alessandro felt the need to show off, including taking us to the island in his new boat, which I think he named after me.'

'He's definitely trying to mark his territory. And you told me, every summer you return, it's a given, you fall into his arms.'

'I don't think I want to this time,' I murmured.

Clara sucked in a breath. 'This is huge, Fran. So… you're going to make a move on Jae-seung?'

'I told you: he doesn't see me like that. He even called me a friend when we were returning from the island this evening and said that he wanted us to get to know each other better tomorrow.'

Clara tutted. 'Friendship is the solid foundation of the best relationships, in my opinion.'

'Then why do you insist on dating Philippe?' I regretted the words as soon as they were out of my mouth. 'I'm sorry, Clara. I didn't mean that.'

'No, no, it's fine. What we have is different, passionate...' She trailed off and I wished I could see her expression to know how deeply my words had hurt.

'Anyway, who am I to judge? My love life is in a confusing state: one guy who no longer makes me quake with desire but calls me the love of his life and another who makes me crave his touch every time I look into his eyes but who has already "friend-zoned" me.'

'*Meu amor.* You need to be braver; tell Jae-seung how you feel.'

'But it's complicated now. He's not a barista/handyman. He's an idol. Adored by millions, no doubt.'

'*Merda*, I forgot about that. *Espera...*' While she was thinking, I quickly laid my phone down on my bed and changed into a vest top and cotton shorts as I waited. 'Woah, woah, woah,' she said as I placed my mobile by my ear.

'What?'

'I can't believe this is the same guy. He can throw some moves.'

'What are you looking at?'

'I googled him. Haven't you?'

'No. I haven't had a moment to myself since I clapped eyes on him at the concert.'

'His voice is beautiful. And he is sexy AF in this tuxedo.' She whistled.

I blushed at the thought of him this afternoon surfacing from the sea a few paces behind me. It was impossible to resist peering over my shoulder, albeit briefly, as he strode from the waves, like he was walking in slow motion, a slight shake of his head to throw his wet hair off his forehead. His swim trunks had sat lower on his torso, revealing a lot more than I think he had noticed. I inwardly sighed and squeezed the nearest cushion to my chest.

'Francesca?'

'Hmm?' I said, shaking myself from my idle daydreaming.

'You were moaning.'

'Was I?' I stroked the cushion.

'Yes, you were. Now, to recap. Jae-seung's willing to trade getting to know you more for a ticket to NYC? Why are you even hesitating to say yes?'

'It's too big a gift.'

'He's a K-pop star. I doubt he's short of a penny or two. Stop overthinking this. Taylor wouldn't hesitate. What was it she said about love? It's maddening, horrible, wonderful, magical. I don't remember all the words she used but she believes in it. And if she gets hurt, she channels all that angst into writing more mega hits. Make it your mission tomorrow. Tell him how you feel. A three-day Italian affair is better than no affair, no? Then grab that ticket, say "*arrivederci*" in New York and go find your mum.'

'I don't want an affair, Clara. I want—'

A knock on my door startled me. 'Cesca?' Dad's voice whispered my name. 'Are you awake?' he said in Italian.

'*Un minuto*,' I shouted. 'I'm going to have to call you back. I think my dad wants to say good night.'

'I've got to get back to the bar. Call me tomorrow. I'll send your love to Steve.'

I gave a half laugh. My London life suddenly felt like a million miles away and I had no doubt Steve would reply: *Francesca who?*

'I'm happy to fill in for you for the next ten days, *meu amor*, but I don't think I can stay in your flat much longer. There's an odd smell in there and it's making me feel queasy all the time. Think it's one of your pot plants. Can I chuck them out?'

'If you're sure that's what's causing the smell then yes, go ahead.'

Clara ended the call after saying goodbye and '*beijos*' several times. Lifting myself off my bed, I opened the door to see Dad sitting in the wicker chair in the hallway dressed in his summer pyjamas. A smile washed over his face.

'Cesca. I came to say good night,' he said. 'Can I come in?'

'Of course, Papà.'

I patted the pillows and settled into them. Dad sat on the end of my bed and fiddled with my quilt. Nonna had made it for me. A moment passed between us, and I knew we were both thinking the same thing: that we missed her.

'I am so happy you are here, Cesca.'

'Me, too.'

'Finally, we get some peace so we can talk,' he continued in Italian.

'*Tutto OK?*' I said, bracing myself for what I guessed would be some well-meaning fatherly advice.

'I wanted to ask how your grandmother was?'

My shoulders dropped at the mention of her. 'She's not great. They're taking good care of her in the home, but the manager has some concerns and thinks she will need more specialist care soon. She no longer recognises me when I visit.'

'I'm sorry to hear that.'

'Actually…' I grabbed one of my cushions again and held it close to my chest, tugging at the tassels on the corner. 'She said something to me during my last visit that was quite surprising.'

'Really? What was that?'

'She said Mum had lived in Seoul, and perhaps even New York,' I lied, not wanting to confess how I had heard that bit of information.

Dad jerked his head. 'Oh. That's interesting.'

'I know you don't like talking about her, Papà, but recently, she's all I think about. These are the first clues I've been given as to where she might be.'

'You still care enough to want to know?' Dad's tone came across harsh, almost accusatory.

'I know she abandoned us, Papà, but don't you think I have a right to find her? Maybe she has tried to reach us, and she didn't know we moved here,' I said, throwing my hands around my room, some of my old frustrations bubbling to the surface every time I mentioned her in front of Dad. 'And if she couldn't find our new home, had no way of contacting us, then how would she know I had moved to England?'

Dad's shoulders tightened. 'Why would she care to find out about us after so many years?'

'I don't know, but I want to know. I thought moving to England might bring me closer to her, but it didn't. Gran hated talking about her as much as you.'

'Well, that's one thing Ava and I agree on.'

'I thought...' I trailed off, my breathing becoming more laboured, an increasingly heavy ball of stress sitting on my chest, the need to speak my truth finally overwhelming me. 'I thought that if I landed a big role, became famous, she would find me. And then maybe she would regret that she ever left me and would be proud of me.' I could feel the build-up of tears and the pressure behind my eyes and swiped the moisture away. This was the first time I had said out loud the real reason why I had wanted to move to England.

'Oh, Cesca,' Dad said soothingly, putting an arm around me. As he stretched out his legs, I curled into him and let his embrace calm me. 'This is why you wanted to be an actress? So she would come to you?'

I nodded in his hold, and he tightened his grip.

'But it hasn't worked out the way you wished, so now you come home?'

Shocked at his abruptness, I shuffled out of his arms. 'There'll be other roles,' I said defensively. 'It's a long road. Becoming famous doesn't happen overnight.'

'But do you think maybe it hasn't happened yet because you're not emotionally invested in it? Wanting to act, find fame solely because you have an ulterior motive and not because you feel truly passionate about it – I don't believe this is the best path. And you said yourself over dinner you had turned down something only last week that would have been merely a stand-in. What are these roles that you audition for? How will you pay your bills, build a future for yourself with this life you lead?'

I breathed in sharply, folding my arms around my knees.

'Cesca, come on,' he said, patting my leg. 'You know I talk sense. I am your father and I care for you. You have a life here, a chance to be happy and settled. I could talk to the manager at the hospital. They would welcome you there in a heartbeat.'

'But what if I don't want my old life? What if I have discovered that I *do* want to act, not only to become famous so Mum will find me but also because I am good at it?'

'What evidence do you have for this? When was your last big role? You're still a shop worker and a waitress in a club. This has been your life for years now. At some point, Cesca, you have to mature and make adult decisions. What will you do if this mysterious role of your dreams doesn't happen? What then?'

I tried to swallow away the effect his words were having on me, not wanting to crumble and instead stand firm in my resolve – my resolve to tell him I was trying, trying hard to build a life for myself in England.

'Thirty is not far off,' he continued. 'You want to get married one day, no? Start a family.'

'With Alessandro, I assume.' I scoffed in irritation.

'Yes, with Alessandro. Why suddenly you are dismissive of him? He cares for you deeply. He is solid, dependable. He would never leave you.' Dad turned his head with those words, and I knew he was thinking about Mum. Nonna had always described her leaving as a shameful, unforgivable act and I wondered if Dad still felt this way. 'Is this not the life you want?'

'I don't know.'

'What changed, *amore mio*?' he said, softening his tone. 'Why suddenly all this interest in your mother? She left us. She hurt us. We cannot return to the past. It took me years to heal from the pain.'

'I know, Papà. *You* eventually got closure, you found Sandra, you built a life for yourself. But I want this closure too. She must have said something when she left. She must have told you where she was going. And if she carried on writing to

Gran, why did she not at least continue writing to me? Was I a nightmare tween?'

Dad shook his head. 'No, you were a lovely young girl,' he said, placing a section of my hair behind my ear.

'There's this memory that plays in my mind sometimes: Mum and I shopping in Palermo, days before she left to go on tour, the last visit she ever made. She said she would come back for me. It seemed such a strange thing to say at the time. I laughed it off, I think, thought nothing of it. Why would she say it if she never planned to return? None of it makes sense. I'm sorry, Papà. I know you want me to have a life here in Sicily, but I don't think I can. Being here makes me feel sad. The memory of Mum is all around me, even though you've done your best to wipe her from our lives. You never speak of her. There are no photos of her. But she's here.' I held my hand over my chest. 'She's in me. And I feel stuck. Clutching at fragments of her. And I think the only way I can move on, and maybe finally accept what happened, is if I find her and have her explain everything to me.'

Dad nodded. 'It's getting late. I think you need your rest. We'll talk more in the morning.'

And with those words, the conversation was over. Was he willing to continue this chat tomorrow or was this a brush-off? Tomorrow he would be at the hospital, and I would be sightseeing with Jae-seung.

Jae-seung.

I flopped on my bed, head buzzing with all that had happened over the last few days. Three doors down the hallway there was a guy I met a week ago, who had quite literally turned my life upside down and I couldn't wait to have some alone time with him tomorrow to find out more about him. Twisting my wet hair on top of my head, I thought about what I'd been about to say to Clara when Dad interrupted. That I didn't want a summer affair with Jae-seung. I wanted more.

If this were a love match
It would never end right
And it pains me to tell you
I have no strength for the fight
And to tell you of my fear

Chapter 17

A sound roused me. I opened my eyes to moonlight filtering through the blinds and the ceiling fan whirring overhead. Despite the breeze it created, it was still hot in my room and perspiration made my pink cami top stick to my skin. A shadow passed at the foot of my door, and I wondered if it was one of the twins unable to sleep, on their way to the main bedroom.

I shuffled across the room, feeling my way around the bed. Even though this was my bedroom, it wasn't the room I grew up in and I had only spent two summer holidays here, so it still felt unfamiliar.

Opening my door, I peered down the hallway but couldn't see anyone. My mouth was dry, and I realised I had forgotten to place my usual cup of water by my bedside, so I headed to the kitchen and poured myself a glass. As I took a refreshing sip, my cat – Marilyn – weaved in and around my feet, clearly thinking it was feeding time. As I reached for one of her treat packets, I saw movement out the window in the garden. I strained my eyes and that's when I realised it was Jae-seung. He was sitting on one of the garden chairs, taking in the moonlit ocean. I gave Marilyn a few biscuits and headed outside to join him.

'Hey,' I said, and he flinched, holding his hand to his chest. 'Sorry, I didn't mean to scare you.'

'I wasn't expecting to see anyone.'

'Couldn't sleep?' I sat down in the chair next to him.

He dipped his head. The muscles in his shoulders appeared tense – the contours visible in the soft glow of the solar lamps that lit the perimeter of the garden. I noticed he was only wearing a pair of black Calvins. His legs stretched out, feet on the grass. 'Yes,' he said. 'I couldn't sleep.'

'I'm sorry. I thought today would have wiped you out. Jet lag won't be helping either. I don't think I was in Seoul long enough to suffer from it.'

'I'm exhausted but my mind can't switch off. As soon as I lay down, it was like my brain came to life, thoughts racing round my head.' He held his hands to his temples and slowly rubbed as if he was trying to rid himself of something painful.

'You said you slept the other day, when you were in my flat. Perhaps…' I swallowed hard. '…we can try and replicate that. Maybe that might work.'

He turned to face me. 'I think I would like that but—'

'You're right,' I interrupted, assuming he would shoot down my suggestion. 'I don't have my sound machine.'

'But your bedroom faces the sea, right?'

I nodded. 'If I turn off the fan and open the window, you can hear the distant waves. It's the hum of cicadas that I find soothing, too,' I said, peering at the night sky and closing my eyes for a beat, letting the sound of them in the trees around us wash over me.

'Won't it get too hot in your bedroom?'

There it was again: that flutter, building slowly in my chest. Did he mean if he was in my bed, our bodies next to each other, or because the fan would be off?

'If I prop open my door a fraction, we should be able to get a nice breeze flowing through the room. And there's no need to sleep with the sheet.'

'OK,' he said. 'But I'll be gone by dawn. I don't want to cause any problems with your family.'

'Probably best. Dad's pretty old-fashioned and I said we were… friends.'

Jae-seung's lips parted, and he focused on my mouth for a second before lowering his eyes.

'How about I make that tea and I'll meet you in my bedroom?'

He smiled and got off the chair, standing tall in front of me. 'Thank you, Francesca.' With a brief bow, he left.

Oh boy. What had I agreed to do? Clara would no doubt be giving me a high five right about now, but he needed to sleep, nothing more, I reminded myself.

Returning to my bedroom a few minutes later with two mugs of chamomile tea, I found Jae-seung standing at my open window, his silhouette illuminated by the moon. The blinds were open, the view stretching out past the front garden to the sea. I handed him a mug, which he took, murmuring his thanks, and I went to wedge my door open a fraction.

He sat down on my bed in the darkness and crossed his legs. I adopted a similar pose and settled in front of him, our knees brushing against each other as we positioned ourselves. Blowing the steam away, he took a sip.

Silence hung heavy between us, but we sat like this, breathing together, synchronising without even meaning to in time to the waves, intermittently taking sips.

'It's so peaceful here,' he said finally.

'When my brothers are asleep.' I smiled.

'They're sweet. They remind me of when I lived with my aunt and uncle. My other younger cousins were always visiting.'

'Do they all know about you being a pop star?'

He shook his head. 'Only my aunt and uncle, Hana and Sun-hee. They're all sworn to secrecy. I hadn't been to visit since I left when I was seventeen. That visit was very unexpected, and they did their best to keep me under the radar, though I know it stressed my aunt out. And then I spent all that time with you, and they didn't know where I was. I caused them unnecessary worry.'

'Why did you spend so much time with me when you had so desperately wanted to be with your family?'

He took a long sip. 'I liked that you didn't recognise me, that for a moment I didn't have to be JC or see that my family were constantly on edge. I could be me, a version of me I hadn't been in many years.'

'Oh,' I said, hoping the tone in my voice didn't have traces of disappointment in it. It was proof yet again that he had seen me as a friend he could joke around with.

'But you're right, I should have spent more time with them, and I was going to but then I got recognised. The truth is, I didn't know what I was searching for when I got on that plane to London. I hadn't been with my family in years and years: the only family I have left. I wanted to feel a connection to those who knew me before all this craziness – the fame, the die-hard fans.'

He shifted position and his knees came closer to mine, the hairs on them tickling my skin.

Remembering that morning, I sighed. 'I should never have accepted that lift to my audition. The trains were running again. I should have insisted on taking one. Piccadilly Circus is a hotbed of tourists. I'm sorry.'

'Don't be.' My hand was resting on my leg; he reached out and touched the back of it.

These touches. They were becoming more frequent. And every time they happened, the spark that ignited on my skin intensified. Could he feel something too?

'You said your... *only* family.'

He nodded. 'Something happened with my mum when I was seventeen.'

'The year you returned to Seoul?'

'Yes. After my father passed, my mother struggled to look after me. I was a bad student in school, always getting into trouble. Money was tight. My father's company's insurance hadn't paid out after his death, claiming he took his own life. My mother thought differently and tried to prove that he was overworked and tired and hadn't seen the car that hit him that night he left us after dinner to go for a walk. I never understood the full story. I was young.'

He paused and I studied his face, the anguish that was building as he recalled these painful memories, a heavy sensation swelling inside me as his words sank in and I acknowledged his pain.

'But my mother firmly believed I could have a better life,' he continued, 'more opportunities if I lived with my aunt and uncle in England. And she was right.' He let a soft smile play on his lips. 'I thrived at the school I attended. I owe my aunt and uncle everything. They gave me a stable, loving home full of kindness and a sense of security. At school I joined the choir, played guitar and acted in plays with the drama department.'

I guess that partly explained how he had helped me with my audition. I never acted in any of my high-school productions. Dad always said it was because I was too shy, but I could have sworn I appeared in some plays when I was at elementary school.

I suddenly realised Jae-seung had paused. 'Go on,' I encouraged.

He swallowed deeply. 'I used to try and go home to Seoul once a year. It was always a Christmas gift from my aunt and uncle. The trip during the Christmas holidays, the year I turned seventeen, my mother was acting very strangely. She finally admitted that a few months before she had found out my father had led a double life.'

I clutched my mug tightly, wondering where this was going and dreading it for the seventeen-year-old Jae-seung.

'He had another woman and a… child. Five years old. They had come to her begging for money, the woman claiming she was owed something, that my dad wouldn't have wanted to leave a child of his own flesh and blood to starve. The night he had died had been the night this woman had told him she was pregnant. Mum loved Dad more than life itself. Their story was that of fairy tales, she had often told me. But now the memory of their marriage was marred. Ruined. She…'

Jae-seung tensed, his jaw tight, bottom lip quivering ever so slightly.

'She began to suffer, mentally, and I didn't realise what she had been going through. She pitied this woman and her child, worked extra shifts to send them what little money she had. I tried reasoning with her, telling her she owed them nothing. She had begun to take some anti-depressants. I didn't know where she had got them from, but they didn't seem to agree with her. I begged her to see a doctor, but she kept insisting she was fine. It was the day before I was due to leave for England. She… hanged herself,' he said, sucking in a breath.

I stilled, ice shooting through my veins, suddenly chilled to the bone. 'Oh, Jae-seung. I am so, *so* sorry.'

His expression hardened. 'She left me a letter. Her heart was broken, and she didn't know how to heal it. She had thought that caring for the other woman who Dad had loved would have united them. Crazy thoughts. *Love*,' he uttered, tone cold and stark. 'Love is a destructive force.'

There was no way I could contradict him. He needed empathy, not someone to question his belief.

It was hard not to notice that his eyes were glistening. 'I couldn't save her,' he whispered.

I placed my mug on my bedside table and held my hands over his knees, rubbing them gently.

He focused on the movement of my fingers. 'I am so tired, Francesca.'

His quiet words shattered something inside of me, and I could feel my own tears building. 'I know you are.'

His shoulders appeared weighed down with grief. He had once mentioned that he was a couple of years younger than his cousin Hana, which made him twenty-six. Nine years. Nine years he had obviously borne some sense of guilt, though I didn't want to pry as to how he believed he could've saved her.

I took his empty mug and rested it next to mine. 'Lie down, Jae-seung,' I said softly. 'Lie down next to me.'

I pulled down the quilt from my side and lay down on the cool cotton sheet beneath.

After a few moments, I felt the mattress shift and then his body was flush behind me. Without a second thought, I reached behind and found his hand, sliding it across my hip to my chest, where the beat of my heart pulsed, steady and deep. Then I brought his hand to my lips and placed a gentle kiss on his skin before lowering it to my heart once more.

'Rest a while,' I whispered. 'Let it all go.'

As soon as those words floated from my mouth, I felt his body tremble behind me. And with the movement came a sniff, then a sharp intake of breath.

Silent sobs. I felt his breath on my shoulder before he buried his head there.

I turned in his embrace and pulled him close, as close as I could, almost as if I was trying to help him snuff out the tears and the pain. His head was by my neck, his lips on my collarbone.

Minutes drifted by. The tears decreased, his breathing becoming softer, the sound of the far-off waves filling the silence.

Pulling back a little, I wiped his tears with my thumbs. There was an intensity in his eyes that I had not seen before; his breathing began to quicken again, along with my own breath, as I cradled his head in my hands, my fingers threading through his hair. Heat pulsed between us, sweat building beneath my vest top.

Inching closer, I wondered if he would flinch, but he met me halfway. Our lips touched for a second. It was the sweetest sensation.

He lifted his hand, and his thumb traced the outline of my mouth, softly, tenderly. A groan emitted from my throat. But my longing was filled with hesitation. Jae-seung was in pain, and I didn't want to take advantage of that, so I waited for him to lead. His hand held my cheek and I leaned into it, turning slightly to place a kiss on that scar, which still remained a mystery to me.

His lips were on my neck then, his tongue tasting the tears he had left there, leaving electric fire in its wake. When his mouth fell on mine again, he left it there as if a battle was raging in his head as to whether we should continue.

And then he kissed me. I tasted the salt from his tears. The kiss deepened; tongues explored. His mouth possessed me, those full lips tender and soft. When we finally pulled apart, he dipped his head and couldn't look at me. Sensing the awkwardness, I turned away from him, grabbing his hand as I had before and bringing it to my chest.

As our breathing eventually steadied, I felt his body slacken. That's when I knew he had let go. Finally, he was asleep.

If this were a love match
It would never end right
And it pains me to tell you
I have no strength for the fight
And to tell you of my fear
My fear to give you my heart

Chapter 18

'Why did no one wake me?' I asked Dad as I shuffled into the kitchen, my eyes bleary, that weird feeling you get when you have slept too much fogging my head.

The clock on the wall ticked close to ten. The aroma of freshly brewed coffee on the stove and toasted brioche on the kitchen table permeated the room and I breathed in deeply. A memory stirred of Nonna and all the mornings I had woken to home-made *cornetti*, the *crema pasticciera* filling oozing out as soon as I took a bite. Nonna always scolded me for not using a plate and the trail of crumbs I would leave around the kitchen, but her scolding always came with a toothy smile not long after the ticking-off.

'*Amore mio*,' Dad said, pouring me a cup of black coffee and passing over a plate. 'You were fast asleep. I didn't want to wake you.'

'Where's Jae-seung? Still sleeping?' I asked, slipping into one of the kitchen chairs. I thanked Dad for the coffee, peeking inside the bag from the local bakery that I knew my stepmother would have got first thing this morning.

'No, no,' Dad said before sipping his coffee. 'He went out. Sightseeing.'

'Sightseeing?' I questioned as I pulled out a jam-filled *cornetto*. 'We were meant to go together, do some more exploring.'

'I told him I wanted to talk with you. Don't worry, he has a map, and I gave him directions to the *castello*. I thought he might enjoy the cable ride.'

I bit into my pastry, the crumbs trickling down my chin. Wiping my fingers with a serviette, I savoured the jam filling. 'What did you want to talk about, Papà?'

Marilyn weaved in and around my chair and I patted my lap. She jumped onto it, her grey fur soft against my bare thighs.

Dad was clutching the counter tightly, his knuckles whitening.

'What's the matter?'

He turned over his shoulder and there was a pained look on his face. 'There is something I need to tell you, Cesca, or rather show you, and it isn't easy for me. But last night, our conversation...'

'I didn't mean to upset you. Honestly.'

'I know, *amore mio*, but I think it is *I* who should be apologising to *you*.'

Dad opened the drawer under the counter and pulled out something that appeared to be a stack of letters. He held them in his grasp and began turning them in his hands. Sitting down in the chair opposite mine, he lowered his head. 'Please understand, Cesca. I believe she did this to protect you.'

I stroked Marilyn with measured movements. 'Who?'

'Nonna.'

Slowly, he pushed the stack towards me. Marilyn jumped off my lap as I scraped my chair closer to the table. They were not letters but postcards, bound in a red ribbon. My throat went dry when I saw the name of the city adorning the top one – Seoul. Landmarks of the South Korean city filled the space around it, and they were similar to the ones I had seen in Gran's velvet box.

'Are these...?' My fingers trembled.

He nodded.

'Where did you find them?'

'When we moved from the apartment, we had to clear out Nonna's things. We discovered them buried in a box at the foot of her wardrobe.'

'Two years,' I said, my voice cracking a little. 'You've had these for two years and you didn't say anything to me? I don't understand. You sat on my bed last night and continued to let me believe that she didn't care about me, hadn't tried to reach me. When did she send these?' I asked, suddenly ripping off the ribbon. Postcard after postcard, at least twenty of them. Turning them over briefly, I clocked dates. Six years' worth. She had written to me for the next six years, until I was eighteen. Until I was an adult.

I got to my feet. 'You knew about this for two years…' I repeated. 'Nonna hid these from me for six years. I grew up believing Mum had simply forgotten about me.'

'Cesca, please try and understand. Nonna obviously—'

'Nonna isn't here to defend her actions, and we can speculate all we want as to why she did it, why she believed she was protecting me, from what, I have no idea. But you…' My breathing was too fast, erratic; that ball of anxiety that had sat inside my chest for so long was bubbling on the surface, desperate to break free. I needed air.

I grabbed the ribbon and tied the postcards, but Dad stood before I could leave and held on to my elbow.

'Where are you going, Cesca? Please, can we talk?'

'I can't talk to you, not about this. This is too huge. You lied to me. I won't ever forgive you for this. I'm going out, to the one place I promised Jae-seung isolation, and that's what I want more than anything right now.'

'Where is that?'

'I want to be alone.' I pushed past him, ignoring his question, and went to my bedroom, picking up my rucksack from the floor and shoving the postcards inside, along with my suncream, sun hat, towel and other hiking essentials. Throwing on some clothes, I then grabbed a couple of bottles of water from the fridge. Dad beseeched me in Italian as I ran around the villa trying to find my hiking shoes. I had wondered if the sight of them would tip him off as to where I was going. The only words I uttered were to ask him if I could borrow the old Cinquecento. He tried to persuade me to let him drive me wherever I wanted to go so we could talk, but I told him I didn't want him near me until I had read these postcards.

He finally handed over the keys and let me pass. As I drove off, I didn't allow myself to think of what words had been written on those cards or whether they gave information as to Mum's whereabouts, instead focusing on the unfamiliarity of driving on the other side of the road.

Forty minutes later I parked by the northern entrance to the *riserva* at San Vito Lo Capo. Grabbing my rucksack, I put my sun hat on and headed off on the coastal path. It was the simplest one and the route I found most beautiful. It was also the quickest way to my favourite beach – where we had come, as a family, that last summer Mum was with us. A hard lump formed in my throat at that thought. Mum. Mum had thought of me. She hadn't forgotten about me. I was desperately hoping her words would give me something tangible, some clues as to what had happened.

Almond and ash trees lined the dusty path. The rockface containing the mid-coast route and the high path loomed large on my right, while the endless green-blue sea lapped the coast invitingly on my left. My fingers grazed along a thyme bush, bursts of purple flowers sitting atop. I plucked a leaf and inhaled. Closing my eyes, the image of Nonna placing a sprig in a small vase next to my bed came to my mind – to ward off nightmares, she had always told me. Apparently, they had plagued me, Dad had once told me when I had woken from one after a long night shift at the hospital.

Nonna.

Instead of her image invoking warmth and comfort inside me, anger crackled beneath my skin. 'Why, Nonna?' I whispered, the air around me heavy with heat.

I threw the leaf away and took a swig of water before continuing on the track. My limbs grew wearier and wearier as the path cut in and out of the rocks, but I didn't want to stop at any of the other beaches to rest or cool off.

When I finally reached Cala Capreria, sweat was pouring down my face, my vest sticking to my back and my head heavy. I drained the first water bottle and took in my surroundings. Zingaro was my version of paradise – black and grey rugged cliffs shooting to the sky and the deepest turquoise water calling to you like the sirens tempting Odysseus, urging you to come in for a swim after a dusty hike.

I peeled off my shorts and vest, black bikini on underneath, and slipped on my sea shoes. There were at most three other people dotted in the water and several more on dry land.

I felt safe here. I felt free.

Striding into the water, this time with no hesitation, I dove in, and the cold slapped me hard, prickling my skin. I floated on my back, the peerless sky above, my ears submerged, a strange blankness filling my head. But I knew I couldn't escape the inevitable. My body was tired, my mind clear. The water had washed away any lingering doubts. I was ready – ready to face what was written in those postcards.

After drying off with my towel, I laid it out on the rocks and sat down. Unearthing the stack, I untied the ribbon and began reading. Three times I read each one. They averaged three or four every year. The birthday ones contained simple messages: hope for a happy day, a joyous new year, and a wish to see me soon. There were mentions of the dance studio she had established in Seoul, talk of this dancer and that dancer – performers I had never heard of who had been discovered not long after attending classes at the studio in Mapo-gu.

My first thought was that it was obvious that if I had wanted to find her, I could have. Every card contained an address scrawled in one corner. She had moved around Seoul over those years, the districts changing three times.

Then they stopped. There was no 'happy eighteenth' card, which seemed odd as she hadn't forgotten a single one of my previous milestones.

A dizzy feeling suddenly fizzed in my head and I realised I had forgotten to put my sun hat on after my swim, nor had I reapplied my sunscreen. Cicadas buzzed incessantly around me, and my skin stung with heat. Shade eluded you here unless you were smart and strong enough to carry a parasol with you from your car. The scarcity of beach dwellers was a reminder that the heat at this time of day was brutal – easily pushing the mercury to thirty-six degrees. I pulled my hat low over my forehead and popped open the second bottle of water and took a sip.

A noise startled me, and I turned, stunned to see Jae-seung descending the path to the beach in a blue vest top and khaki-green shorts, a navy cap on his head. I wiped my mouth and stood shakily. That's when the full extent of my crazy hike hit me hard. A chill spread over me and my eyes blurred. I was swaying and then everything went black.

Blinking, I tried to make sense of the fragments of my new view. Jae-seung was above me, staring at me, concern etched into his face. As I tried to sit up, another rush of wooziness washed over me and I lay back down.

'Take it easy,' he whispered, rubbing an ice pack over my forehead and cheeks.

'What happened? Where did you come from?'

'I returned to your home and your dad was frantic. He said you were upset and that you had gone to a place that you had told me about – the place of isolation. He begged me to tell him where it was, but I said he should not worry and that I would find you. He gave me his moped, a map and lots of provisions.' He held the ice pack aloft before placing it on my cheek again, his thumb grazing my lips. 'And this is it. The place you told me about.' He took in his surroundings, scanning the horizon.

'But how did you know this was the beach I would come to? There are five other coves.'

'It's like the photo on your wall. I told you I have a photographic memory. Every inch of this view is like your picture. It's… breathtaking.' His eyes locked on mine as he said that word and it was impossible to turn away, to not want to remember last night, the comfort that had radiated from his hold. That kiss. I wanted his presence to snuff out the pain in the same way I had tried to block *his* last night.

'Thank you,' I said finally. 'For coming.'

'You're welcome,' he said. That smile was healing in itself, I noted as I felt my surroundings return to sharp focus and the light-headedness begin to abate.

Jae-seung helped lift me into a sitting position and handed over the ice pack – it was like a balm against my sun-scorched skin. I rested next to him on a rock, our knees pressed together.

'Is everything OK with your father?'

'It's fine.' I waved away his concern. 'We had a stupid argument and I had to get out. But I wasn't thinking straight. Usually, I rely on Dad to pack all the essentials. Coming here and conserving two small bottles of water wasn't very bright of me, in hindsight. And walking to the furthest beach from the north entrance was stupid too. Think my skin has been softened by living in England too long. I didn't even bring any food either.' On cue, my stomach grumbled.

Jae-seung unpacked his rucksack to reveal an insulated pack with several bottles of water and snacks. 'Your Dad let me raid your fridge and snack drawer. We're covered for a few hours.' His smile continued to be like a salve, and I felt mellow in his presence, grateful at his thoughtfulness. There was an ease about him, I noticed, his shoulders not locked, his movements sure and fluid. Sicily was obviously having its magic effect on him.

Jae-seung offered me a granola bar and a flavoured energy drink. Devouring both in contemplative silence, my sugar levels rose and the lightness in my head completely dissipated.

'I'm glad you came,' I said after a few minutes.

'Me, too. I wouldn't want to miss out on being here.'

'Did you… sleep OK?'

He nodded. 'Did you?'

My pulse thrummed in my neck, wondering if he would mention that kiss. 'Yes,' I whispered. 'I must have been exhausted, though, because I didn't feel you leave, nor did I hear the mad school-rush.'

'I felt a little uncomfortable when your father said he wanted me to go. I hate being an inconvenience.'

I nudged him. 'You're not an inconvenience at all. I love having you here.'

We turned at the same time – our faces inches apart, shoulders pressed together. The rim of my hat touched the edge of his cap and knocked it. Jae-seung dipped his head and turned his cap. That's when he noticed the cards that I had left on top of my rucksack.

'What are those?' he asked.

I handed them to him. 'Look familiar?'

He smiled. 'My home. Changdeokgung Palace, Jeonju and the pavilions in Gyeongbokgung Palace. All the major tourist sites. So many cards.'

He didn't turn them over but passed them back to me. 'Who are they from?'

'My mother,' I said. 'She sent them to me after she left me, only I never received them. My *nonna* – Dad's mum – intercepted them and hid them.'

'Why did she do that?'

I stroked the satin ribbon. 'No idea. She died when I was eighteen, bizarrely when these postcards stopped.'

Jae-seung propped his arms on his knees. 'Why do you think your mother stopped writing then?'

'Perhaps she lost faith. I hadn't replied in six years. Six years.' The words caught in my throat. 'Maybe she thought I didn't care. I was an adult by then, capable of making my own decisions. But the truth is, I'm not sure what hurts me more: that Mum stopped writing, that Nonna hid them or that my father had these in his possession for two whole years and didn't show them to me.'

His face was full of understanding. 'I don't know. Perhaps all of those things hurt equally. Our caregivers have a responsibility to do their best by us, but when what they think is best causes pain – whether that comes in the form of giving up or lying – you are entitled to feel these actions deeply, without the need to justify one being less hurtful than the other.'

Jae-seung's empathy lifted a weight I hadn't known I was carrying, leaving me feeling lighter than I had since this morning's revelations – my mind a lot clearer. 'I do know one thing,' I said brightly.

'What's that?'

'I want to go with you to New York. I want to find out what happened when she moved there. Maybe I can go to this studio the lady in Seoul told me about and get some information. And I can't deny I've always wanted to go to the city that never sleeps.'

Jae-seung's face tightened and my stomach tied itself in knots at his reaction.

'But I… I don't have to go with you if you've changed your mind. I have enough money to cover a plane ticket. I can—'

'No,' he said quickly. 'I haven't changed my mind. But things will be different when I go there. I won't be able to spend any more time with you once I start rehearsals. Once I am there, we can't be seen together. And my life will return to how it was.'

'So, the no-dating rule is true, huh?'

He furrowed his brow. 'Yes. It is forbidden. No member of the group can date.'

'You can't ever fall in love?'

'I don't believe in love. The only love I know is destructive.'

Jae-seung clutched his hands tightly, stroking the scar between his fingers. I assumed he was thinking about his mum and dad with that sweeping statement.

'Love is a risk,' I said, my chin raised. 'And when the risk pays off, it's magical. At least… that's what the movies will have us believe. But I believe it too.'

Jae-seung smiled. 'Movies aren't real life.'

'I know that,' I said, nudging him in the arm. 'But I believe in finding someone that you connect with, someone you want to build a life with, watch each other grow, support each other. I can't ever imagine not falling in love.'

'Francesca…' Jae-seung's shoulders instantly locked at the utterance of my name, and I knew he was struggling to find the words as his mouth opened and closed. 'That kiss,' he said, tightening his lips. 'I shouldn't have done that. I'm sorry.' He sank into his shoulders.

His words were like a punch to the gut, but from deep within I found my voice. 'Don't be sorry. It was a heat of the moment thing. You were feeling vulnerable; I shouldn't have taken advantage of you like that.'

He shook his head. 'You didn't. But I can't forget who I am, what is expected of me, and I can't lead you on.'

I nudged him again, forcing a smile on my face. 'It was just a kiss. Let's forget about it. You're feeling better, right?'

He nodded.

'So… mission accomplished. Let's get out of here; let's go to New York. We could tour the city, see the sights – no one will recognise you out of context if we're careful. We could only go out when it's dark maybe or do the whole cap-sunglasses combo. Wouldn't you love to enjoy some more anonymity but somewhere a little more public? If we leave today, we'll have time to squeeze all that in before you have to start rehearsals.'

'You make it sound very tempting. I would love to spend some more time with you… but—'

'As friends,' I clarified. 'Nothing more. I understand your life. I know this is how it has to be. You can help me find more clues about my mother and then get back on that stage. And this time we have spent together will be one fleeting, crazy moment in time. A meeting of two souls who benefitted from each other's help.'

Jae-seung scanned the sea and breathed in and out deeply, before finally twisting his body towards me. 'OK,' he said simply.

We shook on it, but I couldn't deny it any longer. My heart cracked a little as I had said those words, like a rockfall into the sea.

That kiss was not only a kiss to *me*.

There is no other option

Chapter 19

As the yellow cab wound its way from JFK airport to Manhattan, the lights of Brooklyn illuminated the night sky outside the window. Never in my wildest dreams could I have imagined being here.

I sank into the leather seat, leaned my head against the glass and thought about the sequence of events since leaving the *riserva* in Sicily. Jae-seung had used my phone to book us on the next available flight via Rome. Dad had begged me to stay, at least another day, so we could talk. Guilt poured through me when he said how disappointed the twins would be when they got home to find me gone, but for the first time, I stood strong in my resolve. This was a journey I should have taken two years ago. Two years ago, Gran could still recognise me. I could have pushed her for more information. Maybe Mum had written to her once she had moved to America, and she had an address for her there.

But there was one thing Dad agreed with me on: that I had a right to find her and discover the truth as to why she had left. He drove us to the airport, and we said our goodbyes. I told him to tell Alessandro that I was sorry not to see him before I left. I couldn't think of my life in Sicily or London right now – my mind was filled with nothing but the thought of finding my mother.

Dad had hugged me tight and whispered in my ear that I should always remember that he loved me more than life itself and that what he had done had been out of love. I gave him no response but headed over to security without turning back.

Love. It was a feeble excuse, and not one I could reconcile with right now.

As we'd waited to board our flight to Rome, I had messaged Clara and she had quickly called me to tell me how proud she was. My eyes filled with tears when she said those words. I missed her and a part of me wished she was on this adventure with me. When she had asked about Jae-seung, I whispered that he was sitting right next to me, and she told me to call her from New York so I could fill her in on everything that had happened. But I couldn't resist typing out a quick message about our kiss. She had sent back the eyes-and-mouth-wide-open-in-shock emoji and I promised her more details the next time we spoke.

The twelve-and-a-quarter-hour flight from Rome had been a lot more relaxed than the one Jae-seung and I had taken from Seoul. We watched the same two movies for half of it, and slept for the other half, content in each other's company. I tried to snuff out the feelings of attraction when, at one point, with the lights of the cabin dimmed, I had stirred to find him holding his arm around my waist, his head on my shoulder. His scent invaded me – cedar and peppermint from his soft hair brushing my cheek.

But we had agreed on being friends and nothing more.

The taxi stopped outside a building in the heart of Chelsea forty-five minutes later. This was the only place we had found last minute in the area close to the dance studio, an Airbnb that I thought would be a good base and was affordable. I had booked it for a couple of nights, but the owner said it was available after that should I need to extend my stay.

Jae-seung had suggested checking us into the hotel he would be staying in, but I said that probably wasn't the greatest idea considering the attention it might draw and I also couldn't accept yet another gift from him. The five-star price tag was way over my budget.

As I stepped out of the taxi, a gust of wind whipped my hair against my cheeks and dust blew into my eyes. In its path, humidity followed.

'There's a storm coming,' the taxi driver said with a thick New York accent as he helped us get our cases from the boot. 'You guys are lucky; there's talk of them shutting the airports. It's coming down from Massachusetts and could reach typhoon status.'

As he said those words, the sky rumbled with thunder.

'This is only the start. If it hits, it'll be in a couple of days. You'll be fine to do some sightseeing tomorrow.'

He sped off and we dragged our cases to the entrance, locating the keys from the lockbox. The studio apartment was in a four-storey walk-up, and we were on the third floor. A white oasis greeted us when we opened the door and flicked on the switch: two large windows at the far end of the room with a view of the street, the double bed awash with white cotton sheets and a collection of different-sized cushions, in varying shades of cream and light grey. One small kitchenette stood in front of us, and the space in between the sleeping and eating areas was filled with a white sofa and two armchairs – the former convertible into a bed.

I pulled my case into the centre of the room. 'I need to have a shower, then how about we go out and get some food? I honestly have no clue what time it is, but I reckon the dance studio is long closed.'

'I'm happy with whatever you have in mind.'

Was it my imagination or had Jae-seung uttered those words with a slight eyebrow arch? Was he flirting?

That kiss had been playing on my mind throughout the flight over, and it was going to take a lot of willpower to forget it had happened and ignore the fact this was a studio apartment. But we had made a pact. A friendship pact. And there was no point in wishing for anything more.

Half an hour later, we stepped outside into the windy, muggy night. I pinned my curls on the top of my head and tucked my green T-shirt into my black shorts. Jae-seung had opted for grey cargo shorts and a navy-blue tee, which matched the cap he wore. We both scanned the brooding sky. The clouds had tinges of white and purple. An electric storm was brewing.

'Shall we be tourists – see Manhattan by night? At least while it's not raining,' I suggested. 'We could head a couple of blocks that way' – I pointed to my left – 'and then walk down Fifth Avenue. I don't think we can go wrong heading north on there, maybe grab a slice of pizza or a hot dog on the way. Isn't that what a true New Yorker would do?'

I smiled and Jae-seung returned the gesture. 'Sounds good.' He held his arm out for me to lead the way, and we headed down West 17th Street.

'I hope the band will be OK to fly in,' Jae-seung said, taking in the sky again.

'That's the first time you've mentioned them in a while. Do you miss them?'

He nodded. 'Yes, I do. They're like brothers to me. Noodle in particular. We joined as trainees at the same time. I have let him down – let all of them down. This is the longest we have been apart.'

'But you've spoken to them, right? When you check in every day.'

He nodded again. 'They were given two days' leave but now they will be rehearsing in the studio in Seoul without me. It feels wrong.'

'You'll see them soon enough,' I said.

'I also feel bad that you are being my guide again. And in a city you've never been to.'

'I feel like I know this city already,' I said as I stepped into the road and a car hooted at me. Jae-seung grabbed me by the arm and pulled me towards him before I was flattened. 'Thanks,' I said, my cheeks flushing at his close proximity. 'Well, I thought I knew this place.' His hold lingered a little longer, until the light turned green and we could safely cross.

As we stepped onto Fifth Avenue, the city sprawled ahead, art deco buildings soaring.

'It really is a concrete jungle,' I said as I breathed it all in.

Jae-seung hummed the tune to 'Empire State of Mind' and I looked at him in surprise. 'Jay-Z and Alicia Keys. I love that song.'

'Me too.' He laughed.

'If you can make it here, Jae-seung, you can make it anywhere,' I said, deadpan.

At those words he hunched slightly, putting his hands in his pockets.

'Are you nervous about performing here?' I asked.

'It's the first time we've toured outside of Seoul. My management team had to pull a lot of strings to accompany BTS here. I have no idea how they arranged it.'

'Because you guys are amazing.'

He ducked his head shyly. 'Thanks.'

'I mean it. Those first two songs I heard were incredible. The way you sync the words to the dance moves, how high your voice goes…'

He chuckled to himself.

'What's so funny?'

'I appreciate your kind words, but the truth is… it's not my kind of music. But promise me you won't say anything?'

I pressed my lips shut, mimicking zipping them.

He nudged me. 'I'm serious.' His eyes crinkled deeply as he said those words. 'I could imagine the headlines now. I would be sunk if word got out that I didn't like our music.'

'I promise I don't have a direct link to the tabloids in the UK, but it would make a good story, I agree.'

'Have you not told anyone about me? Who I am?'

'Only my best friend, but she's sworn to secrecy. She might make a good journalist with her invasive questioning, including that grilling she probably gave you at your uncle and aunt's coffee shop, but she's the most loyal friend I have ever had.'

'You're lucky to have her.'

'I am,' I said wistfully. I had left a voice note for her when we landed. She had already told me she was proud of me for having taken this leap in the quest to find Mum but still, I wanted to hear her reassuring voice again.

'But why don't you like your music, if you don't mind me asking?'

'They're good songs, don't get me wrong. We have an amazing songwriter who works on our albums. He's an ex-K-pop star from the early 2000s, before it got so popular internationally. The truth is... I want to write my own music, but it isn't allowed. And there's no time anyway. The rehearsing, performing, recording, promoting... It occupies most of the day, every day, sometimes more than twenty hours in the day.'

'No wonder you're exhausted. But you're feeling more rested and healthy, right?'

The nod of affirmation was brief, and I sensed this mission to provide Jae-seung with respite and relaxation was only covering his problems superficially. There was more paining him, I knew it, but I wasn't sure how or when he might be willing to confide further.

As we made our way down Fifth, we marvelled at the Flatiron Building, walked through Madison Square Garden and got neck ache staring at the Empire State Building. I fished out my phone and took several pictures. As I did, it vibrated in my hand with an incoming videocall from Clara.

'It's my best friend,' I said. 'Sorry, I've got to take this.'

'Go ahead,' Jae-seung said, and we headed over to two chairs in Bryant Park.

The moment the call connected, she squealed and began a rendition of Taylor Swift's 'Welcome to New York'. 'I can't believe it, *meu amor.* You rock. Is hot Korean guy with you? Any more smooching?' she asked, with full sound effects.

I didn't know why her voice always reverberated so loudly, but Jae-seung stifled a laugh as my eyes widened and cheeks burned.

'*Desculpa*, he's right next to you, isn't he?'

I pulled my phone away from my face and panned it to take in Jae-seung, who waved shyly.

'Oh hey, Jae-seung. How you doing?' she said casually.

'I'll go over there for a minute,' I said, pointing in the distance.

'It's fine. I'll go.' Jae-seung headed over to sit on the grass.

'Can't believe you said that,' I hissed. 'Your intros need working on. I wasn't expecting you to call back so soon. What time is it over there?'

'Almost five. I couldn't sleep. Think I have caught some bug. Thought it was your pot plants but I'm at my flat now and I feel even worse. Keep running to the bathroom but *nada*. And my exam is in two days and I'm freaking out.'

'You're gonna ace it, Clara. Maybe you should go and see the doctor, though.'

'Nah, if I have caught some stomach bug it'll be gone by the time I can get an appointment. And there's no cure for norovirus. Gotta ride it out. Anyway, enough about me and my nausea. How are things going? Any leads on your mum?'

'The studio opens at eleven in the morning so we're going to head there tomorrow and see what we can find out. Meantime, as much sightseeing as we can pack in.'

'When are you coming home?'

Home. A breeze blew through my hair, and I patted down my curls. Where was home?

'Honestly, Clara. I don't know what I am doing in the next few hours, let alone days.'

'But you *are* coming back, right?' A panicked look coated her face. It was the most worried I had ever seen her.

'Of course I am, but I don't know when. It all depends on what I find out.'

'Meantime? More smooching?' She winked and, in a flash, she was her old self.

I sighed. 'I don't think so. He called it a mistake.'

'*Oh, não*. Brutal. Anyway, plenty more fish in the sea.' She did her customary head flick before letting out a yawn. 'Right?'

My shoulders slumped. 'I kinda liked this fish,' I said, giving a cursory glance in Jae-seung's direction. He was taking in the scene around him – his mouth gaping wide, in awe of the Empire State Building glowing purple in the distance. 'But it's as I first thought. He's never seen me in that way. We've become friends now and we agreed it was an "in the heat of the moment" kinda kiss. Nothing more. My mission is to find my mum and to get him back on stage, and hopefully I'm getting close to both. After that, we'll return to our separate lives.'

A hollowness filled my chest as those words drifted into the sticky night. Right then, Jae-seung turned and smiled at me. That look he gave me made me melt. The truth was, I didn't want to go back to our separate lives.

There is no other option
From now, from here

Chapter 20

The next morning, we stood outside the entrance to Body & Pole on West 27th Street and I craned my neck as I took in the whole building. Releasing my hair from its clip, I ran my fingers through my curls and straightened my pleated green skirt, tucking in my pale pink T-shirt. Peering through the glass frontage, I could see a large reception desk with two young women standing behind iMacs on the left, and several rows of dance gear displayed on metal poles along the wall on the right. In the distance, the words *Own Your Unknown* were painted above the entrance to what I assumed were all the studios. I chewed my bottom lip, running through my mind what I wanted to say.

I'd fallen asleep last night imagining possible conversations – thoughts and words I would want to say – and had risen early with a jolt, gasping for breath as if I had woken from a bad dream but couldn't remember what it had been about. Jae-seung had been sitting at the window, writing in a notebook, and had a look of concern on his face. He soothed me with reassuring words, reminding me where we were and that dawn had only just passed. When I questioned how long he had been awake, he said he hadn't been able to drift off. He blamed the jet lag, and I was hoping it was nothing more than that.

After a morning of walking the High Line, drinking coffee and marvelling at the city that clearly never slept, we had headed to the studio. The sky was the lightest blue – the heat intense. The barista at the independent coffee shop we had discovered at the foot of one of the exits along the High Line had called it the calm before the storm. It didn't seem possible when there was not even a breeze.

A touch on my hand startled me. Jae-seung was holding it, the firmness of his grip taming my nerves. With a gentle squeeze, he gave a small nod. His blue cap was tilted low over his face, his V-neck white T-shirt loose on his frame, green cargo shorts skimming his knees. I lifted my chin, and we went inside.

'Welcome to Body & Pole,' one of the receptionists said, her smile broad, ponytail swinging behind her. 'How can I help?'

'I…' The words lodged in my throat, but there it was again, a touch. A reassuring hold on my hand, Jae-seung's fingers laced through mine. 'I was looking for someone that I think works here, or perhaps used to work here. I think she was one of the founders. Marie Cavalieri-Lee is her name.' I paused. Maybe Mum had dropped the Italian part of her double-barrelled surname that we used to share. Once she left, Dad insisted on dropping the 'Lee' from *my* name. Then I remembered what I had unearthed at JK Dance Studio. 'Or maybe she's known as MJ.'

'Let me look her up on the system. I'm quite new here so I don't know all the names of our instructors.'

'Francesca?'

I turned at the sound of my name, dropping Jae-seung's hand. Behind me stood a woman with long flowing chestnut hair, lines etching her forehead, dance gear adorning her toned frame.

'Wow,' she said, staring at me intensely. 'The similarities are uncanny.'

'I'm sorry, do I know you?'

'No, but I knew your mum very, very well and she had hoped that one day you would come and find her. I'm Lacey, and I founded this studio with her and Ara.'

Her words shocked me. Mum *had* wanted me to find her but wait… '*Knew*, past tense?' I asked, my voice cracking a fraction.

'Oh God, no.' She smiled broadly, two straight rows of white teeth on display. 'Not past tense. She no longer works here. Listen, honey, I have a class I have to co-teach in a few minutes. I'm retiring soon and it's going to be one hell of a wrench handing over the reins but it's my time to move on now. Please, stay.' She reached out to grab both my hands. Her tone and openness were soothing and instantly I felt relaxed in her company. 'I want to find out all about you and I have lots to tell you about your mama.'

'Like where she is?'

She nodded. 'Come.' She tugged at my arm. 'Why don't you come sit in on the class? Bring your friend. Have some fun.'

I shook my head. 'Oh no, I don't dance.'

'That surprises me.'

'Why?'

'Something your mama once said… that you were the most graceful ballerina, always dancing in the kitchen of your home in Sicily, I seem to remember.'

'Surreal' was an understatement. I was standing here listening to a woman I had never met who knew Mum well enough to recall childhood memories that I had no recollection of.

'Now, *this* guy,' she said, turning to Jae-seung, and stroking his arms with her red-tipped fingernails, 'is most definitely a dancer. Am I right?' Her eyes twinkled and he turned his head with a bashful expression on his face.

'Yes,' he said quietly.

'Perfect.' She clapped her hands. 'This is a couples pole class and it always helps when one partner knows a little of what they're doing.'

'But we're not a… I mean, this isn't my—'

'Honey,' she said, reaching out and holding my chin gently – the hold taking me by surprise. 'The pairs here come in all shapes and sizes, no labels. "Couple" is another way of saying "two people of any relationship status", including friendship.'

'But I can't dance in this,' I said, pointing to my T-shirt and skirt combo.

She waved away my protesting. 'We'll lend you both some gear.'

I gave Jae-seung an *are you sure about this?* eyebrow raise, but he appeared excited by the prospect of dancing again.

After changing into tight black gym shorts and a fitted Body & Pole cropped black top, I emerged from the changing room, holding my arms tight across my chest. Jae-seung was waiting for me outside decked in black biker shorts and a white branded vest top.

'Are you sure you're OK with this?'

He stretched out his hand. 'If it means I get to dance with you again, then... yes.' He winked.

My fingers threaded through his and my nerves abated as I remembered back to the last time we had danced, at Havana Club. The hand-holding was also becoming more and more frequent – it felt natural, comforting.

In a flash we were ushered inside the studio by the main teacher and asked to go and stand by a pole. I chose one tucked away by the frosted windows, hoping to be inconspicuous. No such luck. After a warm-up session, which I was able to follow, Lacey made a beeline for us and helped us with the basics while the rest of the couples – a mix of opposite sex and same sex – began adding moves to a routine they had been working on in previous lessons.

I followed Lacey's instructions and began to walk around the pole, each step in time to the beat of the music, my hand high on the metal post. I learned my first spin after a few attempts during which my hand kept slipping. She was encouraging and at one point came and tickled me as she said my expression was too serious and my shoulders too stiff. Jae-seung caught my eye once I composed myself and I wondered whether he was thinking about that night in my studio.

When it was Jae-seung's turn, he moved fluidly, and I was stunned to see him lift himself up so he could reach higher and spin with both legs off the floor. Lacey clapped and went over to help another pair with a descent, telling us to keep practising those moves until we had smashed them.

'You've done this before,' I said, poking him in the ribs once Lacey was out of earshot.

He shrugged his shoulder. 'I did a few lessons a couple of years ago. It's good for upper body strength.'

'OK, everyone,' the other teacher hollered from the front of the class. 'Now it's time to learn the next few moves.'

As she and Lacey worked through the routine, my jaw dropped at what we were expected to do next. It involved the first partner pulling themselves up the pole as far as they could go, locking one of their legs around it, with the other partner spinning around at the bottom before providing the other with a shoulder lift to propel them higher. From this height, both would spin round before the one on top would slide down slowly into the arms of the other, before spinning around again. *Got that?*

We practised and practised, Lacey helping me improve my frame and hold, spritzing my hands with pole spray for a better grip. She told me how to pull with my arms and not strain my neck. When we finally mastered the lift, my breath left my body in one rush: a surge that electrified me. Coming down the first time, I didn't hold on tightly enough and fell on my tailbone. Embarrassment flooded my face, but Lacey laughed and said now I could call myself a pole dancer – a fall was a rite of passage apparently. My butt throbbed with pain, and I couldn't quite see the funny side of it, knowing the bruise would be epic.

The music began again, and I counted the beat in my head. Stepping forward, my bare feet cold against the wooden floor, I began the opening sequence that we had already mastered. When Jae-seung joined in so we were both spinning, our hands at intervals apart on the pole, we locked eyes with each other and suddenly I couldn't look away. There was a connection that sizzled between us, and in that moment, I blocked out everyone and everything around me. The only sounds were the deep bass of the music, pulsating in time to my heart. Jae-seung's body slipped and rolled, and he effortlessly lifted me high. This time I came down more elegantly and my body was flush with his. Leaning my arms behind me, I wrapped them around his waist. His arms flexed as he held my weight, and then we were spinning and spinning. My head turned against his chest, breathing him in, a feeling of floating making me feel weightless.

Once we stopped, his heartbeat thrummed against my ear. Lifting my head, our mouths were tantalising close as he leaned down, our breathing ragged. I tried to calm my racing pulse, but it was impossible when I gazed into his eyes and was met by the same intensity that I knew was in mine.

A slow clap sounded around me, and the spell was broken. Jae-seung steadied me as we prised apart.

'Well, well, well,' Lacey said, her finger tapping her chin. 'Are you sure you haven't done this before, you two?'

Jae-seung's bottom lip was folded inside his mouth. No way would I blow his cover. 'We're amateurs,' I confirmed.

'Well, that set my pulse racing,' she said with her hand on her chest. 'It's time for a warm-down now. Why don't you go and get showered and changed, and I'll meet you in my office? There's so much to talk about.'

I held my hands on my hips, still unable to catch my breath. Taking one of the provided hand towels, I dabbed the sweat from my neck and face, before wiping down the pole, the whole time not able to stop sneaking glances at Jae-seung. His chest was rising and lowering as he breathed deeply and evenly. He took the edge of his shirt and wiped his brow, his naked torso glistening with sweat.

I was struggling to contain the thoughts that were crowding my mind: images of being in his arms, remembering his lips on mine in the darkness of my bedroom in Sicily. It was getting harder and harder to deny the attraction.

That class was… *piccante*. It hadn't felt like dancing. There was a fervour that had filled my core and pulsed between my legs. The routine was sexy and liberating, a heady mix of emotions. And they were feelings I would never forget.

There is no other option
From now, from here
Until the end of days

Chapter 21

'Are you sure, Jae-seung?' I said as we stood outside the Dollar car rental place on West 52nd Street, my hand clutching a piece of paper with an address north of Wilmington in North Carolina. 'It's a ten-hour drive.'

'Which you don't have to do alone.'

My hair whipped against my face as I stared deeply into his eyes. The sky was awash with greys, turning darker in places. Traffic was building as people were no doubt trying to get home or wherever they needed to go before the storm hit, and the sidewalk was eerily empty.

'I know how to drive,' I said, battling to keep my curls off my face.

'With an incoming storm?'

'I checked the news on my phone. It said it was likely to blow east, lose its power over New York State and roll into the Atlantic.'

'Are you sure you don't want to wait it out?'

I shook my head vigorously. 'I've come this far; I can't wait. But you don't have the time to drive with me and get back for rehearsals.'

'Hopefully, by the time we get there, the airports will have reopened, and I can fly back to New York. If not, there's time. Don't worry about me. Besides, I'm fully invested now; I want to make sure you find her and a ten-hour drive will be much more bearable if we share it.'

Tears pricked my eyes as he said those words. I had found her. An address had been written on a Christmas card from

Mum to Lacey only six months ago, with best wishes for the new year and an update on her life in North Carolina. Lacey didn't have a number but didn't hesitate in telling me that Mum would without doubt want her details passed on.

Lacey and I had sat and chatted over a couple of smoothies in her office while Jae-seung had headed to the apartment. She had a whole album of photos of Mum and her and the Korean woman I had seen in that photo at the dance studio in Seoul. Mum had met Lacey at one of the classes that she was running from her apartment in Brooklyn, and they had become friends. Lacey had been well known for a pole-dance programme that she had rolled out over various gyms in NYC and was captivated by Mum's ideas, which she had learned in Seoul. Wanting to invest in a new venture (having sold their share of JK Dance Studio), Mum and Ara had decided to put money behind a Manhattan-based business, with the three of them as founders. Once word spread, and the pole programme took off, they had moved from a studio in Park Slope to Chelsea, buying the second floor once it became available.

But two years ago, Mum had decided to sell her share and move for a beach life in North Carolina, though Lacey couldn't tell me why. She thought it best I hear it from her. With trembling hands, I had returned to the apartment, and Jae-seung had held them as we sat and talked about what to do. All airports had grounded their local flights and our only option of getting to the address scrawled on that piece of paper was to drive through five states to reach it.

Jae-seung's hand reached for mine again as the fingers of his other pulled my hair off my face. His touch soothed me, and I leaned into his hold. 'I would like to do this with you,' he said.

I lost myself in the moment and the ability his hold had to calm my racing thoughts. 'OK,' I said finally, 'let's do this… together.'

He dropped his hand and put a closed fist out towards me, and I bumped it with mine, a smile breaking free on my lips. The adventure continued.

We handed over our licences and passports at the counter and Jae-seung laid down his card to give a deposit despite my protest. Grabbing the keys, we loaded the Jeep Cherokee with our cases. Inputting Mum's address into my phone, I locked it into the phone holder as Jae-seung navigated his way out of Manhattan, through the Holland Tunnel and into Jersey City. I let him concentrate on the road ahead while I stared out of the window, the rush of racing thoughts flooding my mind again.

But this time I couldn't clear my head. It had been a crazy week. From London to Seoul, to Sicily then New York and now on to North Carolina. My bank balance wasn't going to thank me but the things I had experienced over these seven days had been priceless.

I snuck a glance at Jae-seung, and he caught me staring.

'You OK?' he asked before fixing his attention on the Garden State Parkway ahead, changing into cruise control as the traffic cleared and we had a fairly open road.

'I'm fine. I'm trying to think through everything that's happened. I'm going to meet my mum. And she has no clue I'm coming. Feels weird. Can't think what I am going to say to her, even though I have replayed possible conversations in my mind for years.'

'It'll be emotional.'

'That's what I'm worried about.' I twisted in my seat to face him more fully. 'While it was lovely to hear those stories from Lacey, I couldn't deny the anger that was bubbling beneath the surface. It keeps reappearing. Or maybe it's never left. Discovering she wanted me to find her one day was nice to hear, but why was it my responsibility? Why was it so hard for her to stay in touch? I don't know. Some things don't quite make sense.'

'I hope you get the answers you'll need to move on,' Jae-seung said quietly, sincerely.

'Move on to where, though?' I slid down my seat a fraction.

'Don't you want to return to London?'

I took in the freeway ahead – the hazy heat rising from the tarmac, the clouds dark and brooding. 'Yes and no. I don't want to leave Clara but what else have I got to go back for? The last call I had with my agent was frosty. She was so brisk in the exchange. I don't think she believes I have what it takes.'

'I do.'

Our eyes met briefly before he fixed his attention on the road.

'That's very kind of you—'

'I'm not being kind,' he said, his tone direct. 'What you lack is self-belief. And I bet when you arrived for your last audition, you had it in spades – that belief that you could do it, because that is what I saw when we rehearsed together.'

A flush filled my cheeks as he said those words.

'It wasn't the right part,' he continued. 'And maybe the next one will be.'

'Maybe,' I said, my eyes lowering to my lap.

It was lovely to hear his words of encouragement; I now had two people in my support bubble. But in ten hours, I'd be saying goodbye to one of those champions.

'How are *you*, anyway?' I asked.

He paused, breathing in deeply. 'The honest truth?'

I shifted my body closer to his seat. 'Yes. Always.'

'I'm scared.'

'Of what?'

'Getting back on stage.'

'Turn around,' I said sharply.

'What?' He gripped the steering wheel tightly.

I pointed ahead at the spaghetti-like junction of exits. 'Turn off here and let's return to Manhattan. We're not even an hour in. If you're worried about making it in time, I don't want you to risk this long drive. I'll be fine to do this on my own.'

He rested his hand on my leg for a moment. 'That's not what I meant, Francesca. The guys won't get in for another two days at the earliest. Our tour manager always likes to build extra time into our schedule in case of any issues, like incoming tropical storms,' he said, the corner of his mouth lifting. 'I'll make it on time.' He sucked his bottom lip inside his mouth before slowly releasing it. 'I meant I'm scared to physically get back on stage. It's hard to explain. I haven't processed what happened last week. I felt like running away was the safest thing for me to do, but I can't keep running. Too much depends on me returning to perform.'

'You're the "J" in JYNKS, the lead vocalist. I can't even imagine the pressure you must be feeling right now.'

'It didn't start out that way. We were all equals. Having a lead singer wasn't part of the original plan for the band when we formed, or at least that was what we were told. But management kept a close eye on everything – fans' reactions, press coverage. I was the chosen one. It happens to a lot of bands. But it comes at a price. Jungkook has spoken a lot about the pressure of being lead vocalist of BTS, the self-doubt he sometimes feels.'

'Is that what you feel?'

'Yes and no. My years as a trainee, the vocal lessons I received – they all helped in building some level of confidence and resilience but…'

He paused and I sensed there was more he wanted to say. His jaw pulsed and I wondered if that night was coming back to the forefront of his mind.

'But what?' I asked softly.

'Something was different about that night. I'm not sure what happened. We warmed up the same way, the guys and I reciting positive affirmations to get the adrenaline pumping. But there was something off. I usually push myself hard but I found myself going through the motions.'

'What is the last thing you remember before you fell?'

'I was singing a duet with Noodle.'

'"Five Minutes",' I said. 'That was the song. It was so beautiful. Your voice is…' I turned then and quietened.

Jae-seung's mouth was open, his breathing short, chest rising rapidly beneath his grey T-shirt. It was barely noticeable, but I could see his hands shake a little, too. I leaned over and rested one of mine on his. 'It's OK. You're safe. Nothing can hurt you right now.' I knew them all too well, the signs of a panic attack. 'Breathe. Breathe with me. In.' I inhaled deeply with my nose to four beats. 'And out.' I counted to eight out loud. 'In to four, and out to eight.' We did this several times, and I held the wheel as straight as I could until I felt his hand stop shaking beneath mine.

He pulled into the nearest layby and hit the brakes. Laying his arms on the wheel, he sank his head into them.

I slipped a reassuring arm around his shoulder. 'Hey, it's OK. You're going to be fine.' I stroked his back in rhythmic circles. 'Maybe I should do the first shift, huh?'

He didn't argue but got out of the car and went round to my side. The wind whipped me against the bonnet and I had to hold on to the car to steady myself. The sky was dark, even though it was early afternoon. A bolt of concern ran through me at how bad this storm might get.

I adjusted the seat, clicked my belt and pulled out onto the freeway. Silence fell between us and when I finally peered over at Jae-seung, I saw his eyes were closed and he was asleep.

I remembered how he told me this morning that he hadn't slept last night and wondered what was going on in his head. Was it only rest he needed? Had he fallen at that moment because of exhaustion and the pressure to perform or was there something else that had troubled him at that time? Perhaps he needed to open up more, talk about his fear. Maybe that was the only way he could move forward.

Easy for me to say – I had kept thoughts about my mother hidden in the depths of my mind, and I had let them fester there, not even sharing them with Clara. Jae-seung was the first person who I had felt comfortable confiding in. He had given me space and understanding.

The next few hours slipped by. Jae-seung periodically stirred and changed position. After a three-hour nap, he took on the next shift. We then swapped over again before I pulled in for gas when we got onto Interstate 95 in Springfield, Virginia. Together, we headed into the adjoining shop and bought some snacks while the pump handler filled the car.

'My turn,' Jae-seung said, grabbing the keys the guy handed over before refusing to let me get my card out to pay. There was humour in his expression. The nap had obviously helped.

I folded my arms in mock offence before swiping the keys back. 'No way. That last shift wasn't that long. Besides, I owe you,' I said as he slipped in beside me.

'You owe me nothing.'

'You're travelling over six hundred miles away from the venue where you're going to be performing in front of thousands in a few days and you keep paying for things. I think I do owe you something.'

'I'm happy to be a part of this adventure with you.'

'I'm happy you're with me, too.'

When our eyes met, it was almost impossible not to focus on his lips as the memory of that kiss stirred in my mind again.

'You sure you're OK to drive?' he asked as I pulled away.

'I'm fine,' I said, looking in the wing mirror as I changed lanes. 'The truth is… I was more worried about you.' My tone was measured, not wanting to dwell too much on what he'd shared earlier in case it triggered another reaction.

'That was a blip earlier.'

I didn't question him but instead asked him other things about being an idol – got him to talk about what he did enjoy about performing and to share some of his favourite moments of his career to date. His posture was relaxed as he spoke. He said what he loved most was the camaraderie between him and the other members, Noodle in particular. They always had supported each other in the early years, before they knew they were going to be in the band – when they were trainees – always joking around, pulling pranks on each other.

He also told me how he had been discovered: busking outside a shopping mall, a chance discovery one evening after his shift at a local convenience store. His life turned upside down overnight. Signed the next day by one of the top management companies in Seoul, he then finished his high school studies over the next year while training. After that it was a rigorous training programme. JYNKS' meteoric rise over the last two years had surprised all of them and being chosen to perform with BTS had been one of their biggest achievements to date, he said, alongside their most recent album topping the charts in South Korea. But global domination wasn't yet in sight, not until they had put in a good performance on the tour.

I clutched the steering wheel tight, steeling myself to say the next words. 'Do you think that song is a trigger for you, Jae-seung?'

He paused, leaning his arm on the window, his fist clenched by his mouth. Another glance in his direction and I could see him putting into practice the breathing technique we had done a few hours ago. 'Yes,' he whispered.

'Do you feel comfortable talking about it?'

He removed his fist from his mouth and rubbed that patch between his thumb and forefinger and nodded. We sat in silence for a while, but no words came.

'Does it have something to do with your scar?' I asked hesitantly.

He closed his eyes for a beat. 'I found my mum… I found her…' He breathed harder and harder. 'She had a rope around her neck. I tried. I tried hard to get it off her. It left a rope burn. Here,' he said, pointing to the puckered skin.

I kept my hands steady on the steering wheel but the image of seventeen-year-old Jae-seung attempting to save his mother played out in my mind.

'When a neighbour heard me screaming, they rushed in and found me cradling her and called for an ambulance. We were both taken to the hospital. It's a second-degree burn.'

He paused again and I wondered if that was where his fear of going to a hospital stemmed from.

'I was in the waiting room,' he continued, 'down the corridor, when the doctors came from her room. They said something about if she had been found five minutes earlier, she would've had a chance. It was my fault. I was having a farewell party with some of my old friends. My flight to London was that night. Five minutes.' His voice cracked. 'If I had left them five minutes earlier, she would have been fine.'

'You've carried this guilt for all these years?'

'Yes. But I thought it was buried, deep inside, but every time my voice soars to that high note, it's a reminder. My screams. My pain. My fault.'

What could I say? I doubted I was the first person to tell him it wasn't his fault – he must have heard that before. 'Thank you for telling me. I can't even begin to imagine what that would have been like for you.'

Jae-seung didn't answer but fixed his focus on the empty freeway ahead. His eyes appeared to water, his lips trembling, and that's when I knew what was about to happen. I couldn't bear seeing him in so much pain, unable to comfort him. I spotted a layby up ahead, checked my mirrors and pulled over. The Jeep hit the gravel and came to a stop.

'Let's get some air,' I said, stepping out.

I came to his side of the car as he leaned against it, raising his eyes to the sky, desperately trying to hold his tears in. I tugged his hand and encouraged him forward and then he crumpled into my arms and cried.

There is no other option
From now, from here
Until the end of days
Even though I don't want it to be

Chapter 22

I held him. Stroked his back. The pain obviously went deep – deeper than I could ever have imagined. His body shook in my embrace. Humid, gritty air whipped my bare arms and my curls danced in the wind. I had no idea how long we stood there like this.

A drop landed on my cheek, but it wasn't a tear; it was from the sky.

Jae-seung finally shifted from my hold, swiping his face with his T-shirt sleeve. He gulped a mouthful of air and ruffled his hair as he breathed out deeply.

'Feel better?' I asked tentatively.

He smiled and nodded. 'Much.' Leaning forward, he held the side of my face and brushed a thumb over my cheek. The movement sent a wave of yearning through to my gut, stealing my breath at the sheer beauty – inside and out – of this man before me. He spoke deeply in Korean, and I was caught under the spell of his words even though I had no clue what he was saying. But then he uttered two English words: 'Thank you.'

I was lost. Lost in his eyes, those sorrowful eyes.

'That's twice I've cried on you,' he said. 'What must you think?'

'Here's a brave guy willing to be true to his feelings and unafraid to express them,' I reassured him.

More drops landed on us. The clouds were darkening above and soon it began to rain, light at first, slowly increasing in intensity. The wind whipped, debris from the layby swirling around.

'I guess we had better get back in the car,' I said, even though I didn't want to move from this spot, from his touch.

'My turn,' Jae-seung said, grabbing the keys from my hand. 'I'm all cried out now. You have nothing to worry about.' He smiled and I returned the gesture, taken aback by his strength and resolve to carry on after baring something so painful.

Back in the car, we sat beside each other in companiable silence. As the miles slipped by, I noticed Jae-seung's posture was more relaxed: one hand on the wheel, that smile firmly etched on his face.

He turned the radio on, and a local station filled the car. A few songs in, our heads turned, and we mirrored each other's shocked expression. It was 'Empire State of Mind'. Our heads began nodding to the beat and then Jae-seung broke into song – singing Jay-Z's rap word-perfect. I laughed as he body-rolled in his seat.

And then…

With a deep breath, I sang out Alicia Keys' part, my voice soaring higher and higher, bopping in my seat, losing myself to the rhythm. I beamed as Jae-seung hit rap after rap, and I let go during my solo, the acoustics surprisingly good within the confines of the Jeep.

When the song ended, Jae-seung turned the volume down and stared at me for a moment, his mouth wide open.

'Um… wow,' he said. 'I didn't know you could sing.'

I blushed. 'Not really.'

'Yes, really. You hit those high notes perfectly. Have you ever auditioned for musicals?'

'God, no. I can't hold a tune on my own. And I certainly can't dance.'

Jae-seung didn't contradict me but a frown settled on his face, leaving me wondering what he was thinking.

The radio hummed in the background as the rain pounded the roof of the car and the windscreen. Jae-seung turned the wipers on to full swipe, but it was beginning to get harder and harder to see through the glass. Flashing signs began to appear on the side of the road, warning us of potential flooding and to slow down.

We glanced at each other, and I chewed my bottom lip as the noise of the rain now drowned out the din of the radio.

'Maybe we need to pull in somewhere and wait until the worst has passed,' I said. 'But then... it'll be gone midnight by the time we get there. *Cazzo*, I didn't think this through. Arriving in the middle of the night, knocking on Mum's door – she'll probably think I'm a ghost and have a heart attack.'

'We passed a sign for a motel. Think it said five miles. Maybe we could stop there for a while or... overnight?' he suggested, his voice low, removing one hand from the wheel to stroke the back of his neck.

Another sign came into view warning us of a crash ten miles ahead.

'I think that's probably a great idea,' I said, suddenly acutely aware of his proximity to me, heat filling the small space between us despite the aircon being on.

Even running from the car to the motel entrance rendered us drenched. The guy at reception was decked out in a blue chequered shirt, his long hair ruffling every time the fan behind him oscillated past. His shoulders sagged. 'One night?' he said, slowly chewing gum, his attention fixed on his computer screen.

'Yes, please,' I said, clocking the *All visitors welcome* sign on the wall behind him, yet feeling anything but. At a guess, business was probably slow until nights like these, when travellers were forced off the road for a brief respite.

Jae-seung wandered over to the seating area, where there was a guitar sitting beside an armchair. He sat down and inspected the instrument, marvelling at it.

'Whose guitar is this?' he asked the receptionist.

'It was left behind by someone a few weeks ago and no one has come to reclaim it. It's yours for the night if you want.' He tapped away on his keyboard. 'One room or two?'

My mouth opened and closed but then I glanced over at Jae-seung. Something passed between us and the hairs on the nape of my neck rose. Knowing what I did about his sleep issues meant there was only one answer to that question.

'One please,' I stammered, my mouth suddenly dry.

Collecting the key, I headed to our room while Jae-seung ran out to the car to grab our things. It was a double room with brown carpet, a small flatscreen on a chest of drawers and a wooden desk with two chairs in the corner. The quilt had a gold brocade pattern with a burgundy backdrop. I shivered beneath the aircon unit and tried but failed to turn it down.

A knock at the door. I opened it and Jae-seung stood there weighed down with our things, the guitar and a white plastic bag, raindrops falling down his face, his T-shirt sticking to his chest. I relieved him of my case, hauling it onto the bed before passing him one of the hand towels that had been left on the quilt.

'Thanks,' he murmured as he wiped his face and ran the towel through his hair.

'What's in there?' I said, nodding at the plastic bag.

'I raided the vending machine for snacks.' He raised the bag proudly.

'Ooh, noodles,' I said as he laid out the contents and I inspected each item. 'Lays, Twizzlers and Sprite.' I chuckled. 'This will be a gourmet feast.'

A shiver suddenly rippled along my arms and I shook a bit.

'You cold?' he asked.

'I can't get the aircon down but I'm sure I'll warm up once I have a shower and get into some dry clothes.' I picked out a white vest and grey jersey shorts from my case.

'The guy at reception also gave me these.' He took out several tea lights and a box of matches. 'He said it's more than likely we'll lose power at some point. And he said we did the right thing in coming off the road. That storm is going to be a direct hit. If we hear banging, it'll be someone securing a few planks against the window, apparently. I'll make the instant noodles while you shower.'

'Sure you don't want to go first? I'm not that wet.' My mind went to an alternate meaning for that statement. 'I mean soaked,' I stammered. OK, now I was making things *much* worse. A flashback to the first moment I met Jae-seung came to the forefront of my mind. The way his presence had rendered me a stuttering mess.

'I'll be fine to go second,' he said, letting a slow smile build.

I let the hot water soothe me as I stood in the bath under the shower head. It was on the highest heat setting, and I resembled a lobster when I stepped out. Changing into my shorts and strappy vest, I towel-dried my hair. I hesitated before turning the handle and stepping back into the room. How was this going to play out? One double bed, zero sofa bed. I closed my eyes and centred myself. Maybe, for once, I shouldn't overthink it and just go with the flow. *Air tick.*

Jae-seung was sitting by the TV, blowing steam away from his pot.

'Bathroom's yours,' I said.

Jae-seung slipped past me and shut the door while I turned on the radio. The weather report confirmed that for the next few hours, we would be in the eye of the storm.

When the bathroom door opened, my first forkful of noodles hovered in the air, sauce dripping off it. Jae-seung had stepped out in a cloud of steam, a small towel hugging his hips.

He cleared his throat. 'I… um… forgot to take in some fresh clothes.'

'Right,' I said, not able to drag my eyes away from him as he moved to his case, giving him the longest once-over – his wet naked skin, those undulating muscles on his arms and chest – before he disappeared back into the bathroom.

I cursed myself again for not being able to resist ogling his taut physique and reminded myself what he had to go through to maintain it. A minute later he returned wearing a grey T-shirt and black sport shorts.

We sat and ate and listened to the radio, singing along to any tracks we knew. The wind rattled the windowpanes, but we were lost in our haven, oblivious to the world outside this room. Even the sudden banging against the frame didn't startle us. It was as if we were in our own bubble.

As we placed the packaging of our snacks in the dustbin, the room plunged into darkness, an eerie silence filling the space as the radio went dead.

A dog barked outside, and voices could be heard from down the corridor. My eyes took a while to adjust to the lack of light, but I could make out Jae-seung moving across the room and as he struck a match against its box, his face was bathed in a gentle glow. He set about igniting the tea lights and placed them all around.

'I guess we will have to make our own music, then,' he said as he grabbed the guitar and sat on the floor against the bed.

I slipped down next to him and watched as he tuned the strings and strummed a few chords.

'Who's your favourite artist?' he asked.

I smiled. 'Taylor Swift. Clara and I are huge fans.'

'She's very talented, a brilliant lyricist,' he said. 'It would be a dream to do a duet with her.' He plucked the opening chords to 'The Joker and the Queen'. 'Sing with me?' he asked.

I hesitated. This time there was no backing track, only the gentle twang of a guitar. 'OK,' I whispered as I watched Jae-seung's long fingers stroke the strings. He began with Ed Sheeran's part. I took a deep breath and sang when it came to Taylor's verse.

Our eyes met as we harmonised, his encouraging smile lifting me, our shoulders periodically pressing together as I swayed to the music. Once we had completed a repertoire of her greatest hits, breaking into some more upbeat ones, we paused to catch our breath.

Then Jae-seung's fingers strummed a sequence of chords that were unfamiliar.

'I don't know this one.'

'It's... um... something I wrote.'

'So, you *do* write?'

'It's all I've ever wanted to do but my management team don't encourage it and I've never had the time to devote myself to it. Since going to London, I have felt inspired.' He flicked his fringe off his forehead.

'Can I hear it?'

'I only have a couple of verses and the chorus. The rest is... still unwritten.'

He sucked his bottom lip inside his mouth and slowly released it, and once again, I couldn't look away. He plucked the strings with his fingertips before singing the sweetest tune.

It took me one look
One look to know
To know I wanted you
And couldn't let you go

When I saw you that day
I couldn't silence my heart
And when I held you close
I knew we could never be apart
But I can't let you into my world
Because a love like this
Will bleed if it unfolds

If this were a love match
It would never end right
And it pains me to tell you
I have no strength for the fight
And to tell you of my fear
My fear to give you my heart

There is no other option
From now, from here

Until the end of days
Even though I don't want it to be...

He paused, strumming one final chord, the notes lingering in the increasingly humid air of the room. As he placed the guitar on the carpet, he shook his head. 'It's not that great, I—'

'It's beautiful,' I interrupted, touching his arm.

He clasped his hands on his lap. 'Thank you.'

'It's very different to what you sing with your band. The lyrics are quite melancholy. Is it about you?'

'Yes, it is.' He lifted his head and took in my face. 'I'm afraid.'

'I know you are.'

'Not only to get back on stage.' He pulled his legs to his chest and hugged his knees. The movement brought him closer to me, so we weren't only touching on our shoulders, his face inches from mine. 'I'm afraid of these feelings, these feelings I have... for you.'

I pointed at my chest as if I hadn't heard him right. '*Per me?*'

There was a slight uplift in the corner of his mouth. '*Sì*,' he said.

At that I laughed but when I saw the seriousness in his expression, I remembered that he was baring his soul to me and was reminded of the opening words of the song.

'You want me?'

'Very much. I've been sinking... further and further into you. The only time I have felt at peace these last few weeks is in your arms. You have provided me with a safe space to be vulnerable with no judgement – a space I have never had with anyone else; your kindness and thoughtfulness soothe me. But every scenario that runs through my head of how it could be between us doesn't end well. You said that kiss in Sicily was a mistake—'

'I didn't truly believe it.'

'But I can't hurt you.'

'I wouldn't let that happen.'

'How could you be so sure?'

'You've told me you can't be involved with someone. You've been honest about your feelings towards love. I wouldn't be getting involved blindly. I know this would only be one night. I know our worlds couldn't be further apart. But right now,' I said, dropping my focus to his mouth, 'all I can think of is kissing you again and getting lost in you.'

He took a sharp intake of breath and then his lips were on mine, feverishly, not chastely like before, devouring me like he was starving, and I was a feast.

Before I could catch my breath, he had lifted me into his strong arms, mine wrapped tightly around his neck, legs around his waist. His movements were gentle, his ability to hold me effortless. Pressed against the wall, an ache built inside me as he kissed me. I didn't want this to go fast but how could it not?

His lips were on my neck, tasting my skin, breathing me in. My hands were in his damp hair, gently tugging.

He rested his forehead on mine. 'I don't have any—'

'I got it covered. The zipped pocket of my suitcase still has some from last summer's trip home.'

'Oh.'

I knew what he was thinking with that 'Oh'.

'He couldn't be further from my thoughts right now.'

At that he smiled – those cheekbones. I trailed my finger over the side of his face, across his lips. He held my thumb captive in his teeth.

Our lips found each other's again as I trailed my hands over his taut shoulders. Then I felt myself falling until the softness of the mattress pressed into my back. Jae-seung released his hold on me and in one swift move peeled his T-shirt off.

His body glowed in the candlelight as he stood there, illuminating the tattoo around his arm, the numbers 234 catching my eye. Jae-seung had opened up to me, bared his soul, and I wondered when he would feel comfortable sharing the symbolism of it. He caught me staring and covered up the ink with his hand. Then he faltered, sat on the bed and closed his eyes.

I stroked his shoulder, touching his chin with my fingertips. He opened his eyes and looked at me. 'Hey,' I said. 'What's wrong?'

'Are you sure this is what you want? One night?'

I kissed his lips again. 'Yes,' I said against his hot breath.

His eyes searched mine. 'It's been so long since I have been with someone. I'm scared of—'

'Jae-seung. You need to stop being so scared of hurting me. Come, lie down with me. Remember that first time, when you held me in the night?' I tugged his arm, so he was lying flush behind me. It was impossible not to feel his hardness, and the fire that was building inside me was fed another piece of kindling at the thought of making love to him.

He brushed away my curls and nuzzled my neck, his lips caressing my skin, and the movements sent tingles down my spine. Then his arm slid across my waist, and he pulled me against him. I brought his hand to my lips and dropped a kiss on his knuckles.

'Tell me,' he whispered. 'Tell me how you like to be touched. I don't want to rush this. I don't want the control.'

A breath caught in my throat at being the one to set the pace. No one had ever asked me what I liked. Passive. That was the role I had always taken in these encounters. Passive and the pleaser.

I closed my eyes and tuned in to the sensations I was feeling. The release of oxytocin as his arms held me in a tight hold, the tenderness of his embrace.

Taking his hand, I touched the tips of his fingers. 'I'd like to be stroked all over with these.'

Jae-seung traced my arm, my thigh, all the way down to my ankle and up again before finding the underside of my other arm and the inside of my other leg. Over and over again, he caressed me, and every graze of skin on skin inflamed me like two live wires connecting.

I was lost to his touch, the distant swell of waves in my mind. 'I can hear it. The ocean. Can you?'

'Yes,' he said, his lips brushing my ear, as his hand moved to my stomach where he traced circles in time to the waves of Cala Rossa against the rocks.

What I wanted him to do next, I couldn't articulate into words, so I grabbed his hand and slipped it under my vest. At this, his leg shifted and lay over mine, pinning me to the mattress. Moving his hand upwards, the fabric rucked up until he lightly grazed my breasts. I moaned as he circled the tips until they hardened beneath his touch, arching my back into him, his hardness pressing into me. I made him pinch his fingers and squeeze each nipple tightly, the way I enjoyed being touched when it was me alone, pleasuring myself, the way no guy had touched me before because it had never seemed in the least bit romantic to give someone instructions in the heat of the moment.

'Show me,' he whispered, 'show me how you like to be touched.'

I moaned as I let other desires overtake me.

Lower and lower I led his hand, until his fingers traced the outline of my jersey shorts, lifting the elastic to gain entry beneath the fabric. His breathing became more ragged in my ear as I slowly brought our hands in between my legs. I was *so*, so wet. Sliding back and forth between the lips, rubbing my mound with our fingers, I savoured the feeling, the building of near unbearable pleasure. He didn't pull his hand away but let me drive the movement, the speed, the intensity with which he touched me there.

After a while I wasn't entirely sure if I was leading, or he had taken over – those long fingers that I had noticed when we first met luxuriating inside me. Over and over again they moved and teased.

The sound of the ocean in my head grew louder and louder until finally the waves broke – my body shuddered, helplessly, pulsating around our hands, my mouth open on a silent moan.

Kisses trailed my shoulder, down my arm, at my hip. He turned me onto my back and I sighed deeply.

When his lips found mine again, I brought my hands to his face, not wanting to let him go. He slipped down the straps of my top and tugged my vest down, kissing every new spot of naked skin revealed. Further and further the fabric moved, until it met my shorts, which he wriggled down my legs until I was completely naked beneath him.

He stripped off his shorts and boxers, releasing himself. Sitting down on the chair by the table, he stroked himself, gently, watching me, devouring my nakedness with his eyes.

'I'm not going to be able to hold on when I am inside you, so please, take the lead again. *You* take control.'

A thrill shot through me. I hopped off the bed and retrieved a condom from my case, tearing the packet with my teeth before placing it on him. I climbed on gently, mouth dropping open as I lowered myself. He filled me completely, and unadulterated pleasure shot through me to my very core. A shaky breath came from his mouth as he grasped me tightly, pulling my body towards him so we were closer. Using my tiptoes to thrust up and down, I set the pace until I couldn't hold my balance any longer.

'Let go, Jae-seung,' I said. 'Let go.'

He shuddered beneath me as he found his release. I held his head in my hands and kissed him before noticing a single tear fall down his cheek.

There is no other option
From now, from here
Until the end of days
Even though I don't want it to be
We must go our separate ways

Chapter 23

Leaning my arm on the car window, I gazed out at the bright blue sky. The storm was over, and in its wake contentment and calm had settled over my body like a weighted blanket.

I snatched a look at Jae-seung and smiled. When he caught me staring, he took one of his hands off the wheel and held mine in the space between our seats.

A memory of last night filtered across my mind. The conversations between endless hours of lovemaking, words borne from deep within our souls – Jae-seung's pain that he wanted to be released from, the guilt of his mum's death he didn't know how to expunge. Showing one's feelings was not encouraged in Korea, he had said. He hadn't shared any of his torment until he had opened up to me. He said he felt lighter.

In return, I shared some memories of my childhood – fragments that had played on my mind over the course of the last week as more information about Mum's life since she'd left me had emerged. In each mental snapshot I was happy, and it still didn't make sense to me why she had never returned.

The road sign welcoming us to Wilmington came into view, and we took a left and headed to Holly Ridge. Butterflies camped in the base of my stomach, along with a hollow feeling, as the satnav showed we were only a few minutes away from our destination. This was it. A goodbye and a hello. As we reached South Anderson Boulevard, Topsail Beach could be seen in between houses and apartment compounds.

The Jeep came to its final stop in the visitor spot of the car park. It had been a three-hour drive from our motel.

Leaving Jae-seung's arms, that bed – the heat between our bodies extinguished as daylight peered through the window when the boards were removed – had been one of the hardest things I'd ever done.

I had lied to him. I'd known this was going to hurt but I had willingly accepted the one night with him – wanted that one night to explore the attraction between us. There was a pain I felt as soon as we headed off on the last leg of our epic journey. It ached deep in my chest. Having experienced now how good we were together, the chemistry, the connection, how could I go on knowing that I would never have that again with him?

The compound stood in front of us, turquoise-blue wood panelling adorning the upstairs apartments, whitewashed walls coating the ones on the ground floor. It was a weathered building, unsurprising considering it was right on the beach. To my right was a walkway, a teasing glimpse of the sea in the distance. The wooden structure appeared to melt into the sand.

Jae-seung leaned on the Jeep and clutched his hands, his head dipped low. I moved closer to him, shifting myself into his space. There it was again. Sadness in his eyes.

'Thank you for getting me here,' I said as I placed both my hands on his chest, stroking his white T-shirt.

His arms enveloped me then. It wasn't a hug; it was so much more. He held me, his strong arms wrapped around like a windbreaker sheltering me from the elements. The embrace felt like home, like belonging. Such unusual sensations because I had never stopped to consider where home was. But his touch soothed the very tips of me, the scent of fabric conditioner and herbal shower gel invading my nose, intermingled with sea wash and sunshine. I laid my head on his chest then, his heart reverberating in my ear, and waited for the rush of endorphins to overtake me. And when it came, it was the greatest high.

I wasn't entirely sure who broke the embrace, but our foreheads were suddenly resting against each other's.

'I tour in London in ten days. Do you think that maybe you…' His jaw locked and I knew this was a battle for him. It could never be like this again. He knew it and I knew it.

'I would love to watch you perform,' I said, stroking his cheek.

He smiled. 'I'll leave you two tickets at the box office. You could bring your friend.'

Clara. *Dio mio*. There was so much to catch up on, but I still couldn't tell her when I would return. It all depended on what was behind the door to apartment 2b.

'Thanks, Jae-seung, for coming on this journey with me.'

He shook his head. 'I have a lot more to thank *you* for. Do you want me to stay until I know you're together?'

I trailed my hand along his arm. 'I'm OK. I can wait for her if she's out. If she's gone away, then… I'll ask around. Someone might know something.'

He cupped my face in his hands and held them there. 'This is hard. Harder than I thought it would ever be.'

I took a snapshot of this moment in my mind, so I could recall it at a later date: the squawk of seabirds mixing with the distant sound of waves against the shore, the tenderness of his hands on my skin, of his legs pressed against mine, and every inch of his face – those liquid eyes and tender mouth.

'Goodbye, Francesca.' His lips brushed mine briefly and then the weight of his hold disappeared.

In a flash, he was at the wheel of the Jeep, reversing and driving into the sun. I knew where he was headed to: Wilmington International Airport. We had studied flight schedules on my phone. He would be at LaGuardia in a matter of hours, ready to get back into training, hitting the gym and beginning the intense rehearsal schedule. The rest of the band were in the air now that their delayed flight could leave Seoul.

Jae-seung had begun his healing process, but he knew there was more work to be done with his mental health, and I still had this sinking feeling that he hadn't shared everything with me. I hoped he could find the headspace to do that work and carry on with his life.

I tugged at my green shorts and readjusted the straps of my floaty white top. The heat was more bearable with the breeze floating off the ocean. I took a deep breath and knocked on the door. It was like pulling off a plaster. If I gave any more thought to what was waiting for me, I knew I would buckle and run.

A minute passed. Then another. I knocked again. A curtain twitched in apartment 2a and a door opened.

'She'll be down at the beach, honey,' a woman with a floral dress and beads in her hair said. 'Was quite the storm and she told me this morning she'd be out there to help clear the debris.'

'Oh,' I said, rolling on the balls of my feet.

'The door's always open. I'm sure she wouldn't mind if you left your case in there.'

'Thanks,' I said, and she shut her door.

I hesitated before turning the handle. Inside, the lingering scent of her perfume hit me hard, and memories stirred of bright lights and dressing rooms, the big top and aerial acrobatics. The room was narrow with an L-shaped grey sofa facing a small flatscreen, a kitchen at the end. The décor was minimal with white walls and rattan furniture dotted around, large canvases of seascapes on the walls. One such canvas drew me forward. It was so familiar; I could sense I had been there but couldn't immediately place it.

I walked over to the sideboard, which was covered by framed photographs. In the centre was a picture of Mum and me at the Cirque du Soleil in Naples. It was an image that had been ingrained in my mind because I had the same photo. Other pictures were of Mum with Lacey and the other founder – including the same photo I'd seen in the Seoul studio. Then there were some beautiful portrait-style photos of Mum on the pole – some black and white, all graceful.

Needing some air, I left the apartment and headed out across the walkway, the breeze ruffling my hair, which I struggled to curb. Holding on to the rail, I walked across the sand-coated steps over to the other side. Pulling off my sandals, my toes sank into the warm sand. A few paddlers waded in and screamed as the waves took them under and they resurfaced, laughing. The sea drew me closer, the water lapping rhythmically against the shore, and I walked until the sand became wet and firm beneath my feet.

Then I saw them. Far in the distance – a group with bin bags and sticks, collecting litter from the ground.

I moved closer and closer until I saw her.

She was talking animatedly with the others but when she noticed me, she froze. Dropping the bag on the ground, she stepped forward and her mouth fell open. Her long green sundress billowed in the breeze, but her curls were pinned tightly on top of her head, her skin tanned.

The waves hitting the shore grew quieter; the chatter of those around her dropped away.

It's you.

Five thousand, five hundred miles from New Malden to Seoul.

Five thousand, seven hundred miles from Seoul to Sicily.

Four thousand, five hundred miles from Sicily to New York City.

Five hundred and ninety-two miles from the city to here.

Over sixteen thousand miles I had travelled and there she was. I had found her. I had found my mother.

It took me one look
One look to know
To know I needed you
And couldn't let you go

Chapter 24

'CiCi?' she said.

That word caught me by surprise, but it was the name she had written on all those postcards – a nickname I hadn't heard in years.

I nodded. 'It's me.'

She held her hand over her eyes to shield them from the sun. 'You found me.'

'I didn't know I was meant to be looking.' The words came out accusatory but were the first that sprang to mind.

She nodded solemnly. 'I deserved that. I… I don't even know where to begin. How did you find me?'

I folded my arms across my chest. 'It's a long story.'

'I'd love to hear it. Would you like to come to mine, talk a while?'

'Sure,' I said, in a non-committal way. There it was. The anger. I could feel it fizzing inside my chest, aching to break free.

Mum said her goodbyes to the other debris collectors and ushered me towards her home. We walked in silence. Inside the apartment, I explained my interaction with her neighbour and her expression appeared to fill with hope that I had brought a suitcase with me.

A tray with ice-cold lemonade and a plate of cookies was brought to the living area. I sat at the edge of the sofa, not able to feel relaxed enough to sit back, while Mum sank into the armchair beside me.

'You're even more beautiful than I could ever have imagined you would be.'

'Thanks,' I said, not knowing how to respond. Every possible reply would be tinged with bitterness.

An uncomfortable silence descended between us. I sipped my drink and broke a chunk of the cookie, the chocolate chips melting in my fingertips as I stared at it.

'Sixteen years,' I said finally. 'Why?' No other words came. They were enough.

She ducked her head. 'I don't think any explanation will ever comfort you, CiCi.'

'My name is Francesca. My friends call me Fran and my *family* call me Cesca.' A hot, angry flush coated my skin.

'I'm sorry,' she said, straightening up and tightening her hold of her highball glass. 'You have every right to be angry.'

'Don't tell me what I have a right to feel. You lost any grounds to say those things to me the day you left and never returned. Remember that day? The one where you said you would come back for me, only you didn't.' My voice began to tremble, as the image of us shopping together in Palermo flashed across my mind. We had sat wearily in a café, sipping granitas, our purchases at our feet, and she had uttered those very words to me.

'I did come back.' She said it in almost a whisper.

'No, you didn't.'

'Please understand, Francesca. I don't know what you know or were told, but I didn't only return to see you. I came to take you with me.'

I rubbed my forehead, my mind going blank. 'What? When?'

'I had finished my last tour. My damaged ankle still plagued me, and my contract wasn't being renewed because of it. I had to start all over again, but I couldn't do that in Sicily.'

'Why not?' I dropped the half-eaten cookie on the plate. 'You had a family. You had me; you had Dad. I don't understand how someone could be so heartless to want to leave their child behind like that, or worse, come to take them away from their loving family.'

She placed her glass on the table and smoothed her hands over her dress. 'I've thought over many scenarios where I might finally be able to tell you the truth, but in none of them would I ever expect you to properly understand my decisions or forgive me for them. It's probably best if I tell you everything and you make of it what you will. I know I lost the right to be your mother years ago, Francesca, but please hear me out.'

I sat silently and settled back into the sofa.

'I fell in love with someone else,' she said, rolling the bangles on her wrist along her arm. 'Someone I shouldn't have. I knew that loving them would be the hardest thing I ever did, because in the process of loving that person, I would lose a daughter. Everything finally made sense, when she walked into my life.'

My throat went dry, her words rendering me speechless. *She.* Flashes of the photos Lacey had shown me at Body & Pole filtered into my mind. Then the penny dropped. *Air tick*. God, I wished Clara was here to steady me.

I went over to the sideboard, locating a replica of the snap I had seen in the JK Dance Studio. 'Did you fall in love with *her*?' I tipped my chin at the picture.

'Yes,' she said as her eyes welled with tears, staring at the ceiling to avert their fall.

'Where is she now?'

The question hung heavy in the air.

'She's gone.' A single tear spilled, and she swiped it away, sniffing.

'Gone where?'

'Ara died ten months ago.'

'Oh,' I said, aware that it came across as uncaring but unable to inject any sympathy into my tone while my head was buzzing with all this new information.

'She was first diagnosed with breast cancer when we lived in Seoul. That's partly why we left to live in New York, so she could be close to her family. She fought so bravely but two years ago, things took a turn for the worse. She had been in remission, but the cancerous cells had returned. She had always wanted to live close to the ocean and…' She paused then, the emotion beginning to choke her, and the tears began to fall.

Numb, I felt like I was having an out-of-body experience, as if another Francesca Cavalieri was having this conversation with their mother.

'She always said—'

'Stop!' My hands gripped the edge of the sideboard, trying to steady myself as a rush of dizziness overcame me. 'You want me to feel sorry for you that you lost the woman you left me and Dad for?'

'No, CiCi – I mean – Francesca, that's not what I want.'

'Then how dare you cry in front of me. This is surreal. I can't…' My chest tightened, and I tried to take a deep breath but couldn't. 'I need air,' I gasped. The walls were closing in. 'I have to get out of here.'

I ran out of the door, across the walkway, onto the sand until I reached the sea, the water lapping over my sandals. I peeled them off, took some hesitant steps and sank into the sand.

The tears came in ugly sobs and when I scanned the horizon, I realised there was one person I wished was by my side more than anyone else. Fishing out my phone, I hit the call button and held it to my ear, praying she wasn't busy.

When the call connected, I told Clara everything: from the pole-dancing lesson to the night with Jae-seung and then my first meeting with my mother in sixteen years. Hardly the reunion I had dreamed of.

Clara whispered the words '*meu amor*' a few times, but apart from that she listened, let me ramble on incoherently. When I stopped talking, she breathed deeply down the line. Her words then were soothing and before long, the view in front of me became less blurry and I wiped my face with the edge of my top.

'What are you going to do, Fran?' she said.

'I don't know. I feel awful. I was so mean. Not sure I can face her, but I've left my case in there, Jae-seung is long gone, and I am going to have to figure out what to do next.'

'But you haven't heard her full story, right?'

'Do I want to hear it?'

'Yes. Yes, you do. Because it is the only way you can process everything. *Meu amor*, I know this hard, and I wish more than anything I could sweep you in my arms and hold you close, but you need to be brave. Listen to her. You don't owe her any apologies but maybe if you hear the rest of her story, you can at least move forward.'

I let Clara's words sink in and thanked her. Luckily, I had caught her post-afternoon exam. She said she couldn't wait for them to be over, then she would sleep for a week, but she also reassured me that she would be covering for me at our Zara job and that I shouldn't give a second thought to my life in England. When I told her that Jae-seung was leaving us tickets for his London concert at the O2, she squealed with delight.

Jae-seung. I held my head in my hands as I thought over the last week with him. The ache that had lodged in my chest when we said goodbye was growing by the hour and I rubbed my hand over my T-shirt to try and ease the throbbing pain. But I had known what I was doing. He had given me the chance to not let things go further because he knew that sleeping with him would make things deeper between us and he hadn't wanted to hurt me. But somehow, I had to put what happened between us behind me.

I wiped the sand from my shorts before heading to Mum's apartment. She was at the kitchen sink and dropped the scourer sponge when she saw me. Wiping her hands on a tea towel, she stepped towards me hesitantly.

'I've come back,' I announced, stating the obvious. 'I am going to sit here' – I pointed at the sofa – 'and I want to hear your story. All of it. I will try and listen, but I won't apologise for how I reacted earlier because the hurt I have inside me has

There is no other option
From now, from here
Until the end of days
Even though I don't want it to be
We must go our separate ways

Chapter 23

Leaning my arm on the car window, I gazed out at the bright blue sky. The storm was over, and in its wake contentment and calm had settled over my body like a weighted blanket.

I snatched a look at Jae-seung and smiled. When he caught me staring, he took one of his hands off the wheel and held mine in the space between our seats.

A memory of last night filtered across my mind. The conversations between endless hours of lovemaking, words borne from deep within our souls – Jae-seung's pain that he wanted to be released from, the guilt of his mum's death he didn't know how to expunge. Showing one's feelings was not encouraged in Korea, he had said. He hadn't shared any of his torment until he had opened up to me. He said he felt lighter.

In return, I shared some memories of my childhood – fragments that had played on my mind over the course of the last week as more information about Mum's life since she'd left me had emerged. In each mental snapshot I was happy, and it still didn't make sense to me why she had never returned.

The road sign welcoming us to Wilmington came into view, and we took a left and headed to Holly Ridge. Butterflies camped in the base of my stomach, along with a hollow feeling, as the satnav showed we were only a few minutes away from our destination. This was it. A goodbye and a hello. As we reached South Anderson Boulevard, Topsail Beach could be seen in between houses and apartment compounds.

The Jeep came to its final stop in the visitor spot of the car park. It had been a three-hour drive from our motel.

been there for years, and one conversation won't fix it. But I can't move on until I know everything.'

With my speech over, I sat down and took a long sip of my lemonade, the sweetness giving me a much-needed sugar rush.

Mum sat down and talked. She told me of her return to Sicily, how Dad had refused to let me go. She didn't say anything bad about him, only that she understood why he wouldn't agree to her wishes. What life would I have led, away from Sicily, he had asked her. Dad had apparently begged her not to return, not to make things harder. Maybe that's why Nonna hid those postcards. Mum said she had to send those – she needed me to know that she was still thinking of me and that as an adult I could decide what I wanted.

When she paused to take a breath, she went over to her writing desk and pulled open a drawer. Unearthing an envelope, she handed it to me.

'I sent you this for your eighteenth birthday.'

It was unopened. On the front was my old address in Trapani, which was crossed out with a *return to sender* written on it. As I turned it around, I held my hand to my mouth. There was Mum's full address in Seoul with a note written underneath it:

Never write again.

The handwriting was familiar. It was Nonna's. I knew it was, because for my birthday she had given me a notebook full of her recipes. 'Top secret' recipes, she had called them, including the one for cannelloni that I loved to make once a week. At that point, she had been getting frailer by the day. She had celebrated my eighteenth from her bed and died only two months later. Perhaps she had been worried about more letters or postcards coming after she was gone and what Dad or I would have done with them.

'I don't expect you to want to read it,' Mum said, 'or understand why I stopped writing after seeing that message, but I guess deep down I knew I had done nothing but bring you pain, and I couldn't continue doing that. I foolishly thought I could have love and you in my life, but that proved impossible. Don't worry, it's not lost on me that I am now on my own. A widow in my fifties.'

'You were… married?' I finally met Mum's gaze and something in my heart shifted.

She nodded, her shoulders lowered, seemingly more fragile than when I had first seen her on the beach.

'Do you have pictures? Of the wedding.'

'You… want… to see them?' she stuttered.

I gripped the edge of the sofa. 'Yes.' I nodded. 'Yes, I do.'

Mum went over to the bookcase in the corner and pulled out an album from the top shelf. She cleared some dust off it and handed it over to me.

As I flipped through each page, I didn't pause too long. The ceremony was on the beach – Topsail Beach, I assumed.

'Are these her parents?' I pointed at the two older people in the picture.

'Yes, and that's her sister from California.'

I flicked through to the next page. A party full of guests sipping cocktails at an outside bar. Barefoot in the sand. A look of love in their eyes. Mum and Ara.

'Francesca, please understand. I loved your father very much. What we had was different but…'

'You hardly knew him before you got married. You regretted getting pregnant because it forced you into a life you didn't want.'

'No,' she said, touching my knee. 'That's not true.'

I stared long and hard at her hand, the wrinkled, weathered skin. It was the first touch I had felt from her in sixteen years. Closing the album, I placed it on the coffee table and shifted my position, so her hand dropped from its hold.

'You can say all you want to convince yourself that we didn't trap you, but it's obvious that we did.'

Mum sat silent for a while, and I wondered what thoughts were filling her mind.

The letter sat unopened underneath the album, but I didn't have the strength to open it – yet.

'I'm sorry for your loss,' I said finally.

Mum pinched her lips tightly, staring into my eyes. 'Thank you for your kind words, Francesca. I wish you had known her. We had a good life together, but there was always one thing that tested our relationship. She knew it. I knew it. I gave you up for her and on occasion the pain of that loss created a wedge between us. But she always believed you and I would be reunited one day.' Mum stared at the ceiling, and it made me wonder what she believed in – the afterlife, heaven? I simply didn't know this woman sitting inches from me.

'Why did you make it so hard for me to find you, then? If you thought we would be reunited. Why couldn't I find a trace of you online?'

'I created a new persona for myself when I moved to Seoul and then when I came to the US, I took Ara's name when we married. I'm sorry. I never thought that you hadn't seen those postcards. I really believed you had read them but didn't want me in your life.'

A thought suddenly came to my mind and I went over to the sideboard. When I had first stepped through the door, I hadn't taken in all the pictures but now I did. And there in the centre was the one I had dismissed as a picture of Mum because our similarities were so striking. But it wasn't Mum. It was me. And I wasn't a child. I was an adult.

How on earth could Mum have this if she had never laid eyes on me in sixteen years?

I held the frame in my hand and turned it, holding it out to her. 'How do you have this?'

She straightened. 'I returned. I went back to Sicily.'

The sun in your hair

Chapter 25

Hours drifted by, shadows from the trees outside the apartment moving across the living room. Mum had made me some lunch and, after we finished, we took a walk along the beach.

The anger bubbling inside me had moved from simmer to high heat again. I still only had Mum's version of events, but I couldn't get my head around what she had said. Mum had returned to Sicily with Ara, merely weeks after I had left for London when I was twenty-two. They had sat and had coffee with Dad and had met the twins and Sandra. Dad had told her I had moved to London but not where. He had convinced her that I had made my choices in life, and they didn't involve her. She had left with that photograph.

Mum had hugged herself tightly when I told her I had gone to New Malden in the hope she would find me there, but she explained why she hadn't. Gran had disapproved bitterly of her continuing to perform with the Cirque du Soleil once she had me and she could never accept Mum being in love with a woman. Her eyes watered when I told her Gran now had dementia and was in a care home. She clasped my hands tightly and thanked me – thanked me for the years I had cared for Gran, told me my grandmother had loved me deeply and it would have given her so much joy to have had me in her life for those four precious years.

We strolled along the beach in silence and Mum let me sit with my thoughts, giving me space. When I finally asked if she wanted to know about my life, her face lit up and it was hard not to be captivated by that smile – the one I had imprinted in my mind from the times when she returned from being on tour.

Having bought two sorbets from the ice-cream truck further down the beach, we sat on the sand, and I let the early evening sun warm my face. After talking through the years I spent as a nurse, dating Alessandro and my life in Trapani, I moved on to how I had decided to move to England, the years of taking acting classes and doing amateur plays.

'I've been trying to be a professional actress for the last two or so years,' I said as the waves lapped gently on the shore. 'I have an agent, been to more auditions than I care to mention, but I haven't made it. The last role I auditioned for was a big new Netflix show. I thought that would be it. My big chance. My chance at stardom. And that then...' I brushed the sand with my fingers. 'Then maybe... you would come and find me.'

At those words our eyes met, and Mum's face crumbled, and I couldn't rein in the emotion any longer. We dropped our empty sorbet cups and hugged each other. Tears flowed freely. The ache I had felt for so long was lifting but being replaced with a sadness. Mum had cared. Mum had wanted me. And now she finally knew how much I had wanted to find her.

I had no idea how long we sat there holding each other but soon we felt the water at our feet. The tide was coming in, beach dwellers were packing up and a sunset hovered on the horizon.

Mum held my face in her hands, a smile breaking through the tears. 'My brave, brave girl. I'm so proud of you.'

'But it wasn't the role of my dreams,' I said, pulling her hands off my face. 'It was the stand-in for the main actress. My agent had messed up and I rejected it.' I waited for her to tell me I had been foolish, that you don't turn down roles, no matter how insignificant they are, but she continued smiling.

'I'm still proud of you,' she said, laying a hand on my knee, 'for pursuing this dream and not giving up. You always wanted to be an actress. And sing and dance.'

I swiped my hand over my tear-stained face. 'Did I? I know I wanted to act but I have two left feet and my voice is far from angelic.'

'Says who?'

'Dad and Nonna. I have this memory of them watching me practise for my audition to play Annie when I was in middle school. I vaguely remember running through my lines, then breaking into song and attempting to do a spin. I fell flat on my face, and they laughed.'

The memory hit me like a tidal wave, and I hunched my back. For how long had I buried that memory? Was this the reason why I hated dancing and had no conviction in my singing voice?

I became faintly aware of another touch. Mum was rubbing my arm. 'I remember that audition. You told me about it when we went shopping that time in Palermo. The last time I... saw you.'

'You said you would come back to see me perform.'

She nodded. 'I said it didn't matter what role you got, whether it was the lead, or in the chorus or one of the dancers. Because to me you were always a star, no matter what.' She pulled strands of my hair behind my ear and the movement felt intimate – something a mother would do to a child – and the compression that had sat on my chest intensified, thinking of all those lost moments when I had longed for such a gesture from my mother.

'I never did it,' I said, twirling my fingers in the sand. 'I remember now. I went into school and crossed out my name. I never even tried to audition.'

Mum leaned in and held her arm on my shoulder. 'The important thing is you didn't let it stop you from pursuing acting eventually. But trust me when I say you were so graceful. I remember once when you came into my dressing room, one of the dancers taught you a routine with these ribbons. You learned the moves instantly and everyone was in awe of you. I think you were only nine. And when I used to tuck you in bed at night, we would sing this song together—'

'"Mr Sandman",' I interrupted.

'Yes, you remember?'

'Over the last week, the closer I came to finding you, all these fragments of memories kept resurfacing in my dreams. And then when I sang with Jae-seung, it was like I had found my voice for the first time in years.'

'Who's Jae-seung?'

'Um...' A flush coated my cheeks. 'He's someone I met in New Malden. It's complicated.'

'I'd love to hear about him. I want to know everything, Francesca. I know I have hurt you; I've let you down. No matter what your father and grandmother did with my postcards, I was still an absent mother and there's nothing that will ever erase that. But I'm here now, and you have *no* idea how happy I am that you found me. I haven't smiled in months. And seeing you on the beach, it was the most amazing sight. I don't expect you to forgive or to forget, but if there is any way I can now be a part of your life, then that would be incredible.'

I smiled and those balls of anxiety burrowed deep in my shoulders appeared to diminish as I was swept away by her words, tension-free for what felt like the first time in weeks. 'I think I'd like that.'

'Then we need food. Lots of food. What do you fancy? There's a store a mile down that way.' She pointed over my shoulder. 'Let's go and stock up.'

It was impossible not to feel buoyed by her enthusiasm. The walls around me had begun to crumble.

We headed into town in Mum's battered Chevrolet. She took me to her local coffee shop, deli store and the studio where she used to give pole-dancing classes. She told me she hadn't set foot inside since Ara died. She had been feeling very lost and didn't know what to do with her life. The more she revealed about their lives together, the more I softened inside. It had obviously been a very supportive and loving relationship. The way Mum spoke of her with so much pride and devotion in her voice made me think they must have been soulmates – two halves of a whole.

–

Later on in the evening, we were sitting around Mum's kitchen table filling taco shells with shredded chicken, lettuce and cheese, sauces spilling out from the sides as we attempted to fit them in our mouths. We laughed at our ineptitude at eating them.

The photos of Mum at Body & Pole suddenly grabbed my attention.

'I liked the class I did at your old studio,' I said, wiping my chin with a napkin.

Mum followed my eyeline. 'Lacey's a great teacher, isn't she? We had some good times together.'

'I felt something in my body when I did the class. Hard to explain.'

Mum held her taco by her mouth. 'An unlocking sensation?'

I popped a strand of cheese into my mouth. 'Something like that.'

She crunched the shell and chewed. 'It's why I became so passionate about pole dancing. The classes I ran in Seoul were for women who had lost all sense of who they were. They're healing. Do you think it was because you did it with this boy that you felt this way?'

'I think I was able to let go because I knew he was there to catch me if I missed a step. Well, apart from this one time.' I chuckled, remembering my embarrassing fall. 'I felt safe with him.'

'You're in love.'

I coughed on a mouthful of taco and hastily sipped some water. 'It's not love. I hardly know him.'

'I accept I have no right to say it's a mother's intuition, but I recognise when someone is talking about a person they love. You told me all about Alessandro and Jae-seung, and there's this look you have when you talk about the Korean boy. He's helped you find your voice and rekindle your love of movement. He believes in you, your dreams. Finding someone who will support you as you grow is a wonderful feeling if you can find it.'

'He said the only love he knows is destructive.'

She wiped her mouth and nodded. 'Ara said something similar about our love.'

'Really?'

'Oh yes. We faced many obstacles, and our love destroyed my family. And then we knew it would eventually be broken when the cancer returned. But to us, it was a risk worth taking.'

'I can't help thinking the life he leads, the fame, it doesn't bring him happiness and I have no idea why he wants to continue doing it.'

'He must have some unresolved issues he needs to work through. How did you leave things between you?'

'A simple goodbye. I have no means to contact him. There will be a concert ticket awaiting me at the O2 arena in London in a few days.'

'So, you can't stay here longer?' There were lines etched into her forehead – a look of disappointment on her face.

I pushed my plate away. 'I don't know what I want to do any longer. I can stretch this trip for another couple of days but then yes, I need to return to my life in London, figure things out. My best friend has been stepping in to cover my two jobs there, but Dad thinks they aren't sustainable, that my whole *existence* in London isn't sustainable.'

Mum pursed her lips.

'What? You're dying to say something, aren't you?'

She tutted. 'Francesca, I have no right to comment on your father's parenting. He has cared for you, nurtured you. I owe him everything.'

'But…' I arched an eyebrow, knowing full well she had thoughts and I wanted to hear them.

'But… my feeling is you need to find out what you truly feel passionate about, harness those feelings, pursue them and don't give up. It will be hard, exhausting, overwhelming at times, but it will be worth it. You're young; you have a life ahead of you. Things will work out if you are patient. Don't be forced into doing something if your heart isn't in it.'

A memory stirred in my mind of me on that stage in the church in New Malden, the buzz I felt as the applause rang in my ears, the electrifying rush that washed over me as I lived and breathed the character of Jo for weeks on end. I then thought of all the walk-on roles I had had, the enthusiasm I had tried to show with my one-liners, the intensity of the camera in your face, the actors on set and how I had wished for more. And that's when it hit me.

I didn't want to give up on my dream.

The sun in your hair
That smile only for me

Chapter 26

The room was empty, my bare feet not making any sound on the polished wooden floor as I stepped closer to the pole at the down beat of the music, wearing a black cropped top and thong. The song was 'Earned It' by The Weekend. Slow, deliberate steps took me forward, my body relaxed, ready.

The pole was in the centre of the room, mirrors lining every wall, a red filter displacing the yellow light from a single lamp in the top corner of the studio. I circled the metal bar, my hand gripping it gently before locking my leg around it and tipping my head, my curls tickling my back. When I came to stand, you were there, watching me, drawing me in with your eyes.

I was spinning now, using my newfound strength in my upper arms to lift my legs off the ground where they wrapped around the pole. When I stopped and slid down gracefully, I locked against your chest. Your skin was soft, and your arms wrapped around me to hold on to the pole. I turned in your embrace, so we were facing each other. My hands trailed down your naked torso, luxuriating in the smooth, undulating curves of your muscles.

We were moving in time; we were synchronised. And then we were spinning, and I was floating. I was safe, in your arms. The song came to an end and our chests were rising and falling, beads of sweat glistening on our skin. Your fingers found my waist; they were drawing me in before they trailed my chest, where you could feel my heart reverberating beneath my bra top. You bent down, your mouth achingly close to my face.

Your lips fell on mine as your hands roamed over my body, freeing my breasts from my top. Your tongue circled my nipples as I groaned with desire. I turned and grasped the pole, the metal cold against my skin. Your hand lowered down my back, teasing my thong to one side, sliding your fingers between the lips, one finger plunging inside, then two, before you let me taste my wetness as your fingers found my mouth. And then you filled me, my arms stretching higher and higher up the pole with each thrust.

A chime rang in my ear. It got louder and louder, but I wanted it to stop. I wanted to be here in this room with you, with no distractions. But something was drawing me away, a familiar sound. It was…

WhatsApp.

I sucked in a breath as I roused myself from my sleep, my skin slick with sweat. The surroundings were unfamiliar. It took me a second to remember where I was because I had woken in so many different places over the last few days. This was Mum's spare room, the ocean audible and rhythmic through the open window. Jae-seung would love it here.

It was a video call from Clara. I hit accept and her face came into view.

'*Meu amor*,' she sobbed. 'I can't see you.'

I flicked on the bedside table light, and my face appeared in the box in the corner of the screen. 'What's the matter?' I asked, rubbing my hand over my eyes, noticing the digital clock in the corner of the screen read half-five.

What followed was an incoherent rambling, some words in Portuguese, others in English. My eyes widened when she said the last two words.

'You're pregnant?'

'Yes,' she wailed.

'Hey, hey, it's going to be OK. Does Philippe know?'

'He's travelling to London this weekend. When I got his message, I was so annoyed because I had been feeling sick and didn't know how I would be able to meet him. Then this thought hit me hard. I couldn't remember the dates of my last period. That time I saw him, the one before the last meet, I had forgotten to take my pill packet with me. I thought missing a day wouldn't make a difference but…' She dropped her head into her hand and her shoulders began to shake.

'It's gonna be OK, Clara.'

'Please come home, Fran. Please. I don't know what to do. I need you.'

Clara was my best friend, my confidante. I couldn't imagine what she must be feeling right now. But as much as I wanted to be there for her, a niggling thought was playing in my mind. I had only just found Mum. Was I ready to say goodbye?

'I'll change my flight. I promise. We'll work this out.'

'Oh, *meu amor*. Thank you.'

'Never any need to thank me. We'll get through this. You're strong. What would Taylor say?'

'Fuck knows. Taylor wouldn't get herself in this mess,' she said with a hint of a smile before her face contorted. 'I have no right to bring a child into this world, Fran. I haven't found myself; I am not standing on my own two feet. I haven't got my act together. I'm up shit creek without a paddle. Oh my God, so many bloody idioms to describe my life right now.'

'None of that's true.' I yawned and held my hand over my mouth to hide it.

'*Merda*, what time is it?'

'It doesn't matter, honestly. It's been such a crazy week. I have no clue what time zone I am in anymore. We crashed at two last night, or this morning, I guess.'

'Everything's OK? You're working things out?'

I let a smile play on my lips. 'We tried to squeeze sixteen years apart into sixteen hours together.'

'I feel bad. You want to stay?'

I shook my head. 'You're my family too, Clara. And I need to get back anyway, figure things out. I'll do my best to get on a flight tonight if I can get my ticket changed, OK?'

She rang off with a multitude of kisses and '*obrigada*'s and I flopped on my pillow. Searching for the airline's website, I noticed my message icon had a '2' beside it and voicemail had a '1'.

I opened my texts to find one from Dad. He was worried, asking me to get in touch and wishing I hadn't left the way I had. This was a repeat of every other message he had sent since I left Sicily. The other was from Alessandro, asking me why I hadn't responded to his last message where he questioned why I had left so suddenly and told me how much he loved and missed me.

The voice message had come through three hours ago when I must have been in the deepest part of my sleep cycle.

'This is a message for Francesca Cavalieri. My name is Sheila, and I am one of the night carers at Speirs House. Please call me back at your earliest convenience. Thank you.'

My fingers quivered as I called the number for Gran's care home, praying that it was only a routine check-in. But that thread of optimism snapped as soon as I was asked to take a deep breath. The voice of the manager was calm as she relayed that Gran had been taken to Kingston Hospital as she had had a fall getting out of bed and fractured her hip. Her mobility had been decreasing over the last week and she had been monitored more carefully but had gotten out of bed in the night to go to the bathroom and tripped.

It was too much to take in. I told the manager that I was currently in America visiting family and that I was trying to get a flight to London this evening. As I disconnected the call, the emotion choked me. All of it. This last week. Dad's lies, Nonna's interference, Alessandro's declaration of love, saying goodbye to Jae-seung, reuniting with Mum, Clara's pregnancy and now Gran.

I couldn't see the light. Curling into a ball, I wrapped my arms around my knees, sank my head down and let the tears fall again. Rocking forwards and backwards, my nose began to stream.

And then there was a voice. It was soothing – a tissue placed in my hand, a tentative touch on my shoulder. When I lifted my head and saw Mum's face, I collapsed into her arms and fully let go.

As I wiped away my tears, I told Mum everything. Everything that was clouding my head. She listened and nodded as tissue after tissue appeared to wipe every new flow.

'This is too much for one person to take on, Francesca.'

I waited but no more words came. As I searched her eyes, the next words came from deep within. 'I don't want to say goodbye to you, Mum.'

Her bottom lip quivered and then I was in her arms again. She held me, tightly, smoothed my hair, the comfort I had longed to feel finally here in abundance. It was like I had received an injection full of maternal love straight into my heart.

She suddenly took hold of my arms. 'Right, Francesca Marie Cavalieri. Your father and Alessandro can be held off with a simple text. Tell them we've met, it's going OK, but you are heading home to London because your grandmother is in the hospital. But tell them they needn't worry because you won't be alone.'

My eyes widened.

Mum smiled and wiped the last tear from my cheek. 'You will never *ever* be alone.'

The sun in your hair
That smile only for me
Why can't I find the strength

Chapter 27

The Uber driver pulled into Kingston Hospital and dropped us off at the main entrance. The seven-storey grey-brick building reminded me of check-ups and blood tests from when I had accompanied Gran here when I lived with her.

We wheeled our cases down endless sterile corridors, our shoes squeaking on the mopped floor, doctors and nurses in blue scrubs hurrying around in various directions. When we came out of the lift on the third floor, we entered the intensive care unit and walked to reception.

Once I explained that we were Ava Lee's daughter and granddaughter, we were ushered to a waiting room where we were told to wait for the consultant, who was doing her rounds and would come in to give us an update.

As we absorbed the information we were given about Gran's current situation, Mum and I held each other's hands in the space between our yellow plastic chairs. Gran was heavily sedated because she was struggling to understand why she was in hospital and had kept getting agitated. They recommended we go in one at a time and sit and talk to her, even though she was sleeping.

A nurse was attending to her vitals when I stepped foot over the threshold, Mum having said she would stay in the waiting room.

There were tubes connected to Gran, bruises lining her arms where blood had obviously been drawn. Numbers and lines on the monitor indicated a steady heart rate and pulse. My days at Azienda Sanitaria Provinciale Di Trapani came flooding back to me, and I gave the nurse a friendly smile, wondering what hour of her shift this was.

'It's OK, my dear,' she said in a strong foreign accent that I couldn't place, 'sit with her. Don't be afraid of all this.' She pointed at the tray of needles sitting atop a clipboard with medication charts ready to be filled in.

'I'm a nurse,' I said, my throat dry, 'or rather, I used to be. I'll probably understand what it's all for.'

'That will make my job easier.' She smiled and there was so much sympathy in that smile that I felt my shoulders drop a little, knowing that Gran was in good hands. 'I'll leave you to it for now. I can return to give her her meds later. I'm sure she'll be happy to hear your voice.'

Would she, though? I thought and my body caved.

'Sometimes, in these late stages, there can be flashes of recognition. Sit close to her. Hold her hand. Go slow.'

I thanked the nurse, and she left the room.

I pulled my chair close to the side of Gran's bed and laid my fingers lightly on her hand – the wrinkles more pronounced, the liver spots more noticeable.

'Hey, Gran. It's me, Francesca. Your granddaughter.' I said these words calmly, watching to see if there was any reaction. It had been so long since I had uttered those words. 'I'm sorry,' I said, squeezing her hand. 'I came as soon as I heard. You'll never believe where I was. In fact, it's been quite the adventure and I have you to thank for that. I found Mum. She's here, with me.' I tipped my head back and stared at the corkboard ceiling for a moment, still in disbelief that she had accompanied me on that long flight back to England. 'It's been a crazy journey, Gran: from Seoul to Sicily, then to the US, but I am here now, and all is fine. I'm fine,' I lied, because I could hear the words floating out of my mouth but there was no strength in them. My voice was cracking.

No movement. Gran lay there unresponsive, and I didn't know what to do. If I was working in my old job at the hospital in Trapani, I could at least attend to her, do something useful. Maybe I should call the nurse in.

'Please wake up, Gran.' I gave her arm a gentle shake. 'Remember that movie we watched – *The Notebook*? She had that short period of recognition right at the end. She knew who Noah was. Remember?' Tears were blurring my vision and I swiped them away and sniffed hard. This wasn't going to get me anywhere: wishing we could turn back the clock three years. During that time, we were living together, and she was well. Before the fall, she was agile, full of energy, encouraging me to take acting classes, handing me her pension money to do her groceries.

It was getting harder to take a deep breath – there was a compression on my chest. I had lost the old Gran a long time ago. What was the point in me being here? None of my thoughts were making any sense.

I headed to the door and when I opened it, Mum's face was the first I saw, and it soothed me.

'What's the matter?' she said, focusing on my wobbling bottom lip.

'I don't know what to say, what to do. Someone should be watching her,' I said, as a wave of anxiety flushed my skin. 'I need to call the nurse.'

Mum held on to my arm reassuringly. 'I'm sure the nurse will go in when it's necessary. Come on, let me go in with you.'

'Are you sure?'

She tucked her shirt into her jeans and lifted her chin as if she was mentally and physically preparing herself. 'I promised I would be by your side, Francesca. And while it is too late to make amends with my own mother, it doesn't mean I can't sit with you and support you.'

We sat on either side of Gran's bed, the intermittent beep of the monitors and the distant rumble of construction outside the window filling the room. Mum pulled her chair closer and centred herself while I clutched Gran's hand in mine.

'Hey, Mum. It's Marie. I'm back.' She emitted a hollow laugh, but I could see from the expression on her face that it was tinged with sadness. 'I know you said you never wanted to see me again and that I let you down, that I was the worst daughter and mother imaginable, but I have come here for Francesca's sake.'

Mum raised her head and found my eyes. She hadn't shared with me what had happened after she had written that letter to Gran, the one I'd caught her rereading in the care home. But Gran's response must have been bad because she had alluded to Gran's disgust of her sexuality when we were in North Carolina.

'She's amazing, isn't she?' Mum smiled at me before turning to Gran. 'This girl. This amazing girl that I left behind. She has your strength and resolve, Mum. I know you always joked that you were a battle-axe, that you only ever did what you thought was in my best interest, but I understand now that you were right. How could I have left this incredible girl? She was my world, my light, my heart. I put my own selfish needs ahead of hers. I regret so much some of the things that happened, but the truth is, I didn't understand at the time why I couldn't have it all. Isn't that what you told me I should strive for? And you were right: Davide did do everything in his power to make sure I wasn't a part of her life in any way.'

Those words made the anger bubble inside me again.

'But...' She leaned her arm over the bed and I held on to it, her strength radiating through me. 'I don't blame him for doing that, because he thought he was doing the best for his little girl, no matter what anyone else might think. And I now realise, now that I have lost the love of my life, that our time on earth is too short and too precious to hold grudges.'

I didn't know whether those words were directed at me or Gran, but I knew that I needed to speak to Dad. I needed to hear his side of the story. It was hard to get my head around what Mum had told me about her trip to Sicily when I had moved to London. I had been twenty-two. Old enough to make my own decisions about my life. But Dad had deprived me of that opportunity in the same way he had hidden the postcards for two years.

A movement. A twitch. At first, I thought I had imagined it, but there it was, the slightest movement in Gran's fingers.

'She moved,' I whispered, not wanting to startle Gran.

'What?' Mum said, grabbing hold of Gran's other hand. 'I felt it.' Mum took some shaky breaths as she stroked Gran's arm gently.

Gran moved her head from side to side and a moaning, grumbling sound came from her mouth. Her lips were dry and a little cracked, and I made a mental note to bring her lip balm the next time I visited. Her eyes slowly opened, and she blinked as she stared at the bright lights of the ceiling before scanning her surroundings. Then she settled on Mum, her eyebrows rising. The edge of her mouth twitched and slowly but surely lifted.

'Marie,' she said quietly. 'You're here.'

Mum's eyes widened, and she nodded. 'Yes, Mum, I'm here and Francesca is here too,' she said, acknowledging my presence.

Gran turned her head, her hair brushing against the pillow. She sank back into it, and blinked a few more times. 'Do I know you?'

I dropped Gran's hand and held my palm against my chest, but Mum clutched my fingers tighter.

'It's OK, Mum. Do you know where you are?'

'Looks a lot like a hospital to me. What happened? Is your father with you?'

Mum's eyes lowered. 'No, Mum, he's not here right now.'

'Couldn't tear himself away from the rugby, I suppose. That and his incessant cough drive me mad.'

An ache nestled deep inside me. Mum had always spoken so fondly of my grandfather. But that incessant cough had been down to years of smoking cigars, which had eventually led to lung cancer.

Gran winced then, grinding her teeth.

'Try not to move, Mum. You had a fall and broke your hip.'

'Oh, blast. That's not very convenient. Who's going to look after your father now?'

'I'm here, Mum. I'm not going anywhere.'

'But what about the tour? You were so excited to visit Italy. It's all you've talked about for weeks.'

A single tear rolled down Mum's cheek as the realisation of what point in time Gran's mind was stuck in dawned on her. She had been on tour when her dad was diagnosed, and it was a rapid six-month decline during which she hadn't been here in England. And I didn't think Mum had ever forgiven herself for putting her touring ahead of being here to support Gran and to say goodbye to Grandpa.

Mum squeezed my hand tighter. 'I have time before it starts. And I have this feeling it's going to be the most amazing time in my life. Something's going to happen that will make my world complete.'

I smiled at her. That summer had been life-changing.

'Maybe I'll meet someone.'

'Oh, no, no,' Gran said. 'Don't you dare go falling for an Italian man. Hot-headed. Terribly unreliable. And they're all too devoted to their mothers.'

Mum laughed and it was hard not to join in.

Gran suddenly turned to me. 'Are you a nurse, dear? You seem terribly familiar. Have you been with me since I got here?'

'I... Yes, I am a nurse,' I said before realising that I was sitting here in jeans and a pink T-shirt.

She nodded. 'Such a beautiful face; you look like someone famous.' She turned to Mum. 'Don't you agree, Marie? That face should be on the telly not stuck in a hospital ward, though we are mighty glad for your service, dear,' she continued, turning to me. 'Your eyes are so similar to my Marie's.' She patted Mum's hand, and I could see it was getting harder for Mum to hold the tears. 'Could I trouble you for a water, perhaps? My throat is all scratchy.'

I stood shakily. 'Of course.'

Mum threw me an *it'll be OK* look. At least I think that's what it was. I didn't know her well enough to know. But what I did know was this was her chance to be with her own mother without addressing all the pain of what had happened to fracture their relationship. This moment could last seconds, minutes or even hours. And it wasn't a time for me to be here.

I had done mountains of research on dementia – how periods of recognition were unlikely but still possible. And I had also read some anecdotal, unscientifically proven ideas that when a sufferer suddenly had occurrences of remembering distant memories, it could signal that the brain was about to completely shut down.

This could be the beginning of the end.

The sun in your hair
That smile only for me
Why can't I find the strength
To be the one you need me to be?

Chapter 28

'I'm so sorry, Fran,' Clara whispered into my hair, pulling me into one of her crushing hugs. '*Meu amor.* It's so good to have you home.'

I accepted the hug gratefully, and the hint of her vanilla body spray filling my nose felt like putting on the fluffiest cardigan and sitting in front of a fire at the start of winter. Only, it was hot again in London, and the sun was heating the glass frontage of the café. The aircon wasn't working and there were pedestal fans dotted around the place trying to create a fresh breeze.

I had left the hospital at Mum's insistence, taking both our cases on the 213 bus from Norbiton to New Malden and lugging them upstairs into my studio. Mum would be staying with me one night before finding a place of her own. I told her she could stay as long as she wanted but she had insisted she didn't want to impose.

Before I had left the hospital, another doctor had done his rounds and raised some concerns over Gran's heart, and was running some more tests, so a move back to the care home wasn't on the horizon. Mum had sworn she wouldn't leave her side until visiting hours were over. Gran had drifted off to sleep and I hoped for Mum's sake she would wake again remembering who she was, even though I knew it was highly unlikely.

After a shower and a change into some clean clothes, I felt more refreshed and had messaged Clara to say we could meet for coffee downstairs. The sight of her in her short-sleeved baby-pink summer dress was like a solace to my travel-weary soul. I had missed her.

She sniffed. 'Ugh, I'm not sure how long I can sit inside here. The smell of coffee now makes me so nauseous, I've had to switch to iced tea.' She pinched her nose and wafted her other hand. 'And those fans are blowing the aroma right into my face.'

'We can sit outside if you want?'

'It's too hot out there,' she said, sliding into the chair opposite mine. 'Honestly, this country. When did it start behaving like Brazil with its crazy heat?'

One of the university students brought our iced drinks to the table as Clara grabbed her boobs and squeezed them.

'They're so sore,' she said.

The barista's cheeks flushed pink, and he made a hasty retreat before we had a chance to thank him.

Clara caught me laughing. 'I'm glad my predicament amuses you. Delighted that you find it hilarious that I am "up the duff" and "have one in the oven".'

These idioms came with no air ticks.

I patted her hand. 'I'm sorry. How are you feeling?'

'Moody, irritable, bloated, queasy.' She squeezed her boobs again and slumped in her chair. 'The doctor gave me all these pamphlets about termination, said he could refer me to a clinic, or I can self-refer myself.'

'You've made your decision?'

She tutted and shook her head. 'I only went there to confirm the pregnancy, even though I took three tests, but I wanted to know all the information, how long do I have to decide, etc. But, Fran, what can I offer a baby? *Sério.* No permanent job, renting a room in a house with three others, working two night shifts and doing a little waitressing. All I have to my name is a signed photo of Taylor Swift and a qualification in fashion designing.'

'*Aspetta,*' I said, leaning forward over the table. 'You've got what?'

A broad grin washed over her, and she ran her finger up and down the plastic cup. 'I got the email this morning. I passed.'

I clapped my hands. '*Felicitazioni*. I'm so proud of you.' But her joyful expression dropped as soon as I uttered my word of congratulations.

'This isn't the time to be pregnant. But… I don't think it is that easy. Even though my childhood was awful, I always imagined having a baby of my own one day. And I know I am a lapsed Catholic but…' She took a long sip of her iced drink, brow furrowed.

'Are you going to tell Philippe?'

She clutched her stomach protectively. 'I am seeing him this Sunday. He had to delay his trip, thank God. He's staying at that same hotel in town for three nights. Oh Fran, I am so nervous.'

I tilted my head. 'Don't be. Remember, it's your decision. Be strong. Be fearless. You'll figure out what the right thing for you is. And you know I am always here for you, no matter what you need or decide.'

'This is going to sound stupid but… I was daydreaming about living in one of those houses by Richmond Green, you know the ones with four floors, the big bay window facing the grass, a basement floor for Clara Designs, and Philippe coming home from his travels to scoop baby Francisca into his arms and shower us with gifts.' She sighed wistfully.

'Francisca?'

'It's a boy or girl Brazilian name. I thought it was *perfeito*. It means "from France", which it will half be, and it is similar to my best friend's name.'

I didn't want to throw cold water over this image, but I had major reservations about how Philippe was going to take her news. All I could do was be there for her, whatever the fallout from her meeting with him would be.

'That's very sweet.' I let a smile across my face mask my concerns. 'God, I have missed you.'

'I've missed you, too. Steve keeps sending me daily texts, asking me if I would think about working permanently at the bar.'

'Oh,' I said, trying to hide my disappointment.

'And you've basically got one life left at Zara after missing the last two shifts.'

My shoulders dropped. 'I knew it was a mistake going. I've left three messages with my agent to say I've returned and *niente*.' I swept my hand across the table in a cutting motion.

Clara reached to grab my hand. 'No, no. I told Steve it would be a huge catastrophe to lose you and I think he's got the message, and Ricardo is always making these threats, but you know he will never fire us. And I am one hundred per cent sure your agent will call. And if she doesn't, her loss. Maybe it's time you took a different direction, sign with someone new. Tell them only good roles. Convince them why you are worth it.'

Her encouraging smile soon turned down at the corners as she contorted her face and did a retching movement.

'*Va bene?*' I asked.

She held her hand over her mouth. '*Desculpa*, I need the bathroom. Enjoy your coffee.'

I caught sight of Hana in the kitchen as Clara left the table. She noticed me staring but carried on with preparing a smoothie – tipping an assortment of rainbow-coloured fruit into a blender, wiping her hands on her apron, which covered her white lace shirt and grey skirt. I wondered what she knew about my time with Jae-seung, if anything at all. Sun-hee had been sworn to secrecy and I hadn't heard from her since she went to her aunt's place. I wondered if 'confinement' meant no phone use, but that seemed a little extreme. I sent her a quick message to ask her how she was and to let her know that I was in New Malden and that Jae-seung had returned to rehearsing.

That thought reminded me of my erotic dream about us pole dancing together, intermixing with flashes of him at the class in Chelsea and the way we had danced together at the club. It was like my body had been locked down for years and he had found the key. The class at Mum's old studio had me wondering whether I should join a class locally. Maybe it was time to renew my love of dancing – something I had obviously buried for years without ever realising.

As Hana returned to the coffee machine to prepare an order, I went to the counter. The barista guy asked me what I wanted, and I pointed to a croissant, something that would be welcoming to settle Clara's stomach.

I held the plate with the French pastry on it and waited for him to collect the coffees that Hana had prepared and take them to the waiting customers. She hovered in front of me, busying herself with a wad of receipts.

'Is there anything else you need?' she asked, nudging her glasses.

Her formality saddened me. 'I was wondering how Sun-hee was getting on?'

'She's fine.' Her tone was snappy.

'We had fun in Seoul,' I said, beads of sweat building on my neck.

She slammed the cash register drawer. 'You can stop the lie, Fran. She confessed. But don't worry, I didn't tell my parents.'

I shifted my weight from one foot to the other. 'Thanks,' I said.

'You didn't heed my warning, though.' A steely glare pinned me to the spot. 'I told you my cousin didn't need these complications.'

'But he needed *someone*, Hana. He was broken, making himself unwell.'

'And you fixed him? You think a few days off can make this all disappear?'

I assumed she was referring to the guilt he felt about his mother's death.

'I think having someone to confide in has helped, yes. I don't believe it's a good idea to bottle feelings. The consequences can be horrific.'

'What exactly did he tell you?'

'I know about his father dying, and that's why he came to live with you and how when he was seventeen, well... he told me how his mum passed away and that not long after he was discovered by his management team when he was busking.'

'Right.' She nodded, collecting the empty cups the university student handed over. 'Well, anyway, I'm sure he's fine now. Thank you for caring for him but he's where he belongs, with his band, performing.' She seemed exasperated and I couldn't understand why. All I had done was be a support to him. Why wasn't she able to accept that my intentions towards him were sincere and that I wouldn't ever tell anyone about what had happened over the last two weeks?

'I promise, Hana. His secrets are safe with me.'

'Is that for me?' Clara appeared beside me and grabbed the plate. 'What are you two whispering about? Your amazing trip with her hot cousin?' She did a head flick in the direction of Hana while I sank on the spot.

'Can we have this croissant to go, please?' I took the plate from Clara and shoved it over the counter. Hana whipped out a paper bag and took a pair of tongs and placed the pastry inside before handing it over. With a bow, she returned to the kitchen.

I grabbed Clara by the arm and told her we were going. We left the café with our iced drinks and I slumped into one of the outdoor chairs.

'Did I say something wrong?' Clara asked, biting into the croissant, flakes of pastry trickling down her chin.

'Please don't mention Jae-seung to anyone, especially not in front of Hana. She gave me another one of her "back off" lectures.'

'What is her problem? You've done nothing but be nice and loving to Jae-seung. It's thanks to you that he's returned to his band.'

'Hmm.'

'What?'

'I hope he has. I don't know, Clara. I have this sinking feeling in the pit of my stomach. He spoke about all these triggers he has, how this one song in particular sets him off, but all I did was listen and give him a shoulder to cry on—'

'Which is more than he has probably ever had.'

'But it won't make the guilt disappear overnight.'

'True. But you'll see him again in a few days, no?'

'In an arena of twenty thousand fans.'

'At least it will give you reassurance that he's fine, that's he's coping the best way he can.'

I held my head in my hands. 'Why didn't I listen to my gut? One-night stands are still a horrible idea.'

Clara peeled my hands off my face. 'No, I don't believe this was a one-night stand. You did not have a sexual encounter with a complete stranger after getting plastered, then never saw him again. There was no alcohol involved, you'd spent the previous few days with him, *and* you drove many hundreds of miles with him post-coitus.'

I smiled. Clara always loved to see the positives in any situation. 'But I will never see him again, never feel his touch, never sing with him again.'

'You *sang* with him? Little Miss Francesca "I refuse to do karaoke with my bestie" Cavalieri.'

'There's a lot I did with him.' I wiggled my eyebrows and she nudged me in the ribs.

'*Meu amor*, it's good to see you smile. I am truly sorry that you fell for an idol. But at best, you chalk it up to an amazing experience that will serve you well for future encounters.'

I straightened in my seat. 'You're right. No good moping over a boy. I have my gran to worry about now, building a relationship with my mother, figuring out what to do about my dad and Alessandro, oh and figuring out if I have a job anywhere.'

'It will all work out, Fran, trust me.'

The sun in your hair
That smile only for me
Why can't I find the strength
To be the one you need me to be?
There is no other way

Chapter 29

'You're scaring the customers away,' Steve said as I shook the cocktail shaker at a mediocre pace.

I had drifted off again. Brain fog. It hadn't lifted since I had landed in London. It was as if there was a spin cycle going on in my mind: Gran, Mum, Clara, Dad, Alessandro and Jae-seung. They all occupied my thoughts.

'I'm sorry,' I said and forced a smile as I dropped an umbrella into a piña colada, passing over the highball glass to the customer in front of me.

'If you needed another night off, you could have asked Clara to fill in again,' he said as he poured a beer while grabbing the bottle of house white. It was hard to gauge his tone with those words, but it was warning enough, and I pinned back my shoulders and smiled as I scooped a measure of mixed nuts into a dish and handed them over with a glass of wine.

'She's meeting her boyfriend tonight,' I said to Steve, wiping the counter where the shaker had left water marks.

'Oh,' he said. Was it my imagination or did he look like someone had pierced his heart with an arrow? Clara had that effect on people so I wouldn't be surprised if Steve was one in a long line of suitors hoping she would turn his way.

At that moment, the doors to the bar burst open and Clara stepped inside, radiant in a blue satin knee-length dress. Her ears must have been burning. But my joy at seeing her soon turned to concern as she stepped closer. Her cheeks were smeared with mascara as tears poured down her face.

She slumped on the bar stool in front of me and sank her head in her hands, her shoulders shaking.

I raced out from the bar and was beside her in a flash. 'What's happened? Talk to me, Clara.'

Her eyes were watery and she shook her head. 'He ended it; doesn't want me or the baby,' she whimpered, collapsing onto the bar.

I stroked her bare back, trying to comfort her. When I caught Steve's concerned expression, he mouthed, 'Take five,' and I escorted Clara to the staff room.

I handed her a pack of tissues, and she sat in the chair beside barrels of beer and boxes of mixers and blew her nose. Kneeling in front of her, I rubbed her knees, waiting for the tide of emotion to abate.

'He told me it was my fault, that I should've been more careful. Said if this news reached his wife, he would be ruined.'

My mouth dropped open. 'He said what?'

'And it turns out he isn't this big-shot corporate guy. He's some two-bit salesman, maxing out credit cards trying to impress clients by staying in fancy hotels. He's a kept man. Married to some French aristocrat older woman. She has him by the balls.' She flicked her hair in agitation. 'Was never ever going to leave her. He only said that so he could keep having his cake and eating it.'

There were no ticks for either of those idioms. She was broken.

I sat on my heels. 'You know what I am going to say, right?'

'It's time for a Taylor marathon and a tub of Häagen?' She scrunched the wet tissues in her hands.

'"Illicit Affairs" on repeat is definitely a good idea. But what I wanted to say was that I know it hurts, but better to hear these things now and not further down the line.' I stroked her knees. 'And you know you're worth so much more than this, than him, than everything.'

'Is it so hard to find a good guy? Honestly, Fran. I thought I would have it all figured out by now. Having a baby at twenty-eight isn't scandalous, is it? But I thought I could do this with someone that cared about me.'

Before I could utter a response, there was a knock on the door and Steve entered. 'Sorry to interrupt,' he said. 'Francesca, your mum has been trying to reach you on your mobile, so she rang the landline. She said you need to come to the hospital. It's your gran. She's had a heart attack.'

I stood shakily, reaching to the nearest shelf to steady myself. It was suddenly hard to breathe. Clara rose and gripped my hand. 'Go, *meu amor.*'

'But you—'

'I'm fine and I'll cover for you,' she said.

'She's right. We've got this,' Steve said, throwing a smile at Clara. 'Get your things and go.'

The confines of the room closed in on me and I tried to implement the breathing technique I had shown Jae-seung that time in the Jeep, but I couldn't. A squeeze of my arm brought me back to the room. I nodded at Clara, grabbed my handbag and headed out.

Numbness coated my suddenly heavy limbs as I made my way to the Underground. Once I emerged at Waterloo, I tried calling Mum, but it went straight to voicemail. Stations whizzed by in a dark blur; passengers got on and off, but I wasn't taking in the scene around me. All I could think of was my grandmother.

At Norbiton station, I stepped off the train and broke into a run. Reaching the hospital, I tried to catch my breath as the lift took me to the third floor. In the intensive care reception, I stopped briefly to sign in and studied the nurses' faces for a hint that everything was OK, but there was nothing but sympathetic expressions.

No, no, no.

All my worst fears were realised as soon as I reached the room and saw Mum's hand grasping Gran's, her head slumped on the bed. She turned when she heard the door. Her eyes were bloodshot, a wad of wet tissues balled in her other hand.

'She's gone,' she whispered. 'Mum's gone.'

The sun in your hair
That smile only for me
Why can't I find the strength
To be the one you need me to be?
There is no other way
It pains me to set you free

Chapter 30

Rain battered my umbrella as Mum and I huddled underneath it. The weather matched our mood – grey and stormy. By my side was Clara and the manager from the care home. The rest of the funeral cortege would be at the Royal Oak pub – Gran's old local – eating canapés and drinking tea and coffee in the function room on the first floor, waiting for our arrival. The whole plan for the day had been discussed with me when Gran was first diagnosed with dementia and had cried, 'Oh blast. At least Pops went quickly.' I hadn't ever met my grandfather, but she had told me of his six-month battle with lung cancer.

As the coffin was lowered into the plot next to Grandpa's grave, I clutched Mum's arm tightly and squeezed but she didn't turn my way. She had been lost the last few days – lost in a tidal wave of… well, I didn't know exactly – grief and sadness, obviously, but there was something else. This woman who I had met only ten days ago still felt like a stranger to me. Since our arrival in London, Mum had decided to rent a room in a town house across the road from the hospital. She had found it online. A short-term let while someone was abroad. We had tag-teamed our visits to the hospital and since Gran passed, our conversations had been about the funeral. The initial energy that had flowed out of her when we had first met on that beach in North Carolina was long gone.

At the wake, Mum and I mingled and chatted with people who had known Gran through the church and her time helping at the local girls' state school across the road as a receptionist. I had been shocked to see Steve from Havana Club make an appearance with a bouquet of peonies, which he had heard were Gran's favourites.

Clara's nausea was beginning to lift so she was playing hostess, making sure everyone's tea was topped up and paper plates laden with sandwiches and crisps. She had also stayed with me last night and helped prepare the food.

As I grabbed an empty silver foil tray to fill with more sausage rolls from the kitchenette at the far end of the hall, I gasped when I saw who was standing in the doorway.

'Dad?'

There was a small suitcase at his feet, and he was wearing a smart navy-blue suit with a coat draped over his arm. He stepped tentatively towards me.

'What are you doing here?' I asked.

'*Amore mio*, how could I not come? I am only sorry that my flight was delayed, and I missed the service. I am so sorry for your loss.'

'Thanks.'

'Davide?' Mum's voice was behind me, and I turned. Her face paled, as if she had seen a ghost.

'Marie.' He nodded his head. 'Francesca messaged to say her grandmother had passed and I wanted to be here to pay my respects.'

'It's good of you to come,' she said, in a monotone, no hint of emotion. 'But if you'll excuse me, I have a headache. Will you be OK, Francesca, if I head back to my place? I'll call you in the morning, OK?'

'Are you sure you don't need company?'

She patted my arm. 'I'll be fine. How about we meet at your café tomorrow at around eleven?'

I nodded and she grabbed her things and left.

I knew Mum was consumed with grief, but it saddened me that she couldn't even be in the presence of my father for longer than a minute.

An awkward silence filled the space between me and Dad.

'I need to... um...' Words failed me. My messages to Dad since finding Mum had been brief, but I knew I couldn't put off talking with him forever – but not today of all days.

'I understand,' he said. 'You're busy. Maybe you have time for a drink downstairs later? I have booked a room here for two nights. I know this is a terrible, sad time for you, *amore mio*, but I think it is important that we talk. I don't want to lose you, Cesca.'

'Well, maybe you should have thought about that when you turned my mother away six years ago when I had first moved here,' I said, harshly.

He nodded. 'Yes, you are right. But I would like you to understand my version of what happened that day. You probably won't forgive me still, but at least you will understand better.'

I held the edges of the silver tray tightly, the ridges marking my fingers. 'OK. I will meet you downstairs in an hour.'

After he left, Clara found me in the kitchenette staring at an empty plastic container.

She laid her head close to mine. 'That's your dad, huh?'

'I don't know if I have the strength to talk to him today, but he's come all this way...'

She rubbed my arm, the warmth soothing. 'I know you will find the resolve to keep going, Fran. And maybe you need to hear him out. He loves you, that much is obvious from all the stories you have told me about your childhood, the summers you spend in Sicily.'

'But he lied, Clara.'

'I know,' she said. 'But you still don't know *why* he lied. And he has been in your life a lot longer than your mother. I'm not saying you've done the wrong thing in accepting her into your life so readily, but I think you need the full picture. You have such a good heart, Fran, so loyal and caring. You knew Philippe was a *bastardo*, but you also knew how crazy I was for him. You stood by me as I made one mistake after the other. But maybe in this case, things aren't so black and white. We can't know what went through your father's mind when he found out the woman he loved and had a daughter with wanted to run off with someone else. He probably did what he did to protect you. I'm not excusing him, but as someone who has zero relationship with her father, and a mother I see once in a blue moon, you now have the opportunity to have them both in your life.'

I flung my arms around her. 'You're the best, you know that, right? The best friend I could ever have hoped to find.' I pulled back and smiled at her.

'I'll always be your shoulder to cry on because birds of a feather flock together.' She twitched her head, and I laughed through my sadness.

'I think you would make an amazing mother.'

She nodded. 'So do I.'

–

I found Dad an hour later downstairs in the pub. He was sitting alone in a booth, nursing a pint of beer. The bar had a few punters perched on stools, absorbed in a rugby game on the TV screens dotted around, periodically raising their fists in glee as a try was scored. There was a soft glow throughout the room – stained-glass dividers throwing pools of rainbow light.

It was surreal seeing him sitting there. Not once had he visited me in all the years I had lived in New Malden. And tonight should have been spent with twenty thousand people at the O2 arena, seeing Jae-seung one last time. I had told Clara she should go, but she said she was exhausted and would be heading home to crash into bed. Now Jae-seung would never know the reason for our absence. But this wasn't the time to dwell on that. That chapter of my life was over.

'*Ciao*, Papà,' I said as I slid beside him with a lemonade. I didn't want an alcoholic drink. I knew I needed a clear head. I smoothed the pleats of my funeral dress, not sure where to begin.

'Thank you for coming, *amore mio,*' he said in Italian. 'How are you?'

'Numb. Confused. Hurt. Angry. You name the feeling and I have probably felt it in the last two weeks.'

'Your mother hasn't changed one bit.'

'You mean since you saw her when she visited Sicily six years ago,' I said curtly, picking at the label on my bottle.

He took a slow sip of his beer. 'It was a shock to see her that day and with that… woman. You often speak of this "closure" that you think I have but this is not true. Your mother was… the love of my life.'

His eyes turned sad as he said those words and something in me thawed.

'She came into my life,' he said, 'and it all made sense. The girls I had dated before her could not compare. Her beauty, her charm. I will never forget when she had that fall and I scooped her into my arms…' He trailed off, his cheeks pinkening. '*Scusa.* You don't need to hear these things.'

I laid a reassuring hand on his arm. 'I want to. I want to hear everything.'

'Then first we must go back to the day she returned when you were only twelve.'

I clasped my bottle of lemonade tighter, bracing myself for what he had to say about a day I had never known existed until recently.

'She came to tell me it was over between us and that she wanted to take you with her. "Shocked" was an understatement. She was presenting me with a life without her or you. I was enraged. I didn't even have time to process the words she said about our marriage having been broken for a while, how she couldn't live this confined lifestyle if she could no longer perform. And she didn't like the way my mother was such a strong presence in our lives. She had no relationship with hers because her mother always tried to control what she did. I couldn't listen to these reasons because all I kept thinking about was you.'

He popped the buttons of his cuffs and rolled the sleeves of his shirt.

'The one thing your mother never understood,' he continued, reaching out and cradling his beer, 'probably because I never had the chance to share with her, was how much her touring impacted you. Every time she left, you would cry and cry and cry. It broke me to see you in pain. Usually after a few days, we would return to our routine, and you would begin your countdown to her return. But when you turned ten, things became harder. You would have these night terrors. They were…' He ran his hand over his beard as if the memories were raw. 'Terrifying.'

'I don't remember them. What were they like?'

'It was like you were awake but still in a deep sleep. You were agitated, roaming around the house. Once you…' He sucked in a breath and released it slowly. 'You unlocked the door to the apartment, and I found you out in the street. You told me you needed a glass of water.'

'I would speak?'

'Not always. Sometimes I would find you tucked in bed with Nonna. She was always on alert too.'

'Is this why you always made me have a glass of water by my bedside?'

He nodded. 'Anything could have happened to you that night you left the apartment. I was so scared. But these episodes. They would last only a week or two after your mother left.'

'But my difficulty sleeping never went away,' I said, taking a sip of my drink to soothe my suddenly dry throat, thinking of a few instances where I had woken early fully dressed, with vague recollections of stirring in the night thinking it was morning. Now I knew this had been going on a lot longer than I thought.

'You still have problems?' Dad asked.

'They come and go. But maybe now I have a better understanding of when they began. Night terrors are caused by stressful periods in one's life. So… you sent her away so I wouldn't suffer these anymore?'

'*Amore mio*, I sent her away because I didn't think she was a good presence in your life.'

'But I grew up believing she didn't care at all. Is that a right way to have lived?'

His back stiffened against the booth. 'My mother made me believe that what we had between the three of us was all you needed. I'm not sure what I would have done if I had known about those postcards your mother wrote you that Nonna hid. I truly believed Marie had left and had finally understood that it was better not to be in your life.'

I fell silent at those words. A protective father and grandmother. The Italian way. 'Is that why you discouraged my love of singing and dancing and then of acting? Were you scared I would become like her?'

He rubbed the back of his neck. 'Yes. All I had seen with her lifestyle was nothing but chaos, uncertainty. I don't think she ever recovered from that initial fall – the one where we met. Her injuries plagued her. So yes, perhaps I saw your love of dancing as something similar. But the singing? No. I loved listening to you sing in your room, playing your CDs.'

As long as there was no audience.

'But I will now apologise for everything that happened after. I am sorry I didn't hand you those letters when we cleared out Nonna's things. I should have trusted you with them. You should have made a decision about contacting her then. But you must understand one more thing. When your mother came to me with her lover that summer – the summer when you had moved to England – I told her you had moved to the UK.'

'I know. She told me.'

'But that is not all.' He paused and met my eyes, steeling himself to say the next few words. 'I also told her you were here in New Malden.'

My eyes widened and my hand knocked into the lemonade bottle, tipping it over. 'No,' I said, in denial, mopping up drops of liquid from the table with a tissue. 'That couldn't have happened. Surely Mum hadn't known where I was. No. I don't believe you.'

Dad grasped my hands on the table and I hadn't realised they were shaking. 'That's not all. I told her who you were living with.'

His words rang in my ears. Mum had known I was here, but she had chosen not to find me. Six years. For six years I had lived in New Malden and she had known how to reach me yet decided against it. The news crushed me like a ton of bricks had been thrown off a ledge onto my body. It was too much to process.

Maybe it can be

Chapter 31

Mum was sitting at the far-right corner table of 63 High Street, cradling her mug, when I approached.

'Hey,' I said, my tone low.

'Francesca.' She smiled but it didn't reach her eyes.

I confirmed my usual order with Mr Son and sat down in front of her, laying my shoulder bag on the table.

Mum appeared frail in her pale blue short-sleeved shirt and jeans. I couldn't ignore what I now knew but I wanted to phrase my words carefully.

'I've booked my flight to Wilmington,' she announced.

'Oh,' I said. 'You're leaving?'

She paused, her fingers tapping the table as if she had a plane to catch this afternoon and needed to rush off. 'I'll help you clear out Gran's things from the care home, but then yes, I need to go back.'

'For what, Mum? For whom?'

'I can see you're angry, Francesca. I assume your father told you everything.'

'Yep. He told me everything.'

She cradled her cup. 'And?'

'And what? You want another forgiveness card?' An indescribable pain was jarring on my right temple, and I tried to rub it away but it kept pulsing as I thought back to that day in her apartment, as revelation after revelation surfaced but I accepted them all. 'What I don't understand is how I have had four adults in my life who lied to me in some shape or form, all with the premise of doing what they thought was best for me. What's your excuse this time? Six years ago, you knew I was here in New Malden. We could have reconnected, but you chose not to. Yes, I can be mad at Dad for his part in all of this, but *you*. It's you. All paths lead to you.' I almost spat out the last word.

'Francesca, I—'

'No.' I stood up as Mr Son laid my coffee down and I asked him to put it in a take-away cup. 'You don't get another chance to say you're sorry.'

'I was scared.' In that moment, it felt as though I was the parent, and she was the child. There was a vulnerability to her that I hadn't seen before in her deer-in-headlights eyes.

'I'm scared too,' I said. 'I'm scared of never finding my purpose in life, a place in this world, of following intangible dreams, of never seeing again the one guy I have ever connected with. But I don't run away. I give everything and everyone another chance even when it seems impossible. And I gave you a chance to be honest and truthful with me, though I probably should never have given you the time of day. But I am done with being the good little girl who lets her parents continue to think they know what is best for her. So, I wish you a safe flight home. I've found you, we connected, we shared some moments but now we can return to our old lives.'

My hands were shaking as I grabbed my take-away cup and left. As I opened the door and turned sharply left, I came face to face with Dad.

'*Amore mio, cosa c'è che non va?*' he said, his hands holding on to my arms to steady me.

'Not now, Papà. Please, not now.' I shook myself from his hold. 'I don't want to talk; I don't want to go through the past any longer. I'm tired. Tired of all this,' I said, pointing through the glass. 'Safe flight tomorrow, OK? I am meeting my friend now, then I have work tonight. Sorry I can't spend any more time with you.'

The lines on his forehead intensified but I didn't have the strength to say any more. I headed towards New Malden station and didn't look back.

Maybe it can be
This problem I can solve

Chapter 32

'I'm so proud of you, Clara,' I said, flinging my arms around her.

'I can't believe it happened,' she said as she squeezed me tightly.

'I can.' I stroked her arm. 'You're phenomenally talented.' Today's outfit was evidence of that – a cream silk tea dress with sweetheart neckline that she had made last week.

She placed her hands on my cheeks and rubbed her nose against mine. 'You are the best support team a girl could ask for.'

Clara spread out on the coffee table the sketches that she had shown the visiting designer who had attended her college's closing exhibition, and I marvelled at each one, running my finger over her exquisite designs.

We were sitting on her living room sofa, her flatmates thankfully all out at work so we had peace and quiet. She had texted me this morning to say she had something to tell me, and I could not have guessed that she had been offered a two-year paid apprenticeship.

'These are amazing,' I said, lifting each one in turn.

'It's the maternity ones she liked the most. Can't believe those were middle-of-the-night additions to my portfolio. And I have my *sementinha* to thank for that.' She patted her stomach. 'Brave or stupid, I don't know, but telling them I was pregnant during the interview didn't make a difference. There was no way I could put myself forward without them knowing what was going to be pretty obvious in a few months.'

'Good for you.'

'It is. The owner of the label commended my honesty but said it obviously wouldn't have mattered if I hadn't said anything. She's a mum of three and she gets it. They even offered to create an on-site creche if I wanted it.'

'That's amazing. I'm happy it's going to work out for you.'

She closed her portfolio. 'But I can hear sadness in your tone.'

I waved away her comment. 'No, no, I am *really* happy for you. This is what you have worked on for years. You found your passion, and you didn't give up.'

'I know you are proud, *meu amor*, but you are sad because you said goodbye to your grandma, and you haven't filled me in on what you spoke to your dad about. Something else has happened, no?'

I took a deep breath and leaned on the sofa, letting the words tumble out. They were highlights of the lengthy conversation with Dad yesterday after the funeral and the brief one with Mum in the coffee shop earlier.

Clara curled her legs under herself, smoothing her dress over her thighs. 'Oh boy, that's a lot to take in. They all lied to you, then.'

'So many secrets, I don't think I can even keep track.'

'And now what?'

'Now Dad goes home to Sicily and Mum flies to America. They both continue with their lives, and I am here wondering what the hell I am doing with *my* life. I put so much time and energy into finding Mum, and where has it left me?'

'With the truth. And that's important. You no longer have this void.'

'Don't I? I still have no relationship with my mother, my father and I…' I shifted my position to mirror Clara's, thinking back to the conversation with him at the pub. How could we go back to the way we were before I began this search? 'It will take a while to forgive the part he played in keeping Mum away from me. I can't reconcile what Nonna did because she's dead;

I am grieving Gran, someone who was only in my life a short time but still had a big impact. And I'm meant to forget about *him*. Pretend what we had meant nothing, that I am OK with that.'

'You're talking about Jae-seung?'

'Sorry, yes, Jae-seung.' I chewed the inside of my mouth as I thought of our wild adventure together. That last kiss when we had said goodbye. I closed my eyes at the memory of his lips against mine.

She stroked my hand, breaking my reverie. 'Who says you have to forget him?'

'He's the lead singer in a band. He can't date, he lives in another country, I can't even communicate with him. How could that ever lead to more? This was doomed from the start, and I should have listened to my gut and not got involved.'

She shook her head and crossed her legs in front of me. 'OK. One thing at a time. I think it's for the best that your mother is going home to North Carolina. She's obviously sorry for hurting you but you don't need her in your life right now until she sorts her shit out. She didn't have a relationship with her own mother for half her life. She'll need to work through all that past unresolved' – she waved her hand around – 'trauma before she can even hope to make amends with you. And your dad and all that Sicilian stuff that keeps rumbling away in the background – your safety bubble. Let's puncture a hole in it once and for all.'

'How?'

'Do you love Alessandro?'

'No.'

'Do you want to be a nurse again?'

'No.'

She held her arms out. '*Excelente*. That wasn't so hard.' She pretended to hold a pair of scissors and snip. 'The umbilical cord is cut. Sicily will always be your home, but you have used it as a fallback plan for too long. In a way, my parents did me a favour. Home was so awful, why would I ever return?'

'Oh, Clara. I am so sorry.'

She waved her hand. 'Completely selfishly, I am telling you to turn your back on Sicily.' She winked and I laughed.

'But honestly,' she said, touching my arm, 'I am very lucky. You are like a sister to me and now... I have my little seed – my *sementinha*.' She hugged her stomach. 'That's all I need. Men can take a back seat. But for *you*... I am happy you had this experience with Jae-seung. It's what you needed.'

I let a smile play on my lips as I thought of that night in the motel with the storm raging around us.

'Do you feel comfortable sharing more of what happened? I feel like we have glossed over your trip because you got so bogged down with everything with your mum and then your gran...'

I clutched a cushion to my chest and sighed.

Clara pinched my arm. 'Look at you. Your cheeks are flushed. He had a huge effect on you, didn't he?'

'It was this crazy, fantastical journey. We travelled so far together, shared our life stories and connected on a level I've never experienced before. And he even wrote me a song.'

She clapped her hands and held them on the side of her face. '*Tão romântico*.'

'The gesture was romantic, but the song was sad. It was about him not being able to give his heart to me because he was afraid. It was only half the song – the rest was still unwritten.'

'Because he didn't know how your affair would end?'

'I guess so.' Stroking the velvet of the cushion, I thought of only a sad ending to that song. 'The stories he told me about his mother were tragic. I now understand the pain he has lived with for years.'

'He's one complex guy. International pop idol, damaged past. And both of you with unresolved mum issues. A perfect meeting of two souls who benefitted from a brief time together. I don't see there is anything to regret there. It was sad we couldn't go to the concert, but...'

She hopped off the sofa and went into her bedroom, coming out moments later with her laptop. 'I'm sure someone streamed some of it in one corner of the Internet. Shall we get snacks and make an afternoon of it?' She laid the machine on the coffee table.

I checked the time on my phone. 'Why not? We can head out together tonight to Zara. I don't need to go home and change.'

She clasped her hands in front of her and swayed on the spot. 'I've handed in my notice.'

'Already?'

'I'm sorry, Fran.'

I tutted. 'No, don't be sorry. I told you, I'm happy for you. I'll miss you, that's all.'

'We'll make my last night shift epic.' She bounced on the balls of her feet before heading to the kitchen.

Opening her laptop, I smiled at the Taylor screensaver and thought of the early days of our friendship. Our lives were changing. Clara was going to have more regular work hours, and these impromptu midday meets and late-afternoon coffees at 63 High Street would become a thing of the past. Change was good, though. Only trouble was, *my* life wasn't changing. I was still working at Zara and Havana Club, and my agent had messaged a few days ago to say she would get in touch if anything materialised. Usually by now, I would have at least some possibility of a walk-on extra role built into my schedule, but as things stood there was nothing on the horizon.

I googled Jae-seung's band and the O2, and my eyes widened as I absorbed all the articles that surfaced.

'OK, what do you fancy?' Clara said, reappearing laden with various food packets. 'Popcorn or I could throw together a couple of cheese tacos. What? What's the matter?'

I turned the screen towards her. 'He never performed at the concert in New York. Jae-seung quit the band.'

Maybe it can be
This problem I can solve
And the fear in my heart

Chapter 33

Fold, fold, fold.

I was going through the motions. Clara was beside me, chatting away, but I wasn't taking in anything she was saying. The bright lights of the shop floor were giving me a headache and all I could think about was Jae-seung.

The clock on the wall was ticking closer to finishing time. Our team wanted to celebrate Clara gaining her freedom, but I had told her I wanted to go to my flat and that we could celebrate privately another time.

Clara and I had pored over every article and YouTube video we could find about JYNKS and the tour but there were conflicting opinions. Some stated that Jae-seung's departure was only temporary, because of his injury, but others spoke of a falling-out with the band members.

Deep inside, I knew neither of these stories rang true.

As I arrived at my flat a little after eight, I noticed the lights of the coffee shop were on. My chamomile tea and bed were calling to me, but I knew I wouldn't be able to fall asleep so easily with thoughts of Jae-seung spinning in my mind.

I opened the door to 63 High Street, and the bell above tinkled.

'We're not open yet,' Hana said, her back to me, watering a pot plant with her green can. She turned. 'Oh, it's you.' Again, her tone was wary.

'Where is he?' I asked.

'Where is who?' She climbed down from her little stepladder and watered the pots on the ground.

'Your cousin – Jae-seung. Is he OK?'

'He's fine.' Her tone was clipped.

I walked over to where she was crouched down, stroking a large leaf from one of the pots. 'But he's not fine, is he? Why do you freeze me out, Hana, every time I talk about him? Why?'

'Because you weren't meant to know his secrets.'

'What?'

She laid the can down on the ground and went behind the counter, tying her apron over her pale blue buttoned shirt and beige trousers. 'No one was ever meant to know. They were family secrets. We swore by them. He didn't want the press to hound us; he didn't want anyone knowing about his private life. But then you came along and...' She took a pair of tongs and fished the pastries from boxes into the glass display case.

'And what?'

'You... complicated things.'

'I'm sorry, Hana. I never meant for that to happen. But I care about him. A lot. And I have this ache deep in my chest. I don't think it will lift until I know he's all right.'

She took a cloth and began wiping the surface in slow circles. 'He left a message on the answer machine at home. He told us not to worry, that he was fine.'

'That's it? Did he not say what happened?'

Hana scrunched the cloth and held it close to her chest.

'Please, Hana. Tell me.'

'His management company called us. He didn't attend the rehearsals in New York. They were furious. Threatened legal action. They kept badgering my parents for information but then two days ago we got that message from him.'

'And he didn't say where he was?'

She shook her head. 'I'm worried about him.' Her voice was a whisper. 'I know the pain he carries with him.'

'And I know why one of his songs is triggering for him – the reason he had the fall at the concert. "Five Minutes" reminds him of the death of his mother.'

She laid the cloth down and patted it. 'Let me make us a coffee. There are things you need to know.'

Finally. Finally, I could detect the thawing of Hana's icy exterior. I sat at one of the tables and watched as she brought the coffee machine to life and prepared us each a drink. When she brought them to the table, I thanked her and scooped some frothed milk from the top. Drinking coffee would mean falling asleep anytime soon was out of the question, but it didn't matter. Not now.

Hana breathed in and out deeply. 'My aunt, Jae-seung's mother… she isn't dead.'

The spoon dropped from my hold. 'What?'

'Did he tell you she had died?'

I wracked my brain for details of that conversation we had had while we were driving though Virginia. 'He said she had hanged herself and that if he had got there five minutes earlier, things would have been different. I assumed…'

'Wrong. When they found her, they managed to resuscitate her and took her to the hospital. There was severe brain damage and she fell into a coma.' Her eyes watered. 'She has remained in that state ever since. Jae-seung refused to turn off her life support. He worked round the clock at a local convenience store to pay for her care. She was moved to a specialist care hospice once he was discovered for the band, somewhere in the suburbs of Seoul. No one knows where it is. All I do know is that he carries the pain of her suicide attempt. That's what drives him. To be successful. It costs a lot of money for her care. And now he has left JYNKS…'

Her voice trailed off as a tear slipped down her cheek. She removed her glasses and wiped her eyes with a serviette.

I reached over and held her arm. The edge of her mouth turned upwards a fraction before falling.

'Do you think that is where he has gone?' I asked. 'To where his mum is.'

'I don't know, Francesca, but I am so, so worried about him. He became like my little brother when he lived with us. He was the glue that stuck our family together. Sun-hee and I used to fight all the time, we drove our parents mad, but when Jae-seung came to stay with us, he acted like a buffer and we both grew to adore him. That's why we would protect him no matter what. I didn't realise he was struggling. I wish he had reached out to us sooner.' Her bottom lip wobbled.

The door tinkled. Hana's chair scraped as she stood, bowing with her usual Korean greeting. It was the hairdresser from the shop next door.

'I must return to work,' Hana announced and left me to my coffee and my thoughts.

The first thing that came to mind was him. Where was Jae-seung? Had he returned to Korea? If he had left the band, I remembered what he told me the implications would be. How much money had he been able to save? How much did he need to care for his mother?

I hugged myself, an overwhelming thought washing over me as my arms tightened. I wanted to hold him or let him hold me. He shouldn't be alone to deal with this.

Draining my coffee, I went upstairs to my studio – with a promise to Hana that I would return during her lunch break if she wanted to talk more. At the kitchen table, I began searching again on the Internet to get more of a picture of Jae-seung's life, or rather what the press had uncovered of it.

Time slipped by and my eyes grew weary.

The doorbell roused me, and I realised I had fallen asleep on my bed with my laptop discarded beside me. It was too early for Clara to be at my door – she was no doubt still asleep after our night shift.

I lifted the intercom receiver and said, 'Hello.' A muffled sound came through.

'Hi, Francesca… it's me.'

It was Mum.

'I know you said your goodbye yesterday, but I can't leave things like that. Can I come up? Please?'

My finger hovered over the buzzer before finally pressing it. I went to the bathroom to splash water over my face before flipping the switch to the kettle. Answering the knock at the door, I hovered in the doorway before firming my resolve and stepping aside, letting her in.

'Do you want a tea?' I asked.

'Yes, that would be lovely,' she said as she took a seat at the kitchen table, fiddling with the bracelets on her wrist.

I was glad for something to do. The anger was beginning to bubble on the surface of my skin again. I placed a mug of PG Tips with a dash of milk in front of her then passed over the sugar, and she spooned in one scoop before stirring.

'Why are you here?' I said a little bluntly.

'I don't expect much of your time. But I couldn't leave with yesterday being our goodbye. Your father and I let you down.'

I shook my head. 'No. Don't include him in that statement.'

'But I have to. When you left yesterday, your father walked into the café, and we spent the rest of the day together. We talked and we talked and we… talked.' She took a sharp breath in. 'Words we should have said many, many years ago to each other.'

I added some milk to my own tea and stirred it. 'About what?'

'About you. About how we messed up – well, about how *I* did. And how, one by one, me, your dad and both your grandmas let you down in some way or another.'

'It's in the past. I'm moving forward.'

'Are you?'

'I'm trying.'

'With what support?'

'I've got Clara—'

'Whose life will change once she has the baby.'

'What are you trying to do, Mum? Make me feel lower than I already do? I'm trying, *really* trying.' The words caught in my throat and the emotion was beginning to choke me. I blamed the tiredness. I swiped my eyes and took a sip of tea, trying to steady myself.

'Oh, Francesca.' She reached out to hold my hand that was cradling the mug. 'It shouldn't be this hard. You're working two night shifts, one very long evening at a club and before that you were a carer for your gran for four years. I had abandoned her.'

'You had your reasons.'

'Yes, I did. But they stopped me from reconnecting with you. Because I was too scared to confront everything, I lost out on coming into your life without all this… this…'

'Shit?' I let a small smile creep in the corner of my mouth and Mum mirrored it.

'Yes, shit. I regret so many things I have done in my life.'

'Life's too short for regrets.'

'When did you get so wise?'

'When I had to mature fast after you left.'

I could tell that that comment was like a dagger to the heart.

'Yes. Yes, you did. And it's about time the adults in your life stepped up. I want you to have something.'

She reached into her handbag and passed over a cheque. The amount of digits next to the number one made my eyes pop.

'What is this?'

'Your gran never changed her will. I have no idea why. I wasn't around when she had her fall, I didn't nurse her, care for her, get her to hospital appointments, help sell her house, look after her when her memory began to lapse and get her into a care home. I didn't do any of those things. The proceeds of her house were meant to pay for her care for years so this is what remains. The lawyer rang me and told me it would be transferred to me. *My* bank account. But I don't deserve it.'

I fingered the cheque in my hands, wordlessly.

'I want you to have a fresh start, Francesca. I'm going back to the US, but only to sort through loose ends. I have decided that there isn't anything there for me anymore. I want my life to continue here. In England. I don't expect you to welcome me with open arms; I only want you to know that you can begin to consider me as someone to turn to, at some point in the future. I need to work on myself, figure things out, reconcile all the fractures of my own relationships with my parents, Davide and you, and I know that will take time and probably a lot of therapy,' she said with a wry smile. 'But I have thought of maybe establishing a dance studio here – a pole-dancing one, helping other women heal, in the same way it helped get me through some challenging times. I won't tell you what to do with the money, but I am hoping it will alleviate some of the worries you have about juggling auditioning with your night jobs. If acting is what you want to do, maybe this will help in some way.'

'If you want to set up a studio, you will need this,' I said, passing over the cheque.

She pushed it towards me again. 'I was fortunate to spend sixteen years of my life with a wonderful woman who I married and when she passed, I inherited more than enough to see me right. And I have been quite frugal over the years. We never led a lavish lifestyle, and we sold our share in Body & Pole for a good sum. This' – she tapped a finger on the cheque – 'is yours. It's not guilt money; it comes with no strings attached. If you choose to take it and still have nothing to do with me, I will respect that decision. But I don't want it.'

I couldn't give her speech more than a second's thought. There was only one thing that came to mind when I contemplated that money going into my account. I wanted to get on a plane. To Seoul. To find him.

Maybe it can be
This problem I can solve
And the fear in my heart
Will finally dissolve

Chapter 34

Mum and Clara thought my plan to go and find Jae-seung was brilliant. He had captured my heart with his soul; he had gone with me on this grand adventure which had led me to my mother and now he needed me. At least, I thought he did. I desperately tried to recall the lines from the chorus of the song he had written for me. He had told me it had taken him one look, one look to know he… was it needed me or wanted me? Agh, I couldn't remember. I knew I couldn't fix him, that's not what this was about, but he needed support and, right now, he must be feeling very alone.

I had messaged Sun-hee and she had told me she would help in whatever way she could. When I had locked the door to my studio a couple of days later and dragged my case into the coffee shop, Hana had thrown her arms around me, thanking me, telling me to keep her posted. Her mum and dad were also very grateful and anxious to hear any news.

As I sat in the boarding lounge waiting for my midday flight to Incheon International, I thought of the last time I had been here. Then, I had the address of the dance studio. Now I had nothing. No clues.

I searched Jae-seung's name on my phone browser, pressing the image tab. My pulse quickened as I took in those eyes. Those sorrowful eyes. Full lips that had inflamed my skin with every point of contact. And as for those long fingers… I sighed before shaking myself from my idle daydreaming, remembering that he was in a bad mental state, and this wasn't the time to be reminiscing about that passionate night we had spent together.

One image made me take notice. It was of him shirtless. When I clicked on it, a few more pictures popped up beneath, one at the gym, one on a photo shoot and various other poses – all with his naked torso on display. But more importantly, all showcasing his tattoo. That tattoo around the rim of his bicep that I had touched when he had been washing dishes in my kitchen in New Malden. When I had asked him if they were coordinates, he had merely said yes but hadn't revealed what of. I studied the pictures and wrote down some of the numbers I could see – the degrees, minutes and seconds north of the Equator, plus some other numbers representing the longitude location. But I couldn't see all the numbers as I couldn't find a picture that showed what digits were on the inner part of his arm.

Googling 'Jae-seung tattoo' was the obvious next step, and I found an article in which he said it was where he'd lived as a kid. Surely Sun-hee would know that.

My flight was called, and I switched off my phone, thoughts of finding a lead to his whereabouts giving me hope.

–

As I walked through immigration, pushing my case along on its wheels, I could see Sun-hee in the distance, the absence of brightly coloured hair the first thing I noticed. She flung her arms around me and squeezed me tight. 'Thank God, someone reasonably close to my age.'

I laughed into her hair as she continued with this comforting embrace.

'How's confinement?' I asked finally as she dropped her hold.

'The pits. But I have been granted leave.'

'How did you manage that?'

'I said it was a matter of life and death – said my friend from home needed my help, and they know vaguely about Jae-seung. My aunt is on my dad's side, not my mum's, but you know...' She gripped the straps of her tote bag. 'I said it was a family emergency and that if they had an issue with that, they should address it with my parents. I got your link to our Airbnb, and checked in, so let's go there first and formulate a plan.'

'I think I know where he might be.'

'Where?'

'What was his hometown?'

'A suburb called Goyang – why?'

'Oh. Well, the tattoo on his arm has some coordinates but that wasn't the location of it, I don't think.'

'Hmm. It's definitely something worth exploring. Surely coordinates will give us the exact location?'

'That's the problem. They aren't complete. I assume when he got the tattoo, he didn't want people to know what it referenced but it was clearly a place that meant something to him. I thought it might have been his childhood home.'

'He didn't have the tattoo when he came to stay with us. Mum and Dad would have freaked if he had got one, so I don't know anything about it. But if it represents a district, it would still be hard to pinpoint a location there.'

We headed over to the subway and emerged an hour later in the centre of Seoul. Mum had insisted on choosing and paying for our accommodation. She told me all about the risks she had taken with her love, and she said she wanted to help out.

Love. I had questioned her use of this word again.

'Of course this is love, Francesca,' she had said. 'I saw it in your eyes the second you mentioned his name to me when we were sitting in my apartment. Your body language, the way your cheeks flushed. You obviously care deeply about this boy. And if you can't rest, can't move on with your life until you know he is OK then yes, sweetheart, it is love. And this is why you might end up getting hurt, but you can't not try to find him and check he is OK.'

After freshening up, I came out of the bathroom of our accommodation to find Sun-hee on the sofa with her laptop on the coffee table. 'Hit me with those coordinates.'

I reached for my phone and went to my Notes app, where I had written them down, before sitting beside her. As she typed them in, she discovered they represented an area called Paju.

'It's a city in the Gyeonggi province,' she said. 'A very famous area for tourists to visit because you can go to the demilitarised zone and peek into the north. There's also a cool museum of modern history that I vaguely remember being dragged to when I was little. Other than that...' She peered closer at the screen as she scrolled. 'It's an area 672.78 km squared.'

'A needle in a haystack,' I said, thinking of Clara. 'Why do you think he would tattoo this area on his arm?'

She flicked her fringe from her forehead and placed her hands behind her head. 'No idea.'

I mulled over what I knew about Jae-seung, what he cared about, what drove him to be the man he was. He was a pop idol but so much more. What came to mind most was his devotion to his family. 'Maybe it has something to do with his mum.'

Sun-hee sat forward, pointing her knees towards me. 'You know?'

'Hana told me. Jae-seung was so distressed when he was with me in Sicily that first night he stayed in my home. He broke down and told me that she had attempted suicide and then when we drove to North Carolina he confessed how he had found her, how he...' I swallowed hard as I remembered what he'd told me. What a thing for a kid to witness.

'Yeah, I know, pretty horrific. My aunt and Mum weren't close. She never approved of Jae-seung's dad. I know my grand-parents treated Mum as the golden child and viewed my aunt as the quiet, weaker one, never able to compete with her big sister.' She turned away at those last few words, and I wondered if she was thinking of her relationship with her own sister and parents.

A thought popped into my mind. 'What if this area is where your aunt is? A hospital or something.'

She grabbed the laptop, leaning it on her legs. 'I'll google it.' Her finger moved over the pad. Left. Right. Up. Down.

'Hmm. If you exclude the public hospitals, there are three.' She swivelled the machine to show me the screen. It was all in Korean. She scrolled down to the three listings and in turn went to the Google Maps tab and showed me where they were.

'That one.' I pointed at the last one. 'It's close to a patch of water.' Jae-seung loved the sound of water, of waves.

She turned the screen. 'It's more of a care centre for the elderly and infirm. Look at these pics. They even bring the beds outside so those who are immobile can get fresh air and take in the view of the lake.'

'If Jae-seung's management company didn't want anyone to find out about her, couldn't that be a place where she was being cared for?'

'I don't know, but there's only one way to find out.' She tapped on her phone for a minute. 'It's a bus ride from *here*.' She pointed on the map. 'Takes about fifty minutes. Shall we give it a go? We could always bus it to the other two hospitals if it isn't the one. Do you want a nap first?'

I shook my head. 'I'm too wired. Maybe I'll drift off on the journey. I *will* have a shower, though, and get changed into fresh clothes.'

-

As the hot water soothed me, a sudden jolt rushed through me at the idea that this could be nothing more than a wild goose chase. Jae-seung could be anywhere in the world. But knowing what he'd told me about the repercussions of him leaving the band, something told me he had come here to try and absolve himself of his guilt. Another thought snuck into my mind as I lifted my face to the rush of water. What if Jae-seung didn't want to be found?

Maybe it can be
This problem I can solve
And the fear in my heart
Will finally dissolve
But know this for always

Chapter 35

As we walked the half mile from the bus stop, sweat poured down my back, my white sleeveless shirt sticking to me as the sun beat down on us. Sun-hee said an early evening downpour was inevitable but even then, it wouldn't lift the humidity. At the end of a gravel path, the care centre stood in front of us – a four-storey red-brick building with gleaming windows.

A large expanse of grass was to the side, a glass barrier far in the distance running along the edge of it. Some residents were sitting in wheelchairs under canopies, with drips on stands beside them – a carer next to each resident – their focus the beautiful Majang Lake. In the background was the suspension bridge taking tourists from one side of the water to the other.

Sun-hee and I went through the main entrance to reception, where a host of staff in blue scrubs milled around carrying clipboards, some typing on computer screens. Along the hallway in both directions, the place was filled with residents being pushed in wheelchairs or being walked with arm support. Others were waiting in their beds, ready to be moved out into the garden as we had seen in those online pictures.

I skulked behind Sun-hee while she spoke to one of the ladies behind the desk. Her words were met with a soft response, but several shakes of the head.

'Hmm,' Sun-hee said, joining my side. 'This is going to be a tough one to crack. She wouldn't tell me anything. Patient confidentiality.'

'Probably should have thought about that before setting off.'

Sun-hee folded her arms across her chest, lost in thought as she stared out the front of the building. 'Come with me,' she said after a while.

I followed her outside, and she went and sat over in the covered area. She struck up a conversation with one of the male nurses who was sitting beside an elderly man. I lingered in the background, watching her. Laughs punctuated her conversation with him, and her head kept leaning in ever so slightly. Was she flirting with him? The man in the wheelchair laughed at something she said. She appeared settled in for a long chat.

Unearthing my bottle of water from my rucksack, I found a shady spot by a tree and sat down, taking in my surroundings. The lake glistened in the distance and through the humid haze, I could see dots of people crossing the suspension bridge.

Where are you, Jae-seung?

My thoughts were broken when Sun-hee finally came and sat down beside me, the hint of a smile breaking in the corner of her mouth.

'Good news and bad news,' she announced as she accepted the water bottle. She took a swig and wiped her mouth before flapping her Queen T-shirt to create a breeze. 'He's been here.'

My mouth dropped open in disbelief before a smile broke freely.

'Don't get too excited. Here's not here now. He's been coming daily, visiting someone for hours on end and singing to the residents. It's thanks to that old man.' She tipped her head in his direction. 'He kept saying "singing man", "singing man". The hot nurse said he thought he was famous. It all made sense.'

'*Hot* nurse?' I nudged her.

'What? He is,' she said, her cheeks pinkening. 'And I may or may not have scored a date with him later on.'

'I'm happy for you. But wait. There's bad news, isn't there?'

She changed position, her legs tucked beneath her. 'He didn't turn up today. Ji-hun – the nurse – said he didn't know why.'

'So, we've lost him, then. Where could he have gone?'

She puffed out her cheeks. 'I don't know, Fran. But I don't think we can hang around here much longer. People will get suspicious. Maybe during my date, I can press Ji-hun for some more information – tell him that he's a relative and that we would appreciate him messaging when he next sees him. Ugh.' She held her head in her hands. 'That sounds so stalkerish.'

'Where are you meeting him for your date?'

'He said he would text me the address of a café in town. It's about a twenty-minute walk there.' She leaned on her hands and stretched her legs out.

I crossed mine and plucked a blade of grass. Rolling it in my fingers, I wondered where we could go from here. How long could we get away with staying in this spot in case he returned?

'It's hard to believe that my aunt is here,' Sun-hee said, turning her head towards the entrance. 'I have these memories of her, very vague ones of visiting the apartment where she and Jae-seung lived. I must have been seven or eight. She was so kind and welcoming, unlike his dad, who was always so grumpy and worked crazy hours. There was always a pot of *jjamppong* on the stove, Jae-seung once told me. When he came to stay with us, he asked Mum to make it for him because it reminded him of his old life here.' She shook her head. 'How do you heal from something like this? When do you let go? She's not going to recover. When Jae-seung dropped by unannounced a couple of weeks ago and gave me those tickets, I heard Mum having words with him that afternoon. I was upstairs. She kept telling him it was wrong to keep her in this state. He got upset, headed off on his motorbike for hours. When he returned, he said he didn't want to talk about it. He had travelled to our home to forget, to not have to think about his life here in Korea. But we couldn't give him that respite.'

'Do you know if he had been visiting her here regularly before these last few days?'

'No idea. I doubt it. Since being discovered, he's had no time or freedom to do anything. His lifestyle is crazy.' She trailed her fingers over the grass. 'I wished I'd known, Fran, how badly he was feeling.'

'Do you think he still wants to be a K-pop star?'

'If he didn't need to fund her place here...' She shook her head slowly. 'No, I don't think he would want this life. He loves his family, was a huge hit with the girls when he lived in New Malden as a teen. I think he misses aspects of his old life. But then again, he's talented. Loves singing and playing the guitar and is damn ace at both.'

That last statement made me think of our music-making session, my cheeks heating at the memory of how that evening ended.

'We've got to find him,' she said.

'How about we head into town and grab some lunch, formulate a plan.'

I stood and brushed the grass from my shorts and Sun-hee joined me.

We headed away from the care centre, Sun-hee throwing a wave at 'hot' nurse guy on her way. As we walked in the shade of the trees lining the road, Sun-hee fished out her phone and simpered at it. I knew that look all too well.

'Is that from Ji-hun?'

'Yeah. He swapped shifts with someone. He wants to meet in half an hour. I can say no. This is far more important, formulating a plan.'

'Don't be silly. Meet him.'

'I promise I will drop in some questions, see if he knows anything. He recommended *this* place.' She turned her phone to me. It was a café with an unusual water feature out in the garden.

'Is that real?'

She clicked on the photo and scrolled down to read the Korean. 'No,' she said. 'It's artificial. It's meant to replicate a waterfall. It says: "sit a while, enjoy some good food, close your eyes and imagine you are at one with nature and let the swell of the water soothe your stresses".' She laughed. 'Sounds like a riot.'

'Jae-seung loves the sound of the ocean. He finds it soothing.' I let my mind drift to every single occasion where he had felt at peace: that time in my New Malden studio listening to my sound machine, snorkelling at Cala Rosa, sitting with me at the *riserva* and in my bed in Sicily, wrapped in each other's arms with the distant sound of the Mediterranean drifting through my window.

'Does it sell *jjamppong*?' I asked.

She paused and clicked on the menu. 'Yeah, it does.'

We both looked at each other, obviously thinking the same thing.

'I'm going there anyway. Wouldn't hurt to ask.'

When we arrived at the café, we were greeted with a wooden-slat-fronted building surrounded by trees. It was the first stop on the way into town, so it would be a convenient place for the care centre's workers to hang out in. Sun-hee went to the counter while I took in the space. Inside there were tables made from tree trunks low on the ground with mats for sitting on. The exterior drew me towards it. A waitress opened the glass door, and the rush of water became more audible. Outside, diners sat cross-legged on raised platforms and some were dipping their feet in the water while they ate. 'Bizarre' was an understatement.

A tap on my arm brought me back to the room. I turned to see Sun-hee, her eyes wide and a little teary.

'What?' I asked.

'He's been coming here every day for lunch, same time, same table.' She pointed to the far end of the restaurant. 'And he's booked it for today, for lunch.'

As the words came from her mouth, a strange sensation washed over me. It was so familiar.

I felt him before I saw him. Stage right. A movement flickering in the corner of my eye as he neared.

Turning to the entrance, I stilled.

I found you.

Maybe it can be
This problem I can solve
And the fear in my heart
Will finally dissolve
But know this for always
As you go your own way

Chapter 36

The embrace was sweet and tender. Sun-hee didn't want to let him go. He had told me he saw his cousins as sisters, and this was evidence of that. Her head was on his chest and her arms wrapped around his waist. He laid his cheek on the top of her head and closed his eyes.

When they finally pulled apart, she playfully slapped him on the arm and began berating him in Korean. He bowed several times, his voice soft.

And then he lifted his head.

It took me one look. One look to know. To know I… *loved* him. And couldn't let him go.

We stepped towards each other, tentatively. His eyes were dull and puffy as if he had been crying for days. Then I was in his arms. It was like I had been injected with a shot of endorphins, dopamine and oxytocin – one heady cocktail of molecules.

'You came all this way to find me,' he whispered into my hair, stroking my back, the touch from his fingertips lighting my soul. 'You came to find me,' he repeated, his voice cracking.

I was lost. Lost in his tender embrace, soothed by his soft words.

'OK you two, break it up,' Sun-hee said, her words puncturing the spell.

We pulled apart and stood with our arms hanging down by our sides as if they no longer served a purpose if they weren't holding us together.

'People are staring. Don't think these folks are used to such public displays of affection.' She laughed. 'Now, *you*,' she said, pointing at Jae-seung. 'You are not going to move from this spot until I have gone into town and bought you a mobile.'

'You don't have to do that, cuz,' he said.

'Duh. Yes, I do. Mum and Dad have been freaking out about you, your management company keep calling them and I've been fielding a million messages from Hana, too, which is my least favourite occupation.'

'I didn't mean to cause so much trouble,' he said, pinching his lips tight.

'Jae, you don't have to do this alone anymore. Let us in. Now.' She pointed at him and then me. 'You're going to sit and have lunch with Francesca while I get you gadgeted and then I am going to hang out at the opposite end of this establishment' – she swept her hand across the room – 'and have a date.'

'Nice, cuz.' Jae-seung let a smile break over his face. 'Where did you meet her?'

'It's a guy this time. He's into K-pop and is a terrible liar. He's one of the nurses at the care centre and I knew he was talking about you when I probed him for information about this singer guy that kept coming to visit someone.'

'I thought I'd got away with it. It's why I didn't go today. Probably wasn't the best idea agreeing to do some singing for the residents. *They* certainly didn't know who I was, but I should have guessed the staff could put two and two together.'

'Does it even matter anymore?' she asked.

He let the question hang in the air.

'You don't need to work through all this alone, Jae,' she said, stroking his arm comfortingly. 'Now go and eat. Peace out.'

With a couple of high fives, she left the restaurant.

'She's a whirlwind,' I said, tucking some errant curls behind my ears.

Jae-seung smiled and then he stepped forward, his nearness causing me to hold my breath in anticipation. He took my hand in his, lacing his fingers in mine. 'I thought I'd never see you again.'

'You can't get rid of me that easily. And goddammit, Jae-seung,' I said, lightly slapping him on the chest – the second scolding he'd had in a matter of minutes. 'We were worried about you.'

'I'm sorry, I didn't mean to cause so much concern. How did you find me?'

I reached out tentatively and skimmed my fingertips across his bicep, and this time he didn't flinch. Tracing my fingers over the numbers and coordinates that decorated his arm, I sighed. 'I guessed these represented something important to you.'

He held his fingers lightly over mine. 'I got this done not long after my mother was moved here. I wanted to feel some pain and for it to act as a reminder of why I was doing everything I was doing, the endless rehearsing, the days when I thought I would pass out from exhaustion. It served as a wake-up call, to dig deep, to keep going.'

The waiter came over to us and we dropped our hold. Jae-seung nodded at him as he spoke in Korean, before being ushered to a table in the corner, behind a screen. As I sat down on the floor, tucking my legs to the side, Jae-Seung sat opposite me. The waiter laid out some menus and retreated.

'Don't you want to sit outside?' I asked.

'It's lovely out there but not so good if you want to have a conversation. And even though the tables are under a canopy, the humidity gets to you after a while.'

I turned the menu in my hand. There was no English.

He smiled at my confused expression. 'What's your favourite Korean food?'

'I like it all. You can choose for me.'

We ordered two set menus, and the waiter typed our order into his handheld machine before laying down two green teas, a small dish of kimchi and a cold glass noodle salad.

'What happened, Jae-seung?' I asked once the server left. 'After you drove off in North Carolina.'

Jae-seung fiddled with his chopsticks. 'I couldn't do it. I couldn't get back on stage. When I arrived back in New York,

I took a cab over to the venue and watched as they constructed the plinth for that solo. All I could think about was how that song would trigger me again, that the memory of her suicide attempt would fill my mind.'

'I didn't know about your mother still being alive. Hana told me.'

'I'm sorry, I—'

'No,' I interrupted and reached over to hold his hand, tightening my grip. 'You need to stop saying sorry. You've never lied to me, Jae-seung. You never confirmed or denied what I asked you about her.'

His shoulders dropped then, and I could see the anguish on his face. 'For too long I haven't visited. I've relied on reports from the hospital, sent to my management company and then shown to me. I also had no direct contact with paying the bills. When they signed me, they promised to take on that burden and suggested she was moved to somewhere where no one would find her to avoid any stories appearing about my personal life. It was an offer I couldn't refuse.'

'I bet. It must have been a large expense for you. And you were only seventeen. That's a huge responsibility to take on so young.'

'It was. At the time, I had a weekly job at a convenience store, and in the evenings and at weekends, I would busk, partly to top up my earnings but also because I couldn't bear being on my own in our apartment, knowing she was lying in a coma in the hospital. It was an emotional release for me too, losing myself in the words I sang. The day the scouts saw me singing and playing guitar outside a mall, they asked me what I was collecting money for, and I said to pay for my mother's care. Becoming a pop star seemed to solve everything. But I don't think I ever had the same passion that all the other trainees had. What pushed me was the thought that she would be cared for, would get better.'

I squeezed his fingers before pulling my hand away when the waiter brought over our meal. When he'd laid out an assortment of rice dishes, soups and shredded chicken and pork, we broke our chopsticks and tucked in. I let the spices tickle my tongue and a slurp of the vegetable broth tempered the tang. In between mouthfuls, I asked him to tell me more about those days following his mother's suicide attempt. He spoke about how his aunt had come over from New Malden and sat with him and cared for him while he stayed by his mother's bedside. The statistics and neurological information they were given, the second opinions he insisted they sought, had given him this tiny sliver of hope but it was a one-in-a-million type of recovery. And even if that did happen, if she did wake, she would have severe brain damage.

'I was consumed by something,' he said, laying down his chopsticks. 'It wasn't grief but it felt similar.'

'Grief is an emotional response to loss, not only when someone dies.'

'I guess.' He took a long sip of his green tea before placing it down on the table and cradling it in his hands. 'Shock, disbelief, denial. I think I experienced all those emotions. After a couple of weeks, I told my aunt to go home, that I could take care of my mother and myself on my own. And I did. Continuing to believe she was going to get better meant I kept going, kept pushing myself, to ensure I made it into the band, became the lead, got this endorsement, that photo shoot. But then when we recorded that song, I felt like I'd been hit by a tidal wave of emotion, and I was drowning. When I escaped to New Malden, my family were pleased to see me, but my aunt berated me for not dealing with the situation here, that it was cruel to keep her sister alive like that. When I arrived in New York after I left you in North Carolina and saw that stage, I knew I couldn't even start rehearsals. I knew I needed to come home and face what I had left behind first.'

I pushed my plate away. 'So, what now?'

His shoulders dropped and eyes watered. The table was a wedge between us, not enabling me to do what I wanted to do – hold him, comfort him.

'Now…' His chin trembled. 'Now, I have to find the strength to let her go.'

Maybe it can be
This problem I can solve
And the fear in my heart
Will finally dissolve
But know this for always
As you go your own way
Know I'll love you forever

Chapter 37

The next few days were filled with great sadness. Sun-hee and I remained by Jae-seung's side until his mother passed away a few hours after her life support was switched off. Sun-hee's parents, Hana and other family members came over from London for the funeral. I helped where I could, but this was a family affair, and I took my lead from Hana and her sister about what I could be a part of and when to be respectful and not involved.

Clara had agreed to cover my shifts at Havana Club, especially when Steve offered to double her wage, but I had decided it was time to quit my Zara job. Being here in Seoul had given me time and space away from everything in England, and that was one part of my life I knew I didn't want to return to.

But I still felt lost. Touring some of the remote parts of the city, connecting with nature, helped clear my head but after a couple of weeks, I knew it was time to say farewell to Korea.

Jae-seung and I hadn't spent any time together following his mother's funeral. He was consumed with grief and at times inconsolable, Hana had told me when I had met up with her for dinner one night. She told me not to take it personally, but that his way of dealing with difficult times was to shut everyone out. While it saddened me that he felt he couldn't reach out, I also respected his decision.

I had messaged him this morning to say goodbye and told him that I was leaving on the evening flight to London but wasn't surprised I hadn't received a reply. Sun-hee had already said her goodbye. She was now officially dating the 'hot' nurse and seemed excited by the prospect of not returning to London anytime soon. She had applied for a two-year set production design course in Seoul a few weeks back, with a dream of working for K-pop bands one day, and been accepted, starting in September. She had persuaded her parents to let her rent a room in the centre while she studied, promising to pay her way with odd jobs and waitressing. An image of Clara came to mind – Sun-hee had that same drive that she did; she had only needed to find her passion.

Passion.

Had I found mine?

I checked in my suitcase at the airline's counter and headed towards security, clutching my passport and boarding pass in my hand, my legs heavy. I heard my name from a distance and turned to see Jae-seung running down the concourse. Dropping my rucksack to the ground, I beamed with surprise and delight. He stood inches from me, breathing heavily.

'I thought I had missed you,' he said.

'You came.' My voice sang with joy.

He held his hands on his hips, his cap tilted low over his face, before taking a few deep breaths. 'I couldn't let you leave without saying a proper goodbye. I'm sorry I haven't messaged before today. I've been a mess.'

'You don't owe me any explanations, Jae-seung.'

'I do. You came all this way to Seoul to find me and then support me through a really difficult time. How can I ever repay you?'

'There's nothing to repay.'

'But your kindness, your friendship. I wish…' He sucked his lip inside his mouth and paused.

I stepped a little closer. 'You wish what?'

'I wish things could be different for us, Francesca, I wish… I wish I could be the man that you deserve to have in your life. Those days we spent together in Sicily and in America were some of the happiest in my life.'

'I don't need you to be anything for me. You have done so much for me, too. You helped me find my mother—'

'And you helped me let go of mine.'

What could I say? I couldn't tell him that we could try and find a way to be together. He was grieving, still in pain. What would a relationship even look like right now?

'You don't have to answer,' I said, 'but… do you know what you're going to do next?'

He shook his head slowly. 'Keep a low profile probably. Wait until the media interest about me leaving JYNKS dies down. I want to find the time to see the rest of the band, sit with them, explain why I have done what I've done. I promised my aunt and uncle I would keep an eye on Sun-hee, too.'

'I bet she would love that,' I said but could hear my voice cracking a bit. That all meant he was staying here in Seoul.

'Starting over seems part terrifying, part thrilling,' he continued. 'What about you? Do you have a plan?'

'Nothing concrete. I don't want to give up on my dream yet. I think I am going to sign with a new agency and give everything one more shot. If it *then* doesn't work out…'

'I believe it will.'

'You do?'

'I think you've known for a long time what you were truly passionate about but somewhere along the line you lost faith. When I first danced with you at Havana Club, your body was so tense. You said you didn't dance, didn't enjoy it. But then the way you began to move at that class in New York…' He puffed his cheeks and slowly exhaled. 'Wow, it took my breath away.'

I rocked on my heels, suddenly feeling shy in his presence.

'And your voice, Francesca. It still enters my dreams at night and the memory of it, of singing with you in the motel…' He held my face and brushed his thumb over my bottom lip.

All other sounds dropped away as I lost myself once more in his eyes. They were still sorrowful but the pain I had seen in them that first eventful moment we met at 63 High Street was gone.

'I'll always remember our jamming session and that song,' I said. 'Have you finished it?'

He nodded, dropping his hand.

'How does it end?' Did I want to know the answer to that question, or did I already know?

'It ends with hope,' he said with a smile. 'So, you'll stay in London?' he asked, changing the direction of the conversation.

'Yes. I will.' That part of my life was now a certainty. I had called Dad yesterday and told him all about the last conversation I had had with Mum. He was happy I was willing to give her a chance to make peace for all those lost years and said he would be thrilled if I made it to Sicily for Christmas.

Jae-seung stepped a little closer, hesitant in his approach.

'Francesca, I…' But there were no more words. In an instant, I was in his arms, and that rush of molecules shot through me like it had done every time he had held me. He whispered words in Korean, words I ached to understand, wishing he could speak from his heart in a way I could comprehend. But right now, I knew that was impossible for him to do. He had warned me before. I hadn't been led blindly down this path with him. And the reality was we both needed to move on, apart from each other.

There was nothing more to say except…

'Goodbye, Jae-seung.' I broke the embrace and his arms hung heavy beside him. It was taking all my resolve not to sink back into them. 'Goodbye.' The word lodged in my throat, the emotion beginning to choke me, but I didn't want him to see me cry. He didn't need to absorb my sadness on top of his.

I grabbed my hand luggage, turned and didn't look back.

Maybe it can be
This problem I can solve
And the fear in my heart
Will finally dissolve
But know this for always
As you go your own way
Know I'll love you forever
Forever you'll hear me say

Chapter 38

Six months later

'How did it go?' Clara asked as I held my mobile in the crook of my neck and attempted to zip my coat.

'I think it went great. Took me ages to peel off all my layers and thaw out before my slot.'

I shivered in the January chill. An arctic freeze had thrown a white frost over London. Thankfully, the train from New Malden had brought me into town on time and the Tube was running, but now that I was outside again and the sun had made an appearance, I felt like walking to Waterloo and unwinding from an intense audition. The part was for a musical – the first one my new agent had put me forward for – an Amazon Prime adaptation of an old classic. When she told me part of the audition would be dancing with a pole, I knew the classes I had undertaken over the last few months at Mum's studio would pay off. Singing while slinking down the metal rod was a first, though, and I was grateful for the voice coach lessons I had taken to help me practise. The role was a supporting one, but it would be perfect for me, and I was buoyed when I saw the director nod and whisper something to the producer, who had smiled and nodded as well.

'*Excelente, meu amor*. I have a good feeling about thiiiiis.' She squeaked the last word.

'You OK?'

'Yeah, I'm fine. A little indigestion. She literally is leaving me no room to breathe.'

Clara was officially overdue, and induction was on the horizon if the baby didn't make an appearance in the next couple of days.

'I'm coming straight home,' I said.

'No, no, no. Don't do that.'

'Why not?'

'Hmm, no reason. Where are you, anyway?'

'Piccadilly Circus, why?'

'I know you're *there*. But what can you see?'

I took in a sweep of my surroundings. 'Hordes of tourists taking selfies in front of the fountain.'

'Why don't you join them?'

'I'm exhausted, Clara. I hardly got any sleep last night. My stomach was twisted in knots. I'm thinking we could watch a movie tonight or something.'

'I'm spending the evening with Steve.'

'I thought he was working tonight?'

'He messaged to say he was free. Or rather… I told him he *had* to be free.'

Clara and Steve's relationship had been a shock, but it was going from strength to strength. He had declared his undying love the night Gran passed away, but she had chided him for his timing and had decided not to confide in me until I had returned from Seoul. She thought I had too much on my plate and wasn't sure how she felt about him. But as the days and weeks had gone by, he had proved himself reliable and dependable. He was prepared to support her when the baby was born, he had told her several times. She appreciated the sentiment but told him she didn't need him, that she was capable of caring for herself and the baby. *Wanting* him was another matter. She had been horny as hell, she had repeatedly told me during her second and third trimesters, and Steve had willingly obliged. They weren't official yet. Clara said she wanted to keep him on his toes. Or rather, have her cake and eat it. *Air tick*.

'That poor boy. When are you going to put him out his misery? He's crazy about you and willing to take time off from the bar to look after Francisca so you can get all those designs ready for your first show.'

'I know, I know. I got a good egg there. But you know. Treat 'em mean, keep 'em keen. These idioms are there for a reason, Francesca.'

I laughed. Clara was never mean to Steve. They were adorable together and I was so happy for her. She was obviously a smitten kitten.

'Are you at the fountain?' she asked.

'No. I'm still on Haymarket.'

Clara spouted Portuguese at me in exasperation. 'Please. Will. You. Go. To. The. Fountain,' she panted.

I stopped dead in the street, a pedestrian knocking into me from behind as I did. 'Are you in labour, Clara?' I said, apologising to the irate gentleman in a long coat.

'Yes, but don't you dare come home yet. The contractions are only eight minutes apart. It will be hours until I am fully dilated. And your mum is downstairs anyway if I need her.'

Clara, Mum and I had been renting a lovely house in Richmond for the last two months – one of the ones with the bay windows that Clara had dreamed of. Mum's studio was in the town centre, so it was convenient. We all had our own space and Mum was insistent she wanted to help out when Clara's baby was born.

Mum and I were healing. Together. And I had never been happier to have both my parents in my life.

'You *have* to go to the fountain,' Clara continued, 'because you're meant to meet—'

I stopped still. Surely that couldn't be… 'Jae-seung.'

'You guessed?'

My breathing stuttered. 'He's here. How did you know?' I asked, still in disbelief as I broke into a run. He hadn't seen me yet, but he was there standing in front of the Eros statue, in a sea of camera-wielding tourists. I pinched my arm to check this wasn't a dream.

'Hana called me. He asked her where you were and wanted to surprise you. Now go and talk to him, then get your ass to the hospital.'

She had disconnected the call before I could object. Crossing at the lights, I walked over to him. When he saw me, a smile flooded his face. There was no sadness in his eyes, only joy.

'You're here,' I said.

'I am. How did the audition go?'

My eyes widened and I wobbled on the spot as a group of kids swept past. 'How did you know?'

'My cousin. I dropped by the coffee shop hoping you would be there. Yeah, I know, I'm asking this question about seven months too late.' He dipped his eyes.

I smiled at the thought of him remembering that day. 'It went well. I think I have a chance this time, for an *actual* role.'

'I'm happy for you. You deserve it.'

'Why are you here? Are you visiting your family?'

'Sort of. But I also came for this.' He pulled out his phone from his rucksack as well as a pair of AirPods Max. 'Do you want to listen?' As he held out the headphones towards me, I pulled off my woolly hat and placed them on my ears. He mouthed some words, but I couldn't hear him.

I lifted one side from my ear. 'What did you say?'

He held his palm out to me and I took it in mine. 'Squeeze my hand if it's too loud.'

I nodded and he pressed a button on his phone. A beat. A drum. A violin. Then a voice, deep and low in a fast-paced rap. It was the song. *The* song he had written about me. About us. The words I had imprinted in my mind from the time Jae-seung sang them to me in the motel in America. I sat down on the steps, and he followed me down, his knees close to mine. I gazed at him as the chorus came. Three times. His hand still nestled in mine, but I didn't squeeze it. I held it, my fingers lacing in his, remembering the last time I had felt this tender touch, when I'd thought I would never feel it again.

My face broke into the widest smile as the last chorus floated through my mind. It had taken him one look. One look to know. To know he loved me.

'It's beautiful,' I said, pulling off the headphones once the song ended. 'But it's not your voice.'

He shook his head. 'No, it isn't. I came to London to have it recorded with an up-and-coming rapper. I connected with one of the band's songwriters in Seoul, told him this had always been my dream and he took me under his wing, and we worked on the music together. I don't want the spotlight. I'm happy to take a back seat. The new lead singer of JYNKS is a good guy and I am happy the band will continue without me, but I know now I was pursuing that life for one reason only. And when that obligation fell away, I felt free for the first time – free to pursue my passion.'

It made me so happy to know that Jae-seung was following his dream. That dream that he had spoken of during our epic American road trip.

'But...' He stroked his thumb over my hand. 'I also returned... for another reason. For you.'

My mouth dropped open.

'I know, I know. It is cheeky of me to assume you've been waiting for me to get my life together.'

'No,' I said, squeezing his hand reassuringly. 'That's not what I was going to say. I guess I am still in shock that you're here. I'm also freezing.' I laughed as my teeth chattered.

'We can go somewhere inside if you want.'

'I actually have to go. Clara's in labour and I think she'll be on her way to the hospital soon. But... she told me I had to hear you out first.'

'Hana messaged her to find out where you were. And don't worry, I will get you to the hospital in record time. I have the motorbike with me.'

Relief flooded me that I would get there easily and not have to take the train.

'Are you… staying in London?' I asked tentatively.

'Yes. Yes, I am. I heard a couple of days ago. The record company producing the song want me to write a whole album. My family's here. And most importantly… you. My muse.' He took my other hand then and brought them both to his chest, my fingers brushing against the leather of his jacket. 'I would like to be in your life, if you'll have me.'

My body began to defrost as he shuffled closer. The chatter of tourists became louder around us, but he didn't turn in the direction of the Korean voices; he only had eyes for me.

Our adventure together was about to begin another chapter, but how could we resume from where we had left things?

Before I could spiral into negativity, I reminded myself: I was no longer the girl I was when we first met. I had healed the pain from my mother's abandonment and found a way to forgive her. I was comfortable in my own skin, in the way my body moved, and I believed in my passion for acting, singing and dancing. I also had a support network here in London that I'd never thought possible, with extended family in Sicily. Jae-seung was the icing on the cake. *Air tick*, I thought and smiled to myself.

'Shall we start over?' Dropping his hands, I offered one of mine in greeting. 'I'm Francesca Cavalieri-Lee, actress, singer, dancer.'

He shook it. 'It's a pleasure to meet you. I'm Choi Jae-seung, former K-pop idol, singer, songwriter, handyman, barista. I am no longer afraid, Francesca Cavalieri-Lee, to give you my heart if you'll have me. Yes, love is a risk. But it's a risk worth taking with *you*.'

The world around us dropped away as his lips found mine. This was the start of our story. It was time to begin again.

'It took me only one look, too, Choi Jae-seung,' I whispered against his lips.

It took me one look
One look to know
To know I wanted you
And couldn't let you go

When I saw you that day
I couldn't silence my heart
And when I held you close
I knew we could never be apart
But I can't let you into my world
No, I can't let you into my world
Because a love like this
Will bleed if it unfolds

If this were a love match
It would never end right
And it pains me to tell you
I have no strength for the fight
And to tell you of my fear
My fear to give you my heart
It took me one look x 2

There is no other option
From now, from here
Until the end of days
Even though I don't want it to be
We must go our separate ways
One look to know x 2

It took me one look
One look to know
To know I needed you
And couldn't let you go

The sun in your hair
That smile only for me
Why can't I find the strength
To be the one you need me to be?
There is no other way
It pains me to set you free
But I can't let you go x 2

Maybe it can be
This problem I can solve
And the fear in my heart
Will finally dissolve
But know this for always
As you go your own way
Know I'll love you forever
Forever you'll hear me say

It took me one look
One look to know
To know I loved you
And couldn't let you go

Repeat chorus x 2

End

Acknowledgements

Still Unwritten is my third novel. I never thought I would be writing that sentence, but I am, thanks to the amazing support of my agent, Kate Burke. Thank you, Kate, for always having my back and your unfailing encouragement. I am also fortunate to have Sian Ellis-Martin supporting me, too. Sian's pep talks get me through many a low phase during the publishing process and for that I am very grateful. Huge credit also to the rest of the Blake Friedmann team who work behind the scenes on my books.

I am very lucky that this novel found a home at Canelo. From the moment I had a Zoom call with my editor, Emily Bedford, I knew she was the one! Emily, from being a fellow Swiftie, to your love of K-pop and all your boundless enthusiasm for the book, I have loved working on *Still Unwritten* with you – your editing expertise really transported this book, and I am truly thankful. Immense gratitude also to the rest of the Canelo team: Thanhmai Bui Van, Nicola Piggott, Kate Shepherd, my cover illustrator Sophie Melissa and designer Emily Courdelle, my incredible copy editor, Becca Allen, and my proofreader, Daniela Nava.

Still Unwritten is set in New Malden – the town I grew up in – and 63 High Street where Fran and Clara meet regularly is the best coffee shop on the high street (in my humble opinion). It's managed by Anselmo and ably assisted by his lovely sisters: Amie and Anaïs. Thanks, Ans, for fuelling many writing sessions with delicious coffee and to Amie for sharing your experiences of growing up in New Malden and your travels to Seoul. Jae-seung was inspired by my favourite actor, Kim Soo-hyun, and my love of K-drama and K-pop, while I owe the inspiration of Francesca to my sweet Italian friend – Francesco Oddo. I am so pleased that we connected, Francesco, and that you opened up about your life here in England and back in Sicily and the trials and tribulations of being an actor. *Grazie mille!* A debt of gratitude also to my Brazilian friend Elenice Pérēs for checking all the Portuguese words and saving my blushes.

Writing a novel can be a very solitary business and fraught with uncertainty so I am very appreciative of my author friends, for the WhatsApp chats we share, reading early proofs and graciously quoting. Shout-outs to Lorraine Brown, Emma Hughes, Sara Jafari, Nicole Kennedy, Emma Cowell, Lorna Cook, Holly Miller, Zoë Folbigg, Olivia Beirne, Lucy Keeling, Sophie Cousens and Fiona Schneider.

I have so much love for the #bookstagram community on Instagram, which has championed my books from the start. I have made many good friends on that platform – wonderful women who read my books and recommend them. A special mention to: Steph, Emma, Emily, Lisa, Nicole, Vicky, Ruby, Lily, Kathryn, Louise, Becky, Carley, Marie, Zoë, Tara and Charlotte. You ladies rock!

This book is dedicated to my best friend, Dee Spence. I can't express enough how much your friendship means to me, Dee, and how it has carried me forward these last few years. You've been my rock, my confidante and my adopted co-parent and I couldn't imagine going through this stage of my life without you. And to your gorgeous daughter, Laila, a huge thanks for imparting your superior K-drama knowledge on me. My friendship appreciation also extends to my other close girlfriends: Sarah Brett, Minal Choksey, Hannah Tigg and Katie Davis – you have all been amazing. Family friends continue to support me behind the scenes, so an immense debt of gratitude to Jan, Auntie Farida, Peter, Rachael, Pamela and David.

Traversing my new world of singledom has been quite the adventure but meeting a lovely Greek guy during the writing of this book was a heady tonic. You made me feel young again, Kostas, brought me a lot of joy during our dates, and you also restored my faith in romance. ευχαριστώ πολύ.

My Pressdee family are my constant. I can't thank them enough for their support, especially my brother Piers, who is an absolute star, my sis-in-law Sally, who is a gem, and my mother, who has stood by me on my author journey from the start with endless uplifting chats and loads of plot advice. I love you all so much.

To my girls – Miranda and Rose. Watching you grow into incredible young women is a huge source of pride for me and I love you both beyond words. We make a great team along with our furry quartet – Biscuit, Flair, Eloise and Oleg!

And finally, but by no means least, thank YOU! for buying this book and hopefully reading it too. Please do get in touch and let me know what you think. I'm @carolinekauthor on Instagram and Threads.

Australian Children's Books 1774–1972

Australian Children's Books

A BIBLIOGRAPHY

Volume One 1774–1972

Marcie Muir

MELBOURNE UNIVERSITY PRESS 1992

First published 1992

Printed in Australia by
Australian Print Group for
Melbourne University Press, Carlton, Victoria 3053
U.S.A. and Canada: International Specialized Book
Services, Inc., 5602 N.E. Hassalo Street, Portland,
Oregon 97213-3640
United Kingdom and Europe: University College
London Press, Gower Street, London WC1E 6BT, UK

Designed by Arthur Stokes

Published with the generous assistance of the Australian Council of Libraries and Information Services

National Library of Australia
Cataloguing-in-Publication entry

Muir, Marcie.
Australian children's books, a bibliography. Volume one, 1774–1972.

[New ed.].
Includes index.
ISBN 0 522 84431 6.
ISBN 0 522 84456 1 (set).

1. Children's literature, English—Bibliography. 2. Children's literature, Australian—Bibliography. 3. Children's literature, English—Oceania—Bibliography. 4. Australia—Juvenile literature—Bibliography. I. Muir, Marcie. Bibliography of Australian children's books. II. Title. III. Title: Bibliography of Australian children's books.

011.62

This book is number seven
in the Miegunyah Press Series,
the establishment of which was made possible
by bequests under the wills of
Sir Russell and Lady Grimwade

MIEGUNYAH WAS THE HOME OF MAB AND
RUSSELL GRIMWADE FROM THE YEAR 1911

To my late husband, Harry Muir,
and to Kathie and Rory

Contents

Introduction

This work is not just an updated edition of my two-volume *A Bibliography of Australian Children's Books* So much has changed over the years since I began working on it that the whole field has had to be re-surveyed and charted afresh. My original work was an attempt to discover and record Australian children's books, working on my own with almost no sources of reference. Indeed there was hardly any interest in the subject and booksellers did not even list their children's books. The holdings in Australian libraries consisted of deposit copies (often uncatalogued) and an assortment of books dispersed in the general collections, as indeed, they still are, in most libraries.

Now children's books provide a strongly collected field, which is gradually being researched. Some booksellers have issued reliable and informative catalogues justifying the high prices asked. After the early pioneering works, authors like Brenda Niall, the late John Ryan, Ian McLaren, Robert Holden, Marion Amies, Patricia Clarke, Maurice Saxby, Maureen Walsh and Walter McVitty have published books and articles providing much useful information. The *Australian Dictionary of Biography* has entries for a number of children's authors, and information on children's books is to be found in some other entries. The *Australian National Bibliography* includes children's books published between 1900 and 1950, and the Australian Bibliographical Network is also useful but by no means comprehensive, especially with earlier works. These published sources and the accessibility of far more children's books in some public and other specialized libraries and private collections have combined to present quite a different aspect. By examining and recording all the books available, and comparing titles listed with my own checklists, and by noting information from all these and other published sources, I have been able to provide a more comprehensive view of the entire subject of Australian children's books.

For example, the whole publishing history of one of our most famous classics, *The Magic Pudding*, makes intriguing reading. I have been able to identify undated editions and find their correct dates. Collectors' points, such as the size of the first edition, the 'remaindering' of part of it, the vexed matter of copies with the 'A.& R.' printed endpapers, the date when a totally new illustration by Norman Lindsay appeared on a new dustjacket design, and so on, are all discussed; and the conclusions drawn from years of experience in handling these books and from much patient research are published here. Wherever possible I have provided information of this sort about any works mentioned, whether famous or obscure. Patterns emerge, and depending on the readers' interests they can discover when Australian writers, compared with overseas ones, began to be more popular, when publishing of Australian children's books in this country became more common, when fairy stories began to give way to animal stories, when Australian illustrators emerged, and so on, and many other matters of quite different interest.

It was a daunting task to undertake the integration and revision of my two original volumes, as well as to examine all the newly-found books acquired in recent years. I hesitated a long while before committing myself. Then I resolved I would not attempt to go beyond my previous cut-off point of the end of 1972. There was so much to occupy me with books of the earlier periods—of greater interest to me because I enjoyed historical research. I also dreaded attempting to come to terms with the proliferation of children's books published in the years following 1972. I had some idea of their extent and I was determined I would go no further. Providentially, at the time when I had just begun to work seriously on the project, in 1987, I was approached by Kerry White, then unknown to me, enquiring if I would mind if she worked on bringing the bibliography up to date. We met, and discussed the whole idea, liked each other, and felt we could work together. We seemed to spend the next few years in constant correspondence, or on the telephone between Adelaide and Wollongong. Fortunately, we were able to arrange to be in Melbourne, Canberra or Sydney working at the same time on some occasions, and Kerry had several long visits to Adelaide where she found the resources of the Children's Literature Research Collection of the State Library here invaluable. We have had an excellent relationship and I greatly admire the way she attacked the huge masses of recently published material with such energy and lively spirits. Her enthusiasm and verve made her a good companion and a supportive colleague.

Naturally, we discussed our standards, methods and definitions, in general agreeing and accepting a common process of arrangement, description, and so on. The development of children's book publishing in Australia affected our criteria for inclusion of some books. Very few children's books were actually published in the Australian Colonies last century; many books written, illustrated and published overseas relating to Australia were of interest and have been included in my book. But with the huge increase in local publication in recent years, Kerry found it necessary to define her own boundaries to suit her subject which she has set out in her Bibliography.

I have found the volume of entries now demands a rigid standard, and books written by non-Australian authors and published overseas are only eligible for inclusion if a substantial proportion of their content relates to Australia. An exception of course is made for very early children's books. Volumes of Cook's Voyages were popular, and eighteenth-century children's books which mention New Holland or New South Wales are sufficiently rare to warrant attention. The Bibliography actually covers over two centuries, my earliest book being published in 1774 or 1775 (the exact date being unknown) and extending to the end of 1972, whilst Kerry's volume brings the work up to the end of 1988.

I have included children's books by Australian authors whatever their subject, except where modern publishing techniques have created a vast, even world-wide proliferation of books by some extraordinarily successful authors. Three principal exceptions are as follows; Pamela Travers, whose Mary Poppins books achieved enormous sales in many languages, shapes and sizes as a result of the successful film. The second is Joseph Jacobs, the eminent nineteenth-century Jewish historian and folklorist, born here, but not writing about this country. His collections of folk tales first published last century have often been reprinted and have served as the sources for many modern books in different languages and editions. The third is Dr Paul White, a most prolific author whose 'Jungle Doctor' books have been published in a very large number of native African and other languages in numerous editions. Born in New South Wales, his missionary work is known widely in other countries.

I found that unless I adopted a rigid criterion for inclusion of books relating to Australia or the Pacific by overseas authors the bibliography would be bloated by entries of books which merely mentioned the word 'Australia'. I cannot see the justification for including such a book as Charlotte M. Yonge's *A Book of Golden Deeds*—a favourite compendium volume a century or more ago and reprinted many times—because in its four hundred or more pages it includes a two-page article on the lost Duff children. And yet at times the decision as to whether or not a book is a children's book is a subjective one. In all honesty it must be admitted that I have sometimes been influenced to include a book that appeals to me in preference to some drab volume of marginal relevance. The little volumes of Emigrant Tracts, for example, published in the 1850s, were intended to encourage prospective emigrants, giving information concerning the voyage to the colonies and conditions of life here. They were written in story form for family reading without being directed specifically to children. I admit I was influenced in my decision to include them because I found them engagingly written. There is also the fact that attitudes towards children are continually changing. Adolescent fiction had not been thought of in the days of Ethel and Lilian Turner, and many young adult women were among their readers. Publishers, naturally seeking the widest market for their books, were ambivalent at times and were not always a reliable guide. It is usually safe to include books awarded as school or Sunday School prizes, and prize labels are also useful in indicating the approximate date of an undated book. Sometimes if it were not for the prize label one would not think of including some large, closely-printed volume. What stamina young Victorian readers were expected to have! Some dry-looking little books turn out to be valuable examples of early voyages published for children in a 'Juvenile Library' when children's knowledge of geography was expanded by the accounts written of the great voyages of discovery at the end of the eighteenth century and later. Indeed volumes of Cook's Voyages were said to be among those most commonly read along with other early voyages and the Mutiny of the *Bounty*, accounts of shipwrecks and so on.

The Bibliography provides a select guide to children's books relating to the South West Pacific area, as did the previous volumes. This is highly relevant to the early period especially. Australia and the neighbouring regions were regarded as a whole by early voyagers, and by writers of accounts of travels and discovery. Our early history was inextricably mixed with that of other parts of the region. New Guinea, Norfolk Island and Pitcairn Island were closely related to events that happened in our continent and on the surrounding seas. There were many tales of adventure about early whaling voyages which demanded to be included. Books relating to Antarctica will be found in the main text as they were in the preceding volumes, but not those about New Zealand which has its own literature.

In looking through books of last century and the first half of this I was struck by the number of stories of missionary endeavour and adventure. Though not fashionable at present, the powerful influence such books had on children of earlier generations should not be forgotten. At least two of the ships used by missionaries in their work in the South Seas were bought with funds raised by Sunday School children, who contributed a penny a week each. They felt a close connection, and in one ship, the *Daydream*, they were regarded as part-owners. Many of these missionaries came from different parts of Australia, or retired here later, and children from schools and parishes all over the country were involved.

Annuals have not been included, apart from one or two volumes optimistically published here; these were usually solitary volumes which met with insufficient public response and were not continued. Paperbacks are included, the boys 'Penny Dreadfuls' being a fascinating category of their own. Comics and periodicals are not included. The 'Ginger Meggs' and 'Fatty Finn' 'annuals' were different from both the usual annual and the comic. Each year in time for Christmas the newspaper in which these comic strips appeared weekly brought out a collection of that year's strips, bound in irresistible vivid picture wrappers and called 'annuals'. On the whole, educational books have been omitted as they form a large class of their own, but there is often a shadowy area between general and educational children's books. Some readers and anthologies are very appealing and may contain original material not published elsewhere and these are listed. So are books descriptive of some particular aspect of Australian history or geographic area if they are not just formal textbooks. The proliferation of series of social history works in the past few decades has made it possible to make series entries of such books without duplication.

The general arrangement is as before, with books arranged so that the authors' names appear in alphabetical sequence. Individual titles of an author's works are entered chronologically, and all variant editions and translations of the title following according to date of publication. For example, every edition or translation of Ethel Turner's *Seven Little*

Australians is listed in order of appearance before one moves on to *The Family at Misrule*. Anonymous books are entered under title in the general alphabetical sequence. Cross-references are given for pseudonyms and where an author's books are entered in a series entry. Each separate title is numbered as are variant editions but not simple reprints. There is a title index and also an illustrator index.

The method of entry is as follows. A complete transcription of the title page of the book is given, with the actual title in capitals and an oblique stroke indicating the end of a line. The date and place of publication follows if not already shown. A bibliographical description follows, showing the number of pages of text and extraneous matter, the number of illustrations and some description of them and the artist's name, if known. The binding is then mentioned, and the page size, height followed by width, is given in millimetres. A comment may follow about the contents of the book or other relevant matter, followed by the location in which the book was seen, and no attempt has been made to discover other copies of the item. A typical example follows:

VILLIERS, Alan J.
JOEY/GOES TO SEA/by/Alan Villiers/[drawing]/ Illustrated by Victor J. Dowling/New York/Charles Scribner's Sons/1939
66pp, col. frontis. & b/w drawings throughout, clo., 205x163mm ANL
The life of a ginger kitten on board the ship *Joseph Conrad*.

Square brackets indicate that the word enclosed, in this case 'drawing', did not appear on the title page.

I have built up my own collection of books over the years mainly to enable me to consult them more readily and compare copies. Naturally, living in Adelaide, I have availed myself of the splendid resources of the Children's Literature Research Collection of the State Library of South Australia, which is without comparison in any state. One of its great advantages is that the children's books are together in one single collection, on site, in the one location, catalogued and under the care of knowledgeable and helpful staff led by Juliana Bayfield, so thoroughly at home in all aspects of the whole field of children's literature. I have also found much interesting material in the Barr Smith Libary, University of Adelaide, especially among the Maude Collection of books relating to the Pacific. As always, periods of work at the Mitchell Library, Sydney and the National Library in Canberra were very rewarding, working in both these great collections providing the opportunity to handle rare and precious books and to appreciate some of the treasures of both libraries. Naturally the breadth of these collections revealed many items of interest for inclusion. Similarly I found many items in the State Library of Victoria, mainly in the La Trobe Collection, but also in the music collection in The Queen's Hall.

Among private collections the most cursory glance will show my original indebtedness to the late Marjorie and Alan Grant of Melbourne, with their great pioneer collection, and their eagerness to help me. Fortunately for me, they were succeeded by Ron Maria of Sydney with his passion for boys' books, which he was able to indulge in his many trips to England. It is sad to think his collection too has now mostly been dispersed, but it provided me with some exciting finds and many entries which I would not otherwise have had. Recently his interest has revived and he is again supplying me with information about his acquisitions. In 1982 I first met Robert Holden, then beginning to build up the James Hardie Library, later to become the Museum of Australian Childhood. Here was someone with the invaluable and unusual combination of both a fine arts and a library training, and someone with a passion for book illustration, and an eagerness to form a great children's collection. I learnt to appreciate Robert's scholarship at close range when we collaborated in our book on Ida Rentoul Outhwaite. The many exhibitions of Australian children's book illustrators, about whom little was previously known, which he has arranged, and whose work he has carefully researched, have brought to our attention much that had otherwise been forgotten. The Museum of Australian Childhood has provided me with some entries of very rare and choice books, as well as extending my entries of Australian plays and other interesting works.

While I was working on Ida Rentoul Outhwaite I received a letter from Ken Pound of Fitzroy, Victoria, telling me about the windows she designed in the church hall of St Mark's, Fitzroy. Although I already knew of the windows, Ken's admiration for Outhwaite's work and his great zeal as a collector eventually led him to the discovery of two hitherto unknown books written and illustrated by her. His tremendous collection has been a joy to work in. I know of nowhere else where up to seven or eight copies of the one book, with some, often slight, variations, can be seen side by side. This is not unusual in this collection as Ken has a keen eye for any variation in a book's production. I have spent many days working there, going straight through from early morning until dark without stop, making the most of the availability of such a magnificent collection, and sustained by kind hospitality and numerous cups of tea.

Naturally one hopes that not too many omissions will be found. However, as work progressed I came to the conclusion that the time has now come for more individual studies on different aspects of Australian children's books of the past. The field has become so wide that it would be useful to see more specialized work, such as Ian McLaren's valuable Whitcombe's Story Books bibliographies. The many editions of the thirty-nine Ethel Turner titles and the thirty-eight Mary Grant Bruce titles (and one suspects some competition here!) cry out for a more exact and detailed guide to the publications than has been possible in this volume. I would also like to see more work done on foreign translations and children's books relating to Australia in other languages. A related area is that of the little editions specially for children of the early voyages of discovery, a fascinating field especially as the books are so rare. The 'Penny Dreadfuls' is another specialized field. To be of use, these studies need to be well defined in scope, and thorough in their coverage.

No bibliography is ever complete, and it is a sign of a lively interest in a subject when new discoveries are being made. The chance of finding some unknown, important book can sweeten the work of any researcher and no one would want an end to such possibilities.

Acknowledgements

My thanks for help received in compiling this bibliography go back a long way and I shall not repeat acknowledgements made in my two previous volumes except where they are directly relevant to the present volume.

First I would like to thank ACLIS (Australian Council of Libraries and Information Services, then AACOBS) who, in 1987 when I was still considering the idea of this new edition of my work, generously awarded me a grant to cover the costs of interstate travel so that I could do the very necessary work in major interstate libraries and private collections, and obtain help with secretarial assistance. Of course it is impossible to assess such expenses in advance, as no one can foretell all the contingencies or the time or amount of material needed to be transcribed. Nevertheless, the grant towards these costs was very helpful indeed. I am indebted to Kerry White and Etta Clark who initially put the whole bibliography on computer for me.

I have already mentioned certain private collectors whose alertness in finding relevant books, and enthusiasm in bringing such finds to my attention, enlivened the whole work and made up for much of the necessary drudgery. They were responsible for many entries, writing to tell me of their finds and generously sharing their pleasure in their books with me. Lindsay Shaw of Melbourne brought over items of interest on frequent visits to Adelaide, writing of his finds at other times. John Holroyd promptly replied to any query, sharing his wide knowledge generously as always. Marie Cosh of Adelaide kept a list of books I still needed to check and filled a number of gaps for me. Other Adelaide collectors regularly left boxes or packets of their most recent purchases for me to examine, and some invited me to their homes to check their books. The friendship and practical help of librarians too has always been noticeable. Interstate I particularly appreciated the friendship and help of Margy Burn, Mitchell Librarian, and Jean James of the Petherick Room, Australian National Library. In Canberra I also greatly benefited from several visits to the Lu Rees Archives. Naturally I have worked most in the companionable atmosphere of the State Library of South Australia, where a cheerful wave from rare books librarian Valmai Hankel brightened the task, and her wide knowledge often clarified some doubtful point. I have already mentioned Juliana Bayfield and the Children's Literature Research Collection. I owe much to her unstinted and kindly help, and that of Valerie Sitters and Lindy Hillman, present staff, and Bev Murray there previously. I also appreciated the help I had from the Barr Smith Library, at Adelaide University, from Flinders University and the Thiele Library at the South Australian College of Advanced Education, Magill Campus.

Overseas I was fortunate to be able to check the numerous books by the first Australian author of boys' stories, Robert Richardson, at the National Library of Scotland. I also spent a good deal of time working at the Renier Collection of the Bethnal Green Museum of Childhood, part of the Victoria and Albert Museum. Although I had friendly help from Ms Tessa Chester I was not able to see the whole collection as not all had then been received or catalogued.

It goes without saying that I am most grateful to all the private people mentioned in the Location list. Looking back on the earlier volumes I remember with gratitude how much I owed to my friends Marjorie and Alan Grant and the pleasure they had too, in helping with the work. I also remember how overawed I felt on my first visit to work at the National Library, then only a group of prefabricated buildings, and the friendship shown me by Mrs Pauline Fanning. This outstanding librarian and generous friend has always made my working visits to Canberra rewarding in every way. I was originally encouraged to compile the bibliography by my husband, Harry Muir, who generously supported and advised me, personally, and through his business, the Beck Book Company Proprietary Limited. Throughout the years I have had much kindly help from individuals in the book trade, both publishers and booksellers. In more recent years my children have actively helped me sort our my ideas by listening patiently and offering constructive criticism, encouragement and some fresh ideas. The confidence shown by friends and family are what sustains one over the long haul.

Locations

AJH	The late A.J.Halls, Adelaide
AMc	Mrs Anne McCormick, Sydney
ANL	Australian National Library
AP	Albert Puddy, Adelaide
ATL	Alexander Turnbull Library, Wellington, NZ
BBC	Beck Book Company, Adelaide (now closed)
BL	British Library
BMC	British Museum Catalogue
BP	Bibliotheca Polynesiana
CLRC	Children's Literature Research Collection, State Library of South Australia
Dromkeen	Dromkeen, Victoria
EC	Etta Clark, Adelaide
GI	Goodwood Institute, S.A. (now defunct)
GK	Gary Krohn, Adelaide
Grant	Collection of the late Alan & Marjorie Grant, Melbourne (now dispersed)
HBM	H. B. Muir, Adelaide
IFA	Information from author
IFP	Information from publisher
IMc	Dr Ian McGill, Perth
JBP	J. B. Prentice, Melbourne
JC	Judith Crabbe, Adelaide
JH	J. Hobson, Adelaide
JMcG	The late Mrs J. McGinlay, Victoria
JR	The late John Ryan, Brisbane
K&NI	Kensington & Norwood Institute, S.A. (now defunct)
KMM	K. M. Muir, Adelaide
KP	Ken Pound, Melbourne
KW	Kerry White, Wollongong
LRA	Lu Rees Archives, Canberra
MAC	Museum of Australian Childhood, Sydney
MC	Mrs Marie Cosh, Adelaide
MCa	Max Cannon, Melbourne
MD	Michael Dugan, Melbourne
MK	Mrs M. Knight, Melbourne
NKP	Mrs N. K. Perry, Melbourne
NLS	National Library of Scotland, Edinburgh
NSL:M	N.S.W. State Library, Mitchell Library
NU	Fisher Library, University of Sydney
NUC	National Union Catalogue
PAI	Port Adelaide Institute, S.A. (now defunct)
PH	Sir Paul Hasluck, Perth
PR	P. Richardson, Melbourne
QSL	Queensland State Library
RC	Renier Collection of Children's Books, Bethnal Green Museum of Childhood, London
RH	Robert Holden, Sydney
RM	Ron Maria, Sydney
SCAE	S.A. College of Advanced Education (now University of S.A.)
SFU	Flinders University of S.A.
SLCSR	State Library of the Czech Socialist Republic
SSL	State Library of South Australia
SUA	Barr Smith Library of Adelaide University
TG	Trevor Guess, Adelaide
TI	Thebarton Institute, S.A. (now defunct)
TSL	Tasmanian State Library
VECD	Melbourne College of Advanced Education
VMOU	Lindsay Shaw Collection Children's Books, Monash University Library
VSL	State Library of Victoria
WRT	W. R. Thompson, Adelaide

References

ADB *Australian Dictionary of Biography*, 12 vols, Melbourne University Press, Melbourne, 1966–90

ANB *Australian National Bibliography 1901–1950*, National Library of Australia Canberra, 1988, 4 vols

BEDDIE, M. K. *Bibliography of Captain James Cook*, 2nd edition, Mitchell Library, Library of N.S.W., Sydney, 1970

BMC British Museum Catalogue (now British Library Catalogue, but earlier vols provided information relevant to books published during the period covered here)

CARPENTER, H. & PRITCHARD, M. *The Oxford Companion to Children's Literature*, Oxford University Press, London, 1984

CARPENTER, Kevin *Penny Dreadfuls and Comics: English Periodicals for children from Victorian times to the present day*, Bethnal Green Museum of Childhood, London, 1983

DU RIETZ, R. *Bibliotheca Polynesiana*, privately published, Almqvist & Wikselle, Oslo, 1969

FERGUSON, J. A. *Bibliography of Australia*, Vols 1–7, Angus and Robertson, Sydney, 1941–65

FERGUSON, J. A. *Addenda 1784–1950*, ANL, Canberra, 1986

JOHANNSEN, A. *The House of Beadle and Adams and its Dime and Nickel Novels*, 2 vols, Norman, Oklahoma, University of Oklahoma Press, 1950

JULES-VERNE, J. *Jules Verne: A Biography*, Macdonald and James, London, 1976

McLAREN, Ian F. with GRIFFITHS, George *Whitcombe's Story Books: A Trans-Tasman Survey*, University of Melbourne Library, 1984
First Supplement, 1987

MILLER, E. Morris *Australian Literature*, 2 vols, Melbourne University Press, with Oxford University Press, Melbourne, 1940

NUC *National Union Catalog Pre 1956* Imprints, Chicago, Ill., American Library Association, 1968–1980

O'NEILL, T. & F. *Australian Children's Books to 1980*, Canberra, Australian National Library, 1989

ST JOHN, J. *The Osborne Collection of Early Children's Books*, 2 vols, 2nd ed., Toronto Public Library, Toronto, 1975

Abbreviations

adv	advertisement(s)
ANB	Australian National Bibliography
bd	board(s)
bdg	binding
b/w	black and white
clo.	cloth
col.	coloured
dec.	decorated, decorative
d/w	dustwrapper
ed.	edition(s), edited by, editor
e/p	endpapers
ext.	extended
f/p	full page
frontis.	frontispiece
g.e.	gilt edges
illus.	illustrated, illustrator, illustration(s)
imp.	impression
inc.	including
lam.	laminated
ltd.	limited
mm	millimetres
n.d.	no date
n.p.	no place of publication
p, pp	pages
part.	partially
pic.	pictorial
prelims	preliminary pages
pub.	published, publisher
rev.	revised
rpt	reprint, reprinted
sgd	signed
sim.	simulated (e.g. sim. cloth)
t.p.	title page
trans.	translated by
vol.	volume (s)

Bibliography

The ABC and 123 Book
1 THE/ABC/and/123/BOOK
n.p., n.d. (back cover missing)
64pp, part col. illus. throughout, col. pic. wrappers, 260x184mm. KP

The A.B.C. Bird Book
2 THE A.B.C./BIRD/BOOK/For/Boys/and/Girls
n.p., n.d. [194-?]
12pp, b/w drawings throughout, col. pic. wrappers, 240x180mm. KP
An 'ABC' painting book of unsigned illus. Front cover design repeated on back.

ABC Coloring Book
3 ABC/COLORING BOOK
Gunn & Taylor, Melbourne, n.d.
12pp, b/w illus., col. pic. wrappers, cover title, 186x244mm. MAC
No 21 Gunn & Taylor Melb. on back cover.

ABC for Tiny Tots
4 ABC/For Tiny Tots/A Pyramid/Production/Series PP100
[1948]
[cover title on col. pic. cover]
8pp, part col. illus. throughout, pic. wrappers, 124x184mm. NSL:M

The ABC in Nursery Picture Rhymes
5 THE ABC/IN/NURSERY PICTURE/RHYMES/[drawing]/Little Boy Blue &c
John Sands Pty Ltd, n.d. [194-?]
[24]pp, 12pp col. illus., others b/w, col. pic. wrappers, 237x245mm. KMM
None of the illus. are signed or initialled.
6 Another copy, but
18pp (inc. 10pp in col. & others b/w). KP

ABC of Simple Things
7 ABC OF/SIMPLE THINGS
Ayers & James Pty Ltd, Sydney, n.d. [1949]
16pp, col. illus. throughout, pic. wrappers, cover title, 325x245mm. ANL
Short rhyming text to each illustration.

A.B.C. Picture Book
8 A.B.C./Picture/Book/A Pyramid/Publication PP107
8pp, col. illus., col. pic. wrappers, cover title, 240x180mm. KP
Little Folks Series: Old Mother Hubbard, Tom Tom the Piper's Son, Jolly Animal Book, ABC Picture book.

ABC Picture Book
9 AB/C/PICTURE/BOOK/A Pyramid/Publication
1948
[12]pp, part col. illus. throughout, col pic. wrappers, cover title, 124x184mm. NSL:M
Tiny Tots Series.

A.B.C. Tiny Toddlers' ABC
10 A.B.C./TINY TODDLERS'/ABC/[illus.]
Adv. in The Booksellers, Stationers & Fancy Goods Journal Sept. 10 1931). Retail 9d per copy. Unseen.

ABBOTT, Hilda [Mrs Charles Lydiard Aubrey, née Hamett]
11 AMONG THE/HILLS/By/Hilda Abbott/Illustrated by/Leslie Greener/Australasian Publishing Company/Sydney Wellington London
1948
159pp, 14 f/p b/w illus., clo., 180x115mm. KMM
Story of a childhood spent on the Monaro tableland in New South Wales; not specifically a book for children.

ABBOTT, J. H. M.
12 THE STORY OF/WILLIAM DAMPIER/by/J. H. M. Abbott/Sydney/Angus & Robertson Ltd./89 Castlereagh Street/1911
101pp (inc. 1p preface), b/w portrait frontis., limp clo., 180x120mm. Australian Story series. ANL

13 DOGSNOSE/By/J. H. M. Abbott/Author of "Castle Vane", "Sydney Cove", etc./Australia:/Cornstalk Publishing Company/89 Castlereagh Street, Sydney/1928
237pp, illus. by Edgar A. Holloway, b/w frontis. & 2 f/p b/w illus., clo., 180x115mm. NSL:M

ABBOTT, Joyce
14 PLAYABOUT/A/Picture-Story Reader/By/Joyce Abbott/Angus and Robertson
1955
30pp, dec. t.p., limp pic. clo., 235x180mm. CLRC
Story of Aborigines told in comic strip form.

15 ULLAGULBRA/A Picture-Story Reader/By/Joyce Abbott/Angus and Robertson
Sydney 1959
31pp, part. col. illus. throughout, pic. wrappers, 250x185mm. ANL
Simple story about Aboriginal children at play.

ABICAIR, Shirley
16 Shirley Abicair/tells/TALES/OF TUMBARUMBA/with pictures by Margaret Cilento/©Shirley Abicair and Margaret Cilento 1962/Printed in Great Britain by Fletcher and Son Norwich/Max Parrish—London
40pp, extended t.p., 2 double-spread pages of col. illus., b/w drawings throughout, bd., 245x185mm. KMM
17 Australian edition as above, but after 'Cilento' /Sydney/Australasian Publishing Company/in association with/Max Parrish & Co. Ltd./London
1963
32pp, b/w frontis., title on 2 pp, b/w drawings, limp clo., 247x183mm. KP

Aboriginal Tribes and Customs
ABORIGINAL TRIBES AND CUSTOMS. The Sanitarium Children's Library—Volume 4.
See McCarthy, Frederick David

Aborigines
18 ABORIGINES/Contents [8 chapter titles]/Education Department of Western Australia
Govt Printer, Perth, 1972
48pp, b/w & part col. drawings, b/w photographic illus., pic. wrappers, 210x267mm. KP
Although intended for schools, an attractively produced book of general interest. *See* WA Education Dept.

ABRAHALL, C. H.
19 C. H. Abrahall/PRELUDE/Illustrated by/Anna Zinkeisen/[Decoration]/Oxford University Press/ Geoffrey Cumberlege/1947
240pp (inc. 1p foreword), part. col. & b/w illus. throughout, clo., 190x120mm. KMM
A biography of Eileen Joyce, the Australian pianist.
20 C.H. Abrahall/PRELUDE/Illustrated by/Anna Zinkeisen/[Decoration]/Second Edition/Geoffrey Cumberlege/Oxford University Press/1950
Details as above. CLRC
• Rpt 1950. KP
21 2nd impr. 1951, as above. KP
22 C. H. Abrahall/PRELUDE/Illustrated by/Anna Zinkeisen/[Decoration]/London/Oxford University Press/1959
240pp, 6 f/p b/w illus. & drawings in text, clo., 195x125mm. Oxford Children's Library edition. CLRC
• Rpt as above, 1966. KP

ABRAM, Mrs Leonard
See Basser, Kathleen Veronica

ABSON, Phillip
THE MAN WITH THE MONEY. *See* Australian Youth Plays

Ace Flying Book
23 ACE/FLYING/BOOK/with compliments of Ace Chewing Sweets
Ace chewing gum Pty Ltd, Brown St, South Melbourne, n.d. [193-?]
32pp, b/w photographic illus., pic. wrappers, 246x184mm. KP
Numerous Australian references

Aces of all Sports
24 ACES OF ALL SPORTS
n.d.
[24]pp. Unseen

Ackman's Booklet for Children
See Outhwaite, Ida Rentoul

ADAMS, Arthur
25 Imperial Edition No. 126/Revised edition with additional rhymes/NURSERY RHYMES/with/music/ Traditional Tunes/Arranged by/Arthur Adams/ Copyright/Allan & Co. Pty Ltd./Melbourne Adelaide Bendigo/Printed in Australia
n.d. [advertised in the *Argus* 15/11/1913]
41pp, b/w illus. throughout, pic. frontis., wrappers, adv. on back wrapper, 300x237mm. KMM
Words & music of traditional nursery rhymes; illus. Beryl Reid.

ADAMS, Bertha Southey [Mrs. T. C. Brammall]
26 DUSKY DELL/By/Bertha Southey Adams/ Launceston, Tasmania/Printed and Published at the "Examiner" Office/1898/(All rights reserved)
200pp, 1p preface, unillus., wrappers, 210x135mm. NSL:M
The author claims in preface: 'This is a story written ostensibly for children'.
Also the author of *The Little Sister* (Hobart Stationery Co. 1916): unseen, & not known whether or not a children's book.

ADAMS, Rev. John
27 MODERN VOYAGES:/containing/A Variety of useful and entertaining Facts, respecting the Expe-/ditions and the principal Discoveries of/Cavendish, Dampier, Monk, Spilbergin,/Anson Byron, Wallis, Carteret,/ Bougainville, Dixon, Portlock,/Paterson, and others./ Comprehending/The most interesting Particulars of Brisson's Narrative of his/Shipwreck and Captivity;— The Shipwreck of the Antelope,/East India Packet, and a Description of the amiable Inhabi-/tants of the Pelew Islands, never before known to any Euro-/pean;—Aso, [*sic*] the latest authentic Accounts from Botany/Bay;— as well as curious Information from several ingenious Writers and Travellers./For the Amusement and Instruction of Youth of both Sexes./Volume I/By the Reverend John Adams, A.M./[quote]/Dublin:/Printed for Chamberlaine and Rice, P. Wogon,/P. Byrne, B. Dugdale, J. Moore, J. Jones,/Grueber and M'Allister, W. Jones,/and R. White./MDCCXC. 1790
xvipp, 296pp, unillus. calf, 170x100mm. CLRC
Chapter 23, Dampier, Chapters 56, 57, 58, 59, Cook
Vol. 2
xivpp, 296pp
Chapter 66, A Brief Detail of Governor Phillip's Voyage to Botany Bay. CLRC
28 MODERN VOYAGES:/Containing/A variety of useful and entertaining/facts, respecting the Expeditions/and the Principal Discoveries of/[3 lists follow as in Irish ed.]/Comprehending/The most interesting Particular of Brisson's Narrative of/his Shipwreck and Captivity;—the Shipwreck of the/ Antelope, East India Packet, and a Description of the/ amiable Inhabitants of the Pelew Islands, never before/ known to any European;—also the latest authentic Accounts from Botany Bay;—as well as curious Information/from several ingenious Writers and Travellers. For the amusement and instruction of/ Youth of Both Sexes./in two volumes./Volume 1./By the Reverend John Adams, A.M./Orbem Terrarum Circumdederunt./[4 line quote]/London:/Printed for G. Kearsley, at Johnson's Head, in Fleet Street,/MDCCXC 1790
xiipp (inc. 2pp adv.), 358pp, unillus., marbled bd., 3/4 calf, 172x105mm. NSL:M
Vol. 2 as above
xiipp (contents), 374pp & 10pp adv., unillus., 3/4 calf. NSL:M
29 CHOIX/DE/VOYAGES MODERNES,/pour l'instruction et l'amusement/des deux sexes;/Contenant une varieté de faits utiles et agréables,/relatif aux expéditions et aux principales découvertes/faites autour du monde, ainsi que la description des/moeurs et usages des peuples /Par John Adams/Traduit de l'Anglais par J. F. André/Ornés de deux jolies figures/[device]/A Paris/à la Librairie Economique,/rue de la Harpe, n°94/ancien Collége d'Harcourt./MDCCCV 1805
Vol. 1
xpp, 407pp (inc. 2pp preface, 6pp index), engraved frontis., quarter calf, 195x117mm.
Vol. 2
vipp, 411pp (inc. 7pp index), engraved frontis., quarter calf, 195x117mm. CLRC

ADAMS, K. M.
30 K.M. Adams/Seeing History—1/THE FIRST AUSTRALIANS/Pre-History—1810/Illustrated by Genevieve Melrose/Lansdowne Press
Melbourne 1968
98pp (inc. 2pp index, 4pp notes), b/w line drawings & photographic illus. throughout, stiff pic. wrappers, 240x180mm. BBC
• Rpt 1970, 1972. KP

31 Seeing History 2 AUSTRALIA: GAOL TO COLONY 1810–1850.
Melbourne 1969
110pp. KP

32 Seeing History 3 AUSTRALIA: COLONIES TO COMMONWEALTH 1850–1900.
Melbourne 1971
122pp.
• Rpt 1972. KP

33 Seeing History 4 TWENTIETH CENTURY AUSTRALIA 1900–1960. illus. Shane Miller.
Melbourne 1972
128pp. KP
Background social studies series. Uniform histories for schools & general reading.

ADAMS, Lee

34 Australian Legend Series/THE TALE OF THE/PLATYPUS/By Lee Adams/illustrated by Artstaff/[drawing]/[device]/Artstaff Sydney Australia
Artstaff Pty Ltd, 89 Berry St, North Sydney, n.d. [1972]
25pp, col. illus. throughout, pic. bd., pic. e/p, 280x215mm. Australian Legend Series Book 1. ANL
Based on story from *Australian Legendary Tales.*

ADAMS, W. H. Davenport

35 NEPTUNE'S HEROES:/or, the/Sea-Kings of England./From Sir John Hawkins to Sir John Franklin./By/W. H. Davenport Adams./[quotation—Shakespeare]/with Illustrations by W. S. Morgan and John Gilbert./London:/Griffith and Farran,/(Successors to Newbery and Harris)/Corner of St. Paul's Churchyard./MDCCCLXI 1861
440pp & 2pp preface & 32pp adv. Griffith & Farran's 'Original Juvenile Library.' Engraved frontis. & 5 f/p engravings, dec. clo., 171x105mm. CLRC
First ed. Contents include: William Dampier, the Buccaneer pp119–160; Capt James Cook pp213–43; Sir John Franklin pp420–40.

36 SOME HEROES OF TRAVEL/or, Chapters from the/History of Geographical Discovery/and Enterprise/With Map/Compiled and Rewritten by/W. H. Davenport Adams/[quotation]/Published under the direction of the committee/of general literature and education appointed by the Society for Promoting Christian Knowledge/London:/Society for Promoting Christian Knowledge:/Northumberland Avenue, Charing Cross;/43 Queen Victoria Street; and 48 Piccadilly./New York: Pott Young and Co./1880
2pp preface, 404pp, 4pp index, 4pp advts, unillus., one map[copy seen re-bound], 180x115mm. HBM
Only Australian section: Colonel Egerton Warburton, & Exploration in Western Australia (32pp).
• Rpt 1893 as above, but
'by the late W. H. Davenport Adams' and 'with maps' as before, & 2 tinted maps frontis. and 2 tinted maps printed on one page, dec. clo., 182x120mm. CLRC

37 JESSIE OGLETHORPE:/The Story of a Daughter's Devotion./And other Tales./By/W. H. Davenport Adams/Thomson & Niven,/Publishers,/Melbourne, Sydney and Adelaide/1885
viiipp & 312pp, engraved frontis. & 6 f/p engravings & small illus. in text, dec. clo., gilt edges, 185x104mm.
On front cover 'The/Young Folks/Library' CLRC
An anthology of prose & verse with the title story printed in sections like a serial. Only Australian content: Uncle Godfrey—Stories of Life in the Bush, 6pp & 3pp.

38 HEROES OF THE SEA/and/Their Achievements/By/W. H. Davenport Adams,/Author of "Great Names in European History", "The Mariners/of England", etc./London:/Gall and Inglis, 25 Paternoster Square;/and Edinburgh
n.d. [1882]
286pp, b/w frontis. & 4 f/p b/w illus., pic. clo., 185x120mm. HBM
Contents include: Ferdinand Magellan (29pp); William Dampier (45pp); Bougainville (16pp) & articles on other explorers who discovered territories in the Pacific, including Wallis, Carteret, etc.

39 HEROES OF/MARITIME DISCOVERY/and/Their Achievements/By/W. H. Davenport Adams,/Author of "Great Fames [*sic*] in European History", "The Mariners/of England," Etc./London:/Gall and Inglis, 25 Paternoster Square;/and Edinburgh.
n.d. [copy inscribed 1891]
287pp, 2pp adv., b/w frontis. & 4 f/p b/w illus., pic. clo., 178x120mm. KMM
Contents the same as in *Heroes of the Sea.*

ADAMSON, Bartlett

40 MYSTERY GOLD/By/Bartlett Adamson/With illustrations by Edgar A. Holloway/Australia/Cornstalk Publishing Company/89 Castlereagh Street, Sydney/1926
286pp, b/w frontis. & 3 f/p b/w illus., clo., 185x120mm. KMM

41 MYSTERY GOLD/By/Bartlett Adamson/Australia:/Cornstalk Publishing Company/89 Castlereagh Street, Sydney/1929
286pp, b/w frontis. only (Edgar A. Holloway), clo., 175x110mm. Platypus series. KMM

"Advance Australia" ABC

42 Mounted on Linen Untearable/"ADVANCE/AUSTRALIA"/AB/C/Ward Lock, Bowden & Co./London, New York Melbourne and Sydney
n.d. [copy inscribed 1893]
14pp, 6pp printed in col., others printed in green. Alphabet in verse inside front & back covers; letters, drawings & words on illus. pages, pic. wrappers, mounted on linen, 274x216mm. NSL:M

Advance Australia

43 ADVANCE AUSTRALIA/A Pageant of the Year
The Sanitarium Health/Food Company, 118 Union St, Prahran Victoria, n.d. [194-?]
16pp, 60 spaces left for cards printed in col. to be pasted in, wrappers with col. illus. of wartime Australians pasted on front covers, 210x282mm. KP

Adventure Series

Format example:

44 Book by Barker "Adventure" Series No. 1/THE/ZOO GARDEN/MYSTERY/[drawing]/A Fantasy
By John Tombs, publ. by "The House of Barker" 476–90 LIttle Lonsdale St, Melbourne and Sydney, [1948]
16pp, col. illus. throughout, col. pic. wrappers, cover title, 280x215mm. KMM
Uniform titles:

45 No. 2 THE STORY OF THOUGHT CASTLE by Elsie Sheppard. KMM

46 No. 3 EXCITEMENT ON ELF ISLAND by Elsie Sheppard. KMM

47 No. 4 FAIRY/GRANDMOTHER'S STORY by "Blossom Ballantyne" [illus. Jean Elder]. NSL:M

Adventure and Adventurers

48 ADVENTURE AND ADVENTURERS/Being/True Tales/Of/Daring, Peril, and Heroism/Selected by the Editor/of/'Recent Travel and Adventure;' 'Great

Thinkers and Workers;'/'Beneficent and Useful Lives;' Etc./W. & R. Chambers, Limited/London and Edinburgh/1895
288pp & 36pp adv., b/w frontis. & b/w engravings, dec. clo., 180x120mm. KMM
Contents include: The Ironclad Bushrangers (Ned Kelly's Gang) 15pp; A Secret of the Solomon Islands (Ben Boyd) 11pp; A Real Romance of the South Seas; or the Captivity of Herman Melville among the Cannibals of Nuka-hiva (in the Marquesas) 13pp.

The Adventure Book for Boys
49 THE/ADVENTURE BOOK/FOR BOYS/OPC Publication/Fun and Laughter Series A56
[12]pp, 6 col. & other b/w illus., col. pic. wrappers, 275x213mm. JH

Adventure in the Sky
50 ADVENTURE IN THE SKY/Edited by/The Nestlé Company (Australia) Ltd.
On verso of t.p.: 'Adventure in the sky is published by/The Nestlé Company (Australia) Ltd./in collaboration with Qantas Empire Airways Ltd.,/to whom the publishers are indebted for their/co-operation and assistance./Adventure in the Sky is produced by/Lawson Press Pty. Ltd. and/edited by C. S. Richardson'
Sydney, n.d. [1959?]
80pp (inc. 1p foreword), col. illus. to be collected & pasted in, b/w drawings, pic. bd., 275x210mm. KMM

Adventure on the Seven Seas
51 ADVENTURE ON/THE SEVEN SEAS/[drawing]/With Sixteen Full Colour Plates/The Sunshine Press/London and Glasgow
n.d. [Inscription in copy seen dated 1944]
63pp, col. frontis. & 15 f/p col. illus., 6 f/p b/w illus., diagrams & b/w drawings in text, clo., dec. e/p, 255x200mm. HBM
Contents include: 'The *Resolution* and Captain Cook', 'Bligh and the *Bounty*', 'Whaling in the Antarctic'.

Adventure Stories for Boys
52 ADVENTURE STORIES/FOR/BOYS/Adventure Stories for Boys 1949
Offset Printing Co Ltd. Melbourne, 1949
108pp, 1 f/p col. illus, 2 f/p b/w illus. & b/w photographic illus. & part col. drawings throughout, pic. bd., 265x210mm. KMM
Fiction and Fact.

Adventure Stories for Boys
53 ADVENTURE/STORIES FOR BOYS/[illus]/Printed at the Snelling Printing Works Pty Ltd, 52 Bay Street Broadway, Sydney/for the Offset Printing Coy Pty Ltd, 169 Phillip Street, Waterloo, Sydney[n.d.]
16pp, col. pic. wrappers, part col. illus. throughout, sgd'McGregor', 273x217mm. CLRC

Adventure Tales for Boys
54 ADVENTURE/TALES/FOR BOYS
Offset Printing Coy Syd. [194-?]
32pp, b/w & part col. illus. (Betty Lou James), pic. wrappers, 240x176mm. KP
Australian content includes 'A Hunting Adventure' by James Reeson, 'Ordeal by Water' by M. Love.

Adventures Ashore and Afloat
55 ADVENTURES/ASHORE AND AFLOAT./[vignette]/London:/Published at the "Leisure Hour" Office,/56, Paternoster Row, and 164, Piccadilly./Sold at Railway Stations and by the book sellers.
n.d. [1866]
288pp, engraved frontis. (of boat approaching a wreck) & 4 f/p engravings, dec. clo., 180x130mm. CLRC
Short stories, half of which have either an Australian background or describe incidents at sea on a voyage either to or from Australia.
56 [vignette]/ADVENTURES/ASHORE AND AFLOAT/[vignette]/London: The Religious Tract Society,/56 Paternoster Row, 65, St. Paul's Churchyard,/and 164, Piccadilly.
n.d. [1887]
383pp, engraved frontis. & 4 f/p b/w engravings, dec. clo. (with adv. on front & back e/p), 175x115mm. KMM
57 ADVENTURES/ASHORE AND AFLOAT/With Coloured illustrations by/W. B. Handforth/London/The Religious Tract Society/4 Bouverie Street & 65 St. Paul's Churchyard
n.d.
327pp, col. frontis. & 3 f/p col. illus., part. col. t.p., pic. clo., 200x135mm. KMM
58 ADVENTURES/ASHORE AND/AFLOAT/with fifteen full-page illustrations/London/The Religious Tract Society/4 Bouverie Street and 65 St. Paul's Churchyard
n.d.
333pp, 9pp adv., b/w frontis. & 14 f/p b/w illus., pic. clo., 200x135mm. Grant
Contents as for previous entry; advertisements describing 'The Brave Deeds Series', 'The Boys' Own Series', &c.

Adventures in Field, Flood and Forest
59 ADVENTURES/IN/FIELD, FLOOD, AND FOREST./Stories of danger and daring/Illustrated/[device]/London/Blackie & Son, Limited, 50 Old Bailey, E.C./Glasgow and Dublin
n.d. [1885]
256pp (inc. 1p preface) & 32pp adv., b/w frontis. & 3 f/p b/w illus., pic. clo, 175x115mm. MK
Contents include: 'The Bushrangers of Australia'; 'How an Irish Sailor became King of New Guinea'; &, 'An Incident of Savage Life in New Zealand'.
60 Another copy as above but imprint: 'London, Glasgow and Dublin', illus. Frank Feller, details as before. PR

The Adventures of "Bennie and BILLY" the Goat
61 The Adventures of "BENNIE/AND BILLY"/THE GOAT
Macarthur Press Pty Limited, 66 Macarthur St Parramatta
An "Uncle John" Book
[8]pp, printed throughout in blue with illus. on every page, col. pic. wrappers, cover title, 246x180mm. JH

The Adventures of Billy Whiz
62 THE/ADVENTURES OF/BILLY WHIZ
Photogravures Pty Ltd., n.d.
[12]pp (inc. covers), col. illus. throughout, col. pic. wrappers, cover title, 235x160mm. JH
Front cover illus. signed 'D. Taylor.'

The Adventures of "Chunder Loo"
See [O'Ferrall, Ernest]

The Adventures of Flip and Flap
63 THE ADVENTURES/OF/FLIP AND FLAP/[illus.]/Lutterworth Press/London and Redhill
n.d. [195-?]
16pp, part col. illus. throughout, pic. wrappers, cover title, 245x180mm. KP

As Penguins are found only in Antarctica this story should be set there. However, the text refers to the North Pole, polar bears &c, as well as penguins. The setting is certainly imaginary.

The Adventures of Tom Twist and Other Stories

64 THE ADVENTURES OF/TOM/TWIST/AND OTHER STORIES
[cover title]
Colourtone Pty Limited for Ayers & James Pty Ltd, Syd., n.d. [194-?]
16pp (inc. wrappers), 4pp printed in col., b/w illus. throughout, pic. wrappers, 175x236mm. CLRC

The Adventures of Wirra Wirra

65 Whitcombe's Story Books [No. 568]/THE ADVENTURES/OF/WIRRA WIRRA/(For ages 10 to 12 years)/[Drawing of an Aboriginal child]/Whitcombe and Tombs Pty. Ltd./Melbourne and Sydney
[1943]
64pp, b/w frontis. & b/w drawings in text, wrappers, 180x115mm. ANL
See McLaren 568

The Adventures of Woofy the Pup

66 THE ADVENTURES OF/WOOFY/THE PUP/[drawing]/A Pyramid Publication
Sydney 1947
16pp, illustrated by Mollie Quick, col. illus. throughout, dec. bd., 240x180mm. NSL:M

Adventures with Wool

67 ADVENTURES WITH WOOL/Published by the Australian Wool Bureau, 414–418 Collins St, Melbourne
n.d.
64pp, patterns & directions, b/w illus., dec. wrappers, 208x132mm. KP
Publ. "to keep in Training young children in the pleasure & satisfaction of working with wool."

68 Another copy with Wool Bureau's address amended to 578 Bourke St, Melbourne. KP

AESOP

THE DOVE AND THE ANT
THE WIND AND THE RAIN
See Blue Wren Books

69 Aesop/THE TORTOISE AND THE HARE/Illustrated by Douglas Annand
Melbourne 1950
43pp, col. & part. col. illus. throughout, dec. bd., dec. e/p, 195x165mm. Little Wonder Books. ANL

70 AESOP/Three of his Fables/Illustrated by Peter Bennett/[device]/Melbourne Technical College/1953
12pp, 4 part col. illus., pic. wrappers, t.p. printed in 2 col., 140x120mm. VSL

Against All Odds

71 AGAINST/ALL ODDS/[drawing]/John F. Shaw & Co., Ltd./4 & 5 Friar Street, Carter Lane, E.C.4
n.d.
[156]pp, col. frontis., 3 f/p col. illus. & b/w drawings in text, col. pic. bd., 240x180mm. MK
Collection of anonymous short stories of which the following three relate to Australia: 'Camel Trains', 'Midshipman's Apprentice', 'The Settler's Yarn'.

The Age of Speed

72 THE AGE OF SPEED/in three/sections/Land/Sea and Air A Series of 52 plates published by the Sanitarium Health Food Co.
Wahroonga NSW, n.d. [1950?]
16pp album with text & spaces left for col. cards to be pasted in, cover title, 135x210mm. WRT

AGUILAR, Grace M.

73 WOMAN'S POWER/A Children's Play in 2 Acts/and an Adult Play in 3 Acts/By/Grace M. Aguilar/Copyright in Australia and U.S.A./Wholly set up and printed in Australia for Grace M. Aguilar/Elizabeth Street, Brisbane, by The Carter Watson/Company, 65 Elizabeth Street, Brisbane
n.d. [1917]
32pp, unillus., wrappers, 220x95mm. NSL:M
The children's section of the book consists of an 8-page didactic play to promote the author's ideas on marriage, social evils, &c.

74 WHO IS OUR/FAIRY-/GODMOTHER?/A Story for Young and Old/By/Grace M. Aguilar
New Thought Centre, Sydney 1932
20pp (inc. 1p introduction & 1p addendum), unillus., wrappers, cover title, 210x135mm. ANL
A moral tale for children with an introduction by Willoughby Connor, president of the Hobart Metaphysical Society; addendum by Henry Aguilar.

The Airman Color Book

75 THE/AIRMAN/COLOR BOOK/[drawing]/An Australian Production by/No. 224 Gunn & Taylor Pty Ltd./Melbourne
n.d. [194-?]
16pp, b/w illus. throughout & 4pp in col., pic. wrappers, 277x212mm. KMM
Painting book depicting planes, personnel &c relating to RAAF.

AITCHINSON, C. V.

76 Whitcombe's Story Books/HOW THE BEARS/CAME TO BUSHLAND/And Other Stories/By/C. V. Aitchinson/Illustrated by Nancy Drake/For Children aged 7 to 8 years/[drawing]/Whitcombe & Tombs Pty. Ltd./Melbourne Sydney Perth
n.d. [1952]
31pp, b/w drawings, illus. wrappers, 180x115mm. ANL
Short stories & some verses.
See McLaren 256

AITKEN, Ian

77 ACTION/MAN/ANTARCTIC/EXPLORER/General Edition/Ian Aitken/Design and Illustration/Leslie Marshall, MSIA/Contents/[listed]/Brockhampton Press [col. illus.]
Leicester, Eng., 1971
32pp, col. illus. & diagrams, pic. wrappers, 240x160mm. KP

ALANSON, Alfred Godwin ['Russell Allanson']

78 TERRAWEENA/A Story of/A Mid-Winter Vacation in Australia/By/Russell Allanson/Illustrated by W. H. C. Groome/London/Wells Gardner, Darton & Co., Ltd./3, Paternoster Buildings
1905
105pp, 6pp adv., b/w frontis. & 3 f/p b/w illus., dec. bd., clo. spine, 190x125mm. Chatterbox Library Series. KMM
First published in serial form in 'Chatterbox', London, 1899, in 19 parts, with 20 f/p b/w illus.

79 TERRAWEENA/A story of/A Mid-winter Vacation in Australia/by/Russell Allanson/Illustrated by W. H. C. Groome/Boston/Dana Estes and Co.
Chatterbox Library, [1905?]
185pp & 1p adv., b/w frontis. & 3 f/p b/w illus., dec. clo., 187x120mm. ANL
Copy has different cover design from the English ed.

80 BEN HALYARD/A Story of Bass and Flinders./By/A. G. Alanson/Headmaster Randwick S. Public School/Sydney/Dymock's Book Arcade,/Educational Booksellers/428 George Street/1907
102pp, b/w frontis. by D. H. Souter, limp clo., 185x120mm. 'Australian Supplementary Reader' Series. KMM

81 THE DIGGERS OF/BLACK ROCK HILL/By/A. G. Alanson/Author of "Terraweena", etc./Illustrated by H. J. Rhodes/London/Wells Gardner, Darton & Co., Ltd./3 Paternoster Buildings, E.C./and 44, Victoria Street, S.W.
1908
186pp, b/w frontis. & 3 f/p b/w illus., pic. bd., 185x120mm. CLRC
On front cover: 'Chatterbox Library'.

82 THE DIGGERS OF BLACK ROCK HILL
As above, but with clo. cover dec. on spine & front and totally different from paper bds above. VSL

ALBERT, Marvin H.

83 THE/LONG/WHITE ROAD/Sir Ernest Shackleton's Antarctic Adventures/by Marvin H. Albert/Line illustrations by/Patricia Windrow/London/Lutterworth Press
1960 [First published by Van Rees Press, New York 1957]
175pp, map frontis. & b/w drawings, clo., 200x130mm. BBC

ALBERT, Max

84 Max Albert/ABENTEUER/IN AUSTRALIEN/UND ALASKA
Alfred H. Linde Verlag, Berlin 1948
127pp, 1p advt., illustrated by Willy Helwig, b/w drawings throughout, dec. map e/p, dec. bd., 210x150mm. NSL:M
The first 55 pages are of Australian subject matter.

ALBISTON, Barbara

See Craddock, Vaughan Alfred & Albiston, Barbara

ALDERSON, Helen

85 FOAMO/BUBBLO/By/Helen Alderson/Drawings by/Peggy Oldfield/Frank Johnson/350 George Street, Sydney
1942
48pp, b/w drawings throughout, bd., 240x190mm. ANL

86 LUCKY/ROLLING STONE/[drawing]/By/Helen Alderson/Illustrations by/Peggy Oldfield/Published by/Frank Johnson/350 George Street, Sydney/Tel: B.W. 6463
1944
46pp, col. frontis. & b/w drawings throughout, bd., 245x185mm. ANL

ALDERTON, Dick

87 KOKO/AND/KATIE/By/Dick/Alderton
Frank Johnson, Sydney 1944
12pp, b/w illus. throughout, wrappers, cover title, 275x200mm. ANL

88 LITTLE FOLK/STICK DOWN/BOOK/by Dick Alderton [cover title] No. 7
New Century Press Pty Ltd, Sydney 1950
[10]pp, col. illus. on alternate pp, pic. wrappers, 220x285mm. TG

Aldine Adventure Library

89 CAPTAIN LIGHTNING/A Tale of the Australian Bush/4d net/Aldine Adventure Library No. 6
n.d. [1927?]
[64]pp, unillus., pic. wrappers, cover title, adv. on back wrappers, 184x130mm. ANL
In same series & uniform with above:

90 THE LAST OF THE/BUSHRANGERS/By Reid Whitly/4d./net/[illus.]/Aldine Adventure Library No. 1. RM

The Aldine 'Boys' First Rate Pocket Library'

See HEMYING, Bracebridge

Aldine Romance of Invention, Travel & Adventure

91 The Aldine Romance of Invention; Travel & Adventure/Library/Jules Verne Outdone!!!/THE/ABANDONED/COUNTRY/[coloured illustration]/No. 139/[caption]/1d./London: Aldine Publishing Company, Limited
n.d.
32pp, unillus., col. pic. wrappers (with adv. verso front wrapper, verso/recto back wrapper), cover title, 205x135mm. RM
An extravaganza in which the young hero & friend sail for Antarctica in the hero's own invention, an electric ship. On landing, they not only find brown bears & animals resembling panthers inhabiting the continent, but a ruined & abandoned city as well! Truly, Jules Verne outdone!
Aldine Romances, listed on back wrapper of *The Abandoned Country:*
KANGAROO KIT, or, The Mysterious Miner (No. 182)
KANGAROO KIT'S RACQUET, or, The Pride of Played Out (No. 183)
Not Australian

92 The Aldine Romance of Invention, Travel, & Adventure/Library/Jules Verne Outdone!!!/JACK WRIGHT'S/PRAIRIE ENGINE/[coloured illustration]/AMONG/THE BUSHMEN/OF/AUSTRALIA/No. 218/[caption]/1d./London: Aldine Publishing Company, Limited
n.d. [advt. on inside front cover dated 1901]
32pp, unillus., col. pic. wrappers (adv. verso front wrapper, verso/recto back wrapper), cover title, 210x135mm. RM
See also ENTON, Harry

Aldine War Stories

93 RALSTON'S PENNY CRUISER by Reid Whitly—Aldine War Stories No. 20
62pp, pic. wrappers, cover title by Savile Lumley, 185x130mm. ANL

ALDOUS, Allan

94 McGOWAN CLIMBS/A MOUNTAIN/By/Allan Aldous/Illustrated by/Miguel Mackinlay/Geoffrey Cumberlege/Oxford University Press
London 1945
165pp, col. frontis., 3 f/p b/w drawings & 1 diagram, clo., 185x120mm. KP
• Rpt 1947, as above. KMM

95 McGOWAN CLIMBS/A MOUNTAIN/By/Allan Aldous/Illustrated by/Miguel Mackinlay/Geoffrey Cumberlege/Oxford University Press/Leighton House, Melbourne
1947 [first Australian edition]
191pp, 4 f/p b/w illus. & 1 diagram, bd., 180x120mm. KMM
French edition

96 Collection "Les Amis des Jeunes"/22/Allan Aldous/MacGOWAN/A/L'HIMALAYA/(MacGowan Climbs a Mountain)/Traduction de S. de Sechelles/Illustrations et Couverture de Th.-J. Delaye/B. Arthaud/Paris VI/6 Rue de Mézières/Grenoble/23 Grande-rue

254pp, col. frontis. & b/w illus. throughout, clo., 190x125mm. ANL

97 McGOWAN GOES TO/SEA/Allan Aldous/Illustrated by/Miguel Mackinlay/[device]/Oxford University Press/London New York Toronto
1945
154pp, col. frontis., 4 b/w illus., clo., 185x172mm. KP
• Rpt 1947, 1950, as above, but no frontis. KMM
98 First Australian edition 1947
192pp, 4 f/p b/w illus., bd., 185x120mm. KMM
German edition
99 Das ZeitungsBuch/Fur 80 pfg./Ein Vollständiges Buch von 244 Seiten Umfangi/UNTER SEGEL IN DER SÜDSEE/von A. Aldous/[chapter headings follow]/ 1948, Komet-Verlag (Wilhelm Hagemann) Düsseldorf
244pp, b/w illus. [as English edition], paper wrappers, stapled, 310x230mm. Unseen. IFA
Swedish edition
100 Allan Aldous/GARRY GAR TILL SJOSS/Illustrerad av Miguel Mackinlay/Stockholm/Natur och Kultur
1949
211pp, 4 f/p b/w illus., bd. (clo. spine), 190x120mm. Unseen. IFA
French edition
101 Collection "Les Amis des Jeunes"/27/Allan Aldous/ MacGOWAN/DANS LES/MERS DU SUD/ (MacGowan Goes to Sea)/Traduction de S. de Sechelles/Illustrations et couverture de Th.-J. Delaye/ B. Arthaud/Paris VI/6 Rue de Mézières/Grenoble/23 Grande Rue
1951
254pp, b/w illus. throughout, wrappers, 190x140mm. ANL

102 QUITTERS/CAN'T/WIN/by/Allan Aldous/F. W. Cheshire Pty. Ltd./Melbourne and London
1946
224pp, b/w frontis. & 7 b/w illus., illustrations signed 'Wiz', board, 185x120mm. ANL
Italian edition
103 Allan Aldous/FORSA RON!/Illustrazioni di A. Molinari/Genio S. A. Editrice Genio, Milan 1950
175pp, 4 f/p b/w illus., wrappers, 185x120mm. ANL

104 DANGER/ON THE MAP/By/Allan Aldous/Author of "Quitters can't win", "McGowan goes to/Sea" etc. etc./F. W. Cheshire Pty. Ltd./Melbourne and London
1947
219pp, b/w frontis. & b/w drawings throughout, illus. by Alan McCulloch, clo., 185x120mm. ANL
Italian edition
105 Allan Aldous/IL TESORO DELLA/TERRA DI ARNHEM/Illustrazioni di Roveroni/Genio
Milan 1950
173pp, 4 f/p b/w illus., illus. wrappers, 185x120mm. ANL
Translation by Enzo Peru.

106 McGOWAN GOES/MOTOR RACING/Allan Aldous/Illustrations by Norman Keene/Geoffrey Cumberlege/Oxford University Press/1947
London
184pp, b/w frontis. & 6 f/p b/w illus., clo., 180x120mm. ANL
107 McGOWAN GOES/MOTOR RACING/Allan Aldous/Illustrations by Norman Keene/Geoffrey Cumberlege/Oxford University Press/Leighton House, Melbourne/1949
191pp, b/w frontis. & 6 f/p b/w illus., bd., 180x120mm. CLRC

108 COLIN McKEE/ADVENTURER/By/Allan Aldous/ Geoffrey Cumberlege/Oxford University Press/ Leighton House, Melbourne
1948
155pp, unillus., bd., 180x120mm. KMM

109 COLIN McKEE/VOYAGER/By/Allan Aldous/ Geoffrey Cumberlege/Oxford University Press/ Leighton House, Melbourne
1948
144pp, unillus., bd., 180x120mm. CLRC

110 McGOWAN GOES FISHING/Allan Aldous/ Illustrated by/Harold Ing/Geoffrey Cumberlege/ Oxford University Press/1948
London
176pp, b/w frontis. & 5 f/p b/w illus., clo., 185x120mm. KMM
111 Australian ed. as above, but
Leighton House Melbourne/1949, KMM

112 McGOWAN GOES TO HENLEY/Illustrated by/ Hailstone/Geoffrey Cumberlege/Oxford University Press
London 1949
224pp, b/w frontis. & 4 f/p b/w illus., clo., 185x120mm. CLRC

113 KIEWA ADVENTURE/Allan Aldous/Geoffrey Cumberlege/Oxford University Press/London Melbourne New York
1950
192pp, 2 b/w maps, clo., 180x120mm. KMM

114 THE NEW/AUSTRALIANS/Allan Aldous/ Illustrated by/Selby Donnison/The Bodley Head/ London
1956
180pp, 8 f/p b/w illus., clo., 200x130mm. CLRC

115 THE TENDRILLS/IN AUSTRALIA/By/Allan Aldous/1959/Chatto and Windus/London
152pp, b/w frontis. map, clo., d/w by Geoffrey Brown, 185x120mm. CLRC
The setting is a Northern Territory cattle station.

116 DOCTOR/WITH/WINGS/Allan Aldous/Drawings by/Roger Payne/Brockhampton Press
London 1960
126pp, col. frontis., 2 b/w maps, 4 f/p line drawings & others in text, clo., 210x130mm. CLRC
• Rpt 1961. KP
3rd ed. 1964 b/w illus. only. KP
117 DOCTOR/WITH/WINGS/[drawing]/Allan Aldous/ Drawings by/Roger Payne/Criterion Books New York
1961
126pp, b/w frontis. map, 4 f/p b/w illus. & line drawings in text, clo., d/w by H. Lawrence Hoffman, 210x135mm. ANL

118 Allan Aldous/OLYMPIC KAYAK/illustrated by Barry Sutton/[extended frontispiece]/Brockhampton Press
Leicester, England, 1968
121pp, (inc. 3pp appendix), 2 b/w plans, b/w frontis. & 13 b/w drawings, bd., 215x135mm. KMM
Finnish edition
119 Allan Aldous/KUTSUKAA LANTÄVÄ LÄÄKÄRI/ Romaani/Helsingissä/Kustannusosakeyhtiö Otava
Helsinki 1962
171pp, unillus., bd., clo. spine, 180x120mm. Unseen. IFA

120 Allan Aldous/BUSHFIRE/Illustrated by Laszlo Acs/ Brockhampton Press
Leicester, England, 1967

120pp, b/w frontis. & b/w drawings in text, clo., 210x135mm. CLRC

ALDRIDGE, James

121 James Aldridge/THE FLYING 19/Illustrated by Raymond Briggs/Hamish Hamilton
London 1966
95pp, extended dec. t.p., b/w drawings in text, printed clo., 180x120mm. Antelope Book Series. BBC
Story about a flying bus.

ALEXANDER, Ruth

122 SEE-SAWS AND SWINGS/and/Other Children's Songs/by/Ruth Alexander/Illustrated by/Joan Turner/With a Foreword by Janet Mitchell/[device]/Georgian House/Melbourne/1948
31pp (inc. 1p foreword), b/w drawings, dec. wrappers, 280x215mm. ANL
Includes words & music of 25 songs.

ALFRED DUDLEY; or, The Australian Settlers

See [PORTER, Sarah (Ricardo)]

ALGER, Horatio Jnr

123 FACING THE WORLD/or, The Haps and Mishaps of Harry Vane/By/Horatio Alger, Jr./Author of "Risen from the Ranks", "The Store Boy",/"Adrift in New York", "The Cash Boy",/"The Young Outlaw" etc/[device]/The Mershon Company/Rahway, N.J. New York
n.d. [1900?]. First publ. 1893
268pp, unillus., pic. clo., 180x120mm. RM
Has only 2 pages set in Melbourne, telling of the adventures of 2 American boys, Harry Vane & his friend Jack, who while on a voyage round the world are shipwrecked on a desert island & picked up by a vessel bound for Melbourne. The sequel was publ. in many ed. in America under the title of *In a New World*, or *Harry Vane, or In a New World*, & in England as *The Nugget Finders*.

124 IN A NEW WORLD/or/Among the Gold-fields of Australia/By/Horatio Alger, Jr./Author of "Facing the World", "Do and/Dare", "Ragged Dick Series", "Luck/and Pluck Series", etc./[device]/Philadelphia/Porter & Coates
verso t.p. 1893
323pp, 8pp adv., b/w frontis., 2 f/p b/w illus., dec. clo., 185x125mm. RM
First appeared in *Golden Argosy* 1885; first publ. in book form 1893; first British ed. *The Nugget Finders* 1894.

125 Another ed. as above, pub. by The John C. Winston Co, Philadelphia, Chicago Toronto. RM

126 IN A NEW WORLD/or/Among the Goldfields of Australia/By Horatio Alger Jr./Author of ... [4 titles etc. etc.]/A. L. Burt Company, Publishers/New York
n.d. [1905?]
287pp, 10pp adv., b/w frontis. only, pic. clo., 182x130mm. RM

127 HARRY VANE/or/In a New World/By/Horatio Alger Jr./Author of/[8 titles follow]/[device]/New York/The New York Book Company/1910
168pp, 1p adv., b/w frontis. only, pic. clo., 175x120mm. RM

128 IN/A/NEW/WORLD/or Among the Goldfields/of Australia/by Horatio Alger Jr./Media Books/New York 1972
217pp, unillus., clo., 207x137mm. CLRC

129 THE NUGGET FINDERS/A Tale of the Gold Fields/of Australia by/H. Alger/London/John F. Shaw and Co./48 Paternoster Row
n.d.
224pp, b/w frontis. & 1 f/p b/w illus. by E. Fagan, clo., 180x125mm. AJH

130 THE NUGGET/FINDERS/A Tale of the Gold Fields/of Australia/By H. Alger/John F. Shaw & Co., Ltd.,/3, Pilgrim Street, London, E.C.
n.d. [awarded as school prize for the year 1908–9]
192pp, unillus., pic. clo., 180x120mm. RM
The oval vignette pasted on the front cover depicts two young men digging for gold, & is the same as the frontispiece entitled 'He struck, and lo! a yellow streak' used in one of the other copies.
Many copies with minor variation in binding & illus. were issued by this publisher who is said to have moved from 48 Paternoster Row to Pilgrim Street 1907–8. (Denis R. Rogers—*Dime Novel Round-Up* Vol. 41, No. 1, Jan. 1972)

ALLAN, Ella

131 DRESS YOUR DOLLY./In Knitting and/Crochet/By/Ella Allan/Copyright/Registered at the General Post Office, Melbourne for transmission/through the post as a book/1932/Wholly set up and printed in Australia by/The Specialty Press Pty Ltd, 174 Little Collins Street/Melbourne
32pp, b/w portrait of author frontis., b/w photographic illus., pic. wrappers, 184x125mm. KMM
Adv. inside & out of back cover.

ALLAN, Henry

132 THE/HAPPY FOREST/A Story Book for Boys and Girls/By/Henry Allan/Wholly set up & printed in Australia by Victory Publicity Pty. Ltd./262 Queen Street, Melbourne
1944
32pp, 8 f/p b/w illus. & many drawings in text, wrappers, cover title, 245x185mm. KMM
Story about Australian animals.

'ALLANSON, Russell'

See Alanson, Alfred Godwin

ALLEN, Gwenda

133 LINDY AND JAMES/IN LONDON/by/Gwenda Allen/Illustrated by Evelyn Clouston/[publisher's device]/Angus and Robertson
Sydney 1961
48pp, 16 b/w drawings in text, pic. bd., 235x155mm. KMM
The 'Lindy and James' stories were originally published in the *School Journal* of the New Zealand Department of Education.

134 The Lansdowne Readers/MARCO DISCOVERS/AUSTRALIA/Grade Three/Book 2
Whitcombe & Tombs Pty Ltd, Melbourne, n.d. [196-?]
32pp, part. col. illus. throughout, illus. by Marjorie Howden, pic. wrappers, cover title, 210x135mm. KMM

ALLEN, James

135 HISTORY/OF/AUSTRALIA,/from/1787 to 1882,/By James Allen/Melbourne:/Mason, Firth & M'Cutcheon,/51 & 53 Flinders Lane West./MDCCCLXXXII 1882
320pp, unillus., clo., 180x120mm. CLRC
Not really children's.

ALLEN, L. H.

136 BILLY-BUBBLES/Child Songs/By/L. H. Allen/Sometime Senior Lecturer in English/The Teachers' College, Sydney/Professor of English, Royal Military/College. Duntroon
n.d. [1920 pencilled on cover]
Publisher not named, but W. A. Pepperday & Co.,

Printers, 119a Pitt Street, Sydney, appears in one line at the foot of p. 32.
32pp, unillus., wrappers, cover title, 180x120mm. Grant

137 BILLY-BUBBLES/Child Songs/By/L. H. Allen/ Sometime Senior Lecturer in English/The Teachers' College, Sydney/Professor of English, Royal Military/ College. Duntroon./Sydney/Angus & Robertson Ltd./ W. A. Pepperday & Co., Pitt Street, Sydney.
n.d. [1924]
48pp, unillus., wrappers, cover title, 180x120mm. KMM
Another copy, identical apart from the imprint on front cover as follows:
Published by/Teachers' College Press/Sydney N.S.W. KMM

Allied Bomber and Fighter Aircraft of Today

138 ALLIED/BOMBER AND/FIGHTER/Aircraft Of Today/[illus. of plane]/All designed in Colour
Offset Printing Coy, Sydney, n.d.
16pp, 8 f/p col. illus., b/w diagrams, pic. wrappers, 180x240mm. KP

The Allied Forces Cut-Out Book Air Force Army Navy

139 THE ALLIED FORCES/CUT-OUT BOOK/AIR FORCE ARMY NAVY
Offset Printing Co., Sydney, n.d. [194-?]
16pp. Book printed in col. on one side of pp only on light bd. so that figures & objects can be cut out and stood up. Col. pic. cover, cover title, 250x365mm. JH

140 LOTS OF FUN CUT OUT BOOK FOR BOYS AND GIRLS
Uniform with above. Noah's Ark, Animals, Trains, Dolls. JH

"The Allies"

141 "THE ALLIES"/Children's Drawing Book/Issued by the Proprietors of/Nestle's Infants Foods/By Appointment to H.M. the King/Head Office for Australasia 347 Kent Street, Sydney/Branches [2 lines] Price One Shilling
n.d. [1916?]
14pp, 6 col. illus., wrappers, 216x377mm. MAC
The date is prior to 1917 as the US is not included among the Allies. Each Ally [i.e. Britain, France, Belgium, Russia, Servia, Italy] is represented with a col. illus. of a soldier with the text, in English, of the national anthem on the opposite page. The illus. are initialled H.J.W. and are by H. J. Weston.

ALLINSON, A. A. & HOTCHIN, F. E.

142 14–16: A Reading Guide/BIOGRAPHY AND/ AUTOBIOGRAPHY/F. W. Cheshire Melbourne Canberra Sydney
1969
42pp, 10 b/w illus. by Elizabeth Howell, stiff dec. wrappers, 195x125mm. BBC

143 14–16: A Reading Guide/WAR/A. A. Allinson and F. E. Hotchin/F. W. Cheshire Melbourne Canberra Sydney
1969
39pp, 10 f/p b/w illus., illus. by Jonathan Howell, stiff dec. wrappers, 195x125mm. BBC
Other books in series (listed in above vols).

144 ADVENTURE
145 MYSTERY AND CRIME
146 RACE AND PREJUDICE
147 S.F.
148 TRAVEL AND EXPLORATION
149 WILD LIFE
150 THE WORLD THROUGH THE EYES OF YOUTH

ALLSOPP, F. J. & HUNT, O. W. (ed.)

151 THE SPIRIT OF MAN/A Book of Adventure/ Selected and edited by/F. J. Allsopp and O. W. Hunt/ Angus and Robertson
Sydney 1959
145pp, b/w chapter headings, clo., 195x120mm. BBC
Extracts include 'Adventures on the Murray' from *Who Rides on the River* by J. K. Ewers; & from P. G. Taylor's *Frigate Bird*, Shackleton's *South*, &c.

152 School ed. as above, limp clo., 1960. KP

'Alouette'

153 RIPPARD,/THE OUTLAW./By/Alouette,/Author of "Jules Gerard, the Lion Killer."/New York:/M. J. Ivers & Co.,/86 Nassau Street.
n.d.
76pp, b/w frontis. & 2 f/p b/w illus. [E. A. H. Westock], col. pic. wrappers, 185x120mm. CLRC
Convict story set in Van Diemen's Land of escaped convict, Aborigines &c.

Alpha and Omega

154 ALPHA AND OMEGA/A Biblical Play/Compiled and arranged by/Geelong Church of England Grammar School/Corio [Victoria]
n.d., printed in Geelong. Preface dated 1936
96pp (inc. 2pp preface), b/w photographic frontis., clo., 182x124mm. KP

An Alphabet

155 AN ALPHABET/Being a Book of/Designs and Rhymes/By Students of the/Applied Art School/ Working Men's College/Melbourne—MCMXXXII 1932
56pp, b/w illus., dec. cover, dec. e/p, 280x220mm. Grant
Printed at the Working Men's College. Each letter followed by a few lines of verse; e/p dec. with names of artists.

Alphabet Book, with bright coloured pages

See Gunn & Taylor

ALSOP, Johanne

156 [drawing]/NUNEE/by Johanne Alsop/An Aboriginal folk story, full of mythological beings and strange happenings
Vacuum Oil Company, Melbourne 1952
44pp, frontis. photograph & biographical note on author, b/w drawings, illus. by author, wrappers, 180x210mm. NSL:M

157 3rd printing, n.d. "With the compliments of the Vacuum Oil Company Pty Ltd . . . Marketers of Plume Motor Spirit &c". KMM

158 4th printing, n.d.
Variant inscriptions (Mobilgas, Mobiloil, &c.) on back page, otherwise as above. KP

ALSOP, Marion & McCRAE, Dorothy Francis [Mrs C. E. Perry]

159 SOME/CHILDREN'S/SONGS/By/Marion Alsop &/Dorothy Frances McCrae/Designed by/Edith Alsop/George Robertson & Company/Proprietary Ltd./Melbourne, Sydney, Adelaide, Brisbane./Printed in Scotland.
n.d. [1910]
20pp, 5 f/p col. illus., clo., 340x300mm. NSL:M
Contents include: 'Paddling Song', 'The Jackass', 'Bubbles', 'Song of the Water-Babes', 'The Rebel'.
Published in variant bindings (paper, clo., & leather) *see* advt. in the *Argus* 12/11/1909.

AMADIO, Nadine

160 THE MAGIC SHELL/Photographed and Written by/ Nadine Amadio/[photograph] Ure Smith—Sydney
1958

64pp, b/w photographic illus. throughout, dec. bd., dec. e/p, 280x210mm. KMM
Story, told mostly in picture form, of a country boy's first visit to Sydney & the beach.

161 AMANDA/AND THE/DACHSHUND/[photograph]/Photographed and Written by/Nadine Amadio/Published by/E. N. Thorne—Sydney
1965
[32]pp, b/w photographic illus. throughout, pic. bd., 260x180mm. CLRC

162 JAMIE'S ADVENTURES/IN THE/LAND OF MUSIC/Photographed and Written/by/Nadine Amadio
Published by E. N. Thorne, Sydney, n.d. [1965?]
[32]pp, photographic illus. throughout, pic. bd., pic. e/p, 260x185mm. CLRC

'Amanda'
163 [drawing]/TOMMY'S/TEDDY/BEARS,/A Story for the Two and Three Year Olds,/Written by Amanda/Illustrated by Mosgar
McNiven Bros Ltd, Sydney, n.d. [194-?]
[20]pp, 10 f/p col. illus., stiff pic. wrappers, 180x236mm. KMM
Printed by Northwood Print, Camperdown, NSW for McNiven Bros Ltd, Manufacturers of Pure Ice Cream.

The Amazing Adventures of Anthony Arrowroot
164 THE AMAZING/ADVENTURES/OF ANTHONY/ARROWROOT./[drawing]
Publ. for William Arnott Ltd by Publicity Studios, 3 Castlereagh St, Sydney
n.d. [1930]
32pp, col. frontis. & 1 f/p col. illus. & b/w drawings, wrappers, 247x185mm. KMM
165 THE AMAZING ADVENTURES/OF ANTHONY ARROWROOT./[drawing]
Published in Australia for William Arnott Pty. Ltd., Homebush, N.S.W. by Marchant & Co. Pty. Ltd., Printers, Sydney
n.d. [194-?]
32pp, b/w frontis. & 1 f/p b/w illus., b/w drawings throughout, wrappers, 215x140mm. KMM
An advertisement for the well-known firm of biscuit manufacturers.
166 Facsimile of first ed.(1930)
n.d. [1960?]. Grant

AMBLER, C. Gifford?
167 OLD MAN/HODGE/HE HAD A FARM/[illus.]/By C. Ambler/A CMC Production/wholly set up. printed and bound in Australia for/Consolidated Merchandising Co. 325 Bourke Street, Melbourne
n.d. [1947]
24pp col. illus., pic. bds, 233x180mm. KP

AMESS, James
168 Whitcombe's Story Books/TOM FINCHAM/The boy who sailed with Flinders and Bass/By James Amess/For ages 11 to 13 years./[device]/Whitcombe & Tombs Limited/Auckland, Christchurch, Dunedin, Wellington, N.S.W/Melbourne, Sydney and London
n.d. [192-?]
97pp, 6pp notes, 1p advt., b/w frontis. & 6 f/p b/w illus. by M. Napier Waller, 2 b/w reproductions of portraits, pic. wrappers, 180x110mm. HBM
See McLaren 626

Among the Islands
AMONG THE ISLANDS: Life in the Pacific Isles
The 'British Empire' Library No. 9
See LEFT ASHORE, OR LIFE AT CORAL CREEK

AMOS, Peter
169 JOLLY JO JUMBO/and his Friends 6d./A Trunk Load of Mischief/Published by NSW Bookstall Co, Castlereagh St, and printed by Publicity Press (1938) Pty Ltd, 71–75 Regent St., Sydney
28pp, b/w drawings throughout, pic. wrappers, cover title, 210x270mm. KP
Illus. by Brodie Mack.

ANCELON, Douglas
See Pedley, Ethel C.

ANDERSON, Alan
170 This thrilling Route/ENGLAND TO AUSTRALIA/By BOAC Constellation/by Alan Anderson/Brockhampton Press. Leicester
n.d. [195-?]
64pp (last adv.), b/w photographic illus. on alternate pages, col. pic. bd., 80x140mm. RC

ANDERSON, Ellery
171 EXPEDITION/SOUTH/by/Ellery Anderson/Cadet Edition/[device]/London/Evans Brothers Limited
1960
192pp, (inc. 1p foreword), b/w photographic frontis. & 8pp b/w photographic illus., b/w map, clo., 195x125mm. KMM
The account of an exploring & survey expedition to the Falkland Islands Dependencies in 1954–55.

ANDERSON, Florence S.
172 DRAMATIZED FAIRY TALES/AND/NURSERY RHYMES/Set to Music/By/Florence S. Anderson/Copyright/Hutchinson's Bookshop Pty. Ltd./174 Little Collins Street Melbourne
1928
32pp, wrappers, 180x115mm. NSL:M

ANDERSON, Hugh
173 AN OUTLINE OF/AUSTRALIAN HISTORY/Book One/Hugh Anderson//London/Macmillan & Co. Ltd./1958
58pp, 3pp glossary, b/w maps & illus. in text, wrappers, 205x165mm. BBC
174 Book Two, 1960, 74pp. KP
175 Book Three, 1960, 62pp. KP
All school histories.

AUSTRALIAN INDUSTRIES SERIES. 16 titles in series. Format example:
176 Australian Industries Series/FRUIT/AND IRRIGATION/by/Hugh Anderson/Illustrated by/Daryl Teschendorf/[drawing]/Lothian Publishing Company Pty Ltd/Melbourne Sydney
1970 [1st publ. 1964,1967, rev. 1968]
55pp (inc. 3pp index), b/w drawings in text, stiff pic. wrappers, 215x140mm. CLRC
Also author of a series of 16pp booklets on THE WHEAT INDUSTRY
Macmillan, Melb., 1968. KP

ANDERSON, John
177 Picture Story Books/A TRIP IN A/CAR/By/John Anderson/Geoffrey Cumberlege/Oxford University Press/Leighton House, Melbourne
n.d. [194-?]
22pp, 4 f/p col. illus., b/w illus. in text, pic. wrappers, 274x214mm. TG
One of a number of books by this author first publ. in London & rpt in Melbourne during WW2 & of no Australian interest.

ANDERSON, Lois
178 FLASHTAIL
The Specialty Press, 174 Little Collins St., Melbourne, n.d.

[16]pp, col. illus. throughout, pic. wrappers, cover title 295x246mm. KP

ANDERSON, Marjorie
179 BUCKETTY/[drawing]/By Marjorie Anderson
Angus & Robertson, Sydney 1953
30pp, 7 f/p col. illus. (inc. 1 double spread), b/w drawings wrappers, cover title, 150x115mm. NSL:M

ANDERSON, Maybanke [Mrs Francis Anderson née Wolstenholme]
180 AUSTRALIAN/SONGS FOR/AUSTRALIAN/CHILDREN/By Maybanke Anderson/Angus & Robertson/Sydney and Melbourne.
1902
16pp, unillus., pic. wrappers, 280x220mm. NSL:M
Contents: 'Australia Fair', 'The Gum Tree', 'The Waving Lucerne', 'The Bonnie Orange Tree', 'Sweet Bush Flowers', 'The Little Grey Bandicoot', 'The Possum'. Music accompanies each verse.
Also the author of *Mother Lore*, on the upbringing & education of children.

ANDREWS, Jane
181 GEOGRAPHICAL PLAYS/By/Jane Andrews/Author of Seven Little Sisters, Each and All/Australia and the islands/Boston/Lee and Shepard Publishers/New York Charles T. Dillingham/1881
22pp (inc. preface & directions), unillus., wrappers, 180x125mm. MAC

ANDREWS, John
THE SECRET OF THE REEF. *See* Boys' Friend Library

182 THE JOLLY/PETS/John/Andrews
Dunvegan Publications, Box 4614, Sydney
18pp (inc. 8pp f/p col. illus.) & b/w illus., stiff pic. wrappers, cover title, 244x180mm. KP

183 WHAT MAKES IT GO/No. 1/John/Andrews
Dunvegan Junior Library
Dunvegan Publications, Box 4614, Sydney
[16]pp (inc. 8 f/p col. illus., b/w drawings in text, text printed inside both wrappers, stiff pic. wrappers, 170x240mm. KP

ANDREWS, Ron
184 GRANDFATHER AND THE/BUSHRANGERS/Ron Andrews, B.A., B.Sc. (Gen. Sc.)/School Projects Pty. Ltd.
Sydney 1965
40pp, b/w frontis. extending on to t.p., map & 8 b/w illus. in text, stiff pic. wrappers, 210x130mm. KMM
Stories of Ned Kelly, Ben Hall, & other Australian bushrangers.

ANDRIESSE, Nancy
185 THE HOUSE OF LITTLE CATS/By/Nancy Andriesse/Illustrated by Mary Robinson/Printed and Published in Australia by/Cheviot Printers/Copyright, etc. [6 lines]
Collaroy, N.S.W., n.d. [1971?]
[24]pp, b/w illus. on alternate pages, dec. wrappers, 230x175mm. NSL:M

ANDRIST, Ralph K.
186 [device]/A/Cassell/Caravel/Book/HEROES OF POLAR/EXPLORATION/By the Editors of/Horizon Magazine/Author/Ralph K. Andrist/In consultation with Rear Admiral George J. Dufek, U.S.N. (Ret.)/Director, The Mariners Museum, Newport News, Virginia/[woodcut illustration]/Cassell—London/Copyright 1962 by American Heritage Publishing Co. Inc. 551 Fifth Avenue, New York 17./New York. All rights reserved under Berne and Pan-American Copyright Conventions./First published in Great Britain in 1963
152pp (inc. 1p foreword by George J. Dufek, 1p acknowledgements & notes, 2pp index), col. frontis. & 49 col. illus. & maps, b/w photographic & other illus. in text throughout, col. dec. clo., col. map e/p, 255x175mm. BBC
About half the book deals with the history of Antarctica.

ANGWIN, Aldyth
187 GABSY/the Little White Kitten/by/Aldyth Angwin/illustrated by/Douglas Maxted/[device]/George G. Harrap & Co. Ltd./London Toronto Wellington Sydney 1960
80pp, b/w drawings in text, clo., 190x135mm. MD
Also Rigby, Adelaide 1961, as above.

Animal Alphabet Book
188 ANIMAL/ALPHABET/ BOOK
Printed by Arbuckle, Waddell Pty. Ltd, Melbourne, for Bushells Ltd, Sydney, n.d. [copyright 1918]
16pp, inc. 4pp col. illus., pic. bd., 245x180mm. NSL:M
The book was produced as an advertisement & consists of an alphabet with a drawing of an animal & a rhymed couplet illustrating each letter. Cover reads: A to Z Animals'.

Animal Alphabet Book
189 ANIMAL ALPHABET BOOK
Presented/To/[blank line]/From/[blank line]/Published by/Gordon & Gotch Pty Ltd./Melbourne, Sydney, Brisbane, Adelaide, Perth./Launceston & New York
n.d. [192-?]
[20]pp (inc. covers), 4 col. plates & drawings in text throughout, pic. bd., t.p. verso front cover, printed throughout in blue, 2 drawings & verses to each p. VSL

Animal Antics
190 ANIMAL ANTICS
Photogravure Pty Ltd. [Melbourne], n.d.
[12]pp (inc. covers), col. illus. throughout, pic. wrappers, cover title, printed on light bd. (stiffened paper), 240x175mm. KP

Animal Frolics
191 ANIMAL FROLICS
Photogravure Pty Ltd, Melbourne, n.d.
[8]pp, col. illus. throughout, col. pic. wrappers, cover title, 295x180mm. Grant
Contains rhymes & illus. which begin verso front cover & end recto back cover.

Animal Fun
192 ANIMAL FUN
ANIMAL FUN, Fun Series No. 2
Uniform booklets published by Barker & Co. Ltd, Melbourne 1942
8pp, col. illus. throughout dec. wrappers, cover title, 285x215mm. NSL:M
193 Another copy as above, but
16pp, part col. illus., 284x216mm. CLRC

The Animal Kingdom
194 THE/ANIMAL/KINGDOM/[device] Paul Hamlyn/London New York Sydney Toronto
1971
61pp & 2pp index, b/w photographs through, pic. e/p, col. pic. bd., 246x175mm. KP
Book prepared for The Nestlé Company (Australia) Ltd with spaces provided for col. project cards to be pasted in.

Animal Life
195 ANIMAL LIFE/Pictures for Little Children/An/OPC/Untearable/Book
[Offset Printing Coy, Sydney], n.d. [194-?]
8pp, f/p col. illus., printed on bd. with spirax bdg, 270x205mm. KP
Illus. signed 'Percival.' (1p kangaroos, 1p koalas.)

Animal Pets
196 ANIMAL PETS [cover title]
No author, no place, n.d. [copy inscribed 1949]
[10]pp, col. illus. on every page & on front & back covers, 236x180mm. TG
Two lines of text on each page; one illustration shows an Australian scene.

Animals of the World
197 ANIMALS/OF THE WORLD/Album & Story/[drawing]/The story of animals of all countries written/especially for Australian boys and girls by/a famous naturalist—and providing spaces/for the 64 beautifully coloured picture cards/issued in packets of Weeties, Vita-Brits and/Crispies
no place, n.d.
12pp, spaces for cards to be pasted in, pic. wrappers, cover title, 280x217mm. CLRC

Animals of the World
198 ANIMALS/OF THE WORLD/Nestlé Collectors Series
Nestlé Company (Australia) Limited, n.d.
48pp, b/w drawings & text on each page with space for cards to be pasted in, stiff col. pic. wrappers & col. illus. inside front & back covers, 247x210mm. KP

Ann and Donald's Trip to Bunnyland
199 ANN AND DONALD'S TRIP TO BUNNYLAND
Pantheon Publications, Melbourne, n.d. [1950?]
16pp, col. illus., col. pic. bd., cover title, 275x215mm. Grant
See also [GRIEVE, David]—*The Magic Egg*

Annie Carr
could be earlier →
200 ANNIE CARR/A Tale of Both Hemispheres/By the Author of 'Adventures in the South Pacific'/With Three Illustrations by/Raymond Potter/[device]/London/The Religious Tract Society/4 Bouverie Street and 65 St Paul's Churchyard, E.C.
n.d. [school prize 1903]
245pp & 10pp adv., b/w frontis. & 2 f/p b/w plates, red clo., dec. in gilt, 185x120mm. KMM
201 ANNIE CARR./A Tale of Both Hemispheres/By the author of/"Adventures in the South Pacific"/With coloured illustrations/London/The Religious Tract Society/4 Bouverie Street and 65 St. Paul's Churchyard/E.C.
n.d.
245pp (inc. 4pp introduction), 10pp adv., frontis. & 1 col. illus. by Francis C. Hiley, clo. (col. medallion on front cover), 190x120mm. KMM
Another copy, variant bdg of plain clo. KP

Antarctica
202 ANTARCTICA/Drawing/Science Program
Nelson Doubleday Inc & Odhams Books, 1968. Printed in USA
64pp, b/w photographs & part col. drawings throughout, 4pp col. photographs to be pasted in, pic. wrappers, 208x140mm. KP

A.N.Z. Savings Bank Fun Book
203 A.N.Z./SAVINGS/BANK/FUN/BOOK
no place,n.d. (presumably prior to 1966 as money is mentioned in pounds)
[12]pp (inc. covers), col. & b/w illus. throughout, pic. bd., cover title, 175x190mm. VMOU

APSLEY, Lord
204 Historical Biographies/(Empire Series)/No. 2./AUSTRALIA/[col. illus. "Australia's Emblem: The Golden Wattle"] Edited by Lord Apsley, D.S.O., M.C., M.P./Foreword by The Marquess of Salisbury, G.C.V.O., K.G./"If" by Rudyard Kipling/Price Sixpence/Published by The British Empire Educational Press Limited, 180 Mansion/House Chambers, London, E.C.
n.d. [1927]
40pp (inc. 1p introduction, 1p foreword), b/w illus. throughout, dec. wrappers, cover title, 225x140mm. KP
Biographies written for "girls and boys of from 12 to 18".

ARIA, George
205 THE "ARIA"/KIDS/[on col. background illus.]/From the Comic Kids series by "Aria" appearing in/The Australian/Woman's Mirror/Wholly set up and printed in Australia by Messrs. Waite & Bull, 81 Campbell Street, Sydney/for the Bulletin Newspaper Co. Ltd., 252 George Street, Sydney./Registered by the Postmaster-General for transmission through the post as a book. Price 1/-
n.d. [1934]
24pp (inc. 2pp introduction & 1p cut-out model of Kingsford-Smith's Altair aircraft), col. comic strip cartoons throughout, col. pic. wrappers, cover title, 310x260mm. RM
Strip printed in b/w on yellow panel.

ARMITAGE, Hazel
206 KEN AND JOYCE IN SEARCH/OF THE/KING KANGAROO
Published by the Amalgamated Press Ltd, The Fleetway House, London, n.d. [195-?]
64pp, 1 b/w chapter heading, pic. wrappers (with adv.), dec. cover title, 180x140mm. The Schoolgirls' Own Library No. 236. KMM

ARMOUR, R. Coutts
Wrote boys books under various pseudonyms, inc. 'Brisbane, Coutts', 'Whitly, Reid', & 'Whitly, Brett'.

ARMSTRONG, Richard
207 THE DISCOVERERS/By Richard Armstrong/[doublespread b/w illus.]/Ernest Benn Limited—London
1968
Vol. 2 in "A History of Seafaring"
Maps & drawings by Ivan Lapper
128pp (inc. 4pp index), 14 b/w maps & b/w illus. in text, clo., 247x185mm. KMM
Includes chapter The Circumnavigators—Magellan, Drake; and Terra Incognita Australis (17pp inc. Dampier and Cook).
Also author of The Mutineers [1968], of only slight Australian interest, about a group of boys emigrating to Australia under a training scheme.

ARNEGUY, Michèle
208 COMPAGNONS/DE LA TERRE ADÉLIE/Delagrave
Paris 1967
138pp, part. col. frontis., part. col. illus. throughout, pic. bd., pic. e/p, 205x170mm. NSL:M
Story set in Antarctica after beginning in Hobart.

[ARNHIM, Countess Mary Annette von]
209 THE/APRIL BABY'S BOOK OF TUNES/With/The

Story of How they came to be written/By the author of/'Elizabeth and her German Garden'/Illustrated by Kate Greenaway/London/Macmillan and Co., Limited/New York: The Macmillan Company/ 1900/All rights reserved
77pp, col. frontis. & 15 col. illus., clo., 180x190mm. NSL:M
Countess von Arnhim, née Beauchamp, a cousin of Katherine Mansfield, was born in Sydney; she later married the second Earl Russell.

ARNOLD, George
See Henri, René & Arnold, George

ARNOLD, Malcolm
OFF TO AUSTRALIA. *See* The Boys' Friend Library

ARONSTEN, Joan
210 Mullens' Plays for Children/No. 2/MRS. KIND RABBIT/And Five Other Playlets for Children/7 to 8 years old/by/Joan Aronsten/Wholly set up and Printed in Australia. Registered at the/G.P.O. Melbourne, for transmission by post as a book/ Robertson & Mullens Ltd./Melbourne.
n.d. [1952]
52pp, b/w frontis. & 6 b/w chapter headings, wrappers, 180x115mm. ANL

211 JOLLY/THE POLAR BEAR/By/Joan Aronsten/ Illustrated by/Florence Warburton/Angus and Robertson/Sydney London Melbourne Wellington/ 1957
14pp, part. col. illus. throughout, stiff wrappers, 250x190mm. KMM

212 CHARLEY/THE/CONCRETE-MIXER/by/Joan Aronsten/Illustrated by/Adye Adams/Music by Dulcie Holland/Angus and Robertson/Sydney London Melbourne Wellington
n.d.
[16]pp, part. col. illus. throughout, stiff dec. wrappers, 240x180mm. KMM
Text includes music of two songs.

Around Australia Program
Format example:
213 AUSTRALIA'S/ISLAND/TERRITORIES/[drawing printed in 2 cols.]/Ronald Rose/Around Australia Program
Nelson Doubleday (Australia) Pty. Ltd, Lane Cove, NSW, 1967
64pp b/w & part col. photographic & other illus, 22 col. illus pasted in, dec. wrappers, 210x140mm. WRT
Others in series:
214 AUSTRALIA AND ANTARCTICA, by John Bechervaise, 1967. KP
215 THE AUSTRALIAN ABORIGINES, by A .P. Elkin, 1966. KMM
216 AUSTRALIAN LIGHTHOUSES, by Capt. John Noble, 1967. KMM
217 AUSTRALIAN MOUNTAINS AND RIVERS, by John Bechervaise, 1968. KMM
218 AUSTRALIAN PLANT LIFE, by Thistle Harris, 1966. KP
219 AUSTRALIAN RAILWAYS, by C. C. Singleton, 1967. KP
220 AUSTRALIAN WILD LIFE, by A. H. Chisholm, 1966. KP
221 BRISBANE, by Clem Lack, 1967. KMM
222 COMMERCIAL AVIATION, by Stanley Brogden, 1967. KMM
223 ELECTRIC POWER, by Allen Crawford, 1968. KP
224 THE GREAT BARRIER REEF, by Jim Thomson, 1966. KMM
225 HOBART, by Michael Sharland, 1967. KMM
226 THE NORTHERN TERRITORY, by Ronald Rose, 1966. KMM
227 PAPUA AND NEW GUINEA, by Ronald Rose, 1966. KMM
228 QUEENSLAND, by Clem Lack, 1966. KMM
229 THE SNOWY MOUNTAINS SCHEME, by B. N. Pratt, 1966. KMM
230 SOUTH AUSTRALIA, by Elizabeth Johnswood, 1967, KMM
231 STEEL FOR AUSTRALIA, by Derek Sawer, 1967. KMM
232 TASMANIA, by Michael Sharland, 1966. KMM
233 WESTERN AUSTRALIA, by William King, 1967. KMM

Around the Farm
234 AROUND THE/FARM/series B3
Printed & publ. by Offset Pty Coy P.L., Sydney, n.d. [194-?]
16pp (inc. covers), col. illus. throughout, wrappers, cover title, 262x215mm. KMM
Pictures with caption to each page.

ASCOTT, John
BOOMERANG BOB. *See* Boys' Friend Library

ASHMORE, Jane [pseud. C. E. Little]
235 BETSY/By/Jane Ashmore/Ward Lock & Co. Limited/London and Melbourne/1927
320pp, unillus., clo., 180x115mm. ANL

ASHTON, Helen [née Willis]
236 "THE KING'S COLONISTS"./A Little Play for Little Australians./By/Helen Ashton/[List of characters] William Brooks & Co. Ltd, Sydney, n.d. [1910?]
20pp, 9 b/w drawings in text, (sgd 'H.A.) pic. wrappers, 285x225mm. KMM
Play written mainly in verse, with music of 7 songs included.

At the Circus with Johnny, Jane and Jason
237 AT THE/CIRCUS/WITH JOHNNY, JANE AND JASON
238 AT THE/ZOO/WITH JOHNNY, JANE AND JASON
239 IN THE OUTBACK/A JOHNNY, JANE AND JASON BOOK
240 ON THE FARM/A JOHNNY, JANE AND JASON BOOK
Uniform booklets published by Frank E. Cork, Adelaide, n.d. [1944]
16pp, col. & b/w illus. throughout, illus. by Trevor Clare, wrappers, cover title, 240x180mm. ANL

At the Seaside
241 AT THE SEASIDE
Georgian House, Melbourne, n.d. [1944]
18pp, 8 f/p col. illus. & line drawings in text, pic. wrappers, cover title, 240x195mm. ANL
Coloured illustrations signed 'J.H.'
Also published as a board picture book with 8 plates only. KMM

At the Zoo
242 AT/THE ZOO/Meet/Jimmie/Queenie/and Co.
n.d., printed in Australia (J.T.K. copyright) by Renwick Pride, Melb.
8pp, b/w illus. & text, col. pic. wrappers, 258x185mm. KP
Kangaroos & kookaburra depicted in one illus. & koalas in another.

ATKINS, Charles
243 AUSTRALIA/AND/THE GREAT WAR/Told to/ Australian Children/[contents]/Presented to the

Scholars of the State Schools of the Albert Ward,/ Melbourne to commemorate Peace/By/Cr. Capt. Charles Atkins,/Melbourne:/Rennie & Pelzer, Printers, 341 Queen Street./1919
14pp, unillus., wrappers, 215x140mm. Grant
Title repeated on cover with sketch of soldier.

ATKINSON, R. C. Everitt
244 HYGIENE JINGLES/By/R. C. Everitt Atkinson, M.A., M.D., D.P.H./Commissioner of Public Health/ Western Australia/Published by Hospital Electrical & Radium Ltd./British Medical Association Building/ Hindmarsh Square/Adelaide/1924
48pp (inc. 1p preface), unillus., clo., 180x120mm. KMM
245 2nd ed. as above, but /[vignette]/Brown, Prior & Co. Pty. Ltd./Printcraft House, Melbourne/1926
52pp, 1p preface, 31 b/w drawings, dec. bd. with linen backstrip, dec. e/p, 250x190mm.
Author's preface & foreword by W. S. Littlejohn, M.A. (Aberdeen), Principal of Scotch College, Melbourne, loosely inserted. A deluxe illus. ed. with marginal drawings throughout & a 'health barometer' printed in red & black. KMM
246 HYGIENE JINGLES/by/R. C. Everitt Atkinson, M.A., M.D., D.P.H./Commissioner of Public Health/ Western Australia/[vignette]/Brown Prior & Co. Pty. Ltd./Printcraft House, Melbourne/1926
54pp, illus. wrappers, 180x115mm. KMM

AUCHMUTY, J. J.
JOHN HUNTER. *See* Great Australians

AUDEBRAND, Philibert
247 UN PETIT-FILS/DE ROBINSON/Par/Philibert Audebrand/Illustrations/de G. Fath et Freeman/ [vignette]/Paris/Théodore Lefèvre Libraire-Éditeur/ Successeur de J. Langlumé./Rue des Poitevins, 2 [1864?]
364pp (inc. 4pp index), engraved frontis. & 19 f/p engraved plates, chapter headings & end pieces, 1/2 leather, gilt title on spine & g.e., 238x154mm. ANL

'Auntie Muriel'
See Levy, Muriel

AUSTEN, Ina L.
248 Mothers' Perplexity Series—No. 1/HOW ALYCE WAS/TOLD AT SIX/By Ina L. Austen/[quotation]/ Copyrighted/Wholly set up and printed in Australia at/The Snelling Printing Works, 130 Sussex Street, Sydney
n.d. [1915]
30pp (inc. 1p preface by Mrs Harrison Lee Cowie & 1p introduction), 1p adv., b/w photographic frontis. & 3 b/w photographic illus.., bd., 175x115mm. NSL:M

249 Mothers' Perplexity Series—No. 2/WHAT ALYCE LEARNT/AT NINE/By Ina L. Austen/[two quotations]/Copyrighted/Wholly set up and printed in Australia at/The Snelling Printing Works, 130 Sussex Street, Sydney
n.d. [1915]
30pp (inc. 1p introduction, 1p preface & 1p dedication), b/w photographic frontis. & 3 f/p b/w illus.., bd., 175x115mm. NSL:M

250 Mothers' Perplexity Series—No. 3/ALYCE ON THE/THRESHOLD/By Ina L. Austen/[two quotations]/Copyrighted/Wholly set up and printed in Australia at/The Snelling Printing Works, 130 Sussex Street, Sydney
n.d. [1915]
32pp (inc. 1p introduction & 1p verse), b/w photographic frontis. & 2 b/w illus.., bd., 175x115mm. NSL:M

251 Mothers' Perplexity Series—No. 4/ALYCE IN THE/ COUNTRY OF TEENS/By Ina L. Austen/[two quotations]/Copyrighted/Wholly set up and printed in Australia at/The Snelling Printing Works, 130 Sussex Street, Sydney
n.d. [1915]
31pp (inc. 1p preface & 1p verse), 1p adv., b/w photographic frontis. & 3 f/p b/w illus.., bd., 175x115mm. NSL:M
The above four booklets are an attempt to teach a girl something about sex in a story form.

AUSTIN, A. G.
THE AUSTRALIAN SCHOOL. *See* Australian Landmarks

AUSTIN, Florence
252 THE WONDERFUL FAIR/A Play for Girls and Boys/by/Florence Austin/[verse]/Adelaide: The Hassell Press/1941
16pp, unillus., wrappers, 215x140mm. KMM
Partly verse.

AUSTIN, Ianel
253 FOUR/ABORIGINAL PLAYS/for/Fourth Grade/By Ianel Austin/Shakespeare Head Press/Sydney 1956
62pp, unillus., wrappers, 180x120mm. ANL
Contents: *Doolook and the Bunyip, One Good Deed, Salt on his Tail, Bush Picnic.*

Australia
254 AUSTRALIA/[drawing]/Around the World Program Nelson Doubleday Inc & Odhams Books Inc 1971, printed in U.S.A.
64pp, b/w photographic & part col. drawings & col. paste-in photographs, pic. wrappers, 210x140mm. KP
On front cover—American Geographical Society/ Australia.

Australia at Work
Format example:
255 Australia at work/OUR SUGAR/By/Helen G. Palmer, B.A.(hons), Dip.Ed./Longmans Green & Co./ London Melbourne New York
1949
64pp, b/w photographic illus. & diagrams, maps &c, wrappers (copy seen re-bound), 214x164mm. CLRC
In same series:
256 OUR COAL, by A. G. L. Shaw. Unseen
257 OUR FOOD, by Marjorie Coppel. CLRC
258 OUR IRON AND STEEL, by Mollie Bayne. Unseen

Australia Discovered The Voyages of Captain James Cook RN
259 AUSTRALIA/DISCOVERED/THE/VOYAGES OF/ Captain James Cook RN./1770–1970/[10 lines text]/ CBC/The Commercial Banking Company of Sydney Limited/C.B.C. Savings Bank Limited
1970
46pp, b/w portrait frontis. of Cook, col. & b/w illus. throughout, col. pic. bd. covers, 215x137mm. KP

Australia Past and Present
Series of booklets for school libraries & general reading.
Format example:
260 Australia Past and Present/General Editor: Geoffrey Atkinson/SOME AUSTRALIAN HOUSES/by Jean Chapman/Illustrated by Noela Young/Wentworth Books/Sydney 1969/[device]
32pp (last blank), marginal b/w drawings, stiff pic. wrappers, 215x162mm. KMM

Other titles in series:
261 THE BLUE MOUNTAINS CROSSING, by John Kennedy, illus. Anne Pickering, 1969. NSL:M
262 THE GREAT SOUTH LAND, by Eve Pownall, illus. Christine Shaw, 1969. BBC
263 JAMES COOK. by George Finkel, illus. Ammon Sadubon, 1969. CLRC
264 JAMES RUSE, by Jean Chapman, illus. Christine Shaw, 1969. BBC
265 SUN, WIND AND CORAL; AUSTRALIA'S GREAT BARRIER REEF, by Jean Chapman, illus. Billy Robinson, 1972, 28pp. CLRC

Australia views Her Past
266 AUSTRALIA/VIEWS HER PAST/A Commonwealth Jubilee Pageant/Commonwealth Office of Education [1951]
1p acknowledgements & 54pp diagrams, wrappers, 205x130mm. MAC

Australia Yesterday and Today
267 AUSTRALIA/YESTERDAY/AND TODAY/A Pictorial Album/for Every Boy and Girl
Sanitarium Health Food Co., Sydney 1949
[12]pp, 50 col. pictures [to be collected & pasted in appropriate spaces in text], wrappers, cover title, 280x215mm. KMM

The Australian A.B.C. Book
268 THE/AUSTRALIAN/A.B.C./BOOK/Published by Valentine and Sons Ltd, Melbourne
Atlas Press Pty. Ltd, Melbourne, n.d. [copyright 1918]
16pp [also printed inside front & back covers], col. illus. throughout, dec. bd., dec. cover title, 180x260mm. Marlborough Series. NSL:M
Simple verses.

Australian ABC
269 AUSTRALIAN/ABC
Photogravure Pty. Ltd, Melbourne n.d. [194-?]
16pp, col. illus. throughout, stiff wrappers, cover title, 240x180mm.
A 4-line verse accompanies each letter. KMM
Many undated variants.

The Australian Aboriginal's First Book
270 THE AUSTRALIAN/ABORIGINAL'S/FIRST BOOK
Issued by the Dept of Native Affairs Brisbane; Printed by A. H. Tucker, Government Printer Brisbane, n.d. (copy inscribed Dec. 1948)
26pp & 2pp note for teachers, b/w illus. throughout, pic. wrappers, 125x180mm. VMOU
See also MACKENZIE, G. The FIRST AUSTRALIANS' FIRST BOOK, which appears to be a revised edition.

Australian Aborigines
271 AUSTRALIAN ABORIGINES/Our Book Corner Second Shelf
W. & R. Chambers Ltd, Edinburgh 1961
16pp, 7 f/p col. illus. & 2 b/w drawings, illus. by Sally Michel, stiff dec. wrappers, cover title, 150x120mm. NSL:M
Contains mostly pictures with slight text.

Australian Alphabet Book
272 AUSTRALIAN ALPHABET BOOK/Illustrated by/ Emilie Beuth/[coloured illustration]/Australia is a land of unusual/animals and birds, most of/which are found nowhere/else in the world./Readabout Books.
Readabout Publishers Pty. Ltd, Crow's Nest, N.S.W. 1964
16pp, col. illus., stiff wrappers, 205x175mm. BBC
Illustrations of Australian animals, birds & plants with brief description to represent each letter of the alphabet.

The Australian Alphabet of Natural History
273 THE AUSTRALIAN ALPHABET OF NATURAL HISTORY
26 illus., sixpence plain, one shilling col.
Advertised on back of *Cowanda and the Veteran's Grant* Sydney J. R. Clarke 1859 and (with 26 engravings) on *Peter Possum's Portfolio* Sydney, J. R. Clarke, 1858.
Unseen

Australian Animals
274 AUSTRALIAN/ANIMALS/[illus. & word 'Koala']
Bancroft Books London, 1971, copyright Novalit Pty Ltd., [Melb.]
6pp, col. illus. & caption on each page, cover title, 240x160mm. KMM
Rag book.

The Australian Babes in the Wood
See [Fry, Sarah Maria]

Australian Birds ABC Book
275 AUSTRALIAN/BIRDS/[Illus.]/ABC/Book
'Australian Birds A.B.C. Picture Book, as illustrated. A large-size book [12½ x 9¾ inches, i.e. 320x250mm] printed in six colours throughout. Alphabet set to rhyme, with typical Australian illustrations all in full colour. Retail 1/6 per copy. *Booksellers Stationers & Fancy Goods Journal* 10/9/31 adv. (Gordon & Gotch).
Unseen

Australian Boys' Adventure Library
A series of paperback boys' stories published by Alexander McCubbin & printed by J. Roy Stevens, Melbourne, n.d. [191-?]. Most are anonymous & not all have been seen, & whether they were all actually published is also unknown.
Format example:
276 [front cover] Australian Boys Adventure Library/ THE SECRET/OF MURRIGAN'S No.9 [cover illus. of a man being throttled] THE SECRET OF MURRIGAN'S A Thrilling Story of School-boys and Hidden/Gold in the Australian Bush/[device]/By R. S. Jackson
62pp, 11pp blank, 1p adv., headpiece & 2 maps, pic. wrappers, 208x155mm. KMM
Imprint on back cover & list of other titles in series (not known if all were actually published)
277 1. THE VEILED RIDDLE OF THE PLAINS, unseen
278 2. THE GREAT ROUND UP, unseen
279 3. ADVENTURES ON THE GOLD RIDGE. uniform with above, ANL
280 4. OUTWITTING THE SPIES, unseen
281 5. THE HEROES OF THE H.M.S. "HEROIC" (No Australian references. Story of 2 English boys who enlist in the RN). Uniform with above, ANL
282 6. LIFE AMONG THE GOLDEN GRAIN, unseen
283 7. THE SECRET OF THE SUBMARINE, unseen
284 8. THE "SPITFIRE" AND THE SPIES, unseen
285 10. A YEAR AT SUNBURY COLLEGE, uniform with above, MAC
286 11. THE PRAIRIE BOYS, unseen
287 12. THE WILD RIDERS OF TEXAS by O. W. Tavon, no t.p., but uniform with others. RM

The Australian Broadcasting Coy's Childrens Hour
288 THE AUSTRALIAN BROADCASTING COY'S/ CHILDRENS HOUR/[part col. illus.]/Issued by/The Australian/Broadcasting/Company Ltd.,/Supplying the National/Broadcasting Service for/The Commonwealth/Government of Australia/2/-
Sydney, n.d. [adv. inside back cover dated 1930]

64pp, b/w drawings, photographs &c, pic. wrappers, cover title, 250x184mm. CLRC
Contains articles on programs, photographs of presentation of different sessions, stories, adv. &c. Cover design by Jack Earl.

Australian Christmas Plays and Sketches
289 AUSTRALIAN/CHRISTMAS PLAYS/AND SKETCHES/The Clifford Press/Melbourne Victoria Australia 3122
n.d.
44pp, unillus., wrappers, 210x140mm. MAC

Australian Chronicle
290 AUSTRALIAN CHRONICLE/A miniature newspaper of Australia's first 200 years/prepared as a souvenir of Captain Cook's discovery of Australia/Vol. 1 1861–1870 No. 9
Sanitarium Health Food Coy, Sydney, 1969
Publ. for SHFC by W. C. Penfold & Co. Pty Ltd.
8pp, printed in brown on stiff buff col. paper, drawings throughout, 178x117mm. CLRC

Australian Commemorative Stamps
291 AUSTRALIAN/COMMEMORATIVE/STAMPS/[drawing]/Bank of New South Wales
Sydney, April 1955; 2nd ed. (revised) March 1956; 3rd ed. (revised) May 1958; 4th ed. (revised) November 1959; 5th ed. (revised) June 1961
26pp, (inc. 2pp glossary), wrappers, cover title, 245x155mm. KMM
Includes descriptions & illustrations of 57 Australian commemorative stamps from 1927 to the present.
• Rpt 1962. KP
292 AUSTRALIAN/COMMEMORATIVE/STAMPS/[drawing]/The Wales/Bank of New South Wales
Sydney, 8th ed. (revised) July 1965
32pp (inc. 2pp glossary), b/w illus. throughout, illus. wrappers, 240x122mm. KMM
Describes & illustrates 72 commemorative stamps.

Australian Explorers
A series of booklets of from 30 to 32 pp
Format example:
293 Australian Explorers/LUDWIG LEICHHARDT/Renee Erdos/Melbourne/Oxford University Press/London Wellington New York.
1963
33pp, b/w illus, map in text, stiff illus. wrappers, 194x124mm. KMM
Others in series:
294 ANTARCTICA, by J. M. Béchervaise, 1959. KP
295 AUGUSTUS CHARLES GREGORY, by W. Birman & G. Bolton, 1972. KP
296 TASMAN, by C. M. H. Clark, 1959, rpt 1969. KP
297 JOHN OXLEY, by E. Dunlop, 1960. HBM
298 THOMAS MITCHELL, by L. Gardiner, 1962. ANL
299 ERNEST GILES, by L. Green, 1963. KMM
300 GREGORY BLAXLAND, by V. Hyde, 1958, rpt 1969. KP
301 NEW GUINEA, by R. Joyce, 1960. KP
302 CAPTAIN CHARLES STURT, by D. Kennedy, 1958, rpt 1967. KMM
303 MATTHEW FLINDERS & GEORGE BASS, by D. Mattingley, 1961. KMM
304 JOHN FORREST, by D. Mossenson, 1960. KP
305 JOHN McDOUALL STUART, by D. Pike, 1958, rpt 1969. KP
306 HAMILTON HUME & WILLIAM HOVELL, by J. Prest, 1963. KMM
307 JAMES COOK, by R. Rienits, 1969. KP
308 EDWARD JOHN EYRE, by M. Uren, 1964. KP

Australian Explorers
309 Cottees Present/5 cents/AUSTRALIAN EXPLORERS
Cottees Foods Ltd., n.d., n.p., The Cottees General Food Companies
16pp, decorations and text relative to explorers with 20 spaces left for cards to be pasted in, pic. wrappers, cover title, 180x230mm. KP

Australian Explorers and Pioneers
310 AUSTRALIAN/EXPLORERS/AND/PIONEERS/Illustrated by Dagmar Dawson/[drawing]/Paul Hamlyn/London New York Sydney Toronto/Published by Paul Hamlyn Pty Ltd 176 South Creek Road,/Dee Why West, New South Wales 2099/Copyright Paul Hamlyn Pty Ltd 1969 [2 lines]
32pp, b/w illus. [to be col.] with slight text, col. pic. wrappers, 295x215mm. KP

The Australian Fairy Tale of the Three Koala Bears and Little Goldilocks
311 THE AUSTRALIAN/FAIRY TALE/OF THE/THREE KOALA BEARS/AND/LITTLE GOLDILOCKS/Illustrated by/Actual Photographs/taken by Cinesound Productions Ltd./Australia
Printed by John Sands, Sydney, n.d. [1930]
24pp, illus. t.p., photographic illus. throughout, pic. bd., 288x224mm. KMM
Text and illus. printed in green.

Australian Heroes and Adventurers
See PYKE, W. T.

Australian Junior Red Cross First Aid Primer
312 AUSTRALIAN JUNIOR RED CROSS/ FIRST AID PRIMER/'Fourth Impression 1955'/[device]
F. W. Niven Pty Ltd, Printers Flinders st Melb.
100pp, b/w diagrams & part col. illus., 176x12mm. KP
As above, 1957 ed. KP
As above, 1964 ed.
No place, details as above. KP
313 Australian Junior Red Cross/FIRST AID MANUAL/1968 Edition/[Red Cross]/The Australian Red Cross Society/122 Flinders Street, Melbourne, 3000
114pp, part col. illus. throughout, pic. wrappers, 182x120mm. KP

Australian Landmarks
A series of booklets based on Australian social history, for schools & general reading.
Format example:
314 Australian Landmarks/Edited by Renee Erdos/ENTER THE SQUATTER/by/Jill Ker/Illustrated by/Iris Millington/[device]/Longmans
Melbourne, 1961
62pp, b/w drawings in text, stiff pic. wrappers, 215x140mm. KMM
Others in series:
315 THE ABORIGINAL AUSTRALIANS, by A. P. Elkin, illus. Pamela Johnston, 1962, 56pp. NSL:M
316 THE AUSTRALIAN BROADCASTING COMMISSION, by T. Fehlberg, illus. Don Angus, 1964, 63pp. KMM
317 THE AUSTRALIAN LIBERAL PARTY, by K. West, illus. Frank Pash, 1968, 64pp. VMOU
318 THE AUSTRALIAN SCHOOL, by A .C. Austin, illus. Jill Mounsey, 1966, 61pp. KMM
319 THE AUSTRALIAN SUGAR INDUSTRY, by E. G. Docker, illus. Jill Mounsey, 1966, 64pp. KP
320 AUSTRALIA'S FIRST ARCHITECT, FRANCIS GREENWAY, by M. Barnard, illus. Iris Millington, 1961, 64pp. KP
321 ENTER THE MERCHANT, by D. A. Macmillan, illus. Camilla Watt, 1961, 54pp. KP

322 EXPLORING THE AIR, by S. Brogden, illus. Jolanda Calkoen, 1961, 63pp. KMM
323 FENCING AUSTRALIA, by H .G. Palmer, illus. Pamela Johnston, 1961, 63pp. KP
324 IRON AND STEEL, by D. A. Macmillan, illus. William Mahony, 1964, 55pp. KMM
325 SQUATTER AND SELECTOR AT TONGALA, by H. W. Forster, illus. Leslie Stack, 1964, 47pp. KMM
326 THE SYDNEY GAZETTE, by R. Erdos, illus. Sylvia Parrett, 1961, 64pp. KMM
327 TALL SHIPS AND STEAMBOATS, by D. A. Macmillan, illus. Sylvia Parrett, 1961, 56pp. KP
328 W. G. SPENCE & THE RISE OF THE TRADE UNIONS, by H .G. Palmer and J. MacLeod, illus. William Mahony, 1964, 56pp. KP

Australian Men of Stamina
See MEN OF STAMINA

'An Australian Mother'
See [Mrs Frances Lettice Smith]

Australian Nursery Rimes [*sic*]
329 AUSTRALIAN/NURSERY RIMES/Selected from/ The Bulletin/for the/Children's Hospital
[12]pp, 6pp full col., 2pp sepia & others b/w, pic. linen wrappers, cover title, 185x162mm. ANL
Col. cover illus. H. J. Weston, Col. illus. by D. H. Souter, M. G. N. (Muriel Nicholls), "Low" (David Low), Harry J. Weston, Norman Lindsay. Sepia, N. Lindsay, D. H. Souter, B. E. Minns, b/w Percy Leason (2) & text drawings D. H. Souter.

Australian People Series
Format example:
330 Australian People 17/THE DROVER/Gerald Williams
Longmans, Melbourne, 1963
16pp, b/w & part col. illus. throughout, stiff pic. wrappers, cover title, 145x115mm
Illus. Iris Millington (series illustrator). KMM
Others in series (1–16, 1963; 17–24, 1965):
331 1. THE LIFE SAVERS, by N. Shelley. KP
332 2. DRIVERS & TRAINS, by M. Fatchen. KP
333 3. THE POSTMAN, by N. Shelley. KP
334 4. THE BAKER, by N. Shelley. KP
335 5. KEEPERS & LIGHTHOUSES, by M. Fatchen. KP
336 6. THE MILKMAN, by J. Redshaw. KP
337 7. THE DENTIST, by N. Shelley. KP
338 8. BALLET DANCERS, by J. Redshaw. KP
339 9. THE FLYING DOCTOR, by N. Shelley. KP
340 10. THE PLUMBER, by M. Fatchen. KP
341 11. THE BLACK TRACKER, by N. Shelley. VSL
342 12. THE ELECTRICIAN, by M. Fatchen. KP
343 13. THE NURSE, by J. Redshaw. KP
344 14. THE FORESTER, by G. Williams. KP
345 15. PILOT & AIRHOSTESS, by J. Redshaw. KP
346 16. THE CORRESPONDENCE SCHOOL, by N. Shelley. VMOU
347 18. THE COAL MINER, by J. Redshaw. KP
348 19. THE BUS CREW, by M. Mead. KP
349 20. TRAWLERS & FISHERMEN, by N. Shelley. KP
350 21. THE TRANSPORT DRIVER, by M. Fatchen. KP
351 22. THE CARPENTER, by M. Fatchen. KP
352 23. THE FARMER, by M. Fatchen. KP
353 24. THE SHEARER, by N. Shelley. VMOU

Australian Plays and Sketches
354 AUSTRALIAN/PLAYS AND SKETCHES/No. 2/The Clifford Press/Melbourne, Victoria, Australia
n.d.
46pp, contains 8 plays, wrappers, 215x135mm. KP
Stories for all ages for Church & Sunday School use. *See* Griffith, Florence L. for first book in series.

Australian Scrapbook
355 AUSTRALIAN/SCRAPBOOK/Paul Hamlyn/ London/Sydney/New York/Toronto
1971
[56]pp, col. & part. col. reproductions from early prints pic. bd., 275x195mm. CLRC

Australian Sugar
356 AUSTRALIAN/SUGAR 1969/Published by The Colonial Sugar Refining Company Limited on behalf of the Australian Sugar Industry/[col. illus.]/[3 lines text] Printed by Halstead Press, Sydney
14pp, col. photographic illus. throughout, pic. wrappers, 240x180mm. KP
357 Published by The Colonial Sugar Refining Company Limited on behalf of the/Australian Sugar Industry. Distributed free on request. Printed by Halstead Press, Sydney/AUSTRALIAN SUGAR 1972 [illus.] [long caption]
16pp, col. photographic illus. throughout, pic. wrappers, 175x240mm. KP

Australian Territories Today
358 AUSTRALIAN/TERRITORIES/TODAY/Published by the Department of Territories and issued under the Authority of the Minister for Territories the Hon. C. E. Barnes, M.P.
Canberra, n.d. [1970?]
32pp, b/w photographic illus. on frontis., t.p. & in text, pic. wrappers (with b/w maps verso/recto back cover), 205x255mm. CLRC

Australian Underwater World
359 AUSTRALIAN/UNDERWATER/WORLD/a 1964 Sanitarium album
Sanitarium Health Food Company NSW
12pp, spaces for pasting in cards, col. pic. wrappers, cover title, 240x180mm. KP

The Australian Uncle
360 THE/AUSTRALIAN UNCLE;/or,/Help in Time of Need/[quotation]/Gall & Inglis/Edinburgh:/Bernard Terrace/London:/25 Paternoster Sqr.
n.d. [1873]
64pp, col. lithographic frontis., repeated as col. onlay on front cover, dec. clo., 140x90mm. KMM
Evangelical tale of well-to-do English family who are left penniless & orphaned, & their rescue from poverty by the unexpected return of the uncle who has made good in Australia.
361 Another copy as above with dec. clo. bdg. Grant Author's initials appear to be "J.C.O." from t.p. of another contemporary book.

Australian Verse for Children
362 AUSTRALIAN VERSE/FOR/CHILDREN/Wholly set up and printed in Australia. Registered at the/ General Post Office, Melbourne, for transmission by post as a book/J. J. Gourley, Government Printer, Melbourne.
n.d. [foreword dated 9 May 1946]
101pp (inc. 1p foreword), 47 b/w drawings, clo., 210x130mm. KMM
Illustrated by Pixie O'Harris, & others; foreword by J. A. Seitz.

The Australian Wonder Book
See Gunn, Jeannie

The Australian Wonder Book of Knowledge
Vols 1 & 2. *See* Blanche, Horace (ed.)

Australian Youth Plays
All publ. Angus and Robertson, 1948.
Format example:
363 Australian Youth Plays/General Editor;/Leslie Rees, B.A./THE KOOKABURRA WHO/COULDN'T LAUGH/A Comedy by/Peter Batten/Junior Series No. 1/Angus and Robertson/Sydney London/1948
21pp, unillus., wrappers, 185x120mm. ANL (as all other titles)
Others in series:
364 THE HAPPY REVOLUTION, by H. T. M. Middleton (Senior Series No. 1).
365 THE LION-TAMER, by H. Drake-Brockman (Senior Series No. 5).
366 THE MAN WITH THE MONEY (Adapted by Leslie Rees from Phillip Abson's radio play—Leave it to George) (Senior Series No. 4).
367 OVER THE RANGES, by M. Dalton (Junior Series No. 4).
368 PRESENTED WITHOUT COURTESY, by 'M. Morell' (Senior Series No. 2).
369 THE SQUEAKING POWDER—A Fairy Play in Verse, by E. Pearson (Junior Series No. 3).
370 THREE BAD BOYS, by M. Hewitt (Junior Series No. 2).
371 THE UNINVITED GUEST, by R. Park (Junior Series No. 7).
372 VENDETTA, by B. Garde (Senior Series No. 3).
373 WAIT TILL WE GROW UP, by C. Rees (Junior Series No. 5).

Australians
374 AUSTRALIANS
n.p., n.d. 'Printed by Photogravures'[*sic*] on back cover
[16]pp, col. illus. throughout, pic. wrappers, cover title, 175x240mm. KMM
Drawings in col. of Australian animals & birds with name of animal &c printed below.
Several widely different variants seen. KP, KMM

L'Australie
375 L'AUSTRALIE/Découverte—Colonisation—Civilisation/Troisième Edition/Revue et Corrigée/[device]/Tours/Ad Mame et Cie, Imprimeurs-Libraires/MDCCCLXI 1861
236pp (inc. 6pp table), b/w frontis. only, dec. clo., 211x130mm. RM
Appears to be a general book for children & not a school textbook, being elegantly bound in royal blue grained cloth with decorations in gilt on front cover & spine.

Australia's Animal Wealth
376 Nabisco/AUSTRALIA'S/ANIMAL WEALTH/A Rural Industry Project/25 cents A Vita-Brits Project Card Series/Registered trade mark of/National Biscuit company
Nabisco Pty Ltd, Melbourne, n.d.
24pp (inc. 2pp text & doublespread map), spaces left for cards to be pasted in, col. pic. card wrappers, cover title, 235x185mm. KP

Australia's Dollars and Cents
377 AUSTRALIA'S/DOLLARS AND CENTS/[14 lines text]/Published by the Reserve Bank of Australia/September/1968
Ambassador Press, Sydney
[20]pp, col. illus. throughout, col. pic. wrappers, 240x180mm. KP

AUVRAY, Michel
378 UN HÉRITAGE/EN/AUSTRALIE/par/Michel Auvray/[monogram]/Limoges/F. F. Ardant Frères/Avenue du Midi, 7./Paris/F. F. Ardant Frères/Quai du Marché-Neuf, 4.
n.d. [1879]
128pp, engraved frontis., dec. bd., 197x120mm. ANL

AVERY, Harold
379 "NO SURRENDER!"/The Story of Captain Scott's/Journey to the South Pole/By/Harold Avery/With photographs by/Capt. Scott and H. G. Ponting/[2 line quotation]/Thomas Nelson and Sons Ltd./London Edinburgh New York Toronto Paris
First publ. Sept. 1933; rpt. 1934, 1936, 1937, 1947
viiipp, 253pp & 2pp adv., b/w photographic frontis. & 9 b/w plates, clo. (copy re-bound), 197x127mm. CLRC

AYREY, Jane
380 MEET ME AT FIVE/by/Jane Ayrey/aged/5/F. W. Cheshire Pty. Ltd, Melbourne/1946
40pp, b/w illus. throughout, illus. by author, bd., 170x200mm. ANL
Verses.

AYSCOUGH, A. L.
381 THE STORY OF/ALLIE THE CROCODILE/A Few Pages of Laughter/for Youths and Adults/(Copyright)/By A. L. Ayscough/Illustrations by Geo. W. Dickinson/Melbourne 1931
51pp, b/w drawings, wrappers, 200x140mm. NSL:M
382 THE STORY OF/ALLIE THE CROCODILE/A Few Pages of Laughter/for Youths and Adults/(Copyright)/(Second Edition)/By A. L. Ayscough./Illustrations by Geo. W. Dickinson
On back page: 'Wholly set up and Printed in Australia by Hickling & Powell, 48 Lygon St., East Brunswick, N.11' [Victoria], n.d.
51pp, 7 b/w drawings in text, dec. wrappers, 215x155mm. KMM
On front cover: 'Net proceeds of sale in aid of Melbourne Hospital'.

'B, A. A. and Helumac'
383 AUSTRALIAN WONDERLAND/A Fairy Chain/By/A. A. B. and Helumac/Illustrated by Louise M. Glazier/London/Ward, Lock and Co., Limited/New York and Melbourne/All rights reserved/1899
75pp, 4pp adv., b/w frontis. & 6 f/p b/w illus. & b/w drawings in text, clo., 240x180mm. KMM
A fantasy of a boy's adventures in the bush.

'B, L. F. P.'
384 BILLY AND BOBBIE/A Story for children/Written by/L.F.P.B./Brighton
Brighton, S.A., n.d. [1948]
13pp, line drawings, wrappers, 170x180mm. CLRC

'B, M. A.'
385 MONA DESMOND/and other Stories/By/M. A. B./The Catholic Depot/Pellegrini & Co./Catholic Furnishers, Catholic Booksellers/543 George St. Sydney/244 Elizabeth St. Melbourne
n.d. [192-?]
110pp, clo., 190x120mm. VSL

'B. S. A.'
See [Booth, S. A.]

Baby Animal Pets
386 BABY ANIMAL PETS
Offset Publishing Co., Sydney, 1948
8pp, col. illus. throughout, printed on bd., spirax bdg, 270x215mm. NSL:M
Brief rhyming text to each page, subject matter not Australian.

Baby Animals
387 BABY ANIMALS/OPC/Series E6
Printed and Published by Offset Printing Coy Pty Ltd, 169 Phillip St, Waterloo Sydney, n.d. [194-?]
16pp, inc. 8pp printed in col., sepia illus. throughout, pic. wrappers, 266x215mm. KMM
Adv. on back wrapper: Jolly Zoo Book; Jolly Farm Book; Baby Animal Pets, &c.

Baby's Album
388 BABY'S ALBUM [cover title]
A BOOK/FOR YOU/AND BABY
Published by Nestlé, n.d.
22pp, col. illus. throughout, stiff pic. wrappers, 200x240mm. KMM
389 Another copy, illus. of baby koalas on p1 & kangaroos on p2 &c.
Bd. covers with Baby's Album & picture of child & toy tiger on front cover. KP
390 Another copy
Printed on pink paper; photograph of toy kangaroo on p1 'A book/for you and baby' & photographs in b/w of toy animals printed on pink on white paper throughout. Pink bd., spirax bdg, 190x235mm. KP

BACH, John
WILLIAM BLIGH. *See* Great Australians

A Back-Answer
See Blake, Harold Sidney

BACKHOUSE, Elizabeth
391 ENONE AND QUENTIN/By/Elizabeth Backhouse/ Wholly set up, printed and bound in Western Australia by/C. H. Pitman/Bookbinder and Publisher/973 Hay Street, Perth/1946
88pp, col. frontis. & 13 col. plates, b/w drawings, col. illus. by Irene Carter, clo., 235x205mm. KMM
Fairy story.

BACON, Phillip
392 Book 6/AUSTRALIA/OCEANIA/and the POLAR REGIONS/With a special section/of statistical maps and index/By Phillip Bacon/Professor of Geography,/ Teachers' College Columbia University/Statistical maps by Richard Edes Harrison/THE GOLDEN BOOK/ PICTURE ATLAS/OF THE WORLD/in six volumes/ Illustrated with more than 1,000 Color Photographs and Maps/Golden Press New York/Copyright 1960
87pp, & 9pp index, col. illus. & maps throughout, dec. bd., dec. e/p, 260x185mm. ANL

BADER, Douglas (ed.)
393 MY FAVOURITE/STORIES OF/COURAGE/edited by/Douglas Bader/[drawing]/with drawings by Mike Charlton/Lutterworth Press/London
1963
159pp (inc. 1p acknowledgements & 2pp introduction), 10 b/w chapter headings, clo., 195x125mm. BBC
Includes one chapter of 10 pages entitled 'A Terrible Fix' by Ernest Giles, reprinted from Kathleen Fitzpatrick's *Australian Explorers.*

BAGSHAW, Thomas Wyatt
394 POMPEY/WAS A PENGUIN/[drawing]/By/ Thomas Wyatt Bagshaw/Decorations by/Joan Kiddell/ Monroe/Oxford University Press/London New York Toronto
1st publ. 1940; rpt 1942, 1944
64pp, part col. frontis. & 9 f/p part col. illus. & b/w drawings in text (? dec. bd—copy seen re-bound), 235x175mm. CLRC

BAILEY, Charles S.
395 [drawing]BUTTON/BUSTERS/Written by Charles Bailey/and illustrated by E. Bailey/Proceeds in aid of Red Cross
Melbourne, the author, 1944
24pp, b/w drawings throughout, col. pic. card wrappers, cover title, 270x214mm. KMM
Humorous verses with foreword by Lord Mayor of Melbourne.

BAILEY, W. A.
396 THE STOWAWAY/By W. A. Bailey/London/Arthur H. Stockwell Ltd./29 Ludgate Hill, E.C.4
n.d.
112pp, unillus., clo., 185x125mm. ANL

BAILLIE, Arthur J.
397 OUR/SUNBURNT/COUNTRY/An illustrated history of Australia/by Arthur Baillie B.A. (Syd.)/[drawing]/illustrated by Molly G. Johnson A.R.A.S./Universal Books Pty. Limited/Sydney
Southern Cross International Pty Ltd, 1964
128pp, (inc. 1p foreword by A. H. Chisholm & 1p preface), col. & part. col. drawings throughout, pic. clo., 240x160mm. CLRC

BAILLIEU, Vere Latham
398 ARAMINTA POPKINS' PRUE/By Vere Latham Baillieu/Illustrated by/Irene Heath/[drawing]/Heath Cranton Limited/6 Fleet Lane London EC4
1939
55pp, 24 f/p col. illus., pic bd., 288x220mm. KMM
Verses. Author a Melbourne woman who moved to London in the 1930s.

BAKER, Eleanor Zuckerman
399 Eleanor Z. Baker/THE/AUSTRALIAN/ ABORIGINES/Steck-Vaughn Company/Austin, Texas
1968
37pp, 1p introduction, b/w photographic illus., part. col. decorations, part. col. dec. t.p., map, clo., 230x185mm. NSL:M

400 Eleanor Z. Baker/AUSTRALIA/TODAY/ Steck-Vaughn Company/Austin Texas
1969
86pp, col. frontis., col. & b/w photographic illus. throughout, col. dec. t.p., clo., 230x180mm. NSL:M

BAKER, Gilbert Maxwell
401 HOW THE BUNNIES/GOT TO/AUSTRALIA/ G. Maxwell Baker/[copyright]/Alpha Printing Company/71-73 Hardware Street, Melbourne.
1944
58pp, b/w & part. col. drawings throughout, bd., 240x190mm. ANL

BAKER, Robin
402 [drawing]/A/MAP/FOR GIANTS/As told to Robert Bateman/by Robin Baker/Illustrated by/Nancy Parker/Constable Young Books Ltd./London
1964
126pp, b/w frontis. map, 10 b/w chapter headings, clo., 195x125mm. CLRC

BAKKER, Piet
403 AUSTRALIE/[vignette]bewerkt door/Piet Bakker/ material van de/Informatie-afdeling/van de Australische Ambassade/omslag, Kaart van Australië, illustraties en lay-out/F. Ten Have V.R.I./Uitgave van Douwe Egberts N.W. joure (Friesland) en utrecht/ Opgericht 1753
n.d. [1951?]
79pp (inc. 1p preface & 10pp introduction), 1p adv., 57 spaces for col. photos to be collected & pasted in, bd. (front e/p & col. map of Australia), 310x240mm. RM

BALDERSON, Margaret
404 Margaret Balderson/WHEN JAYS/FLY TO BARBMO/[drawing]/Illustrated by Victor G. Ambrus/Oxford University Press/1968
202pp (inc. 2pp glossary), 1p acknowledgements, b/w drawings in text, clo., 215x135mm. KMM
Winner CBCA Award 1969.
405 Margaret Balderson/WHEN JAYS/FLY TO BARBMO/Illustrated by Victor G. Ambrus/The World Publishing Company/New York and Cleveland 1969
239pp (inc. 2pp glossary, 1p biographical note about author & artist), b/w drawings in text, clo., 200x130mm. ANL
406 Margaret Balderson/WHEN JAYS/FLY TO BARBMO/Illustrated by/Victor G. Ambrus/London/Oxford University Press/1970
First published 1968, rpt 1969; this edition 1970
220pp (inc. 3pp glossary), 1 b/w chapter heading, pic. wrappers, 195x130mm. Oxford Paperbacks. KMM

BALDOCK, Cecil R.
407 DEMON ISLAND/by/Cecil R. Baldock/[drawing]/Tower House Series/Illustrated by/W. Bryce Hamilton/London/George Newnes Limited/Tower House/Southampton Street, Strand, W.C.2.
First published 1946; second edition 1948
128pp, b/w frontis. & 12 b/w illus., bd., 180x120mm. CLRC
Adventure story set in Queensland & an offshore island.

BALDWIN, Gerald E.
408 THE REPROBATE/Gerald E. Baldwin/Published by Alexander McCubbin/9 Queen Street, Melbourne. n.d. [1922]
175pp, unillus., ?wrappers (copy seen rebound), 175x115mm. KMM
Boys' story with New Zealand setting by Australian author; t.p. has Gerald E. Baldwin, but the cover Gerald R.

BALDWIN, Helen
409 LITTLE/ALEXANDER/By Helen Baldwin/[drawing]/Jons.
Sydney, n.d. [1944]
27pp, 12pp col. illus. & b/w illus. throughout, pic. bd., 210x230mm. ANL
410 LITTLE ALEXANDER/By Helen Baldwin [drawing] Printed in Australia by Colourtone Pty Ltd, for Jons Productions Sydney
Details as above. KP

411 MARTIN AND MAISIE/MOUSE/By Helen Baldwin/[drawing]/A Dawfox Production.
Dawfox Productions, Sydney, n.d. [1944]
59pp, 27pp col. illus., pic. bd., 115x100mm. NSL:M

412 TILLY AND FRILLY/AND AMANDA/by/Helen Baldwin/[drawing]/A Dawfox Production.
Dawfox Productions, Sydney, 1944
59pp, 26pp col. illus., pic. bd., 112x102mm. ANL
413 TILLY AND FRILLY/AND AMANDA/By/Helen Baldwin/[drawing]/A Jons Production/Lithographed in Australia by Posters Pty. Ltd. for Jons Productions Pty. Ltd. Sydney.
Sydney, n.d. [1950]
16pp, alternate col. & b/w illus. throughout, pic. bd., dec. e/p, 160x155mm. KMM

414 SHY/GEORGIANA/By Helen Baldwin/[drawing]/Jons Sydney.
Jons Productions, Sydney, n.d. [1945]
28pp, 12pp col. & b/w illus. throughout, pic. bd., 210x225mm. ANL

415 CHICKY CHICK/By Helen Baldwin/[drawing]/A/Colour Production
Colour Productions, Sydney, n.d. [1946]
32pp, col. & b/w illus. throughout, pic. bd., 215x235mm. ANL
416 CHICKY CHICK/By Helen Baldwin/[drawing]/A Jons Production/Lithographed in Australia by Posters Ltd for Jons Productions Pty Ltd, Sydney n.d. [194-?]
18pp, col. & b/w illus. throughout, pic. bd. & pic. e/p, 165x155mm. JH

417 RAMBLER/THE FROLICSOME KID/[drawing]/A/Colour/Production/By Helen Baldwin
Colour Productions, Sydney, n.d. [1946]
[32]pp, col. & b/w illus. throughout, pic. bd., 215x230mm. KMM

418 LITTLE BILLY BUNNYKIN/By/Helen Baldwin/[drawing]/Registered at the G.P.O. Sydney for transmission by post as a book
Colour Productions, Sydney, n.d. [1947]
56pp, 27 col. illus., dec. bd., 120x100mm. ANL

BALDWIN, May
419 HILDA'S EXPERIENCES/By/May Baldwin/Author of 'A City Schoolgirl', 'Corah's School Chums', 'A Schoolgirl of Moscow'/'Teddy and Lily's Adventures',/'Holly House', &c./With six coloured illustrations/by/W. Rainey/London: 38 Soho Square, W./W. & R. Chambers, Limited/Edinburgh: 339 High Street/1913
386pp, col. frontis. & 5 f/p col. illus., pic. clo., 185x130mm. NSL:M

420 A SCHOOLGIRL'S DIARY/The Story of her Holiday beyond/The Seas/By May Baldwin/Author of 'Hilda's Experiences' 'Moll Meredyth' 'Troublesome Topsy;/'A City Schoolgirl' ''Corah's School Chums' &c/with six coloured illustrations/by/W. A. Cuthbertson/London: 38 Soho Square, W./W & R Chambers, Limited/Edinburgh: 339 High Street n.d.
300pp, col. frontis. & 5 f/p col. plates, pic. clo., 184x128mm. ANL
A story of a schoolgirl on a round voyage from England to Australia and South Africa, with sections on visits to Darwin, Port Moresby, Townsville, Sydney & Adelaide (pp93–180).

'BAMBI, Moan'
See Tindale, Will

BAMFORD, Emma Josephine
421 GROWING/AND/KNOWING/A Simple Story of/Life for Girls and/Boys/by/E. Josephine Bamford
Printed in Australia by Armstrong Bros, Kyneton, Victoria, n.d.
44pp, b/w photographic frontis. & 2 b/w illus. in text, wrappers, 180x125mm. KMM
• Rpt as above. KP
4th ed. March 1942
4th ed. March 1943, both as above but 1943 ed. pub. S. John Bacon, Melbourne, both KP
422 GROWING/AND/KNOWING/A Simple Story of/Life for Girls and/Boys/by/E. Josephine Bamford/S. John Bacon/Australian and New Zealand Representative for/Marsbell, Morgan & Scott Ltd/317 Collins Street Melbourne
1944

48pp, b/w photographic illus., wrappers, 180x120mm. KP

423 "THE/HOUSE NOT/MADE WITH/HANDS"/Talks to older girls/By/E. Josephine Bamford
1935. Printed by Armstrong Bros./Printers and publishers/Kyneton
32pp (inc. 1p foreword by J. Horace Downing & 1p introduction by Donald, Bishop of Bendigo & 1p author's note, unillus., wrappers, 168x110mm. KMM
Religious talks on sex, hygiene &c.

424 Rev. ed., 44pp, Melbourne, S. John Bacon, Sept 1935. KP

425 Rev. ed. (completing 40 000), 1935. KP

426 3rd ed., n.d. (completing 55 000), S. John Bacon. KP

427 5th ed., n.d. (completing 60 000), S. John Bacon. KP

428 THE HOUSE/NOT MADE/WITH HANDS/Talks to Older Girls/by E. Josephine Bamford
Printed in Australia by Armstrong Bros, Kyneton, Victoria, revised ed. (copyright 1935); revised & enlarged ed. 1939, rpt 1941, 1942; revised & enlarged 1943
44pp, wrappers, 180x125mm. KMM

429 [dedication—4 lines]/JINGLES FOR JUNIORS/ Written by/E. Josephine Bamford/illustrated by/ C. Kingsley-Smith/with acknowledgements to/Carol Day/[col. drawing]/published by/S. John Bacon/317 Collins St./Melbourne/International Copyright/ Wholesale distributors/Lantern House Publishing Co. Pty Ltd./Melbourne
n.d.
[22]pp, col. illus. throughout, col. pic. wrappers, 272x208mm. JH
Devotional and hygiene.

430 JINGLES FOR JUNIORS/Written by/E. Josephine Bamford/illustrated by/C. Kingsley-Smith/published by/S. John Bacon/317 Collins St./Melbourne/ (International Copyright)
n.d. [1944]
24pp, dec. t.p., 11 f/p col. illus., stiff pictorial wrappers, 270x200mm. ANL

431 JINGLES FOR JUNIORS [No. 2]/Written by/ E. Josephine Bamford illustrated by/C. Kingsley-Smith/ with acknowledgements to Carol Day published by/ S. John Bacon/317 Collins St./Melbourne/ (International Copyright)
n.d. [1946]
24pp, dec. t.p., col. illus., stiff pictorial wrappers, 270x200mm. ANL
Front cover reads: 'Furs and Feathers No. 2'.

BAMMAN, Henry & WHITEHEAD, Robert

432 FLIGHT TO THE/SOUTH POLE/By/Henry Bamman/Robert Whitehead/Illustrations/William Humrickhouse/Benefie Press Chicago/Publishing Division of Beckley-Cardy Company/Atlanta Dallas Long Beach Portland
1965
72pp, illus. t.p., b/w illus. throughout, col. pic. bd., 230x170mm. KP

BANCKS, James C.

433 THE "SUNBEAMS" BOOK/ADVENTURES/OF/ GINGER/MEGGS/2/-
Sun Newspapers Ltd, Sydney, [1924]
[24]pp (inc. 21pp comic strips), pic. wrappers, cover title, 310x250mm. MAC

434 THE "SUNBEAMS"/BOOK/[drawing]/FURTHER ADVENTURES/OF/GINGER MEGGS/[drawing]/ 2/-/Series 2 Bancks 1925
Sun Newspapers, Sydney
[32]pp, inc. 26pp comic strips printed in b/w with addition of red & yellow, 2pp are competition pages, the backs printed with b/w comic strips, 1p col. illus., 1p verse, col. pic. wrappers, 310x245mm. MAC
Results of competition to be publ. in "Sunbeams" Supplement Feb. 28, 1926.

435 Another copy as above but publ. by *The Saturday Express*, King William Street, Adelaide; competition results to be announced in *The Saturday Express* Feb. 27, 1926. KMM

436 THE "SUNBEAMS"/BOOK/[col. illus.]2/-/Series 3 "Bancks"/MORE/ADVENTURES OF GINGER/ MEGGS/Registered by the/Postmaster General. . . &c/Wholly set up and printed in Australia for Sun Newspapers Ltd/by Marchant & Co. Ltd. Sydney 1926
[32]pp (inc. 28pp comic strips, 2pp blank, 1p drawing, 1p verse), pic. wrappers, cover title, 310x240mm. CLRC

437 THE "SUNBEAMS" BOOK/FURTHER ADVENTURES/OF/GINGER MEGGS/[drawing]/ 2/-/Series 4/Registered by the Postmaster-General. . . &c/Wholly set up and printed in Australia/for Sun Newspapers Limited by/Simmons Limited, Sydney/ 1927
[32]pp. (inc. 28pp comic strips, 1p col. illus., 1p verse, pic. endpiece, col. illus. on back wrapper, col. pic wrappers, cover title, 310x245mm. CLRC

438 THE 'SUNBEAMS' BOOK/MORE/ADVENTURES/ OF/GINGER MEGGS/[drawing] Series 5 2/-/Registered by the Postmaster-General for/ transmission through the Post as a Book./Wholly set up and printed in Australia/For Sun Newspapers Limited by/Simmons Limited/Sydney/1928
[32]pp (inc. 28pp col. comic strips, 2pp f/p illus. & 1p illus. & verse, col. illus. on outside back cover, 305x245mm. KMM

439 THE SUNBEAMS BOOK/MORE/ADVENTURES/ OF/GINGER/MEGGS/Series/6/Registered by the Postmaster General for/transmission through the Post as a Book/Wholly set up and printed in Australia/for the Sun Newspapers Limited by/Mortons Limited, Sydney/1929/2/-
[32]pp (inc. frontis. & preliminary poem), col. comic strip cartoons throughout, col. pic. wrappers, cover title, 300x243mm. RM
The frontis. is a b/w photograph of the author; poem entitled "Ginge".

440 THE/SUNBEAMS/BOOK/[drawing]/GINGER/ MEGGS/in a/7th Series of/Adventures/2/-/Wholly set up and printed in Australia for Sun Newspapers Limited/By Morton Limited, Sydney, 1930. Registered by the Postmaster-/General for transmission through the Post as a Book.
[32]pp (inc. 28pp comic strips, first 3 preliminary pages col. drawings & 1p drawing after text, pic. wrappers, 305x247mm. KMM

441 THE/SUNBEAMS BOOK/[col. illus.]/More/ Adventures/of/2/-/GINGER MEGGS/Series 8/Wholly set up and printed in Australia for Sun Newspapers Limited by S. Bennett Limited, Sydney, 1931/Registered at the General Post Office Sydney, for transmission through the Post as a Book.
[32]pp, col. frontis. & 2pp col. illus. & poem, [28]pp comic strip, 1p col. illus. & col. illus. on back cover, col. pic. wrappers, cover title, 310x245mm. CLRC

442 THE SUNBEAMS BOOK/GINGER MEGGS/ [drawing]/In a/9th Series of ADVENTURES/ 2/-/Wholly set up and printed in Australia by Sun Newspapers/Limited, 60 Elizabeth St, Sydney, 1932. Regd. at GPO. Sydney, for transmission through the post as a book
[32]pp (inc. 28pp comic strip, 4pp col. illus.), col. illus.

throughout, b/w photograph of author, col. pic. wrappers, 310x250mm. KMM

443 THE SUNBEAMS BOOK/[col. illus.] 2/-/More/ Adventures/of/GINGER MEGGS/Series 10/Wholly set up and printed in Australia by Sun Newspapers [&c as before]1933
[32]pp (inc. 28pp strips), col. illus. on front & back cover, col. pic. wrappers, 305x247mm. MAC

444 THE/SUNBEAMS BOOK/[col. illus.] Bancks/ 2/-/Further/Adventures of GINGER MEGGS/Series 11/Wholly set up & printed in Australia by Sun Newspapers Ltd 60-66 Elizabeth Street Sydney/1934
[32]pp (inc. 28pp strips), col. pic. wrappers, 305x248mm. MAC

445 MORE ADVENTURES/OF/GINGER MEGGS/[col. illus.]/Sunbeams/Book/Series/12/Two shillings/ Wholly set up and printed in Australia by Sun Newspapers Ltd. 60-66 Elizabeth St, Sydney/1935. Registered at General Post Office [&c]
[32]pp (comprising 28pp comic strips, 3 preliminary pp col. illus. & 1p col. illus. at end), col. illus. on back wrapper, cover title, 305x244mm. CLRC

446 MORE ADVENTURES/OF/GINGER MEGGS/ 2/-/[drawing]/Bancks/Sunbeams Book/Series 13/Wholly set up and printed in Australia by Sun Newspapers Ltd 60-66 Elizabeth St/Sydney, 1936. Registered at GPO Sydney, for transmission through the post as a book
[32]pp (inc. 28pp comic strips), col. illus., col. pic. wrappers, 305x245mm. MAC

447 MORE ADVENTURES/OF/GINGER MEGGS/ 1/3/[col. illus.]/Sunbeams Book/Series 14/Wholly set up and printed in Australia by Associated Newspapers Ltd 60-66 Elizabeth Street/Sydney 1937 [etc.]
[32]pp (comprising all comic strips), col. illus. on front & back wrappers, 305x246mm. MAC

448 MORE ADVENTURES/OF/GINGER MEGGS/ Sunbeams Book/Series 15/1/3 [i.e. price] /[col. illus.]/ Wholly set up and printed in Australia by Associated Newspapers Ltd Sydney 1938 [etc.]
[32]pp (comprising 31pp comic strips), col. pic. wrappers, 310x250mm. MAC

449 MORE ADVENTURES/OF/GINGER MEGGS/[col. illus. & price]1/3/Bancks/SUNBEAMS BOOKS/Series 16/Wholly set and printed by Associated Newspapers Limited Sydney [2 lines] 1939
[32]pp (comprising 31pp comic strips), col. illus. front & back covers, 305x246mm. MAC

450 MORE ADVENTURES/OF/GINGER MEGGS/ [drawing]/[circle cut out showing 1/6 from page beneath]/Bancks/SUNBEAMS BOOK/Series 17/Wholly set up and printed by Associated Newspapers Ltd Sydney[2 lines]
1940
[28]pp (comprising 27pp comic strips), col. pic. wrappers, 304x244mm. MAC

451 MORE ADVENTURES OF/GINGER/MEGGS/[col. illus.]/Series 18/1/6/Bancks/SUNBEAMS BOOK/ Wholly set up and printed in Australia by Associated Newspapers Ltd 60-70 Elizabeth St, Sydney 1941.
[32]pp (comprising 31pp comic strips), col. illus., wrappers, 305x245mm. MAC

452 MORE ADVENTURES OF/GINGER/MEGGS/[col. illus.]/1/6/Series 19/SUNBEAMS BOOK/Bancks/ Wholly set up and printed in Australia [2 lines as before] 1942
[24]pp, col. pic. wrappers, 310x240mm. MAC

453 MORE ADVENTURES OF/GINGER/MEGGS/ 1/6/Series 20/Sunbeams Book/Bancks/Wholly set up and printed in Australia by Associated Newspapers Ltd [as before]1943
[32]pp (inc. col. frontis. & 31pp col. comic strips), col. pic. wrappers, cover title, 272x210mm. KP

454 MORE ADVENTURES OF/GINGER/MEGGS/ 1/6/Series 21/Sunbeams Book/Bancks/Wholly set up and printed in Australia by Associated Newspapers Ltd., 60-70 Elizabeth St.,/Sydney, 1944. Registered at the GPO, Sydney [etc.]
[28]pp (1p, 27pp comic strips), col. pic. wrappers (blank inside), 272x210mm. CLRC

455 MORE ADVENTURES OF/GINGER/MEGGS/Series 22/1/-/Sunbeams Book/Wholly set up and printed in Australia by Associated Newspapers Ltd., 60-70 Elizabeth St.,/Sydney, 1945. Registered at G.P.O. Sydney [etc.]
[32]pp (inc. 1 f/p col. illus. & 31pp col. comic strips, stiff col. pic. wrappers, cover title, 271x212mm. KMM

456 MORE ADVENTURES/OF/GINGER MEGGS/ [drawing]/1/-/Series 23/Sunbeams Book/Wholly set up and printed in Australia/by Associated Newspapers Ltd, 60-70 Elizabeth St.,/Sydney 1946 [etc.]
[32]pp (inc. 31pp comic strip & 1p t.p. illus.), col. pic. wrappers, 275x215mm. KMM
Printed in col. throughout.

457 MORE ADVENTURES OF/GINGER MEGGS/ 1/-/Series/24/Sunbeams Book/Wholly set up and printed in Australia by Associated Newspapers Ltd. 60-70 Elizabeth St./Sydney 1947 [etc.]
[48]pp (comprising col. frontis. & 47pp col. comic strips), col. pic. wrappers, 270x200mm. CLRC

458 MORE ADVENTURES OF/GINGER MEGGS/ [drawing] 1/-/Series/25/Sunbeams Book/Wholly set up and printed in Australia by Associated Newspapers Ltd. 60-70 Elizabeth St/Sydney 1948
[40]pp (comprising 1p frontis. & 39pp col. comic strips), col. pic. wrappers, cover title, 270x200mm. CLRC

459 MORE ADVENTURES OF/GINGER/MEGGS/ 1/-/[drawing]/Series 26/SUNBEAMS BOOK/Wholly set up and printed in Australia by Associated Newspapers Ltd., 60-70 Elizabeth St.,/Sydney 1949. Registered at GPO, Sydney, for transmission through the post as a book.
[40]pp (inc. 1p drawings surrounding a presentation label & 39pp comic strips printed in col.), col. pic. wrappers, cover title, 270x195mm. KMM

460 MORE ADVENTURES OF/GINGER MEGGS/ [drawing]/1/-/Series/27 Bancks/Sunbeams Book/ Wholly set up and printed in Australia by Associated Newspapers Ltd., 60-70 Elizabeth St./Sydney, 1950. Registered at GPO Sydney [etc.]
[40]pp (inc. 1p col. illus. & 39pp comic strips), col. illus. wrappers (insides blank), 273x200mm. CLRC

461 GINGER/MEGGS/ANNUAL/2/-/[drawing]/ Bancks/Xmas 1952/Distributed by/Consolidated Press Ltd./Registered for transmission by Post in Australia as a book.
Publ. by Shakespeare Head Press Pty Ltd, Sydney
[32]pp, col. comic strips throughout, pic. front & back wrappers, cover title, 270x188mm. CLRC

462 GINGER/MEGGS/ANNUAL/2/-[drawing]/Xmas 1953/Distributed by Consolidated Press Ltd Sydney/ Registered for transmission by Post in Australia [etc.]
[28]pp, col. comic strips throughout, 270x190mm. CLRC

463 1954 GINGER/MEGGS/ANNUAL/2/-/[drawing]/ Registered for transmission/by Post in Australia as a book/Distributed by Consolidated Press Ltd. Xmas 1954
[32]pp comic strips, adv. inside both covers & col. strip on back cover adv. Ginger Meggs Crockery. Col. comic strips throughout. 282x192mm. CLRC

Adv. for Chucklers Weekly inside front cover. *See also* The COR Road Safety Colouring Competition.

464 GINGER/MEGGS/ANNUAL/[drawing]/2/-/Distributed by Consolidated Press Ltd/Registered for transmission by/post in Australia as a book. Xmas 1955
[32]pp, col. comic strips throughout, col. pic. wrappers, cover title, adv. on back wrapper, 270x210mm. KMM

465 GINGER/MEGGS/2/- ANNUAL/[drawing]/Xmas 1956/Distributed by Consolidated Press Ltd./Registered for transmission/by post in Australia as a book
[32]pp, col. comic strips, col. pic. wrappers (adv. on back), cover title, 275x190mm. CLRC
Each page headed 'Ginger/Meggs/Created/by Bancks'.

466 GINGER/MEGGS/Annual 2/-/Xmas 1957 Distributed by Australian Consolidated Press Ltd./Registered for transmission by/post in Australia as a book
[32]pp, col. comic strips throughout, col. pic. wrappers, adv. on back wrapper, cover title, 277x190mm. JH

467 GINGER/MEGGS/ANNUAL/[drawing]/2/-/Xmas 1958/Distributed by Australian/Consolidated Press Ltd./Registered for transmission by/post in Australia as a book
[32]pp, col. comic strips throughout, pic. wrappers (adv. on back), cover title, 255x187mm. KMM

468 GINGER/MEGGS/ANNUAL/2/-/Xmas 1959/Distributed by Australian/Consolidated Press Ltd./Registered for transmission by/post in Australia as a book
[32]pp, col. comic strips throughout, col. pic. wrappers (blank inside), 260x180mm. CLRC
'Created by Bancks'.
NOTE: Bancks died 1 July 1952 and Ron Vivian continued the strips. There was no annual published for 1951 and the last Ginger Meggs Annual appeared in 1959.

469 Jimmy Bancks/GINGER/MEGGS/and HERBERT/THE BILLY GOAT/ [drawing]/The Golden Press/Sydney
n.d.
24pp, col pic. t.p., col & b/w illus. throughout, col. pic. boards,195x150mm. KMM

470 Jimmy Bancks/GINGER MEGGS'/LUCKY BREAK/[col. illus.]/The Golden Press Sydney
n.d. [1957]
22pp, col. illus. throughout, col. pic. boards, 195x150mm. CLRC

471 Jimmy Bancks/GINGER MEGGS/AND THE/COUNTRY COUSIN/[col. illus.]/The Golden Press/Sydney
n.d. [195-?]
[28]pp, col. illus. throughout, pic. boards, 195x155mm. CLRC

BANKS, Mrs G. Linnaeus
MISS PRINGLE'S PEARLS
Hutchinson, Lond., 1894
Though the hero was born in Australia & there are numerous Australian references the action all takes place in England; insufficient interest for inclusion. CLRC

[BANNISTER, J. A.]
472 A BOOK FOR/ TIRED BABIES/BY ONE WHO LOVES THEM
W. C. Penfold & Co., Printers, Sydney 1904
32pp, wrappers, 245x180mm. NSL:M
Inscribed on last blank page and signed 'J. A. Bannister', and inside is written 'Miss Bannister, 1904'.

BARBER, Noel
473 ADVENTURES AT BOTH POLES/by/Noel Barber/Illustrated with photographs/[device]/Heinemann/London Melbourne Toronto
London, 1963
106pp, b/w photographic frontis. & 8pp photographic illus., clo., 195x130mm. NSL:M
Includes extracts from *South with Scott* (Mountevans), *Under Sail in the Frozen North* (Worsley) and *Operation Deep Freeze* (Dupek).

BARCLAY, R. M.
474 GEMS/OF THE/AUSTRALIAN BUSH/And Other Poems/by/R. W. Barclay/Illustrations/by/Rachel Tonkin
First publ. 1968, publ. by the author. Printed by Heidelberg City News Pty Ltd.
60pp (inc. 6pp acknowledgements &c), b/w drawings on t.p. & marginal drawings throughout, clo., 200x135mm. KMM

BARKER, Eric J.
475 Our Overseas Friends: 3/AN AUSTRALIAN/FAMILY/by/Eric J. Barker, B.A., F.R.G.S./Senior Lecturer in Geography and Social Studies,/Trent Park Training College/[drawing]/Evans Brothers Limited: London
1962
24pp, b/w illus. in text, dec. bd., 205x150mm. CLRC

BARKER, Lady [née Mary Anne Stewart, Lady Broome]
476 TRAVELLING ABOUT/over/New and Old Ground/by/Lady Barker/Author of "Stories about Station life in New Zealand" etc/[vignette]/with maps and illustrations/London: George Routledge & Sons:/The Broadway, Ludgate/New York: 416 Broome Street
Inscribed 1876
2pp preface & 353pp, frontis. (portrait of Richard O'Hara Burke), b/w engravings & maps, pic. clo., 185x124mm. KP
Pp1-44 deal with Australian exploration, inc. Burke & Wills, Sturt, Stuart. Preface indicates written for the young.

477 Another copy as above, but
n.d. (prize 1881)
175x115mm. KP

478 LETTERS TO GUY/By Lady Barker/(Lady Broome)/Author of "Station Life in New Zealand",/"Stories About." etc./London/Macmillan and Co./1885
227pp, b/w map frontis. only, clo. [with vignette in gilt and black of some black swans on front cover], 188x124mm. KMM
Letters to her 13-year old son at school in England, describing the author's arrival in Australia from Mauritius, and life at Government House, Perth.
Rpt Melbourne 1963, O.U.P., under the title *Remembered with Affection*, ed. Alexandra Hasluck, 137pp. Not produced as a book for children.

BARKER, Victor
479 INSIDE THE REEF/A Journey through the Fiji Islands/Victor Barker/Lansdowne
Melbourne 1968
113pp, b/w extended frontis., b/w photographic illus., b/w map, dec. chapter headings, clo., dec. e/p, 240x180mm. Pacific Journey Series. KMM

[Barker Bros]
A Surprise for Shirley. *See* Joy Series

BARNARD, Alan
THOMAS SUTCLIFFE MORT. *See* Great Australians

BARNARD, Amy B.
480 THE GOLDEN BOOK/OF YOUTH/Noble Deeds of Boys and Girls/By/Amy B. Barnard, L.L.A./Author of/ "The Girls' Encyclopaedia", "The Home Training of Children"/Etc. Etc./With illustrations specially prepared by Colbron Pearse,/W. M. Bowles, and others./London:/The Pilgrim Press/16 Pilgrim Street, E.C.
n.d.
272pp (inc. 4pp index), 3pp author's foreword, b/w frontis. & 6 f/p b/w illus., dec. clo., 190x135mm. KMM
Contents include: 'An Australian Girl's Courage' (the wreck of the *Quetta*), 2pp; 'A Small Heroine of the Bush' (Jane Duff), 1p; 'An Australian who Saved a Township' (— Rawson), 1p; 'What a Tasmanian Did' (Lt Guy G. E. Wylly in the Boer War), half page.

BARNARD, H. Clive
481 AUSTRALIA, NEW ZEALAND/AND OCEANIA IN PICTURES/By/H. Clive Barnard, M.A., B.Litt./ Examiner in Geography to the College of Preceptors and/Assistant Examiner for the London University Matriculation/and the Northern Universities Matriculation/Containing fifty-nine illustrations, thirty-two of which are/in colour, including maps and diagrams/[drawing, kookaburras]/Published by A. J. C. Black, Limited,/4, 5 & 6 Soho Square, London, W.1/1923
64pp, col. frontis. & others, dec. clo. with col. onlay on front, 245x180mm. KP
Illus. Percy F. Spence, Norman Hardy, J. Williamson &c.

BARNARD, Marjorie Faith
482 THE IVORY GATE/By/Marjorie Barnard/Illustrated by/Leyshon White/H. H. Champion,/Australasian Authors' Agency/Melbourne/1920
96pp, col. frontis & 5 f/p col. illus., bd., half clo., 245x170mm. KMM
Also as above but issued in wrappers. VSL

AUSTRALIA'S FIRST ARCHITECT—FRANCIS GREENWAY. *See* Australian Landmarks

LACHLAN MACQUARIE. *See* Great Australians

BARNARD, Peggy
483 MICHAEL THE MALLEE CHICK/IN SEARCH OF A MOTHER/by/Peggy Barnard/[coloured drawing]/ Illustrated by Mollie Quick
Consolidated Press, Sydney 1946 [?1947]
32pp, col. illus. throughout, pic. wrappers, 180x240mm. ANL

484 WISH/AND THE MAGIC NUT/Written by Peggy Barnard/Illustrated by Sheila Hawkins/[coloured drawing]/Published by John Sands Pty. Ltd./Sydney Melbourne Brisbane Adelaide Perth Hobart
Sydney, n.d. [1956]
33pp, col. illus. throughout, dec. bd., e/p, 180x155mm. KMM
Joint winner CBCA Award 1956.

BARNARDO, T. J.
485 TWELVE/SHEEP/FROM/AUSTRALIA/By T. J. Barnardo, F.R.C.S.E./London Offices/18 to 26 Stepney Causeway E.1
n.d.
32pp, 3 b/w illus., pic. wrappers, 120x90mm. VSL
Written to interest people in Dr Barnardo's Homes for orphaned children. Tells of 12 frozen sheep carcases sent from Australia in 1888 & a note at the end states that the number of children had been brought up to date & that the story was written 'about thirty years ago' (making date of publication 1923? though Ferguson suggests 1891).

BARNES, Ethel [Mrs Aubrey W. Barnes, née John]
486 "SILHOUETTE"/by/Ethel John/(Mrs Aubrey W. Barnes)/Illustrated by/Geoff W. Ridley/Printed and Published by/Paterson's Printing Press Ltd., 882 Hay St. Perth, W.A.
n.d.
34pp, b/w drawings throughout, bd., 240x140mm. ANL
Verses.
487 "SILHOUETTE"/by/Ethel John/(Mrs Aubrey W. Barnes)/Illustrated by/Geoff W. Ridley/Second Edition/Printed and Published by/Paterson's Printing Press Ltd., 882 Hay St. Perth, W.A./1939/(Copyright)
34pp, b/w drawings throughout, bd., 240x140mm. NSL:M
488 "SILHOUETTE"/by/Ethel/John/(Mrs Aubrey W. Barnes)/Illustrated by/Geoff W. Ridley/Third Edition/ Printed and Published by/Paterson's Printing Press Ltd., 65 Murray St. Perth, W.A./1943/(Copyright)
32pp, b/w drawings, bd., 240x170mm. ANL

BARNES, John
JOSEPH FURPHY. *See* Great Australians

BARNES, Victor Dominic Suthers
489 SKIPPY THE BUSH/KANGAROO/[col. illus]/ Written by Victor Barnes/Illustrated by Walter Stackpool/Golden Press [device] Sydney
Copyright 1968
[26]pp, col. illus. throughout, col. pic. bd, pic. e/p, 312x255mm. KP
• Rpt 1969 (twice), rpt 1970. KP
490 SKIPPY/THE BUSH/KANGAROO/[drawing]/ Written by Victor Barnes/Illustrated by Walter Stackpool/Golden Press Sydney
1969
[24]pp, col. illus. throughout, pic. bd., 195x155mm. A Little Golden Book. KMM

491 SKIPPY TO THE/RESCUE/[col. illus.]/Written by Victor Barnes/Illustrated by Walter Stackpool/Golden Press Sydney
1969
[24]pp, col. illus. throughout, dec. bd., dec. e/p, 310x250mm. KMM
• Rpt 1971. KP
492 SKIPPY TO THE/RESCUE/[col. illus.]Written by Victor Barnes/Illustrated by Walter Stackpool/Golden Press [device] Sydney
Copyright 1969
24pp, col. illus. throughout, pic. bd., dec. e/p, 195x155mm. KP
Numerous rpts as above. KP

493 WOOBINDA/Animal Doctor/[col. illus.]/Written by Victor Barnes/Illustrated by Walter Stackpool/Golden Press Sydney
1969
24pp, col. illus. on every page, col. pic. bd., pic. e/p, 313x230mm. WRT
• Rpt 1971. Copyright 1971 by Western Pub. Coy Inc. As above. KP
494 WOOBINDA/(Animal Doctor)/Sticker Fun/Book/

Push out/stick and/colour/Authorised/Edition/Based on the/Famous Thames/Television/Series
World Distributors (Manchester) Ltd., 1970
16pp, col. & part col. illus., pic. wrappers, cover title, 300x214mm. KP

495 WOOBINDA/TO THE RESCUE/[col. drawing]/ Copyright 1972 Published by Golden Press Pty. Ltd., 2-12 Tennyson Road,/Gladesville, Sydney. Printed in Singapore by The Toppan Printing Company Ltd./ Written by Victor Barnes/Illustrated by Walter Stackpool/Based on the TV Series Woobinda—Animal Doctor/Golden Press Sydney
[24]pp, col. illus on every page, pic. bd., dec e/p, 195x152mm. KMM

496 WOOBINDA/TO THE RESCUE/[drawing]/Written by Victor Barnes/illustrated by Walter Stackpool/Based on the TV Series Woobinda—Animal Doctor/Golden Press Sydney
1972
26pp, col. illus. on every page, pic. bd., pic. e/p, 310x254mm. KP

497 SKIPPY AND THE/INTRUDERS/[coloured illustration]/Adapted by Victor Barnes/Illustrated by Walter Stackpool/Golden Press Sydney
1970
[24]pp, col. illus. throughout, col. pic. bd., pic. e/p, 310x250mm. CLRC
• Rpt as above 1971. KP

498 BARRIER REEF/ADVENTURES OF/MINUS FIVE/ [drawing]/Written by Victor Barnes/Illustrated by Walter Stackpool/Golden Press Sydney
1971
[24]pp, col. illus. throughout, pic. bd., pic. e/p, 310x250mm. CLRC

499 Another edition as above, but published as a Little Golden Book, 195x155mm. KP

500 THE BUNYIP/AND THE BULL-BIRD/[col. illus.]/ Written by Victor Barnes/Illustrated by Hal English/ Golden Press [device] Sydney
1971
[25]pp, col. illus. on every page, pic. bd., pic. e/p, 306x250mm. KMM

501 THE LEGEND OF/THE THREE SISTERS/ [drawing]/Written by Victor Barnes/Illustrated by Hal English/Golden Press Sydney
1971
[24]pp, col. illus. throughout, pic. bd., pic. e/p, 310x250mm. CLRC

502 Another edition as above but published as a Little Golden Book, 1971, 195x155mm. KP
• Rpt 1971. KP
• Rpt 1972. CLRC

503 LITTLE BINJY/[drawing]/Written by Victor Barnes/ Illustrated by Hal English/Golden Press Sydney
1971
[24]pp, col. illus. throughout, pic. bd., pic. e/p, 310x250mm. CLRC

504 LITTLE BINJY/[col. illus.]/Written by Victor Barnes/ Illustrated by Hal English/Golden Press Sydney
1971
[24]pp, col. illus. throughout, pic. bd., 195x152mm. CLRC
• Rpt 1971. KP

505 ABORIGINAL/TALES/Written by Victor Barnes/ Illustrated by Hal English/Copyright 1971. Published by Golden Press Pty Ltd. 2-12 Tennyson Road./ Gladesville, Sydney. Printed in Singapore by The Toppan Printing Company Ltd./Golden Press—Sydney
[24]pp, col. illus., bd., 194x152mm. CLRC
A Little Golden Book.

506 ABORIGINAL/TALES/Written by Victor Barnes/ Illustrated by Hal English/Golden Press Sydney
1972
[26]pp, col. illus. throughout, pic. bd., pic. e/p, 310x250mm. CLRC

507 MINUS FIVE/AND THE MOUNTAIN OF GOLD/ Written by Victor Barnes/Illustrated by Peter Chapman/Golden Press Sydney
1972
24pp, col. illus. throughout, col. pic. bd., pic. e/p, 310x245mm. KP

508 THREE ABORIGINAL/LEGENDS/Written by Victor Barnes/Illustrated by Hal English/Golden Press Sydney/Copyright 1972. Published by Golden Press Pty Ltd, 2-12 Tennyson Road,/Gladesville, Sydney. Printed in Singapore by The Toppan Printing Company Ltd.
n.d.
[24]pp, col. illus. on t.p., col. illus. on every page, col. pic. bd., 196x154mm. KMM
A Little Golden Book.

509 THREE ABORIGINAL/LEGENDS/Written by Victor Barnes/Illustrated by Hal English/Golden Press Sydney
1972
[24]pp, col. illus. on every page, pic. e/p, col. pic. bd., 313x250mm. CLRC
Contents the same in both books.

BARNETT, Frederick Oswald

510 HAPPY/ENDINGS/TO OLD NURSERY RHYMES/ Rhymes by/F. Oswald Barnett/pictures by/Dorothy Dibdin/Published in 1945 by/The Book Depot/288 Little Collins Street/Melbourne
15pp, 1p foreword by author, 14 col. illus., dec. bd., 250x185mm. ANL

511 HAPPY/ENDINGS/TO OLD NURSERY RHYMES/ Rhymes by/F. Oswald Barnett/pictures by/Dorothy Dibdin/George G. Harrap & Co. Ltd./London Sydney Toronto Bombay
London 1947
Details as above, but foreword omitted; cover & picture reproduced on d/w differ from Australian edition. NSL:M

BARNETT, Leonard Palin

512 Len Barnett/LIVE FOR KICKS/A New Kind of/Book for Youth/The Joint Board of Christian Education/of Australia and New Zealand/147 Collins Street, Melbourne
First publ. 1964; rpt 1965, 1967
190pp, unillus., stiff wrappers, 177x110mm. NSL:M
Talks on faith & moral problems addressed to young people

513 THIS I *CAN* BELIEVE!/A book for young people/ Leonard Barnett/The Joint Board of Christian Education/of Australia and New Zealand/147 Collins Street, Melbourne
1969
128pp, unillus., wrappers, 185x120mm. CLRC

BARNSLEY, Katharine Fielding

514 MR PALEY/DOG ABOUT TOWN/Katharine Fielding Barnsley/Illustrated by/Bruce Petty/[device]/ Hutchinson of London
First publ. 1957

91pp, part col. illus. throughout, clo., 214x157mm. ANL
Story of a chow puppy

'BARR, Donald'
See Barrett, Charles

BARRABEE, Austin
515 BING BING/BUNGARRA/& other Stories/by/Austin Barrabee/Decorations by/Margaret Tait
n.p., n.d.
32pp, col. frontis. & 2 f/p col. illus., b/w drawings & decorations in text, stiff col. pic. wrappers, cover title, 366x250mm. MAC
Contents lists three stories. Aboriginal stories set in WA & the Nullarbor Plain. Text printed in script.

BARRETT, Charles [pseud. 'Donald Barr']
516 THE/BUSH RAMBLERS/A Story for Australian/Children/By/Charles Barrett/Illustrated with photographs by the Author/Melbourne/T. Shaw Fitchett, 376 Swanston Street/1913
128pp, b/w photographic frontis. & illus.., wrappers, 175x120mm. VSL
A supplementary reader written for the Education Department of Victoria.

517 THE/ISLE OF PALMS/A Story of Adventure/By/Charles Barrett/Author of "From Range to Sea" ,"The Wide/Horizon" etc./Lothian Book Publishing Co. Pty. Ltd./Melbourne Sydney/Printed in England.
n.d. [1915]
224pp, col. frontis. & 4 b/w illus. by C. Nuttall, clo., 190x120mm. CLRC
518 Another copy, as above, but bound in bd. with clo. spine. KMM

519 Whitcombe's Story Books/RALPH IN THE BUSH/by/Charles Barrett, C.M.Z.S./Author of/"In Australian Wilds"/"The Isle of Palms" Etc./For children aged 9 to 10 years/[device]/Whitcombe and Tombs Pty Ltd/Melbourne, Sydney, Perth/Associated Houses:/Christchurch, Auckland, Wellington, Dunedin/Invercargill and London
n.d. [1921]
59pp, 5pp adv., b/w frontis. & 9 b/w photographic illus., pic. wrappers, 180x120mm. MK
See McLaren 407

520 RAMBLES/ROUND THE ZOO/By/Charles Barrett, C.M.Z.S., Author of/"In Australian Wilds"/"The Isle of Palms"/"The Golden Hawk" etc./Whitcombe & Tombs Limited/Melbourne, Auckland Christchurch/Dunedin, Wellington/and London/1923
123pp, 1p adv., b/w frontis. & 42 b/w illus., clo., 180x115mm. ANL
Simple articles on zoo animals, not specifically for children.

521 BUSHLAND BABIES/By/Charles Barrett/C.M.Z.S., M.B.O.U., Author of 'From Range to Sea'/'The Isle of Palms', 'In Australian Wilds', Etc./With 26 illustrations/Australia/Cornstalk Publishing Company/Arnold Place, Sydney/1924
158pp, frontis. & b/w photographic illus., clo., 175x110mm. Platypus Series. KMM

522 THE/WEEKLY TIMES/WILD NATURE BOOK/By Charles Barrett, C.M.Z.S./Author of "In Australian Wilds" "Egyptian/Hours" Etc./Melbourne/Printed and Published by/The Herald and Weekly Times Ltd/Wholly set up &c 1931
96pp, b/w frontis. & 34 col. illus. & b/w photographs in text, col. pic. wrappers, 223x155mm. KP
Based on author's nature notes for boys in the *Weekly Times.*

523 AUSTRALIAN WILD LIFE/By/Charles Barrett/Author of "The Sun Nature Books"/[device]/Georgian House/Melbourne/1946/An Australiana Society Publication.
1st publ. Sept 1943; rpt. 1946
x,116pp, col. frontis. & 6 col. plates & 16 b/w plates, clo., 230x165mm. CLRC

524 THE SECRET OF COCONUT/ISLAND/A Treasure Quest in/Torres Strait/By/Charles Barrett/Author of "The Isle of Palms"/"The Golden Sphinx" etc./Cassell & Company Ltd./London, Toronto, Melbourne/and Sydney
August 1946
240pp, b/w frontis. & 3 f/p illus.(sgd. 'Crampton') drawings in text, clo., 180x120mm. KMM
525 Second edition September 1947
Contents as above. KMM

526 WARRIGAL JOE/A Tale of the/Never Never/by/Donald Barr/Cassell & Company Ltd. London Toronto Melbourne/and Sydney.
1946
255pp, b/w frontis. & 3 f/p b/w illus., clo., 180x115mm. KMM
• Rpt 1948. KMM

527 THE/PENGUIN PEOPLE/by/Charles Barrett/F.R.Z.S./Cassell & Company Ltd./London New York Toronto Melbourne
1948
64pp, col. frontis. & 7 col. illus., b/w photographic illus. throughout, b/w drawings in text, dec. bd., dec. e/p, 245x180mm. CLRC
Coloured illustrations by R. Malcolm Warner

528 WILD LIFE OF AUSTRALIA/AND NEW GUINEA/By/Charles Barrett/F.R.Z.S., C.M.Z.S. (London and New York) with 83 illustrations/William Heinemann Ltd./Melbourne London Toronto
1954
229pp (inc. index), 1p acknowledgements, 1p introduction, col. frontis. & 24pp b/w photographic illus., numerous b/w drawings in text, clo., 215x135mm. BBC

529 WILD LIFE/IN/AUSTRALIA/Illustrated/By Charles Barrett F.R.Z.S./A Colorgravure publication
Melbourne, n.d. [1950]
240pp, (inc. 5pp index), col. & b/w photographs throughout, clo., 235x175mm. CLRC

BARRETT, Charles (ed.)
530 THE/AUSTRALIAN JUNIOR/ENCYCLOPAEDIA/Editor: Charles Barrett, F.R.Z.S., C.M.Z.S./Assistant Editor: Brian W. Harris/With an introduction by/Professor Walter Murdoch, C.B.E., M.A./Volume one/Published by/Georgian House/for The Australian Junior Encyclopaedia Pty. Ltd./Melbourne
1951
2 vols, 998pp (inc. index), 24pp col. illus. & 7pp maps, b/w photographic illus. throughout, clo., 240x180mm. NSL:M
531 THE/AUSTRALIAN JUNIOR/ENCYCLOPAEDIA/Editor: Charles Barrett, F.R.Z.S., C.M.Z.S./Revision Editor: R.P.C. Bower, M.A. (Oxon.)/With an introduction by/Professor Walter Murdoch, C.B.E., M.A./Volume one/Published by/The Australian Educational Foundation/Sydney
1956; new editions 1958, 1959, 1961

3 vols, 996pp (inc. index), 65pp col. & part. col. illus., 8pp maps, clo., 240x180mm. NSL:M

BARRETT, Charles & SHEAD, Isobel Ann

532 KOOBORR THE KOALA/by Charles Barrett & Isobel Ann Shead/decorations by/Joan Kiddell-Monroe/[drawing]/Oxford University Press/London New York Toronto
n.d. [1940]
48pp, part-col. frontis. & throughout & b/w drawings in text, pic. bd., pic. e/p, 250x190mm. NSL:M
1st publ. 1940, 2nd imp. 1942, 3rd imp. 1944, 4th imp. 1946, 5th imp. 1953. KMM

533 1942 and 1943 eds as above & bound in pic. clo. KP
Later eds bound in pic. bd.

BARRETT, Michael

534 TRAITOR/AT TWENTY/FATHOMS/Michael Barrett/[drawing]/Illustrated by John Robinson/Collins/St. James's Place, London/1963
192pp, b/w headpieces, bd., 190x125mm. Grant

535 ANTARCTIC/SECRET/Michael Barrett/With illustrations by/Stuart Tresilian/J. M. Dent & Sons Ltd./London
1965
170pp, b/w frontis. & b/w drawings in text, clo., 190x120mm. CLRC

Barrier Reef Annual 1972

536 BARRIER/REEF/ANNUAL/1972
Copyright 1971 by Norfolk International Films Ltd. Publ. in Great Britain by World Distributors (Manchester) Limited. Printed in Italy
79pp, col. & part-col. illus. throughout, pic. bd., pic. e/p, 263x190mm. WRT

BARRINGTON, G. W.

537 G. W. Barrington/BROKEN VOYAGE/[vignette]/Hutchinson of London
1958
214pp, unillus., clo., 185x120mm. CLRC
The story of two teenage boys who set out to sail a yawl to Australia but get involved in adventure in the Greek islands. No further reference to Australia.

538 DESERT GHOST/G. W. Barrington/Hutchinson of London
1959
164pp, unillus., clo., 185x120mm. CLRC
The story describes the adventures of two boys in the Western Australian desert, & is a sequel to *Broken Voyage.*

BARRINGTON, George

539 CAPTAIN GEORGE BARRINGTON,/THE GENTLEMAN HIGHWAYMAN,/and the/White Sybil of St James's;/or, the/Perils of the Road in the Days of Sheppard, Turpin and Claude Duval/[illus. with 4 scenes]/7 Red Lion Court, Fleet St London W.C.
n.d. [1860?]
16pp & illus. wrappers. Back wrapper advertises sheets of scenes of a play 'The Heart of Fire' in a series entitled 'The British Boys Model Theatre' comprising 8 sheets with the book of the play &c, 260x195mm. ANL
Story begins p1 with illus. captioned 'Your blood be upon your own heads', another ⅔ page engraving, p9 showing Barrington conversing with a girl in bed. One Penny Weekly No. 2.

BARROW, Freda

540 THE TRANSIT OF NAN/By/Freda Barrow/The Lothian Book Publishing Co. Pty. Ltd./Melbourne and Sydney/1923
86pp, unillus., dec wrappers, 180x110mm. ANL
Although classified by the publishers as a children's book, this story of the activities of an imaginary adopted child does not appear to have been intended for children.

BARROW, John (ed.)

541 COOK'S VOYAGES/OF DISCOVERY/Edited by/John Barrow, Esq. F.S.A/With eight illustrations in colour by/John Williamson/London/Adam and Charles Black/1904
417pp, viii (inc. 2pp preface), 2pp advts, col. frontis. & 7 f/p col. illus., 1 fold-out facsimile of a page of Cook's Log-book, 11 titled vignettes throughout text, half page map, pic. clo., 195x130mm. HBM
• Rpt as above 1910. KP

542 COOK'S/VOYAGES OF DISCOVERY/Edited by/John Barrow, F.R.S., F.S.A/with four illustrations/in colour/A. & C. Black, Ltd./4, 5 & 6 Soho Square, London W.1.
1904; rpt 1910, 1919; reissued in Black's Boys' and Girls' Library, 1925; rpt 1930
417pp, 2pp preface, 2pp adv., col. frontis. & 3 f/p col. illus. by John Williamson, pic. clo., 185x130mm. HBM
Includes a 7-page 'Life of Captain James Cook' by Captain J. King.

BARROW, Lyn

543 YOU'RE TOO YOUNG!/YOU'RE TOO OLD!/Solutions to the Problems of Teenagers/—and their parents/Lyn Barrow/[illus.]/R. J. Cleary Publishing Pty Ltd. Sydney
1971
84pp, b/w illus., pic. wrappers, 184x120mm. KP

BARROWCLIFF, C. B.

The KOALA BEAR. *See* Barry Books No. 2

BARROWS, Marjorie

544 JO JO/By Marjorie Barrows/Illustrated by Ivy L. Wallace./Rand McNally & Company. Chicago/Established 1856/Copyright MCMLXIV by Rand McNally & Company. Copyright MCMLXIV under International Copyright/Union by Rand McNally & Company. All Rights reserved. Printed in U.S.A. 1964
20pp, col. illus. throughout, pic. bd., 200x160mm. KMM

BARRY, John Arthur

545 A SON OF/THE SEA/By/John Arthur Barry/Author of/"Steve Brown's Bunyip", "In the Great Deep",/"The Luck of the Native Born", etc./[publisher's device]/London/Duckworth & Co./3 Henrietta Street, Covent Garden, W.C.
1899; reissued 1909
352pp, unillus., pic. clo., 185x120mm. NSL:M

546 SEA YARNS/By/John Arthur Barry/Author of/'Steve Brown's Bunyip' 'The Luck of the Native Born'/'In the Great Deep' 'A Son of the Sea' &c/with eight coloured illustrations/by/Charles Pears/London: 38 Soho Square, W.& R. Chambers, Limited/Edinburgh: 339 High Street
[1910]
300pp, col. frontis. & 7 col. plates, pic. clo., 185x130mm. KMM
Books for Boys series.

BARRY, Margaret

547 JULIE/WESTAWAY/by Margaret Barry/Cover frontispiece by L. F. Lupton/[device]/Kingfisher Books/5 Wigmore Street, London, W1
1958
185pp, b/w frontis., clo., 184x120mm. KP

Barry Books
Format example:
548 THE KOALA BEAR/A Book for children of all ages/from five to seventy five/Written by C. B. Barrowcliff/Illustrations by Ambrose/2/[device] Barry/Book/The "Barry Books" series/[six titles listed as below]/Published by/C. B. Barrowcliff 173 Pitt St. Sydney NSW/(Next to New G.P.O.)
n.d. [194-?]
16pp col. illus., col. pic. bd., 230x185mm. VMOU
Others in series:
549 No.1. IF THE ZOO GOT THE FLUE, unseen
No.2. as above
550 No.3 KOOKABURRAS CALLING, unseen
551 NO.4 KANGAROO CAPERS, unseen
552 No.5 THE 'K' CORROBOREE, unseen
553 No.6 RINGTAIL RHYMES, by E.W.K. details as above, WJSB
Unlisted:
554 THE/CIRCUS/Written and illustrated/by/Mattie and Ambrose/[drawing]/[device—Barry/Books]/Published by C. B. Barrowcliff 173 Pitt St, Sydney NSW./(Next to the new G.P.O.)
12pp, part col. illus. throughout, col. pic. bd., 240x187mm. WRT

BARTLEET, Margaret Traill
555 WILDERNESS/HOUSE/A Story for Girls/By/Margaret Traill Bartleet/Sydney/Dymock's Book Arcade Limited/1952
104pp, unillus., clo., 210x135mm. KMM

BARTLETT, Evelyn
556 ROSEMARY IN/RHYMELAND/Written and illustrated by/Evelyn Bartlett/Coloured frontispiece by/Edith Flaherty/Printed and Published by/Paterson's Printing Press Ltd./882 Hay Street Perth/Western Australia/Price:/Three shillings and ninepence
n.d. [1939]
95pp, col. frontis., b/w drawings in text, bd., 250x175mm. NSL:M

557 DUMPER/THE/KANGAROO/By/Evelyn Bartlett/Illustrated by/Audrey Addison/Angus and Robertson/Sydney London Melbourne Wellington
1955
82pp, part. col. & b/w drawings in text, clo., 235x160mm. BBC
• Rpt 1957. KMM

558 DUMPER AND/THE CIRCUS/[drawing]/by/Evelyn Bartlett/Illustrated by/Irene Maher/Angus and Robertson
Sydney 1958
121pp, b/w frontis. & 7 f/p b/w illus., b/w drawings in text throughout, clo., dec. e/p, 230x145mm. KMM

BARTLETT, Stephen
See 'Slade, Gurney'

[BARTON, Charlotte (née Waring) by first marriage, Atkinson]
559 A/MOTHER'S OFFERING/TO HER/CHILDREN:/By a Lady,/Long Resident in/New South Wales/[6 line quotation]/Sydney:/Printed at The "Gazette" Office, Lower George Street
1841
viii+216pp (inc. 'Lines written during a Storm in the Bay of Biscay'), unillus., bd. with clo. spine, 170x110mm. CLRC
The first book for children publ. in Australia.

BARTON, E. M.
560 A FEW OF GRANDMAMMA'S PRIZES/FOR THE LITTLE ONES
Gibbs Shallard & Co., Sydney [1855]
[32]pp, unillus., paper wrappers, cover title, 180x120mm. NSL:M
Verses printed only on recto of pages; many of the poems are dated 1882–1884. One page opening is blank.

BARTON, F. K. (ed.)
561 NINE PLAYS FOR/PLAY DAYS/(For Upper Primary Classes)/Collected and Edited by F. K. Barton/[device]/The Shakespeare Head/London: New York: Sydney: Durban: Paris
n.d. [inscribed 1947]
134pp (inc. 3pp preface &c, 6pp notes), 9 f/p b/w illus., limp clo., 177x110mm. MC
9 plays by Musette Morell, Kenneth McKeown, Brian Vrepont, & others. School ed.

BASSER, Kathleen Veronica [Mrs Leonard Abram]
562 FRIA/AND THE/SEA/WITCH/Written/by Vron/Basser/Illustrated by Silvia/Tiarks
Clock Publishing Co., Sydney, n.d. [1944]
32pp, col. frontis. & 3 col. illus., b/w drawings throughout, pic. bd., dec. e/p, 240x180mm. ANL

563 GLORY/BIRD/Pictures by/Elaine Haxton/Story by Veronica Basser/John Sands Pty. Ltd. Publishers Sydney and Melbourne.
n.d. [1947]
28pp, col. illus. throughout dec. bd., dec. e/p, 190x240mm. ANL

564 THE MARTINS/OF MONTROSE/by/Veronica Basser/Australasian Publishing Company/Sydney Wellington London.
1948
251pp, b/w frontis., (sgd,'Adye')clo., 185x115mm. ANL

565 PONNY THE/PENGUIN/by/Veronica Basser/Illustrated by/Edwina Bell/Australasian Publishing Company/Sydney Wellington London
1948
90pp, 6 f/p b/w drawings & drawings in text, dec. bd., 190x135mm. The York Series. KMM
566 PONNY THE/PENGUIN/by/Veronica Basser/Illustrated by/Edwina Bell/Australasian Publishing Company/Sydney Wellington London/in association with George G. Harrap & Co. Ltd.
1948; rpt 1949, 1950, 1954
As above. KMM

567 ROUND/THE/YEAR/VERSES/by/Veronica Basser/School Projects Pty. Limited/Rockdale N.S.W.
n.d. [1956]
32pp, b/w illus. throughout, dec. wrappers, cover title, 200x130mm. ANL

568 BRIGHT-EYES/THE GLIDER POSSUM/by/Veronica Basser/illustrated by/Richard Richardson/Sydney/Australasian Publishing Company/in association with George G. Harrap Ltd./London
71pp, b/w frontis. & 22 b/w illus., pic. clo., 210x135mm. KMM
569 BRIGHT-EYES/THE GLIDER POSSUM . . . [School edition as above]/Australasian Publishing Company/Sydney Wellington London
• Rpt 1958
Bound in limp clo., 185x120mm. KMM

BATEMAN, Robert
570 QUEST/FOR NUGGETS/Robert Bateman/Ronald Whiting & Wheaton/London
1967

157pp (inc. 2pp preface), b/w frontis. & 17 b/w illus., clo., 195x125mm. CLRC
Story about the search for gold in Australia during the nineteenth century. Frontis. is a facsimile of an entry in the original diary; other illustrations are reproductions of contemporary engravings from the *Illustrated London News.*

BATES, Daisy
571 TALES TOLD TO/KABBARLI/Aboriginal Legends collected by/Daisy Bates/retold by Barbara Ker Wilson/illustrated by Harold Thomas/Angus and Robertson
Sydney 1972
101pp (inc. 7pp biographical note by Elizabeth Salter, 2pp editor's note), 26 b/w illus., clo., 240x180mm. KMM

572 TALES TOLD TO/KABBARLI/Aboriginal Legends collected by/Daisy Bates/retold by Barbara Ker Wilson/illustrated by Harold Thomas/Crown Publishers, Inc. New York
1972
Details as in Australian ed. KMM

BATES, Frederic
573 [drawing]/SALLY/THE/CALF WHO STRAYED/ Story and/Illustrations/by/Frederic Bates
Sydney [Offset Printing Co.] 1949
25pp, col. & part. col. illus. throughout, dec. bd., dec. e/p, 180x120mm. ANL

574 A tale of ten of the Birds/and Animals of the/ Australian Bush on their/annual picnic/PERCY/ 'POSSUM'S/PICNIC [drawing]
Young's Merchandising Company, 8 Spring St., Sydney, n.d. [195-?]
16pp, col. & b/w illus. on alternate page openings, col. pic. wrapper, 300x245mm. TG

BATESON, C. E.
575 EXIT BOGIE!/Story for Children,/By/C. E. Bateson./Price—Sixpence—J. Bryan, Print
[Perth], n.d. [190-?]
12pp, 1 f/p b/w illus., adv. inside front & back covers, cover title, wrappers, 210x140mm. WJSB
Adv. are for Perth businesses. Includes a song 'Little Fairies' by O.G.

BATESON, Charles
A CHARTMAKER
A GOLD COMMISSIONER
A SAILOR
A SOLDIER
A SURVEYOR *See* Early Australians

BATTEN, Peter
THE KOOKABURRA WHO COULDN'T LAUGH. *See* Australian Youth Plays

BATTERSBY, Marie A.
576 LITTLE KANGA'S/POCKET/[col. illus.]/Pictures by Mary A. Brooks/Story by Marie A. Battersby/Made and Printed in Great Britain/Published by Sampson Low, London
n.d. [195-?]
[26]pp, col. illus. throughout, col. pic. e/p, col. pic. bd., 180x115mm. CLRC

BAUM, Jiri
577 KOLEM ZEMEKOULE (Around the Earth)
Mlada fronta, Prague 1956
247pp. SLCSR

BAVIN, Edyth Ellen [Lady Bavin, née Winchcombe]
578 BABY/BALLADS/Edyth Bavin
Printed by Smith & Lane, Sydney 1927; edition limited to 275 copies
46pp, b/w drawings, illus. by Bertha Sloane & Margot Finlayson, wrappers, dec. cover title, 130x215mm. NSL:M
Verses.

BAWDEN, Sharman N. & STONE, Douglas M.
GOLDEN STAMP BOOK OF AUSTRALIAN GEMSTONES and
GOLDEN STAMP BOOK OF/AUSTRALIAN/ROCKS &/MINERALS. *See* Golden Stamp Books

BAXTER, Fred
579 Fred Baxter/ALL THAT MONEY/Illustrated by Sandra Hargrave/[device]/Angus and Robertson
Sydney 1967
151pp, b/w frontis., b/w chapter headings throughout, clo., 195x130mm. KMM

580 SNAKE/FOR/SUPPER/Fred Baxter/illustrated by/ Genevieve Melrose/Lansdowne Press
Melbourne 1968
173pp (inc. 1p preface), b/w frontis. & 5 f/p b/w illus., map e/p, clo., 215x135mm. CLRC
Story based on the pioneers of the East Gippsland area in Victoria.

BAXTER, Robyn
581 AUSTRALIAN/CAMPING/by/Robyn Baxter/ illustrated by/Litho colour/Readabout Books
Readabout Publishers Pty Ltd, Crow's Nest, N.S.W., 1964
24pp, col. & part. col. illus. throughout, stiff pic. wrappers, 215x180mm. KMM
Practical handbook on camping.

BAYLEY, George
582 FIFTY FABLES/FOR/LITTLE FOLKS,/Versified from the Italian/of/Pignotti, Gozzi, Bertola, Rossi, Clasio,/ Passeroni, etc./By/Rev. George Bayley, M.A. Oxon./ [quotation]/Sydney:/Printed and Published by Reading and Wellbank/1861
138pp (inc. 2pp notes), stiff wrappers, 170x100mm. ANL

BAYLIS, Richard
583 To my Mother and Father/SIX AUSTRALIAN BUSH SONGS/Words by Richard Baylis/No 1 The Land of "Who Knows Where!"/[other titles listed]/Music by/ William G. James/Composer of "The Sun-God" [&c 3 lines]/All rights reserved 118896 Net Price 4s0d./G. Ricordi & Co./265 Regent Street/London. W./[3 lines]/Copyright MCMXXII by G. Ricordi & Co. 1922
28pp, unillus., wrappers, 340x260mm. ANL

BAYLISS, A. E. M. (ed.)
584 DAMPIER'S VOYAGES/Edited by/A. E. M Bayliss, M.A./Editor of "A Pageant of History"/"Pen Portraits and Character Sketches"/etc./[device]/George G. Harrap & Co. Ltd./London Toronto Bombay Sydney
1931; first Australian edition 1945
219pp, 4pp exercises, unillus., dec. map e/p, clo., 170x120mm. KMM
Produced as a school textbook.

BAYLY, Elisabeth Boyd
585 UNDER THE SHE-OAKS/By/Elisabeth Boyd Bayly/ Author of/'A New Zealand Courtship', 'Jonathan Merle', 'Alfreda Holme'/'A Bit of Wool', etc./London/ The Religious Tract Society/4 Bouverie Street and 65 St. Paul's Churchyard, E.C.
n.d. [1903]

383pp, b/w frontis. & 6 b/w plates, by J. Macfarlane, clo., 194x130mm.
A doubtful children's book, unless classified as a romance for older girls. NSL:M
586 Second ed. as above with 16pp advs. KP
Also author of *Alfreda Home*, not a children's book

BAYNE, Mollie
OUR IRON AND STEEL. *See* Australia at Work

BEACH, Charles A.
587 THE WAY TO WIN;/A Story of Adventure/Afloat and Ashore./by Charles A. Beach,/Author of "Lost Lenore". "Ran away from Home" etc. etc./ London:/ Lockwood & Co.,7 Stationers' Hall Court./1869
278pp & 16 pp adv., b/w frontis. & 3 f/p b/w illus, dec. clo., 170x105mm. CLRC
Story of adventures of boy emigrant to Australia who eventually makes good & returns to England.
588 THE/WAY TO WIN/or,/Afloat and Ashore./By/ Charles A. Beach,/Author of "Waifs of the World", "Too Good for Anything", etc./with original illustrations/London:/ Frederick Warne and Co.,/ and New York
n.d.
218pp & 2 pp preface, engraved frontis. & 3 f/p engravings, dec. clo., 180x120mm. KMM
See also Thomas Mayne Reid who edited Beach's *Lost Lenore* and under whose name the book was published, thus achieving greater sales for the book

'Beacon' series
Anonymous uniform booklets publ. by W. H. Honey Pub. Co. Sydney
n.d. [copyright 1943]
16pp, 4 col. illus. & b/w drawings throughout, pic. wrappers, cover title, 250x185mm. NSL:M
Titles include:
589 A DAY AT THE ZOO, illus. by L. G. Jordan
590 JACK AND THE BEANSTALK
591 MY FAVOURITE COLOURING BOOK, illus. M. Crisp
592 MY NURSERY RHYME BOOK, illus. by M. Crisp
593 NURSERY RHYMES, illus. L. G. Jordan
594 THE PAINTING BOOK
595 THE SLEEPING BEAUTY, illus. Rhys Williams
596 TEN LITTLE TOMMYCODS, illus. by "Gilly" [D. H. Gilmore]
Some titles also occur in same publisher's 'Moonbeam Series'.

BEADLE & Co. [Publishers]
STARBUCK, Roger. THE BOY SEA-THUGS; or, The Pirate's Daughter. A Romance of the Lost Islands, July 1, 1877 (Starr's Ten Cent Pocket Library Series). Unseen
Another ed. entitled "The Boy Captain;" or The Pirate's Daughter, 1878 (Beadle's Half-Dime Library) & another as above 1884 (Beadle's Pocket Library). Unseen
CLARK, C. Dunning. THE FLYAWAY AFLOAT; or, Yankee Boys' Round the World, VIII, No 390—Sept 1 1877 to No 400, Nov 10, 1877 (The New York Saturday Journal) (NY. Beadle & Adams). Unseen
BADGER, Joseph E. BUSH AND DIGGINGS; or, Wild Life in Australia. XII, No 590, July 2 1881 to No. 604, Oct 8, 1881 (The NY Sat. Journal) (NY. Beadle and Adams). Unseen
Information from Johannsen, *The House of Beadle and Adams*

BEAL, Dawn & David
597 I WANT TO BE/A MODEL/Dawn and David Beal Thomas Nelson (Aust.) Ltd, Melbourne, 1971
30pp, b/w & col. photographic illus., pic. bd., 245x180mm. CLRC
Other titles in series:
598 I WANT TO BE AN AIRLINE HOSTESS
599 I WANT TO BE AN AIRLINE PILOT
600 I WANT TO BE AN ARTIST
601 I WANT TO BE A FERRY BOAT CAPTAIN
602 I WANT TO BE A VET

BEAL, George
603 THE/QUESTION AND ANSWER/BOOK OF AUSTRALIA/Written by George Beal/[contents]/ Odhams Books/London New York Sydney Toronto Published for Odhams Books by Paul Hamlyn Pty Ltd, 176 South Creek, Dee Why West, NSW, 1968
64pp (inc. covers), 1p index (inside back cover), extended col. illus. t.p. (on frontis, e/p & flyleaf), col. & part. col. illus. on alternate page openings, pic. bd., 270x200mm. CLRC
• Rpt 1969 as above. KP

BEAMAN, S. G. Hulme
604 WALLY/THE KANGAROO/[drawing]/Frederick Warne & Co. Ltd.
London, n.d.
12pp (inc. 6pp col. illus.), dec. t.p., col. pic. wrappers, 155x120mm. KMM
'Out of the Ark' Books.
Simple story about toy animals with no reference to Australia.
French edition
605 JUMBO/LE KANGOUROU/par S. G. Hulme Beaman/Frederick Warne & Co. Ltd
London, Warne, n.d. [195-?]
14pp (inc. 6pp printed in col.)
Collection 'Arche de Noé'. ANL

BEANEY, Ailsa
606 GUMLEAF/FARM/By/Ailsa Beaney/Illustrated by/ Fay Crozier [b/w drawing on t.p.]
Davies Bros Ltd, Hobart, n.d. [194-?]
30pp, 6 f/p col. illus., 7 smaller col. & numerous b/w illus., 202x155mm. NSL:M

'BEAR, Humphrey B.'
See Rule, Gordon A.

BEARD, H. Allen
607 COMPANIONS/OF THE BUSH/by/H. Allen Beard/London/The Boys' Own Paper Office/4 Bouverie Street, E.C.4.
n.d. [1936?]
192pp, col. frontis., [sgd. 'Arch Webb'] clo., 180x120mm. KMM

608 THE/LITTLE BROWN HORSE/By/H. Allen Beard/ Illustrated by Radcliffe Wilson/Blackie & Son Limited/ London and Glasgow
n.d.
208pp, b/w frontis. & 2 f/p b/w plates, clo., 182x120mm. ANL
The story of an Australian horse trained for a little girl to ride. The Sceptre Library—Boys.

BEARNE, David
609 PORTRAITS/Stories for Old and Young/by/David Bearne, S. J./Melbourne/William P. Linehan/309-11 Little Collins Street/1906
108pp, 4pp advts, b/w portrait frontis. & 9 photographic illus., dec. clo., 180x135mm. CLRC
Biographical religious sketches of unlikely interest to children.

BEATTY, Bill
610 AMAZING AUSTRALIA/By/Bill Beatty/[portrait]/[8 lines]/Sandman Series/Printed and Published by/John Sands Pty Ltd, Sydney, NSW Australia
n.d.
64pp, b/w illus. throughout by Harry Wann, wrappers, 180x115mm. KP

611 AUSTRALIAN/WONDERS/Believe Bill Beatty/Illustrations/By/Seale/Amazing Australia/Publishers/Sydney NSW Australia
1945
104pp, b/w illus. throughout, bd., 210x120mm. KP

BEAUCHAMP, Mary Annette
See [ARNHIM, Countess von] THE APRIL BABY'S BOOK OF TUNES

Beauty and the Beast and Rapunzel
612 BEAUTY AND/THE BEAST/AND/RAPUNZEL/[4 lines text]
Publ. by Australian Universities Press Pty Ltd, Chatswood NSW 1971
[25]pp, col. illus. throughout, col. pic. bd. & e/p, 318x232mm. KP
Fairy story with col. photographs of dolls. 7 other titles in series listed on back cover. No Australian subject matter.

BEAVER, Racey
613 Imperial Edition no. 297/MORE CHILDREN'S/SONGS/Words by/Racey Beaver/Music by/Edith HARRHY/[10 songs listed]/Allan & Co.,/Melbourne/Sydney Adelaide Bendigo
n.d. [stamped 1934]
16pp, unillus., wrappers, 307x233mm. VSL
Advertised in the *Argus* 24/9/27.

BÉCHERVAISE, John M.
ANTARCTICA. *See* Australian Explorers

AUSTRALIA AND ANTARCTICA. *See* Around Australia Program

AUSTRALIAN MOUNTAINS AND RIVERS. *See* Around Australia Program

MOUNTAINEERING. *See* Life in Australia

BECKE, Louis
614 TOM WALLIS/A Tale of the South/Seas by Louis Becke/Author of "Wild Life in Southern Seas"/"By Reef and Palm","Admiral Philip" *[sic]* etc./with eleven illustrations by/Lancelot Speed/[device]/London The Religious/Tract Society/56 Paternoster Row and 65 St./Paul's Churchyard
n.d. [first edition 1900]
320pp, b/w frontis. & 10 f/p b/w illus., pic. clo., 195x130mm. KMM

615 TOM WALLIS/A Tale of the South/Seas by Louis Becke/Author of "Wild Life in Southern Seas"/"By Reef and Palm", "Admiral Philip" *[sic]* etc./with eleven illustrations by/Lancelot Speed/[device]/Second impression/London The Religious/Tract Society/56 Paternoster Row and 65 St./Paul's Churchyard
Details as above. CLRC
3rd imp. n.d., as above. KP
5th imp. n.d., as above. KP
6th imp. n.d., as above. KMM

616 TOM WALLIS/A Tale of the South Seas/By/Louis Becke/Author of/'Wild Life in Southern Seas'. 'By Reef and Palm'./'Admiral Philip'*[sic]* etc./Seventh impression/R.T.S., 4 Bouverie Street, London, E.C.4
320pp, col. frontis. & 1 col. plate, clo., col. onlay on front cover, 186x120mm. KMM

617 THE SETTLERS OF/KAROSSA CREEK/And other Stories of Australian Bush Life/By/Louis Becke/Author of 'Tom Wallis', 'Wild Life in the Southern Seas', etc. etc./with three illustrations by J. Finnemore/London/The Religious Tract Society/4 Bouverie Street and 65 St. Paul's Churchyard E.C.
n.d. [First published 1906]
240pp, 16pp adv., b/w. frontis. & 2 b/w plates., clo., 195x130mm. KMM

618 Rpt as above but with col. frontis & 2 b/w plates. KMM

619 THE/SETTLERS OF KAROSSA CREEK/and other stories of/Australian Bush Life/By/Louis Becke/Author of/'Tom Wallis', 'Wild Life in the Southern Isles' *[sic]* etc./with coloured and other illustrations/London/The Religious Tract Society/4 Bouverie Street and 65 St. Paul's Churchyard
n.d. [inscribed 1920]
240pp, 16pp adv., col. frontis. & 2 b/w illus., pic. clo., 195x125mm. KMM
One illustration from book printed in colour on front cover, with title & author in gilt, & a drawing of a man with a miner's pick on spine.

620 THE SETTLERS OF/KAROSSA CREEK/and other stories of Australian Bush Life/By/Louis Becke/Author of 'Tom Wallis', 'Wild Life in the Southern Seas', etc. etc./with three illustrations by J. Finnemore/Philadelphia/J. B. Lippincott Company/London: The Religious Tract Society
n.d.
240pp, b/w frontis. & 2 f/p b/w illus., both frontis. & t.p. printed on coated paper, pic. clo. with only book title in gilt, 190x135mm. Grant
Other variations seen in pic. cloth bdg, and some with t.p. printed in red and blue. KP

BECKLEY, Rene
621 Folk/Tales/of the/World/AUSTRALIA/Rene Beckley/Illustrations by Dean Mitchell/E. J. Arnold & Sons Limited Leeds
1965
80pp, part. col. frontis. & 8 f/p part. col. illus., part. col. chapter headings, etc., clo., 205x155mm. KMM

BEDFORD, Eric
622 SCUM O'THE SEAS/by/Eric Bedford/The Currawong Publishing Company/32 Jamieson Street, Sydney
n.d. [1944]
240pp, bd., 180x120mm. ANL
Adventures of a boy who ran away from Sydney during the gold rush period.

BEDFORD, H. Louisa
623 LOVE AND A WILL-O'-THE-WISP; with 3 illustrations by J. Macfarlane
London, n.d. [1908]
'The story tells of the devotion of a sister who, to be near her brother ordered to Australia to save his life, renounces a coveted appointment in the very moment of delight at its attainment.' Set in South Australia.
Unseen: Advertised with other children's books in *Wallaby Hill*, M. Bradford Whiting (R.T.S., 1895)

624 JACK, THE ENGLISHMAN/By/H. Louisa Bedford/Author of/"Her only son, Isaac", "Mrs. Merriman's Godchild", etc./Illustrated by Wal Paget/London:/Society for Promoting Christian Knowledge/Northumberland Avenue, W.C.; 43, Queen Victoria St., E.C./Brighton: 129 North Street/New York: E. S. Gorham
n.d. [school prize 1914]
160pp, 16pp advts, tinted frontis. & 2 other f/p tinted

illus., clo. (with frontis. onlay on front cover), 190x120mm. KMM
625 Another copy as above, but London/Society for Promoting/Christian Knowledge/ New York and Toronto: The Macmillan Co.
Details as above. KP

626 A HOME IN THE/BUSH/By/H. L. Bedford/Author of 'Barbara's Heroes', 'Under One Standard' etc/ London/Society for Promoting Christian Knowledge/ Northumberland Avenue, W.C.; 43, Queen Victoria St., E.C./Brighton: 129 North Street/New York: E. S. Gorham
n.d. [1913]
120pp, 8pp adv., part. col. frontis. & 10pp b/w drawings by Ernest Prater, pic. clo., 190x120mm. VSL
Also author of,
THE OTHER ONE, Collins 1922
About an Australian boy in England
UNDER ONE STANDARD; or, The Touch that Makes us Kin, Illus. H. Piffard, S.P.C.K. 1923 (Story of the Maori War)
BARBARA'S HEROES, Sheldon Press 1931 (unseen)
NETTA'S CALL, R.T.S. 1931 Not Australian

BEDFORD, Ruth M.
627 ROSYCHEEKS &/GOLDENHEAD/Verses by Ruth M. Bedford/with sixteen colour illus-/trations by Mabel L. Webb/[publisher's device]/London: Alston Rivers, Limited/16 Gray's Inn Road, Holborn, W.C.
n.d. [1913]
63pp, col. frontis. & 15 f/p col. illus., bd., 240x180mm. NSL:M

628 FAIRIES/AND/FANCIES/[drawing]/By/Ruth Bedford/with seventeen page illustrations by/Mela Koehler Broman/A. & C. Black Ltd./4, 5, & 6 Soho Square London W.1./1929
67pp, col. frontis. & 7 col. illus., 9 f/p b/w illus., dec. bd., 235x170mm. NSL:M
Children's verses.

629 HUNDREDS AND/THOUSANDS/By/Ruth Bedford/with decorations by/Pixie O'Harris/ [drawing]/Sydney/Dymock's Book Arcade Ltd.
1934
49pp, b/w drawings throughout, clo., 145x95mm. CLRC
Verses.

630 WHO'S WHO IN RHYME/AND WITHOUT REASON/by/Ruth Bedford/Australasian Publishing Company/Sydney Wellington London
1948
33pp, b/w drawings throughout, bd., 215x130mm. NSL:M
Humorous verses.
RHYMES BY RUTH By a child
1893, 1896
Written between the author's eighth & fourteenth year; not a book for children. NSL:M

BEDNALL, Colin
DINGOES. *See* Life in Australia

Bedtime Stories for Tiny Tots
BEDTIME/STORIES/[drawings]/for TINY TOTS. *See* Gunn & Taylor

Bedtime Stories for Young Australians
631 BEDTIME/STORIES/FOR YOUNG AUSTRALIANS/illustrated by Gwen Lovell/Paul Hamlyn/Sydney, London, New York, Toronto
Dee Why West NSW, 1971
208pp, 27 f/p col. illus. & b/w illus. in text, bd. (with pic. d/w), pic. e/p, 280x200mm. CLRC
13 Australian authors contributed 26 unpubl. stories. Listed on back flap 366 Goodnight Stories; Giant all Colour Book of Fairy Tales.

BEEBY, Ida
632 DANCE CHILD DANCE/By/Ida Beeby/in collaboration with Joan Wilkinson/Mary Senior and Morry Hertz of the/Patch Theatre Perth, W.A./Second impression January 1955/[drawing]/[5 lines of notes relating to copyright]/Paterson Press Limited, Publishers/65 Murray Street Perth, W.A.
104pp, music, movement, sketches &c, pic. bd., 275x225mm. KMM

BEER, Alfred
633 THE HEIR OF/BRAGWELL HALL/By Alfred Beer/ With Seven Illustrations by J. Finnemore/London/The Religious Tract Society/4 Bouverie Street and 65 St. Paul's Churchyard, E.C.
n.d. ?1904
316pp, 4pp adv., b/w frontis. & 6 f/p b/w illus., pic. clo., 195x135mm. RM
Story tells of a boy who emigrates to Australia & eventually makes good; pp165–316 entirely set in Australia.

'BEETLE, Bertie'
See De Jaunay, Hubert

BEETON, Samuel Orchart
634 BEETON'S/FAMOUS VOYAGES,/Brigand Adventures,/Tales of the Battlefield/Life and Nature./ Illustrated by separate plates, and numerous/woodcuts inserted in the text./Edited by S. O. Beeton/Ward, Lock and Co,/London: Warwick House, Salisbury Square, E.C./New York: Bond Street
n.d. [1873]
384pp, 10pp adv., col. frontis., b/w engravings, pic. clo., 210x130mm. NSL:M
Contains articles on the following individuals relating to Australia: Cook (pp143–200); Fernand Mendez Pinto (pp 201–56); La Pérouse (pp 257–99); Flinders (pp 360–71); Eyre, Governor and Explorer (pp 372–84).

BEGBIE, Donald R.
635 PETER FORGETS/A Story of One Little Pig/by/ Donald R Begbie/Dedicated/To all Children /Christian Press/Sydney Australia
1949
30pp, 2 f/p col. illus., some drawings by author in text, pic. bd., 195x195mm. TG

BEGBIE, Donald Ridley (ed.)
636 PETER, PORKY & PODGE/A Story of Three Little Pigs/Adapted by/Donald R. Begbie/Dedicated to/My own three, Ian, Malcolm,/Graeme, in the confidence/ that by its influence they may/build upon that ONE found-/ation, which makes for cour-/age, cleanliness of character/and real manhood./S. John Bacon [drawing] Melbourne, Victoria.
n.d. [1947]
12pp, 4 f/p col. illus. (inc. one on front wrapper), 3 col. illus. in text, wrappers, 245x185mm. NSL:M

BEHREND, Felix Adalbert
637 Felix Behrend/ULYSSES' FATHER/[drawing]/ Illustrated by Anthony Harvey/F. W. Cheshire/ Melbourne: Canberra: Sydney
1962
84pp, 19 b/w chapter headings, clo., 210x135mm. KMM

BEIER, Ulli (ed.)
638 WHEN/THE MOON/WAS BIG/and other

Legends/from New Guinea/Compiled by Ulli Beier/Illustrated by Georgina Beier/Collins/Sydney London
1972
64pp, sepia/white drawings, clo., dec. e/p, 240x180mm. CLRC

BEISEL, W.

639 COLLECTION/OF/VERSES, POEMS AND PLAYS/By/W. Beisel/South Australia/Scopus meus excelcior est/Good character is destiny/Ambition—1916—Determination/Designed by W. Beisel
Hussey & Gillingham, Adelaide 1916
48pp (inc. author's preface), dec. t.p., dec. wrappers, 180x120mm. CLRC
Verses, with two short plays for children: *With God for King and Empire* & *Heroes of the Dardanelles.*

BELL, Athalie Jean

640 FAIRY FANCIES/Fun for Little Folk/by/Athalie Jean Bell/[drawing]/Publishers/W. R. Rolph & Sons Pty. Ltd., Launceston, Tasmania.
1946
31pp, b/w drawings, bd., 255x180mm. ANL

BELL, Diana Frances

641 Diana Frances Bell/THE REBELS OF JOURNEY'S END/[drawing]/Illustrated by Douglas Hall/Hutchinson of London
1966
119pp, b/w drawings in text, clo., 205x130mm. BBC
Animal story written by a thirteen-year-old Australian girl.

642 THE/REBELS/OF JOURNEY'S/END/Diana Frances Bell/[drawing] Penguin Books/by arrangement with Hutchinson of London
Publ. in Puffin Books 1969
124pp & 4pp adv. &c, b/w drawings in text by Douglas Hall, pic. wrappers, 180x110mm. CLRC

BELL, Enid

643 LEGENDS OF THE/COOCHIN VALLEY/by/Enid Bell
Bunyip Press, Brisbane, n.d. [194-?]
38pp (inc. 1p dedication & 1p preface by Lady Gowrie), b/w frontis. & b/w drawings in text, illus. by Marjorie de Winter, clo., 245x165mm. CLRC

644 DAVID/AND HIS AUSTRALIAN FRIENDS/[drawing]/Written by Enid Bell/Illustrated by Noela Young/With a foreword by Sir Laurence Olivier/A Ure Smith Publication
n.d. [1952]
32pp, col. illus. throughout, bd., 235x170mm. CLRC

BELL, Esme Elliott

645 THE RAINBOW PAINTER/[coloured illustration]/Written and illustrated by/Esme E. Bell/John Sands Pty. Ltd., Sydney, Melbourne and Brisbane/Registered in Australia for transmission by post as a book
1939
32pp, 8 f/p col. illus., b/w drawings throughout, dec. bd., 220x280mm. NSL:M

BELL, Leigh [Alison Clare Harvey Bell]

646 COLIN'S/STORY-BOOK/By/Leigh Bell/With Illustrations by Hugh McCrae/Australia/Cornstalk Publishing Company/Arnold Place, Sydney/1924
168pp, b/w frontis. & b/w drawings throughout, clo., 175x110mm. ANL

647 BREAKERS/ON THE BEACH/By/Leigh Bell/Author of 'Colin's Story Book'/Illustrated by Edgar A. Holloway/Australia/Cornstalk Publishing Company/89 Castlereagh Street, Sydney/1926
286pp, b/w frontis. & 2 b/w f/p illus., clo., 175x115mm. KMM

BELLCHAMBERS, T. P.

648 NATURE: OUR MOTHER/By/T. P. Bellchambers/[rpt from *Saturday Journal*]/Copyright/Adelaide:/W. K. Thomas & Co., Printers, Grenfell Street/1918
47pp (inc. 1p preface, written for young folk), b/w photographs throughout, dec. wrappers, 205x137mm. KP

BELLHOUSE, Dulcie

649 DOLLY/SHOWS/THE WAY/by/Dulcie Bellhouse/[illus.]/Printed by Morris & Walker, Melbourne,/for the Publishers, Offset Printing Coy Pty Limited. Sydney
n.d.
8pp (inc. 4pp part col. illus.), stiff pic. wrappers, 175x120mm. KP
'Before Bedtime Series'
In same series & uniform with above:

650 BARBARA LEARNS TO KNIT. Illus. Betty James. CLRC

651 BETTY'S NEW HAIR-RIBBON [cover by Kay Druce]. CLRC

652 THE DISOBEDIENT LIZARD. VMOU

653 FLOWERS FOR MUMMY. Illus. de Kriek. ANL

BELLING, Mabel R.

654 MOLLIE THE FAITHFUL/or/SALTBUSH AND CLOVER/by/Mabel R. Belling/Sunshine Series/London:/Pickering & Inglis/Glasgow Edinburgh
n.d. [192-?]
94pp, 2pp adv., b/w frontis., clo., 185x120mm. KMM

655 MOLLIE THE FAITHFUL/or/Saltbush and Clover/By/Mabel R. Belling/Sunshine Series/[device]/London:/Pickering & Inglis Ltd./14 Paternoster Row, E.C.4/and at Glasgow, Edinburgh, Manchester, Liverpool
n.d.
Details as above. KMM

BELLIS, H.

656 CAPTAIN COOK/H. Bellis/McGraw-Hill. London/New York Sydney Toronto Mexico Johannesburg
1968
60pp (inc. 2pp glossary), b/w frontis., b/w drawings in text, pic. clo. 132x185mm. KP
Drawings are unsigned; some maps included. Frontis. portrait anonymous.

657 CAPTAIN COOK/H. Bellis/McGraw-Hill Far Eastern Publishers Ltd—Singapore/New York, St. Louis, San Francisco, Dusseldorf, Johannesburg, Kuala Lumpur/London, Mexico, Montreal, New Delhi, Panama, Rio de Janeiro, Sydney, Toronto
1970
58pp (inc. 1p glossary, 1p 'Important Dates'), col. photographic illus. & maps throughout, pic. bd., 200x200mm. KMM

BENAUD, L. R.

658 THE YOUNG/CRICKETER/L. R. (Lou) Benaud with foreword and photo demonstrations by Richie Benaud/[device]/Angus and Robertson
Sydney 1964
87pp (inc. 1p foreword & author's note), b/w photographic illus. & diagrams throughout, pic. clo., 245x185mm. CLRC

BENJAMIN, Arthur & Others

659 PIPER'S MUSIC/by/Arthur Benjamin/Peggy Glanville Hicks/Ester Rofe/John Tallis/Editions de

L'Oiseau Lyre/Chez Louise B. M. Dyer/122, Rue de Grenelle/Paris VII/July 1934
'This Edition, printed & made in France, consists of 1,000 copies in one volume on "Oiseau Lyre" paper & numbered from 1 to 1,000. This is number 740'
36pp (inc. 14pp preface, quotations, publisher's note, &c.), stiff dec. paper covers, spirax bdg, 160x245mm. Grant
Australian music by Australian composers.

BENJAMIN, Gordon
660 Gordon Benjamin/MYSTERY ON/MINNAMURRA/ Illustrated by Colin Wheeler/[device]/Longmans Young Books
London 1968
142pp, b/w frontis. & 3 f/p b/w illus., clo., 215x135mm. Out and About Books Series. KMM

BENNETT, Deborah Elizabeth
661 JEAN'S/BLACK/DIAMOND/A Story of Australia/ by Deborah Bennett/Illustrations by L. F. Lupton/ [device]/C.S.S.M. 5 Wigmore St., London, W.1
First published 1951; rpt 1953, 1954, 1957
205pp, b/w frontis., b/w chapter headings, clo., 180x120mm. KMM

662 SON OF/DIAMOND/A Story of Australia/by/ Deborah Bennett/Illustrations by L. F. Lupton/ [device]/C.S.S.M. 5 Wigmore St London. W.1
First publ. 1952; rpt 1954
Copyright 1952 in the USA by the Children's Special Service Mission
ivpp, 175pp, b/w frontis. & illus., clo., 180x120mm. Grant
Sequel to *Jean's Black Diamond*.

663 SUSAN'S/CONQUEST/A story of Australia/by/ Deborah Bennett/Illustrations by L. F. Lupton/ London/C.S.S.M., 5 Wigmore Street, W.1.
1956
176pp, b/w frontis. map & 9 b/w illus., clo., 180x120mm. ANL
Publisher's 'blurb' describes this as the third book by Deborah Bennett, a young Australian.

BENNETT, Franklin [illustrator]
664 THE ANIMALS'/TRIP TO SEA/[drawing]/ Illustrated by/Franklin Bennett/The House of/Offset
Sydney 1947
16pp, 8 col. illus. & b/w drawings throughout, dec. wrappers, 280x22mm. NSL:M
Another copy as above but 'The House of Offset' omitted. KP

BENNETT, Steve
665 Whitcombe's Story Readers/HOMEWARD BOUND/ by Steve Bennett/(For Ages 12 to 14 years)/Whitcombe & Tombs Limited/Melbourne,/ Auckland, Christchurch, Dunedin and Wellington, N.Z.; and London.
n.d.
148 pp, b/w frontis. & 3 f/p b/w illus., stiff dec. wrappers, 185x115mm. KMM
Story of a boy's adventures sailing from Melbourne to London on a windjammer.
See McLaren 618

BENWELL, W. S.
WINE. *See* Life in Australia

[BÉRENGER, J. P.]
666 LE COOK/DE/LA JEUNESSE,/ou/Extrait/Des Voyages les Plus récents/dans les régions éloignées/ Orné de figures./Tome Premier./A Paris, Chez Giguet et Michaud, Imp. Libr./rue des Bons-Enfants/ MDCCCIV–AN XII
Prize label dated 24 Sept. 1814
Vol. 1 189pp (inc. 4pp adv.) & 3 pp contents, 3 folding engravings, calf, 160x90mm. ANL
Vol. 2 186pp & 3pp contents, 2 folding engravings, and as above. ANL
Vol. 2 contains 2 chapters on NZ & 3 chapters on different islands in SW Pacific.
667 As above, but
A Avignon,/Chez Chaillot, Imprimeur-Libraire,/Place de l'Horloge./MDCCCIV AN XII
Vol. 1 178pp (inc. 4pp adv.) & 2pp contents, 3 folding engraved plates, calf, 130x80mm.
Vol. 2 174pp (inc. 3pp contents) & 4pp adv., 2pp folding engraved plates, calf, 130x80mm. NSL:M
668 Rpt as above, but
Chez Ét. Chaillot, Impr. Libraire,/Place du Change/ 1808
Vol. 1 176pp (inc. 4pp adv.) & 2pp contents, 3 folding plates, ¾ leather, 130x80mm.
Vol. 2 180pp (inc. 3pp contents), 2 folding plates complete
Abridged for children from the life by J. P. Bérenger. ANL
669 LE COOK/DE/LA JEUNESSE./ou/Extrait/des voyages les plus récents/dans les régions les plus éloignées./Suivi de l'Abrégé de la vie du Capitaine/ Cook, par M. le Capitaine Bxx.*[sic]*/Orné de trois grandes Planches/Tome Premier/A Paris/1808
Vol. 1 viipp (adv.), 182pp, 2pp contents, 2 (large) engraved folding plates, calf, g.e., 163x90mm.
Vol. 2 183pp & 3pp contents, 1 folding engraved plate. NSL:M
670 LE COOK/DE/LA JEUNESSE,/ou/Extrait/des Voyages les plus récents/dans les régions éloignées./ Orné de figures/Tome premier./A. Avignon,/Chez Ét. Chaillot, Imprimeur-Libraire;/place du Change./1819
Vol. 1 162pp (inc. 4pp foreword), 2pp contents, 3 folding plates
Vol. 2 bound together, 165pp & 3pp contents, 2 folding plates, calf, 120x70mm. NSL:M

BERESFORD, Elisabeth [Mrs Max Robertson]
671 THE/FLYING DOCTOR/MYSTERY/Elisabeth Beresford/Max Parrish/London
1958
180pp, unillus., clo., 180x115mm. ANL
• Rpt 1959 as above. BBC
672 Second edition 1961 as above. KP
673 THE/FLYING DOCTOR/MYSTERY/Elisabeth Beresford/[device]/Sydney/Australasian Publishing Company/in association with/Max Parrish & Co. Ltd./ London
First publ. in Australia 1960—School ed.
144pp, unillus., limp clo., 184x120mm. KMM

674 THE FLYING DOCTOR/TO THE/RESCUE/ Elisabeth Beresford/Max Parrish London
1964
140pp, unillus., clo., 184x120mm. CLRC

BERNA, Paul
675 LE VOYAGEUR/DE SYDNEY/by/Paul Berna/ Edited by/J. Milne/Dollar Academy/Illustrated by/ Richard Kennedy/Oxford University Press/1961
101pp, 27pp vocabulary, b/w drawings throughout, wrappers, 185x125mm. NSL:M
School reader, adapted from *Le Kangourou Volant* by Paul Berna, by permission of Editions G. P. Paris.

BERNEY, Mrs Eva Rose
See 'Wendy'

BERRILL, Jacquelyn

676 WONDERS/OF THE ANTARCTIC/by Jacquelyn Berrill/Illustrated by the author/[drawing]/Dodd, Mead & Company/New York 1958
96pp (inc. index), maps & b/w drawings throughout, clo., 220x155mm. NSL:M

677 WONDERS/OF THE ANTARCTIC/by Jacquelyn Berrill/Illustrated by the author/The World's Work (1913) Ltd/Kingswood Tadworth Surrey
1968
Details as above, but 230x165mm. KP

BERRISFORD, Judith M.

678 Far and Wide Stories/3/SON OF DARKY/By/Judith M. Berrisford/[drawing]/Illustrated by Norman Howard/London/Macmillan & Co. Ltd./New York St Martin's Press/1956
First edition 1953; rpt 1955, 1956
62pp, 1p exercises, b/w drawings throughout, dec. wrappers, 180x130mm. ANL
A school reader set on a sheep station in Australia.

679 Also an Australian edition 1956, rpt 1959. Details as above. ANL
• Rpt 1960. KP

BERRY, Eliza

680 AUSTRALIAN EXPLORERS/(From 1818 to 1876)/In Rhyme/By/Eliza Berry/Head Teacher of the State School for Girls, Kangaroo Point,/Brisbane/Second Edition/(With map showing Explorers' Routes)/Brisbane/Gordon and Gotch,/Melbourne, Sydney and London/1893
39pp, folding map, clo., 180x120mm. ANL

BERRY, W. Grinton (ed.)

681 MEN OF GRIT/Edited by/W. Grinton Berry, M.A./Narratives of some famous heroic figures/emphasising the active and stirring/sides of their characters/London/The "Boy's Own Paper" Office/4 Bouverie Street, E.C.
n.d. [1916]
221pp, 2pp adv., col. frontis. & 2 f/p col. illus., t.p printed in red & black, illus. by Ernest Prater, pic. clo., 195x125mm. RM
Contents include: 'John G. Paton of the New Hebrides' (24pp); 'Burke and Wills, Across Australia from South to North' (10pp).

682 Another copy as above, but t.p. printed in black. KP

Bertie and the Bullfrogs
See [Clark, John Howard]

BESSELL-BROWNE, Gwen

683 CIRCUSES/AND THINGS/By/Gwen Bessell-Browne/(Author of "The Road to Kokoda")/Illustrated by Diana Gibson/[publisher's device]/Book Depot/Melbourne/1945
32pp, b/w illus., dec. wrappers, 175x115mm. ANL
Verses for children.

'BETTY AND JOHN' [pseud. Linda May Cook]

684 OUR DAY AT THE ZOO/by/Betty and John/with illustrations by Alfred H. Cook
Offset Printing Co., Sydney 1946
34pp, 8pp col. illus. & part. col. illus. throughout, dec. bd., dec. e/p, 210x265mm. ANL

Betty Ann's Birthday
See Barker & Co. Publications

BETTANY, G. T.

685 THE/RED, BROWN, AND BLACK MEN/OF/AMERICA AND AUSTRALIA/and Their white supplanters/by/G. T. Bettany, M.A., B.Sc., F.L.S./With many illustrations./Ward, Lock and Co.,/London, New York, and Melbourne./1890/(All rights reserved)
289pp, 6pp introduction, 2pp adv., b/w engravings in text throughout, dec. clo., 180x115mm. KMM
Title on front cover, & also 'The Youth's Library'
Contents include section (101pp) on 'The Inhabitants of Oceania' containing 'The Inhabitants of Australia' (28pp).

'BETTY SUE'

686 THE ADVENTURES OF/BONNIE & BONZA
Modern Printing Co., Melbourne, n.d. [1946]
16pp, 2 f/p col. illus. & part. col. illus. throughout, dec. wrappers, cover title, 325x230mm. NSL:M

BEVAN, Ian

687 KEEFI HER BOOK/by/Ian Bevan/with/photographs/by/R. A. Patten
F. H. Johnston Publishing Company, Sydney 1945
24pp, b/w photographs, pic. wrappers, 240x180mm. ANL
The true story of the first chimpanzee born in Australia & reared like a human baby in the home of the curator of the Taronga Park Zoo by his wife.

BEVAN, Tom & 1924

688 BOB BLAIR/—Plainsman/By/Tom Bevan/Author of/"The Mystery Trail" "Doing his Bit"/"Runners of Contraband" etc/[device]/London/Sampson Low, Marston & Co., Ltd.
n.d.
282pp & 32pp adv., b/w frontis. & 7 b/w plates, pic. clo., 182x120mm. NSL:M

BICHONNIER, Henriette
See Tubiana, Josiane & Bichonnier, Henriette

The Big Little Man
See DOONGALLA DAYS STORIES

BIGLAND, Eileen

689 THE TRUE BOOK ABOUT/SISTER KENNY/by/Eileen Bigland/Illustrated by/F. Stocks May/Frederick Muller Ltd./London
1956
142pp, b/w frontis. & 14 f/p b/w illus., clo., 185x125mm. ANL

'Billabong Readers'

Format example:

690 THE EMU/That was not a Pet/Billabong/Readers/School Projects Pty Ltd Rockdale
[by J. Paton]
NSW, n.d. [195-?]
8pp, part col. illus., dec. wrappers, 140x100mm. KP
Supplementary Readers—*Billabong Readers* (adv. on back cover as listed, unseen)
The Pet Kookaburra
Maggie Magpie
The Pet Kangaroo
The Emu that was not a Pet
The Bower Bird
Spiney Ant Eater

Bill's Bottle

691 BILL'S BOTTLE/Paterson Press Ltd. Publication/65 Murray Street, Perth, W.A.
1946
22pp, col. illus. throughout, illus. by 'Such', bd., 240x190mm. ANL

Billy Bottle's Colour-in Story Book

692 BILLY BOTTLE'S/ COLOUR-IN/ STORY BOOK
Glass Packaging Institute of Australia, 60-62 York St., Sydney, n.d.

14pp, 6 f/p b/w illus., col. pic. wrappers, 240x174mm. KP

'Billy Bluegum'
See [Innes, Alistair Doig]

BILSTON, Ruby A.
693 Imperial Edition NO 396/HERE AND THERE/ SONGS FOR CHILDREN/Words by/Ruby A. Bilston/ Music by/O. G. Campbell Evans/Contents/[12 songs listed]/Price 1/6 net/Allan & Co., Prop Ltd./Melb Syd. A B
Allan & Co., Melbourne, 1936
16pp, unillus., wrappers, 254x177mm. VSL

BINDER, Vladislav
694 AUSTRALIE A TICHOMORI V DOBRODRUZNYCH ROMANECH A CESTOPISECH (Australia and Pacific Ocean—Stories of Adventure and Travel)
Brno 1941
24pp. SLCSR

BINGHAM, Barbara
See Gunn, John & Bingham, Barbara

BINGHAM, Lorna
695 THE SEARCH FOR THE GOLDEN BOOMERANG/ [photograph of George Edwards &c.]/'The Search for the Golden/Boomerang' both as a/radio serial and in the form/presented in this book, is/the work of Miss Lorna/Bingham of the/George Edwards Production/ Company/Registered at the GPO Sydney for/ transmission through the post as a book/Printed and Published by/Winn & Co., Printers/Balfour Street, Sydney/1941
32pp, 8 f/p col. illus., b/w drawings throughout, stiff wrappers, 280x205mm. KMM
Coloured illustrations signed [Hartmut] 'Lahm'.

696 FURTHER ADVENTURES OF/TUCKONIE/From The Golden Boomerang Serial
Winn & Co. Printers, 1942
32pp, 4 f/p col. illus., b/w drawings (by Hottie Lahm), col. pic. card, cover title, 280x215mm. KP
Note on back cover of Two Grand Golden Boomerang Competitions with col. illus. advertising Violet Crumbles Hoadley's Chocolates. Includes an inset pp16a, 16b The Search for the Golden Boomerang Game, 2pp light board printed in col.

697 'THE LOST TRIBE'/George Edwards/George Edwards sends greetings to kiddies all over/Australia who listen to and enjoy "The Search for the/Golden Boomerang" Radio Serial. Mr Edwards has/great pleasure in making this book available to his/many friends./[photograph of Miss Bingham]/Authoress of the Radio Serial and the book/"The Search for the Golden Boomerang"./Sydney/Printed and Published by Winn & Co.,/Printers, Balfour Street,/1943
32pp, 3 f/p col. illus. & 12 b/w illus., by H. Lahm, pic. wrappers, 275x200mm. KMM

698 TUCKONIE'S/WARRIOR FRIEND/[photograph of George Edwards]/[message from G. E., producer of "The Search for the Golden Boomerang" Radio Serial]/ [photograph of author]/"Tuckonie's Warrior Friend" is written by Miss/Lorna Bingham of George Edwards Players, who/also writes the script of the Radio serial, "The/Search for the Golden Boomerang"/Sydney;/ Printed and Published by Winn & Co./Printers, Balfour Street/1944
Sydney
40pp, 3 col. illus. & b/w drawings throughout, stiff dec. wrappers, 235x180mm. KMM

699 TUCKONIE ON TOUR/[photograph]/Mr George Edwards has pleasure in presenting/another series of adventures, taken from "The/Search for The Golden Boomerang". Peggy, Tuckonie and their friends are happy to be with/you once again in book form, and send listeners/and readers a cheery "Coo-ee"!/ [photograph]/"The Search for the Golden Boomerang" is/written for radio by Miss Lorna Bingham of the/ George Edwards Players. This book has been/adapted from the serial by Miss Marianne Martin/Sydney:/ Printed and Published by Winn & Co./1946
40pp, 3 f/p col. illus. & b/w drawings, stiff dec. wrappers, 240x180mm. ANL
See also Martin, Marianne—BOOMERANG STORIES

BINGLEY, Rev. William
700 BIOGRAPHICAL CONVERSATIONS/ON THE/ MOST EMINENT VOYAGERS/OF DIFFERENT NATIONS/from Columbus to Cook/comprehending/ distinct narratives of their personal adventures./By the/Rev. William Bingley, M.A., F.L.S./Late of Peterhouse, Cambridge,/and author of Animal Biography, etc./Designed for the use of young persons./New edition, with woodcuts./London:/ Printed for the/Society for Promoting Christian Knowledge:/sold at the Depository,/Great Queen Street, Lincoln's Inn Fields;/and by all booksellers./ 1840
360pp, 3pp introduction, engravings in text throughout, dec. clo., 170x105mm. CLRC
Contents include: Dampier (pp125–49); Cook (pp 248–360).

The Bird Who Could Not Fly
701 THE BIRD/WHO COULD NOT FLY
Wee Folks Productions, 45 Queen St., Melbourne, n.d. [194-?]
10pp, col. illus. on alternate pages, stiff dec. wrappers, cover title, 240x240mm. CLRC

Birds & Animals of Australia
702 BIRDS & ANIMALS/[illus.]/OF AUSTRALIA
Aust News & Information Bureau Publication, Melbourne, n.d.
22pp, col. & b/w photographs throughout, pic. wrappers, 180x180mm. KP

Birds & Animals of Australia
703 BIRDS &/ANIMALS/OF AUSTRALIA/Issued by Sanitarium Health Food Company
Petersham, NSW, n.d.
12pp text & sketches & spaces left for 25 cards to be pasted in, pic. wrappers, 240x165mm. KP

Birds of the Sunny South
704 BIRDS OF THE SUNNY SOUTH/with/Australian Flowers/Produced entirely by Australians/[8 lines Longfellow, 4 lines Wordsworth]/From [space for name]
Melbourne, n.d. [191-?]
26pp, 12 f/p col. illus., stiff pic. col. wrappers with cord ties, 168x137mm. ANL
Front cover reads: Greetings from Australia/BIRDS/OF THE/SUNNY SOUTH/with/Australian Flowers/Birds by/V. Teague,/I. Gregory/G. Rede/Flowers by/Alf Ashley/Produced/Entirely by Australians.
'The Laughing Jackass', Rose Eucalyptus'

Vita-Brits Birds of the World Album
705 Vita-Brits/BIRDS/OF THE/WORLD ALBUM
Nabisco Pty Ltd, Victoria, n.d.
12pp descriptions of birds with spaces for cards to be pasted in, col. pic. covers, cover title, 176x216mm. KP

BIRD, Bettina
COFFEE AT CHARLIE'S & other titles. *See* Trend Books

Birds of Paradise and Bower Birds
706 BIRDS OF PARADISE AND BOWER BIRDS/Album 1/-/presented by the makers of/Malties/The Build-up Food you really enjoy
Melbourne (no name of printer), n.d. [1954?]
12pp text, spaces for 40 coloured pictures to be collected & pasted in, stiff pic. wrappers, cover title, 240x180mm. KP
Information inside back cover: 'Junior Birds Club, Roy Wheeler, R.A.O.U. Secretary', etc. Advertisement mentions a similar volume already published on cars.

BIRKS, Fay
707 KITTY KANGAROO/and other Stories/by/Fay Birks/Illustrated by M V. Cox/Arthur H. Stockwell Ltd./Ilfracombe, Devon.
n.d. [195-?]
70pp, 6 f/p b/w illus.,clo., 180x120mm. K&NI

BIRMAN, Wendy & BOLTON, Geoffrey
AUGUSTUS CHARLES GREGORY. *See* Australian Explorers

BIRMINGHAM, Karna Marea
708 SKIPPETY SONGS/written and illustrated/by/Karna Birmingham/The Endeavour Press, 252 George Street, Sydney/1934
35pp, dec. t.p., b/w drawings throughout, wrappers, 215x140mm. NSL:M
Verses.

The 'Birth of a Nation'
709 THE/'BIRTH OF A NATION'/150 Years of Progress/in the History of/Australia Price 6d.
Issued by Hoadleys Chocolates Ltd; printed by J. T. Picken, Sons, Melbourne, n.d. [1938?]
16pp text, spaces for 50 coloured pictures to be collected & pasted in, wrappers, 250x185mm. Grant
Photographs on verso of front cover of Sir Edmund Barton & the Rt Hon. J. A. Lyons, P.C., Prime Minister of Australia 1932–38.

BIRTLES, Dora Eileen [Mrs Herbert Victor, née Toll]
710 PIONEER/SHACK/by/Dora Birtles/The Shakespeare Head/London New York Sydney Capetown Paris/1947
171pp, unillus., clo., 210x130mm. KMM
Story set in Newcastle district of New South Wales.

711 BONZA THE/BULL/by/Dora Birtles/The Shakespeare Head/London New York Sydney Paris
n.d. [1949]
127pp, b/w drawings throughout, clo., 180x120mm. NSL:M

BISSETT, Peggy
712 AMBER MAE'S/STORY BOOK/Written by/Peggy Bissett/Illustrated by/Anne Drew/[drawing]
Whitcombe & Tombs Ltd, Melbourne, n.d. [1946]
48pp, col. & b/w illus. throughout, dec. bd., 240x180mm. ANL
Rhymes, stories.

713 AMBER MAE/GOES TO/KINDERGARTEN/Written by Peggy Bissett/Illustrated by Anne Drew/Authors of/"Amber Mae's Story Book"/Whitcombe & Tombs Pty. Ltd./Melbourne Sydney Perth
n.d. [1947]
64pp, col. & b/w illus. throughout, dec. bd., 240x180mm. KMM

BISSETT, Donald
714 KANGAROO/TENNIS/by Donald Bissett/[drawing]/Illustrated by B. S. Biro, F.S.I.A./Ernest Benn Ltd. London 1968
28pp, 25 col. illus., clo., 200x140mm. KMM
• Rpt 1971. KMM

BLACK, Errol (illustrator)
715 AUSTRALIAN/ANIMAL/AND BIRD ABC/Illustrated by/Errol Black/Golden Press Sydney 1970
[22]pp, col. & part. col. illus. on alternate page openings, dec. bd., illus. e/p, 235x210mm. CLRC

The Black Troopers
716 THE BLACK TROOPERS/And other stories/[engraving of 2 wolves]/London/The Religious Tract Society/56 Paternoster Row, 65 St Paul's Churchyard/and 164 Piccadilly
School prize 1889 [serialized in the *Leisure Hour*, June–July 1870]
384pp, b/w frontis. (Bobby Peel's Escape) & 6 f/p b/w illus., clo., 182x120mm. KP

717 THE BLACK/TROOPERS/And Other Stories/with fifteen illustrations/London/The Religious Tract Society/56 Paternoster Row and 65 St. Paul's Churchyard
n.d. [prize label 1902]
320pp, 16pp adv., b/w frontis. & 14 f/p b/w illus., pic. clo., 195x130mm. KP

718 Another copy as above but address 4 Bouverie St. & 65 St Paul's Churchyard, n.d. KP

719 THE BLACK/TROOPERS/and other stories/with fifteen illustrations/London/The Religious Tract Society/4 Bouverie Street and 65 St. Paul's Churchyard
n.d. [copy inscribed 1907]
Details as above. MK

720 THE BLACK/TROOPERS/and other stories/With Coloured and other illustrations/London/The Religious Tract Society/4 Bouverie Street and 65 St. Paul's Churchyard
n.d. [191-?]
320pp [no adv.], col. frontis., two-coloured t.p. (printed in red & blue), 3 f/p b/w illus. (sgd 'Norman Ault'), pic. clo., 195x130mm. KMM
Other copies seen with slight variations in binding, type face, &c, all undated, and too numerous to define individually. KP & others

BLAIR, Elizabeth
721 Imperial Edition NO. 248/THE/SWEET SHOP/A Juvenile Review/(Duration: About 45 minutes)/Words and Music/by/Elizabeth Blair/Price/2/6/Allan & Co., Prop. Ltd./Melb. Syd. Ad. Bend.
n.d. [stamped 1936]
31pp & 1p adv., pic. wrappers, 254x177mm. VSL

BLAIR, Jim
722 THE SECRET/OF THE REEF/[drawing]/Rigby Limited/Adelaide
1963
164pp, 1 b/w map, otherwise unillus., clo., d/w by Trevor Clare, 200x125mm. KMM

BLAKE, Harold Sidney
723 THE/TALE/OF/THE/LITTLE/WHITE/FOX/by H. S. Blake/illustrated by/Albert & Kathleen Collins/Printed and Published by Waite & Bull/81 Campbell Street, Sydney, N.S.W.
n.d. [1932]
49pp, part. col. & b/w illus. throughout, pic. bd., dec. e/p, 240x190mm. NSL:M

724 A BACK-ANSWER/with all good wishes/from/The Land where, a Poet has told us/Bright Blossoms are scentless/and songless, Bright Birds
Angus & Robertson, Sydney, n.d. [1932]
12pp (inc. 2pp index), b/w drawings, dec. wrappers, 140x185mm. NSL:M
Written by H. S. Blake; illus. by M. S. Roe
Humorous verses; doubtful children's book.

725 ALL THE WAY/TO BARCELONA/By H. S. Blake/ Illustrated by/A. & K. Collins/Australia/Angus & Robertson Limited/89 Castlereagh Street, Sydney/1935
71pp, col. frontis. & b/w drawings throughout, pic. bd., 240x180mm. KMM

BLANCHARD, Pierre

726 PETIT VOYAGE/autour/DU MONDE./Ouvrage amusant,/Propre à préparer les enfants à l'étude de la Géographie,/Par Pierre Blanchard./Onziéme édition,/ avec gravures/[device]/Paris,/Librairie de l'enfance et de la jeunesse./Lehuby,/successeur de M. Pierre Blanchard,/Rue de Seine, 48./1836
263pp (inc. 2pp index), engraved frontis. & 3 (?4) engraved plates, dec. bd., 160x104mm. ANL
Pp252-9 'L'Océanie'.

727 PETIT VOYAGE/AUTOUR/DU MONDE/Ouvrage amusant/propre à préparer les enfants a l'étude de la Géographie,/par Pierre Blanchard/Quartorzième Édition/avec gravures/[publisher's device]/Paris./ Libraries de l'enfance et de la jeunesse,/P.-C. Lehuby, Libraire-éditeur,/Rue de Seine, 55, S.-G.
n.d. [copy inscribed 1851]
288pp (inc. 2pp preface), engraved frontis. & 4pp b/w engravings, dec. bd., 175x105mm. NSL:M

BLANCHARD, Victor

728 VOYAGES/DE/LA PÉROUSE/Autour du Monde,/ Par Victor Blanchard/[device]/Paris/Chez Martial Ardant frères,/rue Hauteveuille, 14/Limoges/Chez Martial Ardant Frères,/rue des Taules./1848
Bibliothèque Religieuse, Morale, Littéraire, de l'enfance et de la jeunesse
252pp, engraved frontis., dec. bd., 171x104mm. BL
Last 6 pages describe the French visit to Botany Bay & the subsequent search for La Pérouse.

BLANCHE, Horace (ed.)

729 THE AUSTRALIAN/WONDER BOOK/OF KNOWLEDGE/Volume One/[drawing]/A Colorgravure Publication
Melbourne, n.d. [1950?]
236pp, col. frontis. & 12pp col. illus., b/w photographic & other illus. throughout, clo., dec. e/p, 235x180mm. BBC
Contributors include Keith McKeown, Theodore Roughley, Vivian Stratford, Commander A. K. Calder, Edmund Gill, Robert Lee, John Feely, Ada Jackson, Francis Wilson, A. W. Norrie. Subjects include Natural History, Astronomy, Henry Lawson, Engineering, &c.

730 THE AUSTRALIAN/WONDER BOOK/OF KNOWLEDGE/Volume Two/[drawing]/[quotation]/A Colorgravure Publication
Melbourne, n.d. [195-?]
243-472pp [pagination continues from Vol. 1], col. frontis. & 12pp col. illus., b/w photographic & other illus. throughout, clo., e/p, 240x175mm. KMM
Contributors include R. P. Pescott, Thistle Harris, Lt. Cmdr. Geoffrey Rawson & others, writing on such subjects as Australian Pearling, Natural History, Shipwreck Mystery in Pacific Waters (the wrecks of the *Grafton*, the *Invercauld*, & the *General Grant*), The Conquest of the Air, Discovering Australia by Sea (23pp & col. illus.), Pages from Australia's Romantic Past (11pp account of Kennedy's expedition to Cape York Peninsula).

731 THE STORY OF/AUSTRALIA/Written and Edited by/H. Blanche, B. A./[vignette]/North York Publishing Company.
Sydney, n.d. [1956?]
240pp (inc. index), b/w illus. throughout, clo., dec. e/p, 240x180mm. NSL:M

BLENCOWE, Carlyne

732 HILL TOP FARM/Written and illustrated/by/ Carlyne Blencowe/Hutchinson's Books for Young People/London New York Melbourne Sydney Cape Town
Melbourne n.d. [1948]
31pp, dec. t.p., col. illus. throughout, dec. bd., 260x210mm. ANL
Verse.

Blick, the Cock-a-Too

733 Whitcombe's Story Readers/(No. 11)/BLICK, THE/ COCK-A-TOO/(For the Sixes)/[drawing]/Auckland, Wellington, Christchurch, Dunedin and Invercargill, N.Z./London, Melbourne and Sydney/Whitcombe & Tombs Limited
n.d. [1925]
12pp, b/w frontis., pic. wrappers, 185x125mm. KMM
See McLaren 11

BLIGH, William

Swedish edition of Bligh's Voyage

734 ENGELSKE CAPITAINENS/WILHELM BLIGHS/ RESA/GENOM SÖDRA WERLDS-HAFVET,/tolf hundrade Sjömil/. . . in öpen. . . båt,/från Tofoa till Timor/[device]/Upsala/Tryckt hos Direct. Joh. Edmans Enka,/på eget forlag, 1792
119pp (inc. 2pp foreword signed S. Ö., unillus., paper bd. marbled, 150x87mm. NSL:M

735 DANGEROUS VOYAGE./Containing/An account of the wonderful and truly pro-/vidential Escape of CAPTAIN BLIGH/and a Part of the Crew of his Majesty's/ship BOUNTY: and of their safe Arrival at/ TIMOR, in the year 1789; after having/sailed over twelve hundred Leagues of the/Ocean, in an open Boat, surrounded by/Perils of various Kinds./To which is added,/An Account of the Sufferings and Fate of/ the Remainder of the Crew of the said Ship./WITH AN APPENDIX;/In which is contained an Account of the Island/of Otaheite, and of some Productions of/the Countries which they visited,/Dublin:/Printed by Graisbery and Campbell,/10, Back-Lane/1817
246pp & 2pp index, unillus., copy re-bound in marbled bd. & 3/4 leather, 128x84mm. SUA
Voyage ends at p151 & p153 appendix begins.
(Ferguson 670 records 6 woodcut illus.)

736 Juvenile Library/—/An Account/of the/Dangerous Voyage,/performed by Captain Bligh,/with a part of the Crew of/His Majesty's Ship Bounty,/in an open boat,/Over twelve hundred Leagues of the Ocean,/ with an Appendix,/in which is contained an Account of the Island of/Otaheite, &c/[woodcut]/London: Printed for S. & A. Davis, Radcliffe-Highway/1818./J. Jordan, Printer./(Price eighteen-pence)
178pp & 2pp index, engraved frontis. & 5 other engravings, bd., 140x86mm. ANL
(Appendix pp 107-78)

737 DANGEROUS VOYAGE/OF/CAPTAIN BLIGH,/in an open Boat,/over 1200 Leagues of the Ocean,/in the year 1789/with an appendix,/containing/An Account of Otaheite, and of some Produc-/tions of that Island./ London:/Printed and Published by John Arliss,/ Juvenile Library, Newgate-Street/1818/Price 2s6d.

179pp, engraved frontis. (Dangerous situation of Capt Bligh & his crew) & 6 engravings, wrappers, 140x85mm. NSL:M

738 THE/DANGEROUS VOYAGE/PERFORMED BY/ CAPTAIN BLIGH,/with a Part of the Crew of/His Majesty's Ship Bounty,/in an open boat,/over Twelve Hundred Leagues of the Ocean:/in the year/1789/To which is added,/An Account of the Sufferings and Fate of the/Remainder of the Crew of said Ship./Dublin:/ Printed by R. Napper, 140, Capel St./1824
175pp, woodcut frontis., contemporary calf, 140x90mm. HBM

739 THE/DANGEROUS VOYAGE,/PERFORMED BY/ CAPTAIN BLIGH,/with a/part of the Crew of His Majesty's/Ship Bounty,/in an open boat,/over twelve hundred leagues of the Ocean,/in the year 1789./Published/by the Society for promoting the United and Scriptural/Education of the Poor of Ireland,/Kildare-Place, Dublin./Dublin:/Printed by P. D. Hardy, Cecilia-St./and sold at the Society's Depository, Kildare-Place.
[1825?]
176pp (last blank), woodcut frontis. ('Dangerous situation of Capt Bligh and his Crew'), calf, 133x83mm. ANL

740 THE MUTINY/ON BOARD/H.M.S. BOUNTY/ William Bligh/Airmont Publishing Company, Inc./22 East 60th Street, New York 10022
1965
189pp (inc. 5pp introduction) & 3pp adv., unillus., pic. wrappers, 180x105mm. RC
Introduction by Nathan R. Teitel, N.Y. University.

BLOOMFIELD, Kate

741 LET'S BE HEALTHY/A Guide for Young People/to Cleanliness, Strength and Activity/Kate Bloomfield, B.A., M.B.B.S./[device]/F. W. Cheshire/Melbourne
1960
59pp, b/w diagrams, pic. wrappers, 240x150mm. KP

Blossom in the 'Land of Sunshine' Gift Book

742 BLOSSOM/IN "THE LAND OF SUNSHINE"/GIFT BOOK/Published by/Whitefield's Institute/ Hindmarsh/June, 1930/Copyright registered. Vardon & Sons, Printers, Adelaide
68pp, dec. t.p., 2 f/p col. illus. & many b/w illus., bd., 275x210mm. NSL:M
Coloured illustrations by Hans Heysen and other artists. Contributors include Isobel Ann Shead, May Gibbs, etc.

The Blue Bus Takes a Holiday

743 THE/BLUE BUS/TAKES A HOLIDAY/A Jons Production
[cover title]
Lithographed in Australia by Deaton & Spencer Ltd for Jons Productions, Sydney
n.d. [194-?]
[8]pp & story & illus. continue inside both covers, col. illus. throughout by Hal English, col. pic. wrappers, 280x215mm. TG

Blue Cap the Bushranger
See Borlase, James Skipp

'BLUEGUM, Tom'
See Payne, G. Warren

Blue Wren Books

744 Aesop's Fables Re-told/THE DOVE AND/THE ANT/Illustrated by Sally Medworth/Angus & Robertson/Sydney London
[1951]
32pp, 4pp col. illus. & b/w illus., dec. wrappers, 155x120mm. ANL

745 Aesop's Fables Re-told/THE/WIND/AND THE/ SUN/Illustrated by Margaret Horder/Angus & Robertson/Sydney London
[1951]
32pp, 12pp col. illus. & 6 b/w drawings, dec. wrappers, 155x115mm. ANL

746 GOOD/KING WENCESLAS/[drawing]/Angus & Robertson/Sydney London
[1951]
32pp, 1pp col. illus., dec. wrappers, 155x115mm. ANL

747 LAVENDER'S BLUE/and Two other Rhymes/ Illustrated by/Margaret Horder/[decoration]/Angus & Robertson/Sydney London
[1951]
32pp, 12pp col. illus. & b/w illus. in text, dec. wrappers, 155x115mm. ANL

748 MOOGRABAH/An Australian/Aboriginal/Legend/ [decoration]/Illustrated by/Margaret Horder/Angus & Robertson/Sydney London
[1951]
32pp, 22pp col. illus., dec. t.p., dec. wrappers, 155x120mm. ANL
Retold from the story recorded by Keith McKeown in *The Land of Byamee.*

749 PRETTY/POLLIE/PILLICOTE/[decoration]/ Illustrated by/Margaret Horder/Angus & Robertson/ Sydney London
[1951]
32pp, 10pp col. illus. & b/w illus. in text, dec. wrappers, 155x115mm. ANL

750 THE 12 DAYS OF/CHRISTMAS/Illustrated by Diana Medworth/Angus & Robertson/Sydney London
[1951]
32pp, 2pp introduction, 20 col. illus., dec. wrappers, 155x120mm. ANL

751 WHAT THEY WORE/A First Book of English Costume/From 300 BC to 1422AD /[decoration]/ Written and illustrated by/Margaret Horder/Angus & Robertson/Sydney London
[1951]
32pp, 12pp col. illus. & b/w illus. in text, dec. wrappers, 155x115mm. ANL

752 CHRISTMAS/IN THE SUN/by/Joan Phipson/ illustrated by/Margaret Horder/Angus & Robertson/ Sydney London
1952
32pp, dec. t.p. & 19 col. illus., dec. wrappers, 155x115mm. ANL

753 THE BALLAD OF/LITTLE BILLEE/By/William Makepeace Thackeray/Illustrated by/Sally Medworth/ Angus & Robertson/Sydney London
1952
32pp, 16 col. illus., wrappers, 155x120mm. ANL

BLUNDEN, Godfrey

754 THE LAND/AND PEOPLE/OF/AUSTRALIA/ Godfrey Blunden/Portraits of/The Nations/Series/ [publisher's device]/J. Lippincott Company: Philadelphia & New York
1954
128pp (inc. 4pp index), frontis. map & 16pp photographic illus., clo., 195x140mm. CLRC

755 THE LAND AND PEOPLE OF/AUSTRALIA/by Godfrey Blunden/Revised edition 1972/Portraits of the Nations Series/J. B. Lippincott Company/Philadelphia New York
144pp (inc. 4pp index), b/w photographic illus. throughout, pic. clo., 202x150mm. CLRC

756 AUSTRALIA/AND/HER PEOPLE/By/Godfrey Blunden/[device]/Lutterworth Press/London

First published 1959; second impression 1960; revised edition 1963
112pp (inc. 4pp index, 2pp bibliography), b/w double-spread map, b/w photographic illus. throughout, clo., 205x145mm. Portraits of the Nations Series. BBC

BLUNDEN, Pandy
757 KIM'S ADVENTURES/by/Pandy Blunden/ [drawing]/Kimmy the Dog with majic [*sic*, subtitle]
Privately published, no imprint, 1952
13pp, dec. bd., 100x160mm. MD

[BLYTHE, Delma]
758 DRIP/AND/DROP
'Dinkie' Book, Product of Photogravures, Melbourne, n.d. [194-?]
[16]pp, col. illus. on every page, col. pic. bd., cover title, 177x117mm. KMM

759 PETER/PEBBLE
'Dinkie' Book, Product of Photogravures Melbourne, n.d. [194-?]
[16]pp, col. illus. on every page, col. pic. bd., cover title, 177x114mm. KMM
Companion volume to *Drip and Drop*.

BOADEN, Betty M.
760 THE A.I.F. IN THE/FIRST WORLD WAR/ (1914–1918)/Betty M. Boaden/School Projects Pty. Ltd.
Sydney 1965
40pp, 3 maps & b/w drawings in text, stiff dec. wrappers, 210x130mm. Australian Scene Series. BBC

Bobbie in the Bush
761 BOBBIE/IN THE BUSH [drawing]
Peter Huston, Sydney (Deaton & Spencer Pty Ltd, Printers, Sydney), n.d. [195-?]
[20]pp printed in red & black with drawings on each text page, includes 8pp col. illus., pic. bd., 155x222mm. KMM
Contains 8pp of stiffened paper folded in half with col. illus., the frontis. illus. having movable parts operated by tag. Appears to be possibly the first Australian movable picture book.

BOCK, Alfred (ed.)
762 THE/ALLIANCE CHOICE BUDGET OF/NURSERY RHYMES/Original, Wise & Otherwise,/Collected & Edited by/Alfred Bock/Printed & Published/By/Alfred Bock/Oldina/Tasmania/Price 1 shilling & 6 pence
n.d. [192-?]
34pp, wrappers, cover title, 170x105mm. TSL
Nursery rhymes with some additional improvised rhymes.

'BOLDREWOOD, Rolf' [T. E. BROWNE]
763 The Kennett Library [device]/Rolf Boldrewood/ ROBBERY/UNDER ARMS/retold by John Kennett/ Glasgow/Blackie & Son Limited/London
1970
132pp & 4pp introduction, glossary &c, b/w frontis. & 3 b/w illus., pic. bd., 184x120mm. KP
The Kennett Library. Abridgement for children.

BOLTON, Geoffrey
See Birman, Wendy & Bolton, Geoffrey

BONE, Walter H.
764 HOPPITY/(Being the adventures of an Albino/ Kangaroo)/—/By/Walter H. Bone/1933
Wholly set up & printed in NSW by W. H. Bone & Co., Sydney
69pp, 12 b/w illus., illus. by author, bd., 240x180mm. ANL

765 WHAT BECAME OF THEM?/Australian Stories for Children/Written and Illustrated by/Walter H. Bone/ [drawing]
Set up and printed by W. H. Bone & Co., Sydney 1952; edition limited to 1000 copies
67pp, part. col. frontis. & marginal drawings, dec. clo., 300x180mm. NSL:M
Short stories about Australian animals.

BONWICK, James
766 READER/FOR/AUSTRALIAN YOUTH:/Part 1./By/James Bonwick,/Author of Geography for Australian Youth, etc./Adelaide:/Printed for the author, by T. Strode,/And sold by all Australian Booksellers./1852
viipp, 112pp (1p adv. precedes text), unillus., paper covered bd., 174x105mm. HBM
The reader contains 'extracts from approved authors, selections from the writings of Australian explorers and naturalists, & original articles upon Familiar Science, as well as Australian History and Discovery'. Many of the liveliest pages of the book were written by Bonwick himself always aware of the need of capturing the young reader's attention. Some articles are written in dialogue form & some directly relate the author's own experiences in the Colonies. A second projected vol. was never publ. Also poems by Jane Taylor, Mrs Hemans, Eliza Cook &c.

767 BIBLE STORIES/FOR/YOUNG AUSTRALIANS./ By/James Bonwick,/Author of "Geography of Australia", etc. etc./Part 1./(To be continued)/Melbourne:/James J. Blundell & Co., Collins Street./1857
[First edition, Adelaide 1852]
59pp, 2pp introduction, unillus., (paper covers, according to Pescott; copy seen rebound), 135x80mm. ANL
E. E. Pescott, in *James Bonwick* &c., Melbourne 1939, states that part 2 was not issued.

768 EARLY DAYS/OF/ENGLAND./By/James Bonwick,/Inspector of Denominational Schools, Victoria./Author of "Geography of Australia and New Zealand,"/&c. &c./James J. Blundell & Co., Melbourne;/Sands & Kenny, Sydney/1857
53pp (inc. 1p introduction), 1p adv., engravings in text, (?clo., copy seen rebound), 135x85mm. ANL

769 EARLY DAYS/OF/MELBOURNE./By/James Bonwick,/Author of "Geography of Australia and New Zealand",/"Discovery and Settlement of Port Phillip", &c. &c./Melbourne:/Jas. J. Blundell & Co., Collins Street./1857
40pp, 1p introduction, engraved frontis., (?clo., copy seen rebound), 130x85mm. ANL

770 HOW DOES A TREE/GROW?/or/Botany for Young Australians./By/James Bonwick,/Sub-Inspector of Denominational Schools, Victoria,/Author of "Geography of Australia and New Zealand",/&c. &c./James J. Blundell & Co., Melbourne;/Sands & Kenny, Sydney/1857
42pp, 1p preface, 1p adv., wrappers, 130x90mm. ANL

771 ASTRONOMY/FOR/YOUNG AUSTRALIANS/By/ James Bonwick/Formerly Inspector of Schools, Author of/"Geography of Australia," etc. etc./Melbourne:/

Published by Thomas Harwood,/Collins Street East./
1864
99pp (inc. 1p preface), 1p adv., unillus., clo., 140x90mm. HBM

772 ASTRONOMY/FOR/YOUNG AUSTRALIANS./by/ James Bonwick, F.R.G.S./Author of "Geography of Australia," etc. etc./Melbourne:/Published by Samuel Mullen,/Collins Street, East./1866
ii+70pp, 1p preface to 2nd edition [dated 'St. Kilda, Nov. 1st 1866'], 2pp adv., stiff paper wrappers, 140x90mm. Grant

773 ASTRONOMY/FOR/YOUNG/AUSTRALIANS,/ By/James Bonwick, F.R.G.S.,/Author of "Geography of Australia," etc etc./Melbourne/Published by W. B. Stephens/Collins Street West./1866
iipp, 70pp & 2pp adv., unillus., clo., 140x80mm. Grant
'A cheap edition of "Astronomy for Young Australians" having been designed to meet the requirements of the Public Schools'

774 LITTLE JOE;/a Tale of the Pacific Railway./By/ James Bonwick,/Author of "The Last of the Tasmanians", "Geography/of Australia", &c./London:/William Tweedie, 337, Strand.
n.d. [1872]
96pp, b/w engraved frontis., (copy seen rebound), 160x95mm. ANL

775 LITTLE JOE;/A Tale of/The Pacific's Railway./ second edition./By/James Bonwick,/Author of "The Last of the Tasmanians", "Geography/of Australia," &c./London/National Temperance Publication Depot/ 337, Strand, W.C.
n.d. [1882]
124pp, 4pp adv., b/w engraved frontis., pic. clo., 165x100mm. NKP

776 ORION AND SIRIUS/By/James Bonwick, F.R.G.S./Author of "Geography of Australia" —"Astronomy for Young Australians"—"Last of the Tasmanians", etc./London:/E. A. Petherick, 33 Paternoster Row/Harrison & Hill, Upper Norwood/ 1888
110pp, 2pp preface, 1p epilogue, b/w frontis diagram, clo., 140x105mm. HBM
Bonwick wrote some of the first school textbooks produced in Australia. The books included here, though of an instructional nature, would have also provided recreational reading for the young for whom they were intended.

BONWICK, Walter [brother of James]

777 Registered under [space] The Copyright Act/THE AUSTRALIAN/SCHOOL SONG BOOK,/containing/ Sixty-Six Original Songs/composed by/Walter Bonwick,/of Hawthorn, Melbourne/With notes and Lessons on "Programme"/Price One Shilling./ Melbourne:/Printed for the Author, by Clarson, Massina and Co./72 Little Collins Street East
n.d. [1871?]
ivpp, 60pp (inc. 1p contents), unillus., printed bd., 173x115mm. CLRC
• Rpt as above, third thousand, n.d. VSL

Boobook

778 BOOBOOK/An Uncle Ted's Tale [colophon]/ Produced and Published by/E. W. Kaye/Sydney/ Printed by/Hollander & Govett Pty. Limited/Sydney
n.d.
16pp, part col. illus. throughout, stiff pic. wrappers, 235x180mm. KP

A Book for Boys

See DAWFOX PRODUCTIONS

A Book for Tired Babies

See [J. A. BANNISTER]

The Book of Amazing Wonders

779 THE BOOK OF/AMAZING/WONDERS/Published by the Sanitarium Health Food Company
Sydney, n.d.
[12]pp, part col. illus. throughout, col. pic. wrappers, cover title, 195x242mm. WRT
Spaces left for 50 cards to be pasted in.

Book of Animals

780 BOOK OF/ANIMALS/B2 series
Printed & publ. by Offset Ptg Co., Sydney, n.d.
16pp (inc. covers), col. illus. throughout, paper wrappers, cover title 267x200mm. KMM

A Book of Australian Birds

781 A BOOK OF/AUSTRALIAN BIRDS
Supertone Co., 200 Chalmers St., Sydney, n.d. [194-?]
[8]pp of alternately col & b/w illus. with brief captions, stiff pic. wrappers, with b/w illus. inside front & back covers, 340x240mm. KMM

The Book of Birds Beasts and—No Fishes

782 THE/BOOK OF/BIRDS/BEASTS/AND—NO FISHES/Published in aid of/Red Cross Funds/M.B. Ferguson & Osborn Ltd., Printers, Wellington, N.Z., n.d. [NSL:M copy rebound January 1919]
16pp, illus., wrappers, 195x115mm. NSL:M
Simple illustrated verses.

Books for the Bairns

W. T. Stead, journalist and philanthropist, publ. a series of illustrated books for children which were sold for one penny each. The series ran from 1896 to 1920. A second series was publ. by his daughter in the first half of 1923. Stead's Review of Reviews for Australasia was publ. monthly in Melbourne 1892 to 1914; an Australian edition of Books for the Bairns was publ., of which only No. 1 Aesop's Fables, has been seen. It appears to have been uniform in format with the overseas publication. 12 titles were listed but none of Australian content. MC
Format example:

783 208 Feb 1913 THE/STORY OF WANGO/By/Jessie Phillips./Author of"The Adventures of Bright Eyes"/(No. 197 "Books for the Bairns")/Illustrated by Brinsley Le Fanu,/Stead's Publishing House,/Bank Buildings, Kingsway, London, W.C./Depot Exclusif pour la France;/Librairie Larousse, Rue Montparnasse 13-19 Paris.
56pp, 6pp adv. (& 2pp adv. preceding t.p.), 24 f/p b/w illus., dec. wrappers, 180x115mm. Grant
Title on cover 'The Story of Wango:/An Exciting Tale of the Australian Bush'.
In same series:

784 No 95, Jan 1904 FAIRY TALES FROM THE SOUTH PACIFIC Collected by Constance Barnicoat, 58pp

785 No 197, May 1912 ADVENTURES OF BRIGHT-EYES, by Jessie Phillips. Illus. C. S. Hayward and B. Le Fanu

786 No 226, April 1915 FAIRY TALES FROM AUSTRALIA by Ethel Buckland. Illus. B. Le Fanu
Also New Series:

787 No 4, RONNIE and THE KANGAROO by Jessie Phillips. Illus. B. Le Fanu
Titles unseen but listed in Sally Wood's *W. T. Stead and his "Books for Bairns"*, Salvia Books, Edinburgh 1987

Boomerang Stories for the Children

788 BOOMERANG/STORIES/FOR/THE CHILDREN/ Sydney:/Printed and Published by/Winn & Co., Printers/53-55 Balfour Street/1942

44pp, dec. t.p., 4 f/p col. illus., wrappers, 270x195mm. KMM
Illustrations signed 'J. & H.'
From the George Edwards Radio Serial 'The Golden Boomerang'; *see also* Bingham, Lorna, for The Golden Boomerang Series.

BOOTH, Alice Marie
789 CHRISTINE/[drawing]/Book 1/For Children aged 7 to 9 years
The author, Sydney 1947
56pp, 2 fly sheets, b/w illus., dec. wrappers, 245x150mm. ANL
Preface by author & foreword by Edwina Mountbatten
Instructions for making doll's clothes.

[BOOTH, S. A.]
790 ORIGINAL/RHYMES/FOR THE YOUNG./By S. A. B./Adelaide:/John Thomas Shawyer, Printer, 71 King William Street./1866
8pp, unillus., wrappers, 134x83mm. VSL

BOOTHBY, Guy & others
UNCLE JOE'S LEGACY & other stories. Not children's

BOOTHBY, Mabel F.
791 AN/AUTOBIOGAPHY/OF A/LAUGHING JACKASS/by/Mabel F. Boothby/Published by/Robert Jolley/Melbourne
n.d. [inscribed by author 1915]
12pp, 1 f/p col. illus. pic. paper covers, 170x150mm. KMM
Pasted in at end of book is folded page with photograph of eleven kookaburras, entitled 'An Australian Eleven'.
792 AN/AUTOBIOGAPHY/OF A/LAUGHING JACKASS/By/Mabel F. Boothby/Published by/P. T. Law & Co./Melbourne
n.d. [1916]
12pp, 1 col. & 1 b/w illus. by author, wrappers, illus. front cover, 175x150mm. KMM
The text of this second edition is headed by a 4-line verse written by Hallam, Lord Tennyson.

BORDEN, Charles A.
793 HE SAILED WITH/CAPTAIN COOK/By Charles A. Borden/Illustrated by Ralph Ray/New York: Thomas Y. Crowell Company
1952
248pp (inc. 4pp bibliography & 1p biographical note), b/w frontis. & 11 f/p b/w illus., clo., dec. e/p, 205x130mm. ANL
794 Illustrated by/H. Tom Hall/HE SAILED WITH CAPTAIN COOK/Charles A. Borden/Macrae Smith Company/Philadelphia
1968
203pp (inc. 3pp bibliography), 1p biographical note on author, extended illus. t.p., b/w drawings in text, clo., 200x130mm. ANL

BORER, Mary Cathcart
See Smart, Ralph & Borer, Mary Cathcart

BORLASE, James Skipp
795 THE NIGHT FOSSICKERS,/and other/Australian Tales of Peril and Adventure./By/James Skipp Borlase./[device]/London:/Frederick Warne and Co.,/Bedford Street, Covent Garden./1867
248pp, unillus., pebbled clo., 160x100mm. NSL:M
The 16 stories included are those later published as *Daring Deeds.*
796 DARING DEEDS; and/TALES OF/PERIL AND ADVENTURE/By/James S. Borlase./[device]/With Coloured Illustrations./London:/Frederick Warne and Co.,/Bedford Street, Covent Garden./New York: Scribner, Welford, and Co./1869
viii, 248pp, col. frontis. & 3 f/p col. illus., [copy rebound], 160x110mm. KMM
797 Another copy as above but undated, dec. clo, 165x110 mm. CLRC
798 DARING DEEDS/AND/TALES OF PERIL AND ADVENTURE/By/James S. Borlase/[device]/with illustrations/London and New York/Frederick Warne and Co.
n.d. [awarded as school prize 1886]
Details as above but with b/w frontis. & 3 f/p illus. NSL:M
799 DARING DEEDS/AND/TALES OF PERIL AND ADVENTURE/By/James S. Borlase/[device]/with illustrations/London and New York/Frederick Warne and Co.
n.d. [prize 1886]
viii, 248pp, b/w frontis. & 3 b/w illus., pic. clo. (with 2 illus. reproduced in gilt on front cover & another on spine), 180x120mm. NSL:M
Contents as before.
800 DARING DEEDS;/and/TALES OF/PERIL AND ADVENTURE./By/James S. Borlase./With Illustrations/[device]/London:/Frederick Warne and Co./Bedford Street, Strand.
[1894]
viii, 248pp, b/w frontis. & 3 f/p b/w illus., dec. clo., 160x110mm. KMM
On front cover: 'Daring Deeds Library'.

[BORLASE, James Skipp]
801 AUSTRALIAN/TALES/OF/PERIL AND ADVENTURE/In Town and Bush/Told by an Officer/of the/Victorian Police/[contents]/Melbourne/E. W. Cole, Book Arcade/Bourke Street, East
n.d. [1893?]
viii, 248pp, unillus., wrappers, 180x120mm. NSL:M
The contents are identical with *Daring Deeds;* the front yellow paper wrapper has similar wording to the t.p. but in addition lists the contents & bears the price 'one shilling'. NSL:M

802 BLUE CAP/THE BUSHRANGER;/or,/THE AUSTRALIAN DICK TURPIN/Illustrated./London:/Charles Fox, Victoria House, Newcastle Street, Strand, W.C.
n.d. [186-?]
104pp, 11 f/p b/w illus. [& 1 f/p b/w illus. loosely inserted], col. pic. wrappers (with adv. outside back wrapper), 245x165mm. RM
Charles Fox is said to have been a publisher for only approximately ten years, from 1860 to 1870 when his business was taken over by Hogarth House. This copy varies from the Hogarth House edition, having the price 'One Penny' on front wrapper & a one-line caption below the front cover illustration, whilst the Hogarth House edition has 'One Shilling' & four lines of caption.
803 BLUE CAP/THE BUSHRANGER;/or,/THE AUSTRALIAN DICK TURPIN/Illustrated./London:/Hogarth House, 32, Bouverie Street, E.C.
n.d.
104pp, 11 b/w illus., pic. wrappers, 255x165mm. Hogarth House Library. NSL:M

804 No.1–Weekly–One Penny/NED KELLY/THE/IRONCLAD/AUSTRALIAN BUSHRANGER/[illustration]/London: Published at the Office of the "Illustrated London Novelette", 44, Essex Street, Strand,/and 125, Fleet Street, E.C.
n.d. [1881]

456pp (continuous pagination), 38 f/p b/w illus., paper wrappers, 260x195mm. RM
From a newspaper review printed preceding Part 18 & dated July 1881, it seems that publication of the series began February or March 1881. The following inscription appears on the front fly leaf of this copy which came from the library of J. Medcraft, well-known collector of 'bloods' earlier in the century: 'Extracts from Desmond Coke/*Ned Kelly/The Ironclad Australian Bushranger*/A/Flatulent Farrago/of/Fatuous Fiction/Conceived by G. D. Boucicault/commenced by Borlase/continued by Percy St John/completed by M. Vizetelly/cut up generally (under the pretext of sub-editing & otherwise improving)/by G. D. Boucicault'.

805 NED KELLY/THE/IRONCLAD/AUSTRALIAN BUSHRANGER/[on b/w illus. background with caption]
n.d. [Publisher's imprint running from bottom to top of L.H. side of illus.] No. 1, Price One Penny Weekly–London: Published at the Office of the Illustrated Novelette, 280, Strand, and 125, Fleet Street, E.C.
456pp (continuous pagination in 38 separate parts, adv. at foot of each part), 38 f/p b/w illus., half calf & buckram bd., 252x190mm. RM
Printed by "Shaw & Co, Plough Court, Fetter Lane"

806 1d Weekly Re-Issue/Complete in 38 Numbers./NED KELLY/THE/IRONCLAD AUSTRALIAN BUSHRANGER/The Volume Complete/containing nearly 500/pages and 38 illustra-/tions, price 3/6./[bordered by 8 b/w illus.]/The General Publishing Co., 280 Strand, W.C.
n.d.
Advt. Broadsheet; this issue of the book itself is unseen. RM

807 NED KELLY:/THE/IRONCLAD AUSTRALIAN/ BUSHRANGER/Complete/London:/Alfred J. Isaacs & Sons, 16 Camomile Street, E.C.
n.d.
456pp, b/w frontis. & 37 f/p b/w illus., col. pic. wrappers, 275x210mm. RM
Advertisements appear at the foot of each chapter & on the outside of back wrapper.

808 NED KELLY:/THE/IRONCLAD AUSTRALIAN/ BUSHRANGER./Complete/London:/Charles Henry Clarke, 11 Red Lion Court,/Fleet Street, E.C.
n.d.
456pp [in 38 parts], pic. wrappers, whole bound in col. pic. wrappers, 280x200mm. NSL:M

809 STIRRING TALES/OF/COLONIAL ADVENTURE/ A Book for Boys/By/Skipp Borlase,/Author of/ "Daring Deeds", "Tales of the Bush", "The Mysteries/ of Melbourne", "Yackandandah Station"./Etc. Etc./ [device]/With illustrations by Lancelot Speed/ London:/Frederick Warne & Co./and New York./(All rights reserved)
1894
viii, 376pp, b/w frontis. & 7 f/p b/w illus., pic. clo. blocked in black & gilt on col. background, 190x130mm. KMM
Australian contents include: 'The Overseer at Cooinda'; 'The Black Bloodhound'; 'Saved by Shadows'; 'Perils amongst Papuans'; 'A Slip between two Oceans'; 'Morning Call on Zebra Wolves'. Printed here for the first time in volume form.

810 STIRRING TALES/OF/COLONIAL ADVENTURE/ By/Skipp Borlase/Author of "Daring Deeds" "Tales of the Bush"/London/C. Arthur Pearson Limited/ Henrietta Street/1899
376pp, b/w frontis. by Lancelot Speed, (copy rebound), 180x120mm. KP

BORY, Eva

811 TEACHING/CHILDREN/TO SWIM/Eva Bory/Paul Hamlyn/Sydney London/New York Toronto
1971
140pp (inc. 1p preface), b/w photographic illus. throughout, sim. clo., pic. e/p, 220x145mm. NSL:M

BOSANQUET, June

812 FROM THE ASPARAGUS CASTLE/and other stories/[illus.]/June Bosanquet
Printed by Ambassador Press, Granville, NSW for British and Foreign Bible Society, n.d.
iv+43pp, b/w text illus. throughout, wrappers, cover title, 182x118mm. CLRC
Illus. Dixie Le Quesne. Title story tells of a boy born in Vienna whose family comes to Australia as refugees. He eventually becomes a minister in a mining town on the south coast of NSW. Another story 'The Man with the Book' tells of a man with a van full of Bibles who travels outback Australia.

BOSLEY, Keith

813 Keith Bosley/AND I DANCE/poems/original and translated/illustrated by/Richard Kennedy/Angus and Robertson
1972
96pp (inc. 3pp notes on poets), b/w illus., clo., 215x130mm. KP
Doubtful Australian authorship.

BOSWORTH, Ellen

814 SHELLEY/AND THE PONY OF THE YEAR/by/ Ellen Bosworth/Golden Press/Sydney
1972
154pp, 3 f/p b/w illus., pic. clo., pic. e/p, 208x132mm. ANL

815 SHELLEY/AND THE BUSHFIRE MYSTERY/by/ Ellen Bosworth/Golden Press/Sydney
1972
131pp, 3 f/p b/w illus., pic. clo., 210x132mm. ANL

BOURKE, P. A.

816 BIRDS IN YOUR GARDEN/by/P. A. Bourke/ Principal/Tenambit Primary School/New South Wales/[device]/1/Illustrated by John Truscott/ Longmans 1965
Melbourne
16pp & bibliography, part. col. illus. throughout, stiff pic. wrappers, 210x160mm. Australian Nature Series No. 1. BBC

817 BIRD MIGRATION/by/P. A. Bourke/Principal/ Tenambit Primary School/New South Wales/ Illustrated by/John Truscott/[device]/9/Longmans
1965
Melbourne
32pp & bibliography, part. col. illus. throughout, stiff pic. wrappers, 210x160mm. Australian Nature Series No. 9. BBC

[BOURLIN, V.]

818 ABC BOOK
Printed & publ. by Offset Printing Coy Pty Ltd, Sydney (copyright 1952)
12pp, col. illus. on every page, pic. wrappers, 265x210mm. NSL:M
Drawing on last page signed Victor Bourlin.

BOURNE, Ella F.

819 MEET JEREMY JONES/GREGORY GOODE/AND OTHERS/by/Ella F. Bourne/Illustrated by/Joan

Storie/Published for the Author by/Whitcombe & Tombs Pty. Ltd./Melbourne, Sydney and Perth
1945
51pp, col. frontis & b/w drawings throughout, dec. bd., 240x185mm. ANL
Children's verses.

BOURNE, Lawrence R.

820 CAPTAIN COPPERNOB/The Story of a Sailing Voyage/by/Lawrence R. Bourne/[b/w illus.]/ Humphrey Milford Oxford University Press
Oxford, 1929
158pp, col. frontis. & 12 b/w illus., dec. bd., 205x156mm. ANL
Illus. Savile Lumley. Adventure story of conflict between British sailing vessel & Japanese in the Pacific with voyage ending at Sydney.

821 CAPTAIN/COPPERNOB/The Story of a Sailing/ Voyage/By/Lawrence R Bourne/[device]/London: Humphrey Milford/Oxford University Press
1931
192pp, col. frontis. & 4 f/p b/w illus. (G. S. Bayley), blind stamped clo., 182x120mm. ANL
The Challenge Series

822 THE VOYAGE OF THE/LULWORTH/A Story of/ The Great Days of Sail/By/Lawrence R. Bourne/ Illustrated by/Norman Hepple/[device]/Oxford University Press/London: Humphrey Milford
1932
287pp, col. frontis., 4 f/p b/w plates, clo., 190x125mm. KMM
Nautical adventure in the seas north of Australia, with the last chapter taking place in Sydney.

823 As above but with col. frontis. & 4 f/p b/w plates, illus. of a square rig ship on front cover & ship's officer on spine, 192x130mm. KMM

BOUSSENARD, Louis

824 LE TOUR DU MONDE/D'UN/GAMIN DE PARIS/ Par/Louis Boussenard/Illustré de dessins par Férat, gravés par D. Dumont/[illus.]/Paris/C. Marpon et E. Flammarion, Éditeurs/Galerie de l'Odéon, 1 à 9, et Rue Racine, 26/Tous droits réservés.
n.d. [1876?]
662pp (inc. 15pp table of contents & epilogue), 80 b/w illus. in text, ¼ calf & marbled bd. with title in gilt on spine, marbled e/p, 265x185mm. RM
Book has continuous pagination & is divided into 4 titled parts, namely, Part 1, 'Les Mangeurs d'Hommes'; Part 2, 'Les Bandits de la Mer'; Part 3, 'Le Vaisseau de Proie'; Part 4, 'Les dix Millions de l'Opossum Rouge'. The last 3 chapters & epilogue of Part 3 relate to the Gamin's voyage to Australia (i.e. pp392-452). The Swan River, Perth, Melbourne & Sydney etc. are mentioned. Part 4 is set entirely in Australia, the action taking place in Victoria & SA & Cooper's Creek is mentioned. 26 of the 80 plates are Australian.

825 AVENTURES/D'UN/GAMIN DE PARIS/A TRAVERS L'OCÉANIE/par/Louis Boussenard/ Illustrées de dessins de J. Férat, gravés par D. Dumont./[engraving]/Paris/C. Marpon et E. Flammarion, Éditeurs,/Galeries de l'Odéon, 1 à 9, et rue Racine, 26./Tous droits réservés.
n.d. [187-?]
608pp (inc. 10pp contents), engraved t.p., b/w engravings throughout, embossed clo. bd., dec. in gilt, all g.e., 267x182mm. KMM
1st part Les Cannibales de la Mer de Corail; 2nd part Le Sultan de Bornéo; 3rd part Les Bandits Australiens.

826 Aventures d/un Gamin de Paris/A Travers l'Océanie/LES PIRATES/DES CHAMPS D'OR/Par/ Louis Boussenard/[device]/Paris/A la Librairie Illustrée/8, Rue Saint-Joseph, 8/Tous droits réservés.
n.d. [1877?]
300pp (inc. 4pp table of contents), b/w frontis. & 7 f/p b/w illus., ¾ cloth & marbled boards with title in gilt on spine, 175x115mm. RM
One of a series by this author. *Un Gamin en Brazil, French Guiana, South Africa, Borneo* and *Among the Bison.*

827 AVENTURES/D'UN/GAMIN DE PARIS/A TRAVERS L'OCÉANIE/Par/Louis Boussenard/ [device]/Paris/A la Librairie Illustrée/8, Rue Saint-Joseph, 8/Tous droits réservés.
n.d. [1877?]
403pp (inc. 7pp table of contents), b/w frontis. & 7 f/p b/w illus., 3/4 clo. & marbled bd. with title in gilt on spine, 175x115mm. RM
Story begins in Macao & continues on board a ship *en route* to Sydney. Pirates are encountered before the ship reaches a nameless coral island where Darwin & Torres Strait are mentioned & finally the greatest part of the story is set in New Guinea. A history of the discovery of the Pacific is interspersed with the action.

828 Louis Boussenard/LES/PIRATES DES CHAMPS D'OR/Roman d'Aventures/[device]/Bibliothèque des Grandes Aventures/Éditions Jules Tallandier/75, Rue Dareau, Paris (XIVe)/Tous droits réservés.
n.d. [1924?]
222pp, unillus., col. pic. wrappers, 186x110mm. ANL

BOWDEN, Isobel Kendall

829 STORIES AND RHYMES/by/Isobel Kendall Bowden/Foreword by/Miss Zoe Benjamin/ Vice-Principal, Sydney Kindergarten and/Preparatory Teachers' College/Several of the verses in this book have/appeared in the "Sydney Morning Herald" &c [2 lines]
1936
55pp (inc. 1p foreword), some text drawings, pic. wrappers, 217x140mm. NSL:M

BOWES, Joseph

830 PALS/Young Australians/in sport and adventure/ By/Joseph Bowes/With eight full-page coloured illustrations/by John Macfarlane/London: James Glass/28 Newgate Street
n.d. [1910?]
311pp, 1p adv., col. frontis & 7 col. plates, pic. clo., 185x125mm. KMM

831 Second ed. as above with bdg variation. KMM

832 COMRADES/A Story of/The Australian Bush/By/ Joseph Bowes/Author of 'Pals'/Illustrated in colour by Cyrus Cuneo/London/Henry Frowde/Hodder and Stoughton/1912
288pp, 16pp adv., col. frontis. & 5 col. plates, pic. clo., 185x120mm. CLRC
• Rpt 1919 as above, but no adv. KMM

833 COMRADES, London 1912
Variant bindings. First copy is bound in light blue or green cloth with the figure of a horseman blocked in col. on front & title 'Comrades' in gilt, & a group of boys on horseback on spine. Second copy (possibly a later binding, is in red clo. with a col. onlay on front surrounded by dec. scrolls. Title & author's name blocked in col. & similar design on spine. KMM

834 COMRADES/A Story of/The Australian Bush/By/ Joseph Bowes/Author of "The New Chums" etc/ Illustrated in colour by Cyrus Cuneo/Humphrey Milford/Oxford University Press, London, Edinburgh Glasgow/Toronto, Melbourne, Cape Town, Bombay
• Rpt 1917

288pp, col. frontis. & 5 col. plates, clo. with col. onlay on front cover & on spine, 184x120mm. KP

835 Another copy as above but bound in the bdg used for *The Anzac War-Trail* with the officer grasping a bugle against the background of a Union Jack. KP

836 THE NEW-CHUMS/A Jungle Story/By/Joseph Bowes/Author of "Pals", "Comrades"/Illustrated in colour by Cyrus Cuneo/London/Henry Frowde/Hodder and Stoughton/1915
[a copy seen with an inscription as follows: 'With the author's best wishes Xmas 1914']
308pp (inc. 1p author's foreword), col. frontis. & 5 col. illus., pic. clo., 190x130mm. ANL

837 THE YOUNG ANZACS/A Tale of the Great War/By/Joseph Bowes/Author of "The New Chums"/Illustrated by/Howard Elcock/Humphrey Milford/Oxford/University Press/London Edinburgh Glasgow/Toronto Melbourne Cape Town Bombay
1917; rpt 1918
276pp (inc. 1p dedication, 1p quotation), col. frontis. & 3 f/p col. illus., pic. clo., 190x120mm. KMM

838 THE YOUNG ANZACS/A Tale of the Great War/By/Joseph Bowes/Author of "The New Chums"/Illustrated by/Howard Elcock/Humphrey Milford/Oxford University Press/London Edinburgh Glasgow/Toronto Melbourne Cape Town Bombay/1918
276pp (inc. 1p dedication & 1p quotation), col. frontis. & 3 f/p col. illus., pic. clo. (depicting 2 soldiers, one with machine-gun & one with rifle, on front cover), 190x120mm. KP
Although the second ed. (identical with above apart from date on t.p.), says on verso 'First printed 1917; Reprinted 1918', this seems to be the first edition.

839 THE YOUNG/ANZACS/Joseph/Bowes/Humphrey Milford/Oxford University Press/London
n.d. [prize 1919]
276pp+32pp advs., col frontis, pic. e/p, clo., 184x120mm. KP

840 Another copy as above, variant bdg in blue clo. & illus. arranged in different order. KP

841 THE/YOUNG/ANZACS/Joseph/Bowes/Humphrey/Milford/Oxford University/Press London
• Rpt 1921
276pp (inc. 1p dedication & 1p quotation), dec. t.p., col. frontis., clo., dec. e/p, 160x105mm. Boys Pocket Library. KMM

842 Another copy as above but plain e/ps, variant bdg & illus. from first ed. as frontis. KP

843 THE/ANZAC WAR-TRAIL/With the light horse in Sinai/By/Joseph Bowes/Author of/"Pals", "Comrades", "New Chums", "The Young Anzacs"/Humphrey Milford/Oxford University Press/London, Edinburgh, Glasgow/Toronto, Melbourne, Cape Town, Bombay/1919
281pp, 7pp adv., col. frontis. & 3 col. illus., pic. clo., 190x110mm. CLRC
Illustrations signed 'Arch. Webb'
Author states: 'This book is a story and not a history'.

844 THE ANZAC WAR-TRAIL 1919
As above with variant pic. cover, one has two soldiers with rifles climbing a hill & the other has an officer grasping a bugle in front of the Union Jack, & on spine, has a soldier running with a flag. KP

845 THE/ANZAC/WAR-TRAIL/Joseph/Bowes/Humphrey/Milford/Oxford/University/Press London
• Rpt 1919
281pp & 7 pp adv., col. frontis. (Arch Webb) only, clo., pic. e/p, 185x120mm. KP
The Boy's New Library.

846 THE/AUSSIE CRUSADERS/With Allenby in Palestine/by/Joseph Bowes/Author of/'The Young Anzacs' 'The Anzac War Trail'/Illustrated in colour by/Wal Paget/Humphrey Milford/Oxford University Press/London Edinburgh Glasgow/Toronto Melbourne Cape Town Bombay/1920
[Morris Miller gives dates of first publication as 1918].
270pp, col. frontis. & 3 col. illus., pic. clo., 180x115mm. CLRC

847 THE/AUSSIE/CRUSADERS/Joseph Bowes/Humphrey Milford/Oxford University Press/London
n.d. [1920]
270pp, col. frontis. only, clo., 190x120mm. The Boys New Library. KMM
Several copies seen as above although using a different illus as frontis. KP

848 THE HONOUR OF/JOHN TREMAYNE/By/Joseph Bowes/London/The Epworth Press/J. Alfred Sharp
n.d. [1926] [According to Morris Miller, first published by Angus & Robertson, Sydney 1920]. This historical novel does not in fact appear to be a boys' book.
303pp, unillus., clo. ANL

849 THE JACKAROOS/Life on a Cattle Run/By/Joseph Bowes/Author of/'Comrades'/'The New Chums' ,'The Young Anzacs' etc./with illustrations by Archibald Webb/Humphrey Milford/Oxford University Press/
1923
287pp, col. frontis. & 3 f/p col. illus., clo., 185x120mm. CLRC

850 THE/JACK-/AROOS/by/Joseph Bowes/Humphrey/Milford/Oxford/University/Press London
1926
287pp, 1p adv., dec. t.p., col. frontis. sgd Arch Webb, clo., dec. e/p, 160x110mm. KMM

851 THE/JACK-/AROOS/By/Joseph/Bowes/Humphrey/Milford/Oxford/University/Press London
1926
The Boys Pocket Library; as above but a different Arch Webb illus. used as frontis. & another copy with yet another illus. & variant binding—green clo. with title & pattern of palm trees printed in different col. KP

852 THE FUR-HUNTERS/IN AUSTRALIAN WILDS/By/Joseph Bowes/Author of "The New Chums", "Comrades" ,"The Jackaroos"/With illustrations by D. C. Eyles/[device]/Humphrey Milford/Oxford University Press/London Edinburgh Glasgow/Toronto Melbourne Cape Town Bombay
1925
280pp, 8pp adv., col. frontis., 4 f/p b/w illus.., clo., 190x125mm. KMM

853 THE/YOUNG SETTLER/The Story of a/New-Chum in Queensland/By/Joseph Bowes/Author of/'The Young Anzacs', 'The Honour of John Tremayne'/etc./London/The Epworth Press/J. Alfred Sharp
1927
272pp, b/w frontis. & 2 b/w illus. sgd 'D.W.A.', clo., 190x125mm. ANL

854 THE/YOUNG SETTLER
London, J. Alfred Sharp, 1927
As above. The order in which the 3 illus. were bound in the book was somewhat haphazard as 3 copies of the 1927 (and probably only) ed. have been seen, each with a different illus. used as frontis. Two copies have the publisher printed as 'Sharp' on the spine & the other 'Epworth Press'. KP

BOWMAN, Anne

855 THE/KANGAROO HUNTERS/or/Adventures in the Bush/by/Anne Bowman/Author of "Esperanza"

"The Castaways" "The Young Exiles"/etc. etc./[verse]/London/G. Routledge & Co., Farringdon Street/New York: 18 Beekman Street/1859
iv+444pp (inc. preface), engraved frontis. & 7 b/w engravings, dec. clo., 170x105mm. Grant

856 THE/KANGAROO HUNTERS/or/Adventures in the Bush/by/Anne Bowman/Author of 'Esperanza' 'The Castaways' 'The Young Exiles'/etc./[quotation]/A New Edition/London:/Routledge, Warne & Routledge/Farringdon Street/New York 56 Walker Street/1860
iv+444pp, b/w frontis. & 7 b/w engravings, clo., 180x115mm. ANL

857 THE/KANGAROO HUNTERS;/or./Adventures in the Bush./By/Anne Bowman,/Author of "Esperanza", "The Castaways" ."The Young Exiles"/etc. etc./[verse, Schiller]/London:/George Routledge and Sons,/The Broadway, Ludgate,/New York: 416 Broome Street
n.d. [inscribed 1870]
iv+444pp (inc. 2pp preface), b/w frontis. & 7 f/p engravings, dec. clo., 165x100mm. CLRC
Native with spears and hunting dog on front cover.

858 THE KANGAROO/HUNTERS/or/Adventures in The Bush/by/Anne Bowman/Author of "Esperanza" "The Castaways" ,"The Young Exiles"/etc. etc./[verse]/London/George Routledge and Sons/Broadway, Ludgate Hill/New York 9 Lafayette Place
n.d. [inscribed 1885]
iv+444pp, engraved frontis. & 7 f/p b/w illus., pic. clo., dec. in gilt, 185x120mm. GK
Title in gilt with 2 kangaroos on front and 2 boys on spine.

859 THE KANGAROO/HUNTERS/or/Adventures in the Bush/by/Anne Bowman./Author of "Esperanza", "The Castaways" "The Young Exiles",/etc. etc./with Full-page Plates./[device]/London/George Routledge and Sons, Limited/Broadway House, Ludgate Hill/New York: E. P. Dutton and Co.
n.d.
iv+444pp, b/w frontis. & 7 f/p b/w plates, pic. clo., gilt edges, 190x120mm. Grant

860 THE/KANGAROO HUNTERS;/or,/Adventures in the Bush./By Anne Bowman,/[verse]/Boston:/Crosby, Nichols, Lee and Company./1860
xii+463pp, b/w frontis. & 7 b/w illus., clo., 170x110mm. Grant
• Rpt 1860, 1861, as above, unseen. NUC

861 Another copy, as above but "Boston:/Crosby and Nichols./New York: Oliver S. Felt, 36 Walker Street./1864'
xii+463pp, 2pp preface, engraved frontis. & 7 b/w engravings, clo., 170x110mm. NSL:M

862 THE/KANGAROO HUNTERS;/or/Adventures in the Bush/By Anne Bowman/Author of 'Esperanza', 'The Castaways', 'The Young Exiles'/etc. etc./[quotation]/Philadelphia/Porter & Coates
n.d. [Preface dated 1858]
xii+463pp & 4pp adv., b/w frontis., clo., 188x122mm. ANL

863 Another copy, as above but 'Philadelphia:/Porter & Coates,/822 Chestnut Street.'
n.d.
xii+463pp, 2pp preface, b/w frontis. & 6 f/p b/w engravings, pic. clo., 170x110mm. RM
The singularly inappropriate cover design shows an Indian on horseback spearing a buffalo.

864 THE/KANGAROO HUNTERS;/or,/Adventures in the Bush./by/Anne Bowman./Author of "Esperanza" "The Castaway", "The Young Exiles",/etc. etc./[quotation]/Boston:/Woolworth, Ainsworth & Co./New York: A. S. Barnes & Co.
n.d.
xii+463pp (inc. preface), unillus., marbled bd., half calf, 170x110mm. Grant

865 THE/KANGAROO-HUNTERS/by/Anne Bowman/E. W. Cole, Book Arcade, Melbourne/333 George Street/Sydney/67 Rundle Street/Adelaide
n.d. [inscription 1906]
444pp, b/w frontis., dec. clo., 180x115mm. Cole's Popular Library. Grant

866 VOYAGE/AU/PAYS DES KANGAROUS/adapté de l'anglais/par/Bénédict-Henry Révoil/Tours/Alfred Mame et fils, éditeurs/1876
254pp, engraved frontis., clo., 240x150mm. ANL

BOWMAN, Gerald

867 FROM SCOTT/TO FUCHS/by/Gerald Bowman/Cadet Edition/[publisher's device]/London/Evans Brothers Limited
1960
192pp, frontis. & 8pp b/w photographic illus., clo., 200x125mm. ANL
A book of Antarctic exploration.

868 Adventures in Geography Series/General Editor: Nina Gardner/WITH FUCHS AND HILLARY/ACROSS ANTARCTICA/by/Gerald Bowman/Illustrated by/Lunt Roberts/Frederick Muller Limited/London
1961
143pp (inc. 2pp note & 3pp index), frontis. & 18 b/w maps, 17 b/w photographic illus., line drawings, clo., 185x125mm. BBC

The Boy in the Bush
See Rowe, Richard

BOYD, A. J.

869 THE EARTH'S HISTORY/FOR BOYS/Or,/Geology in Verse./by A. J. Boyd/Headmaster of The Toowoomba Grammar School/Brisbane:/Watson, Ferguson & Co./1889
vipp, 66pp (inc 18pp appendix & glossary) & [16]pp sketches of birds, animals &c, clo., 156x102mm. CLRC

BOYD, Jessie

870 MY LEARN TO GARDEN BOOK/by Jessie Boyd/illustrated by Tony Hudson/Contents [14 lines]/Paul Hamlyn/London/Sydney/New York Toronto
1971
62pp, col. decorations throughout, pic. e/p, pic. bd., 315x230mm. CLRC

BOYD, Martin

871 THE/PAINTED PRINCESS/A Fairy Story/By/Martin Boyd/Illustrated by Jocelyn Crowe/[decoration]/Constable & Co. Ltd./London
1936
71pp, col. illus. throughout, clo., dec. e/p, 210x165mm. KMM
Also with variant bdg & plain e/p.

BOYD, Robin

872 The Story of/Australian Architecture/THE/WALLS/AROUND/US/Told and Illustrated/for Young Readers by/Robin Boyd/F. W. Cheshire/Melbourne Canberra Sydney
1962
90pp (inc. 8pp glossary & notes), dec. t.p., 49 part. col. drawings, clo., 235x155mm. KMM

BOYLAN, Rev. Eustace

873 THE/HEART/OF THE SCHOOL/An Australian School Story/By/Eustace Boylan/J. Roy Stevens, Printer and Publisher/1, 3, 5 & 7 Knox Place, Victoria
[1920]

399pp (inc. 1p foreword), 1p verse, 4 f/p b/w illus. by Colin Colahan & others, clo., 180x110mm. ANL
Second imp. as above but 'Knox Place, Melbourne,Victoria'. KP

874 MRS THUNDER/and Other Stories/By/Eustace Boylan/Author of "The Heart of the School": An Australian/School Story./All rights reserved./Second impression/Wholly set up and printed in Australia./ Registered by the Postmaster-General for transmission through the/post as a book./J. Roy Stevens, Printer and Publisher,/1-7 Knox Place, Melbourne./1923
255pp, b/w frontis. & 2 f/p b/w illus., clo., 180x120mm. ANL
Although this does not seem specifically a children's book, according to Morris Miller: 'The title-piece is an aeronautical novelette for juveniles, set in England, with a sequel, "The Bird of Destiny"; other stories are located in Melbourne and Sydney'.

The Boy's Birth-day Book

875 THE/BOY'S BIRTH-DAY BOOK;/A Collection of/ Tales, Essays, and Narratives of Adventure./By/Mrs S. C. Hall, William Howitt, Augustus Mayhew./Thomas Miller, and George Augustus Sala./Illustrated/with nearly one hundred original engravings/London:/ Houlston and Wright, Paternoster Row.
n.d. [1859]
428pp, engraved frontis. & numerous text illus., dec clo., title in gilt, g.e.,178x120mm. ANL

Boy's Book of Action

876 BOY'S BOOK/OF/ACTION/The Boy's Book of Action 1949
OPC Quality Productions, Sydney, March 1949
220pp, 2pp col. maps, 3pp col. drawings, b/w photographic illus. & some text illus., pic. e/p, pic. bd., 266x210mm. KMM
Stanley Brogden, Alex Chisholm, Douglas Nicholls, mostly factual articles.

The Boys' Friend Library

A series of popular paperback books for boys publ. in London during the 1920s and 1930s.
Format example:

877 BOOMERANG BOB/[in a shield: "The/Boys' Friend/Library/No. 191/(New Series) 2/3/29"]/by John Ascott/4d./A Breathless Story of/Australian Adventure.
The Amalgamated Press, London, 1929
64pp (inc. 2pp extraneous material), unillus., col. pic. wrappers (with adv. verso front wrapper & both sides back wrapper), cover title, 175x135mm. RM
Others in series:

878 THE SECRET OF THE REEF, no. 366, by John Andrews, 5/1/33, 96pp. RM
879 OFF TO AUSTRALIA, no. 270, by Malcolm Arnold, n.d., 120pp. RM
880 PADDY LEARY'S SCHOOL DAYS, no. 180, by T. C. Bridges. RM
881 PADDY LEARY MILLIONAIRE, no. 182, by T. C. Bridges. RM
882 THE AUSSIE AT HIGHCLIFF, no. 708, by T. C. Bridges, 1940, 64pp & 1p adv. KMM
883 LONG ODDS, no. 46, by G. Chester, 1926, 64pp. Unseen
884 CRUSOE ISLAND,Adventures in Solomon Islands and New Guinea, by M. Everard, n.d., 130x180mm. RM
885 SOUTH SEAS GOLD, no. 304, by Maj. C. Gilson, 1931. RM
886 KING OF THE ISLANDS, no. 331, by C. Hamilton, 1932, 96pp. Solomon Islands. RM
887 GALLEONS GOLD, no. 341, by C. Hamilton, 1932, 96pp. RM
888 CHUMS OF THE ISLAND, no. 365, by C. Hamilton, 1933, 96pp. Fiji setting. RM
889 THE HAUNTED ISLAND, no. 434, by C. Hamilton, 1934, 96pp. VMOU
890 PALS OF THE PACIFIC, no. 623, by C. Hamilton, 1938, 96pp. VMOU
891 SOUTH SEAS TREASURE, no. 666, by C. Hamilton, 1939, 64pp. VMOU
892 SHIPWRECK KELLY, no. 484, by A. S. Hardy, 1935, 96pp. New Guinea. RM
893 NED KELLY: A TALE OF TROOPER AND BUSHRANGER, no. 44, by C. Hayter. n.d., 120pp. RM
894 TROOPER AND BUSHRANGER; OR, THE LAST DAYS OF NED KELLY, no. 45, by C. Hayter, n.d., 120pp. RM
895 BANDITS OF THE BUSH, no. 652, by S. C. Hook, 1923, 64pp. RM
896 VOLCANO ISLAND, by S. C. Hook, 1924, 64pp. South Pacific. RM
897 CORNSTALK BOB, no. 524, by B. Kent, 1920, 64pp. ANL
898 THE GOLDEN CREEK, no. 553, by N. Owen, (193-?), 64pp. Victorian background. RM
899 BEYOND THE DESERT, no. 584, by R. Randolph, 64pp. RM
900 THE LAST CHOICE, no. 624, by R. Randolph, 64pp. Australian cricket. RM
901 YOUNG YARDLEY, no. 626, by R. Randolph, 64pp. Cricket. RM
902 BUCKAROO OUTLAW, no. 699, by G. E. Rochester, 1939, 64pp. NT setting. RM
903 THE MISSING HEIR, no. 17, by 'Maxwell Scott' (i.e. J. W. Staniforth), 120pp. ANL
904 THE FINAL ROUND, by 'Maxwell Scott'. Unseen
905 THE SILVER DWARF, by 'Maxwell Scott'. Unseen
906 THE DIGGER 'TEC, no. 111, by 'H. Teed', 1927. ANL
907 BEYOND THE DESERT, no. 584, by 'R. Whitly', 1922, 64pp. RM
908 THE SCHOOL OF SECRETS, no. 624, by 'R. Whitly', 1927, 96pp. RM

The Boy's Own Sea Stories

909 THE/BOY'S OWN SEA STORIES/Being/The Adventures of a Sailor,/in/The Navy, The Merchant Service, and on/A Whaling Cruise./Narrated by himself/With Numerous Illustrations./London:/Ward, Lock, and Tyler./Warwick House, Paternoster Row.
n.d. [inscribed 1874] [1st publ. 1859; new ed. 1880]
viii+424pp, 16pp adv., engraved frontis. & additional engraved t.p. & 10 other engravings, clo. dec. in gold, 170x110mm. KP

910 THE/BOY'S OWN SEA STORIES:/Being/The Adventures of a Sailor/in/The Navy, The Merchant Service,/and on/A Whaling Cruise./London:/Ward, Lock & Co., Limited, Warwick House, Salisbury Square, E.C./New York and Melbourne
n.d.
vii+424pp & 14pp adv., unillus. apart from chapter heading vignettes, clo., 190x122mm. CLRC

911 THE/BOY'S OWN SEA STORIES:/Being/The Adventures of a Sailor/in/The Navy, The Merchant Service,/and on/A Whaling Cruise/Illustrated/Ward, Lock & Co., Limited, London, Melbourne, and Toronto.
n.d.
x+424pp, & 4pp adv., b/w frontis. by Charles de Lacey, clo., 183x122mm. CLRC

912 THE/BOY'S/OWN SEA STORIES;/Being/The Adventures of a Sailor/in/The Navy, The Merchant

Service,/and on/A Whaling Cruise./Illustrated/ London:/Ward, Lock & Co., Limited/Warwick House, Salisbury Square, E.C./New York and Melbourne
n.d. [190-?]
x+424pp, &14pp adv., b/w frontis & 1 b/w plate, by F. Jack, b/w chapter headings & tailpieces, clo., 189x122mm. KMM

913 Cole's Favourite Library/THE/BOYS' OWN SEA STORIES/being/The Adventures of a Sailor/in/The Navy, The Merchant Service/and on/a Whaling Cruise/Illustrated/Printed in England for/E. W. Cole/ Book Arcade, Melbourne; 333 & 346 George St. Sydney/67 Rundle Street Adelaide.
n.d.
424pp, 2pp preface, 1 f/p b/w illus., illus. chapter headings & tailpieces, clo., 190x210mm. Grant

The Boys' Wireless Book

914 THE/BOYS' WIRELESS BOOK/: a concise and reliable guide/for the wireless amateur/in the construction/of his apparatus and/to the better/ understanding/of his/hobby/[device]/Australia/ Cornstalk Publishing Company/Arnold Place, Sydney/ 1924
Eagle Press
90pp (8 leaves of plates), b/w frontis., clo., 245x180mm. ANL

BRACKEN, Anne

915 THE/ADVENTURES OF/FLOPSIE FLAT-FOOT/ The/Walking/Toy/[drawing]/By/Anne Bracken
Dawfox Productions, Sydney 1944
31pp, 14pp col. illus. & b/w drawings, dec. bd., 215x240mm. ANL

916 THE TAIL (OR TALE)/OF/PATCH/THE/PUPPY/ [illustration]/By Anne Bracken
Jons Productions, Sydney, n.d. [1944]
27pp, 12 f/p col. illus. & b/w drawings in text, dec. bd., 215x230mm. NSL:M

917 THE TAIL (OR TALE)/OF/PATCH/THE/PUPPY/ [illustration]/By Anne Bracken/A Jons Production/ Lithographed in Australia by Posters Pty. Ltd. for Jons Productions Pty. Ltd., Sydney
n.d. [1950]
17pp, col. & b/w illus. throughout, dec. bd., dec. e/p, 155x150mm. KMM

918 JANCY WINS THROUGH/By Anne Bracken/A Jons Production/Made and printed in Australia for Jons Productions/by Colourtone Pty. Ltd., Sydney Australia
n.d. [1945]
253pp, 4 b/w f/p illus., clo., 205x130mm. ANL
3rd ed. 1947, 4th ed. 1952, as above. KMM

919 BEING/THE/(MIS)ADVENTURES/OF/PODGY/ THE/PENGUIN/By Anne Bracken
Jons Productions, Sydney, n.d. [1946]
28pp, dec. t.p., 12 f/p col. illus., b/w drawings in text throughout, pic. bd., 215x230mm. KMM

920 THE TWINS TAKE CHARGE/By/Anne Bracken/A Jons Production/Made and printed in Australia for Jons Productions/By Colourtone Pty. Ltd. Sydney Australia
n.d. [1946]
251pp, unillus., clo., 215x140mm. ANL
2nd edition 1947, as above. KMM

921 THE TWINS/TO THE/RESCUE/By Anne Bracken/ A Jons Production/Jons Productions Pty. Ltd./Sydney Australia
n.d. [1947]
229pp, 3pp adv., unillus., clo., 210x130mm. ANL

922 JANCY SCORES AGAIN/By Anne Bracken/A Jons Production/Made and printed in Australia for Jons Productions/by Colourtone Pty. Ltd. Sydney Australia
n.d. [1947]
250pp, 4pp adv., 3 b/w illus., clo., 215x135mm. ANL
• Rpt 1948, 1952 as above. KP

923 PENNY AND DORABELLA/AT THE BEACH/ [drawing]/A Jons Production/By Anne Bracken
Sydney, n.d. [1947]
32pp, col. & b/w illus., dec. bd., 215x230mm. ANL

924 PENNY AND DORABELLA/AT THE CIRCUS/ [drawing]/A Jons Production/By Anne Bracken/ Registered at the GPO Sydney for transmission by post as a book
n.d. [1947]
32pp, col. & b/w illus. throughout, dec. bd., 215x230mm. ANL

925 THE/TUPPITY/TWINS/by Anne Bracken
Jons Productions, Sydney, n.d. [1947]
28pp, col. & b/w illus. throughout, dec. bd., cover title, 215x235mm. ANL

926 A Tale of Two Tails/PATCH/A Jons Production/ AND HIS FRIEND/POM-POM/By Anne Bracken
Jons Productions, Sydney, n.d. [1947]
28pp, dec. t.p., 12 f/p col. illus. & b/w drawings in text, dec. bd., 215x235mm. ANL

927 JANCY IN PURSUIT/By/Anne Bracken/Jons Productions Pty. Ltd./Sydney Australia
n.d. [1950]
224pp, unillus., clo., 215x140mm. ANL

928 JANCY STANDS ALONE/By/Anne Bracken/Made and printed in Australia for Jons Productions Pty. Ltd./ by Deaton & Spencer Pty. Ltd., Sydney Australia
n.d. [Copy seen inscribed 1955]
200pp, unillus., bd., 205x135mm. KMM

BRACKEN, ANNE & 'PIERS' [pseud. SENIOR, Margaret]

929 THE LOST TOYSHOP/By Ann *[sic]* Bracken & Piers
Colour Productions, Sydney, n.d. [1946]
28pp, dec. t.p., col. & b/w illus. throughout, dec. bd., 210x225mm. ANL

930 MEG & PEG/Adventures of Two Peg Dolls/By Ann *[sic]* Bracken & Piers
Jons Productions, Sydney, n.d. [1946]
27pp, dec. t.p., col. & b/w illus. throughout, dec. bd., 215x230mm. ANL

BRADDON, Russell Reading

931 WOMAN IN ARMS/The Story of/Nancy Wake/by/ Russell Braddon/Special edition abridged/for young readers/Collins/Sydney/1963
192pp, b/w map & 14 b/w photographic illus., clo., 200x135mm. KMM
Original edition of this biography of the Australian war heroine published in 1956.
• Rpt 1964, 8 b/w plates, 198x132mm ANL

'BRADLEY, J. J, G.'

See Borlase, James Skipp

BRADY, E. J.

932 TOM PAGDIN/PIRATE/By/E. J. Brady/With four full-page illustrations by Lionel Lindsay/Sydney/ N.S.W. Bookstall Co./1911
202pp, 24pp adv., b/w frontis. & 3 f/p b/w illus., pic. wrappers, 185x110mm. KMM
Humorous adventures of two boys who run away from home in the northern rivers district of New South Wales.

BRAGG, W. H.

933 THE/WORLD OF SOUND/Six lectures delivered before/a juvenile auditory at the/Royal Institution, Christmas, 1919/By/Sir William Bragg, KBE, D.Sc., F.R.S./Hon. Fellow of Trinity College, Cambridge/ Quain Professor of Physics in the University of London/[device]/London/G. Bell and Sons Ltd./1920
viii+196pp, b/w chapter headings & tailpieces, photographic illus. & diagrams, pic. clo., 185x122mm. SUA
Author's name, title & decoration in gilt on front cover & spine. Drawings by Audrey Weber. Professor of Mathematics & Physics at Adelaide University from 1886 to 1907.

BRAHE, May H. [née Dickson, Mary Hannah] 1970s

934 Imperial Edition/No. 104/LOVE AND LIFE/Five Little Songs/with/Piano Accompaniment/By/May H. Brahe/[titles listed]/Copyright for all countries. Price 2/6 Net/Allan & Co.,/Proprietary Limited./276-278 Collins Street,/Melbourne./Bendigo, Geelong and Adelaide/Printed in England
n.d.
12pp (last blank), unillus., wrappers, 310x233mm. NSL:M
Spring Blossoms: 4 Little Songs adv. on back cover.

935 Both Notations/DAME DURDEN'S/SCHOOL;/A Juvenile Cantata for School Entertainments/By/May H. Brahe./Copyright Price 1/- nett./Allan & Co. Proprietary Limited, 276-278 Collins Street,/ Melbourne./And at Bendigo Geelong and Adelaide
[1934]
31pp, 1p adv. & adv. inside front wrapper & both sides of back wrapper, unillus., wrappers, 250x157mm. VSL
Adv. *Argus* 29/11/1913
See also Taylor, Helen

936 Both Notations/THE/MAGIC WOOD/A Juvenile Cantata for School Entertainments/By/May H. Brahe/ Copyright Price 1/6 nett/Allan & Co.,/Melbourne/ Sydney, Adelaide/and Bendigo. Printed in England
[copy acquired 4 Aug. 1934]
37pp & 1p adv. unillus., wrappers, 250x166mm. VSL

937 Imperial Edition/No. 106/Both Notations/THE MAGIC WOOD./A Juvenile Cantata for School Entertainment/By May H. Brahe/copyright/Allan & Co. Prop. Ltd./Melbourne Sydney Adelaide, Bendigo
As above, pic. wrappers, 242x176mm. KP
Price 3/6 on front cover. Adv. *Argus* 29/11/1913.

REAL AUSTRALIAN SONGS. *See* Dickson, Madge

BRAIN, Paula

938 NOBODY'S FAIRY/Being a story/with illustrations/ By Paula Brain
Vardon & Sons, Adelaide, n.d. [1921]
24pp, 10pp col. illus., marginal drawings, pic. wrappers, cover title, 245x155mm. KMM
Subtitle on cover: 'Idealism, The Doctrine of Ideal Existence'.

BRAMMALL, Mrs T. C.

See Adams, Bertha Southey

BRAND, Mona

939 An Australian Space Fantasy/For Children/FLYING SAUCERY/By Mona Brand/Music for Songs by Robert MacDonough/Will Andrade/275c Pitt Street/Sydney NSW Australia 2000
n.d. [1972?]
45pp (inc. 1p notes), unillus., wrappers, cover title, 220x165mm. KMM

BRASSEY, Annie (née Allnutt) Baroness

940 AROUND THE WORLD IN THE YACHT 'SUNBEAM' our home on the Ocean for eleven months.
N.Y.1878. First US edition (later presented as 'A Voyage in the Sunbeam'). (unseen) NUC
The author, the first wife of Lord Brassey died aboard the *Sunbeam* 14 September 1887, seven days out of Darwin on their third voyage. Lord Brassey remarried and was appointed Governor of Victoria in 1895 and served till January 1900. About 100 pages of this popular book are set in the Pacific.

941 AFLOAT AND ASHORE, or A Voyage in the "Sunbeam" our home on the ocean for eleven months
n.d., n.p. Juvenile Pub. Co. NUC
Hungarian edition
Utazas a "Napsugaron" angol..Budapest. NUC

942 VOYAGE D'UNE FAMILLE AUTOUR DU MONDE, Traduit de l'anglais par J. Butler [abridge]
Paris [1878] pp.xiv,360. NUC

943 LE TOUR DU MONDE EN FAMILLE; Voyage de la famille Brassey, dans son yacht le Sunbeam, raconté par la mère, Traduit de l'anglais par Richard Voet, Tours, A. Mame et fils, 1885, illus; 3rd ed. 1887; new ed. 1893. NUC

944 A VOYAGE IN THE 'SUNBEAM'/by/Mrs. Brassey/ Adapted for School and Class Reading/[illustration with caption]/With illustrations/London/Longmans Green & Co./1880
376pp, 16pp adv., engraved frontis., 3 maps, 4 f/p engravings & 32 engravings in text, dec. clo., 170x110mm. KMM
• Rpt 1881, KMM

945 A VOYAGE IN THE 'SUNBEAM'/By/Lady Brassey/ Adapted for School and Class reading/[illustration with caption]/With illustrations/London/Longmans, Green and Co./and New York: 15 East 16th Street/1890
376pp. b/w map, 35 engravings, dec. clo., 165x105mm. KMM
Swedish edition

946 EN SJÖRESA I TROPIKERNA/Af/Lady A. Brassey/ (Förf: a till "En Sjöförd omkring Jorden".) Med Talrika illustrationer och karta
Unseen: Advertised among other books for the young on the back of Swedish edition of Meissner's *Cook's Voyages*. Information RM

BRATTON, John W.

947 TEDDY BEARS/PICNIC/Big note version/For Piano (with words)/by/John W. Bratton/40c/Allan & Co. Pty Ltd/Melbourne Adelaide Bendigo/authorized for sale in Australia and New Zealand only
n.d. [1947]
6pp, pic. cover in 2 col. by Ida Rentoul Outhwaite, cover title, 310x235mm. KP

BRAUN, Kathy

948 KANGAROO/&/KANGAROO/by Kathy Braun/ Illustrated by/Jim McMullan
Ronald Whiting & Wheaton, London 1965
36pp, col. dec. t.p., col. & part. col. illus. on alternate pages, pic. clo., dec. e/p, 200x260mm. KMM
There is nothing Australian in the story, which is told in verse, & the drawings of the kangaroos are very stylized.

The Brave Dog and the Big Bad Wolf

See DOONGALLA DAYS STORIES

Bravery at Sea

949 BRAVERY/AT SEA
n.d., no imprint, [? the author, Sydney, 194-?]
12pp, (inc. 4pp f/p col. illus.), 2 f/p green & white

illus. & drawings throughout, pic. wrappers, cover title, 230x175mm. KP
Illus. signed by J. H. Guerin. Exploits of Australian Navy in WWII recounted.

BRAY, J. R.
950 TEA TOWN/PAINTING/BOOK 3d./TEA REVIVES/YOU
n.p., n.d., ?Aust.
12pp, 6 col. pictures on 3pp & b/w pictures to paint, 2pp story, col. pic. wrappers, 193x122mm. KP

BREMER, Lady J. J. Gordon
At one time thought to be author of A MOTHER'S OFFERING TO HER CHILDREN.

BRENT-DYER, Elinor M.
951 A QUINTETTE IN/QUEENSLAND/By/Elinor M. Brent-Dyer/W. & R. Chambers, Ltd./Edinburgh and London 1951
80pp, frontis. map, 11 f/p photographic illus., 3 small b/w illus., pic. bd., 195x120mm. KMM

BRETON, J. B. J.
952 PREMIER VOYAGE/DE/JAMES COOK,/autour du Monde,/Fait en 1768, 1769, 1770 et 1771,/précédé des Relations de Mm. Byron, Carteret, et Wallis/Traduction nouvelle, par J. B. M. Breton./Tome Premier./A Paris,/ Chez la veuve Le Petit Librairie,/rue Pavée Saint-André-des-Arts, no 28./An XII-1804
xx + 249pp, unillus., polished calf with title in gilt & gilt dec. on spine, 125x75mm. CLRC
Vol. 1 of the 3 Voyages of James Cook in 15 vols, part of "Bibliothèque Portative des voyages [vol. 1 is 'tome-dix-septième'(i.e. Vol. 17) of series]. Preface indicates this ed. was also intended for children.
Vols 1, 2, 3 & 4 narrate the first voyage & vol. 5 atlas
Vols 6, 7, 8 & 9 narrate the second voyage & vol. 10 atlas
Vols 11, 12, 13 & 14 narrate the third voyage & vol. 15 atlas

BRETT, Bernard
953 CAPTAIN/COOK/Written and Illustrated by/ Bernard Brett/Collins/London Sydney Auckland
n.d. [1970]
64pp (inc. 2pp glossary), b/w portrait frontis., col. map, col. & b/w illus. throughout, clo., col. e/p, 210x245mm. KMM

BRETT, Edwin J.
See Hemyng, Bracebridge

BRETT, Mary
954 £100 Ginger Meggs Prize Song Awarded by "The Sunday Sun"/"JUST A LITTLE/GINGER HEADED/ FELLER"/[illus.]/By Mary Brett/Copyright/Chappell & Co. Ltd/(incorporated in Great Britain)/National Building,/250 Pitt Street, Sydney. Price/2/-/Net
n.d.
4pp (1p words of song, 3pp music), adv. verso back wrappers, unillus., col. pic. wrappers, cover title, 30x235mm. KP

BRICKHILL, Paul
955 REACH/FOR THE SKY/The/Story of Douglas Baden/CBE, DSO, D.F.C./by/Paul Brickhill/Collins/St James's Place, London
This ed. specially edited for young people 1957, rpt 1958, rpt 1962.
256pp, portrait photographic frontis., clo., 198x130mm. VMOU

BRIDGES, Hilda
956 Whitcombe's Story Books/JOCK WHITEHEAD/An Australian Fairy Story/By/Hilda Bridges/For Children Aged 9 to 10 years/[drawing]/Whitcombe & Tombs Limited/Melbourne and Sydney/Auckland, Wellington, Christchurch, Dunedin/Invercargill and London
n.d. [1922]
72pp, b/w frontis. & 11 b/w drawings, illus. by Zoe Rothwell, dec. wrappers, 185x125mm. KMM
See McLaren 411

957 Whitcombe's Story Books/BOBBY'S FIRST TERM/A Schoolboys' Story/By/Hilda Bridges/(For ages 10 to 12 years)/[drawing]/Whitcombe and Tombs Limited/ Christchurch, Auckland, Wellington, Dunedin, Invercargill, N.Z./London, Melbourne and Sydney
n.d. [1924]
86pp, 2 pp adv., b/w frontis. & 2 b/w illus., pic. wrappers, 185x125mm. KMM
Frontispiece signed 'J. M. Thomasson'.
See McLaren 516

958 Whitcombe's Story Books/CONNIE OF THE/ FOURTH FORM/By Hilda Bridges/For Ages 10 to 12 years/[drawing]/Whitcombe and Tombs Limited/ Auckland, Christchurch, Wellington, Dunedin, Invercargill, N.Z./London, Melbourne and Sydney
n.d.
88pp (inc. 5pp notes, &c.), b/w frontis. & 2 b/w illus., wrappers, 185x120mm. KMM
See McLaren 542

959 Whitcombe's Story Books/CARNABY'S BOY/A Tale of the Founding of Melbourne/By Hilda Bridges/(For ages 12 to 14 years)/[drawing]/Whitcombe and Tombs Limited/Auckland, Christchurch, Dunedin and Wellington, N.Z./Melbourne and London
n.d. [1926]
109pp, 1p adv., b/w frontis. & 3 f/p b/w illus., 1p portraits & 1 b/w reproduction of early print, illus. by W. S. Wemyss, pic. wrappers (with adv. verso front cover, verso/recto back cover), 175x110mm. CLRC
See McLaren 624

BRIDGES, Roy
960 Hodder & Stoughton's/Man & Boy/Books/[coloured decorative device]/DEAD MEN'S GOLD/By/Roy Bridges/Hodder & Stoughton Ltd. London
n.d. [1916]
268pp, col. frontis. sgd 'E.H.', clo., 175x100mm. ANL

BRIDGES, T. C.
961 ON LAND AND SEA/AT THE DARDANELLES/ T. C. Bridges/[photograph]/London and Glasgow/ Collins/Clear-type Press
n.d. [1915]
198pp, b/w photographic frontis. & 12 f/p b/w photographic plates (of action in the Dardanelles Campaign), clo. with col. onlay on front cover, 220x170mm. VMOU
Adventure story based on the Anzac action in the Gallipoli campaign.

962 THE/CHILDREN'S BOOK OF/DISCOVERY/By/ T. C. Bridges/Author of/"Martin Crusoe", "The Sky Riders" etc./With illustrations in colour/and black and white/[decorative device]/George G. Harrap & Co. Ltd./London Calcutta Sydney
1924
288pp, col. frontis. & 7 f/p col. illus., b/w illus.. throughout, clo. (with col. illus. pasted on front cover), 210x140mm. KMM
Coloured illustrations by Stephen Reid; others by various artists.

Contains sections on voyages of discovery in the Pacific, the Antarctic, &c.

963 A FIGHT/FOR FORTUNE/By/T. C. Bridges/Dean & Son, Ltd./Debrett House, 41/43 Ludgate Hill,/ London, E.C.4
n.d. [193-?]
248pp, col. frontis. only, clo., 195x130mm. KMM
Boys' adventure story with South Pacific setting.

964 THE BUSH BOYS/A Story of the Australian Desert/ By/T. C. Bridges/Frontispiece by/F. R. Grey/London/ The Sheldon Press/Northumberland Avenue, W.C.2
n.d. [1932?]
128pp & 8pp adv., col. frontis. only, clo., 185x120mm. KP

965 WARDENS OF THE/WILD/By/T. C. Bridges/ Author of "The Book of Invention"/"The Book of the Sea"/etc./With thirty-one illustrations in half-tone/ [device]/George G. Harrap & Co. Ltd./London Bombay Sydney
1937
271pp (inc. 5pp preface), frontis. & b/w photographic illus. throughout, clo., 210x140mm. KMM
Includes one chapter 'Murder in Australia—the Butchery of Teddy Bear and Billy 'Possum; and how at last they are being saved' (12pp); & one chapter 'A One-Man Sanctuary—The Lonely Naturalist of Humbug Scrub, Thomas Paine Bellchambers' (13pp).

PADDY LEARY MILLIONAIRE; THE AUSSIE AT HIGHCLIFF.
See The Boys' Friend Library

BRIDGES, T. C. & TILTMAN, H. Hessell

966 HEROES OF/MODERN ADVENTURE/By/T. C. Bridges/and/H. Hessell Tiltman/Joint authors of "More Heroes of Modern Adventure"/"Recent Heroes of Modern Adventure"/"The Romance of Motoring" etc./With thirty-two illustrations/in half-tone/[device]/ George G. Harrap & Company Ltd./London Bombay Sydney
First pub. Sept 1927; rpt Jan, Oct 1928; Aug 1929; April, Sept 1931; Jan, Oct 1932; May, Nov 1933; May 1934
277pp, 2pp authors' note, frontis. & 31 b/w photographic illus., 1 b/w map, clo., 210x135mm. KMM
Contents include: 'Sir Alan Cobham—The Knight of the Air' (10pp); 'Captain E. R. G. R. Evans in the Heart of the Antarctic' (17pp); 'Skipper Gowen and his *Speejacks*—An account of a yacht voyage from New York to Sydney, up the Queensland coast to New Guinea and the Pacific islands, through Indonesia and back via the Mediterranean to Miami' (16pp); 'Michael Terry's Journey across Empty Australia in a Ford Car' (21pp).

967 MORE HEROES OF/MODERN ADVENTURE/By/ T. C. Bridges/and/H. Hessell Tiltman/Authors of "Heroes of Modern Adventure"/"Recent Heroes of Modern Adventure", "Heroes of/Everyday Adventure", "The Romance of Motoring" etc/with thirty-two illustrations/in half-tone/[device]/George G. Harrap & Co. Ltd./London Bombay Sydney
1st publ. 1929
266pp & 2pp author's note, b/w frontis. & other b/w plates, clo., 210x140mm. KP
Contains Bert Hinkler, By Air to Australia (14pp); Robert Macdonald prospecting the Owen Stanley Ranges (12pp); Sir Douglas Mawson & the Antarctic (13pp); A. J. Villiers, Racing round Cape Horn (18pp). KP

• Rpt Jan, Oct 1931, Aug 1932, May 1933, Jan, Oct 1934
As above. KP
First ed. lists 'Heroes of Modern Adventure'
Also HEROES OF FORGOTTEN ADVENTURE.
Variant eds
As above.
1 Australian & 1 Pacific item. KP

968 EPIC TALES OF/MODERN ADVENTURE/By/T. C. Bridges/and/H. Hessell Tiltman/Authors of "Heroes of Modern Adventure"/etc./with thirty illustrations in/half-tone/[device]/George G. Harrap & Co. Ltd., London Bombay Sydney
287pp (inc. 4pp authors' preface), b/w frontis. & 29 f/p b/w illus., clo., 205x140mm. KMM
Contents include: 'The Tale of the Comets: Drama of the Great Air Race from Mildenhall to Melbourne' (15pp); 'Adventuring with a bible: The Story of the Rev. V. H. Sherwin, a Pioneer of the Pacific' (15pp).

969 RECENT HEROES OF/MODERN ADVENTURE/ By/T. C. Bridges/and/H. Hessell Tiltman/Authors of "Heroes of Modern Adventure"/etc./with thirty-two illustrations/in half-tone/[device]/George G. Harrap & Co. Ltd./London Bombay Sydney
First pub. 1932; rpt Jan, Sept 1933; May, Nov 1934; June 1936
284pp (inc. 3pp preface), frontis. & 31 b/w photographic illus., clo., 205x140mm. KMM
Contents include: F. D. Burdett—Queensland, W. A. & the Philippines (12pp); Flying to the South Pole—Admiral Byrd (12pp); The World's Super Airman—Charles Kingsford Smith (9pp).

BRIDGLAND, Elizabeth [Mrs Walter Lewis Bridgland]

970 POEMS FOR CHILDREN/By/Elizabeth Bridgland/ All proceeds from this booklet/Donated to the Red Cross Society/(S.A. Division)
Thornquest Press, Adelaide, 1940
16pp, unillus., 180x115mm. ANL

971 POEMS FOR CHILDREN/By/Elizabeth Bridgland/ Illustrations by/Margot Bridgland/[drawing]
Thornquest Press, Adelaide, 1946
26pp, b/w drawings in text, bd., 185x120mm. KMM

[BRIERLEY, Alec]

972 LOOKING BACK/ON THE EARLY DAYS/with the compliments of the Neptune Oil Co. Pty Ltd./ (Incorporated in N.S.W.)
10th ed. (25,000 copies), Melbourne, n.d.
[50]pp & 6pp adv., b/w illus., pic. wrappers, 137x214mm. KMM

973 LOOKING BACK/AGAIN /Early Australian Transport/with the compliments of the Neptune Oil Co. Pty. Ltd. Inc. in N.S.W.
Melbourne, n.d. [second ed.] [1952?]
[34]pp, b/w illus. throughout, col. pic. wrappers, 137x214mm. KMM
1p foreword by Daryl Lindsay.

BRIGGS, Allie

974 "TONY THE TUG"/Words and Pictures/by/Allie/ Briggs/Angus and Robertson Limited Sydney/Wholly set up, printed and bound in Australia by The Macarthur Press/66 MacArthur Street, Parramatta/ 1947/Registered in Australia for transmission through the post as a book
32pp, col. illus. on alternate pages, dec. bd., 180x235mm. ANL

BRIGGS, Philip

975 MAN OF/ANTARCTICA/The Story of Captain Scott/Philip Briggs/Lutterworth Press/London
1959
96pp, col. frontis., double-spread b/w map, clo., 185x120mm. NSL:M
• Rpt as above, 1963, 1966. KP

BRIGHT, Robert

976 Robert Bright/WHICH IS WILLY?/[drawing]/A World's Work Children's Book/Copyright 1963 by Robert Bright. All rights reserved//First published in Great Britain 1963 by The World's Work (1913) Ltd /[2 lines]
30pp, part col. pictures throughout, col. pic. bd., 205x255mm. KP
Picture book about penguins.

BRINDLEY, Elsie

977 STORY HYMNS/FOR/LITTLE FOLK/Words by Miss Elsie Brindley/Music by Miss Gertrude Harris/Copyright 1933/Melbourne 1933
Published by author
23pp, wrappers, 215x140mm. ANL
Includes 34 religious songs with music.

BRINSMEAD, H. F.

978 H. F. Brinsmead/PASTURES/OF THE BLUE CRANE/Illustrated by/Annette Macarthur-Onslow/London/Oxford University Press 1964
223pp, b/w drawings throughout, clo., 210x140mm. KMM
Won CBCA Award 1965.
• Rpt 1965, 1969, as above. KP

979 PASTURES/OF THE BLUE CRANE/H. F. Brinsmead/Coward-McCann Inc. New York
1966
250pp, unillus. (with original jacket), clo., 210x135mm. Unseen: IFA
2nd imp. as above. KP

980 H. F. Brinsmead/PASTURES OF THE BLUE CRANE/Illustrated by/Annette Macarthur-Onslow/London/Oxford University Press/1970
First published 1964, rpt 1965, 1968, 1969; first published in this edition 1970
219pp, 1 b/w drawing in text, pic. wrappers, 195x125mm. Oxford Paperback Series. KMM
German edition

981 Hesba F. Brinsmead/DAS MÄDCHEN/UND/DER BLAUE KRANICH/Verlag Carl Ueberreuter/Wien-Heidelberg
n.d.
256pp, b/w frontis. & b/w illus. throughout, sim. clo., 198x120mm. LRA
Danish edition

982 H. F. Brinsmead/I DEN BLÅ TRANES LAND/Oversat of Michael Tejn/[device]/Jesperson og Pios Forlag/København 1968
184pp, unillus., wrappers (col. pic. Mac. O.), 214x135mm. LRA

983 [drawing]/SEASON OF THE BRIAR/H. F. Brinsmead/Illustrated by William Papas/London/Oxford University Press/1965
202pp, b/w drawings throughout, clo., 220x135mm. KMM

984 SEASON/OF THE/BRIAR/H. F. Brinsmead/Coward-McCann Inc. New York
1967
252pp, unillus. (with original jacket), clo., 205x130mm. Unseen: IFA
German edition

985 Hesba F. Brinsmead/SOMMER/DER/HECKENROSEN/Verlag Carl Ueberreuter/Wien—Heidelberg
1967
207pp, unillus., embossed clo., 205x130mm. Translated by Inge Artl. IFA
Italian edition
The author mentions an Italian edition, but was unable to give details.

986 H. F. Brinsmead/BEAT OF THE CITY/[drawing]/Illustrated by William Papas/London/Oxford University Press/1966
204pp, b/w drawings in text, clo., 215x135mm. BBC

987 BEAT OF/THE CITY/by H. F. Brinsmead/Coward McCann Inc., New York
1968
277pp, unillus., clo., 205x140mm.
D/w by anonymous artist. Unseen: IFA
German edition

988 Hesba F. Brinsmead/TREFFPUNKT/PARADIES/[device]/Verlag Carl Ueberreuter/Wien—Heidelberg
n.d. [1968]
208pp, unillus., clo., 200x120mm. LRA

989 H. F. Brinsmead/A SAPPHIRE FOR SEPTEMBER/[drawing]/Illustrated by/Victor G. Ambrus/London/Oxford University Press/1967
179pp (inc. 2pp glossary), b/w drawings in text, clo., 215x135mm. KMM

990 H. F. Brinsmead/A SAPPHIRE FOR SEPTEMBER/Illustrated by/Victor G. Ambrus/London/Oxford University Press/1970
First published 1967, rpt 1968; first published in this edition 1970
188pp (inc. 2pp glossary), 1 line drawing in text, pic. wrappers, 195x125mm. Oxford Paperback Series. KMM
German edition

991 Hesba F. Brinsmead/ZEIT/DER/BUNTEN/STEINE/Verlag Carl Ueberreuter/Wien-Heidelberg
n.d.
208pp, b/w illus. throughout, sim. clo., 200x120mm. LRA

992 H. F. Brinsmead/ISLE OF THE SEA HORSE/[drawing]/Illustrated by Peter Farmer/London/Oxford University Press/1969
191pp, 1p acknowledgements, b/w drawings throughout, clo., 215x135mm. KMM
Danish edition

993 Det Danske Forlag, 1971
Unseen: IFA

994 H. F. Brinsmead/LISTEN TO THE WIND/[drawing]/Illustrated by Robert Micklewright/London/Oxford University Press/1970
214pp, 1p acknowledgements, b/w chapter headings, clo., 215x135mm. KMM
German edition

995 Hesba F. Brinsmead/DAS LIED/DER FISCHER/Verlag Carl Ueberreuter/Wien-Heidelberg
n.d. [1971]
207pp, unillus., clo., 200x120mm. LRA

996 H. F. Brinsmead/WHO CALLS FROM AFAR?/[drawing]/Illustrated by/Ian Ribbons/London/Oxford University Press/1971
184pp, 1p acknowledgements, b/w drawings throughout, clo., 215x135mm. KMM

997 LONGTIME/PASSING/Hesba Brinsmead/Angus and Robertson
Sydney 1971

183pp, 1p preface, unillus., clo., d/w designed by Victor G. Ambrus, 215x135mm. KMM
Won CBCA Award 1972.
• Rpt 1972. KP

998 [drawing]/ECHO/IN THE WILDERNESS/Illustrated by Graham Humphreys/H. F. Brinsmead/London Oxford University Press 1972
152pp, extended t.p., b/w map, b/w drawings in text, clo., 215x135mm. KMM

BRISBANE, Coutts [pseud. R. Coutts Armour]
999 THE/SECRET OF THE/DESERT/by/Coutts Brisbane/Illustrated by/John Turner/Thomas Nelson and Sons Ltd./London Edinburgh Paris Melbourne/Toronto and New York
First pub. March 1941; rpt 1943, 1953 (twice), 1955
230pp, b/w frontis. & 2 f/p b/w illus., clo., 185x125mm. KMM

1000 WHEELS OF/FORTUNE/by/Coutts Brisbane/Illustrated by/Drake Brookshaw/Thomas Nelson and Sons Ltd/London Edinburgh Paris Melbourne/Toronto and New York
1st publ. 1948, rpt 1956
219pp, b/w frontis. & 3 f/p b/w illus., clo., 188x125mm. VMOU
• Rpt 1957 as above. KP

THE SECRET OF THE LOCH. *See* The Sexton Blake Library no. 400

BRISTOW, Joan
1001 A World Explorer/ROBERT/FALCON SCOTT/By Joan Bristow/Illustrated by William Hutchinson/Garrard Publishing Company/Champaign, Illinois 1972
96pp, part col. illus. & some b/w photographic illus., clo., pic. e/p, 228x155mm. KMM
In the same series:
1002 FRIDTJOF NANSEN, by E. Berry
1003 ROALD AMUNDSEN, by C. De Leeuw
1004 SIR EDMUND HILLARY, by F. Y. Knoop. All unseen

The British Empire Industries Alphabet
1005 THE/BRITISH EMPIRE/INDUSTRIES/ALPHABET/Established 1913/copyright throughout/The British Empire/Commonwealth Edition/1934-5/Victorian/Issue
Robert Westfield, Melbourne
32pp, part col. & b/w illus. throughout, col. pic. wrappers, cover title, 248x187mm. KP
Government publication advertising Australian household products.

BRITT, Maxwell J.
1006 SHOPPING/IS FUN!/Maxwell J. Britt/photographs by/J. C. Rewell/Nelson
Thomas Nelson (Australia) Limited, Melbourne 1967
32pp, b/w photographic illus. throughout, pic. bd., dec. e/p, 245x185mm. CLRC
Picture book with slight text.

BRITTEN, David
1007 THE MAKING OF/STEPHEN HALL/By/David Britten/[device]/C.S.S.M./5 Wigmore Street, London, W.1.
1953; rpt 1954 [Copyright 1953 in U.S.A. by the Children's Special Service Mission]
188pp, b/w drawings in text, clo., 180x120mm. KMM
Australian boys' school story.

BROADLEY, Ron
The following publications bearing this author's name are simple paper-covered booklets of from 8 to 16 pages of drawings with captions. All were published by Frank Johnson, Sydney, between 1942 & 1945. All ANL
1008 A.B.C. STORYTELLER
1009 THE BUSH BOYS
1010 EMMA THE EMU
1011 HAVE YOU PLAYED JUMBLEZOO?
1012 THE MAGIC PAINTING BOOK
1013 THE MOVING PICTURE BOOK
1014 NU ZOO
1015 NURSERY VERSERY
1016 PETER'S PARTY
1017 PIDGIN: THE PICCANINNY
1018 THE PUZZLE PICTURE BOOK
1019 QUIZZO
1020 RON BROADLEY'S COLOURING BOOK
1021 THE SECOND NURSERY VERSERY
1022 SUSIE GOES SHOPPING

The Brockhoff Baker's Painting Book
1023 THE BROCKHOFF BAKER'S /PAINTING BOOK/with the compliments of Brockhoff
n.p., n.d.
4pp, pic. wrappers, b/w drawings, 245x205mm. KP

BROCKMAN, H. Drake-
See Drake-Brockman, Henrietta
See also Parker, K. Langloh

BROCKMAN, Janie
WHIFFLES
n.d. [inscribed 1907] CLRC
Only very slight Australian interest. Family story set in England telling how the children fare while their parents go on a voyage to Australia for the sake of the mother's health.

BROCKWELL, Peggy
1024 PHOEBE/Story by Peggy Brockwell/[drawing of dog]/Pictures by Jan Smith/Published by D. M. Jones, Collaroy, N.S.W./Plates by K & H Plates Pty Limited, Brookvale, N.S.W./Printed by Dynamic Press Pty Ltd., Brookvale, N.S.W.
n.d.
16pp, 6 f/p drawings, pic. wrappers, pic. e/p, 151x151mm. KMM
Printed throughout in sepia.

BRODERICK, Jessica Potter
1025 HOP-/AWAY/JOEY/By Jessica Potter Broderick/Illustrated by Seymour Fleishman/Rand McNally & Company/Chicago/Established 1956/Copyright MCMLVII [7 lines]/[col. illus.]
[24]pp, col. illus. on every page, col. pic. wrappers, 200x160mm. KMM
On front cover 'This start-right Elf Book is educationally sound'.
Copies with 29c, 39c and 49c on front cover & variant adv. on back cover, KP

BROGDEN, Stanley Marcel William
1026 FIRST TO FLY/From Roger Bacon to/Sir Charles Kingsford-Smith/A brief account of some of the men who pioneered/aviation/by Stanley Brogden/Whitcombe & Tombs Pty. Ltd./Melbourne Sydney Perth
n.d. [1945?]
170pp (inc. 4pp chronological table), 51pp b/w photographic illus. & diagrams, clo., 180x120mm. KMM

1027 THE CATTLE DUFFERS/Adventure in the Kimberleys/By/Stanley Brogden/Cassell and Company Ltd./London Toronto Melbourne and Sydney
1948

254pp, 3 b/w illus. by Bruce Crampton, clo., 180x120mm. ANL

EXPLORING THE AIR. *See* Australian Landmarks

COMMERCIAL AVIATION. *See* Around Australia Program

BROOKES, Noel P. (ed.)

1028 RADIO COMIC/ANNUAL/Editor Noel P. Brookes/Art Editor Royce Bradford/Asst Art Editor J. Wilkinson/Engravers Letts & Co./Published by/ Meteor Publications/and Publicity Pty Ltd/Printed by Cumberland Newspapers Ltd, Argus Lake, Parramatta/ Bound by Conpress, Sydney.
n.d. [194-?]
157pp, printed throughout in sepia, comic strips & drawings throughout, bd., 250x187mm. KP
Features radio personalities of 1940s.

BROOKS, A. E.

1029 AUSTRALIA/IN THE/MAKING/A. E. Brooks/ Lothian Publishing Co. Pty. Ltd./Melbourne Sydney Auckland
1970
90pp (inc. 2pp index), b/w photographic illus. throughout, clo., 245x180mm. CLRC

BROOKS, Edwy Searles

1030 New Complete Detective Story of Nelson Lee!/The Nelson Lee 2d/Library/These/two/magnificent/ photographs/of/famous/footballers/given away this week./[illus.]/THE CANNIBAL HORDE!/An exciting story of schoolboy adventure/with cannibals of a south sea island./no 370, Every Wednesday July 8 1922
40pp (& story continued inside back wrapper), b/w illus., pic. wrappers, 182x130mm. KP

1031 New Holiday Adventure Series just begun!/The Nelson Lee/Library/2d./[illus. with caption]/THE DEMON OF/THE REEF/a story of wonderful adven-/ture with the Boys of St./Frank's on the South Seas/No 535 out on Wednesday September 5 1925
35pp & 5pp other material, b/w frontis. & 5 text illus., pic. wrappers, cover title, 184x130mm. ANL
Uniform with above:

1032 530 THE/WANDERER'S QUEST Aug 1 1925. ANL

1033 531 THE ISLE/OF CORAL/An extra long story of the/wonderful adventures of the/Boys of St Frank's with Lord/Dorrimore in the South Seas: Aug 8 1925. ANL

1034 532 THE PEARL HUNTERS Aug 15 1925, b/w frontis. & 6 text illus. ANL

1035 533 THE SECRET OF THE LAGOON Aug 22 1925. Unseen

1036 534 BESET BY CANNIBALS Aug 29 1925. ANL
535 See above

1037 536 THE TERROR OF THE PACIFIC Sep 12 1925. ANL

1038 THE BOY FROM THE "BUSH"!/or, The Brand of the Twin Stars/[then, in a shield] THE MONSTER/ LIBRARY OF/COMPLETE/STORIES/No. 9/1/-/A Splendid Yarn of/Schoolboy Adventure/and Test Match Cricket/By/Edwy Searles/Brooks
Amalgamated Press Ltd, London, 20th July 1926
128pp (inc. 2pp extraneous material), illus. heading over Chapter I otherwise unillus., pic. wrappers, adv. verso front wrapper & both sides back wrapper, cover title, 270x175mm. RM
The story of an Australian boy boarding at St Frank's School in England.

1039 The Nelson Lee/School Story Library/[drawing—2d.]/TRAPPED BY/BUSHRANGERS!/A magnificent long complete yarn of schoolboy adventure/in Australia, featuring the cheery chums of St. Frank's./New Series No. 142—Out on Wednesday—January 19th, 1929
Amalgamated Press Ltd, London
44pp (inc. approx. 2pp adv., 8pp extraneous matter [serial, cricket notes, etc]), b/w frontis., b/w drawings in text, pic. wrappers, cover title, 220x150mm. RM
This & the following 9 entries are complete items in a series of 12 stories numbered 140–51 concerning the boys of 'St. Frank's' who journey by ship to Australia to see the test cricket series. This story tells of the arrival of some of the boys (who travelled by air) in Adelaide, & their trip up the Murray River; the next tells of one boy lost in the bush near Renmark, & the others are as described. The first two stories in the series, *St. Frank's Afloat* & *St. Frank's in South Africa,* have not been included in this bibliography, as they do not relate to Australia. They are all roughly uniform in format & published by Amalgamated Press, London.

1040 The Nelson Lee/School Story Library/2d. [drawing]/LOST/IN THE BUSH!/A vivid, long complete schoolboy adventure yarn featuring Archie Glen-/thorne and his cheery chums of St. Frank's in Australia./New Series No. 143—Out on Wednesday—January 26th, 1929. RM

1041 "THE ADELAIDE TEST MATCH SENSATION!"/Grand Complete Yarn inside/The Nelson Lee/School Story Library 2d./[reproduction of 4 badges with portraits of test cricketers, & information about these free souvenirs] New Series No. 144—February 2nd, 1929. RM

1042 You'll all Enjoy this Amazing Long Story of Sport and Adventure/ST. FRANK'S AT THE TEST MATCH!/[vignette]/By Edwy Searles Brooks/Author of...etc./New Series No. 145. RM
The whole of the front cover of this issue is devoted to advertising the free album of the test matches, & 4 tokens with portraits of cricketers given away with the booklet. The t.p. of this & the following 4 items occupies the top half of the first page of text.

1043 Follow the Amazing Adventures of Nipper and Co./IN UNKNOWN AUSTRALIA!/[vignette]/By Edwy Searles Brooks/Author of [etc.]/New Series No. 146. RM
The front cover is again devoted to an advertisement for free badges of cricketers.

1044 The White Master's Secret!/Amazing Schoolboy Adventure!/THE VALLEY OF SURPRISES!/[vignette]/ By Edwy Searles Brooks/Author of...etc./New Series No. 147. RM
No frontispiece in this booklet, the space being taken up by an advertisement. The front cover is also devoted to an advertisement for free badges. The story is set in Queensland.

1045 Handforth the Host! St. Frank's in Victoria!/"HARD LINES, HANDY!"/[vignette]/By Edwy Searles Brooks/Author of...etc./New Series No. 148. RM

1046 St. Frank's in Melbourne! Schoolboy Cricket Thrills!/THE MELBOURNE/TEST MATCH TRIUMPH!/[vignette]/By Edwy Searles Brooks/Author of...etc./New Series No. 149. RM

1047 Goodbye to Australia! Exciting Schoolboy Adventure!/ST. FRANK'S IN/NEW ZEALAND/ [vignette]/By/Edwy Searles Brooks/Author of the St. Frank's Stories...etc./New Series No. 150. RM

First 3 chapters set in Tasmania, followed by chapter on crossing the Tasman, & chapter on New Zealand.

1048 The Nelson Lee/School Story Library/ 2d./[illustration]/THE PERIL OF/THE PACIFIC!/A gripping long complete story of thrilling school-boy adventure, featuring/the chums of St Frank's./New Series No. 151 Out on Wednesday March 23rd 1929. RM
Story takes place on the journey home to England from Auckland, via Panama, & concludes the series.

BROOKS, Mary
1049 ANIMAL ADVENTURES/by Mary Brooks/Ward Lock & Co. Limited/London and Melbourne
1967
22pp (inc. frontis. & back pastedowns), col. illus. throughout, pic. bd., 275x210mm. KP
Double-spread t.p. illus. in col.; title on cover 'Australian Animal Adventures'. Illus. author. KP

1050 ANIMAL/PARADISE/by Mary Brooks/Ward Lock 1967 (2866)
Ward Lock & Co. Limited London and Melbourne
47pp, col. illus., pic. bd., 270x210mm. KP
Picture book featuring Australia's birds & animals. Cover title 'Australian Animal Paradise'. KP

1051 ANIMAL/WONDERLAND/by Mary Brooks/Ward Lock & Co. Limited. London and Melbourne 1967
20pp, col. frontis., 25 col. illus., pic. bd., 275x210mm. Grant
Two young children visit a sanctuary for Australian animals.

BROOME, Lady [née Mary Anne Stewart, later Lady Barker, under which name her books were written, but *see also* [Timperley, W. H.] for *Harry Treverton* ed. by Lady Broome

BROUGHTON, Gordon
1052 THE SLIPRAILS/ARE DOWN/by/Gordon Broughton/Illustrated by/Michael Brett/Macmillan/ Melbourne London Toronto/St. Martin's Press/New York/1966
142pp, 1p foreword by Kylie Tennant, 1p bibliography, part. col. & b/w drawings throughout, clo., 215x135mm. Great Stories of Australia Series No. 8. CLRC

BROWN, Barry
1053 THE FLYING/DOCTOR/John Flynn and the Flying Doctor Service/Barry Brown/Lutterworth Press London 1960
95pp, col. frontis., double-spread b/w map, clo., 185x120mm. KMM
• Rpt 1962, 1963 as above. KMM

BROWN, David
See Michell, Barbara Ann & Brown, David

BROWN, Judy
1054 THE/GARDEN OF EDENS/by/Judy Brown/ Illustrated by Roderick Shaw/Imprinted by Richard Edwards/& Roderick Shaw at the/Barn on the Hill/ over St. Columbkille's
Sydney 1939; edition limited to 600 copies
33pp, hand-printed, hand-col. frontis., 7 linocuts, line drawings in text, hand-bound in dec. clo., 255x190mm. KMM

BROWN, Judy & HILL, Mirrie
1055 KINDERGARTEN/SONGS/by/Judy Brown/and/ Mirrie Hill/Pictures by/Tricia/The Currawong Publishing Co. Pty. Ltd./Royal Chambers/3 Castlereagh Street, Sydney/1946
18pp, 1p adv., b/w illus. throughout, dec. wrappers, 215x285mm. ANL
Contains 12 songs with music.

BROWN, Margaret
1056 BLACK/TUPPENNY/By/Margaret Brown/Sheila Hawkins/has drawn her/[drawing]
Printed in Great Britain at the Windmill Press, Kingswood, Surrey, n.d. [1932?]
24pp, drawings throughout, bd., 240x190mm. NSL:M

BROWN, Margaret Wise
1057 YOUNG KANGAROO/By Margaret Wise Brown/ [drawing]/Illustrated by Symeon Shimin/New York: William R. Scott, Inc., Publisher, 1955
44pp, part. col. lithographic illus. throughout, dec. bd., dec. e/p, 215x160mm. NSL:M
1058 YOUNG KANGAROO/By Margaret Wise Brown/ [drawing]/Illustrated by Symeon Shimin/The World's Work (1913) Ltd./Kingswood Surrey
Copyright 1955 by William R. Scott, Inc.; first published in Great Britain 1959, rpt 1960
44pp, 20 sepia/white illus., dec. e/p, pic. bd., 210x170mm. Grant
1059 YOUNG KANGAROO
First Australian edition 1961
Details as above, but limp clo., 210x165mm. Grant

BROWN, Maurice
FOOD; LIVING IN CITIES. *See* Life in Australia

BROWN, Michael
1060 SHACKLETON'S EPIC VOYAGE/Raymond Briggs/Text by Michael Brown/Hamish Hamilton London/First published in Great Britain 1969/By Hamish Hamilton Ltd./90 Great Russell, Street, London WC1 [copyright &c]
[40]pp, col. frontis. & t.p., col. illus. on alternate page openings, b/w on others, pic. bd., 204x194mm. KMM

BROWN, Rhoda E.
See Lockhart, Margaret D. & Brown, Rhoda E. GOUROU

BROWN, R. N. Rudmose
See Scott, G. Firth. THE ROMANCE OF POLAR EXPLORATION

BROWNE, Elsie M.
1061 NATURE'S/HUMBLE/TEACHERS/By/Elsie M. Browne/Signs Publishing Company/(A.C.A. Ltd. Proprietors)/Warburton, Victoria, Aust./Wholly set up and printed in/Australia, 1929/Registered by the Postmaster-General, etc.
96pp, dec. t.p., 59 col. drawings in text, pic. wrappers, 205x135mm. Grant
Contents: 13 stories & 3 songs with music from *Song Stories of Australia for Little People* by Edith G. Walker & Jeanie G. Dane.

BROWNE, Helen de G.
See Simpson, Helen

BROWNE, Mrs W. C.
1062 THE/THREE SISTERS/By/Mrs W. C. Browne./ Parramatta:/Fuller's Lightning Printing Works Company,/1892
20pp, unillus., colophon last page, wrappers, 130x125mm. Grant

BRUCE, Charles
1063 UNCLE JOHN'S/FIRST SHIPWRECK/or/The Loss of the Brig 'Nellie'/By/Charles Bruce/Author of/'Lame Felix', 'Noble Mottoes', 'How Frank began to Climb'/'The Book of Noble Englishwomen' etc./ Edinburgh/W. P. Nimmo, Hay, & Mitchell
n.d. [1876]

124pp, 16pp adv., b/w frontis., dec. clo., dec. e/p, 180x120mm. NSL:M
As above, but
1064 William P. Nimmo & Co./Edinburgh./1880
124pp, col. frontis., clo. with col. pic. onlay on front cover, 164x100mm. RC
1065 New ed. 1885. Imprint W. P. Nimmo, Hay & Mitchell
Dec. chapter headings &c, 168x118mm. VSL
Another copy, n.d. (adv. 1891), col. frontis., 16pp adv. RC
Another copy, n.d. (adv. 1892), b/w frontis. RC
1066 Another copy as above, but
/London/Sampson Low, Marston & Co. Ltd.
n.d. [prize 1935]
124pp & 32pp adv., col. frontis. (unsigned), dec. clo., 185x120mm. RC

BRUCE, Major George Evans
1067 Whitcombe's Southern Cross Story Readers/TOM IN THE/ANDAMANS/by/Major G. E. Bruce/(For Children aged 10 to 12 years)/[device]/Whitcombe & Tombs Limited/Melbourne, Auckland, Christchurch, Dunedin, Wellington/and London
n.d. [1924]
89pp (inc. 1p notes & meanings), 3pp adv., frontis. map, 8 b/w illus. by R. Wenban, pic. wrappers (with adv. verso front cover, verso/recto back cover), 175x120mm. Grant
See McLaren 525

1068 THE LION'S SON/by/Major George Bruce/Australia/Cornstalk Publishing Company/89 Castlereagh Street Sydney/1928
283pp, b/w frontis. by Edgar A. Holloway, 2 b/w illus., clo., 190x130mm. ANL
Boy's adventure story with Indian setting by the husband of Mary Grant Bruce.
1069 Another copy as above, 1929; Platypus edition, with b/w frontis. only, clo., 170x110mm. KMM

1070 THE RAINBOW OF/SABA/A Novel by Major George Bruce/Thomas Nelson & Sons, Ltd./London, Edinburgh, New York/Toronto, and Paris
First publ. Feb. 1928
375pp & 8pp adv., unillus., clo., map e/p, 182x120mm. KMM
Historical novel about Africa but doubtful children's book
1071 THE/RAINBOW OF SABA/By/Major George Bruce/Thomas Nelson and Sons Ltd./London Edinburgh New York/Toronto and Paris
n.d.
375pp, 9pp adv., clo., 175x110mm. ANL

1072 RED DEVIL/By/Major George Bruce/Angus and Robertson Ltd./Sydney: London/1940
269pp, unillus., clo., 185x120mm. Grant

BRUCE, Mary Grant
1073 A LITTLE BUSH/MAID/By/Mary Grant Bruce/With eight illustrations by J. Macfarlane/Ward, Lock & Co., Limited/London, Melbourne and Toronto/1910
254pp, 18pp adv., b/w frontis. & 7 b/w plates, dec. clo., 185x120mm. KMM
'M. Grant Bruce' on front cover & spine.
1074 A LITTLE BUSH/MAID/By/Mary Grant Bruce/Author of "Mates at Billabong" etc./With eight illustrations by J. Macfarlane/Ward, Lock & Co., Limited/London, Melbourne and Toronto
n.d.
254pp, 2pp adv., b/w frontis. & 7 b/w plates, dec. clo., 185x120mm. KMM
1075 A LITTLE BUSH MAID/by/Mary Grant Bruce/Author of "Timothy in Buckland" [*sic*] "Glen Eyre", etc./Abridged and Edited for Victorian Schools/Illustrated by Thos. Shield/George Robertson and Company/Propy. Ltd./Melbourne, Sydney, Adelaide and Brisbane/by arrangement with/Ward, Lock & Co., Limited/(All rights reserved)
n.d. [Probably 1913 or 1914 as *Mates at Billabong, Norah of Billabong, Timothy in Bushland & Glen Eyre,* published between 1910 & 1913, are mentioned in the preface or advertisements]
163pp (inc. 2pp introduction, with photograph of author, & 4pp notes), 3pp adv., b/w frontis. & 3 f/p b/w illus., stiff pic. wrappers, 185x110mm. KMM
Printed on front cover: 'Price sevenpence'.
1076 A LITTLE BUSH/MAID/By/Mary Grant Bruce/Ward, Lock & Co., Limited/London and Melbourne
n.d. [1940?]
254pp, b/w frontis. by J. Macfarlane, clo., 180x120mm. KMM
1077 A LITTLE BUSH MAID/by/Mary Grant Bruce/Ward, Lock & Co., Limited/London and Melbourne
1965
224pp, b/w frontis. by J. F. Campbell, clo., 185x120mm. BBC
Danish edition
1078 C. W. K. Gleerups Ungdomsböcker. N.r 51/EN LITEN AUSTRALISKA/(A Little Bushmaid)/av/Mary Grant Bruce/Bemynddigad översättning av Hedvig av Petersens/[device]/Lund/C. W. K. Gleerups Förlag
1923
253pp, unillus., bd. with col. illus. (after J. W. Macfarlane) on front cover, 192x124mm. ANL
A Little Bush Maid, like most of the 'Billabong' books, was very popular, & has been reprinted many times. However, it was not the publisher's practice to date these books, apart from the first edition & some more recent reprints. Although many changes have been made over the years, particularly with illustrations, which were reduced in number, & in some editions omitted altogether, & later a frontispiece by a different artist was substituted for the original illustrations, & other changes in type & binding were made, many of these variant editions have not been noted. The publisher's records were lost during the war, & it is not possible to date the various editions, or to trace any clear picture of the publishing history of these books.

1079 MATES/AT BILLABONG/By/M. Grant Bruce/Author of "A Little Bush/Maid" etc./Illustrated by J. Macfarlane/Ward, Lock & Co., Limited/London, Melbourne and Toronto/1911
252pp, 4pp adv., b/w frontis. & 7 b/w plates, dec. clo., 190x120mm. KMM
Page of reviews &c. of *A Little Bush Maid* precedes t.p.
• Rpt 1913 as above. Grant
1080 MATES AT BILLABONG/by/Mary Grant Bruce/Abridged for the use of schools/by/Gladys A. Taylor, M.A. LL.B./Gladys A. Taylor, Melbourne/E. W. Cole, Book Arcade, Melbourne/Sydney and Adelaide.
n.d.
127pp (inc. 2pp introduction & 2pp notes), 2pp adv., 4 f/p b/w illus. by B. E. Merfield, Percy Leason, wrappers, 180x120mm. KMM
1081 MATES/AT BILLABONG/By/Mary Grant Bruce/Ward, Lock & Co., Limited/London, Melbourne and Cape Town
[On verso of title: MGB 1911—reprinted 1911, 1912,

1914, 1918, 1920, 1922, 1923, 1926, 1929, 1934, 1937, 1939, 1942, 1947, 1949, 1951, 1953, 1956, 1959]
223pp, b/w frontis. by J. F. Campbell, clo., 185x125mm. K&NI

1082 TIMOTHY IN/BUSHLAND/By/Mary Grant Bruce/Author of/"A Little Bush Maid","Mates at Billabong" etc. etc./Illustrated by J. Macfarlane./Ward, Lock & Co., Limited./London, Melbourne, and Toronto/1912
239pp, 1p adv., b/w frontis & 7 b/w plates, dec. clo., 190x120mm. KMM
Advertisement contains notices of author's previous books.
Another copy as above, but additional 16pp adv. KMM

1083 GLEN EYRE/By/Mary Grant Bruce/Author of "A Little Bush Maid," "Mates at/Billabong," etc./ Illustrated/Ward, Lock & Co., Limited./London, Melbourne, and Toronto/1912
256pp, 16pp adv., b/w frontis. & 7 b/w plates. by J. Macfarlane, dec. clo., 190x120mm. KMM
Another copy as above, but n.d. KMM

1084 NORAH/OF BILLABONG/By/Mary Grant Bruce/ Author of "A Little Bush Maid," "Mates at Billabong"/"Glen Eyre," "Timothy in Bushland," etc./ Illustrated by J. Macfarlane/Ward, Lock & Co., Limited./London, Melbourne, and Toronto/1913
256pp, 16pp adv., b/w frontis. & 7 b/w plates, dec. clo., 185x125mm. KMM
Another copy as above but n.d. TG

1085 NORAH/OF BILLABONG/By/Mary Grant Bruce/ Author of "A Little Bush Maid", "Mates at Billabong"/"Glen Eyre", "Timothy in Bushland," etc./ Illustrated by J. Macfarlane/Ward, Lock & Co., Limited./London and Melbourne
256pp, b/w frontis. & 3 b/w plates, clo., 180x120mm. CLRC

1086 NORAH/OF BILLABONG/By/Mary Grant Bruce/ Ward, Lock & Co., Limited./London and Melbourne
n.d.
256pp, b/w frontis. by J. Macfarlane, clo., 180x120mm. KMM

1087 NORAH OF BILLABONG/by/Mary Grant Bruce/ Ward, Lock & Co., Limited./London, Melbourne and Cape Town
n.d. [195-?]
224pp, b/w frontis. by W. Spence, clo., 185x120mm. K&NI

1088 GRAY'S/HOLLOW/By/Mary Grant Bruce/Author of "Norah of Billabong", "A Little Bush Maid,"/"Glen Eyre"/Ward, Lock & Co., Limited./London, Melbourne, and Toronto/1914
304pp, 2pp & 16pp adv., b/w frontis. & 7 b/w plates by Stanley Davies?, pic. clo., 185x125mm. KMM

1089 GRAY'S/HOLLOW/By/Mary Grant Bruce/Author of "Norah of Billabong", "A Little Bush Maid"/"Glen Eyre"/Ward, Lock & Co., Limited/London and Melbourne
n.d.
304pp & 16pp adv., b/w frontis. & 7 f/p b/w plates, clo. with b/w medallion on front cover, 182x125mm. TG

1090 FROM/BILLABONG/TO LONDON/By/Mary Grant Bruce/Author of "Mates at Billabong", "Glen Eyre",/"Timothy in Bushland," etc./Ward, Lock & Co., Limited./London, Melbourne, and Toronto/1915
320pp, 2+16pp adv., b/w frontis. & 7 b/w plates by Fred Leist, pic. clo., 185x120mm. KMM
• Rpt as above, but 'twenty-seventh thousand' n.d. TG

1091 FROM/BILLABONG/TO LONDON/By/Mary Grant Bruce/Ward, Lock & Co., Limited/London and Melbourne
n.d. [193-?]
320pp, b/w frontis. & 3 b/w plates, clo., 185x125mm. KMM

1092 FROM BILLABONG/TO LONDON/by/Mary Grant Bruce/Ward, Lock & Co., Limited/London and Melbourne
n.d. [1950?]
256pp, b/w frontis. by J. F. Campbell, clo., 185x120mm. K&NI

1093 JIM AND WALLY/By/Mary Grant Bruce/Author of "Mates at Billabong," "Norah of Billabong," etc./ Ward, Lock & Co., Limited./London, Melbourne, and Toronto/1916
256pp, 2pp & 16pp adv., b/w frontis. & 7 b/w plates by Balliol Salmon, pic. clo., 185x120mm. KMM

1094 JIM AND WALLY/By/Mary Grant Bruce/Ward, Lock & Co., Limited./London and Melbourne
n.d. [195-?]
224pp, b/w frontis. only, by different artist, clo., 185x120mm. PAI

1095 'POSSUM/By/Mary Grant Bruce/Author of "Glen Eyre", "Mates at Billabong",/"Norah of Billabong", "Jim and Wally"/etc. etc./Ward, Lock & Co., Limited./ London, Melbourne, and Toronto/1917
312pp, 8pp adv., b/w frontis. & 7 b/w plates. by J. Macfarlane, dec. clo., 185x120mm. KMM
• Rpt as above, but n.d. TG

1096 'POSSUM/By/Mary Grant Bruce/Author of "Little Bush Maid" [*sic*], "Mates at Billabong"/"Norah of Billabong", "Jim and Wally"/etc. etc./Ward, Lock & Co., Limited./London and Melbourne
1948 [First Australian edition]
255pp, no adv., unillus., clo., 180x120mm. PAI

1097 DICK/By/Mary Grant Bruce/Illustrated by/J. Macfarlane/Ward, Lock & Co., Limited./London, Melbourne, and Toronto/1918
256pp, 16pp adv., b/w frontis. & 7 b/w plates, clo., 185x125mm. KMM

1098 DICK/By/Mary Grant Bruce/Illustrated by/J. Macfarlane/Ward, Lock & Co., Limited./London and Melbourne.
n.d.
256pp, b/w frontis. & 7 b/w plates, clo., 185x125mm. KMM

1099 CAPTAIN JIM/By/Mary Grant Bruce/Author of "Mates at Billabong," "Norah at [*sic*]/Billabong", "Jim and Wally" etc./Illustrated by/J. Macfarlane/Ward, Lock & Co., Limited./London, Melbourne, and Toronto/1919
311pp, 8pp adv., b/w frontis. & 7 b/w plates, dec. clo., 180x120mm. NSL:M

1100 CAPTAIN JIM/By/Mary Grant Bruce/Author of "Mates at Billabong," "Norah at [*sic*]/Billabong", "Jim and Wally" etc./Illustrated by/J. Macfarlane/Ward, Lock & Co., Limited./London and Melbourne.
n.d.
As above, but one plate reproduced as onlay on front cover. KMM

1101 CAPTAIN JIM/By/Mary Grant Bruce/Ward, Lock & Co., Limited./London and Melbourne
n.d.
311pp, unillus., clo., 180x120mm. KMM

1102 CAPTAIN JIM/By/Mary Grant Bruce/Ward, Lock & Co., Limited./London and Melbourne
1952

256pp, b/w frontis. by J. F. Campbell, clo., 180x120mm. TI

1103 DICK LESTER/OF/KURRAJONG/By/Mary Grant Bruce/Ward, Lock & Co., Limited/London and Melbourne/1920
256pp, b/w frontis. & 7 b/w plates by J. Macfarlane, clo., 185x120mm. KMM
Sequel to *Dick*

1104 BACK TO/BILLABONG/By/Mary Grant Bruce/[quotation]/Ward, Lock & Co., Limited/London and Melbourne/1921
252pp, 4pp adv., b/w frontis. & 5 f/p b/w plates by J. Macfarlane, pic. clo., 185x125mm. KMM

1105 Another copy as above, n.d.
252pp, [no adv.], b/w frontis only, by J. F. Campbell, clo., 185x120mm. K&NI

1106 THE STONE AXE OF/BURKAMUKK/By/Mary Grant Bruce/Illustrated by J. Macfarlane/Ward, Lock & Co., Limited/London and Melbourne/1922
256pp (inc. 2pp author's foreword), b/w frontis. & 5 b/w plates, clo., 185x125mm. KMM
Aboriginal legends retold.

1107 THE TWINS/OF EMU PLAINS/By/Mary Grant Bruce/Illustrated/Ward, Lock & Co., Limited/London and Melbourne/1923
256pp, b/w frontis. & 3 b/w plates by Dewar Mills, clo., 185x126mm. KMM

1108 THE TWINS/OF EMU PLAINS/By/Mary Grant Bruce/Ward, Lock & Co., Limited/London and Melbourne
n.d.
256pp, b/w frontis. & 3 b/w plates clo., 185x126mm. TG

1109 Whitcombe's Story Books/ROSSITER'S/FARM/By/Mary Grant Bruce/For Children aged 10 to 12 years/[device]/Whitcombe & Tombs Pty. Ltd./Melbourne, Sydney, Perth
n.d. [1923?]
95pp, 1p adv., b/w frontis. & 3 f/p b/w illus. by Esther Paterson, stiff pic. wrappers, 185x110mm. KMM
See McLaren 521

1110 Whitcombe's Story Books/THE COUSIN/FROM TOWN/By/Mary Grant Bruce/For children aged 10 to 12 years/Whitcombes [*sic*] & Tombs Limited/Melbourne, Sydney/Auckland, Wellington, Christchurch, Dunedin/Invercargill and London
n.d. [1923]
108pp, b/w frontis. & 3 f/p b/w illus. by Esther Paterson, stiff pic. wrappers [with adv.], 185x115mm. KMM
See McLaren 522

1111 BILLABONG'S/DAUGHTER/By/Mary Grant Bruce/Illustrated/Ward, Lock & Co., Limited/London and Melbourne/1924
256pp, no adv., b/w frontis. & 7 f/p b/w plates. by J. Macfarlane, pic. clo., 185x120mm. KMM

1112 BILLABONG'S/DAUGHTER/By/Mary Grant Bruce/Ward, Lock & Co., Limited/London and Melbourne
n.d.
256pp, b/w frontis only, by J. Macfarlane, clo., 185x120mm. KMM

1113 BILLABONG'S/DAUGHTER/By/Mary Grant Bruce/Ward, Lock & Co., Limited/London, Melbourne and Cape Town
1959
256pp, b/w frontis only, by J. F. Campbell clo., 185x125mm. K&NI

1114 BILLABONG'S/DAUGHTER/By/Mary Grant Bruce/Ward, Lock & Co., Limited/London and Melbourne
Copyright 1924; 2nd imp. 1925; 3rd imp. 1926; 4th imp. 1928; 5th imp. 1931; 6th imp. 1936; 7th imp. 1939; 8th imp. 1943; 9th imp. 1946; 10th imp. 1948; 11th imp. 1950; 12th imp. 1943; 13th imp. 1956; 14th imp. 1959; 15th imp. 1964 [from verso of t.p.]
256pp, b/w frontis. by J. F. Campbell, clo., 185x120mm. BBC

1115 THE HOUSES OF/THE EAGLE/By/Mary Grant Bruce/Ward, Lock & Co., Limited/London and Melbourne/1925
247pp, 8pp adv., b/w frontis. & 3 b/w plates by Harold Copping, clo., 185x125mm. KMM

1116 Another copy as above, but n.d.
255pp, no adv., unillus., clo., 185x120mm. VSL

1117 THE HOUSES OF/THE EAGLE/By/Mary Grant Bruce/Ward, Lock & Co., Limited/London and Melbourne
1948 [First Australian edition]
255pp, unillus., clo., 180x120mm. K&NI

1118 HUGH STANFORD'S/LUCK/By/Mary Grant Bruce/Author of A Little Bush Maid, Mates of [*sic*] Billabong, Norah of Billabong,/'Possum, etc./Australia:/Cornstalk Publishing Company/Arnold Place, Sydney/1925
233pp, b/w frontis. by Edgar A. Holloway, clo., 185x120mm. KMM
• Rpt as above Sept. 1925;
• Rpt as above Dec. 1926 (both unseen, but on verso of t.p. of later copy)

1119 HUGH STANFORD'S/LUCK/By/Mary Grant Bruce/Author of A Little Bush Maid, Mates of [*sic*]/Billabong/Norah of Billabong/Possum etc/Australia:/Cornstalk Publishing Company/89 Castlereagh Street, Sydney/1928
233pp, b/w frontis. by Edgar A. Holloway, clo., 175x110mm. Grant

1120 First Platypus ed. March 1928, 2000, as above,

1121 Second Platypus ed. Oct 1928, 2000. " "

1122 Third Platypus ed. 1931, as above, CLRC

1123 HUGH STANFORD'S/LUCK/By/Mary Grant Bruce/Author of A Little Bush Maid, Mates of [*sic*] Billabong, Norah of Billabong,/'Possum, etc./Australia/Angus & Robertson Limited/89 Castlereagh Street, Sydney/1937
233pp, unillus., clo., 185x120mm. PR

1124 THE/TOWER ROOMS/By/Mary Grant Bruce/Ward, Lock & Co., Limited/London and Melbourne/1926
252pp, 4pp adv., b/w frontis. & 3 b/w plates by Dewar Mills, clo., 185x125mm. KMM

1125 ROBIN/By/Mary Grant Bruce/Author of Hugh Stanford's Luck, A Little Bush Maid,/Mates of [*sic*] Billabong, Norah of Billabong, 'Possum, etc./Australia:/Cornstalk Publishing Company/89 Castlereagh Street, Sydney/1926
287pp, b/w frontis. & 2 b/w plates by Edgar A. Holloway, clo., 180x120mm. KMM

1126 ROBIN/By/Mary Grant Bruce/Author of Hugh Stanford's Luck, A Little Bush Maid,/Mates of [*sic*] Billabong, Norah of Billabong, 'Possum, etc./Third Edition/Australia:/Cornstalk Publishing Company/89 Castlereagh Street, Sydney/1927
287pp, b/w frontis. & 2 f/p b/w plates by Edgar A. Holloway, clo., 180x120mm. KMM

[1st Bellbird ed. June 1926; 2nd Bellbird ed. Aug. 1926; 3rd Bellbird ed. May 1927 [from verso of t.p.]

1127 ROBIN/By/Mary Grant Bruce/Author of Hugh Stanford's Luck, A Little Bush Maid,/Mates of [sic] Billabong, Norah of Billabong, 'Possum, etc./ Australia:/Cornstalk Publishing Company/89 Castlereagh Street, Sydney/1928
287pp, b/w frontis. by Edgar A. Holloway, clo., 175x110mm. KMM
[1st Platypus ed., April 1928, 2000 copies; 2nd Platypus ed., July 1928, 2000 copies [from verso of t.p.]

1128 ROBIN/by/Mary Grant Bruce/Author of Hugh Stanford's Luck, A Little Bush Maid,/Mates of [sic] Billabong, Norah of Billabong, 'Possum, etc./ Australia/Angus & Robertson Limited/89 Castlereagh Street, Sydney/1933
287pp, b/w frontis. only, clo., 174x110mm. TG

1129 As above, but unillus., 1934, 180x120mm. Grant

1130 ROBIN/By/Mary Grant Bruce/Author of Hugh Stanford's Luck, A Little Bush Maid,/Mates of [sic] Billabong/Norah of Billabong, 'Possum, etc./Angus & Robertson Limited/Sydney and London/1938
287pp, unillus., clo., 180x120mm. KMM
D/w signed Dorothy Wall.

1131 ROBIN/By/Mary Grant Bruce/Author of Hugh Stanford's Luck, Mates of [sic] Billabong/Norah of Billabong, Karalta, etc./Angus & Robertson Ltd./ Sydney London/1941
233pp, b/w frontis., clo., 185x120mm. PAI
Another copy as above, 1948. KMM

1132 ANDERSON'S JO/By/Mary Grant Bruce/Author of Robin, Hugh Stanford's Luck, A Little Bush Maid/ Mates of [sic] Billabong, Nora [sic] of Billabong etc./ Australia:/Cornstalk Publishing Company/89 Castlereagh Street, Sydney/1927
250pp, b/w frontis. & 2 b/w plates, clo., 185x115mm. KMM

1133 ANDERSON'S JO/By/Mary Grant Bruce/Author of Robin, Hugh Stanford's Luck, A Little Bush Maid/ Mates of [sic] Billabong, Nora [sic] of Billabong etc./ Australia:/Cornstalk Publishing Company/89 Castlereagh Street, Sydney/1928
250pp, b/w frontis. by Philip Brown, clo., 175x110mm. NSL:M

1134 Rpt 1st Platypus ed. 1928, 3rd Platypus ed. 1931, unseen

1135 BILLABONG/ADVENTURERS/By/Mary Grant Bruce/Illustrated by/J. Macfarlane/Ward, Lock & Co., Limited/London and Melbourne/1927
250pp, 6pp adv., b/w frontis. & 7 b/w plates, pic. clo., 185x125mm. KMM

1136 BILLABONG/ADVENTURERS/By/Mary Grant Bruce/Illustrated by/J. Macfarlane/(Fifteenth Thousand)/Ward, Lock & Co., Limited/London and Melbourne/1928
250pp, 4pp adv., b/w frontis. & 7 f/p b/w plates, clo., 185x125mm. PAI
Other undated copies as above, one with 4 b/w illus. by J. Macfarlane, one with b/w frontis. only by Macfarlane.

1137 BILLABONG/ADVENTURERS/by/Mary Grant Bruce/Ward, Lock & Co., Limited/London and Melbourne
250pp, b/w frontis. by J. Pollack, clo., 185x120mm. KMM

1138 BILLABONG/ADVENTURERS/By/Mary Grant Bruce/Ward, Lock & Co., Limited/London and Melbourne
Copyright 1927; 2nd imp. 1928; 3rd imp. 1929; 4th imp. 1933; 5th imp. 1936; 6th imp. 1939; 7th imp. 1943; 8th imp. 1946; 9th imp. 1948; 10th imp. 1950; 11th imp. 1953; 12th imp. 1957; 13th imp. 1964
250pp, b/w frontis. by J. Pollack, clo., 185x120mm. BBC

1139 GOLDEN FIDDLES/By/Mary Grant Bruce/Ward, Lock & Co., Limited/London and Melbourne/1928
256pp, b/w frontis. & 3 b/w plates by J. Dewar Mills, clo., 180x120mm. KMM

1140 Another edition as above, but n.d. [195-?]
256pp, b/w frontis. only, by different artist, clo., 180x120mm. KMM

1141 THE/HAPPY TRAVELLER/By/Mary Grant Bruce/ With illustrations by/Laurie Tayler/Ward, Lock & Co., Limited/London and Melbourne/1929
253pp, 2pp adv., b/w frontis. & 3 b/w plates, clo., 180x120mm. KMM

1142 THE/HAPPY TRAVELLER/By/Mary Grant Bruce/ Ward, Lock & Co., Limited/London and Melbourne 1948 [First Australian edition]
255pp, unillus., clo., 185x120mm. VSL

1143 BILL OF BILLABONG/By/Mary Grant Bruce/With illustrations by/A. A. Kent/Ward, Lock & Co., Limited/London and Melbourne/1931
256pp, b/w frontis. & 3 b/w plates., clo., 180x120mm. KMM
Another copy as above, n.d. CLRC

1144 BILL OF BILLABONG/By/Mary Grant Bruce/ Ward, Lock & Co., Limited/London and Melbourne n.d.
256pp, unillus., clo., 180x120mm. KMM

1145 BILL/OF/BILLABONG, By/Mary Grant Bruce/ Ward, Lock & Co., Limited/London and Melbourne 1954
220pp, 4pp adv., b/w frontis. by J. F. Campbell, clo., 185x120mm. K&NI

• BILL/OF/BILLABONG/By/Mary Grant Bruce/Ward, Lock & Co., Limited/London, Melbourne and Cape Town
1954; rpt 1957
As above. K&NI

• BILL/OF/BILLABONG/By/Mary Grant Bruce/Ward, Lock & Co., Limited/London and Melbourne
1954; rpt 1957, 1967
As above, but 185x115mm. BBC

1146 ROAD TO ADVENTURE/By/Mary Grant Bruce/ With illustrations by/Laurie Tayler/Ward, Lock & Co., Limited/London and Melbourne
1932
256pp, b/w frontis. & 3 b/w plates, clo., 185x125mm. KMM

1147 ROAD TO ADVENTURE/By/Mary Grant Bruce/ New York/Minton, Balch & Company/1933
248pp, unillus., peacock blue clo. with multi-coloured d/w, 195x130mm.
Minton, Balch & Company are a division of G. P. Putnam's Sons, New York; this was a limited edition.
Unseen: information from J. E. Bruce

1148 BILLABONG'S/LUCK/By/Mary Grant Bruce/ Ward, Lock & Co., Limited/London and Melbourne 1933
256pp (inc. 4pp author's foreword), b/w frontis. & 3 b/w plates by Laurie Tayler, clo., 190x125mm. KMM

1149 BILLABONG'S/LUCK/By/Mary Grant Bruce/ Ward, Lock & Co., Limited/London and Melbourne n.d.
As above, with frontis. & 3 b/w plates by Laurie Tayler, but with d/w by J. F. Campbell, whereas 1st ed. has d/w by Laurie Tayler. KMM

1150 Another copy, as above, but b/w frontis. only by J. F. Campbell. KMM
1151 BILLABONG'S/LUCK/By/Mary Grant Bruce/ Ward, Lock & Co., Limited/London and Melbourne
Copyright 1933; 2nd imp. 1935; 3rd imp. 1937; 4th imp. 1940; 5th imp. 1943; 6th imp. 1946; 7th imp. 1948; 8th imp. 1950; 9th imp. 1953; 10th imp. 1957; 11th imp. 1963
256pp, b/w frontis. only, clo., 185x120mm.
Frontispiece signed 'J.F.C.' (J. F. Campbell). BBC

1152 "SEAHAWK"/By/Mary Grant Bruce/Ward, Lock & Co., Limited/London and Melbourne
1934
256pp, b/w frontis. & 3 b/w plates (by J. F. Campbell), clo., 185x125mm. KMM
1153 Another copy as above, but 256pp & b/w frontis. by R. W. May, 185x115mm. KMM

1154 WINGS/ABOVE BILLABONG/By/Mary Grant Bruce/Ward, Lock & Co., Limited/London and Melbourne
1935
252pp, 4pp adv., b/w frontis. & 3 f/p b/w plates by J. F. Campbell, clo., 190x120mm. NSL:M
Another copy as above, but n.d. KMM
1155 WINGS/ABOVE BILLABONG/By/Mary Grant Bruce/Ward, Lock & Co., Limited/London, Melbourne and Johannesburg
n.d. [195-?]
252pp, b/w frontis. by J. F. Campbell, clo., 185x120mm. BBC

1156 CIRCUS RING/By/Mary Grant Bruce/Ward, Lock & Co., Limited/London and Melbourne
1936
256pp, b/w frontis. & 3 b/w plates by J. F. Campbell, clo., 185x120mm. KMM
1157 Another copy as above, but London, Melbourne and Cape Town, n.d.
192pp, b/w frontis. only, clo., 185x120mm.
Frontispiece signed 'M.T.' (? Margaret Tarrant). K&NI
1158 CIRCUS RING
New York, G. P. Putnam's Sons, 1937
'A Minton Balch Book'
Unseen: NUC

1159 BILLABONG/GOLD/By/Mary Grant Bruce/Ward, Lock & Co., Limited/London and Melbourne
1937
256pp, b/w frontis. & 3 b/w plates, by J. F. Campbell, clo., 185x125mm. ANL
1160 BILLABONG/GOLD/By/Mary Grant Bruce/Ward, Lock & Co., Limited/London and Melbourne
n.d.
256pp, b/w frontis., clo., 185x120mm. KMM

1161 TOLD BY PETER/By/Mary Grant Bruce/Ward, Lock & Co., Limited/London and Melbourne
1938
256pp, 1p adv., b/w frontis. & 3 b/w plates by J. F. Campbell, clo., 185x125mm. KMM
1162 Rpt as above. 1948
256pp, unillus., clo., 185x120mm. PAI
• Rpt 1949 as above. TI

1163 SON OF/BILLABONG/By/Mary Grant Bruce/ Ward, Lock & Co., Limited/London and Melbourne
1939
255pp, 1p adv., b/w frontis. & 3 f/p b/w plates by J. F. Campbell, pic. clo., 185x125mm. KMM
• Rpt September 1939, 1943, as above. GI
1164 SON OF/BILLABONG/By/Mary Grant Bruce/ Ward, Lock & Co., Limited/London, Melbourne and Cape Town
1939; rpt 1939, 1943, 1946, 1949, 1951, 1953, 1957
255pp, b/w frontis. only by J. F. Campbell, clo., 185x125mm. BBC
• Rpt as above 1964. BBC

1165 PETER & CO./By/Mary Grant Bruce/Ward, Lock & Co., Limited/London and Melbourne
1940
254pp, 2pp adv., b/w frontis. & 3 b/w plates by J. F. Campbell, clo., 185x125mm. KMM
1166 Rpt as above. 1948
254pp, b/w frontis. only by J. F. Campbell, clo., 185x120mm. PAI

1167 KARALTA/By/Mary Grant Bruce/Author of Mates of [sic] Billabong/Norah of Billabong/Robin, etc./ Angus and Robertson Ltd./Sydney London/1941
233pp, b/w frontis, clo., 185x120mm. PAI
Other copies as above, rpt 1942, 1946, 1947, 1948. KMM

1168 BILLABONG RIDERS/By/Mary Grant Bruce/ Author of/Mates of [sic] Billabong/Norah of Billabong/ Robin, etc./Ward, Lock & Co., Limited/London and Melbourne
1942 [Australian printing]
262pp, b/w frontis., clo., 180x120mm. TI
1169 BILLABONG RIDERS/By/Mary Grant Bruce/ Author of/"Mates of [sic] Billabong", "Nora [sic] of Billabong", "Son of Billabong", etc./Ward, Lock & Co., Limited/London and Melbourne
1946
262pp, b/w frontis., clo., 180x120mm. KMM
4th imp. 1967, as above. TG
1170 BILLABONG RIDERS/By/Mary Grant Bruce/Ward, Lock & Co., Limited/London and Melbourne
1952 [First English edition]
192pp, b/w frontis. (different from Australian editions), clo., 185x120mm. KMM
• Rpt 1956, 1963, as above. BBC
See also Gunn, Jeannie. LITTLE BLACK PRINCESS OF THE NEVER NEVER, 1922

BRUNATO, Madeleine
1171 WORRA AND THE/JILBRUKE LEGEND/ Madeleine Brunato/Illus. by/C. Dudley Wood/Rigby/ Opal/Books
Adelaide 1972
38pp (inc. 1p acknowledgements), 7 f/p sepia/white illus., map inside back cover, clo., 255x190mm. KMM

BRYANT, Joseph
1172 THE STORY OF AUSTRALIA/For Boys and Girls/ By/Joseph Bryant/Corresponding Member of the Royal Scottish/Geographical Society/Hodder and Stoughton/ London New York Toronto
n.d. [1919?]
232pp, 1p author's preface, 3pp foreword by Sir W. P. Cullen, b/w frontis. & 7 b/w illus. by W. R. S. Stott, clo., 185x120mm. KMM

1173 GREAT EVENTS IN/AUSTRALIAN HISTORY/ By/Joseph Bryant/Author of "The Story of Australia for Boys and Girls"/With illustrations by Percy Lindsay/Australia:/Cornstalk Publishing Company/ Arnold Place, Sydney/1925
178pp (inc. 10pp tables, 8pp index), 1p preface, col. frontis. & 6 f/p col. illus., clo., 175x105mm. ANL
1174 Rpt Platypus Series, as above. KMM
1175 GREAT EVENTS IN/AUSTRALIAN HISTORY/ By/Joseph Bryant/Author of "The Story of Australia for Boys and Girls"/Fifth Edition/Australia/Angus &

Robertson Limited/89 Castlereagh Street, Sydney/1932
First pub. Dec. 1924; 2nd ed. March 1925; 3rd ed. Feb. 1928; 4th ed. Feb. 1930
183pp (inc. 11pp chronological table & 9pp index), 10 author's preface, col. frontis. & 6 f/p col. illus. by Percy Lindsay, clo., 175x110mm. KMM

1176 CAPTAIN/MATTHEW FLINDERS/R.N./His Voyages, discoveries, and fortunes/by/Joseph Bryant/Author of/Great Events in Australian History, Coral Reefs and Cannibals/With a foreword by/Sir Flinders Petrie/London/The Epworth Press/J. Alfred Sharp
1928
194pp (inc. 1p appendix, 1p foreword & 2pp author's preface), b/w portrait frontis. only, clo., 184x120mm. CLRC

"The Brymay Toy Book"
1177 "THE BRYMAY TOY BOOK"/Sent to you with the Compliments of/Bryant & May Pty. Ltd./Richmond, Vic.
Bryant & May Ltd, Richmond, Victoria, n.d. [1928?]
24pp (inc. 1p note & 1p foreword), col. illus. throughout, pic. wrappers, 195x150mm. KMM
Instructions on toys to make from match boxes. Booklet produced as an advertisement for Bryant & May's matches.

BUCHANAN, E. (illustrator)
1178 MOTHER GOOSE
Ayers & James Pty Ltd, Sydney, n.d. [194-?]
[16]pp (& printed inside both covers), 8 f/p col. illus. & b/w drawings throughout, pic. wrappers, cover title, 323x243mm. KMM

BUCK, Madeline
1179 DOROTHY PERKINS/CHILDREN'S VERSE/By/Madeline Buck
The author, Kogarah, N.S.W., 1943
40pp, b/w illus. by pupils of St. George Girls Public High School, dec. wrappers, cover title, 235x165mm. ANL

BUCKINGHAM, Marjorie
1180 IN ALL THESE THINGS/By/Marjorie Buckingham/[device]/Oliphants Limited/London Edinburgh
1953; rpt 1953, 1954, 1955
224pp, unillus., clo., 180x120mm. KP

1181 BROAD IS THE WAY/By/Marjorie Buckingham/[device]/ Oliphants Limited/Edinburgh
1953; rpt 1954, 1955
216pp, unillus., clo., 180x117mm. KP

1182 "THEY SHALL BE MINE"/A School Story/by/Marjorie Buckingham/[device]/Oliphants Ltd/London Edinburgh
1954
127pp, col. frontis., clo., 183x180mm. KP
Christian novel for young people, written by Victorian author
• Rpt as above 1956, 1958. KP
• Rpt as above 1961. KP

1183 THE/ADVENTURES OF/TINA AND TIM/A Story for Girls and Boys/By/Marjorie Buckingham/[device]/Oliphants Ltd./London Edinburgh
1st printed 1954
159pp, col. frontis. only, clo., 180x120mm. KP
• Rpt 1956 as above. KP

1184 STRAIT IS THE GATE/By/Marjorie Buckingham/[device]/Oliphants Limited/London Edinburgh
1956
224pp, unillus., clo., 180x117mm. KP

1185 THIS MY SON/by/Marjorie Buckingham/[device]/Oliphants Limited/London Edinburgh
1960
190pp, unillus., clo., 185x122mm. KP

1186 Marjorie Buckingham/MANY/WATERS/A Novel/[device]/Oliphants
1965
190pp, unillus., clo., 184x120mm. KP
Adult novel rather than children's fiction.

BUCKLAND, Ethel
FAIRY TALES FROM AUSTRALIA. *See* Books for the Bairns

BUCKLAND, John
1187 ADRIATIC/ADVENTURE/Squadron Leader John Buckland/R.A.A.F./Illustrated/Melbourne/Robertson and Mullens/1945
87pp, b/w photographic frontis. & 8 half-page photographic illus., bd., 210x150mm. Adventurous Youth Series No. 2.
Part of 'blurb' reads: 'A thrilling tale of air crew adventure, told by its navigator, one of three Australians in a crew of six manning a Marauder aircraft operating from Africa over the Mediterranean'. Grant

BUDDEE, Paul
1188 THE COMICAL ADVENTURES/OF/OSCA AND OLGA/A Tale of Mice in Mouseland/By/Paul Buddee/Illustrations by/C. H. Percival/Published by/The Currawong Publishing Co./32 Jamieson Street/Sydney
n.d. [1943]
135pp (inc. 2pp introduction & acknowledgements), b/w illus. throughout, dec. wrappers, 180x130mm. KMM

1189 THE REMARKABLE RAMBLINGS/OF/RUPERT AND RITA/By/Paul Buddee/Illustrations by/C. H. Percival/Published by/The Currawong Publishing Co./32 Jamieson Street/Sydney
n.d. [1944]
112pp (inc. 1pp adv. & 2pp preface), b/w illus. throughout, wrappers, 180x130mm.
Cover title reads: 'Rupert and Rita'. KMM

1190 SIX/COMICAL STORIES/ABOUT/RATTIGAN RAT/By Paul Buddee/Illustrations by Neves Cherry/Copyright/1947/Registered at the G.P.O. Perth for transmission by post as a book/Printed and Published by/Imperial Printing Co. Ltd./397 Hay Street Perth W.A.
74pp, b/w illus. throughout, wrappers, 215x140mm. ANL

1191 Paul Buddee/THE MYSTERY OF MOMA ISLAND/Illustrated by Peter Kesteven/Brockhampton Press
Leicester, England, 1969
120pp (inc. 3pp preface, etc.), b/w drawings throughout, clo., 180x130mm. KMM
Story of illicit search for treasure off the west coast of Australia.

1192 THE ESCAPE OF THE FENIANS/Paul Buddee/Longman
Longman Australia Pty Ltd, Camberwell, Victoria, 1971
176pp (inc. 5pp notes & bibliography), 1p acknowledgements, 1p note, map frontis., b/w drawings in text, illus. by Anne Culvenor, clo., map e/p, 195x125mm. KMM

1193 Another edition, as above
Longman Young Books, England, 1972
Unseen: IFA

1194 Paul Buddee/THE UNWILLING ADVENTURERS/ Illustrations by Gareth Floyd/Brockhampton Press Leicester, England, 1967
120pp, b/w frontis., b/w drawings in text, clo., 185x130mm. KMM

BUESST, Marie
1195 THE CRAIGS OF/COLLINS STREET/By/Marie Buesst/Melbourne/The Hawthorn Press/1971
134pp, 11 b/w engravings in text, clo., dec. e/p, 250x170mm. KMM
Story of a family living in Melbourne in the 1860s.

BUETTEL, N. E.
1196 FIFTEEN NORTH/OF HOOK/N. E. Buettel/ [drawing]/[device]/Angus and Robertson
Sydney, 1965
151pp, 5 b/w maps & diagrams, clo., 215x135mm. KMM

BULCOCK, Roy
1197 NO WIDER/LAND/By Roy Bulcock
Refulgence Publishers Pty Ltd, 28 Baynes St, Margate, Queensland, 1971
111pp, 7 b/w illus., illus. by David Cox, clo., 190x125mm. ANL

BULEY, Bernard
1198 No 95 Price 2½d./JUNE AND THE KANGAROO/ [illus.]/Modern Fairy Tales
(Anglo-American Magazine Co. Ltd) Publ. by Popular Fiction (London) Ltd, n.d.
16pp, b/w illus., pic. wrappers, cover title, 178x124mm. ANL
Illus. Jack Greenall.

BULEY, Ernest Charles
1199 A CHILD'S HISTORY/OF ANZAC/By/E. C. Buley/Author of "Glorious Deeds of Australasians"/Hodder and Stoughton/London New York Toronto/1916
231pp, b/w photographic frontis., 4 f/p photographic plates, pic clo., 190x120mm. ANL

BULLEN, Frank T.
1200 THE BITTER SOUTH/By/Frank T. Bullen/Author of 'With Christ at Sea', 'The Cruise of the Cachalot', etc/With twelve illustrations/by/Arthur Twidle/ London/Robert Colley/25–35 City Road, and 26 Paternoster Row, E.C.
294pp & 2pp adv., b/w frontis. & 11 b/w plates, pic. clo., 190x120mm. KP

BULLER-MURPHY, Deborah [née Drake-Brockman]
1201 AN ATTEMPT TO/EAT THE MOON/And other stories recounted from/the Aborigines by/Deborah Buller-Murphy/Illustrated by/Elizabeth Durack/ [drawing]/Georgian House, Melbourne.
1958
50pp, b/w drawings throughout, dec. clo., dec. e/p, 235x180mm. KMM
Contains 15 Australian Aboriginal legends.

Bumper Book of Sea Stories
1202 BUMPER BOOK/OF SEA STORIES/[drawing]/ [device]/London & Glasgow/Collins' Clear-type Press
n.d.
[160]pp, 2pp adv., col. frontis. & 4 f/p col. illus., b/w illus. in text, pic. bd., 215x160mm. KMM
Contents include: 'A Tragedy of the Pacific', by Herbert Hayens (17pp); 'The Pearl Poachers', by D. F. Seton-Carruthers (action moves from Sydney to a Pacific island; 16pp).

A Bunch of Heartsease
By A.B.S. *See* Shaped Books

BUNGEY, Nyorie
1203 KATFISH/AND/HAROLD HORSE/AND THE/ SAND CASTLE COMPETITION/Written and illustrated by Nyorie Bungey/Ure Smith Sydney London
1969
41pp, col. illus. throughout, pic. clo., dec. e/p, 280x205mm. KMM

1204 TIFFANIE TEAPOT/AND THE LION ON THE WALL/Written and illustrated by Nyorie Bungey/ [device]/Ure Smith—Sydney
1972
[32]pp, col. illus. throughout, col. pic. bd., 285x210mm. BBC

BURES, Karel
1205 SETKANI/POD JIZNIM KRIZEM/aneb/Vypraveni o Australii, olympijskych hrachv Mel-/bournu a o vecech a lidech v pozadi teto udalosti/[map]/Praha 1957/Mlada fronta, nakladatelstvi Ceskoslovenskeho svazu mladeze
1957
125pp, b/w chapter headings & some text illus., 32pp b/w photographs, bd., pic. e/p, 205x150mm. CLRC
Geography of Australia in Czech.

BURKE, Alfred [pseud. 'Teresa Tagg', Timothy Tagg]
1206 I'M A CAPTAIN/By/Timothy Tagg
Playground Publishing, Rozelle, N.S.W., n.d. [1945]
24pp, col. illus. throughout, bd., cover title, 235x180mm. ANL
Verses.

1207 JEEP/A Story of four Dogs/by/Timothy Tagg/ Playground Publishing/Nelson and Darling Streets, Rozelle, N.S.W.
n.d. [1945]
24pp, col. & b/w illus. throughout, bd., 235x180mm. ANL

1208 POT AND PAN/By/Timothy Tagg/Illustrated by/ Bill Davies/Second impression/Playground Publishing, Nelson and Darling Streets, Rozelle, N.S.W.
Printed by The Standard Publishing House, 69 Nelson St, Rozelle, n.d. [1945]
[24]pp, 4pp f/p col. illus., sepia/white illus. throughout, col. pic. bd., 235x183mm. KMM

1209 WHEN I GROW UP/[drawing]/By Timothy Tagg/ Illustrated by Alan Rigby & Laurie Greenacre
Peter Huston Publishing Co., Sydney, n.d. [1945]
32pp, col. illus. throughout, bd., 240x185mm. ANL

1210 "WHEN I GROW UP"/[drawing]/by Teresa Tagg/ Illustrated by Richard Inman and Clyve Elliott
"An Uncle Peter Book"
Peter Huston Publishing, Sydney, n.d. [1945]
32pp, col. illus. throughout, pic. bd., pic. e/p, 240x180mm. KP
Adv. on back page 'Uncle Peter Playbooks'
1 When I grow up (for boys)
2 The Sand-man
3 Wacky the small boy
4 Waggles the chick

1211 CHILDREN/OF/FAR OFF LANDS/By/Alfred

Burke/illustrated by/David Hegarty/Playground Publishing, Sydney
n.d. [1948]
46pp, 11 col. illus., b/w drawings & maps, bd., 235x180mm. ANL

1212 MY PUSS PENNY/By/Teresa Tagg/Playground Publishing/Dick St., Balmain N.S.W.
n.d. [1948?]
39pp, 4 col. illus. & b/w drawings throughout, bd., 240x180mm. ANL

BURKE, Kay
1213 SKWEEKY/SPIDER/By/Kay Burke/Age 6/Written 1932—Printed 35
Printed by Arthur McQuilty & Co., no place of imprint; edition limited to 100 copies
11pp, col. illus., wrappers, 185x120mm. ANL

BURLAND, C. A.
1214 Round the World Histories/JAMES COOK,/CAPTAIN, R.N./by C. A. Burland/illustrated by/D. G. Valentine/Hulton Educational Publications, Ltd. London 1967
32pp, b/w & part. col. illus. throughout, double spread part. col. map, stiff col. pic. wrappers, 210x140mm. KMM

BURLEY, Winifred
1215 Imperial edition No. 378/[2 lines acknowledgement]/SIX/SONGS OF PLAYTIME/Words and Music/by/Winifred Burley/Contents/[6 songs listed]/Price 1/3 net/Allan & Co. Prop. Ltd./Melb. Syd. A.B.
n.d. [stamped 1936]
8pp, unillus., pic. wrappers, 254x180mm. VSL

BURNET, Noel
1216 THE BLUEGUM FAMILY AT KOALA PARK/By Noel Burnet/with Photographs by/Harold Cazneaux/by courtesy "Art in Australia" "Sun" Feature Bureau/Squire Morgan Phil Ward and—/E. B. Studios The Author/[photo of koala]/Price 2/-/Copyright/Wholly Set Up and printed in Australia by:/W. A. Pepperday & Co. Limited/757a George Street, Sydney/1932
35pp, col. frontis. (unsigned), sepia photographs throughout, col. pic. wrappers, 270x216mm. KP
Front cover reads 'The Native Bear Book/The Blue Gum Family/at Koala Park/Noel Burnet'. Not specifically a children's book.

BURNS, Keith
1217 OUR/TRANSPORT/by/Keith Burns, B.A./A Background of Australia Book/Shakespeare Head Press/Sydney/1956
128pp (inc. 3pp projects), b/w photographic illus. throughout, (copy seen rebound), 200x130mm. CLRC
Textbook of some general interest.

BURNS, Roger
1218 "Seeing the World" Series/Edited by Rodney Bennett/TWO BOYS IN AUSTRALIA/By/Roger Burns/Thomas Nelson and Sons Ltd./London, Edinburgh, New York/Toronto and Paris
n.d. [1936?]
130pp, col. frontis. & 12 b/w illus. by R. H. Brock, clo., 160x110mm. NSL:M

BURNS, Win
1219 AUSTRALIAN STORIES/AND ANIMAL ALPHABET/for Children/by/Win Burns/Arthur H. Stockwell Ltd/Ilfracombe Devon
n.d. [1963?]
21pp, 4 b/w drawings, wrappers, 181x122mm. NSL:M

BURRAGE, A. Harcourt
1220 BENDING THE SAILS/By/A. Harcourt Burrage/Wells Gardner, Darton & Co., Ltd./Redhill Surrey 1949
189pp, 3pp adv., unillus., clo., 180x120mm. KMM
Adventure set aboard a Finnish windjammer on a modern voyage from London to 'Port Lagroon', an Australian wheat port.

[BURRAGE, E. Harcourt]
1221 CHEERFUL—DARING—WONDERFUL!/CHING-CHING/Sequel to "Handsome Harry."/[b/w drawing, with caption 'Ching-Ching leaped into the air and clasped the iron rod of the sign-post'./No. 1 Price One Penny
'Best for Boys' Library. Publ. by W. Lucas, 26 Dean St, Fetter Lane, London, n.d.[188-?]
532pp. Publ. in 17 parts, b/w cover title, b/w cover illus. & 1 f/p b/w illus. in each part, wrappers, 230x170mm. CLRC
Sequel to 'Handsome Harry of the Fighting Belvedere'.

1222 Author's Edition—Price One Penny./DARING CHING-CHING./Sequel to 'Handsome Harry' and 'Cheerful Ching-Ching.'/[illus.]
Charles Fox, 4 Shoe Lane, Fleet Street, London, E.C., n.d.
119pp, 13 f/p b/w illus., b/w pic. wrappers, cover title, 213x133mm. RM
Title over chapter one reads: 'Daring Ching-Ching;/or, The Mysterious Cruise of the Swallow'
Continuous pagination in 8 parts; the book contains 51 chapters, the Australian section being from Chapter 32 to Chapter 40 (20pp). The ship sails across the Indian Ocean to Spencer Gulf, South Australia. Ching-Ching and his friends go into the bush where they have adventures with Aborigines and bushrangers.

1223 TOM WILDRAKE'S SCHOOLDAYS/By/George Emmett/Author of "Boys of Bircham School', &c/Profusely Illustrated by Eminent Artists/Hogarth House, St Brides Avenue, Fleet St,/London EC.
n.d. [1875?]
890pp, adv. both sides back wrappers, 64 f/p b/w illus. (inc. cover illus.), pic. wrappers, 205x145mm. RM
Australian section pp785–890. Although credited to George Emmett, actually written by E. H. Burrage & originally printed in *The Young Englishman* from 26 July 1873 to 14 March 1874 with illus. by Harry Maguire and 'Phiz' (Hablot K. Browne).

BURRAGE, E. Harcourt
1224 THE WURRA WURRA BOYS/by E. Harcourt Burrage/author of 'The Vanished Yacht', 'Carbineer/and Scout' etc. etc./four coloured/Illustrations/Collins/Clear-type Press/London and Glasgow
n.d. [1903]
132pp, 10pp adv., col. frontis. & 3 col. illus., dec. bd., 180x120mm. Grant

1225 THE WURRA WURRA BOYS/By/E. Harcourt Burrage/London and Glasgow/Collins Clear-Type Press
n.d. [192-?]
126pp, col. frontis. only, bd., 180x120mm. KMM

BURROW, Aileen L. [pseud. 'Neelia']
1226 THE THINK MAN/By/"Neelia"/(Aileen L. Burrow)/Illustrated by the Author/[drawing]/Sydney/Printed by/Websdale, Shoosmith Limited/1911
9pp, dec t.p.
Bound together with:

1227 THE SUNSET FAIRIES/By/"Neelia"/(Aileen L. Burrow)/[drawing]/Illustrated by Author
Cover reads: THE/THINK/MAN/and/THE/SUNSET/

FAIRIES/By/"Neelia"/(Aileen L. Burrow)/Illustrated by the/Author
Altogether: 18pp, b/w drawings, bd., 230x180mm. NSL:M

1228 Southern Cross Story Readers/LITTLE SHEPHERD/The Life Story of a Little Dog/Founded on Fact/By/Aileen L. Burrow/For Children aged 9 to 10 years/Melbourne/Auckland Christchurch Dunedin Wellington/and London/Whitcombe & Tombs Limited
n.d. [1920?]
64pp, b/w frontis. & 16 line drawings, wrappers, 185x125mm. KMM
See McLaren 410

1229 Whitcombe's/Southern Cross Story Readers/GOBLIN GREENLEAF/Life Stories of some Australian Insects/By/Aileen L. Burrow/("Neelia")/Author of "Little Shepherd", etc./For Children aged 10 to 12 years/[drawing]/Illustrated by the Author/Whitcombe & Tombs Limited/Melbourne/Auckland, Christchurch, Dunedin, Wellington/and London
n.d. [192-?]
96pp, b/w frontis. & line drawings in text, stiff dec. wrappers, 180x115mm. KMM
'Price 9d.' printed on front cover, & advertisement on outside back cover for *Squirmy and Bubbles* by Lilian M. Pyke [192-?]
See McLaren 514

1230 THE ADVENTURES/OF MELALEUCA/By/Aileen L. Burrow/For children aged 9 to 10 years/Australia/Cornstalk Publishing Company/89 Castlereagh Street, Sydney/1928
92pp, b/w frontis. & b/w illus. throughout, illus. by 'Neelia', wrappers, 180x115mm. Gumnut Reader Series. NSL:M

1231 THE ADVENTURES/OF MELALEUCA/By/Aileen L. Burrow
Cornstalk Pub. Coy, Sydney, rpt. 1929
As above. Illus. signed 'Neelia'. The Gumnut Readers. CLRC

1232 Whitcombe's story Books/THE QUEST OF THE/CROWN JEWELS/By Aileen L. Burrow/Author of Little Shepherd, Goblin Greenleaf, etc/For Children aged 10 to 12 years/[device]/Whitcombe & Tombs Pty. Limited/Sydney./Associated Houses at/Auckland, Christchurch, Dunedin/Wellington, Invercargill, (N.Z.),/Melbourne and London
[1929?]
76pp & 4pp questions & notes, b/w frontis. & drawings in text, pic. wrappers, 182x122mm. KP
See McLaren 535

BURROWS, Denys

1233 ABOVE/THE SNOWLINE/By/Denys Burrows/The Educational Press/Sydney
1959
190pp, b/w drawings throughout, illus. by Graham Wade, clo., 220x135mm. KMM
A serial of the same name, based on this story, was broadcast by the Australian Broadcasting Commission prior to publication in book form.
• Rpt 1963, 1965 as above. KP

1234 STAGECOACH/WEST/By/Denys Burrows/[device]/The Educational Press/Sydney
1964
174pp (inc. 1p author's note & 4pp notes), b/w frontis., b/w chapter headings & line drawings in text, illus. by Graham Wade, clo., dec. e/p, 215x135mm. CLRC
Incidents relating to bushrangers, coaches and early railways are introduced into the story.

1235 CLIPPER SHIP/[drawing]/by Denys Burrows/The Educational Press Sydney
1965
184pp (inc. 4pp notes), b/w frontis., b/w chapter headings & drawings in text, illus. by Graham Wade, clo., 215x135mm. KMM

1236 FIGHT/FOR/GOLD!/by Denys Burrows/[drawing]/The Educational Press—Sydney
1966
152pp, 1p adv., b/w frontis. & 5pp b/w illus., chapter headings & drawings in text, illus. by Graham Wade, clo., 215x135mm. CLRC
Illustrations contain reproduction of posters & gold licences from the Gold Rush period.

1237 LIVING/IN/AUSTRALIA/Denys/Burrows/[drawing]/Educational Press/Sydney/[device]
1967
142pp, b/w photographic illus. throughout, sim. clo., pic. map e/p, 242x180mm. WRT

BURSTALL, Tim

1238 THE PRIZE/By Tim Burstall and Gerard Vandenberg/Based on the film "The Prize" written and directed by/Tim Burstall and photographed by Gerard Vandenberg/London: Michael Joseph
1962
32pp, b/w frontis., 3pp col. illus., b/w photographs on alternate pages, dec. bd., 250x185mm. KMM

1239 SEBASTIAN/AND THE/SAUSAGES/by/Tim Burstall/Puppet created by Peter Scriven/Photographed by Gerard Vandenberg/Based on the Eltham Films Series/The Adventures of Sebastian Fox/Lansdowne/Melbourne and Sydney/1965
[30]pp, b/w photographic illus. throughout, col. pic. bd., 245x180mm. KMM

BURTON, Hester

1240 Hester Burton/NO BEAT OF DRUM/Illustrated by/Victor G. Ambrus/London/Oxford University Press/1966
184pp, 1p author's note, b/w illus. throughout, clo., 215x140mm. KMM
The story tells of the transportation to Van Diemen's Land of a seventeen-year-old farm labourer, arrested for participation in the English land riots of the 1830s.

BURTON, J. W.

1241 BROWN FACES/A Missionary Book for Methodist Boys/and Girls/By J. W. Burton/Author of "The Fiji of Today", "Snapshots of India",/"The Call of the Pacific". Etc./[device]/Published by/The Methodist Missionary Society/of Australia
Melbourne, n.d. [1920?]
64pp, b/w photographic illus., double spread b/w map, dec. wrappers, 215x135mm. KMM
Map illustration by T. C. Camm
Story of missionary activities in the south-west Pacific area.

BURTON, Maurice

1242 ANIMALS/OF AUSTRALIA/Maurice Burton/Illustrated by David Parry/[drawing]/Abelard-Schuman/London New York Toronto
First publ. in Great Britain 1969; first publ. in USA 1970
138pp, b/w map & 4pp list of animals mentioned with their scientific names, 16 f/p b/w illus., bd., 210x140mm. KMM

BURTON, Muriel
1243 KANGA/THE/COWBOY/MPA
Story:/Miss Muriel Burton/Illustrations:/Adrian Bain /based on original drawings by/some of the native young people/from the Baptist Mission,/Warrabri Native Settlement, N.T./Published and Printed by:/ Mission Publications of Australia/19 Cascade Street, (P.O. Box 21),/Lawson, NSW 2783/Revised Edition 1970
31pp, 15 f/p part col. illus., pic. wrappers, 203x250mm. KP

BURTON, Robert
1244 ANIMALS OF/THE ANTARCTIC/Robert Burton/ Illustrated by David Parry/[drawing]/ Abelard-Schuman/London New York Toronto
1970
142pp (inc. 6pp index, glossary &c), 14 f/p b/w illus., clo., 208x136mm. KP

BUSH, Roger
1245 THE/LITTLE WHITE/SCHOOL BOOK/by/Roger Bush/[device]/Brolga Books/Adelaide
1972
151pp (inc. 4pp adv. & 2pp notes), b/w frontis. portrait of author, stiff wrappers, 127x90mm. JH
Homilies &c by the author, a Methodist minister.

The Bush Books
Produced by the Commonwealth Office Of Education, Australia. Illustrated by Katherine Morris
16pp, alternate pp. col & b/w ills, stiff pic. paper covers, 200x150mm. KP
1246 THE BUSH BOOKS—Book 1
1247 THE BUSH BOOKS—Book 2
1248 THE BUSH BOOKS—Book 3 (24pp)
1249 THE BUSH BOOKS—Book 5 (32pp)
Supplementary readers with notes for teachers; book 4 unseen

Bush Children
1250 [drawing]/BUSH CHILDREN/This book is a supplementary reader incorporating the/words used in the first five of the Bush Book series./Produced by the/Commonwealth Office of Education/Australia/ Illustrations by Mary Gilhalm
n.d. [195-?]
16pp, b/w illus. throughout, dec. wrappers, 208x165mm. CLRC

The Bush Twins
1251 THE BUSH TWINS. *See* Shaped Books

The Bushland Ballet
1252 THE/BUSHLAND/BALLET
No publisher's imprint, n.d. [? t.p. missing]
25pp, 9pp col. illus. & b/w illus. throughout, dec. bd., cover title, 295x22mm.
Illustrations signed 'J.E.' [Jean Elder]. KMM

'BUSHMAN, Jim'
See Sayce, Conrad H.

BUSONI, Raffaello
1253 Lands and Peoples/AUSTRALIA/Written and Illustrated/By/Raffaello Busoni/[col. illus.]/Cassell and Company Ltd./London, Toronto, Melbourne and Sydney
1939
28pp, numerous col. illus., pic. bd., 240x164mm. CLRC
Printed in Great Britain.
1254 [drawing]/AUSTRALIA/By Raffaello Busoni, Holiday House
No publisher's imprint, n.d. [Printed in U.S.A., copyright 1942]
25pp, 3 col. illus., bd., 235x160mm. NSL:M

Busy Little Folk
1255 BUSY/LITTLE/FOLK/[illus.]/Printed and Published by Offset Printing Coy Pty Limited/169 Phillip Street, Waterloo, Sydney
n.d.
"Wattle Series" from The House of Offset
32pp, part col. illus. throughout, pic. wrappers, 240x180mm. KMM
Cover illus. by Kay Druce. Illus. Betty van der Pot.

BUTCHER, T. K.
1256 The Great Explorations/ASIA and AUSTRALASIA/ T. K. Butcher/London/Dennis Dobson Limited
1955
171pp, 11 f/p b/w illus., clo., 190x120mm. NSL:M
Chapters include: 'Cook's Voyage in the South Pacific' (16pp); 'Inside Australia' (Sturt, Burke & Wills, 14pp).

BUTLER, Geoffrey Travers
1257 UNDER AGE/By/Geoffrey Butler/Illustrated by/ Rosamond McCulloch/To Janet/Copyright reserved
Cox, Kay Pty Ltd, Printer, Hobart, n.d. [193-?]
28pp, b/w drawings throughout, wrappers, 210x130mm. TSL
Children's verses.

Buttercup in Bushland
1258 BUTTERCUP/IN BUSHLAND
Cryter Products Trademark Copyright, n.p., n.d. [194-?]
8pp, col. illus. on every page, stiff pic. wrappers, cover title, 245x166mm. KMM

Butterflies of Australia
1259 A Vita-Brits/card series/BUTTERFLIES/OF AUSTRALIA/2/-
Nabisco Pty Limited, Melbourne, n.d.
12pp (inc. 4pp text) & spaces left for cards to be pasted in, col. pic. bd. covers, cover title, 240x182mm. KP

BUTTERWORTH, Hezekiah
1260 ZIGZAG JOURNEYS/IN/AUSTRALIA;/or,/A Visit to the Ocean World/By/Hezekiah Butterworth/Fully Illustrated/Boston:/Estes and Lauriat,/Publishers
1891
319pp & 8pp adv. (inc. 1p preface, 1p contents, 2pp illus.), b/w frontis., engravings throughout, pic. clo., pic. e/p, 210x160mm. ANL
'The Zig Zag Series.'P87 'Young Australians' solecism as figures resemble Red Indians with feathers in hair &c. In same series, *Zigzag Journeys in the Antipodes* deals only with Siam and Sumatra.

BYSTRÖM, Dan
1261 STILLA HAVETS ERÖVRARE, Kapten James Cooks underbara Ievnadssaga. Bearbetning från engelskan. Stockholm, 1933
192pp, printed bd.
Swedish biography of Cook written for children. Info. from Dahlia Books cat. no. 7, Sweden, 1976. Unseen

BYTOVETZSKI, Pavel L.
See Cormack, Maribelle

CAIRNS, G. O. & J. F.
1262 The Lands and Peoples Series/AUSTRALIA/by/ G. O. and J. F. Cairns/with four plates in colour/ twelve photographs and a map/London/Adam and Charles Black
1953
90pp (inc. appendix, index, bibliography, &c), col. frontis. & 3 f/p col. illus., double-spread b/w map, 8pp b/w photographic illus., clo., 195x120mm. KMM
1263 The Lands and Peoples Series/AUSTRALIA/by/ G. O. and J. F. Cairns/with nineteen photographs and

a map/London: Adam & Charles Black/New York: The Macmillan Company
1st ed. 1953; 2nd ed. 1955; 3rd ed. 1962
90pp (inc. 5pp appendix, 2pp bibliography & 2pp index), frontis. & 18 b/w photographic illus., double-spread b/w map, clo., 195x120mm. BBC

CAIRNS, Sylvia
1264 UNCLE WILLIE MACKENZIE'S/LEGENDS OF THE GOUNDIRS/told by Sylvia Cairns/illustrated by Fred Cobbo/The Jacaranda Press
Brisbane 1967
46pp, col. & part. col. illus. on alternate pages by Aboriginal artist Fred Cobbo, pic. clo., 210x270mm. KMM
Aboriginal legends told to the Aboriginal author by her uncle, the last surviving member of the Darwarbada tribe.

CALDER, Freda Mary Bussell
See 'Vines, Freda'

CALDER, Jean McKinlay
1265 THE STORY/OF NURSING/by Jean McKinlay Calder/M.B.E., S.R.N./Formerly Chief Nursing Officer of the/London County Council Illustrated by/Roy Spencer/Methuen's Outlines/Methuen and Co. Ltd. 36 Essex Street London W.C.2.
First pub. May 1954; rpt with minor corrections 1955; 2nd ed. 1958; 3rd ed. 1960; 4th ed. (revised) 1963
108pp (inc. 4pp index & 3pp bibliography), b/w frontis. & 3 f/p b/w illus., b/w drawings in text, clo., 210x165mm. BBC

CALDWELL, John C.
1266 John Caldwell/DESPERATE VOYAGE/Abridged New Windmill Edition/[device]/Heinemann Educational/Books Ltd. London
First publ. in the New Windmill Series 1957, rpt 1963, 1964
xivpp, 202pp (inc. 2pp glossary), b/w frontis. photograph of author, 2 f/p b/w photographs, 3 b/w sketches of the 'Pagan', dec. map e/p, 184x124mm. KMM
4pp intro. by Ian Serraillier; abridged for young readers.

1267 LET'S VISIT AUSTRALIA/John C. Caldwell/ Burke—London
1965
95pp (inc. 3pp index), extended b/w photographic frontis., b/w map & 39 b/w photographic illus., pic. clo., 205x150mm. BBC

1268 LET'S VISIT AUSTRALIA/John C. Caldwell/ Burke—London
Revised & reprinted October 1966
Details as in previous edition, but 41 b/w photographic illus. BBC
Publishers claim that new material has been introduced into this edition.

1269 LET'S VISIT/AUSTRALIA/John C. Caldwell/Burke London, new ed. 1971
96pp (inc. 2pp index), double-spread col. pic. t.p., b/w map, col. & b/w photographic illus., col. pic. clo., 202x150mm. KMM

CALÉ, R. H.
1270 CASTLE OF DREAMS/(Copyright)/By/R. H. Calé/Wholly set up and printed in Western Australia by/C. H. Pitman, Bookbinder and publisher,/973 Hay Street, Perth
n.d.
156pp, paper wrappers. PH
Borderline children's book.

CALVERT, William & Samuel
1271 THE/YOUNG AUSTRALIAN'S/ALPHABET/ [quotation]/Printed & Published at W. Calvert's Chromo-Typographic Printing Office, 89 Little Collins St. East
Melbourne, 1871
[12]pp, 6pp col. illus., calico covers, cover title (with adv. surrounding illus. title panel), 275x210mm. VSL
Adv. states available 'on calico eighteenpence' on back 'In preparation—The Australian Book of Beasts and Birds—Calvert's Australian Series of Children's Book, No. 2'.

1272 Calvert's Australian Colored Picture Books/THE/ AUSTRALIAN/A,/B, C,/Book/Large Letters./Printed and Published by/W. Calvert, 87 Little Collins St East, Melbourne
14pp, col. pic. every page, pic. wrappers, 210x131mm. NSL:M
On back cover 'Calvert's/Australian Picture Book,/ Printed at the/Melbourne/Intercolonial Exhibition/of 1875./The Young Australian's Alphabet
This is the Hut
Little Chinkey
The Aust ABC Book (Large Letters)
Price tinted 6d, on cloth 1s. Full Colour 9d. On Cloth 1s6d.'

1273 Calvert's Illustrated Series/of Australian Story Books/LITTLE/CHINKEY/CHOW-CHOW/The Boy that Ran/Away!/Printed in the Exhibition Building./87 & 89 Little Collins Street, East, Melbourne
n.d. [1871]
[12]pp (inc. 4pp blank, 4pp col. illus., 4pp text), cover title printed in black on green stiff paper, back cover blank (inside both covers blank & not inc. in pagination), wrappers, 274x218mm. KMM
Advertised Book of Australian Animals.

1274 LITTLE CHINKEY CHOW-CHOW
Second copy differs from first in having yellow border & lettering to front cover & with the words 'Printed & Published at W. Calvert's Chromo-Typographic Printing Office 89 Little Collins St East'.
The text is the same though printed in smaller type. NSL:M

1275 Calvert's Australian Picture Books/THIS IS THE HUT/THAT JACK BUILT/IN AUSTRALIA
Melbourne, n.d. [187-?]
[16]pp (inc. 6pp blank & 4pp text & 4pp col. illus., pic. wrappers, cover title, 275x215mm. NSL:M

1276 Calvert's Australian Picture Books/PICTURES/OF/ AUSTRALIAN/BIRDS/Part 1/[drawing]/W. Calvert 87 & 89 LIttle Collins Street East, Melbourne
n.d. [187-?]
[16]pp (comprising 6pp blank, 4pp col. illus., 4pp text), pic. wrappers, cover title, 275x205mm. NSL:M
Back wrappers advertise Calvert's Australian series of Six-Penny Picture Books, printed in col., and Calvert's Australian Series of Three-Penny Picture Books printed in tint.

CAMERON, Hector
See Finch, Tamara & Cameron, Hector

CAMERON, Innes
1277 THE UNCLOUDED/YEARS/Marion Thomas/ Photographs/Innes Cameron/Stories/Georgian House
Melbourne 1948
71pp, b/w photographic illus. on alternate pages, clo., 235x180mm. NSL:M

CAMERON, Toby

1278 THE MAGICAL HAT/By/Toby Cameron
Currawong Publishing Co., Sydney, n.d. [copyright 1943]
48pp, b/w illus. throughout by author, dec. wrappers, 135x215mm. NSL:M

1279 OUR/FUNNY MUMMY/Written and Illustrated by/Toby Cameron/[drawing]/The Currawong Publishing Company/32 Jamieson Street, Sydney
n.d [1943]
42pp, 2pp adv., b/w drawings throughout, bd., 200x150mm. ANL

1280 DORA DROMEDARY, DETECTIVE/Written and Illustrated by/Toby Cameron/[drawing]/The Currawong Publishing Company/32 Jamieson Street, Sydney
n.d. [1944]
59pp, 4 f/p b/w illus. & b/w drawings throughout, bd., 200x140mm. ANL
A sequel to *Our Funny Mummy.*

CAMPBELL, Mrs A.

1281 ROUGH AND SMOOTH:/or,/Ho! for an Australian Gold Field./—/By Mrs A. Campbell,/ Author of "Inner Life," etc./—Quebec:/Hunter, Rose & Co., St Ursula Street./1865
138pp (inc. 1p preface & 1p contents), unillus., clo., 195x125mm. Grant dispersed

CAMPBELL, Ellen

1282 AN/AUSTRALIAN CHILDHOOD/By/Ellen Campbell/London/Blackie & Son, Limited, 49 Old Bailey, E.C./Glasgow, Edinburgh and Dublin
n.d. [Publishers advise 1892]
96pp, 8pp adv., b/w frontis., clo., 165x105mm. NSL:M
Frontispiece signed 'L.L.B.' [Leslie Brooke].

1283 AN/AUSTRALIAN CHILDHOOD
n.d. [inscribed 1895]
As above, but address "50 Old Bailey, E.C./Glasgow and Dublin." KMM

1284 AN/AUSTRALIAN CHILDHOOD/By/Ellen Campbell/With Frontispiece/Blackie & Son Limited/ London and Glasgow
n.d. [192-?]
96pp, b/w frontis., dec. clo., 170x110mm. CLRC

1285 Another copy , n.d.. as above with a d/w depicting children dressed as in the 1920s & the author's name appears as 'Helen Campbell'. KMM

1286 TWIN PICKLES/a story of Two Australian Children/by/Ellen Campbell/Author of "An Australian Childhood"/[device]/London/Blackie & Son, Limited, 50 Old Bailey E.C./Glasgow and Dublin
n.d. [1898]
127pp, 12pp adv., b/w frontis., pic. clo., 180x115mm. Grant

1287 TWIN PICKLES/a story of Two Australian Children/by/Ellen Campbell/Author of "An Australian Childhood"/Blackie & Son Limited/London Glasgow and Bombay
n.d. [prize label 1913]
127pp, 8pp adv., col. frontis. by Paul Hardy, pic. clo., 175x115mm. KMM

CAMPBELL, Frances

1288 TWO QUEENSLANDERS/AND THEIR FRIENDS/ By Frances Campbell/Alexander Moring Limited The/ De La More Press 32 George St./Hanover Square London W. 1904
1st imp. Oct. 1904; 2nd imp. Dec. 1904
284pp, unillus., clo., 180x120mm. KMM
Not a children's book, although about children.

CAMPBELL, R. G.

See 'Morgan, W. Ingram'

CAMPBELL, Peter

1289 THE KOALA PARTY/Peter Campbell/[drawing]/ Methuen Children's Books London
1972
[24]pp, part. col. illus. throughout, col. dec. bd., 210x165mm. BBC
Stylized drawings of bears in domestic setting; nothing Australian.

1290 THE KOALAS SPRING/CLEAN/Peter/Campbell/ [drawing]/Methuen Children's Books London
1972
[24]pp, part. col. illus. throughout, col. dec. bd., 210x165mm. BBC

CAMPE, Joachim Heinrich

1291 SAMMLUNG/INTERESSANTER/UND/ DURCHGÄNGIG ZWECHMÄSSIG/abgefasster/ Reisebeschreibungen/für/die Jugend/von/J. H. Campe/1786-1790
4 vols. pp 328, 287, 270, 304, map, ¾ leather, 170x100mm. NSL:M

1292 GEOGRAFISKT/BIBLIOTEK/FOR/UNGDOM,/ Eller/Samling/Af/Interessanta Resebeskrifningar,/till /den uppväxande ungdomens nytta och nöje,/Af/ J. H. Campe./Öfversättning/Af/D. Krutmejer./Sextonde Delen./Stockholm, 1816./Tryckt nos Fr. Cederborgh & Comp.[series title]
Innhall./BARRINGTON'S RESA OCH DEPORTATION/TILL BOTANY-BAY I NYA HOLLAND.
148pp, engraved frontis. only, half calf (with marbled bd.), 155x90mm. RM
Swedish translation of Vol. 16 of J. H. Campe's *Geographic Library for Young Folk,* telling the story of George Barrington, the celebrated London pickpocket, transported to Botany Bay.
Other vols in same series, nos 3 and 4 contain Byron-Wallis-Carteret voyages. Vol. 10 contains 'A Swedish version of Campe's German compilation for children of Bligh's narrative, translated by D. Krutmejer from the French version' (Stockholm 1807), and Vols 11, 12, 13 contain Cook's First Voyage, Stockholm 1805–8, from the same translation. Unseen BP

1293 DES/CAPITÄNS JAMES COOK/ BESCHREIBUNG/SEINER/REISE UM DIE WELT./Ein nützliches Lesebuch/für/die Jugend, nach Campe's Lehrärt bearbeitet/von Fridrich Wilhelm von Schütz/ Erster Theil./Neuste Auflage/Wien und Krems/Bev. B. Ph. Bauer./1820
Vol. 1—136pp & engraved frontis. only
Vol. 2—135pp & engraved frontis. only
Vol. 3—124pp & engraved frontis. only, marbled bd., ¼ leather, 155x90mm
Written in form of a family's conversation & broken into successive evenings. NSL:M
Swedish edition
Includes Vols 3 & 4, containing the Byron-Wallis-Carteret Voyages & Vols 11–13 containing Cook's First Voyage. Unseen. BP
Danish edition

1294 CAPITAIN/JAMES COOKS/Reise Omkring Jorden./En/Laesebog for Ungdommen,/efter Campes Laeremaarde/med illuminerede koppere./oversat/af/ H. C. Lund/Dryker af Naturviden steahen, Isar Dens/ Laegevidens—tabelige dele/[vignette]/Ferste Deel/ Risvenhavn 1803

3 vols bound together, 124, 128, 120pp, col. frontis. & 5 col. engravings, bd., 165x100mm. NSL:M
French Edition
1295 Bibliothèque/Géographique et Instructive/des/Jeunes Gens,/ou/Recueil/de Voyages Intéressants,/pour/l'instruction et/l'Amusement de la Jeunesse;/par Campe./Traduit de l'allemande par J. B. J. Breton,/et orné de cartes et figures./Seconde Année/Tome Huitième/VOYAGE DE BARRINGTON/de l'Imprimerie de Guilleminet/à Paris/chez J. E. Gabriel Dufour, librairie, rue/des Mathurins, no 374/Et à Amsterdam, chez la même/AN XII 1804
203pp, engraved frontis., marbled bd., ¾ calf bound together with Vol. 7 NAUFRAGE DE WILSON (not of Australian interest). 132x80mm. KMM
Uniform with these 2 vols:
1296 Tome onzième./VOYAGE AUX TERRES AUSTRALES./A Paris/Chez J. E. Gabriel Dufour . . . [as before] 1806
216pp, engraved frontis. marbled bd., ¾ calf, 132x80mm. KMM
Chapters on Magellan, Drake, Lemaire & Schouten, Pelsart & Tasman.
Bound together with (Vol. 12) VOYAGES DE ROGERS ET ANSON (not Australian).
Uniform with these vols:
1297 VOYAGE DE COOK, SECOND VOYAGE DE COOK, ET TROISIEME VOYAGE DE COOK. 8 vols bound in four. Unseen

CANNON, Arthur Elliott
1298 AUSTRALIA/A. Elliott Cannon/with drawings by/John Dugan/[device]/Oliver and Boyd Quest Library 1962
68pp (inc. 2pp index & 7pp appendix), b/w photographic illus. throughout & b/w drawings in text, pic. bd., dec. map e/p, 190x135mm. ANL

CANNON, Lexie
See Trend Books

CANTLE, J. M.
1299 GUM-TREE/GOSSIP/Series by J. M. Cantle./With the Season's Greetings./To—/From—/Copyright Sydney NSW Bookstall Co., n.d. [1910?], Marchant & Co Ltd, Printers, Sydney
24pp (last blank) with 11 f/p half-tone plates, pic. wrappers, 224x168mm. KMM
Humorous verses with painting of a variety of Australian animals & birds on opposite page

Captain Cook's Colouring Book
1300 CAPTAIN COOK'S/COLOURING BOOK/illustrated by Hutchings/[drawing]/Paul Hamlyn/London New York Sydney Toronto/Published by Paul Hamlyn Pty. Ltd., 176 South Creek Road,/Dee Why West, New South Wales 2099/Copyright Paul Hamlyn Pty. Ltd. 1969/First published 1969/Reprinted 1970/Printed for Paul Hamlyn Pty. Ltd. by the Griffin Press, Adelaide/Registered in Australia for transmission by post as a book.
[64]pp, b/w drawings, stiff pic. wrappers, 295x215mm. BBC
B/w drawings, etc. to be coloured in, with brief captions.

Captain Cook's Third and last Voyage to the Pacific Ocean
1301 CAPTAIN COOK'S/third and last/voyage/to the/Pacific Ocean,/in the years 1776, 1777, 1778, 1779 and 1780/Faithfully abridged from the Quarto Edition,/published/by order of/His Majesty./Illustrated with copper plates./[device]/London:/Printed for John Fielding Pater Noster Row; and/John Stockdale, Piccadilly
n.d. [1785]
xii+372pp (inc. 2pp introduction & 3pp biographical note), engraved frontis. & 6 f/p engravings, calf, 170x100mm. NSL:M
1302 CAPTAIN COOK'S/Third and Last/Voyage,/to the/Pacific Ocean,/in the years 1776, 1777, 1778, 1779 and 1780./Faithfully abridged from the Quarto Edition,/Published by/Order of His Majesty./Illustrated with copper plates./Dublin:/Printed by J. Jones (III) Grafton Street./MDCCLXXXVIII 1788
xii+372pp (inc. 2pp introduction), unillus., calf, 140x80mm. NSL:M

Captain Cook's Voyage to the Pacific Ocean
1303 CAPTAIN COOK'S/VOYAGE/TO THE/PACIFIC OCEAN./for the Juvenile; or, Child's Library./London:/Printed and Sold/By John Marshall./No. 4, Aldermary Church-yard, Bow-/Lane, Cheapside
n.d. [1800]
60pp, engraved frontis. & 4 f/p engravings, bd., 900x770mm. MAC
Frontis. a view of a Maori at Tongataboo.

Captain/Cook's/Voyages
See Strang, Herbert

Captain Cook's Voyages
1304 CAPTAIN COOK'S/VOYAGES/With Four Full-Page Illustrations by/E. S. Hodgson/Cassell and Company, Ltd./London, New York, Toronto and Melbourne
n.d.
446pp, col. frontis. & 3 f/p b/w illus., dec. clo. (with col. frontis. reproduced in rectangle on front cover), 185x120mm. KMM

Captain James Cook
1305 Whitcombe's Story Books/CAPTAIN JAMES COOK/For ages 12 to 14 years/[device]/Whitcombe & Tombs Limited/Auckland, Wellington, Christchurch, Dunedin/and Invercargill/Melbourne, Sydney, London
n.d.
59pp (inc. 6pp notes, etc.), 1p adv., b/w portrait frontis., b/w photographic illus. & maps, stiff pic. wrappers (with adv. verso/recto back cover), 185x120mm. NSL:M
See McLaren 653

Captain James Cook bi-centenary celebrations
1306 CAPTAIN/JAMES COOK/bi-centenary celebrations/Queensland schools/souvenir/1970
Campbell Advertising, Brisbane 1970
32pp, part. col illus. throughout (inc. diagrams, maps, portraits, etc.), pic. wrappers, cover title, 185x245mm. KMM
Compiled by Queensland Department of Education & authorized by the Captain Cook Bi-Centenary Celebrations Committee, Brisbane.

Captain James Cook the First Voyage 1768-1771
1307 CAPTAIN JAMES COOK the first voyage 1768-1771
Publ. by The Sun-Herald Sydney in conjunction with Shoalhaven Paper Mill, The Wiggins Teape Australia Group, [1968]
Folder of facsimile documents including an account of Cook's first voyage by Commander George Finkel R.N. (Ret'd). KP
See also Captain Cook on Orbit round the World

Captain Kangaroo
1308 Magnificent Real Photo of a Famous Knock-out! Free!/The/Rocket/Full of Thrills Yarns/For You and Your Pal/Vol 1 No 4 Every Wednesday Week Ending March 10th 1923/CAPTAIN KANGAROO!/A Stirring Yarn/of/Australian Bush Life/The Kidnapped Policeman!/A Striking Incident from this Great Story/ Introducing the Most Amazing Character/Ever Created!/The Big Paper with the Big Thrills!
Pp85–112, pic. wrappers, 330x230mm. CLRC

Captain Lightning
See Aldine Adventure Library

CAREY, Patricia
1309 BOBBY BLUEGUM PLAYS/FATHER CHRISTMAS/Written and Illustrated by/Patricia Carey/[drawing]/Methuen & Co. Ltd, London/36 Essex Street, Strand, W.C.2.
1947
45pp, t.p. in 2 col., col. illus. & text on 41pp, pic. bd., 208x165mm. KMM
The story of a koala who helps Father Christmas deliver his presents. Appears to be non-Australian apart from the fact that the hero is a koala.

CARISBROOKE, Donald
1310 AUSTRALIAN/ABORIGINES/by/Donald Carisbrooke/[drawing]/Illustrated by/Molly G. Johnson/Readabout Books
Readabout Publishers Pty Ltd, Crow's Nest, N.S.W., 1964
24pp, col. & part. col. illus. throughout, stiff pic. wrappers, 215x180mm. BBC

CARISBROOKE, Donald & Betty
1311 THE/ILLUSTRATED/ENCYCLOPAEDIA/OF/ AUSTRALIA [3 vols.]/by/Donald and Betty Carisbrooke/Illustrated by Peter Chapman/Collins' Book Depot/Melbourne
1964
[Copyright Southern Cross International Pty Ltd]
Vol 1: 168pp, 2pp foreword by A. H. Chisholm, 2pp preface, col. illus. & maps throughout, pic. clo., 245x158mm. All CLRC
Vol. 2: 165pp, as above.
Vol. 3: 168pp, as above.
• Rpt 1967, as above. KP

1312 THE YOUNG PEOPLE'S ENCYCLOPAEDIA/ Donald and Betty Carisbrooke, B.A./Southern Cross International
Sydney, 1967
5 vols (on front cover 'Deluxe Children's Library Edition'), each vol. 95pp, t.p. on 2pp, col. illus. throughout, col. pic. boards, 246x162mm. KMM
1313 THE YOUNG PEOPLE'S ENCYCLOPAEDIA/ Donald and Betty Carisbrooke, B.A./Paul Hamlyn/ London New York Sydney Toronto
Dee Why West, NSW, 1969
452pp (inc. 2pp preface by authors & acknowledgements), col. illus. on every page, col. pic. bd., 236x158mm. KMM
Title on 2pp. Cover reads: 'The Young People's Encyclopaedia of Australia'. Illustrator not named & illus. unsigned.

CARNE, T. C.
1314 CHILDREN OF INDIA/The Story of Premi/by Rev. T. C. Carne, B.A./Azamgarh, India/The Methodist Missionary Society of Australasia/139 Castlereagh Street/Sydney/1925
63pp, b/w photographs & dec. initial letters, pic. wrappers, 220x137mm. CLRC
The 'Children' Series. Initial letter drawings Mernie Albiston.

1315 THE LILY AND/THE LOTUS/By/Rev T. C. Carne, B.A.,/Author of "Premi, an Indian Child,"/"The Christ of the Indian Mind"/Cover and Chapter Decorations by/Ruther Carne/[device]/The Book Depot,/ Melbourne./1944
32pp, b/w chapter headings, stiff dec. wrappers, 182x122mm. ANL
On cover 'The Bible/seen through/Indian Eyes' 'Stories/for/Children.'

CARNEGIE, Dorothy
1316 KAKA THE COCKATOO/by Dorothy Carnegie/ Illustrated by Genevieve Melrose/Lansdowne Press Melbourne 1967
80pp, b/w drawings in text, clo., 225x160mm. KMM

CAROZZI, Barry
1317 THE/GREATEST/JUGGLER/IN/THE/WORLD/ Barry Carozzi/Illustrated/by/Neil Curtis/Rae Dale/ and Anne Sulzer/Cassell Australia
Melbourne 1972
100pp, 8 f/p b/w illus., pic. wrappers, 180x110mm. Patchwork Paperbacks. NSL:M
Traditional fairy tales retold.

CARRINGTON, Edith
COLE'S ANIMAL PICTURE BOOK. *See* Cole, E. W.

CARRISON, Daniel J.
1318 Immortals of History/CAPTAIN/JAMES COOK:/ Genius Afloat/by/Daniel J. Carrison,/Captain U.S.N. (Ret.)/Franklin Watts, Inc./575 Lexington Avenue/ New York, N.Y. 10022
1967
197pp (inc. 14pp references, chronology & index) & 1p preface, 3 f/p maps, pic. clo., 210x136mm. SSL

CARROLL, Herbert
1319 The Wireless 'Bed-time Stories' song/ BUNKY-DOO/dedicated to/'Uncle George'/sepia/ white illus. with inset photo. [sgd 'Uncle George']/ J. Albert & Son/Boomerang House, 137-139 King St Sydney/...&c. 2/-
1927
4pp (inc. pic. covers) music & words, 315x240mm. KMM

CARROLL, Ruth & Latrobe
1320 LUCK/OF THE/ROLL AND GO/by/Ruth and Latrobe Carroll/Illustrations by Ruth Carroll/ [drawing]/A. & C. Black Ltd./4, 5 & 6 Soho Square, London, W.1
1936
132pp, b/w frontis., 6 f/p b/w illus. & drawings in text, clo., dec. e/p, 222x160mm. KMM
Adventures of a cat on an expedition from US to Antarctica via NZ.

CARRUTHERS, Clancy
1321 MY LEARN TO TAKE PHOTOS BOOK/by Clancy Carruthers/illustrated by Allan Stomann/technical adviser: Ted Ashby/[contents]/Paul Hamlyn/London Sydney New York Toronto
61pp, col. illus. throughout, b/w photographic illus., col. dec. e/p, pic. bd., 315x230mm. CLRC

CARSTAIRS, John Paddy
1322 LOLLIPOP/WOOD/A Story for Children/by/John Paddy Carstairs/illustrated by/Hilda Boswell/ Hutchinson's Books for young people/10 Great Queen Street/London W.C.2
Second impression 1947

128pp, col. frontis. & 3 f/p col. illus., b/w drawings in text, clo., 240x180mm. Grant
The adventures of three koalas in the land of 'Can-You-Imagine'.

CARSTAIRS, Sheila
See Castley, Dora, &c.

CARTER, Alex S. (ed.)
1323 THE/RHYTHM/OF OUR/FOOTSTEPS/A collection of Modern verse/by/Australian children/Collected and Edited by/Alex S. Carter/Lowden Publishing Co./Kilmore, Victoria
1969
88pp (inc. 2pp introduction, 2pp editor's note, etc.), unillus., stiff wrappers, 215x140mm. BBC
Poems written by the students of the Reservoir West State School.

CARTER, Dorothy
1324 JAN FLIES/DOWN UNDER/by/Dorothy Carter/[publisher's device]/Lutterworth Press/London and Redhill
1948
175pp, b/w frontis., clo., 185x120mm. NSL:M

1325 THE CRUISE OF THE/GOLDEN DAWN/By/Dorothy Carter/[device]/Latimer House Limited/33 Ludgate Hill, London E.C.4
1949
199pp, b/w frontis., clo., 190x125mm. KMM
Girls' adventure story set in Sydney & on an island somewhere near Lord Howe Island.

1326 MISTRESS/OF THE AIR/by/Dorothy Carter/The Children's Press/London and Glasgow
1958
156pp, unillus., pic. lam. bd., 178x110.8mm. LRA
The Challenge Series.

CARTER, M. E.
1327 CAPTAIN SCOTT/Explorer and Scientist/by/M. E. Carter, M.B.E., B.A./Illustrated by/Louis Ward/Longmans, Green and Co/London New York Toronto
First publ. 1950; new imp. 1953
118pp, b/w frontis. & b/w illus. throughout, wrappers, 185x125mm. VMOU
Lives of Achievement.

CARTER, Margaret Agnes
1328 AUSTRALIAN FAIRY STORIES/by Margaret A. Carter/Drawings by I. G. Hill/Domus Publishing Co./100 Queen Street/Melbourne
n.d. [1944]
78pp, dec. t.p., b/w drawings throughout, bd. (clo. spine), 240x180mm. KMM
Fairy stories & verse.

1329 THE ADVENTURES/OF/BILLY BEE/By/Margaret A. Carter/(Author of Australian Fairy Stories)/Domus Publishing Company/100 Queen Street, Melbourne
n.d. [1945]
79pp, 4 f/p col. illus.. & drawings in text, illus. by I. G. Hill, bd., 240x180mm. ANL
1330 Rpt Nov 1946 as follows:
THE ADVENTURES/OF/BILLY BEE/By/Margaret A. Carter/Background Books Limited/143 Cannon Street, London, E.C.4
Details as above. RC

CARTER, Mary
1331 FRIENDS OF EMPIRE/By/Mary Carter, F.R.G.S./Illustrated by/George Dixon/[publisher's device]/George G. Harrap & Co. Ltd/London Sydney Toronto Bombay
1947
192pp, b/w frontis. & 9 b/w illus., clo., 180x120mm. KMM
Contents include one Australian story entitled 'A Queensland Holiday' (15pp).

CARTER, Theo
1332 IN A STRANGE LAND/Pioneers of Australia/Theo Carter/London. Dennis Dobson
1964
223pp (inc. 8pp notes), b/w portrait frontis., 8pp b/w photographic plates, b/w drawings in text, clo., dec. e/p, 195x125mm. CLRC

CASH, C. G.
1333 THE LIFE AND VOYAGES/OF/CAPTAIN JAMES COOK/Selections/With Introductions and Notes/by/C. G. Cash, F.R.S.G.S./Geography Master at the Edinburgh Academy/London/Blackie & Son, Limited, 50 Old Bailey, E.C./Glasgow and Dublin
n.d.
186pp, 12pp adv., b/w frontis., dec. clo., 180x120mm. Grant
1334 Another copy as above, but:
192pp, 8pp adv., 2pp introduction, b/w frontis., clo., 180x120mm. HBM
On front cover: 'Blackie's School and Home Library'.
1335 Another copy as above, but
Copy inscribed 1901
192pp & 4pp adv., b/w frontis. (Paul Hardy), dec. clo., 180x125mm. KP
Other slightly variant imprints. KP
1336 THE LIFE AND VOYAGES/OF/CAPTAIN JAMES COOK/Selections/With Introductions and Notes/By/C. G. Cash, F.R.S.G.S./Geography Master at the Edinburgh Academy/London/Blackie and Son Limited/London Glasgow Bombay
n.d.
192pp, 16pp adv., col. frontis. & 3 col. illus. by Jas. F. Sloane, dec. clo., 180x120mm. Blackie's Crown Library. KP
1337 Rpt 1905 as above, but
192pp & 16pp adv., sepia & white frontis. & 3 plates, t.p. printed in red & black, clo., 190x134mm. KP

CASLEY-SMITH, J. R. (ed.)
1338 BIRDS AND/ANIMALS OF/AUSTRALIA/and its neighbours/Text by Roby/Illustrations by Robert Dallet/Edited by J. R. Casley-Smith D.Sc., D. Phil., M.B., B.S., F.R.M.S., F.R.S.M./Rigby/Opal/Books Adelaide 1972
126pp (inc. 1p preface by the Duke of Edinburgh), col. frontis. & col. illus. throughout, pic. bd., 350x250mm. BBC

CASSON, Marjory Rose
See Walker, Marjorie

The Castle Annual for Boys
1339 THE CASTLE/ANNUAL/FOR BOYS
Dunvegan Publication, Box 4614, GPO Sydney
127pp, b/w illus. & col. pic. bd., clo. spine, 254x195mm. JH
Cover illus. signed John Andrews. Written by various contributors.

CASTLE, Jean
1340 HERE'S MY/STORY/BOOK
Printed by R. M. Osborne Ltd, 95 Currie Street, Adelaide, n.d. [193-?]
20pp, b/w drawings throughout, stiff pic. wrappers (with adv. on both sides of back cover), cover title, 240x185mm. KMM
Stories by Jean Castle; illus. by Vanessa Lamb
Published in aid of the Adelaide Children's Hospital.

CASTLEY, Dora, FOWLER, Kathleen, & CARSTAIRS, Sheila

1341 THE FLYING/KANGAROO/[coloured illustration]/By Dora Castley, Kathleen Fowler/and Sheila Carstairs/Illustrated by Edward W. Robertson/ Thomas Nelson and Sons Ltd./London Edinburgh Paris Melbourne Johannesburg/Toronto and New York 1961
16pp, col. illus. throughout, dec. bd., dec. e/p, 185x140mm. BBC
Variant eds differing slightly in imprint from above. Several have 'The McKee Platform Readers D1' on front cover or 'Enchantment Books'. The imprint is also simply 'Nelson' or Nelson followed by a serial number. Most other copies have covers of a lighter bd. with no e/p. KP

CATHERALL, Arthur

1342 VANISHED/WHALER/by/Arthur Catherall/ Illustrated by S. Drigin/Thomas Nelson and Sons Ltd./ London Edinburgh Paris Melbourne/Toronto and New York
First pub. 1939; rpt 1953 (twice)
188pp, b/w frontis. & 3 f/p b/w illus.., clo., 185x125mm. KMM
Story of whaling in the Antarctic.
• Rpt 1955, as above. KP

The Cavalcade of Tea

1343 THE/CAVALCADE/OF TEA
Tea Market Expansion Board, n.p., n.d.
23pp, b/w photographic illus., wrappers, 180x120mm. KP
References in text give the impression that book was produced or written in Australia.

CAVANNA, Betty

1344 The Around the World Today Book/DOUG/OF AUSTRALIA/By/Betty Cavanna/Photographs by George Russell Harrison/Chatto and Windus, London 1965
69pp, b/w frontis. map & b/w photographic illus. throughout, clo., dec. e/p, 230x155mm. KMM

CAVANOUGH, Elizabeth

1345 SYDNEY/HOLIDAY/Elizabeth Cavanough/ photography/Jutta Malnic/Lansdowne Press Melbourne 1967
56pp, col. photographic illus. & b/w photographic illus. on alternate pages, col. pic. bd., dec. map e/p, 280x210mm. KMM

'C., W. A.' [W. A. Cawthorne]

1346 [drawing] WHO KILLED/COCKATOO?/BY/ W.A.C./Adelaide, South Australia/J. H. Lewis, Printer, Hindley Street
n.d. [187-?]
20pp, engravings throughout, wrappers, 200x130mm. CLRC
Verse based on 'Who killed Cock Robin?' with engravings of Australian animals & birds.

CAYLEY, Neville W. (ed.)

1347 FEATHERED FRIENDS/A Gould League Annual/ By/M. S. R. Sharland K. A. Hindwood/Norman Chaffers David Leithhead/Alex H. Chisholm F.R.Z.S. P. A. Gilbert/Neville W. Cayley, F.R.Z.S./Edited by/ Neville W. Cayley, F.R.Z.S./Australia/Angus & Robertson Limited/89 Castlereagh Street, Sydney/1935
55pp (inc. 1p foreword), col. frontis. & 5 col. plates & 12 f/p b/w photographs, pic. wrappers, 235x173mm. ANL

CAZNEAUX, [Harold]

1348 THE AUSTRALIAN/NATIVE BEAR BOOK/ [woodcut illus.]/Wholly Set Up and printed in Australia by/Arthur McQuitty, McQuitty House, Regent/Street Sydney, and published by Sydney/Ure Smith, at 24 Bond Street, Sydney, for/the proprietors. Art in Australia Limited./Registered at the GPO, Sydney, for/transmission through the post as a book/ 1930/Photographs by Cazneaux
23pp, sepia photographs throughout, pic. wrappers, 250x190mm. KP
Photograph of Mr Noel Burnet, curator of West Pennant Hills reserve. Woodcut illus. Margaret Preston on front cover, printed in brown on light rust col. paper. Shows koalas in reserve at West Pennant HIlls. Includes 4pp story rpt from *Young Australia* 20/12/29—'Jackie—A True Story'.

1349 Rpt as above, but
1931/Second Edition/Photographs by Cazneaux
Pic. wrappers Second edition/[photograph of a koala replaces the M. Preston woodcut]. KP

1350 Rpt 1932, third Edition as above with photograph of koalas. KP

Centenary Painting Book

1351 CENTENARY PAINTING BOOK/Issued by/The State Savings Bank of Victoria/[picture of a kookaburra on a fence]
Melbourne, n.d. [1934]
[12]pp (inc. covers), 4 f/p b/w illus. of historic interest to be painted, strip of paints pasted on to book with page of instructions for children, cover title, pic. wrappers, 216x140mm. ANL

CHADS, Ellen Augusta ['E.A.C.']

1352 TRACKED BY BUSHRANGERS/and/Other Stories,/Together with/WORK FOR THE MASTER,/a series of Papers for Women/By/Mrs Chads,/ (E.A.C.)/Author of "The Snowdrops' Message" "Tried as Pure/Gold." etc./[quotation]/George Robertson & Company,/Melbourne and Sydney./1891/(All rights reserved)
95pp (inc. 1p preface), 1p adv., unillus., bd., 185x120mm. ANL
Contents include 'Floral Legends' & some other sketches for young people.
Also by the same author: *Tried as Pure Gold* Melbourne 1882, & *The Snowdrops' Message* Melbourne 1888, neither of which is a children's book.

CHADWICK, Doris

1353 JOHN OF THE/SIRIUS/Doris Chadwick/ Illustrated by Margaret Senior/Thomas Nelson and Sons Ltd./London Edinburgh Paris Melbourne/ Toronto and New York
1955
244pp, col. frontis. & 4 f/p b/w illus., b/w drawings in text, map e/p, clo., 190x130mm. KMM

1354 JOHN OF THE SIRIUS/Doris Chadwick/Illustrated by Margaret Senior/Thomas Nelson and Sons Ltd./ London Edinburgh Paris Melbourne Johannesburg/ Toronto and New York
First published in this edition 1960
244pp, 4 f/p b/w illus. & drawings in text, pic.wrappers, 185x115mm. KMM

1355 JOHN/OF SYDNEY COVE/Doris Chadwick/ Illustrated by Adye Adams/Thomas Nelson and Sons Ltd./London Edinburgh Paris Melbourne/Toronto and New York
1957
264pp, col. frontis., b/w drawings throughout, map e/p, clo., 190x130mm. KMM

1356 JOHN AND NANBAREE/Doris Chadwick/ Illustrated by Margaret Senior/Thomas Nelson and Sons Ltd./London Edinburgh Paris Melbourne Johannesburg/Toronto and New York
1962
243pp, b/w frontis. & 27 b/w drawings, map e/p, clo., 200x130mm. KMM

CHAFFEE, Allen
1357 PENN,/THE PENGUIN/By Allen Chaffee/(author of "Wandy"/[col. drawing]/Illustrated by Henry Suskind/London/John Murray, Albemarle Street, W.
1934
103pp & 6pp adv., part-col. frontis., 10 f/p part col. illus. & other part. col. illus. throughout, pic. bd., pic. map e/p, 190x128mm. RC

CHAFFEY, M. Ella
1358 THE YOUNGSTERS OF/MURRAY HOME/By M. Ella Chaffey/With illustrations by A. J. Johnson/ [drawing]/[quotation]/Ward, Lock & Bowden, Limited/ London, New York and Melbourne/1896/(All rights reserved)
326pp, 10pp adv., b/w frontis. & 3 f/p b/w illus., b/w drawings in text, pic. clo., 180x120mm. KMM
1359 Rpt as above, but imprint 'Warwick House, Salisbury Square, E.C./ New York and Melbourne.' n.d. and different pic. design on front cover. KMM

CHALLANDS, Mary Ethel & MYLNE, Kathleen
1360 THE WAY OF THE/GOLDEN DAWN/Some Simple Thoughts and Stories/for Mothers and their Children/[quotation]/By/Mary Ethel Challands/and/ Kathleen Mylne/1929/Cover by R. G. White
Smith & Paterson Ltd, Brisbane
100pp, 5pp introduction, dec. bd., 195x150mm. ANL
Religious stories & verses for children.
1361 THE WAY OF THE/GOLDEN DAWN/Some Simple Thoughts and Stories/for Mothers and their children/from/Kathleen A. Mylne/and/Mary Ethel Challands/[quotation]/W. R. Smith & Paterson Ltd./ Brisbane, Queensland/1949
119pp (inc. 1p foreword to new edition), col. frontis., clo., 180x120mm. KMM

CHAMPAGNAC, Jean Baptiste Joseph de ['C. H. de Mirval']
1362 LE/COOK DE L'ENFANCE/ET/DE LA JEUNESSE/ou/Choix des Particularités les Plus interéssantes des détails/Les plus instructifs et la plus curieux/contenus dans les Relations des trois Voyages/ de ce célèbre navigateur autour du Monde/précédé d'une notice sur sa vie;/par J. B. J. Champagnac/avec quatre jolies gravures./[device]/Paris,/Fruger et Brunet, Libraires,/Rue Mazarine, n° 30./1836
319pp, engraved frontis. & 3 engravings, wrappers, 186x110mm. ANL

1363 LE PETIT/MATELOT/ou/Voyage en Océanie./ Relation attachante et animée/des moeurs, usages, coutumes, etc./des/différents peuples de cette cinquième partie du monde/etc./par
C.-H. de Mirval./avec gravures/Paris 1838/Lehuby/ Rue de Seine no. 48
326pp (inc. 3pp index), 2pp adv., engraved frontis. & 2 engravings in text, dec. t.p., bd. (with vellum spine), 170x100mm. NSL:M
Sections on Bligh, the *Bounty*, La Perouse, Cook, Tahiti & Australia.
1364 LE/PETIT/MATELOT,/ou/Voyage en Océanie,/ Relation attachante et animée/des moeurs...peuples/de cette[4 lines description] par/C.-H. de Mirval/avec gravures/Paris/P.-C. Lehuby, Libraire-Editeur, 53
1842
286pp (inc. 4pp index), engraved frontis. & 2 engravings in text, dec. clo., 170x105mm. NSL:M

1365 LE/VOYAGEUR/DE LA JEUNESSE/dans les cinq parties du Monde/contenant/La description Géographique et Pittoresque des divers pays./[5 lines description]/par/Mm. Champagnac et Olivier/Illustré de 22 gravures par M. M. Rouarque frères/[vignette]/ Paris/Belin-Leprieur et Morizot, Editeurs/3 Rue Pavée Saint-André-des-Arts
1840
644pp (inc. 2pp index), b/w engraved frontis., 16 col. & 5 b/w engravings, dec. clo., 260x170mm. NSL:M
Sections on Australia (pp601-10) & New Guinea (pp610-13).
1366 LE/VOYAGEUR/DE LA JEUNESSE/dans les cinq parties du Monde/contenant/La description Géographique et Pittoresque des divers Pays/ L'esquisse des moeurs de chaque peuple [&c 5 lines] par/Mm. Champagnac et Olivier/Illustré de 22 gravures par MM. Rouarque frères./[vignette ship in full sail]/Paris/Morizot, Libraire. Éditeurs/3, Rue Pavée-Saint-André-des-Arts.
n.d.
viiipp, 645pp (inc. 3pp contents), engraved frontis., 16 col. plates & 5 b/w, calf, g.e., 264x174mm. ANL
Pp600-1 relate to Australia & the South Pacific.

1367 VOYAGE/AUTOUR DU MONDE/contenant/La Description Géographique et Pittoresque des divers Pays/[5 lines description]/par/M. M. Champagnac et Olivier/illustrés de 22 gravures par M. M. Rouarque frères/[vignette]/Paris/Morizot Libraire-Éditeur/3, Rue Pavée Saint-André-des-Arts
n.d.
645pp (inc. 3pp index), 3pp preface to new edition, engraved b/w frontis., 16 col. & 5 b/w engravings, 1/2 leather, 260x170mm. NSL:M

Champion Library
Format example:
1368 CYCLONE ZIP/The Aussie Speedster/By Edwin/ Dale/[part.col.illus]/4d./No.169 Champion Library Amalgamated Press London 1936
64pp, b/w title heading on p.1 only, pic. wrappers, cover title, advs inside front wrapper & both sides back wrapper,180x138mm. KMM
1369 FROM BUSH TO SPEEDWAY, no. 77. 1932, by E. Dale, unseen
1370 LONE-HAND LAWRENCE, no.145;1935 by E. Dale (The Aussie Speedster), RM
1371 THE FLYING FREELANCE, no.159 (story about Gallipoli) by Herbert Macrae, 1935, VMOU
1372 KING FLAME, no. 194, 1937 (A horseracing story) by E. Dale, unseen

CHANDLER, L. G.
1373 Australian Nature Story Readers/JACKY/THE BUTCHER BIRD/By/L. G. Chandler/For Children aged 9 to 10 years/[device]/Melbourne/Auckland, Christchurch, Dunedin, Wellington N.Z./and London/ Whitcombe & Tombs Limited.
n.d.
36pp, b/w frontis. & 5 b/w photographic illus. in text, pic.wrappers [with adv.], 180x120mm. KMM
1374 Whitcombe's Story Books/JACKY/THE BUTCHER BIRD/By/L. G. Chandler/For Children aged 9 to 10 years/Whitcombe & Tombs Pty.Ltd./Melbourne and Sydney/Associated Houses:/Christchurch, Auckland, Wellington, Dunedin./Invercargill and London
n.d.
36pp, b/w frontis. & 5 b/w illus., wrappers, 185x120mm. KMM

Also author of *Bush Charms;* not a children's book.
See McLaren 310

CHAPMAN, Ernest
See 'Hatfield, William'

CHAPMAN, Frances
1375 THE WITTY/WIZARD OF/WARRANDYTE/A Magical Hour in Fairyland/By/Frances Chapman/ Illustrated by/Armstrong/Published by Boobook Productions, Melbourne./Text and Illustrations copyright in Australia and British Dominions/Printed in Australia by Morris and Walker Pty. Ltd., Melbourne/Registered at G.P.O. Melbourne, for transmission through the post as a book
n.d. [1944]
80pp, dec. t.p., 8 col. illus. & b/w drawings throughout, dec. bd., dec. e/p, 290x215mm. ANL

CHAPMAN, Jean
1376 AMELIA MUDDLE/Stories by/Jean Chapman/ [drawing]/Illustrated by Adye Adams/Angus & Robertson/Sydney—London
1963
64pp, part. col. drawings throughout, clo., 220x140mm. CLRC
Contains 7 stories.

1377 THE WISH CAT/by Jean Chapman/Drawings by Noela Young/Photographs by Dean Hay/Angus and Robertson
Sydney 1966
66pp, dec. t.p., 6 f/p & other b/w photographic illus., drawings in text, clo., 245x180mm. CLRC
German edition
1378 DIE WUNSCH-KATZE/Jean Chapman/Illustrated by Bettina Hullsman/translated by Helga von Wimmer
Obelisk Verlag, Hamburg 1969
116pp, 12 f/p b/w drawings, clo., 195x135mm. unseen IFA
Awarded first prize in Austrian Children's Book Contest 1969/70.
Danish edition
1379 ØNSKEKATTEN/Jean Chapman/photographs by Dean Hay
Borgen forlag, Copenhagen 1970
78pp, clo., 220x150mm. Unseen: IFA

1380 [drawing]/COWBOY/by Jean Chapman/drawings by John Watts/Angus and Robertson
Sydney 1967
[31]pp, part. col. illus. throughout, pic. clo., 175x125mm. KMM

1381 SANDY/THE CANE TRAIN/story by/Jean Chapman/drawings by/Walter Cunningham/Angus & Robertson
Sydney 1967
[30]pp, col. dec. t.p., col. illus. throughout, pic. clo., 180x235mm. KMM
1382 SANDY/THE CANE TRAIN/story by/Jean Chapman/[drawing]/drawings by/Walter Cunningham/Angus & Robertson
First publ. 1966, rpt 1971, printed in Hong Kong
30pp, col. dec. t.p., col. illus. throughout, col. pic. bd., 180x245mm. KP
This rpt states that book first publ. 1966 by Angus and Robertson, 221 George Street, Sydney. Yet in 1966 & 1967 Angus & Robertson's address on their imprint was still 89 Castlereagh Street. The first ed. was bound in green clo. with lettering & picture of cane train blocked in white & with a col. d/w & was publ. in 1967.

1383 THE/SOMEDAY/DOG/Jean Chapman/ Photographs by Dean Hay/Angus and Robertson
Sydney 1968
67pp, b/w photographic frontis. & b/w illus. throughout, pic. clo., col. e/p, 245x180mm. CLRC

1384 DO YOU REMEMBER/WHAT HAPPENED/by Jean Chapman/Illustrated by Edward Ardizzone/ [drawing]/Angus and Robertson
Sydney 1969
[38]pp, part. col. illus. throughout, clo., 215x135mm. KMM

SOME AUSTRALIAN HOUSES; JAMES RUSE. *See* Australia Past and Present

1385 [drawing]/WOMBAT/by Jean Chapman/drawings by John Watts/Angus and Robertson
Sydney 1969
[32]pp, part. col. t.p., part. col. illus. throughout, pic. clo., 175x125mm. KMM

1386 DER KLEINE LÖWE/Jean Chapman/Illustrated by Von Sieflinde/translated by Lotte von Polak
Obelisk Verlag, Wien-Innsbruck 1972
95pp, b/w illus. throughout, pic. plasticized bd., 180x110mm. IFA
Contains 5 stories all from Kindergarten of the Air anthologies published by Angus and Robertson 1961–70.

SUN WIND AND CORAL: AUSTRALIA'S GREAT BARRIER REEF. *See* Australia Past & Present Series

CHAPMAN, Stella & ANCELON, Douglas
See Pedley, Ethel, DOT AND THE KANGAROO, adapted for stage presentation

CHARDONNET, Janine
1387 Janine Chardonnet/Illustrations de Michèle Le Bas/ ZOUZOU/PETIT PINGOUIN/[col. illus.]/Éditions G.P.—Département des Presses de la Cité/©1970 Éditions G.P.—Département des presses de la Cité, Paris
1970
36pp, col. illus. throughout, col. pic. bd., dec. e/p, 263x193mm. KP

CHARLES, Harold
1388 AUSTRALIAN NURSERY RHYMES/and/The Playlet "FRIENDS OF THE BUSH"/by/Harold Charles/Illustrated by Betty and Esther Paterson/ Foreword by Kate Baker, O.B.E./1st. Edition 1945/Copyright—All rights reserved
J. Roy Stevens, Melbourne
46pp (inc. 2pp foreword & 1p author's note), b/w drawings in text, dec. wrappers, 250x185mm. ANL

1389 NEW/NURSERY/RHYMES/By/Harold Charles
[16]pp, 7 f/p illus. & other drawings printed in sepia or green, by H. B. M. Armstrong, col. pic. bd., cover title, 370x250mm. KP

CHARLTON, L. E. O.
1390 DEEDS THAT HELD/THE EMPIRE/BY AIR/Air Commodore L. E. O. Charlton,/C.B., C.M.G., D.S.O./John Murray/Albemarle Street/London
1940
280pp (inc. index), b/w photographic illus., 186x120mm. VMOU
Includes Ross and Keith Smith, Kingsford Smith & P. G. Taylor &c.

CHARLTON, Mrs Leonard
See Curlewis, Jean

CHARLWOOD, D. E.

1391 ALL/THE/GREEN/YEAR/[drawing]/D. E. Charlwood/[device]/Angus and/Robertson Sydney, 1965
183pp, unillus., clo., 215x140mm. KMM
Book about author's adolescence, but read widely by older children.

1392 ALL/THE/GREEN/YEAR/D. E. Charlwood/ Angus and Robertson
First publ. in Pacific Books, 1967
183pp, unillus., wrappers, 184x110mm. LRA

1393 ALL/THE/GREEN/YEAR/D. E. Charlwood/ [device] Pacific Books
First publ. in Pacific Books in 1967, rpt 1968 (twice), 1969 (twice), 1970 (twice)
xpp (inc. author's notes), 183pp, unillus., wrappers, 180x105mm. KMM

CHARPENTIER, Henri

1394 Henri Charpentier/DIE LETZTE FAHRT/DES WELTUMSEGLERS/Hoch-Verlag. Düsseldorf
1972
159pp (inc. 2pp foreword), 8 f/p b/w illus. & 1 map, clo., 186x130mm. RM
The last voyage of the circumnavigator; illus. are photographic reproductions of the original illus. of Cook's Voyages.

CHASELING, W. S.

1395 CHILDREN/OF/ARNHEM LAND/(North Australia)/By/Rev. W. S. Chaseling/The Department of Overseas Missions/of/The Methodist Church of Australasia/139 Castlereagh Street/Sydney/1939
64pp, b/w photographs throughout, map, wrappers, 220x140mm. ANL

CHASELING, Wilbur

1396 Light of the Pacific Series No 2/A BOY FROM/ GEELONG/The Adventures of/William Bromilow/By/ Wilbur Chaseling/Drawings by/Beverley Dunphy/ Published by/The Committee for Promotion and Literature/Head Office:/Methodist Overseas Missions/ 13a Castlereagh Street/Sydney
1960
35pp, b/w drawings throughout, pic. wrappers, 172x115mm. NSL:M
Story of a Geelong boy who became a missionary in Papua in the late 19th & early 20th centuries.

CHAUNCY, Nancen Beryl [née Masterman]

1397 THEY FOUND/A CAVE/Nan Chauncy/[drawing]/ Illustrated by/Margaret Horder/Geoffrey Cumberlege/ Oxford University Press/1948
195pp, b/w frontis. & b/w drawings throughout, clo., 180x120mm. KMM

1398 THEY FOUND/A CAVE/Nan Chauncy/[drawing]/ Illustrated by/Margaret Horder/London/Oxford University Press
'First edition 1949, First issued in this series 1958' [on verso of t.p.]
195pp, b/w frontis. & b/w drawings throughout, clo., d/w by William Stobbs, 195x130mm. Oxford Children's Library Edition. KMM
• Rpt as above, 1963. BBC

1399 THEY FOUND/A CAVE/Nan Chauncy/Illustrated by Margaret Horder/[drawing]/Franklin Watts, Inc. 575 Lexington Ave./New York 22 New York/[publisher's colophon]
1961 [First American edition]
180pp, 2pp glossary, b/w drawings throughout, clo., 205x135mm. KMM
A note from the author states that permission had been given for this book & all other of her children's books to be published in Braille. A film of the book was made in Eastman colour by Columbia Moving Pictures, 1962.
Portuguese edition

1400 AGRUTA/Nan Chauncy/Illustrated by Margaret Horder/1965/Companhia Editora do Minho/Barcelos
214pp, b/w drawings throughout, hard cover, 175x120mm. Unseen: IFA
German edition

1401 HÖHLENMENSCHEN IM CAPRA-TAL/Nan Chauncy/Illustrated by von Ulrike Ulrich/ 1968/Englebert-Verlag/Balve/Westf.
154pp, b/w drawings throughout, hard cloth cover, 200x135mm. Unseen: IFA

1402 Nan Chauncy/WORLD'S END WAS HOME/ Illustrated by/Shirley Hughes/[vignette]/Geoffrey Cumberlege/Oxford University Press/1952
202pp, b/w drawings throughout, clo., 180x120mm. KMM

1403 Nan Chauncy/WORLD'S END/WAS HOME/ Illustrated by/Shirley Hughes/[vignette]/London/ Oxford University Press
1958
202pp, b/w drawings throughout, clo., d/w by William Stobbs, 195x130mm. Oxford Children's Library Edition. BBC
• Rpt as above, 1964. BBC

1404 WORLD'S END/WAS HOME/Nan Chauncy/ Illustrated by Shirley Hughes/[vignette]/Franklin Watts, Inc. 575 Lexington Ave./New York 22 New York/[publisher's colophon]
1961 [First American edition]
181pp, 2pp glossary, b/w drawings throughout, clo., 205x135mm. KMM
Swedish edition

1405 NYBYGGAR-FLICKA (Av Nan Chauncy) Rabén & Sjögren/Stockholm
1955
165pp, unillus., hard cover [using original jacket illustration], 175x125mm. Unseen: IFA
Dutch edition

1406 Nan Chauncy/EEN TOEKOMST VOOR ELLIE/ Illustrated by Shirley Hughes/1964/Prisma-Boeken/ Utrecht/Antwerpen
187pp, stiff paper cover, 180x105mm. Unseen: IFA

1407 A FORTUNE FOR THE/BRAVE/Nan Chauncy/ [decoration]/Illustrated by/Margaret Horder/Geoffrey Cumberlege/Oxford University Press/London/ Melbourne Wellington/1954
[Printed in Australia]
198pp, b/w drawings in text, clo., 185x120mm. KMM

1408 A FORTUNE/FOR THE BRAVE/Nan Chauncy/ [decoration]/Illustrated by Margaret Horder/Franklin Watts, Inc. 575Lexington Ave./New York 22 New York [publisher's colophon]
1961 [First American edition]
216pp, b/w drawings in text, clo., 205x135mm. KMM

1409 A FORTUNE/FOR THE BRAVE/Nan Chauncy/ Illustrated by/Margaret Horder/Melbourne/Oxford University Press/London Wellington New York
1954; rpt 1964
198pp, b/w chapter headings & b/w drawings in text, clo., 215x140mm. BBC
German edition

1410 Nan Chauncy/DER SCHATZ AM KLAUENFELSEN/Illustrated by von Ulrike Ulrich/ 1968/Englebert-Verlag. Balve/Westf.
186pp, b/w drawings throughout, hard cloth cover, 200x135mm. Unseen: IFA

1411 TIGER/IN THE BUSH/Nan Chauncy/Illustrated by Margaret Horder/[drawing]/London/Oxford University Press/1957
171pp, b/w frontis. & line drawings in text, clo., 185x120mm. KMM
Won CBCA Award 1958.
• Rpt as above 1958, 1959, 1961, 1965. BBC

1412 TIGER/IN THE BUSH/Nan Chauncy/Illustrated by Margaret Horder/[drawing]/Franklin Watts, Inc. 575 Lexington Ave./New York 22 New York/[publisher's colophon]
1961 [First American edition]
152pp, 1p author's note, 2pp glossary, b/w frontis. & line drawings in text, clo., 205x135mm. KMM

1413 Nan Chauncy/TIGER IN THE BUSH/Illustrated by/Margaret Horder/London/Oxford University Press/1971
First edition 1957, rpt 1958, 1959, 1961; first published in this edition 1971
119pp, 1p author's note, b/w chapter headings, pic. wrappers, cover design by Doreen Roberts, 190x125mm. Oxford Paperback Series. KMM

Swedish edition

1414 BOB HITTAR EN TIGER/Av Nan Chauncy/Rabén & Sjögren/Stockholm
1959
145pp, cover illus. only by Eric Palmquist, hard cover, 180x125mm. Unseen: IFA

Danish edition

1415 DRENG I/TASMANIEN/Nan/Chauncy
Hernovs Forlag [Kobenhavn 1960]
124pp, unillus., hard cover, 200x120mm. Unseen: IFA

Italian edition

1416 Nan Chauncy/IL SEGRETO/DELLA/VALLATA/Illustrated by R. Squillantini
Bemporad Marzocco 1962
139pp, col. illus. throughout [some f/p], paper cover, 125x190mm. Unseen: IFA

1417 IL SEGRETO DELLA VALLATA
Illustrazioni di R. Squillantini; trans. by Antonio Lugli
C. E. Giunti, Firenze 1962, rpt 1968
138pp, col. illus., 26cm.[*sic*] Unseen: ANB 1970

French edition

1418 LE VALLON SECRET/Editions de l'amitié G. T. Rageot/Paris Bruxelles/Illustrations de H. M. Horder [*sic*]/Photographies de D. Anderson
1961
155pp, extended illus. t.p., 5 f/p coloured photographs of Tasmania, double-spread map, all original illustrations by Margaret Horder included, some enlarged from English edition & another colour (green) added, hard cover illus. with col. photograph, 190x140mm. Unseen: IFA

Norwegian edition

1419 Nan Chauncy/DEN TASMANSKE/TIGEREN
Glydendals Gode, n.d.
135pp, unillus., clo., 185x120mm. Unseen: IFA

Russian edition

1420 BARSUK VYSLEZHIVAET TIGRA; povest' v dvykh chastiakh
[Perevod s anliiskogo M. Abkinoi] Moskva, Gos.
12d-vo detskoi lit-ry. 1963
255pp, illus, 21cm.[*sic*]
Contents: PO sledam tasmanskogo tigra—Chertov Kholm, translations of *Tiger in the Bush* & *Devils' Hill*.
Unseen: ANB 1964

Dutch edition

1421 DE WOLFSBERG/ Nan Chauncy: vertaald door An Rutgers van der Loeff. [Netherlands]
Wolters-Noordhoff, c.1969
156pp, illus. Junior Tierner Club. Unseen, ABN

1422 Nan Chauncy/DEVILS' HILL/[drawing]/Illustrated by/Geraldine Spence/London/Oxford University Press/1958
159pp, b/w drawings throughout, clo., 215x135mm. KMM
Joint winner CBCA Award, 1959.
Nan Chauncy/DEVILS' HILL/[drawing]/Illustrated by/Geraldine Spence/London/Oxford University/Press
1958, rpt 1963
Details as above. KP
• Rpt 1959 as above, KP
• Rpt 1960 as above, KP

German edition

1423 Nan Chauncy/DIE HÖHLE IM TEUFELSBERG/Abenteuerliche Erlebnisse/der Lorennie-Kinder/im Tasmanischen Busch/Hermann Schaffstein Verlag—Köln
1960
156pp, 25 b/w illus. by Walter Rieck, pic. hard cover [? bd.], 200x125mm. Unseen: IFA

1424 Nan Chauncy/DEVILS' HILL/Illustrated by/Geraldine Spence/Franklin Watts Inc./575 Lexington Avenue, New York 22, N.Y.
1960 [First American edition]
153pp, b/w drawings throughout, clo., 205x135mm. Unseen: IFA

1425 Another copy as above, but a Book Club edition, being a Junior Literary Guild of America selection. Details are the same as in the Franklin Watts edition, but the cloth cover has printed on it a coloured illustration, the same as that used on the d/w of the Franklin Watts edition. (The d/ws for the Franklin Watts editions are all different from those issued by Oxford University Press.) Unseen: IFA

1426 Nan Chauncy/DEVIL'S [*sic*] HILL/Illustrated by Geraldine Spence/London/Oxford University Press/1971
First edition 1958, rpt 1963; first published in this edition 1971
122pp, b/w drawings throughout, pic. wrappers, cover design by Doreen Roberts, 190x125mm. Oxford Paperback Series. KMM
DEVILS' HILL

Japanese edition

Kodansha 1968

Danish edition

1427 Nan Chauncy/DJAEVLE BJERGET/Hernovs Forlag
1960
155pp, 30 b/w illus., illus. by Geraldine Spence, pic. wrappers, 200x125mm. Unseen: IFA

Dutch edition

1428 Nan Chauncy/EXPEDITITE/"DE VERDWENEN KOE"/Vertaling van An Rutgers van de Loeff—Basenau/Illustraties van Geraldine Spence/Omslag van Jenny Dalenoord/Uitgeverij Ploegsma—Amsterdam MCMLXI
168pp, 30 b/w illus., pic. clo., 215x150mm. Unseen: IFA

Dutch Book Club edition

Unseen

Swedish edition

1429 Nan Chauncy/BOB FÖLJER ETT SPÅR
Raben & Sjogren, 1961
156pp, unillus., hard cover, 185x125mm. Unseen: IFA

Italian edition

1430 Nan Chauncy/LA COLLINA/DEI DASIURI/Paravia
Paravia, Torino 1964
145pp, col. illus. throughout by Guido Bertello, hard cover, 240x180mm. Unseen: IFA

Russian edition
See TIGER IN THE BUSH, the two books being published in one volume in the Russian edition

1431 Nan Chauncy/TANGARA/[motto]/[drawing]/ Illustrated by/Brian Wildsmith/London/Oxford University Press/1960
180pp, b/w illus. throughout, clo., 215x135mm. KMM
Won CBCA Award 1961, & the 'Diploma of Merit', Hans Christian Andersen Award, 1962.

1432 Nan Chauncy/THE SECRET FRIENDS/[drawing]/ Illustrated by/Brian Wildsmith/[device]/Watts/ International/Franklin Watts, Inc./575 Lexington Ave., New York 22.
1962 [First American edition of *Tangara*]
180pp, b/w drawings in text throughout, clo., 200x135mm. CLRC

1433 Nan Chauncy/TANGARA/"Let us set off again"/Illustrated by/Brian Wildsmith/London/Oxford University Press/1972
First edition 1960, rpt 1961, reset 1961, rpt 1970; first published in this edition 1972
121pp, 10 b/w chapter headings, pic. wrappers, 190x130mm. Oxford Paperback Series. KMM
Japanese edition
Kodansha ?date
Danish edition
Branner Og Korch, 1971
Unseen: Information for both editions from Oxford University Press
German edition

1434 Nan Chauncy/'O DAS JUNGE EMU...'/Claudius 1965
158pp, unillus., hard cover, 220x145mm. Unseen: IFA

1435 Nan Chauncy/HALF A WORLD AWAY/Illustrated by/Annette Macarthur-Onslow/[drawing]/Oxford University Press/London 1962
195pp, 1p acknowledgements, b/w frontis. & line drawings throughout, clo., 215x140mm. KMM
• Rpt 1963, details as above KP

1436 HALF A WORLD AWAY, Illustrated by Annette Macarthur-Onslow
Franklin Watts, New York, 1963
194pp, illus., 21cm.[*sic*] Unseen: ANB May 1963
HALF A WORLD AWAY
E. M. Hale & Company, Wisconsin 1966 [by arrangement with Franklin Watts]
First Cadmus Edition [in braille]. Unseen: IFA

1437 HALF A WORLD AWAY
German edition
Englebert Verlag, 1969
Unseen: Information from Oxford University Press

1438 Nan Chauncy/THE ROARING 40/Illustrated by/ Annette Macarthur-Onslow/The Children's Book Club/121 Charing Cross Road/London W. C.2
1963
161pp
Identical with first edition except for blue instead of yellow cloth bdg, & new d/w designed by Leslie Wood. Ths edition is apparently the Foyle's Book Club edition; jacket has device incorporating the initials 'F.B.C.' on base of spine. KMM
• Rpt 1965, as above. KP

1439 Nan Chauncy/THE ROARING 40/Illustrated by/ Annette Macarthur-Onslow/London/Oxford University Press/1963
161pp, 1p author's note, b/w map frontis. & 25 b/w drawings, clo., 215x135mm. KMM

1440 THE ROARING 40, Illustrated by Annette Macarthur-Onslow
Watts, New York 1963
161pp, illus., map, 21cm.[*sic*] Unseen: ANB 1964
Dutch edition

1441 DE SPOOKKUST/Nan Chauncy
Uitgeverij Ploegsma, Amsterdam 1964
190pp, b/w illus. (as in original edition), clo., 220x140mm. Unseen: IFA
German edition

1442 DAXI, TOM UND TOLLE VIER i Wie Vater Lorennies Jüngster an Tasmaniens einsamer Küste statt Gold einen Freund fand. [Köln] Hermann Schaffstein Verlag [1965]
151pp, illus., 22cm. [*sic*] Unseen: ANB July 1966
Italian edition

1443 Nan Chauncy/40° PARRELLELO/Parvia
Parvia 1965
163pp, col. & b/w illus. throughout [some f/p], col. illus. by Guido Bertello, hard cover, 240x180mm. Unseen: IFA
Afrikaans edition

1444 DIE SPOOKKUS/Nan Chauncy
J. L. van Schaik Beperk, Pretoria 1966
152pp, b/w illus. (as in original edition), 210x135mm. Unseen: IFA
Finnish edition

1445 Nan Chauncy/KULTARETKI TASMANIASSA/Ned Otava
1966
202pp, unillus., clo., 180x120mm. Unseen: IFA
Slovak edition

1446 Nan Chauncy/NED,/ZAJATEC/MORA
Publisher [?] Vydali Mlade, 1967
216pp, part. col. illus. by Radomir Kolar, hard cover, 185x170mm. Unseen: IFA
French edition

1447 N. Chauncy/LA COTE DES NAUFRAGES/ Editions de l'Amitié—G. T. Rageot/Paris—Illustrations de M. Barcilon
1970
184pp, 1p adv., extended illus. t.p., 3 f/p col. photographic illus., part. col. & b/w drawings, pic. bd., map e/p, 185x145mm. ANL

1448 Nan Chauncy/HIGH AND HAUNTED/ISLAND/ Illustrated by/Victor G. Ambrus/London/Oxford University Press/1964
145pp, b/w drawings throughout, clo., 215x135mm. KMM

1449 HIGH AND HAUNTED ISLAND, Illustrated by Victor G. Ambrus
W. W. Norton, New York 1965
145pp, illus., 22cm.[*sic*] Unseen: ANB1965
German edition

1450 VERSCHOLLEN IN PORT DAVEY [von] Nan Chauncy
F. Schneekluth, Darmstadt 1966
159pp, illus., maps (on lining papers), 20cm. Unseen:[*sic*] ANB 1967

1451 THE/SKEWBALD PONY/Nan Chauncy/with drawings by/David Parry/[drawing]/Nelson London 1965
48pp, b/w drawings in text throughout, dec. clo., 185x120mm. KMM

1452 PANIC/AT THE GARAGE/by/Nan Chauncy/ illustrated by/Peter Lloyd/[device—Flamingo Books]/ Oliver & Boyd
Edinburgh, first publ. 1965, rpt 1967, 1972
24pp, 11pp with col. illus., stiff pic. wrapper, 190x135mm. SFU
School reader with Australian setting.

BEEKEEPING. *See* Life in Australia

1453 Nan Chauncy/MATHINNA'S PEOPLE/[drawing]/ Illustrated by Victor G. Ambrus/London/Oxford University Press/1967
163pp (inc. 3pp glossary), 1p note, b/w map, b/w chapter headings & drawings in text, clo., 210x130mm. KMM
Story about the dispossession of the Tasmanian Aborigines of their lands by the white settlers.
Danish edition
Branner Og Korchs Forlag A/S, 1968
Italian edition
Paravia, Turin 1969 [permission given them in 1970 to issue an English reprint for use in Italian schools]
Unseen: Information for both editions from Oxford University Press

1454 Nan Chauncy/LIZZIE LIGHTS/Illustrated by/ Judith White/London/Oxford University Press/1968
134pp, b/w frontis. & b/w drawings in text throughout, clo., 210x135mm. KMM

1455 THE LIGHTHOUSE/KEEPER'S SON/[drawing]/ Illustrated by Victor G. Ambrus/London/Oxford University Press/1969
133pp, b/w drawings in text, clo., 215x137mm. KMM

PRIMARY INDUSTRIES. *See* Life in Australia

CHAUVEL, Charles
1456 EVE IN EBONY/the story of "JEDDA"
Columbia Pictures Propy Ltd 251a Pitt St., Sydney, 1954
[14]pp, 6pp, col. photographic illus. & b/w illus., col. pic. wrappers, cover title, 275x214mm. KP
Story of the making of the film. Doubtful children's.

CHAUVIN, V.
See Denis, F. & Chauvin, V.

[CHAVANNE, Herminie]
1457 UN/JEUNE SUISSE EN AUSTRALIE/Suite des/ Soirées de famille et des lettres d'une Famille Suisse/ Par l'auteur de/La Vie d'Elisabeth Fry, etc. etc./ [verse]/—/Geneve/Emile Beroud, Libraire-Editeur/ Successeur de Mmes Ve Beroud & S. Guers./Paris/J. Grassart, Libraire/Rue de la Paix 11, Marc Ducloux, Libraire,/Rue Tronchet, 2/1852
203pp (inc. 4pp introduction) folding map & 9pp b/w engravings, wrappers, 180x120mm. NSL:M
Author mentions a dinner with Governor Gipps, a visit to Camden & describes the Macarthur home & property, the Rev. S. Marsden, Aborigines, &c.
1458 UN/JEUNE SUISSE EN AUSTRALIE,/Suite des/ Soirées de famille et des lettres d'une Famille Suisse,/ Par l'auteur de/La Vie d'Elisabeth Fry, etc etc./[verse]/ Toulouse,/Société des Livres Religieux./Dépôt: Rue du Lycée, 14./1858
219pp (inc. 4pp introduction & 3pp table of contents), 8 f/p b/w engravings, marbled bd., 185x120mm. RM
This copy has been re-bound & contains 8 plates only & no map.
1459 UN/JEUNE SUISSE/EN AUSTRALIE,/par l'Auteur/de la Vie d'Elisabeth Fry, des Soirées de famille, des Lettres/d'une famille suisse, etc./[4 lines quotation]/Troisième édition./Toulouse,/Société des Livres Religieux/Dépôt: Rue Romiguieres, 7/1874
215pp (inc. 4pp introduction & 3pp contents), 8pp b/w illus., dec. clo., 170x105mm. CLRC
Does not contain a map. Contains 7pp appendix to the 2nd ed. of the book describing how, if the author had lived, he would certainly have included details of the discovery of gold in Australia. The editor then proceeds to reproduce 'Les Lingots d'or en Australie' from the third chapter of M. VULLIET'S *'Quelques merveilles de la nature et de l'art.*

CHEESMAN, Lucy Evelyn
1460 EVERYDAY DOINGS/OF INSECTS/By/Evelyn Cheesman, F.E.S., F.Z.S./Curator of Insects to the Zoological Society of London/With illustrations by/ Hugh Main, Dr. Herbert Shirley, Peter Scott/The Author and others/[publisher's device]/George G. Harrap & Co. Ltd./London Bombay Sydney
1924, rpt 1930
240pp, 2pp foreword, 5pp index, b/w photographic frontis. & 157 b/w illus., clo., 180x125mm. CLRC

1461 CAMPING/ADVENTURES/IN NEW GUINEA/ By/Evelyn Cheesman, F.R.E.S./With illustrations/and two maps/George G. Harrap and Company Ltd./ London Sydney Toronto Bombay
1948
160pp, b/w frontis. & line drawings, clo., 180x115mm. NSL:M

1462 CAMPING/ADVENTURES/ON/CANNIBAL ISLANDS/By/Evelyn Cheesman, F.R.E.S./With illustrations/and two maps/George G. Harrap and Company Ltd./London Sydney Toronto Bombay
1949
168pp, b/w frontis. & drawings in text, 2 b/w maps, clo., 180x115mm. CLRC
• Rpt 1950 as above. NSL:M
1463 CAMPING/ADVENTURES/ON/CANNIBAL ISLANDS/By/Evelyn Cheesman, F.R.E.S./with illustrations/and two maps/Medill McBride Company/ New York
1950
168pp, b/w frontis., 2 f/p b/w illus., 2 b/w maps & b/w drawings in text, clo., 185x120mm. AJH

1464 LANDFALL/THE UNKNOWN/Lord Howe Island/ 1788/By Evelyn Cheesman/[drawing of a compass]/ Penguin Books/Harmondsworth, Middlesex
1950
192pp (inc. 5pp notes), 2 b/w maps, dec. wrappers, 180x105mm. A Puffin Book. KMM

1465 MAROONED IN/DU-BU COVE/Evelyn Cheesman/Illustrated by Jack Matthew/Bell Publishing Company, Penna
n.d.
190pp, dec. t.p., 2pp illus. [facsimile], b/w map, b/w illus. in text, bd., 180x115mm. NSL:M
1466 Another copy, G. Bell & Sons, London 1950.
Unseen: Information from publisher's catalogue

1467 SEALSKINS FOR SILK/Captain Fanning's Voyage round the World/in a brig in 1797–99/by/Evelyn Cheesman, F.R.Ent. Soc./Illustrated by/Geoffrey Whittam/[device]/Methuen & Co., Ltd. London/36 Essex Street, Strand, W.C.2
1952
214pp (inc. 5pp postscript) 1p author's foreword, b/w frontis. & 19 b/w drawings, dec. map e/p, clo., 185x120mm. HBM
The story of Captain Edmund Fanning's voyage in the brig *'Betsey'* from New York to China via Cape Horn & his westward return to America & his trading exploits.

1468 CHARLES DARWIN/AND HIS PROBLEMS/by/ Evelyn Cheesman/F.R.E.S., formerly Curator of Insects

at/the London Zoo, author of "Marooned in/Du-Bu Cove", "Camping Adventures on Cannibal Islands", "Insects Indomitable"/Illustrated by/Geoffrey Whittam/G. Bell and Sons, Ltd./London 1953
163pp, 3pp index, map frontis. & 9 b/w illus., clo., 180x115mm. CLRC

CHESNEY, Anne
1469 LESLIE WINS/THROUGH/(A School Story for Girls)/By/Anne Chesney/[device]/The Shakespeare Head/London New York Sydney Capetown Paris/ 1947
163pp, unillus., clo., 176x124mm. ANL

CHESTER, G.
LONG ODDS! *See* The Boys' Friend Library

CHETWODE, R. D.
1470 THE MARBLE CITY/Being the Strange Adventures/of Three Boys/By/R. D. Chetwode/ Author of "The Fortune of the Quittentuns",/with illustrations/New and Cheaper Edition/London/ Sampson Low, Marston & Company/Limited/St. Dunstan's House/Fetter lane, Fleet Street, E.C.
n.d. [1895]
312pp, b/w frontis. & 15 f/p b/w illus., pic. bd., 170x115mm. KMM
Adventures of three boys shipwrecked *en route* to Australia, their capture by savages, discovery of secret treasure & eventual arrival at the Queensland coast.

CHEW, Sylvia
1471 LITTLE CHIU"/Written by Sylvia Chew/(A Series of Stories)/Book 1—Kwong Chiu's NEW YEAR CLOTHES/[publisher's device]/Printed in Australia by Queen City Printer Pty. Ltd., Melbourne, for the/ Publishers, Murfett Pty. Ltd., 364 Lonsdale Street, Melbourne
n.d. [1947]
36pp, 8 col. illus. & b/w drawings throughout, illus. by Jean Elder, dec. bd., 245x235mm. KMM
Contents consist of one story only, including a song with music.

CHEYNE, Irene
1472 THE GOLDEN/CAULIFLOWER/By/Irene Cheyne/illustrations by/Jean Elder/Hutchinson & Co./(Publishers) Ltd./London
n.d. [Library copy acquired 1937]
219pp, col. frontis. & b/w drawings throughout, clo., 215x155mm. ANL

1473 ANNETTE/OF RIVER BEND/By/Irene Cheyne/ Angus and Robertson Ltd./Sydney London/1941
229pp, b/w frontis. only, clo., 185x125mm. ANL
• Rpt 1942 (twice),1946, 1947, 1948. KP

1474 ANNETTE & CO./By/Irene Cheyne/Angus and Robertson Ltd./Sydney London/1942
214pp, unillus., clo., 185x120mm. ANL
• Rpt 1945, 1948. KP

1475 DAVID OF THE/STARS/By/Irene Cheyne/Angus and Robertson Ltd./Sydney: London/1942
204pp, unillus., clo., 185x120mm. ANL
• Rpt 1946. KP

1476 THE LITTLE BLUE/MOUNTAIN/By/Irene Cheyne/Angus and Robertson Ltd./Sydney: London/ 1944
210pp, unillus., bd., 180x120mm. KMM
• Rpt 1947 as above. BBC

1477 DINNIE,/BINNIE,/and JINKS/by/Irene Cheyne/ [drawing]/Whitcombe & Tombs Pty. Ltd./Melbourne Sydney and Perth
n.d. [1945]
59pp, col. frontis. & b/w drawings throughout, bd., 180x130mm. ANL
Reprinted by permission of the Victorian School Paper.

1478 PACKMAN'S/PIPE/by/Irene Cheyne/[drawing]/ Whitcombe & Tombs Pty. Ltd./Melbourne Sydney Perth
n.d. [1946]
47pp, col. frontis., 4 f/p b/w illus., b/w drawings throughout, dec. bd., 185x135mm. ANL

CHILD, John
1479 AUSTRALIAN SEA SHELLS/An introduction for young biologists/and collectors/by/John Child/M.A. (N.Z.) D.Phil. (Oxon.)/First edition/Periwinkle Press
n.d. [1959]
viipp, 59pp (inc. 2pp introduction & 4pp index), col. frontis., b/w drawings, dec. card covers, 186x122mm. KP
• Rpt 1959, as above but revised, KP
1480 AUSTRALIAN SEA SHELLS/An Introduction for Young Biologists/and Collectors/By/John Child/M.A. (N.Z.) D.Phil. (Oxon.)./Periwinkle Press
Sydney 1959; revised & rpt 1959; 2nd ed. 1961
1p preface, 63pp (inc. index), col. frontis. & 4pp b/w photographic illus., b/w drawings & diagrams in text throughout, bd., 185x125mm. KMM
1481 AUSTRALIAN SEA SHELLS
2nd ed. rev. & rpt 1963; 3rd ed. 1965
Details as in previous edition. CLRC

1482 AUSTRALIAN INSECTS/An introduction for young biologists/and collectors/by/John Child/M.A. (N.Z.) D.Phil. (Oxon.)./Periwinkle Press
Sydney 1960
88pp (inc. 2pp introduction, 1p bibliography, & 5pp index), 1p preface, col. frontis. & 1 f/p col. illus., b/w illus. throughout, dec. bd., 180x120mm. CLRC
Rev. ed, 1961 as above. KP
• Rpt 1964, 3rd ed. 1966
97pp (inc. 5pp index, 1 bibliography) & 1p preface, col. frontis., 1 f/p col. plate, 10 f/p b/w photographic plates, bd., dec. e/p, 185x120mm. KP

1483 AUSTRALIAN SEASHORE LIFE/An Introduction for Young Biologists/and Seashore Explorers/By/John Child/M.A. (N.Z.) D.Phil. (Oxon.)./Periwinkle Press
Gladesville, NSW, 1962
1p author's preface, 74pp (inc. index & bibliography), col. frontis. & 1p col. illus., 9 f/p b/w photographic illus. & diagrams in text, bd., 185x125mm. CLRC

1484 AUSTRALIAN ROCKS AND MINERALS/An Introduction to Geology/By/John Child/M.A. (N.Z.), D.Phil. (Oxon.)/Periwinkle Press
Sydney 1963
74pp (inc. 3pp index & 1p bibliography), 1p preface, b/w photographic frontis. & 15pp b/w illus., 3pp col. illus., b/w drawings & diagrams in text, bd., 185x120mm. KP
Revised & rpt 1963, as above. KP
• Rpt 1964, 1965, as above. KP
• Rpt 1966, as above. KP

1485 AUSTRALIAN SPIDERS/By/John Child/M.A. (N.Z.), D.Phil. (Oxon.)/Periwinkle Press
Sydney 1965

87pp, 1p preface, b/w photographic frontis. & 15pp b/w photographic illus., 2pp col. photographic illus., diagrams in text, pic. bd., dec. e/p, 180x120mm. BBC

1486 INSECTS/ARE ALL AROUND US/[device]3/ Illustrated by Margaret Senior/Longmans 1965 Melbourne
16pp (inc. bibliography), part. col. illus. throughout, stiff pic. wrappers, 210x155mm. BBC Australian Nature Series No. 3.

1487 INSECTS AND THEIR HABITS/by/John Child/ Illustrated by/Margaret Senior/Australian/Nature Series/10/Longmans 1966
Longmans Green & Co. Ltd, Croydon, Victoria
32pp, col. illus. throughout, pic. wrappers, 210x155mm. BBC

GOLDEN STAMP BOOK OF/AUSTRALIAN/SEA SHELLS. *See* Golden Stamp Books

'CHILDREN'

1488 STORIES FOR CHILDREN/By/CHILDREN/ Copyright. Published by W. F. McConnell Co-operative Publicity/Grenfell Street, Adelaide/and printed at the Hassell Press, Currie Street/1923
48pp (inc. 1p preface by W. F. McConnell), b/w illus. throughout, illus. by John Goodchild, dec. bd., 245x185mm. KMM
Illustrated advertisements inside front cover, & inside & outside back cover and throughout for various household products. The stories were prize ones submitted by children to illustrate the drawings accompanying them.

Children of Down-Under

See [James, Henry Colbert]

Children on the Farm

1489 CHILDREN/ON THE/FARM/[illus.]/Offset Printing Coy Pty Limited Sydney
n.d. [inscribed Christmas 1946]
32pp, part col. illus., col. pic. wrappers, 240x175mm. JH
Wattle Series from the House of Offset.

The Children's Book of Australian Animals and Birds

1490 THE CHILDREN'S/BOOK OF/AUSTRALIAN/ ANIMALS AND BIRDS/Mrs Kangaroo/and her baby/ in her Pouch
An 'Uncle John' Book, Printed by Macarthur Press Pty Limited, 66 Macarthur Street, Parramatta, n.d. [194-?]
6pp, illus. throughout, col. pic. wrappers, cover title signed 'J.D.', 248x180mm. KMM
Illus. printed in blue with slight caption.

The Children's Colouring Book of Birds & Butterflies

1491 THE CHILDREN'S/COLOURING BOOK/OF BIRDS & BUTTERFLIES
The Central Press Pty Ltd, Castlereagh St, Sydney, n.d.
8pp (inc. covers), 4pp col. illus. & illus repeated in b/w, wrappers, cover title, 180x120mm. KP

The Children's Dictionary in Pictures

1492 THE/CHILDREN'S/DICTIONARY/IN PICTURES/ A Colorgravure Publication/Registered at the GPO Melbourne/for transmission by Post as a Book
n.d. [1953]
128pp, dec. t.p., col. illus. throughout, clo., dec. e/p, 275x210mm. ANL

Children's Favourite Stories in Pictures

1493 CHILDREN'S/FAVOURITE STORIES/IN PICTURES/Selections from the famous stories by Hans Andersen/and Jakob and Wilhelm Grimm, and from the Arabian/Nights, Australian Aboriginal Folklore, Aesop's Fables,/Greek Mythology and Old English Fairy Tales./[coloured drawing]/The News & the Mail Adelaide, n.d. [195-?]
96pp, 32pp col. illus. & b/w illus. throughout, dec. bd., dec. e/p, 275x215mm. KMM
Stories told in comic strip form; includes Australian stories (7pp) illus. by John L. Curtis: 'Wayambeh the Turtle'; 'How the Southern Cross was formed'; 'The Brolga'.

Children's Highway Code

1494 CHILDREN'S/HIGHWAY/CODE/[drawing]/ Issued by the/Australian Road Safety/Council/with the co-operation of/BP Australia Ltd./Fifth Edition 1964
16pp, col. illus. throughout, pic. wrappers, 202x126mm. KP
• Rpt 1966 as above, seventh ed. KP

1495 Another ed.
Children's Highway Code/[drawing] This book belongs to .../and I live at .../Issued in the interests of Road Safety by the Commonwealth Department of Transport in co-operation with the Traffic and Road Safety authorities of the Australian States and Territories
Printed at The Dominion Press, North Blackburn, Victoria, n.d.
18pp, col. illus., pic. wrappers, 202x126mm. KP

1496 CHILDREN'S/HIGHWAY/CODE/Produced by the/Commonwealth Department/of Shipping and Transport/for the Australian Road Safety/Council/ with the co-operation of/BP Australia Ltd./Tenth Edition—1970
16pp, col. illus. throughout, col. pic. wrappers, 200x125mm. KP

The Child's Companion and Juvenile Instructor

1497 THE/CHILD'S COMPANION,/AND/JUVENILE INSTRUCTOR/New Series/1846/Religious Tract Society/56 Paternoster Row
[Title within decorative border]
380pp, col. frontis. (Baxter print), engravings in text, ¾ leather, 144x90mm. CLRC
Contains 'Little Mickey, the South Australian Boy' pp25–32. A tale of a young Aboriginal boy who steals bread from the missionary who has befriended him & eventually repents & is forgiven. Also included in French in *Le Petit Messager.*

A Child's First Cook Book

1498 A CHILD'S FIRST COOK BOOK/For Boys and Girls/A Happy Hour Book
40 Play Ideas for Boys and Girls
Jon Sales Pty Ltd
48pp, cover in col. 200x165mm. Unseen

Chips

1499 CHIPS
Photogravure, Melbourne
12pp, col. illus. by N. E. Mumford throughout, cover title, 235x170mm. KP

CHISHOLM, Alexander Hugh

1500 HAIL, THE KOOKA BURRA/By A. H. Chisholm/ LAUGHING JACK/By Dorothy Drewett/[drawing]/ Wholly set up and printed in Australia by/Pratten Bros. Ltd. Sydney N.S.W./1931
12pp, 3 col. plates (inc. 1 double spread), b/w drawings, illus. by S. Long & N. Cayley, stiff pic. wrappers, 270x205mm. ANL

1501 SOME FAVOURITE/BIRDS/Introduced by/A. H. Chisholm/Wholly set up and printed in Australia by/ Pratten Bros. Ltd. Sydney N.S.W./1931
12pp, 4 col. illus. & b/w drawings, illus. by N. W.

Cayley & others, stiff dec. wrappers, 280x220mm. NSL:M
The same author's *Mateship with Birds* (Melbourne 1922) is not a children's book.

FERDINAND VON MUELLER. *See* Great Australians

AUSTRALIAN WILD LIFE. *See* Around Australia Program

CHISHOLM, Janet
1502 PADDY THE AUSTRALIAN PONY/by/Janet Chisholm/Publishers:/Arthur H. Stockwell, Ltd./ Ilfracombe, Devon
n.d. [1956?]
30pp, 2 b/w drawings [unsgd.], wrappers, 180x120mm. ANL

1503 TIMMY CATERPILLAR/by/[coloured drawing]/ Janet Chisholm
No publisher's imprint [on verso of t.p.: 'Wholly set up and printed in Australia by the Bridge Printery Pty. Ltd. 117 Reservoir Street, Sydney'], n.d. [195-?]
[25]pp, alternate pages blank, 5 f/p col. illus. by the author, col. illus. wrappers, 130x220mm. KMM

CHITTY, A. W. I.
1504 FOURTEEN/ROAD SAFETY SONGS/For little children/[device]/[drawing]/Issued with the compliments of the/Australian Road Safety Council/ Printed by arrangement with/W. Paxton & Co. Ltd./ London
16pp songs with music, illus. wrappers, 280x266mm. KP

The Chocolate Project
1505 THE/CHOCOLATE/PROJECT
n.p., n.d. [1970?]
With compliments of the Nestlé Company (Australia) Limited
12pp, col. illus. throughout, wrappers, cover title, 227x175mm. KMM
Features the chocolate 'Yogi Bear'.

CHOMLEY, C. H.
1506 THE/FLIGHT OF THE BLACK SWAN/A Tale of Piracy and Adventure/By/C. H. Chomley/With four plates by H. L. Shindler/[device]/London/George Routledge & Sons Ltd./New York: E. P. Dutton & Co.
Presented as a prize for an essay on Australia 1916
308pp & 4pp adv., b/w frontis. & 3 others, pic. clo., 185x120mm. KP
Doubtful children's book.

CHRISTENSEN, E. E. & others
1507 HOW TO PLAY/RUGBY LEAGUE/by/E. E. Christensen/K. McCafferey/D. Brown./Southern Cross International Sydney
1964
96pp, b/w photographic illus., pic. wrappers, 202x134mm. KP

CHRISTIE, Connie
1508 THE/ADVENTURES/OF/PINKISHELL/By Connie Christie
The author's first book. Specialty Press Melbourne, n.d. [1939?]
16pp, 4 f/p col. plates, b/w illus. & 4pp part col., col. pic. wrappers, 277x217mm. KP
'Pinkishell's Adventures' title on p.1.
1509 PINKISHELL'S ADVENTURES
n.d., n.p. (? rpt, inscr. 1942)
12pp (inc. cover), 6pp col. illus., col. pic. wrappers, 277x217mm. KP

1510 ANIMAL/ABC
Digest Juvenile Productions, 170 Little Collins St., Melbourne, n.d.
16pp, alternate page openings printed in col., others in b/w, illus. throughout, stiff pic. wrappers, 280x215mm. KP

1511 ANIMAL/NURSERYLAND/Connie Christie
Digest Juvenile Productions, Melbourne, n.d. [inscribed 1947]
[16]pp, 8pp f/p col. illus., other pages printed in green, stiff col. pic. wrappers, cover title, 280x215mm. ANL

1512 BABY BUNTING/COMES/TO/TOWN/By Connie Christie
Digest Juvenile Productions, Melbourne, n.d.
[16]pp, illus. on every page printed in col. & part col., col. pic. wrappers, 278x215mm. CLRC

1513 WEE ONE/from/Hans Andersen's "Thumbelina"/The story of a fairy child, who/was no bigger than your thumb/Adapted and/Illustrated by/ Connie Christie/Digest Juvenile Productions/ (Registered)/170 Little Collins Street/Melbourne, Australia
n.d.
28pp, b/w illus. throughout, 6pp col. illus., pic. bd., 246x183mm. KMM
In the same series 'Baby Bunting Comes to Town'.

1514 THE/MAGIC/SHELL/by/Connie Christie
Digest Juvenile Publications, Melbourne, n.d. [194-?]
16pp, 8 f/p col. illus. & 8 part. col. illus., pic. wrappers, cover title, 275x210mm. Grant

1515 THE/MAGIC BUCKET/Connie Christie
Digest Juvenile Publications, Melbourne, n.d. [194-?]
16pp, 8 f/p col. illus. & b/w drawings in text, stiff wrappers, cover title, 275x215mm. KMM

1516 THE/QUEEN OF HEARTS
Digest Juvenile Publications, Melbourne, n.d. [194-?]
16pp, 8 f/p col. illus. & b/w drawings in text, illus. wrappers, cover title, 280x215mm. KMM

1517 NUMBER/FUN/drawing]/Connie Christie
Digest Juvenile Publications, 170 Little Collins Street, Melbourne, n.d.
16pp, col. & b/w illus. throughout, stiff pic. wrappers, 275x210mm. KMM
Nursery rhyme captions, with page openings illustrated alternately in colour or b/w.

1518 SUSAN THE RAG DOLL
Printed by/The Specialty Press Ltd/174 Little Collins St. Melbourne
n.d.
[16]pp, each page opening alternately with col. or b/w illus., col. pic. wrappers, b/w pic. e/p, 246x184mm. KMM

1519 NURSERYLAND
Printed by Specialty Press Pty Ltd, 174 Little Collins Street, Melbourne, n.d.
[16]pp, col. illus., b/w illus. e/ps, pic. wrappers, cover title, 270x220mm. Grant
Each page has a coloured illustration of a nursery rhyme with the verse printed below.
1520 LET'S COUNT
1521 MOTHER GOOSE
uniform booklets
Digest Juvenile Publications, Melbourne, n.d. [1945]
20pp, illus., 245x185mm. ANL

1522 THE/MERRY-/GO-ROUND./Connie Christie
n.p., n.d. [copy inscribed 1947]
[20]pp, pic. wrappers, 8 col. illus., 243x180mm. KMM

1523 Spring Summer/HAPPY/DAYS/Autumn Winter
Specialty Press Ltd, Melbourne, n.d.
[12]pp, alternate col. & part col. page openings, pic. wrappers, cover title, 276x214mm. KP

1524 A/B/C/S. S. ALPHABET
The Specialty Press Limited, 174 Little Collins St, Melbourne, n.d.
[16]pp, col. f/p illus. and b/w drawings inside covers, col. pic. wrappers, cover title, 265x215mm. Grant

1525 A/CHILD'S GARDEN/OF VERSE/[col. illus.]/Connie Christie
Specialty Press, Melbourne, n.d. [195-?]
16pp, 8 col. illus. & 8 part col. illus., pic. wrappers, 270x215mm. KP

1526 BUNTY'S PIXIES
Specialty Press, Melbourne, n.d. [copy inscribed 1950]
16pp (inc. 8pp in col.), b/w illus on other pages, col. pic. wrappers, 245x180mm. KP

1527 SIMPLE SIMON/RHYMES
Digest Juvenile Productions, Melbourne, n.d. [1950?]
16pp (inc. 8pp in col., others in part col., col. pic. wrappers, cover title, 275x215mm. KP

1528 KIT KATS/Story of Two Kittens
Specialty Press, Melbourne [n.d.]
16pp, 4pp col. illus. & b/w illus. with text on each page, 275x215mm. VMOU

1529 JUDY'S HOLIDAY/By/Connie Christie
Digest Juvenile Productions, Melbourne, n.d.
[16]pp, 8 f/p col. illus. & drawings in text, col. pic. wrappers, 275x215mm. CLRC

1530 JILL'S BUBBLE/Connie Christie
Digest Juvenile Productions, Melbourne, n.d. [194-?]
[16]pp, 8 f/p col. illus. & b/w drawings in text, stiff pic. wrappers, cover title, 276x215mm. KMM

1531 A HAPPY/DAY./A Child's Day/from Sunrise/to Sunset/Connie Christie
Digest Juvenile Productions, Melbourne, n.d. [194-?]
16pp with 8 f/p col. illus & numerous b/w illus., pic. card wrappers, 280x215mm. CLRC

1532 MERRY TALES
Digest Juvenile Productions, Melbourne, n.d.
16pp, 8pp in col., other illus. printed in green, col. pic. wrappers, 280x216mm
Contains: The Little Red Hen, The Elves & the Shoemaker, The Gingerbread Boy, The Three Bears. KP

1533 LITTLE RED RIDING HOOD
Digest Juvenile Productions, Melbourne, n.d.
16pp (inc. 8pp printed in col.), other illus. part col., col. pic. wrappers, cover title, 280x210mm. KP

1534 CINDERELLA
Digest Juvenile Productions, Melbourne, n.d. [194-?]
16pp, 8 f/p col. illus., card wrappers, 280x215mm. CLRC

1535 HANSEL/AND/GRETEL
Digest Juvenile Productions, Melbourne (Specialty Press), n.d.
16pp (inc. 8pp in col. & 8pp part col.), col. pic. wrappers, cover title, 280x210mm. KP

1536 THE/FAIRY MERMAID/by/Connie Christie
Digest Juvenile Productions (Registered) 170 Little Collins St, Melbourne, n.d. Printed by The Specialty Press
12pp, 6pp f/p col. illus. & drawings in text, stiff col. pic. wrappers, cover title, 276x216mm. KMM

1537 STORY TIME
n.p., n.d.
16pp, b/w illus. throughout, some illus. sgd 'Splash', col. card pic. wrappers, cover title, 244x184mm. JH

1538 4 FAIRY/TALES
n.p., n.d.
[20]pp, 8 f/p col. illus., col. pic. wrappers, 250x180mm. KP
Includes Ali Baba, Red Rose and Snow White, Sleeping Beauty, Cinderella.

1539 THE FLOWER/BABIES
Specialty Press, Melbourne, n.d.
16pp (inc. 4pp in col.), b/w illus. other pages, col. pic. wrappers, cover title, 270x210mm. KP

1540 NURSERY RHYMES. Connie Christie
Digest Juvenile Productions/(Registered)/174 Little Collins Street/Melbourne Australia
n.d. [1945]
[20]pp (inc. pic. covers), 8pp col. illus., other pages text & line drawings, stiff pic. wrappers, cover title, 276x220mm. ANL
Uniform with above:
1541 Little Rhymes
1542 Mary Lou in Candyland
1543 Mops, A Fairy Story. All ANL
Also uniform but [1948] also ANL
1544 The Fairy Knight
1545 Nursery Numbers
1546 Sally's Sea Party [*sic*]

1547 THE/CONNIE CHRISTIE/ANNUAL/Fairy/Stories/and/Verse/A Digest Juvenile Production
Australian Digest Pty Ltd, Melbourne, n.d. [1947]
[66]pp, 32pp col. illus. & b/w drawings in text, dec. bd., cover title, 280x215mm. ANL
Contents include: Judy's Holiday; Animal Nurseryland; A Happy Day; Merry Tales. Cover shows children with an open book entitled 'Fairy Stories & Verse'.
1548 THE CONNIE CHRISTIE/ANNUAL/(Illustration)/A Digest Juvenile Production
Australian Digest Pty Ltd, Melbourne, n.d. [1948]
[64]pp, 32 col. illus. & b/w drawings, dec. bd., cover title, 280x215mm. KMM
Contents include: The Fairy Mermaid; Number Fun; Sleepy Time Rhymes; Animal ABC.
Cover shows children on magic carpet.
1549 THE/CONNIE CHRISTIE/ANNUAL/Fairy Stories/and Verse/A Digest Juvenile Production
[1949]
[64]pp, col. & b/w or sepia & white illus. on each alternate page opening, pic. bd., dec. e/p, 275x215mm. CLRC
Cover title showing boy paddling a canoe with dog & girl passenger among fairies, a duckling &c. Nursery rhymes &c, Hansel & Gretel, Mother Goose, Jill's Bubble, The Magic Bucket.
1550 THE CONNIE CHRISTIE ANNUAL
Digest Juvenile Production, 1950
[64]pp, col. & part col. illus., pic. bd. (cover showing children on a rocking horse), 270x208mm. Unseen. IFA
Contents: Simple Simon, Wee One, Happy Days, Baby Bunting.
1551 THE CONNIE CHRISTIE/ANNUAL/OF/FAIRY/STORIES/and/VERSE/A Digest Juvenile Production
Aust Digest Pty Ltd, 170 Little Collins St, Melbourne, n.d. [1951]
[64]pp, col. & part col. illus. throughout, pic. bd., 270x208mm. KP
An elf boy with pointed red shoes striding across the

cover. Contents: Mother Goose; Mops, A Fairy Story; Little Rhymes; Mary Lou in Candyland.

1552 THE CONNIE CHRISTIE/ANNUAL/Fairy/Stories/and/Verse/Here
Aust Digest Pty Ltd by Specialty Press, Melbourne, n.d. [1952]
[62]pp (64pp inc. fly leaf & blank page at back), inc. 28pp in col., others in part col., bd., 280x210mm. KP
Contents: Simple Simon, A frog he would awooing go, Baby Bunting, Thumbelina & selection from *A child's garden of verse.*
Cover title shows a boy & a girl with a sign 'Fairy Stories and Verses Here'.[*sic*]

1553 THE/CONNIE CHRISTIE/ANNUAL (for 1953)
Aust Digest Pty Ltd, 174 Little Collins St, Melbourne. Printed by The Specialty Press
[64]pp, col. & part col. illus. throughout, pic. bd., cover title, 274x216mm. KMM
Picture of children in toy car on front cover on brown background.
Contents include: Cinderella, Nursery Rhymes, The Fairy Balloon, Happy Thought & verses.

1554 THE/CONNIE CHRISTIE/ANNUAL
Australian Digest Pty Ltd, Melbourne, n.d. [1954]
64pp, 32 col. illus., b/w & part. col. drawings, pic. bd., dec. e/p, 270x215mm. KMM
Contents include: The Queen of Hearts; The Little Red Hen; The Elves and the Shoemaker; The Gingerbread Boy; The Three Bears; Little Red Riding Hood.
Cover shows boy beating a drum.

1555 SUNNY DAYS/ANNUAL
Aust Digest Pty Ltd, Melbourne, n.d.
[61]pp, 8pp col. photos of dolls, 8pp col. plates nursery rhymes &c, 8pp col. plates counting rhymes &c, pic. bd., cover title, 270x210mm. ANL
Nursery Rhymes, The Fairy Mermaid, Counting with Nursery Rhymes.

CHRISTIE, Mrs George

1556 MIRANDA/THE/MONKEY/AND/HER MATES;/especially written for Australian children/By Mrs George Christie/And illustrated by G. Rosalie Wilson/Publisher: Mrs G. Christie, Roseville, Sydney
Printed by G. Arthur McQuilty, Kent St, Sydney [n.d.]
[21]pp, line drawings each page, 187x250mm. Dromkeen
Alphabet rhymes of animals.

Christine
See Booth, Alice Marie

The Christmas Story

1557 THE CHRISTMAS STORY/for Australian children
n.p., n.d. (copy acquired Dec. 1971)
16pp (inc. covers), 8 f/p illus. & slight text, wrappers, 150x185mm. NSL:M

Christmas Tales
See SPOTTY AT THE CIRCUS

The Christmas Tree

1558 THE/CHRISTMAS TREE;/A/Book of Instruction and Amusement,/for/All Young People/with numerous illustrations./[vignette]/London:/James Blackwood, Paternoster Row/MDCCCLIX 1859
viii, 192pp, dec. t.p., col. frontis. & 6 f/p col. illus., numerous b/w sketches in text, clo. blocked in gilt, 170x120mm. CLRC
Contains three chapters entitled Australian Sketches—'Summer Hill Creek' (pp58–61), 'Mount Alexander (pp70–4), 'The Blue Mountains' (pp115-18)—all dealing with gold & the diggings, & each with a coloured illustration of the area.

CILENTO, Ruth

1559 Ruth Cilento/MORETON BAY ADVENTURE/[drawing]/Illustrated by Margaret Cilento/London/Michael Joseph
1961
143pp, 1p glossary, 8 f/p b/w illus. & b/w chapter headings, clo., 185x120mm. KMM

Cinderella's Dream
See Outhwaite, I. R.

The Circus

1560 THE CIRCUS
Photogravures Pty Ltd, Melbourne, n.d.
235x175mm. Grant
This 'book' is made up of 3 sheets of bd., printed in col. on both sides with pictures & verses, folded & stapled in the centre, thus making12pp. The centre fold is one picture covering both pages.

CLAIR, Colin

1561 Figures of the Commonwealth/CAPTAIN JAMES/COOK/The Navigator/by/Colin Clair/Bruce & Gawthorn Limited/Hunters Lane, Leavesden, Watford, Herts.
1963
112pp (inc. 2pp index & 5pp bibliography, &c.), b/w portrait frontis. & 34 b/w illus.(inc. 2 maps) by Anton Lock, clo., 220x140mm. HBM

1562 Figures of the Commonwealth/LACHLAN/MACQUARIE/Father of Australia/by/Colin Clair/Bruce & Gawthorn Limited/Hunters Lane, Leavesden, Watford, Herts.
1963
96pp (inc. 1p index), b/w portrait frontis. & 26 b/w photographic illus., clo., 220x140mm. HBM
Colin Clair was also the editor of the *Commonwealth and Empire Annual.*

CLARK, C. M. H.
ABEL TASMAN. *See* Australian Explorers

CLARK, Charles

1563 AN/ANTARCTIC QUEEN/By/Captain Charles Clark/Author of "My Yarns of Sea Foam" etc./"The Story of an Ocean Tramp"/with original illustrations by/J. B. Greene/[device]/London/Frederick Warne and Co./and New York/All rights reserved.
n.d. [1902]
360pp, 8pp adv., b/w frontis. & 7 b/w illus., pic. clo., 195x130mm. KMM
The adventures of a party shipwrecked on an island in the Antarctic circle south of Cape Horn.

CLARK, Dennis

1564 BOOMER/The Life of a Kangaroo/by/Dennis Clark/Illustrated by/C. Gifford Ambler/1954/Hutchinson & Co. (Publishers) Ltd./Hutchinson House/London, W.1.
135pp (inc. 1p glossary), b/w frontis. & 7 b/w illus., [? clo.; copy seen rebound], 195x130mm. CLRC

1565 BOOMER/The Life of a Kangaroo/by Dennis Clark/Illustrated by C. Gifford Ambler/The Viking Press/New York 1955
144pp [no glossary], b/w frontis. & 7 b/w illus., clo., 210x135mm. ANL
BOOMER/The Life of a Kangaroo/Dennis Clark/Illustrated by/C. Gifford Ambler/Hutchinson of London
2nd imp. March 1957
135pp (inc. 1p glossary), b/w frontis. & 7 b/w illus., clo., 200x135mm. The New Chestnut Library. BBC

French edition
1566 Denis Clark/JOE/SOUS LES EUCALYPTUS/Texte française d'/Alain Valière/Illustrations de René Péron/ Fernand Nathan, Editeur—Paris/18, Rue Monsieur-le-Prince, 18/(vi°)
1958
125pp, col. frontis. & 7 f/p col. illus. & b/w drawings, pic. bd., 210x140mm. LRA

[CLARK, John Howard]
1567 BERTIE/AND THE/BULLFROGS/An Australian Story for Big and/Little Children/Reprinted from the Christmas number of/the Adelaide Observer/ Adelaide/Printed for Private circulation/1874
23pp, unillus., wrappers, 170x100mm. NSL:M
The author was editor of the *South Australian Register* from 1870 to 1878.

CLARK, M. T. [CLARK, Mavis Thorpe, Mrs Harold Latham]
1568 HATHERLEY'S/FIRST FIFTEEN/By/M. R. Clark [*sic*]/Illustrated by F. E. Hiley/Humphrey Milford/ Oxford University Press/London, Edinburgh, Glasgow/Toronto, Melbourne, Cape Town, Bombay
n.d. [1930?]
254pp, col. frontis. & 4 b/w illus. by Francis E. Hiley, clo., 185x120mm. ANL
A boys' school story.
1569 HATHERLEY'S/FIRST FIFTEEN/By/M. R. Clark [*sic*]/Illustrated by F. E. Hiley/Whitcombe & Tombs Ltd./Auckland, Christchurch, Dunedin/Wellington N.Z.; Melbourne, Sydney/London
n.d. [1930?]
Details as in previous edition. VSL
The author states: 'My first published book, *Hatherley's First Fifteen*, was produced by the Oxford Press in London, for Whitcombe & Tombs, when I was eighteen' (*The Singing Roads*, Hugh Anderson, 1965).

1570 DARK POOL ISLAND/By/M. Thorpe Clark/ Geoffrey Cumberlege/Oxford University Press/ Leighton House Melbourne
1949
112pp, unillus., bd., 180x120mm. KMM

1571 MISSING GOLD/by/Mavis Thorpe Clark/Girls' Adventure Series/Hutchinson's/Books for Young People/Hutchinson House/London, W.1.
n.d. [publisher's advise: first pub. October 1949; 2nd ed. April 1951; 3rd ed. 1958]
224pp, unillus., clo., 185x115mm. PAI

1572 THE TWINS/FROM TIMBER CREEK/By/Mavis Thorpe Clark/Geoffrey Cumberlege/Oxford University Press/Leighton House/Melbourne
1949
112pp, unillus., bd., 180x120mm. KMM

1573 HOME AGAIN/AT TIMBER CREEK/M. Thorpe Clark/Geoffrey Cumberlege/Oxford University Press/ Melbourne Wellington
1950
110pp, unillus., clo., 180x120mm. KMM

1574 JINGAROO/Mavis Thorpe Clark/[drawing]/ Geoffrey Cumberlege/Oxford University Press/ Melbourne Wellington
1951
186pp, unillus., clo., 185x120mm. KMM

1575 Mavis Thorpe Clark/THE/BROWN LAND WAS GREEN/Illustrated by/Harry Hudson/William Heinemann Ltd./Melbourne: London: Toronto
1956
219pp, b/w frontis. & 5 b/w illus., clo., 210x140mm. KMM

1576 Second edition 1957
Details as above, but limp clo. (some copies paper-bound), 185x120mm. KMM
This edition was published at the request of the NSW Education Department for use as a school reader.
1577 Mavis Thorpe Clark/THE/BROWN LAND WAS GREEN/Illustrated by/Genevieve Melrose/Lansdowne Press
Melbourne 1967
219pp, b/w frontis. & 5 f/p b/w illus., clo., 200x125mm. CLRC

1578 Mavis Thorpe Clark/GULLY OF GOLD/Illustrated by/Anne Graham/William Heinemann Ltd./ Melbourne: London: Toronto
1958
194pp, b/w frontis. & 5 b/w illus., clo., 210x140mm. BBC
1579 GULLY OF GOLD/Mavis Thorpe Clark/Illustrated by Rachel Tonkin/Lansdowne
Melbourne 1969
191pp, b/w frontis., 4 f/p b/w drawings & 1 b/w drawing in text, clo., d/w designed by Genevieve Melrose, 210x130mm. CLRC

1580 Mavis Thorpe Clark/PONY/FROM TARELLA/ Illustrations by Jean M. Rowe/Heinemann/London Melbourne Toronto
1959
222pp, 6 f/p b/w illus., clo., 190x135mm. NSL:M
1581 PONY/FROM TARELLA/Mavis Thorpe Clark/ Illustrated by Rachel Tonkin/Lansdowne
Melbourne 1969
205pp, 5 f/p b/w illus., clo., d/w designed by Genevieve Melrose, 210x130mm. KMM

JOHN BATMAN. *See* Great Australians

FISHING. *See* Life in Australia

1582 Mavis Thorpe Clark/THEY/CAME/SOUTH/ Illustrations by Joy Murray/Heinemann/London Melbourne Toronto
1963
234pp, 4 f/p b/w illus., clo., 195x130mm. KMM
Pioneering story of early Victoria.
1583 THEY CAME SOUTH/Mavis Thorpe Clark/ illustrated by Peter McMahon/Lansdowne
First published 1963; this edition Melbourne 1971
234pp, b/w frontis. & 4 f/p b/w illus., clo., dec. e/p, 215x135mm. BBC

1584 Mavis Thorpe Clark/THE MIN-MIN/Illustrated by/Genevieve Melrose/[drawing]/Lansdowne Press
Melbourne 1966
206pp, b/w drawings in text, clo., 210x130mm. KMM
Won CBCA Award, 1967.
• Rpt as above, May 1967. KP
• Rpt as above, November 1967. KP
1585 Mavis Thorpe Clark/THE MIN-MIN/The Macmillan Company
New York: Collier-Macmillan, Canada Ltd., Toronto
1969
216pp, 2pp glossary, unillus., pic. clo., cover design by Muni Lieblein, 205x135mm. ANL
German edition
1586 Mavis Thorpe Clark/SYLVIA UND DER TAUGENICHTS/[device]/Signal Verlag—Baden-Baden
1969
192pp, unillus., clo., 205x140mm. LRA
Japanese edition
Kodansha (Publisher), 1972
310pp, illus., 215x155mm. Unseen: IFA

1587 BLUE ABOVE/THE TREES/Mavis Thorpe Clark/[vignette]/Illustrated by/Genevieve Melrose/Lansdowne Press
Melbourne 1967
198pp, 1p preface, b/w drawings in text, clo., 210x135mm. CLRC

1588 BLUE ABOVE THE TREES/Mavis Thorpe Clark/illustrated by Genevieve Melrose
Meredith Press, New York 1968
248pp, 2pp preface, b/w drawings, clo., 210x130mm. Unseen: IFA

A PACK-TRACKER. *See* Early Australians

1589 SPARK OF OPAL/Mavis Thorpe Clark/Illustrated by/Genevieve Melrose/Lansdowne Press
Melbourne 1968
173pp, 1p author's preface, 7 f/p b/w illus., clo., dec. e/p, 215x140mm. KMM

1590 SPARK OF OPAL [by] Mavis Thorpe Clarke [*sic*]
Illus. by Genevieve Melrose, London Methuen 1971
Details as in Lansdowne edition, but with a glossary & plain e/p. Unseen: IFA
German edition

1591 Mavis Thorpe Clark/DIE STADT/DER FUNKELNDEN STEINE/[device]/Signal-Verlag Baden-Baden
1970
183pp, b/w illus., clo., pic. e/p, 206x142mm. LRA

1592 NOWHERE TO HIDE/Mavis Thorpe Clark/Illustrated by/Genevieve Melrose/Lansdowne Press
Melbourne 1969
188pp, b/w frontis. & 6 f/p b/w illus., clo., pic. e/p, 210x135mm. KMM
The story of two escaped German P.O.W.s in wartime Australia.

OPAL MINING. *See* Life in Australia

1593 IRON MOUNTAIN/Mavis Thorpe Clark/Illustrated by/Ronald Brooks/Lansdowne
Melbourne 1970
182pp, 6 f/p b/w illus., map e/p, clo., 210x135mm. KMM

1594 IRON MOUNTAIN/Mavis Thorpe Clark/The Macmillan Company, New York
1970
204pp, 2pp glossary, unillus., pic. clo., 200x135mm. Unseen: IFA

1595 IRON/MOUNTAIN/Mavis Thorpe Clark/Methuen London
1st publ. in Australia 1970 by Lansdowne Press, publ. in Great Britain 1972
176pp & 1p glossary, unillus., clo., map e/p, 218x136mm. KP
German edition

1596 Mavis Thorpe Clark/DAS ERZ IN DEN BERGEN/[device]/Signal-Verlag Baden-Baden
1972
208pp, unillus., sim. clo., 206x140mm. LRA

CLARK, Olive

1597 OUR GARDEN/Little Story Pieces for very young pianists/Words and music/by/Olive Clark/[12 songs listed] Allan & Co Pty Ltd/Melb. Ad. Bend./Printed in Aust 1/- ea
1953
4pp, b/w illus., col. pic. covers, 306x242mm. VSL
Each of 12 songs publ. uniformly & independently.

CLARK, Roland Cuthbert

1598 THE ADVENTURES/OF/ALFRED—/THE FISH/By/Roland C. Clark/Printed and Published by/Winn & Co., Balfour Street/Sydney
n.d. [1948]
30pp, 5 f/p b/w illus., illus. by Delcie Silvia Ferguson, dec. wrappers, 215x135mm. ANL

[CLARK, Samuel]

See [Goodrich, Samuel Griswold]. Peter Parley's Tales About The World

CLARK, William R.

1599 William R. Clark/EXPLORERS/OF THE WORLD/with paintings by Hans Schwarz/Aldus Books London/in association with W. H. Allen London
1964
252pp (inc. 4pp index, 1p acknowledgements &c), col. frontis., fully illus. throughout with numerous col. & b/w illus. & maps, dec. map e/p., clo., 264x186mm. HBM
Cook 9pp, Exploring the Antarctic 24pp, The Australian Deserts, 11pp.

CLARKE, Dorothy

1600 THE TALE OF TERRIGAL BILL/THE LIZARD/By/Dorothy Clarke
Printed by Watkins & Murphy Pty Ltd [Sydney], n.d. [196-?]
46pp, b/w drawings in text, wrappers, cover title, 140x220mm. KMM
Dec. by J. & J. McAdam Studio. Story of a 'skink'.

CLARKE, Mrs Henry [Amy, née KEY]

1601 THE/BUSHRANGER'S SECRET./By/Mrs Henry Clarke, M.A./Illustrated by W. S. Stacey./[device]/London:/Blackie & Son, Limited, 49, Old Bailey, E.C./Glasgow, Edinburgh, and Dublin
n.d. [first pub. 1892, this copy inscr. 1892]
191pp, 32pp adv., b/w frontis., 2 f/p b/w illus., pic. clo., 180x120mm. KP

1602 Another copy as above but after author's name [device]/London/Blackie & Son Limited, 50 Old Bailey, E.C./Glasgow and Dublin. KP

1603 THE/BUSHRANGER'S SECRET/By/Mrs Henry Clarke, M.A./Author of "The Fairclough Family" "The Ravensworth Scholarship"/"The Mystery of the Manor House" &c./Illustrated by W. S. Stacey/Blackie and Son Limited/London Glasgow and Dublin
n.d. [prize 1903]
As before but variant pic. bdg showing spears & figures silhouetted against a panel on front cover. KP
Another copy [prize 1912]. Same cover design. KP

1604 Another copy
Blackie & Son Limited, London and Glasgow
n.d.
Details as above, but
b/w frontis. only (& different illus. used in this ed.)
The Capitol Library. KP

1605 THE/BUSHRANGER'S SECRET/by/Mrs Henry Clarke/Author of "The Ravensworth Scholarship"/"The Mystery of the Manor House", &c./Illustrated by W. S. Stacey/Blackie and Son Limited/London Glasgow and Bombay
n.d. [inscribed 1923]
191pp, b/w frontis. & 3 f/p b/w illus., dec. clo., 175x120mm. RM
The additional illus. here used as frontis. (caption 'So you haven't left me to the crows') is not reproduced in other earlier ed.
Variant imprint, London and Glasgow. KP
Like others of Blackie's popular children's books many variants have been seen, all undated & with at least 4 totally different col. & designs of bdg & numerous slightly different imprints & variations in adv.

CLARKE, Marjorie
1606 SAWDUST/AND SPANGLES/by/Marjorie Clarke/illustrations by/Irene Maher/Angus and Robertson
Sydney 1959
218pp, b/w frontis. & drawings in text, clo., 200x130mm. KMM

1607 KANGAROO/PAWS/by/Marjorie Clarke/ Illustrated by/Leslie Green/[drawing]/London: Dennis Dobson
1964
172pp, b/w illus. in text throughout, clo., 200x130mm. CLRC

CLARKE, Percy
1608 THE VALLEY COUNCIL/or Leaves from/The Journal of Thomas Bateman/of/Cambelego Station, N.S.W./Edited by/Percy Clarke, LL. B./Author of/ "Three Diggers", "The New Chum in Australia",/&c. &c./Illustrated/London/Sampson, Low, Marston & Company/Limited/St. Dunstan's House/Fetter Lane, Fleet Street, E.C./1891
356pp, 2pp preface, b/w frontis. & 4 b/w illus., dec. clo., 190x120mm. ANL
An adventure story, possibly intended for boys, which deals with an imagined community hidden in the bush.

CLARKE, Phyllis Mary [Mrs R. Power]
See Power, Phyllis Mary

CLARKE, Ron (ed.)
1609 ATHLETICS/The Australian Way/Edited by Ron Clarke/Lansdowne
Melbourne, 1971
128pp, b/w photographic frontis. & b/w illus. throughout, pic. bd., 275x200mm. KMM
Australian athletes write for young people on their competitions.

CLEARY, Sheila & Others
1610 AUSSIE/ANIMALS/Stories/Sheila Cleary/ Rhymes/Bartlett Adamson/Drawings/Harry MacDonald & Jack Childs/Book Design by Roderick Shaw
Current Book Distributors, Sydney 1946
28pp, b/w illus. on alternate pages, dec. wrappers, 285x215mm. Aussie Series No. 1. KMM

1611 AUSSIE/BIRDS/Stories—Sheila Cleary/ Drawings—Tina Grace/Book Design by Roderick Shaw
Current Book Distributors, Sydney, n.d. [1948]
32pp, dec. t.p., b/w illus. throughout, dec. wrappers, 270x215mm. Aussie Series No. 2. ANL

CLEGG, Thomas Bailey
1612 THE CHILDREN/OF/THE FIRE MOUNTAIN/A Story of/Adventures in the South Seas/By/T. B. Clegg/London:/Biggs & Co., 139–140, Salisbury Court,/Fleet Street, E.C.
n.d. [1892]
191pp, wrappers, 180x110mm. NSL:M
The action of the story takes place first in Queensland, & then in the South Pacific.

CLELAND, E. Davenport
1613 THE WHITE KANGAROO/A Tale of Colonial Life/Founded on Fact/By/E. Davenport Cleland/ Illustrated/London:/Wells Gardner, Darton & Co./2 Paternoster Buildings, E.C./and 44 Victoria Street, Westminster, S.W.
1890
177pp, 6pp adv., b/w frontis. & 7 b/w illus., dec. clo., 180x130mm. KMM
Illustrations signed 'A.M.S.'
This adventure story with a South Australian background was serialized in *Sunday Reading for the Young*, Wells, Gardner & Darton, London 1889, in 29 instalments with 26 f/p b/w illustrations.
• Rpt 1891, 1893, as above. RM

1614 THE WHITE KANGAROO./A Tale of Colonial Life./Founded on Fact./by/E. Davenport Cleland./ Illustrated/London:/Wells, Gardner, Darton & Co./3, Paternoster Buildings, E.C./and 44, Victoria Street, Westminster, S.W.
1898
Details as in first edition. CLRC

1615 THE WHITE KANGAROO/A Tale of Colonial Life,/Founded on Fact./by/E. Davenport Cleland./ Illustrated/London:/Wells Gardner, Darton & Co./3, Paternoster Buildings, E.C./and 44, Victoria Street, S.W.
1904
Details as in first edition. KMM

CLEVELAND, Brian
1616 PUFFER PETE/Written by/Brian Cleveland/ Illustrated by/Thelma Knight/[drawing]/Lothian Publishing Company/Melbourne Sydney Auckland
1963
28pp, 6 col. illus. & 6 b/w illus., bd., 240x180mm. KMM

CLIFFORD, Graeme
1617 THE OYSTER/AND THE/SNAIL/By Graeme Clifford/[coloured illustration]/[quotation]
The author, Melbourne 1947
16pp, col. illus. on alternate page openings by T.A.Guerin, dec. wrappers, 275x210mm. KMM

CLIFTON, Meda Carlotta Leschen
1618 PANDORA'S BOX/A Book of Family Verse/By Meda C. Leschen Clifton/Price: Two Shillings/Printed and Published by/Paterson's Printing Press Ltd., 882 Hay Street, Perth, W.A.
1940
24pp, b/w drawings, illus. by B. L. C. Clifton, dec. bd., 215x125mm. ANL

CLOVER, Sam T.
1619 PAUL TRAVERS'/ADVENTURES/Being a faithful narrative of a/boy's journey around the world;/showing his mishaps, privations/and ofttimes [*sic*] thrilling experi-/ences and how he won his re-/porter's star/By/Sam T. Clover/Chicago/Way & Williams/1897
368pp, b/w frontis. & 11 b/w plates, pic. clo., 185x120mm. VMOU
Adventure of a Chicago boy who works his way around the world, sailing across the Pacific to NZ and Australia & returning via the UK. Pp183-306 tell of his experiences during a shipwreck off the NZ coast, then rescue on a ship bound for Melbourne & his exertions in Australia to support himself, selling ink, home-made whistles & acting as a bookmaker's clerk.

CLUCAS, Alice
1620 BEHIND THE HILLS/By/A. Clucas/Lothian Publishing Company Pty. Ltd./Melbourne and Sydney
1926
66pp, 1p glossary, unillus., wrappers, 180x120mm. NSL:M
A fantasy of the Western Australian bush.

1621 THE ADVENTURES OF CAROL/IN/BUSHLAND/ By Mrs. Alice Clucas/[drawing]/E. B. Bayliss Print, Publishers/13 Pier Street, Perth, Western Australia
1935

144pp, b/w drawings throughout, dec. bd., 220x130mm. NSL:M

CLUNE, Francis Patrick
1622 Wild Colonial Boys/NED KELLY/by Frank Clune Illustrated by Walter Stackpool/[coloured illustration]/ First published in 1970 by/Angus and Robertson Ltd./ © Frank Clune 1970/ISBN 0 207 12028 5/Registered in Australia for transmission by post as a book/Printed in Australia by Halstead Press, Sydney
[26]pp, col. illus. throughout, pic. bd., pic. e/p, 295x240mm. Young Australia Series. CLRC

1623 BURKE AND WILLS/Frank Clune/Illustrated by Wolfgang Graesse/Angus and Robertson/First published in 1971 by/Angus and Robertson (Publishers) Pty. Ltd./Sydney...etc.
[30]pp [printed on both endpapers], col. illus. throughout, pic. bd., 285x215mm. Young Australia Series. KMM

CLYNE, Densey
Golden Stamp Book of AUSTRALIAN/INSECTS; GOLDEN STAMP BOOK OF AUSTRALIAN WILDFLOWERS. *See* Golden Stamp Books

COBB, James F.
1624 MARTIN/THE SKIPPER/A Tale/For Boys and Seafaring Folk/By/James F. Cobb, F.R.G.S./Author of/ "The Watchers on the Longships"/"Silent Jim" etc./ [quotation]/London/Wells Gardner, Darton & Co., Paternoster Buildings
n.d. [1883?]
403pp, 8pp adv., b/w frontis. & 4 f/p b/w illus., pic. clo., 190x120mm. CLRC
Three chapters are set in Melbourne & the Victorian gold diggings.
1625 Another copy with 35pp adv. Inscribed 1887. RM

COCK, Gwen M.
See 'O'Harris, Pixie'. THE PIXIE O'HARRIS FAIRY BOOK

COCKING, Thelma
1626 TALES FROM THE/SECRET BUSHLAND/by/ Thelma Cocking/Illustrated by/[device]/Sally Medworth/Australasian Publishing Company/Sydney Wellington London
1952
92pp, 7 f/p b/w illus. & b/w drawings in text, bd., 185x135mm. York Series. KMM
• Rpt as above 1954. KP

Cocky in Cage Cut-Out Book
1627 COCKY/IN/CAGE/CUT-OUT/BOOK
n.p., n.d.
4pp, illus., bd., 255x370mm. MAC

COGGER, Harold G.
1628 ANIMALS AND THEIR YOUNG/by/Harold G. Cogger, M.Sc./Curator of Reptiles and Amphibians/ The Australian Museum, Sydney/Illustrated by/Brian Bertram/[device]/7/Longmans 1965
Melbourne
16pp, part. col. illus. throughout, stiff pic. wrappers, 210x160mm. Australian Nature Series
No. 7. BBC

COHN, Ola
1629 THE FAIRIES' TREE/By/Ola Cohn/in collaboration with Norman Davies/Illustrations and Decorations by Marjorie Wood/Music by Tom King/ [drawing]/Australia/H. Tatlock Miller, The Book Nook/Geelong/1932
62pp, b/w frontis. & 9 b/w illus., pic. bd., 250x185mm. ANL
1630 Sgd ed. limited to 110 copies. RM

1631 MORE ABOUT/THE FAIRIES' TREE/By/Ola Cohn/Australia:/Ola Cohn, A.R.C.A. (London)/9 Collins Street/Melbourne/1933
39pp, b/w frontis. & 3 b/w photographic illus., bd., 240x180mm. ANL
Photographs of the carvings by the author on the Fairies' Tree, Fitzroy Gardens Melbourne, & stories which are depicted there.

1632 CASTLES IN THE AIR/By/Ola Cohn/A.R.C.A. (London)/Author of "The Fairies' Tree" and/"More about the Fairies' Tree"/Illustrations by Ola Cohn/ Australia:/Ola Cohn, A.R.C.A. (London)/46 George Street/East Melbourne/1936
48pp, 6 b/w photographic illus., bd., 240x180mm. ANL

Coins of Australia/A Vita-Brits card series
See Skinner, Dion H.

COLACINO, Antonio
1633 SUSAN/AND/SPOTTY/by Antonio Colacino/Ure Smith Sydney London
1967
24pp, col. photographic illus. throughout, pic. bd., 215x180mm. CLRC

COLBECK, Maurice
1634 Eagle Books No 81/SISTER KENNY OF/THE OUTBACK/by/Maurice Colbeck/London/Edinburgh House Press/1965
31pp, unillus., pic. wrappers, 185x120mm. KMM

COLCLOUGH, Ellie P.
1635 THE/MARY-ROSE/SONG BOOK FOR CHILDREN/Words by Ellie P. Colclough, B.A./(Lecturer in Speech, Melbourne Teachers' College.)/Music by Jessie A. Lanphier, Mus.Bac./ (Music and Speech Staff, Education Department,/ Melbourne.)/Illustrations by Jean A. Brown./Wholly set up and printed in Australia./Registered at the General Post Office, Melbourne, for transmission through/the post as a book/Whitcombe & Tombs Pty. Ltd./Melbourne, Sydney, Perth, Geelong
n.d.
23pp, b/w illus. throughout, dec. wrappers, 280x215mm. Grant
Dedicated to the memory of Mary Rose Williams, late lecturer in Music at the Melbourne Teachers' College.

COLE, E. W.
1636 COLE'S FUNNY PICTURE BOOK, published 24 December 1879 by E. W. Cole, Melbourne, price 1/- The book contained 62pp, and no copies so far have been traced.
1637 COLE'S/FUNNY/PICTURE/BOOK/The Funniest/ Picture Book in the world.
E. W. Cole, Melbourne n.d. [1882?]
ii+79pp & 1 p adv. (comprising 63pp & [16] pp supplement) b/w illus., cover title printed in gold on red clo. with gold rainbow design, 275x215mm. Grant
1638 COLE'S/ FUNNY PICTURE BOOK/Price/ Eighteen/Pence/
[rainbow design with wording]/Book/Arcade/ Melbourne/The/Cheapest/Picture Book/in the World./Look through it yourself
n.d. [pres.1883 or after. On pp 40 & 41, a prize of £1000 is offered for a flying machine sgd E. W. Cole Oct. 31st 1882; illus. of the new Book Arcade, opened Cup Day 1883 are included]

86pp, b/w illus. throughout, col. pic. bds, cover title, 274x210mm. VSL
Contents as in previous edition with the omission of 'Strange Stories', including 'An Account of a race of men with Tails'. A supplement (pp78-85) is unillustrated and lists series of children's books sold at the Book Arcade. This copy is bound together with 'Cole's Book Arcade Fun Doctor, the third edition of 10,000 copies in a year'.

1639 COLE'S/FUNNY PICTURE BOOK No.1/or Family/Amuser/and/Instructor/To/delight/the children/and/make/Home Happier/The/Best/ Children's Picture Book/in the World/it contains also choice Riddle Games/and pieces of reading/for Adults./Look through it yourself
E. W. Cole, Melbourne, June 1905 [286 000 copies printed to the time, 2/6]
224pp (inc. covers), dec. cover title with the rainbow & its message in colour intersecting the design, b/w illus. throughout, pic. bds, 270x215mm. KMM

1640 COLE'S FUNNY PICTURE BOOK No.1
E. W. Cole, Melbourne n.d. [presentation page gives date as 19 April 1906]
223pp, b/w illus., pic. bds, 280x220mm. Grant

1641 COLE'S No.1/FUNNY PICTURE BOOK/[rainbow design]/or/Family Amuser/and/Instructor/The/Best/ Child's Picture Book/in the World [as before]
42nd edition totalling 378 000, June 1914
222pp (text preceded with 2pp col. illus., and followed with 2 additional col. pp), b/w illus. throughout, pic. bds, cover title, 275x215mm. AP

1642 COLES/FUNNY PICTURE BOOK No.1/[Rainbow sign, etc.]/or/Family/Amuser/and/ Instructor/[as before]
44th edition, Cole's Book Arcade, Melbourne, Dec.1915
230pp, [4] pp (col. inserts) b/w illus. throughout, pic. bds, cover title, 280x220mm. KMM
(pp193-6 contain adv. material, & reviews &c. and foll. pp. contain biographical notes, photographs & further advs.)

1643 51st Edition/Totalling 500,000 copies/September 1920/COLE'S/FUNNY PICTURE/BOOK/ No.1/Compiled by E. W. Cole/E. W. Cole, Book Arcade/Melbourne
206pp (and 6pp col & b/w insert inc. t.p.) b/w illus. throughout, pic. bds, clo. spine, 275x215mm. KMM
Contents as in 1915 ed. but omitting some advertising material

1644 53rd Edition/Totalling 540,000 copies/October 1921/COLE'S/FUNNY PICTURE/BOOK/No.1/ Compiled by E. W. Cole/E. W. Cole, Book Arcade/ Melbourne
206pp (not inc. covers & pastedowns) and 5 insert pp in col. & b/w inc. t.p with col. illus. of palm trees & waterfall, b/w illus. throughout, col. pic. bds, 276x213mm. KMM

1645 54th Edition 1922, 560 000 copies, unseen, Edmonds Book Gallery cat. 1982

1646 56th Edition/Totalling 600,000 copies/ COLE'S/FUNNY PICTURE/BOOK/No.1/Compiled by E. W. Cole/E. W. Cole, Book Arcade/Melbourne
n.d.[1923]
206pp (portrait of E. W. Cole verso t.p. & 4pp col. insert), b/w illus. throughout, pic. bds, clo. spine, 280x215mm. KMM

1647 61st Edition/Totalling 660,000 copies/COLE'S FUNNY PICTURE/BOOK/No.1/Written and/ Compiled by E. W. Cole/E. W. Cole, Publishers/ McEwan House/Melbourne
n.d. [inscr. 15/7/45]
(vipp & front pastedown, inc. t.p., printed in col.), 206pp, b/w illus., pic. bds, 280x210mm. KP

1648 64th Edition/Totalling 695,000 copies/ COLE'S/FUNNY PICTURE/BOOK/No.1/Written and Compiled by/E. W. Cole/E. W. Cole. Publishers/ McEwan House,/Melbourne
n.d.
206pp & 1 p. adv., col. illus. & poem inside front cover & col. illus. of palm tree on t.p., b/w portrait of E. W .Cole in blue border verso t.p., b/w illus. throughout, col. pic. bds, clo. spine, 280x215mm. KMM

1649 65th Edition/Totalling 720,000 copies/ COLE'S/FUNNY PICTURE BOOK/NO. 1/Written and Compiled by E. W. Cole/E. W. Cole Publisher/ McEwan House, Melbourne.
n.d. [1946?]
206pp, col. dec. t.p. & 3 col. pp., b/w illus. throughout, pic. bds, 280x210mm. CLRC

1650 67th Edition/Totalling 800,000 copies/ COLE'S/FUNNY PICTURE/BOOK/No.1/Written and Compiled by/E. W. Cole, Publisher/McEwan House/ Melbourne/Registered at the GPO Melbourne, for transmission by post as a book/Printed by Wilke & Co. Pty Ltd.,19-47 Jeffcott Street, Melbourne
n.d.
[6] pp col., & 206pp, b/w illus. throughout, col. pic. bds, 275x215mm. KMM

1651 68th Edition/Totalling 800,000 copies/COLE'S/ FUNNY PICTURE/BOOK/No. 1/(Copyright)/Written and Compiled by/E. W. Cole/E. W. Cole Publishing House/Melbourne/[3 lines as before]
n.d.
206pp & 4pp in col. (inc. t.p.), b/w illus. throughout, pic. clo., 275x215mm. KMM
Cole's Nursery Rhyme Stories, & Cole's Funny ABC Book adv; verse & rainbow sign printed in col. on front pastedown.

1652 69th Edition/Totalling 860,000 copies/ COLE'S/FUNNY PICTURE/BOOK/No. 1/(Copyright)/ Written and Compiled by E. W. Cole/ E. W. Cole Publishing House/Melbourne/[as before]
n.d. [1951]
206pp, inc. 6pp col., b/w illus. throughout, pic. bds, 275x215mm. CLRC

1653 70th Edition/Totalling 870,000 copies/ COLE'S/FUNNY PICTURE/BOOK/No. 1/Written and Compiled by/E. W. Cole/E. W. Cole, Publishing House/Melbourne[as before]
n.d.
206pp, col. pic t.p.& 3 pp col. illus., b/w illus. throughout, pic. bds, 275x210mm. KMM

1654 71st Edition/Totalling 885,000 copies/COLE'S/ FUNNY PICTURE/BOOK/No. 1/(Copyright)/Written and Compiled by/E. W. Cole/E. W. Cole/Melbourne [as before]
n.d.[1965?]
Details as in 70th ed. KMM

1655 72nd Edition/ Totalling 900,000 copies/ COLE'S/FUNNY PICTURE/BOOK/No.1/(Copyright)/ Written and Compiled by/E. W. Cole/E. W. Cole Publications/Melbourne [3 lines as before]
n.d.[1971]
vii pp printed in col (inc. pastedown & t.p.), 206pp. b/w illus. throughout, pic. bds, 270x215mm. KMM

1656 COLE'S FUNNY PICTURE BOOK [Sequel]
COLE'S FUNNY PICTURE BOOK/Juvenile Half/ Funny Pieces/Sequel/Adult Half/Instructive Pieces/ [rainbow sign with lettering'The Family Amuser and Instructor','To Delight the Children and make Home Happier' &c.]

E. W. Cole, Book Arcade, Melbourne, n.d. [1905]
254pp, b/w illus., pic. bds, cover title, 280x220mm. KMM
Later known as Cole's Funny Picture Book No. 2; date established from advertisements in the *Argus* and the *Herald* 1905.

1657 Rpt [1906?] inscribed Feb. 1907. As above with 'No.2' on front cover instead of 'Sequel'. Unseen (info. from Cat.27, 1984, of Antique Books & Curios, Sydney)

1658 Sequel/to/COLE'S/ CHILD'S FUNNY PICTURE BOOK/[contents]/Serious Supplement for Older Readers/Funny Picture Book No. 2. 3rd Edition, Totalling 25,000. November 1914
256pp, b/w illus., col. pic. bds, 275x220mm. CLRC

1659 Sequel to Cole's Funny Picture Book, No. 1/COLE'S/FUNNY PICTURE BOOK/No. 2/Compiled by/ E. W. COLE/4th Edition10,000 Copies, totalling 35,000 copies/March, 1920/Printed and Published by/ E. W. Cole, Book Arcade, Melbourne
206pp, 7 col. & part-col. illus., b/w illus. throughout, pic. bds, 275x215mm. KMM

1660 Another copy dated March 1920 as above but 223pp, the additional pages being of adult material such as 'What Books have done and will do for Mankind', by E. W. Cole, etc. KMM

1661 Sequel to Cole's Funny Picture Book No. 1/COLE'S/FUNNY PICTURE BOOK/No. 2/Compiled by/ E. W .Cole/6th Edition 20,000 copies, totalling 75,000 copies/May, 1922/Printed and Published by/ E. W. Cole, Book Arcade, Melbourne
206pp., b/w illus. & 6pp in col. (inc. col. photograph of Cole's Book Arcade shop front with an advertising jingle based on 'This is the House that Jack Built'), pic. bds, 275x215mm. CLRC

1662 [COLE'S FUNNY PICTURE BOOK] No. 2 [part of t.p., i.e. inside front cover, missing] Compiled by/E. W. COLE/7th Edition 20,000 Copies totalling 95,000/May 1925/Printed and Published by/E. W. Cole, Book Arcade, Melbourne
206pp, b/w illus. (no col. pages, at least in this copy), pic. bds, 275x215mm. CLRC

1663 58th Edition/10 000 copies, totalling 100 000 copies/COLE'S/FUNNY PICTURE/BOOK/ No.2/ Compiled by E. W. Cole/E. W. Cole Book Arcade/ Melbourne.
n.d.
206pp (inc. 7 pp col. illus., col. illus. t.p. on front pastedown), b/w illus., col. pic. bds, 276x214mm. KMM
Printed and published by E. W. Cole

1664 60th Edition/Totalling 110,000 copies/COLE'S/ FUNNY PICTURE/BOOK/No. 2/Written and/ Compiled by E. W. Cole, Publishers/McEwan House/ Melbourne
206pp, 6pp col. & part-col. illus., b/w illus., col. pic. bds, 275x215mm. CLRC

1665 63rd Edition, 20,000 copies/Totalling 185,000 copies/COLE'S/FUNNY PICTURE/BOOK/No. 2/Written and Compiled by/E. W. Cole/E. W. Cole, Publishers,/McEwan House,/Melbourne
n.d. [1948?]
198pp, pic. t.p. & 3pp col. illus., b/w illus., col. pic. bds, 280x210mm. CLRC

1666 65th Edition/Totalling 215,000 copies/COLE'S/ FUNNY PICTURE/BOOK/No. 2/(Copyright)/Written and Compiled by/E. W. Cole/E. W. Cole Publishing House/Melbourne/[2 lines, Registered at the GPO, &c.] Printed by Wilke & Co.
n.d.[1950?]
198pp, pic. t.p., & 3 pp col. illus., b/w illus., col. pic. bds, 280x210mm. TG

1667 66th Edition/Totalling 255,000 copies/COLE'S FUNNY PICTURE/BOOK/No.2/Copyright)/ Written and Compiled by/E. W. Cole/E. W. Cole Publishing House/ Melbourne/[2 lines]
n.d. [195-?]
198pp. as above CLRC

1668 67th Edition/Totalling 285,000 copies/COLE'S/ FUNNY PICTURE/BOOK/No.2/(Copyright)/ Written and compiled by E. W. Cole/E. W. Cole/Melbourne/ Registered at the GPO Melbourne, for transmission by post as a book./Printed by Wilke & Co. Ltd., 19–47 Jeffcott Street, Melbourne
n.d. [196-?]
198pp, as above. KMM

1669 69th Edition/Totalling 860,000 copies./COLE'S/ FUNNY PICTURE/BOOK/No. 2/(Copyright)/ Written and Compiled by/E. W. COLE/E. W. Cole, Publishing House/Melbourne/Registered at the GPO Melbourne/[2 lines]
n.d.[1970?]
198pp, as above. CLRC

1670 COLE'S/CHILDLAND/or/Pleasing Poems/For/ Pretty Pets/Pleasant Learning Land/Number One The Book Arcade, Melbourne n.d. [189-?]
130pp, b/w illus. throughout, pic. bds, cover title, 270x210mm. Grant
Booklets, Baby Land, Mama Land. Boy Land, Naughtiness Land, Dolly Land, &c. published separately at threepence each were intended to be part of 'a Kindergarten Cyclopaedia, for all ages'.

1671 COLE'S CHILDLAND/or/Pleasing Poems/for/ Pretty Pets/Pleasant Learning Land/Number/ One no t.p. but preface & contents inside front cover.
78pp (continuous pagination) advs both sides of back cover, limp pic. boards, 280x210mm. KP

1672 Rpt as above but without continuous pagination containing [115pp] . KMM

1673 COLE'S/DOLLYLAND/A Kindergarten Book,/ Containing 100 pictures and poems,/Being a Specimen part of Cole's Childland/[etc. list of other parts and subject dealt with, drawing]/ Printed and Published by E. W. Cole./Book Arcade, Melbourne/Sold by all booksellers/Number eleven
n.d.
20pp(inc. both wrappers) b/w illus. green & black pic. wrappers, with advs inside front & both sides of back wrapper, 280x220mm. RM
One of a series of 18 uniform booklets also bound together to form Cole's Child Land

1674 COLE'S COMIC/ANIMAL STORY BOOK/Telling Why the Animals do/all sorts of Funny Things/ [drawing of two bears]/E. W. Cole,/Book Arcade, Melbourne; 333, George Street Sydney;/67, Rundle Street Adelaide./(Printed in Great Britain)
Printed by Cassell & Company, n.d.[1907?]
109pp & 1p drawing, f/p b/w illus. & 18 f/p & numerous other b/w illus. by Harry B. Neilson, pic. bd., 255x192mm. KP
No Australian content.

1675 COLE'S/KINDERGARTEN/FIRST BOOK/FOR/ LITTLE AUSTRALIANS/Bright Pictures/and/Easy Lessons/E. W. Cole/Book Arcade, Melbourne: 333 George Street, Sydney/67 Rundle Street, Adelaide/(All rights reserved)
n.d. [copy inscribed 1908]
95pp, col. frontis. & 6 f/p col. illus. & 4pp with some col. illus., col. pic. bd, 254x194mm. KP

1676 Rpt as above, n.d.(on t.p. 'Printed in Great Britain') [78pp, inc. pastedowns] col. frontis & 5 f/p col. illus.,

& 2 pp part-col. illus, b/w illus. throughout, col. pic. bds, 255x190mm. KMM
No Australian content in either ed.

1677 COLE'S/KINDERGARTEN/FAIRY TALES/with numerous illustrations/ E. W. Cole: Book Arcade/ Melbourne/Sydney Adelaide
n.d.
57pp, col. frontis. & 1 f/p b/w illus. & 38 text illus. pic. bds, cover title, 230x190mm. Grant

1678 COLE'S/KINDERGARTEN/POETRY BOOK/with numerous illustrations/[drawing]/E. W. Cole: Book Arcade/Melbourne/Sydney Adelaide
[58]pp, col. frontis. & b/w illus. throughout, pic. wrappers with rainbow sign & 'Cole's/Kindergarten/ Poetry Book 'etc., 235x190mm. VSL
Printed in Great Britain. No Australian content.

1679 COLE'S/FIRST BOOK/FOR LITTLE AUSTRALIANS/Printed in Great Britain/E. W. Cole/ Book Arcade, Melbourne/333 George St, Sydney; 67 Rundle St., Adelaide
n.d.
96pp, col. frontis. & 13 f/p col. illus., 2 half-page col. illus. & b/w illus. throughout, dec. bds, 235x190mm. Grant

1680 Rpt as above, n.d.
64pp, col. front & 7 f/p col. illus., b/w illus. in text, pic. bds, 235x190mm. KMM

1681 COLE'S/FUN AND FROLIC/FOR/TINY TOTS/ Coloured Pictures/and Bright Stories/E. W. Cole/Book Arcade, Melbourne; 333 George Street, Sydney/67 Rundle Street, Adelaide/[All rights reserved]/Printed in Great Britain
n.d. [191-?]
[159pp] col. frontis. & 5 col. plates, b/w illus. in text, dec. bd., 255x190mm. KMM
No Australian content, but familiar rainbow design on the front cover.

1682 COLE'S/ROSEBUD/STORY BOOK/[rainbow]/ Full/of/Tales, Talks/and/Pretty Pictures/ Commonwealth of Australia/E. W. Cole Book Arcade Melbourne/346 George St, Sydney/67 Rundle Street Adelaide/Printed in Great Britain
n.d. [1911?]
174pp (possibly pp missing), line drawings, pic. bd., 240x187mm. KP

1683 COLE'S/ROSEBUD STORY/BOOK/[drawing]/ Melbourne: E. W. Cole, Book Arcade
n.d. [inscribed 1921]. Printed in Great Britain by T. Nelson and Sons
64pp, col. frontis. & 7 f/p col. plates, b/w illus. in text, pic. bd. ('Coles/Rosebud/Story Book/For Little Australians' with rainbow sign), 250x193mm. VSL
No Australian content.

1684 COLE'S/MERRY-GO-ROUND/ STORY BOOK/ Melbourne: E. W. Cole, Book Arcade
n.d. [1913?]
64pp, col. frontis. & 7 f/p col. illus., b/w text illus., pic. wrappers, 250x190mm. Grant

1685 COLE'S MERRY/BIRD/AND ANIMAL/PICTURE BOOK/[rainbow]/Full/of Coloured Pictures/ and/Jolly Rhymes/Commonwealth of Australia/E. W. Cole/ Book Arcade Melbourne/346 George Street Sydney/67 Rundle Street Adelaide
n.d. [1921]
40pp, col. & b/w illus., pic. bds, 240x180mm. KP
Contents include 'TheWagtails' Wedding' by C. E. James, also published separately by E. W. Cole.

1686 COLE'S CHUMMY BOOK OF LITTLE AUSTRALIANS, new 2/6, Rainbow cover, unseen, adv.
Argus, 8 Nov. 1913

1687 COLE'S EMPIRE PICTURE ANNUAL, 2/6, adv.
Argus, 29 Nov. 1913

1688 COLE'S/PEEP SHOW/STORY BOOK/[drawing]/ E. W. Cole Book Arcade, Melbourne; 346 George St. Sydney/67 Rundle St., Adelaide
n.d. [copy inscribed 1916]
[194]pp, 46 f/p col. plates & numerous b/w drawings, pic. bd., 222x180mm. TG
Printed in Great Britain. Contents not Australian.

1689 COLE'S/JINGLE JUNGLE BOOK/Pictures and Verse for/Little Folk/[drawing]/Illustrated by Harry B. Neilson/E. W. Cole/Book Arcade, Melbourne: 333 George Street, Sydney/67 Rundle Street, Adelaide/(All rights reserved)/Printed in Great Britain
n.d. [1919?]
[72]pp & 3 double-spread col. illus., b/w illus. throughout, 255x195mm. MC

1690 COLE'S/JOLLY BOOK/FOR/LITTLE AUSTRALIANS/[drawing]/Printed in England/E. W. Cole/ Book Arcade, Melbourne/333 George St., Sydney; 67 Rundle St., Adelaide
n.d.
318pp, b/w frontis., numerous b/w illus., pic. bds, pic. e/ps, 255x190mm. Grant

1691 COLE'S/JOLLY WORKERS BOOK/For Little Australians/Full of Bright Colored Pictures/[rainbow]/ In every rank,/Great or small,/'tis industry/supports us all./Commonwealth of Australia/E. W. Cole Book Arcade, Melbourne/346 George Street, Sydney/67 Rundle Street, Adelaide./Printed in America
n.d., no t.p. in copy seen
58pp (?pp missing), col. illus. throughout, col. dec. border to each page of text, pic. bd., 254x200mm. KP
Various occupations described in verse & opposite col. illus. by H. D. Kennedy. No Australian content.

1692 A RAILWAY BOOK FOR LITTLE AUSTRALIANS Ed. Lilian M. Pyke Author of 'Max, the Sport' .'Camp/ Kiddies' ,'Jack of St Virgils', etc./With Coloured Pictures, Line Illustrations and an Alphabet in Black and White by Linden Miller.
E. W. Cole Book Arcade, Melbourne, 246 George Street, Sydney, 67 Rundle Street, Adelaide, n.d. [1920?]
40pp, col. frontis. & 3 f/p col. illus., 2 col. illus. in text, bd., 245x180mm.
On front cover: 'Cole's Railway Picture Book. A Jolly Book for Little Australians full of bright pictures Commonwealth of Australia E. W. Cole Book Arcade Melbourne' LRA

1693 COLE'S HAPPY TIME PICTURE/AND NURSERY RHYME BOOK/By Lillian M. Pyke/Author of 'Max the Sport', 'Camp Kiddies'.'Jack of St Virgil's', etc./with 8 coloured pictures and 35 line illustrations in black and white/by/Percy Leason/E. W. Cole,/Book Arcade, Melbourne/346 George St, Sydney: 67 Rundle St., Adelaide/Principal Bibliopole [*sic*] to the Commonwealth
n.d. [1920]
48pp, 8 col. plates & 35 b/w drawings, pic. bds, 250x187mm. ANL

1694 COLE'S HAPPY TIME/PICTURE AND NURSERY/RHYME BOOK/No. 2/By/Lillian M. Pyke/Author of/"Max, the Sport", "Camp Kiddies"/"Jack of St. Virgils" etc/With Coloured

Pictures and Line Illustrations in Black and White,/and an Alphabet by Percy Leason/E. W. Cole/Book Arcade, Melbourne/346 George St, Sydney: 67 Rundle St., Adelaide/Principal Bibliopole to the Commonwealth
n.d. [1921]
48pp, 2 f/p col. illus., 12 f/p part col. illus., b/w drawings in text, pic. bd. (with rainbow design), 242x186mm. VSL

1695 COLE'S/LITTLE BOOK OF/RIDDLES/AND JOKES/E. W. Cole, Book Arcade/Melbourne/346 George St.,/Sydney/67 Rundle St.,/Adelaide
n.d. [192-?]
48pp, unillus., wrappers, 155x80mm. CLRC
Not specifically for children

1696 AUSTRALIAN ALPHABET with 26 eight-line rhymes by Lillian Pyke, unseen, adv. *Argus*, 17 Dec. 1921

1697 ROBINSON CRUSOE/and the/SWISS FAMILY ROBINSON/Retold in easy Words for Little Australasians [*sic*] Full of Pictures/[vignette]/ Commonwealth of Australia:/E. W. Cole Book Arcade Melbourne/346 George Street, Sydney/67 Rundle Street, Adelaide
Printed in Great Britain by Thomas Nelson & Sons, n.d.
128pp [i.e. 64 & 64pp], col. frontis. & 5 col. plates, b/w text drawings, pic. bds, 255x195mm. KMM
Title page & rainbow-patterned cover Cole's only contribution to this publication.

1698 COLE'S HOLIDAY BOOK/ For Boys and Girls/ Edited by Lilian [*sic*] M. Pyke/Author of Sheila at Happy Hills/Camp Kiddies/Max the Sport, etc/ [device]/E. W. Cole Book Arcade, Bourke St., Melbourne/Sydney Adelaide
n.d. [inscr. Jan. 1929]
72pp, 4 col. illus., b/w drawings in text, pic. bds, 240x180mm. KMM
Col. illus. repro. paintings by F. W. McCubbin; some drawings sgd 'C .E. James'. Editor's preface refers to the book as the 'Southern Seas Story Book' which is the title heading throughout. Ref. also made to the Southern Seas Story Book coming out as a children's monthly.The contents are the same as Pyke's 'Southern Seas Story Book' except for the covers, the front cover of this book having the famous rainbow design.

1699 COLE'S/ABC/AND/OTHER JOYS/FOR LITTLE AUSTRALIAN/GIRLS AND BOYS./With/pictures Bright/to give Delight/Commonwealth of Australia/E. W. Cole Book Arcade Melbourne/346 George St., Sydney/67 Rundle Street, Adelaide./Printed in Great Britain
n.d.
Contains 8 books originally published by Blackie & Son Ltd, bound together with separate pagination, *ABC* (10pp), *One Two Three; Playtime; Funny Things, Little Ones; Trains; Bo Peep; Red Riding Hood* (each 12 pp) col. & b/w illus., pic. bds, 220x170mm. Grant

1700 COLE'S/ANIMAL PICTURE BOOK/By/Edith Carrington/[drawing]/E. W. Cole/Book Arcade Melbourne; 333 George Street, Sydney/67 Rundle Street, Adelaide/(All rights reserved)/Printed in Great Britain
n.d. [inscribed 1919]
[66]pp, 3 double-spread col. illus., 2 f/p col. illus., b/w drawings throughout, 3 col. illus. inside front & back covers, pic. bd., 250x195mm. KMM
Factual articles with accompanying illus. (inc. 2pp on The Kangaroo, with 1 p. illus, though nothing else Australian).

1701 COLE'S/NURSERY RHYME/STORIES/[drawing]/ Nursery Rhyme Continuations by Jean E. Turnley/ Illustrations by J. Ferguson/Registered at G.P.O. Melbourne for transmission by post as a book/E. W. Cole Melbourne
n.d. [1946]
[48]pp, part-col. & b/w illus., dec. wrappers, 275x210mm. ANL

1702 [drawing]/COLE'S/GREAT BOOK/FOR BOYS/ E. W. Cole/Melbourne
n.d. [1948]
192pp, col. frontis., b/w illus., pic. bds, 245x185mm. KMM
Ed. Turner Lee, illus. by Ian Cole

1703 COLE'S/FUNNY A.B.C. BOOK/[drawing]/E. W. Cole Melbourne/[6 lines contents]
n.d.
[48]pp , 8 f/p col. illus., part-col. & b/w illus., stiff pic. wrappers, 270x210mm. KMM
Reprints material from previous Cole publications & includes new material by Jean Turnley, & others.

1704 Rpt, with some variations, some illus. redrawn, different cover designs and different text inside front cover. KMM

1705 COLE'S/NOISY/PICTURE BOOK/Specially written and illustrated/by/Douglas Tainsh/Registered at the G.P.O. Melbourne/for transmission by post as a book
E. W. Cole, Melbourne, n.d. [1950]
[48]pp, col. & b/w illus. throughout, dec. t.p., stiff pic. wrappers, 240x180mm. CLRC

1706 COLE'S GREAT/BOYS' BOOK/No.2 /E. W.Cole/ Melbourne
n.d. [1950]
192pp, col. frontis, b/w illus., pic. bds, 240x180mm. ANL
ed. Turner Lee; illus. Noel Rhoden; authors include Darcy Niland, Stanley Brogden, M. Thorpe Clark.

1707 COLE'S GREAT/GIRLS' BOOK/E. W. Cole/ Melbourne/Registered GPO Melbourne, for transmission by post as a book.
n.d. [1950]
192pp, dec. t.p., b/w illus. by G. F. Rhoden, pic. bds, 240x180mm. ANL

1708 COLE'S/FUNNY DRAWING/BOOK/specially written and illustrated/by/J. W. Sampson/ Registered at G.P.O. Melbourne for transmission by post as a book/Printed for the publishers, E. W. Cole Publishing House, 343 Little Collins Street, Melbourne/by Wilke & Co. Ltd.,19-47 Jeffcott Street, Melbourne, Victoria
n.d. [1951]
48pp, 16pp col. illus., b/w drawings throughout, pic. wrappers, 245x180mm. ANL
Cole's Intellect Sharpener, and *Cole's Fun Doctor* have not been included as appearing to have been intended for general and family reading, rather than especially for children.

COLE, Ida J. L.

1709 Whitcombe's Story Books/"KOO"/THE KOOKABURRA/By/Ida J. L. Cole/For ages 8 to 9 years/[drawing]/Whitcombe & Tombs Ltd./ Christchurch, Auckland, Wellington, Dunedin, Invercargill, N.Z./London Melbourne Sydney, Perth
n.d. [1941]
39pp & 1p adv. & adv. inside front cover & both sides

of back, b/w frontis. & 4 b/w illus. in text, pic. wrappers, 182x120mm. CLRC
See McLaren 360

COLE, P. C.

1710 Imperial Edition NO. 259/SIX/ACTION/SONGS/ Words by/P. C. Cole/Music by/Frederick Hall/Allan & Co.,/Proprietary Limited/Melbourne Sydney Adelaide Bendigo
n.d. [193-?]
20pp (inc. 3pp adv.), unillus., pic. wrappers, 305x230mm. KP

1711 Another copy as above, but
Allan & Co 276 Collins St
18pp (inc. 1p adv.), pic. wrappers, 305x230mm. KP
Has '40c' printed on front cover, hence post-1966. Contents the same.

COLE, Percival R.

1712 Imperial Edition No 488/ONCE UPON A TIME/ or/A Trip through Storyland/a musical playlet/for youngsters/Dialogue and lyrics by P. R. Cole, music by Arthur Loam/Musical contents [listed]/copyright 1951 by Allan & Co Pty Ltd 276 Collins St, Melbourne/ Allan & Co. Pty Ltd/Melbourne Adelaide Bendigo
28pp, unillus., dec. wrappers, 245x180mm. VSL

1713 GREAT AUSTRALIANS/A Reader for Schools,/ Percival R. Cole, M.A., Ph.D./Ninepence/Second and Revised Edition/Sydney./George B. Phillip & Son./298 George Street.
n.d.
95pp, b/w photographs, limp clo., 180x115mm. CLRC

1714 GREAT AUSTRALIANS/A reader for Schools/ Revised and Enlarged Edition./By Percival R. Cole, M.A., Ph.D., F.C.P./with the collaboration/of the late John Cole, J.P./Sydney/George B. Philip & Son./451 Pitt Street
1928
128pp, 1 b/w map & 8 plates, wrappers, 180x120mm. KMM
Adv. on back cover: Great Australian Explorers by K. R. Cramp, Pioneers of Australian Industry by Percival R. Cole.

1715 MYTHS AND LEGENDS/OF/MANY LANDS/By/ Percival R. Cole./M.A. (Sydney) Ph.D. (Columbia) FC8/[8 lines]/Humphrey Milford/Oxford University Press/Cathedral Building, Melbourne/And at London Edinburgh Glasgow New York/Toronto Bombay Capetown/1933
xpp, 127pp, b/w photographic frontis., bd., 190x120mm. ANL

COLEMAN, Frederick

1716 WHITE MAGIC/Adventures in search of oil and a/kidnapped explorer in New Guinea/By/Fred Coleman/Angus and Robertson Ltd./Sydney London/ 1941
219pp, unillus., clo., 185x125mm. CLRC

COLEY, John

1717 MAKE-AND-DO/50 Things for Boys and Girls to make and do/John Coley/No. 1 40c
Page Publications, Surry Hills NSW, n.d.
50pp, b/w illus., col. pic. wrappers, 272x210mm. KP

COLLIER, Madeline

1718 THE LOST/PRINCESS/by/Madeline Collier/with four illustrations/in colour by/Ida Rentoul Outhwaite/ A. & C. Black Ltd./4, 5, & 6 Soho Square, London, W.1. 1937
64pp, col. frontis. & 3 f/p col. illus., clo., 180x120mm. KMM
Doubtful Australian author.
• Rpt 1942. KP

COLLIER, R. Stephen

1719 SHORT STORIES/OF AUSTRALIA'S MANUFACTURING/INDUSTRIES and the Lives of/ Some of Our Business Men,/A Reader for Schools/for Civics, Morals, Geography,/and Supplementary Reading./By S. Collier/Public School Spencer./Price 1/-/Sydney./George B. Philip & Son./451 Pitt Street
n.d.[192-?]
94pp (inc. 1p preface, 1p foreword, 1p 'Duty's Call'), unillus., wrappers, 180x120mm. ANL
Rubber industry, Tents, Tarpaulins, Canvas, The Golden Fleece, Meggatt's Linseed &c.

COLLINGRIDGE, George

1720 ALICE/IN/ONE DEAR/LAND/By George Collingridge
No place of imprint [? privately printed by author], n.d. [1922]
41pp, de luxe ed., col. frontis, col. & b/w woodcut illus., 2 original sgd. etched illus., wrappers, 270x200mm. NSL:M

1721 ALICE/IN/ONE DEAR/LAND/by George Collingridge
Printed by W. C. Penfold & Co., Sydney, n.d. [1922]
34pp, col. frontis. & 15 loose illus., wrappers, 260x205mm. VSL
Full-page adv. on verso of title page: 'Alice in one dear land (An Appreciation) by Arthur J. Vogan'.

1722 THROUGH/THE/JOKE IN CLASS/By/Geo Collingridge/Hornsby NSW./Australia/Price, five shillings
The author, n.d. [1923]
20pp, 1p adv., map frontis. & b/w woodcut illus. throughout, wrappers, 280x210mm. NSL:M

Collins Children's Encyclopedia of Knowledge

1723 COLLINS CHILDREN'S ENCYCLOPEDIA OF KNOWLEDGE Book of Wild Life
Collins Book Depot, Melbourne 1962.
One of several vols with different subtitles but containing virtually no Australian content. VSL

COLLINS, Cuthbert Dale [pseuds 'Stephen Fennimore', 'Michael Copeland']

1724 LOST/Dale Collins/Author of/"Ordeal" "Jungle Maid"/"Rich and Strange" "The Fifth Victim"/etc./ London/George G. Harrap & Co. Ltd./Bombay & Sydney
1933
304pp, unillus., clo., 180x120mm. NSL:M
The story, which has an Antarctic setting, is *about* children & is said to be *for* children.

1725 THE VOYAGE OF/THE LANDSHIP/By/Dale Collins/Illustrated by/Grace Golden/London/The Pilot Press Ltd./1947
213pp, b/w drawings throughout, clo., 185x120mm. ANL

1726 THE HAPPY EMIGRANTS/By/Dale Collins/ Author of/Winds of Chance; Ah, Promised Land!;/Ordeal; Bright Vista; Far-off Strands;/Utility Baby; A Sister for Susan;/etc. etc./London/Herbert Jenkins Limited/3 Duke of York Street, St. James's, S.W.1
n.d. [1948]
172pp, unillus., clo., 185x120mm. ANL

1727 ROBINSON CAREW—/CASTAWAY/by/Dale Collins/Author of "The Voyage of the Landship" etc./London/The Pilot Press Ltd./1948
224pp, 9 b/w illus., (sgd 'Golden') clo., 185x120mm. ANL

1728 BUSH HOLIDAY/by/Stephen Fennimore/Illustrated by/Sheila Hawkins/William Heinemann Ltd./Melbourne London Toronto
1948
180pp, 6 f/p b/w illus., clo., 195x130mm. KMM
• Rpt 1963. KP

1729 Stephen Fennimore/[vignette]/BUSH HOLIDAY/Illustrations by Nino Macknight/Garden City N.Y./Doubleday & Company Inc./1949
242pp, 7 f/p b/w illus. & b/w drawings throughout, clo., 210x145mm. ANL

1730 BUSH HOLIDAY/by/Dale Collins/Illustrated by/Sheila Hawkins/William Heinemann Ltd./Melbourne London Toronto
1949 [First Australian edition]
192pp, 6 f/p b/w illus., clo., 195x130mm. KMM
• Rpt 1950, 1951, 1952. KMM
• Rpt 1963. KP

1731 BUSH HOLIDAY/—/Stephen Fennimore/Illustrated by/Sheila Hawkins/Penguin Books
1958
187pp, 2pp adv., 6 f/p b/w illus., dec. wrappers, 180x110mm. A Puffin Book. KMM

1732 Another edition, Penguin Books 1966
Details as above, but with new cover design by Elizabeth Grant. KMM

French edition

1733 Stephen Fennimore/VACANCES/EN AUSTRALIE/Traduit de l'anglais par E. Vincent/Illustrations de Claire Marchal/[vignette]/Editions de l'Amitié/G. T. Rageot/Paris—Bruxelles
n.d. [1957?]
206pp, b/w drawings throughout, clo., dec. e/p, 175x115mm. ANL

1734 THE VANISHING BOY/by/Dale Collins/Illustrated by/Margaret Horder/[drawing]/William Heinemann Limited/Melbourne London Toronto
1949
167pp, b/w frontis. & 5 f/p b/w illus., b/w drawings in text, clo., 195x130mm. KMM

1735 BUSH VOYAGE/by/Stephen Fennimore/Illustrated by/Margaret Horder/[drawing]/William Heinemann Ltd./Melbourne London Toronto
1950
238pp, b/w frontis. & 30 b/w illus., clo., 195x130mm. ANL

1736 BUSH VOYAGE/by/Dale Collins/Illustrated by/Margaret Horder/William Heinemann Ltd/Melbourne London Toronto
1950
238pp, b/w frontis. & 30 b/w illus., clo., 180x120mm. KMM

1737 CORAL SEA/ADVENTURE/by Dale Collins/Illustrated by/M. Brailey/William Heinemann Ltd./Melbourne London Toronto
1951
187pp, b/w frontis. & 5 b/w illus., clo., 190x130mm. ANL

1738 [drawing]/SHIPMATES/DOWN UNDER/by Dale Collins/Illustrated by Raffaello Busoni/Holiday House New York 1950 [First American edition of *Coral Sea Adventure*]
188pp, b/w illus. throughout, clo., 190x135mm. ANL

1739 SUNSET PLAINS/by/Stephen Fennimore/and/Dale Collins/Illustrated by/Margaret Horder/William Heinemann Ltd./Melbourne London Toronto
1953
196pp, b/w frontis. & 13 b/w drawings, clo., 180x120mm. CLRC

1740 STORM OVER SAMOA/by/DALE COLLINS/Illustrated by/Vera Jarman/William Heinemann Ltd./Melbourne London Toronto
1954
170pp, 1p author's note, b/w frontis. & 5 b/w illus., clo., 185x120mm. KMM

1741 ANZAC/ADVENTURE/The Story of Gallipoli told for Young Readers/by/Dale Collins/Illustrated by/Frank Norton/Angus and Robertson
Sydney 1959
168pp, extended b/w frontis., b/w drawings in text throughout, clo., map e/p, 215x140mm. KMM

[COLLINS, Rev. W. M. pseud. 'Peggy Gogg']

1742 Copyright/A/FANCY DRESS/BALL AT THE ZOO/Verselets/for/Terselets/[drawing]/By Peddy Gogg/Price 1/6 Wholly set up, designed, and printed in Australia by The Advocate Press,/309–313 Little Lonsdale Street, Melbourne
n.d. [1923]
32pp, 2 col. illus. & b/w drawings throughout, dec. bd., cover title, 250x180mm.
Humorous verses. ANL

COLOMBINI, Jolanda

1743 Jolanda Colombini/AUSTRALIAN JOURNEY/Illustrated by Mariapia/Edited in English by Charlotte Penn/©1963 by Casa Editrice "Piccoli"/Publishers Piccoli Milan
20pp (inc. 1p adv.), 9 f/p col. illus., pic. bd., 230x180mm. KP

Columbus and Cook

1744 COLUMBUS AND COOK/The Story/of their/Lives, Voyages, and Discoveries/W. & R. Chambers, Limited/London and Edinburgh
n.d. [prize label 1902]
152pp (inc. 1p quotes, 1p preface), 1p adv., b/w frontis., b/w portrait of Cook, pic. clo., 177x120mm. KP
The *Santa Maria* and the *Endeavour* are depicted on front cover which has the title as 'The Story of Columbus and Cook'. Cook pp87-152.

1745 COLUMBUS/AND COOK/The story of their lives, Voyages/and Discoveries/London: 38 Soho Square. W./W. & R. Chambers, Limited/Edinburgh: 339 High Street
n.d. [school prize 1918]
Details as above. KP

COLVIN, Robert

CAROLINE CHISHOLM. *See* Great People in Australian History

COLWELL, Max

1746 PETER THE WHALER/IN SOUTHERN SEAS/by/Max Colwell/[drawing]/Illustrated by/Geoffrey C. Ingleton/Melbourne/London Toronto/Macmillan/New York/St. Martin's Press
1964
118pp (inc. 2pp editor's note), part. col. b/w frontis. & 12 part. col. illus., b/w drawings in text, dec. clo., map e/p, 215x135mm. KMM
Great Stories of Australia Series No. 5 (edited by Kylie Tennant).

1747 THE JOURNEY OF/BURKE AND WILLS/by Max Colwell/Illustrated by John Sykes/Paul Hamlyn/London Sydney New York Toronto
1971
59pp, 2pp index, col. illus. throughout, extended col. dec. t.p., extended col. map, pic. bd., pic. e/p, 310x230mm. KMM

1748 CAREERS/WITH ANIMALS/Max Colwell/Macmillan of Australia/1968
Melbourne
47pp, 1p adv., unillus., stiff wrappers, 180x115mm. CLRC
Uniform books the same series, by the same author, all CLRC
1749 CAREERS IN AVIATION
1750 CAREERS IN NURSING
1751 CAREERS IN WRITING
By Guy Saunders:
1752 CAREERS IN ADVERTISING
1753 CAREERS IN THE RETAIL TRADE

1754 THE VOYAGES/OF/MATTHEW FLINDERS/By Max Colwell/Illustrated by Hutchings/Paul Hamlyn/London New York Sydney Toronto
1970
64pp (inc. 2pp index), col. frontis., col. illus. throughout, pic. bd., pic. e/p, 310x230mm. KMM

COMFORT, John
1755 TOBY'S LUCK/By/John Comfort/with a Frontispiece by/R. Petherick/London/The Sheldon Press/Northumberland Avenue, W.C.2/New York and Toronto: The Macmillan Company
n.d. [1927, first publ. 1922]
120pp, 10pp adv., col. frontis., pic. clo., 184x120mm. ANL

COMFORT, Mildred Houghton
1756 PETER AND NANCY/IN AUSTRALIA/and Islands of the Pacific/By/Mildred Houghton Comfort/Author of 'Peter and Nancy in Europe'/'Peter and Nancy in South America'/'Peter and Nancy in Africa'/'Peter and Nancy in Asia'/Beckley-Cardy Company/Chicago
1937
320pp, col. frontis. & many b/w illus., pic. clo., dec. map e/p, 190x130mm. NSL:M

Commonwealth of Australia Jubilee 1901–1951
1757 [Coat of Arms] COMMONWEALTH/OF AUSTRALIA/JUBILEE/1901–1951
Published by the Commonwealth of Australia, n.d. [1951]
38pp, b/w photographic illus. throughout, map, dec. wrappers, cover title, 165x145mm. KMM
Presented to school children to commemorate Fifty Years in the Life of the Commonwealth of Australia.

The Commonwealth of Nations
1758 THE COMMONWEALTH OF NATIONS
n.d. [1954?]. The Specialty Press Ltd, Melbourne
[12]pp, b/w photographs inside covers & in text, double-spread col. photograph of the Queen on her 1954 Royal Tour in Ceylon, wrappers, 207x137mm. KP
Front cover photograph of the children Prince Charles & Princess Anne.

Commonwealth Savings Bank
1759 COMMONWEALTH/SAVINGS/BANK [col. illus.]
n.p., n.d.
6pp folding leaflet, col. illus. throughout, 180x110mm. KP
Illus. signed 'Bron' and 'G. PIKE'. Savings promotion.

The Commonwealth Savings Bank Colouring Book
1760 THE/COMMONWEALTH/SAVINGS BANK/COLOURING BOOK/[illus.]/No. 2
Printed by Simmons Limited, 32 Parramatta Rd, Glebe, Sydney, n.d.
12pp, b/w pictures to be col., by G. Pike, pic. wrappers, 240x180mm. KP
1761 Another copy, but
16pp, col. pic. bd. JH

CONLEY, Enid
1762 THE DANGEROUS/BOMBORA/Enid Conley/Illustrations by Jeff Conley/Coolarlie Pty. Ltd./Sydney/1968
117pp, b/w frontis., 2 b/w illus., map, clo., 210x135mm. ANL

CONNELL, Mary and MORRIS, Erica
1763 SEVEN/PRIMARY SCHOOL PLAYS/by/Mary Connell and Erica Morris/[drawing]/Whitcombe & Tombs Pty. Ltd./Melbourne, Sydney, Perth
n.d.
62pp, b/w drawings, wrappers, 240x180mm. ANL

Conquest of the Air
1764 Nabisco/From Fable to Fact/CONQUEST/OF THE AIR/A Vita-Brits Project Card Series/30c
n.d. [1966?]
[16]pp (inc. 4pp text), 2pp col. maps of world, spaces for cards to be pasted in, col. pic. wrappers, cover title, 240x180mm. KP

CONYERS, Evelyn
1765 BABES IN THE BUSH/And other verses/[decoration]/By/Evelyn Conyers/Edward A. Vidler/178 Collins Street, Melbourne
n.d. [1927]
38pp, b/w drawings, illus. by Hazel Grant, dec. bd., 190x140mm. CLRC

'COOEE'
See Walker, William Sylvester

COOK, Deborah & GALLASCH, Keith
1766 IMPROVING/ON THE/BLANK/PAGE/Selected by deborah cook & keith gallasch/illustrated by ann newmarch/rigby
1972
114pp (inc. index, acknowledgements), 7 f/p col. illus., b/w drawings & b/w photographs, stiff wrappers, 210x150mm. KP
Anthology of poems from Australia & overseas.

COOK, Hume
1767 AUSTRALIAN/FAIRY/TALES/By Hume Cook/With illustrations by/Christian Yandell/Published by J. Howlett-Ross/Melbourne/all rights reserved/Registered by the Postmaster-General for transmission through the post as a book
1925
140pp (inc. 1p author's preface, 2pp foreword by W. M. Hughes & 2pp notes), col. frontis. & 5 col. illus., 11 f/p b/w illus. & other b/w drawings, clo., 280x215mm. KMM

Le Cook du Jeune Age
1768 LE COOK/DU JEUNE AGE,/ou/Abrégé des Voyages/de ce Célèbre Navigateur
388pp, bd., 175x100mm. NSL:M
Mitchell Library copy has title page & frontispiece of another work inserted as follows:
BEAUTÉS/DES VOYAGES DU/CAPITAINE COOK,/ou/Relation Historique/du premier et du plus intéressant des voyages de cet/illustre marin/Paris,/Librairie enfantine et juvénile/de Pierre Maumus,/

éditeur de la Bibliothèque populaire,/1, rue du Jardinet, quartier de l'École-de-Médecine
NSL:M

Le Cook de la Jeunesse
See Bérenger, J. P.

COOK, James
1769 Nos 1 & 2, in a wrapper, Price One Penny, to be continued in Penny Weekly Numbers./THE/ ADVENTURES AND VICISSITUDES/OF/CAPTAIN COOK,/MARINER./Showing How by Honesty, Truth, and Perseverance, a Poor, Friendless Orphan Boy became a/Great Man./[engraving, with caption— 'James Cook attacked by the Farmer's Dog']/Beautifully Illustrated./London: E. Harrison and all Newsagents./ Gratis with No. 3, a Portrait of Captain Cook
T.p. reads: The/Adventures and Vicissitudes/of/ Captain Cook,/Mariner./Showing how in Honesty, Truth and/Perseverance, a Poor, Friendless Orphan Boy/became a Great Man./with Illustrations./ London:/E. Harrison, Salisbury Square, Fleet Street./ 1870
158pp in 45 chapters, 20 engraved illus. together with the b/w engraved portrait, 270x185mm. BL
Fictitious & sensational ventures of J. Cook in his days as an apprentice, written for boys. BL
See also "James Cook" under 'J 'for several anonymous items.

[COOK, Kerry]
1770 A/LETTER/TO THE/POPE/from a sixteen year old Australian school girl
Patrician Publications, Sydney 1969
[64]pp, b/w photographic illus. throughout, illus. by 'Megan' (author's sister), stiff dec. wrappers, 210x270mm . BBC
Pictorial & written account of an Australian family's adventures in Rome.

COOK, Linda May
See 'BETTY AND JOHN'

COOKE, Beryl
1771 A/FISHY/TALE/by/Beryl Cooke/illustrated by/ Nicholas Fisk/Published by Angus & Robertson/ London. Sydney. Melbourne. Wellington
1957
69pp, col. dec. t.p., b/w frontis. & part. col. illus. throughout, dec. e/p, clo., 235x155mm. BBC

COOKE, Mervyn A.
1772 TELL ME A TALE/Written by/Mervyn A. Cooke/ illustrated by/Neroli Mondon/Printed and Published by/Paterson's Printing Press Ltd./882 Hay Street Perth/Western Australia/Price/Three shillings and sixpence
n.d. [1940]
57pp, 1 f/p b/w illus., line drawings, 270x165mm. VSL
Includes some verse & stories first broadcast by the Australian Broadcasting Commission.

1773 MORE ADVENTURES/OF SONNY JIM/By/ Mervyn A. Cooke/Stories and Verses/for Children/ Price 3/6/Printed and Published by/Paterson's Printing Press Ltd./65 Murray Street Perth, W.A.
n.d. [1944]
56pp, unillus., 240x165mm. VSL

1774 A DATE/WITH DESTINY/by/Mervyn A. Cooke/ illustrated by/Richard Ressom/[device]/Longmans Longmans Green, Croydon, Victoria, 1965
161pp, 10 b/w illus. in text, clo. (with drawing printed in white on front cover), 215x130mm. KMM
Adventure story of a search for lost treasure from a Dutch ship wrecked 300 years ago, set in the Yanchep Caves of Western Australia.

COOKE, N. G.
1775 Parish of Holy Trinity/Grenfell/[photograph]/THE CHILDREN'S CORNER/Motto:/[2 lines]
Printed by D. S. Ford, Sydney, n.d. [1940]
32pp (inc. introduction & foreword dated 1937), b/w photographic illus., wrappers, 180x120mm. ANL
Book of prayers & devotional pictures.

COOPER, Janet
CATHERINE SPENCE. *See* Great Australians

COOPER, Leone Brook
1776 OOGOOZOO/and other Verse/(Written and Illustrated by Leone Brook Cooper)/[vignette]/ Australia/Shipping Newspapers Limited/16 Bond Street, Sydney/1936
47pp, b/w frontis., 1 f/p b/w illus. & b/w drawings in text, pic. bd., 240x175mm. Grant

COOPER, Nelle Grant
1777 AUSTRALIANS ALL/Bush Folk in Rhyme/By Nelle Grant Cooper/[decoration]/Illustrations by Dorothy Wall/Australia/Angus & Robertson Limited/ 89 Castlereagh Street, Sydney/1934
30pp, b/w illus. throughout, dec. bd., 210x160mm. CLRC

1778 MORE AUSTRALIANS/Land and Sea Folk in Rhyme/By Nelle Grant Cooper/[drawing]/Illustrations by Phyllis Shillito/Australia/Angus & Robertson Limited/89 Castlereagh Street, Sydney/1935
24pp, b/w drawings throughout, bd., 210x160mm. KMM

1779 AUSTRALIANS ALL/Land and Sea Folk in Rhyme/By Nelle Grant Cooper/[drawing]/Illustrations by Dorothy Wall/and Phyllis Shillito/Angus & Robertson Limited/Sydney: London/1939
54pp, b/w drawing throughout, bd., 240x185mm. KMM
This book comprises the author's two books previously published noted above.
• Rpt as above, 1940. KMM

1780 PLAY SONGS FOR/CHILDREN/By/Nelle Grant Cooper/Music by/Dorothy R. Mathlin/Decorations by/Pat O'Harris/[drawing]/Angus and Robertson Ltd./ Sydney: London
1941
32pp, b/w drawings in text, dec. bd., 285x22mm. Bunyip Song Book No. 1. KMM
Contains 12 songs with music.

1781 RHYMING/ABC/[drawing]/by/Nelle Grant Cooper/decorations by Pat O'Harris
Ross Brothers Pty Ltd Print, 45 Kent Street, Sydney [1945]
16pp, printed in col. and drawings throughout, pic. wrappers, cover title, 273x212mm. ANL
Author publ. adult humorous verse under the pseud. 'Kay Grant'.

COOPER-VINES, J.
1782 Make it yourself handbooks/THE AUSTRALIAN BOYS'/BOOK OF BOATS/Sailing Models/By/ J. Cooper-Vines/with numerous illustrations/Australia/ Angus & Robertson Limited/89 Castlereagh Street, Sydney/1934
71pp (inc. 3pp glossary), 2pp preface, diagrams, stiff wrappers, 185x120mm. NSL:M

1783 THE BOY SCIENTIST'S/NOTE BOOK/By/J.

Cooper-Vines/[device]/Shakespeare Head Press/310 George St. Sydney/1936
72pp (inc. 1p foreword & 2pp preface & 8pp adv.), b/w diagrams, pic. wrappers, 177x117mm. ANL

'COORIES, The' [pseud. Edward Haughton]
1784 THE RUNAWAY/ROCKING/PONY/by/the Coories
Printed by Renwick Pride, Melbourne, n.d.
8pp, illus., 2 drawings & photographic illus., pic. wrappers, cover title, 245x185mm. ANL

1785 THE/WONDERFUL JOURNEY/The Story of Three/Little Troutlings/by/The Coories/Pictures by/ Graham Thorley
The Lantern House [Bacon] Melbourne, n.d. [1949]
16pp, b/w drawings, map inside front cover, dec. wrappers, cover title, 285x220mm. ANL
1786 Another copy with no imprint but 'Renwick Pride' on back wrapper. KMM

COPE, Gwen
1787 FAIRY VERSE/FOR/LITTLE FOLK/By/Gwen Cope/Illustrated by Pixie O'Harris/[drawing]/Angus & Robertson Limited/89 Castlereagh Street, Sydney/1936
75pp, b/w photograph of author, b/w drawings throughout, dec. bd., 215x165mm. ANL
Author a girl of thirteen years of age.

1788 UNDER THE JOY/OF THE SKY/And other verses/By/Gwen Cope/Illustrated by Pixie O'Harris/ [drawing]/Angus and Robertson Limited/89 Castlereagh Street, Sydney/1936
45pp, b/w frontis. photograph of author, b/w drawings throughout, dec. bd., 180x125mm. ANL
1789 UNDER THE JOY/OF THE SKY/And Other Verses/By/Gwen Cope/Illustrated by Pixie O'Harris/ [drawing]/Angus & Robertson Limited/89 Castlereagh Street, Sydney/1937
68pp, b/w frontis. photograph of author, 24 f/p b/w illus. & b/w drawings in text, dec. bd., 200x145mm. ANL
Includes 4 additional poems.

'COPELAND, Michael'
See Collins, Dale Cuthbert

COPLEY, Roger
HARTOG AND TASMAN; DAMPIER AND COOK.
See Great People in Australian History

COPP, Lillian Grace
1790 SUE/STANWOOD/By/Lillian Grace Copp/ Australia/Cornstalk Publishing Company/ 89/Castlereagh Street, Sydney/1927
303pp, b/w frontis., clo., 180x115mm. ANL
U.S.A. setting, doubtful Australian.

COPPEL, Marjorie
OUR FOOD. *See* Australia at Work

C.O.R. Merrythought Nursery Rhymes
1791 C.O.R./MERRYTHOUGHT/NURSERY RHYMES/ [drawing]/With Compliments from/The Commonwealth Oil Refineries Limited/Melbourne/ [drawing]
n.p, n.d. [192-?]
[12]pp, b/w drawings throughout, pic. bd., cover title, 230x183mm. KMM
No imprint; rhymes accompanied by drawings on every page.

The C.O.R. Road Safety Colouring Competition
1792 A contribution to the Australian Road Safety Council's Campaign/THE C.O.R. ROAD SAFETY/ COLOURING COMPETITION/1954/South Australian Section (including Northern Territory)
Printed by the Premier Printing Co. Pty Ltd, 27-31 Little Bourke St, Melbourne
12pp, 5 f/p b/w illus., pic. wrappers, cover title, 186x250mm. CLRC
Col. illus. of 'Ginger Meggs' on front & back covers; the b/w illus. taken from Ginger Meggs comic strips publ. in the S.A. *Sunday Mail*. To be col. in for competition.

CORBIN, Iris
1793 BY WIRELESS AND/PLANE/and other tales/By/ Iris Corbin/London/Society for promoting/Christian Knowledge
n.d.
32pp, b/w frontis. & 2 f/p b/w illus., illus. by R. H. Brock, pic. wrappers (with frontis illus. reproduced on front cover & adv. inside & outside back cover), 165x105mm. KMM
St. Christopher Books No. 45.
Consists of 3 missionary stories, the first concerning Flynn of the Inland; the second, missionaries at Kwato, an island off the New Guinea coast.

CORMACK, Maribelle & BYTOVETZSKI, Pavel L.
1794 ROAD TO/DOWN UNDER/by Maribelle Cormack/Illustrations by/Edward Shenton/D. Appleton-Century Company/Incorporated/New York London
1944
301pp, 1p foreword, b/w drawings throughout, clo., 190x130mm. NSL:M
Written in collaboration with Pavel L. Bytovetzski. A story of the emigration from the island of Eday in the Orkneys to Australia in the middle of the nineteenth century.

CORNISH, T. S.
1795 BLESSED PETER CHANEL: A Play for Children
No 209 ACTS Publication

1796 BERNADETTE: A Play for Children
No 181 ACTS Publication
Both unseen, listed on back of 'Little Therese' by 'Miriam Agath' publ. by The Australian Catholic Truth Society.

A Coronation Booklet
1797 A CORONATION BOOKLET/Presented to Young People/Empire Youth Sunday 3rd May 1953
Printed by The Specialty Press Ltd, Melbourne
16pp, b/w photographic illus. & col. inset, col. pic. wrappers, map of royal procession through London on back wrapper, 210x135mm. KP
Separate 4pp leaflet from Sir Dallas Brooks, Governor of Victoria, inserted.

The Coronation Queen Elizabeth
1798 THE CORONATION/QUEEN ELIZABETH/June 2nd 1953
Litho. in Australia by Deaton & Spencer Pty Ltd, Sydney
A gift [to school children] from the Australian Commonwealth Government
Fold-out panoramic book of 20pp printed on both sides with col. lithographic figures & b/w London scenes (verso)
B/w photographs of Royal family & 4pp printed matter, 102x110mm. KP

CORRELL, Valeria
1799 GAY GAMBOLS/A Nonsense Story/Written and

Illustrated by/Valeria Correll/Commonwealth of Australia:/Edward A. Vidler/Melbourne
n.d. [1923]
39pp, b/w frontis. & 9 b/w line drawings, bd., 240x185mm. VSL

COSTELLO, Michael
1800 HAROLD EFFERMERE/A Story of the Queensland Bush/By/Michael Costello/George Robertson & Company/Melbourne, Sydney, Adelaide/Brisbane, Perth and London/1897
309pp, unillus., clo., 185x120mm. Grant
The story begins with the hero at school, where he is interested only in sport; his guardians take him away from school & send him into the bush, & the book tells of his adventures in Queensland. Not specifically a boys' book.

Cottee's Children's Party Book
1801 COTTEE'S CHILDREN'S PARTY BOOK/For Fun and Fare
Publ. by Cottee's Passiona Ltd & printed by Wm Brooks Printers, Sydney, n.d.
40pp (inc. 8pp col. illus. & col. illus. inside covers), part col. illus., pic. wrappers, cover title, 135x215mm. KP
Recipes, games &c.

COTTON, Emily Alice
1802 POEMS OF PEM/FOR PETS/By/Emily Alice Cotton/(Emily McGregor)/Price—Two shillings/ Printed and Published by/Paterson's Printing Press Limited/882 Hay St., Perth—Western Australia
n.d. [1940]
27pp, b/w drawings throughout, dec. bd., 245x140mm. ANL

COTTRELL, Dorothy [Mrs Walter Wilkinson]
1803 'WINKS/HIS BOOK/By/Dorothy Cottrell/Author of.../With illustrations by/J. Nicholson, A.R.E., R.W.S./and/Paul Bransom/Jarrolds Publishers London/Limited 34 Paternoster Row E.C.4/MCMXXXIV 1934.
122pp, col. frontis. & 5 col. illus., 10 b/w illus., clo., 220x140mm. VSL

1804 WILDERNESS/ORPHAN/The Life and Adventures of Chut/the Kangaroo/By/Dorothy Cottrell/Author of 'The Singing Gold'/Australia:/Angus & Robertson Limited/89 Castlereagh Street, Sydney/1936
68pp, unillus., clo., 185x120mm. KMM
1805 Dorothy Cottrell/[drawing]/WILDERNESS/ ORPHAN/Ian Novak—Sydney
1961 [printed in the Netherlands] Illustrated by Grant Roberts
64pp, part. col. t.p., 2 part. col. & 16 b/w illus., clo., 210x155mm. BBC

COULTER, E. L.
1806 THE/WISE OLD ELEPHANT/Forty Story Talks to Boys and Girls/By E. L. Coulter/Hodder and Stoughton/Limited London
n.d. [NSL:M copy acquired 1928]
202pp, unillus., clo., 185x120mm. NSL M

COUNSEL, June
1807 MOSTLY TIMOTHY/by June Counsel/Illustrated by Anne Knight/Longman Young Books
London 1971
111pp, b/w drawings throughout, clo., 195x125mm. BBC
This English author spent three years travelling round Australia & New Zealand. Three of Timothy's toys, about whom the stories are written, are stuffed koalas from Australia, otherwise there is no Australian content.

Country Friends
1808 COUNTRY FRIENDS
Photogravure Pty Ltd (Melbourne), n.d.
16pp (b/w illus. inside covers), f/p illus. in full col., part col. & b/w, cover title, no text, 232x172mm. KP
Some of the illus. have an Australian subject (e.g. platypus, &c).

COUPER, John Mill
1809 THE THUNDERING/GOOD TODAY/J. M. Couper/[device—A Book for new adults]/The Bodley Head/London Sydney/Toronto
1970
140pp, unillus., clo., d/w designed by Bernard Blatch, 215x135mm. KMM

COUPER, Sue
1810 Sue Couper/THE LEMON THIEVES/Illustrated by M. J. Couper and L. N. Mitchell/Acacia Press Pty Ltd, Blackburn Victoria
1972
89pp, 5 f/p & several smaller b/w illus., dec. bd., 210x160mm. CLRC

COUTTS, A. J.
1811 PLAYS/One Act and Entr'acte/A Collection for Amateur Groups/and Secondary Schools/By/A. J. Coutts, M.A., Dip. Ed./Sydney/Dymock's Book Arcade Ltd./1950
126pp, 10pp introduction, diagrams &c., otherwise unillus., wrappers, 180x120mm. KMM

COUTTS, David Boyd
1812 THE/EMPIRE SHOP/A One-Act Play./Suitable for Performance by/Young People/By/D. B. Coutts, B.A., Dip. Ed./(Copyright)
The author, Melbourne, Vic., n.d. [1931?]
16pp (last blank), unillus., stiff wrappers, 193x130mm. ANL

COWARD, Max
1813 LET'S MAKE/SIMPLE PUPPETS/written and illustrated/with lino-cuts/by/Max Coward
Lansdowne Press Pty Ltd, Melbourne, n.d. [1961?]
47pp, dec. t.p., part. col. & b/w lino-cuts throughout, dec. wrappers, 230x155mm. BBC

COWEN, Zelman
ISAAC ISAACS. *See* Great Australians

COWIE, Mrs Harrison Lee [Bessie, née Vickery, later Cowie]
AUNTIE FAITH'S TRAVELS. *See* LEE, Mrs Harrison

COX, W. H.
1814 THE/SUNSHINE/BOOK/[drawing]/With pictures to color/No 67 An Australian Production by/Gunn & Taylor Pty Ltd. Melbourne/[one line 'distributors' &c]
n.d. [194-?]
[16]pp, b/w illus. throughout, col. pic. wrappers, 277x210mm. ANL

CRABBE, Kenneth Wallace
See Wallace-Crabbe, Kenneth

CRADDOCK, Vaughan Alfred and ALBISTON, Barbara
1815 Rivers of the World—2/THE MURRAY/by V. A. Craddock and Barbara Albiston/Oxford University Press
Melbourne, n.d. [1960]
32pp, 1 map & 16 b/w illus., limp clo., cover designed by Jack Townend, cover title, 200x155mm. ANL
• Rpt 1963, 1966. KP
THE MURRAY RIVER. *See* Life in Australia

CRAIG, Shaun
1816 THE COLOURFUL TALE OF/EEK/THE EMU/by Shaun Craig/design: bruno grasswill/a colouring book/big enough to enjoy/use the finished/pictures as posters/published by Paul Hamlyn pty. ltd./176 south creek road dee why west new south wales 2099/first published 1972 printed in australia
51pp, drawings (printed in blue) on alternate pages & additional pages at end of book, wrappers, 495x335mm. CLRC

CRAMERI, Talbot
SNOW AT TATARU. *See* Trend Books

CRAVEN, John [ed.]
1817 John Craven/FOOTBALL THE/AUSTRALIAN WAY/[device]/Lansdowne/[b.w photograph]
Melbourne 1969, rpt 1970
122pp, b/w photographic illus., pic. clo., 282x205mm. KP

CRAWFORD, Allen
Electric Power. *See* Around Australia Program

CRAWFORD, Raymond Maxwell
1818 A/PICTURE HISTORY/OF/AUSTRALIA/Prof. R. M. Crawford/Illustrated by/Clarke Hutton/[vignette]/Oxford University Press/London/1962
62pp, col. t.p., col. illus. throughout, dec. bd., map e/p, 280x210mm. KMM
1819 A PICTURE HISTORY OF AUSTRALIA
Watts, New York 1963
62pp, col. illus. by Clarke Hutton, col. maps (inc. e/p), 29cm. [*sic*] Unseen: ANB 1964
1820 A/PICTURE HISTORY/OF/AUSTRALIA/Prof. R. M. Crawford/Illustrated by/Clarke Hutton/[drawing]/Melbourne/Oxford University Press/London Wellington New York
First Australian edition 1970
62pp, col. illus., stiff pic. wrappers, col. e/p maps, 280x210mm. BBC

CREED, Mrs J. P.
See Mack, Louise Marie

Crinkle the Caterpillar
1821 CRINKLE/THE/CATERPILLAR/"New Friend of the Little Folk"
Magician Publications, Melbourne, n.d. [1945]
16pp, 6 f/p col. illus., b/w drawings, col. illus. by Rosemary B. Smith, dec. wrappers, cover title, 240x180mm. ANL

CRISP, Frank
1822 THE/SEA ROBBERS/Frank Crisp/Illustrated by/A. K. Lee/[device]/Hamish Hamilton/London
First published 1949; first published in Great Britain 1963
215pp, b/w frontis., 20 b/w chapter headings & tailpieces, pic. clo., cover designed by Bernard Wragg, 185x120mm. Big Reindeer Edition. CLRC
Adventure story set in New Guinea, the hero being the sole survivor of an Australian cargo ship wrecked by a gang seeking its precious cargo of pearls.
1823 Frank Crisp/The SEA ROBBERS/illustrated by R. M. Powers/Coward-McCann, Inc. New York
1953
247pp, b/w extended frontis., 9 b/w drawings, b/w chapter headings, clo., 205x135mm. KP

1824 A Dirk Rogers Adventure/THE GIANT OF/JEMBU GULF/by/Frank Crisp/London/Hodder and Stoughton
1959
160pp, col. frontis. only, clo., 184x118mm. ANL

1825 A Dirk Rogers Adventure/THE ICE DIVERS/by/Frank Crisp/London/Hodder and Stoughton
1960
126pp, col. frontis. only, clo., 180x120mm. TI
Boys adventure story which takes place on a whale factory ship in the Antarctic.

CRIST, Alice Guérin
1826 "GO IT! BROTHERS!!"/By/Alice Guérin Crist/Registered by the Postmaster-General/for transmission through the post as/a book printed in Australia/Wholly set up and printed in Australia by/Pellegrini & Co./Sydney Melbourne Brisbane.
n.d. [1929]
155pp, unillus., clo., 190x130mm. KMM
A school story for boys which first appeared in serial form in the *Catholic Advocate*, Brisbane.

CROFTS, Rhona Reidy
See MacGillivray, Mona & Crofts, Rhona Reidy

CROKER, T. Crofton (ed.)
1827 THE/CHRISTMAS BOX/An/Annual Present for Children/Edited by T. Crofton Croker, Esq., F.S.A./Author of The Fairy Legends of the South of Ireland/[vignette]/London:/William Harrison Ainsworth/Old Bond Street/MDCCCXXVIII 1828
232pp, clo., 165x100mm. NSL:M
A Collection of stories, verses &c. for the young, including 'A Voyage to New Holland' (anon., 12pp).

CROMBIE, Isabel
1828 My Home No. 10/MY HOME IN/AUSTRALIA/[drawing]/Isabel Crombie
Longmans Green, London 1960
17pp, col. illus. throughout, stiff dec. wrappers, cover title, 150x120mm. NSL:M
• Rpt as above, 1961. KMM

CRONIN, Bernard
1829 THE TREASURE OF/THE TROPICS/By/Bernard Cronin/Ward, Lock & Co. Limited/London and Melbourne/1928
256pp, b/w frontis. & 3 b/w illus., clo., 185x120mm. KMM

CRONIN, Bernard & KERR, Doris Boake
See 'Grey, Stephen'

CROPP, Ben
1830 SAMMY THE SEAL/Ben Cropp/[device]/Rigby Limited
Adelaide 1966
61pp, 14 b/w photographic illus., clo., 210x130mm. CLRC
The story of a young seal who is captured & tamed, & becomes an attraction at a Sydney aquarium.

1831 CHEEKY/THE DOLPHIN/Ben/Cropp/Rigby/Limited
Adelaide 1968
51pp, 8pp col. photographic illus., 16pp b/w photographic illus., pic. clo., 210x135mm. CLRC

CROSS, Constance
1832 SAILOR JACK/A Tale of the Southern Seas/By/Constance Cross/Author of 'After Twenty Years', 'Stanley's Summer Visit'/etc. etc./London/The Religious Tract Society/56 Paternoster Row, 65 St. Paul's Churchyard/and 164 Piccadilly
n.d. [first published 1888]

160pp (inc. preface), 16pp adv., b/w engraved frontis. & 2 f/p engravings, clo., 180x115mm. Grant
Story of a voyage to Melbourne & return to England after a stay of three weeks. Grant

1833 SAILOR JACK/A Tale of the Southern Seas/By/C. Cross/Author of 'After Twenty Years,' etc./London/The Religious Tract Society/4 Bouverie Street & 65 St. Paul's Churchyard
n.d.
157pp (inc. preface) & 8pp adv., col. frontis. & col. dec. t.p. (with col. border), 2 f/p b/w illus., pic. clo., 180x120mm. KMM

1834 Rpt as above, fifth impression, n.d.
155pp & 24pp adv., col. frontis. only, clo., 180x120mm. KP

CROSS, Zora

1835 THE CITY OF/RIDDLE-ME-REE/By/Zora Cross/Illustrated by Olive Crane/Angus & Robertson Ltd. Sydney
n.d. [1918]
16pp, 2pp adv., col. frontis. & 1 col. illus., b/w drawings throughout, dec. wrappers, 180x130mm. KMM
Verses

CROSS, Zora (ed.)

AUSTRALIAN NURSERY RHYMES
Unseen: Advertised inside front cover of Barrett's *Bushland Babies,* Platypus Series, 1924. Never published

CROW, Alexander

1836 GUM LEAVES/Addresses for the Young/By/Alexander Crow/Minister of Albany, Western Australia/With Introductory note by/The Rt. Rev. Dr. George H. Morrison/Moderator of the General Assembly, United Free Church of/Scotland/London/James Clarke & Co. Limited/9 Essex Street, Strand W.C.2
n.d. [193-?]
159pp, 1p adv., clo., 185x120mm. CLRC
Second imp. as above. KMM

CROWCROFT, Peter

1837 A Bodley Head Natural Science Picture Book/Scientific Adviser: Dr. Gwynne Vevers/AUSTRALIAN MARSUPIALS/Peter Crowcroft/Illustrated by/Colin Threadgall/[device]/The Bodley Head/London Sydney Toronto
1970
32pp, col. & b/w illus. on alternate page openings, pic. bd., pic. e/p, 250x195mm. KMM

CROZIER, Cecily (ed.)

1838 TAILS UP
A Comment Publication, Melbourne, n.d. [1944]
39pp, lino-cut illus. throughout, dec. wrappers, cover title, 235x170mm. ANL
Stories & poems by Sylvia Green, tales by Eila Green, lino-cuts by Irvine Green, edited by Cecily Crozier.

CUMMINS, Jule

See 'Douglas, Mary'

CUNNINGHAM, Peter

1839 Taschenbuch/der/neueren, für die Jugend bearbeiteten/Entdechungs-Reisen./Drittes Bändchen/Enthaltend./P. CUNNINGHAM'S REISE NACH NEU-/SÜD-WALLIS;/Hërausgegeben/von/Carl Friedrich Dietzsch,/Dekanund Stiftsprediger in Oehringen./Mit 4 Kupfern./Leipzig, 1832./Ch. G. Kayser'sche Buchhandlung.
ivpp, 158pp & 4pp adv., engraved frontis. & 3 plates, clo., 164x102mm. ANL
Peter Cunningham's *Two Years in New South Wales* abridged for children & translated into German.

CUPPLES, Mrs George [Anne Jane Cupples]

1840 TERRAPIN ISLAND:/or,/Adventures with the "Gleam"./by/Mrs. George Cupples./Eight woodcuts./Gall & Inglis/Edinburgh:/Bernard Terrace/London:/25 Paternoster Sqr.
n.d. [1876]
288pp, 32pp adv., b/w frontis. & 7 f/p b/w illus., b/w head & tailpieces, dec. clo., 170x110mm. Grant

1841 THE CASTAWAYS/OR/TERRAPIN ISLAND/By/Mrs George Cupples,/Author of "The LIttle Captain", "Young Bright Eye",/&c/with eight illustrations/by J Lawson/London:/Gael and Inglis, 25 Paternoster Square;/and Edinburgh
n.d. [1903]
274pp, part col. frontis. & 7 f/p b/w illus., pic. clo., 190x120mm. KP
Rpt of *Terrapin Island.*

1842 Rpt as above, but with col. frontis., inscribed 1910. KP

1843 CARRY VANCE/and her/Adventures on Terrapin Island/By/Mrs George Cupples,/Authoress of "Young Bright Eye", "The Little Captain",/etc./London:/Gall and Inglis, 25 Paternoster Square;/and Edinburgh
n.d. [1890?]
274pp, b/w engraved frontis. & 7 f/p b/w engravings, dec. clo., 185x120mm. KMM
The story of a family of Australian settlers returning to England, shipwrecked on an island south of New Guinea, their rescue & return to Sydney. A reprint of *Terrapin Island.*

1844 THE OLD "DOLPHIN"./by/Mrs George Cupples,/Author of "The Little Captain", "Young Bright Eyes",/"Terrapin Island", etc./With illustrations/Gall & Inglis/London:/25 Paternoster Square./Edinburgh: 20 Bernard Tce.
n.d. [1885]
128pp, engraved frontis. & 2 engravings, dec. clo., 185x115mm. Grant

THE REDFORDS: An emigrant story, 1887, Blackie & Son Ltd.
128pp, 12pp adv., 1 b/w plate, clo., 180x120mm. Unseen
NZ setting.

'CURFEW, John'

See Shann, Richard Ernest Churchill

CURLEWIS, Mrs H. R.

See Turner, Ethel Sybil

CURLEWIS, Edith Jean [Mrs Leonard Charlton, née Curlewis]

1845 THE SHIP THAT/NEVER SET SAIL/by/Jean Curlewis/Ward, Lock & Co Limited/London and Melbourne/1921
249pp, b/w frontis. & 5 b/w plates by J. Macfarlane, clo., 190x125mm. KMM
The author was the daughter of Ethel Turner.

1846 THE SHIP THAT/NEVER SET SAIL/By/Jean Curlewis/Author of "Drowning Maze"/Ward, Lock & Co., Limited/London and Melbourne
n.d.
249pp, 6pp adv., b/w frontis. & 5 b/w plates by J. Macfarlane, clo., 180x125mm. MK

1847 DROWNING/MAZE/By/Jean Curlewis/Author of "The Ship that never set sail"/Ward, Lock & Co. Limited/London and Melbourne/1922

255pp, b/w frontis. & 5 f/p b/w plates by J. Macfarlane & 1 b/w map, clo., 185x125mm. KMM

1848 BEACH BEYOND/By/Jean Curlewis/Author of "The Ship that Never Set Sail", "Drowning Maze", etc./Ward, Lock & Co., Limited/London and Melbourne/1923
242pp, 12pp adv., b/w frontis. & 7 f/p b/w plates by J. Macfarlane, clo., 190x130mm. VSL

1849 THE DAWN/MAN/By/Jean Curlewis/Illustrations by/Harold Copping/Ward, Lock & Co. Limited/ London and Melbourne/1924
251pp, 4pp adv., b/w frontis. & 3 b/w plates, clo., 190x130mm. VSL

CURLEWIS, Jean & TURNER, Ethel
THE SUNSHINE FAMILY. *See* Turner, Ethel

CURLY WEE and GUSSIE GOOSE
The six booklets of this children's comic strip publ. by the *Age*, Melbourne, from 1938 are not Australian. It was of English origin; the author was Maud Budden & the artist Roland Clibborn & the strip was publ. in the Liverpool *Echo* in the 1930s. It also appeared in the Melbourne *Age* from 18 Oct. 1937 till 24 Feb. 1967.

CURREY, C. H.
1850 NOTABLE PATHFINDERS/TO/ANTARCTICA/ by/C. H. Currey, M.A., LL.D./Teachers' College, Sydney/[device]/Whitcombe & Tombs Pty Limited/ Sydney & Melbourne/Associated Houses at/ Christchurch, Auckland, Wellington, Dunedin, Invercargill (NZ)/and London
1941
64pp, maps & b/w photographic illus., pic. wrappers, 180x122mm. KMM

CURREY, John [ed.]
1851 Southern Cross Series/AUSTRALIAN EXPLORERS [no t.p.]
Cassell Australia, Melbourne 1972
117pp, 10 f/p and other col. & b/w illus. by Peter Cuffley, pic. bd., dec. e/p, 245x185mm. CLRC
Compilation of extracts from: Beale, *Kennedy of Cape York;* Chisholm, *Strange New World;* & articles on Charles Sturt, Governor George Grey, Eyre, Burke & Wills, Ernest Giles, Mawson & Ivan Champion in New Guinea.

1852 Southern Cross Series/AUSTRALIAN SEA/ STORIES/Edited by John Currey/Illustrated by Don Angus/Cassell Australia
Melbourne 1972
117pp, 10 f/p ,and other col. & b/w illus., pic. bd., col. e/p, extended illus. t.p., 245x185mm. HBM
Compilation including extracts from: Ian Mudie, *The Wreck of the Admella;* K. A. Austin, *The Voyage of the Investigator;* Ronald McKie, *Proud Echo;* & articles on 'The Mutiny of the *Bounty*'; 'The Sinking of the *Emden*'; 'The Sinking of the *Perth*'; 'The Wreck of the *Quetta*', etc.

CURRY, Mrs Winifred J. P.
See 'Primrose Jane'

CUSACK, Dymphna
1853 KANGA-BEE and KANGA-BO/[drawing]/Written by/Dymphna Cusack/[drawing]/And/Illustrated by/ Matt-Slater-Wigg/[drawing]/Botany/House/ Publishers/Box 4357 GPO Sydney
1945
54pp, 8 f/p b/w illus. & drawings in text, wrappers, 245x170mm. KMM

CUSACK, Dymphna & JAMES, Florence
1854 Dymphna Cusack/and/Florence James/FOUR WINDS/AND A FAMILY/Illustrated by Nan Knowles/[vignette]/The Shakespeare Head/London New York Sydney Capetown Paris
n.d. [1947]
133pp, 14 f/p b/w illus. & drawings in text, dec. e/p, clo., 210x135mm. KMM

1855 FOUR WINDS/AND A FAMILY/Dymphna Cusack/and Florence James/[drawing]/Illustrated by/ Virginia Sikorskis/Lansdowne/1965
First pub. 1946 [*sic*]; new ed. [Melbourne] 1965
137pp, 8 f/p b/w illus. & drawings in text, dec. e/p, clo., 210x135mm. KMM

CUTHILL, William John
1856 THE RIVER OF/LITTLE FISH/A History of Traralgon written for/Girls and Boys of the City/by William J. Cuthill/Chief Stipendiary Magistrate for the State of Victoria/Vice-President of the Traralgon and District/Historical Society/and/A Resident of Traralgon from 1934 to 1953/Copyright/First published 1970/Registered in Australia...etc./Wholly set up and printed by the L.V. Printers, Traralgon/ Victoria, Australia
On front cover: 'Published by The Traralgon and District Historical Society'
106pp (inc. 1p author's foreword), b/w photographic illus., pic. wrappers, 240x140mm. ANL

D'AGRAIVES, Jean
1857 Jean D'Agraives/LE FILLEUL DE/LA PÉROUSE/ Illustrations de J. Touchat/[drawing]/Hachette Paris, 1947
253pp, 8 f/p b/w illus., wrappers, 185x115mm. NSL:M
English 'The Godchild of La Pérouse'.

DAIBER, Albert
1858 GESCHICHTEN/AUS AUSTRALIEN/von/Dr Albert Daiber/mit acht Vollbildern auf Taflen/[device]/ Leipzig/Druck und Verlag von B. G. Teubner./1902
310pp & 2pp adv., b/w frontis. & 8 plates, dec. clo., 180x120mm. NSL:M
Chapters on Ophir goldfields, Edmund Kennedy, Flinders & Bass, William Buckley, &c.

DALE, Edwin
LONE-HAND LAWRENCE. *See* Champion Library No. 145

FROM BUSH TO SPEEDWAY. *See* Champion Library No. 77

KING FLAME. *See* Champion Library No. 194

CYCLONE ZIP/The Aussie Speedster. *See* Champion Library No. 169

DALE, Judith
1859 SHIRLEY FLIGHT—AIR HOSTESS/PACIFIC CASTAWAYS/by/Judith Dale/Published by/World Distributors (Manchester) Limited/London Manchester/England/MCMLX 1960
183pp, unillus., dec. clo., 190x125mm. Grant

1860 SHIRLEY FLIGHT—AIR HOSTESS/AND THE/ FLYING DOCTOR/Published by/World Distributors (Manchester) LImited/London—Manchester/England n.d.
184pp, unillus., dec. clo., 185x125mm. KMM

DALE, Norman
1861 THE PIED PIPER/OF/MEDENHAM/Norman Dale/[drawing]/Illustrated by Jean Harper/Hamish Hamilton/London
1959

137pp, 4 f/p b/w illus. & b/w drawings in text, clo., 185x120mm. Reindeer Books. NSL:M
The hero is an Australian, although the setting of the book is England.

1862 ALL CHANGE FOR/MEDENHAM/by Norman Dale/[drawing]/Illustrated by Jean Harper/Hamish Hamilton/London
1959
126pp, 9 b/w illus. & b/w drawings in text, clo., 185x120mm. Reindeer Books. MK
The story is set in England like *The Pied Piper of Medenham;* the hero is an Australian.

DALE, W. S.
1863 GOLDEN HAIR/By/W. S. Dale/Illustrated by/S. Woolcott/[drawing printed in blue]/Copyright and Radio Rights Reserved/A Dawool Story
An Empire Production, U.B.D., Adelaide
16pp, 6 col. illus. (S. Woolcott), others in blue ink, col. pic. wrappers, 242x183mm. JH

1864 THE STORY OF/PETER PIG/By/W. S. Dale/ Illustrated by/S. Woolcott/[drawing]/Copyright and Radio Rights Reserved./A Dawool Story
An Empire Publication, Universal Business Directories (Aust) Pty Ltd, Adelaide, n.d. [194-?]
16pp, 6 col. illus., b/w drawings, pic. wrappers, 240x180mm. KMM

1865 SHAKABAK/THE GOBLIN/By/W. S. Dale/ Illustrated by/S. Woolcott/Copyright and Radio Rights Reserved/A Dawool Story
An Empire Publication, Universal Business Directories, Adelaide, n.d. [194-?] Printed by The Collotype Ltd, Adelaide
16pp, 6 col. illus., drawings in text, pic. wrappers, 245x184mm. WRT

DALGARNO, Ann Patricia
1866 THE/BORED DUCK/By/Ann Dalgarno/ Illustrations by/Peg Minty
The author, 8 Torres St, Red Hill, Canberra ACT [1972]
[12]pp, 6 f/p col. illus., stiff pic. wrappers, 205x290mm. ANL

DALRYMPLE, E.
1867 WHEN/THE STARS LOOK DOWN/By/ E. Dalrymple/The F. J. Thwaites Publishing Co./Head Office/47 Burwood Road/Sydney
n.d. [1930?]
62pp, 8 col. illus. & b/w drawings in text, illus. by author, bd. & half clo., 245x190mm. KMM

DALTON, Muriel
OVER THE RANGES. *See* Australian Youth Plays

1868 CHILDREN OF THE CIRCUS/story by/(Miss) Muriel Dalton/33 Dixon St., Malvern, S.E.4/Wholly set up and printed in Australia by/Tooronga Press, Malvern Road,/Malvern
n.d. [1955?]
32pp, illus., wrappers, 240x190mm. MD

DALY, Kathleen N.
CBS Television's/CAPTAIN KANGAROO. *See* Memling, Carl

DALY, Mary
1869 CINTY/AND/THE LAUGHING JACKASSES/and other Children's Stories/by/Dame Mary Daly, D.B.E./with illustrations by/Sir Hans Heysen/Evelyn M. Baxter, Dermont Hellier,/Allan Bernaldo, Robert Johnson/Shirley Bourne, Laurence D. Kermond,/Ernest Buckmaster, Dudley Parker,/George Colville, Betty Paterson,/William Dargie, Esther Paterson,/William Dobell, John Rowell,/Nornie Gude, Phyl Waterhouse/ Copyright reserved
Herald Gravure Printers, Melbourne October 1961; 2nd impr. August 1962
30pp (inc. 1p foreword by Sir Dallas Brooks, Governor of Victoria & 1p biographical notes on artist contributors), 20 col. & part. col. illus. & b/w drawings, dec. bd., 265x195mm. KMM
Published in aid of the Hospital School for Crippled Children, Yooralla; includes 4 short stories.

1870 TIMMY'S CHRISTMAS/SURPRISE/By Dame Mary Daly, D.B.E./[drawing]/With Illustrations by/George Arnold Max Middleton/Dudley Drew Betty Paterson, M.B.E./Ambrose Griffin Esther Paterson
The author, Herald Gravure Printers, Melbourne, n.d. [1967]
[28]pp (inc. 1p foreword by Dame Pattie Menzies [dated June 1967] & 1p dedication & quotation), 9 col. illus. & b/w drawings, pic. bd., col. illus. front e/p, 185x145mm. KMM
Proceeds of sale of the book for Yooralla Hospital School for Crippled Children, Victoria.

DALZIEL, Ken
1871 PENGUIN/ROAD/by/Ken Dalziel/Illustrated by/ Frank Norton/[drawing]/Angus and Robertson/ Sydney London Melbourne Wellington
1955; rpt 1956
80pp (inc. 2pp foreword by P. G. Law), 8pp photographic illus., line drawings in text, dec. e/p, dec. clo., 235x155mm. KMM
Experiences of the author during a year spent at Heard Island Antarctic Research Station; originally written as letters to his children.

1872 PENGUIN/ROAD/by/Ken Dalziel/Illustrated by/ Frank Norton/Angus and Robertson/Sydney London Melbourne Wellington
First pub. 1955; first school edition 1956
64pp (inc. 1p foreword by P. G. Law), extended part. col. frontis., b/w part. col. illus. throughout, limp clo., 180x120mm. KMM

DAMES, E. L. [?Pilkington]
1873 BEHIND THE STARS/and Other Fairy Tales/By/ E. Longworth Dames/London/T. Fisher Unwin/ Paternoster Square/1897
Pencilled beneath the author's name 'Mrs R. R. Pilkington, late of Perth.' Copy acquired 1953
68pp, unillus., rebound, 130x100mm. WJSB
European fairy tales.

DAMES, Helen
1874 Imperial Edition No. 770/PLAY RHYMES/9 Pieces for Piano/words by/Helen Dames/Music by/Arthur S. Loam [9 songs listed]/Allan & Co. Pty Ltd./Melbourne Adelaide Bendigo/Printed in Australia 3/-
20pp (last adv.), unillus., dec. wrappers (signed M.H.), 310x234mm. EC

1875 Imperial Edition NO. 692/THE MANTIS & THE BUTTERFLY/and other Songs/Words by/Helen Dames/Music by/Evelyn Wales/Allan & Co. Pty Ltd./ Melbourne Ad. Bendigo/Printed in Aust. 2/6
1953
28pp, unillus., dec. wrappers, 246x176mm. VSL

1876 AN AUSTRALIAN/LULLABY/Words by/Helen Dames/Music by/Edith Harrhy/2/6/Allan & Co Pty Ltd./Melbourne Ad. Ben/Printed in Aust.
Acquired 1954
6pp, unillus., wrappers, 310x237mm. VSL

DAMPIER, William

1877 THE/LIFE AND ADVENTURES/OF/WILLIAM DAMPIER/With a History of/The Buccaneers of America/London/Blackie & Son, Limited, 50 Old Bailey, E. C./Glasgow and Dublin
n.d. [1894?]
224pp, 2pp & 8pp adv., b/w frontis. by Paul Hardy, clo., lettering in gilt on front cover & spine, 180x120mm. Blackie's Library of Famous Books. HBM
A number of undated rpt have been seen with slight variations, some with sepia frontis. KP and others

Dandy Dick or the King of the Bushrangers

1878 The Dandy Dick Series/No. 1—One Penny/ DANDY DICK/OR/THE KING OF THE BUSHRANGERS/[illustration]/London: Hogarth House, Bouverie Street, Fleet Street, E.C.
n.d.
32pp, 2 b/w illus., pink pic. wrappers (printed in black; with adv. verso front cover), cover title, 220x150mm. RM
The prologue of this melodramatic tale is set in England where a duke's infant son is abducted before his father is shot dead; the rest of the action takes place twenty years later on the banks of the Murray River, Australia, where the duke's heir has become a gentleman bushranger.

DANE, Jeanie G. & WALKER, Edith G.

1879 SONG STORIES/OF/AUSTRALIA/for/Little People/with an Appreciation/by/Frances E. Newton/ Music/and/Illustrations by Edith G. Walker/Words by Jeanie G. Dane
No publisher's imprint [Device: 'W.B. and Co. Ltd.' Sydney, ?William Brooks & Co. Ltd], n.d.
[1905?]
54pp (inc. 2pp author's preface), 1p appreciation, dec. t.p., 8 col. & part. col. illus., pic. bd., 245x275mm. CLRC
Appreciation by Frances E. Newton, Principal, Kindergarten Training College, Sydney 1905
Words & music of 32 songs for children.

DANIEL, Elizabeth

1880 DORINA THE DAYDREAMER/by/Elizabeth Daniel/Illustrated by Rod Fowler/Horwitz-Martin Sydney 1965
44pp, 4 f/p b/w illus., pic. wrappers, 180x120mm. KMM
The story of the abduction of a native girl by a hostile tribesman in New Guinea.

DANIELL, David Scott

1881 FLIGHT ONE:/AUSTRALIA/[decoration]/[coat of arms]/Story by/David Scott Daniell/Illustrated by/Jack Matthew/Publishers: Wills & Hepworth Ltd., Loughborough/First published 1958 Printed in England
51pp (inc. 24pp col. illus.), bd., dec. e/p, 170x110mm. ANL A Ladybird Book of Travel & Adventure.

1882 FLIGHT ONE:/AUSTRALIA
Variant colophon otherwise identical with above. The ladybird colophon appears with open wings in no. 1; the second copy has the ladybird shown with closed wings. KP

1883 Another copy as above but with advertising material opposite t.p. with the words: 'A ladybird travel adventure book 2/6 net'. This copy has no d/w but the d/w illus. is printed in col. on the bd. cover & on back mention is made of 180 Ladybird titles. KP

1884 Another copy as 3 'There are now 280 ladybird titles'. This copy has smaller lettering on spine. KP

DANIELL, Michael

1885 THE ISLAND OF THE/BLIND HIPOPOTAMIE/ [*sic*]/And other Stories/By Michael Daniell/[device]/ Wentworth Books Pty. Ltd./48 Cooper Street/Surry Hills 2010
[NSW] 1970
29pp, b/w illus. throughout, stiff pic. wrappers, 260x200mm. KMM

1886 IT PAYS/TO BE/WEALTHY/by/Michael Daniell/ [device]/Wentworth Books Pty. Ltd./48 Cooper Street/ Surry Hills 2010
[NSW] 1970
32pp, b/w drawings throughout, stiff pic. paper wrappers, 300x205mm. KP Story & drawings by a nine-year-old boy.
• Rpt 1970, as above. KP

DANIELSSON, Bengt

1887 Bengt Danielsson/TERRY IN/AUSTRALIA/ Translated from the Swedish/By Reginald Spink/ Illustrations by/Pierre Heyman/Ruskin House/George Allen & Unwin Ltd./Museum Street London
First published in Great Britain 1961
180pp, 9 f/p b/w illus., b/w chapter headings & tailpieces, clo., 215x140mm. KMM
First edition, in Swedish, published by Saxon & Lindströms Förlag 1958.

DANKS, Bertha M.

1888 JANET/AND THE/FAIRIES/By/Bertha M. Danks/ With four illustrations/in colour by/Ida Rentoul Outhwaite/A. & C. Black Ltd./4, 5 & 6 Soho Square, London, W.1
1937
64pp, col. frontis. & 3 f/p col. illus., clo., 180x120mm. Grant
Uniform with *The Lost Princess* by Madeline Collier, but this book has an Australian setting.
• Rpt 1942 as above. KMM

DARBY, H. F.

See Humphreys, W. G. & Darby, H. F.

DARE, Eveline

1889 Whitcombe's Story Books/THE/ELFIN HOUSE/ and other Stories/(for ages 8–9 years) [drawing]/ Whitcombe & Tombs Pty. Ltd./Melbourne Sydney Perth
n.d. [1945]
32pp, 6 b/w illus. by W. M. Rolland, wrappers, 185x120mm. Grant
See McLaren 372

1890 Whitcombe's Story Books/MR. SPIDER'S WALK/ and other Stories/By/Eveline Dare/For Ages 7 to 9 years/[drawing]/Whitcombe & Tombs Pty. Ltd./ Melbourne Sydney Perth
n.d. [1946]
32pp, b/w frontis. & 5 f/p b/w illus., dec. wrappers, 180x120mm. ANL
See McLaren 254

1891 Mullens' Stories for Children/(No. 102)/THE ELF WHO/LIVED IN A TEAPOT/By Eveline Dare/(For ages 7 to 8)/[drawing]/Robertson & Mullens Ltd./ Melbourne
n.d. [1951]
30pp, b/w frontis. & b/w drawings throughout, pic. wrappers, 180x120mm. ANL

1892 Mullens' Stories for Children/(No. 101)/ MADELINE,/THE MUSICAL MOUSE/By Eveline Dare/(For ages 7 to 8)/[drawing]/Robertson & Mullens Ltd./Melbourne
n.d. [1951]

30pp, b/w frontis. & 3 b/w illus., illus. by Marjorie Howden, pic. wrappers, 180x120mm. ANL

1893 OFF TO THE BEACH/by Eveline Dare/Illustrated by John Mason/Golden Press/Sydney
1970
[29]pp, col. illus. throughout, pic. bd., 280x230mm. CLRC

1894 TINY THE AUSTRALIAN TERRIER/and his friends/by Eveline Dare/Illustrated by John Richards/[drawing]/Golden Press Sydney
1970
[20]pp, col. & part. col. illus. throughout, pic. bd., 240x190mm. CLRC

1895 TRAIN TRIP TO THE BUSH/by Eveline Dare/Illustrated by John Mason/Golden Press Sydney
1970
[28]pp, col. illus. throughout, pic. bd., pic. e/p, 280x225mm. CLRC

1896 BUSH/PICNIC/Written by Eveline Dare/Illustrated by John Richards/Golden Press Sydney
1970
[29]pp, col. illus. throughout, pic. bd., 280x230mm. CLRC

Daring & Danger
1897 DARING &/DANGER/[illustration]/With Numerous coloured and Black and White Illustrations/London & Glasgow/Collins Clear Type Press
n.d.
128pp, col. frontis., 7 f/p b/w illus. & b/w drawings in text, bd. (with col. illus. pasted on front cover), clo. spine, 255x195mm. Grant
Contents include: 'How I Ran the Booroomana Sawmill', by S. Le Satgille; & 'My Palaver with the Black Fellows', by John Mackie.

DARLING, Louis
1898 KANGAROOS/AND OTHER ANIMALS WITH POCKETS/Written and Illustrated by Louis Darling/William Morrow & Company/New York 1958
64pp, b/w lithographic illus. throughout, clo., 215x165mm. WRT
1899 Rpt as above, but
/Angus & Robertson Ltd./London & Sydney
1960
Details as above. BBC
• Rpt 1961. WRT

1900 [drawing] PENGUINS/by Louis Darling/Angus & Robertson
Sydney 1961 [Copyright 1956]
64pp, b/w lithographic illus. throughout, clo., 210x160mm. BBC

1901 SEALS AND/WALRUSES/[drawing]/by/Louis Darling/Angus & Robertson
Sydney 1961 [Copyright 1955, apparently in USA]
63pp, b/w lithographic illus., clo., 210x160mm. CLRC

DARVILL, Daisy
1902 THE/COMING OF CHLOE/A Story of the Australian Bush/by/Daisy Darvill/Illustrated in Colour and Pen/and Ink by Gordon Browne, R.I./London/The Religious Tract Society/4 Bouverie Street, E.C.4
n.d. [1924]
233pp, 6pp adv., col. frontis. & 10 f/p b/w illus., pic. bd., 195x130mm. Grant

DARWIN, William
See 'Niwrad, William'

DASKEIN, Tarella Quin [née Quin]
1903 GUM TREE BROWNIE/and other Faërie Folk of the Never-Never/By Tarella Quin/Illustrated by Ida S. Rentoul/[drawing]/George Robertson & Co./Propy. Ltd./Melbourne, Sydney, Adelaide & Brisbane
n.d. [1907]
184pp, 1p foreword by Ethel Turner, b/w frontis. & 30 f/p b/w illus., b/w drawings in text, dec. clo. (mottled e/ps), 180x215mm. ANL
1904 GUM TREE BROWNIE/and other Faerie Folk of the Never Never/By Tarella Quin Illustrated by/Ida S. Rentoul/[drawing]/George Robertson & Co./Propy. Ltd./Melbourne, Sydney, Adelaide & Brisbane.
n.d. [1910]
vipp, 184pp, b/w frontis. as before but 180x214mm. KMM
The 1907 edition is bound in heavy, bevelled green cl. bd. with an illus. of a brownie in a spider's web & title, author &c printed in red & black. The e/p are of green & brown marbled paper; and no printer's name is to be found inside the book. This new ed. is bound in orange cl. bd. with plain edges & the same cover design. The e/p are plain. The individual t.p. to the eight stories are printed in a different & larger old English typeface & on the last page of the text is a colophon which reads 'B. R. Gowan & Co, Printers, Melbourne'.
1905 GUM TREE BROWNIE/and other Faerie Folk of the Never Never/by/Tarella Quin/Illustrated by/Ida S. Rentoul/Robertson & Mullens Limited/Elizabeth Street, Melbourne
1925
165pp, [no foreword], b/w frontis. & 12 f/p b/w illus., 11 half-page & 5 smaller b/w illus., pic. bd. with red backstrip, 175x210mm. KMM
This ed. has 18 fewer b/w illus., & t.p. for 'September Gold' and 'Exit to Faerieland' have been changed.

1906 FRECKLES/By/Tarella Quin/London/Alexander Moring Limited/The de la More Press/32 George Street Hanover Square W./1910
154pp, b/w frontis. & 4 f/p b/w illus., b/w drawings in text, illus. by Jack Somers, clo., 200x140mm. KMM

1907 BEFORE THE LAMPS ARE LIT/By Tarella Quin/[drawing]/Illustrated by/Ida Rentoul Outhwaite/George Robertson & Company/Propy. Ltd./Melbourne Sydney/Adelaide Brisbane
n.d. [1911]
190pp, 1p verse, b/w frontis. & 25 f/p b/w illus., b/w drawings in text throughout, dec. clo., 185x215mm. KMM
Contains 6 stories.

1908 CHIMNEY TOWN/By Tarella Quin Daskein/Author of Gum Tree Brownie/Before the Lamps are Lit, etc./Illustrated by Ida Rentoul Outhwaite/A. & C. Black Ltd./4, 5 & 6 Soho Square, London W.1.
1934
238pp, 1p & 2pp adv., col. frontis. & 1 col. illus., 27 f/p b/w illus. & b/w drawings in text, dec. clo., 205x145mm. KMM

1909 THE OTHER SIDE/OF/NOWHERE/Stories by/Tarella Quin Daskein/Illustrations by/Ida Rentoul Outhwaite/Melbourne/Robertson & Mullens Limited
1934
171pp, 18 f/p b/w illus. & b/w drawings in text, clo. [wrappers seen on one copy], 180x210mm. KMM
This book contains 7 stories, the title story & 3 others being reprinted from *Gum Tree Brownie;* also included is a song 'Over the Water from Nowhere', with music by Kenneth L. Duffield.
See also Gunn, Jeannie & Others, THE AUSTRALIAN WONDER BOOK, in which is included *The Other Side*

of Nowhere. Mrs Daskein also wrote *Paying Guests, & Kerno, a Stone* which were not children's books.

Date with Disaster
1910 an Action Man adventure/DATE WITH DISASTER/[illus.]/Purnell/MCMLXVII, BPC. Publishing Ltd as to the/stories and artwork herein/ Action Man Palitoy Regd.
64pp (inc. 1p adv.), b/w frontis. & 7 f/p b/w illus., pic. wrappers, 124x120mm. KP

DAVEY, Cyril J.
1911 SAMUEL MARSDEN/by/Cyril J. Davey/Oliphants Ltd./London Edinburgh
1957
93pp, col. frontis., clo., 185x120mm. NSL:M

1912 Eagle Books No 77/CHIEF OF CHIEFS/Samuel Marsden of Australasia/by/Cyril J. Davey/author of/ They Called Him Traitor etc./London/Edinburgh House Press/1961
32pp, unillus., pic.wrappers, 185x120mm. KMM

DAVID, Tova
1913 RUTH/Tova David/Copyright reserved
n.p., n.d. [197-?]. Stanmore Press
38pp (last blank), unillus., stiff pic. wrappers, 186x120mm. ANL
Girls' story set in Victoria.

DAVIDSON, Alan
1914 Alan Davidson's/CRICKET BOOK/by/Alan Davidson/(NSW and Australian XI)/edited by/Phil Tresidder/[device]/Shakespeare Head Press/10-16 Dowling St, Potts Point/Sydney
1965
104pp, b/w photographs throughout, bd., 240x180mm. KP

DAVIES, Bill
1915 THE STOWAWAYS/[drawing]/By Bill Davies/ Playground Publishing/Wingello House, Angel Place, Sydney/Registered at GPO Sydney for transmission by post as a book
n.d. [1945]
24pp, 8 col. illus. & b/w drawings in text, dec. bd., dec. e/p, 180x245mm. ANL

DAVIES, E. Harold
1916 FIVE SONGS/OF/CHILDHOOD/Composed by/E. Harold Davies/Price/two shillings/net./London/ Novello & Co., Ltd./Copyright, 1912, by Novello and Company, Limited
Title &c in dec. borders
17pp & 1p adv. & adv. both sides of back wrapper, dec. wrappers, 305x240mm. MC
Author was director of the Adelaide Conservatorium of Music for many years.

DAVIES, Eleanor [or Eleanore Davis]
1917 Soper Productions/presents/"TALES OF/ ENCHANTMENT"/by/Eleanor Davies/Illustrated by/ Bill Davies/Copyright 1944/All rights reserved; no/ part of the Book may be/reproduced in any form/ without the permission of the Publisher
Soper Publications, Sydney
24pp, 11 f/p col. illus., col. pic. bd. with t.p. repeated on back cover, 295x210mm. Grant
Contains 2 stories, 'The Bushland Trial' & 'The Enchanted Princess', the second story being the same as that published separately under the title of *The Magic Orchid.* On title page & back cover the author's name is spelt 'Eleanor Davies' but on front cover 'Eleanor Davis'.

1918 THE "MAGIC ORCHID"/A New/Enchanting Fairy Tale/by/Eleanore Davis/Acme Publishing Co., Sydney, n.d. [Copyright 1944]
16pp, 1 f/p & 3 b/w illus. in text, col. illus. wrappers, 200x125mm. KMM

DAVIES, M. Catherine
1919 ADVENTURES/WITH THE MERMAIDS/By/ M. Catherine Davies/Illustrations by/Enid MacDonald/Samual Wood/433 Kent Street, Sydney
1929
128pp, b/w frontis. & 1 f/p b/w illus., b/w drawings in text, clo., 190x125mm. NSL:M

DAVIES, Mrs
See 'Desda'

DAVIES, Norman
See Cohn, Ola. THE FAIRIES' TREE
See also Pirani, Leila & Davies, Norman

DAVIS, Anthony
1920 SIR/DONALD BRADMAN/by/Anthony Davis/ Red Lion Lives/Cassell—London
1960
122pp, 4 f/p b/w illus., clo., 185x125mm. NSL:M

DAVIS, Charles
1921 ZOOLETTERS/NOAH'S RIVAL
The author, Sydney 1922
49pp, illus., dec. wrappers, cover title, 280x220mm. NSL:M
Alphabetical rhymes with illustrations & descriptive prose paragraphs about the various animals, & many advertisements interspersed with the text.

DAVIS, Howard G.
1922 STORIES FROM/GOD'S BOOK/And Simple Lessons/from the/Things God has Made/Number One By/Howard G./Davis/Line Drawings by/Joan Storie/ and/Beatrij's Jansz-Ensink/Copyright/Printed and Published by/Signs Publishing Company/Warburton Victoria Australia
n.d.
64pp, col. frontis. & 3 f/p col. illus., part col. & b/w illus., pic. wrappers, 245x185mm. KP
Doubtful if any of the contents are Australian.

DAVIS, John P.
1923 TOLD BY DIGGER/(The Autobiography of a Dog)/to/John P. Davis/Nash & Grayson/Curzon Street/Mayfair London
1931
126pp, b/w drawings in text throughout, clo., 195x125mm. NSL:M
An Australian sheepdog—stories first appeared in *The Morning Post.*

DAVISON, Frank Dalby
1924 "MAN-SHY"/By/F. D. Davison/Author of "Forever Morning"/The Australian Authors/Publishing Co./Sydney/1931
150pp, 2pp adv., unillus., clo. [only 200 copies bound in clo.], 190x125mm. ANL
1925 Another copy as above, bound in stiff, pebble-grained paper, 180x115mm. HBM
1926 MAN-SHY/By/Frank Dalby Davison/Author of Forever Morning/Illustrated by Frank Whitmore/ Second Edition/Australia/Angus and Robertson Limited/89 Castlereagh Street, Sydney/1932
153pp, 26pp adv., b/w frontis. & 8 f/p b/w illus., 2 b/w drawings, clo., 185x115mm. CLRC
1927 MAN-SHY/By/Frank Dalby Davison/Author of Forever Morning, The Wells of Beersheba/Third

Edition/Australia/Angus & Robertson Limited/89 Castlereagh Street, Sydney/1933
144pp, 27pp adv., unillus. (apart from tailpiece on last page), clo., 180x120mm. HBM

1928 MAN-SHY/By/Frank Dalby Davison/Fourth Edition/Australia/Angus & Robertson Limited/89 Castlereagh Street, Sydney/1935
188pp, unillus., clo., 180x120mm. ANL
• Rpt as above, Sydney & London 6th edition 1939. CLRC
• Rpt as above, 7th ed. 1941. CLRC
• Rpt as above, 9th ed. 1943. KMM
• Rpt as above, 10th ed. 1944. KMM

1929 MAN-SHY/By/Frank Dalby Davison/Angus and Robertson Ltd/Sydney: London/1944
116pp, unillus., wrappers, 185x115mm. Australian Pocket Library. KMM

1930 MAN-SHY/A Story of Men and Cattle/By/Frank Dalby Davison/Angus and Robertson/Sydney: London/1946
13th ed., completing 54,000 copies
185pp, unillus., clo., 185x120mm. KMM

1931 MAN-SHY/A Story of Men and Cattle/By Frank Dalby Davison/Angus and Robertson/Sydney: London/1947
13th ed., completing 61,000 copies
183pp, unillus., limp clo., 180x120mm. NSL:M

1932 MAN-SHY/A Story of Men and Cattle/By/Frank Dalby Davison/Angus and Robertson/Sydney: London/1948
16th ed., completing 66,500 copies
183pp, unillus., stiff paper wrappers, 185x125mm. KMM

1933 MAN-SHY/By/Frank Dalby Davison/Author of "Children of the Dark People" and "Dusty"/[publisher's device]/Angus and Robertson Sydney, First pub. 1931; rpt 1931, 1932, 1933, 1935, 1937, 1939, 1941, 1942, 1943, 1944 (twice), 1946 (twice), 1947, 1948, 1949, 1950, 1951, 1952, 1953, 1954 (twice), 1956, 1958, 1959, 1960, 1961
New illustrated edition 1962
160pp, b/w frontis., 2 f/p b/w illus. & 14 chapter headings, clo., some copies bound in pic. wrappers, 195x125mm. BBC
The illustrations consist of the same frontispiece as that used in the Junior Library edition, but the other illustrations are different, & are not signed or initialled, nor is the artist's name given.

1934 MAN-SHY/By/Frank Dalby Davison/Author of "Children of the Dark People" and "Dusty"/Angus and Robertson
Sydney First pub. 1931; new illustrated edition 1962, rpt 1964
The b/w frontispiece used in the first edition of the New Illustrated Edition which had been retained from earlier editions has been replaced by a drawing used on the d/w of the New Illustrated Edition, & which extends on to the title page.
160pp, b/w frontis. extended on to t.p., 2 f/p b/w illus. & b/w chapter headings, stiff pic. wrappers (reproducing frontis.), 180x120mm. KMM
• Rpt 1963. CLRC

1935 The Junior Library of Australian Books/ MAN-SHY/By/Frank Dalby Davison/Author of "Children of the Dark People" and "Dusty"/Angus and Robertson/Sydney—London
1949 [Junior Library edition]
153pp, b/w frontis. & 2 f/p b/w illus., [sgd 'J.B.G.']bd., 180x125mm. KMM
• Rpt as above, 1950. KMM

1936 MAN-SHY/By/Frank Dalby Davison/Author of "Children of the Dark People" and "Dusty"/[publisher's device]/Angus and Robertson/Sydney—London
Junior Library 16th ed. completing 74,000 copies January 1950, Junior Library Edition 1949, 2nd impr. 1950; 3rd impr. 1951; 4th impr. 1952; 5th imp. 1953; 6th imp. 1954
153pp, b/w frontis. & 2 f/p b/w illus., stiff wrappers, 185x120mm. KMM
• Rpt as above, 1958. KMM

1937 MAN-SHY/By Frank Dalby Davison/Author of "Children of the Dark People" and 'Dusty"/[device]/ Angus and Robertson
Sydney 1959
153pp, b/w frontis. & 2 f/p b/w illus., wrappers, 180x120mm. Australian Junior Library. KMM
• Rpt as above, 1960. KMM

1938 MAN-SHY/A Story of Men and Cattle/by/Frank Dalby Davison/Author of Forever Morning/Illustrated by/Frank Wallace/London/Eyre and Spottiswoode/ 1934
204pp, b/w frontis. & 7 f/p b/w illus., clo., 215x135mm. HBM

1939 RED HEIFER/By/Frank Dalby/Davison/London/ Eyre & Spottiswoode
1949 [Second English edition; first English edition 1934 under title *Man-Shy*]
127pp, unillus., clo., 190x125mm. ANL

1940 Frank Dalby Davison/MAN-SHY/Penguin Books Harmondsworth, Middlesex, England [First published in Australia 1931; First English edition 1934; Second English edition 1949 under the title *Red Heifer;* Published in Puffin Story Books 1956]
117pp, 6pp adv., unillus., pic. wrappers, cover designed by David Cox, 180x110mm. KMM

1941 MAN-SHY/A Story of Men and Cattle/Frank Dalby Davison/[drawing]/[device]/Pacific Books Sydney 1969
160pp, 2 f/p b/w illus., b/w chapter headings, pic. wrappers, 180x110mm. KMM

U.S. edition

1942 RED HEIFER/A story of Men and Cattle/Frank Dalby Davison/Introduction by/Kermit Roosevelt/ Illustrated by Frank Wallace/The Junior Literary Guild/and Coward McCann/New York 1935
214pp (inc. introduction, dedication, etc.), b/w frontis. & 7 f/p b/w illus., clo. (with frontis. reproduced on cover), 205x130mm. Grant

1943 CHILDREN/OF THE/DARK PEOPLE/An Australian Folk Tale/By/Frank Dalby Davison/Author of Man-Shy, Forever Morning, The Wells of/ Beersheba, Caribbean Interlude, joint author of/Blue Coast Caravan/Illustrations by/Pixie O'Harris/ Australia/Angus & Robertson Limited/89 Castlereagh Street, Sydney/1936
218pp, 1p acknowledgements, 1p prologue, b/w frontis., b/w chapter headings & tailpieces, clo., 195x125mm. KMM

1944 Second edition, Sydney 1937
Details as in first edition. KMM

1945 CHILDREN/OF THE/DARK PEOPLE/An Australian Story for/Young Folk/By/Frank Dalby Davison/Illustrated by/Pixie O'Harris/Angus and Robertson Ltd./Sydney: London/1946
219pp, 1p acknowledgements, 1p prologue, b/w frontis. & 6 f/p b/w illus., b/w chapter headings & tailpieces, clo., 185x120mm. KMM
The frontispiece, & some chapter headings & tailpieces, differ from those in the first edition.

1946 CHILDREN OF THE/DARK PEOPLE/An

Australian Story/for Young Folk/by/Frank Dalby Davison/Illustrated by/Pixie O'Harris/Angus and Robertson/Sydney: London/1948
First pub. 1936; rpt 1938, 1946; 5th ed. (revised) completing 33,500 copies 1948
247pp, 2pp note, 1p prologue, b/w frontis. & 7 f/p b/w illus. (one additional to those in 1946 edition), b/w chapter headings & tailpieces, clo., 185x120mm. CLRC

1947 The Junior Library of Australian Books/—/CHILDREN OF THE DARK PEOPLE/—/By/Frank Dalby Davison/Author of "Man-shy" and "Dusty"/Angus and Robertson/Sydney: London
First pub. 1936; 5th ed. (revised), completing 33,500 copies 1948; Junior Library edition 1949
154pp, 1p note, 1p prologue, b/w frontis. & 2 b/w illus. by Pixie O'Harris, bd., 185x120mm. ANL

1948 CHILDREN OF THE/DARK PEOPLE/An Australian Story for Young Folk/by/Frank Dalby Davison/Illustrated by/Pixie O'Harris/[device]/Angus and Robertson
Sydney 1966 [school edition]
xiv, 175pp, 3pp dedication, note etc., b/w frontis. & 7 f/p b/w illus., b/w chapter headings & endpieces, pic. paper wrappers, 185x120mm. KMM
• Rpt 1967, as above. KMM

1949 DUSTY/The Story of a Sheep Dog/By/Frank Dalby Davison/Angus and Robertson/Sydney—London/1946
242pp, 1p acknowledgement, 1p foreword, unillus., clo., 180x120mm. CLRC
The MS. of this book, entered under the title *Stranger* & the pen-name 'Tarboy', was the winner of the *Melbourne Argus and Asian Post* £500 novel competition 1946.

1950 DUSTY/A Dog of the Sheep Country/By/Frank Dalby Davison/Angus and Robertson/Sydney: London/1947
First pub. October 1946; rpt May 1947
242pp, 1p acknowledgement, 1p foreword, unillus., clo., 190x120mm. KMM

1951 DUSTY/A Dog of the Sheep Country/By/Frank Dalby Davison/[device]/Angus and Robertson/Sydney London
First pub. 1946; rpt 1947, 1948, 1949, 1950; School Edition 1950
244pp, 1p acknowledgements, 1p foreword, unillus., bd., 180x120mm. ANL
This edition contains footnotes for school use.

1952 DUSTY/A Dog of the Sheep Country/By/Frank Dalby Davison/Abridged and provided with footnotes/for use in Schools/[device]/Angus and Robertson/Sydney London
1952
244pp, 1p acknowledgements, 1p foreword, unillus., stiff wrappers, 180x120mm. KMM

1953 DUSTY/A Dog of the Sheep Country/By/Frank Dalby Davison/Abridged and provided with footnotes/for use in Schools/[device]/Angus and Robertson/Sydney London Melbourne Wellington
First pub. 1946; rpt 1947; revised 1948; rpt 1949, 1950, 1954, 1958; School edition 1950; rpt 1951, 1952, 1956, 1958
244pp, 1p acknowledgement, 1p foreword, unillus., clo., 180x120mm. BBC
• Rpt 1959, as above, but with stiff paper wrappers. KMM

1954 DUSTY/A Dog of the Sheep Country/By/Frank Dalby Davison/[device]/Angus and Robertson
Sydney, first pub. 1946; rpt 1947, 1948, 1951, 1952, 1954, 1956, 1958, 1959; School edition 1950, rpt 1951, 1952, 1954, 1956, 1958, 1959; new ed. 1962, rpt 1963, 1964, 1965 (twice)
244pp, 1p acknowledgement, 1p foreword, 2pp glossary, unillus., clo., 180x120mm. BBC

1955 DUSTY/A Dog of the Sheep Country/By/Frank Dalby Davison/Angus and Robertson
• Rpt 1966, 1967, 1968; this edition Sydney 1972
244pp, 1p acknowledgement, 1p foreword, 2pp glossary, unillus., clo., d/w from painting by Wolfgang Grässe, 180x120mm. BBC

1956 DUSTY/A Novel by Frank D. Davison/New York/Coward McCann, Inc.
1946 [First American edition]
211pp, unillus., clo., 205x130mm, ANL

1957 DUSTY/The Story of a Sheepdog/by/Frank Dalby Davison/[device]/Eyre & Spottiswoode's/Popular Fiction Series
London, first pub. 1947; first issued in Eyre & Spottiswoode's Popular Fiction Series 1952
234pp, 1p foreword, unillus., clo., 185x120mm. KMM

DAVISON, Fred

1958 DUCK WILLIAMS AND/HIS COBBERS/By/Fred Davison/Angus and Robertson/Sydney and London/1939
287pp, unillus., clo., 180x125mm. KMM

DAVY, G. C.

1959 GENTLEMAN JUNIOR/A Junior Book of Politeness/by G. C. Davy/Illustrated by Marjorie Matthews/Angus and Robertson
Sydney, 1966
43pp, b/w drawings in text, stiff wrappers, 182x172mm. CLRC

DAWE, M. I.

1960 COOKERY/FOR YOUNG AUSTRALIANS/by/M. I. Dawe/Teacher of Home Economics/Education Department/Perth W.A./Whitcombe & Tombs Pty Ltd
1970
109pp, unillus., pic. bd., 210x135mm. NSL:M

DAWES, John

1961 THE TALES/OF TICKERY TOO/Verses for children/from Six to Sixty/By John Dawes/Illustrated by Elaine Jamison
Printed by A. J. Colley, 76–80 King Street, Newtown, n.d.
32pp, 3 f/p b/w illus. & drawings in text, pic. wrappers, 225x175mm. Grant

Dawfox Productions D.F. Series 135

Uniform booklets published by Dawfox Productions, Sydney, n.d. [1946]
14pp, 4 col. illus., b/w illus. on other pages, wrappers, 350x235mm. ANL
Picture books with brief rhyming text.

1962 A BOOK FOR BOYS
1963 DING DONG BELL
1964 PAINTER PETER AND OTHER PICTURES
1965 PERCE PARROT AND OTHERS

DAWLISH, Peter

1966 THE FIRST/TRIPPER/by/Peter Dawlish/Illustrated by/P. A. Jobson/Geoffrey Cumberlege/Oxford University Press/1947
158pp & 1p author's note, b/w frontis., 1 f/p b/w illus. & 1 diagram, b/w illus. in text, clo., 196x176mm. KP
The story of a young English naval cadet's first voyage from England to Australia.

1967 Rpt 1949, 1954
162pp (inc. 4pp author's note to the second ed.), b/w

frontis., 1 f/p b/w illus., 12 b/w chapter headings & 1 f/p plan of ship, clo., 196x125mm. KMM

1968 Peter Dawlish/MacCLELLAN'S LAKE/Illustrated by/Roy Sharp/[drawing]/Geoffrey Cumberlege/ Oxford University Press/1951
London
229pp, b/w frontis. & 6 f/p b/w illus., drawings in text, clo., 180x125mm. KMM

1969 JOHNNO/THE DEEP-SEA DIVER/The Life-Story of/Diver John Johnstone/as told to/Peter Dawlish/ with 24 illustrations in half-tone/George G. Harrap & Co. Ltd./London Toronto Wellington Sydney
160pp, b/w photographs, clo., 195x130mm. BBC
The life-story of a famous deep-sea diver most of whose work was done round the Australian coast.
• Rpt 1961. KP

DAWSON, Alec John

1970 FINN/THE WOLFHOUND/[drawing]/By A. J. Dawson/Author of "The Message", "The Genteel A.B.", etc./Illustrated by/R. H. Buxton/London: Grant Richards Ltd./Publishers, 7 Carlton Street, S.W.
First pub. Nov. 1908; reissued Sept. 1911
487pp, b/w frontis. & 15 f/p b/w illus., drawings in text, dec. e/p, pic. clo., 205x135mm. KMM

1971 A. J. Dawson/FINN THE WOLFHOUND/ Illustrated by Richard Kennedy/[device]/Longmans (on verso of t/p 'Longmans Green in association with Brockhampton Press, London, 1964')
251pp (inc. 1p foreword by Maxwell Knight), b/w drawings throughout, clo., 195x130mm. Modern Reading Series. KMM

1972 A. J. Dawson/FINN THE WOLFHOUND/ Illustrated by Richard Kennedy/[device]/Brockhampton Press—Leicester England
First pub. 1908; This edition first printed 1962; 2nd imp. 1964; 3rd imp. 1966
251pp (inc. 2pp foreword by Maxwell Knight), b/w frontis. & drawings throughout, clo., 200x135mm. BBC
According to the foreword, the present edition, edited by Antony Kamm, is about 20 000 words shorter than the original edition.
A publisher's advertisement in *The Times Literary Supplement*, 9 December 1965, claims that: 'Since its publication in the Brockhampton edition...[it] is now published also in the U.S.A., Denmark, Sweden, Germany, Czechoslovakia and in Afrikaans...film rights have been bought by Walt Disney'.

1973 A. J. Dawson/FINN THE WOLFHOUND/ Illustrations by Richard Kennedy/[drawing]/Penguin Books
First pub. 1908; this (abridged) edition first published by Brockhampton Press 1962; published in Peacock Books 1964
283pp (inc. 2pp introduction by Maxwell Knight), 3pp adv., 28 b/w illus., dec. wrappers, 180x110mm. KMM
Edition abridged by about 20 000 words
• Rpt as above, 1970. CLRC

1974 A. J. Dawson/JAN SON OF FINN/Illustrated by Richard Kennedy/Brockhampton Press
Leicester, England, 1963 [First published Constable, London 1917]
246pp (inc. 2pp foreword by John Dawson [son of author]), b/w frontis. & 8 f/p b/w illus., b/w drawings in text, clo., 205x130mm. CLRC
While most of the action of *Finn, the Wolfhound* took place in Australia, this book has an English & Canadian background. Dawson, though English born, spent some time in Australia, & wrote a number of adult novels with an Australian background.
• Rpt as above, 1966. CLRC

DAWSON, Dagma

1975 LADYBIRD GARDEN/Written and illustrated by/ Dagma Dawson/Aged 11 years/[drawing]/Australasian Publishing Company/Sydney Wellington London
1949
25pp, 9 col. illus., bd., 180x220mm. ANL

DAWSON, E. C.

1976 HEROINES OF/MISSIONARY ADVENTURE/True stories of the intrepid Bravery/and patient endurance of missionaries/in their encounters with uncivilized/ man, wild beasts and the forces of/nature in all parts of the world/By/E. C. Dawson, M.A. (Oxon.)/Canon of St Mary's Cathedral and Rector of St Peters, Edinburgh/Author of "The Life of Bishop Hannington"/"Lion-Hearted" "In the Days of the Dragons"/&c &c &c/with twenty-four illustrations/ London/Seeley, Service & Co. Limited/196 Shaftesbury Avenue/MDCCCCXXV
1st ed. 1909
340pp (inc. 3pp preface) & 20pp adv., b/w frontis. & 23 b/w plates, dec. clo., 195x125mm. KP
Contains 'Among the "Blackfellows" of North Australia' (Mrs Arthur Ward & the Moravian Mission at Mapoon), 19pp & 1 plate.

1977 Another copy as above, but
with eight illustrations/London/Seeley, Service & Co. Limited/38 Great Russell Street/1912
169pp, 20pp adv. & 2pp adv. preceding text & 4pp preface, b/w frontis. & 7 f/p b/w plates, dec. clo., 195x125mm. WRT
Contains 'Among the "Blackfellows" of North Australia' pp143—69. 'The contents of this volume have been taken from Canon Dawson's larger book entitled "*Heroines of Missionary Adventure*" published at five shillings.'

DAWSON, Helen

1978 THE HOUSE IN/HAVEN STREET/by/Helen Dawson/with a frontispiece by/Brian Wildsmith/ London/J. M. Dent & Sons Ltd.
1960
151pp, clo., 190x125mm. NSL:M

DAY, A. Grove

1979 THE STORY OF/AUSTRALIA/by A. Grove Day/ Illustrated by W. R. Lohse
Random House, New York, 1960
171pp, 4pp index, 3pp chronology, 2pp adv., dec. map frontis., double spread map, 17 f/p part. col. illus., illus. chapter-headings, dec. e/p, clo., 215x140mm. World Landmark Books. NSL:M

1980 ALL ABOUT/AUSTRALIA/By/A. Grove Day/ Illustrated by/W. R. Lohse/[publisher's device: "All-About Books"]/W. H. Allen/London 1961
116pp, 8pp chronology & index, double-spread dec. map frontis., 1 double-spread map & 17 f/p or extended part. col. illus., illus. chapter headings, dec. e/p, clo., 215x140mm. KMM

1981 THEY PEOPLED/THE PACIFIC/[drawing]/By A. Grove Day/Illustrated by George Wilson/London: G. Bell and Sons Ltd.
Copyright 1964; Published by Duell, Sloane & Pearce, New York; British edition first published 1965
166pp (inc. 6pp index), b/w chapter headings & two-page b/w map, clo., 195x125mm. CLRC
• Rpt 1966. CLRC

DE BURGH, Jane

1982 Imperial Edition No. 275/GUM-TREES/Seven Australian Songs/1, Rain,/2 The Wallaby Rat,/3, The

Platypus, 4, The Train with the Forty Trucks/5, Little Brother Possum/6, Tinkle, Tinkle Cow Bells/7, Gum-Trees/Words by Jane de Burgh, Music by Mirrie Solomon,/Illustrations by Kathleen Ussher/Allan & Co.,/Melbourne Sydney Adelaide Bendigo
n.d. [Copyright 1925]
20pp, line drawings & decorations, dec. wrappers, 320x240mm. CLRC

DE CRESPIGNY, Mary Champion
1983 Imperial Edition No. 1078/MORE FOLK SONGS/FOR YOUNG SINGERS/Selected by Mary Champion de Crespigny/Allans Music/(Australia) Pty Ltd. Melbourne Adelaide Geelong/Bendigo Hobart Launceston/Printed in Australia
144pp, pic. wrappers, 250x185mm. KP
Few of the songs are of Australian origin though the compiler is an Australian.

DE FOSSARD, Esta
1984 PUFFING BILLY/A Story for Children by Esta de Fossard/Illustrated by John Mason/Lansdowne Press
Melbourne, 1967
[26]pp, dec. col. t.p., col. illus. throughout, clo., 280x210mm. KMM

1985 BARRENJOEY/by Esta de Fossard/Illustrations by John Mason/Lansdowne
Melbourne, 1971
[23]pp, col. illus. throughout, pic. bd., 280x210mm. CLRC

1986 LET'S GO SAILING/by Esta de Fossard/Illustrated by John Mason/[illustration]/Golden Press Sydney
1971
[29]pp, col. illus. throughout, pic. bd., 280x230mm. CLRC

DE GARIS, C. J. (ed.)
1987 "SUN-RAYSED"/CHILDREN'S FAIRY STORY BOOK/Edited by C. J. De Garis/[drawing]/68 pages, containing/Fairy Stories/Nursery Rhymes, Limericks/Parodies Acrostics/F. W. Niven & Co. Printers and Publishers,/40–42 Flinders Street, Melbourne
n.d. [1919]
52pp (inc. 1p preface), 8pp f/p col. illus., line drawings in text, bd., 240x170mm. NSL:M
Book of stories & verses; produced to advertise the dried fruit industry in the Murray irrigation settlements.

DE JAN, Mrs
See James, Winifred

DE JAUNAY, Hubert [pseud. 'Bertie Beetle']
1988 GILBERT/GUINEA PIG/and other Tales/by/Bertie Beetle/(H. de J.)/Illustrated by The Santrys/Consolidated Press Limited, Sydney
1943
56pp, 11 col. illus. & b/w drawings in text, dec. bd., dec. e/p, 230x180mm. ANL
Verses, &c.

DE LEEUW, Adele
1989 [device]/A World Explorer/JAMES COOK/By Adele De Leeuw/Illustrated by Nathan Goldstein/Garrard Publishing Company/Champaign, Illinois
1963
96pp, col. illus., clo., map e/p, 230x155mm. Grant
1990 [device]/A World Explorer/JAMES COOK/By Adele De Leeuw/Illustrated by Nathan Goldstein/Frederick Muller Limited/London
1966
96pp, part. col. illus. throughout, clo., map e/p, 225x160mm. A World Explorer Book (edited by Elizabeth Minot Graves). KMM

DE LEEUW, Cateau
1991 [device]/A World Explorer/ROALD/AMUNDSEN/By Cateau de Leeuw/Illustrated by George I. Parrish/[device]/Frederick Muller Limited
London, 1967
96pp, part col. frontis. & 18 f/p part col. illus. & other illus. in text, clo., dec. map e/p, 226x160mm. KMM

DE MOLE, Evelyn
1992 FOR THE YOUNG IN HEART/By/Evelyn de Mole/Illustrated by C.C./[drawing]/Adelaide: The Hassell Press/1936
First pub. October 1936
41pp, b/w drawings throughout, wrappers, 245x170mm. CLRC
1993 2nd imp. Feb. 1937, as above. KMM
1994 Another copy as above, but with band on wrapper containing a recommendation by the Duchess of Devonshire dated September 1938. CLRC

DE ROUGEMONT, Louis
1995 THE ADVENTURES OF/LOUIS DE ROUGEMONT/As told by Himself/with Forty-six Illustrations/London/George Newnes, United/Southampton Street, Strand/1899/(All rights reserved)
396pp, xipp, 32pp, b/w illus. (A. H. Pearse), pic. clo., 185x120mm. TG

DE SELINCOURT, Aubrey
1996 Aubrey de Selincourt/MR. ORAM'S STORY/The Adventures of Capt. James Cook, R.N./Illustrated by/John Baynes/"The Story of Two Ships and of a Man"/Methuen & Co. Ltd./London 36 Essex Street, Strand, W.C.2
1949
142pp, 7 f/p b/w illus., 8 b/w drawings in text, dec. e/p, clo., 190x125mm. HBM

DEAN, Sheila Helen
1997 ROSEMEE/'N'/EVERYBODY/by/Sheila Dean/Illustrated by/The Santrys
Consolidated Press, Sydney, 1946
40pp, dec. t.p., 11 col. illus. & b/w drawings, dec. e/p, dec. bd., 230x170mm. ANL
Children's verses.

1998 Mullens' Stories for Children/No. 204/SAMMY SILVERFISH/And Other Stories/by/Sheila Dean/(for Ages 8–9)/Robertson & Mullens Ltd./Melbourne
n.d. [1952]
31pp, b/w frontis. & 3 f/p b/w illus., wrappers, 180x115mm. KMM

DEANE, Bernard
1999 MASTER/OF THE MOUNTAIN/A Story of the Australian Bush/by/Bernard Deane/London/R. T. S.—Lutterworth Press/4 Bouverie Street E.C.4
1939
221pp, col. frontis., clo., 185x120mm. CLRC

DEANE, Shirley
2000 VENDETTA/A Story of/the Corsican Mountains/Shirley Deane/Illustrated by Batia Valero/Macmillan
London, 1969 [copyright Shirley Deane 1967]
121pp, b/w illus. throughout, clo., 200x125mm. KMM

DEANS, Leslie
2001 THE IMP AND THE/FAIRY/By Leslie Deans/Drawings by/Esther and/Betty Paterson
Victory Publicity, Melbourne, n.d. [1945]
16pp, part. col. drawings throughout, bd., cover title, 240x180mm. ANL

DEARDEN, R. L.

2002 JIM/OF THE/"VALFREYA"/By/R. L. Dearden/A. & C. Black, Ltd./4, 5 & 6 Soho Square/London, W.1/1925
256pp, col. frontis. only, clo., 186x120mm. CLRC
The experiences of a boy in the merchant navy in a sailing ship on a voyage from England to Port Pirie, SA, Cape Town, Sydney, thence to Valparaiso and home via Cape Horn.

'DEBBY'

2003 KITCHEN FUN/COOKING WITH DEBBY/A Cook Book for children
Publ. for the Australian Egg Industry, n.d. [197-?]
32pp, col. illus. throughout, col. pic. wrappers, cover title, 204x135mm. KMM
Recipes for children advertising certain well-known trade products.

DEE, Laurie

2004 CHILDREN'S/HIVE/OF/HAPPINESS/by/Laurie Dee
Laurie Dee Publications, Wahroonga, NSW, n.d.
42pp, numerous b/w text illus., dec. wrappers, spiral bdg, 180x220mm. NSL:M

DEEGAN, T. P.

2005 THE COMEDY OF/THE MILKY WAY/AND THE/MYSTIC AND MAGIC/FOLKLORE OF THE/ABORIGINES/By/T. P. Deegan
J. Roy Stevens, Melbourne, n.d. [NSL:M copy received 1946]
30pp (inc. preface), unillus., pic. wrappers, 220x135mm. NSL:M
Cover illustration signed 'Crampton'
A fairy tale in verse. Although the book does not appear to have been intended for children some of the verses are suitable for them.

Deep Sea Wonders

2006 A 1965 Sanitarium Picture Card Album/DEEP SEA WONDERS
Sanitarium Health Food Co., P.O. Box 40, Summer Hill, NSW
12pp [with spaces left for 25 cards, collected from the firm's products, to be pasted in], pic. wrappers, cover title, 240x180mm. KMM
• Rpt as above, 1965. KP

DELANDER, Sonja

2007 OLA/COHN'S/FAIRIES'/TREE/text/Sonja Delander/Photography/Rick Buckingham/Mullaya
Mullaya Publications, Canterbury, Victoria, 1972
29pp, b/w photographic illus. throughout, clo., 240x180mm. CLRC

DELLE, Hilary

2008 THE/THREE LITTLE PIGS/by/Hilary/Delle/Pictures by E. H. Davie
Ayers & James, Sydney, 1949
15pp, col. illus. throughout, wrappers, cover title, 310x250mm. NSL:M
Song, with music by Barry Gray, printed on back wrapper.

The Demon McGuire

See [Grundy, Francis H.]

DENIS, F. & CHAUVIN, V.

2009 THE/TRUE ROBINSON CRUSOES/Stories of Adventure./Abridged from the French of F. Denis/and V. Chauvin./By/Charles Russell./Illustrated./Cassell & Company, Limited:/London, Paris, New York & Melbourne
n.d. [inscribed Christmas 1891]
222pp (inc. 2pp preface), 16pp adv., b/w frontis. & 7 f/p b/w illus., dec. clo., 180x120mm. RM
Contents include: 'The Mutiny of the *Bounty*' (13pp); 'A Woman among Savages' (the wreck of the *Stirling Castle)* (8pp); 'The Wreck of the *Duroc*' (off the coast of New Guinea) (13pp).

DENNIS, C. J.

2010 A BOOK FOR KIDS/By C. J. Dennis/[coloured illustration]/Australia:/Angus & Robertson, Ltd./89 Castlereagh Street/Sydney
n.d. [First edition 1921]
117pp (inc. 1p dedication), col. frontis. & b/w illus. throughout, dec. e/p, col. pic. bd., 245x185mm. KMM
Frontis. & title page illustrations by Hal Gye; b/w e/p & cover illus. by the author (d/w different from board cover design)
Verses, with 2 short stories.
A special issue of 12 copies of the first edition was published with the wrappers bound in. See *C. J. Dennis: His Life and Work* by Ian McLaren, Melbourne 1961.

2011 ROUNDABOUT/By/C. J. Dennis/Author of The Sentimental Bloke/Australia/Angus & Robertson Limited/89 Castlereagh Street, Sydney/1935
117pp (inc. 1p dedication), col. frontis. by Hal Gye & b/w illus. throughout by author, dec. e/p, bd., 240x180mm. KMM
A re-issue of *A Book for Kids.* This edition omits 5 verses from the first edition ('The Funny Hatter', 'The Publisher', 'Bessie and the Bunny', 'Good Enough' & 'The Unsociable Wallaby'). In the first edition only one Bird Song is listed in the contents, though both are included in the text; in this edition both are included in the text & in the list of contents.

2012 A BOOK FOR KIDS/by/C. J. Dennis/with illustrations by the author. [publisher's device]/Angus and Robertson
Sydney 1958
100pp (inc. 3pp introduction by Alec Chisholm & 1p dedication), b/w drawings throughout, illus. by the author, dec. e/p, clo., 235x155mm. KMM
Contents the same as *Roundabout,* although one extra poem is listed in the contents. This is actually included in the texts of both the first edition & *Roundabout,* though as two separate poems neither of which are included in the list of contents in either volume.
• Rpt as above 1961, 1962, 1965. BBC

2013 A BOOK FOR KIDS/by/C. J. Dennis/with illustrations by the author/[device]/Angus and Robertson
Sydney 1970
100pp, b/w illus. throughout, pic. bd., dec. e/p, 235x150mm. BBC

DENNIS, C. J. & Others

MORE POEMS TO READ TO YOUNG AUSTRALIANS. *See* Rowe, Jennifer [ed.]

DEPASQUALE, Paul

2014 GRANDPAPA IN/DREAMLAND/by/Paul Depasquale/Illustrations and Cover by/Sr. M. Julian, O.P./Published by Academy Enterprises/Printed by Hyde Park Press, Adelaide/Copyright reserved June 1968
19pp & 1p blank, 3 line drawings, pic. wrappers, 210x136mm. CLRC

DEPPING, George Bernard

2015 VOYAGE/D'UN ÉTUDIANT/DANS LES CINQ PARTIES DU MONDE,/ouvrage/destiné à faciliter l'étude de la géographie aux jeunes gens,/et orné de huit cartes/Par M. Depping, Tome Premier. à Paris/à

la Librairie ancienne et moderne/de Méquignon Junior, Libraire,/Rue des Grands-Augustins, No. 9/A Lyon/ Chez Périsse Frères, Libraires,/des Mercière, No. 35/MDCCCXXII
2 vols. Vol. 1, viii+419pp, 4 folding maps, calf, and Vol. 2, iv+319pp, 4 folding maps, calf, 190x115mm. NSL:M

2016 VOYAGES/D'UN ÉTUDIANT/DANS LES CINQ PARTIES DU MONDE,/ouvrage/destiné à faciliter l'étude de la géographie Aux Jeunes Gens,/Par G-B. Depping./Nouvelle édition, ornée de vues et de cartes/ tome premier./A Paris/chez delamarche,/ingénieur mécanicien pour les globes et sphères,/Rue du jardinet, N°12/1835
viiipp (inc. 3pp preface to new ed.), 419pp (inc. 5pp index), folding engraved frontis. & folding engravings in text
Vol. 2 1st ed. 319pp (inc. 5pp index), frontis., folding b/w map of Africa, 2 folding b/w maps of Americas & one of l'Océanie, both bound in calf, 200x120mm. NSL:M
The Fifth Book (pp225—48) deals with the islands in the Pacific (pp249—65 with New Zealand and New Holland).

DERHAM, Enid

2017 EMPIRE/A Morality Play for Children/Written for the Victoria League/of Victoria by Enid Derham/ Melbourne/1912/All rights reserved
[Serle gives Osboldstone & Co. Pty. Ltd., Melbourne]
16pp, unillus., wrappers, 215x140mm. CLRC
A verse play written for performance on Empire Day.

DERWENT, Lavinia

2018 Collins Happy Readers/FIN, THE FISH/By/Lavinia Derwent/[drawing]/No. 6 Collins Clear-Type Press Collins Ltd, Glasgow, 1st imp. April 1938; rpt 1946, 1953, 1955
30pp, col. illus. throughout, illus. by Mollie Brett, dec. wrappers, cover title, 220x145mm. NSL:M

'DESDA' [Mrs Davies]

2019 THE RIVAL FAIRIES/or/Little Mamie's Troubles/ An Australian Story for Children:/by/Desda/Sydney/ Edward Turner, Publisher/Hunter Street
n.d. [1871]
24pp, unillus., stiff wrappers, 165x100mm. NSL:M
A moral tale.

DESMOND, Alice Curtis

2020 TEDDY KOALA/Mascot of the Marines/By Alice Curtis Desmond/Illustrated by Sam Savitt/[drawing]/ Dodd, Mead & Company, New York
1962
92pp, 3pp b/w drawings, 1p biographical note, b/w frontis. & 15 f/p b/w illus. & drawings in text, clo., 230x145mm. ANL

DESSARE, Eve

2021 Eve Dessare/Illustrations de Vanni Tealdi/TIMMY/ LE PETIT KOALA/[col. illus.]/Éditions G.P.—Département des Presses de la Cité/©1970 Éditions G.P.—Département des Presses de la Cité Paris
36pp, 28 col. illus., pic. bd., 264x195mm. KMM

Destination Moon

2022 DESTINATION MOON/The Story of Man's First Venture into Space/Published by Sanitarium Health Food Company
Sydney, n.d.
[12]pp, part col. illus., col. pic. wrappers (adv. on back wrapper), cover title, 196x244mm. WRT
Spaces for 50 cards to be pasted in.

DEVANEY, James

2023 THE/VANISHED TRIBES/By/James Devaney/ Second Edition/Australia/Cornstalk Publishing Company/89 Castlereagh Street, Sydney/1929
246pp (inc. 10pp glossary), b/w frontis. & 7 b/w plates, clo., 195x120mm. KMM

2024 THE WITCH-DOCTOR/and other Tales of/The Australian Blacks/By/James Devaney/Author of The Vanished Tribes/Australia:/Angus & Robertson Limited/89 Castlereagh Street, Sydney/1930
64pp (inc. 3pp glossary), 2pp foreword, unillus., pic. wrappers, 185x120mm. Grant
Adapted from the author's *The Vanished Tribes.*

2025 THE GIRL OONA/And other tales of/the Australian Blacks/By/James Devaney/Author of The Vanished Tribes/Australia:/Cornstalk Publishing Company/89 Castlereagh Street, Sydney/1929
64pp (inc. 1p foreword & 3pp glossary), b/w frontis. & 1 f/p b/w illus., pic. wrappers, 184x120mm. NSL:M
Illus. R. Wenban; cover uniform with other 2 titles. The Gumnut readers. Contains 4 stories.

2026 I-RINKA/THE MESSENGER/And other Tales of/ the Australian Blacks/By/James Devaney/Author of The Vanished Tribes/Australia:/Angus & Robertson Limited/89 Castlereagh Street, Sydney/1930
64pp (inc. 1p foreword & 4pp glossary), b/w frontis. & 1 f/p b/w illus., pic. wrappers, 184x120mm. NSL:M
Illus. R. Wenban. Same cover illus. as other 2 books in series. The Gumnut Readers. Contains 5 stories.

2027 THE FIRE TRIBE/and other Tales of/the Australian Blacks/By/James Devaney/Author of *The Vanished Tribes*/Australia/Angus & Robertson Limited/89 Castlereagh Street, Sydney/1930
63pp (inc. 1p preface & 3pp glossary), b/w frontis. (R. Wenban), pic. wrappers (same), 184x120mm. NSL:M
The Gumnut Readers. Includes 4 stories.

Diamond Library

Format example:
2028 Diamond Library. Complete Novel no. 37/1d./PALS/IN PERIL/[illus.]/Weird Adventures in the Australian Wilds.
Active Publishing Co., Ltd., Goodship House, Crown Court, Chancery Lane, London, W.C., n.d. [cover illus. signed, R/P/.16]
[32]pp, unillus., col. pic. wrappers, cover title, 185x130mm. RM
Adv. verso front wrapper & both sides back wrapper.
In same series:
2029 No 31 DUBBS FROM DOWN UNDER—The Australian Chum and his pet kangaroo, by Wingrove Willson
40pp, unillus., pic. wrappers, cover title, 184x130mm. CLRC
2030 No 82 THE KINGS OF COOLGARDIE
20pp, pic. wrappers, cover title. Unseen

DICKENS, A.

2031 OUR BABY/BOOK/[drawing]/Illustrated by/A. Dickens
n.d., printed in Australia by Colourtone Pty Ltd for Jons Productions, Sydney
30pp, part col. illus., pic. bd., 245x184mm. KP
Designed to record the baby's progress.

DICKS, H. G.

THE ROYAL FLYING DOCTOR SERVICE. *See* Life in Australia

DICKSON, Madge

2032 SONGS/FOR/AUSTRALIAN CHILDREN/Words

by Madge Dickson/music by/May H. Brahe/Contents/ 1. I wish I were a Possum...etc. [9 songs listed] Copyright price 2/6 net/Allan & Co. Prop. Ltd./ Melbourne, Adelaide, Bendigo, Geelong/Printed in England
n.d.
32pp [last blank], 6 col. illus., wrappers, 310x245mm. Grant

2033 REAL/AUSTRALIAN CHILDREN/SONGS/Words by/Madge Dickson/Music by/May H. Brahe./Contents [9 songs listed]/copyright price 2/6 nett/Allan & Co. Prop. Ltd/Melbourne Adelaide Bendigo Geelong/ Printed in England
Melbourne, 1911
32pp (inc. covers—last blank), 6 col. illus. (initialled ATM), wrappers, 310x245mm. NSL:M

2034 Rpt as above, but
Allan & Co./Melbourne Sydney Adelaide Bendigo/ Printed in England
32pp (not inc. covers—last blank), col. pic. wrappers,310x245mm. KP
Allans 50 Nursery Rhymes advertised on back cover.

2035 [col. illus.]REAL/AUSTRALIAN CHILDREN/ SONGS/By/Madge Dickson/and/May H. Brahe/ Copyright./Allan & Co./Melbourne Sydney Adelaide Bendigo/printed in England Price 2/6 nett
n.d. [acquired 1934]
31pp & 1p blank, pic. wrappers, 310x245mm. VSL

Difficulty Hill and Some Lads who climbed it

2036 DIFFICULTY HILL/AND/SOME LADS WHO CLIMBED IT./Two Tales founded on fact./Published under the direction of/The Committee of general literature and education,/appointed by the Society for promoting/Christian Knowledge./London:/Society for promoting Christian Knowledge:/sold at the depositories:/77 Great Queen Street, Lincoln's Inn Fields,/4, Royal Exchange; 48, Piccadilly;/and by all book sellers./New York: Pott, Young, & Co.
n.d. [1866] [awarded as school prize 1878]
179pp & 4pp adv., engraved frontis. & 3 f/p engravings, dec. clo., 144x95mm. CLRC
The second story (pp55–179) 'Thomas Kew', tells of a poor farm boy who emigrates to Australia, his experiences in Victoria with his brothers who follow him out & the family's successful life in the colony.

DILLBERG, Gustaf

2037 GENOM DEN FÖRSVUNNA SYDPOLEN
Lund 1909 (first published 1902)
iv, 284pp, printed bd.
'Translated from the English [?] by Disa Törnquist; a novel on the South Pole. The author (1858 to1934) was a Swede who for many years lived in New Zealand.'
As I have not seen this book, nor any other reference to it, I cannot comment as to whether or not it is a children's book.
Unseen: Catalogue No. 4, 1975, Dahlia Books, Uppsala

DINGWALL, Alexander

2038 THE/GREAT CAPTAIN/The Story of Captain Cook/Alexander Dingwall/[device]/Lutterworth Press/ London
1964
94pp, col. frontis., double-spread b/w map, clo., 180x115mm. NSL:M

The Dinkum Aussie Painting Book

2039 THE/DINKUM AUSSIE/PAINTING BOOK
n.p., n.d. [1934?]
24pp, col. & b/w drawings, slight text, wrappers, cover title, 280x275mm. MAC

As the Sydney Harbour Bridge, and the Shrine, Melbourne, are depicted the date must be 1934 or later.

Discovery

2040 DISCOVERY/An authentic account of the discovery, settlement and exploration of Australia by land, sea and air...from the voyage of the "Duyfken" in 1606 to the Mackay Aerial Expedition of 1937
Gregory's Guides & Maps Pty Ltd, Sydney 1961
40pp (inc. foreword by Dr G. Mackaness), 4pp col. adv., part. col. portraits & maps, maps by Clive Barrass, wrappers, 280x215mm. ANL

2041 Another copy as above but published by Cottee's General Foods Ltd, Brookvale, NSW, n.d. WRT

Discovery and Adventure

2042 DISCOVERY AND ADVENTURE/Christopher Columbus, 15th Century./LA PÉROUSE,/17th Century/[vignette]/London:/Burns and Lambert./ MDCCCLIX 1859
142pp, dec. clo., 165x100mm. KMM
Comprises 'The Life & Voyages of C. Columbus' (71pp), 'The Voyages of La Pérouse' (48pp) & 'Arctic Voyages and Discovery,' 'The Exploring Voyages of Dr Kane' &c.

DISNEY, Walt

MICKEY'S KANGAROO/by Walt Disney/[drawing]/ John Sands Ltd, Sydney n.d.
48pp, illus. throughout, col. pic.wrappers, 245x245mm. Grant
Comic strip cartoons.

DITCHAM, Louisa M.

2043 [drawing]/MOTHER/MADGE/By/Louisa M. Ditcham/Launceston/A. J. Pasmore, 51 Patterson Street/1899
164pp, unillus., limp clo., 180x120mm. TSL

2044 NELL/Sequel to "Mother Madge"/By/Louisa M. Ditcham/Tasmania: Heather Brae, Launceston/1901
331pp, unillus. (copy seen re-bound), 215x130mm. TSL

DIVINE, David

2045 SIX GREAT/EXPLORERS/Frobisher—Cook—Mungo Park—/Burton—Livingstone—Scott/By/David Divine/[publisher's device]/Hamish Hamilton/London
First pub. 1954; 2nd imp. Nov. 1954; 3rd imp. Nov. 1957; 4th imp. July 1959
216pp (inc. 2pp acknowledgements & bibliography, & 2pp author's foreword), 6pp b/w portrait illus. & 5pp maps, map e/p, clo., 185x120mm. HBM

DIXON, Franklin W.

2046 The Ted Scott Flying Stories [underlined]/FIRST STOP HONOLULU/or/Ted Scott over the Pacific/By/ Franklin W. Dixon/Author of/"Over the Ocean to Paris"/"Over the Rockies with the Air Mail"/"The Hardy Boys: The Tower Treasure," etc./Illustrated by/ Walter S. Rogers/New York/Grosset & Dunlap/ Publishers/Made in the United States of America
1927
vipp (inc. 1p dedication), 216pp & 2 adv., b/w frontis. only, by V.S.Rogers, clo., 185x120mm. NSL:M

2047 The Ted Scott Flying Stories [underlined]/ACROSS THE PACIFIC/or/Ted Scott's Hop to Australia/By/ Franklin W. Dixon/Author of/"Over the Ocean to Paris",/"First Stop Honolulu", "The Hardy Boys, The/ Tower Treasure", Etc./Illustrated by/Walter S. Rogers/ New York/Grosset & Dunlap/Publishers
1928
216pp, 1p dedication & 2pp adv., b/w frontis. only, dec. clo., 187x126mm. NSL:M

Adventure story set in the US, which then develops into a flight across the Pacific ending in Sydney.

2048 The Ted Scott Flying Stories/LOST AT THE/SOUTH POLE/or/Ted Scott in Blizzard Land/By/Franklin W. Dixon/Author of/"Over the Ocean to Paris",/"The Lone Eagle of the Border"/"The Hardy Boys: The Secret of the Old Mill", etc/Illustrated by/Walter S Rogers/New York/Grosset & Dunlap/Publishers
1930
vipp, 214pp, 4pp adv., b/w frontis. only, clo., 185x120mm. KMM

DOBSON, Melanie
DR GUMNUT. *See* Gunn & Taylor 92, Junior Library No. 2

DOBSON, Rosemary [ed.]
2049 SONGS FOR ALL SEASONS/100 Poems for Young People/Chosen by/Rosemary Dobson/Drawings by/Margaret Horder/Angus and Robertson
Sydney, 1967
177pp (inc. 9pp notes, index &c), line drawings throughout, clo., 215x137mm. KMM
Some of the drawings are printed in black & some in green.
2050 Rpt as above. 1971
The first edition has a gilt decoration running up the spine which does not appear in the reprint; the lettering also varies. The reprint was printed in Hong Kong & is not as well printed as the first imp. KMM

DOCKER, E. G.
THE AUSTRALIAN SUGAR INDUSTRY. *See* Australian Landmarks

DOCKER, Ted
SISTER/KENNY. *See* Famous Australians

DODWELL, A. L. V.
2051 THE CHILDREN'S PRINCE./Dedicated to the Helpless./All profits for Minda./By Mrs. G. F. Dodwell./Adelaide:/Hussey & Gillingham Limited, Printers, Currie Street./1920
12pp double-spread b/w reprod. of aerial photograph of children forming the P of W's crest on the Adelaide oval, stiff pic. wrappers, 140x110mm. SSL
Verses for children & others celebrating the visit of HRH the Prince of Wales to Adelaide in 1920.

D'OMBRAIN, Arthur Wolseley
2052 O NITA RINKUS/The Story of an Easter Egg/By A. W. D'Ombrain/[drawing]/Illustrated by Mary M. Abbott/By the same Author: "A Gallery of Gum Trees," "Boomerang Verses"
Australasian Medical Pub. Co., Sydney, 1946
37pp, 2 f/p col. illus. & b/w drawings throughout, dec. bd., col. illus. pasted on front cover, 275x220mm. ANL
The story of a platypus.

Don Bradman
2053 DON BRADMAN/"Flicker" No. 1/On Drive/and/Off Drive/John Wisden & Co. Ltd./Mortlake SW 14
Flicker Productions Ltd/113b Earl's Court Road London SW5
Flicker Sports Series [1930]
50 leaves unpaged of photographic illus. of the batsman in action; when booklet is reversed another series of photographs is seen, wrappers, cover title, 74x54mm. KMM
A "Flicker book" designed to be flicked through so the rapid succession of pictures gives the impression of movement.
2054 Uniform with this book—Vol. 2. Unseen
2055 Also Vol. 3 Don Bradman/"Flicker" No. 3/Leg Glance/and Pull
As above. KMM

DONALD, Will
2056 DAD, DAVE,/& DAISY/[illustration]/The New Aussie Comic
Sydney, n.d. [1917]
16pp, b/w drawings, wrappers, 270x210mm. NSL:M

2057 Price 2/-/KIDS'/CANNON/Written/&/Illustrated/by/Will Donald/[drawing]/for/The War Chest Fund
Printed by W. C. Penfold, Sydney, 1917
28pp, b/w drawings & verse on each page, khaki col. paper wrappers, printed in black & red, 305x242mm. KMM
Adv., with drawings, & rhymes inside front & back covers. T.p. reads: "War Babies/ABC/[drawing]/The Bombardment opens on/the next page." Humorous wartime cartoons arranged alphabetically with rhymes ostensibly for children.

DONATH, E. J.
WILLIAM FARRER. *See* Great Australians

DONKIN, Nance (ed.)
2058 AUSTRALIAN/CHILDREN'S/ANNUAL/[drawing]/Edited by Nance Donkin/illustrations by—Henry Ford/Jack Truscott/Cecily Fricker/Lothian Publishing Company/Sydney Melbourne Auckland
1963
114pp, b/w drawings throughout, pic. bd., 248x188mm. KMM
Prose, verse & miscellaneous. Contributors include Nan Chauncy, Ivan Southall, Alan Marshall.

DONKIN, Nance Clare
2059 ARALUEN/ADVENTURES/by Nance Donkin/Illustrations by/Edith B. Bowden/F. W. Cheshire Pty. Ltd./Melbourne and London
1946
175pp, b/w frontis. & 5 b/w illus., bd., 180x115mm. VSL

2060 NO MEDALS/FOR MEG/by/Nance Donkin/F. W. Cheshire Pty. Ltd./Melbourne and London
1947
148pp, b/w frontis. & 4 b/w illus., clo., 185x120mm. ANL
New edition 1948. ANB

2061 JULIE/STANDS BY/by/Nance Donkin/F. W. Cheshire/Melbourne and London
1948
139pp, b/w frontis., front & d/w by Joan Turner, bd., 175x115mm. ANL

2062 BLUE RIBBON BETH/Nance Donkin/[drawing]/Geoffrey Cumberlege/Oxford University Press/Melbourne Wellington
1951
153pp, unillus., clo., 185x120mm. KMM

SHEEP; SUGAR. *See* Life in Australia
AN EMANCIPIST; A CURRENCY LASS; AN ORPHAN. *See* Early Australians

2063 HOUSE/BY THE/WATER/[drawing]/Nance Donkin/Illustrated by Astra Lacis Dick/Angus and Robertson
Sydney, 1969
141pp, b/w drawings in text, clo., 215x135mm. KMM

2064 Nance Donkin/JOHNNY NEPTUNE/Angus and Robertson
Sydney, 1971
146pp, 1p preface, unillus., clo., 215x135mm. KMM

Doongalla Days Stories
2065 THE BIG/LITTLE MAN
2066 THE FOUR/CLEVER BROTHERS
2067 THE FOX/AND THE/LITTLE BROWN HEN
2068 THE BRAVE DOG/AND THE/BIG BAD WOLF
[cover reads 'The Clever Dog']
Uniform booklets published by Georgian House Melbourne 1946
16pp, 4–6 part. col. illus., stiff dec. wrappers, (sgd 'J.H.') 180x120mm. ANL

DORÉ, L. M.
2069 SMALL FRIENDS/An/Uncle Lee Book By L. M. Doré
Publ. by L. M. Doré, Sydney, printed by Simmons Ltd. 31-33 Parramatta Rd, Glebe, n.d.
[10]pp, pictures every page, 4 printed in col. others b/w, col. pic. wrappers, cover title, 237x180mm. KP

2070 THE/MAGIC/FLUTE/An "Uncle Lee" Book/By L. M. Doré
n.p., n.d.
[10]pp (inc. covers), col. illus. throughout, pic. wrappers, cover title, 235x180mm. ANL

2071 DILLY:/The Runaway Doll/[drawing]/An "Uncle Lee" Book by L. M. Doré
The author, Sydney, n.d. [194-?]. Printed by Simmons Ltd, 31-33 Parramatta Road, Glebe
[12]pp, alternate pages printed in col., others in b/w, illus. throughout, pic. wrappers, cover title, 277x217mm. KMM

2072 "UNCLE LEE'S"/A/B/C
Publ. by L. M. Doré, Sydney, n.d.
[12]pp (inc. covers), col. drawings of objects beginning with the same letter on every page, col. pic. wrappers, cover title, 273x216mm. ANL

2073 RHYME TIME/Verses and Illustrations/By/L. M. DORÉ/[dedication—11 lines]/Printed by/Hollander & Govett Pty Ltd., Sydney
n.d., [194-?]
On front cover: 'Rhyme Time with Uncle Lee'
16pp, col. illus with verse & dec. b/w border on each page, pic. wrappers, 365x244mm. KMM
Another copy:
2074 RHYMETIME/An/"Uncle Lee" Book/By L. M. DORÉ [on front cover]
Publ. by L. M. Doré, Sydney, printed by Simmons Ltd, 31 Parramatta Rd, Glebe. Copy inscribed 1950
[10]pp, col. illus. & verse on each page, col. pic. wrappers, 245x180mm. KMM

2075 SMALL/CREATURES/An/"Uncle Lee" Book/L. M. Doré
10pp, col. illus. on every page, col. pic. wrappers, 245x177mm. KP

DORIAN, P. F.
2076 THE/YEARS/BETWEEN/A Guide for Catholic Boys/by/Patrick Dorian/B.A., D.P.A. M.I.E.D. (Lon.)/The Polding Press/Brisbane
1st ed. July 1962, rpt Nov. 1962, Sept. 1963, Jan. 1965
148pp, unillus., dec. wrappers, 202x134mm. KP

'DOUBLECLEFF, Miss'
See [Pye, Moira P.]

DOUGLAS, Lorna
2077 THESE/GOLDEN DAYS/Verses by/Lorna Douglas/Illustrations by/Betty Paterson/Copyright all rights reserved
Printed by Morris & Walker Pty Ltd, 243 Smith St, Fitzroy (Victoria), n.d.
26pp, b/w drawings throughout, dec. bd., 175x205mm. NSL:M

'DOUGLAS, Mary' [Jule Cummins]
2078 THE ROCKING DONKEY/also/Sylvester goes a-seeking/and The Three Lost Toys/The stories by/Mary Douglas/& the pictures by/Wally Driscoll/E. W. Cole/Melbourne
n.d. [1953]
128pp, col. frontis. & 9 col. illus., 7 f/p b/w illus. & b/w drawings in text, clo., dec. e/p, 215x140mm. VSL

DOVE, Castleden
2079 LOWANNA/An Australian School Story/By/Castleden Dove/Illustrated by/J. Dewar Mills/Humphrey Milford/Oxford University Press/London Edinburgh Glasgow Copenhagen/New York Toronto Melbourne Cape Town/Bombay Calcutta Madras Shanghai
1925
256pp, col. frontis. & 4 f/p b/w illus., clo., 185x120mm. ANL
2080 LOWANNA/An Australian School Story/By/Castleden Dove/[publisher's device]/London/Humphrey Milford/Oxford University Press
1929
256pp, col. frontis. only, clo., 185x120mm. KMM

DOW, Hume & BARNES, John [ed.]
2081 WORLD UNKNOWN/An Anthology of Australian Prose/Selected by/Hume Dow and John Barnes/[vignette]/Drawings by Alison Forbes/Melbourne/Oxford University Press/London Wellington New York/1960
147pp (inc. 11pp notes & acknowledgements), b/w drawings throughout, limp clo., 210x130mm. KMM
A school anthology of extracts from the works of Australian authors writing about childhood.
• Rpt 1963, 1964, 1968, 1970. KP
2082 2nd ed. as above, 1970
187pp (inc. 12pp notes &c), other details as before. KP
Includes a 6th section reproducing work by Hal Porter, Judith Wright, Randolph Stow.

DOWKER, Helen
2083 CHILDREN'S/STORIES/By/Helen Dowker
G. W. Archer & Son, Printers, 431 Vincent St, Leederville [Perth, W.A.], n.d. [1931]
24pp, portrait frontis. (of author), b/w drawings, wrappers, 180x110mm. NSL:M
Simple stories written by a girl in her teens.

2084 STORIES/FOR CHILDREN/[device]/By Helen Dowker/The Associated Printers./319 Lennox Street,/Richmond, Victoria./Sept. 1933
34pp, b/w frontis., portrait of author, b/w drawings, wrappers, 180x105mm. Grant

2085 BED-TIME/STORIES/By Helen Dowker
Printed by Gordon Chandler, Printer, 13 Carlisle Street, St Kilda [Vic], n.d.
48pp, b/w frontis. portrait of author, 7 b/w illus., pic. wrappers, 170x104mm. KMM

DOWLING, Dorothea
2086 BUNNY SLIPPERS/and/other Poems/[drawing]/Dorothea Dowling/Illustrated by/Mavis Dowling
Printed by Highway Press, Marrickville, NSW, [1968]
28pp, b/w drawings, wrappers, 212x130mm. ANL

2087 POEMS/FOR RECITATION/[drawing]/Dorothea Dowling/Illustrated by/Mavis Dowling
Highway Press Pty Ltd, Marrickville, NSW, 1972

52pp, b/w drawings in text, wrappers, 210x125mm. KMM
Some of these poems were originally published in the school magazines of the Education Departments of New South Wales and Queensland.

Down on the Farm Cut-Out Book
See Offset Publishing Cut-Out Books

DOWNES, Marion Grace

2088 FLOWER O'/THE BUSH/By/Marion Downes/ Author of "Swayed by the Storm", etc./Ward, Lock & Co., Limited/London, Melbourne and Toronto/1914
320pp, 16pp adv., 1 f/p b/w illus. & 1 plate, illus. by J. Macfarlane, clo. (with coloured oval medallion on front cover), 185x125mm. KP

2089 IN THE TRACK/OF THE SUNSET/An Australian Story/for Girls/By/Marion Downes/Author of/ "Swayed by the Storm", "Flower o'the Bush", etc./ 1919
Modern Printing Co., [Melbourne]
313pp, 6pp adv., unillus., clo., 180x115mm. KMM

DOWNIE, James M.

2090 WARRIGAL/The Story of a Wild Horse/By/James M. Downie/[drawing]/Illustrated in Line & Colour/ By/John C. Downie/London/Hutchinson & Co. (Publishers) Ltd.
1935
190pp, col. frontis. & 2 col. illus., 22 f/p b/w illus., clo., 226x175mm. VSL

2091 WARRIGAL/The Story of a Wild Horse/by/James M. Downie/[drawing]/Illustrated in Line and Colour/ by/John C. Downie/London:/Hutchinson & Co. (Publishers) Ltd.
As entered above. The same t.p. with 1935 on verso. However, this is probably a re-issue [1939] as the title &c on front cover & spine is blocked in black instead of gilt & the e/p are white instead of red as in other ed. Original ed. was bound up in a cheaper bdg in 1939 as internally text is the same, both copies being printed by Taylor Garrett Evans & Co. Ltd, Manchester. KP
Swedish edition

2092 WARRIGAL. VILDHÄSTEN, BERÄTTELSE FOÖR UNGDOM
Tr. Emil Langlet
B. Wahlström, Stockholm, 1939
190(1)pp, 8 photographic illus.
2nd ed. 1944; 3rd ed. 1950. Unseen

2093 KILLER-DOG/By/James M. Downie/With 17 illustrations/by John C. Downie/Hutchinson & Co./ (Publishers) Ltd./London
1936
223pp, 40pp adv., col. frontis. & line drawings, clo., 185x120mm. ANL
Swedish edition

2094 WOMBA, EN BERÅTTELSE FOÖR UNGDOM OM DEN AUSTRALISKA VILDHUNDEN OCH ANDRA DJUR
Tr. V. Davidson
Förord av författaren, Stockholm, B. Wahlström, 1936
188(1)pp, photographic illus.
2nd ed. 1941, 3rd ed. 1949. Unseen

2095 THE TREASURE/OF THE NEVER-NEVER/By/ James M. Downie/Author of "Warrigal: the Story of a Wild Horse"/Illustrated by John C. Downie/Blackie & Son Limited/London and Glasgow
n.d.
256pp, b/w frontis. & 17 f/p b/w illus., drawings in text, clo., 210x150mm. KMM

2096 THE TREASURE/OF THE NEVER-NEVER/By/ James M. Downie/Author of "Warrigal: the Story of a Wild Horse"/Illustrated by John C. Downie/[device]/ M. S. Mill Co., Inc./Publishers/New York, N.Y.
1st American ed., 1937
254pp, f/p b/w frontis., 18 f/p b/w illus & b/w drawings in text, clo., 210x150mm. RM

2097 MUTINY IN THE AIR/By/James M. Downie/ Author of 'The Treasure of the Never-Never' etc./Illus. by Reginald Cleaver/Blackie & Son Limited/London and Glasgow
1937
255pp, col. frontis. & 7 f/p b/w illus., clo., 200x135mm. VSL

2098 MUTINY IN THE AIR/By/James M. Downie/ Author of "The Treasure of the Never-Never" etc./ Illus. by Reginald Cleaver/Blackie & Son Limited/ London and Glasgow
n.d. [1943]
255pp, b/w frontis. & 2 f/p b/w illus., clo., 180x115mm. Grant

2099 Another copy, as above, but with b/w frontis. & 3 f/p b/w illus. RM

2100 ALVACORE'S ISLAND/By/James M. Downie/ Author of "Mutiny in the Air" "The Treasure of the/ Never-Never" &c./Illustrated by M. Mackinlay/Blackie & Son Limited/London and Glasgow
n.d. [194-?]
256pp, b/w frontis. & 3 f/p b/w illus., clo., 185x120mm. KMM
Boys' adventure story set in the New Hebrides.

2101 THE YELLOW/RAIDERS/by/James M. Downie/ The Children's Press/London and Glasgow
n.d.
224pp, col. frontis. (sgd 'Eyles'), clo., 175x120mm. BBC

2102 THE YELLOW/RAIDERS/by/James M. Downie/ [device]/Collins/London and Glasgow
1940
224pp, b/w frontis. only, clo., 180x120mm. KMM
• Rpt 1945, Feb. 1946. KP
• Rpt 1958, 1960. KP

2103 SKIP OF/THE ISLANDS/By/James M. Downie/ Round the Globe/Stories/Frederick Warne & Co., Ltd./London and New York
1948
63pp, b/w map, b/w drawings in text, wrappers, 185x130mm. MK

2104 GAUNT OF PACIFIC COMMAND/By/James M. Downie/[device]/Frederick Warne and Co. Ltd./ London and New York
1948
256pp, tinted frontis. only, clo., 190x125mm. KMM

2105 THE/PIRATES OF PAPUA/By/James M. Downie/ Frederick Warne and Co. Ltd./London and New York
1949
249pp, col. frontis., clo., 190x120mm. ANL

2106 THE/SECRET OF THE LOCH/By/James M. Downie/W. & R. Chambers Limited/London and Edinburgh
[1949]
232pp, unillus., clo., 184x120mm. ANL
• Rpt as above, 1957. ANL

2107 THE/MYSTERY OF/THE SANTA CRUZ/by/ James M. Downie/Frederick Warne & Co., Ltd./ London and New York
1951
256pp, col. frontis. (sgd 'G.P.'), b/w map, clo., 195x130mm. PAI

2108 THE ROCKET/RANGE PLOT/James M. Downie/Frederick Warne & Co. Ltd./London & New York
1952
256pp, b/w frontis. by W. Spence, clo., 190x120mm. CLRC

2109 GAUNT OF THE/PEARL SEAS PATROL/By/James M. Downie/W. & R. Chambers Limited/London and Edinburgh
First published 1950; rpt 1954
247pp, 2 b/w maps only, clo., 185x120mm. K&NI
Set in Broome.

2110 THE FLYING/DOCTOR/MYSTERY/James M. Downie/[drawing]/Frederick Warne & Co, Ltd./London & New York
1954
256pp, b/w frontis. by S. Drigin, clo., 185x120mm. CLRC

DOWNIE, John C.

2111 GALLOPING HOOFS/A Story of Australian/Men and Horses/Written and illustrated/by/John C. Downie/Thomas Nelson & Sons Ltd./London Edinburgh Paris Melbourne/Toronto and New York
1936
213pp, 14pp adv., col. frontis. & 6 f/p b/w illus., b/w drawings in text, clo., 210x140mm. ANL
• Rpt 1937. KP
• Rpt 1953, 1957. KP

2112 Another edition, t.p. as above; Printed in Australia, n.d.
191pp, b/w drawings in text, illus. by author, clo., 180x120mm. KMM

DOWNING, Brownie

2113 A TALE OF MISCHIEF/[drawing & dedication]/Story and/Pictures/by/Brownie Downing
'Published by Brownie Downing Gift Books/1963/Made and Printed in the/Republic of Ireland by/Hely Thom Ltd, Dublin'
[29]pp (inc. 1p biographical note with photograph), col. illus. throughout, pic. bd., 245x185mm. KMM
• Rpt 1963. KP

2114 CHILDREN OF THE DREAMING/Brownie Downing/[coloured illustration]/Nelson
Thos. Nelson (Australia) Ltd, Melbourne, 1966
26pp, col. illus. throughout, pic. bd., dec. e/p, 275x215mm. CLRC

2115 TINKA/AND THE BUNYIP/[coloured illustration]/Nelson
Thos. Nelson (Australia) Ltd, Melbourne, 1966
[25]pp, col. illus. throughout, illus. by author, pic. bd., dec. e/p, 275x210mm. KMM

DOWNING, Brownie & MANSFIELD, John

2116 TINKA/AND HIS FRIENDS/by/Brownie Downing/and/John Mansfield/Nelson
Edinburgh, 1960
48pp, double-spread dec. col. t.p., col. illus. throughout, dec. bd., 270x205mm. KMM
• Rpt as above, 1964. KP

2117 Rpt 1969
As above, but
46pp, double-spread t.p., col. illus. throughout, pic. bd., 280x215mm
This copy does not reproduce illus. on pp39, 40, 47 and 48 of previous ed. & the foreword is printed on verso of t.p. KP

DRAKE-BROCKMAN, Henrietta

THE LION-TAMER. *See* Australian Youth Plays
See also Parker, K. Langloh. AUSTRALIAN LEGENDARY TALES, selected & edited by H. Drake-Brockman

DREW, Barbara

2118 LET'S DRESS/A DOLL/By Barbara Drew/Photographs by Dean Hay/Angus and Robertson
Sydney, 1968
98pp, 7pp introduction, 10 f/p col. plates, 15 f/p b/w illus., patterns, diagrams & directions, clo., 240x180mm. CLRC
Introduction by Kathleen M. Mellor, Pre-school adviser, Kindergarten Union of South Australia.

DREWETT, Dorothy

2119 SUNDOWN STORIES/The Home of the Nursery Rhymes and/Other Fairy Tales/By/Dorothy Drewett/Illustrated by/Ethel Wood/Sydney/Tyrrell's Limited/99 Castlereagh Street/1918
36pp, b/w drawings throughout, wrappers, 190x120mm. NSL:M

2120 NURSERYLAND/MEMORIES/[drawing]/by Dorothy Drewett/Printed and Published by Offset Printing Coy. Pty. Ltd., 169 Phillip St., Waterloo, Sydney
n.d. [1947]
17pp, col. illus. throughout, illus. by Jean Elder, dec. wrappers, 275x215mm.
Short rhyming text on alternate pages. ANL

2121 CHARLIE/THE/CHIMP/OPC/Publication
Offset Printing Co., Sydney, n.d. [194-?]
[24]pp, 13 f/p b/w illus., pic. wrappers, 140x140mm. KP

2122 TOBY THE/PUP/Printed & Published by Offset Printing Coy Pty Limited, 169 Phillip Street, Waterloo (All rights reserved)
[24]pp, b/w illus. on alternate pages, pic. wrappers, 134x130mm. KP

LAUGHING JACK *See* Chisholm, Alexander Hugh—HAIL, THE KOOKABURRA

DREWETT, Dorothy & Others

2123 THE/FORGOTTEN JAR/and other stories for children/[drawing]/Printed by Morris & Walker, Melbourne/for the Publishers, Offset Printing Coy Pty Limited, Sydney
n.d. [194-?]
16pp, 1 f/p & 10 other part. col. illus., pic. wrappers, 240x175mm. Grant
Contents: 'The Forgotten Jar', by Dorothy Drewett; 'The Music Makers', by Edith Becket (verse); 'The Lonely Rocking Horse', by Dulcie Bellhouse

DREYER, Anne Hope

2124 THE LITTLE COAL TRUCK/and/Other Favourites/Re-told for very little children/By/Anne H. Dreyer/All royalties from this book will benefit the Kindergarten Holiday/Home, Forest Hill, Victoria, which is maintained by the Graduates of the/Kindergarten Training College, Melbourne. This home provides a holiday/for Kindergarten children of the industrial areas of Melbourne./Wholly set up and printed in Australia. Registered at the/G.P.O. Melbourne, for transmission through the Post as a book./Whitcombe & Tombs, Pty. Ltd./Melbourne, Sydney, Perth
n.d. [First pub. 1944]
24pp, col. & part. col. illus. throughout, dec. wrappers, 240x180mm. BBC
Foreword by R. Bronner, Chairman, National Kindergarten of the Air Advisory Committee.

2125 ANNE DREYER'S/ALBUM OF/CHRISTMAS/

SONGS/[illus.]/D. Davis & Co. Pty Ltd 250 Pitt Street, Sydney
1950
22pp, b/w illus. throughout by Judith Perrey, col. pic. wrappers, 278x220mm. ANL

2126 ANNE DREYER'S/ALBUM OF CHRISTMAS SONGS/Music by/Robin Wood/Illustrated by/Judith Perrey/[photograph of author & paras of biographical notes of author & illustrator]
n.d. [1966? as front cover price given as 4/6 or 45c]
21pp (inc. back cover), b/w illus. throughout, dec. wrappers, 246x184mm. ANL

2127 Anne Dreyer's/LITTLE SONGS FOR YOU AND ME/Music by/Robin Wood/Illustrated by/George Santos/[photograph & biographical note of author]/[note on Robin Wood]
D. H. Davis & Co. Pty Ltd, 250 Pitt St, Sydney, n.d. [1950]
20pp (last song printed inside back wrapper), 7 f/p b/w illus. & pic. contents page, col. illus., wrappers, 250x218mm. EC

2128 LITTLE SONGS/FOR YOU AND ME/Words by/Anne Dreyer/Music by/Robin Wood/D. Davis & Co. Pty Ltd./(incorporated NSW)/Melbourne Adelaide Bendigo/Printed in Australia
n.d. [*c.* 1966] (decimal currency & imperial price given)
21pp, b/w illus. throughout, pic. wrappers, 245x185mm. KP
Photograph of Anne Dreyer & biographical note & also of Robin Wood. Illus. George Santos. 10 songs listed.

2129 ANNE DREYER'S LITTLE HYMNS FOR YOU AND ME
Music by Robin Wood; illus. Judith Perrey
D. Davis & Co, Sydney, 1st ed. 1951
23pp, numerous b/w illus., pic. wrappers, 280mm. Unseen

2130 SING WITH ME/CHILDREN/by/Anne Dreyer/Music by Robin Wood/Illustrated by Judith Perrey/(Copyright)/Published for the Author by/Whitcombe & Tombs Pty. Ltd./Melbourne, Sydney and Perth
n.d. [1951]
23pp, 10 f/p b/w illus., dec. wrappers, 245x180mm. ANL
Foreword by Janet Mitchell; includes 10 songs.

2131 Anne Dreyer's/ABORIGINAL SONGS/FOR YOU AND ME/Music by Robin Wood/D. Davis & Co. Pty. Ltd. (Incorporated in N.S.W.)/Melbourne Adelaide Bendigo
n.d. [1954]
21pp, 10 f/p b/w illus. by Marjorie Howden, dec. wrappers, 305x238mm. KMM
Imperial Edition No. 640; contains 10 songs

DREYFUS, George
See Strahan, Lynne; Kellaway, Frank Gerald; Hall, Rodney

DRUCE, Kay
Kay Druce, a Canadian-born artist, wrote & illustrated the following books whilst living in Australia during & after the Second World War. Her many booklets sold in large numbers at a time when the importation of overseas books was restricted because of the shortage of paper.

2132 ONCE UPON/A/TIME/FAIRY TALES
Offset Printing Coy Pty Ltd, Sydney, n.d. [inscribed 1944]
12pp, 2 f/p col. illus., b/w illus. throughout, col. pic. wrappers, cover title, 360x245mm. TG
Contains traditional fairy tales.

2133 POPSY'S/PICNIC/[drawing]/introducing/Jeffrey Alexander Jones/Kay Druce
Offset Printing Co., Sydney, n.d. [1945?]
16pp, col. illus. throughout, dec. wrappers, 270x200mm. ANL

2134 POPSY AT THE/SEA-SIDE/by Kay Druce
Offset Printing Co., Sydney, 1946
16pp, col. illus. throughout, 255x200mm. ANL

2135 THE STORY/of/LITTLE DUFFY/AND HIS DOG/[drawing]/by Kay Druce
Offset Printing Co., Sydney, n.d. [1946]
16pp, col. illus. throughout, pic. wrappers, cover title, 265x210mm. KMM

2136 LITTLE DUFFY/AND/HIS DOG
Sydney, n.d.
[14]pp story printed inside covers & 1 illus. outside back wrapper, col. illus. throughout, 265x210mm. KP

2137 LITTLE DUFFY/GOES FISHING/by Kay Druce
Offset Printing Co., Sydney, n.d. [1946]
16pp, col. illus. throughout, pic. wrappers, cover title, 265x210mm. ANL

2138 POPSY'S/BUMPER/BOOK/by/Kay Druce
Offset Printing Co., Sydney, 1946
85pp, col. & b/w illus. throughout, dec. bd., dec. e/p, 260x215mm. NSL:M
Consists of the following books, bound together: *Popsy's Picnic, Popsy's adventure down on the farm, Popsy's A.B.C., Popsy at the Sea Side, Popsy's Holiday.*

2139 GOOD TIMES: Stories and Pictures
Offset Printing Co., Sydney, n.d. [1947]
20pp, 4pp col. illus., b/w drawings throughout, pic. wrappers, 275x215mm. ANL

2140 MOTHER GOOSE/NURSERY RHYMES/Illustrated by/Kay Druce
Offset Printing Co., Sydney, n.d. [1947]
16pp, 8pp col. illus., b/w drawings throughout, pic. wrappers, 275x215mm. NSL:M

2141 MY/BIG BOOK/OF STORIES
Offset Printing Co., Sydney, n.d. [1947?]
20pp, 4pp col. illus., b/w drawings throughout, pic. wrappers, 275x210mm. ANL

2142 NURSERY RHYME/BOOK
Offset Printing Co., Sydney, n.d. [1947]
20pp, 4pp col. illus. throughout, pic. wrappers, cover title, 280x215mm. ANL

2143 NURSERY/RHYMES/For Little Folks
OPC Publications Series A196, n.d.
12pp, b/w illus. on every page, col. pic. wrappers, 235x180mm. TG
Colouring book

2144 NURSERY RHYMES/Contents—Pictures/Rhymes/Pictures to Paint/This book belongs/To—
Offset Printing Coy. Sydney, n.d. [194-?]
20pp, 4pp col. illus., b/w illus. throughout, pic. wrappers, 276x214mm. KMM

2145 POPSY'S/ADVENTURES/DOWN ON THE FARM/also/POPSY'S ABC/By Kay Druce
Offset Printing Co., Sydney, n.d. [1947]
24pp, col. & b/w illus. throughout, wrappers, 270x210mm. ANL

2146 POPSY AND JIMMY/AT THE/ZOO/by/Kay Druce
Offset Printing Co., Sydney, n.d. [1947]
24pp, col. & b/w illus. throughout, wrappers, 270x215mm. ANL

2147 POPSY'S/HOLIDAY/MORE/ADVENTURES WITH/THE BUNNY TWINS/[drawing]/By Kay Druce
Offset Printing Co., Sydney, n.d. [1947]
24pp, col. & b/w illus. throughout, wrappers, 275x210mm. KMM

2148 POPSY'S TRIP/TO/NURSERYLAND/Illustrations & Introduction/By/Kay Druce
Offset Printing Co., Sydney, n.d. [1947]
24pp, col. illus. throughout, dec. wrappers, 280x210mm. KMM

2149 POPSY/AND THE/BUNNY TWINS/By/Kay Druce/[drawing]
Offset Printing Coy. Sydney [1947]
12pp, b/w illus. throughout, col. pic. wrappers, 280x220mm. CLRC

2150 Another copy, n.d., as above but
[24]pp, 4 col. & b/w illus. Otherwise same. WRT

2151 THE TOYS VISIT/THE CIRCUS/by Kay Druce
Offset Printing Co., Sydney, n.d. [1947]
20pp, 4pp col. illus., b/w drawings, pic. wrappers, 275x215mm. ANL

2152 LITTLE DUFFY AT THE FARM
Offset Printing Co., Sydney, n.d. [1948]
16pp, col. illus. throughout, pic. wrappers, cover title, 265x210mm. ANL

2153 LITTLE DUFFY/A/Kay Druce/BUMPER BOOK
Offset Printing Co., Sydney, n.d. [1948]
46pp, col. illus. throughout, dec. bd., dec. e/p, cover title, 275x210mm. ANL
Three paper-covered books bound together with no title page or pagination, being: *Little Duffy at the Farm; Little Duffy goes Fishing; Little Duffy and his Dog.*

2154 LITTLE THUMBELINA/A FAIRY TALE/Illustrated by/Kay Druce
Offset Printing Co., Sydney, n.d. [1948?]
20pp, 4pp col. illus., b/w drawings throughout, pic. wrappers, 285x220mm. NSL:M

2155 THE BIG BOOK/[drawing]/FOR/LITTLE PEOPLE/Kay Druce
Offset Printing Co., Sydney, n.d. [1948]
60pp, 12 col. illus. & b/w drawings throughout, dec. bd., dec. e/p, cover title, 265x210mm. ANL
Contents include: 'Little Thumbelina: A Fairy Tale', 'Fun: Nursery Rhyme Book'.

2156 BUNCHY/AND/THE FAIRY/Written and illustrated/by Kay Druce
Children's Press, Sydney, n.d. [1949]
16pp, col. illus. throughout, dec. wrappers, cover title, 270x215mm. NSL:M

2157 BUNCHY'S ADVENTURE
Children's Press, Sydney, n.d. [1949]
16pp, col. illus. throughout, dec. wrappers, cover title, 265x205mm. NSL:M

2158 COME TO THE/PARTY/PAINT BOOK
Offset Printing Coy Pty Ltd, Sydney, n.d. [194-?]
[20]pp, b/w illus. throughout & 4pp printed in col., col. pic. wrappers, 278x216mm. TG
Mother Hubbard Series which includes Nursery Rhymes; Little Thumbelina; Fun.

2159 POPSY/GOES/SHOPPING/Series E 216/Kay Druce
Offset Printing Co., Sydney, n.d. [1950?]
16pp, col. illus. throughout, wrappers, 255x210mm. ANL

2160 THE STORY OF/SMALL SAM/by/Kay Druce
Children's Press, Sydney, n.d. [1950]
15pp, col. illus. throughout, dec. wrappers, 275x215mm. ANL

2161 TEENY/FOLK/Nursery Rhymes
Offset Printing Co., Sydney, n.d. [1950]
16pp, 6pp col. illus. & b/w drawings, pic. wrappers, 275x215mm. ANL

2162 SMALL SAM/AT THE ZOO/By/Kay Druce
Children's Press, Sydney, 1951
15pp, col. illus. throughout, dec. wrappers, 275x215mm. NSL:M

2163 THE POPSY/BUMPER BOOK/Kay Druce
Offset Printing Co., Sydney, 1952
44pp, col. illus. throughout, dec. bd., cover title, 265x205mm. NSL:M
Consists of the following books bound together: *Popsy goes shopping, Popsy at the Sea Side, Popsy's Picnic.*

2164 FUN TO/LOOK AT THE PICTURES/READ THE STORIES/PLAY THE GAMES
Offset Printing Co., Sydney, n.d.
20pp, 4pp col. illus., b/w drawings, pic. wrappers, 280x215mm. NSL:M

2165 OUR/BABY BOOK/A record of Baby's/First Three Years/Designed by Kay Druce./Printed and Published by Offset Printing Co. Pty Ltd, 169 Phillip St, Waterloo Sydney. (All Rights Reserved.)
n.d.
16pp, col. illus. throughout with spaces left to be filled in, dec. bd., dec. e/p, 278x220mm. KMM

2166 CUT OUT/POPSY/AND HER/LOVELY FROCKS/Druce/Printed and Published by Offset Printing Coy Pty Ltd Sydney
n.d.
14pp (printed on one side of paper only. Dresses &c to be cut out), col. illus. throughout, light bd., cover title, 280x215mm. MAC

2167 HAPPY DAYS/PICTURE AND STORY BOOK
Offset Printing Coy. Sydney, n.d.
12pp (inc. 2pp with col. illus.), b/w illus on other pages, col. pic. wrappers, 354x250mm. KP

2168 MOBBIN AND WOBBIN/Woods School/By Kay Druce/Series No. E229
n.p., n.d.
31pp, col. illus. throughout, col. pic. wrappers (lacks back cover), 280x194mm. KP

2169 MORE/NURSERY JINGLES/[col. illus.]/FOR LITTLE FOLK
Offset Printing Coy Pty Ltd. Sydney, n.d. Printed by the Qld Can Co Ltd for the publishers
12pp, 2 f/p col. illus., b/w illus. throughout, col. pic. wrappers, cover title, 355x250mm. TG

2170 POPSY'S PARTY/Written & Illustrated by/Kay Druce
Offset Printing Coy, Sydney, n.d.
24pp (inc. 12pp full col. illus. & numerous b/w), pic. wrappers, 280x210mm
A col. illus. from inside the book is repeated inside the cover; this appears to vary in different copies. KP

2171 THE/TEDDY BEAR TWINS/Written and Illustrated by/Kay Druce/The Children's Press, 141 York St, Sydney
n.d.
16pp (inc. covers), col. illus. on every page, cover title, 267x210mm. MAC

2172 TWICE TOLD TALES/Cinderella and/Red Riding Hood
Printed & Publ. by Offset Printing Coy Pty Ltd, Sydney, n.d.
12pp (inc. 6pp f/p col. illus., b/w illus on other pages), col. pic. wrappers, 280x220mm. KP

DU BOIS, William Pène
BEAR PARTY/By/William Pène du Bois/[drawing]/ New York The Viking Press MCMLI
Publ. in part in *Life* 1960. Also publ. simultaneously by The Macmillan Company of Canada Ltd
48pp, col. illus. throughout of koalas, pic. bd., 210x135mm. KP
Not Australian. This famous American writer & illustrator delights in using Australian animals in some of his fantasy picture books but this hardly allows us to claim them as Australian children's books. Several later titles are referred to by White.

DUFF, Douglas V.
2173 THE TREASURE/OF THE ANTARCTIC/By/ Douglas V. Duff/Author of "Harding's Quest" etc./ Illustrated by John de Walton/Blackie & Son Limited/ London and Glasgow
1940
223pp, b/w frontis. & 3 b/w illus., clo., 185x120mm. ANL
2174 THE TREASURE/OF THE ANTARCTIC/By/ Douglas V. Duff/Author of "The Lost Admiral" "Peril on the Amazon" &c./Illustrated by John De Walton/ Blackie & Son Limited/London and Glasgow
n.d. [inscribed 1949]
223pp, b/w frontis. & 2 b/w plates, clo., 180x120mm. KP

DUGAN, Michael
TRAVEL AND TRANSPORT. *See* Life in Australia

DUKE, Madelaine [*sic*]
2175 Madelaine [*sic*] Duke/THE SECRET PEOPLE/ Illustrated by Mona Killpack/Brockhampton Press Leicester, England, 1967
128pp, b/w frontis. & b/w drawings in text, clo., map e/p, 215x135mm. KMM
Adventure story about white men & Aborigines in Central Australia.
2176 THE/SECRET/PEOPLE/Madelaine [*sic*] Duke /Illustrated by Ken Longtemps/Doubleday & Company Inc./Garden City, New York
1967
125pp, extended dec. t.p., b/w drawings in text, clo., 205x135mm. ANL
D/w design by Isabelle Coutrot, d/w painting by Ken Longtemps.

DUKERT, Joseph M.
2177 THIS IS/ANTARCTICA/Joseph M. Dukert/Angus and Robertson
First published by Coward-McCann Inc., New York 1965; this edition Sydney 1968
162pp (inc. 7pp index, etc.), b/w photographic frontis., maps, b/w photographic illus., clo., 220x135mm. KMM
Photographs & maps by John T. Gorsuch & others.

DULCKEN, H. W.
2178 THE/WORLD'S EXPLORERS./By H. W. Dulcken, Ph.Dr./including/Livingstone's discoveries/and/ Stanley's Search./Illustrated with/many engravings from designs by eminent artists./[vignette]/Ward, Lock and Co./London: Warwick House, Salisbury Square, E.C./New York, 10 Bond Street.
n.d. [1868]
472pp, 24pp adv., engraved frontis., 15 f/p illus. & engravings in text throughout, dec. clo., 200x130mm. Beeton's Boys' Own Library. HBM
Contents include: 'Captain Cook and His Discoveries' (57pp); 'The Voyage of La Perouse' (42pp); 'Captain Flinders' (11pp); 'Eyre: Governor and Australian Explorer'. (12pp).
2179 THE/WORLD'S EXPLORERS;/or,/Travel and Adventures./By H. W. Dulcken, Ph. Dr. [*sic*] /Illustrated with/Many Engravings from Designs by Eminent Artists/[device]/London:/Ward, Lock, and Tyler,/Warwick House, Paternoster Row
n.d. [1876?]
384pp, col. frontis. & additional col. pic. t.p., 12 f/p b/w engravings & engravings in text, dec. clo., 185x120mm. CLRC

DUNLOP, Eric
JOHN OXLEY. *See* Australian Explorers

DURACK, Mary [Mrs H. Miller] [Dame]
2180 LITTLE POEMS/OF SUNSHINE/By An Australian Child/Mary Durack
R. S. Sampson, Perth, n.d. [1923]
56pp (inc. 2pp preface by Muriel Chase), portrait frontis., wrappers, cover title, 150x90mm. ANL
Preface states that the author was ten years old when the poems were written.

2181 PICCANINNIES/By/Mary & Elizabeth Durack
n.p., n.d.
[20]pp & back pastedown, b/w illus. throughout, pic. bd., 237x210mm. KMM
Front pastedown & t.p. unillus., verse on back pastedown. ?first ed.; drawings printed showing pencil tones.
2182 Rpt as above in pic. wrappers. RM
2183 PICCANINNIES/By/Mary & Elizabeth Durack
Printed Offset Printing Coy Pty Limited
[22]pp, b/w illus. throughout, pic. wrappers, 244x220mm. KP
Better printed early ed. showing pencil tones.
2184 PICCANINNIES/By/Mary & Elizabeth Durack
Offset Printing Co., Sydney, n.d. [1940]
20pp, b/w illus. throughout, dec. bd., cover title, 235x210mm. KMM
2185 PICCANINNIES/By/Mary & Elizabeth Durack
Offset Printing Coy Pty Ltd, 169 Phillip Street, Waterloo, Sydney, n.d.
[20]pp & printed inside cover, illus. inside front cover & on t.p., b/w illus. pic. bd., 265x210mm. KMM
Seems to be later ed. though copy bears price in both shillings and cents.

2186 THE WAY/OF THE/WHIRLWIND/Mary & Elizabeth Durack/Consolidated Press Ltd./168-174 Castlereagh Street, Sydney/1941
79pp, 9 col. & 3 b/w tipped in plates, pic. bd., clo. spine, pic. d/w, col. pic. e/p, 370x240mm. KMM
2187 THE WAY/OF THE/WHIRLWIND/Mary & Elizabeth Durack/Consolidated Press Ltd./168–174 Castlereagh Street, Sydney/1943
79pp, 9 col. & 3 f/p b/w illus., b/w drawings in text, pic. bd., clo. spine, dec. e/p, 365x235mm. KMM
• Rpt 1944, as above. KMM
2188 THE WAY/OF THE/WHIRLWIND/Mary & Elizabeth Durack/Consolidated Press Ltd./168–174 Castlereagh Street, Sydney/1945
79pp, 9 col. illus. & 3 f/p b/w illus., b/w drawings in text, bd., 360x240mm. CLRC
2189 THE WAY OF/THE WHIRLWIND/By/Mary and Elizabeth Durack/Angus and Robertson/Sydney—London—Melbourne—Wellington
Second edition 1956

78pp (inc. 1p dedication), 9 col. & 3 b/w f/p illus., b/w drawings in text, clo., 280x220mm. KMM

2190 THE WAY OF/THE WHIRLWIND/By/Mary and Elizabeth Durack/Angus and Robertson
Sydney, first pub. 1941; rpt 1946; 2nd ed. 1956; rpt 1963
Details as in 1956 edition. BBC

2191 THE WAY OF THE/WHIRLWIND/Mary and Elizabeth Durack/(School Edition)/[drawing]/Angus and Robertson
Sydney 1968
95pp, 1p dedicatory verses, b/w drawings, pic. wrappers, 180x110mm. KMM

2192 THE WAY OF THE/WHIRLWIND/Mary and Elizabeth Durack/[drawing]/Angus and Robertson
• Rpt Sydney 1969, details as previous school edition. KMM

2193 A BOOK OF/PICTURE STORIES/By/Mary and Elizabeth Durack/with acknowledgements to Consolidated Press for/permission to reprint from "Sunday Telegraph", Sydney, N.S.W./Printed by Imperial Printing Co. Ltd./397 Hay Street, Perth, W.A.
n.d. [some illustrations dated 1942]
[56]pp, col. illus. throughout, pic. wrappers, 275x275mm. CLRC
Contains 3 stories in comic strip form: 'The Magic Bone'; 'The Young White Chief'; 'The Great Drought'.

2194 THE/MAGIC TRUMPET/By/Mary & Elizabeth Durack/Cassell & Company Limited/London; New York: Toronto: Melbourne: Sydney
n.d. [1946]
46pp, col. & part. col. illus. throughout, dec. bd., dec. e/p, 240x180mm. KMM
Fantasy in verse.

2195 KOOKANOO/&/KANGAROO/[drawing]/Mary and/Elizabeth Durack
Rigby Ltd, Adelaide 1963
44pp, 20 f/p col. illus., line drawings in text, dec. clo., dec. e/p, 230x260mm. KMM
Text in verse.

2196 KOOKANOO/AND THE/KANGAROO/[drawing]/By Mary and Elizabeth Durack/[device]/Lerner Publications Company/Minneapolis, Minnesota
1st publ. in the US 1966; 2nd printing 1967; 3rd printing 1968
48pp, 20 f/p col. illus., additional col. illus & b/w drawings throughout, pic. paper bd., 224x257mm. KMM

2197 Great Stories of Australia/TO RIDE/A FINE HORSE/By/Mary Durack/Illustrated by/Elizabeth Durack/Melbourne/Macmillan & Co. Ltd./1963
137pp, 2pp author's foreword, 33 col. & part. col. illus., clo., dec. e/p, 215x135mm. KMM
A version for children of the author's biography of her grandfather, Patsy Durack, published under the title of *Kings in Grass Castles.*

2198 Great Stories of Australia/TO RIDE/A FINE HORSE/By/Mary Durack/Illustrated by/Elizabeth Durack/Macmillan/Melbourne London Toronto/St Martin's Press Inc./New York 1965
vipp, 137pp, col. & part col. illus., clo., dec. e/p, 212x135mm. WRT

2199 THE COURTEOUS SAVAGE/Yagan of Swan River/By Mary Durack/Illustrated by Elizabeth Durack/Thomas Nelson and Sons Ltd. Edinburgh
1964
84pp, b/w frontis., 7 part.-col. double-spread illus., b/w drawings in text throughout, clo., dec. e/p, 240x180mm. KMM

2200 Rpt 1965, as above, but pic. bd., 240x175mm. KMM

A PASTORAL EMIGRANT. *See* Early Australians

ALL-ABOUT, The Bulletin, Sydney 1935

CHUNUMA, The Bulletin, Sydney, 1936

SON OF DJARO, R. J. Sampson, Perth, 1940
The books listed above, illustrated by Elizabeth Durack, are not children's books. The large format of the books, allowing space for the many marginal drawings, gives them the appearance of children's books, & *Chunuma* particularly contains sketches children would enjoy. The books were very successful, *All-about* appearing in its seventh edition in 1944.

DUTTON, Geoffrey

2201 ON MY ISLAND/Poems by/Geoffrey Dutton/Illustrations by/John Perceval/F. W. Cheshire
Melbourne Canberra Sydney
1967
42pp, b/w frontis. & drawings throughout, clo., 275x210mm. KMM
Authors and Artists for Australian Children Series
Poems for children about Kangaroo Island.

DUTTON, Geoffrey & HAY, Dean

2202 TISI AND/THE YABBY/by Geoffrey Dutton/and Dean Hay/Collins/London—Sydney/1965
[48]pp, b/w photographic illus. throughout, dec. bd., 255x190mm. KMM

2203 TISI AND/THE/PAGEANT/Geoffrey Dutton/Dean Hay/Rigby Limited/Adelaide,/Sydney, Melbourne,/Brisbane, Perth/For/Bill Hayward
1968
[36]pp, col. photographic illus. throughout, pic. clo., col. e/p, 250x190mm. KMM

2204 SEAL BAY/by Geoffrey Dutton/and Dean Hay/Collins/London—Sydney/1966
48pp, b/w photographs throughout, pic. bd. with clo. spine, col. e/p, 250x185mm. KMM
A photographic book of two small boys' holiday at Seal Bay, Kangaroo Island, South Australia; text by Dutton, photographs by Hay.

DWYER, Vera Gladys [Mrs W. Coldham-Fussell]

2205 WITH BEATING/WINGS/An Australian Story/By/Vera G. Dwyer/Ward, Lock & Co., Limited/London Melbourne and Toronto/1913
304pp, 16pp adv., b/w frontis. & 3 f/p b/w illus. by Victor Prout, dec. clo., 185x120mm. KMM

2206 MONA'S/MYSTERY MAN/By/Vera G. Dwyer/Author of "With Beating Wings"/Ward, Lock & Co., Limited/London, Melbourne and Toronto/1914
320pp, b/w frontis. & 3 f/p b/w illus. by J. Macfarlane, pic. clo., 180x120mm. KMM
This book, & Vera Dwyer's first book *With Beating Wings,* were both considered on publication as 'juveniles' although they appear to be light romances probably intended for older girls. Her other books were considered as adult novels although there is not a great difference in style.

2207 A WAR OF/GIRLS/By/Vera G. Dwyer/Author of.../Ward, Lock & Co. Limited/London Melbourne and Toronto/1915
320pp, 16pp adv., b/w frontis. & 7 f/p b/w illus., clo., 190x130mm. VSL

2208 CONQUERING/HAL/By/Vera G. Dwyer/(Mrs. Warwick Coldham-Fussell)/Author of "With Beating

Wings", "Mona's Mystery Man",/"A War of Girls", etc. etc./Ward, Lock & Co., Limited/London, Melbourne and Toronto/1916
319pp, 2pp & 16pp adv., b/w frontis. & 7 f/p b/w illus. (by ?Charles Dixon), pic. clo., 185x115mm. ANL

2209 THE KAYLES OF/BUSHY LODGE/An Australian Story/By/Vera G. Dwyer/London/Humphrey Milford/Oxford University Press
n.d. [1922]
288pp, col. frontis., clo., 185x120mm. KMM

2210 THE KAYLES OF/BUSHY LODGE/An Australian Story/By/Vera G. Dwyer/Humphrey Milford/Oxford University Press/London, Edinburgh, Glasgow/ Toronto, Melbourne, Cape Town, Bombay
n.d.
288pp, col. frontis. & 4 b/w plates (sgd.'Burden'), clo., 190x125mm. KMM
Sequel to *A War of Girls.*

2211 THE/KAYLES OF/BUSHY LODGE/Vera Dwyer/ Humphrey Milford/Oxford University/Press London
n.d.
288pp, col. frontis., clo., 165x105mm. The Girls Pocket Library. MK

2212 THE MARCHES/DISAPPEAR/by/Vera G. Dwyer/ [device]/Robert M. McBride & Company/New York
1929
301pp, unillus., clo., 190x130mm. Grant
Pictorial d/w by Charles Bowman. 'Blurb' suggests book for teenage girls.

DYSON, Edward

2213 THE GOLD-STEALERS/A Story of Waddy/By/ Edward Dyson/Author of "Rhymes from the Mines" and "Below and on Top"/With eight illustrations by/ G. Grenville Manton/Longmans, Green and Co./39 Paternoster Row, London/New York and Bombay/
1901
310pp, 4pp adv., b/w frontis. & 7 f/p b/w illus., pic. clo., 195x125mm. KMM

2214 Longmans' Colonial Library/THE GOLD-STEALERS/A Story of Waddy/By/Edward Dyson/Author of "Rhymes from the Mines" and "Below and on Top"/with eight illustrations by/G. Grenville Manton/Longmans, Green and Co./39 Paternoster Row, London/and Bombay/1901/This edition is intended for circulation only in India and the/British Colonies.
310pp, b/w frontis. & 7 f/p b/w illus., dec. clo., 195x125mm. ANL

Swedish edition

2215 C. W. K. Gleerups Ungdomsböcker No. 06./GULDTJUFVARNA/En Historia Från Australien/ af/Eduard Dyson/öfversättning af M.R-G/Med 8 helsides-Illustrationer/[device]/Lund/C. W. K. Gleerups Förlag
1911
243pp, b/w frontis. & 7 f/p b/w illus., illus. by C. Grenville Manton, pic. bd., clo. spine, 200x135mm. RM

2216 Rpt Lund, Stockholm 1920, as above, but with different printed bd.
Unseen: Catalogue No. 4, 1975, Dahlia Books, Uppsala, Sweden

2217 BILLY BLUEGUM/or/Back to the Bush/by/ Edward Dyson/Illustrations by Norman Lindsay/The Shepherd Press/Sydney, Australia/1947
66pp, 65 line drawings in text [although publisher's 'blurb' claims there are 69], pic. bd., 240x165mm. KMM
First published in The *Lone. Hand* as a serial in 1912. Although this edition was published as a children's book with numerous amusing line drawings, the satire does not seem to have been originally written for children.

Early Artists of Australia

2218 EARLY/ARTISTS/OF AUSTRALIA/Frontispiece:/ Augustus Earle, a professional and versatile/artist, painted this watercolour of 'Cabbage Tree/Forrest, Illawarra, New South Wales' around 1827./Paul Hamlyn/London/Sydney/New York/Toronto
1971
58pp, col. frontis., col. & b/w reproductions from early prints, etc., pic. bd., 275x195mm. CLRC

Early Australians

Social history presented in an attractive form for primary school children.
Format example:

2219 DONKIN, Nance, EARLY AUSTRALIANS/AN EMANCIPIST/Nance Donkin/illustrated by/Jane Robinson/Melbourne/Oxford University Press/London Wellington New York/1968
32pp, b/w illus., stiff pic. wrappers, 197x54mm. KMM

2220 A SAILOR by C. Bateson, illus. R. Isaacs, 1968. KP
2221 A SOLDIER, by " " " 1968. CLRC
2222 A SURVEYOR, by " illus. J. Bell, 1972. CLRC
2223 A CHARTMAKER, by C. Bateson, illus. J. Bell, 1972. CLRC
2224 A GOLD COMMISSIONER, by C. Bateson, illus. R. Brooks, 1972. CLRC
2225 A PACK TRACKER, by M. T. Clark, illus. S. Turner, 1968. KP
2226 A CURRENCY LASS, by N. Donkin, illus. J. Walker, 1969. KMM
2227 AN ORPHAN, by N. Donkin, illus. A. Culvenor, 1970. KMM
2228 A PASTORAL EMIGRANT, by M. Durack, illus. D. Parry, 1965. KP
2229 A WHALER, by F. Kellaway, illus. P. Thomas, 1967. KP
2230 A GOLDSEEKER, by J. Nicholson, illus. J. Jones, 1970. KP
2231 A PIONEER DAUGHTER, by E. Pownall, illus. J. Walker, 1968. KMM
2232 A DROVER, by E. Pownall, illus. A. Culvenor, 1969, 1970. KMM
2233 A POST BOY, by L. Quinlan, illus. B. Turner, 1970. KMM
2234 A CONVICT, by L. L. Robson, illus. R. Isaacs, 1968. KP
2235 A SCHOOLMASTER, by E. Spence, illus. J. Walker, 1969. KMM
2236 A CEDAR-CUTTER, by E. Spence, illus. G. Spence, 1971. KMM

Early English Voyagers

2237 EARLY ENGLISH/VOYAGERS;/or,/The Adventures and Discoveries/of/Drake, Cavendish, and Dampier./[verso]/London:/T. Nelson and Sons, Paternoster Row./Edinburgh: and New York/1889
458pp & 6pp adv., additional illus. t.p., engraved frontis. & 14 f/p engravings, pic. clo., 188x126mm. KP

2238 Rpt as above. 1892
Details as above, but with g.e. & front cover & spine decorations blocked with gilt & col. KP

Early Governors of Australia

2239 EARLY/GOVERNORS/OF AUSTRALIA/ Frontispiece:/Lachlan Macquarie—fifth Governor of/ New South Wales—who was probably/the most able governor of all/Paul Hamlyn/London/Sydney/New York/Toronto
1971

[56]pp, col. frontis., col. & b/w reproductions from early prints, etc., pic. bd., 275x195mm. CLRC
Studies of the first ten governors.

EARNSHAW, Ewart Hurlstone

2240 EAGLEHAWK/Chief of the Tribes/of Arunta/by/E. H. Earnshaw/[vignette]/Wholly set up and printed in Australia/by William Brooks & Co. Ltd./44 Pitt St., Sydney/1929
47pp, 2pp b/w illus., wrappers, 180x120mm. Boys' Bookstall Series. NSL:M

2241 YARRAGONGARTHA/Stirling Castle and Yarragongartha/by/E. H. Earnshaw/The two stories in this book are true. The first tells of/the wreck of the brig Stirling Castle in 1836, and gives an/exciting and truthful account of the adventures of the captain/and crew. The second story describes the attack made by/aboriginal warriors in 1874 upon Barrow Creek Telegraph/Station, a lonely link in the great chain of telegraph stations/connecting Adelaide with Darwin./Copyright./All rights reserved./Published Privately by the Author at—/398 Rawson Chambers,/Rawson Place/Sydney/Illustrations from Tyrrell's Museum of/Antiques, Books and Curios,/143 Castlereagh Street,/Sydney./Wholly set up and printed in Australia/by William Brooks & Co. Ltd.,/44 Pitt Street, Sydney/1930/Registered by the Postmaster-General for transmission through the post as a/book
48pp (inc. preface, foreword, verse, &c.), 2 b/w illus., wrappers, 180x120mm. ANL

2242 THE EXPLORER HEROES/OF AUSTRALIA/Part I/An Authentic Account of the Adventures/of the Brave Explorers told/in Story Form/by/E. H. Earnshaw/Registered at the General Post Office, Sydney, for transmission through/the post as a book/Wholly set up and printed in Australia/by William Brooks & Co. Ltd./35 Pitt St., Sydney/1933
80pp, b/w photographic illus., wrappers, 185x120mm. NSL:M

2243 A Book for Every Australian/THE EXPLORER HEROES/OF AUSTRALIA/Part I—New Edition/Thrilling True Adventures of the Explorer Heroes/on the rolling waves and in the wild bush/[illustration]/The Australian Boys' Series/"Australian Books for Australian Boys"
The author, Sydney 1945
96pp (inc. 1p foreword &c.), 15 b/w illus., wrappers, cover title, 185x120mm. ANL

2244 A Book for Every Australian/THE EXPLORER HEROES/OF AUSTRALIA/Part II/A Book glowing with the grandeur of the/adventures, courage, and achievements of the Explorers/[illustrations]/The Australian Boys' Series/"Australian Books for Australian Boys"
The author, Sydney 1944
92pp (inc. author's foreword), 11 b/w illus., wrappers (with additional b/w illus. on front cover), cover title, 185x125mm. ANL
Includes sections on Leichhardt, Giles, Warburton, Forrest, Eyre, &c.

2245 AUSTRALIA'S EXPLORER/HEROES OF THE AIR/by/E. H. Earnshaw/A book of exciting adventure stories about famous Aus-/tralian Airmen, their great inventions, glorious achieve-/ments, and daring exploits with aeroplanes in which they/gained the mastery of the skies./[photograph]
The author, Sydney 1946
100pp, 1p author's preface, 15 b/w illus., wrappers, cover title, 180x120mm. ANL The Australian Boys' Series, 'Australian Books for Australian Boys'.
• Rpt as above, 1947. WJSB

2246 THE BOYS' BOOK OF WARRIORS; Thrilling Adventures of the Pioneers amid hostile savages in the dawn of Australian settlement [cover title] Title page reads: The Australian Boys' series/Australian Books for Australian Boys/[dedication]/[note]/[Copyright etc.]/Wholly set up and printed in Australia by/Robert Dey, Son & Co.,/66–68 Bathurst St./Sydney/1946
86pp (inc. author's foreword & notes), 11 b/w illus., wrappers, 185x120mm. ANL
Stories about Australian Aborigines.

2247 THE BOYS' BOOK OF BUSHRANGERS/Stories of the Bushrangers adapted for reading/by Australian Schoolboys/by E. H. Earnshaw/[illustration]/Exciting Stories depicting the thrilling encounters of/the Australian Mounted Police with the bushrangers/The Australian Boys' Series/'Australian Books for Australian Boys'
The author, Sydney 1947
68pp, 2pp author's preface, 4 b/w illus., wrappers, cover title, 185x125mm. ANL
Bushrangers mentioned include: William Dunne; Ben Hall; Johnny Gilbert; Johnny Dunn; Dan Morgan; Captain Thunderbolt; Ned Kelly; Captain Moonlight.

2248 AUSTRALIA'S TREASURE HUNTERS/The Australian Boys' Series/Australian Books for Australian Boys/[dedication]/[note]/[Copyright] etc./Wholly set up and printed in Australia by/Robert Dey, Son & Co.,/66–68 Bathurst St./Sydney./1948
64pp, introduction & bibliography, 5 b/w illus., wrappers, 215x140mm. ANL

EASON, Victor

2249 THE/FROLICSOME/MONKEYS/by/Victor Eason
Victory Publicity Pty Ltd, 262 Queen St, Melbourne, n.d.
32pp, 14 f/p part. col. illus., 5 other illus., pic. wrappers, cover title, 240x180mm. Grant
Cover illustrations signed George Needham.

EASTWOOD, Jill

CHARLES JOSEPH LA TROBE. *See* Great Australians

EBBELL, Bendix

2250 Bendix Ebbell/DEN NYSESTE/VERDEN/Australias/opdagelse/Fortalt for/Ungdom/Kristiania/Gyldendalske Bokhandel/Kjøbenhavn London Berlin/MCMXXII
140pp, 14 f/p b/w illus. & 1 endpiece, col. pic. bd. (clo. spine), 190x125mm. ANL

EBERLE, Irmengarde

2251 KOALAS LIVE HERE/By Irmangarde Eberle/Doubleday & Company, Inc., Garden City, New York 1967
60pp & 1p biographical note on author, b/w photographic frontis., illus. throughout, col. pic. wrappers, 178x230mm. KP

EDEL, May

2252 [drawing] THE STORY/OF PEOPLE/Anthropology for Young People/by May Edel/Illustrated by Herbert Danska/[drawing]/The Bodley Head—London
First pub. 1954; rpt 1954
160pp (inc. 3pp index), extended t.p., b/w illus., maps, diagrams &c. throughout, clo., 200x125mm. ANL
Includes one chapter (7pp) on 'The Desert Australians'.

EDEN, Charles Henry

2253 THE/FORTUNES OF THE FLETCHERS:/A Story of/Life in Canada and Australia/By/Charles Henry Eden/Author of "My Wife and I in Queensland"/

Published under the direction of The Committee of General Literature and Education,/Appointed by the Society for Promoting/Christian Knowledge/London:/Society for Promoting Christian Knowledge:/sold at the Depositories:/77 Great Queen Street, Lincoln's Inn Fields;/4, Royal Exchange; 48 Piccadilly;/and by all booksellers./New York: Pott, Young & Co.
n.d. [preface dated 1873]
237pp (inc. 1p preface), 2pp adv., b/w frontis. & 2 f/p b/w illus., clo., 180x110mm. ANL

2254 Another copy as above but SPCK's address, 'Northumberland Avenue, Charing Cross;/43 Queen Victoria Street/and 48, Piccadilly.
n.d. [inscribed 1881]
Details as before. RM

2255 CORALIE/or/THE WRECK OF THE SYBILLE/By/Charles H. Eden/Author of "Ralph Somerville" "The Twin Brothers of/Elfvedale", &c./London:/Marcus Ward & Co., 67, Chandos Street/and Royal Ulster Works, Belfast, 1877
323pp (inc. 13pp preface), col. frontis. & col. dec. t.p. [preceding b/w t.p.], 13 b/w illus., dec. clo., 180x120mm. ANL
Preface states that the story was suggested by the loss of La Perouse & the wreck of the frigates *Astrolabe* & *Boussole*.

2256 GUINEA GOLD,/or/The Great Barrier Reef/By/Charles H. Eden,/Author of "Australia's Heroes" "The Fifth Continent",/"My Wife and I in Queensland", etc./Published under the direction of the committee/of general literature and education appointed by the/Society for Promoting Christian Knowledge/London:/Society for Promoting Christian Knowledge;/Northumberland Avenue, Charing Cross;/4 Royal Exchange; 48 Piccadilly./New York: Pott, Young and Co.
n.d. 1879
160pp, 4pp adv., b/w frontis. & 2 b/w illus., clo., 180x115mm. NSL:M

2257 Another copy as above but address given as (after 'Charing Cross'), '43 Queen Victoria Street, E.C./Brighton: 135 North Street: New York: E. & J. B. Young and Co.'
n.d. [inscribed 1892]
Details as before. KMM
This author, who lived in Australia for eight years, published a number of boys' adventure stories of non-Australian interest in the 1870s and 1880s, & also wrote a popular book for the general reader, entitled *Australia's Heroes*, in which are retold the experiences of some of the discoverers & explorers of the Australian continent.

EDMUNDS, Alan

2258 A/JACKAROO'S/JINGLES/About Australian Animals and Birds/[drawing]/Written by/Alan Edmunds/Poetaster/Illustrations by/A Real old fashioned Artist...etc. [text]/Engravings by/A team of craftsmen known as Modern Reproduction Pty. Ltd., Wills Street, Melbourne./Wholly set up printed...etc. by/Horticultural Press Pty. Ltd., Orr Street, Melbourne, Victoria [text]
1940
32pp (inc. introduction by E. E. Pescott), illus. throughout by Quentin Sutton, dec. wrappers, 280x220mm. KMM

2259 A/JACKAROO'S/JINGLES/About Australian Animals and Birds/[drawing]/written by/Alan Edmunds/Poetaster/Illustrations by/A Real old fashioned Artist/[4 lines]/Publisher/Marjorie Miller/1416 South Harvard Boulevard/Los Angeles. California
Copyright throughout Australia & New Zealand 1941; copyright USA 1943
Details as above. Grant

2260 A/JACKAROO'S/JINGLES
• Rpt as above, n.d. [1954?]
Letter from Government House Melbourne quoted inside front cover dated 1946, & one dated 1954 from the Queen acknowledging copy of book.. KP

EDQUIST, Alfred George

2261 NATURE STUDIES IN/AUSTRALASIA/By/Alfred George Edquist/Supervisor in Nature and Science in Primary Schools, Education/Department, South Australia/The Lothian Book Publishing Company/Proprietary Limited/Melbourne and Sydney/Printed in England
First publ. Sept 1916
176pp, 16pp adv. & 23pp preliminaries, col. frontis., 1 col. plate & 22 b/w plates, dec. clo., 185x120mm. KMM
Front cover title reads: The Commonwealth Nature Study Series/Part 1/Alfred George Edquist/[drawing].

Edward's Adventures in Nursery Rhyme Land
See Grieve, David

EDWARDS, Bruce
AUSTRALIAN ANIMALS. *See* Golden Stamp Books

EDWARDS, Bruce & BURTON, Barbara (ed.)

2262 MY GOLDEN/WONDER BOOK/Edited by/Bruce Edwards/Barbara Burton/OF AUSTRALIA AND NEW ZEALAND
Golden Press, Potts Point, NSW, 1972
255pp, extended t.p. (on front e/p & fly-leaf), col. & part. col. illus. throughout by various artists, pic. bd., 280x205mm. CLRC

2263 Young Nature Library/KANGAROOS/AND/WALLABIES/Bruce Edwards/Lansdowne Press Melbourne 1972
[38]pp [printed on both e/p], col. & b/w photographic illus. throughout, diagrams, col. pic. bd., 190x245mm. BBC
Also in series, details as above:
2264 KOOKABURRAS AND KINGFISHERS. 1972
2265 POSSUMS. 1972
2266 THE PLATYPUS. 1972 with Barbara Burton, all CLRC

EDWARDS, Don

2267 THE ADVENTURES OF/JAN AND JENNIFER/by/Don Edwards/Illustrated by/Edwina Bell/Australasian Publishing Company/Sydney Wellington London 1948
96pp, b/w drawings in text throughout, dec. bd., 175x130mm. York Series. ANL

2268 Rpt 1952. 88pp, limp clo., 185x120mm. Grant
Also 'issued as a school reader, printed in the *Sydney Morning Herald* magazine, *Playtime*, the New South Wales *School Magazine*, and broadcast over the Australian Broadcasting Commission' (*The Singing Roads*).

EDWARDS, George [pseud. Hal Parks]

2269 DAVID AND DAWN WITH GEORGE/EDWARDS IN FAIRYLAND/Broadcast from Station 2 U.W.[*sic*]
Shepherd & Newman Ltd, Printers, Sydney, n.d. [194-?]
20pp, 8 f/p col. illus., (cover title, illus. H. Lahm), col. pic. wrappers, cover title, 280x220mm. KMM

2270 DAVID AND DAWN with George Edwards/UNDER THE SOUTHERN CROSS

Snows Ltd, Sydney, n.d. [194-]. Winn & Co Printers 53-55 Balfour St, Sydney
[38]pp (inside of front & back wrappers on which an illus. is printed), 11 f/p col. plates & 2 inside cover, col. pic. wrappers, cover title, 280x213mm. ANL
Illus. Hottie Lahm. 'Listen in to stations 2UW & 3KZ each evening Mon–Fri 6pm. Book presented by Snows.'

2271 DAVID & [*sic*] DAWN WITH GEORGE EDWARDS/AND THE SEA FAIRIES
n.d. [194-]. Printed by Winn & Co Printers 53-55 Balfour Street Sydney
[28]pp, 1 f/p b/w plate & 8 f/p col. plates & col. pictures on front & back wrappers, cover title, 280x216mm
Illus. Hottie Lahm. *David and Dawn* appeared as a comic strip in *Smith's Weekly* July 1938 to July 1939. KMM

GEORGE EDWARDS RADIO PRODUCTION—THE SEARCH FOR THE GOLDEN BOOMERANG (Radio Serials, parts of which were published as separate books). *See* Bingham, Lorna. TUCKONIE'S WARRIOR FRIEND; Martin, Marianne. BUSHLAND TALES; Anon. BOOMERANG STORIES FOR THE CHILDREN

EDWARDS, Hugh
2272 CAPTAIN/WILLIAM BLIGH/RN/Written by Hugh Edwards/illustrated by Arthur McNeil/Paul Hamlyn/Sydney London New York Toronto
Dee Why West, NSW, 1972
77pp (inc. 2pp index, extended t.p., col. frontis. extended on to t.p., col. & part. col. illus. throughout, pic. bd., 270x200mm. HBM
Cover title: 'The Trials and Triumphs of Captain William Bligh RN'.

2273 THE TRIUMPHS AND TRAGEDIES OF/PEARL DIVERS/OF AUSTRALIA/written by Hugh Edwards/Paul Hamlyn/Sydney London New York Toronto
1972
77pp (inc. 2pp index, 2pp col. dec. map), frontis. extended on to t.p., col. & sepia/white illus. throughout by Tiffany Art Studios, pic. bd., 270x200mm. CLRC

EDWARDS, Sylvia
2274 SALLY BAXTER—GIRL REPORTER/IN AUSTRALIA/by/Sylvia Edwards/Published by/World Distributors (Manchester) Limited/London—Manchester/England
n.d. [1959]
184pp, clo., 185x120mm. NSL:M
• Rpt 1960, as above. KP

[EGERTON-WARBURTON, A.]
2275 MORE/STRANGE ANIMALS/I'VE NEVER MET/Drawn by/Marion H. Hart/Verses by/A. E-W./Adelaide: G. Hassell & Son/1918
21pp, illus. throughout, grey paper wrappers, 180x120mm. NSL:M
See also [Hart, M. H.] for previous volume

EGGLESTON, Roland
2276 Roland Eggleston/with illustrations by Grace Huxtable/WHEN YONDI PUSHED UP THE SKY/[drawing]/[publisher's device]/Jonathan Cape/Thirty Bedford Square London
1963
127pp, extended t.p., 15 f/p b/w illus. & dec. initials at beginnings of each story, clo., 200x130mm. KMM
Contains 15 Aboriginal legends.

2277 Roland Eggleston/with illustrations by Grace Huxtable/WHEN YONDI/PUSHED UP THE SKY/[drawing]/London/Jonathan Cape/in association with/Australasian Publishing Company/Sydney
First publ. in Australia 1964
128pp, double-spread t.p., details as above, but limp clo., 184x120mm. KMM
School ed.

'EIRENE'
See Searle, M. Lila

ELDER, Jean
2278 SOXY/AND THE/BUSHLAND/QUEEN/by/Jean Elder
[Offset, Sydney, 1950]
26pp, dec. t.p., 8 f/p col. illus. & b/w illus. in text throughout, dec. bd., 270x220mm. ANL

2279 NURSERY LAND/ADVENTURES
n.p., n.d.
[16]pp, 7 f/p col. illus. & other illus. throughout, pic. wrappers, 243x183mm. TG
Nursery rhymes. Each page of illus. signed 'Jean Elder'.
2280 Another copy
n.p., n.d.
[12]pp, 10pp col. & 2pp b/w illus. sgd 'Jean Elder', 243x183mm. KP
See also Johnson, Phyllis & Elder, Jean

ELDRIDGE, Denise
2281 KINDLE A CANDLE/Denise Eldridge/[drawing]/Illustrated by Jocelyn Jones/Macmillan
Melbourne 1971
115pp, b/w drawings in text, clo., 200x125mm. CLRC

ELEY, Annie W.
2282 THE/DAWN MAIDEN/and/DIONE'S VISIT TO AUSTRALIA/By/Annie W. Eley/with illustrations from Sketches by the Author/Commonwealth of Australia/Edward A. Vidler/Melbourne
n.d. [1922?]
56pp, col. frontis. & 3 other col. illus., 10 b/w illus., bd., 255x190mm. ANL
2283 THE DAWN MAIDEN
Limited de luxe edition, Melbourne, n.d. [1922?]
Details as before, but with add. 2pp (Edition-de-luxe: list of subscribers), clo. (with title in gilt). Grant

THE ELFIN HOUSE *See* Dare, Eveline

ELIAS, Edith L.
2284 IN THE/GREAT COLONIAL/BUSH/By/Edith L. Elias/Author of 'In Tudor Times'/'Stories from Bunyan', etc./With twelve illustrations by/Helen A. Gray/Methuen & Co. Ltd./36 Essex Street W.C./London
1910
203pp, 8pp adv., b/w frontis. & 11 illus., clo., 165x100mm. NSL:M
A small girl's imaginary experiences in the Australian bush.

2285 THE BOOK OF/POLAR EXPLORATION/by/E. L. Elias, M.A., Author of/"Abraham Lincoln" etc./With a Foreword by/R. E. Priestley/M.C./Fellow of Clare College Cambridge/Geologist to the Shackleton Expedition of 1907–9/and to the Scott Expedition of 1910–13/[vignette]/George G. Harrap & Company Ltd./London Bombay Sydney
1928
302pp, col. frontis. & 3 f/p col. illus., 32 f/p b/w illus. & numerous b/w illus. in text, dec. clo. (with col. illus. pasted on front cover), map e/p, 210x140mm. KP

'ELIOTT, E. C.' [Martin, Reg. A.]
2286 TAS AND THE/SPACE MACHINE/by/E. C. Eliott/Illustrated by A. Bruce Cornwell/Thomas Nelson and Sons Ltd./London Edinburgh Paris Melbourne/Toronto and New York
1955
119pp, b/w frontis. & 10 b/w illus., clo., 185x120mm. KMM
• Rpt 1958, as above. KMM
2287 School ed., 1960
136pp (inc. 16pp notes). KP

2288 TAS AND THE/POSTAL ROCKET/by/E. C. Eliott/Illustrated by A. Bruce Cornwell/Thomas Nelson and Sons Ltd./London Edinburgh Paris Melbourne/Toronto and New York
1955
119pp, b/w frontis. & 8 f/p b/w illus., clo., 180x120mm. KMM
Boys' adventure fantasy of the future based in 'Woomera City' & elsewhere.
2289 Rpt 1958 as above. CLRC

ELIOTT, Lydia Susanna
2290 LITTLE/TEDDY BEAR/By Lydia S. Eliott/With a foreword by/Frank L. Edwards/Secretary of the Koala Club of Australia/Drawings by Alan Wright/[drawing]/Collins/London and Glasgow
n.d. [1939]
80pp (inc. 2pp foreword), b/w frontis., part. col. photographs & b/w drawings in text throughout, clo., 250x185mm. KMM
2291 Rpt 1944, 1947, as above, but pic. bd. CLRC
• Rpt 1951, 1952. KP

2292 THE KOALA FAMILY/AT HOME/by/Lydia S. Eliott/M.A., F.Z.S./The Falcon Nature Stories/Frederick Warne & Co. Ltd./London and New York
1949
62pp, b/w frontis. & 9 b/w illus., wrappers, 180x130mm. ANL

2293 KANGAROO/COOLAROO/By/Lydia S. Eliott, M.A., F.Z.S./[drawing]/Illustrated by Joyce Horne/Frederick Warne & Co. Limited/London and New York
1950
115pp, b/w frontis. & 8 f/p b/w illus., b/w drawings in text, clo., 215x160mm. VSL

2294 TUFTY THE TEDDY/by/Lydia S. Eliott/With 33 photographs Lutterworth Press/London
1950
90pp, b/w frontis. & b/w photographic illus. throughout, clo. (copy seen re-bound), 180x115mm. KMM

2295 KANGAROO COUNTRY/by/Lydia S. Eliott/Lutterworth Press/London
1955
96pp, col. frontis., clo., 180x115mm. ANL
• Rpt as above, 2nd imp. 1957. BBC
• Rpt as above, 3rd imp. 1959. KMM
• Rpt as above, 4th ed. 1962. KP
• Rpt as above, 5th ed. 1966. KP

2296 AUSTRALIAN/ADVENTURE/Lydia S. Eliott/Lutterworth Press/London
1956
120pp, b/w frontis., clo., 180x115mm. CLRC
2297 AUSTRALIAN/ADVENTURE/Lydia S. Eliott/Lutterworth Press/London
First published 1956; second impression 1962; third impression 1965
120pp, col. frontis., clo., 180x115mm. KMM

ELIOTT, Lydia Susanna & NOYLE, George
2298 GLIMPSES OF/FAMILY/LIFE/by/Lydia Eliott and George Noyle/AUSTRALIA
Macmillan, London 1959
64pp, part. col. illus. throughout, wrappers, cover title, 180x130mm. KMM
This is actually a social studies school textbook. The author states that a Dutch edition has also been published.

ELKIN, A. P.
THE ABORIGINAL AUSTRALIANS. *See* Australian Landmarks

THE AUSTRALIAN ABORIGINES. *See* Around Australia Program

ELLIOT, Dorothy
2299 AUSTRALIAN/SEASONS/by Dorothy Elliot/Illustrated by Peter Chapman/Readabout Books
Readabout Publishers Pty Ltd, Crow's Nest, NSW, 1964
24pp, dec. t.p., col. & part. col. drawings & diagrams throughout, stiff pic. wrappers, 215x180mm. BBC

ELLIOT, G. F. Scott
2300 THE WONDERS OF/SAVAGE LIFE/By/G. F. Scott Elliot/M.A. Cantab., B.Sc. Edin., F.R.G.S., F.L.S., &c./Author of *The Romance of Plant Life/A Naturalist in Mid Africa*/&c. &c./With fourteen illustrations/London/Seeley, Service & Co. Limited/38 Great Russell Street/1914
162pp, 2pp adv., b/w illus., clo., 195x125mm. PAI
Contains many references to Australian Aborigines & the Pacific peoples. The contents of this book were taken from the author's larger book entitled *The Romance of Savage Life.*

ELLIOTT, Brian
MARCUS CLARKE. *See* Great Australians

ELLIOTT, Dawn
2301 JOHN/NARDOO/FINDS/THE WAY/Story:/Adapted from an original story/by Miss Dawn Elliott/Illustrations:/Adrian Bain/Published and Printed by:/Mission Publications of Australia/19 Cascade Street,/Lawson, N.S.W. 2783/First edition 1969
16pp, part col. illus. on alternate pages, pic. wrappers, spirax bdg, 205x250mm. KMM
'This book is designed to be used as a flash card story. Missionaries, ministers, Sunday School teachers & youth workers will find it a useful way to warn against the evil power of strong drink.'

ELLIOTT, Mary
2302 CLARE CARSON/AND THE GOLD RUSH/Bush Nurse in the Australian Outback/[drawing]/by/Mary Elliott/Illustrated by Rachel Tonkin/Rigby Limited
Adelaide 1970 [copyright 1970 by Lloyd O'Neil Pty Ltd]
187pp, 11 f/p b/w illus., b/w drawings in text, pic. bd., pic. e/p, 210x135mm. CLRC

2303 CLARE CARSON/AND THE RUNAWAYS/Bush Nurse in the Australian Outback/[drawing]/by/Mary Elliott/Illustrated by Rachel Tonkin/Rigby Limited
Adelaide 1970 [copyright 1970 by Lloyd O'Neil Pty Ltd]
188pp, 10 f/p b/w illus., b/w drawings in text, pic. bd., dec. e/p, 210x135mm. CLRC

2304 CLARE CARSON/AND THE SHEEP DUFFERS/Bush Nurse in the Australian Outback/[drawing]/by/Mary Elliott/Illustrated by Rachel Tonkin/Rigby Limited

Adelaide 1970 [copyright 1970 by Lloyd O'Neil Pty Ltd]
187pp, b/w frontis. & 13 f/p b/w illus., b/w chapter headings, pic. bd., dec. e/p, 210x140mm. CLRC

2305 CLARE CARSON/AT WILGA JUNCTION/Bush Nurse in the Australian Outback/[drawing]/by/Mary Elliott/Illustrated by Rachel Tonkin/Rigby Limited 1970
188pp, 11 f/p b/w illus. & drawings in text, pic. bd., dec. e/p, 210x140mm. WRT

ELLIS, C.

2306 A/TALE/OF/TWO STOWAWAYS/By/C. Ellis/ The Religious Tract Society/56, Paternoster Row London, n.d. [1901]
80pp & 16pp adv., b/w frontis. & 5 b/w drawings (Victor Prout) in text, pic. clo., 169x117mm. KMM

2307 A TALE OF TWO/STOWAWAYS/By/C. Ellis/ London/The Religious Tract Society/4 Bouverie Street & 65 St Paul's Churchyard
London, n.d.
121pp & 22pp adv., col. frontis. by Maud Rhodes, & col. dec. t.p., b/w drawings in text, pic. clo., 185x124mm. KP

2308 A TALE OF/TWO STOWAWAYS/By/C. Ellis/ London/The Religious Tract Society/4 Bouverie Street and 65 St. Paul's Churchyard
n.d.
121pp, 18pp adv., b/w frontis. & 5 b/w drawings in text, illus. by Victor Prout, pic. clo., 180x120mm. KMM

ELLIS, C. Hamilton

2309 RAILS ACROSS THE/RANGES/By/C. Hamilton Ellis/Illustrations by/Terence Cuneo/[device]/Oxford University Press/London New York Toronto
1941
254pp (inc. 1p preface), col. frontis. & 6 f/p b/w illus., dec. clo., map e/p, 185x125mm. KMM
Story set in Qld.

ELLIS, Peter

2310 PETER/ELLIS/TELLS/STORIES OF/FAIRYLAND Morris & Walker Pty Ltd, Melbourne, n.d. [194-?]
32pp, 5 f/p b/w illus. & drawings in text, illus. by Mary Gilbert, dec. wrappers, cover title, 240x180mm. ANL

ELLISON, Norman

2311 DAREDEVILS/OF THE SKIES/By/Norman Ellison/With foreword by/Sir Keith Smith, K.B.E., F.R.G.S., F.R.Ac.S./Angus and Robertson Ltd./Sydney London/1940
139pp, 1p foreword, col. frontis. & b/w drawings, clo., 230x175mm. CLRC

2312 DAREDEVILS OF/THE SKIES/By/Norman Ellison/With foreword by/Sir Keith Smith/K.B.E., F.R.G.S., F.R.Ac.S./Angus and Robertson Ltd./Sydney London/1941
250pp, 2pp foreword, b/w frontis. only, clo., 180x120mm. KMM

ELRINGTON, Clement C.

2313 ALFRED THE GREAT/A Poem,/addressed to/The Youth of Australia/By Mr. C. C. Elrington/[two quotations]/Goulburn:/Printed by Benjamin Isaacs, Auburn Street/1853
24pp (inc. 1p preface), unillus., wrappers (copy seen re-bound), 185x115mm. NSL:M
The title poem (3pp) is addressed to youth; the remainder of the volume consists of adult verses.

ELY, George Herbert

See 'Strang, Herbert'

EMBURY, E. M.

2314 Shakespeare Head Australian Nature Books./ General Editor: [publisher's device] David G. Stead/ No. 3/THE GREAT BARRIER/REEF/[drawing]/By E. M. Embury,/Marine Zoologist/(drawings by Misses G. Lochrin and E. M. Nangle)/Sydney: The Shakespeare Head Press Ltd.,/1933
95pp (inc. 1p foreword by Sir Philip Game & 1p note), 1p bibliography, b/w drawings, diagrams & photographic illus. throughout, wrappers, 185x115mm. CLRC

EMBURY, E. M. & A. F.

2315 Whitcombe's Nature Story Books/BILLY FLYING-FOX/By/E. M. Embury and A. F. Embury/For ages 7 to 8 years/Whitcombe & Tombs Limited/ Sydney and Melbourne/Auckland, Christchurch, Dunedin, Wellington N.Z./and London
n.d. [1934]
20pp, 4 b/w photographic illus. in text, wrappers, 180x115mm. NSL:M
See McLaren 216

EMERSON, E. S.

2316 SANTA CLAUS AND A/SUN-DIAL/An Australian Christmas Fantasy/By E. S. Emerson/ Illustrations and Decorations by/Percy Lindsay/George Robertson & Co./Propy. Ltd./Melbourne Sydney Adelaide and Brisbane
n.d. [1909]
88pp, b/w frontis. & 19 f/p b/w illus., marginal drawings throughout, clo., 235x180mm. KMM

Emigrant Tracts

2317 Emigrant Tracts No IV/THE/AUSTRALIAN CHRISTIAN BOY./(A True Narrative.)/Published under the direction of/the Committee of General Literature and Education,/Appointed by the Society for Promoting/Christian Knowledge./London:/Printed for the /Society for Promoting Christian Knowledge:/Sold at the Depository,/Great-Queen Street, Lincoln's Inn Fields;/No. 4, Royal Exchange;/and by all booksellers./1850
vipp, 35pp, engraved frontis. ("Encampment of Natives"), wrappers, 140x90mm. ANL

2318 Emigrant Tracts—No. V./THE/YOUNG EMIGRANTS;/or,/A Voyage to Australia./Part I/Published under the direction of/The Committee of General Literature and Education/Appointed by the Society for Promoting/Christian Knowledge./London:/ Printed for the/Society for Promoting Christian Knowledge:/Sold at the Depository,/Great Queen-Street, Lincoln's Inn Fields,/No. 4 Royal Exchange;/and by all Book Sellers./1850
47pp
3 tracts (nos 5-7) with identical t.p. pp 47, 48, 52, with separate t.p., Parts I, II and III bound together in blind stamped clo. with title in gilt on front cover, 130x85mm. KMM

2319 Emigrant Tracts No. XII/THE/EMIGRANT FAMILY./By/C. P. Ford./Published under the direction of/the Committee of General Literature and Education,/Appointed by the Society for Promoting/ Christian Knowledge./London:/Printed for the/Society for Promoting Christian Knowledge;/Sold at the Depository/Great Queen Street, Lincoln's Inn Fields;/4 Royal Exchange;/and by all Book Sellers/1851/Price fourpence/London: Printed by James Truscott, Nelson Square
vipp, 60pp & 4pp adv., frontis. of a family with a bullock waggon, wrappers, 140x90mm. ANL

1p adv. 'The following narrative is written by a person who has lived for ten years in New South Wales The farm on which they are supposed to be employed is intended for that of the Messrs James and Wm Macarthur at Taralga to the north of Goulburn near to which the author lived for some years.'

2320 Emigrant Tracts No XIII/THE/SUNDAY-SCHOOL BOY/IN/AUSTRALIA/By the author of/"The Emigrant Family" "Remarks for the/Use of Emigrants."/Published under the direction of/the Committee of General Literature and Education,/ appointed by the Society for Promoting/Christian Knowledge/London:/Printed for the/Society for Promoting Christian Knowledge./Sold at the Depository,/Great Queen Street, Lincoln's Inn Fields,/ No. 4, Royal Exchange,/and by all Booksellers/1851
ivpp, 59pp & 4pp adv., engraved frontis., wrappers, 140x90mm. ANL

[EMMETT, Evelyn Temple?]

2321 Issued by the Tasmanian Government Tourist Department, Treasury/Buildings, corner Macquarie and Murray Streets, Hobart./TOMMY'S/TRIP TO/ TASMANIA/John Vail/Government Printer/Tasmania
Fifth ed., n.d. [1913]
30pp, 1 double-spread illus. & 7 f/p & drawings in text, pic. wrappers, cover title, 145x120mm
Frontis. illus. with man's smiling face with hat forming outline of Tasmania, KP

'EMMETT, George'

See Burrage, E. H.

Empire Youth Council of Victoria

2322 Untitled booklet publ. by Empire Youth Council of Victoria for Empire Youth Sunday, 2 May 1954
Melbourne
[16]pp, col. pic. wrappers, b/w illus. throughout, 210x137mm. KP
Another copy, n.d. [1955?]
16pp, col. pic. wrappers, col. pic. photographic inset, wrappers, 210x137mm. KP
Centrepiece shows HM the Queen opening the Parliament of Ceylon on her 1954 Royal Tour.

EMSLIE, M. L.

2323 Far and Near Readers/Second Series/Book M.1/BLACK FELLOWS AND BUFFALOES/M. L. Emslie/Illustrated by Stuart Tresilian/W. & R. Chambers Ltd./London and Edinburgh
1959
32pp, b/w drawings & 1 map, limp dec. clo., 195x146mm. KP

Endeavour and Achievement

2324 ENDEAVOUR/AND/ACHIEVEMENT/Highlights/ in the Story of/Australian Development/Bank of New South Wales/Sydney/1962
First pub. Feb. 1952; 2nd ed. (revised) 1953; 3rd ed. 1955; 4th ed. 1957; 5th ed. 1957; 6th ed. 1958; 7th ed. (completely revised) Feb. 1961; 8th ed. (revised) Feb. 1962
32pp, 28 b/w photographic illus., 1 map, 1 b/w drawing, col. illus., wrappers, 245x155mm. KMM
Description of the growth of various industries &c., together with a time chart (3pp); text prepared by Mr Brian H. Fletcher of the Department of History, University of NSW. KMM

Endeavour Books

Endeavour Reading Program. A series of school readers of different grades, some of which contain original Australian stories, noted here, as follows:

2325 Endeavour Reading Programme/[drawing]/THE LOST/BOOMERANG/The Jacaranda Press
Melton, Qld, 1967
32pp, part col. drawings on every page by Mollie Horseman, stiff col. pic. wrappers, 186x130mm. KMM

2326 Endeavour Reading Programme/BENNELONG/ [drawing]/The Jacaranda Press
Milton, Qld, first publ. 1970
48pp (inc. 1p vocabulary), b/w & part col. illus.by Mollie Horseman throughout, stiff pic. wrappers, 187x130mm. KMM

2327 Endeavour Reading Programme/UNDER THE/ SOUTHERN CROSS/[col. illus.]/The Jacaranda Press
Milton, Qld, 1970. Rpt in Hong Kong 1972 (twice)
94pp & 2pp vocabulary & adv. for series inside back cover, col. illus. throughout (Mollie Horseman), col. pic. sim. limp clo., 185x130mm. KMM
Contents include: 'The Endeavour' (Cook); 'Buckley's Hope' (William Buckley) & 3 other stories including one on Eyre's exploration.

2328 Endeavour Books/[drawing]/UNCLE HARO'S/NEW GUINEA/STORIES/The Jacaranda Press
Milton, Qld. First publ. 1967; rpt. 1971
48pp (inc. 1p notes), part col. illus. throughout by Genevieve Melrose, stiff pic. wrappers, 190x130mm. KMM

2329 Reading for Pleasure/WOMBAT'S GOLD/and other stories/[device]/The Jacaranda Press
1972
144pp (inc. acknowledgements &c), 44pp with col. illus., pic. wrappers, col. pic. wrappers, 185x130mm. KMM
Australian authors include: S. A. Wakefield, Mavis Scott, Judith Wright, W. N. Scott, Michael Dugan.

England

2330 Nestle's/Album No 3./"ENGLAND"/Adventure, Romance, Discovery/in Words and Pictures
17 Foveaux St, Sydney, n.d. [1937?] [accession of Edward VIII in 1936 is recorded]
28pp (inc. 4pp description, with photographs of Nestle's Abbotsford factory), text & sketches relating to English history with spaces for 136 cards to be pasted in, col. pic. card covers, cover title, 264x206mm. KP

'ENGLISH, Ethel Emily' [Emily E. Henstock]

2331 AUSTRALIAN/FAIRY TALES/By/Ethel E. English/George A. Jones, Printer and Publisher
[Sydney] 1925
58pp, 3 f/p b/w illus. by 'Rita' [McKenzie], clo., 210x130mm. ANL
Contains 15 stories.

2332 AUSTRALIAN/FAIRY TALES/By/Ethel E. English/1st Edition October 1925/2nd. Edition, February 1926
Wholly set up & printed by G. A. Jones, Sydney
92pp, col. frontis. & 4 b/w illus. by 'Rita' [McKenzie], clo., 185x120mm. ANL
Contains 1 additional story, 'Pixie and the Brownie'.

2333 AUSTRALIAN/FAIRY TALES/By/Ethel E. English/Illustrated by/Rita McKenzie/1st. Edition, October 1925/2nd. Edition, February 1926/School Edition April 1927/G. A. Jones, Printer, 167 Castlereagh St., Sydney
71pp, 4 b/w illus., limp clo., 160x115mm. KMM
Contains 16 stories & 1 verse.

ENGLISH, George Selwyn

2334 "DOWN BY THE BAY"/Six Australian/Nature Songs/Contents/"March of the Soldier Crabs" [&c listed]/W. H. Paling & Co. Limited/Sydney—

Brisbane/and established throughout N.S.W. & Queensland
1954
13pp & 1p blank, 1p adv., 1p blank, unillus., wrappers, 247x185mm. KMM

Enoch Roden's Training
See 'Stretton, Hesba' [pseud. Sarah Smith]

"Entertain Em" [*sic*]
2335 A Book of/Games for Young and Old/Games and/Competitions/For Parties, Entertainments, Evenings/Socials, Family Entertainments, etc./Suitable for Young Children, Boys/and Girls, Young People and Adults./Compiled by'Entertain em'/Published by/John Pollard/Winfield Building, 495 Collins Street, Melbourne, C.1
n.d. [1945?]. Wilke & Sons Printers 19–47 Jeffcott St, Melbourne
64pp (last blank), unillus., pic. wrappers, 180x116mm. CLRC
2336 Another copy as above
[1934]. Printed by Wilke & Co Pty Ltd, 241–5 William St, Melbourne
63pp
Printed plain wrappers, price 1/- on front cover. KP

[ENTON, Harry]
Harry Enton (sometimes given as Enten) 1854–1927 was an American doctor of medicine who created the boys' hero 'Frank Reade' & wrote three books featuring the hero. A quarrel with his publisher Frank Tousey arose when the latter publ. the books under 'Noname'. Enton gave up writing & the series was continued by Lu Senarens & others.
2337 The Aldine Romance of Invention, Travel & Adventure/Library/Jules Verne Outdone!!!/FRANK READE FROM/POLE TO POLE/[coloured illustration]/No. 52/[caption]/London: Aldine Publishing Company
n.d.
32pp, unillus., col. pic. wrappers (with adv. verso front cover, verso/recto back cover), cover title, 215x135mm. RM

2338 The Aldine Romance of Invention, Travel, & Adventure/Library/Jules Verne Outdone!!!/FRANK READE/AMID ICE AND SNOW/[col. illus.]/No. 53/[caption]/1d./London: Aldine Publishing Company.
n.d.
30pp, 2pp adv., unillus., col. pic. wrappers (with adv. verso front cover, verso/recto back cover), cover title, 220x140mm. RM
About half the action takes place in the Arctic when Frank Reade & his friends move under the sea & the Antarctic via the Solomon Islands, New Hebrides, New Caledonia, Norfolk Island and NZ. Sequel to *Frank Reade From Pole to Pole.*

2339 No. 74 as above, but
FRANK READE IN/THE GOLDEN CITY/
n.d.
Details as above. RM
Adventure story based on fantasy of a city of dwarfs in the region of Central Mt Stuart, ending in Sydney. The stories originally appeared in the 'Frank Reade Library' [189-?] in US.

2340 The Aldine Romance of Invention, Travel & Adventure/Library/Jules Verne Outdone!!!/FRANK READE'S/ELECTRIC BUCKBOARD./[coloured illustration]/No. 76/[caption]/1d./London: Aldine Publishing Company, Limited
n.d. [1894?]
31pp (inc. 1p reviews), 1p adv., unillus., col. pic. wrappers, cover title, 210x135mm. RM
Title at head of first page of text reads: 'Frank Reade's Electric Buckboard;/or,/Thrilling Adventures in North Australia'.

2341 The Aldine Romance of Invention, Travel, & Adventure/Library/Jules Verne Outdone!!!./FRANK READE'S/ELECTRIC MAN/IN AUSTRALIA/[col. illus.]/No. 36/[caption]/1d./London: Aldine Publishing Company, Limited
n.d. (English rpt)
32pp, unillus., col. pic. wrappers (with adv. verso front cover, verso/recto back cover), cover title, 220x135mm. RM
Story begins in Sydney then moves to somewhere unspecified in Australia.
2342 Noname's Latest and Best Stories are Published in This Library./Frank Reade/Library/[on background illus.] Entered as second class mail at the New York, N.Y. Post Office, October 5, 1892./No. 37 (complete) Frank Tousey, Publishers, 34 & 36 North Moore Street, New York. (price 5 cents) Vol. II/New York, June 3, 1893/Issued Weekly/THE ELECTRIC MAN:/or,/Frank Reade, Jr., in Australia./By "Noname"./[illus.]
28pp (inc. front & back wrappers), unillus., pic. wrappers, 280x210mm. RM
Adv. on half verso of back wrappers.

2343 No. 90 as above, but
FRANK READE Jr's CATAMARAN OF THE AIR; or,/Wild and Wonderful Adventures in North Australia. by "Noname."
1894
32pp. Uniform with *The Electric Man*. RM

Episodes of Personal Aventure in Field, Flood and Forest
2344 EPISODES/OF/PERSONAL ADVENTURE/IN/FIELD, FLOOD, AND FOREST/A Book for Boys/London:/Blackie & Son, 49 & 50 Old Bailey, E.C./Glasgow, Edinburgh and Dublin./1880
256pp (inc. 1p preface), additional dec. t.p., b/w frontis., clo., 165x105mm. KMM
Includes: 'The Bushrangers of Australia' (9pp); 'How an Irish Sailor became King in New Guinea' (10pp).

EPSTEIN, June
2345 LET'S JOIN/IN AGAIN/For Katharine-Ann/by June Epstein/Published by Whitcombe & Tombs Pty. Ltd./20 Bond Street, Melbourne./Melbourne Sydney Perth Geelong
n.d.
24pp (inc. 1p foreword by C. R. Bull, of the ABC), part col. illus. throughout, pic. wrappers, 240x187mm. KP
Words & music by author.

2346 LITTLE RED ENGINE/AND/MILKMAN'S HORSE/Two Songs by/June Epstein/[illus.]/Allans Music (Australia) Pty Ltd./30c./Melbourne Adelaide Hobart Geelong Bendigo/Dandenong Bentleigh Camberwell Preston/Printed in Australia
Melbourne, 1972
4pp, col. illus. wrappers, cover title, 312x236mm. ANL

EPSTEIN, June Sadie
2347 Mullens' Plays for Children/No. 3/THE NINE MUSES/Five Plays for ages 11 to 13/by/June Epstein/Robertson & Mullens Ltd./Melbourne
n.d. [1952]
91pp (inc. foreword by Dorothy J. Ross & author's notes), b/w frontis. by Marjorie Howden, diagrams &c., wrappers, 185x120mm. ANL

ERDOS, Renée
THE SYDNEY GAZETTE. *See* Australian Landmarks

LUDWIG LEICHHARDT. *See* Australian Explorers

ERGIL, Francis
AVENTURES DE DEUX JEUNES ANGLAIS EN AUSTRALIE *See* Kingston, W. H. G., Adventures in Australia

'ERIC THE RED'
2348 VIC GOES TO WAR/By Eric the Red/Illustrated by John Endean/[device]/Paul Hamlyn Pty. Ltd./Sydney London New York Toronto
1971
[32]pp, col. illus. throughout, pic. bd., pic. e/p, 310x230mm. CLRC

2349 VIC MEETS SLAPPER/By Eric the Red/Illustrated by John Endean/[device]/Paul Hamlyn Pty. Ltd./ Sydney London New York Toronto
1971
[32]pp, col. illus. throughout, pic. bd., pic. e/p, 310x230mm. CLRC

ERNST, Olga Dorothea Agnes [later Waller]
2350 FAIRY TALES/FROM THE/LAND OF THE WATTLE/By/Olga D. A. Ernst/with illustrations by Dorothy Ashley/Melbourne/McCarron, Bird & Co., 479 Collins St.
n.d. [1904]
94pp, 15 f/p b/w illus., endpieces &c., dec. bd., 200x160mm. KMM
Fairy tales about Australian birds, animals, &c. Publisher's note states that the stories are the work of a young Australian girl. Also author of *The Magic Shadow Show* (G. Robertson, Melbourne 1913) which, although consisting of short fantasies, is not a children's book. KMM

2351 SONGS FROM THE DANDENONGS/Mountain Nursery Rhymes/Set to Music for the/Young of all Ages/Contents [10 songs listed]/Words by Olga D. A. Waller, M.A./Music by/Jean M. Fraser/Price 1/3 Net/ [2 lines acknowledgements]
Printed by A. Kynoch & Co. Pty. Ltd., Melbourne, n.d. (Copyright 1939)
24pp (inc. 1p dedication & 1p foreword), line drawings & notes for each song, pic. wrapper, 240x155mm. KMM
• Rpt June 1945, July 1949, as above. KP

ESLER, E. Rentoul
2352 ALMOST A PAUPER/A Tale of Trial and Triumph./By/E. Rentoul Esler./Illustrated by Frank Dadd./Published under the direction of the committee/of general literature and education appointed by the/Society for Promoting Christian Knowledge./London:/Society for Promoting Christian Knowledge./Northumberland Avenue, Charing Cross, W.C.;/43, Queen Victoria Street, E.C./Brighton: 135, North Street,/New York: E. & J. B. Young and Co.
n.d. [school prize 1889]
96pp & 4pp adv., b/w frontis., pic. clo., 168x116mm. KMM
The story first appeared in *All the Year Round* under the title of 'Poor Folk'. It tells of a poor orphan boy who stows away on a ship bound for Australia. He is befriended by a squatter returning to the colonies & makes good on his property.

'EULALIE'
2353 DANCING DINAH/Pictures and Verses by Eulalie Ayers & James, Sydney 1951
15pp, col. illus. throughout, dec. wrappers, cover title, 300x245mm. NSL:M
Song with music by Barry Gray on back cover.

'EUROPA' [pseud. Sarah Welch]
2354 THE/FERNYTHORPE CHORISTERS/A Tale for Boys/By Europa/George Robertson/Melbourne, Sydney and Adelaide/MDCCCLXXVI 1876
103pp, unillus., clo., 170x105mm. NSL:M
Boys' story with religious background.

Eva in Fairyland
See [Hope, J. E. C.]

EVANS, E. R. G. R. [first Baron Mountevans]
2355 SOUTH/WITH SCOTT/by/Rear-Admiral E. R. G. R. Evans,/C.B., D.S.O., R.N./With Three Maps/ [device]/London and Glasgow/Collins Clear-type Press
n.d. [school prize 1931] [first publ. 1921]
xiipp, 284pp & 5pp adv., col. frontis., pic. clo., 200x135mm. KP
2356 SOUTH WITH/SCOTT/By/Admiral E. R. G. R. Evans,/C.B., D.S.O., R.N./London and Glasgow/ Collins' Clear-Type Press
n.d. [preface dated 1921—awarded as Sunday School prize 1938]
xiipp, 284pp, photographic frontis., 3 b/w maps folding together, pic. clo., 185x125mm. KMM
'Written particularly for Britain's younger generation' (from author's preface).
2357 SOUTH WITH/SCOTT
As above, but no device
282pp, no adv. but 3 folding b/w maps, sepia/white photographic frontis., pic. clo., 185x125mm. KP
2358 SOUTH/WITH SCOTT/Admiral/Sir Edward R. G. R. Evans/KCB., D.S.O./[device]/The Scout Book Club/ The Scout Book Club Edition/Not for Sale to the Public
n.d.
285pp (inc. 1p author's preface, 1p foreword by editor of *The Scout*), 3pp personnel of expedition, 3 folding b/w maps, sim. clo., 182x120mm. KP
Also issued in Collins White Circle paperback, an adult series.
2359 SOUTH WITH SCOTT/By/Admiral/Lord Mountevans/K.C.B., D.S.O./[device]/Collins/London and Glasgow
1957
284pp, col. frontis., clo., 210x130mm. KP
The Crusader Series. Frontis. by J. C. Dollman, preface by E. G. R. G. Evans.
2360 SOUTH WITH/SCOTT/By/Admiral/Lord Mountevans/KCB., DSO., LL.D./With Photographs by/Herbert Ponting, F.R.G.S./[device]/Collins/London and Glasgow
This imp. 1961
284pp (inc. 1p preface & 3pp list of personnel), b/w frontis., 14pp b/w photographic illus., clo., 210x138mm. KP
Not specifically children's edition

2361 THE MYSTERY OF/THE "POLAR STAR"/By/ Rear-Admiral/E. R. G. R. Evans, C.B., D.S.O./Author of/"The Adventures of Peter" "South with Scott",/"Keeping the Seas", etc. etc./[device]/S. W. Partridge & Co./4, 5 & 6 Soho Square, London, W.1
1st publ. 1927 [prize 1943]
256pp, col. frontis. (Norman Ellis), pic. clo., 200x134mm. KP

2362 THE MODERN WORLD OF/CONQUEST/ Contributors include:/Admiral Sir E. R. G. R. Evans/

Katharine Trevelyan/'Bartimeus'/London and Glasgow/Collins' Clear Type Press
n.d. [1937?]
[64]pp, b/w photographic illus., dec. t.p., bd., col. photograph pasted on front cover, 245x185mm. KP
Contents include: Evans, 'Sledging with Scott '11pp; W. Bremner Highet ,'South with Byrd' 8pp; Ivy Moore, 'Koala Park' 6pp; Leander Fitzgerald ,'Building a New City: Canberra' 7pp.

2363 HAPPY/ADVENTURER/An Autobiography/By/ Admiral Lord Mountevans/illustrated by/S. Drigin/ [device]/Lutterworth Press/London
1951
131pp, col. frontis., b/w drawings in text, clo., 196x125mm. KP

2364 MAN OF THE WHITE SOUTH/The Story of Captain Scott/by Admiral Lord Mountevans/Illustrated by Robert Hodgson/Thomas Nelson and Sons Ltd./ Edinburgh
1958
83pp, 7 col. lithographs (inc. map) & b/w drawings, clo., dec. e/p, 240x180mm. NSL:M

EVANS, George F.
2365 GRUMBLE-GRUMBLE/By/George F. Evans/ Illustrated by/Peter Fraser/[illus.]/Hamish Hamilton/ London
1947
187pp, b/w drawings in text, clo., 183x120mm. KP
Fantasy about a koala & other Australian animals. B/w drawing of koala in a panel of red on front cover & t.p.

EVANS, I. O.
See Hall, Willis & Evans, I. O.

EVANS, Myfanwy
2366 DIGGORY GOES TO/THE NEVER-NEVER/By/ Myfanwy Evans/Drawings by/Margaret Tempest/ Collins 48 Pall Mall London
1937
32pp, col. illus. throughout, dec. bd., 245x195mm. CLRC

EVANS, Nellie A.
2367 HOW THE KNAVE/STOLE THE TARTS/ [drawing]/and/THE CATVILLE FAIR/Wholly set up and published by the Offset Printing Coy Pty Limited, Sydney [2 lines]
n.d. [194-?]
[16]pp, part col. illus., col. pic. wrappers, pic. e/p, 272x214mm. ANL

EVANS, Sylvia
2368 TAIL UP/The Story of "Manna"/Personality Dog/ [illustration] "Manna"/Copyright (No. 40,173)/1944, by Sylvia Evans/"Alwyn" 16 Loftus Street, Arncliffe/ [2 lines]
56pp, sepia/white photographic illus. throughout, col. pic. bd., clo. spine, 275x195mm. ANL

EVELYN, J.
2369 CAPTAIN KANGAROO/A Story of Australian Life/By/J. Evelyn/London/Remington & Co., Publishers/Henrietta Street, Covent Garden/1889/All rights reserved
277pp, unillus., clo., 180x115mm. NSL:M
Boys' story with bushranging background.

EVERARD, Elizabeth
STORIES OF JESUS—A New Series of Illustrated Bible Story Books for Very Young Folks
Author of several series of religious booklets published between 1946 and 1949 by The Book Depot, Melbourne, but author not Australian.

EVERS, L. H.
2370 THE/RACKETTY STREET/GANG/by/L. H. Evers/London/Hodder & Stoughton
1961
189pp, unillus., clo., 210x135mm. KMM
Joint winner CBCA Award, 1962.
• Rpt 1962. KW

2371 THE/RACKETTY STREET/GANG/[device]/ Brockhampton Press
Leicester, England; Sydney & Melbourne under licence from the Currawong Pub. Co. Pty Ltd, Sydney, 5th impr. 1966
Wrapper design Arthur Horowicz. KP
• Rpt as above, 1969. KP

2372 THE/RACKETTY STREET/GANG/by/L. H. Evers/[device]/Brockhampton Press
Leicester, England, eighth impression 1971 (under licence from the Currawong Pub. Co. Pty Ltd, 129 Pitt Street, Sydney)
As above. BBC

2373 THE RACKETTY STREET GANG/L. H. Evers/ Scholastic Book Services/New York Toronto London Auckland Sydney Tokyo
Printed in Great Britain July 1972
188pp, unillus., pic. wrappers, 198x129mm. KMM

2374 L. H. Evers/DANNY'S/WONDERFUL UNCLE/ Drawings by George Adamson/Thomas Nelson & Sons Ltd.
Edinburgh [Copyright The Currawong Publishing Co. Pty. Ltd. 1963, Publishing by arrangement with The Currawong Publishing Co. Pty. Ltd., Sydney]
121pp, extended b/w frontis. & 11 b/w illus. in text, clo., 200x130mm. BBC

Every Boy's Adventure Omnibus
2375 EVERY BOY'S/ADVENTURE OMNIBUS/[device]/ Published by/Associated General Publications Pty. Ltd./Sydney
1952
126pp, b/w illus. throughout, pic. bd., 240x180mm. CLRC
Short stories and comic strips. 'Decoy Death' relates to action in the Solomons in 1944, 'Point Five Reception' based on the Battle of the Bismarck Sea.

Every Boy's Colour Book of Trains
2376 EVERY BOY'S COLOUR BOOK OF TRAINS
Sydney, Offset Printing & Publishing Co., n.d. [1948]
18pp, 8 f/p col. illus. & b/w drawings, dec. wrappers, cover title, 270x215mm. ANL

EVISON, B.
2377 LITTLE KOALA/AND THE PARROT/English Text by B. Evison/Illustrated by Lucie Lundberg/Copyright by/Lithor Publishers Ltd—Brighton/Danny Books— Montreal/All rights reserved/Printed by Halsingborgs Litografiska AB Sweden
n.d. [196-?]
25pp, 12 f/p col. illus., pic. bd., 210x148mm. CLRC

EWART, Ernest Andrew
See 'Cable, Boyd'

EWERS, John K.
2378 BOY AND SILVER/[illus.]/By/John K. Ewers/With Decorations by/Porter/1929
Porter & Salmon, Fremantle, WA
32pp, drawings printed in brown wrappers, 225x167mm. KP
Poems

2379 TALES FROM THE/DEAD HEART/by/J. K. Ewers/Illustrated by Leo Porter/The Currawong Publishing Company/32 Jamieson Street, Sydney
n.d. [1944]
75pp, 4pp glossary, b/w frontis. & 13 f/p b/w illus., bd., 180x115mm. KMM
American edition

2380 WRITTEN/IN SAND/by/John Ewers/Illustrated by/Avery Johnson/New York/E. P. Dutton & Co. Inc./1947/[decoration]
160pp (inc. 6pp glossary), b/w frontis. & 12 f/p b/w illus., b/w drawings in text, clo., dec. e/p, 205x145mm. NSL:M

2381 WHO RIDES ON/THE RIVER?/By/John K. Ewers/Illustrated by/Elizabeth Durack/[device]/Angus and Robertson
First publ. 1956. First school ed. (abridged) 1964
224pp (inc. 1p author's note & 2pp appendix), b/w frontis., b/w drawings in text, pic. e/p map of Sturt's route, limp pic. clo., 180x120mm. KMM

Exciting Stories of the First Australians

2382 EXCITING STORIES OF/THE FIRST AUSTRALIANS/a Vita-Brit card series
Nabisco Pty Limited, Melbourne, n.d.
8pp, with spaces left for cards to be pasted in, stiff pic. covers, cover title, 240x184mm. KP

Explorers All

2383 EXPLORERS/ALL/[portrait]/London: Humphrey Milford/Oxford University Press
1942
47pp, b/w frontis. & b/w drawings throughout, pic. wrappers, 190x140mm. KP
First 24pp relate to Matthew Flinders.

Explorers and their Ships

2384 EXPLORERS/AND/THEIR SHIPS/2/- (20 cents) A Vita-Brits Project Card Series
Nabisco Pty Ltd, Melbourne, n.d.
12pp, spaces left for cards to be pasted in, double-spread dec. map, stiff pic. covers, cover title, 238x184mm. KP

EYRE, Hal

2385 THE AMAZING/ADVENTURES OF/LITTLE/"OSSIE"/by/Eyre Jr.
Frank Johnson, Sydney, n.d. [1943]
8pp, col. illus. throughout, col. wrappers, cover title, 240x350mm. ANL
Children's comic booklet by the Sydney cartoonist.

2386 BETTY AND THE BEARS/By/Hal Eyre/Author of 'Hilarities'/Illustrated by the author/Methuen & Co. Ltd./36 Essex St. W.C./London
n.d. [1932]
204pp, 8pp adv., b/w drawings in text, clo., 200x130mm. VSL

Ezy-Bilt

2387 EZY-BILT/The Master Toy/[col. illus.]/Instruction Book for Sets 1 to 5/Copyright Colton Palmer and Preston Limited, Southwark, S.A.
36pp, b/w illus. of working models to be constructed, pic. wrappers, 180x232mm. ANL

2388 Another copy as above, but 'copyright by Ezy-Bilt Ltd, Kilkenny, SA'
35pp (& 1p & inside cover 'Diary of Models Built'), cover title, front cover printed in red & black on green background, 178x240mm. CLRC

2389 EZY-BILT/THE MASTER TOY/[illus.]/Instruction for Sets 6, 7 and 8/Copyright by Colton Palmer and Preston Limited, Southwark S.A.
n.d. [195-?]
71pp, diagrams of models throughout, cover title, wrappers printed in 3 col., 180x235mm. MAC

F., K. E.

THE AUSTRALIAN CHRISTIAN BOY. *See* Emigrant Tracts

F., M.

2390 BEN WENTWORTH'S REVENGE,/by M.F./Author of "The Confirmation Class."/Published under the direction of/The Committee of General Literature and Education/Appointed by the Society for Promoting/Christian Knowledge./London:/Society for Promoting Christian Knowledge./Sold at the depositories:/77 Great Queen Street, Lincoln's-Inn Fields;/4 Royal Exchange; 48 Piccadilly;/and by all booksellers
n.d.
102pp, engraved frontis., 2 b/w illus., dec. clo., 140x90mm. MAC
Australian background, mostly Melbourne & Victoria.

FABER, Frederick William

2391 THE CHILD TO WHOM/NOBODY WAS KIND/A Tale of England and Australia/By Father W. Faber/With 12 Coloured and other Illustrations/Boards, 1s net/[illus. with caption]
n.d. [1905]
29pp
As advertised in *NEW NORCIA: The remarkable Aborigine's institution ... in the State of Western Australia* (London, Burns & Oates, 1908). Described by P. Depasquale *In House* No. 6, June 1982. Unseen

FAGRELL, Else

2392 THE LOST/BIRTHDAY/By/Else Fagrell/[drawing]/Illustrated by Julie K. Howard/The Caxton Printers, Ltd./Caldwell, Idaho/1954
124pp, 6 f/p b/w illus. & b/w decorations, clo., dec. e/p, 200 x 135 mm. ANL
Story of two children lost in the Australian bush.

FAIRFAX, Mackenzie

2393 HUMANA'S QUEST/A Rhyme for Children/By Mackenzie Fairfax/A. Brooker/Robertson Street/Hastings [N.Z.] n.d. [1910?]
71pp, col. frontis. & 10 f/p b/w illus., line drawings in text, wrappers, 215x135mm. NSL:M
Frontis. signed Charles E. Dawson, ?Davison.

Fairy Gold

2394 FAIRY GOLD
Whitcombe & Tombs Ltd, Melbourne, n.d. [1945]
15pp, col. illus. throughout, col. pic. wrappers, cover title, 175x330mm. NSL:M
Picture book with slight rhyming text.

The Fairy Ring

2395 Whitcombe's Story Books/THE/FAIRY RING/(For the Sevens)/[drawing & caption]/Whitcombe and Tombs Limited/Auckland, Wellington, Christchurch, Dunedin, Invercargill, NZ/London, Melbourne and Sydney
n.d. [193-?]
14pp, b/w frontis. by J. M. Thomasson, pic. wrappers, 185x125mm. KMM
See McLaren 112

The Fairy Story that came True

2396 [col. drawing] THE FAIRY STORY THAT/CAME TRUE
British Imperial Oil, Melbourne, n.d. [192-?]
16pp, dec. t.p., 5 col. illus. & 1 b/w illus. by Ida Rentoul Outhwaite, pic. wrappers, 245 x 185 mm. ANL

Fairy Tales The Magic Ring and other Stories
2397 FAIRY TALES/THE MAGIC RING/AND/OTHER STORIES
Thomas Tennant, Chatswood, NSW, n.d. [1944]
32pp, b/w drawings in text, wrappers, cover title, 195x120mm. ANL

Fairy Tales Told in Pictures
See Gunn & Taylor

Fairy Tales told in the Bush
See 'Sister Agnes'

Fairyland for Boys and Girls
See Gunn & Taylor

Fairyland Rhymes
2398 FAIRYLAND/RHYMES
W. H. Honey Publishing Co., Sydney, n.d. [Copyright 1943]
96pp, b/w illus. throughout, dec. bd., cover title, 245x170mm. NSL:M

Family Life Movement
2399 No 4 in the Guide series/THE GUIDE/THROUGH BOYHOOD/A reliable book for Australian boys 8 to 11 years/Sydney Melbourne Brisbane Adelaide Newcastle/Family Life Movement of Australia [device]/(a division of Father & Son Welfare Movement)
Sydney, Nov 1970 (completing 175 000 copies)
30pp & 2pp adv., b/w diagrams &c, wrappers, 184x120mm. KP
Uniform with above:
2400 The Guide through Girlhood. KP
and numerous other guides

Famous Australians
A series of 20 booklets published as advertising material by the soap manufacturers of 'Surf', 'Omo', 'Sunlight' &c., Sydney 1969.
Format example:
2401 Famous Australians/WILLIAM/CHARLES/WENTWORTH
by Frank Greenop; W. C. Penfold Pty Ltd for manufacturers of 'Surf', 'Omo' &c.
6pp, sepia/white illus., double-spread col. illus. & col. pic. wrappers, by Monty Webb, cover title 150x75mm. KP
2402 HENRY LAWSON, by Frank Greenop. KP
2403 JOHN MACARTHUR, by Frank Greenop. KP
2404 SIR HENRY PARKES, by Frank Greenop. KP
2405 ALBERT NAMATJIRA, by Ted Docker. KP
2406 DAISY BATES, by Ted Docker. KP
2407 SISTER KENNY, by Ted Docker. KP
2408 SIR CHARLES KINGSFORD SMITH, by Ted Docker. KP
2409 HUME AND HOVELL, by Arthur Rainsford. KP
2410 SIR JOHN MONASH, by Arthur Rainsford. KP
2411 DAME NELLIE MELBA, by Maurice Hehir. KP
Other titles in series: Sturt, Burke and Wills; 'Boy' Charlton; Peter Lalor; Francis Greenway; Lachlan Macquarie; Caroline Chisholm, Flynn of the Inland; Bass and Flinders. Unseen

Famous Australians
2412 FAMOUS/AUSTRALIANS/Book 2/Presented to you by the Commonwealth Savings Bank.
Printed by Bell Press Ltd, Printers, Rockdale, NSW, n.d. [1950-?]
24pp (inc. 1p foreword), dec. wrappers, cover title, 240x180 mm. KMM
Includes brief biographies with portrait illustration of 12 Australian men & women of note.

Famous Explorers
2413 Tidders Book 4/FAMOUS EXPLORERS/Bencroft [device]/London
32pp (& printed inside covers), 16 f/p col. illus., col. pic. wrappers, 62x84mm. RC
2414 FAMOUS EXPLORERS [cover title]
©1966 & 1970 by B.P.C. Publishing Ltd. Printed in Great Britain by A. Wheaton & Co., Exeter
88pp & printed inside back cover, 13 f/p col. illus., col. pic. wrappers, 66x84mm. RC
Contains Vikings, Marco Polo, Christopher Columbus, Ferdinand Magellan, James Cook, Mungo Park, David Livingstone, Robert Falcon Scott, Roald Amundsen, Thor Heyerdahl, Sir E. Hilary, Sir V. Fuchs, Jacques Cousteau, Edwin Eugene 'Buzz' Alain, Michael Collins, Neil Armstrong. Back cover carries an adv. for 'These exciting Nabisco Adventure Books'.

Famous Explorers of Australia
2415 FAMOUS/EXPLORERS/OF AUSTRALIA/Paul Hamlyn/London/Sydney/New York/Toronto
Dee Why West, NSW, 1971
61pp, col. & b/w illus. throughout, pic. bd., 275x195mm. CLRC
Contains accounts of three explorers: Thomas Livingstone Mitchell, Charles Sturt & George William Evans. Illustrated with reproductions of contemporary prints, etc.

Farr Off; or, Asia and Australia Described
See [Mortimer, Mrs M.]

FARINA, Loredana
THE GOLDEN FISH—an adaptation of Pushkin's story by Loredana Farina, translated from the Italian by Barbara McGilvray, pub. Bay Books Pty Ltd, Sydney 1970.
THE GOLDEN FLEECE, narrated and translated by the same authors, pub. Bay Books Pty Ltd, Sydney 1970.
These are not considered Australian children's books.

FARJEON, Benjamin Leopold
2416 THE/GOLDEN LAND;/or, Links from Shore to Shore./By/B. L. Farjeon,/Author of "The Nine of Hearts", "Molka", "Blade o'Grass",/"Grif", etc./With twenty-eight illustrations by Gordon Browne./Engraved and printed by Edmund Evans./London: Ward, Lock, & Co.,/Warwick House, Salisbury Square, E.C./New York: Bond Street./1886/(All rights reserved)
344pp, b/w frontis. & 3 f/p b/w illus., b/w drawings in text, pic. col., 180x120mm. VSL
2417 THE/GOLDEN LAND/or,/Links from Shore to Shore./By/B.L. Farjeon,/Author of "The Nine of Hearts", "Molka", "Blade o'Grass",/"Grif", etc./With twenty-eight illustrations by Gordon Browne./Engraved and printed by Edmund Evans/Second Edition/Ward Lock and Co./London, New York and Melbourne/1890/(All rights reserved)
344pp, 8pp adv., 28 b/w illus., dec. col., 180x125mm. CLRC

Farmyard Friends
2418 FARMYARD FRIENDS
A CMC Production. Lithographed by Modern Printing Co Pty Ltd for Pantheon Publications, Melbourne, n.d. [194-?]
[16]pp, col. illus. throughout, bd. bound with spirax, 245x195mm. KP
Consists of 8pp light bd., illus. both sides with captions only, cover title, one page depicts two cockatoos & a kookaburra perched on a bough of flowering gum.

FARNSWORTH, Vesta J.
2419 THE HOUSE WE LIVE IN/or/The Making of the

Body/A Book for Home Reading, intended to assist/ Mothers in Teaching their children/How to care for their Bodies/and the Evil Effects/of Narcotics and/ Stimulants./Vesta J. Farnsworth/[quotation]/ Melbourne, Australia/Echo Publishing Company, Limited/International Tract Society:/London, Cape Town, Calcutta
n.d. [1900? copy inscribed May 1903]
218pp, 6pp adv., b/w frontis., & b/w drawings in text, pic. col., 220x150mm. NSL:M

2420 THE HOUSE WE LIVE IN
Same till [quotation], then
Signs of the Times Publishing Association, Ltd./ Warburton, Victoria. Australia/London Cape Town and Calcutta/1907
Unillus., limp clo., as above. KP

FARRELL, Monica

2421 THE STORY/OF/TOMMY AND BETTY/"From Pauper's House to Royal Palace"/A Children's Story/ by/Monica Farrell
The author, Light and Truth Gospel Crusade, Sydney, n.d.
51pp, 6 f/p part col. illus., pic. wrappers, 185x122mm. NSL:M

FARRELLY, Alan

2422 for Joe and Kenneth/COUNTRY COUSINS/text by Alan Farrelly/photography by Ron Morrison/Rigby Limited
Adelaide 1968
[48]pp, b/w photographs throughout, pic. clo., 250x190mm. KMM

2423 for Bryn and Janet/DAVID/AT/THE/SHOW/text by/Alan Farrelly/photography by/Ron Morrison/ Rigby Limited
Adelaide 1968
32pp, b/w photographs throughout, pic. clo., 250x190 mm. BBC

2424 for our mothers/HOP/SKIP/AND JUMP/text by/ Alan Farrelly/Photographs by/Ron Morrison/Rigby Limited
Adelaide 1968
[25]pp, col. illus. throughout, pic. clo., col. e/p, 250x185mm. CLRC

2425 for our fathers/TWO BY/TWO/Text by/Alan Farrelly/photography by/Ron Morrison/Rigby
Rigby Ltd, Adelaide 1969
[32]pp, col. photographic illus. throughout, pic. clo., dec. e/p, 250x190mm. KMM
Account of the rehearsing & performance by children of Benjamin Britten's *Noye's Fludde* at Newcastle Cathedral, NSW.

FARWELL, George

2426 Great Stories of Australia/RIDERS TO/AN UNKNOWN SEA/The Story of Charles Sturt: Explorer/[drawing]/By George Farwell/Illustrated by Frank Beck/Melbourne/Macmillan & Co. Ltd./1963
175pp, 2pp foreword, 14 part. col. illus., clo., dec. map e/p, 215x135mm. KMM

2427 SEVEN/THOUSAND/ISLES/Discovering the Philippines/George Farwell/Lansdowne
Melbourne 1968
101pp, b/w photographic frontis., b/w photographic illus. throughout, dec. chapter headings, clo., map e/p, 245x180mm. Pacific Journeys Series. BBC

This Fascinating World

2428 THIS/FASCINATING/WORLD/A Series of 50 picture plates that take you to the four/corners of the earth—that make geography lessons FUN!/Published by the/Sanitarium/Health Food Company
Sydney, n.d.
[12]pp, part col. illus. throughout, col. pic. wrappers, cover title (adv. on back wrapper), 196x242mm. WRT
Spaces for 50 cards to be pasted in.

FATCHEN, Max

2429 THE RIVER KINGS/by Max Fatchen/illustrated by Clyde Pearson/[drawing]/Hicks Smith & Sons Pty. Ltd./Sydney Melbourne Brisbane/in association with/ Methuen & Co. Ltd., London
1966
144pp, (inc. 1p author's note), extended b/w frontis, b/w drawings in text, clo., 180x120mm. KMM

2430 THE RIVER KINGS/by Max Fatchen/illustrated by Clyde Pearson/Methuen & Co. Ltd./11 New Fetter Lane London E.C.4/Hicks Smith & Sons Pty. Ltd./ Sydney Melbourne Brisbane.
• Rpt 1970
144pp (inc. 1p author's note), b/w frontis., & b/w drawings throughout, clo., 195x130mm. KMM
American edition

2431 St Martin's Press, 175 Fifth Avenue, New York 1968
Details as in English edition, but 215x140mm. IFA
Swedish edition

2432 B. Wahlstroms Bokforlag, Stockholm 1968
158pp, clo., 210x125mm. IFA
Danish edition

2433 Gyldendal, Copenhagen 1970
124pp, 210x125mm. IFA
Polish edition

2434 Instytut Wydawniczy, Warsaw 1971
153pp, b/w drawings throughout, illus. by Andrezez Gordon, limp clo., 200x125mm. Unseen: IFA

2435 Max Fatchen/CONQUEST OF THE RIVER/ illustrated by Clyde Pearson/Methuen & Co. Ltd./11 New Fetter Lane, London, E.C.4/Hicks Smith & Sons Pty. Ltd./Sydney Melbourne Brisbane
1970
159pp (inc. 1p author's note), b/w frontis. & 5 f/p b/w illus., b/w drawings in text, clo., 200x130mm. KMM
Sequel to *The River Kings*.

DRIVERS AND TRAINS
KEEPERS AND LIGHTHOUSES
THE PLUMBER
THE ELECTRICIAN
THE TRANSPORT DRIVER
THE CARPENTER *See* Australian People

Father and Son Welfare Movement
See Family Life Movement of Australia

Father Time's Life Story

2436 FATHER TIME'S/LIFE STORY/[vignette]/A History of Time-Keepers/Prepared for 3LO/(with acknowledgements to Elgin Watch Co.)/by courtesy of/Dunklings/Diamond and watch experts/294–296 Collins Street, 313–317 Bourke Street/Melbourne
1927
28pp, 3pp notes, 13 f/p b/w illus. (by G. C Benson), wrappers, 186x220mm. KP
'The purpose of this booklet is to serve as a reminder of the series of lectures on the History of Timekeeping broadcasted [*sic*] by 3LO.' 3LO was a commercial radio station in Melbourne.

Father Time's Xmas Annual

2437 FATHER TIME'S/XMAS ANNUAL/Containing Australian/Stories and Verse /Illustrated by John/ Wiseman /December 1st, 1930/Australia/W. H. Honey Publishing Co./62 Margaret St., Sydney, N.S.W.

61pp, col. frontis. & 8 f/p litho. plates, b/w drawings throughout, pic. wrappers, cover design by R. H. Steuart, 280x215mm. ANL
Stories & verse by Ruth Bedford, Elsie Cole, June Turner, Elizabeth Powell

FAVENC, Ernest

2438 THE SECRET/OF THE/AUSTRALIAN DESERT/ By/Ernest Favenc/Author of "The History of Australian Exploration", "Tales of the Austral/ Tropics", &c. &c./With four illustrations by Percy F. S. Spence/and a Map/[device]/London/Blackie & Son, Limited, 50 Old Bailey, E.C./Glasgow and Dublin/ 1896
223pp (inc. 3pp preface)32pp advs., b/w frontis. & 3 f/p b/w illus. & double-spread tinted map, pic. clo., 177 x 116 mm. HBM
In the preface the author explains how the book is based on the disappearance of the explorer Ludwig Leichhardt.

2439 Another copy as above (n.d.)
Details as before but printed on heavier paper, making book nearly 20mm thicker. RM

2440 THE SECRET OF THE/AUSTRALIAN DESERT/ by/Ernest Favenc/Author of "The History of Australian Exploration", "Tales of the Austral/ Tropics", &c. &c./With Four Illustrations and a Map./ New Edition/Blackie and Son Limited/London Glasgow Dublin Bombay/1910
223pp (inc. 3pp preface), 16pp adv., col. frontis. & 3 b/w plates & double-spread map. pic. clo., 177x117mm. RM
The coloured frontis., signed R. James Williams, replaces a Spence plate. An illus. of two explorers pointing to the distance is blocked in green & yellow on front cover

2441 THE SECRET/OF THE/AUSTRALIAN DESERT/ By/Ernest Favenc/Author of "Marooned on Australia" &c./[device]/Blackie & Son Limited/London and Glasgow
n.d. [1917]
223pp (inc.double spread b/w map) 2pp adv., col. frontis. [by R. James Williams ?] 1 b/w map. clo., 170x110mm. CLRC
Blackie's Library for Boys and Girls (with entirely new dec. bdg design)
Many undated rpts with varying bindings & slightly different imprints have been seen.
Swedish edition

2442 ÖDEMARKENS HEMLIGHET. Äventyr under en upptäektsfärd i Australien
Stockholm 1918
188pp, printed bd., translated by Richard Melander.
Unseen: Catalogue No. 5, 1975, Dahlia Books, Uppsala, Sweden

2443 MAROONED ON AUSTRALIA/Being the Narration by Diedrich Buys of/his discoveries and exploits in Terra/Australis Incognita about the year 1630/By/Ernest Favenc/Author of "The History of Australian Exploration", "Tales of the Austral/ Tropics", "The Secret of the Australian Desert", &c./with four illustrations by Percy F. S. Spence/and a map/[device]/London/Blackie & Son, Limited, 50 Old Bailey, E.C./Glasgow and Dublin
n.d. [1896]
224pp (inc. 2pp author's preface & 6pp appendix), 32pp adv., b/w frontis. & 3 b/w illus. & a map (facing first text page), pic. clo.,175x115mm. HBM

2444 MAROONED ON AUSTRALIA/Being the Narration by Diedrich Buys of/his discoveries and exploits in Terra/Australis Incognita about the year 1630/By/Ernest Favenc/Author of/"Tales of the Austral Tropics" "The Secret of the Australian Desert"/"The History of Australian Exploration", &c./With four full-page illustrations by and a map/ New Edition/Blackie and Son Limited/London Glasgow and Dublin/1905
224pp (inc. 2pp author's preface & 6pp appendix), 16pp adv., b/w frontis. & 3 f/p b/w illus. & a map, illus. by Percy F. Spence, pic. clo. (with title in gilt) 180x115mm. ANL
• Rpt n.d., as above. KP
Several copies as above but imprint 'London Glasgow Bombay' with varying number of adv. pages & col. of clo. bdg. KP

2445 Copy as above but illus. printed in sepia. KP

2446 Rpt as above to 'the year 1630', then, 'By/Ernest Favenc/Author of "The Secret of the Australian Desert" &c./Blackie & Son Limited/London and Glasgow.'
n.d. [prize 1924]
224pp, b/w frontis., map, 2 b/w plates, pic. clo., 180x120mm. KP

2447 MAROONED ON AUSTRALIA
The same but variant imprint
/Blackie and Son Limited/London Glasgow and Bombay
n.d.[1933?]
224pp (inc. 2pp preface, 6pp appendix), b/w frontis. & 3 f/p b/w illus. (only 3 illus. listed on contents page), map, pic. clo., 180x120mm. RM
Swedish edition

2448 I KUNG ZOLCAS LAND. Två skeppsbrutnas äventyr.
Stockholm 1926
160pp, printed bd., translated by Styrbjörn Melander.
Unseen: Catalogue No. 5, 1975, Dahlia Books, Uppsala, Sweden

FAVENC, Ernest & Others

2449 TALES FOR YOUNG/AUSTRALIA/By/Ernest Favenc/"Mab"/and/James and Josephine Fotheringhame/Sydney/Empson & Son, Limited/ Newbery House, 49 York St./Printed in Bavaria
n.d. [1900?]
80pp, b/w frontis. & 1 f/p & other b/w illus. by Percy F. S. Spence, D. H. Souter & others, (copy seen re-bound), 220x170mm. NSL:M

FAVENC, Ernest & SPENCE, Percy F. S.

2450 THE STORY OF OUR/CONTINENT/[vignette]/ Told with Brush and Pen/Edited/by/Ernest Favenc/ Illustrated/by/Percy F. S. Spence/Printed for the Proprietor by W. M. Maclardy, 319 George Street, Sydney,/238 Little Collins Street, Melbourne; 17 Furnival Street, Holborn, London
n.d.
12pp, 1p preface, b/w frontis. & 1 large & several small b/w drawings, dec. wrappers, cover title, 320 x 240 mm. NSL:M
Proposed to be issued in fortnightly numbers. Each set of 21 numbers was designed to form a complete volume, containing 42 original pictures, besides numerous vignettes, & 230 pages of letterpress. Apparently only the first number appeared (*see* Ferguson, Vol. V, 9563a).

Favourite Fairy Tales set to Rhyme

2451 FAVOURITE/FAIRY TALES/SET TO RHYME/[3 illus.]
A "Little Treasure" Book, John Morrissey, Melbourne, n.d. [195-?]

12pp, col. & b/w illus. on alternate page openings, pic. wrappers, cover title, 240x180mm. KP
Illus. John Morrissey.

FEATHERED FRIENDS
See Cayley, Neville W.

FEHLBERG, Tasman
THE AUSTRALIAN BROADCASTING COMMISSION/A NATIONAL SERVICE. *See* Australian Landmarks

FELDMANN, Jules
2452 THE GREAT/JUBILEE BOOK/The Story of the Australian Nation in Pictures/Written by Jules Feldmann/A Colorgravure Publication
Melbourne, n.d. [1951]
240pp (inc. 1p index to col. supplement & inc. 8pp col. illus., b/w illus. throughout, clo., col. e/p, 237x175mm. KP

Felix the Cat
See Sullivan, Pat

FENN, George Manville
2453 BUNYIP LAND:/The Story of a Wild Journey in/New Guinea/By/G. Manville Fenn,/Author of "The Golden Magnet" "In the King's Name" "Nat the/Naturalist" &c./With twelve full page illustrations/London:/Blackie & Son, 49 & 50 Old Bailey, E.C.;/Glasgow, Edinburgh, and Dublin/1885
384pp, 32pp adv., b/w frontis. & 11 f/p b/w illus. by Gordon Browne, pic. clo., 185x130mm. ANL
• Rpt as above, but n.d. NSL:M

2454 BUNYIP LAND./or/Among the Blackfellows in New Guinea/By/G. Manville Fenn,/Author of "The Golden Magnet", "In the King's Name", "Nat the Naturalist",/"Mother Carey's Chickens", "Devon Boys", &c./With six page illustrations by Gordon Browne./New Edition/[device]/London:/Blackie & Son Limited, 49 Old Bailey, E.C./Glasgow, Edinburgh, and Dublin
n.d. [inscribed 1893]
384pp, 32pp adv., b/w frontis. & 5 f/p b/w illus., pic. clo., 185x120mm. KMM

2455 BUNYIP LAND/or/Among the Blackfellows in New Guinea
As previous copy, but
Illustrated by Gordon Browne/New Edition/Blackie and Son Limited/London Glasgow Dublin Bombay/1907
Details as before but 16pp adv. KMM

2456 BUNYIP LAND/Or/Among the Blackfellows in New Guinea/By/G. Manville Fenn/Author of "The Golden Magnet", "In the King's Name"/"Nat the Naturalist"/"Devon Boys" &c./Illustrated by Gordon Browne, R.I./Blackie and Son Limited/London Glasgow Bombay
n.d. [inscribed Xmas 1923]
384pp, b/w frontis. & 5 f/p b/w illus., pic. clo., 185x125mm. RM

2457 BUNYIP LAND/A Story of Adventure in New Guinea/By/G. Manville Fenn/Author of "The Golden Magnet" "In the King's Name"/"Nat the Naturalist" "Devon Boys" &c./Illustrated by Gordon Browne, R.I./Blackie & Son Limited/London and Glasgow
n.d. [192-?]
384pp, b/w frontis. & 3 f/p b/w illus., clo., 190x125mm. KMM

2458 THE DINGO BOYS/or/The Squatters of Wallaby Range/By/George Manville Fenn/Author of/"In the King's Name", "Patience Wins", "Dick of the Fens", "Nat the/Naturalist, "The Golden Magnet", "Rajah of Dah", etc./With six illustrations by W. S. Stacey/W. & R. Chambers, Limited/London and Edinburgh/1892
312pp, 36pp adv., 6 b/w illus., clo., 180x120mm. KMM

2459 THE DINGO BOYS/or/The Squatters of Wallaby Range/By/George Manville Fenn/Author of/"In the King's Name", "Patience Wins", "Dick o'the Fens", "Nat the/Naturalist", "The Golden Magnet", "Rajah of Dah", etc./With six illustrations by W. S. Stacey/W. & R. Chambers, Limited/London and Edinburgh
n.d. [school prize 1898]
312pp, 32pp adv., b/w frontis. & 5 f/p b/w illus., pic. clo., 185x130mm. RM

2460 THE DINGO BOYS/or/The Squatters of Wallaby Range/By/George Manville Fenn/Author of 'The Rajah of Dah;' etc/Illustrated by W. S. Stacey/London: 38 Soho Square, W./W. & R Chambers, Limited/Edinburgh: 339 High Street
1921
312pp, 3 f/p b/w plates, pic. clo., 185x128mm. WRT

2461 THE DINGO BOYS/or/The Squatters of Wallaby Range/By/George Manville Fenn/Author of "The Rajah of Dah", "Real Gold", &c./Illustrated/London: 38 Soho Square, W.1./W. & R. Chambers, Limited/Edinburgh: 339 High Street
On verso of t.p.: 'Original ed. 1892/Latest reprint 1929'
312pp, 4pp adv., b/w frontis. & 3 f/p b/w illus., clo., 185x125mm. KP

2462 FIRST IN THE FIELD/A Story of New South Wales/By/Geo. Manville Fenn/Author of "Steve Young", "The Grand Chaco",/"The Crystal Hunters", "Nolens Volens",/"Dick o' the Fens", etc. etc./Illustrated by W. Rainey, R.I./London/S. W. Partridge and Co./8 and 9, Paternoster Row
n.d. [presumably first edition, inscribed 1894]
416pp, 16pp adv., b/w frontis & 7 f/p b/w illus., dec. clo., 190x135mm. ANL

2463 Second ed. as above, with 'Second Edition' on t.p. KP

2464 FIRST IN THE FIELD/A Story of New South Wales/By/Geo. Manville Fenn/Author of "Cormorant Crag", "Steve Young", "Rob Harlow's Adventures",/"The Crystal Hunters", "Nolens Volens",/etc. etc./New edition/London/S. W. Partridge & Co., Ltd./Old Bailey
n.d. [1900?]
416pp, [no adv.], b/w frontis. & 9 b/w plates by W. Rainey, pic. clo., 185x120mm. KMM

2465 FIRST IN THE FIELD/A Story of New South Wales/By/Geo. Manville Fenn/Author of 'Cormorant Crag', 'Steve Young', 'The Grand Chaco',/'The Crystal Hunters', 'Nolens Volens'/etc. etc./Illustrated by W. Rainey, R.I./Third Edition/London/S. W. Partridge and Co./8 and 9, Paternoster Row
n.d. [school prize 1901]
416pp, 16pp adv., b/w frontis. & 9 b/w plates, pic. clo., 185x125mm. CLRC

2466 FIRST IN THE FIELD
Fourth edition, n.d. [inscribed Xmas 1907]
Details as in third edition, but with 32pp adv. RM

2467 FIRST IN THE FIELD/A Story of New South Wales/By/George Manville Fenn/Author of/"Cormorant Crag", "Rob Harlow's Adventures"/"The Crystal Hunters", "In the Mahdi's Grasp"/Dean & Son Ltd./6 La Belle Sauvage, Ludgate Hill/London E.C.4.
n.d. [192-?]
248pp, col. frontis. by Pryor Clarke, clo., 195x130mm. KMM

2468 FIRST IN THE FIELD/A Story of New South Wales/By/Geo. Manville Fenn/Author of "Steve Young", "The Grand Chaco", "The Crystal/Hunters",

"Dick o' the Fens," etc. etc./Illustrated by W. Rainey, R.I./New York/Dodd, Mead & Company/Publishers
1st US ed., Dodd Mead—The Mershon Company Press, Rahway N.J., 1894
417pp, b/w frontis/& 9 b/w illus., dec. clo., 197x132mm. KMM

2469 KING O'/THE BEACH/A Tropic Tale/By/G. Manville Fenn,/Author of "Young Robin Hood", "The Little Skipper",/"Our Soldier Boy",/etc. etc./London: New York/Ernest Nister—E. P. Dutton & Co./Printed in Bavaria/512
n.d. [school prize 1903]
320pp, 8pp adv., col. frontis., 8 f/p b/w & numerous smaller illus. in text (by J. B. Greene), dec. clo., 185x120mm. KMM
Pearl fishing adventures in Torres Strait.
See also South West Pacific section for other entries by this author

FENNER, Ruth
2470 THE STORY HOUSE/[drawing]/by Ruth Fenner/ pictures by/Elizabeth Macintyre/Angus and Robertson Sydney 1960
32pp, dec. t.p., col. lithographic illus. throughout, dec. bd., dec. e/p, 210x275mm. KMM
Contains 4 stories for young children, including one in verse.

'FENNIMORE, Stephen'
See Collins, Cuthbert Dale

FEREDAY, Mrs R. W.
2471 THE/FAIRIES OF ARBOTH/Scene:/A Forest Clearing/in Samatnia/Written and arranged by/Mrs R. W. Fereday/Smallhorn & Sons, Print.
69 Liverpool Street [Hobart, Tasmania], n.d. [1915?]
7pp (inc. 1p verse), unillus., wrappers, 165x100mm. NSL:M

FERGUS, R. M.
2472 LITTLE AUSTRALIAN/PIONEERS/By/R. M. Fergus, M.A./Hutchinson & Co. (Publishers) Ltd./ Paternoster Row, London, E.C.
n.d. [1928]
256pp, part. col. frontis. & 5 b/w illus., clo., 180x115mm. VSL
• Rpt as above, n.d., b/w illus only. KP

FERGUSON, Henry
2473 SOUTH FOR/ADVENTURE/by/Henry Ferguson/ [publisher's device]/Cassell & Company Ltd./London, Toronto, Melbourne & Sydney
1947
255pp, 4 f/p b/w illus. by Bruce Crampton, clo., 180x115mm. ANL

'FERRES, Arthur' [pseud. John William Kevin]
2474 MY CENTENNIAL GIFT,/or,/Australian Stories/ for Children/by/Arthur Ferres/[drawing]/Sydney/ Turner & Henderson/1887
254pp (inc. 2pp preface), b/w frontis. & 2 b/w illus. by Luc Davis, clo., 185x120mm. NSL:M
Reprinted from the *Sydney Mail*, where they were published as 'Bush Stories for Children'.

2475 HIS COUSIN THE WALLABY/and/Three Other Australian Stories/By/Arthur Ferres/Author of "My Centennial Gift" "His First Kangaroo",/"Bush Stories for Children" etc. etc./George Robertson and Co./ Melbourne, Sydney, Adelaide, Brisbane/and London/ 1896
183pp, b/w frontis. & 3 b/w illus. (signed 'E.F.'), dec. clo., 180x120mm. KMM

2476 HIS FIRST KANGAROO/An Australian Story for Boys/By/Arthur Ferres/Author of "My Centennial Gift" "Bush Stories for Children"/With six full-page illustrations by Percy F. S. Spence/[publisher's device]/ London/Blackie & Son, Limited, 50 Old Bailey, E.C./Glasgow and Dublin/1896
288pp, 32pp adv., b/w frontis & 6 f/p b/w illus., pic. clo., 185x120mm. VSL
2477 HIS FIRST KANGAROO/An Australian Story for Boys/By/Arthur Ferres/Illustrations by Percy F. S. Spence/Blackie & Son Limited/London Glasgow Dublin Bombay
n.d.
288pp, 16pp adv., col. frontis. & 3 b/w illus., pic. clo., 180x115mm. KMM
• Rpt as above, but with 16pp adv., prize 1910. KP

2478 THE PLOUGHBOY PREMIER/A Story for Boys/ By/Arthur Ferres/Author of "My Centennial Gift" "His First Kangaroo"/"His Cousin the Wallaby" etc. etc./[two quotations]/Printed by/Websdale, Shoosmith & Co./Sydney
n.d. [1916]
131pp (inc. 1p preface & 1p dedication), unillus., clo., 185x120mm. ANL

FERRIS, Isabel
2479 ANIMAL AND INSECT/VERSES/by Isabel Ferris/ Illustrations/by/R. E. A. Hawson/1958/Arthur H. Stockwell/Elms Court, Ilfracombe/Devon
59pp, b/w drawings, clo., 185x120mm. TSL
Children's verses.

FEW, Frank & Betty
2480 Alcheringa Series/THE BOOMERANG-MAKER/ Frank and Betty Few/Photography by Frank Few/ [device]/Rigby Limited/Adelaide
1963
43pp, b/w photographic illus. on alternate pages, pic. clo., 240 x 180 mm. KMM
Picture book with slight text based on a television film of the Alcheringa Series, with photographs on back cover of Bill Onus, narrator of the series, throwing a boomerang. KMM
2481 Rpt as above, but
Angus and Robertson London/Rigby Limited Adelaide
Copyright 1963; first publ. 1964
Details as before but plain clo. cover with title & authors' names in gilt. KP

2482 THE STONE-AXE MAKER/Frank and Betty Few/ [device]/Rigby Limited
Adelaide 1966
48pp, b/w photographic illus. on alternate pages, pic. clo., 240x180mm. KMM
Picture book with short text opposite each photograph.

2483 THE FIREMAKER/Frank and Betty Few/Rigby
Rigby Ltd, Adelaide 1969
[47]pp, b/w photographic illus. on alternate pages, pic. clo., 240 x 175 mm. CLRC
Alcheringa Series.
Picture book about Aboriginal firemaking customs.

FIELD, Mrs A.
2484 SATISFYING/STORIES/By Mrs A. Field/True Tales from real life told/for "children under ninety-/nine"/S.A. Press, 508 Albert Street, East Melbourne, Vic
n.d. [192-?]
96pp (inc. 1p foreword by Jas. A. Hawkins, Lt. Col. &

Editor in Chief of Salvation Army Publications in Australia), some line drawings, wrappers, 178x110mm. KP
Collection of contributions by the author to *The War Cry*; dedicated to the children of Australia.

FIELDING, Biron
2485 ADVENTURES/ON/PARROT ISLAND/by Biron Fielding/Illustrated by Rosemary Fielding/[drawing]/ Ward, Lock & Co. Limited/London and Melbourne
1964
95pp, 5 f/p b/w illus., 3 double-spread b/w illus. & drawings in text, extended t.p., clo. (with drawing in gilt of kangaroo on front cover), 230x160mm. KMM

FIELDING, [Rev.] Sydney Glenville
2486 THE/SOUTHERN LIGHT/By/S. G. Fielding/ Illustrated by Warwick Goble/London/Ward Lock & Bowden, Limited,/Warwick House, Salisbury Square, E.C./New York and Melbourne/1895/(All rights reserved)
369pp, 6pp adv., 3 f/p b/w illus., clo., 180x115mm. KMM

2487 "DOWN TO THE SEA/IN SHIPS"/By/S. G. Fielding/Author of "The 'Southern Light' "/Sydney/ William Brooks & Co., 17 Castlereagh Street
1900
293pp, 10pp adv., b/w frontis. & 4 b/w illus. by D. H. Souter, dec. bd. (clo. spine), 185x120mm. VSL
Boys' sea story.

50 Zoo Animals and Birds to Trace and Colour
2488 50 ZOO ANIMALS/AND BIRDS/TO TRACE/ AND COLOUR
n.d., no imprint, no text
8pp, b/w illus. of zoo animals to col., col. pic. wrappers, 284x210mm. KP
Kangaroo, kookaburra, cockatoo, magpie, pelican, platypus, possum, native bear, wombat, native cat, are included.

FIGUEROLA, Carmen
2489 FAMILY/ON/PHILLIP ISLAND/by/Carmem [*sic*] Figuerola/Whitcombe & Tombs Pty. Ltd./Melbourne, Sydney, Perth, Geelong
1955
128pp, b/w frontis. & 4 b/w illus. (signed Mahood), wrappers, 180x115mm. ANL
Author's name spelt 'Carmen' on front cover.

FIKER, Eduard
2490 TRI V PISKU (Three in the Sand)
Volesky, Prague 1937. SLCSR

FILLEUL, Marianne
2491 ELLEN TREMAINE/By/Marianne Filleul/with coloured illustrations./London/The Religious Tract Society/4 Bouverie Street and 65 St Paul's Churchyard EC
n.d. [presentation copy with inscription dated 1910]
254pp, 4pp adv., col. frontis. & 1 f/p col. illus., clo. with medallion pasted on front cover, 190x125mm. KP
'Every Girl's Bookshelf'. Story of a young Cornish woman who with her small son migrates to Tasmania when her fisherman husband is supposedly lost at sea. The latter half of the book is set in Tasmania where eventually the family is reunited to become happy settlers.

2492 ELLEN TREMAINE/By/Marianne Filleul/Fourth Impression/R. T.S., 4, Bouverie Street, London, E.C.4
n.d. [presented 1922]
Details as above. JMcG

Also author of *The Squatter's Home* which is not Australian.

FINCH, Robert J.
2493 The Kingsway Book of/FAMOUS/EXPLORERS/By Robert J. Finch, F.R.G.S./[device]/New Edition with illustrations/Evans Brothers Limited/Montague House, Russell Square, London, W.C.1.
First pub. Jan. 1919; 2nd. ed. Dec. 1919; 3rd ed. Feb. 1923
179pp (inc. 3pp introduction), 1p adv., 13pp b/w illus. by C. C. Titterton, 10 maps, clo., 180x120mm. KMM
Includes 2 chapters on Cook (18pp).

2494 WONDER TALES/OF/GREAT EXPLORERS/By/ Robert Finch/Author of/"Wonder Tales of Past History", etc/Illustrated by Savile Lumley/The Shore Lane Publishing Co./6 Farringdon Avenue, London, E.C.4
n.d. [inscribed 1938]
126pp, col. frontis., b/w text drawings, col. pic. bd., 250x185mm. KP

2495 The London Books of/Discovery and Exploration/ By/Robert Finch/HEROES/OF/DISCOVERY/ [drawing]/First series Book one/University of London Press Ltd./10 & 11 Warwick Lane, London, E.C.4
First printed September 1940
96pp (inc. 1p preface), b/w frontis. & b/w drawings & maps, pic. wrappers, 195x130mm. HBM
Contains chapters on Magellan, Tasman & Cook.
Wrote numerous school histories, including:
The World Discovered (Uni. London Press, 1948)—Explorers of Interior Australia pp9-27. KP
Pioneers of Discovery (Uni. London Press, 4th imp. 1959)—includes 1 chapter Tasman & Dampier pp81-96 & 1 chapter on Cook. KP

FINCH, Tamara & CAMERON, Hector
2496 Tamara Finch and Hector Cameron/THE LITTLE KING/The Book of Twenty/Nights and One Night/ [device]/Angus and Robertson/London Sydney Melbourne Wellington
1958
159pp (inc. 2pp introduction), col. frontis. & 6 f/p b/w illus. (signed 'Constable'), clo., 200x130mm. KMM
A collection of 6 fairy stories.

FINGER, Charles J.
2497 A DOG AT HIS HEEL/The Story of Jock, an Australian sheep dog,/and what befell him and his companions on a/Great Drive/[drawing]/by/Charles J. Finger/Author of Tales from Silver Lands, Courageous Companions, Seven/Horizons/and other books for boys, and men with boys' hearts./Illustrated by/Henry C. Pitz
The John C. Winston Company, Chicago Philadelphia Toronto 1936
301pp, 2pp glossary, col. frontis. & 3 col. illus., 9 f/p b/w illus. & line drawings in text, clo., dec. e/p, 210x140 mm. ANL

2498 Rpt as above, but
Illustrated by/Henry C. Pitz/[device]/George G. Harrap & Co. Ltd./London Bombay Sydney
First publ. 1937 (printed in England)
285pp (inc. 3pp glossary), part col. frontis., b/w & part col. illus. throughout, clo. pic. e/p, 215x135mm. KMM

FINKEL, George
2499 THE MYSTERY OF/SECRET BEACH/by/George Finkel/Angus and Robertson
Sydney 1962
153pp, unillus., clo., 220x135mm. KMM

2500 THE MYSTERY OF/SECRET BEACH/by/George Finkel/Angus and Robertson
Sydney, first supplementary school reader edition 1963
153pp, unillus., limp clo., 195x130mm. Unseen: IFA

2501 SHIP IN HIDING/by/George Finkel/[device]/Angus and Robertson
Sydney 1963
166pp, 3pp prologue, 1 f/p map, otherwise unillus., clo., 215 x 135 mm. CLRC
Adventure story not intended specifically for children.

2502 CLOUDMAKER/by/George Finkel/[device]/Angus and Robertson
Sydney 1965
163pp, unillus., clo., 215 x 135 mm. KMM
Adventure story about spies & an unidentified flying object seen in the Australian alps.

2503 CLOUDMAKER/by/George Finkel/[device]/Angus and Robertson
First school edition, Sydney 1969
163pp, unillus., dec. wrappers, 195x125mm. KMM

2504 THE/SINGING SANDS/by/George Finkel/[device]/Angus and Robertson
Sydney 1966
176pp, unillus., clo., 215x140mm. CLRC

2505 [drawing]/THE LONG PILGRIMAGE/George Finkel/Illustrated by George Tetlow/Angus and Robertson
Sydney 1967
258pp (inc. 2pp note & 3pp glossary), 2pp verse, b/w drawings & maps, clo., 215x135mm. CLRC
Historical novel about a Northumberland outlaw who fights under Charlemagne, & travels widely in Mediterranean countries.

2506 THE LONG PILGRIMAGE/by George Finkel/The Viking Press New York
1969
319pp, 4 b/w maps by the author, clo., d/w by Robin Jacques, 210x140mm. Unseen: IFA

2507 THE 'LOYALL VIRGINIAN'[*sic*]/George Finkel/Angus and Robertson/[drawing]
Sydney 1968
189pp, 3 b/w maps by the author, clo., 215x135mm. KMM
Story of a vessel trading between Virginia & England in 1648, & the effect of the English Civil War on the Virginian colonists.

2508 THE LOYAL VIRGINIAN/George Finkel/The Viking Press New York
1969
282pp, 2 b/w maps by author, clo., d/w by Robin Jacques, 210x140mm. Unseen: IFA

2509 TWILIGHT/PROVINCE/George Finkel/Illustrated by George Tetlow/Angus and Robertson
Sydney 1967
224pp (inc. 1p glossary), extended b/w frontis., 3 b/w maps, chapter headings & drawings, clo., 215x140mm. CLRC
American edition

2510 WATCH FIRES/TO THE NORTH/By George Finkel/The Viking Press New York
1967
311pp, 3 b/w maps by the author, otherwise unillus., clo., d/w by Richard M. Powers, 210 x 140 mm. Unseen: IFA

2511 George Finkel/JOURNEY/TO/JORSALA/Angus and Robertson
London 1969
231pp, 5 b/w maps by the author, clo., 215x135mm. KMM

JAMES COOK. *See* Australia Past and Present

2512 JAMES COOK,/ROYAL NAVY/George Finkel/Decorations by Amnon Sadubin/[drawing]/Angus and Robertson
Sydney 1970
191pp (inc. 2pp Historical Note), 3 f/p b/w maps, b/w decorations in text, clo., 215x135mm. KMM
• Rpt 1971. KP

2513 THE PEACE SEEKERS/George Finkel/Angus and Robertson
Sydney 1970
186pp (inc. 1p Historical Note), 3 f/p b/w maps, clo., d/w by C.R. Evans, 215x135mm. KMM
Story of a Welsh prince & his followers who, when driven out of Wales in the 12th century, eventually sail to North America where they make a treaty with an Indian tribe & settle with them.

2514 WILLIAM LIGHT/[decoration]/George Finkel/Angus and Robertson
Sydney 1972
171pp, 1p bibliography, unillus., clo., 215 x 135 mm. KMM
D/w reproduces a portrait of Light by G. Jones from the National Portrait Gallery, London.

2515 JAMES COOK [pic. cover title]
Decorative contents page:
Contents/[9 headings]/JAMES COOK/by/Commander George Finkel R.N. (Ret'd)/Art Direction by Elaine Rushbrooke/Technical Director—Cyril H. Fisher/Registered at the GPO Melbourne for transmission by post as a book
The Age, Melbourne, in conjunction with Shoalhaven Paper Mill, n.d. [1970]
32pp, pic. wrappers, col. & b/w illus., 295x205mm. VMOU
Commemorative booklet not specifically intended for children.

FINN, F. E. S. (ed.)

2516 MODERN ADVENTURE/Edited by/F. E. S. Finn/[drawing]/John Murray/Fifty Albemarle Street London
First pub. Oct. 1958; rpt Nov. 1959
154pp, 8pp b/w photographic illus., dec. clo., 185x120mm. KMM
The Albemarle Library [books intended for schools].
Contents include extract from *Cullenbenbong* by Bernard O'Reilly (14pp).

FINN, Mary Agnes

2517 MONICA'S TRIAL/A Story for Girls/By/Mary Agnes Finn/Registered by the Postmaster-General/for transmission through the post as/a book printed in Australia/Wholly set up and printed in Australia by/Pellegrini & Co./Sydney Melbourne Brisbane/1929
182pp, unillus., clo., 185x120mm. ANL
Religious story for girls.
Another copy, n.d. TG

2518 MONICA'S VICTORY/A Story for Girls/By/Mary Agnes Finn/[device]/Pellegrini & Co./Pty. Ltd./Sydney Melbourne Brisbane/Adelaide Perth
1944
188pp, unillus., bd., 186x120mm. ANL
Also the author of *A Broken Rosary and Other Stories* (Finn Bros., Sydney 1900) & *Nora's Mission*. These have not been seen & it is not known whether or not they are children's books.

FINNEMORE, John

2519 THE/EMPIRE'S CHILDREN/By/John Finnemore/Author of/'Boys and Girls of other Days'/'Famous Englishmen'/'Men of Renown'/&c./47 Paternoster Row. Lond, E.C./W. & R. Chambers, Limited/339 High Street, Edinburgh/1906
288pp & 48pp adv., b/w frontis. & b/w photographic illus. in text, pic. clo. with background of setting sun in gilt, 179x120mm. ANL
'The Young Australian' pp235–288.

2520 THE LONE PATROL/by/John Finnemore/Author of "Teddy Lester's Chums", "His First Term", "Three School Chums"/"Foray and Fight" etc./With six coloured illustrations/by/W. Rainey/London: 38 Soho Square, W./W. & R. Chambers, Limited/Edinburgh: 339 High Street/1910
316pp, col. frontis. & 5 col. f/p illus., dec. clo., 185x130mm. Grant
A North Queensland story.
• Rpt as above, but n.d. RM
• Rpt 1930, as above. KP

Norwegian editions

2521 John Finnemore/SPIEDERGUTTER/I AUSTRALIA/oversat av Aagot Holst/[device]/Kristiania/N. W. Damm & Søns Forlag
n.d. [inscribed 1919]
133pp, unillus., pic. bd., 183x120mm. ANL

2522 John Finnemore/SPIEDERGUTTER/I AUSTRALIA/oversat av Aagot Holst/Annet Oplag/[device]/Forlagt ov N. W. Damm & Son/Oslo
1925
136pp, unillus., pic. bd., 183x120mm. ANL

2523 THE/BUSHRANGERS OF/BLACK GAP/by John Finnemore/With Eight Full-page Illustrations by/P.W. Caton Woodville/A. & C. Black, Ltd./4, 5 & 6 Soho Square, London, W.1/1920
280pp, b/w frontis. & 7 f/p b/w illus., pic. clo., 195x130mm. KMM
Contains 7 stories of which the first only has an Australian setting. This is the same story as *The Bandits of Black Gap.*

2524 THE/BUSHRANGERS/OF BLACK GAP/By/John Finnemore/Author of "The Wolf Patrol"/"The Red Men of the Dusk"/Etc., Etc./[device]/A. & C. Black Ltd./4, 5 and 6 Soho Square/London W. 1/1928
280pp, 1p adv. (preceding t.p.), col. frontis. only, dec. clo., 185x120 mm. RM

2525 THE BANDITS/ OF BLACK GAP/By/ John Finnemore/ Whitcombe & Tombs Limited /Auckland; Wellington; Christchurch; Dunedin/ Invercargill; London;Melbourne; Sydney.
n.d.[1942]
64pp,b/w frontis., semi-stiff pic. wrappers, 185x120mm. CLRC

2526 Whitcombe's Story Book./THE BANDITS/OF BLACK GAP/by/John Finnemore/Whitcombe & Tombs Limited/Christchurch, Auckland, Wellington, Dunedin, Invercargill, N.Z./London, Melbourne and Sydney
n.d.
56pp, b/w frontis., wrappers, 180x120mm. Grant
See McLaren 566

2527 THE YELLOW/PIRATES/and/other Stories/By/John Finnemore/Author of "The Wolf Patrol"/"The Red Men of the Dusk" etc/A & C Black Ltd./4, 5 and 6 Soho Square/London, W.1/1929
First publ. 1922
248pp, t.p. surrounded by dec. border, col. frontis. (sgd J. M. Hart), clo., 185x120mm. WRT

2528 RIFLE AND/BOOMERANG/by/John Finnemore/Whitcombe & Tombs Limited/Auckland Wellington Christchurch Dunedin/Invercargill London Melbourne Sydney
n.d. [1942]
64pp, b/w frontis., stiff pic. wrappers, 185x115mm. CLRC
Taken from the author's *The Yellow Pirates.*
See McLaren 563

FINNIN, Mary

2529 THE/BOOK OF BAUBLE/By Mary Finnin/Printed and Published by/W. A. Hamer Pty. Ltd./Printers and Publishers 205–217 Peel St. N. Melbourne
n.d. [1945]
61pp, col. illus. throughout, dec. bd., 230x165mm. VSL
Another copy with 2 blank leaves bound in, front & back. KP

Fire! Fire!
See Pearson, Margaret Mary

'FIRENZE'
See Hayward, F.

First Aid Primer

2530 Australian Junior Red Cross/FIRST AID PRIMER/1957 Edition/[device]
Printed by Truth & Sportsman Ltd, Melbourne, n.d.
96pp, part col. illus., pic. wrappers, 177x117mm. KP

The First Australian Governors
See Great Australians series

FISHER, G. A.

2531 FAMOUS/AUSTRALIANS/Presented to you by the Commonwealth Savings Bank
Sydney, n.d. [195-?]
24pp (inc. foreword), illus., wrappers, cover title, 245x185 mm. KMM
Biographies of the following twelve men, each illus. with a b/w portrait: Sir Douglas Mawson, Lawrence Hargrave, Sir Mark Oliphant, William Farrer, King O'Malley, Harold Blair, Sir Charles Kingsford Smith, Sir John Monash, Sir Howard Florey, Rev. Dr John Flynn, Sir Donald Bradman, Sir Hubert Murray.

FISHER, Marjorie
See Mellor, Kathleen & Fisher, Marjorie

FISHER, Vera

2532 TASMANIAN/TALES/FOR/TINIES/by/Vera Fisher/1956/Arthur H. Stockwell Limited/Elms Court/Ilfracombe/Devon [England]
29pp, photographic frontis. & 3 f/p photographs in text, wrappers, 185x125mm. Grant

FISHER-WEBSTER, Wynnefred

2533 [drawing]/AUSTRALIAN SONGS FOR/AUSTRALIAN CHILDREN/By/Wynnefred Fisher-Webster/Foreword by/H. F. Treharne, B.A./(Superintendent of Music, Department of Education, (NSW.)/Price 2/6/Publishers:/George B. Philip & Son,/Sydney
1933
16pp, unillus. (apart from t.p. & same repeated on cover), wrappers, 310x250mm. VSL

Fishes of the World

2534 FISHES OF/THE WORLD/[illus.]/Presented by/Malties
Malties Pty Ltd, East Brunswick, Vic, n.d.
8pp printed on bd. & folding together, 40 spaces for cards to be collected & pasted in, pic. bd., cover title, 320x188mm. KP

FITCHETT, Rev. William Henry [pseud. 'Vedette']

2535 First Series/DEEDS THAT WON/THE EMPIRE/ Historic Battle Scenes./By/"Vedette"./A first series of selections from the articles entitled/"Deeds that won the Empire" now appearing in the/"Argus", and published by special arrangement with the/proprietors of that journal./Revised: with plans & illustrations./ Dedicated to the members of the A.N.A. throughout/ the Colonies./(Copyright)/Australasian Review of Reviews,/Melbourne.
n.d. [1896]
152pp (inc. 1p preface), 3pp & 8pp adv., 9 b/w illus., 4 plans, wrappers, 180x115mm. NSL:M

2536 First Series. Second Edition./DEEDS THAT WON/ THE EMPIRE/Historic Battle Scenes/By/ "Vedette"/first series of selections from the articles entitled/"Deeds that won the empire" now appearing in the/"Argus", and published by special arrangement with the/proprietors of that journal./Revised: with plans & illustrations/Dedicated to the members of the A.N.A. throughout/the Colonies./ (Copyright)/Australasian Review of Reviews,/ Melbourne.
152pp, 1p preface, 2pp & 8pp adv., 1p 'Extracts for Review' (tipped in), 7 f/p b/w illus., & 1 f/p plan, other b/w illus. & plans in text, wrappers (with adv. inside front & back covers), 175x115mm. KMM

2537 DEEDS THAT WON/THE EMPIRE/Historic Battle Scenes/By/The Rev. W. H. Fitchett/("Vedette")/With portraits and plans/Second Edition/London/Smith, Elder, & Co., 15 Waterloo Place/1897
328pp, 2pp preface, 12pp adv., b/w portrait frontis. & 15 f/p portraits, 11 plans, dec. clo., 190x125mm. ANL
First and second series published together.

2538 DEEDS THAT WON/THE EMPIRE/Historic Battle Scenes/By W. H. Fitchett, LL.D./London: John Murray
First pub. (Smith, Elder & Co.) Nov. 1897; 29th imp. Oct. 1914; rpt (John Murray, Cheap Edition) Sept. 1917, Feb. 1921, July 1923 (Crown 8vo.), Feb. 1928 (2/6)
328pp, 2pp preface, 8pp adv., b/w plans, otherwise unillus., clo., 170x110mm. KMM
Smith Elder publ. 27th edition in 1912 (KP) & it was taken over by John Murray (28th ed. 1914, KP). John Murray brought out a cheap ed. in 1917, unillus. apart from battle plans, for the general reader, & also continued publ. the full ed. with 16 portraits, plans & the Waterloo Medallion embossed on the front cover until at least 1928. This ed. also was presented as school prizes. This book eventually ran into 35 editions, selling over 250,000 copies. KMM

2539 DEEDS THAT WON/THE EMPIRE/Historic Battle Scenes/By/The Rev. W. H. Fitchett/("Vedette")/With portraits and plans/[device]/London/George Bell & Sons/and Bombay/1897
328pp, 2pp preface, 1p dedication, 16pp adv., b/w frontis. & 15 f/p b/w portraits, 11 plans, clo., 185x120mm. KP
This edition contains both series.

2540 DEEDS THAT WON/THE EMPIRE/By/The Rev. W. H. Fitchett, B.A., LL. D./Adapted for Use in schools/with illustrations and plans/[device]/London/ George Bell & Sons.
n.d. [1900]
157pp (inc. 1p publisher's note), 3pp notes, 8 f/p b/w illus. & 4 b/w plans, clo., 180x120mm. KMM
Bell's Literature Readers. Geo Bell publ. the book in 25 impr. up to Dec. 1909 in the full ed. as well as in the school ed.

2541 Second Series/DEEDS/THAT WON THE EMPIRE/Historic Battle Scenes/by/"Vedette"/A second series of selections from the articles entitled/ "Deeds that won the Empire" now appearing/in the "Argus", and published by special/arrangement with the proprietors/of that journal./Revised: With Plans and Illustrations./(Copyright)/Australian "Review of Reviews",/Melbourne
n.d. [1897]
145pp (inc. 1p preface), 2pp & 14pp adv., 9 f/p b/w illus., diagrams in text, (?wrappers, copy seen re-bound), 175x105mm. ANL

2542 FIGHTS/FOR THE FLAG/By/W. H. Fitchett/ ("Vedette")/Author of "Deeds that won the Empire"/"What is the flag of England? Winds of the world declare!"/Kipling/With portraits and plans/ [device]/London/George Bell & Sons/and Bombay/ 1898
333pp, 16pp adv., b/w frontis., 14 f/p b/w portraits, b/w plans, clo., 195x125mm. VSL

2543 FIGHTS FOR THE/FLAG/By/W. H. Fitchett, B.A. LL.D./Author of "Deeds that won the Empire"/"How England saved Europe", etc./[quotation]/with a frontispiece and plans/London/Smith, Elder & Co./15 Waterloo Place/1910/(All rights reserved)
333pp, 2pp adv., b/w frontis., b/w plans, clo., 170x110mm. KMM
• Rpt 1912, as above. KMM

2544 THE COMMANDER OF THE HIRONDELLE./A Tale of the Great Blockade/By W. H. Fitchett/Author of "Deeds that Won the Empire" "How England/ Saved Europe," etc/Melbourne:/Fitchett Brothers Proprietary Limited/167–9 Queen Street
192pp, unillus., ?wrappers (cover missing), 210x130mm. KP
Boys' adventure story of Napoleonic War period.

2545 THE COMMANDER/OF THE/"HIRONDELLE"/ By/W. H. Fitchett, B.A., LL.D./With Illustrations/ London/Smith, Elder & Co., 15 Waterloo Place/1904/ (All rights reserved)
390pp, b/w frontis. & 15 f/p b/w plates, pic. clo., 184x120mm. KP

2546 THE COMMANDER/OF THE/"HIRONDELLE"/ By/W. H. Fitchett, B.A., LL.D./with illustrations/ [device]/London/George Bell & Sons/1904
Details as above (Smith Elder copy); illus. A. Pearse. SUA

EPIC PAGES FROM AUSTRALIA'S STORY
5 booklets of Australian history publ. in wrappers for popular reading not intended for children (*From Convicts to Bushrangers*, &c)

FITZGERALD, Elizabeth

2547 FINDERS KEEPERS/[drawing]/Elizabeth Fitzgerald/Illustrated by Marjorie Matthews/[device]/ Angus and Robertson
Sydney 1966
192pp, b/w chapter headings, clo., 210x130mm. KMM

FITZGERALD, Frances

2548 THE CHILDREN AT/KANGAROO CREEK/By/ Frances Fitzgerald/The British Australasian/115 High Holborn, London W.C./1916
215pp, b/w frontis. & 5 f/p b/w illus. by Laurie Tayler, clo., 175x115mm. KMM

FITZGERALD, Mary Anne

2549 AUSTRALIAN/FURS AND FEATHERS,/By/Mary Anne Fitzgerald/Illustrated by W. T. Anderson/Sydney and Brisbane/Edwards, Dunlop and Co. Limted/1889
107pp (some blank), 1p dedication, 1p preface, b/w map, 25 b/w f/p illus., pic. bd., 250 x 185 mm. NSL:M

Studies of Australian birds & animals, each description with a f/p b/w illustration.

2550 KING BUNGAREE'S PYALLA/and/Stories,/ Illustrative of Manners and Customs/that prevailed among Australian/Aborigines,/by/Mary A. Fitzgerald,/(Authoress of "Australian Furs and Feathers")/Sydney 1891/Edwards, Dunlop & Co. Limited/Sydney, Brisbane and London/(Copyright)
78pp, 7 f/p b/w illus., pic. wrappers, 200 x 170 mm. VSL
Illus. printed in brown. Text includes a glossary (2pp) of Aboriginal words.

2551 One Shilling/TALES AND LEGENDS/OF THE/ AUSTRALIAN BLACKS/and/Stories of some of their Manners and Customs./For Australian Children./By Mary A. Fitzgerald./Illustrated by W. T. Anderson./ William Dymock,/Book Arcade,/428 George Street, Sydney.
Cover title of an issue of the remainder sheets of *King Bungaree's Pyalla*, 1891, as above, published at a bargain price. Identical with above, apart from printed wrappers. KMM

2552 KING BUNGAREE'S PYALLA/and/Stories/ illustrative of manners and/customs that prevailed among/Australian aborigines/by/Mary A. Fitzgerald/ (Authoress of Australian Furs and Feathers)/Sydney, 1891/William Brooks & Co., Ltd./Sydney and Brisbane/[Copyright]
111pp (inc. 1p dedication, 1p preface, 2pp introduction, 2p glossary), 11 b/w illus., limp clo., 180x120mm. KMM
Introduction in verse. There are two b/w photographic illus. The other nine are drawings initialled 'W.T.A.'; seven are the same as those used in the Edwards, Dunlop edition, but much reduced, & there are two additional by the same artist. An edition produced for use in schools, printed in brown.

FLEAY, David

2553 TALKING/OF ANIMALS/by/David Fleay/B.Sc., Dip.Ed., C.M.Z.S./London, C.M.Z.S. New York/with photographs by the Author/[quotation]/Jacaranda Press/Brisbane/1956
56pp, b/w photographs throughout, pic. bd., 230x170mm. KP
Factual articles on various Australian animals.

2554 Rpt as above but
Brisbane/The Jacaranda Press/1960. KP

2555 LIVING WITH/ANIMALS/David Fleay/MBE, B.Sc. Dip Ed. CMZS. London and New York/[device]/ Lansdowne Press/Melbourne
1960
64pp, b/w photographs throughout, pic. bd., 235x175mm. KP

FLEMING, Atholl

2556 Imperial Edition 719/HAPPY DAYS/Eight Songs of Childhood/Words by/Atholl Fleming/Music by/ Lindley Evans/[contents]/Allan & Co. Pty Ltd./ Melbourne Ad. Bendigo/Printed in Aust
1954
23pp & 1p blank, unillus., pic. covers, 248x180mm. VSL

FLEMING, W. M.

2557 BUNYIP SAYS SO/A Tale of the/Australian Bush/ W. M. Fleming, M.P./With Illustrations in colour and black/and white by R. W. Sturgess/Commonwealth of Australia/Edward A. Vidler/Melbourne
n.d. [1922]
77pp, col. frontis. & 6 col. illus., b/w drawings in text, pic. bd., 240x175mm. VSL

2558 Australian Young Folks Story Books/BUNYIP SAYS SO/A Tale of the Australian Bush/by/W. M. Fleming/Author of "White Eagles Build" etc./ Illustrated by R. W. Sturgess/Second Edition/ Commonwealth of Australia/Edward S. Vidler/178 Collins Street, Melbourne
n.d. [1925 pencilled on t.p.]
108pp, b/w drawings in text throughout, wrappers, 175x120mm. KMM

2559 BUNYIP SAYS SO/A Tale of the Australian Bush/ By/W. M. Fleming/[drawing]/Sydney/New Century Press Pty. Ltd./3 North York Street
1939
96pp, b/w drawings throughout, dec. bd., 240x175mm. VSL

2560 BUNYIP/TOLD ME/By/W. M. Fleming/[device]/ Edited by/Geoffrey E. Green/B.A./J. M. Dent & Sons Ltd. London & Toronto
First pub. 1926; rpt 1934
138pp, 7pp notes &c., 14pp adv., dec. t.p., b/w frontis., 5 b/w illus. & drawings in text by H. Sands, clo., 145x100mm. Kings Treasury Series. VSL

2561 Another copy as above, but
New York E.P. Dutton and Company J. M. Dent & Sons Ltd London & Toronto
n.d. [1926?]
Details as above, but 150x110mm. KP

2562 THE HUNTED/PICCANINNIES/By/W. M. Fleming/[drawing]/Illustrated by/Kay Edmunds/J. M. Dent and Sons Ltd./London & Toronto
1927
185pp, col. frontis. & 6 f/p col. illus. & line drawings in text, pic. clo., 190x135mm. KMM
• Rpt as above 1934 ANL

2563 JESSIE THE ELEPHANT/Her Life Story/By/W. M. Fleming/[drawing]/Sydney/New Century Press Pty. Ltd./3 North York Street
1939
95pp, 1p adv., b/w photographic illus. & line drawings throughout, pic. paper bd., 235x170mm. VSL

FLETCHER, Helen Jill

2564 THE NATURE BOOK/written and illustrated by/ Helen Jill Fletcher/Instructor—Artist—Designer/Junior Readers' Press/London—New York—Sydney/(All rights reserved etc.)
Sydney, n.d. [1954] [First published in the USA 1953]
58pp, b/w drawings throughout, dec. wrappers, 210x170mm. ANL
Activities & projects for children.

FLETCHER, Jane Ada

2565 STORIES FROM/NATURE/By/J. A. Fletcher/with illustrations/Macmillan and Co., Limited/St. Martin's Street, London/1915
145pp, b/w photographic illus. throughout, clo., 185x120mm. KMM

2566 NATURE & ADVENTURE/for Boys and Girls/by/ Jane Ada Fletcher/with illustrations/Macmillan and Co., Limited/St. Martin's Church London/
1916
151pp, photographic frontis. & 31 photographs in text, clo., 185x120mm. KMM
Title on cover reads: 'Nature and Adventure/in Australasia/for Boys and Girls'.

2567 Whitcombe's Story Books/BRAVE BOYS/And other Stories of Australian/Animals and Birds/by J. A.

Fletcher/For Children aged 10 to 12 years/Whitcombe & Tombs Limited/Melbourne and Sydney/Auckland, Wellington, Christchurch, Dunedin/Invercargill and London
n.d. [1922]
79pp, 1p adv., b/w frontis. & 4 f/p b/w illus. & line drawings in text, wrappers (with adv. on both sides of back cover), 180x120mm. KMM
See McLaren 506

2568 Australian Nature Story Readers/BRAVE BOYS/ and other Stories of Adventure/By J. A. Fletcher/For Children aged 10 to 12 years/[decoration]/Melbourne/ Auckland, Christchurch, Dunedin, Wellington and London/Whitcombe & Tombs Limited
n.d.
79pp, 1p adv., b/w frontis. & 16 b/w drawings by Hans Praetorius, wrappers, 185x120mm. KMM

2569 Whitcombe's Story Books/WANNA/A Small Tasmanian aborigine who made friends/with Captain Cook at Adventure Bay/By/J. A. Fletcher/For children aged 9 to 10 years/[drawing]/Whitcombe and Tombs Limited/Melbourne and Sydney/Auckland, Wellington, Christchurch, Dunedin, Invercargill/and London
n.d. [1938?]
70pp (inc. 6pp notes &c., & glossary), 3pp adv., b/w drawings in text, wrappers, 180x115mm. KMM
See McLaren 448

2570 Whitcombe's Story Books/TOMMY'S RIDE/ON THE EMU/By/J. A. Fletcher/For Children Aged 8 to 9 years/[drawing]/Whitcombe & Tombs Limited/ Melbourne and Sydney/Auckland, Christchurch, Dunedin, Wellington, N.Z./and London
n.d. [1948]
32pp, b/w frontis. & 6 b/w illus. by Hans Praetorius, wrappers, 180x120mm. ANL
See McLaren 314

2571 LITTLE BROWN/PICCANINNIES/OF TASMANIA/By/Jane Ada Fletcher/Illustrated by/ Margaret Senior/Copyright/John Sands Pty. Ltd., Publishers/Sydney Melbourne Brisbane Adelaide Perth
n.d. [1950]
41pp (inc. preface by A.L. Meston, M.A., Education Officer for Schools, Tasmania, & glossary), part. col. illus. throughout, dec. bd., 240x180mm. KMM

FLETCHER, Lionel B.

2572 SKIPPER MY CHUM/and other True Dog Stories/ By/Lionel B. Fletcher/with illustrations by/C. Ambler/ London/The Lutterworth Press/4 Bouverie Street, E.C.4
1935
208pp, b/w frontis. & 13 b/w illus., clo., 215x145mm. ANL

2573 SKIPPER MY CHUM/and other True Dog Stories/ By/Lionel B. Fletcher/with illustrations by/C. Ambler/ Lutterworth Press/London and Redhill
n.d. [First pub. 1935; 2nd. imp. 1936; 3rd. imp. 1938; 4th imp. 1946]
192pp, b/w frontis. & 13 b/w illus., clo., 190x115mm. CLRC
Stories originally broadcast over NZ Radio stations.

FLEURY, M.

This Wonderful World—PLANTS AND FLOWERS. Ayers & James, Sydney
• Rpt of overseas books

Flight to Adventure

2574 Princess/Picture Library No. 72/FLIGHT TO ADVENTURE/Thrills with Beth Lawson,/Australian Flying Nurse
Fleetway Printers Ltd, 17 Summer Street, London, S.E.1, n.d.
58pp, illus. throughout, col. pic. wrappers, 180x135mm. Grant
Story told in pictures.

Flogged to Death

2575 No. 334 Vol. XXXIV/Boys' Weekly Reader/ Novelette/A Complete Story Weekly/FLOGGED TO DEATH/[illus. with caption 'The ruffian was tied up, rods were cut and the flogging commenced.']
Publ. between 1861 and 1870
24pp, unillus., wrappers, with t.p. illus. repeated on front wrapper, 206x140mm. Facsimile. CLRC.
Advertised on back wrapper: Lost in the Bush; or, The Golden Nugget.

FLOWER, John

PETROLEUM & NATURAL GAS. *See* Around Australia Program

FLOWERDEW, Phyllis & SCHONELL, Fred

2576 Happy Venture Library/[drawing—Book 22]/THE LITTLE KANGAROO/WHO JUMPED TOO FAR
Oliver & Boyd Ltd, Edinburgh and London, n.d. [1960?]
32pp, b/w drawings throughout, pic. wrappers, cover title, 135x150mm. KMM

FLYNN, Olive Mary

2577 THE UNHAPPY/BOOK FAIRIES/By/Olive Mary Flynn
Printed by Finn Bros., Ltd, 590 George St., Sydney, n.d.
15pp, unillus., wrappers, 210x130mm. NSL:M
Play for children.

FOA, Mme Eugénie [pseud.]

2578 CONTE HISTORIQUES/POUR/LA JEUNESSE/ Par/Mme. Eugénie Foa/Jean-Jacques Rousseau—Sainte Victoire—Jacques Cook.—Les Élèves d'Écouen— Antoine Gallard—Wolfgang Mozart—.—Les Deux Soeurs d'Écouen—Marie Leezinska— Mariette.Tintorella./Paris/Desforges, Éditeur/25 Rue des Grands-Augustins.
n.d. [1840?]
349pp, engraved frontis. & 3 f/p engravings, dec. clo., 175x100mm. NSL:M
Contents include 'James Cook' (pp 95–157), being the story of Cook's early life told for children.

2579 LE CAPITAINE COOK, ou Le Schelling Marque
No t.p. or wrappers
29pp excerpt (pp175–204), b/w frontis., 195x120mm. NSL:M

FOGARTY, John P.

GEORGE CHAFFEY. *See* Great Australians

FOLKARD, Frederick C. [ed.]

2580 BOYS' BOOK OF/OUTDOORS ADVENTURE/ Compiled by Frederic C. Folkard/[device]/Murray Sydney
K. G. Murray Publishing Co., n.d. [1965]
159pp, 13 f/p b/w illus., many b/w drawings in text, diagrams, clo., 285x215mm. BBC
Contains many practical articles on bushcraft or outdoor life.

FOOT, Katharine B.

2581 THE ROVINGS/OF/A RESTLESS BOY/By/ Katharine B. Foot/Author of "An Orphan in Japan" "My Hard/Money" "Tilda" "The Young/Reformer",

etc. etc./Cassell & Company, Limited/London Paris and Melbourne.
Printed in USA, foreword dated April 1892
294pp (inc. 2pp foreword & 1p preface), 14pp adv., b/w frontis. & 5 f/p b/w plates, pic. clo., 186x125mm. CLRC
Story of an American boy who goes to sea. Pp145–249 set in Victoria. Leaves Sydney on ship bound for London via Cape Horn.

FOOTE, Carol
See Odell, Carol

FOOTE, Kay Stevens
2582 WALKABOUT/DOWN UNDER/By/Kay Stevens Foote/[Coat of Arms]/Illustrated with photographs/ 1944/Charles Scribner's Sons/New York
92pp, b/w photographs throughout, b/w map, clo., dec. e/p, 220x150mm. NSL:M

FOOTT, Mary Hannay
2583 SWEEP/A Comedy for Children/in Three Acts/By Mary Hannay Foott/Brisbane/Gordon and Gotch, Printers, Queen Street
n.d. [1890?]
12pp, unillus, wrappers, 135x100mm. QSL
Play based on Charles Lamb's essay 'The Praise of Chimney Sweepers'.

FORBES, Alison
See Trudinger, R. M. & Forbes, Alison

FORBES, George
2584 ADVENTURES IN/SOUTHERN SEAS/A Tale of the Sixteenth Century/By/George Forbes/Illustrated by/G. Henry Evison/[drawing]/Sydney/The Australasian Publishing Co. Ltd./218–222 Clarence Street/1920
252pp (inc. 4pp introduction), col frontis. & 4 b/w illus., clo., 190x135mm. VSL
Boys' romance based on Dirck Hartog's voyage.
2585 Rpt as above, but
London/George G. Harrap & Company Ltd./2 & 3 Portsmouth Street Kingsway W.C./and at Sydney
First publ. July 1920
252pp (inc. 4pp intro.) & 4pp adv., col. frontis. & 4 b/w plates, clo., 190x135mm. KP
2586 Rpt as above, July 1924
George G. Harrap & Co. Ltd./London Calcutta Sydney
252pp (inc. introduction), col. frontis. & 4 b/w plates, dec. clo., 195x135mm. KP
2587 ADVENTURES IN/SOUTHERN SEAS/A Tale of the Sixteenth Century/By/George Forbes/Illustrated by/G. Henry Evison/John F. Shaw (1928) & Co., Ltd./ Publishers,/3 Pilgrim Street, London, E.C.
n.d. [school prize 1934]
252pp (inc. 4pp introduction), b/w frontis. & 3 f/p b/w illus., dec. clo., 185x120mm. KMM
The illus. are the same in both editions, apart from the omission of the coloured frontis. in this edition.

FORD, Effie
2588 LITTLE PLAYS FOR SCHOOLS AND CONCERTS Sydney, 1909
Lacks t.p. Front cover:
'Little Plays/for/Schools/and/Concerts/By Effie Ford'
viiipp, 80pp, unillus., clo., 214x130mm. MAC
Includes 12 plays, some for children.

FORDWYCH, John Edmund
2589 A Story of Love and Adventure in the Australian Bush/THE HEART OF/NO MAN'S/LAND/3d./ [illustration]/"The Wonder" Library—No. 9
n.d.
120pp, unillus., col. pic. wrappers, cover title, 185x130mm. RM
Back wrapper missing & no publisher's imprint to be found on remainder of copy. Romance for adolescent girls.

FORREST, M.
2590 THE GREEN HARPER/By/M. Forrest/Printers:/ Gordon and Gotch (Queensland) Limited, Queen Street, Brisbane/1915
59pp, wrappers, 180x120 mm. CLRC
Fairy verses & stories reprinted from *Pall Mall Magazine* (London), *Australasian, Sydney Mail & Sunday Times* (Sydney).

FORSTER, Harley W.
SQUATTER AND SELECTOR AT TONGALA. *See* Australian Landmarks

FORSTER, William J.
2591 A TRIP TO MANY LANDS/By/William J. Forster/ Author of/'The Wonderful Half-crown' 'A Change of Weather'/'The Animals in Council' etc/with twenty-six full-page illustrations/London/S. W. Partridge & Co./8 and 9 Paternoster Row
n.d. [1901]
140pp & 2pp adv., b/w frontis. & 25 other f/p illus., pic. clo., 220x170mm. ANL
Pp115–19 Queensland, pp120–4 NSW, pp125–9 NZ, each with f/p illus.
2592 THE/CAPTAIN'S STORY/By/William J. Forster/ Author of 'The Wonderful Half-Crown' 'Leslie's Revenge',/'Cousin Jack's Umbrella' etc./John F. Shaw (1928) & Co. Ltd.,/Publishers,/3 Pilgrim Street, London, E.C.
n.d.
128pp, col. frontis. & 1 b/w illus., clo., 180x115mm. KMM
Temperance story with only 10pp devoted to Australia.

Fortunatus—A Romance
See White, J. H.

The Fortunes of the Charlton Family
2593 THE FORTUNES OF/THE CHARLTON FAMILY/ Illustrated by/W. H. C. Groome/London/Wells Gardner, Darton & Co./Paternoster Buildings
1898
148pp & 4pp adv., b/w frontis. & 3 f/p b/w illus., dec. clo., 186x124mm. ANL
Part of the action takes place in Australia.

FORWARD, R. K.
SAMUEL GRIFFITH. *See* Great Australians

FOSTER, Maude Clifton
2594 THE CUTE BOOK OF VERSE/By Maude Clifton Foster/Illustrations by Maureen C. Kelly/[drawing]/ Retsof Publishing Company/1st. edition, May 1947/Copyright
Designed & Printed by Stuart Taylor, Melbourne
18pp, part. col. illus. throughout, bd., 125x200mm. VSL

FOTHERINGHAME, Josephine
2595 SIR VALDEMAR/THE GANGER/A Tale of the days of King Haco/By/Josephine Fotheringhame/ Illustrations by/D. H. Souter/Young Australia Office/ 76 Pitt Street, Sydney, N.S.W./1905
188pp, 12 f/p b/w illus., dec. clo., 180x115mm. ANL
2596 SIR VALDEMAR/THE GANGER/A Tale of the Days of King Haco/By/Josephine Fotheringhame/ Illustrations by/D. H. Souter/London/Sampson Low, Marston & Company/Limited/St Dunstan's House/

Fetter Lane, Fleet Street, E.C./1905/(All rights reserved)
188pp, 12 plates & b/w drawings, pic. clo., 182x120mm. ANL

2597 A TALE IN A RED/MOROCCO BOOK/Being certain Incidents in the Life of/Merran Douglas, inscribed by that Demoiselle in the aforementioned/ Volume, and prepared for/publication by/Josephine Fotheringhame/Illustrated/[device]/London/George Routledge & Sons Limited/New York: E. P. Dutton & Co.
n.d. [1909]
247pp, b/w frontis. & 3 f/p b/w illus., dec. clo., 185x120mm. NSL:M
The author was editor of *Young Australia,* & also contributed to Favenc's *Tales for Young Australia.*

FOUINET, E. [Ernest]
2598 ALLAN/LE/JEUNE DÉPORTÉ À BOTANY-BAY./ Par E. Fouinet,/Auteur du Robinson des Glaces./ [vignette]/Paris/Désirée Eymery,/à la Bibliothèque D'Éducation,/Quai Voltaire, 15/1836
322pp (inc. table of contents), engraved frontis. & 3 f/p engravings, bd., 154x96mm. CLRC
2599 ALLAN/LE/JEUNE DÉPORTÉ À BOTANY-BAY/ Par E. Fouinet/ouvrage couronné par l'Académie Française, et qui a remporté le prix Monthyon./Édition revue et corrigée./[device]/Librairie des Bons Livres./ Limoges/Chez Martial Ardant Frères./rue des Taules./ Paris/Chez Martial Ardent Frères quai des Augustins, 25/1852
276pp, engraved frontis. & 3 plates, dec. & embossed paper bd., 205x125mm. ANL
The front cover has a rose design in gilt & col. surrounding a col. plate of two male figures in a landscape.
2600 ALLAN/ou/LE JEUNE DÉPORTÉ À BOTANY BAY/par/E. Fouinet/Ouvrage couronné par L'Académie Française/[device]/Limoges/Eugène Ardant et Cic./Éditeurs
n.d.
144pp (inc. 2pp publishers adv.), engraved frontis., dec. bd., 225x145mm. MAC

The Four Clever Brothers
See DOONGALLA DAYS STORIES

Fourteen Explorers of Australia
2601 FOURTEEN/EXPLORERS/OF/AUSTRALIA/ [sketch]/Bank of New South Wales
Sydney 1951
16pp, 15 b/w drawings, b/w maps, wrappers, cover title, illus. by Walter Jardine, 240x150mm. HBM
One page article, with portrait & map, on each of the following: Tasman, Cook, Bass, Flinders, Blaxland, Oxley, Phillip Parker King, Sturt, Eyre, Leichhardt, Edmund Kennedy, Burke, Stuart, Forrest.
Acknowledgements to Mr Kenneth Cable, Dept of History, University of Sydney, & the Gregory Publishing Co. (maps).
2602 SIXTEEN EXPLORERS/OF AUSTRALIA/[sketch]/ Bank of New South Wales
Sydney 1961 [First published as *Fourteen Explorers of Australia* in March 1951 compiled by K. Cable] rpt July 1951; 2nd ed. July 1952; rpt August 1953; 3rd ed. (revised & enlarged as *Sixteen Explorers of Australia* 1956; 4th ed. July 1957; rpt 1959, Nov. 1959, May 1961]
17pp, b/w drawings, b/w maps, illus. by Walter Jardine, wrappers, 245 x 155 mm. KMM
Contents as in previous edition, but also articles, portraits & maps on Mitchell & A. C. Gregory.

2603 SIXTEEN EXPLORERS OF AUSTRALIA
• Rpt July 1962, 1963, 1965, 1967, 1968, 1970
The 1970 ed. no longer uses the portrait of James Cook on the front cover but reproduces a b/w drawing of two men looking out over the country ahead & one departing on horseback. KP

FOWERAKER, Patricia
2604 TIMOTHY JOHN/AND/AMANDA SUE/by Patricia Foweraker/[coloured illus.]/Illustrated by/ Emilie Beuth
Readabout Publishers Pty Ltd, Crow's Nest, NSW, 1964
24pp, col. & part. col. illus. throughout, stiff dec. wrappers, 215x180mm. BBC

FOWLER, Helen
2605 THE FAMILY/AT/WILLOW BEND/By/Helen Fowler/Illustrated by/Irene Maher/Angus and Robertson/Sydney London Melbourne Wellington 1955
180pp, b/w drawings, clo., 190x130mm. CLRC
• Rpt 1957, as above. ANL

FOWLER, Kathleen
See Castley, Dora &c.

FOWLER, Mildred M. (ed.)
2606 LAND OF THE/RAINBOW GOLD/poetry for young Australians/edited by Mildred M. Fowler/ Nelson
Thomas Nelson (Australia) Ltd, Melbourne 1967
109pp (inc. 2pp introduction, 10pp notes & glossary, 1p acknowledgements), col. & b/w drawings in text throughout, illus. by Jack Newnham, Tom Bishop, Rachel Tonkin & Nola Bearlin, pic. bd., 210x135mm. KMM
• Rpt 1968 (omits subtitle), limp pic. clo. KW

FOWLES, E. W. H.
2607 Special C. E. Jubilee Edition/Queensland State Convention, Brisbane July 23–28 1931/YOUNG AUSTRALIA/a four part (S.A.T.B.) Crusader's Call /words and Music by Dr E. W. H. Fowles/Queensland Book Depot, Albert Street/Brisbane
4pp only (back cover blank apart from quote). ANL

The Fox and the Little Brown Hen
See DOONGALLA DAYS STORIES

FOX, Frank
2608 Peeps at Many Lands/AUSTRALIA/By/Frank Fox/ with twelve full-page illustrations/in colour/By/Percy F. S. Spence, etc/London/Adam and Charles Black/ 1911
88pp, col. frontis & 11 f/p col. illus., clo. (with col. illus. pasted on front cover), 190x130mm. KMM

2609 Peeps at Many Lands/OCEANIA/By/Frank Fox/ Author of "Australia", "Ramparts of Empire", and of/ "The British Empire" and "Australia" in the/"Peeps at Many Lands" Series/Containing Thirty-two Full-Page/ Illustrations in Colour/By/Norman H. Hardy, F. & W. Wright/and Percy F. S. Spence/London/Adam and Charles Black/1911
204pp (inc. 4pp appendix), col. frontis. & 30 f/p col. illus., fold-out b/w map, pic. clo. (with col. illus. pasted on front cover), 205x140mm. RM
An omnibus volume of three of the 'Peeps at Many Lands' series, including *The Blessed Isles of the Pacific, Australia & New Zealand.*
2610 Peeps at Many Lands/AUSTRALIA/By/Frank Fox/ With Eight full-page illustrations/in colour/By/Percy F. S. Spence, etc./A. & C. Black, Ltd./4, 5 & 6 Soho Square, London, W. I./1920

88pp, 8 f/p col. illus. (inc. 1 pasted on front cover), b/w double-spread map, 1 b/w drawing, clo., 195x130mm. KMM
2611 3rd ed. as above, but col. frontis. of the new Parliament House, Canberra. KP

FOX, Len
2612 CHUNG OF VIETNAM/by Len Fox/Hanoi/Red River Publishing House/1957
24pp, b/w drawings, illus. wrappers, 265x190mm. ANL
Verses.

FOX, Lorene K.
2613 ANTARCTIC/ICEBREAKERS/By Lorene K. Fox/ Illustrated with photographs/Junior Books/Doubleday, Doran & Company, Inc./Garden City 1937 New York
319pp, 3pp acknowledgements, 1p preface, b/w photographic frontis. & 31pp photographic illus., clo., pic. e/p, 230x150mm. NSL:M
The story of the exploration and discovery of Antarctica.

FOX, Matthew Joseph
2614 UNCLE MATT'S/MODERN/NURSERY PHYMES/ For/Clever Children/by/Matt. J. Fox/Illustrated by/ Walter Dowman/Consolidated Press Ltd., Sydney/ Registered at G.P.O. for Transmission by post as a book
Sydney, n.d. [1947]
17pp, dec. t.p., 7 f/p col. illus., b/w drawings, stiff pic. wrappers, 235x180mm. ANL

FRANC, Maude Jeanne
Though the many works by this author were widely read by girls in the late nineteenth century, they are not entered in this bibliography, having been originally published as adult romances.

FRANCIS, Audrey
2615 THE KING/OF THE/MOUNTAINS/A Fairy/ Story/for the/Tinies/By Audrey Francis/Also "AUSSIE" [quotation]
Frank Johnson, Sydney, n.d. [1944]
12pp, b/w illus. throughout, wrappers, cover title, 280x210mm. ANL

2616 LOLLY/By Audrey Francis/LANDS/Illustrated/by Carl Lyon/A Frank Johnson/Publication
Sydney, n.d. [1944]
12pp, b/w illus. throughout, wrappers, cover title, 265x200mm. ANL

FRANCIS, Vera
2617 THE CALF/WHO COULDN'T MOO/By Vera Francis/Pictures by/George Santos
Colorgravure, Melbourne 1950
42pp, 12 col. illus & b/w illus. on alternate pages, pic. bd., dec. e/p, 195x165mm. A Little Wonder Book. KMM

FRANKLIN, Sir John
2618 A BRAVE MAN and his/Belongings:/Being some passages in the Life/of Sir John Franklin, R.N.,/F.R.S., K.C.H., &c, &c./First discoverer of the North-west Passage/London:/Printed by S. Taylor, Graystoke Place, Fetter Lane,/Holborn, E.C./–/1874.
61pp & 5pp appendices, original portrait photograph frontis., bds.,185x120mm. ANL
'This fragmentary record/is Affectionately Dedicated to/(as it was compiled for)/Sir John Franklin's Grandchildren/and his/great nephews and nieces.'

FRANKLIN, Kathleen
2619 SLIDING DOWN/THE RAINBOW/[drawing]/ Written by/Kathleen Franklin/Illustrated by/Joan Abbott/[device]/Published by/Aidmasta Productions Pty. Ltd., 3 Rawson Place, Sydney
n.d.
24pp, numerous col. illus., pic. wrappers, 230x180mm. Grant

2620 BABY KANGAROO'S/EASTER/EGG/[drawing]/ Written by/Kathleen Franklin/Illustrated by/Dorothy Huffell/[device]/Published by/Aidmasta Productions Pty. Ltd., 3 Rawson Place, Sydney
n.d.
24pp, part. col. drawings throughout, stiff pic. wrappers, 230x175mm. KMM

FRANKLIN, Miles
2621 SYDNEY ROYAL/Divertissement/by/Miles Franklin/Decorations by Nan Knowles/The Shakespeare Head/London New York Sydney Durban Paris
n.d. [1947]
104pp, b/w drawings in text, dec. wrappers, 200 x 135 mm. ANL
The setting of this story is Sydney's Royal Agricultural Show.

FRASER, Alexander A.
2622 DADDY CRIPS' WAIFS./A Tale of Australasian Life and/Adventure./By/Alexander A. Fraser/ [vignette]/The Religious Tract Society,/56 Paternoster Row, 65 Paul's Churchyard,/And 164 Piccadilly
n.d. [1886]
192pp, 16pp adv., b/w frontis. & 2 f/p b/w illus., b/w dec. chapter headings, dec. clo., 180x120mm. ANL
2623 DADDY CRIPS' WAIFS/A Tale of Australasian Life/and Adventure/By/Alexander A. Fraser/London/ The Religious Tract Society/4 Bouverie Street and 65 St Paul's Churchyard E.C.
[1915]
192pp & 6pp adv., b/w frontis. & 2 f/p plates (C. A. Ferrier), dec. clo., 185x125mm. CLRC

FRASER, Alison
2624 FAIRY THOUGHTS/Alison Fraser/11 years/ [printer's device]/Sydney/Arthur McQuilty & Co./ Printers
n.d. [1918]
vi, 47pp (last blank), unillus., dec. paper covered bd., 180x120mm. ANL
Verse.

FRAUCA, Harry
2625 STRIPED/WOLF/A Bush Adventure/Harry Frauca/Illustrated by/Genevieve Melrose/Heinemann Melbourne London
1969
109pp, 1p foreword, 14 f/p b/w illus., pic. clo., 210x135mm. KMM

Fred Malcolm and His Friends
2626 FRED MALCOLM/AND HIS FRIENDS/with illustrations/By/W. H. C. Groome./London:/Wells Gardner, Darton & Co./3, Paternoster Buildings, E.C., and/44, Victoria Street, S.W.
1902
179pp, 1p adv., b/w frontis. & 3 f/p b/w illus., col. pic. bd. (adv. verso back cover), 197x124mm. KMM
Pp1–13 and 160–79 are set in Australia. Chatterbox Library.

FREEDMAN, Helen
2627 LET'S GO TO THE CIRCUS/David and Margaret's Trip to Circus/Land. Told by Helen Freedman/Pictures

by Hal Freedman/Published in Melbourne by Georgian House
n.d. [1949]
16pp, col. & b/w illus. throughout, stiff pic. wrappers, 180x240mm. ANL

2628 THE GIANT BOOK OF/ZOO ANIMALS/[drawing]/with twelve plates in full colour and including/Our Zoo Picnic The Greedy Monkey Queer Birds/and other stories By Helen Freedman/The Giant Books are published [device] in Melbourne by Georgian House
Printed by Morris & Walker
16pp (inc. 6pp in full col. & other pages illus. in b/w by Harold Freedman), col. pic. wrappers, 240x367mm. CLRC
In same series: The Giant Book of Farm Friends; The Giant Engine Book.

FRESCHET, Berniece

2629 KANGAROO RED/By Berniece Freschet/Illustrated by John Schoenherr/A World's Work Children's Book
Copyright 1966, First published in Great Britain 1967 by The World's Work (1913) Ltd, Kingswood, Tadsworth, Surrey
[46]pp, extended part. col. frontis., part. col. drawings throughout, clo., 225x180mm. BBC

FREUCHEN, Peter

2630 PETER FREUCHEN'S/BOOK OF THE/SEVEN SEAS/By/Peter Freuchen/with David Loth/London/Jonathan Cape 30 Bedford Square
First publ. in Great Britain, 1958
512pp (inc. 6pp index), b/w frontis., b/w illus. throughout, clo., dec. e/p, 232x150mm. KP
Numerous references to Australia & SW Pacific.

Friends from the Walkabout

2631 FRIENDS FROM THE WALKABOUT/Brief Studies of the Australian Aborigines/and of/the Work of Presbyterian Missions/in their Midst./[device]/Issued by the Australian Presbyterian Board of Missions,/Assembly Building, Margaret Street,/Sydney Australia
n.d. [1948?]
32pp (inc. 1p foreword by V. W. Coombes for the Australian Presbyterian Board of Missions Publications Committee), b/w frontis. & b/w photographs in text, pic. wrappers, 210x135mm. CLRC

Friends on the Farm

2632 FRIENDS ON THE FARM
Offset Printing Coy. Pty Ltd, Sydney, n.d.
8pp, 3 f/p part col. illus., stiff pic. wrappers, 175x122mm. VMOU

FRISTEDT, Conrad

2633 TVÅ SVENSKA GOSSARS/ÄFVENTYR/BLAND MÄNNISKOÄTARE./berattelse för yngre gossar/Af/Conrad Fristedt,/Fil. Doktor./Med 8 Helsidesplancher./[device]/Stockholm./Albert Bonniers Förlag.
Stockholm, 1893
102pp, f/p b/w photographic frontis. & 7 b/w plates, chapter headings, stiff pic. wrappers, 194x133mm. RM
Title translation: 'Two Swedish Boys' Adventures among the Cannibals'; 3 of the illus. sgd 'D. L. Jundhal, '93'. Adventures of two boys shipwrecked on the barren coast of W.A. who are captured by Aborigines then rescued & taken to Perth, then Sydney before setting sail once more for Sweden.

FRODSHAM, Stanley H.

2634 AROUND THE WORLD/WITH THE/BOOMERANG BOY/By/Stanley H. Frodsham/Author of "The Boomerang Boy and/Other Stories"/Gospel Publishing House, Springfield, M.O., U.S.A.
1926
165pp (inc. 2pp introduction), 1p adv., b/w drawings, wrappers, 190x130mm. ANL
The hero is an Aboriginal boy who stowed away on a boat bound for San Francisco. He was sent to gaol soon after his arrival, and became converted by an Evangelist. Evangelical story of the young convert's travels, written in a naive manner.

FROGGATT, Gladys H.

2635 THE WORLD OF LITTLE LIVES/By/Gladys H. Froggatt/(Millie-Millie)/With 15 full plates and 35 text blocks/[quotation]/Sydney—/William Brooks & Co. Ltd./17 Castlereagh Street/1916
169pp (inc. foreword by Walter W. Froggatt & author's preface), b/w frontis. & 12 f/p b/w illus. sgd 'E.H.Z.' & B.A.T.', other drawings & diagrams in text, clo., 205x150mm. CLRC
Author states in preface that part of the book first appeared in the *Stock and Station Journal.*

2636 THE WORLD OF LITTLE LIVES/By/Gladys H. Froggatt/Second edition, with 50 illustrations/Australia:/Cornstalk Publishing Company/Arnold Place, Sydney/1924
163pp, 1p preface, b/w photographic frontis., 11 f/p b/w illus. signed 'E.H.Z.' & B.A.T.', 2 f/p diagrams, diagrams & photographic illus., etc. in text, clo., 205x150mm. KMM
Illus. same as in first ed., apart from the line drawing frontis., not used in this ed., & the alteration of a few of the text illustrations.

2637 THE WORLD OF/LITTLE LIVES/By/Gladys H. Froggatt/For Children aged 11 to 12 years/Australia:/Angus & Robertson Ltd./89 Castlereagh Street, Sydney/1930
69pp, b/w frontis. & 4 f/p b/w illus., wrappers, 180x120 mm. KMM

2638 MORE ABOUT/THE WORLD OF/LITTLE LIVES/By/Gladys H. Froggatt/For Children aged 11 to 12 years/Australia/Cornstalk Publishing Company/89 Castlereagh Street, Sydney/1929
71pp, b/w frontis. & 4 f/p b/w illus. sgd 'E.H.Z.', wrappers, 180x120mm. KMM
Insect life for children.

2639 MORE ABOUT/THE WORLD OF/LITTLE LIVES/By/Gladys H. Froggatt/For children aged 11 to 12 years/Australia:/Angus & Robertson, Ltd./89 Castlereagh Street, Sydney/1930
71pp, b/w frontis. & 4 f/p b/w illus., wrappers, 180x120mm. Grant
A list of the 'Gumnut Readers' is printed on back cover.

FROGGATT, Walter W.

2640 Shakespeare Head Australian Nature Books/General Editor: [publisher's device] David G. Stead./No. 1/THE INSECT BOOK/[drawing]/By Walter W. Froggatt./F.L.S., F.E.S., F.R.Z.S.,/Formerly Government Entomologist and Special Forest Entomologist/to New South Wales Government./Author of "Australian Insect", "Forest Insects of Australia"/Sydney:/The Shakespeare Head Press Ltd.,/1933
103pp, 1p booklist, b/w diagrams, 2 photographic illus. in text, wrappers, 184x110mm. KMM

2641 Shakespeare Head Publication/[device]/No. 1/THE INSECT BOOK/[drawing]/By Walter W. Froggatt/F.R.Z.S./Formerly Government Entomologist [4 lines]/Shakespeare Head Press/310 George St. Sydney/1936

119pp (inc. foreword &c) & 1p booklist, diagrams & b/w photographs, wrappers, 184x120mm. KP

2642 Consolidated Press Limited/Australian Nature Series/No 1/THE INSECT BOOK/[drawing]/By Walter W. Froggatt/F.R.Z.S./Formerly Government Entomologist [4 lines]/Consolidated Press Ltd/ Sydney/1943.
Details as above. KP

2643 THE INSECT BOOK/[drawing]/By Walter W. Froggatt/FRZS/[4 lines]/[device]/Shakespeare Head Press Pty Ltd./London Sydney New York/1946
128pp, b/w drawings & diagrams, wrappers, 175x110mm. KP

From Colony to Nation

2644 FROM/COLONY/TO/NATION/Knowabout Australia/Horwitz-International Inc.
Compiled by the editorial staff of The Modern Encyclopaedia of Australia & New Zealand
1965 (printed in Hong Kong)
64pp, b/w & part col. illus. throughout, pic. wrappers, 245x180mm. KP
Factual & biographical material arranged in encylopaedic form.

From Holey Dollar to Dollar Bill

2645 FROM HOLEY DOLLAR/TO DOLLAR BILL/Why Money and Banks have Changed/During Australia's Short History/Presented to you by the Commonwealth Banks.
n.p., n.d. [1966?] [on back cover 'Adv. 117B 3/66']
16pp, col. illus. throughout, pic. wrappers, cover title, 240x182mm. KP

From Many Lands Australasia and Africa

2646 Untearable Linen/FROM MANY LANDS/ AUSTRALASIA/AND/AFRICA/[col. illus.]/Father Tuck's /"Useful Knowledge"/Series
Raphael Tuck & Sons Ltd, London, n.d. [190? prize 1908]
14pp (inc. inside of cover), line drawings throughout, 4 f/p col. illus., col. pic. bd., cover title, 270x216mm. ANL
Text printed in green on most pages.

From Trees to Tyres

2647 FROM TREES TO/TYRES/With the Compliments of/Dunlop Rubber Australia Limited
108 Flinders St, Melbourne, n.d. [195-? map of main rubber producers dated 1953]
16pp, col. illus. (mostly comic strip), wrappers, cover title, 230x140mm. KP

[FROST, Anne]

See 'Idie'

FRY, Daisy

2648 FOUR TALES FOR CHILDREN/By/Daisy Fry/The Baby Man/The Electric Fence/Himalaya Bear/Jimmy the Brush Tail Rat/Adelaide/The Hassell Press/1952
28pp, b/w drawings, wrappers, 245x170mm. CLRC

[FRY, Sarah Maria]

2649 THE/AUSTRALIAN BABES IN THE WOOD/A True Story/Told in Rhyme for the Young/By/The Author of "Little Jessie," etc./Illustrated by/Hugh Cameron, A.R.S.A., J. M'Whirter, G. Hay, J. Lawson, etc/and engraved by R. Patterson/London/Griffith and Farran/Successors to Newbery and Harris/Corner of St Paul's Church-yard/MDCCCLXVI 1866
47pp, engraved frontis. & 13 engravings in text, gilt dec. clo., 180x130mm. CLRC
Inspired by the experiences of the Duff children, lost in the bush near Horsham, Victoria in 1864 & found alive after '9 long days & eight long weary nights'.

FUCHS, Sir Vivian

2650 ANTARCTIC ADVENTURE/The Commonwealth Trans-Antarctic Expedition 1955–58 by Sir Vivian Fuchs/Illustrated by Stuart Tresilian/Cassell—London 1959
190pp, extended dec. t.p., 16pp col. photographs, 9pp maps & plans, b/w drawings throughout, clo., 210x140mm. NSL:M

FUCHS, Sir Vivian & HILLARY, Sir Edmund

2651 THE CROSSING/OF/ANTARCTICA/The Commonwealth/Trans-Antarctic Expedition/ 1955–1958/By Sir Vivian Fuchs/and Sir Edmund Hillary/Edited for schools/Andrew Scotland, M.A., Ph.D./[device]/Cassell London
First school ed. 1960
138pp (inc. editor's preface, foreword, 2pp questions for students), maps & b/w photographic illus., clo., 220x136mm. KP

Full Speed

2652 FULL SPEED
George Jaboor, Melbourne, n.d. [194-?]. Printed by Morris & Walker Ltd, Melbourne
8pp (& printed inside covers), 4pp printed in col., others in b/w, pic. paper covers, cover title, 205x137mm. KMM
Picture book of railway engines, with captions.

FULLARTON, Nan

2653 THE/ALPHABET/FROM A TO Z/Written and illustrated/by/Nan Fullerton *[sic]*/Published by/ Invincible Press,/Sydney N.S.W.
n.d. [1945]
32pp, 16pp col. illus., b/w illus throughout, stiff pic. wrappers, 240x180mm. ANL
Rhyming captions.

2654 A DAY IN THE BUSH/[coloured illus.]/Written and illustrated by/Nan Fullarton
Invincible Press, Sydney, n.d. [Copyright 1946]
32pp, 16pp col. illus., b/w drawings throughout, pic. wrappers, 240x180mm. NSL:M

2655 LET'S READ/THUMBELINA:/A Fairy Story; adapted from Hans Andersen's Fairy Story
Digest Juvenile Productions, Melbourne, n.d. [1948]
16pp, 8pp col. illus., b/w illus. throughout, stiff pic. wrappers, cover title, 240x180mm. ANL

2656 LET'S VISIT THE/ZOO/by Nan Fullarton
Digest Juvenile Productions, Melbourne, n.d. [1948]
16pp, 8pp col. illus., b/w illus. throughout, stiff pic. wrappers, cover title 240x185 mm. ANL

2657 LET'S WALK IN/THE BUSH/Written and Illustrated by Nan Fullarton
Digest Juvenile Productions, Melbourne, n.d. [1948]
16pp, 8pp illus. in col., b/w illus. throughout, stiff pic. wrappers, cover title, 245x185mm. ANL

2658 FRISKY/A Story of the Australian Bush/Written and Illustrated by/Nan Fullarton/Angus and Robertson/Sydney—London—Melbourne—Wellington 1956
80pp, col. frontis., b/w drawings in text, clo., 250x180mm. CLRC
Some pages printed in comic-strip form.

2659 LET'S SAY OUR/NURSERY/RHYMES/Illustrated by Nan Fullarton
Digest Juvenile Productions, Melbourne, n.d. [195-?]

16pp, alternate page openings col. or b/w, light bd., col. pic. wrappers, 244x182mm. NSL:M

2660 FURTHER ADVENTURES OF/FRISKY/[drawing]/ Written and Illustrated by/Nan Fullarton/Angus and Robertson
Sydney 1961
80pp, extended b/w frontis., b/w & part. col. illus. throughout, clo., 250x185mm. CLRC
Part printed in comic-strip form.

2661 NEST/IN THE BUSH/written and illustrated by/ Nan Fullarton/Golden Pleasure Books/Westbook House Fulham Broadway London/Copyright Golden Pleasure Books Ltd 1962/Printed in Italy
[20]pp, col. illus. throughout (inc. t.p.), col. pic. bd. & e/p, 315x230mm. NSL:M

FULLER, Katherine
2662 NOISES/CAN BE FUN!/by Katherine Fuller/ Illustrated by/Ella Hansen
Readabout Publications Pty Ltd, Crow's Nest, NSW, 1964
24pp, col. dec. t.p., col. & part. col. illus. throughout, stiff dec. wrappers, 215x180mm. KMM

"FULLERTON, Cyrus"
2663 HAPPINESS AND HEALTH/IN WOMANHOOD/ A guide to better understanding and/closer friendship between mother/and daughter/Revised fourth edition/ By/"Cyrus Fullerton"/Father & Son Welfare Movement/Sydney N.S.W./1945
52pp, b/w illus., wrappers, 180x120mm. KP

FULLERTON, Evelyn
2664 SUSAN'S TALE/by/Evelyn Fullerton/[b/w illus.]/ Illustrated by/Betty Paterson/Hall's Book Store Pty Ltd./Melbourne
n.d. [library copy acquired 1919]
vipp, 87pp, b/w drawings in text, part col. illus. wrappers, 210x138mm. ANL

FULTON, M. J. C.
2665 NO-TIME-/LAND/A Story/for/Girls and Boys/ By/M. J. C. Fulton/Tasmania/Printed at the Examiner Office, Launceston/1901
23pp, 2 f/p b/w illus., wrappers, 140x120mm. KMM
Fairy story for young children.

Fun and Fare
2666 FUN AND FARE/for Children's Parties/Published by the Mothers Club Committee of the/Rose Park Infant Demonstration School,/South Australia/ 1964/Coudrey Offset Press LImited/293 Pirie St., Adelaide 23 3349
64pp, unillus., dec. wrappers, 206x132mm. KP
Games, recipes &c.

Fun at the Zoo
2667 FUN AT THE/ZOO
n.p., n.d. [1950?]
14pp (inc. 6pp f/p col. illus) & col. pic. covers, cover title, 225x175mm. KP
Kangaroos, koalas & kookaburras as well as parrots suggest an Australian origin.

Fun in Cubbing
2668 FUN IN CUBBING/A Book for/Nine-year-old Cubs
Publ. by the authority of the Scout Association of Australia by Educational Division, Horwitz Group Books
1927
132pp & 8pp parents supplement (insert), part col. illus. throughout, stiff pic. wrappers, 210x145mm. CLRC

Funland
2669 FUNLAND
Dawfox Productions, Sydney, n.d.
16pp, b/w illus. throughout, col. pic. wrappers, cover title, 215x135mm. KP

FURNES, Albert
2670 Imperial Edition/No. 151/TINY TUNES/FOR/ WEE AUSTRALIANS/A collection of melodies set with words/for piano solo without octaves/by/Albert Furnes/Copyright/Allan & Co. Pty. Ltd.
Melbourne, n.d.
16pp, unillus., wrappers, 310x235mm. KMM
2671 TINY TUNES/FOR/WEE AUSTRALIANS/A Collection of Melodies set with Words/for Piano Solo without Octaves/Albert Furnes
Allan & Co. [acquired 1934]
Imperial edition 151, 9 songs, 305x230mm. VSL

FYFE, J. Hamilton
2672 BRITISH ENTERPRISE BEYOND/THE SEAS;/or,/ The Planting of our Colonies./By/J. H. Fyfe/Author of "The Triumphs of Invention and Discovery"/London:/ T. Nelson and Sons, Paternoster Row,/Edinburgh; and New York./MDCCCLXIII 1863
viiipp, 263pp, b/w frontis., additional engraved t.p., 2 engraved plates, dec. clo., 177x117mm. HBM
Contains 'Our Antipodes' 41pp; 'The Cannibal Islands' 17pp; 'The Island of the Blest' (Pitcairn) 9pp.

2673 ENTERPRISE/BEYOND THE SEAS;/or,/How Great Colonies were founded./By/J. Hamilton Fyfe,/ Author of "Triumphs of Invention and Discovery"/London:/T. Nelson and Sons, Paternoster Row;/Edinburgh; and New York./1872
247pp (inc. 3pp preface, 5pp appendix), 8pp adv., b/w frontis. & 6 f/p b/w illus., dec. clo., 175x115mm. CLRC
Contains: 'The Australian Continent' (46pp); 'Pitcairn's Island' (10pp).
• Rpt 1874
Details as above. HBM

"G.H."
AUSTRALIA. *See* Shaped Books

GADD, K. M.
2674 SALLY ANN/A Tall Ship/By/K. M. Gadd/ Illustrated by/P. A. Jobson, S.M.A./Ginn and Company Ltd./Queen Square, London. W.C.1
1st pub. 1953; Fourth impr. 1956.
vipp (inc. pref. and frontis. drawing), 170pp (inc. 26pp Glossary etc.) b/w drawings throughout, dec. bd., e/p, diagram of a 4-masted barque, and map of the world, 178x124mm. WRT
'The Active Readers' series.
An account of a voyage from Port Victoria, S.A. to London Docks, written for children and largely based on the book of Commander A. J. Villiers and others.

[GADEN, T.]
2675 STUMPY:/A Cattle Dog/His Own Tale/ Melbourne:/Australasian Authors Agency/1912
16pp, 2 b/w illus., dec. wrappers, 185x120mm. NSL:M

GALBALLY, Ann
ARTHUR STREETON. *See* Great Australians

GALBRAITH, Jean
2676 GRANDMA/HONEYPOT/By Jean Galbraith/ Pictures by Noela Young/Angus and Robertson
Sydney 1962

56pp, b/w frontis. & 40 b/w & part. col. illus., clo., dec. e/p, 235x150mm. KMM
These short stories were originally published in the *School Magazine* of the NSW Department of Education.

2677 Rpt above, school edition 1964
64pp, part. col. frontis. & illus., pic. wrappers, 185x120mm. Grant

2678 FROM FLOWER TO FRUIT/by/Jean Galbraith/[device]/2/Illustrated by Moira Pye/Longmans 1965
Melbourne
16pp, part. col. illus. throughout, stiff pic. wrappers, 210x160mm. Australian Nature Series No. 2. SCAE

2679 FRUITS/by/Jean Galbraith/illustrated by/John Truscott/[device]/13/Longmans 1966
Croydon, Victoria
32pp (inc. bibliography & glossary), part. col. illus. throughout, pic. wrappers, 210x155mm. Australian Nature Series No. 13. SCAE

2680 THE WONDERFUL BUTTERFLY/The Magic of Growth in Nature/Jean Galbraith/Angus and Robertson
1968
50pp, col. photographic illus. clo. 246x185mm. CLRC

GALLASCH, Keith
LASCH, K.

ator]
N/COLOURING BOOK/Can be
colours or Crayons
ey, n.d. [1945]
v illus. (to be coloured) on
, drawings, wrappers, cover title,

GALPIN, Jeanette
2682 A HORSE OF/YOUR OWN/A book for Australian/and New Zealand riders/by/Jeanette Galpin/A. H. & A. W. Reed/Wellington Auckland Sydney Melbourne
1969
162pp, b/w photographic illus. throughout, clo., 210x135mm. CLRC

GAMACK, Ronald S.
2683 WHAT BECAME OF THE/AUSTRALIAN ABORIGINES?/Ronald S. Gamack/designed and illustrated by/Denis Wrigley/Wheaton A member of the Pergamon Group
Exeter, England, 1969
90pp (inc. 2pp index), 16 part. col. illus., b/w drawings in text, clo., 205x150mm. CLRC

'GAMBLER'
OLD MAN/HODGE/HE HAD A FARM/By/GAMBLER. *See* Ambler, C. Gifford

GAMMAGE, John W.
2684 EXPLORATIONS IN/NATURAL SCIENCE/Written by/John W. Gammage/B.A., B.Sc. Agr./Wollongong Teachers' College/Editor-in-Chief:/Alan G. Maclaine,/B.Ed. M.A., Ph.D., A.Mus.A., M.A.C.E., M.R.S.H./University of Sydney/[col. illus.]/Illustrated by:/Tuk Caldwell,/A.T.D./Southern Cross International Sydney
1965
128pp, b/w & part col. illus. throughout, pic. clo., 242x166mm. KP

GARD, Joyce
WOORROO/by/Joyce Gard/Illustrated by/Ronald Benham/London/Victor Gollancz Ltd./1961
This is not an Australian children's book but a fantasy with a number of Australian references. KMM

GARDE, Brian
VENDETTA. *See* Australian Youth Plays

The Garden Year with Mr Bear
2685 6d/THE GARDEN/YEAR/WITH/MR BEAR
Published for Australian Kiddies by Arthur Yates & Co Pty Ltd, 184-186 Sussex St Sydney
n.d.
[24]pp, b/w & part col. illus. throughout, stiff pic. wrappers, cover title, 250x180m. KP
Verses & drawings about gardening pub. by the seed merchant.

GARDINER, Lyndsay Beatrice
2686 Lyndsay Gardiner, M.A./PACIFIC/PEOPLES/Illustrated by/Nancy Parker/Longmans, Green & Co./London Melbourne New York
1957
134pp (inc index), 1p author's note, b/w drawings throughout, maps &c., clo., 215x135mm. ANL

THOMAS MITCHELL. *See* Australian Explorers

GARDINER, Tom James
2687 WIRELESS/AND OTHER/FAIRY STORIES/By T. J. Gardiner/Proceeds for the/Adelaide Children's Hospital/(Copyright)
Whillas & Ormiston, Adelaide, n.d. [1930]
20pp (inc. 1p acknowledgements), unillus., dec. wrappers, 180x155mm. VSL
Booklet contains 6 short stories & some verse.

GARDNER, Rev. John
2688 "In the shadow of the wings will I make/my refuge."/A Sermon/preached to the children/attending the/Sabbath Schools of the Presbyterian Church,/Conway Street, Birkenhead./with/A MEMOIR/of/Elizabeth Hearne,/of Oxton, Cheshire/By the/Rev. John Gardner./1849/Melbourne:/Fergusson and Moore, Printers, 48 Flinders Lane East./1887.
68pp and 1p letter from the author's grandchildren dated Mentone 1887 thanking him for the little book he wrote in England 38 years ago, unillus., clo., 157x104mm. NSL:M
Book comprises Sermon (13pp) and Memoir of the pious child who died in September 1848 aged 11 years and 2 months.
Printed Ferguson & Moore, Melbourne.
Title on front cover: 'Memoir of Elizabeth Hearne by Rev. J. Gardner'.

GARDNER, Russell & ALBISTON, Barbara
AUSTRALIAN CATTLE STATIONS. *See* Life in Australia

GARNER, George J.
2689 Whitcombe's Story Books/AT DRAKE'S RIGHT HAND/A Tale of English Sea-Dog/and Spanish Don/For ages 10 to 12 years/[drawing]/Whitcombe and Tombs Limited/Auckland Christchurch Dunedin Wellington/Melbourne Sydney London
n.d.
87pp (inc. 7pp notes, &c.), b/w frontis. & b/w drawings, pic. wrappers, 180x115mm. ANL
See McLaren 548

2690 Whitcombe's Historical Story Books (No. 432)/A SON OF/MERRIE ENGLAND/A Tale of the Glorious Days/of Good Queen Bess/(For ages 9 to 10 years)/[illustration & caption]/Whitcombe and Tombs Limited/Auckland, Christchurch, Dunedin, Wellington/Melbourne, Sydney and London
n.d. [1928]

64pp (inc. 5pp notes, &c.), b/w frontis. & drawings in text, pic. wrappers, 180x115mm. ANL
See McLaren 432

2691 IN PIRATE WATERS/By/George Garner/Illustrated by/Savile Lumley/Whitcombe & Tombs Ltd./Auckland, Christchurch, Dunedin/Wellington, N.Z.; Melbourne, Sydney/London
1930
256pp, col. frontis. & 4 b/w illus., clo., 180x115mm. ANL

2692 MYSTERY/MEN-O-WAR/By/George Garner/With a Frontispiece by/A. S. Forrest/And Illustrations in Colour and/Black and White by/Claude Muncaster/A.R.W.S., R.O.I./[drawing]/Thomas Nelson and Sons Ltd./London Edinburgh New York Toronto Paris
n.d.
300pp, 11pp adv., b/w frontis., 3 col. illus. & 2 f/p b/w illus., clo., 195x130mm. ANL

GARNET, J. Roslyn
WILSONS PROMONTORY. *See* Life in Australia series

GARNETT, Emmeline
2693 THE TRUE BOOK ABOUT/HEROINES/OF ADVENTURE/by Emmeline Garnett/Illustrated by/F. Stocks May/Shakespeare Head/London New York Sydney Paris
1955
143pp, 18 b/w drawings, clo., 180x115mm. NSL:M
One chapter of 22 pages on Amy Johnson & her flight to Australia.

GARRETT, Edward
2694 THE/MAGIC FLOWER-POT/By/Edward Garrett/New Edition/Sydney/Hugh Macready
n.d.
284pp, b/w front cover, dec. e/p, clo., g.e. 185x117mm. ANL
A collection of stories none of which relate to Australia.

'GARRICK, Donald' [pseud., Donald Keith]
2695 OLD MAKE/BELIEVE/By Donald Garrick
Anjon Publishing Co., Adelaide 1954
14pp, b/w drawings, wrappers, cover title, 240x185mm. ANL
Allee Dollie Book.
Verses.

GARY, John
2696 PERILS OF A/PEARL HUNTER/By John Gary/[drawing]/John Sands Pty. Ltd./Sydney and Melbourne
n.d. [1948]
104pp, 4 b/w f/p illus., drawings in text, clo., 180x120mm. ANL

[GAULT, Mrs A. K.]
See Hawker, Ruth M.

GAY, Florence
2697 THE DRUIDESS./A Story for Boys and Others/By/Florence Gay/London:/John Ouseley,/16 Farringdon Street, E.C./(All rights reserved)
n.d. [1908]
195pp (inc. 1p preface), 5pp adv., unillus., clo., 180x115mm. ANL

GAZE, Harold
2698 THE BILLABONGA BIRD/Written and Pictured by/Harold Gaze/Author of/"The Simple Jaggajay" "The Chewg-um-blewg-um"/"Copper-top" "Omar in Fairyland" etc./[drawing]/Melbourne/Auckland, Christchurch, Dunedin and Wellington, N.Z., and London/Whitcombe & Tombs Limited
n.d. [1919]
[32]pp, 1p preface, 2pp introduction, 2 col. plates, 1 b/w plate. & b/w drawings in text, pic. wrappers, 255x190mm. The Mite Merry Series KMM
Verses.

2699 THE/CHEWG-UM-BLEWG-UM/Written and Pictured by/Harold Gaze/Author of/"The Billabonga Bird" "The Simple Jaggajay"/"Copper-top" "Omar in Fairyland" etc./[drawing]/Melbourne/Auckland, Christchurch, Dunedin and Wellington, N.Z., and London/Whitcombe & Tombs Limited
n.d. [1919]
[32]pp (inc. 1p preface), 2 col. plates, 1 b/w plate & b/w drawings in text, pic. wrappers, 245x180mm. The Mite Merry Series. ANL
Verses.

2700 THE SIMPLE JAGGAJAY/Written and Pictured by/Harold Gaze/Author of/"The Billabonga Bird" "The Chewg-um-blewg-um"/"Copper-top" "Omar in Fairyland" etc./[drawing]/Melbourne/Auckland, Christchurch, Dunedin and Wellington, N.Z., and London/Whitcombe & Tombs Limited
n.d. [1919]
[32]pp, 1p preface, 2pp introduction, 2 col. plates, 1 b/w plate & b/w drawings in text, pic. wrappers, 255x190mm. The Mite Merry Series. KMM
Verses.

2701 The Chap Happy Series/"THE WICKED/WINKAPONG"/Written and Pictured by/Harold Gaze/[drawing]/Published by Gordon & Gotch Pty. Ltd./Melbourne, Sydney, Brisbane, Adelaide, Perth, Launceston/and New York.
n.d. [1919]
12pp, 1p preface, col. frontis. & 1 col. plate., 1 f/p b/w illus. & line drawings in text, pic. bd., 270x215mm. NSL:M
Children's verse.

2702 COPPERTOP/The Queer Adventures of a Quaint Child/By/Harold Gaze/author of/The Mite Merry Stories, War in Faerieland/Omar in Faerieland, etc./Illustrations by the author/Melbourne Publishing Company/Cromwell Buildings/Melbourne
n.d. [1919]
153pp, col. frontis. & 6 col. plates, 10 b/w illus., bd. (with col. illus. on front cover), 220x145mm. KMM

2703 COPPERTOP/The Queer Adventures/of a Quaint Child/by/Harold Gaze/Ilustrations by the Author/Harper Brothers Publishers/New York and London
n.d. [Copyright 1924]
338pp (inc. 1p note), col. frontis. & 11 f/p col. plates, 13 f/p b/w illus. & 6 b/w drawings in text, bd., 230x170mm. ANL
Contents include *Coppertop* and *Coppertop Cruises.*

2704 COPPERTOP CRUISES/The Wonderful Voyage of the good ship/"Queercraft"/By/Harold Gaze/Author of/"Coppertop" "War in Faerieland" "Omar in Faerieland"/"The Mite Merry Stories" "The Peri and the Pearl"/Illustrations by the author/Melbourne Publishing Company/Cromwell Buildings/Melbourne
n.d. [1920]
133pp, col. frontis., 6 col. plates & 10 b/w illus., bd. (with col. illus. on front cover), 245x180mm. KMM

2705 THE CHINA CAT/By/Harold Gaze/Author and Illustrator of "Copper-top"/"The Enchanted Fish", The Mite Merry Series/etc./[decoration]/Whitcombe and

Tombs Limited/Auckland Christchurch Dunedin and Wellington, N.Z./Melbourne and London
n.d. [1921]
44pp, col. frontis. & 2 col. plates, b/w drawings, dec. wrappers (with adv. inside front & back covers), 180x135mm. KMM
Includes verses.

2706 THE ENCHANTED FISH/By/Harold Gaze/Author and Illustrator of "Coppertop"/"The China Cat", The Merry Mite Series, etc./[decoration]/Whitcombe and Tombs Limited/Auckland Christchurch Dunedin and Wellington N.Z./Melbourne and London
n.d. [1921]
52pp, col. frontis. & 2 col. plates, b/w drawings, dec. wrappers, 180x135mm. KMM

2707 WAR/IN/FAIRYLAND/Written and Pictured by Harold Gaze/Published by Gordon & Gotch Pty. Ltd./Melbourne, Sydney, Brisbane, Adelaide, Perth, Launceston/and New York/Printed by Arbuckle, Waddell, Pty. Ltd. McKillop St., Melbourne.
n.d. [1921]
30pp (inc. 1p preface & 1p introduction), 4 col. plates, b/w drawings, dec. bd., dec. e/p, 240x185mm. NSL:M

2708 THE GOBLIN'S/GLEN/A Story of/Childhood's Wonderland/[drawing]/By/Harold Gaze/with/illustrations by the author/Boston/Little Brown and Company/1924
241pp, col. frontis. & 5 col. plates, dec. clo., pic. e/p, 200x130mm. ANL

2709 THE/MERRY PIPER/or The Magical Trip/of the Sugar Bowl Ship/Written and Illustrated by/Harold Gaze/Longmans, Green, and Co./39 Paternoster Row, London, E.C.4/Toronto/Bombay, Calcutta and Madras/1925/All rights reserved
247pp, dec. t.p., col. frontis. & 7 col. plates, 12 f/p b/w illus. & b/w drawings in text, pic. clo., dec. e/p, 210x170mm. KMM

2710 As above but, Boston/Little Brown & Co./1925. ANL

GEDDIE, Rev. John & COPELAND, Rev. Joseph
2711 [engraving of a ship]/APPEAL/FOR/A MISSIONARY SHIP/—/To the Children of the Presbyterian Churches in Australia/and New Zealand./(Ancitcum) New Hebrides Dec 1861
4pp, unillus., leaflet, 230x185mm. NSL:M
Printed by G. R. Addison 411 George Street Sydney.

GEDYE, Ethel R.
2712 EVERY DAY/WITH GOD/daily devotions for children/Ethel R. Gedye/Illustrated by Sadie and Suzanne Pascoe/The Clifford Press/Melbourne/Australia
1964
[40]pp, 5 f/p part col. illus & b/w drawings, clo., 178x115mm. KP

GEEVES, Philip Leslie
2713 THE EXPLORERS
Australian Broadcasting Commission Education Department, Sydney, n.d. [1971?]
31pp, photographic illus. throughout, b/w maps, pic. wrappers, 175x235mm. ANL
Includes articles on: Flinders, Oxley, Hume & Hovell, Cunningham, Mitchell, Eyre, Sturt, Leichhardt, Stuart, Burke & Wills.

GELLERT, Leon
2714 THESE BEASTLY/AUSTRALIANS/Some faunagraphic data compiled for/students of Australian Wild Life/By/Leon Gellert/Illustrated by/Bernard Hesling/Australasian Publishing Co. Pty. Ltd./Sydney N.S.W.
n.d. [1945?]
52pp, b/w drawings throughout dec. bd., dec. e/p, 185x140mm. KMM

2715 BEASTLY/AUSTRALIANS/Some faunagraphic data compiled for/Students of Australian Wild Life/by Leon Gellert/Illustrated by/Bernard Hesling/Hodder and Stoughton
London 1964
[74]pp, b/w drawings, clo., 175x120mm. KMM

GEORGE, Beryl
See Tindale, Norman B. & George, Beryl

GEORGE, Elisabeth
2716 JANUARY AND AUGUST/By/Elisabeth George/Decorations by Esmond George/[device]/Georgian House/Melbourne
1947
202pp, b/w chapter headings & tailpieces, clo., 185x120mm. KMM
The experiences of two children of itinerant workers in the outback. Not a children's book, but sometimes referred to as such.

GEORGE, Gordon
2717 FOREST FRIENDS/Issued by The School Bank Department of/The Savings Bank of South Australia
Adelaide n.d. [195-?]
10pp, 8 b/w illus., col. pic. wrappers, cover title, 186x122mm. CLRC
Illus. by Maxine Harden.

[GEORGE, Mabel E.]
2718 A/PICTURE HISTORY/OF GREAT DISCOVERIES/Clarke Hutton/[Illus.]/Oxford University Press/London
First ed. 1954, rpt 1956, 1957, 1960, 1961
62pp, col. lithographic drawings throughout, pic. bd., map e/p, 277x210mm. KMM
10pp deal with Jas Cook & 7pp with the Antarctic.
• Rpt as above, 1965. KMM

GEORGE, Sidney Charles
2719 THE TROUBLE MAKER/S. C. George/Illustrated by/Arthur Cartwright/E. J. Arnold & Son Limited, Leeds
1965
144pp, b/w frontis & 3 f/p b/w illus. & 4 smaller illus. in text, clo., 180x120mm. KP
Story set in an Aboriginal reserve.

2720 HIDDEN/TREASURE/S. C. George/Lothian Publishing Co. Pty Ltd; Melbourne
1972
74pp (inc. 2pp index, 1p acknowledgements), b/w photographic illus. throughout, bd., 210x146mm. ANL
Archaeology for young people.

GERSTAECKER, Friedrich
2721 DIE/WELT IM KLEINEN/FÜR/DIE KLEINE WELT/Von Friedrich Gerstäcker./POLYNESIAN UND AUSTRALIEN./Mit Zwei Karten./(Der Berfasser Berhält sich das uebersetzungsrecht vor.)/[device]/Leipzig,/Verlag von Bernhard Schlicke./1860
111pp, 2pp adv., 2 folding maps, pic. clo., 180x135mm. RM
This is the fifth volume of a series 'The World in Miniature for the Small World' dealing with different countries, Volume 1 being an introduction; Volume 2 dealing with Europe; Volume 3, North America; Volume 4, South America. Also advertised is a work entitled *Reisen um die Welt/Ein Familienbuch in 6*

Banden ('Trips round the World, a family book in 6 parts'), 2nd ed., by the same author.

2722 DIE BEIDEN STRÄFLINGE./Australischer Roman/von/Friedrich Gerstäcker./Original Ausgabe./Neu durchgesehen und herausgegebem/von/Dietrich Theden/Zehnte Auflage/[device]/Berlin S.W./Verlag von Neufeld & Henius
[1912?]
535pp, b/w frontis & 11 b/w plates, dec. clo., 186x130mm. ANL
Also published in other editions not intended for children

Dutch trans. of Die Beiden Sträflinge
2723 Friedrich Gerstäcker/DONKER AUSTRALIE/Naar de oorspronkelijke uitgave/opnieuw bewerkt door/Henk Schregel/[drawing]/Bandtekening en illustraties van/R. Van Looy/J. Philip Kruseman [device] Uitgever Den Haag
n.d.
320pp (t.p. printed in 2 col.), b/w frontis & 3 f/p b/w illus., col. pic. bd., 234x155mm. ANL
Die Beiden Sträflinge; adapted for children as
2724 UNTER/SCHWARZEN AUSTRALIENS/von/Friedrich/Gerstäcker/Für die reifere Jugend bearbeitet von/Ferdinand Schmidt/mit einem mehrfarbigen Umschlagbild und zwei farbigen/Textbildern nach Aquarellen von M. Wulff/[device]/Johannes Knoblauch Verlag, Berlin S.W.
n.d. [1950?]
174pp & 2pp adv., part col. frontis & 1 part col. plate, pic. bd., 205x142mm. ANL
THE/TWO CONVICTS/By/Frederick Gerstaëcker
Eng. trans. of *Die Beiden Sträflinge*, but not intended for children. NSL:M
2725 THE BUSHRANGER; or, The Half-Breed Brigade. A Romance of the Bush. Jan 28 1871 (American Tales Series)
N.Y. Beadle & Co.
A translation by Francis Johnson of the first part of Gerstacker's DIE BEIDEN STRÄFLINGE.
Other editions 1876, 1881. Continuation pub. in same series Feb. 18 1871 under the title THE OUTLAW HUNTER; or, Red John, the Bush-Ranger. (new ed. 1876, 1881)
From JOHANNSEN, A. 'The House of Beadle and Adams and its Dime and Nickel Novels', 2 vol., Norman, Oklahoma, Uni. of Oklahoma Press, 1950. Unseen

GERVAISE, Mary
2726 THE/RAINBOW COMES/by/Mary Gervaise/[Device]/Frederick Warne and Co., Ltd./London and New York
240pp, t.p. b/w frontis, clo., 180x120mm. JMcG
First pub. 1944; rpt 1948.
Story for older girls set partly on a station in remote outback Australia.

The Giant Book of Trains
2727 THE GIANT BOOK/OF TRAINS
Offset Printing Co, Waterloo NSW
n.d. [194-?]
16pp, b/w illus., 4 f/p col. illus., col. pic. wrappers, cover title, 360x244mm. ANL
Uniform with above:
2728 The Giant Book of Aeroplanes. Grant
2729 The Giant Book of Speed. JH

The Giant Comic Book
With Bright Colored Pages/THE GIANT/COMIC/BOOK. *See* Gunn & Taylor

The Giant Book of Stories
THE/GIANT/BOOK OF STORIES. *See* Gunn & Taylor

GIBB, C. A.
2730 THE ADVENTURES/OF/JOHNNY RABBIT/By C. A. Gibb/Thompson Street, Clifton Gardens/Sydney
The author, n.d. [1931]
72pp, unillus., wrappers, 240x180mm. NSL:M

GIBBS, May [Mrs Cecilia May Ossoli Kelly]
2731 ABOUT US/[drawing]/by May Gibbs/London: Ernest Nister/New York: E. P. Dutton & Co./No. 3529
n.d. [1912]
[32]pp, col. frontis. & 7 f/p col. illus., 7 f/p b/w illus. & line drawings, col. pic. bd., pic. e/p, 227x286mm. NSL:M
This book, the only one of the author's to have been published overseas and her first book, is entirely different in style from the rest of her work.

2732 Words/and/Pictures/GUM/BLOSSOM/BABIES/by/May Gibbs/Sydney: Angus & Robertson Ltd
n.d. [1916] Printed by H. & H. Printing Co., 190a Sussex St Sydney
[56]pp consisting of half-title, 2 blank pp, frontis., t.p.; then 22pp text and illus, blank pp with caption between each page opening of text & illus.; brown paper wrappers, title printed in brown in larger letters than in subsequent editions; externally 250x160mm, page size 224x145mm. Col. illus. on cover & col. frontis; printed throughout in sepia. KMM
This first edition sold at 2s 6d.
2733 Words/and/Pictures/GUM/BLOSSOM/BABIES/as above
n.d. [Rpt 1917, 1918 (twice), 1919 (twice), 1920 (three times)]
[28]pp, col. frontis., dec. t.p., 11 sepia f/p illus., col. illus. pasted on brown paper tied wrapper, 220x142mm. KMM
By the end of 1920 nearly 33 000 copies of this shilling rpt had been sold
2734 Rpt as above but: ...Angus & Robertson Ltd./Wholly set up and printed in/Australia by Shepherd & Newman/Commonwealth Street, Sydney, 1922/Registered by the Postmaster-General for transmission by post as a book.
Details as previous rpt. KMM

2735 Words and/Pictures/by/May/Gibbs/GUMNUT/BABIES/Sydney: Angus & Robertson Ltd.
n.d. [1916]
Uniform with *Gum Blossom Babies* first edition
At first sold at 2s 6d, then a cheap shilling edition was brought out in 1917. CLRC
2736 Words and/Pictures/by/May/Gibbs/GUMNUT/BABIES/Sydney: Angus & Robertson Ltd.
n.d. [Rpt 1917, 1918 (twice), 1919 (twice), 1920 (three times)]
By the end of 1920 over thirty- two and a half thousand copies of this reprint had been sold
[28]pp, col. frontis., dec. t.p., 11 sepia f/p illus., col. illus. pasted on brown tied wrappers, 220x142mm. KMM
2737 Rpt as above but: ...Angus & Robertson Ltd./Wholly set up and printed in/Australia by Shepherd & Newman/Commonwealth Street, Sydney, 1922/&c.
Details as previous rpt. KMM

2738 [dec. border] WATTLE/BABIES/by/May/Gibbs/Sydney: Angus & Robertson Ltd.
n.d. [1918]
[28]pp, col. frontis., dec. t.p., 11 f/p sepia illus., tied

cream wrappers with col. illus. & title in sepia, 220x142mm. KMM
[W. C. Penfold & Co Printers Sydney]
Over 22 000 copies printed up to February 1922 with 5 reprints.
Morris Miller refers to *Water Babies* 1918, a misprint for *Wattle Babies.*

2739 WATTLE BABIES/by/May/Gibbs/Sydney: Angus & Robertson Ltd./Wholly set up and printed in Australia by Shepherd & Newman/Commonwealth Street, Sydney, 1922/Registered by the Postmaster-General...&c.
As before. CLRC

2740 BORONIA/BABIES [within dec. border]/May/Gibbs/Sydney: Angus & Robertson Ltd.
[Printed by W. C. Penfold & Co. Ltd. 183 Pitt St Sydney]
n.d. [1919]
[28]pp, col. frontis. & col. illus. pasted on front cover, dec. borders to each page & 11 f/p sepia illus., brown paper wrappers tied, 220x142mm. KMM

2741 BORONIA/BABIES/May/Gibbs/Sydney: Angus & Robertson Ltd./Wholly set up and printed in Australia by Shepherd and Newman/Commonwealth Street, Sydney, 1922/Registered by the Postmaster-General...&c.
As previous. CLRC
19 450 copies printed up to March 1920. Not known how many in 1922 edition or if there were any later printings.

2742 [dec. border]/FLANNEL/FLOWERS/AND/Other Bush/Babies/May/Gibbs/Sydney: Angus & Robertson Ltd.
n.d. [1920?]
Printed W. C. Penfold,88 Pitt Street, Sydney
[28]pp, col. frontis., dec. t.p., 11 sepia illus. , grey pic. wrappers with col. illus., tied, 220x142mm. KMM
Title printed in larger letters in green. Over 18 000 copies printed up to February 1922 with 5 reprints.

2743 [border]/FLANNEL/FLOWERS/And/Other Bush/Babies/May/Gibbs/Sydney: Angus & Robertson Ltd./Wholly set up and printed in Australia by Shepherd and Newman/Commonwealth Street, Sydney, 1922/Registered by the Postmaster-General...&c.
As in previous ed. unseen

2744 SNUGGLEPOT/AND/CUDDLEPIE/[drawing]/Their Adventures Wonderful/Pictures & Words/by/May/Gibbs/Sydney Angus & Robertson Ltd.
n.d. [1918]
87pp, col. frontis. (frontis. & title printed on coated paper), 22 f/p sepia illus. & drawings in text, pic. bd. with col. onlay pasted on front cover, clo. spine, pic. e/p, 244x188mm. KMM
The first ed. printed by W. C. Penfold 183 Pitt St Sydney has a round vignette on back cover, text is printed in b/w. 5000 copies were printed.
A second printing (also undated) was on sale before the end of March & a third before 30 June 1919.
Penfold moved to 88 Pitt Street during 1919. Some copies with this address have the vignette on back cover. Some are printed thoughout in sepia. Some copies have illus. on pp32 & 36 reversed & on pp42 & 46. Earlier copies seem to have 'The Hat Shop' opp. p32 & the 'Fight with Red Gumnut' opp. p42. 23 000 copies had been sold by early 1922.

2745 SNUGGLEPOT/AND/CUDDLEPIE/[drawing]/Their Adventures Wonderful/Pictures & Words/by/May/Gibbs/Sydney—Cornstalk Publishing Co.
1929
69pp, 4 f/p b/w illus., drawings in text, wrappers, 170x110mm. The Gumnut Readers. ANL

2746 SNUGGLEPOT/AND/CUDDLEPIE/[drawing]/Their Adventures Wonderful/Pictures & Words/by/May/Gibbs/Sydney—Angus & Robertson Ltd.
n.d. [copy inscribed 1931]
87pp, col. frontis., 22 f/p sepia/white illus. & drawings in text, clo., 240x180mm. Grant
Book printed in sepia apart from t.p. which is b/w. Red cloth binding with 'Tales of/Snugglepot/and/Cuddlepie/by May Gibbs' in gilt on front cover & embossed design of gumnuts in bottom right hand corner.

2747 SNUGGLEPOT/AND/CUDDLEPIE/[drawing]/Their Adventures Wonderful/Pictures & Words/by/May/Gibbs/Sydney—Angus & Robertson Ltd.
1934
87pp, col. frontis., 22 f/p sepia/white illus., drawings in text, dec. bd., 240x180mm.
Cover reads: 'Tales of Snugglepot and Cuddlepie'. KMM
• Rpt as above, 1939. KMM

2748 THE COMPLETE ADVENTURES/OF/SNUGGLEPOT/AND/CUDDLEPIE/[drawing]/Pictures & Words by/May Gibbs/Angus & Robertson Ltd/Sydney
1940
[209]pp, col. frontis. & 56 f/p b/w illus., pic. bd., 240x184mm. KMM
The first collected edition of the three books, *Snugglepot and Cuddlepie* (65pp); *Little Ragged Blossom* (78pp) & *Little Obelia* (66pp), each with separate pagination.
This edition omits all but one of the col. plates, 5 of the f/p b/w illus. & a number of text illus., mainly tailpieces. All the f/p b/w omitted are from *Little Obelia* & the endpiece.

2749 THE COMPLETE ADVENTURES/OF/SNUGGLEPOT/AND/CUDDLEPIE/[drawing]/Pictures and Words by/May Gibbs/Angus & Robertson Ltd./Sydney
1942
iv+[209]pp (i.e. 65, 78, 66, sep. pagination), col. frontis. & 52 f/p b/w illus., pic. bd., 242x180mm. CLRC

2750 THE COMPLETE ADVENTURES OF/SNUGGLEPOT/AND/CUDDLEPIE/[drawing]/Pictures & Words/by May Gibbs/Angus & Robertson Ltd./Sydney
1946
219pp, col. frontis. & 4 col. illus., 61 f/p sepia/white illus., bd., dec. e/p, 235x180mm. ANL
• Rpt as above. 1948
Text printed in black. Drawings & chapter headings in sepia, 219pp, col. frontis. & 4 col. plates. KP
• Rpt as above, 1949. ANL
• Rpt as above 1950, but printed in sepia. KP
• Rpt as above 1952, but bound in dec. bd. with clo. spine. KMM
• Rpt 1954 & 1956, as above, but bound in clo. KP
• Rpt 1965, as above. KP
• Rpt 1966, as above. KP

2751 THE COMPLETE ADVENTURES OF/SNUGGLEPOT/AND/CUDDLEPIE/[drawing]/Pictures & Words/by/May/Gibbs/Angus & Robertson Ltd./Sydney
First published in this form 1946; rpt 1947, 1948, 1949, 1950, 1952, 1954, 1956, 1962, 1963, 1965, 1966; reset and rearranged 1968, rpt 1970, 1971, 1972 (twice)
Details as above but pic. bd., KP

2752 LITTLE RAGGED/BLOSSOM/& more about/

Snugglepot &/Cuddlepie/by/May/Gibbs/Sydney—Angus & Robertson Ltd.
n.d. [1920] [inscr.1920]
98pp, dec. t.p., col. frontis. & 1 col. illus., 20 f/p sepia/white illus., line drawings in text, pic. bd., with col. pic. onlay on front cover, pic. e/p, 250x180mm. KP
The text and drawings are printed in b/w & the f/p illus. in sepia. The t.p. is printed on coated paper in b/w.

2753 LITTLE RAGGED/BLOSSOM/& more about/Snugglepot/&/Cuddlepie/by/May/Gibbs/Sydney –Cornstalk Publishing Co.
[Angus & Robertson Ltd] 1929
85pp, b/w frontis. & 3 f/p b/w illus., line drawings in text, wrappers, 185x120mm. The Gumnut Readers. KMM

2754 LITTLE RAGGED/BLOSSOM
Gumnut Reader as above but imprint: Australia/Angus & Robertson Limited/89 Castlereagh Street, Sydney/1932
KP

2755 LITTLE RAGGED/BLOSSOM/& more about SNUGGLEPOT/&/ CUDDLEPIE/ by/May/Gibbs/Sydney Angus & Robertson Ltd
1934
98pp, col. frontis., 20 f/p sepia/white plates, line drawings in text, pic. bd., 245x180mm. KMM
• Rpt 1938, as above. Grant

2756 LITTLE RAGGED/BLOSSOM/& MORE ABOUT/SNUGGLEPOT &/CUDDLEPIE/by/May/Gibbs/Sydney—Angus & Robertson Ltd
1940
78pp, col. frontis., 20 sepia/white drawings, col. pic. bd., 240x180mm.
On front cover: 'Little/Ragged/Blossom/2nd Book/of/Snugglepot & Cuddlepie/May Gibbs'/
KP

2757 LITTLE OBELIA/and/Further Adventures/of Ragged Blossom/Snugglepot &/Cuddlepie/by/May/Gibbs/Angus & Robertson—Sydney
n.d. [1921]
91pp, col. frontis. & 1 col. plate, 19 f/p sepia illus., b/w line drawings & text printed in b/w, pic. bd. with col. pic. onlay, dec. e/p, 245x180mm. The t.p. is printed in b/w on coated paper. ANL

2758 LITTLE OBELIA/Further adventures of/Ragged Blossom/Snugglepot and Cuddlepie [drawing]/By May Gibbs/Australia;/Cornstalk Publishing Company/89 Castlereagh Street, Sydney/1929
77pp, b/w frontis. & 3 f/p b/w illus. & other line drawings, wrappers, cover title, 180x115mm. ANL The Gumnut Readers (other titles in this series advertised on back wrapper)

2759 Rpt of 1929 Gumnut Reader but imprint: Angus & Robertson Limited/89 Castlereagh Street, Sydney/1933 CLRC

2760 LITTLE OBELIA/and/Further Adventures/of Ragged Blossom/Snugglepot &/Cuddlepie/by/May/Gibbs/Angus & Robertson Sydney
1934
90pp, col. frontis., 19 sepia plates, drawings in text, pic. bd., 240x180mm. KMM
• Rpt as above 1938. Grant

2761 LITTLE OBELIA/and /Further/Adventures/of Ragged Blossom/Snugglepot &/Cuddlepie/by/May/Gibbs/Angus & Robertson Sydney
1940
72pp, col. frontis., 19 sepia f/p illus., col. pic. bd., 248x188mm. KP

2762 Rpt 1942, as above, but stiff col. pic. wrappers. KMM

2763 NUTTYBUB/AND/NITTERSING/By/May Gibbs/Australia/Osboldstone & Co. Pty. Ltd.
Melbourne 1923
86pp, pic. t.p., col. frontis., 20 f/p sepia plates, drawings in text, pic. bd., dec. e/p, 245x190mm.
Front cover with col. pic. onlay, title reads: 'The Story of Nuttybub and Nittersing'. VSL

2764 NUTTYBUB/AND/NITTERSING/[drawing]/by May/Gibbs/Australia/Angus & Robertson Limited/89 Castlereagh Street, Sydney/1932
86pp, col. frontis., 20 sepia plates, drawings in text, pic. bd. with clo. spine, 235x170mm.
Cover reads as t.p.; on half title: 'The Story of Nuttybub and Nittersing'. ANL

2765 NUTTYBUB/AND/NITTERSING/[drawing]/by/May/Gibbs/[drawing]/Australia/Angus & Robertson Limited/89 Castlereagh Street, Sydney/1937
86pp, col. frontis., 20 sepia plates (on 10pp), pic. bd., 245x185mm. TG

2766 NUTTYBUB/AND/NITTERSING/by/May/Gibbs/Angus and Robertson Ltd./Sydney: London/1940
106pp, dec. t.p., col. frontis., 10 sepia plates (with 20 illus.), line drawings in text, pic. bd., 240x180mm. KMM

2767 NUTTYBUB/AND/NITTERSING/[drawing]/by/May/Gibbs/Angus and Robertson Ltd./Sydney London/1941
As in 1940 ed. KP

2768 CHUCKLEBUD/AND/WUNKYDOO/by/May Gibbs/Australia/Osboldstone & Co. Pty. Ltd.
Melbourne 1924
47pp, pic. t.p., col. frontis. & 18 part. col. f/p illus., decorations in text, pic. bd., pic. e/p, 240x185mm. VSL
Title on front cover reads: 'Two Little Gumnuts—Chucklebud and Wunkydoo'.

2769 TWO LITTLE/GUM-NUTS/By/May Gibbs/Author of Snugglepot and Cuddlepie, Ragged Blossom, The/Story of Nuttybub and Nittersing, Bib and Bub/Australia:/Cornstalk Publishing Company/89 Castlereagh Street, Sydney/1929
70pp, b/w drawings throughout, dec. wrappers, 185x120mm. ANL
Cover reads: 'Two Little Gumnuts Chucklebud and Wunkydoo—Their Strange Adventures'.

2770 TWO LITTLE GUMNUTS as Cornstalk 1929 ed. but: Angus & Robertson Limited/89 Castlereagh Street, Sydney/1933
Other details as previous entry. Grant

2771 CHUCKLEBUD/AND/WUNKYDOO/by/May Gibbs/Australia/Angus & Robertson Limited/89 Castlereagh Street, Sydney/1932
47pp, dec. t.p., col. frontis. & 18 f/p part. col. illus., decorations in text, dec. bd., 240x180mm. ANL

2772 CHUCKLEBUD/AND/WUNKYDOO/by/May/Gibbs/Australia/Angus & Robertson Limited/Sydney: London/1940
65pp, col. frontis., 18 f/p b/w illus., marginal drawings throughout, pic. bd., 240x180mm. KMM

2773 BIB AND BUB/[coloured illustration]/THEIR ADVENTURES/By/May/Gibbs/Cornstalk Publishing Company Sydney
1925
80pp, col. & part. col. illus. throughout, dec. clo., dec. e/p, 240x210mm. NSL:M
Story told in comic strip form with rhyming text.

2774 BIB AND BUB/[drawing]/Their Adventures/by/

May/Gibbs/In Two Parts/Part 1/Cornstalk Publishing Company Sydney
1925
40pp, dec. t.p., col. illus. throughout, col. pic. wrappers, pic. e/ps, 234x207mm. CLRC
Story told in comic-strip form, with rhyming text.

2775 BIB AND BUB, part 2, uniform with above, KMM
Published as 2 volumes in one, clo., or 2 separate paper-covered bd.

2776 THE FURTHER ADVENTURES/OF/BIB/AND/BUB/by/May/Gibbs/[drawing]/Cornstalk Publishing Company Sydney
[1927]
[100]pp, illus., pic. clo., pic. e/p, 242x270mm. ANL
Comic strips throughout, printed either in blue, green, or reddish-brown. Cover title: The Further Adventures of/Bib and Bub/The Gumnut Babies/and/their/Friends/The Bush Creatures/by/May/Gibbs.

2777 MORE FUNNY STORIES ABOUT OLD FRIENDS/BIB/AND/BUB/May/Gibbs
Cornstalk Publishing Company, Sydney 1928
[94]pp, illus., pic. clo., cover title, 241x274mm. ANL
Comic strips throughout with drawings and caption printed either in green or violet on a pale yellow background.

2778 BIB & BUB/IN/GUMNUT/TOWN
Halstead Printing Co. Ltd, Waterloo, NSW, n.d.
[Copyright 1929]
[44]pp, col. illus. throughout, pic. clo., dec. e/p, 242x270mm. NSL:M
Story told in comic-strip form.

2779 BIB AND BUB/PAINTING BOOK/New Stories/By May Gibbs
Wholly set up and printed in Australia for May Gibbs by W. C. Penfold & Co. Ltd, Printers, Sydney, n.d.
[1932]
24pp, b/w illus. throughout, col. pic. wrappers, cover title, 205x300mm. CLRC
6 pictures in comic-strip form on every page, with 2 lines rhyming text to each.

2780 [decorative device]/GUMNUTS/[decorative device—drawing]/May Gibbs/Angus and Robertson Ltd. Sydney
n.d. [1940?]
48pp, b/w illus. throughout, dec. wrappers, 210x300mm. KMM
Story told in verse in comic-strip form.

2781 SCOTTY IN/GUMNUT/LAND/[drawing]/by/May/Gibbs/Sydney/Angus & Robertson Ltd.
1941
97pp, col. frontis. & 9 f/p b/w illus., drawings in text, bd., 235x180mm. ANL

2782 SCOTTY IN/GUMNUT/LAND/[drawing]/by May/Gibbs/Sydney Angus & Robertson Ltd.
1944
97pp, col. frontis. & 9 f/p b/w illus., drawings in text, bd., 235x180mm. CLRC

2783 SCOTTY IN/GUMNUT/LAND/[drawing]/by/May/Gibbs/Sydney/Angus & Robertson Ltd.
1949
106pp (inc. 9pp illus. not counted as text pages in 1st ed.), col. frontis., 9 f/p sepia illus., drawings in text, printed throughout in sepia, bd., 240x184mm. ANL

2784 SCOTTY IN/GUMNUT/LAND/[drawing]/By/May/Gibbs/Angus & Robertson/Sydney London Melbourne Wellington
First pub. 1941; rpt 1944, 1949; 2nd ed. 1955; rpt 1956
94pp, col. frontis., 5 f/p b/w illus., b/w drawings throughout, clo., 235x155mm. KMM

2785 MR. & MRS. BEAR/AND/FRIENDS/by/[No author's name given] Angus & Robertson Ltd./Sydney
1943 [First edition]
145pp, dec. t.p., col. frontis., 9 f/p b/w illus., drawings in text, bd., 240x180mm. KMM
Half-title reads: 'by May Gibbs'.

2786 MR. & MRS. BEAR/AND/FRIENDS/By/[No author's name given]/Angus & Robertson Ltd. Sydney
1944
145pp, 9 f/p b/w illus. [no frontis.], line drawings in text, dec. bd., 240x180mm. KMM

2787 MR. AND MRS. BEAR/AND/FRIENDS/By/May/Gibbs/Angus & Robertson Ltd. Sydney
1947
145pp, dec. t.p., col. frontis. & 9 f/p sepia illus., drawings in text, dec. bd., 240x180mm. VSL

2788 MR. & MRS. BEAR/AND/FRIENDS/by/May/Gibbs/Angus & Robertson Ltd. Sydney
- Rpt 1949, as above. ANL
- Rpt 1950, as above. BBC

2789 MR. & MRS. BEAR/AND/FRIENDS/by/May/Gibbs/Angus & Robertson/Sydney London Melbourne Wellington
Second edition 1957
124pp, dec. t.p., col. frontis., 10 f/p b/w illus., drawings in text printed in b/w, dec. clo., 235x155mm. KMM

2790 PRINCE DANDE/LION/[decoration]/A Garden/Whim-Wham/by/May Gibbs/A Ure Smith Publication Sydney 1953
117pp (inc. 3pp glossary), col. frontis. & 3 f/p col. plates, 12 f/p b/w illus. & drawings in text, bd., 240x180mm. KMM

2791 SNUGGLEPOT/AND/CUDDLEPIE/MEET MR. LIZARD/[drawing]/Angus and Robertson
Sydney 1970
[26]pp, col. illus. throughout (inc. t.p.), pic. bd., col. e/p, 290x225mm. KMM
Adapted by Carol Edell & redrawn by Noela Young
Publisher's note states that May Gibbs, shortly before her death, 'gave approval for her work to be adapted for the Young Australia series. It was her wish that her original characters should be faithfully reproduced...'.
Adapted from the first 32 pages of *The Complete Adventures of Snugglepot and Cuddlepie.*

GIBBS, Peter

2792 THE TRUE BOOK ABOUT/GOLD/by/Peter Gibbs/Illustrated by/N. G. Wilson/Frederick Muller Limited/London
1959
143pp, 16 b/w illus., clo., 180x120mm. BBC
Chapter 18: 'Australian Gold' (7pp).

GIBSON, Charles E.

2793 DARING PROWS/Great Voyages of Exploration/by/Charles Gibson/Abelard-Schumann London New York Toronto
1963
224pp (inc. 6pp introduction & 6pp index), 8pp b/w photographic illus., 3 b/w maps (2 double-spread), clo., 195x125mm. KMM
Includes one chapter on Magellan (26pp); one chapter on 'The Search for the Southern Continent' (Drake, Janszoon, Quiros, Torres, Dirck Hartog, Tasman, Dampier, &c.) (10pp) & one chapter on Cook (19pp).

GIBSON, Helen

2794 AN/AUSTRALIAN/CHRISTMAS/Story by—

Helen Gibson/Pictures by—Galina Herbert/[drawing]/ Lothian Publishing Co. Pty. Ltd./Adelaide Melbourne Sydney Auckland
1961
32pp, 5 col. illus., b/w drawings throughout, dec. bd., dec. e/p, 245x180mm. ANL

2795 BUSTER/THE/FIRETRUCK/[drawing]/Story by Helen Gibson/Illustrations by Galina Herbert/Lothian Publishing Company Pty. Ltd., Melbourne.
1962
32pp, col. & b/w illus. throughout, bd., 180x250mm. KMM

2796 BUSTER/THE/FIRE TRUCK/[drawing]/Story by Helen Gibson/Illustrations by Galina Herbert/Angus and Robertson Ltd./London Sydney Melbourne Wellington
First pub. in Great Britain in 1963.
34pp, col. & b/w illus. throughout, bd. & pic. d/w, 180x250mm. KP

GILBERT, P. F.

2797 Discovering Australian History/SQUATTERS AND/IMMIGRANTS/P. A. Gilbert, B.A., Dip. Ed./ Audio-Visual Officer (History)/Audio-Visual Education Centre/Education Department, Victoria/The Jacaranda Press
Milton, Queensland, 1970
49pp, 2pp notes &c., col. & b/w illus., pic. clo., 230x170mm. KMM
In same series of background history readers by same author, both KMM:

2798 GOLD. 1970

2799 RURAL LIFE. 1971
and by J. E. Tate:

2800 CONVICTS. 1970

2801 BOOM AND DEPRESSION. 1971, both KMM

GILCHRIST, Elizabeth

2802 THE/HANDCLASP/No. 2/by/Elizabeth Gilchrist/ All proceeds to funds of/Victorian Baptist Home and Foreign Missions/436 Albert Street, Melbourne
n.d. [195?]
24pp (last 2 blank), unillus., wrappers, 214x135mm. ANL
Poems.

GILES, Joanna E.

2803 SEPTIMUS SERPENTINE/and/Other Verses/ Words by/Joanna E. Giles/Pictures by/Audrey Teago/ London/H. F. W. Deane and Sons/The Year Book Press Ltd./31 Museum Street, W.C.1./1919
29pp, col. frontis., b/w drawings throughout, clo., 240x185mm. KMM

GILL, G. Hermon [ed.]

2804 This is a Tots' Book/THE MAGIC MOUSE/ Illustrated by/Esther & Betty Paterson/Published by W. H. McKechnie,/Melbourne
'Wholly set up & printed in Australia by Victory Publicity Pty. Ltd., 262, Queen St., Melbourne', n.d. [194-?]
28pp, b/w & part. col. drawings throughout, pic. bd., 90x120mm. KMM
Advertised inside front cover: 'The/Tots' Tiny Books/ Edited by Hermon Gill: Sammy Sparrow; The Proud 'Possum; The Koalas' Party; Kitten Land; The Magic Mouse; Bunnies at Home; Two Bad Mice; The Naughty Kooka'.
See also Paterson, Betty & Gill, G. Hermon

GILL, Ruby

2805 PRINCESS/VERDURE/A Poetic Phantasy/and other verses/by/Ruby Gill/[drawing]/Copyright. All rights reserved./Wholly set up and printed in Australia by/Building Publishing Co. Pty. Ltd./20 Loftus Street Sydney, New South Wales, Australia
n.d.
80pp (inc. 2pp notes), 8 f/p b/w photographic illus., wrappers, 180x120mm. MAC

GILL, Traviss

See Odell, Gill

GILLIES, William

2806 FIRST STUDIES IN PLANT/LIFE IN AUSTRALASIA/with numerous questions,/directions for outdoor work, and drawing/and composition exercises./by/William Gillies, M.A./Co-Author of "Nature Studies in Australia"./[device]/Melbourne:/ Christchurch, Wellington, Dunedin, and London:/ Whitcombe & Tombs Limited
n.d. [190-?]
xxx+ 177pp, b/w frontis., numerous b/w drawings in text, clo., 180x120mm. KMM
Textbook, also intended for general reading for children with an interest in botany.

2807 Rpt n.d.
xpp +184pp, b/w frontis. & drawings in text, clo., 180x110mm. KP
Price 1/3 on front cover; illus. by Wm Huddlestone

2808 Revised & Enlarged Edition
n.d. KP
Numerous other copies with slight variations in price, size etc. KP

2809 FIRST STUDIES IN INSECT LIFE/IN AUSTRALASIA/with numerous questions, Directions for outdoor work, and Drawing/and Composition Exercises/By/William Gillies, M.A.,/Co-Author of "Nature Studies in Australia",/[device]/Melbourne,/ Christchurch, Wellington, Dunedin and London/ Whitcombe & Tombs Limited.
n.d. [1906]
xviipp+ 178pp, b/w frontis. & b/w illus. or figs. in text, clo., 184x112mm. KMM
On front cover 1/3.

2810 FIRST STUDIES IN INSECT LIFE/IN AUSTRALASIA/with numerous questions,/directions for outdoor work, and drawing/and composition exercises/by/William Gillies, M.A.,/Co-Author of "Nature Studies in Australia"./[device]/Melbourne,/ Christchurch, Wellington, Dunedin, and London/ Whitcombe & Tombs Limited
Second edition, n.d.
178pp, b/w frontis. & numerous b/w drawings in text, clo., 180x120mm. ANL
Textbook, also intended for general reading for children with an interest in insects.

GILLIES, William & HALL, Robert

2811 NATURE STUDIES IN AUSTRALIA/with/A natural history calendar,/summaries of the chapters, and complete index/By/William Gillies, M.A./and/ Robert Hall, C.M.Z.S., F.L.S./Lecturer on Nature Study, Victorian Education Department,/Author of 'Insectivorous Birds of Victoria', and 'Key to the Birds of/Australia and Tasmania'/Introduction by/Frank Tate, M.A., Director of Education, Victoria/[device]/ Melbourne/Christchurch, Wellington, Dunedin, & London/Whitcombe & Tombs Limited
First edition, n.d.
299pp, 1p quotation, 3pp preface, 8pp introduction, col. frontis., b/w illus. in text, clo., 180x125mm. KMM
A simple book on nature study intended to interest senior children in elementary schools; written as a

reader rather than a textbook & advertised as an 'instruction Gift Book for Australian Children'.

2812 NATURE STUDIES/IN AUSTRALIA/By/William Gillies, M.A./Author of "First Studies of Plant Life in Australasia", and/"First Studies of Insect Life in Australasia"/and/Robert Hall, C.M.Z.S., F.L.S./Curator of the Tasmanian Museum and Botanical Gardens, Hobart;/Author of "The Useful Birds of South Australia";/and "Key to the Birds of Australia"/Introduction by/Frank Tate, M.A., Director of Education, Victoria/Melbourne/Christchurch, Wellington, Dunedin, N.Z.; and London./Whitcombe & Tombs Limited
Revised edition, n.d.
308pp (inc. 8pp index, etc.), b/w illus. & diagrams throughout, clo., 180x120mm. KMM
• Rpt as above, but with col. frontis., price 2/6 on front cover. KP

'GILLY' [? D. H. Gilmore]
TEN LITTLE TOMMYCODS. *See* THE SLEEPING BEAUTY (Beacon Series)

2813 'PIG/WON'T GET OVER/THE STILE!' Re-told and illustrated/by Gilly
W.H. Honey Publishing Co., n.d. "Golliwog" Series, n.d. [1945?]
16pp, 8pp illus. in col. & b/w on other pp., pic. card, 245x180mm. KP
See also Moonbeam series

2814 Another copy as above
W. H. Honey 31 Cunningham St Sydney, n.d.
[8]pp inc. cover, printed on card, col. illus. covers, cover title & 2pp col. illus., others printed in deep pink, 200x120mm. JH

GILMORE, David Hunter

2815 THE REMARKABLE/ADVENTURES/OF/CUTHBERT/THE CATERPILLAR/AND/WILFRED/THE WASP/Told in Words and Pictures/by D. H. Gilmore/[drawing]/Registered in Australia for transmission by/post as a book./Sydney, N.S.W. Marchant & Co. Pty. Ltd.
n.d. [1941]
46pp, col. frontis. & 5 f/p col. illus., 10 f/p b/w illus. & drawings in text, dec. bd., 230x160mm. Grant

2816 THE REMARKABLE/ADVENTURES/OF/CUTHBERT/THE CATERPILLAR/AND/WILFRED/THE WASP/Told in Words and Pictures/by D. H. Gilmore/[drawing]/Sydney, N.S.W. Marchant & Co. Pty. Ltd.
1st imp. October 1941; 2nd imp. July 1942; 3rd imp. October 1942
46pp, col. frontis. & 5 f/p col. illus., 10 f/p b/w illus. & drawings in text, dec. bd., 235x165mm. NSL:M
Cover title reads: 'The Adventures of...'
• Rpt 1943, 4th imp. as above. KP

2817 ANTONY/ANT/AND THE/EARWIG PIRATES/Told/in Words & Pictures/by D. H. Gilmore/Wholly set up, Printed and Published in Australia by/Marchant & Co. Pty. Ltd., Sydney N.S.W./Registered at the G.P.O. Sydney for transmission by Post as a Book
n.d. [copy seen inscribed 1942]
[48]pp, col. frontis. & 5 f/p col. illus., 10 f/p sepia/white illus. & drawings in text, pic. bd., 240x165mm. CLRC

2818 ANTONY/ANT/AND THE/EARWIG PIRATES/told/in words and pictures/by D. H. Gilmore/Sydney Wholly set up, Printed & Published in Australia by Marchant & Co. Pty Ltd, Sydney, N.S.W., n.d. [inscription dated Xmas 1945]
60pp, col. frontis. & 5 f/p col. illus., 10 f/p b/w illus. & drawings in text, stiff paper pic. bd., 235x175mm. Grant

2819 ANTONY/ANT/AND THE/EARWIG PIRATES/Written and Illustrated by D. H. Gilmore/Angus & Robertson/Sydney London.
First pub. 1942; rpt 1949
46pp, col. frontis. & 5 col. illus., 10 f/p b/w illus. & b/w drawings in text, bd., 240x180mm. VSL

2820 THE TALE/OF/GREGORY/GRASSHOPPER/Written and Illustrated/by/D. H. Gilmore/Angus and Robertson Ltd./Sydney London/1942
42pp, col. frontis., 3 f/p & 2 small col. illus., 7 half-page b/w illus. & b/w head & tailpieces, bd., 240x180mm. Grant

2821 THE TALE OF/GREGORY/GRASSHOPPER/Written and Illustrated/by D. H. Gilmore/Angus and Robertson/Sydney London/1947
47pp, col. frontis. & 5 f/p col. illus., 10 f/p b/w illus. & b/w drawings in text, dec. bd., 240x180mm. KMM
Text & illustrations differ from 1942 edition.

2822 THE ADVENTURES/OF/CATKIN/AND/CODLIN/Written and illustrated/by D. H. Gilmore/Angus and Robertson Sydney 1946
53pp, col. frontis. & 5 f/p col. illus., 10 f/p b/w illus. & drawings in text, bd., 240x180mm. VSL

2823 THE TALE OF/CHRISTOPHER/CRICKET/Written & Illustrated/by/D. H. Gilmore/Angus & Robertson/Sydney London/1946
47pp, dec. t.p., col. frontis. & 5 col. plates, 10 f/p b/w illus. & b/w drawings in text, dec. bd., 240x180mm. ANL
• Rpt 1948, as above. KP

2824 THE TALE/OF/BENJAMIN/BUMBLE/Written & illustrated/by D. H. Gilmore/Angus & Robertson, Sydney 1947
47pp, dec. t.p., col. frontis. & 5 f/p col. illus., 10 f/p & 16 small b/w illus., dec. bd., 240x180mm. Grant

2825 THE CRUISE OF/THE SAUCY/WALNUT/Written & illustrated/by/D. H. Gilmore/[drawing]/Angus & Robertson/Sydney London.
1948
47pp, dec. t.p., col. frontis. & 5 f/p col. illus., 10 f/p b/w illus. & drawings in text, bd., 235x180mm. ANL

2826 CHRISTOPHER/CRICKET'S/FAVOURITE/TALES/[drawing]/Told and illustrated by/D. H. Gilmore/Angus & Robertson/Sydney London
Omnibus edition first published 1950
185pp, col. frontis. & 7 f/p col. illus., 40 f/p b/w illus. & drawings in text, dec. bd. (clo. spine), 240x180mm. ANL
Contains: *Christopher Cricket, The Tale of Benjamin Bumble, The Adventures of Catkin and Codlin, The Cruise of the Saucy Walnut.*

GILMORE, Mary Jean [Dame]

2827 THE TALE OF TIDDLEY WINKS/By Mary Gilmore/[text]
The Bookfellow, Sydney, n.d. [1917]
4pp, 2 b/w illus. by Eirene Mort, dec. wrappers, 150x115mm. ANLAustralian Poetry Books No. 1.

2828 VERSE FOR CHILDREN/by Mary Gilmore/Drawings by Celeste Mass/[drawing]/First, hand-set, edition/The Writers' Press/Sydney
n.d. [1955]
23pp (inc. 1p author's foreword), b/w drawings throughout, clo., 175x120mm. KMM

2829 [drawing]/THE SINGING TREE/A Selection of Mary Gilmore's Poetry/for Young Readers/Illustrated by Astra Lacis Dick/Angus and Robertson
Sydney 1971
73pp (inc. 4pp introductory note by Barbara Ker Wilson, etc.), b/w drawings in text, pic. bd., 215x140mm. KMM

GILMORE, Mary & PENDER, Lydia
2830 POEMS/TO READ TO/YOUNG/AUSTRALIANS/ by Mary Gilmore and Lydia Pender/illustrated by June Gulloch/Paul Hamlyn/London New York Sydney Toronto
1968
[25]pp, col. illus. throughout, pic. bd., dec. e/p, 285x225mm. KMM

Girl Life in Australia:
A Description of Colonial Life, London, R. A. Elliott, n.d.
Fiction; not children's.

Girls' Realm of Stories
2831 GIRLS' REALM OF STORIES/[drawing]/John F. Shaw & Co. Ltd./3 Pilgrim St London
n.d., inscription dated 1915
[247]pp, col. frontis. & 11 f/p col. plates, b/w drawings in text, dec. clo. with col. medallion on front cover, 225x175mm. KMM
Includes The Most Natural Thing in the World (Grace Bussell & the wreck of the *Georgette* off the W.A. coast) 6pp, and 2 other Australian stories.

Glad Tidings of Good Things
2832 GLAD TIDINGS/OF/GOOD THINGS/Volume 7 of "Evangelic News",/A Monthly Gospel Paper for/ Old and Young/[device]/Sydney/The Central Press/ Printers & Publishers/MDCCCCXXXVI
96pp, b/w photographic illus. throughout, bd., 244x174mm. KP
General religious text; illus. all of Australian scenes etc.

GLASKIN, G. M.
2833 A WALTZ/THROUGH THE HILLS/G. M. Glaskin/[drawing/]London/Barrie and Rockliff
1961
254pp and b/w drawings, clo., 198x122mm. KMM
Drawings by Paul Rigby.
2834 A WALTZ THROUGH THE HILLS/G. M. Glaskin/ [device]/Penguin Books
First published Barrie & Rockcliff, London 1961; revised edition Peacock Books, Harmondsworth, Middlesex, England, 1970
252pp (inc. 1p music), 4pp adv., unillus., pic. wrappers, cover design by Victor Ambrus, 180x110mm. KMM

GLASS, Dudley
2835 ROUND THE WORLD WITH/THE REDHEAD TWINS/[drawing]/Verses by Dudley Glass/Drawings by George Sherigham/Methuen & Co. Ltd./36 Essex St., London, W.C.
1933
49pp, b/w illus. on alternate pages, bd., 220x165mm. VSL

2836 THE SPANISH/GOLD-FISH/By/Dudley Glass/ Illustrated by/A. E. Bestall/[drawing]/Frederick Warne & Co., Ltd./London/Frederick Warne and Co., Inc./ New York
1934
95pp, col. frontis. & 3 f/p col. illus., b/w drawings in text, dec. bd. (clo. spine), dec. e/p, 205x155mm. VSL
Text includes words & music of 'The Ballad of Davy Jones Locker'.

2837 PETER RABBIT/A Musical Play for Children/by/ Dudley Glass/Based on/"The Tale of Peter Rabbit"/by Beatrix Potter/Frederick Warne & Co. Ltd.,/London and New York
1951
24pp, wrappers, 185x120mm. ANL

GLASSOP, Jack Lawson
2838 SUSAN AND THE/BOGEYWOMP/by/Lawson Glassop/Illustrated by/Ron. Madden/Angus and Robertson/Sydney
1947
99pp, col. frontis., 8 f/p & 4 small col. illus., dec. bd. 235x180mm. ANL

'GLEE, Professor'
2839 A JOURNEY/AROUND THE WORLD/Including Interesting Adventures in Many Lands/with/Professor Glee/And his Class of Young People in Their Travels/ Visiting the Historic and Famous Cities and Places of Europe, Asia, Africa,/South America, Australia and many islands of the Atlantic/and Pacific Oceans, including the New Possession/of the United States./A Week at the Pan-American Exposition/The Beautiful Buildings./The Midway and its Strange Shows—The Wonderful/Exhibits in Machinery—Science and Art— The Grand Electrical/Displays at Night—Adventures in this Home City/and a Trip to Niagara, described in a/Delightful Style/Profusely Illustrated with Nearly 200 Fine Engravings.
W. E. Scull, Washington 1901
434pp, col. frontis., b/w photographic illus. & numerous engravings, dec. clo. with b/w onlay on front cover, 240x177mm. KMM
Section on Australia and New Zealand comprises 8pp text, 3 f/p engravings & several text illus.

GLEESON, Horace
2840 SONGS OF/THE BUSH GARDEN/For/Young Australian Singers/Words and Music by/Horace Gleeson/[drawing]/Wholly set up and printed in Australia./Registered in Australia for transmission/ through the post as a book/Publishers: Whitcombe and Tombs Pty. Ltd. Melbourne & Sydney
n.d. [193-?]
24pp, b/w dec. headings, dec. wrappers, 280x220mm. KMM
Cover illustration signed 'J.H.'
Contains words & music of 8 songs.

GLEIG, Rev. G. R. (ed.)
KATHERINE RANDOLPH. or, Self-Devotion
Melb. Syd. & Adelaide, Thomson & Niven, n.d. [188-?]
This book appears to have no connection with Australia except that it was published here. ANL

GLOVER, Dorothy
2841 Imperial edition No. 591/THE TRUTHFUL ELF/a juvenile operetta/—words and music by/Dorothy Glover/Musical Contents/[listed]/Cast/in order of appearance [listed]/2/6/Allan & Co. Pty Ltd./ Melbourne Adelaide Bendigo/Printed in Australia
19pp & 1p blank, dec. wrappers, 246x180mm. VSL

GODFREY, R. J.
2842 JESUS THE CARPENTER/and/other verses for children/(By R. J. Godfrey)
Bridge Print, Murray Bridge, n.d. [1970]
26pp, 1p preface, unillus., wrappers, cover title, 195x125mm. CLRC

GOEBEL, Ferdinand
2843 RUBEZAHL/OR/NUMBER-NIP/Translated from the German/of/Ferdinand Goebel/by/Roland C.

Clark/Illustrations by/Valda Winifred Croll/Published by/Chessell & McCredie/136 Pitt Street, Sydney/All rights reserved
1951
28pp, 8f/p col. illus. & b/w illus. in text, dec. t.p., pic. bd., 240x180mm. CLRC
First publ. in Germany in German 1885. Legend from area between Silesia & Bohemia.

'GOGG, Peddy'
See [Collins, Rev. W. M.]

Golden Hours for You
2844 GOLDEN HOURS FOR YOU
Printed by The Central Press 309 Castlereagh Street Sydney
n.d. [1935]
96pp, sepia photographic illus., clo., 245x183mm. KP
Anonymous religious stories & anecdotes of a proselytizing nature with references to and photographs of Australian scenery.

The Golden Key
2845 THE GOLDEN KEY/and other/Lovely Stories/[drawing]/With Pictures and Texts to Colour
Cover title. Sterling Art Novelties, Melbourne n.d.
Wholly set up & printed at the offices of The Examiner, Launceston
[32]pp, b/w illus. throughout, pic. wrappers, 268x178mm. TG
Bible stories & others with moral message.

Golden Stamp Book Series
Activity books with pages of coloured stamps to be torn out and stuck in the appropriate spaces.
Format example:
2846 GOLDEN STAMP BOOK OF/AUSTRALIAN/BIRDS/Text by Marion Petrie/[instructions and contents]/Golden Press [map] Sydney/First published 1970 by Golden Press Pty Ltd./2-12 Tennyson Road Gladesville, N.S.W./Printed in Hongkong [b/w drawing along outer edge of t.p.]
48pp, 4pp col. stamps, b/w illus. in text, pic. wrappers, 280x210mm. KMM
Illus. Robin Hill.
Other Golden Stamp Books:
2847 AUSTRALIAN ROCKS & MINERALS, Sharman N. Bawden & Douglas M. Stone. Illus. Derrick I. Stone, 1970. KP
2848 AUSTRALIAN GEM STONES, Sharman N. Bawden & Douglas M. Stone. Illus. D. I. Stone, 1970. CLRC
2849 AUSTRALIAN EXPLORERS, Carolyn R. Stone. Illus. J. Papworth, 1970. CLRC
2850 AUSTRALIAN SHIPS, Lynne Stronell. Illus. Andre Sollier, 1971. KMM
2851 AUSTRALIAN CARS, Lynne Stronell. Illus. Lesley Mansfield & Andre Sollier, 1971. KP
2852 AUSTRALIAN PLANES, Lynne Stronell. Illus. Andre Sollier, 1971. KP
2853 AUSTRALIAN TRAINS, Susan Wilkins. Illus. Adrienne Higgs, 1972. CLRC
2854 AUSTRALIAN SEA SHELLS, J. Child. Illus. L. D'Abrera, 1971. KMM
2855 AUSTRALIAN INSECTS, Text & some illus. Densey Clyne, b/w illus. M. Kaighin, 1971. KP
2856 MORE AUSTRALIAN INSECTS, Text & col. illus. Densey Clyne, b/w illus. Marion Kaighin, 1st publ. 1971. KP
2857 AUSTRALIAN WILDFLOWERS, Densey Clyne. Illus. Ninon Phillips, 1971. VMOU
2858 AUSTRALIAN ANIMALS, Bruce Edwards. Illus. Ninon Phillips, 1971. KMM
2859 MORE AUSTRALIAN BIRDS, Marion Petrie. Illus. Robin Hill & Vera Mezaks, 1970. WRT

GOOD, Irene
2860 Child Series No. 1/GOD'S/WORLD/AND/ME/Stories by Irene Good/Foreword by Dr. F. W. Boreham
Clifford Press in co-operation with Bacon, Melbourne, n.d. [194-?]
16pp, 1p foreword, b/w illus. throughout, wrappers, cover title, 155x250mm. ANL
Short religious text, verses, games &c.

Good King Wenceslas
See Blue Wren Books

GOODE, Arthur Russell
See 'Russell, Arthur'

GOODE, Evelyn [Mrs Crawford Vaughan]
2861 DAYS THAT SPEAK/A Story of Australian Child Life/By/Evelyn Goode/Illustrated by J. Macfarlane/London/Ward, Lock & Co., Limited/1908
249pp, 6pp adv., b/w frontis. & 7 b/w plates, clo., 185x125mm. KMM
2862 DAYS THAT SPEAK/A Story of Australian Child Life/By/Evelyn Goode/Illustrated by J. Macfarlane/Ward, Lock & Co. Limited/London and Melbourne
n.d.
As above. CLRC

2863 THE/CHILDHOOD/OF HELEN/By/Evelyn Goode/(Mrs. Crawford Vaughan)/Author of "Days that Speak," etc./Illustrated/Ward, Lock & Co. Limited/London, Melbourne and Toronto/1913
256pp, 16pp adv., b/w frontis. & 7 b/w plates by J. Macfarlane, clo., 185x125mm. KMM

GOODE, Jessie
2864 RHYMES/FOR/A/GRANDCHILD/by/Jessie Goode/Oldfort: G.P.O. Box 707 F/Melbourne/1970
The author; edition limited to 500 copies
14pp, 2 col. illus. & 2 b/w illus., stiff wrappers, 225x140mm. ANL

GOODE, John
2865 WOOD/WIRE/AND/FABRIC/John Goode/A Saga of Australian Flying/Lansdowne Press
Melbourne 1968
109pp (inc. 9pp index, etc.); 3pp introduction, etc., extended illus. t.p., b/w photographic illus., line drawings & chapter headings throughout, clo., pic. e/p, 240x180mm. KMM

2866 [drawing]/SMOKE, SMELL AND CLATTER/The Revolutionary Story of/Motoring in Australia/John Goode/Lansdowne Press
1969
106pp, 2pp introduction, etc., extended illus. t.p., b/w photographic illus. throughout, clo., pic. e/p, 240x180mm. CLRC

2867 TORTOISES, TERRAPINS/AND TURTLES/by John Goode/Illustrated by Alec Bailey/Angus and Robertson
Sydney 1971
64pp, b/w drawings in text, pic. bd., 215x160mm. CLRC

2868 AUSTRALIAN/CARS AND/MOTORING/John Goode/Lansdowne Press [illus.]
Melbourne 1972
40pp, inc. 8pp col., & other b/w photographs throughout, e/p decorations, pic. bd., 190x260mm. KP

GOODENOW, Earle
2869 THE/CARELESS/KANGAROO/Story/and Pictures/by/Earle Goodenow/[drawing]
Henry Z. Walck Inc., New York 1959
31pp, dec. t.p., col. illus. throughout, clo., 245x190mm. KMM

GOODLUCK, John
2870 SUCH IS THE/KINGDOM/Some of Christ's parables/as re-told for Australian/Children/Written and illustrated/by/John Goodluck, B.A./[device]/The Methodist Publishing House/(Aldersgate Press),/Melbourne, Brisbane, Perth, Sydney, Adelaide,/Suva and Apia
1st ed. 3000 copies n.d. [pre 1966 as prices in old currency]
58pp, inc. 1p preface, 2pp list of other books, b/w illus. in text, pic. wrappers, 180x120mm. KP

GOODMAN, Hermea
See Telfer, Phyllis & Goodman, Hermea

GOODRICH, Frank Boott
2871 THE/HISTORY OF THE SEA./A/Graphic description of Maritime Adventures./Achievements, Explorations, Discov-/eries and Inventions./Including/ Hazards and Perils of Early Navigators, &c [6 lines follow] covering the many centuries of development in science/and civilization from/The Ark to the Present Time/By/Frank B. Goodrich, LL.D./Author of "Letters of Dick Tinto," "The Court of Napoleon" etc/To which is added/An Account of Adventures beneath the Sea; Diving, Dredging, Deep Sea Sounding,/Latest Submarine Explorations, etc, etc. prepared with great care by/Edwards Howland Esq,/Author of many popular works/over 250 spirited illustrations/James MacKay/Sydney, NSW. Australia
n.d. [187-?]
785pp (inc. 9pp index & 17pp contents &c), b/w frontis. & b/w engravings in text throughout, leather, heavily embossed & dec. in gilt, 232x150mm. CLRC
Includes Voyages of Cartier, Drake, Quiros, Tasman, Dampier, Cook, Laperouse, Bligh &c. of interest to children but not publ. for them.
Reprint of *The Ocean Story* 1873; later ed. of *Man upon the Sea* 1858—books not intended for children.

2872 [vignette]/THE SEA/AND HER/FAMOUS SAILORS./A History of Maritime Adventure and Exploration/from/the Christian era to the present time/Eight full page cuts/Gall & Inglis/ Edinburgh;/Bernard Terrace/London:/25 Paternoster Square
n.d.
294pp (inc. 5pp preface, etc.), engraved frontis., additional engraved frontis. (with 7 portraits), 6 f/p engravings, dec. clo. (with gilt border & panel), 170x110mm. CLRC

2873 THE SEA/AND/HER FAMOUS SAILORS/of all Ages and Nations/By/Frank B. Goodrich/Gall and Inglis, 25 Paternoster Square/and Edinburgh
n.d. [189-?]
294pp (inc. 1p preface & 4pp introduction), b/w frontis. & 7 f/p engravings, dec. clo., 185x130mm. HBM
An abridgement of the original American book *Man upon the Sea*, edited so that nationalistic allusions &c. are omitted. Contains section on discovery of Australia & Pacific, Botany Bay, Cook, Bligh &c.

GOODRICH, Samuel Griswold [pseud. 'Peter Parley']
2874 TALES ABOUT THE SEA,/AND/THE ISLANDS IN THE PACIFIC OCEAN./By Peter Parley,/Author of Tales about Natural History, etc./—/Embellished with engravings/[vignette]/London:/Printed for Thomas Tegg and Son, Cheapside;/T. T. and H. Tegg, Dublin; R. Griffin and Co. Glasgow;/And J. and S. A.Tegg, Sydney, and Hobart Town,./—/1837
viii, 384pp, f/p engraved frontis. & 74 small engravings in text, f/p map (The Pacific Ocean and Islands), bd., 130x95mm. ANL
Contains chapter on Pitcairn Island, 'Parley goes to New Holland', 'About New Holland' & 'The Story of La Perouse'.

2875 TALES ABOUT THE SEA,/AND/THE ISLANDS IN THE PACIFIC OCEAN/By Peter Parley/Author of Tales about Natural History,etc./Embellished with engravings/[vignette]/Third Edition /London:/Printed for Thomas Tegg and Son, Cheapside[as before]/1838
viii, 360pp, engraved frontis. & engravings in text throughout (copy seen re-bound), 135x100mm. NSL:M
Includes contents of *Tales about the Islands in the Pacific* with a map & an engraving of Sydney not in that volume.

2876 Fourth edition 1841, as above, but
viii, 359pp, 1p adv.135x100mm. HBM
Contents as in previous volume.

2877 TALES ABOUT THE SEA,/AND/THE ISLANDS IN THE PACIFIC OCEAN./By Peter Parley./Author of "Tales about Natural History", Etc./Embellished with seventy-nine Engravings./[vignette]/Sixth Edition./ London:/Printed for Thomas Tegg, 73 Cheapside;/T. Le Mesurier, Dublin; and R. Griffin & Co., Glasgow.
n.d. [copy inscribed July 1850]
viii, 359pp, b/w frontis. & 78 engravings in text, dec. clo., 135x105mm. RM
Contents as in previous editions.

2878 TALES ABOUT THE SEA/AND/THE ISLANDS IN THE PACIFIC OCEAN./By Peter Parley,/Author of "Tales about Natural History", etc./embellished with engravings/[vignette]/London, Grant Richards/48 Leicester Square,W.C./1902
viii,359pp, b/w frontis. (diagram of a sailing ship), b/w map of Sydney & adjacent country, engravings in text, clo.,135x105mm. CLRC

2879 PETER PARLEY'S/TALES/ABOUT THE ISLANDS/IN THE/PACIFIC OCEAN/With a Map and numerous engravings/Philadelphia:/Thomas, Cowperthwait & Co./253 Market Street/1841
144pp, engraved frontis. map & 26 engravings, bd., 140x105mm. NSL:M
[1841]
Contains a chapter on 'Pitcairn's Island', 'Parley goes to New Holland', 'About New Holland', 'Leaves New Holland and goes to New Zealand'.

2880 PETER PARLEY'S/TALES OF THE SEA./ [vignette]/with numerous engravings./London:/Printed for Thomas Tegg and Son, Cheapside,/Tegg, Wise & Co. Dublin; R. Griffin and Co., Glasgow;/and sold by all booksellers./1836
viii+296pp, b/w engravings in text, three-quarters leather, marbled boards,129x100mm. KMM
Last 8 pages contain the 'Story of Perouse'; does not include chapters on New Holland or Pitcairn Island.

2881 PETER PARLEY'S TALES/ABOUT/THE SON OF THE SEA/and other interesting matters./[vignette]/ London/printed for T. Allman, 42 Holborn Hill/and sold by all Booksellers./1839
184pp, engraved frontis., clo., 115x95mm. Grant
The first story, 'The Son of the Sea', contains the only reference to the Pacific Ocean.

2882 PETER PARLEY'S/TALES ABOUT THE WORLD/ Containing/Europe, Asia, Africa, America,/and

Australia/Edited by the Rev. T. Wilson/London:/Darton and Co., Holborn Hill
n.d. [1840]
3 vols bound together, 180pp, 180 & 192, 5 tinted maps, clo., 145x90mm. NSL:M
Two chapters containing 28 pages about Australia. One of the six English writers using the name of 'Peter Parley' was Samuel Clark, partner in the publishing firm of Darton and Clark, who also wrote under the name of 'the Rev. T. Wilson'. (See F. J. Harvey Darton, *Children's Books in England)*

2883 TALES ABOUT AMERICA/AND AUSTRALIA;/by/Peter Parley/Edited by the Rev. T. Wilson/London:/Darton and Clark, Holborn Hill
n.d. [1840?]
iv,192pp, 2 tinted maps frontis, 39 engravings, gilt dec. clo., g.e., 140x90mm. NSL:M
Australian section pp164–92.

2884 TALES ABOUT AMERICA/AND AUSTRALIA/By Peter Parley/London:/Darton and Clark, Holborn Hill
n.d.
iv,192pp, 2pp printed map frontis., 1p tinted in col. inside front cover (Darton's Juvenile Library/London/Darton & Clark/Holborn Hill'), 39 engravings (one variation, p70, from those in previous edition), clo., 145x90mm. NSL:M

2885 TALES/ABOUT/AMERICA AND AUSTRALIA./By/Peter Parley/A New Edition/Brought down to the Present Time/Revised by/The Rev. T. Wilson/London:/Cassell, Petter, and Galpin/Ludgate Hill, E.C.
n.d. [1860?]
iv,207pp, 4pp adv., 2 tinted maps, b/w engravings, dec. clo., 165x100mm. NSL:M
Australian section pp176–207.

2886 TALES/ABOUT/EUROPE, ASIA, AFRICA/AND AMERICA./By Peter Parley,/Author of Tales about Natural History, etc./Embellished with engravings/[vignette of Parley with children & dog]/London:/Printed for Thomas Tegg and Son, Cheapside;/J. T. and H. Tegg, Dublin; R.Griffin and Co. Glasgow;/and J. and S.A. Tegg, Sydney and Hobart Town./1837.
x+516pp, map frontis., three-quarter calf, 126x96mm. CLRC
Pp 506–16 relate to Australia, Polynesia and New Zealand, and the text boosts 'Mr Tegg, bookseller of Sydney'. Copy seen has been re-bound.

2887 TALES/ABOUT/EUROPE, ASIA, AFRICA, AMERICA, & OCEANIA./By Peter Parley, Author of "Tales About Natural History", Etc./The Seventh Edition, Greatly Enlarged, with Maps Engraved/on Steel, and Numerous Illustrations./[vignette]/London:/William Tegg & Co., 85, Queen Street,/Cheapside./MDCCCLIV
xiv+424pp, 4pp adv., b/w engraved frontis., numerous maps & engravings throughout, dec. clo., 135x110mm. RM
Australian section occupies pp409–24 & includes a map of Sydney & one of Oceania.

2888 PARLEY'S TALES ABOUT/EUROPE, ASIA, AFRICA, AMERICA, AND OCEANIA./[vignette]/New Edition, Greatly Enlarged and Improved./Illustrated with 16 full-page and other engravings./London: William Tegg
n.d. [Preface dated 1872]
xiv+492pp (inc. 3pp notes &c., & 5pp index), 2pp preface, engraved frontis., map & engravings throughout, dec. clo., 180x130mm. ANL
Contains section (pp457–84) 'About Oceania' (which includes Antarctica).

2889 TALES ABOUT SHIPWRECKS,/and/DISASTERS AT SEA./By Peter Parley,/Author of "Tales about Europe," etc./Embellished with Forty-nine Engravings./London:/William Tegg and Co., 73, Cheapside;/R. Griffin and Co., Glasgow;/Cumming and Ferguson, Dublin./1847
xv+351pp, 1p adv., engravings throughout, dec. clo., 134x103mm. KMM
Topics include the wreck of the *Essex* in the South Seas in 1820 (9pp); The mutiny of the *Bounty* (15pp); The wreck of the convict ship *Neva* in 1835 near King's Island near Portland Bay with the loss of 225 persons, mostly female convicts (11pp); Wreck of the convict ship *Amphitrite* off Boulogne in 1833 with 108 female convicts & 12 children on board bound for NSW (10pp), Wreck of the *Waterloo* convict ship bound for VDL in Table Bay 1842 (13pp).

2890 One Penny/LA PEROUSE/A List of/Peter Parley's/Popular Stories/[list of 12 titles]/with numerous engravings/London/Orlando Hodgson, 111, Fleet Street
16pp (inc. covers), 8 engravings, wrappers, cover title, 110x100mm. ANL

2891 PETER PARLEY'S/TALES/with/Numerous illustrations/Printed by Ben George/:London:/Ben George, 47 Hatton Gardens./and all booksellers.
n.d. [prize 1895]
296pp, tinted frontis.,13 plates, dec. clo., 187x135mm. ANL
Contains one Australian story, 'The Black Bloodhound' (79pp).

2892 UNIVERSAL HISTORY,/on the/Basis of Geography,/For the use of families and schools./By Peter Parley,/Author of "Tales about Natural History" "The Sea and Pacific Ocean"/etc.etc./with numerous useful maps,/by A.G. Findlay, F.R.G.S./Fifteenth edition,/corrected to date./London, William Tegg.
n.d.
xvi+568pp, col. frontis., 12 f/p maps, dec. clo. 173x132mm. CLRC
Pp502–23 about Oceania, Malaysia, Australia, including 2 maps.

GOODWIN, C. J.

2893 COMING IN TO BAT/A handbook for those who coach/and play cricket/C. M. Goodwin/Hill of Content/Melbourne
1st ed. 1970, rpt 1973
61pp, diagrams & b/w photographs, clo., 202x180 mm. KP
Author a cricket coach in various Vic schools. Includes 2pp foreword by Frank Tyson.

GORDON, Charles

PETER BOBTAIL IN THE CAVES OF THE MITES. *See* Gunn & Taylor

PETER BOBTAIL AND THE FOREST PRINCE. *See* Gunn & Taylor

THE WIGGLY WOGS. *See* Gunn & Taylor

GORDON, Gay

2894 CHANG/AND THE/TOY SOLDIER/by Gay Gordon/[illustration]/and other stories/Wholly set up...by the Offset Printing Coy. Pty. Limited, Sydney/and printed by S. T. Leigh & Co. Pty Ltd, Sydney/(All rights reserved)
n.d.
16pp, part. col. illus. throughout, col. pic. wrappers, 270x210mm. Happy Days Series. CLRC

GORDON, W. J.

2895 THE/CAPTAIN-GENERAL/Being/ The Story of the Attempt of the Dutch/to Colonize New Holland/ By/ W.J.Gordon/[quot.]/ London and New York/ Frederick Warne and Co./ 1888/[all rights reserved]
xvi+304pp (inc. 2pp author's preface),folding map frontis., unillus., clo., 195x120mm. KMM
A factual story, not necessarily for boys, based on the adventures of Captain Pelsart & the *Batavia* at Houtman's Abrolhos off the coast of WA.

2896 THE/CAPTAIN GENERAL/By/W. J. Gordon/ Author of/"Englishman's Haven," "The Treasure Finder",/"Under the Avalanche", Etc./[device]/ London/Frederick Warne and Co./and New York./(All Rights Reserved)
n.d. [3rd ed. 1891]
304pp, 2pp preface & note to the third ed., 1 d/p map (preceding t.p.), unillus., clo., 195x120mm. RM

GOREY, J., A. & N.

2897 LITTLE VERSES/FROM OUTBACK/[drawing]/By/ John, Ann, and Natalie Gorey
Printed by Alice Springs Printing & Publishing for John Gorey Yambah Station Alice Springs
n.d.
[44]pp, unillus., wrappers, 177x117mm. KP
First publ. 1951 verses by Natalie Gorey (with ideas from her children, John and Ann).

GORMAN, J. T. & others

2898 THE/PEARL FISHERS/and other stories/By/Major Gorman, Percy F. Westerman/and others/With Illustrations by/C. E. Brock, R.I., V. Cooley/and others/Raphael Tuck & Sons/Ltd./London Paris New York/Printed in England/Copyright
n.d. [193-?]
186pp, 6pp adv., col. frontis. & 1 f/p col. illus., b/w drawings in text, dec. illus. t.p., pic. bd., 220x170mm. KMM
Title story only, by J. T. Gorman (27pp), set in Broome, relates to Australia.

GOSSETT, Margaret

2899 CHILDREN'S/PICTURE/COOKBOOK/[drawing]/ recipes by Margaret Gossett/designed by Elizabeth Dauber/A Young Scott Book/Published by The Strand Press, Brisbane
n.d. [195-?]
47pp (with e/p inc. in text & pagination), part. col. dec. t.p., part col. illus. throughout, pic. bd., 220x180mm. KMM

GOUGH, Irene

2900 ONE SUNDAY MORNING EARLY/by Irene Gough/illustrated by Noela Young/Ure Smith— Sydney
1963
64pp (inc. 1p notes), part. col. illus. throughout, clo., 235x155mm. KMM
Book designed by Sally Keep
Verses for children.
• Rpt 1968, as above. NSL:M

2901 ONE SUNDAY MORNING EARLY/by Irene Gough/illustrated by Noela Young/The Caxton Press—Christchurch
First New Zealand edition 1964
As above. NSL:M

2902 THE GOLDEN LAMB/by Irene Gough/illustrated by Joy Murray/Heinemann Melbourne/World's Work London
1966
[41]pp, part. col. dec. t.p., part. col. & b/w drawings throughout, 6pp printed on col. paper, col. e/p, pic. bd., 210x170mm. KMM

2903 THE CAT WHO/BELONGED/Irene Gough/ Illustrated by Sue Frankel/[drawing]/Nelson
Thomas Nelson (Australia) Ltd, 1969
42pp, 15 b/w drawings in text, pic. wrappers, 180x120mm. KMM

GOULD, Charles S.

2904 BIFF/By Charles S. Gould/A Jons Production/ Made and printed in Australia for Jons Productions/by Colourtone Pty. Ltd., Sydney, Australia.
n.d. [1945]
221pp, unillus., clo., 205x130mm. CLRC

2905 BIFF FINDS A CLUE/by/Charles S. Gould/A Jons Production/Made and printed in Australia for Jons Productions Pty. Ltd./by Colourtone Pty. Ltd., Sydney, Australia.
n.d. [1947]
243pp, 5pp adv., unillus., clo., 200x130mm. ANL

Gould League Songs & Poems

2906 GOULD LEAGUE/SONGS & POEMS/[within dec. border]/The New South Wales Gould League of Bird Lovers/Sydney/1934
76pp (last blank), inc. 1p foreword, 2 f/p col. illus., b/w photographic illus., 210x134mm. ANL
Foreword by G. Ross Thomas, Director of Education. Col. illus. by Neville Cayley; articles, verses, songs &c.

GOULDEN, Shirley

2907 TALES/FROM/AUSTRALIA/[coloured illustration]/Retold by Shirley Goulden/Illustrated by Benvenuti/W. H. Allen
London 1966
61pp, col. illus. throughout, pic. bd., dec. e/p, 320x240mm. CLRCSplendour Books Series.
Contains what purport to be five Aboriginal legends.

GOW, Gregson

2908 NEW LIGHT/THROUGH OLD WINDOWS:/A Series of Stories/Illustrating Fables of Aesop./By/ Gregson Gow,/Author of "Tales for the Twilight"; "Troubles and Triumphs of/Little Time", etc./[device]/ London: Blackie & Son, 49 Old Bailey, E.C.;/Glasgow, Edinburgh, and Dublin./1883
192pp, 32pp adv., col. frontis. & 2 f/p part. col. illus., pic. clo., 180x120mm. MK
The first story only, 'The Cock and the Jewel; or, Amos Doon's Nugget', relates to Australia, being set in the Victorian goldfields.

2909 NEW LIGHT/THROUGH OLD WINDOWS
[school prize 1893]
As above, but n.d. Part col. frontis. & 2 f/p part col. illus., dec. clo., 178x120mm. KP

2910 New edition as above but publisher's imprint 50 Old Bailey E.C./Glasgow and Dublin
n.d. [prize 1932]
192pp, 26pp adv., b/w frontis. & 2 f/p b/w plates, pic. clo., 180x120mm. KP

2911 A LITTLE ADVENTURER;/or,/How Tommy Treffit went to look/for his Father/By/Gregson Gow,/Author of "New Light through Old Windows" "The Troubles and/Triumphs of Little Tim," &c/Illustrated/[device]/ London:/Blackie & Son, 49 & 50 Old Bailey, E.C.;/Glasgow, Edinburgh, and Dublin
n.d. [1885]
128pp, frontis. printed in sepia, dec. blue clo., (title in rectangular gilt panel), 166x116mm. RC
Others editions listed in collection 189-?, and 191-?, n.d. red cloth.

GOY, André de

2912 AVENTURES/SUR MER ET SUR TERRE/I/LA FAMILLE LAURENCAY/II/HISTOIRE D'UN JEUNE CHERCHEUR D'OR EN AUSTRALIE/Par/André de Goy/Paris/Alphonse Desesserts/Editeur de la Librairie à illustrations pour la jeunesse/Passage des Panoramas, 38, et galerie Feydeau, 12
n.d. [1853]
342pp, 2pp preface, engraved frontis. & 7 engravings in text, clo., 230x140mm. NSL:M
The second story only (pp289-342) relates to Australia, and to gold discoveries.

GRAHAM, Beryl

2913 A VISIT TO THE/AUSTRALIAN/REPTILE PARK/by/Beryl Graham/[drawing]/The Allan Press/Registered at the G.P.O. Sydney, for transmission by post as a book
1966
24pp, b/w drawings throughout, pic. wrappers, 215x140mm. KP
Illus. by Rosemary Beeman.

GRAHAM, Burton

2914 A BOY'S/DOG
F. H. Johnson Pub. Coy. Sydney n.d. [1944]
8pp, line drawings throughout, pic. card wrappers, 160x104mm. ANL
Printed throughout in sepia; cover title.

GRAHAM, Edith

2915 A LITTLE BUSH/POPPY/By/Edith Graham/Illustrated by May Gibbs/Lothian Book Publishing Co. Pty. Ltd./Melbourne Sydney/Printed in England
n.d. [1915]
336pp, col. frontis., 8 f/p b/w plates & b/w drawings in text, pic. clo. with red lettering &c., 190x115mm. KMM

2916 Another copy as above, bound in blue cl. with drawings &c in darker blue
n.d. [inscribed Xmas 1923]. KP

GRAHAM, Ethel

2917 RHYMES AND JINGLES/With Illustrations/FOR LITTLE FOLKS/[medallion]/By Ethel Graham/[medallion]/Melbourne:/Modern Printing Co. Pty. Ltd., 18 to 32 Leicester Street/1920
64pp, 28 col. illus. & many b/w drawings, illus. by author, dec. bd. (clo. spine), (with additional poems printed on both sides of back cover), 235x180mm. ANL

GRAHAM, Jean W.

See 'Hamilton, Mary'

GRAHAM W. Edward

2918 THE/WATTLE FAIRY/A Dream in a Garden/By W. Edward Graham
n.d. [Place of printing & name of printer indecipherable]
6pp, wrappers, 220x170mm. QSL

GRAHAM, William

2919 THE/MOUSE/WHO WAS/BOASTFUL/William Graham/Pictures by/George Santos/& Donald Glue
Colorgravure, Melbourne 1950
41pp, 12 col. illus., b/w illus. throughout, dec. bd., dec. e/p, 195x165mm. Little Wonder Books. NSL:M

Grandmamma's Letters

See H., E.

GRANGER, Walter R. (ed.)

2920 AUSTRALIA'S/STORY/told in more than 400 pictures/Preface/[24 lines text, signed Walter Granger, Editor] To those who desire their copy of Australia's Story in a more permanent form there will/be a limited number of De Luxe copies available at 2/6./Published by/John Sands Pty. Ltd., Sydney./Copyright—Great Britain, Canada, Australia. No portion may be reproduced without consent of the publishers.
n.d. [1938?]
64pp (inc. 3pp adv.), b/w illus. throughout, pic. wrappers, 210x170mm. CLRC
History told in b/w drawings with captions, the artist being anonymous.

'GRANNY'

See Rossiter, Marguerite

GRANT, Alexander Charles

2921 BUSH LIFE IN QUEENSLAND: or John West's Colonial Experiences, 2 vols., Blackwood, Edinburgh, 1881
Although H. M. Green refers to this as a boy's book 'which might alternatively have been included in the station group' (i.e. of adult books), it is not here considered a children's book.

GRANT, Lois

2922 A FOOTIE IS A BALL./Lois Grant/in collaboration with/Wally Miller./Illustrated by/Glenn Mehaffey./The Redlegs Series
Printed by The Griffin Press; published by Advertiser Broadcasting Network, Adelaide 1971
17pp, col. illus. throughout, col. pic. wrappers, 275x210mm. KMM

GRANTHAM, Joy

2923 PLAYETTES/for/Seven Favourite/Nursery Rhymes/by/Joy Grantham
Dominic Publications, French's Forest NSW (n.d. deposit copy 1958)
24pp, unillus., wrappers, 214x137mm. NSL:M
Cover title "Play Time—Seven Favourite Nursery Rhymes."

2924 ANY TIME IS "PLAY" TIME/Six Plays for/any time or place/by/Joy Grantham
Dominic Publications, French's Forest n.d. [1958?]
23pp (inc. introduction), 2pp adv., unillus., wrappers, 210x140mm. NSL:M

2925 The Play Time Series/LET'S "PLAY" OUR FAIRY TALES/by/Joy Grantham
Dominic Publications, French's Forest NSW n.d. [1958]
30pp (inc. 1p introduction), 2pp adv., unillus., wrappers, 210x140mm. NSL:M

2926 SPECIAL PLAYS/FOR/SPECIAL DAYS/by/Joy Grantham
Dominic Publications. French's Forest n.d. [1958]
23pp & 1p blank, unillus., wrappers, 210x140mm. NSL:M
Uniform with above:

2927 SPECIAL PLAYS/FOR/SPECIAL DAYS/by/Joy Grantham/A Horwitz-Martin/Text Book
Sydney n.d. [1964?]
24pp, unillus., stiff wrappers, 210x140mm. NSL:M

2928 PUPPET PLAYS WITH A PURPOSE
23pp & 1p adv., otherwise the same. NSL:M

The Grateful Parrot

2929 [coloured drawing]/THE GRATEFUL PARROT/Illustrated by/Bona Sancipriano Rabaglino/Printed in Italy/for/Rex Publications/Australia
[On last page: 'Nirex Pty. Limited, 545 George St., Sydney (Australia)']
n.d. [194-?]

[24]pp, col. illus. throughout, col. pic. bd., dec. e/p, 210x150mm. KMM

GRATTAN-SMITH, Thomas E.

2930 THREE REAL BRICKS/The Adventures of/Mel Ned and Jim/By/T. E. Grattan-Smith/Illustrated by/Savile Lumley/[vignette]/Sydney/The Australasian Publishing Co. Ltd./218–222 Clarence Street/1920
256pp, col. frontis. (A. B. Nash) & 5 f/p b/w plates, clo., 195x135mm. NSL:M

2931 THREE REAL BRICKS/The Adventures of/Mel Ned and Jim/By/T. E. Grattan-Smith/Illustrated by/Savile Lumley/[vignette]/George G. Harrap & Co. Ltd./London Calcutta Sydney
• Rpt April 1923
256pp, col. frontis. (Nash) & 5 b/w plates, clo 192x134mm. KMM

2932 Rpt as above, but
First published 1920; rpt 1923, 1924, 1927
256pp, 1p adv. (preceding t.p.), b/w frontis. & 3 b/w plates, dec. clo., 190x130mm. RM

2933 THREE REAL BRICKS/The Adventures of/Mel Ned and Jim/By/T. E. Grattan-Smith/Illustrated by/Savile Lumley/J. Coker & Co. Ltd./6 Farringdon Avenue, London, E.C.4
1935
256pp, b/w frontis. & 3 b/w plates, clo., 184x124mm. KP

2934 THE/MAGIC/BILLABONG/by/T. E. Grattan-Smith
John Sands Ltd, Sydney, n.d. [1921?]
24pp, 3 col. illus. & 5 b/w illus. by Edgar A. Holloway, dec. bd., dec. e/p, cover title, 280x215mm. NSL:M
Sunny South Series (for other anonymous titles in this series, see Sunny South Series).

2935 THE/MAGIC BILLABONG/and other stories/for Australian Children/T. E. Grattan-Smith/author of/"Three Real Bricks"/illustrated with Pen Drawings/by/Percy Lindsay./The Grattan Press/Sydney
n.d. [Copyright 1928]
68pp, 15 pen drawings in text, pic. bd., 185x125mm. Grant

2936 THE CAVE OF A/THOUSAND COLUMNS/by/T. E. Grattan-Smith/Containing/five half-tone/plates/Hutchinson & Co./(Publishers) Ltd./London
1938
288pp, b/w frontis. & 4 b/w plates, illus. by E. Boye Uden, clo., 185x130mm. KMM
The story continues the adventures of Ned & Jim (see *Three Real Bricks)* in the discovery of some vast underground caverns in the Australian mountains.

GRAVES, Richard Harry

2937 SPEAR/AND/STOCKWHIP/By/Richard H. Graves/A Tale of the Territory/Dymock's Book Arcade Ltd./Sydney London/1950
162pp, unillus., clo., map e/p, 200x130mm. ANL

2938 TIDBINBILLA/ADVENTURE/A Sequel to/Spear and Stockwhip/By/Richard H. Graves/Sydney/Dymock's Book Arcade Limited/1951
150pp, 3 f/p b/w illus., clo., 200x130mm. ANL

GRAVES, R. P. T.

2939 A VISUAL HISTORY/OF AUSTRALIA/by/R. P. T. Graves, A.Ed.(Q)/Senior History Master,/St Crispin's County Secondary School, Wokingham/illustrated by/Leslie Haywood/[device]/London/Evans Brothers Limited
64pp, maps, b/w illus., pic. wrappers, 245x186mm. ANL
Dedicated 'To my former pupils of the Waiben State School, Thursday Island, North Queensland'.

GRAY, Annie

2940 DENNY/or,/From Haven to Haven./By/Annie Gray,/Author of "On Rocky Soil," "Allie Stuart," etc etc/Third Edition/London:/Sunday School Union,/56, Old Bailey, E.C.
n.d. [1st publ. 1883]
318pp & 2pp adv., b/w frontis., 10 f/p b/w illus. & engravings in text, pic. clo., 180x120mm. ANL
Last third of book set in the Victorian goldfields.

'GRAY, Carol Anne' [pseud. Nola Margot Johnson]

2941 BLACK WARRIGAL'S/TREASURE/By Carol Anne Gray/Wholly set up and printed by W. R. Rolph & Sons Pty. Ltd./The Examiner Press, 71–77 Paterson Street, Launceston, Tasmania.
n.d. [1948]
32pp, b/w frontis. & 3 f/p b/w illus., b/w drawings in text, illus. by J. Barry Laurance, dec. bd., 200x135mm. ANL
Prose, with verses (7pp).

GRAY, Edwina M.

2942 TRUE AUSTRALIANS/Text and Illustration/Edwina M. Gray/a Horwitz-Martin Publication Sydney 1970
44pp, b/w drawings in text, pic. wrappers, 243x187mm. NSL:M
Australian fauna.

Great Australians

A series of short biographies for schools and general reading for secondary children.
Format example:

2943 Great Australians/MARCUS CLARKE/Brian Elliott/Melbourne/Oxford University Press, London Wellington New York
1969, 30pp, b/w illus., stiff dec. wrappers, 184x122mm. KP
Others in series:

2944 JOHN HUNTER, J. J. Auchmuty 1968. KP
2945 WILLIAM BLIGH, John Bach 1967. KMM
2946 THOMAS SUTCLIFFE MORT, Alan Barnard 1962. KP
2947 LACHLAN MACQUARIE, Marjorie Barnard 1964, rpt & rev. 1971. KP
2948 JOSEPH FURPHY, John Barnes 1967. KMM
2949 FERDINAND VON MUELLER, Alec H. Chisholm 1962. KP
2950 JOHN BATMAN, Mavis Thorpe Clark 1962, rpt & rev. 1971. CLRC
2951 CATHERINE SPENCE, Janet Cooper 1972. KMM
2952 ISAAC ISAACS, Zelman Cowen 1962. KP
2953 WILLIAM FARRER, E. J. Donath 1962, rpt & rev. 1970. KP
2954 CHARLES JOSEPH LA TROBE, Jill Eastwood 1972. CLRC
2955 GEORGE CHAFFEY, John P. Fogarty 1967. KP
2956 SAMUEL GRIFFITH, R. K. Forward 1964. KP
2957 ARTHUR STREETON, Ann Galbally 1972. ANL
2958 SIMEON LORD, D. R. Hainsworth 1968. VMOU
2959 C. Y. O'CONNOR, Alexandra Hasluck 1965. KP
2960 JAMES STIRLING, Morton Herman 1963. KP
2961 FRANCIS GREENWAY, Morton Herman 1964. KP
2962 JOHN MONASH, John Hetherington 1962, rpt 1970 rev. KP
2963 CHARLES KINGSFORD SMITH, Frederick Howard 1962. KMM
2964 MELBA, Geoffrey Hutton 1962. KP
2965 RICHARD BOURKE, Hazel King 1963. HBM

2966 HENRY HANDEL RICHARDSON, Leonie Kramer 1967. KMM
2967 ALFRED DEAKIN, John La Nauze 1962, rpt. 1968. KP
2968 J. F. ARCHIBALD, Sylvia Lawson 1971. KMM
2969 MARY GILMORE, Sylvia Lawson 1966. KMM
2970 JOHN BEDE POLDING, Mary Raphael Leavey 1971. ANL
2971 GEORGE GIPPS, S. C. McCulloch 1966. KP
2972 JOHN DUNMORE LANG, D. S. Macmillan 1962, rpt. 1971. KP
2973 EDGEWORTH DAVID, D. S. Macmillan 1965. KP
2974 CHARLES NICHOLSON, D. S. Macmillan 1969. KP
2975 JOHN FLYNN, W. Scott McPheat 1964, rpt. 1969. KMM
2976 HENRY PARKES, A. W. Martin 1964. KP
2977 ROLF BOLDREWOOD, T. Inglis Moore 1968. KP
2978 ERNEST MORRISON, W. A. Morrison 1962. KP
2979 GEORGE FIFE ANGAS, Sally O'Neill 1972. ANL
2980 W. C. WENTWORTH, Michael Persse 1972. KP
2981 CHARLES HAWKER, Douglas Pike 1968. KP
2982 DAVID COLLINS, Rex Rienits 1969. CLRC
2983 JAMES COOK, Rex Rienits 1969. CLRC
2984 PHILIP GIDLEY KING, Michael Roe 1963. KMM
2985 REDMOND BARRY, Peter Ryan 1972. ANL
2986 RALPH DARLING, A. G. L. Shaw 1971. CLRC
2987 A. B. PATERSON, Clement Semmler 1967. CLRC
2988 TOM ROBERTS, Arnold Shore 1964. KP
2989 LAWRENCE HARGRAVE, Ivan Southall 1964. CLRC
2990 ARTHUR PHILLIP, Margaret Steven 1962. KP
2991 JOHN MACARTHUR, Margaret Steven 1968. KP
2992 ROBERT CAMPBELL, Margaret Steven 1969. CLRC
2993 CAROLINE CHISHOLM, Wendy Sutherland 1967. CLRC
2994 DOUGLAS MAWSON, Griffith Taylor 1962. KP
2995 THOMAS BRISBANE, Ruth Teale 1971. KP
2996 ESSINGTON LEWIS, Clive Turnbull 1963. KP
2997 HUBERT MURRAY, Francis West 1962. KP
2998 HENRY LAWSON, Judith Wright 1967. KP
2999 SAMUEL MARSDEN, A. T. Yarwood 1968. KP
Also several vol. issued of six titles bound together, e.g. *First Australian Governors* &c.

Great Explorers
3000 GREAT EXPLORERS/Marco Polo, Ferdinand Magellan, Mungo Park,/Sir John Franklin, David Livingstone,/Christopher Columbus,/Etc. Etc.,/Thomas Nelson and Sons/London, Edinburgh, and New York/1905
224pp, 16pp adv., b/w portrait frontis. & 31 f/p b/w illus. (inc. maps), pic. clo., 180x120mm. KMM
Includes chapters on Magellan, Cook, Sir John Franklin 'The Story of Australia'.

Great People in Australian History
Short illustrated biographies for schools and the general young reader.
Format example:
3001 Great People/In/Australian History/General Editor: J. Mark Howard/HENRY LAWSON/by/K. Levis/illustrated by Margaret Senior/[device] Longmans
Melbourne 1967
30pp, part col. & b/w illus. throughout, stiff pic. wrappers, 210x154mm. KMM
Others in series:
3002 ARTHUR PHILLIP by Eve Levis. Illus. A. van Ewijk, 1965. KMM
3003 'BANJO' PATERSON by H. G. Palmer. Illus. A. van Ewijk, 1966. KP
3004 BASS AND FLINDERS by Eve Levis. Illus. James Phillips, 1965. KMM
3005 BUILDERS OF THE WHEAT INDUSTRY by J. Mark Howard. Illus. Sylvia Parrett, 1967. KMM
3006 CAROLINE CHISHOLM by Robert Colvin. Illus. James Phillips, 1965. KMM
3007 CHARLES KINGSFORD SMITH by K. & E. Moon. Illus. Sylvia Parrett, 1967. KP
3008 CHARLES STURT by J. Mark Howard. Illus. James Phillips, 1966. HBM
3009 DAMPIER & COOK by R. Copley. Illus. Carole Kivinen, 1966. KMM
3010 HARTOG & TASMAN, by R. Copley. Illus. Carole Kivinen, 1965. KMM
3011 HENRY PARKES by L. C. Rodd. Illus. Sylvia Parrett, 1965. KP
3012 JOHN FLYNN & THE FLYING DOCTOR SERVICE by K. Moon. Illus. A. van Ewijk, 1965. KP
3013 JOHN MCDOUALL STUART by D. S. Macmillan. Illus. Will Mahony, 1966. HBM
3014 ROSS SMITH & BERT HINKLER by J. Mark Howard, Illus. A. van Ewijk, 1967. KP

GREEN, Bruce
3015 TOMMY/AND HIS/GARDEN/Bruce Green/Decorations by/Paul Beadle
Colorgravure, Melbourne 1950
41pp, 12pp col. illus., b/w & part. col. illus. throughout, dec. bd., dec. e/p, 190x170mm. Little Wonder Books. KMM

3016 TOMMY/GOES ROUND/THE WORLD/Bruce Green/Pictures by Max Newton
Colorgravure, Melbourne 1950
40pp, col. & part. col. illus. throughout, dec. bd., dec. e/p, 190x165mm. Little Wonder Books. KMM

3017 TOMMY/AND HIS/PONY/Bruce Green/Decorations by/Paul Beadle
Colorgravure, Melbourne 1951
20pp, col. illus. throughout, dec. bd., dec. e/p, 190x165mm. Little Wonder Books. KMM

GREEN, Eila
See Crozier, Cecily (ed.)

GREEN, E. Everett
3018 DADDY'S DUCKLINGS/By/E. Everett Green/Author of "Sweepie" "Aunt Patience"/"The Heron Stroke Mystery"/Etc. Etc./London/The Religious Tract Society/4 Bouverie Street E.C.4
n.d. [prize 1928]
220pp, col. frontis. only, clo. with col. onlay on front cover, 184x120mm. KP
'Uncle Jack' in Australia is introduced on p42 & is a character thereafter.

GREEN, Evelyn Everett
3019 MY COUSIN/FROM AUSTRALIA/by/Evelyn Everett Green/Author of/"Namesakes", "Golden Gwendolyn"/"Dare Lorimer's Heritage", etc. etc./London/Hutchinson & Co./34 Paternoster Row
n.d. [adv. dated 1894]
312pp, 32pp adv., b/w frontis. & 3 f/p b/w illus., dec. clo., 185x120mm. Grant
• Rpt, as above. ANL

GREEN, Henry Mackenzie
3020 CLARENCE AND THE GOBLINS;/or,/Under the Earth./By/Henry Mackenzie Green./(Eleven years of age.)/With Portrait of the Author, and Photograph/of illustration drawn by him./Sydney:/1892
Public Library Press

8pp, 1p preface, b/w frontis. portrait, 1 f/p b/w illus., clo., 220x145mm. NSL:M
Preface by James Norton [the author's grandfather].

GREEN, Louis
ERNEST GILES. *See* Australian Explorers

GREEN, Max
3021 THE GIANT AND THE BUTTERFLIES/and Other Stories/By/Max Green/Illustrations:/Theo. Lippmann/ Mingay Publishing Co., Sydney/Wholly set up and printed in Australia by Radio Printing Press Pty. Ltd. 146 Foveaux Street, Sydney, N.S.W.
n.d. [1944]
20pp, drawings in text, pic. wrappers, 245x185mm. NSL:M

GREEN, Sylvia
See Crozier, Cecily (ed.)

GREENBERG, Joe [illustrator]
3022 THE STORY OF/JOSEPH/Decorations by/Joe Greenberg
Colorgravure, Melbourne 1951
20pp, dec. t.p., col. illus. throughout, dec. bd., 195x165mm. Little Wonder Books. KMM

GREENER, Leslie
3023 MOON/AHEAD/By Leslie/Greener/Illustrated by/William Pène du/Bois/New York/1951/The/ Viking/Press
First published by the Viking Press October 1951; Published on the same day in the Dominion of Canada by the Macmillan Company of Canada Limited
256pp, dec. t.p., 8 f/p b/w illus., clo., dec. e/p, 210x140mm. TSL
3024 MOON/AHEAD/by/Leslie/Greener/illustrated by/William/Pène du Bois/The/Bodley/Head/London 1952
192pp, dec. t.p., 8 f/p b/w illus., clo., 195x125mm. ANL
3025 MOON/AHEAD/Leslie Greener/and/John Hutchinson/Illustrated by/William Pène du Bois/ Penguin Books
Harmondsworth, Middlesex, England 1957
158pp, 1p foreword, dec. t.p., 8 b/w illus., pic. wrappers, 180x110mm. Puffin Books. KMM
The foreword states that this is an abridged edition, and that John Hutchinson was responsible for the abridgement.

3026 THE WIZARD BOATMAN/OF THE NILE/and other Tales from Egypt/By/Leslie Greener/Illustrated in colour/and black-and-white/[device]/George G. Harrap & Co. Ltd./London Toronto Wellington Sydney 1957
64pp, part. col. & b/w illus., clo., 185x125mm. KMM

Greengrocer the Locust
3027 The Enchanted Castle Series/Glen Valley/ presents/GREENGROCER/THE/LOCUST/The Tea for/Quality
W. H. Honey Pub Co., 31 Cunningham St, Sydney n.d. [194-?]
16pp, b/w illus., col. pic. wrappers, 240x185mm. KP

GREENOP, Frank S.
3028 THE LIFE AND ACHIEVEMENTS OF/CAPTAIN JAMES COOK/Adventures and Discoveries of Three Voyages/Frank S. Greenop—Illustrated by Walter Stackpool/[illustration with portrait]
W. C. Penfold & Co. Pty Ltd, Sydney 1969
45pp (inc. 1p foreword by Alec H. Chisholm), 10 col. illus., b/w drawings, maps, etc. in text, pic. bd., map e/p, cover title, 280x215mm. KMM

3029 PATHS OF/THE PIONEERS
Produced for Vita-Brits & printed by W. C. Penfold Pty Ltd Sydney n.d. [1969?]
8pp & text printed inside book cover, col. & part col. illus. to be pressed out & pasted in appropriate places, pic. covers, cover title, 330x230mm. KP
Illus. by Col. Cameron.

3030 CLOSING/THE MILES
Produced by Vita-Brits & printed by W. C. Penfold, Sydney n.d.
[8]pp & maps & diagrams printed inside cover, col. & part col. illus. to be pressed out & inserted, col. pic. wrappers, cover title, 330x230mm. KP
Illus. Hal English. KP

3031 FROM/COLONIES/TO/COMMONWEALTH
Produced for Vita-Brits & printed by W. C. Penfold, Sydney n.d.
[8]pp & info. printed inside both covers, col. & part col. illus. to be pressed out & inserted, col. pic. wrappers, cover title Monty Wedd, 330x230mm. KP
Publ. together with a long-playing record.

3032 THE GREAT/GOLD RUSHES
Produced for Vita-Brits & printed by W. C. Penfold Pty Ltd Sydney. n.d.
8pp & maps & info. printed inside both covers, col. pic. cover, cover title, col. illus. to be pressed out & inserted & part col. drawings, 330x230mm. KP
Illus. Hal English. KP

3033 Moorooba/Books/CATAPULT/FOR TOM/An Australian Story Book
Greenop & Greenhalgh, Sydney n.d. [196-?]
13pp (inc. back pastedown), col. illus. throughout, pic. bd., cover title, 255x185mm. WRT
Illus. by Hal English.

Uniform in the series:
3034 BUNYIP WITH A SWAG, illus. Col. Cameron. KMM
3035 CLARRIE KOOKABURRA AND CHARLIE CROW, illus. Col. Cameron. KMM
3036 FAIRIES OF FLOWERY GULLEY [*sic*] illus. VMOU
3037 FLAME FAIRIES, illus. Col. Cameron. KMM
3038 JUMBO JET & THE ELVES, illus. VMOU
3039 KIT KOALA, illus. Col. Cameron. KMM
3040 KOALAS DRINK DEW, illus. Col. Cameron. WRT
3041 LAZY LOPER, illus. Col. Cameron. KMM
3042 LIGHTHOUSE LAD, illus. Hal English. KMM
3043 THE MAGPIE HERO, illus. Hal English. KMM
3044 WILD WHITE, illus. Hal English. KMM

GREENOP, Frank S. [ed.]
3045 NEW SOUTH WALES/AUSTRALIA/A concise outline/of the history, wealth/and development of the State/with 47 photographs/in colour and black and white/Southern Cross International/Sydney
1968
95pp, inc. 2pp index, pic. bd., map e/p, 235x160mm. KP

Uniform in same series publ. 1968/9. all KP
3046 VICTORIA
3047 WESTERN AUSTRALIA
3048 QUEENSLAND
3049 SOUTH AUSTRALIA
3050 TASMANIA

GREENWAY, Ella
3051 PETER/CAT/Ella Greenway/Pictures by/Kath O'Brien
Colorgravure, Melbourne, 1950

41pp, 12pp col. illus., b/w & part. col. illus. throughout, dec. bd., dec. e/p, 195x170mm. KMM
Little Wonder Books.

GREENWOOD, 'Ted' [E. A.]
3052 [drawing]/AELFRED/Ted Greenwood/Angus and Robertson
Sydney 1970
[52]pp, b/w & part. col. illus. throughout, pic. clo., pic. e/p, 240x150mm. CLRC

3053 OBSTREPEROUS/by Ted Greenwood/Angus and Robertson
Sydney 1970
[48]pp, col. drawings throughout, col. dec. t.p., pic. clo., dec. e/p, 280x185mm. KMM
3054 Rpt 1970. KMM
3055 [drawing]/V.I.P./Very Important Plant/Ted Greenwood/Angus and Robertson
Sydney 1971
[25]pp, col. illus. throughout, pic. bd., dec. e/p, 280x185mm. KMM

3056 JOSEPH/[drawing]/AND LULU/[drawing]/AND THE/[drawing]/PRINDIVILLE HOUSE/PIGEONS/ Ted Greenwood/Angus and Robertson
Sydney 1972
[47]pp, part. col. illus. throughout, pic. bd., 280x175mm. CLRC

GREGORSON, Edith Ray
3057 LEMUEL/[drawing]/by/Edith Ray Gregorson/ Illustrated/by/Peter Scott/[device]/The Owl Press Limited/London WC2
1947
48pp, drawings in text throughout, bd., 230x152mm. KMM
The story of a tree kangaroo from New Guinea.

GREGORY, Olive Barnes
3058 The "Read about it" Series/Book 45/JAMES COOK/by/O. B. Gregory/Illustrated by A. Oxenham/ © O. B. Gregory, 1965/[device]/Wheaton & Exeter
24pp, 10 f/p part col. illus., stiff col. pic. clo. covers, 184x140mm. NSL:M

GREGORY, Richard E.
3059 DON'T SWIM THERE!/An Infants' Story of Pollution/Written and illustrated by Richard E. Gregory/Angus and Robertson
Sydney 1971
32pp, part. col. illus. throughout, stiff pic. wrappers, 215x290mm. KMM

3060 WHAT IS A BANDICOOT?/An Australian ABC/ Written and Illustrated by Richard E. Gregory/Angus and Robertson
Sydney 1971
54pp, b/w & part. col. drawings throughout, stiff pic. wrappers, 215x290mm. VSL

3061 TRICKS WITH/SCIENCE/Written and Illustrated by/Richard E. Gregory/Whitcombe & Tombs Pty Ltd.
Sydney 1972
127pp, part col. illus. throughout, bd., 195x15mm. CLRC

GREGSON, Nell
3062 RHYTHM SONGS/For Children Small/Words and Music by/Nell Gregson/Contents [32 songs listed]/ Copyright Price 2/- net/Allan & Co. Pty Ltd./Melb. Ad. Bend.
1940
24pp, dec. wrappers, Imperial Edition no. 480, 248x170mm. KP

3063 Another ed. as above with price 3/6 35c n.d. [196-?]. KP
3064 Another ed. as above with price 45c n.d. KP

3065 SOUND MATCHING SONGS;/75 songs/for children/under seven/by/Nell Gregson
Melb Allan 1947
48pp, inc. 3pp introduction, words & music of 75 songs, dec. wrappers, cover title, 284x18mm. CLRC
2/6/ 3/- in NZ/Allan & Co. Pty Ltd./Melbourne Adelaide Bendigo
Imperial Edition no. 501.
• Rpt as above price 4/- on front cover. KP

'GREY, Estelle' [pseud. Esta de Fossard]
3066 JULIE GORDON/and the School Fashion Contest/ by/Estelle Grey/Golden Press/Sydney
1972
260pp, 3 f/p b/w illus., pic. bd., pic. e/p, 205x130mm. NSL:M

GREY, Peter
3067 KIT HUNTER—SHOW JUMPER/BUSH ADVENTURE/by/Peter Grey/Published by/World Distributors (Manchester) Limited/London—Manchester/England
183pp, bd., 185x120mm. ANL
Adventures of an English girl on a visit to Australia.

3068 KIT HUNTER—SHOW JUMPER/THE MYSTERY OF THE MINE/by/Peter Grey/Published by/World Distributors (Manchester) Limited/London—Manchester/England
1960
183pp, unillus., clo., 185x120mm. KP
• Rpt n.d. as above. KP

'GREY, Stephen' [pseud. Bernard Cronin & Doris Boake Kerr]
3069 KANGAROO RHYMES/By/Stephen Grey/ Dedicated to the Children of the Commonwealth/[25 lines introduction by Frank Tate, Director of Education, Victoria, June 1922]/Melbourne:/Wholly set up and Printed in Australia by Smithson Bros., Printers and Publishers/369a P.O. Place West.
12pp, 2 f/p b/w illus., b/w decorations in text, wrappers (with b/w illus. reproduced part. col. on front cover), 235x170mm. VSL

[GRIEVE, David]
3070 EDWARD'S ADVENTURES/IN/NURSERY RHYME/LAND
A C.M.C. Production. Lithographed by Modern Printing Co Pty Ltd for Pantheon Publications 20 Queen St, Melbourne
n.d. [1950]
18pp, col. illus. every page by Jean Elder, col. pic. wrappers, cover title, 270x215mm. KMM

GRIEVE, David
3071 ANN AND DONALD'S/TRIP TO BUNNYLAND/ Story and illustrations by David Grieve
Pantheon Publications, 20 Queen Street, Melbourne, n.d. [1950]
16pp (story beginning on verso of front cover & ending on recto of back cover), col.
illus. throughout, col. pic. bd., 275x215mm. KMM

3072 THE MAGIC EGG/An Easter Story
Pantheon Publications, Melbourne, n.d. [1948]
16pp, col. illus., col. pic. bd., cover title, 275x215mm. KMM
The text & illustrations are the same, with minor variations, as *Ann and Donald's Trip to Bunnyland* except for the front cover drawing.

3073 THE ENCHANTED/CHRISTMAS TREE/Story and Illustrations by David Grieve
A CMC Production, Pantheon Publications, 20 Queen St Melbourne
n.d.
18pp (inc. inside of both wrappers), illus. in col. throughout, col. pic. wrappers, 226x215mm. KMM

GRIEVE, Edith [illustrator]
Illustrator of the following uniform picture books:
3074 ANIMAL FRIENDS
3075 AT THE ZOO
3076 AWAY WE GO
3077 SUNNY DAYS
3078 TRAINS
Published by George Jaboor, Melbourne 1943
8pp, board books, illus. throughout, 140x120mm. ANL
Also:
3079 FAVOURITE NURSERY RHYMES
3080 PUPPIES AT PLAY
Published by Georgian House, Melbourne 1944
16pp, 8 col. illus. throughout, pic. wrappers, 250x195mm. ANL
Brief text.
Also published as board books with 8pp, omitting text pages. KMM

GRIFFIN, David
3081 THE/HAPPINESS BOX/by David Griffin/With drawings by/Leslie Greener/The Australasian Publishing Co. Pty. Ltd./Sydney N.S.W.
1947
32pp, 2pp col. illus., b/w drawings, dec. bd., 195x165mm. VSL
Written in Changi gaol for child prisoners.

GRIFFITH, Eugenie V.
3082 THE/FRANCIS XAVIER/STORY/by/Eugenie V. Griffith/Longmans, Green and Co./London Melbourne New York
1957
186pp, b/w drawings, illus. by Margaret R. Dods, dec. map e/p, clo., 180x125mm. KMM

GRIFFITH, Florence L.
3083 AUSTRALIAN/PLAYS AND SKETCHES/No. 1/Florence L. Griffith/The Clifford Press/Melbourne, Victoria, Australia.
n.d. [1962?]
48pp, unillus., dec. wrappers, 215x135mm. ANL
Includes some verse. On front cover: 'Items for all ages for Church and Sunday School use'.

GRIFFITH, George
3084 MEN WHO HAVE MADE/THE EMPIRE/By/George Griffith/Author of "Valdar the Oft-Born", "The Rose of Judah", etc./with illustrations by Stanley L. Wood/[device]/London/George Bell and Sons/and Bombay
n.d. [190-?]
305pp, 4pp author's foreword, b/w frontis. & 7 f/p b/w illus., clo., 195x130mm. KMM
Includes section on James Cook (22pp).

GRIFFITHS, Lexie Rhelba
3085 Imperial Edition NO. 681/MERRY RHYMES FOR/CHILDHOOD TIMES/Piano solos with words/words by Lexie Griffiths/—Music by Anthony Hall/[11 songs listed]/Allan & Co. Pty. Ltd./Melbourne Adelaide Bendigo
1932
19pp & 2pp blank, col. pic. wrapper, 305x230mm. VSL

3086 BETWEEN OURSELVES/By/Lexie Griffiths/Illustrations by/Pixie O'Harris/Angus & Robertson Ltd/Sydney: London/1945
41pp, b/w drawings throughout, bd., 180x115mm. KMM
• Rpt June 1945. KP

3087 BETWEEN OURSELVES/By/Lexie Griffiths/(Author of "A Little Bird Told Me")/Illustrations by/Pixie O'Harris/[publisher's device]/The Book Depot/288 Little Collins Street,/Melbourne/1946
41pp, b/w drawings throughout, stiff wrappers, 180x115mm. ANL

3088 A LITTLE BIRD/TOLD ME/By/Lexie Griffiths/(Author of "Between Ourselves")/Illustrations by/Josselyn Hughes/[publisher's device]/The Book Depot/288 Little Collins Street,/Melbourne/1946
35pp, b/w drawings in text, col. pic. wrappers, 180x120mm. ANL
Verse. ANL

3089 Imperial Edition No. 543/ALONG THE TRACK/Little Tunes for young pianists/Words by/Lexie Griffiths/Music by/Arthur S. Loam/[8 songs listed]/Copyright MCMXLIX by Allan & Co. Pty Ltd./Allan & Co. Pty Ltd./Melbourne Adelaide Bendigo
12pp, unillus., pic. front cover, 307x237mm. KP

3090 Imperial Edition No. 626/THE LEAF AND/THE BUD/and Other Songs for Children/Words by/Lexie Griffiths/Music by/Edith Harrhy/[Titles of 11 songs]/Copyright 1950 by/Allan & Co. Pty. Ltd./Melbourne Adelaide Bendigo
30pp (last 2 blank), pic. wrappers, 240x180mm. Grant

3091 Mullens' Stories for Children/(No. 202)/THE CAT WALK/by/Lexie Griffiths/(For Ages 8 to 9)/[drawing]/Robertson & Mullens Ltd./Melbourne
n.d. [1952]
56pp, b/w frontis. & 3 f/p b/w illus., pic. wrappers, 180x115mm. ANL
Illustrations signed 'Rolland'.

3092 Mullens' Stories for Children/No. 203/RICHARD THE RAT/by/Lexie Griffiths/(For Ages 8 to 9)/[drawing]/Robertson & Mullens Ltd./Melbourne
1952
32pp, b/w frontis. & 3 f/p b/w illus. by Marjorie Howden, pic. wrappers, 180x115mm. ANL

3093 Mullens' Stories for Children/No. 201/WILLIAM WOMBAT/FINDS A HOME/by/Lexie Griffiths/(For Ages 8 to 9)/[drawing]/Robertson & Mullens Ltd./Melbourne
1952
32pp, b/w frontis. & 3 f/p b/w illus. by Marjorie Howden, pic. wrappers, 180x115mm. KMM
Story originally appeared in the Victorian Education Department's School Paper.

GRIGGS, P. G.
3094 TREACHERY/AT/FORTY KNOTS/A Sea Spy Story for Boys/P. G. Griggs/The Shakespeare Head/London New York Sydney Durban Paris/1946
175pp, b/w frontis. & 5 f/p b/w illus., clo., 210x130mm. NSL:M

GRIMWADE, Alice
3095 ONCE UPON A TIME/By/Alice Grimwade/Illustrations by/Una Le Souëf Falkiner and Violet Teague/George Robertson and Company/Propy. Ltd/Melbourne Sydney Adelaide Brisbane
n.d. [1911]
63pp, b/w drawings throughout, b/w frontis., clo., 210x180mm. KMM
Short stories.

GROH, Lynn

3096 [device]/A World Explorer/FERDINAND MAGELLAN/By Lynn Groh/Illustrated by Robert Doremus/Frederick Muller Limited/London
1966 [First published in the United States 1963]
96pp, part. col. illus. throughout, clo., map e/p, 225x160mm. KMM
A World Explorer Book [edited by Elizabeth Minot Graves].

GROOM, Arthur

3097 'FLYING DOCTOR'/ANNUAL/[drawing]/Stories by Arthur Groom/Associated British Corporation, Ltd. 1963/[device—Dean & Son Ltd., London]/Sole Agents for South Africa: Central News Agency Ltd./Sole Agents for Australia and New Zealand: Gordon and Gotch Ltd.
125pp, col. frontis., b/w frontis. & b/w drawings on almost every page, col. pic. bd., dec. e/p, 270x205mm. KMM
Contains 14 stories based on the Royal Flying Doctor Service. Artist's name not given. On cover: 'Exciting Stories from the T.V. and Radio Series'.

GROSER, Thomas Sidney

3098 BOYS/OF BACK O' BEYOND/A Realistic Tale of Sport and Adventure/Typical of the Spirit of Young Australia/By T. S. Groser/Alexander-Ouseley Limited/Windsor House, Victoria St., Westminster London, S.W.1.
1930
viipp, 286pp, col. frontis., 1 col. & 4 b/w plates, illus. Douglas Constable, clo., 185x120mm. KP

[GRUNDY, Francis H.]

3099 THE DEMON McGUIRE
Gibbs, Shallard & Co., General Letterpress and Lithographic Printers, 108 Pitt Street, Sydney, n.d. [1870]
46pp (alternate page openings blank), 12 f/p lithographic illus., stiff wrappers, cover title, 270x215mm. NSL:M
Macabre but humorous tale in verse issued anonymously for the Charles Lascelles Benefit at the Prince of Wales Theatre, November 1870

Gründzuge des Natur—und Menschenlebens in Australien und Polynesien
See RICHTER, Friedrich

GRZIMEK, Bernhard

3100 STVORNOHI AUSTRALCANIA (Four-legged Australians)
Slovak edition
Bratislava 1971
161pp. SLCSR

GUERIN, A. C.

3101 [drawing]/"LOOSIKINS"/A Delightful Story of the Australian/Bush for Young and Old with/Authentic Information on/Birds and Trees/By A. C. Guerin
Laurent Publishing Co., Sydney, n.d. [1946]
64pp (inc. 6pp glossary & 1p foreword by Mary Gilmore), 9 col. illus. & b/w drawings in text throughout, illus. by Harry Wann, dec. bd., 245x185mm. ANL

GUÉRIN, Léon

3102 LE TOUR/DU MONDE/ou les/Mille et une Merveilles/des Voyages./par Léon Guérin/AUSTRALIE/Japon, Archipel Indien et Diverses autres îles/Paris/Langlois et Leclercq/Rue de la Harpe, 81/1842
143pp (inc. 3pp contents), engravings in text, clo., g.e., 153x96mm. ANL
Bound together with VOYAGES/DE/WILLIAMS [*sic*] JARVIS,/en Angleterre,/dans plusiers îles de l'Océan Atlantique, de la mer Sud/et des mers Polaires.
and 2nd vol.
LE TOUR/DU MONDE/ou Les/Mille et une Merveilles/des voyages,/par Léon Guérin,/OCEANIE,/Océan Atlantique, mers Polaires./Paris/Langlois et Leclercq/Rue de la Harpe, 81/1842
143pp (inc. 3pp contents), engravings in text throughout, 153x96mm. ANL
2 vol. bound together in clo., g.e.
Chapter 6 (49pp South Seas, NZ, Tonga, Dumont Durville,[*sic*]] New Hebrides, New Caledonia, La Peyrouse [*sic*] Sandwich Isles, Death of Cook, Tahiti).

3103 LE TOUR/DU MONDE/ou les/mille et une Merveilles/des voyages/par Léon Guérin/—/Australie/Japon, Archipel Indien et diverses autres îles/—/Paris/Langlois et Leclercq/Rue de la Harpe, 81
n.d. [1850?]
144pp (last blank), many text illus., pic. wrappers, title repeated on front cover, 170x105mm. NSL:M
Imaginary travels, carrying instructions in geography for juveniles. First 40 pages relate to Australia.

3104 LES/JEUNES NAVIGATEURS/Autour du Monde./par Léon Guérin/[monogram]/Paris/Mme Ve Louis Janet, Libraire-Éditeur,/Rue Saint-Jacques, 59/[decoration]
n.d.
vipp, 231pp, engraved frontis. & 7 f/p engravings, dec. board, 142x107mm. ANL
Last chapters about New Guinea, New Holland & return via Cape Horn (pp195-231)

A Guide to Manhood

3105 Guide Series:/A reliable Sex Education Book for Young Men/A GUIDE TO MANHOOD/Foreword by/Professor Harvey Sutton, O.B.E./Australian Public Health Authority/Father & Son Welfare Movement Of/Australia/(inc. Mother and Daughter Section)/Sydney Melbourne Brisbane Adelaide/1959
32pp, 4pp adv., b/w drawings, pic. wrappers, 184x120mm. KP

GUILBERT, Rose

3106 SILVERLAND/AND GOLDENSHORE:/a Fairy Tale/By Rose Guilbert/Hobart:/Monotone Art Printers/56-58 Liverpool St./1916
14pp, unillus. wrappers, 190x126mm. ANL

GULLICK, M. E.

3107 Overseas Children/By M. E. Gullick/THE LITTLE/BROWN GIRL/[drawing]/Humphrey Milford/Oxford University Press
n.d.
32pp, col. frontis. & 3 f/p col. illus., pic. wrappers, 160x105mm. KMM

'GUMSUCKER'. *See* Roland, S. A.

GUNN, Florence [illustrator]

3108 THE LITTLE/GINGERBREAD/BOY/Pictures by/Florence Gunn/Georgian House/Melbourne
n.d. [1947]
11pp, 9 f/p col. illus., stiff dec. wrappers, 245x185mm. ANL

GUNN, Jeannie [Mrs Aeneas Gunn, née Taylor]

3109 THE LITTLE BLACK/PRINCESS: A TRUE/TALE OF LIFE IN THE/NEVER-NEVER LAND/By Jeannie Gunn/London/Alexander Moring Ltd./Melbourne/Melville and Mullen. 1905

107pp, 1p acknowledgement, 1p map, b/w frontis. & 24pp b/w illus., pic. clo., 205x140mm. KMM

3110 THE LITTLE BLACK/PRINCESS: A True/Tale of Life in the Never-Never Land/By Jeannie Gunn/ London/Alexander Moring Ltd./Melbourne/Melville and Mullen 1906
Second edition May 1906
Details as before only the pic. cover reads, 'By Mrs Aeneas Gunn' on front cover & spine instead of 'Jeannie Gunn'. KMM

3111 THE LITTLE BLACK/PRINCESS: A TRUE/TALE OF LIFE IN THE/NEVER-NEVER LAND/By Mrs Aeneas Gunn/Third Impression/Alexander Moring Limited The/De la More Press 32 George St./Hanover Square London W. 1906
'1st imp. October 1905; 2nd imp. May 1906; 3rd imp. September 1906' on verso of t.p
107pp, 1p acknowledgement, 2pp adv., 1p map, b/w frontis. & 24pp b/w illus., pic. clo. (design as in first imp.), 205x140mm. NSL:M

3112 THE LITTLE BLACK/PRINCESS OF THE/ NEVER-NEVER/By/Mrs Aeneas Gunn/Author of "We of the Never-Never"/New and revised edition/ Hodder and Stoughton/London MCMIX
107pp, 1p acknowledgements, b/w frontis. (photograph of Bett Bett and Sue), 19pp b/w illus., 1p map, marginal illus., fawn clo. (with vignette of Bett Bett blocked in col. on front cover with black & green lettering & gilt lettering on spine), 200x140mm. KMM
Another edition, Hodder & Stoughton, as above, but n.d. BBC

3113 THE LITTLE BLACK/PRINCESS OF THE/ NEVER-NEVER/By/Mrs Aeneas Gunn/Author of "We of the Never-Never"/Robertson & Mullens Ltd./ Melbourne
n.d. [1922?] [Printed by G. W. Green & Sons, Melbourne]
107pp, b/w frontis. ('Bett Bett & Sue') & 19pp b/w illus. & map, dec. green clo. (tree ferns & lake &c., & rope device on spine), 200x140mm. NSL:M

3114 THE LITTLE BLACK/PRINCESS...Completing the 78th thousand/Robertson & Mullens Ltd./Melbourne n.d. [prize 1925]
Details as before (ferns &c. on cover). KP

3115 THE LITTLE BLACK/PRINCESS OF THE/ NEVER-NEVER/By/Mrs Aeneas Gunn/Author of "We of the Never-Never"/Completing the 92nd thousand/ Robertson & Mullens Ltd./Melbourne
1929
107pp, b/w frontis. & 32 b/w illus. (inc. map), clo. (with tree-fern design printed on front cover), 200x135mm. KMM
- Rpt 119th thousand, 1940. KP
- Rpt 120th thousand, 1947. KP
- Rpt 125th thousand, 1948. KP
- Rpt 130th thousand, 1952. KP

3116 THE LITTLE BLACK/PRINCESS OF THE/ NEVER-NEVER/By/Mrs. Aeneas Gunn/Author of "We of the Never-Never"/Completing the 130th thousand/Robertson & Mullens Ltd./Melbourne. 1952; edition limited to 500 numbered copies (in slipcase) signed by author
107pp, b/w frontis. & 31 b/w illus., 1 b/w map, clo., 215x140mm. CLRC
- Rpt 135th thousand, 1955, plain cream bd. KP
- Rpt 140th thousand, 1957. KP

3117 THE LITTLE BLACK/PRINCESS OF THE/ NEVER-NEVER/By/Mrs. Aeneas Gunn/Author of "We of the Never-Never"/Angus and Robertson Sydney, n.d. [1962]
107pp, (no frontis.), 32pp b/w illus. (inc. 1p map), clo., 215x135mm. BBC
This edition, the first bearing the Angus & Robertson imprint, was published with a new pictorial d/w (sgd ?Quinton P. Davies).
- Rpt as above 1963, 1966. KP

3118 THE LITTLE BLACK/PRINCESS OF THE/ NEVER-NEVER/By/Mrs Aeneas Gunn/Author of "We of the Never-Never"/Angus and Robertson
Sydney, new edition 1962; rpt 1963, 1966, 1968, 1970
Details as in 1962 edition. BBC

3119 THE LITTLE/BLACK PRINCESS/OF THE/ NEVER-NEVER/By/Mrs Aeneas Gunn/
Australian Pocket Library 1947
155pp, 3pp adv., wrappers, 180x110mm. KP

3120 THE LITTLE/BLACK PRINCESS/OF THE/ NEVER-NEVER By/Mrs Aeneas Gunn/Adapted for use in Victorian Schools./Melbourne:/George Robertson & Co. Propy. Ltd./By arrangement with/ Hodder & Stoughton./London
n.d.
164pp (inc. 2pp preface, 2pp 'The Northern Territory' & 14pp 'Notes & Explanations'), 2pp adv., b/w map frontis. & inset b/w portrait of author, 4 f/p b/w illus. & b/w illus. in text by Charles Nuttall, stiff dec. wrappers (with price 'seven-pence' on front cover & adv. on back cover), 180x110mm. KMM
Part 2 of the book, from p125 onwards, contains 'Kur-bo-roo the Koala' & 'Mirran and Warreen' 'from a new book by Mary Grant Bruce, entitled *Kur-bo-roo, and other Legends of the Australian Bush*' (this was *The Stone Axe of Burkamukk*, first published 1922).

3121 THE LITTLE/BLACK PRINCESS/OF THE/ NEVER-NEVER/By/Mrs. Aeneas Gunn/Adapted for use in schools/Melbourne:/Robertson & Mullens Ltd./ 107–113 Elizabeth Street/1935
163pp (inc. 2pp preface, 3pp note & appreciation, 13pp notes & explanations), 3pp adv., b/w map frontis., b/w portrait of author & b/w photographic illus. in text, 5 f/p b/w illus. by Charles Nuttall, pic. wrappers, 185x120mm. KMM
Text includes 'Kur-bo-roo and Other legends', by Mary Grant Bruce (25pp).
This & subsequent school editions contain one additional b/w drawing, replacing a b/w photographic illustration which appeared on p74 of the George Robertson & Hodder & Stoughton edition (1922?). The design on the front cover was also redrawn.

3122 Rpt 1938, new school edition
155pp, 3pp adv. KP
- Rpt 1942, third school ed., as above. KMM
- Rpt 1943, as above. KP

3123 THE LITTLE/BLACK PRINCESS/adapted for use in Schools/by/Mrs. Aeneas Gunn/Author of "We of the Never-Never"/Robertson & Mullens Ltd./ Melbourne
1958
112pp, unillus., limp clo., 180x110mm. KMM

3124 THE LITTLE/BLACK PRINCESS/Adapted for Use in Schools/by/Mrs Aeneas Gunn/Author of "We of the Never-Never"/[device]/Angus and Robertson Sydney 1965
112pp, b/w photographic frontis., 3 b/w maps only, stiff wrappers, 180x120mm. KMM
Also author of *We of the Never Never*, a very popular account of her life on Elsey Station in the Northern Territory. It was abridged and adapted for use in schools, and went into many editions, including one commissioned by the Queensland Education Department. It was not originally written as a book for children, and is not included here.

GUNN, Jeannie & others

3125 THE AUSTRALIAN/WONDER BOOK/Containing/these four complete books:/1. THE LITTLE BLACK PRINCESS/By Mrs Aeneas Gunn/2. THE OTHER SIDE OF NOWHERE/by Tarella Quin Daskein/Illustrated by Ida Rentoul Outhwaite/3. THE PRINCE OF THE TOTEM/by Tarlton Rayment/4. WINKS—The Mystery and Magic of the Bush/by J. J. Hall/Home Entertainment Library
Melbourne 1935
351pp (inc. 1p preface), b/w illus. throughout, dec. bd., 240x185mm. KMM
Illustrations include 'Bett-Bett, The Little Black Princess', 'a hitherto unpublished photograph, taken three years after the close of this story'; cover design by Athol Thompson, 'a youthful artist who was robbed of the use of his arms in boyhood and now paints with his brush between his lips'. The Home Entertainment Library was published by the *Herald and Weekly Times* in an edition of at least 10 000 copies.

GUNN, John

3126 FLYING FOR YOU/A Career in Aviation/by/John Gunn/Lutterworth Press/London
1955
192pp (inc. 2pp foreword by Mike Lithgow & 2pp author's preface), b/w photographic frontis. & 30pp b/w photographic illus., 16 line drawings in text, dec. bd., 185x120mm. CLRC
Author born in Northumberland, but emigrated to Australia at the age of three.

3127 BARRIER REEF ESPIONAGE/A thrilling adventure Story for Boys with/an authentic naval and flying background/by/John Gunn/Illustrated by/Edward Osmond/Lutterworth Press/London
First pub. 1955; 2nd imp. 1958; 3rd imp. 1961
192pp, b/w frontis., 4 f/p b/w illus. (1 double-spread), clo., 195x125mm. KMM

3128 BATTLE IN THE ICE/An exciting "Peter Kent" Story with an/authentic naval and flying background/by/John Gunn/Illustrated by/George Lane/Lutterworth Press/London
1956
184pp, b/w frontis. & 6 f/p b/w illus., b/w drawings in text, clo., 195x130mm. BBC
Second imp. as above, 1961. MK

3129 GIBRALTAR/SABOTAGE/An exciting "Peter Kent" story with an/authentic Naval and Flying background/by/John Gunn/Frontispiece by/George Lane/Lutterworth Press/London
1957
168pp, col. frontis., clo., 200x130mm. BBC

3130 SAILING AND SHIPS/FOR YOU/by/John Gunn/Lutterworth Press/London
1957
178pp (inc. 2pp preface & 5pp appendices), b/w photographic frontis. & 14 b/w photographic illus., diagrams in text, clo., 200x125mm. BBC

3131 SEA/MENACE/[drawing]/by John Gunn/Illustrated by Brian Keogh/London/Constable and Co. Ltd.
1958
192pp, b/w drawings throughout, clo., 200x125mm. KMM
Joint winner CBCA Award 1959.
• Rpt as above, 1959. KMM

3132 SUBMARINE/ISLAND/A thrilling "Peter Kent" adventure story with the/authentic background of flying and naval action/by/John Gunn/Illustrated by/George Lane/Lutterworth Press/London
1958
160pp, b/w frontis. & 2 f/p b/w illus., clo., 195x125mm. BBC

3133 THE HUMPY/IN THE HILLS/[drawing]/John Gunn/Illustrated by/Noela Young/Lutterworth Press—London
1960
190pp, b/w drawings in text, clo., 195x120mm. KMM
• Rpt second imp., as above. Grant

3134 John Gunn/THE HUMPY IN/THE HILLS/Illustrated by/Noela Young/[drawing]/Penguin Books
Harmondsworth, Middlesex, England, 1967
187pp, 1p biographical note, 3pp adv., 4 f/p b/w illus., b/w drawings in text, pic. wrappers, cover design by Douglas Lee Travis, 180x110mm. Puffin Books. KMM

3135 PETER KENT'S/COMMAND/A Thrilling Adventure Story for Boys with the/authentic background of flying and naval action/by/John Gunn/Illustrated by/Horowitz/Lutterworth Press/London
1960
159pp, b/w frontis. & 7 b/w f/p illus., clo., 200x130mm. CLRC

3136 DANGEROUS/ENEMIES/[drawing]/John Gunn/Illustrated by/Brian Keogh/Lutterworth Press—London
1961
182pp, 5 f/p b/w illus. & b/w drawings in text, clo., 195x125mm. CLRC

3137 CITY IN DANGER/A thrilling "Peter Kent" Adventure Story with the/Authentic Background of Flying and Naval Action/by/John Gunn/Illustrated by/Noela Young/Lutterworth Press/London
1962
160pp, b/w frontis. & 8 f/p b/w illus., clo., 200x125mm. KMM

3138 CONQUEST OF SPACE/by/John Gunn, A.R.Ae.S./Published by/The Nestlé Company (Australia) Ltd
Sydney, n.d. [1962?]
58pp, b/w frontis., b/w photographic illus. & diagrams, spaces left for col. illus. to be collected & pasted in, pic. bd., pic. e/p, 275x210mm. KMM

3139 THE GOODBYE/ISLAND/[drawing]/John Gunn/Illustrated by/James Val/Lutterworth Press—London
1963
166pp, 4 f/p b/w illus., line drawings in text, clo., 200x130mm. KMM

3140 SEASPRAY,/THE MAN WHO WAS TOO RICH/John Gunn/Cover illustrations from T. V. Series Seaspray/by permission of Screen Gems Inc./[device]/Armada/Paperbacks/for Boys & Girls
First published May Fair Books Ltd, London 1967
126pp, 2pp adv., unillus., pic. wrappers, 180x110mm. KMM
Front cover title reads: 'The Adventures of/Seaspray/The Man who was too rich'.

3141 John Gunn/SEASPRAY,/THE SPOILS OF WAR/Cover illustration from T.V. series SEASPRAY/by permission of Screen Gems Inc./[device]/Armada/Paperbacks/for Boys & Girls
Surrey, England, 1967
128pp, unillus., pic. wrappers, 180x110mm. KMM

GUNN, John (ed.)

3142 DANGEROUS SECRET/by the girls and boys of

the/A.B.C. Children's Hour Argonauts' Club/Edited by/John Gunn/Australian Broadcasting/Commission [no place of imprint] 1960
68pp (inc. 1p foreword & 1p preface), 6 f/p col. illus., dec. bd., dec. e/p, 230x180mm. KMM
Written & illustrated by child members of the Argonauts' Club, ten different chidren as authors & eight as illustrators.

3143 THE GOLD SMUGGLERS/by the girls and boys of the/A.B.C. Children's Hour Argonauts' Club/Edited by/John Gunn/Lansdowne Press/Melbourne
1962
63pp (inc. 1p foreword by Charles Moses, General Manager, A.B.C. & 2pp photographs & biographical notes on artists & authors), 6 f/p col. illus. & 2 f/p b/w illus., dec. bd., dec. e/p, 245x185mm. KMM

3144 THE GRAVITY STEALERS/Written by Boys and Girls/of Australia/Edited by/John Gunn/Lansdowne Press
Melbourne 1965
64pp (inc. 1p foreword & 2pp photographs & biographical notes on authors & artists), 6 f/p col. illus. & 5 f/p b/w illus., dec. bd., dec. e/p, 250x185mm. KMM
Written & illustrated by the boys & girls of the Australian Broadcasting Commission's Children Hour Argonauts' Club.

GUNN, John & BINGHAM, Barbara
3145 ACTING FOR YOU/by/John Gunn/and/Barbara Bingham/Lutterworth Press/London
1957
184pp (inc. 2pp introduction), b/w photographic frontis. & 14 b/w photographic illus., 6 b/w diagrams, clo., 200x125mm. BBC

GUNN, John & BROWN, Barry
3146 THE WORLD ON WHEELS/Edited by/John Gunn/and/Barry Brown/Published by/The Nestlé Company (Australia) Ltd.
n.d. [196-?] (printed by W. C. Penfold & Co. Pty Ltd, Sydney)
74pp (120 col. illus. to be collected & pasted in), b/w photographs in text, pic. bd., pic. e/p, 280x215mm. KMM
Drawings by Walter Cunningham and Noela Young. Foreword by Jack Brabham.

GUNN, Thos.
3147 NURSERY/RHYMES/[decoration]/By/Thos. Gunn/Old Cashmere/St. George 1917
William Brooks & Co (Queensland) Ltd
12pp (last 3pp blank), unillus., wrappers, 160x102mm. ANL

GUNN, Tom
3148 BUSH NURSERY/RHYMES/In aid of St George Soldiers'/Memorial Hospital/[12 line verse signed 'Tom Gunn']
n.p., n.d. [1920, Stanthorpe. Info. from Hornibrook: *Biblio. of Queensland Verse*]
16pp, unillus., wrappers, 166x106mm. ANL
Some of the contents the same as the author's *Nursery Rhymes*

Gunn & Taylor, Melbourne [publishers]
3149 Australian Productions No 1—COLOURING BOOK/OF STORIES AND RHYMES/FOR/YOUNG ARTISTS
[Sydney 1941]
[16]pp, 4 f/p col. illus., b/w illus. throughout, col. pic. board covers, 178x235mm. ANL

Others in series:
3150 No 2 NURSERY RHYME PICTURES TO COLOR FOR BOYS & GIRLS
3151 No 3 MY FAVOURITE BOOK OF STORIES AND RHYMES
3152 No 4 MY OWN BOOK OF NURSERY RHYMES FOR BOYS & GIRLS
3153 No 5 3 LITTLE PIGS COLOR BOOK WITH BRIGHT COLOR PAGES
3154 No 6 ALI BABA & THE FORTY THIEVES COLORING BOOK
3155 No 7 JACK AND THE BEANSTALK & OTHER STORIES
3156 No 8 CINDERELLA BOOK OF STORIES & RHYMES FOR BOYS AND GIRLS

3157 NURSERY/STORIES/AND/RHYMES/[drawing]/ For/Boys and Girls/with pictures to color/No 17 An Australian Production by/Gunn & Taylor Pty Ltd. Melbourne
[1944]
20pp, b/w illus., stiff col. pic. wrappers, 360x236mm. ANL
In same series:
3158 No 9 THE STORYTELLER FOR BOYS & GIRLS, PICTURES TO COLOR
3159 No 10 MOTHER GOOSE BOOK OF RHYMES
3160 No 11 PLAYTIME STORY BOOK
3161 No 12 FAVOURITE FAIRY TALES
3162 No 13 PETER BOBTAIL IN THE CAVES OF THE MITES (by Charles Gordon, illus. Marna Fitchett)
3163 No 14 THE KOALA KIDS STORY BOOK
3164 No 15 THE PRINCESS BOOK OF FAIRY STORIES
3165 No 16 THE VICTORY BOOK
3166 No 18 HAPPY DAYS—STORIES FOR BOYS AND GIRLS
GUNN & TAYLOR Series. Uniform booklets. All ANL
3167 No 65 THE PRINCESS STORY BOOK, 1944, 16pp, b/w illus., col. pic. wrappers, 270x200mm.
3168 No 66 BEDTIME STORIES FOR TINY TOTS with pictures to color
3169 No 68 THE WONDER BOOK with pictures to color
3170 No 69 MY OWN COLORING BOOK OF NURSERY RHYMES, 32pp, 4pp col.
3171 No 70 THE LITTLE RED HEN COLORING BOOK, 32pp, 4pp col.
3172 No 71 FAVOURITE FAIRY TALES TO COLOR with col. pictures to copy, 32pp, 4pp col.
3173 No 72 THE TODDLERS' COLOR BOOK, 32pp, 4pp col.

3174 FAIRYLAND/[drawing]/For Boys and Girls/No 95 An Australian Production by/Gunn & Taylor Pty Ltd, Melbourne/Distributors for N.S.W. and Queensland: Hamson & Leonard, 101 York Street, Sydney
n.d. [1947]
20pp, 4pp in col., b/w illus. throughout, stiff col. pic. wrappers, 358x235mm. ANL
Stories by Sonia Hardie, Mary Douglas, illus. unsigned. Uniform with above, all ANL:
3175 No 81 STORIES OF ADVENTURE by Louise Kinch. Illus. E. Grieve
3176 No 83 THE TODDLERS BOOK OF NURSERY RHYMES
3177 No 84 PETER BOBTAIL & THE FOREST PRINCE by Charles Gordon, Illus. Marna Fitchett
3178 No 85 TALES OF THE SHOE, by Irene Shackcloth
3179 No 86 THE FUNTIME BOOK
3180 No 87 FAIRY STORIES
3181 No 88 FAIRY TALES TOLD IN PICTURES, 1944
3182 No 89 MORE TALES OF THE SHOE, by Irene Shackcloth,1945
3183 No 90 THE GIANT COMIC BOOK

3184 No 91 THE JUNIOR LIBRARY VOL 1
3185 No 92 THE JUNIOR LIBRARY NO 2. by Phyllis Telfer & others
3186 No 93 FABLES IN PICTURES
3187 No 94 MRS MATHILDA'S KITCHEN by Irene Shackcloth, 1947
3188 No 96 ALPHABET BOOK WITH BRIGHT COLORED PAGES, 1946
3189 No 98 ROBINSON CRUSOE abridged, illus. by Ronald Bunning
3190 No 151 THE BIG ANIMAL PICTURE BOOK (kangaroo, platypus, wombat, goanna)
3191 No 152 THE FARMYARD PICTURE BOOK (includes possum, magpies, kookaburra, koalas)

3192 STORYTIME/FOR BOYS AND GIRLS/[drawing]/Gunn & Taylor Pty. Ltd/The Children's Publishers/Melbourne
n.d. [194-?]
[70]pp, 4pp col. illus., b/w illus. throughout, light pic. bd., 278x208mm. ANL
Books in this series, as above, all bound together in a series of volumes, but some titles missing. ANL:
3193 No 101 STORYTIME
3194 No 102 NURSERY RHYMES
3195 No 103 THE HAPPINESS BOOK
3196 No 104 THE WIGGLY WOGS
Stories, verses, comic strips by various authors, inc. Elizabeth Smalley, Margaret L. Hooper, Kathleen Chapple, C. M. Lewis, Irene Shackcloth, Jack Dunn, &c.
GUNN & TAYLOR books bound as series, but some titles missing.
32pp (some 16pp), b/w illus., col. pic. light card wrappers, 280x200mm. ANL

3197 No 201 THE BUMPER COLORING BOOK, [1947], 32pp, b/w illus., col. pic. wrappers, 280x200mm
3198 No 203 THE GIANT BOOK OF STORIES FOR BOYS & GIRLS
3199 No 204 FARMYARD COLORING BOOK, [1947]
3200 No 205 TRAINS TO COLOR
3201 No 206 SHIPS TO COLOR
3202 No 207 FRUIT & FLOWERS COLORING BOOK
3203 No 208 ANIMAL ABC COLORING BOOK
3204 No 209 THE TIP-TOP COLORING BOOK (FOR BOYS)
3205 No 210 THE TIP-TOP COLORING BOOK FOR GIRLS
3206 No 211 NURSERY RHYME COLORING BOOK
3207 No 212 IT'S FUN TO COLOR
3208 No 251 THE JUNIOR COLORING BOOK, 32pp, b/w & col. illus., col. stiff pic. wrapper, 433x195mm
3209 No 252 TOYLAND COLORING BOOK
3210 No 253 PLAYTIME COLORING BOOK
3211 No 254 THE FAVOURITE COLORING BOOK
3212 No 301 PAINTING BOOK FOR TINY TOTS, 16pp
3213 No 302 PAINTING BOOK FOR BOYS & GIRLS, 16pp
3214 No 303 PAINTING BOOK FOR GIRLS & BOYS
3215 No 304 PAINTING BOOK FOR BOYS & GIRLS
3216 No 305 A BOOK OF TOYS TO COLOR
3217 No 306 PLAYTIME COLORING BOOK
3218 No 307 NURSERY RHYME PICTURES TO COLOR
3219 No 308 TEDDY BEARS BIG BOOK TO COLOR, 16pp (inc. covers)

GUNSTON, David
3220 THE SEA OF WHALES/by/David Gunston/[device—Round the Globe Stories]/Frederick Warne and Co. Ltd./London and New York
Lond. 1948
64pp, map & b/w text drawings, stiff wrappers, 185x137mm. KMM
Adventure story set in the Antarctic; Warne's Supplementary Readers. Illus. signed by Peter Fraser.

GURDON, Captain J. E.
3221 THE/SECRET OF/THE SOUTH/Captain J. E. Gurdon, D.F.C./Author of/Saracen Junior/The King's Pipe/[drawing]/Frederick Warne & Co. Ltd./London & New York
1950
256pp, b/w & ochre frontis. only, clo., 195x125mm. CLRC
Adventure story set in Australia.

GURIK, Robert
See Miller, Patricia K.

GURR, Nancy Stuart [Mrs Eric Thompson]
3222 ANIMAL TALES/FOR ANN/By/Nancy Stuart Gurr/Illustrated by J. Sharp/[drawing]/George G. Harrap & Co. Ltd./London, Toronto Bombay Sydney
1938
95pp, col. frontis., 6 t.p. b/w illus., b/w drawings, bd., 185x135mm. NSL:M

3223 A DOG FOR ROBIN/by/Nancy Stuart Gurr/with line illustrations by/John Auld/Australasian Publishing Company/SydneyWellington London
1950
129pp, 23 b/w illus., clo., 180x115mm. VSL

GURR, Robin
3224 RED PEPPER/The Story of an Australian Horse/Written and illustrated by/Robin Gurr/Australasian Publishing Company/Sydney Wellington London/in association with/George G. Harrap & Co. Ltd.
1954
87pp, b/w drawings throughout, bd., 185x130mm. The York Series. BBC
• Rpt 1955, pic. wrappers. KP

GURR, Thomas Stuart
3225 JUNGLE/VAGABONDS/by/T. Stuart Gurr/Angus and Robertson Ltd./Sydney:London/1942
134pp, 1p preface, 18 b/w illus., dec. bd., dec. e/p, 240x185mm. NSL:M
Illustrations signed 'E.B.'
• Rpt as above, 1946. KMM

3226 THE/CASTAWAYS/by/T. Stuart Gurr/Consolidated Press Limited/Sydney/1944
111pp, unillus., pic. wrappers, 180x115mm. ANL

3227 JAMAICA BAY/A Fantasy for Children/By/T. S. Gurr/Illustrated by Stan H. Clements
Offset Printing Co., Sydney, n.d. [1945]
32pp, dec. t.p., part. col. illus. throughout, stiff wrappers, 175x240mm. KMM

3228 THE/MAGIC/HAT/A Fairy Story/by T. S. Gurr/Illustrated by Betty van de Pot
Offset Printing Co., Sydney, n.d. [1945]
32pp, dec. t.p., b/w drawings throughout, stiff wrappers, 240x180mm. ANL

3229 ROGER/THE/RABBIT/By T. S. Gurr
Offset Printing Co., Sydney, n.d. [1946]
16pp, col. illus. throughout, dec. bd., cover title, 165x240mm. ANL

3230 MOUNTAIN OF THE/SLEEPING GIANT/By/T. Stuart Gurr/Australasian Publishing Company/Sydney Wellington London
1948
93pp, b/w frontis., clo., 180x115mm. ANL

3231 THE VALLEY OF THE/LOST TRAIL/By/T. Stuart Gurr/Angus and Robertson Ltd./Sydney: London/1943
248pp, unillus., clo., 180x115mm. ANL

3232 THE/VALLEY OF THE/LOST TRAIL/Stuart Gurr/Angus and Robertson/Sydney London Melbourne Wellington
First published in Great Britain 1957
192pp, b/w frontis. & b/w drawings throughout, clo., 200x120mm. CLRC
Illustrated by ?Frank Johnson.

GURR, Thomas Stuart & HARROWSMITH, Gwen

3233 BLUE MOUNTAIN STORY/By/T. Stuart Gurr/and/Gwen Harrowsmith/Shakespeare Head Press/Sydney
1949
120pp, facsimile frontis., 16 b/w photographic illus., clo., dec. map e/p, 245x180mm.
Frontispiece facsimile of page from Governor Macquarie's Diary. NSL:M

GUY, Rita

See PERRIE, George & GUY, Rita

H., E.

3234 GRANDMAMMA'S/LETTERS/Dedicated, with loving affection, to all/Little Children./Melbourne:/T. G. Ramsay & Co., Printers and Publishers./1890
104pp, 4 f/p col. illus., 11 b/w illus., dec. t.p., clo., 140x205mm. Grant

H., J. [HASSALL, J.]

3235 JEMMY MULLINS,/or, the/Little Irish Sailor Boy,/By/one of H. M. Chaplains,/N.S.Wales./Sydney:/Printed by W. Welsh, King Street West./1856
19pp (i.e. ivpp, 15pp and 1p blank), cover title, unillus., wrappers, 190x120mm. MAC
Preface signed J. H. but the text is actually written by his father, Thomas Hassall (1794–1868), about the conversion from Catholicism of a poor boy & reflection on his pious life and death.

HAAS, Dorothy

3236 CAPTAIN KANGAROO/AND THE TOO-SMALL HOUSE/Story by Dorothy Haas/Authorized Edition/[col. illus.]/Illustrations by/Mel Crawford/CBS Television Enterprises A Service of CBS Television/© 1958 Keeshan-Miller Enterprises Corp. All rights reserved/Printed in U.S.A. Whitman Publishing Company, Racine, Wisconsin
28pp, col. illus. throughout, col. pic. bd., 157x137mm. RC
Aust. in title only.

HACKETT, E. M.

3237 BILLY CATERPILLAR/By E. M. Hackett Georgian House, Melbourne 1945
[24]pp, 10 f/p col. illus., b/w drawings, stiff dec. wrappers, cover title, 140x195mm. ANL

HACKNEY, Frances Mary Veda

3238 BREAD-AND-BUTTER/MOON/Written and illustrated by/Frances Hackney (handset edition)/The Writers' Press/Sydney
n.d. [1956]
23pp, line drawings, wrappers, 180x115mm. ANL
Verses for children.

3239 THE WORLD OF/NATURE/[coloured illustration]/By Frances M. V. Hackney, D.Sc./Illustrated by Peter Chapman/Readabout Books
Readabout Publishers Pty Ltd, Crow's Nest, N.S.W., 1964
32pp, col. & part. col. illus. throughout, stiff dec. wrappers, 280x210mm. BBC
Cover reads: 'Australian Science'.

[HADDON, J. L.]

See 'Leslie, J.'

HAHN, Arthur

3240 Imperial Edition No. 391/KIDDIES HOUR/SONGS/by/Arthur Hahn/Contents/[11 songs listed]/Copyright price 1/6 net/Allan & Co. Prop. Ltd/Melb. Sy Ad Ben
1935
12pp, unillus. wrappers, 256x180mm. VSL
On front cover—Arthur Hahn ('Bimbo' of 2GB)

HAIG-BROWN, Roderick Langmere

3241 Great stories of Canada/CAPTAIN OF THE DISCOVERY:/the story of Captain George Vancouver,/[part col. portrait]/By Roderick Haig-Brown/Illustrated by Robert Banks/London: 1956: Macmillan
viiipp, 181pp, b/w & part col. illus. throughout, clo., dec. map e/p, 206x135mm. NSL:M
First 30pp describe Vancouver's part in two of Cook's expeditions; next 40pp describe Vancouver's own expedition to SW Australia & the Pacific.

HAINSWORTH, D. R.

SIMEON LORD. *See* Great Australians

HALES, Alfred Arthur Greenwood

3242 A LINDSAY/O' THE DALE/By/A. G. Hales/Author of/"The Watcher on the Tower" "Driscoll, King of Scouts"/"M'Glusky" "Jair the Apostate" etc. etc./With a frontispiece by Stanley L. Wood/Colonial Edition/(This edition is for Circulation in the British Colonies only)/London/T. Fisher Unwin/Adelphi Terrace/MCMVII
341pp, 18pp adv., b/w frontis., clo. (with col. illus. pasted on front cover), 185x120mm. NSL:M
A bushranging story of southern Australia, not specifically a boys' book.

3243 A FIGHT FOR A/FRIEND/By/A. G. Hales/War Correspondent and Editor/Author of "Telegraph Dick", "Angel Jim"/"Campaign Pictures", etc etc./With eight coloured plates/Cassell and Company, Limited/London, Paris, New York, Toronto and Melbourne/MCMVII All rights reserved
279pp, col. frontis. & 7 f/p col. illus., pic. clo., 190x120mm. KMM
Boys' story set in the Gobi desert.
• Rpt as above but Author of "Telegraph Dick", etc etc./With four illustrations/Cassell and Company, Limited/London, New York, Toronto and Melbourne n.d. (inscribed 1919)
As above but 4 b/w plates only. KMM
Swedish edition
First Swedish ed. 1912. Unseen

3244 DÄR ÖKNEN BÖRJAR/Äventyr i Mongoliet/Bevättade av/A. G. Hales/Från Engelskan av Richard Melander/Andra Upplogan/[device]/Stockholm/C. E. Fritzes Bokförlogs Aktiebolag
1925
212pp, unillus., pic. bd., 180x120mm. ANL
Fritzes Scout Bibliotek.

3245 TELEGRAPH DICK/A London Lad's Adventures/in Africa/By/A. G. Hales/With four full-page illustrations/Cassell and Company, Ltd/London, New York, Toronto and Melbourne
n.d. [1st ed. 1907 with 6 b/w illus.]

244pp, frontis. & 3 b/w plates, pic. clo., 190x125mm. KMM
Illus. by F. W. Boyington.

3246 TELEGRAPH DICK/By/A. G. Hales/Author of the famous McGlusky Books/Wright & Brown, Ltd./4 Farringdon Avenue,/London, E.C.4
n.d. [1907?]
249pp, 4pp adv., unillus., clo., 185x120mm. ANL
A boys' book with a South African background.
Swedish edition

3247 BLAND FARMARE/OCH KAFFRER/Äventyr i Sydafrika/Berättade av/A. G. Hales/Från Engelskan/av/Richard Melander/[device]/Stockholm/C. E. Fritzes Bokforlegs Akteboleg
1913
221pp, unillus., pic. bd., 183x123mm. ANL

HALES, Catherine Frances

3248 THE STORY OF JESUE.[*sic*]/Told in simple language, and with such explana-/tions as are suitable for children./By/Catherine Frances Hales,/with a preface/by/Archdeacon Hales./Melville & Mullen,/Publishers,/Melbourne.
n.d. [preface dated 1899]
viiipp (inc. 3pp author's preface), 74pp, unillus., limp clo., 208x132mm. NSL:M

HALL, H. L. *et al.*

3249 NOW AND THEN/A Miscellany for Boys/By/H. L. Hall/A. H. Pike/P. St. J. Wilson/Brighton Grammar School/Melbourne/Ramsay, Ware Publishing Pty Ltd./117-129 King Street.
n.d. [1945]
63pp, 4 f/p b/w photographic illus., stiff wrappers, 180x120mm. ANL
Publ. in aid of the Brighton Grammar School Memorial Fund.

HALL, J. J.

3250 "WINKS"/'Winks' tells Australian/Children what he saw/in the Australian/Bush/By J. J. Hall/Melbourne/George Robertson & Co. Pty. Ltd./Elizabeth Street/1920
191pp, 2pp introduction by R. P. Franklin, b/w drawings in text, clo., 180x115mm. KMM

3251 THE/CRYSTAL BOWL/Australian Nature Stories/By/J. J. Hall/Author of "Winks"/[drawing]/Illustrated by Dorothy Wall/Melbourne/Auckland Christchurch Dunedin/Wellington N.Z. and London/Whitcombe & Tombs Limited
n.d. [1921]
64pp, col. frontis. & 7 f/p col. illus., 8 f/p b/w illus. & drawings in text, clo., 235x180mm. KMM

3252 Whitcombe's Story Books/THE/KANGAROO PAW/The Story of a Strange Australian Flower./By J. J. Hall/Author of "The Crystal Bowl"/For children aged 7 to 8 years/[drawing]/Whitcombe & Tombs Pty. Ltd./Melbourne, Sydney, Perth.
n.d. [192-?]
36pp, 4 f/p b/w illus. & 4 b/w illus. in text, illus. H. Praetorius, wrappers (with adv. inside front cover & on both sides of back covers), 185x120mm. KMM
See McLaren 209
See also Gunn, Mrs Aeneas & others. THE AUSTRALIAN WONDER BOOK

HALL, Willis & EVANS, I. O.

3253 THEY FOUND THE WORLD/by Willis Hall & I. O. Evans/[drawing]/Illustrated by Norman Buchanan/Frederick Warne & Co. Ltd./London and New York
1960
192pp (inc. 2pp publisher's foreword), extended dec. t.p., b/w drawings in text throughout, dec. e/p, clo., 210x155mm. HBM
Contents include sections on Cook, Scott, Richard Byrd, 'Across Antarctica', &c.

"HALLARD, Peter" [CATHERALL, Arthur]

3254 CORAL REEF/CASTAWAY/Peter Hallard/With illustrations by/Terence Greer/Phoenix House Ltd./London
1958
188pp, b/w frontis. & 9 f/p b/w illus., clo., 195x120mm. BBC
Story of adventure & pearling on the Barrier Reef.

3255 Peter Hallard/BARRIER REEF/BANDITS/Illustrated by Hugh Marshall/London: Dennis Dobson
1960
183pp, b/w frontis. & 11 line drawings in text, clo., 195x120mm. KMM
Sequel to *Coral Reef Castaway;* action takes place between Port Moresby & Brisbane aboard a pearling lugger.
Published New York, Criterion Books [196-?], unseen.

HALLS, Elizabeth

3256 NICKY/AND/THE/ZOO TRAIN/[drawing]/By Elizabeth Halls
Paterson's Printing Press, Perth, n.d. [1943]
29pp, part. col. illus. throughout, dec. bd., 230x180mm. ANL

HAMILTON, A. W.

3257 HAJI'S/BOOK/OF/MALAYAN NURSERY/RHYMES/by/A. W. Hamilton/Illustrated by/Nora Hamerton/Music by/H. A. Courtney/The Australasian Publishing Co. Pty. Ltd./Sydney and London
1947
145pp, 2pp preface, 12pp glossary, &c., part. col. frontis. & part. col. illus. throughout, clo., 245x185mm. NSL:M
Nursery rhymes in English with Malayan translation below, some with music. Preface (also in both English & Malay) states: 'Some of the Malayan Nursery Rhymes were first published in pamphlet form at the time of the Malaya-Borneo Exhibition in 1922. They were reprinted in 1923 at the Methodist Publishing House in Singapore...'

HAMILTON, Arthur & KELLY, Gipsy

3258 THE NALLY/NURSERY/BOOK/[device]/with the compliments of Nally Ltd./An Australian Production/original poems by Arthur Hamilton and Gipsy Kelly/original drawings and illustrations by W. N. Millar/[Copyright...etc.]
Wholly set up and printed in Australia by Deaton & Spencer Ltd, 1 Douglas St, Sydney, n.d.
34pp, 1p adv., b/w drawings throughout, col. pic. wrappers [with col. adv. for 'Nally ware' on back cover], 245x180mm. KMM

HAMILTON, Lucy

3259 Junior Red Cross introduces:/"THE FOOD FAIRIES"/By Lucy Hamilton/Illustrated by Margery Luth/[drawing]
Published by Australian Junior Red Cross, Victorian Division, 122 Flinders St, Australian Red Cross Society, Melbourne C.1, n.d. [194-?]
32pp, 8 col. illus., 4 b/w illus. & marginal drawings, dec. wrappers, 220x280mm. KMM
Food facts presented in form of a fairy story.

'HAMILTON, Mary' [pseud. Jean W. Graham]

3260 FERN/PORRIDGE/and/other imagination stories/By/Mary Hamilton/(Jean W. Graham)/Illustrated by K.

Brown/Brisbane:/Watson, Ferguson & Co. Limited/ 1924
37pp, portrait frontis., line drawings in text, wrappers, 195x150mm. QSL
Book includes a memorial notice to the author by her husband, W. E. Graham.

HAMILTON, Patrick
See Rabling, Harold & Hamilton, Patrick

HAMILTON-WILKES, Monty
3261 HOW TO LOOK AFTER/PETS/by Monty Hamilton-Wilkes/photographs by David Cumming/ Angus and Robertson
Sydney 1966
64pp, b/w photographic frontis. & t.p. & b/w photographs throughout, pic. clo., 180x240mm. CLRC

'HAMLINE, Daniel'
See Taylor, Katherine

HAMMILL, Mrs Herbert
3262 THE/LIFE AND ADVENTURES/DOG [*sic*, 'of the' omitted on t.p.]/"OSCAR"/Melbourne/Melville, Mullen & Slade/262 & 264 Collins Street/1889
43pp, title within decorative border, frontis. portrait, pic. wrappers (printed in green) with drawing of a dog, 190x145mm. MAC
Front cover has correct title. Printed by McCarron Bird & Co, Printers, 479 Collins St. Melbourne.
• Rpt as above but 'second edition' on front cover. NSL:M

HANDFORD, Nourma
3263 THREE CAME FROM/BRITAIN/By/Nourma Handford/Wholly set up and Printed in Australia/By/ Pratten Bros. Pty. Ltd./Sydney 1945 [?1946]
[Printed on front cover: 'Currawong Publishing Co. Pty. Ltd./3 Castlereagh Street/Sydney']
148pp, unillus., clo., 210x135mm. CLRC

3264 COTTONTREES/By/Nourma Handford/Illustrated by/David Christian/Collins/London—Sydney/1948
192pp, b/w frontis. & b/w drawings in text, clo., 180x115mm. ANL

3265 CARCOOLA/By/Nourma Handford/A Story for Girls/Dymock's Book Arcade Ltd./Sydney London/ 1950
144pp, unillus., pic. clo., 210x130mm. ANL
• Rpt as above, variant bdg in plain grey clo. KP

3266 CARCOOLA/ADVENTURE/Nourma Handford/ Sydney;/Dymock's Book Arcade Ltd./1952
148pp, 4pp adv., unillus., clo., 205x130mm. ANL

3267 CARCOOLA HOLIDAY/by/Nourma Handford/ Illustrations by Frank Hodgkinson/Sydney/Dymock's Book Arcade Ltd./1953
235pp, b/w drawings, clo., 180x115mm. ANL

3268 CARCOOLA BACKSTAGE/by/Nourma Handford/ A Career Novel for Girls/Illustrations by Kate O'Brien/ Dymock's Book Arcade Ltd./Sydney
n.d. [1956]
256pp, b/w drawings in text, clo., dec. e/p, 205x135mm. ANL

Hanky-Panky
3269 HANKY/-PANKY/Illustrated by/Rufus Morris "Golliwog" Series, W. H. Honey Publishing Co., n.d. [inscribed 1942]
[16]pp, col. & b/w illus. throughout, stiff pic. wrappers, 245x180mm. KMM

HANN, Marjorie
3270 THE/RETURN/OF/CHARLIE/CHEESECAKE/By Marjorie Hann
'Produced with the co-operation of the Road Safety Council of S.A [etc.;] printed at The Griffin Press, Adelaide, n.d.
[32]pp, each page has a flap concealing a picture, 2pp adv., wrappers, cover title, 115x135mm.
Verses. KMM

HANN, Marjorie & WILSON, Lloyd Arnold
3271 THE ADVENTURES OF/CHARLIE/ CHEESECAKE/by/Marjorie Hann and Lloyd A. Wilson
A Child Safety Production Publication, J. H. Sherring & Co. Ltd., Printer, 22 King William St, Adelaide, n.d. [194-?]
32pp, red/black illus. throughout with flaps concealing further pictures, pic. wrappers, 115x135mm . KMM
The authors were 'June and Billy Bouncer' of Radio Station 3KZ Melbourne 1945–49.
'Inside the fold on each side lies the surprising result of Charlie's reckless disregard for danger; so read the poem page, look at the picture opposite, *Then* open the flap.'

HANNAN, L. M. & TICKELL, W. G. (ed.)
3272 THE BAD DEEDS GANG/and other Stories/edited by/L. M. Hannan and W. G. Tickell/Australian Association/for the/Teaching of English
Carlton, Vic., 1971
138pp, unillus., dec. clo., dec. e/p, 212x135mm. KMM

HANSEN, M. P. & McLACHLAN, D.
3273 AN AUSTRAL GARDEN/An Anthology of/ Australian Verse/Selected and Edited by/M. P. Hansen and D. McLachlan/Melbourne/George Robertson & Company/Propy. Ltd.
n.d. [1912]
xvipp, 304pp (inc. 19pp notes &c), unillus., clo., 180x120mm. CLRC
3274 Another ed. as above, n.d. but imprint 'Melbourne, Sydney, Adelaide, and Brisbane' with 12 b/w plates, portraits of poets & inclues brief biographies. KMM
See also McLachlan, Donald

HANSTEIN, Howard A.
3275 AUSTRALIAN WILDLIFE/Birds and Animals of Australia in natural colour/by/Howard A. Hanstein/ [drawing]/Published by/Nucolorvue Productions, Mentone, Australia/Copyright
n.d. [1949?]
42pp (inc. 1p index), col. photographs, f/p col. map, pic. bd., 175x240mm. KMM
Photographic picture book of Australian animals & birds, with brief descriptive text under each picture.

The Happiness Book
See GUNN & TAYLOR

Happy and Sunny
3276 HAPPY AND SUNNY/Rhymes for/Little Children
n.p., n.d. [192-?]
Cover title reads:PAINTING BOOK/AND RHYMES FOR/LITTLE CHILDREN/[illus.] Happy and/Sunny
[24]pp, col. illus. on alternate pages (signed "Gwen Milgate"), stiff pic. bd., 295x235mm. KP
Each page opening reveals a col. illus. with brief rhyming text & the facing page is printed in b/w to be col. by child.

Happy Friends Story Book
3277 HAPPY FRIENDS/STORY BOOK/With Pictures to Colour/Registered at the G.P.O. Hobart, for transmission by post as a book

n.d. [prize label 1946], The Salvation Army Book Department, 69 Bourke Street, Melbourne
[64]pp, b/w drawings throughout, part col. pic. bd., 270x180mm. KP
Anonymous uplifting tales, religious texts, &c.

Happy Hours
3278 HAPPY HOURS
No imprint, n.d. [Copyright 1945]
12pp, 4 f/p col. illus., drawings throughout, dec. wrappers, cover title, 230x180mm. NSL:M
Illustrations signed 'Guerin'
Children's verse.

HARBORD, Ellen M.
3279 DOWN AMONG THE/RED GUMS/A Collection of short poems of the/Great south-western Bushland, written and/Illustrated by/Ellen M. Harbord/("Ellakin")/Printed and Published by/Imperial Printing Company Limited/397 Hay Street (East), Perth/Western Australia/1938
34pp, b/w drawings throughout, pic. wrappers, 216x140mm. CLRC

HARBOUR, Henry
3280 WHERE FLIES THE FLAG/By/Henry Harbour/With/Six Coloured Illustrations/By Arthur Rackham/Second Edition/Collins' Clear-type Press/London and Glasgow
n.d.
286pp, col. frontis. & 5 col. plates, pic. clo., 180x120mm. ANL
pp213-68 relate to Australia.

HARDEN, Maxine
3281 THE ADVENTURES/OF/SNIFF SNUFF AND STICKLES/Story and Illustrations/by/Maxine Harden/Engraved, Printed and Published by/Osboldstone & Co. Pty. Ltd./Melbourne, Australia.
n.d.[194-?]
15pp, 5 f/p col. illus., bd. (dec. inside), col. pic. wrappers, 250x180mm. KMM

HARDIE, Sonia ['Miranda' of the Weekly Times]
3282 STORY TIME/By/Sonia Hardie/With illustrations by Nancy Dobson/[drawing]/Australia:/Angus & Robertson Ltd./89 Castlereagh Street, Sydney/1929
86pp, b/w frontis. & line drawings throughout, clo., dec. e/p, 185x115mm. CLRC
Children's verses.

3283 Imperial Edition No. 372/SIX/ACTION/SONGS/Words by Sonia Hardie Music by Mabel Down/Contents/[6 songs listed]/Allan & Co., Proprietary Limited/Melb. Sy. A. Bend.
n.d. [acquired1934]
16pp, unillus., 305x230mm. VSL

THE LITTLE LAD, Melb. 1933
Book *about*, but not *for* children. KMM

FAIRYLAND. *See* Gunn & Taylor no. 95

SHORT STORIES. *See* Gunn & Taylor no. 92, The Junior Library no. 2

HARDING, Bruce
3284 WINDOWS OF/FAME/A Heroic Chronicle of Australians at War/by/Bruce Harding/Lansdowne Press/Melbourne 1963
100pp (inc. 3pp author's introduction & 1p acknowledgements), 4pp f/p col. illus. & 24pp b/w photographic illus., clo., 235x180mm. BBC
A book intended to be of interest to children as well as adults; illustrations of the stained glass windows of the Australian War Memorial, Canberra.

HARDING, Eric
3285 SALUTE TO THE HORSE/by Eric Harding/illustrations by Fred Whitcroft/[drawing with caption]/A Colorgravure Publication
Melb. n.d.
96pp, inc. 1p index, b/w illus. throughout, clo., pic. e/p, 240x180mm. KP
Note 'during the prep. of this work Mr Churchill is now Rt Hon Sir Winston Churchill [*sic*]'(indicates prob. date of publicaton).

HARDING, T. E. [ed.]
3286 HERE AND THERE/New Stories for Young Children/by Students of Coburg Teachers' College, Victoria/Illustrated by Anna de Polnay/[drawing]/Angus and Robertson
Syd. 1969
vipp, 79pp, 20 drawings in text, t.p. printed in 2 cols, pic. wrappers ,228x150mm. KP
See also Here and Now

HARDWICKE, Elizabeth
POEMS [Davison, Duncan & Co.], Melbourne 1894
Cover reads: 'Numbers for the Old Land and the New'
Although dedicated to the author's children these are not poems intended for children. CLRC

The Hare and the Tortoise Sport
3287 THE HARE/AND THE TORTOISE/SPORT
Presented by the bottlers of Coca Cola, Victoria, n.d.
[24]pp, b/w drawings, col. pic. wrappers, 150x120mm. KP
Booklet on orienteering.

HARE, Robert
3288 TALES OF GRIT/For Boys and Girls/By/Uncle Robert/Robert Hare/Author of "Earth's Last Generation" "Beacon Light"/"Footprints of the Invisible"/[drawing]/Wholly set up and printed in Australia./Registered at the General Post Office, Melbourne,/for transmission through the post as a book/1938/Signs Publishing Company/(A.C.A. Ltd., Proprietors)/Warburton, Victoria, Australia
96pp, b/w frontis. & 8 b/w illus., wrappers, 205x125mm. ANL
Moral stories; not known whether author was Australian, or whether this was a reprint of an overseas publication.

'HARKAWAY, Jack'
See Hemying, Bracebridge

HARMER, Moira
3289 "DINKUM DILLY"/Rhymes/and/Tales/By/Moira Harmer/Illustrated by/C. H. Hunt/Copyright/Sydney 1917
Printed in Australia by J. R. Trenerry, Sydney Road, Manly
36pp, b/w drawings throughout, dec. wrappers, 195x150mm. NSL:M
On front cover, 'War Chest Edition 3/6'.

HARPER, Edith Alice Mary [Mrs P. Hepburn]
3290 THE SEASONS/A Speaking Tableau/For Girls. 100 Performers/Written by Edith Harper
Printed by W. A. Pepperday & Co., 119a Pitt Street, Sydney, n.d. [1902]
20pp, unillus., wrappers, cover title, 215x135mm. NSL:M
Verse. This author also used the pseudonyms 'Anna Wickham' & 'John Oland'.

3291 "WONDER EYES:/A JOURNEY TO SLUMBERTOWN"/Written for/80 Little People/By Edith Harper

W. A. Pepperday & Co., Printers, 119a Pitt Street, Sydney, n.d. [1903]
23pp, unillus., wrappers, cover title, 210x135mm. NSL:M
A play.

HARPER, Theodore Acland
3292 THE/JANITOR'S CAT/By/Theodore Acland Harper/in collaboration with/Winifred Harper/ [drawing]/Drawings by/J. Erwin Porter/Australia: Cornstalk Publishing Company/89 Castlereagh Street, Sydney/1928
214pp, b/w frontis. & b/w drawings in text, clo., dec. e/p, 195x140mm. NSL:M

3293 SIBERIAN GOLD/By/Theodore Acland Harper/In collaboration with Winifred Harper/Hutchinson & Co. (Publishers) Ltd./London
1937
288pp, clo., 210x140mm. NSL:M
Author is a New Zealander, according to the Mitchell Library.
Also author of *Windy Island* (New York 1939, copyright 1931), dealing with the early days of New Zealand & not included here.

HARRHY, Edith and others
3294 SOME/AUSTRALIAN/SONGS/By/Edith Harrhy/ Price 3/- net/W. H. Paling & Co. Limited/Sydney Brisbane/[2 lines]
Copyright 1928
24pp, unillus., words by Charles MacGregor, Richard Lomas, Eleanor Wemyss, wrappers, 250x185mm. KP

3295 Imperial Edition No 571 Vol. 1/SONGS FOR/ MOVEMENT/AND ACTION/[silhouette]/[6 songs listed]/Allan & Co. Pty. Ltd./Melbourne Adelaide Bendigo/Printed in Australia
n.d. [copyright 1935]
15pp & back cover adv., unillus. apart from dec. wrappers, 310x234mm. ANL

HARRINGTON, Harry
3296 CONUNDRUMS/Selected and Collected/by/Harry Harrington/Published by/John Pollard/Winfield Building/495 Collins Street, Melbourne. C.1
n.d.
63pp, unillus., dec. wrappers, 180x117mm. KP

HARRINGTON, John W.
3297 THE/JUMPING KANGAROO/AND THE/APPLE BUTTER CAT/by/John W. Harrington/Illustrated by/ J. W. Condé/New York/McClure, Phillips & Co./MCM
130pp, b/w frontis. & 48 f/p b/w illus., pic. bd., 240x180mm. Grant
Chapter 1 only refers to the kangaroo.

HARRINGTON, Lyn
3298 AUSTRALIA &/NEW ZEALAND/Pacific Community/Lyn Harrington/photographs by Richard Harrington/Sydney Harbor, Australia/Thomas Nelson Inc.
Camden, N. J. and simultaneously Toronto, Canada, 1969
223pp & 1p adv., photographic frontis. & b/w photographic illus. throughout, clo., 214x156mm. CLRC
Factual book in 'World Neighbors' series written for children

HARRIS, Henry
3299 MORAL ADMONITIONS/AND/LESSONS FOR THE YOUNG/compiled by/Henry Harris/[Royal Arms]/ . . ./Melbourne/George Robertson/1874
80pp, 1p quotation from Locke precedes text, unillus., clo., 136x108mm. ANL

HARRIS, Leila Gott & Walter Kilroy
3300 IT HAPPENED IN AUSTRALIA/By/Leila Gott Harris/former kindergarten Primary Directress/Fort William, Ontario, Canada/and/Kilroy Harris, D.S.O., F.R.G.S./Author of "Kangaroo Land" and "Outback in Australia"/Australian and New Zealand Editor of/ Compton's Pictured Encyclopaedia/Published by/ McKnight & McKnight/Bloomington, Illinois
1936
173pp, b/w photographs throughout, clo., map e/p, 190x140mm. NSL:M

3301 BLACKFELLOW BUNDI/A Native Australian Boy/ By/Leila and Kilroy Harris/[illus.]/Pictured by Kurt Wiese/Junior Press Books/Albert Whitman/& Co./ Chicago/1939
63pp, col. frontis., 9 f/p & numerous col. lithographic illus., pic. bd., pic. e/p, 235x180mm. ANL

3302 SUNNY AUSTRALIA/A Photographic Picture Book/By/Leila and Kilroy Harris/[drawing]/With Drawings by Margery Aspen/David McKay Company/ Washington Square, Philadelphia
1941
40pp, photographs throughout, marginal decorations, bd., dec. e/p, 235x185mm. ANL

3303 THE LOST HOLE/OF BINGOOLA/A Story of the Australian Bush/by/Leila and Kilroy Harris/Illustrated by/Will Forrest/The Bobbs-Merrill Company/ Publishers/Indianapolis New York
1942
207pp (inc. 19pp glossary), 8 f/p b/w illus., clo., dec. map e/p, 200x130mm. NSL:M
• Rpt as above, but
/The Children's Book Club/121 Charing Cross Road, London, W.C.2
n.d., copyright 1942, The Bobbs-Merrill Company
150pp (inc. 14pp glossary), 8 f/p unsigned b/w illus., clo., 180x120mm. RC

3304 THE LOST HOLE/OF BINGOOLA/A Story of the Australian Bush/By/Leila and Kilroy Harris/Illustrated by/Will Forrest/John Gifford Limited/125 Charing Cross Road, London, W.C.2
First published in England in 1948
105pp (inc. 14pp glossary), 8 f/p b/w illus., clo. (no e/p), 185x120mm. KMM

3305 [photograph]/Let's read About/AUSTRALIA/By Leila and Kilroy Harris/The Fideler Company/Grand Rapids, Michigan
1950
112pp (inc. index), b/w photographs throughout, clo., dec. e/p, 265x180mm. NSL:M

3306 AUSTRALIA/Leila and Kilroy Harris/The Fideler Company Grand Rapids, Michigan
Copyright 1950, 1955, 1959, 1961
112pp (inc. 2pp notes & 2pp index), maps & b/w photographs throughout, pic. clo., dec. map e/p, 265x195mm. Life in Other Lands Series. CLRC
The book, though mostly pictorial, is intended for use in schools. A note states that Captain Kilroy Harris is a native of Australia, & his wife a former Canadian school teacher.

HARRIS, Mabel
3307 DAWN/MAIDEN/and other/Small Songs/by Mabel Harris./Illustrated by D. L. Wilson
Printed by McCarron, Bird & Co., Melbourne, n.d.
12pp, 14 b/w drawings, dec. song titles, tied in illus. wrappers, 250x315mm. Grant

Both words & music apparently by Mabel Harris. Dora Wilson's name appears on cover; publication presumably prior to 1946, the date when Dora Wilson died.

HARRIS, Pixie O'
See 'O'Harris, Pixie' [Rona Olive Pratt]

HARRIS, Ray
3308 THE SECRET/OF THE TIDE-RACE/By/Ray Harris/Angus and Robertson/Sydney: London/1948
231pp, 4 f/p b/w illus. & 2 diagrams, clo., 185x120mm. KMM

3309 THE ADVENTURES OF/TURKEY/Boy of the Australian Plains/Ray Harris/Illustrated by Geoffrey Whittam/[drawing]/Collins/London and Glasgow
1952
256pp (inc. 2pp glossary), col. frontis., 4 f/p b/w illus. & b/w drawings in text, clo., 180x115mm. KMM
• Rpt as above 1959, Seagull Library. KMM

3310 TURKEY/AND/PARTNERS/Ray Harris/[drawing]/Illustrated by Geoffrey Whittam/Collins/London and Glasgow
1954
256pp (inc. 2pp glossary), col. frontis., 5 f/p b/w illus. & b/w drawings in text, clo., 180x120mm. KMM

3311 THE CRUISE/OF THE/NIFTY DUCK/Ray Harris/[drawing]/Illustrated by Geoffrey Whittam/Collins/London and Glasgow
1955
192pp, col. frontis., 5 f/p b/w illus. & b/w drawings in text, clo., 180x125mm. KMM

3312 TURKEY/AND CO./by/Ray Harris/[drawing]/Collins/London and Glasgow
1961
192pp, col. frontis., 3 f/p b/w illus. & b/w drawings in text, illus. by Geoffrey Whittam, clo., 190x120mm. KMM

3313 THE OPAL SEEKERS/by/Ray Harris/The Children's Press/London and Glasgow
n.d. [Appears to be a cheap rpt; no other edition of the book seen]
256pp (inc. 2pp glossary), 2 b/w maps, otherwise unillus., clo., 180x120mm. KMM

HARRIS, Rolf
3314 THE/ROLF HARRIS/COOJEE BEAR/PAINTING BOOK/[illus. col.]/Brown Watson Ltd./London/Printed in England/© 1967 Published by arrangement with Rolf Harris Enterprises Ltd.
12pp, col. & b/w illus. (unsigned) throughout, pic. wrappers, 297x217mm. RC
Koala character.
Same series listed in above, unseen:
The Rolf Harris Jake the Peg Painting Book
The Rolf Harris Shamus O'Seah Painting Book
The Rolf Harris Six White Boomers Painting Book (kangaroos)

3315 ROLF HARRIS/ANNUAL/Contents/[contents listed in detail]/Rolf Harris Annual Published by Atlas Publishing Co. Ltd, 10 Kennington Park Place London S.E.11 [b/w photographs of author on double spread t.p.]
1969
76pp, col. & b/w illus. & comic strip cartoons throughout, pic. bd., 273x194mm. CLRC

HARRIS, Thistle Y.
3316 NATURE PROBLEMS/A Book of Nature Study for Young Australians/By/Thistle Y. Harris/B.Sc., M.Ed., Lecturer in Biological/Science, Sydney Teachers' College/Illustrated by Jean Poole/and A. Turnidge/(except where otherwise indicated)/Companion volume/A Handbook of suggestions for/Teachers. By the same author./William Brooks & Co. Limited/The Educational Publishers of Australia/99 Pitt Street Sydney/299 Queen Street Brisbane
1945
203pp, col. frontis. & 8 col. plates, b/w illus. throughout, clo., 214x133mm. CLRC
3317 Rev. ed. n.d. [1955] as above. CLRC
AUSTRALIAN PLANT LIFE. *See* Around Australia Program

HARRIS, Walter Kilroy
See Harris, Leila Gott & Walter Kilroy

HARRISON, Herbert Clifford
3318 THE WINDMILL/A book for boys/(Young and old)/by/W/Cdr. H. C. Harrison/A.R.C.Sc., O.B.E./Melbourne/1947
The author, Melbourne
76pp (inc. 3pp glossary), b/w photographic frontis. & 4 b/w photographic illus., 13 f/p b/w drawings & drawings in text, illus. by G. R. Nisbet, clo., 245x185mm. ANL
A description of the mechanics & the history of English windmills.

HARRISON, Launcelot
See 'Perfessor, The & Alter Ego, Esquire'

HARRISON, Mrs Launcelot
See Mack, Amy Eleanor

HARRISON, Lyn
3319 ME TOO/By/Lyn Harrison
Cumberland Newspapers Ltd, Sydney 1955
80pp, b/w photographs, bd., 240x180mm. NSL:M
Photographs & factual report of the tour of Australia by H. M. Queen Elizabeth II written by Lady Harrison, wife of Sir Eric Harrison, minister-in-charge of the tour.

HARROWSMITH, Gwen
3320 HOPPITTY'S HOUSE/By/Gwen Harrowsmith/Made and printed in Australia/For Consolidated Press Limited/168–174 Castlereagh St., Sydney/Registered at the G.P.O., Sydney, for/transmission through the Post as a book./Waite & Bull, Sydney/Illustrated/by/George Finey/Consolidated Press Ltd./1943
63pp, col. frontis., 1 extended col. illus. & 5 f/p col. illus., pic. bd., pic. e/p, 235x165mm. ANL
3321 HOPPITTY'S HOUSE/By/Gwen Harrowsmith/Illustrated/by/George Finey/Consolidated Press Ltd/1943
As above; no printer's name appears anywhere on this copy apart from 'C.P.' on front cover. KMM

3322 PIPPINNY/AND/THE SHADOWS/by/Gwen Harrowsmith/Illustrated by/L. Revill/Consolidated Press Ltd./1944
Sydney
53pp, 1 extended col. illus. & 4 f/p col. illus., b/w drawings, dec. wrappers, 235x180mm. ANL

3323 DINTY/by/Gwen Harrowsmith/Illustrated by/Jackson Hull/The Shakespeare Head Press Pty. Ltd./Sydney
n.d. [1947]
72pp, 4 f/p col. illus., b/w drawings, dec. bd., dec. e/p, 240x170mm. ANL
See also Gurr, Thomas Stuart & Harrowsmith, Gwen. BLUE MOUNTAIN STORY

HARRY, Millicent Kate
3324 PROVED POPULAR/PUPPET PLAYS/By Millicent Harry/Twelve Plays/written especially for/Glove

Puppets/but also suitable for/Marionettes/or/Live Acting/Issued by The Temperance Committee Presbyterian Church, Vic [col. illus. border]
Printed by Cambridge Press, Bendigo, n.d. [1949]
52pp, 4 f/p line drawings, stiff pic. wrappers, 245x185mm. KP
12 plays included.

3325 THE MAGIC SHOP/By Millicent Harry
Published by the Temperance Committee, Presbyterian Church of Victoria, Melbourne, n.d.
[195-?]
28pp (inc. foreword by F. W. Boreham, D.D.), 3 col. illus., b/w drawings, illus. by author, clo., cover title, 195x130mm. ANL

3326 COLOURING/BOOK/No. 2/Designed by/ Millicent K. Harry
Published by the Temperance Committee, Presbyterian Church of Victoria, n.d. [1954?]
24pp, 11 b/w illus. [to colour], wrappers, cover title, 250x185mm. ANL
Colouring book with verse opposite each picture advocating temperance habits.

HART, E. Gertrude & Annie A.
3327 AT THE BEND OF/THE CREEK/A Story of Australia/By/E. Gertrude and Annie A. Hart./Four illustrations by T. W. Holgate/London/S. W. Partridge & Co./8 & 9 Paternoster Row
n.d. [1902]
128pp, 24pp adv., b/w frontis. & 3 f/p b/w illus., pic. clo., 185x125mm. CLRC
Youthful romance rather than a children's book.

3328 THE LAUGHTER LADY/A Story for/Children of Different Ages./By Gertrude Hart/Author of "The Dream Girl", etc./Illustrations by O. A. Garland/ Melbourne Publishing Company/Cromwell Buildings/ Melbourne
n.d. [1914]
207pp (inc. 2pp prologue), col. frontis., 4 f/p b/w illus., clo., 180x120mm. ANL

3329 CHUBBY/by/Gertrude Hart/Hutchinson & Co./ (Publishers) Ltd./London
n.d. [1937]
204pp, b/w frontis. & 4 f/p b/w illus., clo., 185x125mm. ANL

3330 CHUBBY AND PIP/By/Gertrude Hart/Hutchinson & Co./(Publishers) Ltd./London and Melbourne
n.d. [prize 1942]
208pp, b/w frontis. & 2 f/p b/w illus., clo., 185x120mm. RM
Illus. 'Joan Kiddell-Monroe'

3331 WANTED—A SERVANT/(An Australian Story)/By E. Gertrude Hart,/Joint Author of "The Man Next Door" etc etc./[drawing signed Ben Taplin] Text
Publ. John Bateman, 27 Paternoster Sq. London, n.d.
16pp, b/w illus. (lacks covers, ?wrappers), 260x175mm. CLRC

HART, Marion H. [pseud. 'Mirriam']
3332 STRANGE ANIMALS/I HAVE NEVER MET/ Designed and/Drawn by/"Mirriam"
Vardon & Sons Ltd, Printers, Adelaide n.d. [1911]
24pp, b/w drawings throughout, wrappers, 145x180mm. CLRC
Humorous verses.
See also EGERTON-WARBURTON, A. for succeeding volume

HARVEY, Anthony John
3333 THE AUSTRALIAN BOYS'/BOOK OF CRAFTS, PETS,/SPORTS AND HOBBIES/compiled by Anthony Harvey/[device]/Longmans of Australia
Croydon, Victoria, 1968
208pp, b/w photographic illus., drawings & diagrams throughout, illus. by the compiler & others, pic. bd., 245x180mm. BBC
• Rpt, 2nd imp. 1969. KMM
• Rpt, 3rd imp. 1970. KMM

HARVEY, Prudence Despreaux & Anthony John
3334 THE AUSTRALIAN GIRLS'/BOOK OF CRAFTS, PETS,/SPORTS AND HOBBIES/compiled by Prudence and Anthony Harvey/Rigby/Opal/Books
Croydon, Victoria, 1969;
208pp, b/w photographic illus. & diagrams throughout, pic. bd., 245x185mm. CLRC
• Rpt 1971, as above, but Longmans, Australia. KP
• Rpt 1972. KP

HARVEY, Nancy Irene
3335 OVER THE HILLS/Poems for Children/By/Nancy I. Harvey/Illustrated by/M. Lovell-Harvey/[drawing]/ Oswald-Sealy (Overseas) Ltd./Sydney, Australia/ Printed by/Hollander & Govett Pty. Ltd., Sydney
n.d. [1945] [*Annual Catalogue of Australian Publications* 1945 mentions this was published in New Zealand in 1943]
30pp, 8 f/p col. illus., dec. bd., 170x120mm. CLRC

HASLEWOOD, Constance
3336 YOUNG AUSTRALIA'S/NURSERY/RHYMES/ Illustrated/by/Constance Haslewood/Edwards Dunlop & Co. Limited/(Publishers)/Sydney Brisbane & London
n.d. [1894]
80pp, dec. t.p., col. frontis. & col. illus. throughout, dec. bd., 215x160mm, MAC
Nothing about this book relates to Australia apart from the title & publisher. Constance Haslewood illustrated a number of books of nursery rhymes &c publ. in England in the 1880s and 1890s.

HASLUCK, Alexandra
JAMES STIRLING. *See* Great Australians
C. Y. O'CONNOR. *See* Great Australians

HATCHER, Victor
3337 SHIPS AND/SEAFARERS OF THE/SOUTH PACIFIC/Written and illustrated by/Victor Hatcher/ Collins/Sydney London Auckland
1969
[32]pp, col. illus. throughout, dec. t.p., pic. bd., dec. e/p, 285x210mm. KMM

3338 SHIPS AND/SEAFARERS OF/THE ORIENT/ Written and illustrated by Victor Hatcher/Collins/ Sydney London Auckland
1971
32pp, col. illus. on every page with slight text, col. pic. bd., col. pic. e/p, 210x288mm. ANL

3339 SHIPS AND/SEAFARERS OF THE/ MEDITERRANEAN/Written and illustrated by/Victor Hatcher/Collins/Sydney London Auckland
1972
[32]pp, col. illus. throughout, pic. bd., pic. e/p, 210x280mm. CLRC

HATFIELD, Marcia
3340 EDDIE'S/ALPHABET/Based on the television series by Marcia Hatfield/Illustrated by Rowl Greenhalgh/Produced in Australia by Ajax Films/ Odhams Books/London, New York, Sydney, Toronto/

Published for Odhams Books/by Paul Hamlyn Pty Ltd, 176 South Creek Road/Dee Why West, New South Wales 2099/Copyright reserved—Publication rights Paul Hamlyn Pty Ltd/First published 1969/Printed in Hong Kong
[32]pp, col. illus. throughout, t.p. surrounded by col. floral border, col. pic. bd., 314x230mm. KP

3341 LET'S/EXPLORE/WITH/ROSEMARY/By/Marcia Hatfield/in association with/Rosemary Eather/ Illustrated by/Ron/Greenhalgh/and Stan Varley/West Publishing Corporation Pty. Ltd.
Sydney 1970
98pp (inc. 1p foreword), extended t.p., b/w drawings, 2pp b/w photographs, pic. bd., dec. e/p, 265x190mm. KMM
Various articles, puzzles, etc., based on television programmes.

3342 EDDIE'S NUMBERS/Based on the popular television series by Marcia Hatfield/Illustrated by Allan & Giulietta Stomann/[drawing]Paul Hamlyn/Sydney London New York Toronto
1972
[25]pp, col. illus. on every page, col. pic. e/p, col. pic. bd., 310x230mm. NSL:M

'HATFIELD, William' [pseud. Ernest Chapman]

3343 BUFFALO JIM/by William Hatfield/Illustrated by Norman Hepple/[drawing]/Oxford University Press/ London New York Toronto
1938
287pp, col. frontis. & 6 f/p b/w illus., b/w drawings, clo., 190x125mm. KMM

3344 BUFFALO JIM/By William Hatfield/[drawing]/ Geoffrey Cumberlege/Oxford University Press/ Leighton House Melbourne
1946 [First Australian edition]
256pp, col. frontis. only, clo., 180x115mm. KMM
• Rpt Melbourne 1947, 1948, as above.

3345 BARRIER REEF DAYS/By/William Hatfield/ Illustrations by Pat Terry/Geoffrey Cumberlege/ Oxford University Press/Leighton House Melbourne/ 1948
224pp, b/w frontis. & 7 b/w illus. by Pat Terry, clo., 170x110mm. BBC
• Rpt 1949, as above. KMM
A TEACHER'S COMPANION TO *BARRIER REEF DAYS*
A Queensland Syllabus Notes Committee Production, Brisbane 1949
67pp, unillus., wrappers, 180x120mm. KMM

3346 WILD DOG FRONTIER/William Hatfield/ [drawing]/Geoffrey Cumberlege/Oxford University Press/Melbourne Wellington
1951
196pp, b/w chapter headings, clo., 180x115mm. KMM

HATHERLEY, Frank

3347 Piccolo True Adventures/BUSHRANGERS BOLD!/Frank Hatherley/Cover illustration by Alan Lee/Text illustrations by Graham Humphreys/ [device]/A Piccolo Original/Pan Books Ltd./London
1972
132pp, 2pp adv., b/w map frontis., 6 f/p b/w illus., 4 b/w maps & b/w drawings in text, pic. wrappers, 180x110mm. KMM

HAUGHTON, Edward

See 'Coories, The'

HAVERFIELD, E. L.

3348 By E. L. Haverfield/QUEENSLAND/COUSINS/ Thomas Nelson/and Sons/London, Edinburgh/Dublin, and/New York
n.d. [1908]
238pp, 16pp adv., dec. t.p., col. frontis. & 1 col. plate, illus. by A. H. Jenkins, pic. clo., 188x124mm. KMM

3349 QUEENSLAND/COUSINS/By/E. L. Haverfield/ Thomas Nelson and Sons, Ltd./London, Edinburgh, and New York
n.d.
238pp, col. frontis. & 1 col. plate (A. H. Jenkins), pic. clo. (different design from previous edition), 185x120mm. KMM

3350 By E. L. Haverfield/QUEENSLAND/COUSINS/ Thomas Nelson & Sons, Ltd./London, Edinburgh, and New York
n.d. [prize 1926]
238pp (no adv.) dec. t.p., col. frontis., clo. (with oval col. medallion on front cover), 185x120mm. KP
• Rpt as above but with plain clo. bdg. KP

3351 DAUNTLESS PATTY/By/E. L. Haverfield/Author of/"Audrey's Awakening" "The Conquest of Claudia"/Etc. Etc./Illustrated in colour by Dudley Tennant/London/Henry Frowde/Hodder and Stoughton
n.d. [1908]
357pp, 16pp adv., col. frontis. & 5 f/p col. illus., pic. clo., 185x120mm. KMM
The heroine is a young Australian in this girl's school story set in England.
• Rpt Milford, London 1918, 357pp. Unseen

3352 THE GIRL FROM/THE BUSH/by/E. L. Haverfield/Author of "The Mascotte of Sunnyside",/"The Girls of St. Olaves", etc./Collins' Clear-type Press/London and Glasgow
n.d. [1929]
320pp, col. frontis., clo., 180x120mm. KMM

3353 THE GIRL FROM/THE BUSH/By/E. L. Haverfield/Collins/London and Glasgow
First published Collins 1920; First published in this edition September 1940; rpt March 1943
320pp, unillus., clo., 180x125mm. KMM
E. L. Haverfield, who was not an Australian, was the author of a number of other girls' stories which do not relate to Australia.

HAWEIS, Rev. Hugh Reginald [ed.]

3354 [Quot.]/Routledge's/World Library/The Mutiny of the Bounty/Lambs Tales from Shakespeare/The Professor at the Breakfast Table/Chinese Gordon/With introductions/by the/Rev. Hugh Reginald Haweis, M.A./London/George Routledge and Sons/Broadway, Ludgate Hill/New York: 9 La fayette Place/1886
Separate pagination, 160pp, 160pp, 158pp, 160 & 2pp adv. & 2pp precede t.p., unillus., clo., 153x112mm. KP

HAWKER, Ruth M. [Mrs A. K. Gault]

3355 US THREE/By/Ruth M. Hawker/Drawings by/ Nora Young/[drawing]/All the people in this book are real./We hope they like being there/Adelaide/South Australia/John McGrath Ltd./224–226 North Terrace/ 1930
[First edition copyright 1929]
35pp, b/w drawings throughout, wrappers, dec. e/p, 200x165mm. KMM
Verses.
Another copy, as above, bd. KMM

3356 US THREE OUTBACK/by/Ruth M. Hawker/ Author of "Us Three"/Drawings by/Nora Young/ "Allans"/Booklovers' Library/51 Rundle Street, Adelaide
[First edition copyright June 1932]

51p, b/w drawings throughout, dec. bd., 215x170mm. KMM
Stories & verses.

3357 US THREE OUTBACK/by/Ruth M. Hawker/ Author of "Us Three"/Drawings by/Nora Young/ Harman & Jacka/Adelaide, South Australia./Wholly set up and printed in Australia/H. & J.
Details as above. KMM

3358 YESTERDAY/Being/The Adventures of Us Three with the Early Colonists/By/Ruth M. Hawker/Author of "Us Three", "Us Three Outback", etc./Drawings & Cover Design/from handcut linoleum block/by/Nora Young/[drawing]/Adelaide: F. W. Preece & Sons/1936
69pp, b/w frontis & 5 b/w illus., dec. bd., 240x185mm. KMM
Verses included in text.

3359 TWO NEW/AUSTRALIANS/By/Ruth M. Hawker/ Geoffrey Cumberlege/Oxford University Press/ Leighton House, Melbourne
1949
191pp, unillus., bd., 180x115mm. KMM

3360 TREASURE AT/PRINCE'S POINT/By/Ruth M. Hawker/Geoffrey Cumberlege/Oxford University Press/Leighton House Melbourne
1949
191pp, unillus., bd., 180x115mm. KMM

3361 HEATHER AT MAGPIE/CREEK/Ruth M. Hawker/Geoffrey Cumberlege/Oxford University Press/Melbourne Wellington
1950
111pp, unillus., bd., 180x115mm. KMM

3362 THE WARRENS/OF WOMBAT FLAT/Ruth M. Hawker/Geoffrey Cumberlege/Oxford University Press/Melbourne Wellington
1950
192pp, unillus., clo., 180x115mm. KMM

HAWKINS, Sheila

3363 ENA-MEENA-/MINA-MO-/AND BENJAMIN/By Sheila Hawkins/[drawing]/Frederick Warne and Co. Ltd.,/London and New York
1935
57pp, 14 part. col. illus., pic. bd. (clo. spine), 180x215mm. ANL

3364 ENA-MEENA-/MINA-MO-/AND BENJAMIN/By Sheila Hawkins/[drawing]/Frederick Warne and Co., Ltd./London and New York
1935
58pp (last blank), 14 f/p part. col. illus. & 11 f/p b/w illus., pic. bd. (clo. spine), 183x220mm. KMM

3365 ENA-MEENA-MINA-MO/AND BENJAMIN/By/ Sheila/Hawkins/[drawing]/Frederick Warne and Co., Ltd./London and New York
n.d. [1960]
58pp (last blank), 12 part col. & 13 b/w illus., pic. sim. clo., 163x210mm. KMM

3366 APPLEBY JOHN/THE MILLER'S LAD/[drawing]/ By Sheila Hawkins/Hamish Hamilton, Publisher/90 Great Russell Street, London
1938
93pp, part col. illus. on alternate pages, pic. bd. (clo. spine), 275x250mm. ANL

3367 U.S. ed. publ. by Harper & Brothers, New York, 1939. Unseen

3368 PEPITO/By Sheila Hawkins/[drawing]/Hamish Hamilton, Publisher/90 Great Russell Street, London
1938
86pp, part col. illus. throughout, clo., dec. e/p, 270x245mm. ANL

3369 US edition as above, published by Harper & Brothers, New York & London 1940.

3370 PEPITO/ By Sheila Hawkins/ [drawing]/ Hamish Hamilton Ltd./ London
New edition 1948
85pp, part col. ills. throughout, clo., dec. e/p, 265x245mm. KMM

3371 LITTLE GRAY/COLO/The Adventures of a Koala Bear/By/Sheila Hawkins/[drawing]/Colo/Grosset & Dunlap/Publishers New York/Copyright, 1939, by Grosset & Dunlap, Inc./Printed in the United States of America
41pp, col. & b/w illus. throughout, dec. bd., dec. e/p, 195x185mm. ANL

3372 THE PANDA AND/THE PICCANINNY/ [drawing]/Hamish Hamilton London
n.d. [1939]
28pp, col. illus. on alternate pages, dec. bd., 245x180mm. ANL

3373 THE PANDA AND/ THE PICCANINNY/by/ Sheila Hawkins/ [drawing]/ Hamish Hamilton London
First published March 1939, 2nd imp. June 1939, 3rd imp. Oct. 1939, 4th imp Dec. 1939, 5th imp. August 1947, details as before. KMM

3374 BRUZZY BEAR AND THE CABIN BOY
Harper & Brothers, New York and London [1940]
32pp, illus. (part. col.) & illus. t.p. by author, lining papers in cols, 270x210mm. Unseen: NUC

3375 THE/BEARS BROTHERS/by Sheila Hawkins/ [drawing]/Oxford University Press/London New York Toronto
1942
[32]pp, col. & sepia/white illus. throughout, pic. bd., 245x185mm. KMM

3376 THE/BEAR BROTHERS'/HOLIDAY/by Sheila Hawkins/Oxford University Press/London New York Toronto/Publishers
n.d. [1942]
[28]pp, extended title (printed on dec. e/p & front fly-leaf), col. & sepia/white illus. on alternate page openings, pic. bd., 245x180mm. KMM
Note states: 'Big Bear and Little Bear have had one book written all about them, called *The Bear Brothers*. They are also well known to the readers of the *Farmers' Weekly*, where they have often appeared in the children's section'.

3377 A BOOK OF FABLES adapted from Aesop by Sheila Hawkins
Penguin Books, Harmondsworth and New York [1942]
Puffin Picture Books; unseen, BMC

3378 ANIMALS OF AUSTRALIA/by Sheila Hawkins
Penguin Books Ltd., Harmondsworth, England, 1947
32pp, col. & b/w illus. throughout, dec. wrappers, cover title, 180x215mm. Puffin Picture Books. NSL:M

3379 HOMES AND FAMILIES—Africa
Edinburgh House Press, London 1955
24pp, quarto
Pictures to colour & cut out, drawn by Sheila Hawkins
Unseen: BMC

3380 AUSTRALIAN/ANIMALS AND BIRDS/By Sheila Hawkins/[drawing]/Angus and Robertson
Sydney 1962
64pp, part. col. t.p., col. & b/w illus. throughout, pic. clo., dec. e/p, 250x185mm. BBC

Picture book with brief descriptive text.
• Rpt 1966. KMM
• Rpt 1969. KP

'HAWTHORN, J. R. H.'
See Houlding, John Richard

HAWTON, Don
3381 THE/PICTURE BOOK/OF/PLANES/AND/SHIPS/illustrations by/Ray Wenban/narration by/Don Hawton/decorations by/Quinlan
Offset Printing Coy Sydney, 1947
36pp, 15 f/p col. illus. & part-col. decorations throughout, col. pic. bd., 270x220mm. KP
Includes biographical note on the artist.

HAXTON, Elaine
3382 A PARROT IN A FLAME TREE/Adapted from a Medieval Christmas carol—Words and pictures by Elaine Haxton/St. Martin's Press, New York
1968
[30]pp, col. illus. throughout, pic. bd., 190x254mm. ANL
3383 Another copy as above, but 'F.W.Cheshire Melbourne Canberra Sydney'
as above. KP

HAY, Dean
3384 I SEE/A LOT OF THINGS/colour photographs by Dean Hay/Collins/St. James Place, London
1966
47pp, 23pp col. photographic illus., pic. bd., 195x150mm. BBC
A simple 'first' book for a very young child, consisting of coloured photographs of simple objects with the name of the object below & a plain page in contrasting colour opposite.

3385 NOW I CAN COUNT/photographs by Dean Hay/Collins/London Sydney
1968
[53]pp, col. photographic illus. throughout, pic. bd., 190x150mm. BBC
• Rpt 1970, 1972. KMM

3386 THINGS WE DO/photographs by Dean Hay/Collins/London Sydney
1971
[48]pp (last blank), 23 f/p col. photographs, pic. bd., 195x155mm. KMM
Photographs with brief captions of young children's activities.
See also Dutton, Geoffrey & Hay, Dean. TISI AND THE YABBY; SEAL BAY

HAY, Phyllis
3387 THE JOURNEY/OF THE/STAMP ANIMALS/By/Phyllis Hay/Illustrated by Rosamond Stokes/Georgian House/Melbourne
1948
112pp, 8 f/p col. illus. & b/w drawings in text, clo., 210x130mm. KMM
The story of four animals whose pictures then appeared on Australian stamps.

HAYDON, A. L.
HIS SERENE HIGHNESS: A Public School Story [1925] and STAND FAST, WYMONDHAM [1928] are both English school stories with an Australian boy as one of the main characters, but have no other Australian association.

HAYDON, A. L. (ed.)
3388 THE/"BOY'S OWN" BOOK/OF/ADVENTURE/Edited by A. L. Haydon/(Editor of "The Boy's Own Paper")/with coloured frontispiece and/numerous black-and-white/illustrations/[drawing]/London/"Boy's Own Paper" Office, 4, Bouverie Street, E.C.
n.d. [school prize 1923]
128pp, col. frontis., b/w illus. throughout, illus. by various artists, pic. bd., 275x205mm. KMM
Contents include: 'The Affair at Omeo; how we bested the Bushrangers', by W. T. Greene, M.A., M.D. (7pp); 'Our Lucky Strike; A Tale of the Australian Gold Diggings', by W. T. Greene, M.A., M.D. (6pp).

HAYENS, Herbert
3389 FROM/ANZAC TO BUCKINGHAM PALACE/A Tale of the V.C./Herbert Hayens/Author of " 'Midst Shot and Shell in Flanders"/"Britain's Glory on Land and Sea" etc./Coloured Illustrations and Photographs/London and Glasgow/Collins' Clear-Type Press
n.d. [1918?]
232pp, col. frontis. & 3 f/p col. illus., 6 f/p b/w photographic illus., clo. (with illus. pasted on front cover), 250x190mm. Grant

3390 PLAY UP, JACK!/by/Herbert Hayens/[device]/London and Glasgow/Collins Clear-Type Press
n.d.
320pp, col. frontis., clo., 200x140mm. Grant
The setting is Sydney & New Guinea; seven other titles listed in the 'Play Up' series.

HAYENS, Herbert [ed.]
3391 NINETEENTH/CENTURY EXPLORERS/with coloured illustrations/and/eight portraits/London and Glasgow/Collins Clear-Type Press
n.d. [prize 1910]
192pp, col. frontis. & additional col. pic. t.p., 8 b/w plates, clo., 180x120mm. KP
Noble Lives series. Includes John M'Douall Stuart, pp87-110.

3392 THE/SOUTH SEAS PATROL/ADVENTURE BOOK/[illustration]/London & Glasgow/Collins' Clear-Type Press
n.d. [192-?]
[180]pp, col. frontis., col. illus. t.p., b/w illus., col. pic. bd., 225x170mm. CLRC
Contents include: 'A South Sea Adventure', by W. J. Marx (32pp); 'My Palaver with the Black Fellows', by John Mackie (6pp); 'How I Ran the Booroomana Sawmill', by S. Le Sotgille (9pp).

HAYES, D.
3393 NURSERY/RHYME/HOLIDAY/By/D. Hayes/[pic. border round title]/ Offset Printing Coy Ltd Sydney
n.d. [194-?]
16pp, part col. illus., col. pic. wrappers, 272x216mm. CLRC
Happy Days Series, Other Titles uniform with above.
3394 Adventure Stories for boys
3395 Chang & the Toy Soldiers
3396 Chuckles the Jester (KMM)
3397 Happy ABC Book
3398 How the Knave Stole the Tarts
3399 Nursery Rhyme Holiday
3400 Princess who couldn't cry
3401 The Goose Girl

3402 JOHAN MEETS OUR/ANIMALS AND BIRDS/by D. Hayes/School Projects Pty. Ltd.
Sydney 1967
46pp (inc. 2pp verse), dec. t.p., b/w drawings in text, stiff dec. wrappers, 210x130mm. Australian Scene Series. BBC

HAYES, Dorothy
3403 TRADING PORTS OF/AUSTRALIA AND/NEW ZEALAND/By Dorothy Hayes
Viking Books, Curl Curl NSW, n.d. [1970?]
46pp, b/w photographic illus. throughout, pic. clo., dec. e/p, 275x210mm. KP

HAYES, Herbert Edward Elton [pseud. H. E. Elton]
3404 SUMMER LAND/An Unconventional Fairy Tale/ for Children of All Ages/By/Herbert E. E. Hayes/ Author of "Melody of Life", "Halls of Life", "The/ Prince Magician" "Ultimate Values" etc./(Copyright registered in Australia)/Ramsay Publishing Pty. Ltd., 203–7 King St., Melb.
n.d. [1927]
129pp, unillus., wrappers, 175x110mm. ANL
Includes some verse in text.

HAYNES, William & WILLIAMSON, William H.
See 'Willo & Billo'

"HAY-RIC"
3405 The Story of/SILENT NIGHT/by/Hay-Ric/A Christmas Card/over 100 years old/Ric.
Scott Bros, Printers 30-34 Newman St, Mortdale, n.d., [194-?]
20pp, 2 f/p col. illus., 3 b/w illus., bd. with pic. jacket, 255x190mm. KP

[HAYTER, Cecil]
NED KELLY: A Tale of Trooper & Bushranger. *See* The "Boys' Friend" Library No 44

TROOPER AND BUSHRANGER, or the Last Days of Ned Kelly. *See* The "Boys' Friend" Library No 45

HAYWARD, Arthur L.
3406 THE BOYS' BOOK/OF/HIGHWAYMEN/By/ Arthur L. Hayward, F.R.Hist.S./Author of "The Boys' Book of Pirates",/"The Boys' Book of Explorers", etc/ with 8 half-tone plates/By Charles Crombie/[device]/ Cassell and Company, Ltd./London, Toronto Melbourne and Sydney
1931
245pp & 2pp foreword, b/w frontis. & 7 plates, clo., 190x120mm. KP
Includes The Kelly Gang (18pp.)

3407 THE BOYS' BOOK/OF EXPLORERS/By/Arthur L. Hayward,F.R.Hist. S./Author of 'The Boys' Book of Pirates' etc./With 8 half-tone plates/and 12 route maps/Cassell and Company, Ltd/London, Toronto, Melbourne and Sydney.
1929
245pp, b/w frontis. & 7 plates, 12 maps, clo., 190x125mm. WRT
Contents include: Captain Scott reaches the S. Pole (13pp), Magellan (18pp), Australia, N.Z. and Cook (15pp), J. M. Stuart and Eyre (13pp).
3408 Revised ed. 1953, as above, but x+234pp, clo., 184x124mm. KP

HAYWARD, F. [pseud. 'Firenze']
3409 WHY THE/LAUGHING JACK/LAUGHED/A Fairy Story/By Firenze/Illustrated by Esmond George
Rigby Ltd, Adelaide, n.d. [1916?]
36pp, dec. col. t.p., col. frontis. & 3 f/p col. illus., dec. bd., 155x100mm. KMM
On front cover: 'Why the/Laughing Jack/ Laughed'/'The/Bungalow Brownies'/series/by "Firenze"/Illustrated by Esmond George/Rigby Ltd. Publishers/74 King William Street, Adelaide
Book printed on bd., tied with cords.

3410 THE SUNSHINE FAIRIES/& THE/SHADOW GIANTS/THE/BUNGALOW/BROWNIES/Series/No. 2/By "Firenze"/Illustrated by Esmond George
Rigby Ltd, Adelaide, n.d. [1916?]
25pp, dec. t.p., col. frontis. & 3 col. illus., bd., 150x95mm. KMM
Book printed on bd., tied with cords.

3411 TALES/AND TALES OF TAILS/AND/NO TAILS/ By F. Hayward/("Firenze")/Illustrated by Marjorie D. Kay/Adelaide/Pritchard Bros./Printers/1920
86pp, line drawings, dec. wrappers, 180x120mm. KMM
Verse.

HEAD, John
3412 No 1 Series/BIRDS OF AUSTRALIA/By John Head/with Twelve lithographs in Colour/By the Author/Head's Studio,/191 Queen Street,/Melbourne, Australia
[32]pp, col. lithographs & text description of 12 birds illus., paper wrappers, 185x142mm. CLRC
3413 Second ed., as above.

HEADY, Eleanor B.
3414 BRAVE JOHNNY O'HARE/by Eleanor B. Heady/ Parents' Magazine Press—New York—pictures by Steven Kellogg
1969
36pp & 1p introduction, 1p biographical notes, col. illus. throughout, pic. e/p, pic. bd., 183x245mm. KP
American author who became fascinated with tales of the Bunyip & Australian animals & people & wrote the book as a result of her visit to Australia. Australian animals are depicted in a very untypical landscape by well-known American illustrator.

The Health Highway
3415 Whitcombe's Story Books/THE HEALTH HIGHWAY/For ages 10 to 12 years/[device]/ Whitcombe and Tombs Limited/Christchurch, Auckland, Wellington, Dunedin, Invercargill, N.Z./London, Melbourne and Sydney
n.d. [1939]
92pp, diagrams &c in text, dec. wrappers, 184x124mm. WRT
Elementary physiology & health book for schools.
See McLaren 557

[HEARNE, Elizabeth]
A MEMOIR *See* Gardner, J.

HEATON, P. R.
3416 The Rockcliff New Project/Illustrated Geography/ ANTARCTICA/By/P. R. Heaton/B.Sc., F.R.G.S./Author of "Canada"/Headmaster, Holmshill Secondary School, Boreham Wood/Formerly/ Headmaster, Belmont County Secondary/Modern Boys' School, Harrow/Barrie and Rockliff/London
1959
75pp (inc. 3pp bibliography), 1p adv., b/w photographic frontis. & 22 b/w illus., maps &c., clo., 185x120mm. ANL
Background book for school reading.

HEDDLE, Enid Moodie (ed.)
3417 THE/BOOMERANG BOOK/OF/AUSTRALIAN POETRY/Chosen edited and arranged by/Enid Moodie Heddle/Decorations by Margaret R. Dods/Longmans, Green and Co./London Melbourne New York
1956
157pp, 3pp index, b/w drawings in text, clo., 215x130mm. KMM
• Rpt 1957, 1958 as above, limp clo. KMM

3418 THE/BOOMERANG BOOK/OF/LEGENDARY TALES/Chosen/edited and arranged by/Enid Moodie

Heddle/Decorations by Nancy Parker/Longmans, Green and Co./London, Melbourne, New York
1957
150pp, b/w drawings, chapter headings & tailpieces, clo., 215x130mm. HBM
Aboriginal & other native legends &c. by K. Langloh Parker, Roland Robinson, A. W. Reed, Mervyn Skipper, Lorimer Fison, Dal Stivens, Lance Skulthorpe &c.
Winner CBCA Award 1957.
• Rpt 1958. KMM

HEDDLE, Enid Moodie & MILLINGTON, Iris
3419 HOW/AUSTRALIAN LITERATURE GREW/Enid Moodie Heddle/Iris Millington/[device]/F. W. Cheshire/Melbourne Canberra Sydney
1962
90p (inc. 4pp bibliography), dec. t.p., part-col. drawings throughout, illus. by Iris Millington, pic. clo., dec. e/p, 230x150mm. KMM
A description for children of the development of Australian literature.
3420 Copy also seen bound in plain red clo. with silver lettering on spine. KP
See also Samuel, Helen Jo & Heddle, Enid Moodie. BOY ON A HORSE

HEDDLE, John F. Moodie
3421 SEVEN IN THE/HALF-DECK/An Account of the Wreck of the/Barque John Murray/By/John F. Moodie Heddle/(An Apprentice on Board)/Longmans, Green and Co./London, Melbourne, New York
1949
183pp (inc. 1p dedication & 2pp foreword), b/w drawings in text, wrappers, dec. e/p, 185x120mm. KMM
Also produced in cloth bdg. KMM

3422 SON/OF THE/SEA DRAGON/By/John F. Moodie Heddle/Longmans Green and Co./London, Melbourne New York
1953
159pp, b/w drawings in text, limp clo., 180x120mm. CLRC

HEDIN, Sven
3423 FROM/POLE TO POLE/A Book for Young People/By/Sven Hedin/Macmillan and Co., Limited/St Martin's Street, London/1914
407pp & 2pp adv., clo., 195x130mm. NSL:M
Dutch edition
3424 Sven Hedin/VAN POOL TOT POOL/Mijn 75000 Kilometer lange reis door/Oostelijk Europa, Azië en Australië/Amerika en de Poolstreken/Met 50 plateu/be druk/Uitgeversmaatschappij W. de Haan N.V./Utrecht
6th ed. [192?]
414pp, illus. ANL

HEFFERNAN, Ruth
3425 THE/LITTLE/WAVE/Rigby Limited/Adelaide
1961
28pp, dec. t.p., col. & b/w illus. throughout, illus. Pamela Sirkel [author's & artist's names on dec. pastedown] dec. bd., 235x175mm. KMM

HEHIR, Maurice
Dame Nellie Melba. *See* Famous Australians

HEINZE, Bernard
3426 ADVENTURES IN MUSIC/Issued in connection/with series of talks on/Musical Appreciation by/The Australian Broad-/casting Commission
A.B.C. Melbourne, n.d. [1950]
18pp & folded sheet 'Excerpt from conductor's scores', b/w photographs, dec. wrappers, cover title, 210x140mm. ANL

HEMING, J. W.
3427 QUEER ANIMALS/A Collection of interesting Facts/and Pictures/illustrated by C. H. Percival/written by J. W. Heming/The Currawong Publishing Company/32 Jamieson Street/Sydney 1943
16pp, b/w drawings throughout, dec. wrappers, 295x190mm. ANL

3428 QUEER BIRDS/A Collection of Interesting Facts/and Pictures/Illustrated by C. H. Percival/Written by J. W. Heming/The Currawong Publishing Company/32 Jamieson Street,/Sydney
n.d. [1943]
16pp, b/w drawings throughout, stiff dec. wrappers, 300x190mm. NSL:M

3429 THE/PIRATE FAIRIES/A Fairy Thriller/By/J. W. Heming/Illustrations by:/Des Connor/The Currawong Publishing Co./32 Jamieson Street, Sydney/1943
48pp, b/w drawings in text, wrappers, 170x110mm. KMM

AUSTRALIAN NURSERY RHYMES, by J. W. Heming, A real Australian Tiny Tots' Book. Illustrated by John Andrews Advertised by Currawong Pub. Coy, Sydney, in Paul Buddee's *The Comical Adventures of Osca and Olga* (1943).
Unseen: Advertisement as above

3430 BUSH PARTY/and/MOTHER GOOSE ISLAND/by/J. W. Heming/Illustrated by Des Connor/The Currawong Publishing Co./32 Jamieson Street,/Sydney
n.d. [copyright 1944]
64pp, 2 f/p b/w illus. & b/w drawings in text, pic. wrappers, 185x120mm. KMM

3431 QUEER/AUSTRALIAN/FISHES/Pictured by C. H. Percival/Written by J. W. Heming/The Currawong Publishing Company/32 Jamieson Street,/Sydney/1944
14pp (inc. back wrapper & verso of frontis.), b/w illus., with 2 illus. to each page throughout, pic. wrappers, printed throughout in blue ink on stiff paper, 230x185mm. ANL

3432 QUEER/AUSTRALIAN/INSECTS/Pictured by C. H. Percival/Written by J. W. Heming/1944/The Currawong Publishing Company,/32 Jamieson Street,/Sydney
Uniform with above. ANL

HEMMINGS, Ernestine [Mrs E. Hill]
3433 PETER/PAN/LAND/And Other Poems/Brisbane/August, 1916/By Ernestine Hemmings/Wholly set up, printed and published by Hibernian Newspaper Co./Ltd.,/Proprietors "Catholic Advocate", Gotha St. Valley
104pp (inc. 1p foreword by Archbishop Duhig, 2pp preface by J. C. McArdle, Editor, *Catholic Advocate*, & 2pp biographical note), 8pp adv., b/w photographic portrait frontis., b/w photographs & drawings in text, wrappers, 210x125mm. NSL:M
Includes poems & verses by Ernestine Hemmings, then aged sixteen years, & by other youthful writers. The author later wrote a number of very successful adult books under the name of Ernestine Hill.

HEMPHILL, Rosemary
3434 LOOK, YOU CAN COOK!/A Cook Book for Young People/Rosemary Hemphill/Decorations by Claire Simpson/[drawing]/Angus and Robertson
Syd., 1967

105pp, line drawings printed in sepia throughout, clo., 215x135mm. CLRC

3435 COOKING IS FUN/Rosemary Hemphill/Illustrated by Claire Simpson/First published in 1972 by/Angus and Robertson/(Publishers) Pty. Ltd./Sydney, Melbourne, Brisbane,/London and Singapore/ [Acknowledgements, etc.]
26pp, col. illus. throughout, clo., col. dec. e/p, 285x210mm. BBC

HEMPSEED, Leila

3436 TASMANIAN/FAIRY STORIES/Leila Hempseed Walch & Sons, Printers Hobart, n.d.
8pp, unillus., cover title, wrappers, 165x100mm. NSL:M

HEMYNG, Bracebridge

3437 Edwin J. Brett's/JACK HARKAWAY/AND HIS SON'S/ADVENTURES IN AUSTRALIA./Beautifully illustrated./Complete./Office/Harkaway House, 6, West Harding Street,/Fetter Lane, Fleet St., London, E.C./and all Booksellers
n.d. [1893]
187pp, col. frontis. & 12 b/w illus., wrappers, 255x180mm. The Harkaway Series Vol. 13. Grant

3438 As above, but imprint: "Boys of England" Office, 173 Fleet Street, E.C./and all Booksellers
2pp adv. & adv. on back cover, otherwise same. CLRC
Note saying a coloured picture is given away with each number.

3439 JACK HARKAWAY/AND HIS SON'S/ ADVENTURES IN AUSTRALIA/Beautifully illustrated./Complete./London:/"Boys of England" Office, 173 Fleet St., E.C./And All Booksellers
n.d.
152pp (numbered pp447–598), 12 f/p b/w illus., wrappers, 250x160mm. RM
Part of a 2-volume set entitled *Jack Harkaway and his Son's Adventures Around the World.* Vol. 1 includes America & Cuba, & Vol. 2 China, Greece, Australia & 'Jack and his boy Tinka'. The last two chapters of *Jack Harkaway and his Son's Adventures in Greece* (pp443–6) actually relate to Australia, a footnote (p442) saying: 'The next number will contain Nos. 1 and 2 of *Jack Harkaway and his Son's Adventures in Australia,* which will be given away with the concluding pages of "The Adventures in Greece" '.

3440 JACK HARKAWAY/AND HIS SON'S/ ADVENTURES IN AUSTRALIA/By/Bracebridge Hemyng/Complete/Chicago:/M. A. Donohue & Co./ 407–429 Dearborn St.
n.d. [inscribed 1907]
323pp, 3pp adv., b/w frontis. & 5 f/p b/w illus., pic. clo., 180x120mm. NSL:M
Note inserted in this copy states: 'The tales in this volume are the last two of the once-famed "Jack Harkaway" Series, which commenced in No. 249, Vol. 10 of the "Boys of England" Aug. 19, 1871...written by Bracebridge Hemyng...In 1874 he crossed to the U.S. and ran a rival series of "Harkaway" for Frank Leslie's Weekly. The remainder of the "Boys of England" Series was the product of many writers. The publisher, E. J. Brett (in the last paragraph of "Boy Tinker") credits himself with inventing the plots. "Harkaway in Australia" commenced in No. 459, Vol. 18, Aug. 27, 1875 of the "Boys of England", and "Boy Tinker" ended No. 521, Vol. 20, Nov. 10, 1876...The highlight of the story is "Morgan the Bushranger" and the author, whoever he was, had a profound disregard of historical accuracy' (J. P. Quaine). Information from RM

3441 JACK HARKAWAY/AND HIS SON'S/ ADVENTURES IN AUSTRALIA as NSL:M copy but: Book Number Thirteen/Chicago/M. A. Donohue & Company
n.d. [inscribed 1925] Grant

3442 Another variant as above but: New York/William L. Allison & Co./Publishers
Other details as NSL:M copy. Grant

3443 JACK HARKAWAY IN/AUSTRALIA/or/Perils of the New Expedition/By Bracebridge Hemyng/Author of the Famous "Jack Harkaway" stories, a number of which have been published in the Medal/and New Medal Library./[device]/Street & Smith, Publishers/ 79–89 Seventh Ave., New York City
n.d.
349pp, 1p adv., unillus., pic. bd., 185x125mm. RM
Although the pictorial paper wrapper has been pasted on to the board covers, this seems to be how this & the previous book were originally issued.
A compilation, slightly altered, from *Jack Harkaway and his Son's Adventures in Greece,* & *Jack Harkaway and his Son's Adventures in Australia.*

3444 The Five Cent/Wide Awake/Library/Entered according to Act of Congress, in the year 1879, by Frank Tousey, in the office of the Librarian of Congress at Washington, D.C./Vol. 1 (Single Number) Frank Tousey, Publishers, 180 William Street N.Y. (Price 5 cents) No. 178/HARKAWAY IN AUSTRALIA/ [illustration with caption]
16pp (inc. frontis & back wrappers), unillus., pic. wrappers, cover title, 290x210mm. CLRC

3445 Another Five Cent Wide Awake Library edition: entered at the Post Office at New York, N.Y /No 1244 (complete) Frank Tousey Publisher...New York December 6 1895...JACK HARKAWAY IN AUSTRALIA/
Details as above. RM

3446 JACK HARKAWAY/IN AUSTRALIA/By/ Bracebridge Hemyng/Author of "The Harkaway Series"/[device]/Street & Smith, Publishers/238 William Street, New York City
n.d. [30 June 1904]
244pp, 14pp adv., unillus., pic. wrappers, cover title, 122x180mm. The Harkaway Library No. 20. RM

3447 JACK HARKAWAY IN AUSTRALIA/By/ Bracebridge Hemyng/Author of the famous Harkaway Stories/[device]/Printed in the United States of America/Street & Smith Corporation/Publishers/ 79–89 Seventh Avenue, New York
n.d. [1925?]
318pp, unillus., col. pic. wrappers, 175x120mm. Round the World Library No. 16. RM

3448 JACK HARKAWAY AND THE/BUSHRANGERS/ or/The Mysterious Nugget/By Bracebridge Hemyng/Author of the Famous "Jack Harkaway" stories, a number of which have been published in the/Medal and New Medal Library./[device]/Street & Smith, Publishers/79–89 Seventh Ave., New York City
n.d.
383pp, 3pp adv. (2pp following t.p., 7pp. at end of text), unillus., pic. bd., 185x125mm. RM
A compilation, slightly altered, from *Jack Harkaway and his Son's Adventures in Australia,* and *Young Jack Harkaway and his Boy Tinker.*

3449 Another copy as above but wrappers & on front cover: Jack Harkaway Stories No 10 10 cents/JACK HARKAWAY/AND THE/BUSHRANGERS/By Bracebridge/Hemyng/Street & Smith/Publishers/New York
Otherwise as before. RM

JACK HARKAWAY AND THE/BUSHRANGERS published in foll. series:
3450 *The Harkaway Library No 24,* uniform with this series. RM
3451 *Round the World Library No 17,* uniform with this series. RM
3452 *The Five Cent Wide Awake Library No 180.* CLRC
3453 Also 1895 ed. in this library (No.1246). RM

JACK HARKAWAY AND THE CONVICTS
3454 *The Five Cent Wide Awake Library* New York 1895 (No 1245), uniform. RM
3455 Also No 179 in variant of same series. CLRC

3456 The Aldine "Boy's First Rate Pocket Library."/BALLARAT BILL;/or/LUMPS/OF/GOLD./[illustration]/By/Bracebridge/Hemyng/No. 223 [caption]/1d./London: Aldine Publishing Company
n.d.
32pp, unillus., col. pic. wrappers (with adv. verso front wrapper, verso/recto back wrapper), cover illus. signed 'R. Prowse', cover title, 220x140mm. RM

3457 The Aldine "Boy's First Rate Pocket Library."/BALLARAT/BILL;/or/FIGHTING/THE BUSH-/RANGERS./By/Bracebridge/Hemyng./[Illustration]/No. 224 [caption] 1d./London: Aldine Publishing Company
n.d.
31pp, 1p adv., unillus., col. pic. wrappers (with adv. verso front wrapper, verso/recto back wrapper), cover illus. signed 'R. Prowse', cover title, 220x140mm. RM

3458 The Aldine "Boy's First Rate Pocket Library."/BALLARAT/BILL/IN SEARCH/OF THE GREAT/AFRICAN DIAMOND./[illustration]/By/Bracebridge Hemyng/No. 227 [caption] 1d./London: Aldine Publishing Company
n.d.
30pp, 2pp adv., unillus., col. pic. wrappers (with adv. verso front wrapper, verso/recto back wrapper), cover illus. signed 'R. Prowse', cover title, 220x140mm. RM
Story opens in Victoria, & the action then moves to Africa.

HENRI, René & ARNOLD, George
3459 TOBY PRESENTS/ALI/OIGLE/AND/TOITLE/A Tale of the Northern Territory [Cover title only]
A Story for Children from Two to Ten/[drawing]/Written and illustrated by/René Henri and George Arnold
A Hudson Publication; printed by City Printers, 796 George Street, Sydney, n.d. [1955]
[21]pp, 4pp col. illus. & b/w illus. on other pages, pic. bd., clo. spine, 180x250mm. KMM

HENRIQUES, Gillian Adele
3460 The/CITY CHILD'S/NATURE BOOK/Gillian Henriques/1944
Georgian House, Melbourne, n.d. [1945] [T.p. date 1944, last page 1945]
45pp, dec. t.p., col. illus. on alternate pages, dec. bd., 200x245mm. ANL
Illustrations of insects, flowers, birds &c. with a brief explanatory text opposite.

HENRY, Marguerite
3461 PICTURED GEOGRAPHY/AUSTRALIA/In Story and Pictures/by/Marguerite Henry/Pictured by/Kurt Wiese/Albert Whitman and Company/Chicago Illinois/Lithographed in the U.S.A. Copyright 1946 by Albert Whitman and Company
27pp, col. & b/w lithographs throughout, clo., dec. e/p, 140x200mm. NSL:M

HENSTOCK, Ethel E.
See 'English, Ethel Emily'

HENTY, G. A.
3462 A FINAL RECKONING/A Tale of Bush Life in Australia/by/G. A. Henty,/Author of "With Clive in India"; "The Lion of the North"; "In Freedom's Cause";/"The Dragon and the Raven"; "By Sheer Pluck"; "Facing Death"; etc./With Eight Full-page Illustrations/By W. B. Wollen/[device]/London:/Blackie & Son, 49 & 50 Old Bailey, E.C./Glasgow, Edinburgh, and Dublin/1887
352pp, 48pp adv., b/w frontis. & 7 b/w plates, pic. clo., 185x120mm. Grant
List on verso of half-title: 'Books by G. A. Henty' (11 titles).
3463 Rpt as above but,
/London/Blackie & Son, Limited, 50 Old Bailey, E.C./Glasgow and Dublin
n.d.
352pp (inc. 1p preface, slightly abridged from previous edition), 32pp adv., b/w frontis. & 7 b/w plates, pic. clo. (design as in previous edition), 185x120mm. Title & author only on spine. KMM
3464 Another copy as above, but '49 Old Bailey, E.C.' KP
3465 A FINAL RECKONING/A Tale of Bush Life in Australia/By/G. A. Henty/Author of "With Clive in India" "The Lion of the North" "In Freedom's Cause"/"By Conduct and Courage" "With Kitchener in the Soudan" "Facing Death" &c./Illustrated by W. B. Wollen/Blackie and Son Limited/London Glasgow and Bombay
n.d.
352pp, 16pp adv., b/w frontis. & 7 b/w plates, pic. clo., 185x125mm. RM
3466 As above but,
/London and Glasgow
n.d.
352pp (inc. 2pp preface), b/w frontis. & 3 f/p b/w illus., pic.clo., 180x120mm. RM
3467 Blackie's Colonial Library/A FINAL RECKONING/A Tale of Bush Life in Australia/By/G. A. Henty/Author of "With Clive in India", "In Greek Waters", "The Tiger of Mysore",/"The Dragon and the Raven", "By Sheer Pluck", "Maori and Settler", &c./[device]/London/Blackie & Son, Limited, 50 Old Bailey, E.C./Glasgow and Dublin/1896/This edition is for circulation only in India and the British Colonies
352pp (inc. 1p preface), 1p adv. (preceding t.p.), b/w frontis. only (different illustration from any in previous editions), dec. clo., 185x120mm. KMM
3468 A FINAL RECKONING,/A Tale of Bush Life in Australia/By/G. A. Henty/Author of "With Clive in India", "The Lion of the North",/"In Freedom's Cause", "By Conduct and Courage",/"With Kitchener in the Soudan",/"Facing Death", &c./Illustrated/[device]/Blackie & Son Limited/London and Glasgow
n.d. [inscribed 1932]
352pp, col. frontis. by W. Rainey & 4 col. plates by W. B. Wollen, dec. clo., 180x120mm. KMM
3469 The Foulsham Henty Library/A/FINAL/RECKONING/A Tale of Bush Life in Australia/by/G. A. Henty/London/W. Foulsham & Co. Ltd./New York Toronto Cape Town Sydney
n.d. [1955?]
223pp, col. frontis. only, clo., 180x120mm. ANL
Edited & abridged edition.
3470 A FINAL RECKONING/A Tale of Bush Life in/Australia/ By/ G.A.Henty/Author of "With Clive in India","The Lion of the North". "In Freedom's/Cause", "The Dragon and the Raven"By Sheer

Pluck"./"Facing Death",etc./With Eight Full-page illustrations/ by/W. B. Wollen./Chicago./M. A. Donohue & Co./407–429 Dearborn St.
n.d. [189-?]
302pp, 2pp adv., b/w frontis. & 7 b/w plates, pic. clo., 180x120mm. Grant
On front cover: 'Henty Series'.

3471 A FINAL RECKONING./A Tale of Bush Life in Australia/By G. A. Henty,/Author of "With Clive in India", "Under Drake's Flag", "In Freedom's/Cause", "The Young Carthaginian", "For the Temple", "Facing/Death", "By Sheer Pluck", "Bonnie Prince Charlie", etc./Illustrated./A. L. Burt Company,/ Publishers, [space] New York
n.d.[NUC gives eds pub. by Burt 188- , 189-]
vi+381pp, 2pp preface, 12pp adv., b/w frontis. & 7 b/w plates by W. B. Wollen, pic. clo., 185x120mm. RM

3472 A FINAL RECKONING/A Tale of Bush Life in/ Australia/By/G. A. Henty/Author of "With Clive in India", "In Freedom's Cause",/"The Dragon and the Raven", "By Sheer Pluck",/"Through the Fray". etc./ etc./The Mershon Company/Rahway, N.J. [space] New York
n.d. [1900?]
302pp (inc. 2pp preface), b/w frontis. & 6 b/w plates by W. B. Wollen, pic. clo., 180x120mm. RM
A number of other copies with slightly varying imprints, bindings &c have been seen, all undated, and of minor significance

3473 AMONG/THE BUSHRANGERS/From "A Final Reckoning"/By G. A. Henty/Blackie and Son Limited/ London Glasgow and Bombay
n.d. [inscribed 1923]
88pp, b/w frontis. & 2 b/w illus. W. B. Wollen, dec. clo., 170x110mm. KMM

3474 AMONG/THE BUSHRANGERS/From/"A Final Reckoning"/By G. A. Henty/Blackie and Son Limited/ London and Glasgow
n.d. [1929]
95pp, b/w frontis. by W. Rainey, pic. bd., 180x120mm. KMM

3475 AMONG THE BUSHRANGERS/from/"A Final Reckoning"/by/G. A. Henty/with frontispiece by/F. Cockerton/Blackie & Son Limited/London and Glasgow
n.d. [1949?]
92pp, b/w frontis. only, pic. bd., 180x120mm. The Summit Library. KMM

3476 G. A. Henty/AMONG/THE BUSHRANGERS/ from/A FINAL RECKONING/Blackie and Son Limited/London Glasgow and Bombay
n.d.
88pp, b/w frontis. wrappers, 165x107mm. KMM
Blackie's Story Book Readers; fifth series suitable for pupils of 11 to 13

3477 A SOLDIER'S DAUGHTER/and other stories/By/ G. A. Henty/Author of "With Buller in Natal" "The Lion of St Mark"/"The Young Carthaginian" "In Freedom's Cause" &c./Illustrated by Frances Ewan/ Blackie and Son Limited/London Glasgow Dublin Bombay/1906
197pp & 16pp adv., b/w frontis. & 5 f/p b/w plates, pic. clo., 180x120mm. KMM
The story 'A Raid by the Blacks' (pp171-97) is set on an outback Australian station.
Another copy as above but,
n.d. [school prize 1914]
177x120mm. KMM

HENTY, G. A. & Others

3478 THROUGH FIRE/AND STORM/Stories of Adventure and Peril/By/G. A. Henty, Geo. Manville Fenn, and/John A. Higginson/London/S. W. Partridge & Co./8 & 9 Paternoster Row/1898
vi+320pp, 20pp publisher's catalogue, frontis., dec. e/p, pic. clo., 190x128mm. KMM
Contents include: 'A Desperate Gang, a Story of the Australian Bush' (91pp) by G. A. Henty. This story appeared in *Boy's Annual*, Vol. II, 1894. Also included is 'A Secret of the Sea' (87pp) by John A. Higginson, the story of a search for gold bullion on a ship wrecked on the Barrier Reef.

3479 GRIT AND GO/Stories told By/G. A. Henty/Guy Boothby/D. Christie Murray/H. A. Bryden/D. L. Johnstone/Harold Blindloss/F. R. O'Neill/S. Annesley/Eight illustrations by/W. Rainey/London/ 1902/W & R Chambers Limited/Edinburgh
400pp, b/w frontis., 7 plates, pic. clo., 185x130mm. NSL:M
Includes 'Burton & Son' (75pp) by Henty and 'Stephen Whitledge's Revenge' (44pp) by Guy Boothby.

BRAINS & BRAVERY
1903
Not sufficient Australian content for inclusion. NSL:M

3480 STEADY & STRONG/Stories told by/G. A. Henty/G. Manville Fenn/John Oxenham/Louis Becke/ &c./with eight illustrations by/W. H. C. Groome/ London: 47 Paternoster Row, E.C./1905 W & R Chambers, Limited/Edinburgh: 339 High Street
404 pp & 32pp adv., b/w frontis. & 7 f/p b/w plates, pic. clo., 185x128mm. NSL:M
Contains Henty, 'Gerald Mayfield's Reward' (23pp), set partly in Melbourne; Louis Becke, 'Luck' (24pp), set in Sydney & Aust. waters.

HEPBURN, Mrs P.

See Harper, Edith Alice Mary

HEPWORTH, Tom Stanley

3481 CASTAWAYS/OF/THE MONOBOOLA/A Story for Boys/by/T. S. Hepworth/Dymocks Book Arcade Ltd.,/Sydney London/1948
213pp (inc. 2pp foreword), unillus., clo., 180x115mm. KMM
The author states in his Foreword that the story founded on the adventures of two boys, convicts in the Moreton Bay district about 1828, is based on the life of George Barrington, the experiences of Barbara Thompson & Eliza Ann Frazer, the wrecks of the *Matthew Flinders*, the *Stedcombe* & the *Charles Eaton*.

Her Majesty Queen Elizabeth II

3482 HER MAJESTY/QUEEN ELIZABETH II
Publ. by Empire Youth Movement of Victoria, Melb., n.d. [1956]
16pp, b/w photographic illus., col. pic. wrappers, 210x137mm. KP
Publ. to commemorate Empire Youth Sunday, 6 May1969.

HERBERT, Barbara

3483 THE ADVENTURES/OF/PERCY PLATYPUS/ AND HIS FAMILY/[coloured illustrations]/by/Barbara Herbert
n.d. [printed by Streatfield Press Pty Ltd, Sydney]
24pp, 6 col. illus., b/w illus. throughout, dec. bd., 240x180mm. KMM

3484 A/CAMPING/HOLIDAY/[coloured illustrations]/ The Adventures of/WILLY POSSUM/BILLY KOOKABURRA/AND/JACK WALLABY
n.d. [reprinted by Streatfield Press Pty Ltd, Sydney]

24pp, 8 col. illus., b/w illus. throughout, dec. bd., 240x180mm. KMM

HERBERT, Wally
3485 International Library/Wally Herbert/POLAR DESERTS/Collins Publishers/London Glasgow/[device]/Franklin Watts, Inc./New York
1971
128pp (inc. 3pp index), col. & b/w illus. throughout, pic. clo., 250x180mm. KMM

Here and Now
3486 HERE AND NOW/New Poems for Young Children/by Students of Coburg Teachers' College, Victoria/illustrated by Judy Howe/[drawing]/Angus and Robertson
Sydney 1968
63pp, 1p preface by T. E. Harding (Coburg Teachers' College), b/w drawings & drawings (& t.p.), printed in red & blue throughout, stiff dec. wrappers, 235x150mm. BBC
See also Harding [ed.] HERE AND THERE

Here is Faery
HERE IS FAERY/Illustrations and Decorations/by/Percy Leason/George Robertson & Co. Propy. Ltd./Melbourne, Sydney, Adelaide and Brisbane [1915]
Not written for children.

HERMAN, Morton
FRANCIS GREENWAY. *See* Great Australians

The Heroes of H.M.S. "Heroic"
See Australian Boys Adventure Library

HERON, Gilbert Septimus
3487 THE COMMON SENSE/NURSERY RHYMES/A Series of Stories that will/help overtaxed Mothers/of today/[drawing]/Copyright/Arranged and Published by/G. S. Heron, Sydney
Wilson Bros. Printers, Sydney n.d. [1932]
22pp, b/w drawings throughout, (by ? N. Hope) dec. wrappers, 230x180mm. ANL

HERVEY, M. H.
3488 THE REEF OF GOLD/A Story of the South Seas/By/Maurice H. Hervey/Author of/"Dark Days in Chile" etc/London/Edward Arnold/37 Bedford Street, Strand W.C./Publisher to the India Office/1894/All rights reserved/&c
384pp (inc. 2pp preface & 2pp appendix), b/w frontis. & 7 f/p b/w plates by A.Twidle, pic. clo., 180x120mm. MAC
Story set in Queensland & New Guinea.

HESELTON, Beverley
3489 YOUR FIRST PONY/A Complete Beginner's Guide to Care,/Training, Saddlery and Horsemanship/Beverley Heselton/Photography by Ian Brown/Lansdowne Press
Melbourne, 1972
112pp, b/w photographic frontis. & illus. throughout, clo., 230x150mm. CLRC

HESSE, Marjorie A.
7 SONGS FOR CHILDREN. *See* MORGAN, Diana

HETHERINGTON, John
JOHN MONASH. *See* Great Australians

HEWETT, Anita
3490 HONEY MOUSE/and other Stories/by Anita Hewett/[drawing]/Illustrated by/Margery Gill/The Bodley Head
London 1957
70pp, sepia/white line drawings throughout, dec. bd., 250x185mm. KMM
10 stories about Australian animals, &c.
1 undated copy seen bound in dark yellow boards, illus. & lettering in green
1 copy with pink & white-striped boards, illus. & lettering in black, and title, author & publisher on spine, otherwise as above; both KP
• Rpt as above, but, 'first Australian edition 1959; Sydney'
90pp, b/w drawings, pic. wrappers, 182x122mm. KW

3491 KOALA BEAR'S/WALKABOUT/by/Anita Hewett/Pictures/by/Marie Jauss/Stirling Publishing Co., Inc./New York
1959
32pp, dec t.p., b/w drawings in text throughout, clo., 210x155mm. CLRC

3492 THE/ANITA HEWETT/ANIMAL STORY BOOK/Stories by Anita Hewett/illustrated by/Margery Gill and Charlotte Hough/[device]/The Bodley Head/London Sydney Toronto
1972
270pp, b/w drawings throughout, clo., 214x162mm. CLRC
Stories of Aust. Animals pp63-133.

HEWITT, Mary
THREE BAD BOYS. *See* Australian Youth Plays

HEYD, Kurt
3493 Kurt Heyd/CHRISTOPHS ABENTEUER IN AUSTRALIEN/Eine Erzahlung/aus der Goldgraberzeit/mit 30 zeichnunger von Nina Tokumbet/[drawing]/Zweite Auflage/Gustav Kiepenheuer Verlag
1935
192pp, b/w drawings throughout, clo., 205x140mm. NSL:M
Christoph Heyd who visited Australia during the gold-rush period with his father was the author's grandfather, and this children's story tells of his experiences.
3494 KRISTOFFERS ÄVENTYR I AUSTRALIEN. En berättelse från guldgrävartiden
Stockholm 1936
180pp, printed bd.
Illustrated by Nina Tokumbet; Swedish translation by John S. Ericson, from German. Unseen: Catalogue No. 4, 1975, Dahlia Books, Uppsala

HICKS, John
3495 GIRRIKI/teller/of tales:/a series of Aborigine Myths/and legends for children:/by/John Hicks/With a foreword by Neville W. Cayley/and illustrations by Harry Wann
Associated Newspapers Sydney, n.d. [1945]
32pp (inc. 1p foreword), 12 part-col. illus. & b/w drawings in text, dec. wrappers, 260x200mm. ANL

HIGGINS, Kathleen
3496 BETTY IN BUSHLAND/By/Kathleen Higgins/Illustrated by/Pixie O'Harris and E. A. King/Australia/Angus & Robertson Limited/89 Castlereagh Street, Sydney/1937
115pp, 1p preface, b/w frontis. & 7 f/p b/w illus., b/w drawings in text, bd., 215x165mm. KMM
The book is intended to encourage a child to collect Australian wildflowers, & contains descriptions of some flowers as well as stories
• Rpt as above, 1938. KMM

HIGGINSON, John Andrew
3497 THE CRUISE OF THE/"KATHERINA"/A Story for Boys/By/John A. Higginson/(Late Royal Mail Steam Packet Company)/Author of "A Secret of the Sea" etc./Thomas Nelson and Sons/London, Edinburgh and New York/1903
125pp, 2pp adv., dec. t.p. (preceding full t.p.), b/w frontis. by Alan Stewart, clo., 170x115mm. KMM
This boys' adventure story opens in Melbourne, but most of the action takes place in the islands near Malaya & the South Pacific.
• Rpt as above, 1907, 185x120mm. KMM

3498 A BOY'S ADVENTURES/ROUND THE WORLD/By/John Andrew Higginson/Author of/"Four Years abaft the Galley", "Two Chummy Shellbacks"/etc. etc./London/The Religious Tract Society/4 Bouverie Street and 65 St. Paul's Churchyard
n.d. [1908]
223pp, 2 f/p col. illus. & 1 b/w diagram, blind-stamped clo. (with col. illus. pasted on front cover), 185x120mm. KMM
Contains section on Australia.
Another copy as above, 'The School-boy's Library'. KMM
Fourth impression as above, prize label 1920. KP
Fifth impression as above, n.d. KP
Another copy as above, but 'E.C.4' after 'Churchyard", prize 1924. KP
See also Henty, G.A. & others, 'THROUGH FIRE AND STORM'
See also South West Pacific section for other entries by this author

HIGHFIELD, Annina E.
3499 Christmas Fairy Series—No. 1/THE WAYWARD FERN FAIRY/By/Annina E. Highfield/Published by The Read Press/Illustrations by/Esme Duncan/[vignette]/By kind/permission of/Telegraph Newspaper/Coy.
Brisbane, n.d. [1930]
16pp, 5 col. illus. & b/w drawings, dec. wrappers, 140x185mm. NSL:M

Highlights of Australian History
3500 "Sighting the Overland Telegraph Line"/ HIGHLIGHTS OF AUSTRALIAN HISTORY/ (1906–1919)/2/- A Vita-Brits Card Series
Nabisco Pty Limited, Melbourne, n.d.
20pp, stiff pic. covers, cover title, 240x184mm. KP
Notes on various explorers with spaces left for cards to be pasted in.

HILDRETH, C. L.
3501 THE MYSTERIOUS CITY OF/OO/Adventures in Orbello Land/by/Charles Lotin Hildreth/author of/ "Judith", "The New Symphony", "The Masque of Death", etc., etc./Chicago/Belford Clarke Co./109-111 Warbash Avenue
1889
316pp, b/w frontis & 3 f/p b/w illus., map & 95 text illus., floral e/p, pic. clo., 190x130mm. RM
Story of mutiny and desertion from a sailing ship off King Sound, N.W. Australia and landing in an imagined country.
3502 Another copy as above, but 'new edition/with one hundred illustrations/New York/Frederick Warne & Co./3 Cooper Union/1893
A new issue with the Frederick Warne t.p., a cancellan laid down on a stub; the name 'Belford Company' still appears at base of spine. RM

HILL, A. F.
3503 The Boys/Star/Library/Entered etc [2 lines]/No. 230 Complete Price 5 cents/THE SEARCH/FOR THE GOLDEN SKULL./By A. F. Hill/[illus.]
New York, Nov 7 1891
32pp, inc. 4pp adv., pic. wrappers, 255x180mm. CLRC

HILL, Alex
3504 AROUND THE/BRITISH EMPIRE/By/Alex Hill/ Principal of the Harley University College,/ Southampton, Sometime Master of Downing/College, Cambridge/with 24 full-page illustrations/[device]/ Herbert Jenkins Limited/Arundel Place Haymarket/ London S.W. MCMXIII
383pp (inc. 1p preface & 5pp index), b/w photographic frontis. & illus., dec. clo., 184x120mm. KP
Australian section pp115-79. An educational tour by two children accompanying their parents.

HILL, Deirdre
3505 OVER THE BRIDGE/Deirdre Hill/Illustrated by James Hunt/[drawing]/Hutchinson Junior Books London 1969
136pp, b/w extended frontis., b/w drawings in text, clo., 195x120mm. KMM

HILL, Elfrida
3506 GATHERED LEAVES/By/Elfrida Hill/Foreword by Dr C. S. Mead, B.A./The Australian Baptist Foreign Mission (Incorp.)./486 Albert Street, Melbourne, C.2. 1934
109pp, b/w frontis. & marginal drawings by author throughout, wrappers, 245x175mm. KMM
Tales of Indian Mission life for Australian children.

HILL, Ernestine
See Hemmings, Ernestine

HILL, Fitzmaurice
3507 SOUTHWARD HO/WITH/THE HENTYS/The adventures of a pioneer family/who sailed from Sussex, England,/aboard the barque Caroline/in the spring of the year 1829/and/—with Edward Henty— /established the/First Permanent Settlement in Victoria/at Portland Bay/19th Nov. 1834/Whitcombe & Tombs Pty. Ltd./Melbourne Sydney Perth
n.d. [1953]
118pp (inc. preface by G. R. Leggett, B.A. & introduction), b/w frontis., limp clo., 175x145mm. Grant
• Rpt 1957, as above. HBM

3508 BY THEIR ENDEAVOURS/A Pageant and Two One-Act Plays of the Pioneer/Men and Women of Australia who "By Their/Endeavours", made Australia a Nation/By/Fitzmaurice Hill/Author of "Southward Ho with the Hentys"/Whitcombe & Tombs Pty. Ltd./ Melbourne, Sydney, Perth, Geelong
n.d. [1956]
48pp, 9 b/w f/p illus. by Marjorie Howden, wrappers, 245x185mm. ANL
Contents include: 'The Box of Matches'; 'The Wreck of the *Loch Leven;*' 'One Other Vision—a Pageant Play in two Scenes'.

HILL, Martha & Others
3509 HAPPY HOURS FOR CHILDREN/or/THE PARENTS' CABINET/By/Martha Hill and Friends/A New edition/Edited by Constance Hill/Popular Re-issue/Series IV/Sydney C. Mayle 70 High Street Hampstead/1906/all rights reserved
253pp (inc. 1p preface & 1p adv.), b/w map, b/w drawings in text, clo., 180x115mm. NSL:M
Contains an article by Martha Hill on Captain Cook (26pp). An advertisement refers to Series 2 which

includes *'The Breadfruit of Tahiti'*; & to Series 6 which includes *'The Pet Emu and its Australian neighbours'*.

HILL, Mirrie
See Brown, Judy & Hill, Mirrie

HILL, Robin
3510 BUSHLAND/AND/SEASHORE/An Australian Nature Adventure/By/Robin Hill/Lansdowne Press Melbourne 1962
48pp (inc. 2pp introduction by Graham Pizzey, 1p author's preface & 3pp index), 6 f/p col. illus., col. & b/w drawings in text, pic. bd., 280x215mm. CLRC
Not specifically a children's book. An artist's description of wild life observed while sketching & painting.
3511 Another edition as above, but 'Children's Library Guild of Australia 1962/Brisbane Sydney Melbourne'. BBC

HILL, Stan
3512 BUCCANEER BILL/By/Stan Hill/Copyright/Published by W. J. Nesbit,/125 Liverpool Street,/Sydney
n.d. [194-?]
128pp, b/w frontis. & drawings in text, pic. wrappers, 100x132mm. CLRC
Other titles advertised on back cover in same series.

HILL, William T.
3513 Whitcombe's Story Books/THE GOLDEN QUEST/A story of the Eureka Stockade/By/William Thomas Hill, B.A./(For Ages 12 to 14 years)/[device]/Whitcombe & Tombs Limited/Auckland, Christchurch, Dunedin and Wellington, N.Z./Melbourne and London
n.d. [1926?]
122pp (inc. 4pp notes), 6pp adv., b/w frontis. & 3 f/p b/w illus., pic. wrappers, 180x110mm. CLRC
Preceded by preliminary title page. The illustrations are unsigned but appear to be by M. Napier Waller.
See McLaren 627

3514 Australian Young Folks' Story Books/THE MAGIC SPEAR/Or/Camped with the Blacks/A Tale of the Early Days/By Wm. T. Hill, B.A.,/Author of/"The Golden Quest"/Illustrated by R. Wenban/Written, Illustrated and Printed in Australia for/Edward A. Vidler, Publisher/W. A. Hamer, Printer 205–217 Peel St., North Melbourne N.1.
n.d. [1929]
64pp, b/w frontis. & 1 f/p b/w illus., b/w drawings in text, pic. wrappers, 180x115mm. KMM

3515 The Romance of Australian Exploration/MARCHING WITH MITCHELL/The Story of the/Finding of "Australia Felix"/By Wm. T. Hill, B.A.,/Author of/"The Magic Spear" etc./Under the General Editorship of Edward A. Vidler/Written, Illustrated and Printed in Australia/W. A. Hamer Printer and Publisher, 205–217 Peel Street/North Melbourne, N.1./1930/Registered at the G.P.O. Melbourne for transmission through the Post as a Book
32pp, b/w photographic frontis. & 4 small b/w illus., 1 map, pic. wrappers, 180x120mm. Grant

3516 The Romance of Australian Exploration/THE FIRST OVERLANDERS/The Story of/Hume and Hovell/By Wm. T. Hill, B.A./Author of "The Magic Spear" etc./[quotation]/Under the General Editorship of Edward A. Vidler/Written, Illustrated and Printed in Australia/W. A. Hamer, Printer and Publisher/205–217 Peel Street, North Melbourne, N.1.
n.d. [1930]
32pp (inc. 1p notes), b/w photographic frontis. & 2 f/p b/w photographic illus., b/w f/p map & b/w illus. in text, pic. wrappers (with adv. inside front cover, & on both sides of back cover), 180x120mm. HBM
3517 THE FIRST OVERLANDERS...[as above]...Edward A. Vidler/Second Edition/Written, Illustrated and Printed in Australia/W. A. Hamer Pty. Ltd., Printers and Publishers, 205–217 Peel Street,/North Melbourne, N.1/1935/Registered at the G.P.O. Melbourne for transmission through the Post as a Book.
Details as in first edition. Grant

3518 The Romance of Australian Exploration/THE LOST EXPLORERS/The Story of/Ludwig Leichhardt/by Wm. T. Hill, B.A./Author of/"The First Overlanders"/Under the General Editorship of Edward A. Vidler./Second Edition/Written, Illustrated and Printed in Australia by/W. A. Hamer Pty. Ltd., Printers and Publishers/205–217 Peel Street, North Melbourne, N.1./1935/Registered at the G.P.O. Melbourne for transmission through the Post as a Book
[First published 1930. Advertised in first edition of *Eyre's Journey*]
32pp, b/w photographic frontis., 1 map, 2 f/p b/w illus. & 2 small b/w illus., pic. wrappers, 180x120mm. Grant

3519 The Romance of Australian Exploration/A MAKER OF HISTORY/The Story of/Captain Charles Sturt/By Wm. T. Hill, B.A./Author of/"The First Overlanders", "The Lost Explorers",/"The Magic Spear", etc./Under the General Editorship of Edward A. Vidler./Written, Illustrated and Printed in Australia/W. A. Hamer, Printer and Publisher, 205–217 Peel Street, North Melbourne, N.1.
n.d. [1930?]
40pp (inc. 2pp notes), b/w f/p map, 4 f/p b/w photographic illus. & 2 b/w illus. in text, pic. wrappers, 180x120mm. HBM
3520 A MAKER OF HISTORY...[as above]...Edward A. Vidler/Second Edition/Written, Illustrated and Printed in Australia/W. A. Hamer Pty. Ltd., Printers, 205–217 Peel Street,/North Melbourne, N.1./1935/Registered at the G.P.O. Melbourne, for transmission through the Post as a Book
Details as in first edition. Grant

3521 The Romance of Australian Exploration/EYRE'S JOURNEYS/From Adelaide to Albany/By Wm. T. Hill, B.A./Author of/"The First Overlanders", "The Lost Explorers",/"A Maker of History", "The Magic Spear", etc./Under the General Editorship of Edward A. Vidler./Written, Illustrated and Printed in Australia/W. A. Hamer, Printer and Publisher/205–217 Peel Street, North Melbourne, N.1.
n.d. [adv. inside front cover dated March 1930]
32pp, b/w map frontis. & 2 b/w photographic illus., pic. wrappers (with adv. inside front wrapper & on both sides of back wrapper), 180x120mm. HBM
3522 The Romance of Australian Exploration/EYRE'S JOURNEYS/From Adelaide to Albany/By Wm. T. Hill, B.A./Author of/"The First Overlanders", "The Lost Explorers",/"A Maker of History", "The Magic Spear", etc./Under the General Editorship of Edward A. Vidler./Second Edition/Written, Illustrated and Printed in Australia by/W. A. Hamer Pty. Ltd., Printers and Publishers/205–217 Peel Street, North Melbourne, N.1./1935./Registered at the G.P.O., Melbourne, for transmission through the Post/as a Book
32pp, 2 f/p b/w illus., b/w map, wrappers, 185x125mm. KMM

3523 The "Pathfinder" series/of Romances of Australian

Exploration/BURKE AND WILLS/The Story of Their Ill-Fated Expedition/By Wm T. Hill, B.A.,/Author of/ "The First Overlanders," "The Lost Explorers"/"The Magic Spear", Etc/Under the General Editorship of Edward A. Vidler/Written, Illustrated and Printed in Australia/W. A. Hamer Pty Ltd., Printers and Publishers, 205-217 Peel Street, North Melbourne N.1/Registered at the GPO Melbourne for Transmission through the Post as a Book
n.d. [1935]
32pp, b/w frontis. 'The Start from the Royal Park, Melbourne' by William Strutt, 5 photographic illus., pic. wrappers, 185x120mm. ANL
6d on front cover. No 6 in The Pathfinder Series

HILLARY, Edmund
See FUCHS, Sir Vivian & HILLARY, Sir Edmund

HILLSON, Don
3524 HEART OF OAK/The Story of Captain James Cook, R.N./Written and Illustrated by/Don Hillson/ Author of "The Fort in the Forest"/"Ranch on the Plain"/"Crusoes of the Prairie", etc/[vignette]/ Schofield & Sims Ltd./Huddersfield
n.d.
246pp, b/w frontis., 4 f/p & other small b/w illus. in text, clo., 183x120mm. NSL:M

HILSON, Charles
3525 FIDDLE-DE-DEE/(A Book of Verse for Little Children)/by/Charles Hilson/and illustrated/by/Olive Seymour/Introduction by/Dr George Mackaness, M.A., Litt.D./The co-Editor of "Frolic Fair"/[quotation]/Price: Three Shillings/Printed and Published by Paterson's Printing Press Ltd., 882 Hay Street, Perth, Western Australia
n.d. [introduction dated December 1939]
48pp (inc. 1p introduction), b/w drawings throughout, dec. bd., 240x165mm. ANL
3526 FIDDLE-DE-DEE/(A Book of Verse for children)/By/Charles Hilson/and illustrated/by/Olive Seymour/Second edition/Price: three shillings/ [copyright]/Printed and Published by Paterson's Printing Press Ltd., 65 Murray St., Perth, Western Australia
n.d.
48pp, b/w drawings throughout, bd., 215x125mm. KMM
3527 FIDDLE-DE-DEE/(A Book of Verse for Children)/By/Charles Hilson/and illustrated/by/Olive Seymour/Third Edition/Price: Five Shillings/ (Copyright)/Carroll's Ltd., Printers and Publishers, 566 Hay St., Perth
n.d. [1946]
47pp, col. frontis., b/w drawings throughout, bd. (with col. illus. pasted on front cover), 240x140mm. ANL

3528 GUM-TIPS/(A Second Book of Verses for Little Children)/by/Charles Hilson/(Author of Fiddle-de-dee)/and/illustrated by/Olive Seymour/ With an introduction by/T. Sten, Esq., M.A., Dip. Ed./ (Principal, Teachers' College/Claremont, W.A.)/[quotation]/Price: Five Shillings/ (Copyright)/Carroll's Ltd., Printers and Publishers, 566 Hay St., Perth
n.d. [1946]
44pp, col. frontis. & 1 b/w photograph, b/w drawings throughout, dec. bd., 220x140mm. ANL

HILTON, Irene
3529 BLUEY/FROM/DOWN UNDER/by/Irene Hilton/ Illustrated by/James Heugh/The Westminster Press/ Philadelphia
1962
176pp (inc. 2pp glossary & 2pp biographical note), 16 line drawings, clo., 205x130mm. ANL

HINTON, A. Marguerite
3530 PHANTASIES/OF/CHILDHOOD/By/A. Marguerite Hinton/December, 1943
The author. Brisbane
12pp, b/w illus., cover title, wrappers, 210x130mm. ANL
Play for 'the Primary School'.

HINTON, Maurice John
See 'Unwin, M. J.'

HIRST, Rev. Gordon Hamilton
3531 SO THEY PLAYED TOGETHER/By/Gordon Hirst/ Illustrations by the author/(Who can't draw for nuts) Printed and Published in Goulburn by Johnstone and Davie, Printers, for The Church of England, Diocese of Goulburn, N.S.W., n.d. [1939]
40pp, b/w drawings, wrappers, 240x185mm. KMM
Verses.
Another copy, 3rd ed., n.d., as above. ANL

An Historic Retrospect
3532 AN HISTORIC/RETROSPECT/on the occasion of the/150th Anniversary Celebrations/of the founding of/Australia/[illus.—caption 'Captain Arthur Phillip, R.N.']
Presented to the School Children of New South Wales by Australia's 150th Anniversary Celebrations Council; printed by S. T. Leigh & Co. Pty Ltd, Sydney, [1938]
32pp (inc. covers), col. pic. wrappers, 240x154mm. VMOU
Alternate page openings printed with col. reproductions of illus. of historic events. Text explanations on other pages.

An Historical Account of the Circumnavigation of the Globe
3533 An/HISTORICAL ACCOUNT/OF THE/ CIRCUMNAVIGATION/of the/Globe,/and of/the progress of Discovery/in the Pacific Ocean,/from the Voyage of Magellan to the death of Cook,/Illustrated by numerous engravings./New-York:/Harper & Brothers, 82 Cliff-st./-/1839
xvipp + 366pp, incl. 17 engravings, clo., 150x95mm. NSL:M
With additional dec. t.p.: Circumnavigation/of the/Globe/[engraving—"Canoe of the Tonga Islands"/New-York/Harper & Brothers./ 1839
Chapters include Discovery of the South Sea 1513, Magellan, Bougainville, Cook (5 chapters).

The History of a Golden Sovereign
See [Newman, William]

HOARE, Benjamin
3534 LITTLE ERNIE'S/BIRTHDAY/GIFT./By/Benjamin Hoare./Melbourne:/The Australian Catholic Truth Society./309 & 311 Little Collins Street
22pp, unillus., 170x115mm. ANL
Bdg unseen (bound in with other pamphlets).

HOARE, Robert J.
3535 The Champion Library/1/Four-Minute Miler/and/ THE BOY FROM BOWRAL/by/Robert J. Hoare/ London/Macmillan & Co. Ltd/New York St Martin's Press/1962
79pp & 1p adv., b/w photographs & drawings, pic. bd., 190x132mm. KP
Half book deals with career of Don Bradman.

HOBLEY, L. F.

3536 Methuen's [device] Outlines/EXPLORING/THE PACIFIC/by/L. F. Hobley/Illustrated by the Author and G. Randall/Methuen & Co. Ltd./36 Essex Street, Strand, London W.C.2
1957
71pp (inc. index), b/w maps, b/w drawings in text, clo., 210x170mm. BBC
• Rpt 1959, 1965, 1969, as above. KP

HOBSON, Adele

3537 DREAMS/OF/OUTBACK/By/Adele Hobson/ [drawing]/Illustrated by/Laurie Tayler/London/ Frederick Warne & Co. Ltd./& New York
n.d. [1922]
64pp, b/w illus. throughout, dec. bd., 180x140mm. KMM
Verses.

HODDER, Edwin

3538 TOSSED ON THE WAVES/By/Edwin Hodder/ Author of "The Junior Clerk"/"Memories of New Zealand Life" etc. etc./London:/Hodder and Stoughton/27 Paternoster Row/1877
324pp, unillus., pic. clo., 165x110mm. KMM
Part of the action of this moral tale takes place in Melbourne. First published 1864.

3539 TOSSED ON THE WAVES./By/Edwin Hodder,/ Author of "The Junior Clerk,"/"memories of New Zealand Life," etc etc./Third edition/Douglas, Isle of Man:/Jabez S. Doidge,/21 Duke Street./ MDCCCLXXVII
233pp, b/w frontis., unillus., dec. clo., 158x108mm. CLRC

3540 TOSSED/ON THE WAVES/By/Edwin Hodder/ Author of/"The Junior Clerk" "In Strange Quarters", etc./New edition/Illustrated in colour by T. C. Dugdale/London/Henry Frowde/Hodder and Stoughton
n.d. [copy inscribed 1914]
324pp, col. frontis. & 3 f/p col. plates, dec. clo., with 2 of the illus. reproduced in panels on front cover & spine, 186x122mm. KMM

3541 TOSSED/ON THE/WAVES/By/Edwin Hodder/ Humphrey Milford/Oxford University/Press/London
1921
324pp, col. frontis. only, clo., 186x116mm. KP

3542 HEROES OF BRITAIN/IN/PEACE AND WAR/ by/Edwin Hodder/[drawing]/Illustrated/Cassell and Company, Limited/London, Paris, New York and Melbourne/All rights reserved.
n.d.[inscribed 1905, first published 1878, many reprints]
2 vols bound together, 330 and 336 pp., and 8pp advs, b/w frontis. in each and 9 and 8 plates, pic. clo., 250x180mm. MCa
Chapter 8, vol.2 deals with Eyre and the Burke and Wills expedition

HODGE, Harry

3543 WARRUMBUNGLE THE WALLABY/An Australian Animal Story/for Young People/By/Harry Hodge/ [publisher's device]/Angus and Robertson/Sydney— London
1950
128pp, col. frontis. & b/w drawings in text, dec. clo., 235x175mm. ANL

HODGES, Eleanor & BELCHER, Hazel

3544 KATY BROWN/written by Eleanor Hodges and Hazel Belcher/illustrated by Dick Evans/[text].
Joint Board of Christian Education, Melbourne, 1969
16pp, part col. illus. throughout, stiff pic. wrappers, 210x130mm. KMM

HODGES, Ralph Morwell Thomas

3545 BOB BERRELL/IN/NORTH AUSTRALIA/A Story of Adventure and Peril/For Youths of all Ages/By/ Morwell Hodges/A Southern Moon Publication
Melbourne, n.d. [1947]
176pp, 8pp adv., unillus., clo., 180x115mm. ANL

HODGETTS, James Frederick

3546 TOM'S NUGGET/A Story of the/Australian Gold Fields/By/Professor J. F. Hodgetts/Author of/The Treasure of the East, etc./Illustrations by Gordon Browne/First Edition/London/Sunday School Union/ 56 Old Bailey, E.C.
n.d. [1888]
292pp, b/w frontis., dec. t.p., chapter headings & tailpieces, 12 b/w illus., pic. clo., 180x125mm. NSL:M
A boy's adventures on the voyage out, at the Victorian gold diggings, in Melbourne & with bushrangers. The cover design shows a boy holding a pick confronting bearded gold digger.

3547 TOM'S NUGGET/ A Story of the Australian Gold Fields/by/ Professor J.F.Hodgetts/ Illustrations by Gordon Browne/ Third Edition/London:/ The Sunday School Union/57 and 59 Ludgate Hill, E.C.
n.d.
as above, but 'Youth's Own Library' on front cover which has a design of a tree &birds printed in black and grey on a brown background, with title printed boldly in gold panel, repeated on spine. 180x120mm. CLRC

3548 TOM'S NUGGET/A Story of the Australian Gold Fields/By/Professor J. F. Hodgetts/Illustrated by Gordon Browne/Fourth Edition/London:/The Sunday School Union/57 and 59 Ludgate Hill, E.C.
n.d. [inscribed 1913]
292pp, b/w frontis. & 8 f/p b/w illus. & drawings in text, pic. clo., 190x120mm. Grant

HOGAN, Inez

3549 KANGAROO/TWINS/[drawing]/Inez Hogan/ London/J. M. Dent & Sons Ltd.
First published in Great Britain 1939; This edition rpt 1956
48pp, b/w illus. throughout, bd., 215x135mm. KMM
• Rpt 1959. KP

3550 PETER/PLATYPUS/[drawing]/Written and illustrated by/Inez Hogan/London/J. M. Dent & Sons Ltd.
First published in the United States 1948; First published in Great Britain 1953; rpt 1955
33pp, b/w drawings throughout, dec. bd., dec. e/p, 210x130mm. CLRC

3551 KOALA BEAR/TWINS/[drawing]/Written and illustrated by/Inez Hogan/London: J. M. Dent & Sons Ltd.
First published in the United States 1955; First published in Great Britain 1959
52pp, 30 sepia/white illus., dec. bd., dec. e/p, 215x130mm. BBC

HOGARTH, Grace Allen

3552 AUSTRALIA:/The Island Continent/[coat of arms]/ by Grace Allen Hogarth/from material supplied by Joan Colebrook/illustrations by Howard W. Willard/ Houghton Mifflin Company, Boston/1943
60pp (inc. 2pp index), b/w & part. col. illus. & maps throughout, clo., dec. e/p, 280x225mm. KMM

'HOGEN, Kurt'
See Trend Books

HOGG, Garry
3553 Adventures in Geography Series/Editor: Nina Gardner/WITH BURKE AND WILLS/ACROSS/AUSTRALIA/by/Garry Hogg/Illustrated by/Harry Toothill/Frederick Muller Limited/London
1961
144pp (inc. 4pp index), map frontis., 12 b/w photographs, 12 b/w drawings, clo., 185x120mm. HBM

HOGSTROM, Daphne
3554 WHOA, JOEY!/by/Daphne Hogstrom/illustrated by/Charles Bracke/A Whitman Book/Western Publishing Company, Inc. Racine, Wisconsin/© 1968 by Western Publishing Company, Inc./Produced in U.S.A./[etc.]
[28]pp, col. illus. throughout, pic. bd., dec. e/p, 150x135mm. KMM
Story in verse about Australian animals.

HOLDEN, Frances Gillam
3555 THE TRAVELS/OF/RED-JACKET & WHITE-CAP/or/A History of the circulation of the blood/By/Frances Gillam Holden/Sydney/George Robertson & Co., Limited
n.d. [1884]
27pp (inc. 4pp preface &c., 1 f/p b/w diagram only, limp clo., 150x100mm. RM
Book written in a story form; in the preface Andrew Ross M.D. suggests the book might be 'adopted as a text book in the Public and High Schools of the Colony'. The author was Matron of The Children's Hospital and publ. many articles & pamphlets advocating medical & social reform.

3556 HER FATHER'S DARLING/and other/Child Pictures/by/Frances Gillam Holden/[quotation]/Sydney/Turner and Henderson/MDCCCLXXXVII
90pp, unillus., wrappers, 180x110mm. VSL
Verses, with introduction by William Woolls.

HOLFORD, Franz
3557 THE BUILDING OF GOBLIN/TOWN/(A Story in Verse)/Written and Illustrated by/Franz Holford/Deaton & Spencer, Ltd. Printers, Sydney
n.d. [1937]
24pp, col. illus., clo., 125x185mm. Grant

3558 THROUGH/THE CASEMENT/(Poems)/1941
Printed by Deaton & Spencer Ltd, Sydney
32pp, unillus., bd., 182x125mm. KP

Holiday Book
3559 HOLIDAY/BOOK
Printed & Publ. by Offset Ptg Co PL Sydney, n.d.
10pp, col. illus. throughout, cover title, pic. wrappers, 266x216mm. KMM

The Holiday Cut Out Book
See Offset Publishing Cut Out Books

Holidays Beyond the Horizon
3560 HOLIDAYS BEYOND/THE HORIZON
n.d., n.p. Printed in Belgium
[Cover title]
[44]pp, col. illus. throughout, col. pic. bd. & e/p, 328x235mm. KP
Contains two stories; one about a visit to Australia & the other 'Charles and the Whales'.

HOLLAND, Dulcie
3561 YOUNG AUSTRALIA/Songs for Australian Children/by/Dulcie Holland/Contents/[6 songs]/Copyright/W. H. Paling & Co. Limited/Sydney Brisbane/and established throughout N.S.W. and Queensland
n.d. [copyright 1955]
16pp (last blank), unillus., col. pic. wrappers, 245x185mm. ANL

HOLLAND, Julian
3562 LANDS OF THE/SOUTHERN CROSS/By Julian Holland
Aldus Encyclopaedia of Discovery and Exploration, Aldus Books, London 1971
191pp (inc. 4pp glossary, index, etc.), col. extended frontis., b/w, col. & part.-col. illus. throughout, part.-col. maps, clo. (with col. pic. panel pasted on front cover), 260x190mm. BBC
Many of the illustrations are reproductions of historical portraits & prints, etc.

HOLLOW, V. S.
3563 THE LITTLE/SILVER RING/Fables/by/V. S. Hollow/Illustrations by M. McConaghy/F. W. Cheshire Pty. Ltd./Melbourne 1947
32pp, 7 f/p b/w illus., pic. wrappers, 180x125mm. Grant

HOLLOWAY, Edgar A.
3564 TINY TODDLER'S/A.B.C.
Printed and Published by John Sands Ltd, Sydney, Gordon & Gotch (Australia) Ltd, Sole Distributors, n.d. [1931]
12pp, col. illus. throughout, pic. wrappers, 265x205mm. NSL:M
Sunny South Series, rhyming text.

HOLMAN, Mrs W. A. [Ada Augusta Holman]
3565 LITTLE MISS ANZAC/The True Story of/an Australian Doll/[drawing]/By Mrs. W. A. Holman/Illustrations by/Nelle Rodd/London: T. C. & E. C. Jack Ltd./35 Paternoster Row, E.C. and Edinburgh
n.d. [1917]
68pp, col. frontis. & 10 col. illus., b/w drawings, illus. by Mrs Selwyn Betts, bd. (with col. illus. pasted on front cover), 290x240mm. NSL:M

3566 ELKA-REVA-REE/A Story for Children/By/Ada A. Holman/Author of/"My Wander Year" "Little Miss Anzac"/"Sport of the Gods" "Adventures of Woodeny", etc./[decoration/[dedication]
Edwards Dunlop and Company Limited Sydney Brisbane Melbourne [1931]
62pp, b/w drawings in text throughout, dec. wrappers, 275x210mm. ANL

HOLMAN, Mrs W. A. & others
3567 THE ADVENTURES/OF WOODENY/The Story of a Doll/By Mrs W. A. Holman/and other Stories/Thomas Nelson and Sons, Ltd./London, Edinburgh, and New York
n.d. [1923]
121pp, col. frontis., 13 f/p b/w illus., b/w drawings in text, illus. by Nelle Rodd, dec. clo., 170x105mm. ANL
First issued under the title of 'Little Miss Anzac'. Other stories included are 'The Little Robinson Crusoes' by Harold Avery (60pp) & 'The Moat House Mystery' by Ethel Talbot (11pp), neither with Australian content.

HOLMES, F. Morell
JACK MARSTON'S ANCHOR
Cassell, Lond., n.d.
Insufficient Australian material for inclusion. 10pp relating to the hero's being shipwrecked & picked up by the *Portland* en route to London from Melbourne. CLRC

HOLMES, I. M.

3568 I. M. Holmes/GREAT/GOLDRUSHES/Illustrated by/Robin Jacques/Peter Lunn/London/1947
247pp, col. frontis., 2 f/p b/w illus. & b/w chapter headings, clo., 185x120mm.
Pp 51–122 deal with Australian goldrushes. KMM

HOLWOOD, Will

3569 THE TRUE BOOK ABOUT/CAPTAIN SCOTT/By/Will Holwood/Illustrated by/J. M. Haddock/Shakespeare Head/London New York Sydney Paris
1954
143pp, 1p chronology, b/w frontis. & b/w drawings in text, clo., 185x120mm. KP

3570 THE TRUE BOOK ABOUT/CAPTAIN SCOTT/by/Will Holwood/Illustrated by J. M. Haddock/Frederick Muller Ltd/London
1954, as above, KP

3571 THE TRUE STORY OF/CAPTAIN/SCOTT/AT THE SOUTH POLE/By Will Holwood/Children's Press, Chicago
1964, second printing 1965
143pp (inc biographical note on author & artist, chronology & map), col. frontis. & lithographic illus. throughout, pic. clo., 215x140mm. KP

HONEY, Ennis Josephine

3572 JANEY/OF BEECHLANDS/by/Ennis Honey/Bilson-Honey Pty. Ltd./P.O. Box 26, Edgecliff/N.S.W. Australia
n.d. [1947]
287pp, unillus., clo., 180x115mm. ANL

3573 JENNIFER JANE/By/Ennis Honey/Drawings by/L. G. Jordan/[publisher's device]/Bilson-Honey Pty. Ltd./P.O. Box 26 Edgecliff/Sydney
n.d. [1947]
40pp, col. frontis. & 6 f/p col. illus., b/w drawings in text, dec. bd., 235x170mm. ANL

3574 BUSY/MR TOOT-TOOT/Written by Ennis Honey/Illustrated by Gloria Bourner/[device—B. H. Productions]
Bilson Honey Pty Ltd Sydney, [194-?]
32pp, illus. throughout in 2 col., 8pp col. illus., dec. e/p, pic. bd., 174x220mm. NSL:M

3575 THREE LITTLE BUNNIES/Written By/Ennis/Honey/Illustrated by/Marjorie Pritchard/BH/Productions
Edgecliff NSW, n.d. [1948]
[32]pp, t.p. & 10pp printed in col., slight text & drawings on other pages, col. pic. bd., 165x220mm. NSL:M

HONEY, Ennis Josephine (ed.)

3576 MOTHER/GOOSE/Illustrated by/Rufus Morris/Edited by Ennis Honey/Bilson-Honey Pty. Ltd./115 Pitt Street/Sydney
[1946]
46pp, 8 col. illus. & b/w drawings throughout, clo., 240x190mm. NSL:M

HONEY, Lucy Madeleine

3577 DANCING LADY/By/Madeleine Honey/[publisher's device]/Bilson-Honey Pty. Ltd./P.O. Box 26 Edgecliff,/N.S.W., Australia
n.d. [1946]
263pp, unillus., clo., 180x120mm. KMM

3578 THE SECRETS/OF RIVER VALLEY/By/Madeleine Honey/[publisher's device]/Bilson-Honey Pty. Ltd./P.O. Box 26, Edgecliff,/N.S.W., Australia
n.d. [1947]
280pp, unillus., clo., 180x115mm. KMM

3579 DIANA/By/Madeleine Honey/[publisher's device]/Bilson-Honey Pty. Ltd./P.O. Box 26 Edgecliff,/N.S.W., Australia
n.d. [1948]
292pp, unillus., clo., 170x115mm. ANL
PAM and the others
(Advertised in The Secrets of River Valley). Unseen
Published?

HONEY, William Henry

3580 BUSH CREATURES/illustrations by/E. A. King/By/W. H. Honey
Sydney, 1934
12pp, 6 col. plates tipped in, stiff wrappers, cover title, 140x135mm. ANL
Bound together with

3581 SOME/AUSTRALIAN/BIRDS/Illustrations by/Neville W. Cayley/By/W. H. Honey
12pp (2 blank before t.p. & 3 after text), 6 col. tipped illus. with 4 lines text below each illus., stiff wrappers, cover title, 150x150mm. ANL

3582 THE EXCITING ADVENTURES OF/SMOOKIE/Written by W. H. Honey/Illustrated by L. G. Jordan/[drawing]/[publisher's device]/W. H. Honey Publishing Co., 31 Cunningham Street,/Sydney
n.d. [1945]
48pp, col. frontis. & 11 f/p col. illus., b/w drawings in text, dec. bd., 235x165mm. ANL

3583 HOW/THEY COLOURED/AUSTRALIA/and Other Stories/written by W. H. Honey/[coloured drawing]/Published by the W. H. Honey Publishing Co./31 Cunningham Street, Sydney/(Copyright)
n.d. [1945]
62pp, col. & b/w illus. throughout, dec. bd., 240x165mm. KMM
Verse.

3584 [drawing]/THE STORY OF/TOWSER/Verse by/W. H. Honey/Beware of/the Dog/Drawings by/L. G. Jordan/The First Episode in the Life Story of this Delightful Pup/Copyright—Published by W. H. Honey Publishing Co., Sydney
n.d. [1945]
8pp, part-col. drawings throughout, wrappers, cover title, 300x240mm. KMM

3585 ANOTHER STORY OF/TOWSER/[drawing]/Verse by/W. H. Honey/Drawings by/L. G. Jordan/The Second Episode in the Life Story of this Delightful Pup/Copyright—Pub. by W. H. Honey Publishing Co., Sydney
n.d.
8pp, part-col. drawings throughout, wrappers, cover title, 300x240mm. KMM

3586 ANOTHER STORY OF/TOWSER/[drawing]/Verse by/W. H. Honey/Drawings by L. G. Jordan/The Third Episode in the Life Story of this Delightful Pup/Copyright—Pub. by W. H. Honey Publishing Co., Sydney
n.d.
8pp, part-col. drawings throughout, wrappers, cover title, 300x240mm. KMM

3587 [drawing]/Verse by/W. H. Honey/Drawings by L. G. Jordan/ANOTHER STORY OF/TOWSER/The Fourth Episode in the Life Story of this Delightful Pup/Copyright—Published by W. H. Honey Publishing Co., Sydney
n.d.
8pp, part-col. drawings throughout, wrappers, cover title, 300x240mm. KMM

3588 A/MOTHER GOOSE/FANTASY/and other Stories/Written by/W. H. Honey/Published by/W. H. Honey Publishing Co./31 Cunningham Street, Sydney./(Copyright)
n.d. [inscribed Xmas 1944]
62pp, 37 col. illus., b/w drawings, dec. bd., 245x170mm. NSL:M
Illustrated by Rufus Morris & others; cover design by Rhys Williams.

3589 SMOOKIE/& Co./Written by/W. H. Honey/[publisher's device—A Bilson-Honey Production]
Edgecliff, NSW, 1947
46pp, col. frontis. & 7 f/p col. illus., b/w drawings throughout, illus. Rufus Morris, dec. bd., 235x165mm. ANL

HONNYWILL, Eleanor
3590 Eleanor Honnywill/THE CHALLENGE/OF ANTARCTICA/with a Foreword by Sir Vivian Fuchs/Illustrated with/Photographs, maps and diagrams/Methuen & Co Ltd/11 New Fetter Lane London E.C.4
1969
160pp, inc. 3pp index, 3pp chronology & bibliography, b/w photographic illus., maps &c., clo., 216x155mm. KP

HOOD, Alex
3591 BRUMBY JACK/SAVES THE WILD BUSH HORSES/Written by Alex Hood/Illustrated by Susanne Dolesch/Paul Hamlyn/London Sydney/New York Toronto
Sydney 1972
[26]pp, col. illus. throughout, pic. bd., pic. e/p, 310x230mm. CLRC

3592 PUMPKIN PADDY/MEETS THE BUNYIP/Written by Alex Hood./Illustrated by Susanne Dolesch/Paul Hamlyn/London Sydney New York Toronto
Sydney 1972
[28]pp, col. illus. throughout, col. pic. bd., col. dec. t.p. & e/p, 310x230mm. KMM

HOOD, Alex and others
3593 THE WALLABY TRACK/An Australian Folk Opera in Ten Episodes/ABC Education Radio Feature/for Primary Schools/Songs presented by Alex Hood/Accompanist: Brian Godden/Supervision of music teaching: Jeff Rushton/Dialogues for the Plays: Alex Hood/Series devised and produced by/Christopher Koch/Cover picture: Alex Hood and Brian Godden/[8 lines] Published by/The Australian Broadcasting Commission
n.d. [1971]
48pp, part col. illus. by Max Angus, & some photographs, music &c., col. photographic illus., wrappers, 180x236mm. KW

HOOK, Geoffrey
3594 JAMIE/THE JUMBO/JET/Wren Books
Written & illustrated by Jeff Hook
Mt Eliza, Victoria, 1971
[55]pp, col. illus. on alternate pages, pic. bd., 220x265mm. ANL
See also Rankine, David & Hook, Geoffrey

HOOK, S. Clarke
BANDITS OF THE BUSH. *See* The Boys' Friend Library

HOOKEY, Dora
3595 MY LITTLE BOOK/by Dora Hookey/Cover Design by Hope Evershed/Hobart/W. E. Fuller and James Boa/The Bookshelf/99 Collins St./1920
16pp, printed in red, dec. head & tailpieces on most pages, lino-cut cover design & title, wrappers, 205x180mm. KMM
Book consists of 6 nursery poems.

HOOLEY, E. T.
3596 TARRAGAL/OR/BUSHLIFE IN AUSTRALIA/By/E. T. Hooley/[publisher's device]/London/Gay and Bird/22 Bedford Street, Covent Garden/1897
226pp, 32pp adv., b/w frontis. & 7 f/p b/w illus., dec. clo., 190x115mm. CLRC
Frontispiece signed 'R.H.M.'
Adventure story of Australian bush life.

HOOPER, Margaret L. & HARDIE, Sonia
SHORT STORIES. *See* GUNN & TAYLOR, The Junior Library No. 19

HOOPER, Meredith
3597 Round the World Histories/THE GOLD RUSH/IN/AUSTRALIA/by Meredith Hooper/Illustrated by/Michael Hadley/Hulton Educational Publications, Ltd London, 1969
32pp, 14pp illus. in col., other pages illus. in b/w, pic. bd., 200x135mm. KMM

3598 Meredith Hooper/EVERYDAY/INVENTIONS/Angus and Robertson
Cremorne, NSW, 1972
138pp, extended t.p., part. col. photographic illus. throughout, clo., dec. e/p, 245x185mm. CLRC

HOOPER, Paddy
3599 MUSTER UP!/Paddy Hooper/[drawing]/Illustrated by Jim Phillips/Angus and Robertson
Sydney 1965
123pp (inc. 1p author's note), b/w chapter headings throughout, clo., 215x135mm. KMM
Note claims that main facts of the story are true.

HOOVER, Latharo
3600 THE CAMP-FIRE BOYS/IN AUSTRALIAN GOLD FIELDS By Latharo Hoover/Author of/"The Camp-Fire Boys' Treasure Quest", "The Camp-Fire/Boys in the South Seas", "The Camp-Fire Boys/in the Brazilian Wilderness", "The Camp-/Boys [*sic*] in Borneo", "The Camp-Fire Boys/in African Jungles" Etc./A. L. Burt Company/Publishers/New York/Printed in U.S.A.
1932
251pp, 4pp adv., b/w frontis. only, illus. by Lawrence Blair, clo., pic. e/p, 185x120mm. CLRC

HOPKINS, John
3601 INSTRUMENTS/OF THE/ORCHESTRA/Australian Broadcasting Commission/25 cents
Revised Edition May 1969
48pp, b/w photographs throughout, pic. wrappers, 275x185mm. KP

HOPMAN, Harry
3602 BETTER TENNIS/FOR BOYS AND GIRLS/Harry Hopman/Dodd, Mead & Company. New York
1972
95pp, b/w frontis., b/w photographic illus. & diagrams throughout, clo., 175x218mm. KP

HORDER, Margaret
WHAT THEY WORE, A First Book of English Costume *See* Blue Wren Books

'HORN, W. O. von' [pseud. Oertel, F. W.]
3603 JAMES COOK/Leben und Thaten des weltberühmten Seefahrers/und Erdumseglers./Der Jugend und dem Volke erzählt/von/W. O. von Horn,/

Berfasser der Spinnstube/mit vier Abbildungen./ Wiesbaden/Julius Niedner, Verlagshandlung
n.d. [186-?]
136pp, engraved frontis. & 3 f/p engravings, half calf, 150x110mm. NSL:M

3604 JAMES COOK/den namnkunnige verldsomseglaren,/ hans lefnad och bedrifter./skilrade för ungdomen/af/W. O. von Horn,/Författare till Ralf Redstone, En Korsarjagt,/ Ostindiefararen M. Fl./Med fyra plancher. opversattning./ Stockholm./Ebeling & Com.
1867
130pp, engraved portrait frontis. & 3 f/p engravings, pic. wrappers, 155x110mm. NSL:M

3605 JAMES COOK:/Leben und Thaten des weltberühmten Seefahrers/und Erdumseglers./Der Jugend und dem Volke erzählt/von/W. O. von Horn/ Vierte Auflage/mit Abbildungen/Altenburg,/Stephan Giebel, Verlagsbuch-handlung/1894
116pp, b/w frontis. & 3 f/p b/w illus., pic. bd., 155x110mm. NSL:M

HORNADGE, Bill

3606 EXPLORE AUSTRALIA/THROUGH STAMPS/An Illustrated history of Australia as/depicted on the nation's postage stamps/Text by Bill Hornadge/ Cartoon Stories by Monty Wedd/Published by/Review Publications Pty Ltd./Sterling Street, Dubbo NSW Australia 2830
n.d. [1970?]
64pp, 23pp b/w comic-strip cartoons, drawings & reproductions of Australian postage stamps in text, pic. wrappers, 235x180mm. CLRC

HORNUNG, Ernest William

3607 FATHERS OF MEN/By/E. W. Hornung/Author of "Raffles", "Peccavi", "The Rogue's March",/"No Hero", etc./London/G. Bell & Sons, Ltd./1912/(All rights reserved)
371pp, 24pp adv., unillus., clo., 185x120mm. Bell's Indian and Colonial Library. KMM

3608 FATHERS/OF MEN/E. W. Hornung/John Murray/ 1919
First published Smith & Elder January 1912; 2nd ed. Smith & Elder March 1912; Cheaper Edition, John Murray, London September 1919
292pp, 7pp preface, 6pp adv., dec. t.p., unillus., clo., 170x110mm. VSL
Morris Miller states: 'School cricket is featured in "Fathers of Men" which, says Conan Doyle, is "one of the very best school tales in the language" '.

3609 FATHERS OF MEN/By/E. W. Hornung/New York/Charles Scribner's Sons/1912
February 1912
369pp, 4pp adv., unillus., clo., 185x125mm. KMM

HORSEMAN, Mollie

3610 NURSERY RHYMES/Illustrated/by/Mollie Horseman
Offset Publishing Co. Sydney, n.d. [1949]
[26]pp, 12pp col. illus. & b/w illus. on remaining pages, col. pic. bd., pic. e/p, cover title, 175x115mm. ANL

HORSLEY, Reginald

3611 THE YELLOW GOD/A Tale of/Some Strange Adventures/By/Reginald Horsley/With six illustrations/by/W. S. Stacey/W. & R. Chambers, Limited/London and Edinburgh/1895
297pp, 32pp adv., b/w frontis. & 5 b/w plates, pic. clo., 190x125mm. CLRC
Another copy as above, but plain clo. KP

Swedish edition

3612 TILL SJÖSS OCHLANDS./John Brooks Äfventyr Bland Röfvare/och Guldsökare/Af/Reginald Horsley/ ofversattning fran engelskan/Af/H. Nordenadler/med sju illustrationer/[device]/Stockholm/Wilhelm Billes Bokförlags Aktiebolag
1901
214pp, 1p adv. (preceding t.p.), b/w frontis. & 6 f/p b/w illus., pic. bd. (with adv. on verso back cover), clo. backstrip, dec. e/p, 220x155mm. RM
Illustrations signed 'E. A. Bero' (?).

3613 CHUMS EVER!/("The Yellow God")/A Tale of Stirring and Strange/Adventures on Land And Sea/ By/Reginald Horsley/Author of "Hunted through Fiji", "The Red Hussar"/Illustrated by/W. S. Stacey/ London: 38 Soho Square, W.1./W. & R. Chambers, Limited/Edinburgh: 339 High Street
n.d. [1920?]
297pp, b/w frontis. & 5 b/w plates, clo., 185x120mm. KMM
Boys' adventure story dealing with discovery of gold in Australia, Hargreaves, life on the diggings, Aborigines &c. Previously published under the title *The Yellow God.*
See also South West Pacific section for other entries by this author.

HOTCHIN, F. E.

See Allinson, A. A. & Hotchin, F. E.

HOULDING, John Richard [pseuds 'J. R. H. Hawthorn', 'Old Boomerang']

3614 THE PIONEER OF A FAMILY;/or,/Adventures of a Young Governess/By/J. R. H. Hawthorn/London:/ Hodder and Stoughton,/27 Paternoster Row/ MDCCCLXXXI
313pp (inc. 3pp Appendix) & 1p preface, 2pp adv., b/w frontis., pic. clo., title & author's name in gilt, g.e., 186x122mm. CLRC

3615 IN THE DEPTHS OF THE SEA/By/Old Boomerang/Author of/"The Pioneer of a Family", "Launching Away", "The Fortunes of the/Stubble Family", "Australian Tales", etc./With a Frontispiece/ London:/Hodder and Stoughton,/27 Paternoster Row/ MDCCCLXXXV/(All rights reserved)
378pp (inc. 2pp appendix), 1p preface, 8pp adv., b/w frontis., pic. clo., 185x120mm. NSL:M

3616 LAUNCHING AWAY;/or,/Roger Larksway's Strange Mission./Edited by/J. R. H. Hawthorn,/Author of/"The Pioneer of a Family; or, Adventures of a Young Governess," etc././London:/Hodder and Stoughton,/27, Paternoster Row./MDCCCLXXXII./All rights reserved
319pp, 1p Notes, b/w engraved frontis. only, pic. clo. with design & lettering in gilt , black & silver & g.e., 185x120mm. CLRC
This moral tale of the adventures of a young Englishman in Victoria & New South Wales does not appear to be a children's book, but the advertisements all relating to 'Gift Book for the Young' and 'Sunday Library for Young People' suggest that it was in fact intended for young people.

3617 Second ed. 1885, as above but with 'Second edition' on t.p., 360 pp & 32pp advs. KMM

3618 Another ed. 1889, as above. Boys Select Library, unillus. KP

3619 A FLOOD THAT LED ON/TO FORTUNE./By/Old Boomerang,/Author of "In the Depths of the Sea" "Launching Away" "The/Pioneer of a Family" "The Stubble Family," etc/With illustrations/London:/ Hodder and Stoughton,/27, Paternoster Row./ MDCCCLXXXVI/(All rights reserved)

366pp & 1p Appendix, 4pp adv., b/w frontis. & 6 f/p b/w illus., pic. clo., 187x122mm. CLRC

The House that Jack Built
3620 A Nursery Rhyme Book/THE/HOUSE/THAT/JACK BUILT/A Pyramid Production
Sydney 1948
16pp, dec. col. t.p., col. illus. throughout by Mollie Quick, dec. bd., 240x180mm. ANL

How a Road is Built
3621 HOW A ROAD/IS BUILT/Issued by/Department of Main Roads NSW
1951
18pp, b/w photographic illus., wrappers, 200x160mm. CLRC

How Oil is Used
3622 HOW/OIL/IS/USED
Petroleum Information Bureau, Melbourne, n.d. [195-?]
16pp (inc. covers), part col. illus. throughout, stiff dec. wrappers, 212x134mm. ANL

How the Church came to us in Australia
3623 HOW THE CHURCH/CAME TO US/IN AUSTRALIA/An Anglo-Australian/Church of England History,/By the Rev. A. Law, B.D., Th.Schol.,/St John's, Toorak, Melbourne/6th and Enlarged Edition, Illustrated/Copyright./Price 1/-/(Profits devoted to C.E.M.S.)
n.d. [192-?]
24pp, b/w photographic illus., wrappers, 180x120mm. KP
Sketch of first church in Australia reproduced inside front wrapper.

HOWARD, Dais
3624 INDIA/PAINTING BOOK/By Dais Howard/and Elfrida Hill
Australian Baptist Foreign Mission in co-operation with S. J. Bacon, Melbourne, n.d. [1950]
29pp, b/w illus. throughout, dec. wrappers, cover title, 185x245mm. ANL
A painting book about mission stations in Eastern Bengal with a story explaining each picture.

HOWARD, Frederick
CHARLES KINGSFORD SMITH. *See* Great Australians

CHARLES STURT; BUILDERS OF THE WHEAT INDUSTRY; ROSS SMITH AND BERT HINKLER. *See* Great People in Australian History

HOWARD, Peter & LEVY, Wayne [eds]
3625 AUSTRALIAN STORY SAMPLER/Peter Howard and Wayne Levy/from Ivan Southall's/Ash Road/Book 1/[illustration]
Pergamon Press, Australia, 1970
20 booklets in case 130x190mm. Case contains 2 copies each of extracts from 10 titles, with summary of complete story, comprehension exercises & answer key. Each booklet: 12pp, unillus., stiff paper wrappers (with notes, questions & answer key printed verso front cover, verso/recto back cover), 185x120mm. KMM
Other books from which extracts are made include: *Midnite*, by Randolph Stow; *Kings of the Dingoes*, by Judith Wright; *Australian Legendary Tales*, by K. Langloh Parker; *The Magic Pudding*, by Norman Lindsay; *Down to Earth*, by Patricia Wrightson; *The Sun on the Stubble*, by Colin Thiele; *The First Walkabout*, by Norman B. Tindale & H. A. Lindsay; *Patterson's Track* by Eleanor Spence; Henry Lawson's *Fifteen Stories*, selected by Colin Roderick.

HOWARD, Winifred
3626 THROUGH/THE WHITE GATE/By/Winifred Howard/Illustrated/By Richard B. Ogle/London/The Epworth Press/J. Alfred Sharp
[1924]
93pp, col. frontis. & 3 b/w plates, clo., 186x124mm. ANL

3627 OUT OF THE/EVERYWHERE/By Winifred Howard/Illustrated by/Elizabeth Montgomery/[device]/Oxford University Press/London: Humphrey Milford
1929
78pp, b/w drawings throughout, dec. boards, clo. backstrip, dec. e/p,190x127mm. KMM
• Rpt 1929, as above. ANL
First published OUP New York [1929]

HOWARTH, Allison
3628 "COOEE" ENGLAND/A Travel Diary/by/Allison Howarth/Publishers/George Batchelor Pty. Ltd./12 McKillop Street, Melbourne/1937
171pp, 1 f/p col. photograph, 53 full or half page photographs, clo., 240x150mm. Grant
Appears to have been intended for children.

HOWDEN, Marjorie Beatrice
3629 Mullens' Stories for Children/(No. 501)/HALF-WAY HOUSE/By Marjorie Howden/(For ages 12 to 14)/[vignette]/Robertson & Mullens Ltd./Melbourne
n.d. [1951]
96pp, b/w frontis. & 4 f/p b/w illus. by author, dec. wrappers, 180x110mm. ANL

'HOWE, Edward'
See Rowe, Richard

HOWE, Josephine
3630 Whitcombe's Story Books/THE SCHOOL IN/CIGAM SQUARE/by/Josephine Howe/For Ages 9 to 12 years/[drawing]/Whitcombe & Tombs Pty. Ltd./Melbourne, Sydney, Perth
n.d. [1945]
110pp, 2pp adv., b/w frontis. & b/w drawings in text, wrappers, 180x105mm. ANL
See McLaren 457

HOWES, Edith
3631 Whitcombe's Nature Story Books/THE POPPY SEED/and other Nature Stories/By Edith Howes/For ages 7 to 8 years/[drawing—'The Poppy Plant']/Whitcombe and Tombs Limited/Christchurch—Auckland Wellington Dunedin Invercargill/London Melbourne and Sydney
First publ. 1925, rpt. 1926, 1928, 1937, 1943
44pp, b/w frontis. & illus. throughout, pic. wrappers, 184x122mm. KMM
Some of the stories are Australian;
See McLaren 213

3632 Whitcombe's Nature Story Books/WILLIE WAGTAIL/and Other Tales/By Edith Howes/For children aged 9 to 10 years/[vignette]/Whitcombe & Tombs Limited/Auckland Christchurch Dunedin, Wellington/Melbourne Sydney London
n.d. [1929]
64pp (inc. 4pp notes &c), b/w frontis. & illus. in text, pic. wrappers, 184x122mm
Illus. M. Matthews. Some of the stories are of Australia. KMM
See McLaren 430

3633 DRUMS OF THE SEA/The Story of Captain Cook/By/Edith Howes, M.B.E./Illustrated by/Michael D. Gibson/London/Burns Oates & Washbourne Ltd.
1939

146pp, b/w frontis. & 4 f/p b/w illus. by M. D. Gibson, clo., 184x116mm. NSL:M
Australian ed. Whitcombe's Story Books
See McLaren 572

HOWITT, William
3634 A BOY'S ADVENTURES/IN THE/WILDS OF AUSTRALIA;/or, Herbert's Note-Book./By/William Howitt/London:/Arthur Hall, Virtue & Co.,/25, Paternoster Row./1854
376pp, 1p preface, 24pp adv. (dated August 1854), engraved frontis & 11 other engravings, clo., 165x110mm. CLRC
Preface contains a misprint: 'Herbert's cotemporaries'.
3635 New ed. as above, 1855. CLRC
3636 A BOY'S ADVENTURES/IN THE/WILDS OF AUSTRALIA;/or,/Herbert's Note-Book,/By William Howitt./Illustrated by Harvey/Cheap Edition/ London:/Arthur Hall, Virtue, and Co./25, Paternoster Row./1858
x+247pp &1p adv., frontis. & 11 illus., dec. clo., g.e., 160x100mm. KP
3637 A BOY'S ADVENTURES/IN THE/WILDS OF AUSTRALIA;/or/Herbert's Note-Book/by/William Howitt/With Illustrations byWilliam Harvey./ London/George Routledge and Sons/The Broadway, Ludgate
n.d.
376pp, b/w frontis. & 11 b/w illus., clo., 180x115mm. Grant
3638 A BOY'S ADVENTURES/IN THE/WILDS OF AUSTRALIA:/or,/Herbert's Note-Book/By/William Howitt/Author of/"Jack of the Mill" , "A Country Book", etc./With illustrations byWilliam Harvey/ London/George Routledge and Sons/Broadway, Ludgate Hill/New York: 416 Broome Street
n.d.
376pp, 1p preface, engraved frontis. & 11 other engravings, clo., 180x115mm. KMM
Misprint in preface corrected.
3639 Another copy as above, but imprint 'George Routledge and Sons/Broadway,Ludgate Hill/New York:9 La Fayette Place' NSL:M
3640 Another copy as above, but 'George Routledge and Sons,/The Broadway, Ludgate'
376 +32pp adv.(George Routledge & Sons Juvenile Books) front & 11 engravings, clo. with title in gilt & gilt decorations on spine, 168x110mm. KP
3641 Another copy as above, but no adv., n.d. (inscribed 1875), 170x115mm. KP
Title, bird on spray and map of Australia blocked in gilt on front cover, and title & birds & leaves decoration in gilt on spine.
3642 A BOY'S ADVENTURES/IN THE/WILDS OF AUSTRALIA/or/Herbert's Note-Book/ By/William Howitt/Author of/ "Jack of the Mill","A Country Book", etc. with illustrations by William Harvey/ London/George Routledge and Sons, Limited/ Broadway, Ludgate Hill/Manchester and New York
n.d.
viii+376pp., b/w frontis. & 5 illus. (?complete), dec. clo. in two colours, dec. e/p, 182x120mm. CLRC
3643 A BOY'S ADVENTURES/ IN THE/ WILDS OF AUSTRALIA/or/Herbert's Note-Book/By/William Howitt/Author of/"Jack of the Mill" "A Country Book"etc./with illustrations by William Harvey/ London/George Routledge and Sons/Broadway, Ludgate Hill/Glasgow and New York
n.d.
viii+376pp, b/w frontis. & 11 b/w illus., clo. with illus. blocked in two cols & author's name & title in gilt on front cover, 185x120mm. CLRC
3644 A/BOY'S ADVENTURES/IN THE/WILDS OF AUSTRALIA;/or,/Herbert's Note-Book./By/William Howitt./with illustrations./Boston:/Ticknor and Fields./MDCCCLV
vii+359pp, b/w frontis. & 5 f/p. engravings, blind-stamped clo., 170x100mm. CLRC
3645 A/BOY'S ADVENTURES/IN THE/WILDS OF AUSTRALIA;/or,/Herbert's Note-Book./By/William Howitt/With Illustrations/Boston:/Ticknor and Fields./ 1864
359pp+24pp adv., engraved frontis. & 5 other engravings (different from those in English editions), clo., 170x110mm. RM
3646 Another copy as above (Ticknor and Fields), 1865, 359pp, engraved frontis. & illus. as above, 165x100mm. CLRC
German edition
3647 ABENTEUER/IN DEN WILDNISSEN VON AUSTRALIEN./Von/William Howitt/Aus dem Englischen/von/Dr. H. Sebald/Berlin, 1856/Verlag von Otto Janke/(Administration des Puck)
x+358pp+4pp translator's preface, engraved frontis., 4 illus. (repro. from English edition), clo., 150x97mm. NSL:M

HOWSON, John Michael
3648 The Adventure Island Story Books/THE/ BIRTHDAY PARTY/Based on the ABC-TV Children's Programme/Story by John Michael Howson Produced by Godfrey Philipp [*sic*]/[coloured illustration]/ Lansdowne
Lansdowne Press, Melbourne 1969
[22]pp, col. & part. col. illus. throughout, stiff pic. bd., cover title, 240x190mm. KMM
3649 The Adventure Island Story Books/CLOWN/AND THE PIRATES/Based on the ABC-TV Children's Programme/Story by John Michael Howson— Produced by Godfrey Phillip/[coloured illustration]/ Lansdowne
Lansdowne Press, Melbourne 1969
[22]pp (inc. e/p), col. & part.-col. illus. throughout, stiff pic. bd., cover title, 240x190mm. KMM
3650 The Adventure Island Story Books 50c/FLOWER POTTS/AND THE GIANT/Based on the ABC-TV Childrens Programme/Story by John Michael Howson Produced by Godfrey Philipp [*sic*]/[col. illus.]/ Lansdowne
Melbourne, 1969
[20]pp, col. illus. throughout, col. pic. bd., cover title, 240x190mm. KP
3651 The Adventure Island Story Books/FROSTY/THE SNOWMAN/Based on the ABC-TV Children's Programme/Story by John Michael Howson Produced by Godfrey Philipp [*sic*]]/[coloured illustration]/ Lansdowne
Lansdowne Press, Melbourne 1969
[22]pp (inc. e/p), col. & part. col. illus. throughout, stiff pic. bd., cover title, 240x190mm. KMM

HOYT, Olga
3652 Olga Hoyt/ABORIGINES OF/AUSTRALIA/ Illustrated with photographs/Lothrop, Lee & Shepard Co./New York
1969
128pp (inc. 4pp index, 2pp author's acknowledgements), b/w map by Joan Maestro, b/w photographic illus. throughout, clo., 235x160mm. ANL

HUDSON, Harry
3653 EXPLORERS/OF/AUSTRALIA/Written and illustrated for/Trans-Australia Airlines/by Harry Hudson
Melb., n.d. [195-?]

vipp (inc. intro.), 58pp, part col. dec. t.p., double-spread dec. map, sketches of explorers, pic. wrappers, 184x126mm. KP
Accounts of journeys of 54 explorers of Australia & 1p chronology.

HUDSPETH, B. M.
3654 SANTA/CLAUS/AND THE/SHADOW/by/B. M. Hudspeth/S. T. Leigh & Co./Printers, 155 Clarence St./Sydney
n.d. [Morris Miller suggests 189-. Copy examined has inscription dated 1892]
60pp, dec. t.p., bd., 220x170mm. KMM
Short stories, some with Tasmanian background.

HUDSPETH, June & others
THE KOALA KIDS STORY BOOK. *See* Gunn & Taylor

HUE, Fernand
3655 Fernand Hue/ADVENTURES/DE/DEUX FRANCAIS/ET D'UN CHIEN/EN/AUSTRALIE/ Nouvelle édition/[device]/Paris/H. Lecène et H. Oudin, Éditeurs/17, Rue Bonaparte, 17.
n.d.
142pp (inc. 3pp contents &c), 13 engravings in text (S. I. Baer), buckram, 200x125mm. ANL
Adventures in the Victorian goldfields.

HUGHES, Mrs F.
3656 MY CHILDHOOD/IN AUSTRALIA/A Story for My Children/By/Mrs. F. Hughes/Illustrated/London/ Digby, Long & Co., Publishers/18 Bouverie Street, Fleet Street, E.C.
n.d. [1892]
134pp, 1p & 8pp adv., 4 f/p b/w illus. & b/w drawings in text, pic. clo., 190x120mm. KMM
Simple reminiscences of a childhood spent in the bush, near Wellington on the River Murray, with references to Aborigines &c.

HUGHES, Helen [Mrs John Freeth]
3657 THE/ZOOPIE/ZATS/Story by/Helen Hughes/ Illustrated by/Jacki Jones/Horwitz Publications Inc./ London Melbourne Sydney
1969
[28]pp, col. illus. throughout, pic. bd., 280x215mm. CLRC

HUGHES, Walter
See 'Walters, Hugh'

HULST, Willem Gerrit van de
3658 For our Youngsters/BERT/AND LITTLE BERT/By/ W. G. van de Hulst/[drawing]/W. Krins—Melbourne
1960
47pp, b/w illus. throughout by author, dec. bd., 205x150mm. ANL
Original title *Grote Bertus en Kleine Bertus;* translated from the Dutch by O. J. Hofman.

3659 For our Youngsters/THE BOSS AND I/By/W. G. van de Hulst/[drawing]/W. Krins—Melbourne
1960
45pp, b/w drawings throughout, pic. bd., 205x150mm. ANL
Original title *Fik;* translated from the Dutch by O. J. Hofman; printed in the Netherlands. Like the author's *Bert and Little Bert,* this appears to be an Australian translation of a Dutch book.

HUME, Fergus
3660 THE CHRONICLES OF FAIRYLAND/Fantastic Tales for Old and Young
Lippincott 1893
191pp, b/w frontis. (M. Dunlop) & 1 plate, text drawings, pic. clo., 215x160mm. Unseen, info. from R. Muir, Perth

3661 THE CHRONICLES OF/FAIRY LAND/[*sic*] By/ Fergus Hume/with illustrations in color by/Maria L. Kirk/and in the text by/M. Dunlop/[drawing]/ Philadelphia & London/J.B.Lippincott Company/1911
191pp (t.p. printed in 2 cols within a ruled border), col. frontis. & 7 col. plates, b/w drawings, pic. clo., pic. e/p, 200x145mm. ANL

3662 THE/CHRONICLES OF FAERYLAND/Fantastic Tales for Old and Young/By/Fergus Hume/Illustrated by M. Dunlop/[engraving]/London/Griffith Farran & Co./Newbery House, 39 Charing Cross Road
n.d. [inscribed 1905]
192pp [last blank], engraved frontis., 1 f/p & numerous smaller engravings in text, pic. clo., 205x165mm. KMM

HUMMERSTON, R. A.
3663 THE/JOY BOOK/By/R. A. Hummerston/A Feast of Delightful/Entertainment, includ-/ing Games, Tricks,/Puzzles and Solutions,/"How to Makes", and/ various other means of/Amusement/Published by/ United Service Agency/100 Flinders Street, Melbourne./Sole Distributors for Australia and New Zealand:/Gordon & Gotch (Australasia) Limited
n.d. [1922]
174pp, 2pp adv., b/w illus., clo., 237x175mm. ANL
Another copy as above but,
n.d. [prize label 1926]
174pp (inc. 3pp index), 2pp adv., pic. bd., 245x185mm. KP

HUMPHREYS, W. G. & DARBY, H. F. [compilers]
3664 A/COMMONWEALTH/ANTHOLOGY/Selected by/W. G. Humphreys and H. F. Darby/Hamish Hamilton/London
1962
160pp (inc. 1p preface & 1p acknowledgements), 4pp b/w photographic illus., clo., 185x120mm, Oak Tree Books. BBC
Includes extracts from *One Wet Season* by Ion L. Idriess, *Rum Jungle* by Alan Moorehead, and *Cullenbenbong* by Bernard O'Reilly.

HUNGERFORD, Eve
3665 TOMMY IN/By Eve Hungerford/[drawing]/ Illustrated by/Mary M. Abbott/MUSIC-LAND/Ure Smith—Sydney
1955
32pp, 10 col. illus. & b/w drawings in text, dec. bd., 250x185mm. NSL:M

3666 TOMMY IN/By Eve Hungerford/[b/w drawing of violin]/Illustrated by/Mary M. Abbott/MUSIC-LAND/ Aidmasta/Productions
Sydney, n.d.
32pp, part col. illus. throughout, dec. boards, 230x182mm. KP
The same illustrations are reproduced with the addition of one col. throughout. The dec. yellow bd. have a different design from the 1st ed.

HUNT, Madeline Bonavia
AUNT TABITHA'S WAIFS
Cassell & Company Ltd, London, n.d. [189-?]
Insufficient Australian content for inclusion. KMM

3667 MARGARET'S ENEMY/by/Madeline Bonavia Hunt/Author of "Little Hinges" "Little Empress Jean" etc/[vignette]/Cassell & Company, Limited/London Paris & New York/(All rights reserved)/1883
268pp & 4pp adv., b/w frontis., dec. clo., q.c. 190x120mm
Small part of book only Australian. NSL:M

HUNT, Neil
3668 THE WATCH/by/Neil Hunt/Author of/the Thistledown Fairy Queen's Party/A Fairy Story/ Narrandera/Australia
n.d. [1955?]
[22]pp, unillus., clo., 220x164mm. VSL
Printed throughout in red.

HUNT, O. W.
See Allsopp, F. J. & Hunt, O. W.

HUNTER, Christine
3669 THE BOY FROM/DOWN UNDER/Christine Hunter/[device]/London/Pickering & Inglis Ltd/1964
124pp, col. frontis. only, clo., 181x117mm. KMM

HUNTER, J. E.
3670 TWELVE SONGS/OF/THE ZOO/Words and Music by/J. E. Hunter/With illustrations by Jean Plant/Melbourne/Copyright/1944
Printed at The Salvation Army Printing House, Melbourne for the Zoological Board of Victoria
28pp, b/w illus. in text, pic. wrappers, 260x205mm. KMM

HUNTER, Leslie
3671 THE BOYS' AND GIRLS' BOOK OF/THE COMMONWEALTH/Leslie Hunter/Burke London
1962
144pp, b/w photographic frontis. & b/w photographic illus. throughout, b/w maps, clo., 250x185mm. ANL
Contains 17 pages dealing with Australia.

HURLEY, Frank
3672 SHACKLETON'S/ARGONAUTS/A Saga of the Antarctic Ice-Packs/By/Frank Hurley/with photographs by the author/Angus and Robertson/ Sydney; London/1948
140pp, 4pp foreword, 2pp note on illustrations, 47pp photographs, clo., dec. e/p, 215x135mm. KMM
Not originally intended as a children's book, but winner CBCA Award 1948.
• Rpt 1949, 1956, as above. KMM

HURRELL, Marian Isabel
3673 INTO A SUNLIT HARBOUR
Partridge, London [193-?]
Slight Australian interest only. Grant

HURT, Freda
3674 Freda Hurt/NORGY/IN LITTLELAND/Illustrated by/Elizabeth [*sic*] McIntyre [*sic*]/London/The Epworth Press
1955
125pp, 7 f/p b/w illus. & drawings in text, clo., 185x120mm. BBC
Doubtful Australian children's book: fantasy with English setting. Also by the same author *Clever Mr. Twink* and *Mr. Twink takes charge.*

HUTCHESON, John C.
3675 TEDDY/The Story of a "Little Pickle"/By/John C. Hutcheson/Author of "The Wreck of the Nancy Bell" "Picked up at Sea" &c/Illustrated/Blackie and Son Limited/London Glasgow Dublin
n.d. [prize 1905]
192pp & 32pp adv., b/w frontis. & 2 plates, pic. clo., 180x120mm. ANL
Australian section (Melbourne &c) pp149-63, thence in the South Seas pp163-78.

HUTCHINSON, F.
3676 Cantata "WELCOME"/Composed for the visit of/ Lord and Lady Carrington/to/Fort Street Model Public School, Sydney,/on 25th July, 1890/Words by F. Hutchinson/Music by Hugo Alpen/ [Cantata follows]
Publ. by Charles Potter, Government Printer, Sydney
Full morocco bd, title &c in gilt, 355x270mm. MAC

HUTTON, Geoffrey
MELBA. *See* Great Australians

HYDE, Edmund E. C.
See Rejje, E.

HYDE, Miriam
3677 UNDER THE MILKY WAY/Ten elementary/Piano Pieces/which may also/be used as/Songs for/ Children/[titles listed]/Words and Music by/Miriam Hyde/Slightly more advanced than/"My favourite days"/Album complete/2/6 net/Chappell/& Co Ltd/ (incorporated in Great Britain)/National Building/Pitt Street, Sydney/London & New York
1946
12pp, unillus., pic. wrappers, 280x216mm. MC

HYDE, Victor
GREGORY BLAXLAND. *See* Australian Explorers

HYRST, H. W. G.
3678 ADVENTURES/IN/THE GREAT FORESTS/ Romantic incidents & perils of Travel, Sport, and Exploration/throughout the World/By/H. W. G. Hyrst/Author of "Adventures in the Great Deserts",/"Chasma", &c./&c.,/With Sixteen illustrations/London/Seeley and Co., Limited/38 Great Russell Street/1908
330pp (inc. 2pp preface), 14pp adv., b/w frontis. & 15 f/p b/w illus., pic. clo., 190x130mm. RM
Contains: 'The Wild White Man' (Buckley, pp54–64); 'A Teak Forest in Java' (Jukes, voyage of H.M.S. *Fly*, pp111–20); 'Among the Bushrangers' (pp166–76)

3679 DARING DEEDS/IN DARK FORESTS/True Stories of/Adventure and Pluck in many/parts of the world/ by/H. W. G. Hyrst/Author of "The Romance of the world's Fisheries",/"Adventures in Great Deserts",/etc. etc. etc./with illustrations/London/ Seeley Service and Co., Limited/38 Great Russell Street/1919
257pp, col. frontis., 8 f/p b/w illus., pic. clo., 205x145mm. PR
6 illustrations by J. F. Campbell, 1 by Ernest Prater & others unsigned
Contents, first published in the author's *Adventures in the Great Forests*, include: 'The Wild White Man' (Buckley pp54–64); 'Among the Bushrangers' (pp166–76).

IBBOTSON, M. Christine
3680 ROBERTSON,/UGLY AND NOHOW/M. C. Ibbotson/Illustrated by Edward McLachlan/[device]/ Brockhampton Press
Leicester, England, 1968
96pp, b/w drawings in text, clo., 200x135mm. ANL

ICENHOWER, J. B.
3681 THE FIRST BOOK OF THE/ANTARCTIC/by J. B. Icenhower, Capt. U.S.N./Pictures by Rus Anderson/ Franklin Watts/New York/Copyright 1956 by Franklin Watts, Inc.
68pp (inc. 1p index & 1p biographical notes), b/w frontis., b/w & part. col. illus. throughout, clo., dec. map e/p, 215x175mm. NSL:M

'IDIE' [pseud. Annie Frost]
3682 STORIES TOLD BY/"LITTLE MISS KOOKABURRA"/of 3 L.O., Melbourne/Written by "Idie"/Illustrated by Guthrie Grant/Lothian Publishing Co. Pty. Ltd./Melbourne and Sydney
1925

95pp, photographic frontis., b/w drawings throughout, pic. bd., 240x180mm. NSL:M
Frontispiece photograph of Miss Hazel Maude, 'Little Miss Kookaburra'.

IDRIESS, Ion Llewellyn

3683 THE GREAT TREK/One of the greatest feats in Australian/Exploration/By/Ion L. Idriess/[drawing]/Angus and Robertson Ltd./Sydney—London/1940
199pp, 1p author's note, col. frontis. & b/w drawings in text, dec. bd., 235x180mm. ANL
The story is founded on the Jardine expedition in Northern Queensland.

3684 THE GREAT TREK/One of the Greatest Feats in/Australian Exploration/By/Ion L. Idriess/Angus and Robertson Ltd./Sydney—London/1941
231pp (inc. 4pp appendix), 2pp author's note, b/w frontis., clo., 180x120mm. PAI

3685 THE GREAT TREK/One of the Greatest Feats in/Australian Exploration/By/Ion L. Idriess/Angus and Robertson Ltd./Sydney—London/1944
222pp, unillus., stiff wrappers, 180x120mm. ANL

3686 THE GREAT TREK/One of the Greatest Feats in/Australian Exploration/By/Ion L. Idriess/Angus & Robertson/Sydney—London
First publ. 1940; rpt 1941, 1944, 1947, 1948, 1951
211pp, b/w frontis., bd., 180x115mm. NSL:M

3687 THE GREAT TREK/One of the Greatest Feats in/Australian Exploration/By/Ion L. Idriess/Illustrated by Wal Stackpool/Angus and Robertson/Sydney London Melbourne Wellington
First publ. 1940; rpt 1941, 1944, 1947, 1948, 1951; new edition 1956
211pp, b/w frontis. & b/w drawings in text, clo., 195x120mm. BBC
• Rpt 1958, as above. KP

3688 Upper Primary Library/For Students Aged 11–14/THE GREAT TREK/By Ion L. Idriess/Angus and Robertson/Sydney London
First publ. 1940; rpt 1941, 1944, 1947, 1948, 1951; first issued in this edition 1954
128pp (inc. 1p author's note), b/w map frontis. & 4 f/p b/w illus., limp clo., 180x120mm. KMM
Illustrations signed 'H.C.'

3689 HEADHUNTERS/OF THE CORAL SEA/By/Ion L. Idriess/[drawing]/Angus and Robertson Ltd./Sydney—London/1940
196pp (inc. 3pp author's introduction & 1p notes), col. frontis. & b/w drawings throughout, bd., dec. e/p, 235x180mm. ANL
The anonymous frontis. is repeated on front cover. Adventures of two boys, survivors of the wreck of the *Charles Eaton.*

3690 HEADHUNTERS/OF THE CORAL SEA/By/Ion L. Idriess/Angus and Robertson Ltd./Sydney London/1941
ixpp, 234pp, 3pp notes, b/w frontis. by E. Bell, 2 charts & 1 b/w illus., clo., 182x120mm. KP

3691 HEADHUNTERS/OF THE CORAL SEA/By Ion L. Idriess/Angus and Robertson Ltd./Sydney London/1944
220pp, 3pp notes, 4pp introduction, b/w frontis. (E. Bell), stiff wrappers, 180x115mm. KMM
• Rpt as above, but n.d. [1946]. KP
• Rpt 1947 as above, but dec. bd. MK

3692 HEADHUNTERS/OF THE CORAL SEA/By/Ion L. Idriess/Illustrated by/Wal Stackpool/Angus and Robertson Ltd./Sydney London Melbourne Wellington
First publ. 1940; rpt 1941, 1944, 1946, 1947, 1948, 1951; new edition 1955
207pp (inc. 4pp preface & 3pp notes), b/w frontis., 3 f/p b/w illus., 2 maps, b/w drawings in text, clo., 185x120mm. ANL
• Rpt as above, 1957. BBC

3693 NEMARLUK/King of the Wilds/By/Ion L. Idriess/Angus and Robertson Ltd./Sydney—London/1941
221pp, 1p author's note, b/w portrait frontis., clo., 180x120mm. KMM
• Rpt 1946, as above. KMM
• Rpt 1947, 1948, 1951. KP

3694 NEMARLUK/King of the Wilds/by/Ion L. Idriess/[device]/Angus and Robertson/Sydney London Melbourne Wellington
1st publ. 1941; rpt 1946, 1947, 1948, 1951, 1958
1p author's note & 207pp, b/w frontis. & drawings in text, clo., 197x125mm. KP
New frontis. & illus. appear to be by Wal Stackpool.

3695 Upper Primary Library/For Students aged 11–14/NEMARLUK/King of the Wilds/By/Ion L. Idriess/Adapted for schools by/Colin Roderick, M.A., M. Ed./[publisher's device]/Angus and Robertson/Sydney—London
n.d. [1951]
128pp (inc. 1p author's note), b/w frontis. & 5 f/p b/w illus., dec. bd., 185x120mm. ANL

3696 THE OPIUM/SMUGGLERS/A True Story of Our Northern Seas/By/Ion L. Idriess/Angus and Robertson/Sydney London/1948
273pp, 2pp author's note, b/w photographic frontis. & 6 f/p b/w drawings, clo., dec. map e/p, 180x120mm. NSL:M
• Rpt as above, 1951. Grant

3697 THE OPIUM/SMUGGLERS/A True Story of Our Northern Seas/By/Ion L. Idriess/Angus and Robertson/Sydney London Melbourne Wellington
First publ. 1948; rpt 1951; 2nd ed. 1957
216pp, b/w frontis. & 5 f/p b/w illus., clo., map e/p, 180x120mm. BBC

3698 The Junior Library of Australian Books/GEMS FROM/ION IDRIESS/With an Introduction by/Colin Roderick/Angus and Robertson/Sydney London
First publ. 1949; rpt 1951
148pp, 5pp introduction, b/w frontis. & 2 f/p b/w illus., bd., 180x120mm. KMM

The Illustrated Australian Alphabet

3699 THE ILLUSTRATED AUSTRALIAN ALPHABET—New Publication—Price in calico 1/6, posted 1/8d; price on paper 1/-, posted 1/2
W. A. Cawthorne newsagent Waymouth and Morphett Streets Adelaide
Advertised in the *Illustrated Adelaide Post*, 17 June 1871. Unseen

Industry in Australia

Format example:
3700 Industry in Australia/SHEEP/AND WOOL/W. R. Lang/Longmans
Croydon, Victoria, 1967
36pp, b/w photographic illus. & diagrams, pic. wrappers, 215x150mm. KMM
Instructional rather than recreational reading.
Others listed in series:
3701 ALUMINIUM, by Robin F. Dowie
3702 COAL, by M. G. A. Wilson
3703 COASTAL SHIPPING, by P. J. Rimmer
3704 COTTON, by J. J. Pigram, 1970. KMM
3705 FISHING, by R. S. Mathieson
3706 PETROLEUM, by P. J. Rimmer
3707 WHEAT, by Hylda A. Rolfe

I Never Knew

3708 I NEVER KNEW./By/One Who Loves Children/Ballarat:/John Fraser, Printer, Albert Street./1900
42pp, 4pp & 1 plate
and
WHAT BECAME OF A BIRDIE'S BALL
16pp & 2pp adv.
Bound together, bd., 188x118mm. Grant

INGAMELLS, Rex [Reginald Charles]

3709 ARANDA BOY/An Aboriginal Story/by/Rex Ingamells/Illustrated by/Leong Pak Hong/Longmans Green and Co./London Melbourne New York
1952
159pp (inc. 3pp glossary & 1p acknowledgements), b/w drawings in text throughout, clo., 180x115mm. CLRC
• Rpt 1956; 1958 stiff wrappers, as above. KMM
• Rpt 1960, 1961, 1963, 1964, 1968. KP
Also compiler of *New Song in an Old Land,* Longmans Green, Melbourne, first published 1943 & thereafter many times reprinted, an anthology of Australian verse designed as a school textbook & therefore not included.

INGLE, Dorothy

3710 THREE GIRLS AND/AN ISLAND/A Story for Girls/By Dorothy Ingle/Pyramid Publications Pty. Ltd./Sydney n.d. [1947]
184pp, b/w frontis. & 4 f/p b/w illus., clo., 180x115mm. ANL
The setting of the story is the Hawkesbury River district of New South Wales.

INGRAM, Anne Bower (ed.)

3711 SHUDDERS/AND/SHAKES/Ghostly tales from Australia/chosen and edited by/Anne Bower Ingram/Collins/Sydney London
1972
176pp, unillus., clo., 215x135mm. KMM

[INNES, Alistair Doig]

3712 THE/SLEEPY/'POSSUM/A Tale of Billy Bluegum/and his Australian Forest Friends
Associated General Publishers, Sydney, n.d. [1946]
24pp, col. illus. throughout, stiff pic. wrappers, cover title, 235x180mm. ANL
Picture book with brief rhyming text.

3713 BILLY'S FIRE BRIGADE/The Second Tale/of/Billy Bluegum/and his Australian Forest Friends
Associated General Publishers, Sydney, n.d. [1946]
24pp, col. illus. throughout, stiff pic. wrappers, cover title, 235x180mm. ANL
Picture book with brief rhyming text.

3714 PIGGY THE/ROAD HOG/The/Third Tale/of/Billy Bluegum/and his Australian Forest Friends
Associated General Publishers, Sydney, n.d. [1946]
24pp, col. illus. throughout, stiff pic. wrappers, cover title, 235x180mm. ANL
Picture book with brief rhyming text.

3715 STEAMBOAT/The Fourth Tale/of/Billy Bluegum/and his Australian Forest Friends
Associated General Publishers, Sydney, n.d. [1947]
24pp, col. illus. throughout, stiff pic. wrappers, cover title, 235x180mm. ANL
On page 1 the story is entitled 'Steamboat Billy'.
Picture book with brief rhyming text.

3716 PUFFING BILLY/the Fifth Tale of/Billy Bluegum/and his Australian Forest Friends
Associated General Publishers, Sydney, n.d. [1948]
24pp, col. illus. throughout, stiff pic. wrappers, cover title, 235x180mm. ANL
Picure book with brief rhyming text.

3717 THE FOREST AIR MAIL
Listed on back cover of *Piggy the Road Hog.* Unseen

In the Outback/A Johnny, Jane and Jason Book

See AT THE CIRCUS WITH JOHNNY, JANE AND JASON

IRBY, Florence Margaret

3718 SALLY WARNER/by/Florence M. Irby/Illustrated by Edgar A. Holloway/Australia;/Cornstalk Publishing Company/89 Castlereagh Street, Sydney/1926
242pp, b/w frontis. & 2 f/p b/w illus., clo., 185x120mm. CLRC
• Rpt as above 1927, Angus & Robertson, Bell Bird Series. KMM

3719 [Photograph]/MIRRAM—Little Happy One/The Story of a Sugar Squirrel/By Florence M. Irby/Author of "Sally Warner" and "The Waggon of Birds"
Ramsay Pub Pty Ltd, Melb., n.d. [1937]
26pp, b/w photographs, wrappers, 215x140mm. KMM
Also publ. in *The Australian Zoologist* Vol. 7, Part 1, Sydney 1937, 4pp

IRBY, L. G.

See 'Sylvanus'

IRELAND, John

3720 THE/SHIPWRECKED ORPHANS:/A True Narrative of the/Shipwreck and Sufferings/of/John Ireland and William Doyley,/who were wrecked in the/Ship *Charles Eaton,*/on an island in the South Seas./Written by John Ireland./[vignette]/New Haven./Published by S. Babcock. [title in dec. border]
n.d. [author's note 'To my Young readers' dated 1845]
64pp, 8 f/p b/w illus., stiff dec. bd., 142x117mm. RM
Front cover title reads: Teller's Tales/THE/SHIPWRECKED ORPHANS:/A/True Narrative/of/four Years' Sufferings./Edited by Thomas Teller./[vignette]/Embellished with new and/Beautiful Engravings/New Haven./Published by S. Babcock./Chapel Street/New Series Number Five.
First publ. in London 1838. Unseen BMC

IRVINE, R. F.

3721 BUBBLES/HIS BOOK/Written by/R. F. Irvine/Illustrated by/D. H. Souter/Wm. Brooks & Co./Sydney and Brisbane
n.d. [1899]
111pp, col. frontis. & 15 col. illus., b/w drawings in text, clo., dec. e/p, 235x175mm. KMM

IRVING, Kay

3722 21 LESSONS/FOR YOUNG/RIDERS/Kay Irving/Lansdowne
Melbourne, n.d.
96pp, b/w photographic illus. & diagrams throughout, clo., 230x150mm. KP

The Italian Boy

3723 THE ITALIAN BOY;/and/Industrial Men/of Note./with illustrations/[device]/London: Frederick Warne & Co./Bedford Street, Covent Garden./New York: Scribner, Welford, and Co.
n.d. [inscribed July 1871]
122pp, 2pp adv., f/p col. frontis. & 6 b/w illus., clo., 160x110mm. Grant
Contents include: 'Captain Cook' (pp 46–73); 'Alexander Selkirk' (pp 108–22).

3724 Another copy 'Round the Globe Library'. Frederick Warne and Co./Bedford Street Strand
n.d., as above but device, frontis. & adv. differ. Grant

IVATT, Frances Selina Jane [née Combes, Mrs Alfred Ivatt]
3725 PRINCESS HER-/MINIE AND THE/TAPESTRY PRINCE/AND OTHER STORIES/Published by Art in Australia Limited/24 Bond Street, Sydney/ 1922/Written by/Lee Ivatt/and Illustrated/By Barbara/Macdonald/Wholly set-up and printed in Australia by/Shepherd & Newman, Sydney./Blocks by Bacon & Co., Sydney.
79pp, extended t.p., 4 f/p col. illus. &14 f/p b/w illus., wrappers (with col. illus. reproduced on front wrapper), 250x185mm. ANL

J., M. C.
THE WHITE LADIES. *See* Gunn & Taylor, no. 92, The Junior Library, no. 2

Jack and the Beanstalk
See Moonbeam Series

Jack and the Beanstalk and Cinderella
3726 JACK AND THE BEANSTALK/AND CINDERELLA
Phogravures [Melb.], n.d.
8pp, col. illus. throughout, cover title. JH

Jack Horner Nursery Rhymes
3727 JACK HORNER/NURSERY/RHYMES/[drawing]/ Printed & Published by Offset Printing Coy Pty Ltd. [device] 168 Phillip St. Waterloo, Sydney. (All rights reserved)
n.d. [194-?]
24pp, 4 f/p col. illus., b/w illus. throughout, pic. wrappers, 278x214mm. KMM
Illus. initialled 'T.H.R.'

JACKSON, Ada [Mrs Ada Acraman Fawcett]
3728 BEETLES AHOY!/Being a Series of Nature/Studies Specially written/for children/by/Ada Jackson./ Printed and Published by/Paterson Press Ltd./65 Murray Street Perth
n.d. [1948]
160pp, b/w chapter headings, clo., 220x135mm. NSL:M

JACKSON, Alice F.
JACK'S LITTLE GIRLS
Lond. SPCK, n.d. [inscribed 1898]
Insufficient Australian material—English setting with Australian references only. CLRC

JACKSON, Gainor W.
3729 THE AUSTRALIAN/BEACH AND BOATING BOOK/written and illustrated by/Gainor W. Jackson, F.R.G.S./[device]/Cassell, Australia
1963
viiipp, 127pp (inc. 2pp introduction), b/w diagrams, clo., 210x137mm. KP
Practical advice on boats, fishing, aquatic sports, weather &c.

JACKSON, G. Gibbard
3730 THE ROMANCE OF/EXPLORATION/By/G. Gibbard Jackson/Author of "From Post Boy to Air Mail" "The Book of the Ship", Etc./Fully Illustrated/ London/Sampson Low, Marston & Co. Ltd.
n.d.
xvipp, 240pp, 40 b/w plates photographs, 16pp adv., clo., 220x142mm. ANL
'Romance' series. Some Australian content.

JACKSON, R. S.
THE SECRET OF MURRIGAN'S. *See* Australian Boys' Adventure Library

JACOBS, Joseph 1854-1916
The famous Jewish historian was born and educated in Sydney. As an authority on folklore he made a number of celebrated collections of fairy tales, in children's as well as in scholarly editions. His adult life was spent in England & the United States & as his literary work had no connection with Australia I have not included his books here.

JAMES, Anthony
3731 MY DAY/by/Anthony James/aged 7 months/ Sketches by/Unkle/White/[drawing]/Frank Johnson/ Publisher 350 George St.
Sydney, n.d. [194-?]
16pp, b/w drawings throughout, wrappers, 240x180mm. KMM

JAMES, B. E.
3732 DANGEROUS/HOLIDAY/B. E. James/[device]/ Rigby Limited/Adelaide
1963
158pp, 2pp adv., b/w map, otherwise unillus., clo., 190x125mm. KMM

JAMES, Brian
ORCHARDS. *See* Life in Australia

JAMES, C. E.
See Cole, E. W.

JAMES, Dorothy & others
3733 LITTLE BOY BLUE/Farm & Rhyme Book [col. illus.] Back cover repeat of front
Vardon & Son Adelaide, n.d. [copy inscribed 1948] [Printed by R. P. Dean & Co, 178 Rundle St, Adel.]
32pp, inc. 16pp col. illus., pic. bd., cover title, 250x180mm. TG
Illus. by M. M. Brittain. Trad. nursery rhymes.

3734 THE STORY OF LITTLE BOY BLUE/ON THE FARM/[illus. & rhyme]/Farm Rhymes by Dorothy James/copyright
n.d. [inscribed 1948], as above. KP

JAMES, Florence
See Cusack, Dymphna & James, Florence

[JAMES, Harry Reginald]
3735 AUSTRALIAN/BIRDS/AND THEIR/EGGS/A Highly educative/children's book/on Australian/Birds and their/Eggs
H. R. James & Co., Adelaide, n.d. [1945]
16pp, 9 col. illus. by C. E. Stamp, wrappers, cover title, 240x175mm. Southern Series. ANL

3736 BIRDS/WITH THEIR OWN NESTS AGREE/Theirs is the best/that could possibly be./A charming little/ book of Australian/birds and their nests
H. R. James & Co., Adelaide, n.d. [1945]
16pp, 9 col. illus. by C. E. Stamp, wrappers, cover title, 230x175mm. Southern Series. ANL

[JAMES, Henry Colbert]
3737 CHILDREN OF DOWN-UNDER/Hutchinson of London
London, n.d. [1962]
32pp, col. photographic illus. throughout, dec. bd., dec. map e/p, 225x180mm. 'This is our Country' Series No. 9. BBC
Photographs supplied by the Australian News and Information Bureau after an idea by Henry C. James. Brief factual text.
Second printing 1962, with slight variation. KP

JAMES, Marion
3738 YABBA YABBA/(An Aboriginal word meaning

"talks") Stories and Verses/of Australian/Birds—Bush—Blackfellows/By/Marion James/[boomerang]/Some of the illustrations by/V. R. Watt/1943/Registered in Australia for transmission/by post as a Book./Copyright
Wholly set up and printed at/St. Vincent's Boys' Home,/Westmead, Sydney, N.S.W.
96pp (inc. 1p foreword by Mary Gilmore & others), b/w drawings throughout, bd., 210x130mm. Grant

3739 YABBA YABBA
Second & enlarged ed. 1944 as above, but
123pp (inc. 1p glossary, 2pp foreword), b/w drawings throughout, bd., 210x130mm. KMM

JAMES, Richard

3740 ANDREW AND/THE FISHERMAN/A Novel for Young Primaries/By Richard James/Drawings by Cecily Trueman/[device]/Brolga Books Pty. Ltd.
Printed at The Griffin Press, Adelaide, n.d. [1968?]
95pp, 1p adv., b/w drawings in text, pic. wrappers, 180x110mm. KMM

JAMES, Winifred [Mrs de Jan]

3741 SATURDAY'S CHILDREN/A Story of Today/By/Winifred James/Author of "Bachelor Betty"/Illustrated by Frances Ewan/Blackie and Son Limited/London Glasgow Dublin Bombay/1910
392pp, tinted frontis. & 7 other tinted illus., pic. clo., 190x135mm. NSL:M
Also author of *Bachelor Betty* (Constable 1907) & *Patricia Baring* (Constable 1908), books intended for older girls, but not considered children's books.

James Cook

3742 JAMES COOK/1770–1970
Captain Cook Bi-Centenary Commemorative Booklet
Govt Printer NSW, 1970
[32]pp, col. & b/w illus. throughout, double-spread map, pink & black wrappers, 236x180mm. KP
Original drawings by Joyce Abbott, Margaret Senior.
Text begins: 'James Cook was born in a part of England called Yorkshire'.

3743 Another variant copy
Govt Printer NSW 1970
[32]pp, col. & b/w illus. throughout, double-spread map, green & dark blue wrappers, 238x180mm. KP
Text begins: 'Nine days after sighting the East Coast of New Holland'. 1st book appears to be intended for younger readers.

JAMIESON, Molly E.

3744 RUBY./A Story of the Australian Bush./by/Molly E. Jamieson,/Author of "Jack", "At Sunset", "Molly and I", etc./Published under the Direction of the General Literature/Committee,/London:/Society for Promoting Christian Knowledge,/Northumberland Avenue, W.C.:/43, Queen Victoria Street, E.C./Brighton: 129 North Street./New York: E. & J. B. Young and Co.
n.d. [1898]
96pp, 16pp adv., b/w frontis., dec. clo., 165x115mm. KMM

'JANELLE'

3745 HOW/I/DRESS/written and illustrated by Janelle
Australia Lin-Print Book, n.d. [196-?]
[8]pp, numerous illus., rag book, cover title, 185x140mm. ANL
This copy dated 1979.

SAMMY SUN
Uniform with above. Unseen

JANIC, Penelope

3746 THE HA HA BIRD/written and illustrated by Penelope Janic/Paul Hamlyn/London New York Sydney Toronto
1968
[22]pp, col. illus. throughout, col. dec. t.p., dec. bd., dec. e/p, 250x245mm. KMM

3747 THE NO SUCH THING/written and illustrated by Penelope Janic/[drawing]/Paul Hamlyn/London New York Sydney Toronto
Dee Why West, NSW, 1970
[26]pp, col. illus. throughout, pic. bd., pic. e/p, 310x230mm. KMM

3748 Penelope Janic/PERI AND THE WILLOW'S/SONG or TREE MAGIC/Heinemann Melbourne
1971
[39]pp, extended t.p., col. illus. throughout, illus. by author, designed by John Sayers, clo., 280x185mm. KMM

'JANJIC, Penelope' [*sic*]

3749 JAPHET/THE TIGER/[drawing]/Penelope Janjic [*sic*]/Angus and Robertson
Sydney 1965
[32]pp, col. illus. throughout, dec. bd., 185x250mm. KMM

'JARL, Moonie' [pseud. Wilf Reeves]

3750 THE LEGENDS/OF/MOONIE JARL/retold by/Moonie Jarl/(Wilf Reeves)/illustrated by/Wandi (Olga Miller)/[drawing]/The Jacaranda Press
Brisbane 1964
44pp, 9 f/p col. illus., pic. clo., 240x180mm. KMM

Jason & Jan Meet the Little Bush Folk

3751 JASON & JAN/MEET THE LITTLE/BUSH FOLK/A colouring-in comic book story of how to be fire tidy/released by the Country Fire Authority of Victoria/[CFA insignia]
Melb., n.d.
8pp, b/w illus. throughout, pic. wrappers, cover title, 240x185mm. KP
Illus. based on animal characters created by Kerrie Mortison.

Jean and the Shell Fairy

3752 JEAN AND THE/SHELL FAIRY/[drawing]
Published by the Shell Company, n.d. [192-?]
16pp, 5 f/p col. illus., b/w drawings, illus. Sheila Hawkins, wrappers, 245x185mm. KMM
Advertising booklet.
See also [Martin, George W.] THE SENTRY AND THE SHELL FAIRY

JEFFERY, Walter James

3753 A CENTURY OF OUR/SEA STORY/By/Walter Jeffery/Author of "The King's Year," etc/with a portrait of Lord Nelson/London/John Murray, Albemarle Street/1900
xiipp, 381pp (inc. 1p preface & 11pp index), frontis. only, dec. wrappers, 190x120mm. NSL:M
Includes 1 chapter on Arctic & Antarctic Explorations; 1 chapter on The South Seas, &c.

JENKINS, Colin J.

3754 Imperial Edition No. 1119/"ROUNDABOUT"/By Colin Jenkins/Words by/C. J. Dennis A. B. Paterson/Will Lawson Rex Ingamells/[part col. illus.]/Allans Music (Australia) Pty. Ltd/Melbourne Adelaide Hobart Geelong Bendigo/Dandenong Bentleigh Camberwell Preston 75c/Printed in Australia
n.d. [1972?]
25pp, pic. wrappers, 245x185mm. KP
Words & music of 10 songs.

JENKINS, Ruth
3755 VERSES FOR/LITTLE AUSTRALIANS/Written & Illustrated by/Ruth Jenkins
Published by Haldane Publishing Co. Pty Ltd, North Sydney, n.d.
39pp, col. drawings throughout, pic. bd., col. dec. e/p, 255x190mm. Grant

JENKINS, William Stitt [*sic*]
3756 THE/LOST CHILDREN./(In Perpetual Remembrance of Jane Duff)/By/William Stitt [*sic*] Jenkins./Price one shilling./The proceeds of sale will be added to the fund for the/Benefit of the children./ Geelong:/Printed at the office of the "Geelong Advertiser", Malop Street,/1864
[8]pp, unillus., wrappers, 195x125mm. VSL
Verse of sixteen stanzas. Author's correct name is William Still Jenkins.

JENKS, Tudor
3757 THE BOYS BOOK/OF/EXPLORATIONS/True Stories of the Heroes of Travel/and Discovery in Africa, Asia,/and Australia/From the "Dark Ages" to the/"Wonderful Century"/By/Tudor Jenks/[vignette]/ New York,/Doubleday Page and Co./1904
441pp, b/w frontis. & 104 b/w illus. & maps in text, pic. clo., 195x125mm. RM
Chapter 24 (pp393–430) relates to Australia, & Chapter 25 has much Australian content. One map & 18 illustrations are of Australia.

JENNINGS, J. N.
CAVES. *See* Life in Australia

JENNINGS, R. G.
3758 TOLD IN/THE DORMITORY/By/R. G. Jennings/ Melbourne/Thomas C. Lothian/1911/Printed in England
237pp (inc. 1p preface), 16pp adv., part. col. frontis. only, clo., 190x125mm. KMM

3759 THE/HUMAN PEDAGOGUE/By/R. G. Jennings/ Australian Authors' Agency/239 Collins Street, Melbourne
1924
345pp, unillus., clo., 185x120mm. KMM

3760 STORIES OF A/HOUSE MASTER/By/R. G. Jennings/Author of "Told in the Dormitory", "The Human Pedagogue",/"Threads of Yesterday"/Melbourne/Robertson & Mullens Limited.
1933
233pp (inc. 1p preface), unillus., clo., 180x120mm. CLRC
The book consists of a selection of stories from *The Human Pedagogue* & *Told in the Dormitory* & several new stories, all of which boys would enjoy although the collection is not specifically a boys' book.

JEROME, Armand (ed.)
3761 "AUSTRALIAN/BOYS AND GIRLS"/No. 1/An/ Illustrated Annual/of/Stories/By/Australian Writers./ Edited by Armand Jerome./1895/Publishers: Gordon & Gotch/Sydney/Melbourne/Brisbane/Perth/ Capetown/London/W. M. Maclardy & Co., Printers, Sydney
62pp, 4pp+2pp adv., b/w illus. in text, pic. bd. (with adv. inside front cover, inside/outside back cover), 275x215mm. VSL
Illustrations by Walter H. Bone, Bert A. Levy, A. Collingridge
Includes stories by Alex. Montgomery, Louis Becke, Ernest Favenc, Louise Mack, Ethel Turner, & biographical notes on these authors with some photographs.

JESSOP, Gilbert L.
3762 CRESLEY/OF CRESSINGHAM/By/Gilbert L. Jessop/With four full-page Colour Illustrations/by Frank Gillett, R.T./Cassell and Company, Ltd./ London, New York, Toronto and Melbourne
1924
311pp, col. frontis. & 3 col. plates, pic. clo., 200x130mm. KP
Australian cricket novel.

JESSOP, Jessica
3763 CHEERY CHANTINGS/A Book of Rhymes/By Jessica Jessop/A Whisper/[8 line poem]/[monogram 'IFT']/Melbourne/I. Frances Taylor
Printed by the Ramsay Publishing Co. Pty Ltd, 197–207 King Street, Melbourne, 1929
62pp, 56 b/w drawings in text, dec. bd., 240x145mm. KMM

JESSUP, Frank
3764 THE WITCH'S/RING/By/Frank Jessup/Published by/Frank Johnson/350 George Street/Sydney/ Copyright
n.d. [1944]
16pp, col. illus. throughout, wrappers, cover title, 240x180mm. ANL

3765 PICKETTY BO/By Frank/Jessup/Copyright/ Published by/Frank Johnson/350 George St., Sydney/ Simmonds Ltd. Printer 31–33 Parramatta Road, Glebe, Sydney
n.d. [1946]
16pp, col. illus. throughout, wrappers, cover title, 235x170mm. ANL
Brief text in verse.

JEZARD, Alison
3766 ALBERT AND DIGGER/by/Alison Jezard/ Illustrated by/Margaret Gordon/[drawing]/London/ Victor Gollancz Ltd/1972
60pp, b/w illus., clo. bd., 225x150mm. VMOU
Story about the visit to London of an Australian koala who stays with a London teddy bear.

'JOAN'
3767 JOAN'S BOOK OF EVENING/GAMES/A Book of/ Entertaining Games, etc/For Social Evenings and/ Parties/Compiled by/Joan/Registered under The Commonwealth Copyright Act, 1912/Melbourne/ Printers Proprietary Limited/27 Little Bourke Street
111pp, unillus., dec. wrappers, 180x120mm. KP
Not specifically children's but on front cover 'For Young and Old'.
Another copy as above but stapled and printed on cheap yellow paper. KP

JOBBINS, Sheridan
3768 [3 lines]/COOKING WITH SHERI/By Sheridan Jobbins/[¼ page of text]/Printed and Published in Australia/By Sungravure Pty Ltd Sydney/First published, November 1970/Copyright Sheri Jobbins & Melizza Maguire 1970/Registered &c.
64pp, col. photographic illus., stiff pic. wrappers, 284x218mm. ANL
Children's recipes.

JOBSON, Sandra
3769 ONCE UPON A VASE/Text and Illustrations/by Sandra Jobson/[illustration]/Macmillan
Melbourne 1970
45pp, part. col. illus., pic. bd., 210x265mm. CLRC
Stories of ancient Greece retold from the illustrations

on the 'Francois' vase in the Archaeological Museum at Florence.

Joey Koala's Australian ABC

3770 JOEY KOALA'S/AUSTRALIAN/ABC
Supertone Sydney, n.d. [194-?]
8pp, illus. throughout, alternately in col. & b/w, pic. wrappers, cover title, dec. e/p, 350x240mm. NSL:M
Contains 4 lines verse & drawing of an animal for each letter.

JOHN, Beryl

3771 SEASHORES/by/Beryl John, B.A., Dip. Ed./Visual Aids Officer,/Department of Education,/New South Wales/Illustrated by/David Rae/[device]/8/Longmans, 1965
Melbourne
16pp, part. col. illus. throughout, stiff pic. wrappers, 210x155mm. Australian Nature Series No. 8. BBC

JOHN, Ethel

See Barnes, Ethel [Mrs Aubrey W. Barnes]

JOHN, Jaromir

3772 AUSTRALSKA DOBRODRUZSTVI ALOISE TOPICE (Australian Adventures of Aloise)
Melantrich, Prague 1939
175pp
Vol. 2: Melantrich, Prague 1946
139pp
Vol. 3: S.N.D.K., Prague 1954
135pp
Vol. 4: Ceskoslovensky spisovatel, Prague 1969
132pp
Slovak edition
S.N.D.K., Bratislava 1955
144pp
Unseen: SLCSR

'JOHN MYSTERY'

See 'MYSTERY, John'

JOHNS, William Earl

3773 WORRALS/DOWN UNDER/by/W. E. Johns/[publisher's device]/Lutterworth Press/London and Redhill
1948
216pp, col. frontis., clo., 185x120mm. RM

3774 WORRALS/DOWN UNDER/by/Captain W. E. Johns/[publisher's device]/Lutterworth Press/London
New illustrated edition 1950
216pp, col. frontis. & 4 f/p part. col. plates, clo., 185x120mm. KMM

3775 BIGGLES BREAKS/THE SILENCE/An Adventure of Sergeant/Biggleswort, of the special/air police, and his comrades/of the service/By/Capt. W. E. Johns/[b/w drawing]/Illustrated by/Stead/London—Hodder & Stoughton Limited.
1949
191pp, 4 part col. plates, printed in black, blue & white on each side, b/w drawings in text, clo., 185x122mm. GK
- Rpt March 1950, as above. GK
- Rpt third imp. 1951, as above. GK
- Rpt fourth imp. 1955, as above. GK
- Rpt fifth imp. 1959, as above. KP

3776 BIGGLES IN/THE ANTARCTIC/Captain W. E. Johns
Mayfair Books, Armada Books London, 1970
158pp, unillus., pic. wrappers, 180x110mm. KP
Originally publ. 1949 as *Biggles Breaks the Silence*

3777 BIGGLES/WORKS IT OUT/A Story of Air Detective-Inspector Bigglesworth/and his comrades of the air police/By/Captain W. E. Johns/[drawing]/Illustrated by/Stead/Hodder & Stoughton
1951
192pp, part-col. frontis. & 7 f/p part-col. illus., clo., 180x120mm. GK
Action takes place partly in N. Australia.

3778 BIGGLES/WORKS IT OUT/Captain W. E. Johns/[device]/Armada
n.d.
First publ. 1951 by Hodder & Stoughton; first publ. 1971 by W. M. Collins & Co. Ltd.
158pp, 2pp adv., unillus., pic. wrappers, 180x110mm. GK

3779 BIGGLES/IN AUSTRALIA/By/Captain W. E. Johns/[drawing]/With illustrations by/Studio Stead/Hodder and Stoughton
London 1955
188pp, 1p adv., col. frontis. & 5 f/p col. illus., clo., 180x115mm. ANL
- Rpt as above, 1956. GK
- Rpt as above, 1957. KMM

3780 BIGGLES/IN AUSTRALIA/By/Captain W. E. Johns/[drawing of a kangaroo]/Hodder and Stoughton
First publ. May 1955; fourth imp. 1962
188pp, unillus., clo., 184x117mm. GK

3781 Captain W. E. Johns/BIGGLES IN/AUSTRALIA/Cover design by/Peter Archer/[device] Armada
May Fair Books Ltd, London 1970
126pp, 2pp adv., unillus., pic. wrappers, 180x110mm. KMM
Advertised in same series: *Biggles in the South Seas*
Dutch edition

3782 W. E. Johns/BIGGLES/IN AUSTRALIE/[device]Prisma-Boeken/Utrecht/Antwerpen
1965
191pp & 1p adv., 8 f/p b/w illus. by Waldemar Post, pic. wrappers, 180x106mm. ANL

3783 THE/BIGGLES/AIR DETECTIVE/OMNIBUS/by/Captain W. E. Johns/Containing/Sergeant Bigglesworth, CID/Biggles' Second Case/Another Job for Biggles/Biggles works it out/London/Hodder & Stoughton
First publ. 1956; second imp. 1959
640pp (inc. 3pp foreword), 16 f/p b/w illus., clo., 184x120mm. GK

3784 THE/BIGGLES/AIR DETECTIVE/OMNIBUS
As before, but
[device]/Hodder and Stoughton
First publ. in this form 1956; third imp. 1963
184x120mm. GK

3785 BIGGLES FLIES AGAIN/by/Capt. W. E. Johns/Illustrated by/J. E. McConnell/The Thames Publishing Co./London/Designed and Printed in England/Copyright
n.d.[1st publ. August 1934]
141pp, col. frontis. & 4 col. plates, b/w illus., pic. bd., clo. spine, 220x160mm. GK
The Modern Library. Contains 3 stories. Set in Papua & other S.W. Pacific countries pp50-82.

3786 BIGGLES FLIES AGAIN/by/Capt. W. E. Johns/[device Regent/Classics]/The Thames Publishing Co./London
n.d. [prize label 1956]
214pp (inc. 1p adv.), unillus., sim. clo., 204x130mm. GK

3787 BIGGLES/FLIES AGAIN/Capt. W. E. Johns/[device/Kingston/Library]/The Thames Publishing Co./London
As before. GK

3788 BIGGLES FLIES AGAIN/By/Capt. W. E. Johns/By arrangement with/The Thames Publishing Co./ London/[device]/Dean & Son Ltd 41/43 Ludgate Hill London E.C.4
n.d. [copy seen inscribed 1962]
183pp, unillus., clo., 184x124mm. GK
See also South West Pacific section

JOHNSON, Francis
3789 THE BUSH RANGER;/Or,/The Half-Breed Brigade./A Romance of the Bush./By Francis Johnson./New York:/Beadle and Company, Publishers,/98 William Street.
1871
99pp, adv. verso front wrapper & both sides back, unillus., pic. wrappers, 194x135mm. RM
American Tales Series No. 74. Set 'on the Murray River, in the mallee scrub'.

3790 THE OUT-LAW HUNTER;/or,/Red John, The Bush-Ranger./A Romance of the Ranges./By Francis Johnson./New York./Beadle and Company, Publishers,/98 William Street.
1871
100pp, adv. verso front wrappers & both sides back wrapper, unillus., pic. wrappers, 194x135mm. RM
American Tales Series No. 75; adv. for James Fennimore Cooper book on back cover.

JOHNSON, J. C.
3791 THE/ROSE QUEEN,/A Floral Cantata for Schools/ By/J. C. Johnson./Prahran:/Osment and Sons, Printers, Chapel Street,/1898
24pp (last 3 blank), unillus., wrappers, 180x110mm. MAC

JOHNSON, Nola Margot
See 'Gray, Carol Anne'

JOHNSON, Phyllis & ELDER, Jean
3792 ROBBIE'S TRIP/TO/FAIRYLAND/by/Phyllis Johnson/and Jean Elder
Murfett Ltd, Melbourne, n.d. [1946]
36pp, 14 col. & b/w illus., pic. bd., 250x230mm. KP

3793 ROBBIE'S/BIRTHDAY WISH/by Phyllis Johnson/ & Jean Elder
Murfett Ltd, Melbourne, n.d. [1950]
[36]pp, 13pp col. illus., b/w drawings throughout, dec. bd. 250x235mm. ANL

JOHNSSON, Harald
3794 AUSTRALIENS HEMLIGHET. Skildring Från den femte världsdelens Kolonisation
Stockholm 1931
192pp, printed bd., publisher's binding
Illustrated by Werner Liljequist & others
A Swedish children's book on the early days of the Port Jackson settlement & the First Fleet.
Unseen: Catalogue No. 4, 1975, Dahlia Books, Uppsala
3795 Barnbibliotekent Saga/145/Läsebok I Hem Och Skola/AUSTRALIENS/HEMLIGHET/Skildring från den femte världsdelens/kolonisering/Av/Harald Johnsson/teckningar av/Werner Liljequist m. fl./Andra Upplagan/Red.: Signe H. Wraner/Stockholm/Svensk Lärane tidnings Förlag
1946
175pp, 11 f/p b/w illus. & 3 vignettes in text, dec. headpieces, col. pic. bd., clo. spine, 160x105mm. RM

JOHNSTON, Alfred St
See St Johnston, Alfred

JOHNSTON, Annie Fellows
3796 THE LITTLE COLONEL/STORIES/By/Annie Fellows Johnston/Australia/Angus & Robertson Limited/89 Castlereagh Street, Sydney/1935
280pp, unillus., clo., 185x120mm. ANL
Contents not Australian.

JOHNSTON, Harold Crawford
3797 THE VOICE OF THE BUSH/By/Harold Crawford Johnston/[dedication] (All rights reserved)/Copyright by Enid Stewart Delalande, Brisbane/[drawing]/Printed by Martin W. Kennedy, at the Office of The Worker Newspaper Pty. Ltd., Dunstan/House, Elizabeth Street, Brisbane/Registered at the GPO Brisbane, for transmission by Post as a Book/1944
63pp, 2 col. illus. by Harry Campbell, b/w photographic illus., wrappers, 265x210mm. KMM

3798 THE VOICE OF THE BUSH/By/Harold Crawford Johnston/[dedication]/(All rights reserved)/Copyright by Enid Stewart Delalande, Brisbane/[drawing]/ Printed by The Worker Newspaper Pty. Ltd. Dunstan House, Elizabeth Street, Brisbane/Registered at the GPO Brisbane, for transmission by Post as a Book/ 1945
Third imp., as above. QSL

JOHNSTON, Sir Harry
3799 PIONEERS IN/AUSTRALASIA/By Sir Harry Johnston/G.C.M.G., K.C.B./With Eight coloured illustrations/by Alec Ball/Pioneers of Empire/ [decoration]/Blackie and Son Limited/London Glasgow Bombay/1913
308pp, 5pp authors' preface (inc. 2pp bibliography), part. col. t.p., col. frontis. & 7 col. illus., 8 f/p b/w illus. & 3 maps, clo., 195x145mm. Pioneers of Empire Series HBM
An account of the discovery of Australia by sea.
3800 Great Travellers and Explorers/PIONEERS/IN AUSTRALASIA/by/Sir Harry Johnston/G.C.M.G., K.C.B./with eight plates in colours/by Alec Ball/ [drawing]/The Gresham Publishing Company/34 Southampton Street, Strand, London
n.d.
308pp, 4pp author's preface, col. frontis. & 7 col. plates, 8 b/w plates & 3 maps, clo., quarter leather, 200x130mm. KMM
3801 PIONEERS IN/AUSTRALASIA/By Sir Harry Johnston/G.C.M.G., K.C.B/with eight coloured illustrations/by Alec Ball/[decoration]/Blackie & Son Limited/London and Glasgow
308pp (inc. author's preface & bibliography), col. frontis. & 7 col. plates, 8 b/w plates & 3 maps, clo., 184x120mm. KP
3802 PIONEERS IN/AUSTRALASIA/By Sir Harry Johnston/C.C.M.G., K.C.B./with four coloured illustrations/by Alec Ball/and eight half-tone Plates/ [decoration]/Blackie & Son Limited/London and Glasgow
n.d.
308pp, col. frontis. & 3 f/p col. illus., 8 f/p b/w illus., 3 maps, clo., 185x125mm. The Pioneer Library. Grant
3803 PIONEERS IN/AUSTRALASIA/By Sir Harry Johnston/G.C.M.G., K.C.B./with Coloured Frontispiece/byAlec Ball/and eight Half-tone Plates/ [device]/Blackie & Son Limited/London and Glasgow
n.d.
308pp (inc. 5pp preface & 2pp bibliography), col frontis. & 8 half-tone plates (no maps), clo., 185x125mm. KMM
The Pioneer Library.

JOHNSTON, Sir Harry (ed.)
3804 A BOOK OF/EMPIRE HEROES/Edited by/Sir

Harry Johnston/London and Glasgow/Collins' Clear-type Press
n.d. [192-?]
[220]pp (inc. 3pp author's preface), col. frontis. & 2 f/p col. illus., clo., 190x125mm. KMM
Contents include: 'John McDouall Stuart' (24pp).

JOHNSTON, Johanna
3805 PENGUIN'S WAY/By Johanna Johnston/Illustrated by Leonard Weisgard/[drawing]/Doubleday & Company, Inc., Garden City, New York/Library of Congress Catalog Card Number 62,7070. Copyright 1962 by Doubleday & Company, Inc./All rights reserved. Printed in the United States of America. First Edition.
42pp, col. frontis. & col. illus. throughout, col. dec. e/p, clo., 235x205mm. NSL:M
3806 PENGUIN'S WAY/By Johanna Johnston/Illustrated by Leonard Weisgard/[drawing] A World's Work Children's Book/copyright 1962 by Doubleday & Company, Inc./All rights reserved. First published in Great Britain 1963 by/The World's Work (1913) Ltd., The Press at Kingswood, Tadworth, Surrey/Printed in Holland by N. V. Grafische Industrie Haarlem
[41]pp, details as in the Doubleday edition. KMM

JOHNSTON, Nancy
3807 MICHAEL McFUDGE/By/Nancy Johnston/Illustrations by Dorothy Brown/Mingay Publishing Company/1944
Sydney
41pp, b/w drawings throughout, wrappers, 210x135mm. QSL

JOHNSTONE, Bertha A.
3808 CHRISTY-ANN/VISITS TRANA/By/Bertha A. Johnstone/Illustrated by/Gwyn Duncan/Printed by T. Willmett & Sons, Pty. Ltd., Flinders Street, Townsville [Queensland]
n.d. [1944]
51pp, b/w frontis., 8 f/p b/w illus. & b/w drawings in text, wrappers, 235x170mm. ANL

JOHNSTONE, David Lawson
3809 IN THE/LAND OF THE GOLDEN PLUME/A Tale of Adventure/By/David Lawson Johnstone/Author of "The Paradise of the North" "Richard Tregellas"/"The Mountain Kingdom" etc./With six illustrations/By/W. S. Stacey/W. & R. Chambers, Limited/London and Edinburgh/1894
312pp, 32pp adv., b/w frontis. & 5 f/p b/w illus., pic. clo., 180x120mm. KMM
Adventure story set in Papua & North Queensland.
U.S. edition, New York, Whittaker, n.d., Unseen

JOHNSTONE, John
JOHNNO THE DEEP-SEA DIVER. *See* Dawlish, Peter

JOHNSWOOD, Elizabeth
SOUTH AUSTRALIA. *See* Around Australia Program

JOLLY, Alexander Stewart
3810 ADRIFT AT SEA/A Boy's Book of Adventure/by/Alexander Stewart Jolly/Copyright/Sydney/George B. Philip & Son/451 Pitt Street
1932
69pp, unillus., dec. bd., 205x140mm. NSL:M

3811 THE SPIRIT OF THE BUSH/Part One/by/Alexander Stewart Jolly/Copyright/Sydney/William Homer/31 Cunningham Street
1932
53pp, unillus., bd., 205x150mm. NSL:M
Fairy story about bush animals, &c.

Jolly Animal Picture Book
3812 JOLLY/ANIMAL/PICTURE/BOOK
A Pyramid Production No. 106 Sydney [1947]
8pp, col. illus. on each page, pic. wrappers, cover title, 240x180mm. ANL

The Jolly Cafetaria
3813 THE/JOLLY/CAFETERIA/with 4 legs &/a Tail/[picture of a cow]
n.p., n.d.
[Advertising brochure for Nestles Australia]
22pp, part col. illus. & b/w photographs, pic. wrappers, 232x226mm. KP
History of dairying in Australia, description of modern milk-processing, recipes, &c. KP

The Jolly Farm Book
3814 THE/JOLLY FARM/BOOK/16 Beautiful/Colour Pictures/of animals on/the farm
Printed & publ. by Offset Printing Coy. Pty Ltd, Sydney
16pp, f/p col. illus. (inc. both sides of covers) with brief captions, pic. wrappers, cover title, 265x210mm. KP

JOLLY, Kathleen Gladys
3815 "LANNIE"/[drawing]/the Story of a/Collie Dog/By/Kathleen Gladys Jolly
Printed by Oxford Press, 39–41 Little Collins St., Melbourne, n.d. [1946]
163pp, b/w drawings in text, clo., 180x125mm. NSL:M
3816 Second edition as above, but Nat. Press Melbourne
172pp, otherwise same. KP

The Jolly Nursery Rhymes
3817 THE JOLLY/NURSERY/RHYMES
Offset Printing Coy, Sydney, n.d. [1949]
16pp, 3 f/p col. illus., line drawings throughout, col. pic. wrappers, cover title, 274x220mm. ANL
Cover drawing by Rufus Morris; internal col. pages by Franklin Bennett.

JONES, C. Sheridan & MILES, Alfred
3818 HEROIC DEEDS OF/GREAT MEN/By/C. Sheridan Jones/and/Alfred Miles/Illustrated by/Howard Davie/and/Harry Payne/[device]/Raphael Tuck & Sons. Ltd./Publishers to Their Majesties the King & Queen/London Paris New York/Designed & Printed in England/Copyright
n.d. [192-?]
254pp & 2pp adv., col. frontis. & 5 col. plates & one on front cover, b/w drawings in text, 184x120mm. KP
Contains: Allenby, the Liberator of Palestine, by C. Sheridan Jones 14pp; The Last Voyage of Captain Scott, by C. Sheridan Jones 27pp. Plate of Allenby entering Jerusalem on front cover. (The Allenby article has brief reference to Australian troops.)

JONES, Frederic Wood
3819 SEABIRDS SIMPLIFIED/by/Frederic Wood Jones/London/Edward Arnold & Co.
1934
47pp, b/w drawings throughout, dec. bd. (clo. spine), 135x210mm. ANL
Humorous verses, each illustrated with a b/w drawing by the author.

JONES, Helen
3820 COME WITH US TO/AUSTRALIA/by/Helen Jones/George G. Harrap & Co. Ltd./London Toronto Wellington Sydney
1960
62pp (inc. 3pp questions & projects), b/w frontis. & 9 b/w drawings in text, clo., 180x115mm. KMM

JONES, John Joseph

3821 "CONDAMINE BELLS"/Songs and Stories of the Australian Outback/Dedicated to Mary Durack—Her Book of Songs/Music and Stories by John Joseph Jones/Poems by Jack Sorenson, Joseph Jones and Patsy/Durack/Piano arrangements by Billy Edwards/Wholly set up, printed and published by/ Carroll's Pty. Ltd., 566 Hay Street, Perth W.A[10 lines]
1961
31pp, portrait of author, unillus., stiff dec. wrapper, 240x185mm. NSL:M
Words & music of 6 songs for children.

JONES, M.

3822 THE STORY/OF/CAPTAIN COOK'S/THREE VOYAGES/ROUND THE WORLD./Told by M. Jones,/Author of "Stories of the Olden Time", etc./ with numerous illustrations./Cassell, Petter and Galphin,/London and New York
n.d. [preface dated 1870]
264pp, 16pp adv., engraved frontis. & 39 f/p engravings, pic. clo., 175x130mm. NSL:M
Third edition, n.d., as above. NSL:M

JONES, Neil

3823 THE VOYAGES OF THE/LIMPING FLAMINGO/ Written and illustrated by/Neil Jones/Introducing the/ Poggy People/George G. Harrap & Co. Ltd./London Toronto Wellington Sydney
1962
96pp, part. col. frontis. & part. col. drawings in text throughout, clo., 185x120mm. NSL:M
Fantasy with partly Australian background.

JONES, T. M.

3824 SONS OF THE SEA/From Naval Cadet to Captain/By/T. M. Jones/Seaman Torpedoman H.M.A.S. Australia/Angus and Robertson Ltd./Sydney London/1941
207pp, 1p foreword, 2pp author's note, b/w frontis., clo., 180x120mm. CLRC

Joy Series

Uniform booklets publ. by Barker & Co. 476-90 Little Lonsdale Street Melbourne, 1941
Format Example:

3825 No. 1. DAVID'S SEASIDE HOLIDAY/Written and Illustrated by/C. E. Stamp/Published by/Barker & Company/476-90 Little Lonsdale Street, Melbourne/ and at 37-43 Bay Street, Glebe, Sydney/Copyright
15pp, b/w illus. throughout, pic. wrappers, 210x280mm. NSL:M
Another copy as above, but

3826 Joy Series No 1/DAVID'S SEASIDE HOLIDAY./ Produced by/[Coat of Arms]/The House of Barker/ Melbourne and Sydney/Australia
12pp (last page adv.), part col. illus. throughout, col. pic. stiff wrappers, 280x215mm. KMM
Another copy:

3827 Joy Series No. 1/DAVID'S SEASIDE HOLIDAY/ [drawing]/Produced by/[Coat of Arms—The House of Barker]/Melbourne and Sydney/Australia/Copyright
n.d. [copy inscribed Xmas 1944]
The part col. illustrations have been redrawn. There is a new cover design by C. E. Stamp in full col. & the whole book is produced in a landscape format; 12pp, part col. illus. throughout, last page list of other titles in series; cover illus. signed 'C. E. Stamp'. 215x275mm. KMM

Joy Series No. 2

3828 JONATHAN/AND HIS BILLY-GOAT CART/and the strange adventures that can happen/to owners of billy-goat carts/when they look for them/Written and illustrated by/C. E. Stamp/Published by/Barker & Company/476-90 Little Lonsdale Street, Melbourne/ and at 37-43 Bay Street, Glebe, Sydney/Copyright
[1941]
[11]pp & 1p adv., b/w illus., pic. wrappers, 210x280mm. NSL:M
Another copy:

3829 Joy Series No. 2/JONATHAN/AND/HIS BILLY-GOAT CART/and the strange adventures that can happen/to owners of billy-goat carts—/when they look for them/[device]/Produced by/[Coat of Arms]/ The House of Barker/Melbourne and Sydney/Australia Copyright
n.d.
[11]pp & 1p adv., part col. illus. throughout, stiff pic. wrappers, 280x215mm. KMM
Another copy:
n.d.

3830 The same, but with new, brightly col. cover design signed 'C. E. Stamp'. KMM
Another copy:
n.d.
The same, with the new cover but different illus., some in b/w others partly col. These look like an earlier version of drawings in 2 and 3.
Joy Series uniform with above, all KMM

3831 No. 3 PHILIP THE FROG
3832 No. 4 PEPPO THE PONY
3833 No. 5 BETTY ANN'S BIRTHDAY
3834 No. 6 RUPERT THE RABBIT
3835 No. 7 A SURPRISE FOR SHIRLEY—two copies with some variant part-col. illus.
3836 No. 8 THE MISDOINGS OF MICKEY AND MACK
3837 No. 9 KENNY THE KOALA
3838 No. 10 JUDY'S JOYOUS DAY
3839 No. 11 FUN ON A FARM
3840 No. 12 TROUBLE IN TOYLAND

JOY, Charles Rhind [compiler]

3841 YOUNG PEOPLE/OF/EAST ASIA AND/ AUSTRALIA/Their Stories in their own Words/by/ Charles R. Joy/Duell, Sloan and Pearce/New York
1961
183pp (inc. 6pp introduction), b/w maps only, clo., dec. e/p, 205x130mm. ANL
Includes 14pp text & double-spread map of Australia.

JOYCE, Frances

3842 RAINBOW'S END/A Fairy Story by/Frances Joyce/A "Jaycol" Book/No. 97
n.p., n.d.
8pp (inc. covers), col. illus. initialled 'M' throughout, printed on stiffened paper, cover title, 308x242mm. KMM
Author's name spelt 'Francis Joyce' inside.

JUDD, Alfred

3843 THE CONQUEST OF/THE POLES/and Modern Adventures/in the World of Ice/by/Alfred Judd/ Author of "In Quest of Peril", etc./London: T. C. & E. C. Jack, Ltd./35 & 36 Paternoster Row, E.C./and Edinburgh
n.d. [1924]
364pp, b/w photographic frontis. & 16 b/w photographic plates, clo., 200x130mm. Grant

3844 THE CONQUEST OF/THE POLES/and modern adventures/in the world of ice/By/Alfred Judd/author of"In Quest of Peril", etc/Thomas Nelson and Sons, Ltd./(Incorporating T. C. & E. C. Jack, Ltd.)/London, Edinburgh, New York/Toronto, and Paris
n.d. [school prize 1937]

364pp, b/w photographic frontis., 16 b/w plates, 2 maps, pic. clo., 195x136mm. KP

3845 THE/SECRET OF THE SNOWS/By/Alfred Judd/ Author of "The Mystery of the Towers"/"The Young Treasure Hunters", etc./[device]/Cassell & Company, Ltd./London, New York, Toronto and Melbourne
1925
186pp, b/w frontis. only by Arch. Webb, pic. clo., 190x120mm. KMM
Story set in Antarctica.

3846 THE SECRET/OF THE SNOWS/By/Afred Judd/ Author of "The Mystery of the Towers"/"The Young Treasure Hunters," etc/[device]/Cassell and Company, Ltd./London, Toronto, Melbourne and Sydney
New ed. 1931
186pp, b/w frontis. by Arch Webb, clo., 185x120mm. KP

Judy and John's Number Book

3847 JUDY/AND/JOHN'S/NUMBER BOOK
Novelty Publishing Co, Brisbane, n.d. [1945]
8pp, drawings & figures printed throughout on light board, cover title, 230x150mm. ANL

Judy's Joyous Day

See Barker & Co. Publications

Jungle Life

3848 JUNGLE LIFE/Crayon Colouring Book/64 full pages/of Animal/pictures/to colour/[col. picture]/A Winna Production
n.p., n.d.
64pp, b/w outlines with captions, col. pic. wrappers, 248x180mm. KP
Includes some Australian animals.

The Junior LIbrary—Vol. One *See* Gunn & Taylor

JUPP, Eric

3849 Original music composed for the Australian/T.V. Series/SKIPPY/THE BUSH Kangaroo/By/Eric Jupp/ Selection/My Pal Skippy/As recorded by Eric Jupp and his music on Parlophone
Sydney, n.d.
40c, col. pic. wrappers, 280x216mm. KP

Just Me

3850 [col. drawing]JUST/ME/A Record of/My Early Days and/Doings/[5 lines]
[20]pp, col. illus. & spaces left for a baby's record, pic. bd., 190x117mm. KP

The Juvenile Scrap-Book

3851 THE/JUVENILE SCRAP-BOOK/By the Author of/ "The Women of England",/MDCCCXLIV/London:/ Fisher, Son & Co., Newgate Street;/Rue St. Honoré, 108 Paris
100pp, 1p preface, engraved frontis., 14 f/p engravings, dec. clo., 195x135mm. KP
Preliminary t.p. with title: 'Fisher's/Juvenile Scrapbook/[vignette—caption]'
The first story is entitled 'Captain Cook' (pp1–19); frontispiece is engraving of Dance's portrait of Cook, with facsimile of Cook's signature.

K., E. W.

RINGTAIL RHYMES. *See* Barry Books

K., M. J. [Kernot, Mary Jane]

3852 STORIES & FABLES/By M. J. K. [half-title with b/w illus. tipped in]
STORIES AND/FABLES/By M. J. K. [title]
n.p. [Kernot family, Melbourne], n.d. [1933]
[32]pp (last blank) inc. 2pp foreword, 1 illus., brown suede leather wrappers, 180x135mm. ANL
From the foreword it appears that this booklet was privately printed for the author 'Auntie Jeanie's' family after her death in 1932. She was an early pioneer having arrived in Australia in 1850 at the age of 3.

KALAB, Theresa

3853 KOKWA/A Little Koala Bear/Story and Pictures/ By/Theresa Kalab/[drawing]/Hutchinson's Books for Young People/10 Great Queen Street/London W.C.2
n.d. [1945]; [First published in the US 1939]
28pp, part. col. illus. throughout, bd., dec. e/p, 230x190mm. ANL

KAMM, Josephine

3854 HE WENT WITH/CAPTAIN COOK/by/Josephine Kamm/Author of/"African Challenge: The Story of the British/in Tropical Africa"/Etc./George G. Harrap & Co. Ltd./London Toronto Wellington Sydney
1952
176pp (inc. 1p author's note), col. frontis., b/w drawings & map, illus. by G. S. Ronald, clo., 190x120mm. KMM

3855 HE WENT WITH/CAPTAIN COOK/by/Josephine Kamm/Author of/"Men who served Africa" etc./ George G. Harrap & Co. Ltd./London Toronto Wellington Sydney
First pub. 1952; rpt 1952, 1954, 1957, 1960
176pp (inc. 1p author's note), col. frontis., 12 b/w illus. in text & double-spread b/w map, clo., 195x125mm. BBC
• Rpt 1955, 1957. KP

The Kangaroo

3856 Animals of the World/THE KANGAROO/[illus.]/ Illustrations by Nemo/RA Publishers Ltd/17 Bedford Row, London WC1, England
1972. Rentaprint for the English text. Printed in Italy by Rentaprint, Milano
12pp, col. illus. throughout, stiff pic. wrappers, 298x225mm. KP

The Kangaroo and his Friends

3857 Toppan's Foto Books/THE KANGAROO/AND HIS FRIENDS
Froebel-Kan Co. Ltd, Tokyo, Japan, 1967
[12]pp, col. photographic illus., pic. bd., 264x184mm. WRT
Bd. book with slight text, cover title (12 titles listed in series).

The Kangaroo with a Hole in her Pocket

3858 THE KANGAROO/WITH A HOLE/IN HER POCKET
World Distributors (Manchester) Limited, 1968
(Copyright 1968 by Éditions des Deux Coqs d'Or, Paris. Printed in Italy
[31]pp (inc. back pastedown), col. illus. on every page, pic. bd., cover title, dec. e/p, 316x234mm. KMM

Kangi

3859 KANGI/The Adventures/of a small/Kangaroo
PM Productions Ltd, London & Letchworth, n.d. [194-?]. Printed in Australia by Sungravure for Australian Distributors, Ayers & James Pty Ltd., Sydney
16pp, alternate col. & blue & white page openings, pic. wrappers, cover title, 210x240mm. KMM

KAULA, Edna Mason

3860 THE/FIRST BOOK./OF/AUSTRALIA/by Edna Mason Kaula/Franklin Watts, Inc./575 Lexington Ave./New York 22, N.Y.
1960
59pp (inc. glossary & index), dec. t.p., 2 maps & b/w

drawings throughout, illus. by author, clo., dec. e/p, 210x175mm. KMM

3861 THE/FIRST BOOK/OF/AUSTRALIA/by Edna Mason Kaula/Edmund Ward (Publishers) Ltd./194–200 Bishopsgate,/London E.C.2
First published in Great Britain 1963
60pp, 1p drawing, double-spread b/w photographic illus. preceding t.p. [in this edition only], dec. t.p., maps (preceding text), 6 b/w photographic illus. [not in US edition], b/w drawings throughout, clo., 210x175mm. BBC
There are some variations in text. The US edition includes a section on 'Swagmen', mentioned only briefly in the English edition, & the English edition has a section entitled 'Australians at Work' which does not appear in the US edition. The title is printed on front cover & spine in the US edition & on spine only in the English edition.

KAUTER, Frank

3862 OVER THE HILLS/AND FAR AWAY/Verse by/Frank Kauter/Illustrated by/Bill Davies/John Sands/Pty. Ltd.
Sydney, n.d. [1946]
16pp, col. illus. throughout, dec. bd., cover title, 280x220mm. KMM
Young children's verses.

3863 THE/SANDMAN SAYS/Verses by/Frank Kauter/Illustrated by/Bill Davies/John Sands Pty Ltd./Sydney Melbourne and Brisbane
n.d. [1949]
16pp, col. dec. t.p., col. illus. throughout, dec. bd., 280x215mm. ANL

KAY, Nella

3864 WALKABOUT/IN THE/DREAMTIME/By/Nella Kay/[drawing]/Illustrated by Dorothy Huffell Aidmasta/Productions
n.d. [acquired 1968]
[32]pp, 15 f/p col. illus., pic. bd., 228x180mm. NSL:M

3865 LIFE AMONG THE/ABORIGINES/[drawing]/By Nella Kay/[device]/Aidmasta/Productions
n.d.
24pp & 1p glossary, b/w & part col. illus. throughout, pic. bd., 214x164mm. KP

KAY, Timothy

3866 THE ADVENTURES OF/JOKER JACK/Story by/Timothy Kay/Drawings by/Rufus Morris
Dawfox Productions, Sydney, n.d. [1944]
32pp, dec. t.p., col. & b/w illus. throughout, dec. bd., 210x235mm. ANL

3867 BOBBY/RUBBERNOSE/A story about a little/Koala Bear/who lost himself and/was found again/Story by/Timothy Kay/Drawings by/Rufus Morris
Dawfox Productions, Sydney 1944
[32]pp, 14 col. & some b/w illus., pic. bd., 210x235mm. KMM
Copy seen inscribed by author Christmas 1943.

3868 FLOP/The Platypus/Story by Timothy Kay/Drawings by/Rufus Morris/A/Colour/Production
Colour Productions, Sydney, n.d. [1946]
[32]pp, 12 col. illus. & b/w drawings throughout, dec. bd., 215x230mm. KMM

3869 Another copy as above, but on t.p. 'A Jons/Production'. KP

3870 Another copy the same, but 'Lithographed in Australia by Colourtone Pty Ltd for Jons Productions' KP

3871 KOO-LOO/THE 'ROO/Story by Timothy Kay/Drawings by/Rufus Morris/A/Colour/Production
Colour Production, Sydney, n.d. [1947]
32pp, col. & b/w illus. throughout, dec. bd., 215x230mm. ANL

KAYE, E. W.

3872 THE/KOALA TWINS/An/"Uncle Ted's"/Tale/Written & Illustrated/by/E. W. Kaye/Printed by/F. Cunninghame & Co. Pty. Ltd./Sydney
n.d. [194-?]
[16]pp, part. col. illus. throughout, dec. wrappers, 240x180mm. KMM
Verse.

3873 BOOBOOK/[device—An Uncle Ted's Tale]/Produced and Published by/E. W. Kaye/Sydney/Printed by/Hollander & Govett Pty Limited/Sydney
n.d. [194-?]
16pp, part col. illus. throughout, pic. wrappers, 234x182mm. KP
Verse.

KAYE, E. W. [ed.]

See POSSUM BOTHER

[KEALLEY, Frank S.]

3874 BLUE SKIES/Safety Stories/Suitable for Children aged 7–8/National Safety Council S.A. Inc./A Constituent Member of the Australian Road Safety Council
Adelaide, n.d. [1960?]
32pp, b/w illus. in text, by C. J. Burfield, wrappers, cover title, 220x140mm. ANL

3875 Suitable for children aged 9–10/"PLAYTIME"/SAFETY STORIES/National Safety Council S.A. Inc./A Constituent Member of the Australian Road Safety Council
Adelaide, n.d. [1960?]
32pp, b/w drawings in text, by C. J. Burfield, wrappers, cover title, 220x140mm. ANL

3876 Suitable for Children aged 11–12/"ROADS TO ADVENTURE"/Safety Stories/National Safety Council S.A. Inc./A Constituent Member of the Australian Road Safety Council
Adelaide, n.d. [1960?]
32pp, b/w drawings in text, by C. J. Burfield, wrappers, cover title, 220x140mm. ANL

KEARNEY, G. M. V.

3877 A/FAIRY/TALE/OF THE/TRUTH/For the Children/of the/Wonderland Heroes/Written for Australia/Day 1915 by/G. M. V. Kearney
Orange, NSW, 1915
8pp, unillus., wrappers, 160x100mm. NSL:M
Author's inscription reads: 'Written to sell in the streets of Orange N.S.W. on Australia Day 1915. Brought in £25.10.0 for the Australia Day Fund'.

KEAST, Dr Allen

3878 WINDOW/TO BUSHLAND/by/Dr. Allen Keast/Curator of Birds, Reptiles and Amphibians/at the Australian Museum, Sydney/[device]/The Educational Press/Sydney
1959
192pp (inc. 1p editorial note, 2pp introduction, 2pp glossary, & 1p bibliography), b/w photographic frontis., b/w photographic illus. throughout, maps & diagrams, clo., 215x135mm. CLRC
Most of the book is based on articles which appeared in the *Australian Children's Newspaper.*

KEENE, Frances W.

3879 CALTEX/TRAVEL/FUN BOOK/This is the original Travel Fun Book [etc. 4 lines]/by Frances W. Keene/[device]/McGraw-Hill Book Company Australia Pty. Limited,/Sydney/New York London Toronto
1965
96pp, b/w illus. throughout, col. pic. wrappers, 230x175mm. Grant

KEESING, Nancy

3880 Great Stories of Australia/BY GRAVEL AND/GUM/The Story of a Pioneer Family/[drawing]/By Nancy Keesing/Illustrated by Roderick Shaw/Melbourne/Macmillan & Co. Ltd./1963
168pp, 1p acknowledgements, 28 part. col. illus., clo., dec. e/p, 215x135mm. KMM

3881 Great Stories of Australia/BY GRAVEL AND/GUM
New ed. 1966 as above, but
Macmillan/Melbourne London Toronto/St Martin's Press/New York/1966
KP

KEITH, Donald

See 'Garrick, Donald'

KEITH, Elizabeth

3882 FAIRY BLUEBELL AND/ROSAMOND/by Elizabeth Keith/Illustrations by Hilda McGavin/Australian/Women's Weekly/Children's Classics/The Shakespeare Head/London New York Sydney Paris Cape Town
64pp, col. frontis. & 6 f/p col. illus., pic. wrappers, 215x140mm. TG
Content not Australian.

KEITH, James

3883 THE/SCUBA BUCCANEERS/James Keith/Illustrated by Nancy Parker/[device]/Angus and Robertson
Sydney 1966
164pp, map frontis., b/w drawings in text, clo., 215x135mm. KMM

KELLAWAY, Frank

3884 THE QUEST/FOR GOLDEN DAN/F. W. Cheshire/Melbourne—Canberra—Sydney
1962
210pp, 1p preface, 20 b/w illus. by Deborah White, clo., dec. e/p, 215x135mm. KMM

3885 Frank Kellaway/THE QUEST/FOR GOLDEN DAN/Children's Library Guild/of Australia/Melbourne Sydney Brisbane
1962, details as above. KP
A WHALER *See* Early Australians

KELLIE, Ursula E.

3886 THE/WILDFLOWER FAIRIES/and other Stories/by/Ursula E. Kellie/Arthur H. Stockwell Ltd/Ilfracombe, Devon
n.d. [194-?] Printed by M T Stevens Ltd, Church St, Malvern
56pp, 6 f/p b/w drawings, pic. wrappers, 185x125mm. KP

KELLOGG, Eva M. C.

3887 The/World and its people/Book VIII/AUSTRALIA/AND THE/ISLANDS OF THE SEA/by/Eva M. C. Kellogg/Edited by Larkin Dunton, LL.D./Headmaster of the Boston Normal School/[device]/Silver, Burdett & Company./New York...Boston...Chicago/1898
448pp & 2pp. advs, b/w photographic frontis & f/p & other b/w illus., clo. NSL:M
First 60 pp only of this supplementary school reader are devoted to Australia.

Kellogg's Jumbly Jungle Book

3888 KELLOGG'S/JUMBLY JUNGLE/BOOK/over 335 animal combinations
Copyright 1948 by Kellogg Company; lithographed in Australia by Posters Pty Ltd
Board folded into 4 with page attached & cut into 6 strips to make various combinations, col. illus. throughout, 280x210mm. Grant

KELLY, Gipsy

See Hamilton, Arthur & Kelly, Gipsy

KEMPSTER, Madeline (ed.)

3889 VERSE BY/YOUNG/AUSTRALIANS/edited by/Madeline Kempster/Margaret Backhouse/Ella Turnbull/[device]/Rigby Limited
Adelaide 1968
168pp (inc. 5pp acknowledgements), 3pp foreword etc., unillus., clo., 215x135mm. KMM
Note states that the Australian Council for Child Advancement, assisted by Ella Turnbull (then of the World Poetry Day Committee), began to collect these verses in 1965, in memory of Dame Mary Gilmore. Verses collected by teachers of various Australian schools.
• Rpt 1968 (twice). KP

3890 MORE VERSE/BY YOUNG/AUSTRALIANS/Edited by:/Madeline Kempster/Margaret Backhouse/Ella Turnbull/Editorial Assistants:/Jane Diplock/Michael Dransfield/Robert Gay/Rosemary Geikie/Ann Scully/Rigby
Adelaide 1970
151pp, 12pp introduction, etc., unillus., clo., 210x130mm. KMM

KENNEDY, Brian

3891 Cities of the World:/SYDNEY/Brian Kennedy/With 32 photographs and 2 maps/[device]/A. S. Barnes and Company/South Brunswick and New York
1970
80pp (inc. 6pp index), 16pp b/w photographic illus., clo., 195x137mm. KMM

KENNEDY, Donald

CAPTAIN CHARLES STURT. *See* Australian Explorers

KENNEDY, E. B.

3892 BLACKS AND BUSHRANGERS/Adventures in Queensland/by/E. B. Kennedy/Author of "Four Years in Queensland", etc./with illustrations by Stanley Berkeley/London/Sampson Low, Marston, Searle & Rivington/Limited/St. Dunstan's House/Fetter Lane, Fleet Street, E.C./1889/(All rights reserved)
312pp, 3pp preface, 32pp adv., b/w frontis. & 7 f/p b/w illus., pic. clo., 185x120mm. ANL

3893 BLACKS AND BUSHRANGERS/Adventures in Queensland/By/E. B. Kennedy/Author of "Four Years in Queensland" etc./With illustrations by Stanley Berkeley/New and cheaper edition/London/Sampson Low, Marston & Company/Limited/St. Dunstan's House/Fetter Lane/Fleet Street, E.C.
312pp, 3pp preface, 32pp adv., b/w frontis. & 7 f/p b/w illus., clo., 180x115mm. KP
• Rpt 1894, 1895, pic. clo. KP

KENNEDY, John

THE BLUE MOUNTAINS CROSSING. *See* Australia Past and Present

KENNEDY, John J.

3894 THE/INSEPARABLES/By/Rev. John J. Kennedy,/Author of/"Carrigmore."/The Chronicle Printing and Publishing Offices,/Murphy Street, Wangaratta, Victoria./1910

230pp, unillus., clo., 185x120mm. CLRC
First chapter set in Xavier College, Kew, Victoria
Presumably intended for young readers (see last paragraph).

KENNY, Florence
3895 A reliable Booklet for Girls/(From eight to twelve)/[2 lines text]/THE/GUIDE/THROUGH/GIRLHOOD/By/Florence/Kenny/Illustrated/"Youth and Honor" Series No. 3/Edited by/Professor Harvey Sutton/OBE MD ChB DSc DPH/Director, School of Public Health and Tropical Medicine/9d
Copyright 1945
Father and Son Welfare Movement
32pp, b/w illus., wrappers, 185x120mm. KP

J. P. KENNY & Co.
3896 TINY PEOPLE'S PAINTING BOOK/Hints to Little Painters [22 lines text]/Published by/W. F. McConnell Co-operative Publicity/Grenfell Buildings, Grenfell St. Adelaide/Printed by/Vardon & Sons Ltd
[32pp] col. & b/w illus. on alternate pp. by John C. Goodchild, stiff pic. wrappers, 248x185mm. KMM
3897 J. P. KENNY & Co./TINY PEOPLE'S/PAINTING BOOK/With Compliments from/J. P. Kenny & Co./Jetty Road, Glenelg/Opposite Savings Bank [Adelaide], n.d. [193-?]. Printed by Vardon & Co.
[32]pp, col. & b/w drawings on alternate pp, pic. front cover, wrappers, cover title. TG

Kenny the Koala
See Barker & Co. Publications

KENT, Beverley
CORNSTALK BOB. *See* Boys' Friend Library

KENT, Louise
3898 THE WIZARD OF/THE UMBRELLA/PEOPLE/By Louise Kent/Illustrated by Sandra Smith/[drawing]/Ure Smith Sydney
1971
[30]pp, col. illus. throughout, pic. bd., 280x210mm. KMM
American edition
Platt & Munck, New York 1971. Unseen

KENYON, Charles M.
3899 FIRST/VOYAGE/OUT/Charles M. Kenyon/Four Winds Press New York
1970
173pp, b/w frontis. only, pic. clo., 190x135mm. KP
Tale of an American boy's first whaling voyage in the Pacific in 1841.

KENYON, E. C.
3900 THE CAVE BY/THE WATERFALL/And Other Stories/By/E. C. Kenyon/Author of/The Heroines of Brookleigh etc etc,/London/The Sunday School Union/57 and 59 Ludgate Hill, E.C.
n.d. [1898]
248pp, 8pp adv., b/w frontis. & 3 f/p b/w plates, illus. in text, clo. dec. e/p, 190x125mm. ANL
The second story, 'A Heroine of Home' (pp107–77) is set mainly in NSW & tells of a young man's voyage in an immigrant ship & his adventures in the bush including an account of a bushfire. Endeavour Library.

KER, Jill
ENTER THE SQUATTER. *See* Australian Landmarks

KERN, J. D. H.
3901 DE SCHRIK DER ZUIDZEE./Leven en daden van een vrijbuiter uit den/Tegen woordigen tijd/door/J. D. H. Kern/Zutphen/Schillemans & Van Belkum/Thieme's Bock en Muziekhandel
n.d.
448pp, frontis. (printed in blue) & 9 plates, pic. clo., 197x130mm. ANL
'Bully' Hayes. Not really children's.

KERR, Doris Boake & CRONIN, Bernard
See 'Grey, Stephen'

KERR, Hilda C. Temple
3902 THE LITTLE BIRTHDAY QUEEN./By/Hilda C. Temple Kerr/Verse/[photograph of 2 small boys]/verse
The author [Orbost, Victoria, 1907]. Printed by Norman Bros. Melbourne (100 copies printed)
12pp, 6 sepia/white photographs, dec. wrapper, 190x125mm. ANL
Illus. Mr H. Sherwood, Orbost (on front cover). Verses celebrating a young girl's birthday with family photographs.

Kerry the Kangaroo
3903 KERRY/THE KANGAROO/Little Castle Books
Murray Sales & Service Co., London, n.d. [196-?]
8pp, col. illus. throughout, pic. wrappers, 237x170mm. MC

KEVIN, John William
See 'Ferres, Arthur'

KIDDELL, John
3904 THE DAY OF THE/DINGO/John Kiddell/Illustrated by W. Neave Parker/[drawing]/Thomas Nelson and Sons Ltd./London Edinburgh Paris Melbourne/Toronto and New York
1955
201pp, col. frontis. & 3 f/p col. illus., b/w drawings in text, clo., 200x130mm. KMM

3905 GIANT OF THE BUSH/John Kiddell/Illustrated by/Richard Kennedy/Odhams Press Limited/Long Acre, London
1962
160pp, extended b/w frontis. & 23 b/w drawings, clo., 210x130mm. CLRC
• Rpt 1964, 1965. KP
3906 GIANT OF THE BUSH, Illustrated by Richard Kennedy, Indianapolis, Bobbs-Merrill [1963]
156 pp, illus., 220mm. Unseen: ANB 1963

3907 John Kiddell/EULOOWIRREE/WALKABOUT/Hodder and Stoughton Sydney/Brockhampton Press Leicester [England]
First published in Australia 1969; first published in Great Britain 1970
163pp, 2pp author's note, unillus., clo., d/w by Charles Geer, 200x135mm. KMM
American edition
Chilton Book Coy., Philadelphia 1968, Library edition
196
Unseen: IFA

3908 CHOOGOOWARRA/Australian Sheep Station/John Kiddell/Photographs by Joe Molnar/The Macmillan Company, New York, New York/Collier-Macmillan Limited, London
1972
69pp (inc. 3pp glossary), b/w photographic frontis., b/w illus. throughout, clo., 230x175mm. BBC

Kiddies Party Guide
3909 KIDDIES/PARTY/GUIDE
n.p., n.d. Publ. by Coca Cola. Printed in Australia by DWP print
46pp, b/w illus. throughout, pic. wrappers, 180x106mm. KP

KIDDLE, Margaret Loch
3910 MOONBEAM STAIRS/By/Margaret Kiddle/Illustrated by/Anne Montgomery/[decoration]/Australasian Publishing Co. Pty. Ltd./Sydney N.S.W. n.d. [1945]
70pp, col. frontis. & 3 f/p col. illus., b/w drawings in text, dec. bd., 240x180mm. KMM

3911 WEST OF SUNSET/By/Margaret Kiddle/Illustrated by/Anne Montgomery/Australasian Publishing Company/Sydney Wellington London
1949
222pp, b/w frontis. & 3 f/p b/w illus., clo., 185x135mm. KMM
Story based on life of Caroline Chisholm.
3912 Margaret Kiddle/WEST OF SUNSET/Illustrated by/Anne Montgomery/Melbourne University Press
1961
222pp, b/w frontis. & 3 f/p b/w illus., wrappers, 185x115mm. KMM

KIELLY, Theo
3913 GREGORY/THE VAGABOND
Children's Press, Sydney, n.d. [1949]
15pp, col. illus. throughout, pic. wrappers, cover title, 270x210mm. ANL

3914 GREGORY/GOES TO THE SEASIDE/Written and illustrated by/Theo Kielly
Children's Press, Sydney, n.d. [1950]
16pp, col. illus. throughout, pic. wrappers, cover title, 270x210mm. ANL

KILBOURNE, C. E.
3915 BABY KANGAROO/AND LILLY LAMB/by C. E. Kilbourne/Illustrated by Hattie Longstreet/The Penn Publishing Company/Philadelphia/1916
82pp, 11 f/p col. illus., 5 f/p & several smaller b/w illus., bd., col. pic. e/p, 150x110mm. Grant
There is a coloured illustration pasted on front cover which does not appear elsewhere in the book.

KILGOUR, Elma
3916 ROSY SUE/by/Elma Kilgour/[dedication]/Georgian House/Melbourne
n.d. [1950]
24pp (inc. introduction by Anne Dreyer), col. illus. on alternate pages, dec. wrappers, 165x180mm. NSL:M
Verses.

KINANE, Kay
3917 OUR/PRECIOUS SOIL/by/Kay Kinane/Youth Education Department/of the A.B.C./Illustrated by Marjory Penglase/A Background of Australia Book/Shakespeare Head Press/Sydney—1956
126pp (inc. 1p introduction by R. J. F. Boyer, Chairman, A.B.C.), b/w frontis. & b/w drawings in text, illus. by author, bd., 210x130mm. NSL:M
Background book for social studies.

KINCH, Louise
STORIES OF ADVENTURE. *See* Gunn & Taylor

KING, Alec & Catherine
3918 AUSTRALIAN HOLIDAY/Written by/Alec and Catherine King/Illustrated by/Marjorie Rankin/Georgian House/Melbourne
1945
105pp, col. frontis. & 9 f/p col. illus., b/w drawings, dec. bd., 200x275mm. KMM
A book about Australian marsupials told in the form of a story.

KING, Alice
3919 A CLUSTER OF LIVES/By/Alice King/Author of "The Woman with a Secret" "Queen of Herself"/etc. etc./Second Edition/Henry S. King & Co./65 Cornhill, and 12 Paternoster Row, London/1874
291pp, 2pp preface, 32pp adv., unillus., clo., 190x120mm. NSL:M
Biographical studies, including one, Capt. James King, who sailed with Cook.

KING, B.
3920 CAPTAIN/JAMES COOK/AND THE/VOYAGE OF THE/ENDEAVOUR/B. King/School Projects/Pty. Limited
Sydney 1967
41pp, b/w drawings & 2 maps, stiff dec. wrappers, 210x130mm. Australian Scene Series. BBC

KING, Clive
3921 THE TOWN/THAT WENT SOUTH/by Clive King/[drawing]/Illustrated by Maurice Bartlett/The Macmillan Company/New York, 1959
120pp, title on 2pp, b/w illus. throughout, clo., pic. e/p, 215x148mm. KMM
3922 THE/TOWN THAT/WENT SOUTH/by Clive King/[drawing]/Illustrated by Maurice Bartlett/Penguin Books
First publ. in USA 1959; publ. in Great Britain by Hamish Hamilton 1969; Puffin Books 1970
106pp, b/w drawings, pic. wrappers, 180x110mm. KP
The last chapter tells of the town drifting to Australia & then the South Pole (15pp).

KING, HAZEL
RICHARD BOURKE. *See* Great Australians

KING, LEWIS B.
3923 THE/EARTH,/MAN AND/MAPS/by Lewis B. King, F.R.G.S./Registered at the General Post Office, Brisbane/for transmission by post as a book/William Brooks & Co. (Q.) Pty. Ltd./The educational Publishers of Australia...etc.
n.d. [1972]
135pp, b/w & part-col. diagrams, pic. bd., 220x280mm. CLRC
'Designed primarily as a school book'.

King of the Jungle
See The Great White Bear

KING, Percy
3924 THE STORY OF/"THE BABES IN/THE WOOD"/Adapted by/Victor Roberts/from the book by/Percy King/With illustrations/by Angus Winneke/[drawing]/As told in the/Tivoli Theatre Pantomime/"The Babes in the Wood"/Christmas and New Year
Wholly set up and printed by Victory Publicity Pty Ltd, 262 Queen Street, Melbourne, n.d.
[32]pp, 8 f/p col. illus., 1 f/p b/w illus. & b/w drawings, pic. wrappers, 245x1875mm. Grant

KING, William
WESTERN AUSTRALIA. *See* Around Australia Program

KINGSLEY, Henry
3925 TALES OF OLD TRAVEL/RE-NARRATED/by/Henry Kingsley, F.R.G.S./[vignette & verse]/London:/Macmillan & Co./1869/(The Right of Translation and reproduction is reserved.)
368pp, 56pp adv., b/w frontis. & 7 f/p b/w engravings by Huard, clo., 185x125mm. NSL:M
Contents include: 'The Shipwreck of Pelsart' (pp40–55); 'The Foundation of an Empire (Australia: The early settlement)' (pp308–68).
(2nd ed. 1869, rpt 1872,1876 and 1882, unseen)
3926 TALES OF OLD TRAVEL/RE-NARRATED/By/Henry Kingsley,F.R.G.S./Third Edition/with

illustrations./ [vignette and verse]/London:/ Macmillan & Co./1890
Details as in first edition, but pic. clo., 178x120mm. KMM

3927 THE BOY IN GREY/By Henry Kingsley/[device]/ Strahan & Co., Publishers/56 Ludgate Hill, London/ 1871/(Second Edition)
[First edition, London 1871]
194pp, 42pp adv., b/w frontis. & 13 f/p b/w illus. by Arthur Hughes, dec. clo., 175x115mm. CLRC
Part of the story (pp136–94) is Australian.
First published in *'Good Words for the Young'* 1868–69.
Contains 'Eyre's March' (24pp) & 'The March of Charles Sturt' (20pp).
Later reprinted in *Hornby Mills & other Stories,* London, Tinsley, 1872

3928 THE BOY IN GREY/and/Other Stories and Sketches/by/Henry Kingsley/New edition/with a frontispiece by A. Forestier/London/Ward, Lock & Bowden, Limited/Warwick House, Salisbury Square, E.C./New York and Melbourne/1895/(All rights reserved)
328pp, 16pp adv., b/w frontis., clo., 195x130mm. CLRC

3929 THE LOST CHILD/By/Henry Kingsley/[vignette & caption]/Illustrated by L. Frölich/London and New York:/Macmillan and Co./1871
41pp, 1p adv., b/w frontis. & 6 f/p b/w illus., dec. clo., 230x170mm. NSL:M
Reprint of Chapter XXX of *Geoffry Hamlyn.*

3930 THE/MYSTERY OF THE ISLAND/By/Henry Kingsley/Author of "Geoffrey [*sic*] Hamlyn", "Tales of old Travel", &c./[device]/William Mullan & Son/34 Paternoster Row London/4 Donegal Place Belfast/1877
vipp, 266pp, unillus., clo., 170x110mm. SUA
Adventure story, presumably written for boys about a convict sent to WA who discovers treasure on Pelsart's Island.

3931 THE/MYSTERY OF THE ISLAND/A Tale of Treasure Trove/By/Henry Kingsley/Author of "Geoffry Hamlyn", "Ravenshoe",/etc etc/Marshall Brothers, Ltd.,/London, Edinburgh
n.d.
216pp, sepia/white frontis. only, clo., 185x120mm. KP

3932 THE RECOLLECTIONS/OF/GEOFFRY HAMLYN/ By/Henry Kingsley/Author of "The Hillyars and the Burtons" "Ravenshoe" etc etc/with a memoir by Clement Shorter/London:/Ward, Lock & Co., Limited./Warwick House, Salisbury Square, E.C./New York and Melbourne
n.d. [190-?]
xxx+468pp (inc. 16pp introductory notes), & 12pp adv. (some Ethel Turner titles advertised), b/w frontis. & 3 b/w plates, clo., 184x115mm. KP
Some line drawings in introduction. Plates by J. Macfarlane dated 1901. Ed. possibly intended for teenagers.

3933 THE RECOLLECTIONS OF/GEOFFRY HAMLYN./ by/Henry Kingsley,/Author of "Ravenshoe", "The Hillyars and the Burtons"./Selected and edited to suit the requirements of the/Education Department of Victoria by/Carlyle Smythe, B.A./Illustrated by Alek Sass./Melbourne:/Fitchett Brothers Proprietary Ltd./ 376 Swanston Street./1912
160pp (inc. 2pp editorial introduction), f/p b/w frontis. & 1 half-page b/w illus. in text, dec. wrappers, 180x120mm. Grant

3934 Whitcombe's Story Books/GEOFFRY HAMLYN/IN AUSTRALIA/(An Adaptation of the Australian portion of Henry Kingsley's/"Geoffry Hamlyn"/For ages 12 to 14 years/[device]/Auckland, Christchurch, Dunedin and Wellington, N.Z./Melbourne, Sydney, and London:/Whitcombe & Tombs Limited
n.d.
152pp (inc. notes, questions &c., & 2pp biographical note), b/w portrait frontis. & 3 f/p b/w illus., wrappers, 185x110mm. KMM
See McLaren 601

KINGSMILL, Stanley

3935 "WIDGEE"/Adventures/in the Wild Australian Bush/By/Stanley Kingsmill, F.R.G.S./Illustrated by/ Lieut. Charles Bryant/R.O.I./[device]/London/W. Westall & Co., Ltd./8 Adam Street, Adelphi, W.C.2./1919
302pp, 1p verse, 6pp glossary, b/w photographic portrait frontis. & 6 f/p b/w illus. by Charles Bryant, pic. clo., 185x120mm. CLRC

KINGSTON, William H. G.

3936 THE/GILPINS AND THEIR FORTUNES/An Australian Tale/By/William H. G. Kingston./Published under the direction of/the Committee of General literature and education,/appointed by the Society for Promoting/Christian Knowledge/London:/Society for Promoting Christian Knowledge;/Sold at the depositories:/77 Great Queen Street, Lincoln's Inn Fields;/4 Royal Exchange; 48, Piccadilly;/and by all booksellers.
n.d. [1865]
171pp, 4pp adv., engraved frontis. & 3 other engravings, clo., 143x94mm. NSL:M

3937 Another copy as above but, after 'Piccadilly': New York: Pott, Young & Co.
8pp adv. KMM

3938 THE GILPINS/AND THEIR FORTUNES./An Australian Tale./By/William H. G. Kingston/Author of "Owen Hartley", "Ned Garth", etc. etc./Published under the direction of the committee/of general literature and education appointed by the/Society for Promoting Christian Knowledge./London:/Society for Promoting Christian Knowledge/Northumberland Avenue, Charing Cross, W.C./43 Queen Victoria Street, E.C./Brighton, 135 North Street,/New York, E. J. B. Young & Co.
n.d. [inscribed 1889]
159pp, 4pp adv., engraved frontis. & 3 f/p engravings, pic. clo., 185x120mm. KMM

3939 As above, with slightly varying addresses, adv. &c. KMM

3940 THE GILPINS/AND THEIR FORTUNES/A Story of Early Days in Australia/By/William H. G. Kingston,/Author of "Owen Hartley", "Ned Garth", etc. etc./Illustrated by/Archie Webb/London/The Sheldon Press/Northumberland Avenue W.C.2/New York and Toronto: The Macmillan Co.
n.d. [inscribed 1928]
159pp, 17pp adv., unillus., pic. clo., 192x125mm. KMM

3941 JOSEPH RUDGE, THE AUSTRALIAN/ SHEPHERD./A Tale/[vignette with caption]/Griffith and Farran,/successors to Newbery and Harris/West Corner of St Paul's Church-yard, London/E. P. Dutton and Co., New York
n.d. [first published 1867, this copy post 1880]
64pp & 2pp adv., & adv. inside both covers, engraved frontis. & 3 other engravings, dec. clo., with col. onlay, 185x122mm. KMM
The three engravings were first used in Mrs Lee's *Adventures in Australia.* One of a series of four 'Talking Tales, edited by the late W. H. G. Kingston'.

3942 AT THE SOUTH POLE;/or/The Adventures of Richard Pengelley,/Mariner/By/William H. G. Kingston/Author of "Off to Sea" etc./With numerous illustrations/Fourth edition/Cassell Petter & Galpin,/ London Paris & New York
n.d. [first published 1870]
415pp, 2pp preface, 4pp adv., b/w frontis. & 41 engravings, clo., 180x115mm. ANL
Bears, moose &c. are encountered in the story, & Kingston admits he had 'met no other descriptive work' on the southern continent.

3943 AT THE SOUTH POLE
As copy above, but sixth edition [prize 1888]
viii, 351pp, 16pp adv., engraved frontis. & 7 f/p engravings, pic. clo., dec. e/p, 180x120mm. GK
Swedish edition
RICHARD PENGELLEYS ÄFVENTYR VID SYDPOLEN. Unseen

3944 TWICE LOST/A Story of Shipwreck, and of Adventure in/the Wilds of Australia/by W. H. G. Kingston,/Author of "Old Jack", "In the Eastern Seas", "On the Banks/of the Amazon", "In the Wilds of Africa", etc./London:/T. Nelson and Sons, Paternoster Row;/Edinburgh and New York./1878
473pp, engraved frontis., illus. t.p. (preceding typographical t.p.), 33 f/p engraved illus. & 9 vignettes, pic. clo., 185x125mm. Grant

3945 TWICE LOST/A Story of Shipwreck, and of Adventure/in the Wilds of Australia/by the late/W. H. G. Kingston/Author of 'Old Jack', 'In the Eastern Seas', 'On the Banks of the Amazon', 'In the Wilds of Africa',/etc. etc./With forty-six engravings/London:/T. Nelson and Sons, Paternoster Row/Edinburgh; and New York./1881
Details as above. NSL:M
• Rpt as above 1883, 1887. NSL:M
• Rpt as above 1889, The Kingston Library for Boys. KMM
• Rpt as above 1892, The Kingston Library for Boys. KP
• Rpt as above 1897, The Kingston Library for Boys. GK

3946 TWICE LOST./A Story of Shipwreck, and of Adventure/in the Wilds of Australia./By the late/W. H. G. Kingston,/Author of "Old Jack", "In the Eastern Seas", "On the Banks/of the Amazon", "In the Wilds of Africa",/Etc. Etc./With Forty-six Engravings./ London:/T. Nelson and Sons, Paternoster Row./ Edinburgh; and New York,/1901
473pp, 4pp adv., b/w frontis., additional dec. t.p., 34 f/p b/w engravings in text, pic. clo., dec. e/p, 180x125mm. RM

3947 TWICE LOST/By/W. H. G. Kingston/Thomas Nelson and Sons/London, Edinburgh, Dublin/and New York
n.d.
396pp, 4pp adv., part-col. t.p., col. frontis. & additional pic. t.p., 4 col. plates, pic. clo., 185x127mm.
Frontis. by W. S. Stacey, other illus. by C. J. Staniland. Copies seen inscribed 1909, 1914, 1916. Later copies have no gilt on cover & no pic. t.p. KP

3948 ADVENTURES IN AUSTRALIA/By/William H. G. Kingston/Author of "Great African Travellers", "Shipwrecks and Disasters/at Sea", "Digby Heathcote", &c./[drawing]/With thirty-four illustrations/London/George Routledge and Sons/ Broadway, Ludgate Hill/New York: 9 Lafayette Place/ 1885
184pp, col. frontis. & 33 b/w illus., pic. clo., 180x120mm. NSL:M
Serialized in *Every Boys Annual* 1882.

3949 AUSTRALIAN ADVENTURES/By/William H. G. Kingston/Author of "Great African Travellers", "Shipwrecks and Disasters/at Sea", "Digby Heathcote", etc./[drawing]/With thirty-four illustrations/London/George Routledge and Sons/ Broadway, Ludgate Hill/Glasgow and New York
n.d. [inscribed 1889]
184pp, 2pp adv., col. frontis. & 33 b/w illus., pic. clo., 180x120mm. RM
This edition has a variant binding, the pictorial design differing entirely from that of earlier editions, the author's name & all edges being gilt.

3950 AUSTRALIAN ADVENTURES/By/William H. G. Kingston/Author of "Great African Travellers", "Shipwrecks and Disasters/at Sea", "Digby Heathcote", etc./[drawing]/With thirty-four illustrations/London/George Routledge and Sons/ Broadway, Ludgate Hill/Glasgow and New York
n.d.
184pp, 2pp & 4pp adv., 26 f/p b/w illus. & b/w tailpieces, limp dec. clo. (with adv. inside cover), 180x120mm. Every Boys Library. KMM

3951 Another copy but: Manchester and New York
Pic. clo. blocked in colours & gilt. GK
Many undated variations, title in gilt panel on front cover &c. KP
French edition

3952 AVENTURES/DE DEUX JEUNES ANGLAIS/EN AUSTRALIE/ouvrage imité de l'anglais/par/Francis Ergil/Professeur de Langues/Nouvelle édition/ [colophon]/Tours/Alfred Cattier, Éditeur/1894
240pp (inc. 2pp contents & 8pp dedication), b/w frontis. & 6 f/p b/w illus., three-quarter leather & marbled bd., 245x160mm. CLRC
Danish edition

3953 PAA EVENTYR I AUSTRALIEN/af. W. H. G. Kingston/F. Borck/[device]/Kobenhavn/Jul. Gjellerups Forlag/Martius Truelsens Bogtrykkeri/1890
155pp, additional illus. t.p., bd., leather spine, 170x105mm. NSL:M
Abridged & adapted edition

3954 Whitcombe's Story Books/ADVENTURES/IN AUSTRALIA/(for children aged 10 to 12 years)/(Adapted from the story by W. H. G. Kingston/ by permission)/[drawing]/Whitcombe & Tombs Limited/Auckland, Christchurch, Dunedin, Wellington/Melbourne and London
n.d.
87pp, 1p glossary, b/w frontis. & b/w drawings in text, wrappers, 185x115mm. KMM
See McLaren 530

3955 PETER BIDDULPH;/The Rise and Progress of an Australian/Settler/By/William H. G. Kingston/Author of/"A True Hero", "Charley Laurel", "The Boy who sailed with/Blake", etc. etc./London:/Sunday School Union,/56 Old Bailey, E.C.
n.d. [1881]
138pp, 10pp adv., col. presentation page, b/w frontis. & 11 f/p b/w engravings, pic. clo., 185x120mm. CLRC

3956 PETER BIDDULPH/The Story of an Australian Settler/By/W. H. G. Kingston/Author of "The Boy who sailed with Blake"/"A True Hero", "Very Far West Indeed"/etc. etc./London:/The Sunday School Union,/57 and 59 Ludgate Hill, E.C.
n.d.
142pp, 18pp adv., engraved frontis. & 6 f/p engravings, 7 smaller engravings in text, pic. clo., 180x120mm. KMM
• Rpt as above but eleventh thousand. KMM
• Rpt as above but thirteenth thousand. RM

3957 THE/YOUNG BERRINGTONS/or, The Boy

Explorers/by/W. H. G. Kingston/author of "Over the Rocky Mountains", "At the South Pole"/etc. etc./[vignette]/Cassell, Petter Galpin & Co./London, Paris and New York/(all rights reserved)
n.d. [first ed. 1880]
152pp, 4pp adv., engraved frontis. & 6 f/p engravings, numerous engravings in text, pic. clo., 180x120mm. Grant
This story, of young settlers exploring the Australian bush, their experiences with Aborigines &c., originally appeared in a volume of *Little Folks.*

3958 THE/YOUNG BERRINGTONS:/or, the Boy Explorers/By/W. H. G. Kingston/Author of "Among the Red-Skins", "At the South Pole"/etc. etc./[vignette]/second edition/Cassell and Company, Limited/London, Paris, New York/(All rights reserved)
n.d. [copy seen a prize in 1886.]
viii, 152pp, engraved frontis. & 6 f/p engravings, many smaller engravings in text, pic. clo., 185x115mm. VSL
• Rpt as above but sixteenth thousand. KMM

3959 Third edition/Cassell and Company, Limited/London, Paris, New York and Melbourne/(All rights reserved)
Otherwise as above with 16pp adv. ANL

3960 MILICENT COURTENAY'S DIARY:/or the/Experiences of a Young Lady at Home/and Abroad./By/William H. G. Kingston./With Illustrations./Gall & Inglis./London:/25 Paternoster Sq./Edinburgh:/6 George Street
n.d. [inscribed 1884; ?first edition 1873]
448pp, engraved frontis. & 3 f/p engravings, dec. t.p., clo., 180x120mm. Grant
Title in gilt on front cover reads: 'Millicent [*sic*] Courtenay's/Experiences'. Second half of the book tells of the heroine's voyage to New South Wales and experiences in the Colony.

3961 THE DIARY OF/MILICENT COURTENAY/or/The Experiences of a Young Lady/at Home and Abroad/by/W. H. G. Kingston/Author of "The Cruise of the Frolic" "Happy Jack"/"Uncle Bos" Etc./London/Gall and Inglis, 25 Paternoster Square/and Edinburgh
n.d. [Prize label December 1892]
448pp, b/w frontis. sgd 'Williamson' & 4 f/p b/w illus., dec. clo., 190x135mm. Grant
On cover 'Millicent Courtenay's Diary' by W. H. G. Kingston' in gilt, but apparently a misprint; name spelt 'Milicent' elsewhere throughout.

3962 Another copy as above, but 'Millicent Courtenay' on front cover, pic. clo, 200x135mm. KMM

3963 SHIPWRECKS/AND/DISASTERS AT SEA/By/W. H. G. Kingston./Author of "Digby Heathcote" and "Paul Gerard"/[vignette]/with numerous illustrations/London and New York:/George Routledge and Sons./1873
iv, 515pp, engraved frontis. & numerous text engravings, dec. clo., 190x120mm. CLRC
Contains sections relating to Australia & also: several sections of New Zealand interest; the voyage & shipwreck of H.M.S. *Alceste* (China, Korea, Philippines, Borneo); the wreck of the *Antelope* on the Pelew Islands of the Caroline group, & the visit of Prince Lee Boo to England.

3964 SHIPWRECKS/AND/DISASTERS AT SEA/By/W. H. G. Kingston/Author of "Digby Heathcote", "Great African Travellers", etc./[vignette]/with one hundred and eighty illustrations/London/George Routledge and Sons, limited/Broadway, Ludgate Hill/Glasgow, Manchester, and New York
n.d. [school prize 1897]
516pp, 4pp preface, b/w engravings throughout, pic. clo., 190x125mm. KMM

3965 CAPTAIN COOK:/His/Life, Voyages, and Discoveries/By/William H. G. Kingston,/Author of/"Little Ben Hadden", "The Story of a Super-cargo" etc./[vignette]/London:/The Religious Tract Society;/56 Paternoster Row, 65 St. Paul's Churchyard,/and 164 Piccadilly./Manchester: Corporation Street Brighton: Western Road
n.d. [prize 1877]
352pp, double-spread map, engraved frontis. & 59 engravings (inc. 1 map), clo. with gilt medallion & title in gilt, 180x130mm. GK
Another copy as above, n.d. [prize 1879]. CLRC

3966 Another copy as above, with double-spread map & edges in gilt, 177x130mm. GK

3967 CAPTAIN COOK,/His/Life, Voyages, and Discoveries./By/William H. G. Kingston,/Author of/'The Golden Grasshopper'./"A Yacht Voyage Round England'.Etc/London:/The Religious Tract Society,/56, Paternoster Row; 65 St Paul's Churchyard;/and 164, Piccadilly
n.d. (inscribed1891)
368pp. b/w frontis., 6 f/p b/w illus. & 2 b/w illus. in text, dec. clo., dec. e/p, g.e., 180x120mm. RM

3968 CAPTAIN COOK/His/Life, Voyages, and Discoveries/By/William H. G. Kingston/Author of "The Golden Grasshopper", "A Yacht Voyage round/England", etc./London/The Religious Tract Society/56, Paternoster Row; 65 St. Paul's Churchyard
n.d. [prize label 1894]
319pp [no adv.], b/w frontis. & 6 f/p b/w illus., 2 small engravings in text, dec. clo., 180x120mm. RM

3969 CAPTAIN COOK/His Life, Voyages and Discoveries/By/W. H. G. Kingston/London/The Religious Tract Society/4 Bouverie Street and 65 St. Paul's Churchyard
n.d. [1904]
319pp, 16pp adv., t.p. printed in 2 colours, col. frontis. & 2 f/p col. illus., 8 b/w plates, pic. clo., 195x130mm. KMM

3970 CAPTAIN COOK/His Life, Voyages, and Discoveries/by/William H. G. Kingston/Author of "The Golden Grasshopper", "The Cruise of the Mary Rose",/"Ben Hadden" etc./With eleven illustrations/London/The Religious Tract Society/4 Bouverie Street; and 65, St. Paul's Churchyard E.C.
n.d. [inscribed 1909]
319pp, 16pp adv., b/w frontis., 5 f/p b/w photographic illus. & 5 f/p engravings, 2 small b/w illus. in text, pic. clo., 195x130mm. HBM
Another copy as above, but awarded as a Sunday School prize 1916, & 8pp adv. KP

3971 CAPTAIN COOK/His Life, Voyages and Discoveries/By/William H. G. Kingston/Author of/"The Golden Grasshopper",/"The Cruise of the Mary Rose",/"Ben Hadden", etc./London/Boys Own Paper Office/4 Bouverie Street, E.C.4
n.d.
255pp [no adv.], col. frontis., 4 f/p b/w illus., clo., 185x120mm. PR

3972 THE/THREE ADMIRALS/By/W. H. G. Kingston/[vignette]/Griffith Farran Browne & Co. Limited/35 Bow Street, Covent Garden/London.
n.d.
424pp, b/w frontis. & 7 f/p engravings (by C. J. De Lacy), clo., 190x130mm. CLRC
Includes one chapter on Sydney, & several on the Pacific & New Zealand. Two earlier books, to which

this is a sequel, *The Three Midshipmen* & *The Three Lieutenants*, do not relate to Australia.

3973 THE THREE ADMIRALS/And the/Adventures of their Young Followers/By/W. H. G. Kingston/Author of "The Three Midshipmen", "The Three Lieutenants", etc./Illustrated by J. R. Wells and C. J. Staniland/London/Griffith Farran Okeden and Welsh/Newbery House, Charing Cross Road/and Sydney
n.d. [first published 1878]
440pp, 16pp adv., b/w frontis. & 7 f/p b/w illus., clo., 180x115mm. KMM

3974 Another copy as above but: 'etc, etc' after 'The Three Midshipmen'...Griffith Farran & Co.,/39 Charing Cross Road
n.d. [prize 1901]
Details as before but bevelled edges & all edges gilt. KP

3975 THE THREE ADMIRALS/By/W. H. G. Kingston/Author of/"From Powder Monkey to Admiral", "The Three Midshipmen", etc/New edition/Illustrated in colour by Archibald Webb/London/Henry Frowde/Hodder and Stoughton/1912
419pp, 16pp adv., col. frontis. & 5 col. plates, pic. clo., 190x124mm. KP

3976 THE/THREE ADMIRALS/BY/W. H. G. Kingston/Author of/"From Powder Monkey to Admiral", "The Three Midshipmen", etc./New Edition/Illustrated in colour by Archibald Webb/Humphrey Milford/Oxford University Press/London, Edinburgh, Glasgow/Toronto, Melbourne, Cape Town, Bombay
n.d.
410pp, col. frontis. & 5 col. plates, pic. clo., 185x120mm. KMM

3977 WONDERS/OF/THE OCEAN/By/W. H. G. Kingston/With Seventeen Illustrative Cuts./Gall & Inglis/London:/25 Paternoster Square/Edinburgh:/20 Bernard Terrace.
n.d. [school prize 1880]
128pp, b/w frontis. & illus. in text, dec. clo., 160x100mm. CLRC
'In the Antipodes' (61pp), 'Polynesia', 'Coral Islands', &c. to p105.

3978
• Rpt as above inscribed 1886. Cover decorated with gilt leaves &c. Title & vignette of a flying fish printed in black &c. GK

KINGSTON, W. H. G. (ed.)

3979 TALES FOR OLD AND YOUNG/of all Classes/By Many Writers/Edited by/William H. G. Kingston/Author of "True Blue", "Cruise of the Frolic", "The Fire Ships", "My Travels in/Many Lands", "Marmaduke Merry the Midshipman", etc. etc./with numerous Illustrations by various Artists/London/William Kent & Co., Paternoster Row/1862
128 & 208pp, engraved frontis. & small engravings in text, bound three-quarter leather with marbled bd., 180x130mm. CLRC
Copy seen bound together with *Marmaduke Merry the Midshipman.* Contains an anonymous story by Kingston, 'The Bushrangers' (50pp), which has an Australian setting. Story has a three-quarter page illus. by J. B. Zwecker.
See also South West Pacific section

KINGSTON, W. H. G. & FRITH, Henry

3980 NOTABLE VOYAGERS/FROM/COLUMBUS TO NORDEN-SKIOLD/By/William H. G. Kingston/and/Henry Frith/with illustrations/London/George Routledge and Sons, Limited/Broadway, Ludgate Hill/Glasgow, Manchester and New York/1892
[first published Routledge 1885]
621pp, 4pp preface, 6pp adv., b/w engraved frontis. & 63 f/p b/w illus., many small engravings in text, dec. clo., 195x130mm. KMM
Not specifically a boys' book; contains three chapters on Dampier, one on Anson's voyages, & three on Cook, &c.

KINMONT, Joan

3981 GRANDPA/AND ME/By/Joan Kinmont/Distributors:/Oldham, Beddome & Meredith Pty. Ltd./Hobart
n.d. [1944]
78pp, b/w drawings throughout, bd., 205x130mm. KMM
Verses.

3982 TWO LITTLE GIRLS/Photographs and/Verses by/Joan Kinmont/Distributors:/Oldham, Beddome & Meredith Pty. Ltd./Hobart
n.d. [1946]
[46]pp, illus. throughout, bd., 240x180mm. VSL
Verses & photographic child studies.

KINNEAR, Margaret

3983 THE/GIANT'S PANCAKE/An Australian Fairy Story/Written and Illustrated/by/Margaret Kinnear/John Sands Ltd./Druitt Street/Sydney
n.d. [inscribed 1939]
16pp, 4 f/p col. illus., b/w drawings, stiff pic. wrappers, 282x125mm. NSL:M

KINSELLA, Clare & McLEAN, Donald

3984 ADVENTURES/IN POETRY/A/Personal Poetry Book/For You to Illustrate/Selected and annotated by Clare Kinsella and Donald McLean/Illustrated by Jill Blunt/Shakespeare Head Press Pty Ltd
Sydney, 5th ed. 1960 [1st ed. 1949]
80pp, verses with some b/w drawings & spaces left for child to make own illus., pic. wrappers, 213x180mm. KP

KIPLING, Rudyard

3985 Just so Stories. THE SING-SONG OF OLD MAN KANGAROO By Rudyard Kipling, London: A.P.Watt Hastings House, Norfolk Street, Strand 1900
Duodecimo. Issued in green paper wrappers, the front cover lettered 'The Sing-Song of Old Man Kangaroo. Rudyard Kipling'
Collation: 6 leaves, blank leaf, title with copyright notice on verso, 1 leaf, text pp3-7, blank leaf. The story was published in *The Ladies' Home Journal,* June 1900 & was collected in *Just So Stories,* 1902 (*Bibliography of the Works of Rudyard Kipling,* by Flora L. Livingstone, New York, Edgard H. Wells, & Company, 1927), unseen

3986 THE/JUST SO STORIES/PAINTING BOOKS/FOR CHILDREN/THE SING-SONG OF OLD MAN/KANGAROO/[title printed in blue]/By/Rudyard/Kipling/Hodder & Stoughton/Limited London
Engraved and printed by The Sun Engraving Co., Ltd, London & Watford, n.d. [1922]
[28]pp, dec. t.p., 6 col. illus. (by Miss Day Hodgetts) with illus repeated in b/w on opposite page, & last page b/w illus., marginal drawings, col. pic. wrappers, 230x283mm. Grant
Series—The Just-So Stories Painting Books for Children. Also issued by Doubleday Page & Co in America in 1923.

KIPPIS, Andrew

See THE LIFE OF CAPTAIN JAMES COOK, for editions of this work abridged for children

KIRBY, Rev. Reginald
3987 TYING THE ROPE/and/Six Other Addresses/Three on the Trinity/and/Three Bible Readings/by the Rev./Reginald Kirby/Minister of the Collins Street Baptist/Church, and late of Harrogate, England/the Leeson Publishing Coy./174 Collins Street—Melbourne/Copyright—all rights reserved
n.d. [1936]
107pp (inc. 1p foreword), unillus., wrappers, 185x120mm. NSL:M

KIRSTEN, Marcia Meymott (ed.)
3988 YOUTH WRITES/Edited/by/Marcia Kirsten/[device]/Rigby Limited
Adelaide 1967
64pp (inc. 1p foreword, 1p editor's foreword), unillus., pic. wrappers, 215x135mm. KMM
A collection of verse & prose by young writers.

3989 YOUTH WRITES/AGAIN/A collection of verse and prose by young people/of secondary school age in Australia and/Papua-New Guinea/Editor/Marcia Kirsten/B.A., Dip. Ed. (Mod. Lang.) Syd./Assistant Editor/Marjorie Aldred...[etc.]/Rigby Limited
Adelaide 1969
82pp (inc. 3pp list of contributors, instructions, 3pp editor's foreword, introduction by Maie Casey, etc.), unillus., clo., 225x150mm. CLRC
Young people's writing rather than a book for children.

3990 YOUTH WRITES/1971/A Collection of verse and prose/by young writers of secondary school age/in Australia and the/Territory of Papua and New Guinea
A. H. & A. W. Reed, Sydney 1971
96pp (inc. 7pp introduction by Professor Leonie Kramer, etc.), unillus., clo., 235x155mm. KMM

KISCH, Egon Ervin
3991 CESTA K PROTINOZCUM (Road to the Antipodes)
S.N.D.K., Prague 1954
135pp. SLCSR

KITCHING, E. M.
3992 Far and Near Readers B.1/JACKAROOS/By/E. M. Kitching/[drawing]/Illustrated by/Len Fullerton/W. & R. Chamers, Ltd./London and Edinburgh
n.d. [1956]
32pp, b/w drawings throughout, limp clo., 200x140mm. ANL

KITHER, Hilda Turner
3993 GEOFF'S/TEMPTATION/By/Hilda Turner Kither/Adelaide:/W. K. Thomas & Co., Grenfell Street/1898
12pp, unillus., wrappers, 165x100mm. CLRC
Short moral tale about two boys.

KJELGAARD, Jim
3994 BOOMERANG HUNTER/by Jim Kjelgaard/illustrated by W. T. Mars/Holiday House New York N.Y.
1960
172pp, b/w frontis., 12 b/w illus., clo., pic. e/p, 196x134mm. ANL
Danish edition
3995 Jim Kjelgaard/BOOMERANG-/JAEGER/Hernou
n.d. [1963—Copenhagen]
110pp, unillus., pic. bd. (Jean Petersson), 200x125mm. ANL
German edition
3996 Jim Kjelgaard/BALALU UND SEIN DINGO/von Mutigen Taten und Abenteuern Eines/Jungen Jägers in Australischen Wüster/Hermann Schaffstein Verlag
1962
88pp, b/w extended frontis., 14 b/w illus., pic. bd., 202x130mm. ANL

KNIGHT, Frank
3997 THE/GOLDEN MONKEY/By/Frank Knight/Illustrated by/J. S. Goodall, R. I./London/Macmillan & Co. Ltd./New York—St. Martin's Press/1953
196pp, 1p preface, b/w frontis., b/w drawings in text, b/w map & diagram, clo., 200x130mm. ANL
Story based on the races between British & American clipper ships in the Australian goldrush era of the 1850s.
• Rpt 1956, 1958, 1960, 1963, as above. KP

3998 STORIES OF/FAMOUS SHIPS/Frank Knight/Illustrated by/Will Nickless/Oliver & Boyd
Edinburgh 1963
152pp (inc. 2pp introduction), f/p sepia/white frontis. & 7 f/p sepia/white illus., 3 f/p b/w illus. & 1 f/p diagram, b/w drawings in text, clo., 195x130mm. BBC
Includes: 'The *Endeavour* in which Captain Cook explored the Pacific' (6pp), & 'The *James Baines*—Australian emigrant clipper 1854' (6pp).

3999 THE YOUNG/CAPTAIN COOK/Frank Knight/Illustrated by/Joan Howell/Max Parrish
—London
1964
127pp, b/w drawings in text, clo., 195x125mm. HBM
4000 American edition, the same, Roy Publishers, New York 1964. NSL:M

4001 STORIES OF/FAMOUS EXPLORERS/BY SEA/Frank Knight/Illustrated by/Will Nickless/Oliver & Boyd
Edinburgh 1964
160pp, part col. frontis., 7 f/p part-col. illus., b/w drawings, clo., 196x130mm. KP
Contents include: 'Magellan' (7pp); 'Dutch Exploration' (6pp); 'Cook' (21pp); 'Dampier', etc. (7pp); 'Bass and Flinders' (7pp); 'John Franklin' (8pp).
• Rpt 1969 as above, Chatto, Boyd and Oliver. BBC
American edition
Westminster, New York 1966. Unseen

4002 STORIES OF/FAMOUS EXPLORERS/BY LAND/Frank Knight/Illustrated by/Will Nickless/Oliver & Boyd
Edinburgh 1965
160pp, part-col. frontis. & 7 part-col. illus., drawings in text, clo., 195x150mm. BBC
Contents include: 'The White Continent' (Antarctica, 6pp); 'By Way of the South Pole' (7pp); 'Men Who Vanished' (Leichhardt, 8pp).

4003 STORIES OF/FAMOUS/SEA ADVENTURES/Frank Knight/Illustrated by/Will Nickless/Oliver & Boyd
1966
144pp, col. frontis. & 7 f/p col. plates, b/w drawings, clo., 196x130mm. ANL
Contains 'Mutiny on the *Bounty*', 8pp, 'Wreck of the *General Grant*', 7pp.

4004 CAPTAIN COOK/& THE VOYAGE OF THE/ENDEAVOUR/(1768–1771)/Captain Frank Knight/[drawing]/Nelson
Melbourne 1968
174pp, 12pp b/w illus. & b/w map, clo., dec. e/p, 210x135mm. CLRC
Also published in stiff pictorial paper, 1968. KP

4005 Frank Knight/THE/DARDANELLES CAMPAIGN/Illustrated by F. D. Phillips/Macdonald: London
1970

94pp, b/w extended frontis., 4 double-spread b/w illus., 2 f/p b/w illus. & drawings in text, clo., 185x125mm. KMM

KNOOP, Faith Yingling

4006 [device]/A World Explorer/SIR EDMUND/HILLARY/By Faith Yingling Knoop/Illustrated by William Hutchinson/Garrard Publishing Company/Champaign, Illinois
1970
96pp, 12 f/p part-col. illus., b/w photographs & other illus., dec. clo., map e/p, 225x150mm. KMM
Deals with the NZ explorer's Antarctic expedition as well as Everest.

'Know your Ships'

4007 "KNOW YOUR SHIPS"/Presented by Malties
Malties Pty Ltd, Box 3, East Brunswick, Victoria, n.d.
8pp printed on board & folding together, 40 spaces on inside for cards to be pasted in & information about Nos 1–40 printed on other side, pic. bd., cover title, 320x188mm. KP
See also Fishes of the World & Malties Bird Album

Knowledge for Boys and Girls

See Wall, Dorothy [illus.]

KNOWLES, Gaye

4008 TIKO/THE TREE BEAR/Written and pictured by/Gaye Knowles/[drawing]/The Brockhampton Press/Leicester [England] 1951
48pp, 11 f/p col. illus., numerous b/w & part. col. drawings in text, clo. (with col. illus. pasted on front cover), 180x130mm. KMM
Story for young children of koalas, kangaroos &c.

KNOWLES, Marion Miller

4009 CORINNE OF CORRALL'S/BLUFF/By/Marion Miller Knowles/Author of/"Songs from the Hills" (Two Editions) "Fronds from the Blacks'/Spur", "Barbara Halliday" etc./Melbourne/W. P. Linehan, Little Collins Street/1912
197pp, b/w portrait frontis., clo., 180x120mm. KMM
Author of a number of light romances which are not considered books for children.

KNOX, Thomas Wallace

4010 THE BOY TRAVELLERS IN/AUSTRALASIA/Adventures of two Youths in a journey to/The Sandwich, Marquesas, Society, Samoan, and Feejee Islands, and/through the colonies of New Zealand, New South Wales/Queensland, Victoria, Tasmania, and South Australia/By/Thomas W. Knox/Author of "The Boy Travellers in the Far East" "In South America"/"In Russia" and "On the Congo" "The Young Nimrods"/"The Voyage of the 'Vivian'," etc./Illustrated/New York/Harper & Brothers, Franklin Square/1889
538pp, 2pp preface, 6pp adv., col. frontis. & b/w illus. throughout, pic. clo., dec. e/p, 220x160mm. ANL

4011 THE BOY TRAVELLERS IN/AUSTRALASIA
As above, but
New York and London/Harper & Brothers Publishers/1895
Second ed.
538pp & 2pp preface, 4pp adv., b/w illus. throughout, pic. clo., map e/p, 225x165mm. RM
This volume has no frontis. & is printed on lighter paper making the book approx. 10mm thinner than the first ed.

4012 THE BOY TRAVELLERS IN/AUSTRALASIA/Adventures of Two Youths in a Journey to/The Sandwich, Marquesas, Society, Samoan, and Feejee Islands, and/Through the Colonies of New Zealand, New South Wales/Queensland, Victoria, Tasmania, and South Australia/By/Thomas W. Knox/Author of "The Boy Travellers in the Far East", "In South America"/"In Russia" and "On the Congo", "The Young Nimrods"/"The Voyage of the 'Vivian'," etc./With a new appreciation by Charles V. S. Borst/Paul Flesch & Company/Melbourne & Sydney
Published by the Charles E. Tuttle Company Inc., Rutland, Vermont & Tokyo, Japan, 1971 [first published by Harper & Brothers, New York 1889]
538pp, 22pp contents (inc. 4pp Thomas Wallace Knox, an Appreciation & 2pp author's preface), col. engraved frontis., b/w engravings throughout, clo., map e/p etc., 185x130mm. KMM

4013 THE BOY TRAVELLERS IN AUSTRALASIA
Another copy, as above, but with variant t.p., publisher reading: 'Charles E. Tuttle Co: Publishers/Rutland, Vermont & Tokyo, Japan'
538pp, 5pp contents, 4pp Thomas Wallace Knox, An Appreciation, 2pp author's preface. KP

4014 THE/LAND OF THE KANGAROO./Adventures of Two Youths in a Journey through/the Great Island Continent./By/Thomas W. Knox./Author of "In Wild Africa", "The Boy Travellers,/(15 vols.) "Overland through/Asia", etc. etc./Illustrated by H. Burgess./[device]/Boston, U.S.A./W. A. Wilde & Company,/25 Bromfield Street.
1896
318pp (inc. 1p preface), 2pp adv., b/w frontis. & 3 f/p b/w illus., dec. clo., 195x140mm
Travel Adventure Series. KMM

KNUDSEN, Greta

4015 GOLDSEEKERS/Written by Greta Knudsen/Illustrated by Eva Sandor/Cheshire
Melbourne 1969
53pp, 1p acknowledgement, 26 f/p col. illus. & b/w marginal drawings, clo., col. pic. e/p, 275x215mm. KMM
Adventures of a family at Sofala & Hill End during the goldrush era.

Koala Babies

4016 KOALA/BABIES/[b/w drawing]/Collins: London: Glasgow
n.d.
[31]pp, part col. photographic illus. & b/w text drawings throughout, dec. bd., 183x117mm. RC

Koala Friends

4017 KOALA/FRIENDS/[decoration]/Collins: London Glasgow
n.d. [1949]
32pp, 8 part-col. photographic illus., bd., 180x115mm. CLRC

KOCH, Hannelore

4018 CLAUDE/THE COLOUR CHANGING/CAT/Illustrated by/Hannelore Koch/Published 1969 by Horwitz Publications Inc. Pty Ltd/2 Denison Street, North Sydney 2060 Australia/Copyright 1969 by Hannelore Koch/All rights reserved/National Library of Australia Registry No Aus 69-2670/Printed in Hong Kong
28pp, col. illus. throughout, double-spread illus. t.p., pic. bd., 280x215mm. KP

KOHN, Bernice

4019 KOALAS/by Bernice Kohn/Pictures by Gail Harvey/Prentice-Hall, Inc. Englewood Cliffs, N.J./[drawing]
1965

[30]pp, part-col. frontis. & part-col. illus. throughout, clo., 230x170mm. CLRC
Neither author nor illustrator is Australian.
4020 KOALAS/by Bernice Kohn/Pictures by Gail Harvey/A World's Work Children's Book
First published in Great Britain by The World's Work Ltd., Surrey, 1966
[30]pp, part-col. frontis. & part-col. drawings throughout, pic. bd. (clo. spine), 230x170mm. BBC

KORENSKY, Josef
4021 V CIZINE. Kulturni obrazky pro mladez (ABROAD—Cultural Pictures for Youth)
A. Storch, Prague 1899
203pp, 35 pictures in text, 12 supplements, 1 in colour. Unseen: SLCSR
4022 The same
New revised edition, A. Storch, Prague 1921 Unseen: SLCSR

4023 AUSTRALIA. Kulturni obrazy pro mladez (AUSTRALIA—Cultural Pictures for Youth)
A. Storch, Prague 1903
159pp, 50 illus. Unseen: SLCSR
Another edition
A. Storch, Prague 1922
202pp, 47 pictures & 2 maps, SLCSR
4024 NOVÉ CESTY PO SVETE (New Roads round the World)
J. Otto, Prague 1907–10
In eight parts:
4025 1 PLAVBA DO AUSTRALIE (Voyage to Australia), 1907, 92pp
4026 2 NA LABUTI RECE (Swan River), 1907, 101pp
4027 3 CESTY PO AUSTRALII JIZNI (South Australia), 1907, 140pp
4028 4 CESTY PO AUSTRALSKE VIKTORII A TASMANII (Voyage to Victoria and Tasmania), 1907, 143pp
4029 5 NA JIHU NOVEHO ZELANDU (South New Zealand), 1908, 138pp
4030 6 NA SEVERU NOVEHO ZELANDU (North New Zealand), 1908, 89pp
4031 7 V JIZNIM MORI (In the Southern Ocean), 1908, 113pp
4032 8 VE VYCHODNI AUSTRALII (In Eastern Australia), 1908, 85pp

KOTZE, Stepan
4033 LOV NA KLOKANY (Kangaroo Hunt)
Emil Solc, Prague 1919
32pp. Unseen: SLCSR
4034 V AUSTRALSKE BUSHI (In the Australian Bush)
Prague 1921
137pp. Unseen: SLCSR

KOUTSOUKIS, Albert J. (trans.)
4035 INDONESIAN/FOLK TALES/Translated by/Albert Koutsoukis/Illustrated by/Jean Elder/Rigby Limited Adelaide 1970
124pp, b/w frontis. & 15pp b/w illus., clo., 200x135mm. CLRC

KRAG, G. Pederson
See Pederson-Krag, G.

KRAMER, Leonie
HENRY HANDEL RICHARDSON. *See* Great Australians

KÜHNWALD, Gerd
4036 UNTER DEN KANNIBALEN/DER SÜDSEE/Ein Tatsachen-Bericht über James/Cooks Leben und reisen von/Gerd Kühnwald/Mit Bildern von M. Wulff/A. Weichert Verlag Berlin
n.d. [Library copy acquired 1940]
111pp, 1p adv., b/w frontis. & 3 f/p b/w illus., pic. bd., 185x125mm. NSL:M

KUNHARDT, Dorothy
4037 HOP, HOP,/LITTLE KANGAROO/by Dorothy Kunhardt/Pictures by Garth Williams/[col. vignette]/ Simon and Schuster. New York
n.d. [1948]
18pp (inc. t.p.), 2 f/p & 9 half-page col. illus., col. pic. bd., col. illus. e/p, 77x53mm. RM
A 'Tiny Golden Book'.
• Rpt as above
Golden Press, New York, Copyright 1948
80x53mm. KMM

'KUPPORD, Skelton" [pseud. Adams, J.]
4038 THE/UNCHARTED ISLAND/By/Skelton Kuppord/Author of 'Hammond's Hard Lines' 'The Mess that Jack Made'/&c &c/[device]/Thomas Nelson and Sons/London Edinburgh and New York/1899
350pp & 2pp adv, sepia frontis. & dec. t.p. with vignette, 4 sepia f.p. illus, pic. clo., gilt lettering, 190x125mm. KP
Numerous other undated rpts, but only slight Australian content. An adventure story of a voyage in search of missing treasure, considered briefly to be found in Australia, the setting for 20 pp only of the story.

LABORDE, [Jean Benjamin] de
4039 HISTOIRE/ABRÉGÉE/DE LA MER DU SUD/ ornée de plusiers cartes;/dédiée au Roi,/et composée pour l'éducation de Mgr Le Dauphin,/par M. de Laborde,/ancien premier, valet-de-chambre du Roi, et gouverneur du/Louvre, l'un des fermiers généraux de Sa Majesté./Tome premier/A Paris/Chez P. Didot L'Ainé; Imprimeur-Libraire,/rue Pavée Saint-André-des-Arcs./MDCCXCI
3 vols. & atlas
Vol. 1: 416pp, 3 maps, full leather, 220x130mm. CLRC
Vasco Nugnez de Baboa, Magellan, Drake, Cavandish, Hawkins, Mendana, Quiros, Tasman, Dampier, Anson, Byron, Carteret, Wallis, Bougainville
Vol. 2: 412pp, 3 f/p engravings & 1 map
Vol. 3: viiipp, 472pp, 31 latitude & longtitude tables.

LACK, Clem
QUEENSLAND; BRISBANE. *See* Around Australia Program

LACK, Clem & STAFFORD, Harry
THE RIFLE AND THE SPEAR. Fortitude Press, Brisbane 1964
Not intended for children.

LAHM, Hartmut
4040 PADDY/BOW WOW/Words & Drawings by Hartmut Lahm/Angus and Robertson/Sydney/1947
32pp, dec. t.p., col. illus. throughout, dec. bd., 180x240mm. ANL

LAIRD, Eveline & MORRIS, Katherine
4041 DOWN/BY/THE/RIVER/By Eveline Laird and Katherine Morris/Illustrated by Katherine Morris
Whitcombe & Tombs Pty Ltd, Sydney 1967
48pp, part. col. illus. throughout, pic. clo., pic. e/p, 240x175mm. KMM

LAKE, Joshua (ed.)
4042 CHILDHOOD/IN/BUD AND BLOSSOM/A Souvenir Book/of the/Children's Hospital Bazaar/

Compiled and edited by/Joshua Lake/[drawing]/The Atlas Press/Melbourne/1900
Numbered de luxe edition
[106]pp, 16pp adv., 3pp list of subscribers [preceding t.p.], b/w portrait frontis. & b/w illus. throughout, dec. clo., 285x220mm. KMM
Contributors include A. B. Paterson, Ada Cambridge, Donald MacDonald, J. B. O'Hara, &c. Contents of book appear to be about childhood, rather than for children.

LAMB, G. F.

4043 THE SPIRIT OF/MODERN ADVENTURE/Exciting Exploits/of Modern Adventurers/by/G. F. Lamb/Author of/"Modern Action and Adventure"/[device]/George G. Harrap & Co. Ltd./London Toronto Wellington Sydney
First published in Great Britain 1955; First published in this series 1955; rpt 1955, 1957
207pp (inc. 2pp preface & 1p bibliography), b/w photographic frontis. & 6pp photographic illus., 8 b/w drawings, maps, &c. in text, clo., 185x120mm. KMM
Contents include one chapter on 'Flights by Kingsford Smith and Neville Duke' (28pp).

4044 THE TRUE BOOK ABOUT/THE SOUTH POLE/By/G. F. Lamb/Illustrated by/David Cobb/Shakespeare Head/London New York Sydney Paris 1957
143pp, 1p bibliography, 11 b/w illus. & 4 maps, clo., 180x115mm. NSL:M

4045 THE TRUE BOOK ABOUT/THE SOUTH POLE/by/G. F. Lamb/Illustrated by/David Cobb/Frederick Muller Limited/London
First published 1957; 2nd imp. November 1960
143pp, 1p bibliography, 11 b/w illus. & 4 maps, clo., 180x120mm. BBC

LAMBERT, Eric

4046 Eric Lambert/THE TENDER CONSPIRACY/Illustrated by/Iris Schweitzer/Frederick Muller Limited/London
1965
This is not a children's book though about children & produced as if intended for children. KMM

LAMOND, Henry George

4047 AN AVIARY ON THE/PLAINS/By/Henry G. Lamond/Australia/Angus & Robertson Limited/89 Castlereagh Street, Sydney/1934
228pp, 16pp adv., unillus., clo., d/w by Dorothy Wall, 185x115mm. ANL
This book first appeared serially in the *Pastoral Review*, Melbourne.

4048 The Junior Library of Australian Books/AN AVIARY/ON THE PLAINS/by Henry G. Lamond/Author of Tooth and Talon, Amathea, Brindle/Royalist, Dingo: The Story of an Outlaw/Angus and Robertson/Sydney: London
First published in Junior Library series 1949
152pp, b/w frontis. & 3 f/p b/w illus., bd., 180x115mm. KMM

4049 TOOTH AND/TALON/Tales of the Australian Wild/by/Henry G. Lamond
Angus & Robertson, Sydney 1934
226pp, 27pp adv., dec. t.p., unillus., clo., 185x115mm. ANL
'Most of these stories appeared originally in the *Atlantic Monthly, Adventure,* and *Short Stories*, all of the U.S.A.'

4050 AMATHEA/The Story of a Horse/By/Henry G. Lamond/Author of/Tooth and Talon, an Aviary on the Plains, etc/Australia/Angus and Robertson Limited/89 Castlreagh Street, Sydney/1937
133pp, unillus., clo. 200x125mm. KMM
This story first appeared in the *Bulletin*
American edition

4051 by Henry G. Lamond/KILGOUR'S/MARE/Illustrations/by Lajos Segner/[drawing]/William Morrow and Company/New York 1943
124pp, b/w drawings throughout, clo., 205x140mm. ANL

4052 [drawing] DINGO/The Story of an Outlaw/by Henry G. Lamond/Illustrations by/Enos B. Comstock/William Morrow and Company/New York 1945
206pp, 1p author's note, 1p acknowledgements, b/w chapter headings, clo., 195x125mm. CLRC
Published in Australia as *White Ears the Outlaw*. The author states that the US Government 'took 50,000 copies of *Dingo* for Armed Services, and 30,000 for advanced schools'.
German edition

4053 Henry/G. Lamond/DINGO/Geschichte eines Geächteten/Buchergilde Gutenberg Zurich/1948
223pp, 8pp notes & index, unillus., clo., 200x130mm. ANL
German translation of *Dingo*, published in Switzerland.

4054 WHITE EARS/THE OUTLAW/The Story of a Dingo/By/Henry G. Lamond/Angus and Robertson/Sydney London
1949
150pp, unillus., clo., 180x115mm. KMM

4055 DINGO/The Story of an Outlaw/by/Henry G. Lamond/Illustrated by/Enos B. Comstock/[drawing]/Faber and Faber/24 Russell Square/London
1957
203pp (inc. 1p author's note), b/w chapter headings throughout, clo., 200x125mm. ANL
First published in the *Australasian*, Melbourne, in serial form under the title of 'White Ears, the Outlaw'.
French edition

4056 HISTOIRE D'UN HORS-LA-LOI, published by Les Presses de la Cité Paris
Unseen: IFA

4057 BIG RED/by/Henry G. Lamond/Faber and Faber/24 Russell Square/London
1953
284pp (inc. 4pp glossary & 1p author's note), unillus., clo., 200x130mm. ANL
Second imp. 1953. KP
American edition

4058 Henry G. Lamond/KANGAROO/The John Day Company/New York
1953 [slightly different version of *Big Red*]
247pp (inc. 5pp glossary), unillus., clo., 205x140mm. ANL
French edition

4059 GRAND-ROUX, Seigneur de la Brousse
Published by Les Presses de la Cité, Paris, illustrated with photographs
Unseen: IFA

4060 BIG RED/Henry G. Lamond/Sun Books/Melbourne
1965
220pp (inc. 4pp glossary & 1p author's note), unillus., pic. wrappers, 180x110mm. CLRC

4061 THE/MANX STAR/by/Henry G. Lamond/Faber & Faber Ltd./24 Russell Square/London
1954
256pp (inc. 5pp glossary & 1p author's note), unillus., clo., 205x125mm. KMM

4062 TOWSER/THE SHEEP DOG/Henry G. Lamond/Faber and Faber/24 Russell Square/London
1955
270pp (inc. 4pp glossary & 2pp author's note), unillus., clo., 200x130mm. ANL

4063 TOWSER/THE SHEEP DOG/By/Henry G. Lamond/E. P. Dutton and Company, Inc./New York
1956
256pp (inc. 6pp glossary), unillus., clo., 200x140mm. ANL

4064 [vignette]/BRINDLE ROYALIST/A Story/of the Australian Plains/Henry G. Lamond/William Morrow & Company/New York 1946
235pp, 5pp glossary, 1p author's note, 6 f/p illus. by Lajos Segner, clo., 205x135mm. ANL
Another edition, William Morrow 1956, as above

4065 BRINDLE/ROYALIST/A Story of the Australian Plains/[drawing]/Henry G. Lamond/Angus and Robertson/Sydney 1947, London
261pp, 1p author's note, 5 f/p b/w illus.(sgd.'H.C.') , clo., 190x120mm. ANL

4066 BRINDLE ROYALIST/A Story of/the Australian Plains/by/Henry G. Lamond/Faber and Faber Ltd./24 Russell Square/London
1956
207pp (inc. 5pp glossary & 1p author's note), unillus., clo., 205x125mm. KMM

4067 THE RED RUIN MARE/Henry G. Lamond/Faber and Faber/24 Russell Square/London
1958
253pp (inc. 1p glossary & 1p author's note), unillus., clo., 200x130mm. KMM
Second imp. 1963. KP

4068 SHEEP STATION/By/Henry Lamond/Faber and Faber/24 Russell Square/London
1959
224pp (inc. 1p foreword & 2pp glossary), unillus., clo., 200x130mm. ANL

4069 ETIQUETTE OF/BATTLE/Henry G. Lamond/Designed by Robin Hill/Lansdowne Press
Melbourne 1966
187pp (inc. 2pp glossary), 1p acknowledgements, extended t.p., 8 f/p b/w drawings & b/w chapter headings, clo., 235x145mm. KMM
Short stories & sketches.

LAMPEN, C. Dudley

4070 THE STRANDING OF THE/"WHITE ROSE"./A Story of Adventure./By/C. Dudley Lampen,/Author of "The Queen of the Extinct Volcano"/etc. etc./Illustrated by Ernest Prater/Published under the direction of the General Literature /Committee./London:/Society for Promoting Christian Knowledge./Northumberland Avenue, W. C.;/43 Queen Victoria Street, E.C.2/Brighton: 129 North Street./New York: E. & J. B. Young and Co.
n.d. [1899]
222pp, 32pp adv., b/w frontis. & 2 b/w plates, pic. clo., 180x120mm. KMM
Setting is north-western Australia.

4071 Another copy as above, but 3 b/w plates & 16pp adv. KP

4072 THE STRANDING OF/THE "WHITE ROSE"/A Story of Adventure/By/C. Dudley Lampen/Author of "The Queen of the Extinct Volcano," etc./Illustrated by Ernest Prater/London/The Sheldon Press/Northumberland Avenue, W.C./New York and Toronto; The Macmillan Co.
n.d. [inscribed 1928]
221pp & 1p adv., col. frontis. only, pic. clo., 193x130mm. RM

LA NAUZE, J. A.
ALFRED DEAKIN. *See* Great Australians

LANCASTER, William Joseph Cosens
See 'Collingwood, Harry'

Land o' Dreams

4073 LAND O'/DREAMS
n.p., n.d.
10pp, b/w illus. throughout, col. pic. wrappers, cover title, 248x185mm. KMM
Australian content 1p drawing & text of a kangaroo.

LANE, Alfred B. (ed.)
ALLAN'S SCHOOL SONGS
Melbourne n.d. [1931?]
Traditional songs, not Australian

LANE, B. J. (illus.)

4074 THE/ABC BOOK/OF/BEASTS AND BIRDS/and/What I Saw at/The Melbourne Zoo/Specially illustrated by B. J. Lane/[device]/Melbourne:/Andrew Sherar & Co., Printers/101–103 Elizabeth Street/1905
[46]pp, wrappers, cover title, 310x248mm. ANL
Description of animals & birds which are depicted on the verso of each page, the animals of each letter appearing together, with an adv. for Swallow and Ariel's biscuits. Other adv. appear on the recto of each page. Printed throughout in sepia.

LANE, Fred

4075 PATROL/TO THE/KIMBERLEYS/by Fred Lane/Prentice-Hall Inc. New York
1955
218pp (inc. 9pp glossary), 22 b/w photographic illus., clo., 200x130mm. ANL

4076 PATROL/TO THE/KIMBERLEYS/By/Fred Lane/World Adventure Library/Oldbourne/London
1958
216pp (inc. 6pp glossary), 21 b/w photographic illus., clo., 215x140mm. ANL
German translation

4077 DURCH DIE WILDEN KIMBERLEYS: auf Patrouillenrit mit der Australischen Polizei. Zürich, Müller 1959, 273pp, map, 19cm. Unseen: ANB 1962

LANG, Andrew (ed.)

4078 THE RED/TRUE STORY BOOK/Edited by/Andrew Lang/[vignette]/with numerous illustrations by Henry J. Ford/London/Longman, Green, and Co./and New York/1895/All rights reserved
xiipp, 419pp, b/w frontis. & 18 f/p b/w woodcut illus. throughout, clo. with title & decoration in gilt on spine & front cover, g.e., 180x120mm. CLRC
Contents include: The Pitcairn Islanders pp238–46; The Burke and Wills Exploring Expedition pp324–45.

4079 THE RED TRUE STORY BOOK/Edited by/Andrew Lang/(Adapted for School Use) with 41 illustrations/by/Henry J. Ford/[device]/New Impression/Longmans, Green, and Co./39 Paternoster Row, London/New York and Bombay/1898/All rights reserved
viiipp, 165pp & 13pp notes (1p adv. precedes text), b/w frontis., b/w illus. in text, pic. clo., 178x120mm. KMM
Includes The Burke and Wills Exploring Expedition pp80–102. Does not include The Pitcairn Islanders.

LANG, Jean

4080 WITH/BOBBY/AND/ANNE/IN/BEELOO/by/Jean Lang/Being the adventures of two children/

among the wildfowers of the Swan/District of Western Australia/Illustrated by the author
Paterson Press Ltd, 65 Murray St, Perth, n.d. [1946]
17pp, col. illus. throughout, bd., 250x200mm. ANL
As above, but wrappers. KMM

4081 [drawing]/MY/ANIMAL/BOOK/by/Jean Lang
n.d. [1948?]
9pp, col. illus. on every page with 2 lines text, soft pic. bd. (back cover illus. adv.), cover title, 147x124mm. WJSB

LANG, John

4082 THE STORY OF/CAPTAIN COOK/By/John Lang/[device]/London: T. C. & E. C. Jack/34 Henrietta Street, W.C./and Edinburgh
n.d. [copy inscribed 1907]
119pp, col. frontis. & 7 f/p col. illus. sgd 'Will B. Robinson', clo. (with col. onlay on front cover), 145x115mm. The Children's Heroes Series. KMM

4083 THE STORY OF/CAPTAIN COOK/By/John Lang/with pictures by/W. Heath Robinson/[circlet of leaves]/London: T. C. & E. C. Jack/New York: E. P. Dutton
n.d. [prize 1907]
viiipp, 119pp, col. frontis. & 7 f/p col. illus., clo. with col. pic. onlay on front cover, 144x114mm. KP
Illus. as in previous ed. signed Will B. Robinson.

4084 The Children's Heroes Series/THE STORY OF/CAPTAIN COOK/By/John Lang/with Pictures by/Will B. Robinson/London: T. C. & E. C. Jack Ltd., 35 and 36 Paternoster Row, E.C./and Edinburgh
n.d. [prize 1928]
119pp, f/p col. frontis. & 7 f/p col. illus., clo., 160x110mm. KMM

LANG, [Dr] W. H.

4085 Romance of Empire/AUSTRALIA/By/W. H. Lang/With twelve reproductions from original drawings/in colour by/G. W. Lambert/[drawing]/London: T. C. & E. C. Jack/16 Henrietta Street, W.C./and Edinburgh
n.d. [1908]
300pp (inc. 1p note & 4pp index), col. frontis. & 11 f/p col. illus., 2 f/p b/w maps, pic. clo., 210x145mm. ANL

4086 Another copy, as above, but publisher's address 67 Long Acre, W.C. and with col. onlay on front cover. KMM

4087 Another copy as above, n.d. (inscribed 1913) but with dark blue clo. bdg with crown & spray of laurel & title & author in gilt & red on front cover, & title, author and Southern Cross in shield on spine, 210x144mm. KP

4088 Romance of Empire/AUSTRALIA/By/W. H. Lang/With twelve reproductions from original drawings/in colour by/G. W. Lambert/[drawing]/London: T. C. & E. C. Jack/New York: Frederick A. Stokes Co.
n.d.
Details as above. An edition prepared for the American market, although printed by R. & R. Clark, Edinburgh. It has a different title page, with the publisher's imprint reset, & the American publisher's name 'Stokes' appears at the base of the spine. The pictorial binding differs from above. RM

4089 Another copy with publisher's imprint 'Thomas Nelson and Sons Ltd. (Incorporating T. C. and E. C. Jack, Ltd.)'. AJH

4090 Romance of Empire/AUSTRALIA/By/W.H.Lang/with twelve reproductions from original drawings/in colour by/G. W. Lambert/[drawing]/London/The Caxton Publishing Company/Clun [*sic*] House, Surrey St. W.C.
n.d.
Details as before, but plain clo. bdg with gilt dec. on front cover. KP

LANG, W. R.

SHEEP AND WOOL. *See* Industry in Australia

LANGFORD-SMITH, Keith

4091 DRAKE'S DRUM/and other stories from the Sky Pilot's Log/By/Keith Langford-Smith, F.R.G.S./Author of "Sky Pilot in Arnhem Land"/"Sky Pilot's Last Flight"/Christian Press/Sydney/Australia
First edition 1951
141pp, portrait frontis. only, clo., 180x115mm. KMM
Short stories of C.M.S. missionaries based on their experiences at the Roper River & in South Australia, Queensland, central Australia & the Pacific Islands, & broadcast over Station 2CH Sydney.

LANGLANDS, Isobel

4092 SONGS OF THE BUSH/FOR CHILDREN/Written and Composed by/Isobel Langlands/Illustrated by Quentin G. Sutton/Commonwealth of Australia:/Edward A. Vidler/178 Collins Street, Melbourne
n.d. [1926]
28pp, 2pp adv., b/w illus. throughout, wrappers, 300x240mm. CLRC
Words & music of the following songs: 'The Dingo', 'The Possum', 'The Iguana', 'The Crow', 'The Parrot', 'The Lyre Bird', &c. (12 songs in all).

LANGLANDS, Mabel

4093 POEMS/OF A/YOUNG/WEST AUSTRALIAN/Mabel Langlands/Printed and Published by Paterson Printing Press Ltd. 882 Hay Street, Perth, Western Australia
n.d. [1941]
42pp, unillus., wrappers, 185x110mm. NSL:M
Poems of a teenage girl, but not intended for children.

LANGLEY, Nina

4094 Nina Langley/EXPLORATION/IN THE ANTARCTIC/[device]—[Great Endeavour]/Illustrated by Gilbert Dunlop/Blackie & Son Ltd./London and Glasgow/1954
71pp, 1p foreword by Admiral Lord Mountevans & 1p table, b/w frontis. & b/w drawings in text, limp clo., 185x135mm. NSL:M
Contents include: 'The Courage of Three', the adventures of the last supporting party to Captain Scott's Polar Party, 1911–12, & 'Inexpressible Island', the adventures of the northern party in Victoria Land during Captain Scott's Last Expedition to the Antarctic 1911–12.

4095 EXPLORATION/IN THE ANTARCTIC/Nina Langley/[device]/Blackie: London and Glasgow
n.d.
Details as above, Great Endeavour Books. KMM

LANGSFORD, Dorothy M.

4096 THE WATERBABIES/And Other Stories/Dorothy M. Langsford
Hussey & Gillingham Ltd., Adelaide 1913
98pp, 6 b/w illus. by author, dec. wrappers, 115x135mm. CLRC
Contains 14 fairy stories.

LANSER, Edith

4097 SUSAN AND RICHARD/Written and illustrated by/Edith Lanser/Australasian Publishing Company Pty. Ltd. Sydney
1945
34pp, part-col. drawings throughout, bd., dec. e/p, 200x150mm. ANL

4098 CAROLINE LISTENS/Written and illustrated by/

Edith Lanser/Australasian Publishing Company Pty. Ltd., Sydney
1948
32pp, part-col. drawings throughout, dec. bd., dec. e/p, 180x250mm. ANL

LANSING, Alfred
4099 SHACKLETON'S/VALIANT VOYAGE/Alfred Lansing/University of London Press Ltd./Warwick Square, London, E.C.4.
1963
159pp, 8pp b/w photographic illus., b/w map, clo., 185x120mm. KMM
Photographic illustrations provided by the Royal Geographical Society.

LA PÉROUSE
4100 THE LIFE/OF/LA PEROUSE,/the celebrated and unfortunate/French Navigator./Including his/Voyage, Shipwreck, & Subsequent Adventures/in a/Desolate Island,/on the/Northern Coast of Japan;/when he was discovered by/Madame La Pérouse./Third Edition./On this interesting History is founded, the pantomimical/ Drama of/PEROUSE, or The Desolate Island,/ Performing, with unbounded applause, at the Theatre Royal,/Covent Garden;/an accurate description of which,/including the Songs, &c. is also added./ Sommers Town;/Printed and Published by A. Neil, 30 Chalton Street;/and sold by all other Booksellers./ 1801/[price one shilling]
64pp (inc. 2pp preface) & 6pp 'An accurate description of the pantomimical Drama of Pérouse; or The Desolate Island', engraved frontis., wrappers, 165x100mm. NSL:M

4101 Bysh's Edition/of the/VOYAGES AND ADVENTURES/OF/LA PÉROUSE./—/To which is added/the/Life of Hatem Tai,/or the/Generosity/of an/Arabian Prince/—/Embellished with Eight Coloured Engravings./—/London:/John Bysh, 8 Cloth Fair, West-Smithfield,/and/Thomas Richardson, Friar Gate, Derby./—/MDCCCXXIX.
36pp, col. frontis. & 3 other col. illus., pic. wrappers, 136x90mm. ANL

LARSEN, Egon
4102 SIR VIVIAN FUCHS
Phoenix
110pp, b/w photographic frontis. & b/w photographic illus. throughout, clo. ,184x124mm. KP
Lacks t.p.

LARSEN, Heather
4103 THE HAPPY BUSH/by Heather Larsen/illustrated by Patricia Mullins/Paul Hamlyn/Sydney London New York Toronto
Dee Why West, NSW, 1972
26pp, col. illus. throughout, pic. bd., pic. e/p, 310x225mm. ANL

'LATHAM, Mavis'
See Clark, M. T.

LATURNER, Hans-Jürgen
4104 Hans-Jürgen Laturner/GOLD/AM KANGURUH-FLUSS/Franz Schneider Verlag
n.d. [copy acquired 1957]
118pp, 3pp adv., b/w frontis. & b/w drawings in text, illus. by Walter Rieck, pic. bd., 185x120mm. NSL:M

LAUBER, Patricia
4105 Junior Science Book of/PENGUINS/By/Patricia Lauber/Frederick Muller Limited/London
1964
64pp (inc. 1p index), b/w photographs throughout, pic. clo., 222x156mm. KP

4106 THE SURPRISING/KANGAROOS/and other Pouched Mammals/by Patricia Lauber/Illustrated/with Photographs/Random House/New York
1965
81pp (inc. 3pp photographs, 1p preface) & 1p adv., b/w photographs throughout, pic. clo., 230x160mm. NSL:M
Gateway Books.

The Laughing Jack Picture Book
4107 THE/LAUGHING JACK/PICTURE/BOOK/The Most Amusing & Instructive/Child's Book in Australia/For Children of all ages/Look Read/Learn & Laugh/Underneath the Southern Cross/Where the Sky is mostly blue/Here the laughing Jack laughs all day/ And his picture Book makes you laugh too. [T.p. missing in copy seen]
Wholly set up and printed in Australia by the Farrow Falcon Press, 226–230 Little Lonsdale St, Melbourne, n.d. [1914?]
102pp, b/w illus., pic. bd., cover title, 275x210mm. Grant
Stories, poems, jokes, riddles, rhymes, puzzles & drawings from books published in the previous two decades or so. Australian contents include: 'Advance Australia Fair', & several other poems, including 'The Good Little Jackass' from Allan's *Australian Children's Songs* & 'The Kangaroo' by A. Pratt.

LAURENCE, Hugh
4108 LITTLE FOLK/IN MANY LANDS/by/Hugh Laurence/Author of Tales of an Old Yew Tree/ [drawing]/Blackie and Son Limited/London Glasgow Bombay
n.d. [inscribed 20/1/1914]
128pp, 2pp publisher's note, 12 f/p col. illus. & 1 double-spread col. illus., b/w illus. throughout, dec. clo., 210x150mm. Grant
Contains a section on Australia (3pp), & an article (2pp), entitled 'Lost in the Woods' which, with one f/p b/w illustration, relates the story of Jane Duff.

Lavender's Blue
See Blue Wren Books

LAW, Beverley
4109 AN AUSTRALIAN XMAS/a Play/by/Beverley Law/also/Two Australian Poems/The Australian Bush/and/The Two Launcestons/by the same author/ London/Arthur H. Stockwell Ltd./29 Ludgate Hill, E.C.4.
n.d. [1939]
39pp, unillus., bd., 180x120mm. ANL

LAW, Marjorie J.
4110 Whitcombe's Story Books/WENDY FAY/By/ Marjorie J. Law/(for ages 8–9 years)/[drawing]/ Whitcombe & Tombs Pty. Ltd./Melbourne—Sydney—Perth
n.d. [1947]
48pp, b/w frontis. & 3 f/p b/w illus. by F. M. Gunn, wrappers, 180x120mm. *ANL*
See McLaren 374

LAW, Palmer
4111 JOLLY/BUSH COBBERS/words and music by Palmer Law/An Educational nature study of Australian Fauna in a/musical setting. Suitably arranged for Junior Music Students./Six different little songs and melodies
Standard Newspapers Pty Ltd, Cheltenham, n.d. [1952?]

4pp, pic. cover, line drawings, 305x245mm. KP
Art work by F. O'Brien.

LAW, Winifred

4112 THROUGH SPACE/TO THE PLANETS/By/Winifred Law/Illustrated by/Dick Alderton/Sydney/New Century Press Pty. Ltd./3 North York Street/1944
174pp, b/w frontis. & 17 b/w illus., bd., 185x120mm. ANL
• Rpt as above, 1945. TG; 1946, KP

4113 RANGERS OF/THE UNIVERSE/By/Winifred Law/Illustrated by/Dick Alderton/Sydney/New Century Press Pty. Ltd./3 North York Street/1945
176pp, b/w frontis. & 4 f/p b/w illus., line drawings in text, bd., 185x120mm. KMM

4114 Second and third editions 1946, as above. Grant

LAWRENCE, S. A.

See Littlejohns, R. T. & Lawrence, S. A., BIRDS OF OUR BUSH

LAWRENCE, Stephen

4115 CROCODILES/OF THE/GULF COUNTRY/By Stephen Lawrence/School Projects Pty. Limited Sydney 1966
40pp, line drawings & map, illus. by Lenore Andrews, stiff dec. wrappers, 210x130mm. BBC Australian Scene Series.

LAWRENCE, V. L.

4116 BINDI/by/V. L. Lawrence/Harvester Press Canberra 1969. First publ. July 1969; rpt Aug 1969
[32]pp, 3 f/p b/w drawings, b/w text illus. throughout, stiff pic. wrappers, 190x147mm. KMM
Illus. Jill & Judith Clingan. Story of an Aboriginal boy.

LAWRIE, Margaret

4117 TALES/FROM/TORRES/STRAIT/[drawing]/collected and translated by Margaret Lawrie/University of Queensland Press
St. Lucia, Queensland, 1972
53pp (inc. 9pp glossary), col. & b/w illus. throughout, pic. clo. (alternatively available paper bound), map e/p, 235x185mm. KMM
Illustrated by island artists: Kala Waia, Segar Passi, John Baud & George Passi; map by the author
Also the author of *Myths and Legends of Torres Strait* (1970) which was not intended as a children's book.

LAWSON, Henry

4118 Henry Lawson THE LOADED DOG/With illustrations by/Walter Cunningham/[drawing]/Angus and Robertson
Sydney 1970
[26]pp, extended t.p. (with biographical note on author), col. illus. throughout, pic. bd., pic. e/p, 290x225mm. *Young Australia Series.* BBC
• Rpt 1971, KP

4119 The Junior Library of Australian Books/THE CHILDREN'S/LAWSON/Selected by/Colin Roderick/Angus and Robertson/Sydney—London
1949
148pp, 5pp introduction, b/w frontis. & 2 b/w illus., bd., 185x125mm. ANL
Includes some verse as well as stories.
See also Howard and Levy, Australian Story Sampler

LAWSON, Jim

4120 THE LAND/OF/DREAMS/AND MORE/DREAMS/Verses by/Jim Lawson/illustrated by/Unk White
Frank Johnson, Sydney 1944
12pp, b/w drawings throughout, wrappers, cover title, 275x160mm. ANL

LAWSON, Sylvia

J. F. ARCHIBALD
MARY GILMORE *See* Great Australians

LAWSON, Will

4121 WHEN/COBB AND CO./WAS KING/By Will Lawson/Author of "The Laughing Buccaneer"/Angus and Robertson Limited/89 Castlereagh Street, Sydney/1936
305pp, 1p author's note, unillus., clo., 185x120mm. ANL

4122 WHEN COBB AND CO./WAS KING/By/Will Lawson/Angus and Robertson Limited/Sydney: London/1947
306pp, b/w drawings throughout, illus. by Rhys Williams, clo., 185x120mm. ANL

4123 WHEN COBB & CO./WAS KING/By Will Lawson/Frank Johnson Pty Ltd./350 George St. Sydney
n.d. [194-?]
130pp, unillus., pic. wrappers, 185x140mm. KP
A Magpie selected story no. 66.

4124 WHEN COBB AND CO./WAS KING/by Will Lawson/[device]/Frank Johnson Pty. Ltd./350 George St. Sydney
n.d. [presentation copy dated 26/2/54]
132pp, pic. wrappers, 190x135mm. Grant

4125 WHEN COBB AND CO./WAS KING/by/Will Lawson/[vignette]/[publisher's device]/Angus and Robertson
Third edition 1959
241pp, 1p dedication & 2pp author's note to 2nd ed. [preceding text], b/w drawings in text, illus. by Rhys Williams, clo., dec. e/p, 215x135mm. BBC
• Rpt 1961. BBC

4126 WHEN COBB AND CO./WAS KING/by/Will Lawson/[device]/Angus and Robertson
Second ed. 1947; 3rd ed. 1959; rpt 1961; first publ. in Pacific Books 1967
viiipp (inc. 2pp author's note, 1p verse), 241pp, b/w chapter headings & b/w drawings, pic. wrappers, 184x110mm. KP
Illus. Rhys Williams.
• Rpt 1970 as above, but
[device]/Pacific Books.
Angus & Robertson. KMM
As above, but
col. pic. wrappers with variant illus. KMM
A book for children as well as general readers to enjoy

LAWSON, Will & HICKEY, Tom

4127 GALLOPING/WHEELS/By/Will Lawson/and/Tom Hickey/Angus and Robertson/Sydney: London/1947
215pp, 2pp foreword, b/w illus. in text, clo., 185x120mm. ANL

LAWTON, Eva

THE PIXIE O'HARRIS FAIRY BOOK. *See* O'Harris, Pixie

4128 SONGS/OF/FAIRYLAND/by/Eva Lawton Sands & McDougall, Printers Adelaide [1924]
16pp, illus. wrappers?, 180x105mm. NSL:M
Verses.

LE BRETON, Agatha [pseud. 'Miriam Agatha']

4129 GRANNIE'S ROSARY/BEADS/and Other Stories/By/Miriam Agatha (Sydney)/Melbourne:/The Australian Catholic Truth Society,/312 Lonsdale Street
n.d. [1910]
32pp, unillus., 175x115mm. NSL:M

Copy seen bound with the following uniform booklets, all n.d. [1910], 32pp. NSL:M
4130 PEGGY'S PRESENT
4131 FOR THE HOLY SOULS
4132 ROSES AND ROSARIES

4133 NELLIE DORAN/A Story of Australian/Home and School Life/By/Miriam Agatha/With a preface by His Grace the Coadjutor/Archbishop of Brisbane, Queensland/Sydney/E. J. Dwyer/705 George Street/ 1914/Printed in England
240pp (inc. 2pp preface), unillus., clo., 180x120mm. KP
4134 NELLIE DORAN/A Story of Home and/School Life/By/Miriam Agatha/With a Preface by His Grace the Coadjutor/Archbishop of Brisbane/R. & T. Washbourne, Ltd./Paternoster Row, London/and at Manchester, Birmingham, and Glasgow/1915 All rights reserved
Details as above. KP
4135 NELLIE DORAN/A Story of Australian/Home and School Life/By/Miriam Agatha/With a Preface by His Grace The Coadjutor/Archbishop of Brisbane, Queensland/Second Impression/Sydney/E. J. Dwyer/ 711 George Street/1923/Printed in England
240pp (inc. 2pp preface), unillus., clo., 185x120mm. CLRC

4136 "LITTLE THÉRESE"/A True Story for Little/ Readers/By/Miriam Agatha (Sydney, N.S.W.)/Melbourne:/Australian Catholic Truth Society,/312 Lonsdale St./No. 207 One Penny Advocate Press, n.d.
16pp, unillus., wrappers, cover title, 178x120mm. KMM
List of other publications by ACTS inside front cover & inside & outside back cover. Life of St Thérèse.

LE FEBVRE, Joan & others
4137 CAUGHT/RED-HANDED!/and other Stories for Boys/[drawing]/Printed by Morris & Walker, Melbourne./for the Publishers. Offset Printing Coy. Pty Limited, Sydney
n.d. [1945]
32pp, part-col. illus. throughout, pic. wrappers, 240x177mm. KP

LE SOUEF, A. S.
4138 THE/BROWNIE TWINS/The Story of a Ringtail Family/By/A. S. Le Souëf/Illustrated by/Walter Cunningham/[vignette in colour]/John Sands Pty. Ltd./Sydney Melbourne Brisbane Adelaide Perth Hobart
n.d. [1955]
31pp, 7 f/p col. illus. & other col. drawings in text throughout, dec. bd., 235x185mm. KMM

LE SOUEF, J. Cecil
4139 [drawing]/ZOOIE'S/NATURE/BOOK/Number One/THE LYRE BIRD/In which will be found Zooie's adventures while looking for/Lyre Birds/by/J. Cecil Le Souëf/Ilustrated by the author/Copyrighted 1933 by the Author/Wholly set up and printed in Australia by Pelzer J. Lee 309 Queen Street, Melbourne
12pp, b/w illus., dec. wrappers, 240x180mm. NSL:M

LEACH, Jessie
4140 "THE WHIRLIWINDI"/Book of/Nature Study Poems/and/Stories in Verse/by/Jessie Leach, L.A.B./Wholly set up and printed in Australia by/ Carroll's Ltd., Printers and Publishers,/566 Hay Street, Perth./1940/Proceeds in aid of Soldier's Camp Comforts Fund.
39pp, b/w drawings in text throughout, wrappers, 235x140mm. ANL

LEADBEATER, E. H.
4141 Imperial edition No. 481/SONGS OF/ HAPPINESS/Words by/E. H. Leadbeater/Music by/ E. H. Leadbeater & Anthony Hall/[list of contents]/ Allan & Co. Pty. Ltd./Melbourne, Adelaide Bendigo 1940
[16]pp (last page adv.), col. pic. wrappers signed 'Dulcie A', 255x175mm. ANL
4142 Imperial Edition No. 481/SONGS OF/HAPPINESS
Another copy, but
col. pic. wrappers, 1/6 net on front cover, adv. inside & out of back cover & inside front cover. KP

LEAR, Melva
4143 DANGEROUS HOLIDAY/Five Young Treasure-seekers in the/Abrolhos Islands/by/Melva Lear/Illustrations by/Joan Abbott/Angus and Robertson
Sydney 1959
163pp, b/w frontis. & 10 b/w illus., clo., 215x135mm. KMM

4144 RIVER FUGITIVE/The Story of a Boy with a Secret/By/Melva Lear/Author of/Dangerous Holiday/ with illustrations by Wal Stackpool/Angus and Robertson
Sydney 1963
158pp, b/w frontis. & b/w drawings in text, clo., 220x135mm. CLRC

4145 A SECRET TO/SELL/A Story of the First Settlement in Western Australia/by/Melva Lear/ Illustrated by Wal Stackpool/[device]/Angus and Robertson
Sydney 1965
147pp, 1p author's note, b/w chapter headings, clo., 220x135mm. CLRC

Learning about Australia
4146 LEARNING ABOUT/AUSTRALIA/Featuring Working in/Colonial Days/39c/[illus.]/Ideal for School Project Work
Paul Hamlyn, Dee Why West, NSW, 1971
[18]pp (inc. inside both front & back covers), col. illus. with explanatory text below on each page, col. pic. wrappers, 276x200mm. KMM

LEASK, May
4147 Imperial Edition NO 615/RHYME TIME/for piano by/May Leask/Allan & Co Pty Ltd/Melb. Ad. Ben/ Printed in Aust
1949
12pp, unillus., col. pic. wrappers, 310x230mm. VSL

LEAVENS, George
See Newell, Crosby & Leavens, George

LEAVEY, Mary Raphael
JOHN BEDE POLDING. *See* Great Australians

'LEBRUN, Henri' [pseud.]
4148 VOYAGES/ET AVENTURES/DU/CAPITAINE COOK,/Par. Henri Lebrun,/Ornée/de quatre gravures sur acier./Nouvelle édition,/revue et corrigée/Par un Société d'ecclésiastiques./Librairie d'éducation de périsse frères,/Lyon, [space] Paris,/Grande Rue Mecière, [space] Rue de Pot-de-Fer/No. 33 [space] St.-Sulpice, No. 8/Tours,/Ad. Mame et Cie, Éditeurs./ 1839
312pp, b/w engraved frontis. & 3 b/w engravings, marbled paper-covered bd., marbled e/p, 170x100mm. RM

Book divided into 3 parts with continuous pagination. First voyage, pp1–89; Second voyage, pp90–176; Third voyage, pp177–310, & 2pp contents.

4149 VOYAGES ET AVENTURES/DU/CAPITAINE COOK/Par/Henri Le Brun/Nouvelle Edition/ornée de deux gravures sur acier/Revue et approuvée par une société d/Ecclésiastiques/[device]/Tours/Ad. Mame et Cie. Imprimeurs-Libraires/1845
236pp & 2pp contents, engraved frontis. & 1 other engraving, bd., 172x104mm. NSL:M

4150 VOYAGES ET AVENTURES/du/CAPITAINE COOK/Par Henri Lebrun/nouvelle édition/Revue et approuvée par une société d'Ecclésiastiques/[device]/Tours/Ad. Mame et Cie, Imprimeurs-Libraires/1852
236pp, b/w engraved frontis. & 1 f/p engraving, re-bound, 173x100mm. CLRC
Bound together with
VOYAGES ET AVENTURES/de/LAPÉROUSE/par F. Valentin/Auteur de l'Histoire des Croisades, etc/ Quatrième édition/[vignette]/Tours/Ad Mame et Cie, Imprimeurs-Libraires/1844
288pp (inc. 8pp introduction, 4pp appendix & 2pp contents), engraved frontis. & t.p., 2 f/p b/w engravings, 173x100mm. CLRC

LEE, Mrs Harrison [Bessie, née Vickery, later Cowie]

4151 AUNTIE FAITH'S/RHYMES/by Mrs Harrison Lee./[medallion portrait surrounded by flags & wording "For God and Home and Every Land"] Price One Shilling
J. J. Howard Printer, 372 Post Office Place, W. Melbourne, obtainable at Temperance Hall, Russell St, Melbourne, n.d. [copy inscribed 1911]
48pp, cover title—inside 'A Book for Big and Little Children', line drawings & b/w photographic illus., pic. bd., 275x220mm. CLRC
Poems, lessons, stories on Temperance mostly for children.

4152 AUNTIE FAITH'S/TRAVELS/By/Mrs Harrison Lee Cowie/Author of/One of Australia's Daughters, One of God's Lamplighters/Marriage and Heredity, etc/ London/Richard J. James, Temperance Publishing House/London House Yard, Paternoster Row E.C.
n.d. [verses dated '94, '03]
48pp, b/w illus., bd., 275x220mm. NSL:M
Stories, verses, texts on Temperance or religion; contributions by Mabel Beddow, Robert Powell; verse illus. with b/w photograph precedes text.

LEE, Jennifer

4153 The Enchanted Castle Series/BILLY/BLUEGUM/ RHYMES
W. H. Honey Pub. Coy, 31 Cunningham Street, Sydney
16pp, 8 b/w illus., col. pic. card covers, cover title, 240x180mm. JH
Page 1 has b/w drawing then 'Billy Bluegum Rhymes/ By Jennifer Lee'.

LEE, Leslie

4154 THE ROAD/TO WIDGEWONG/By/Leslie Lee/ Australia:/Cornstalk Publishing Company/89 Castlereagh Street, Sydney/1928
259pp, b/w frontis. & 2 f/p b/w illus. by Edgar A. Holloway, clo., 185x120mm. KMM

4155 [drawing]/FURRY TALES/Told By/Leslie Lee/ Illustrated by/Angus McGregor/Dymock's Book Arcade/Limited/Sydney/[drawing]
n.d. [1950]
66pp (inc. 2pp foreword by C. K. Thompson), 2 part. col. illus., 4 f/p b/w illus. & b/w drawings in text, dec. bd., 270x215mm. CLRC

4156 MORE FURRY TALES/Illustrated by/Angus McGregor/Told by Leslie Lee/Dymock's Book Arcade Ltd., Sydney
n.d. [1953]
55pp, col. frontis. & b/w drawings throughout, bd., 270x215mm. KMM

LEE, Norman E.

4157 TRAVEL AND TRANSPORT/THROUGH THE AGES/by/Norman E. Lee/History Master, Scotch College Junior School, Melbourne/Melbourne University Press
1951
154pp (inc. 2pp chronological appendix), b/w photographic illus. throughout, wrappers, 210x130mm. NSL:M
Supplementary history textbook.

4158 SEAWAY/TO/ADVENTURE/by/Norman Lee/ Ward, Lock & Co., Limited/London and Melbourne
1956
160pp, b/w frontis. only, clo., 182x120mm. NSL:M

LEE, Sarah [Mrs Robert, née Wallis, formerly Mrs T. E. Bowditch]

4159 ADVENTURES IN AUSTRALIA;/or, the/ Wanderings of Captain Spencer/in the Bush and the Wilds./Containing accurate/Descriptions of the Habits of the Natives,/and the/Natural Productions and Features of/the Country./By/Mrs R. Lee,/(Formerly Mrs T. E. Bowditch)/Author of "The African Wanderers", "Memoirs of/Cuvier" &c/with illustrations by J. S. Prout,/Member of the New Water-Colour Society./London:/Grant and Griffith,/ Successors to/J. Harris./Corner of St Paul's Churchyard./MDCCCLI
xi+364pp & 20pp adv., engr. frontis. & 3 other f/p engravings, dec. clo, 168x100mm. CLRC

4160 ADVENTURES IN AUSTRALIA;/or the/ Wanderings of Captain Spencer/in the Bush and the Wilds./Containing accurate/Descriptions of the Habits of the Natives,/and the/Natural Productions and Features of/the Country./By/Mrs R. Lee,/(Formerly Mrs. T. E. Bowditch,)/Author of "The African Wanderers", "Anecdotes of Animals", etc./with illustrations by J. S. Prout/Second Edition, revised./ London:/Grant and Griffith./(Successors to J. Harris.)/Corner of St. Paul's Churchyard./MDCCCLIII
xiv+370pp, 24pp adv., engraved frontis. & 3 f/p engraved illus., blind-stamped clo. (dec. gilt spine), 175x105mm. HBM
Advertisements headed: 'Original Juvenile Library'.

4161 ADVENTURES IN AUSTRALIA, 'sixth thousand', n.d. prize label 1879-80, title in gilt on front cover & in gilt panel on spine, otherwise as below. KP

4162 ADVENTURES IN AUSTRALIA:/The Wanderings of Captain Spencer/in the Bush and the Wild./ Containing/Accurate descriptions of the habits of the natives/and the natural productions and features/of the country./By/Mrs R. Lee,/Author of "The African Wanderers", "Anecdotes of Animals", etc./with illustrations by J. S. Prout/Seventh thousand, Revised./[device]/Griffith and Farran,/Successors to Newbery and Harris,/west corner of St. Paul's Churchyard, London./New York: E. P. Dutton and Co.
n.d. [inscribed 1883]
xvi+336pp, 32pp adv. (Griffith & Farran's 'Catalogue of Books for the Young of all Ages'), engraved frontis., 3 f/p b/w engravings, pic. clo., 175x115mm. KMM
Repro. of 'The Kangaroo Hunt' blocked in black on front cover; title in gilt.

4163 ADVENTURES IN AUSTRALIA:/The Wanderings

of Captain Spencer/in the Bush and the Wilds/ containing...[6 lines as above] Griffith Farran Okeden & Welsh/Newbery House, Charing Cross Road/London and Sydney
n.d.[189-? prize label 1902]
xvi+336pp, frontis. & 3 f/p engravings, pic. clo., 185x117mm. KMM
Captain Spencer & Kinchela blocked in col. on front cover; title in gilt.
• Rpt as above, with g.e. & lettering in gilt on front cover, n.d. [prize 1895]. KP

4164 THE/AUSTRALIAN WANDERERS/or the/ Adventures of Captain Spencer/His Horse and Dog/by Mrs. R. Lee/author of "African Crusoes", "Anecdotes of Birds", "Anecdotes of Animals" etc. with illustrations/Boston/Lee and Shepard, Publishers,/ New York./Lee, Shepard and Dillingham, 49 Green Street, 1872
472pp, 8pp adv., b/w engraved frontis. & 3 b/w engravings in text, dec. clo., 170x105mm. Grant

4165 THE/AUSTRALIAN WANDERERS/or The/ Adventures of Captain Spencer,/His Horse and Dog./ By Mrs. R. Lee,/Author of "African Crusoes", "Anecdotes of Birds", "Anecdotes of Animals", &c./with illustrations./Boston:/Lee & Shepard, Publishers,/1876
472pp, engraved frontis. & 3 engraved illus., clo., 195x120mm. CLRC

LEE, Turner (ed.)
COLE'S GREAT BOOK FOR BOYS and COLE'S GREAT BOOK FOR BOYS No. 2. *See* Cole, E. W.

LEETE, Frances
4166 LIFE,/WEALTH/AND/POWER/[quotation—4 lines]/the story of water in Australia/Presented by The Coca-Cola Export Corporation
n.p. [Melbourne], n.d.
60pp (inc. 4pp index & 1p foreword & acknowledgements), col. photographs, maps & diagrams throughout, pic. wrappers, 240x180mm. KP

4167 The same, revised ed. 1971, as above. KP

Left Ashore or Life at Coral Creek
4168 LEFT ASHORE/OR LIFE/AT CORAL CREEK
Published by Mackenzie & Macmillan, 7 Red Lion Court, Fleet Street, London, n.d. [1890?]
32pp, 3 f/p b/w illus., pic. wrappers (with adv. inside front cover & outside back cover), cover title, 185x125mm. The British Empire Library. KMM
Boys' adventure story of Australian life. Price one penny; No. 1 in The 'British Empire' Library advertised on back wrapper. No. 2 listed as 'The Three Young Pioneers: Being the Interesting Sequel to No. 1'. No. 9 in the series was 'Among the Islands; Life in the Pacific Isles with Cannibals, Natives & Kind Folk'.

The Legend of the Coming of the First Kangaroo
4169 THE LEGEND/OF THE COMING OF THE/FIRST KANGAROO/Dedicated/to the patriotic efforts/of The Australia Day Council/to fittingly celebrate/Australia's National Day/January Twenty-six/[device—Les Fryer, Truesdell Press, Caulfield, Victoria]/Melbourne 1948
100 copies printed by Les Fryer and Phillip Chaffey at the Truesdell Press, Caulfield from handset type with col. block cut in linoleum by Lindsay A. Dane to commemorate Australia Day 1984. Copy no. 58
[24]pp (inc. several blank), 2 lino-cut illus., wrappers, 203x140mm. ANL
Text includes Barron Field's 'The Kangaroo' & an anonymous legend. Book printed for fine-book collectors; not for children.

LEGGE, H. S.
4170 ON THE/EDGE OF THE BUSH/By/H. S. Legge/ [device]/Commonwealth of Australia:/Edward A. Vidler/189 Little Collins Street, Melbourne
1925
64pp, unillus., wrappers, 185x125mm. CLRC
Verses, many of which are addressed to children.

LEGRAND, Edy
4171 VOYAGES ET/GLORIEUSES DÉCOUVERTES/ DES/GRANDS/NAVIGATEURS/ET EXPLORATEURS/FRANÇAIS/Illustré par Edy Legrand/[vignette]/Tolmer/Imprimeur Éditeur/À Paris, 13 Quai d'Anjou, dans l'Ile St. Louis.
1921
[32]pp (inc. 3pp introduction), 1 f/p col. illus., 1 double-spread col. illus., col. illus. throughout, 2 fold-out col. maps, col. illus. bd., pic. e/p, 380x275mm. RM
Various French explorers of the Pacific region discussed, including La Pérouse, Bougainville, D'Entrecasteaux, Dumont d'Urville & also Captain Cook. The second map is of the Pacific region. The book is remarkable for the brilliance of the hand-stencilled, water-col. illus. in the Art Deco styles. Legrand appears to have written the text as well as illus. the book.

LEHANE, Wendy (ed.)
4172 ALL ABOUT/AUSTRALIA AND NEW ZEALAND/ edited by/Wendy Lehane/illustrated by/Latif Hutchings/and Cynthia Leech/[device]/Paul Hamlyn/ London New York Sydney Toronto
Dee Why West, NSW, 1970
240pp (inc. 5pp index), col. & part. col. illus. throughout, pic. bd., pic. e/p, 240x180mm. BBC
Factual book in the form of questions & answers.

LEIGH-PEMBERTON, John
4173 AUSTRALIAN/MAMMALS/written and illustrated by/John Leigh-Pemberton/[drawing]/Publishers: Wills & Hepworth Ltd., Loughborough/First published 1970—Printed in England
52pp, 24 f/p col. illus., col. map e/p, pic. bd., 170x110mm. A Ladybird Book. KMM
• Rpt 1972.

LEONETTI, Cynthia
4174 LITTLE/DREAM/by/Cynthia/Leonetti/Illustrated by:/Laurie Sharp/John Taylor/Cynthia Leech/ Copyright 1969 by Artransa Park Television Pty. Ltd. published by Sungravure Pty. Limited of Jones Street, Broadway, at Morley Avenue, Rosebery, N.S.W./on behalf of Artransa Park Television Pty. Limited...
32pp, col. illus. throughout, pic. wrappers, 270x210mm. KMM

LEOPOLD, Keith
4175 EIN ABENTEUER/IN/DEUTSCHLAND/Keith Leopold/Illustrated by/H. E. Oiderman/[device]/ Angus and Robertson
1st publ. 1963, rpt 1964, 1965, 1966, 1967
80pp (inc. 22pp notes &c), b/w illus. throughout, stiff wrappers, 183x123mm. NSL:M
A story for young students of German.

4176 NORA AUS/DER FREMDE/Keith Leopold/ Illustrated by Julie Mattox/Angus and Robertson
Sydney 1968
99pp (inc. 1p introduction, 5pp notes, 21pp vocabulary), b/w frontis. & 11 f/p b/w drawings, limp pic. clo., 180x120mm. NSL:M

Le Petit Messager des Missions Evangéliques
4177 LE/PETIT MESSAGER/DES/MISSIONS ÉVANGÉLIQUES./Dédié a la Jeunesse/Troisième anné./Paris/Librairie de L. R. Delay,/Rue Troncher,2/1846
384pp, engravings in text, marbled boards, 114x72mm. 4 vols, 1844, 1845, 1846, 1847. CLRC
Volume 3 contains 'Mickey, ou le petit garçon de l'Australie du Sud'(pp142-55, with one engraving)
See also Child's Companion & Juvenile Instruction

'LESLIE, J.' [pseud. J. L. Haddon]
4178 YOUTH BUILDS A/MONUMENT/By/J. Leslie/Sydney/N.S.W. Bookstall Company Ltd./Castlereagh and Market Streets/1933
152pp, 2pp foreword, b/w chapter headings, clo., 185x120mm. NSL:M
Experiences of an Australian boy at school & at work in his first job.
• Rpt as above 1934. CLRC

4179 HOME IS THE SAILOR/By/J. Leslie/Author of Youth builds a Monument/Australia/NSW Bookstall Company, Ltd./Castlereagh & Market Streets, Sydney/1934
267pp & 1p foreword, unillus., clo., 184x120mm. KMM

LESSER, Milton
4180 Walt Disney's/STRANGE ANIMALS/OF AUSTRALIA/[col. photograph]/by/Milton Lesser/Whitman Publishing Company Racine, Wisconsin 1963, col. photographs (Alfred & Elma Milotte) throughout, pic. bd., pic. e/p, 232x182mm. ANL
4181 Another copy as above, but imprint Golden Press [device] Sydney. WRT

L'ESTRANGE, Charles James
See 'Strang, Herbert'

LETHBRIDGE, H. O.
4182 Imperial Edition No. 420/AUSTRALIAN/ABORIGINAL SONGS/Melodies Rhythm and Words/Truly and Authentically Aboriginal/Collected and Translated by/Dr H. O. Lethbridge/Accompaniments Arranged by/Arthur S. Loam/Contents [5 songs]/... Allan & Co. Pty Ltd./Melbourne Sydney Adelaide Bendigo . . .
n.d. [196-?]
16pp, pic. wrappers, 303x233mm. KP
Cover dec. with Aboriginal motifs. Price given as 4/- hence pre-1966.

Let's Listen Again
4183 LET'S LISTEN AGAIN/Kindergarten Stories and Verses/Illustrated by Penelope Janic/[drawing]/Angus and Robertson
Sydney 1967
121pp, part-col. t.p. & drawings throughout, dec. clo., dec. e/p. 230x150mm. CLRC

LEVENSON, Dorothy
4184 TOO MANY/POCKETS, Story by Dorothy Levenson/pictures by Ruth Wood/Editorial Consultant: Lilian Moore/[drawing]/Grosset & Dunlap/Publishers/New York, N.Y. 10010
Wonder Books, New York, 1st ed. 1963
60pp, part col. illus. throughout, col. pic. clo., 207x130mm. KP
'Wonder Books easy reader'.
4185 Another copy as above but imprint Wonder Books/1107 Broadway, New York 10 N.Y.
1963
60pp & 1p list of other titles, part col. illus. throughout, col. pic. bd., pic. e/p, 207x127mm. WRT
'Easy Reader' 59c on front cover.

LEVIS, Eva S.
4186 LEAVES/by/Eva S. Levis/Deputy-Principal/Woollahra Demonstration School/New South Wales/[device]/41/Illustrated by James Phillips/Longmans 1965
14pp (inc. 1p notes & bibliography), col. illus. throughout, pic. stiff wrappers, 210x160mm. Australian Nature Series No. 4. KMM

ARTHUR PHILLIP; BASS AND FLINDERS. *See* Great People in Australian History

LEVIS, Ken
HENRY LAWSON. *See* Great People in Australian History

LEVY, Muriel
THE ADVENTURES OF WONK. Wills and Hepworth, Ladybird Books, Loughborough England
1941–1950s
A popular series of six titles (often rpt) each containing two stories about the adventures of a koala, illus. Joan Kiddell-Monroe. They have no other relation to Australia, & are not included here.

LEVY, Wayne
See Howard, Peter & Levy, Wayne [eds]

LEWENHAK, Sheila (compiler)
4187 THE VOYAGES OF/CAPTAIN COOK/Jackdaw No. 20/Jackdaw Publications/A collection of contemporary documents compiled by/Sheila Lewenhak/Founded and distributed by Jonathan Cape Limited, Thirty Bedford Square, London
1965
Contains 16 loose pieces, including maps, illustrations & facsimiles, in folder, 230x350mm. BBC
Jackdaw No. 20.

LEWIS, Eliza
4188 THE RUNAWAY/KANGAROOS/By Eliza Lewis/Illustrated by/Eve Rockwell/[coloured illustration]/Rand McNally & Company—Chicago/Established 1856/Copyright 1959 by Rand McNally[2 lines]
[30]pp, col. illus. throughout, pic. bd., 155x110mm. R. M. Junior Elf Book. CLRC
4189 THE RUNAWAY/KANGAROOS/By Eliza Lewis/Illustrated by/Eve Rockwell/Rand McNally & Company. Chicago/Established 1856/Copyright MCMLIX by Rand/McNally & Company. All rights reserved. Printed in U.S.A./Edition of MXMLXII
[30]pp, col. illus. throughout, pic. bd., col. pic. e/p, 150x110mm. KMM

LEWIS, Kay & Allan
4190 PUPPETS/FOR JUNIORS/by Kay and Allan Lewis/[large red cross]/Australian Red Cross Society/Founded in 1914 Incorporated by Royal Charter 1941 A.R.C.S., 141 Printers Pty Ltd, 27 Little Bourke St, Melbourne, n.d. [1949]
32pp, col. illus. & b/w drawings, pic. wrappers, 180x115mm. Grant

LEWIS, Leonard (ed.)
4191 EPICS/OF THE EMPIRE/Edited by/Leonard Lewis/Dean & Son, Ltd./6 La Belle Sauvage, Ludgate Hill,/London, E.C.4
n.d. [1936]
249pp, col. frontis. only, (sgd. 'Bernard Rutt') clo., 200x130mm. KMM
Contents include: 'Five Englishmen versus the Antarctic—Scott's Expedition', by Lewis Broad (16pp); 'From Typist to National Heroine—Amy Johnson', by George Reid (15pp); 'The Grimmest Landing in History', by E. F. P. Bartlett (Gallipoli: 8pp); 'How the *Emden* went to her Doom', by Campbell Dixon (14pp).

LEWIS, Meg

4192 IT ALL BEGAN/WITH CALAMITY/Meg Lewis/ Illustrations by/Yvonne Bulgin/Angus and Robertson/ Sydney London Melbourne Wellington
1962
150pp, extended part-col. frontis., part-col. & b/w illus. throughout, clo., 215x135mm. KMM

LEYDEN, Peter

Publisher of Educational and Pictorial Australian studies in numerous series & ed. from 1960 onwards & outside the scope of this Bibliography.

LEYLAND, Eric

4193 WINGS OVER/THE OUTBACK/Eric Leyland/ Illustrated by John Woods/Brockhampton Press Leicester
1958
120pp, b/w frontis. & b/w drawings in text, clo., 185x130mm. KMM

The Life and Adventures of William Dampier

See Dampier

Life in Australia

A series of paper-covered social history books about different aspects of Australian life for general reading and for schools.
Format example:

4194 DICKS, H .G., Life in Australia THE ROYAL/ FLYING DOCTOR/SERVICE/H. G. Dicks/Illustrated by Boyd Turner/Oxford University Press Melbourne 1971, 32pp, line drawings, stiff dec. wrappers, cover title,195x150mm. KMM
Others in series:

4195 AGRICULTURAL SHOWS, by H. T. C. Woodfull, illus. Joy Murray, 1965. KP
4196 AUSTRALIAN ABORIGINES, by R. M. Trudinger, illus. Alison Forbes, 1960. CLRC
4197 BEACHES, by Neilma Sidney, illus. Margaret Williams, 1964. VSL
4198 BEEKEEPING, by Nan Chauncy, illus. Jane Walker, 1967. KMM
4199 CATTLE STATIONS, by R. Gardner, illus. B. Albiston, 1959, rpt 1964, 1971. KP
4200 CAVES, by J. N. Jennings, illus. Ron Brooks, n.d. KMM
4201 COUNTRY TOWNS, by Judith Wright, illus. Margaret Duce, 1963. KMM
4202 DINGOES, by Colin Bednall, illus. Roslyn Isaacs, 1967. WSJB
4203 FISHING, by Mavis Latham, illus. Joy Murray, 1963. KMM
4204 FOOD, by Maurice Brown, illus. Genevieve Melrose, 1969. KMM
4205 IRON ORE, by Mavis Thorpe Clark, illus. Jocelyn Bell, 1971. KMM
4206 KANGAROOS, by Edward Osmond, illus. the author, 1960, rpt 1969. KMM
4207 KOALAS, by R. T. M. Pescott, illus. Joy Murray, 1965. KMM
4208 LIVING IN CITIES, by M. Brown, illus. Irina Waloff, 1963. KMM
4209 LYRE BIRDS, by Graham Pizzey, illus. Margaret Williams, 1963. ANL
4210 MOUNTAINEERING, by John Bechervaise, illus. R. Brooks, 1971. CLRC
4211 NEW AUSTRALIANS, by K. & E. Moon, illus. Jane Robinson, 1965. KMM
4212 OPAL MINING by M. T. Clark, illus. Barbara Taylor, 1969. KMM
4213 ORCHARDS, by Brian James, illus. B. Albiston, 1963, rpt 1970. KP
4214 POSSUMS, by R. T. M. Pescott, illus. Joy Murray, 1968. KMM
4215 ROADS, by J. Mathieson, illus. Jocelyn Jones, 1970. KMM
4216 SHEEP, by N. Donkin, illus. Jocelyn Jones, 1967. KMM
4217 SNOW COUNTRY, by Laura Neal, illus. Patricia Cuss, 1963. KMM
4218 SUGAR, by N. Donkin, illus. Jocelyn Jones, 1967. KMM
4219 THE MURRAY RIVER, by Vaughan Craddock, illus. B. Albiston, 1960. KMM
4220 TRAVEL AND TRANSPORT, by M. Dugan, illus. Jocelyn Jones, 1968. KMM
4221 WILD LIFE RESERVES, by J. G. Mosley, illus. Daryl Carnahan, 1972. VMOU
4222 WILSON'S PROMONTORY by J. Ros Garnet, illus. Ron Brooks, 1970. CLRC
4223 WINE, by W. S. Benwell, illus. Jane Walker, 1970. WSJB
Some groups of 6 titles bound together in hard covers under the overall title of Primary Industries, for example, comprising, Beekeeping, Cattle Stations, Orchards, &c. and other titles.

The Life of Adventure in Australia

4224 THE LIFE OF ADVENTURE/IN AUSTRALASIA/ First series/W. & R. Chambers Limited/38 Soho Square, London, W.1; and Edinburgh
Original edition 1936; rpt 1937
96pp, unillus., clo., 180x120mm. CLRC
Cover reads: 'Buckley's Chance and other stories of Australasia'
Contains 6 stories, by Mary Gaunt, W. J. Ogilvie, Erle Wilson, & others.

The Life of Captain James Cook [Adapted from Life by Andrew Kippis]

4225 THE/LIFE/OF/CAPTAIN JAMES COOK/ [engraving]/Dublin:/Printed by Richard Grace, 3 Mary Street/1820./Price, bound in sheep, 8d.; in grain 6d.
179pp (inc. 2pp preface), engraved frontis. & 3 f/p engravings, hard grain morocco, 135x85mm. NSL:M
Preface indicates that the book was intended for children.

4226 THE/LIFE OF/CAPTAIN JAMES COOK./ [engraving]/Dublin:/Printed by John Jones, 40, South Great George's St.,/1824
179pp (inc. 2pp preface), engraved frontis. & 3 f/p engravings, leather, 135x85mm. RM

4227 THE/LIFE/OF/CAPTAIN JAMES COOK./New Edition./London:/W. Wetton, No. 21, Fleet Street;/And sold by all Booksellers
[1830]
vipp, 170pp, 16pp adv., engraved frontis. & 3 f/p engravings, calf, 136x82mm. SUA
Stamped inside front cover Dec 1830, but one section of adv. dated Jan 1831. Abridged ed.

4228 THE/LIFE/OF/CAPTAIN JAMES COOK./A New Edition./London:/Printed for the Executrix of the late W. Wetton;/and sold by/C. F. Cock, 21, Fleet Street,/ And all Booksellers./1834
170pp, engraved frontis. & 3 f/p engravings, bound in leather, 137x87mm. CLRC
'Society for Promoting Christian Knowledge' blind-stamped on front cover.

4229 THE LIFE OF/CAPTAIN JAMES COOK,/The/ Celebrated Navigator./London:/Published by Newman & Co./MDCCCXLIX
122pp, 4pp adv., 1p adv. (preceding t.p.), clo., 135x110mm. NSL:M
Adapted for young readers from the biography by

A. Kippis; listed in one advertisement as being published by W. Tegg & Co.

4230 THE/LIFE,/VOYAGES, AND DISCOVERIES,/OF/CAPTAIN JAMES COOK/[2 medallions]/London:/John W. Parker, West Strand/MDCCCXXXVII
viiipp, 229pp, 4pp adv., engraved frontis. & 11 f/p engravings, ¾ leather, 140x90mm. NSL:M
Adv. all for children's books.

4231 THE/LIFE,/VOYAGES, AND DISCOVERIES,/OF/CAPTAIN JAMES COOK,/[2 medallions]/The Second Edition/London:/John W. Parker, West Strand./MDCCCXL
220pp, engraved frontis. & 11 engravings, clo., 135x90mm. HBM

4232 THE/LIFE,/VOYAGES, AND DISCOVERIES/OF/CAPTAIN JAMES COOK./[2 medallions]/The fifth edition/London/John W. Parker & Sons, West Strand./MDCCCLIII
220pp, 4pp adv. (consisting of booklist of the Society for Promoting Christian Knowledge), b/w frontis. & 10 f/p engravings, clo., 130x90mm. Grant

4233 THE/LIFE/VOYAGES AND DISCOVERIES/OF/CAPTAIN JAMES COOK/[2 medallions]/The Fifth Edition/London/John W. Parker and Son West Strand MDCCCLV
220pp, engraved frontis. & 11 engravings, clo., 137x92mm. KP

The Life of Saint Therese for Children
See A Sister of Mercy

Life on Desolate Islands

4234 LIFE ON DESOLATE ISLANDS;/or,/Real Robinson Crusoes./By the author of/"Tales of the Northern Seas," etc./London: The Religious Tract Society;/56, Paternoster Row; 65 St Paul's Churchyard;/and 164 Piccadilly
n.d. [prize 1881]
128pp (last page adv. 'Monthly Shilling Volumes'), engraved frontis. ('Landing of the Mutineers on Pitcairn's Island'), 8 f/p engravings & smaller one in text, dec. clo., 157x100mm. RC
Contains 'The Pitcairn Islanders' pp30-60 (inc. 3 f/p & 2 smaller engravings relating to this text).

Lifebuoy

4235 [device]/THE LIFEBUOY HEALTH GUARD'S/DO-YOU-KNOW/BOOK
Wholly set up in Australia. Printed by Lever Brothers Limited, Balmain, NSW, n.d. [1935?] [sporting results &c for 1934 given]
96pp, b/w illus. in text throughout, pic. wrappers, 183x123mm. WRT
Compendium of encyclopaedic information about Australia for children.
THE LIFEBUOY HEALTH GUARD'S/AUSTRALIAN/DO-YOU-KNOW/BOOK
As above. KP

4236 THE/LIFEBUOY LEAGUE OF HEALTH/GUARDS/Do-you-know Book No. 3/Pictorial/Atlas of the/Empire
Lever Brothers Prop Ltd, [Sydney], n.d. [King George VI depicted as monarch]
96pp, b/w photographic illus., maps, 210x134mm. KP

4237 LIFEBUOY BOOK NO. 4/PUZZLING/PROBLEMS/AND CLEVER/CATCHES
Printed by Sungravure, n.d. [194-?]
60pp, b/w drawings & diagrams, pic. wrappers, cover title, 187x120mm. KP
Adv. inside front cover & inside & outside back cover.

4238 The "Do-you-Know Book" No 5/LIFEBUOY/HOBBY/BOOK/for girls and boys/Dozens/of useful/things to make/and do
(Presumably Lever and Kitchen, Sydney), n.d. [193-?]
64pp, b/w drawings in text, pic. wrappers (adv. for Lifebuoy Soap inside & outside of covers), cover title,180x124mm. WRT

LIFESAVIUS
The Adventures of Peppy Hector; a little story with a ring in it/written by Lifesavius; illustrated by Harry Clark, Sydney, Central Press [1928]
Printed with the compliments of 'Life Savers'; unseen, ANB 25929

The Life Story of Santa Claus

4239 THE/LIFE STORY OF/SANTA/CLAUS/[drawing]
Ayers & James Pty Ltd. 24 Jamieson St, Sydney, n.d.
111pp, 4 f/p part-col. illus. & 2 f/p b/w illus., pic. wrappers, 245x180mm. WRT
Doubtful Australian.
Another copy as above, but

4240 THE STORY OF/SANTA CLAUS
Cover again printed in red cream & green but different illus., 240x180mm
Contents the same. KP
Also different t.ps though both printed in red & black. Both have the same b/w frontis.

LIGHTFOOT, Sue

4241 THINGS MY/FAMILY MAKE/Written by Sue Lightfoot/(Age 11 years)/Pictures by Peter Clark/(Age 16 years)/Printed and Published by/John Sands Pty. Ltd., Sydney/(Age 118 years)
n.d. [1955]
30pp, col. illus. throughout, dec. bd., 180x230mm. KMM
How to make simple toys, &c.

The Lighthouse

4242 THE LIGHTHOUSE/and Other Stories/with Pictures in Colour/[illus.]/Registered at the G.P.O. Hobart for transmission by post as a book
Printed by W. R. Rolph & Sons, The Examiner Press, 71–77 Paterson Street, Launceston for the Austin Pub. Co., Launceston, n.d. [195-?]
32pp, part-col. drawings throughout (sgd 'E.A.S.'), pic. wrappers, cover title, 265x174mm. KP
Religious story about a family who emigrate to Australia.

Like English Gentlemen

4243 LIKE/ENGLISH GENTLEMEN/To Peter Scott/From the Author of 'Where's Master'/'Our sons will die like English gentlemen.' Wendy/Hodder and Stoughton/London New York Toronto
64pp, unillus., pic. bd., dec. e/p, 185x122mm. KP
Story of Captain Scott at the South Pole.

LIMMER, Hans
MY KANGAROO FANNY...Angus & Robertson 1970
Translation of a German book about a German child, first published by Hanns Reich Verlag, Munich, 1969, & not Australian in content. BBC

4244 MY KANGAROO PHOEBE/Photos: Lies Wiegman/Text: Hans Limmer/Translation: Timothy Cleary/A Terra Magica Children's Book/Hill and Wang: New York
First publ. Hanns Reich Verlag, Munich, 1969
Eng. trans. 1970
[44]pp, b/w photographs throughout, slight text, clo., 230x214mm. KMM

LINDBLOM, Yngve

4245 HAVET VAR HANS ÖDE/Sannsagan om James Cook, Världsomseglaren,/Södershavsoarnas fredlige erövrare/Berättad av/Yngve Lindblom/Tredje-femte

tusendet./[device]/Harriers Bokförlag Aktiebolag—Stockholm
1946
159pp, b/w portrait frontis., otherwise unillus., col. pic. bd. (clo. backstrip), 180x120mm. RM
Swedish children's book based on life of James Cook.

LINDLEY, Augustus F.
4246 THE LOG/OF/THE FORTUNA:/A Cruise on Chinese Waters./Containing Tales of Adventure in foreign climes,/by sea and by shore./by/Captain Augustus F. Lindley,/Author of " 'Ti-ping-tien-kwoh', The History of the Ti-Ping Revolution";/"Theodore's Case", &c. &c./Cassell, Petter, and Galpin,/London and New York
n.d. [1870]
256pp, 16pp adv., 26 f/p engravings & smaller engravings in text throughout, dec. clo., 220x160mm. NSL:M
Only Australian reference contained in 'Stuck up! An Adventure with Australian bushrangers' (22pp).

4246a A CRUISE IN/CHINESE WATERS./Being the Log of "The Fortuna"./Containing Tales of Adventure in Foreign Climes/by Land and Sea./By/Captain Augustus F. Lindley,/Author of "Ti-ping-Tien-Kwoh," "The History of the Ti-ping Revolution,"/"Theodore's Case," &c &c./Fourth edition./Cassell, Petter, Galpin & Co.:/London, Paris & New York.
n.d. [1882]
256pp & 16pp adv., engraved frontis., numerous engravings throughout, pic. clo., 215x164mm. CLRC
Australian section pp115–37. First publ. as 'The Log of the Fortuna' [1870].

LINDSAAR, Peeter
4247 Peeter Lindsaar/VANA HOBUNE/[device]—Kirjastas]/Luvamees/Streatfield Press Sydney 1950
112pp, woodcut illus. throughout, stiff pic. wrappers, 220x160mm. ANL
Illus. Eduard Rüga.

LINDSAY, Harold Arthur
4248 THE/ARNHEM TREASURE/By/H. A. Lindsay/The Waninga Press/Adelaide
1952
172pp, unillus., clo., 185x120mm. KMM
See also Tindale, Norman B. & Lindsay, Harold Arthur

LINDSAY, Hilarie
4249 CARD & BOARD GAMES/TO MAKE/Fully illustrated—easy to follow instructions for children to understand/by Hilarie Lindsay/Ansay Pty Ltd./NSW. Australia
1972
69pp, b/w diagrams, stiff col. pic. wrappers, 216x184mm. KP

4250 ONE HUNDRED AND ONE/TOYS TO MAKE/Fully illustrated—easy to follow instructions for children to understand/by Hilarie Lindsay/Ansay Pty. Ltd/NSW Australia
1972
407pp, b/w illus., col. pic. bd., 216x180mm. ANL
Illus. Christine & Jeff Watson.

4251 SOFT TOYS & DOLLS/TO MAKE/Fully illustrated—easy to follow instructions for children to understand/by Hilarie Lindsay/Ansay Pty Ltd NSW Australia
67pp, b/w illus., col. pic. wrappers, 216x184mm. KP
Illus. as before.

4252 OUTDOOR GAMES/TO MAKE/fully illustrated—easy to follow instructions for children to understand/by Hilarie LIndsay/Ansay Pty Ltd./N.S.W. Australia
1972
89pp, b/w illus. throughout, col. pic. wrappers, 216x184mm. KP
Toys designed & created by author; illus. by Christine & Jeff Watson.

LINDSAY, Jack
4253 RUNAWAY/By/Jack Lindsay/Illustrated by/J. Morton Sale/Oxford University Press/London: Humphrey Milford
1935
255pp, col. frontis. & 6 f/p b/w illus., clo., 190x120mm. ANL
Adventure story about two boys taken slave by the Romans & their escape & adventures.
4254 RUNAWAY/By/Jack Lindsay/Illustrated by/J. Morton Sale/[drawing printed in col.]/Oxford University Press/London: Humphrey Milford
• Rpt 1938, 255pp, col. frontis & 6 f/p b/w illus., clo. 195x125mm. KMM
4255 RUNAWAY/By/Jack Lindsay/Illustrated by/J. Morton Sale/[drawing] in col.]/Oxford University Press/London: Humphrey Milford
• Rpt 1938 'Modern Stories for the Schoolroom' series; contents identical with above, except for bdg and possibly the col. frontis. is omitted (missing in copy examined). KMM

4256 REBELS OF/THE GOLDFIELDS/By/Jack Lindsay/With illustrations by/George Scott/Lawrence & Wishart Ltd./2 Parton Street/London/W.C.1.
1936
264pp, col. frontis. & 3 f/p col. illus., clo., 185x125mm. ANL
Boys' story of the Eureka Stockade.
4257 Another copy as above but 'Left Book Club Edition' on front cover. KMM

4258 TO ARMS!/A Story of Ancient Gaul/By/Jack Lindsay/Illustrated by Martin Tyas/Oxford University Press/London: Humphrey Milford
1938
287pp, col. frontis. & 6 f/p b/w illus., clo., 190x120mm. ANL

4259 THE DONS/SIGHT DEVON/A Story of the Defeat of/the Invincible Armada/By/Jack Lindsay/Illustrations by/E. Boye Uden/[device]/Oxford University Press/London New York Toronto
1941
287pp, col. frontis. & 6 b/w f/p illus., clo., 190x125mm. ANL
4260 THE DONS/SIGHT DEVON/A Story of the Defeat of/The Invincible Armada/By/Jack Lindsay/Illustrations by/E. Boye Uden/Geoffrey Cumberlege/Oxford University Press
First publ. 1941, rpt 1951
287pp, 6 f/p b/w illus., clo., 185x115mm. KMM

LINDSAY, Martin
4261 THE EPIC/OF/CAPTAIN SCOTT/by/Martin Lindsay/The Falcon Press Ltd./7 Crown Passage, Pall Mall/London
First publ. in 1933 by Peter Davies, this new ed. 1948
124pp (inc. glossary &c) & folding map, b/w portrait frontis. & b/w photographic illus., clo., 185x118mm. KP
4262 Martin Lindsay/THE EPIC OF/CAPTAIN SCOTT/[device]/Heinemann Educational/Books Ltd. London
First publ. 1933. First publ. in New Windmill Series 1962, rpt 1965, 1966, 1968, 1970

141pp & 1p glossary, b/w photographic illus., map, pic. clo., map e/p, 185x123mm. KP

LINDSAY, Norman

4263 THE MAGIC PUDDING/Being the Adventures of Bunyip Bluegum/and his friends Bill Barnacle & Sam Sawnoff/by Norman Lindsay/[drawing] Sydney/ Angus & Robertson Limited/Castlereagh Street
1918
171pp, col. illus. t.p. (preceding typographic t.p.), b/w drawings throughout, bd., clo. spine, e/p patterned with green A&R device, 285x220mm. KMM [a review copy]

4263a THE MAGIC PUDDING
The first edition as above, but with plain white endpapers, size 278x220mm and title printed in black instead of gilt lettering on spine. KMM

Note on the special edition with the Angus and Robertson endpapers
Angus and Robertson records show that 3000 copies of the first edition were printed but not all were bound at once. 1292 copies were bound in September 1918 and in January 1919 a further 250 copies were received from the binder. Sales were disappointing and in 1921 the price was reduced from 21 shillings to 7s 6d, and the remaining sheets were bound up, presumably with ordinary white paper. The pages were slightly more closely trimmed, the size being 278x220mm, and the lettering on the spine printed in black not gilt. Both have the same thick brown paper d/w with the col. illus. from the t.p. pasted on the front. There is no record of any specially bound edition and copies with the patterned endpapers are at least as common as those with ordinary white paper.

4264 THE MAGIC PUDDING/Being the Adventures of Bunyip Bluegum/and his friends Bill Barnacle & Sam Sawnoff/by Norman Lindsay/[drawing]/Australia: Cornstalk Publishing Company/Arnold Place, Sydney
1924
171pp, col. frontis. [reproduction of col. illus. t.p.], b/w drawings, clo., 240x180mm. HBM

4265 THE MAGIC PUDDING/Being the Adventures...&c/Sydney/Angus & Robertson Limited/ Castlereagh Street
1930
171pp, b/w drawings throughout, clo., 227x170mm. KMM

4266 THE MAGIC PUDDING...Sydney/Angus & Robertson Limited/Castlereagh Street
[printed by Halstead Printing Company Limited]
n.d. [1935] [on d/w '4th and cheaper edition']
[171]pp, col. frontis., b/w drawings throughout, blue bd., 245x182mm. KMM

4267 THE MAGIC PUDDING/ Being the Adventures of Bunyip Bluegum/ and his friends Bill Barnacle & Sam Sawnoff/ by Norman Lindsay/[drawing]/Sydney/ Angus & Roberston Limited/Castlereagh Street
1937 [on d/w '5th and cheaper edition']
[171]pp, col. frontis., b/w drawings, white bd., 242x182mm. KMM
• Rpt as above, 1938. CLRC

4268 Rpt as above, 1940, col. pic. bd., 240x180mm. Adv. for others in the series on back cover. KMM

4269 THE MAGIC PUDDING/ [title page lettering as before]/Angus & Robertson Limited/Castlereagh Street
1948
171pp, 15 part-col. & other b/w illus., clo., 242x155mm. HBM
The first post-war edition (although later the publisher incorrectly listed a 1947 edition on the verso of the t.p.). For this edition Lindsay tinted 15 of the illus. in terracotta & pale yellow, but the col. frontispiece was not reproduced. Lindsay strongly criticized the dustwrapper, based on the design of the US & English editions printed in dark blue & heavy red, & designed a new jacket for the next edition.

4270 THE MAGIC PUDDING/Being the Adventures of Bunyip Bluegum/and his friends Bill Barnacle & Sam Sawnoff/by Norman Lindsay/[drawing of the 3 friends]/Sydney/Angus & Robertson Limited/ Castlereagh Street
1951
171pp, b/w illus. & 29 part. col. illus., clo., 245x155mm. KMM
This edition had an additional 14 of the illustrations tinted. The new green wrapper reproduced for the first time a drawing of the three friends chasing the puddin' which Lindsay drew especially for the new dustwrapper and which continued to be used until the new edition of 1963.
• Rpt as above, 1954. HBM
• Rpt as above, 1958 (some lines transposed on p171 of the text). HBM
• Rpt as above, 1960. KMM
• Rpt as above, 1961. KMM
• Rpt as above, 1962. KMM

4271 THE MAGIC PUDDING/Being the Adventures of Bunyip Bluegum/and his friends Bill Barnacle & Sam Sawnoff/by Norman Lindsay/[drawing of the 3 friends]/Sydney/Angus & Robertson Limited/ Castlereagh Street
New edition 1963
171pp, col. illus. t.p. [preceding t.p. proper, replica of that in 1st ed.], b/w drawings throughout, clo., 240x185mm. HBM
The coloured illustration is reproduced on the dustwrapper. The illustrations in this new edition were reproduced as well (or even better, Lindsay thought) than in the first edition & it was a handsome book.
• Rpt 1965
This is a reprint of the 1963 edition, with the variation that the coloured reproduction of the original title page is here used as a frontispiece. The binding is brown, instead of red cloth, with slightly different lettering on the spine. HBM
• Rpt 1967 as in 1965 edition, but size 245x185mm. HBM
• Rpt 1968 as above. HBM
• Rpt 1969 as above, but with variation in lettering on spine. BBC
• Rpt twice, Sydney 1970; also 1971, & twice 1972
Details as in 1963 edition, but bound in pink laminated pic. bd., 245x185mm. HBM
See also Howard, Peter & Levy, Wayne [eds]

4272 THE MAGIC PUDDING/Being the Adventures of Bunyip Bluegum/and his friends Bill Barnacle & Sam Sawnoff/by Norman Lindsay/[drawing of the 3 friends]/Sydney/Angus & Robertson Limited/ Castlereagh Street
Jubilee Edition of 2000 copies 1968
171pp, b/w illus. throughout [as in 1963 edition], 8 f/p col. illus., clo. (with special A. & R. medallion e/p printed in orange), 245x175mm. HBM
The new illustrations were painted by Norman Lindsay as a guide for the puppet makers when the story was made into a puppet play.

4273 Norman Lindsay/THE MAGIC PUDDING/Being the Adventures of/Bunyip Bluegum and his friends/ Bill Barnacle and/Sam Sawnoff/[drawing of the 3 friends]/Penguin Books
First published in Australia 1930 [*sic*]; First published in Great Britain 1931 [*sic*]; Published in Puffin Story Books 1957
137pp, 4pp adv., b/w drawings throughout, pic. wrappers, 180x110mm. KMM

The illustrations in this edition were re-drawn by another artist from the original illustrations, which so infuriated Lindsay he would not allow the edition to be sold in Australia.

4274 THE MAGIC PUDDING/Being the Adventures of Bunyip Bluegum/and his friends Bill Barnacle & Sam Sawnoff/by Norman Lindsay/[drawing of the 3 friends]/Penguin Books
Harmondsworth, Middlesex, England, 1972
171pp, 3pp adv., b/w illus. throughout, col. pic. wrappers, 195x130mm. KMM
• Rpt 1972 as above. KP
• Rpt 1972 as above but: in association with H. J. Ashton, Auckland & Sydney
KMM

4275 THE MAGIC/PUDDING/First Slice/Being the Adventures of Bunyip Bluegum/and his friends Bill Barnacle and Sam Sawnoff/By Norman Lindsay/ Angus and Robertson
This edition first published 1971
[28]pp, col. illus. t.p., col. illus. throughout, pic. bd., 285x215mm. Young Australia Series. HBM
Slight variations in text & illustrations: an illustration from p33 (1969 ed.) is omitted, & 2 paragraphs on this page have been transposed to two pages further on.
In same series, uniform with above

4276 THE MAGIC PUDDING Second Slice. 1971. HBM

4277 THE MAGIC PUDDING Third Slice. 1972. HBM
Variations from original edition in text—illustrations moved, omitted &c.

US edition

4278 THE MAGIC PUDDING/Being the adventures...&c./Farrar & Rinehart, Incorporated/On Murray Hill/New York
n.d. [1936]
[159]pp [i.e. vi + 153], no frontis., b/w drawings, clo., 225x150mm. KMM
Only 90 of the 100 b/w drawings in the original edition are reproduced, many of them reduced in size.

English edition

4279 THE MAGIC PUDDING/Being the adventures...&c./[drawing]/[publisher's device]/ Hamish Hamilton Ltd./90 Great Russell Street W.C.1 [London 1936]
159pp, col. frontis. & 89 b/w drawings, clo. [with frontis. illus. reproduced as col. onlay], 230x158mm. KMM
The dark blue & red dustjacket used the same design as the US edition. The 'blurb' described Bunyip Bluegum as a 'Kinkajou bear'. The illustrations used were those of the US edition but the layout was more spacious. Externally too the book was more attractive with the coloured onlay & lettering in silver ink. However, the book did not sell & in November 1938 the publisher issued a cheap edition consisting of the existing sheets bound in plain blue cloth with black lettering.
See White for later editions of *The Magic Pudding*

4280 THE/FLYAWAY/HIGHWAY/By/Norman Lindsay/[drawing]/Australia/Angus & Robertson Limited/89, Castlereagh Street, Sydney/1936
120pp, line drawings in text throughout, bd., 235x180mm. KMM

LINDSAY, Norman & SCRIVEN, Peter

4281 THE/MAGIC/PUDDING/Produced by/The Australian Elizabethan Theatre Trust/[coloured illlustration of the 3 friends chasing the Pudding]/By/ Norman Lindsay/Adapted for Marionettes by Peter Scriven with Music by Hal Evans/Australia's funniest and most famous children's story/Chappell & Co. Ltd./National Building, 250 Pitt St., Sydney/and 39 Lower Cuba St., Wellington, N.Z.
n.d. [copyright 1960]
8pp, music, pic. wrappers, cover title, 280x220mm. NSL:M
Music & words of 'The Pudding Anthem', 'I've got a Stick', 'Spanish Gold', 'Breakfast Ballad'. Green cover design uniform with dustwrapper of book.

[LINDSAY, Philip]

4282 The Little Big Books/A LITTLE BOOK/OF THE/ WATER BABIES/[illus.]/Humphrey Milford/Oxford University Press London
1933
60pp, col. frontis. & b/w illus., some with an additional col. pic. bd., 150x115mm. NSL:M
Illus. May Smith
The Little Big Book, edited by Mrs Herbert Strang. Although published anonymously, this copy has an inscription to Peter Lindsay acknowledging authorship.

4283 THE/KNIGHTS AT BAY/By Philip Lindsay/Tales of Action No. 1/Basil Blackwell, Oxford
n.d. [1935]
190pp, col. frontis. & 9 f/p b/w illus. by H. R. Millar, clo., 205x135mm. NSL:M

4284 THE/KNIGHTS AT BAY/By Philip Lindsay/Basil Blackwell—Oxford
First printed September 1933; rpt 1936, 1946
190pp, col. frontis., 9 f/p b/w illus. (inc. plan), by H. R. Millar, clo., 190x130mm. KMM
A tale of the Knights Hospitaller of St John & the Siege of Malta.

4285 Philip Lindsay/THE/KNIGHTS/AT BAY/ Illustrated by Oscar Ogg/[device]/New York/Loring & Mussey Publishers.
1935
viiipp, 223pp, 8 f/p b/w illus., chapter headings & some text drawings, pic. clo., 205x135mm. KMM

4286 THE KNIGHTS AT BAY/by Philip Lindsay/Walker and Company/New York
1961
112pp, double-spread pic. t.p., b/w drawings in margins throughout, clo., 254x175mm. KMM

LINDWALL, Gustav

4287 GULDARET/En Australisk Pojkes Äventyr/ Berättade Av/Gustav Lindwall/Med Illustrationer Av/ David Ljungdahl/Andra upplagen/[device]/Uppsala/J. A. Lindblads Forlag
1941
120pp, 10 f/p b/w illus., col. pic. bd., clo. backstrip, 185x120mm. RM
One of a few original Australian stories written in Swedish, it was first published in 1918.

[LING, Mrs Mary Ann] [Mrs H. H. Ling, née Moore-Bentley]

4288 SOMETHING TO AMUSE/Published Every Fortnight/(All rights reserved)
n.d. [1920?]
20pp, roneoed pamphlet, 215x140mm. NSL:M
Stapled together with *Fairy Tales* (12pp).
FAIRY TALES [no t.p.]
n.d.
10pp, 1p adv., roneoed pamphlet, 215x135mm. NSL:M
Additional number to third edition of *Something to Amuse*, copyright 1919.

A BULRUSH FAIRY
n.d. [1922?]
11pp, roneoed pamphlet, 205x130mm. NSL:M

LINKLATER, William
4289 THE/MAGIC SNAKE/Being a group of stories for/children concerning the habits,/customs, beliefs, ceremonies,/corroborees and legends of the/Australian Aborigines/Stories by/William Linklater/Illustrated and Edited by/Mavis Mallinson/The Currawong Publishing Company,/Royal Chambers, 3 Castlereagh Street,/Sydney
n.d. [1946]
95pp (inc. 3pp glossary), col. frontis. & b/w drawings throughout, wrappers, 240x180mm. NSL:M
The author is known as Billy Miller of the Northern Territory where he lived for fifty-four years.

LINTON, Faith
4290 AUSTRALIAN/QUESTIONS/CHILDREN/ASK/by Faith Linton/Illustrated by Peter Chapman/[drawing]/Readabout Books
Readabout Publishers Pty Ltd, Crow's Nest, NSW, 1964
24pp, col. & part-col. illus. throughout, stiff pic. wrappers, 215x180mm. BBC
Factual book on Australian insects & animals.

4291 FAMOUS/AUSTRALIANS/By Faith Linton/illustrated by Molly Johnson/douglas/mawson/john flynn/daisy/bates/nellie/melba/francis/greenway/henry/lawson/Readabout Books
Readabout Publishers Pty Ltd, Crow's Nest, NSW, 1964
32pp, col. & part. col. illus. throughout, stiff pic. wrappers, 280x210mm. KMM
Biographical sketches of six Australians whose names appear on the title page.

LINTOTT, Joan
4292 PRAYERS/FOR/LITTLE/ONES/By/Joan Lintott
A Jons Production [Sydney] n.d.
18pp, dec. t.p., col. & b/w illus. throughout, dec. bd., dec. e/p, 175x155mm. KMM
Unknown if author/artist is Australian.

Listen to a Story
4293 LISTEN TO A/STORY/Kindergarten Stories and Verses/Illustrated by Claire Simpson/[drawing]/Angus and Robertson
Sydney 1968; rpt 1971
142pp, line drawings (printed in red) as chapter headings & tailpieces, pic. bd., dec. e/p, 230x155mm. KMM

Listening Time
4294 LISTENING/TIME/"Kindergarten of the Air"/Stories and Verses/[drawing]/ Angus and Robertson/ Sydney London Melbourne Wellington 1961
102pp, part-col. t.p., & drawings throughout, by Margaret Horder, dec.boards, dec. e/p, 235x155mm. KMM.
Includes 37 stories by various authors previously broadcast
• Rpt 1962, 1964, 1966 and 1969 as above. KP

LISTER, Gladys [Mrs Leopold Alfred Lister]
4295 THE/LITTLE ROUND GARDEN/By/Gladys Lister/Decorated by/Pixie O'Harris/[decoration]/Angus & Robertson Limited/Sydney and London/1938
109pp, b/w frontis. & b/w drawings throughout, bd., 240x180mm. CLRC
4296 THE/LITTLE ROUND GARDEN/by/Gladys Lister/[decoration]/Angus & Robertson/Sydney London 1946
111pp, col. frontis., b/w drawings throughout (some variants from earlier edition), pic. bd. (clo. spine), dec. e/p, 240x180mm. CLRC
Sepia illustrations by Pixie O'Harris; frontispiece from Walt Disney's *Fantasia*
Dedicated to Walt Disney.
4297 THE/LITTLE ROUND GARDEN/by/Gladys Lister/[drawing]/Angus and Robertson/Sydney London/1948
1st publ. Nov 1938; rpt Dec 1938; Dec 1946; Sept 1948
111pp, printed throughout in sepia; t.p. printed in 2 col., pic. e/p, 240x184mm. KP

4298 LITTLE ROUND HOUSE/By/Gladys Lister/Author of/"The Little Round Garden"/Decorated by/Pixie O'Harris/[drawing]/Angus and Robertson/Sydney: London/1939
115pp, col. frontis. & sepia/white drawings throughout, bd., 240x180mm. ANL
• Rpt as above, 1940. KP
4299 LITTLE ROUND HOUSE/By/Gladys Lister/Author of/"The Little Round Garden"/"The House that Beckons"/Decorated by/Pixie O'Harris/[drawing]/1943/New Century Press Pty. Ltd./3 North York Street, Sydney
115pp, col. frontis. & sepia/white drawings throughout, bd., 240x180mm. ANL
• Rpt as above, 1946. KP
4300 LITTLE ROUND HOUSE/By/Gladys Lister/Author of/The Little Round Garden/The House that Beckons/Decorated by/Pixie O'Harris/[drawing]/1947/New Century Press Ltd./3 North York Street, Sydney
First published 1939; rpt 1940, 1943, 1945, 1946, 1947
115pp, col. frontis. & 10 f/p sepia/white illus., line drawings throughout, bd., 245x180mm. KMM
• Rpt as above, 1949. TG

4301 THE/HOUSE THAT/BECKONS/By/Gladys Lister/Author of/'Little Round Garden'/'Little Round House'/[drawing]/Decorated by/Pixie O'Harris/With a few drawings/by the author/1940/New Century Press Pty. Ltd./3 North York Street, Sydney
122pp, 10 f/p part-col. illus., pic. bd., dec. e/p, 240x180mm. KMM
• Rpt 1945, 1946, 1947, as above. KP

4302 JENNIFER STANDS BY/By/Gladys Lister/Angus and Robertson Ltd./Sydney: London/1941
245pp, b/w frontis., clo., 185x120mm. KMM
A shorter version of this story appeared in serial form in the *Sydney Morning Herald* under the title 'Phantom Gold'.
• Rpt 1946, as above, but unillus. KP
• Rpt 1948, as above, unillus. KMM

4303 THE SONG GOES ON/By Gladys Lister/Foreword/by/Her Excellency/The Lady Gowrie/[drawing]/Illustrated by R. M. Thompson and Author/['Preface by Meta Maclean' printed but superimposed, is strip of paper with the autograph 'Gladys Lister 1941']/Words of Song by Margaret Osborne/Published by/New Century Press Pty. Ltd./3 North York Street, Sydney
60pp (inc. 1p foreword & 1p verse), part-col. illus. throughout, pic. bd., pic. e/p, 190x160mm. ANL

4304 DAWN MOTHER/By/Gladys Lister/Angus and Robertson Ltd./Sydney London/1942
133pp, col. frontis. & 11 f/p b/w illus., b/w drawings throughout, illus. by J. Abbott, Pixie O'Harris, 'D.H.G.' & others, bd., 240x175mm. CLRC

4305 GRANDPUFF/AND/LEAFY/by Gladys Lister/decorations by/Joyce Abbott/and author/Wholly set up, Printed and Published in Australia by/Marchant &

Co. Pty. Ltd., Sydney, N.S.W./Registered at the G.P.O., Sydney, for transmission by Post as a Book
1st imp. 1942; 2nd imp. 1943
54pp, 1p adv., dec. t.p., col. frontis. & 5 f/p col. illus., b/w drawings throughout, dec. bd., dec. e/p, 235x160mm. KMM
Dedicated 'To Her Excellency, The Lady Gowrie and to every child with a Soldier Daddy'

4306 LEAFY/AND/PRINCE BRUMBY/Written/and/designed/by/Gladys Lister/Drawn by Joyce Abbott
Dawfox Productions, Sydney 1944
32pp, col. & b/w illus. throughout, bd., 240x235mm. ANL

4307 LITTLE ROUND STAIRWAY/By/Gladys Lister/Author of "The Little Round Garden", "Little Round House",/and "The House that Beckons"/Illustrations by/Joyce Abbott and Author/[drawing]/1946/New Century Press Pty. Ltd./Sydney
125pp, col. frontis. & 2 f/p col. illus., b/w drawings throughout, bd., 235x180mm. KMM

4308 Second edition 1949, as above, but with col. frontis. only & b/w drawings in text, bd., 245x180mm. CLRC

4309 LITTLE ROUND STAIRWAY/By/Gladys Lister/Author of/The Little Round Garden, Little Round House,/and The House that Beckons/Illustrations/by/Joyce Abbott and Author/[drawing]/1946/New Century Press Ltd./Sydney
Title surrounded by dec. border printed in blue as is the drawing
32pp, 1 col. illus. in this ed., many others printed in blue & black, dec. bd., 237x180mm. CLRC

4310 I WOULDN'T IF I/WERE YOU/By/Gladys Lister/[14 lines of text appealing for funds for the Sydney Day Nursery & Nursery Schools Association, signed Violet Braddon]/Angus and Robertson—Sydney/Registered in Australia for transmission through/the post as a book
n.d. [1948]
32pp, dec. t.p., b/w drawings throughout, bd., 250x180mm. ANL

4311 LEAFY'S/SEVENTH WAVE/[drawing]/By/Gladys Lister/With coloured illustrations/By/Joyce Abbott/Angus and Robertson/Sydney: London/1948
[32]pp. illus. printed in two cols, pic. bd., 180x240mm. ANL

4312 WHITHER JENNIFER?/A Story of Adventure/By/Gladys Lister/Angus and Robertson/Sydney: London/1948
225pp, unillus., clo., 185x115mm. ANL

4313 TUBBY/THE LITTLE ROUND/BEAR/A Gladys Lister Leafy Book
Leafy Books, Box 444 GPO. Sydney, n.d. [1949?]
32pp, drawings throughout, light pic. bd., cover title, 200x160mm. NSL:M
Leafy series listed. 2 titles as follows unseen: Leafy & the Platy Kittens; Leafy on the Mistletoe Swing; Size & format resembles a Little Golden Book; printed in two col. throughout. Not known if these titles were ever published

4314 STARLIGHT/BELONGS/TO ME/by/Gladys Lister/Illustrated by Frank Varty/Collins/London and Glasgow
First edition 1951
256pp, col. frontis., b/w drawings in text, clo., 180x120mm. VSL
• Rpt 1952, as above. KP

4315 A STAR FOR/STARLIGHT/by/Gladys Lister/Illustrated by Frank Varty/Collins/London and Glasgow
First published in this edition 1953
256pp, col. frontis., b/w drawings in text, clo., 180x120mm. GI
• Rpt 1954. KMM

4316 A STAR FOR/STARLIGHT/by/Gladys Lister/Illustrated by Frank Varty/The Children's Press/London and Glasgow
n.d.
256pp, b/w drawings in text, clo., 180x120mm. KMM

4317 THE/LITTLE ROUND WORLD/By/Gladys Lister/Ward, Lock & Co., Limited/London and Melbourne
First pub. 1954; rpt 1955
160pp, b/w photographic frontis. & 17 b/w drawings, bd. (clo. spine), 210x150mm. KMM

4318 QUEST FOR/STARLIGHT/by/Gladys Lister/Illustrated by Frank Varty/Collins/London and Glasgow
1956
256pp, col. frontis. & 6 f/p b/w illus., clo., 180x120mm. KMM

LISTON, Maud Renner

4319 CINDERELLA'S PARTY/A Fairy Story/By/Maud Renner Liston/Illustrations by/Pixie O'Harris/To the/Children of St. George's School, Goodwood,/for whom this Story was first written/in the form of a Play/[decoration]/Rigby Limited/Booksellers, Stationers, &c./74 King William Street/Adelaide
n.d. [1923]
31pp, b/w frontis. & 5 f/p b/w illus., line drawings in text, wrappers, 270x220mm. KMM
The story originally appeared in the columns of the *Murray Pioneer.*

LITTLE, C. E.

See 'Ashmore, Jane'

LITTLE, M. I.

4320 DUNHAM DAYS/A Sketch/By/M. I. Little/Illustrated by Marian Alsop/Adelaide/E. J. McAlister & Co., James Place/1913
106pp, b/w frontis. & 3 b/w illus., wrappers, 180x115mm. ANL
Girls' school story with religious, Roman Catholic background

Little Boy Blue Nursery Rhymes

4321 LITTLE/BOY/BLUE/[drawing]/NURSERY/RHYMES./Printed and Published by Offset Printing Coy Pty Ltd. [device] 169 Phillip St., Waterloo, Sydney (All Rights Reserved)
n.d. [194-?]
16pp, 4pp f/p col. illus., b/w illus. throughout, col. pic. wrappers, 277x214mm. ANL
Illus. Franklin Bennett.

The Little Corporal

4322 THE/LITTLE CORPORAL/Being the "Young Soldier" Annual/Beautifully Illustrated/Melbourne/Salvation Army Press/Bourke Street East
n.d.
219pp & 3pp contents, b/w illus. by R. Wenban, clo. with 'The Little Corporal' & imprint of Guardsman on front cover, 248x185mm. Grant

Little Folded Hands

4323 LITTLE/FOLDED HANDS/[drawing]/Lutheran Publishing Co./70 Pirie Street Adelaide
32pp, frontis. & e/p illus. printed in sepia & f/p b/w illus., pic. wrappers, 136x104mm. CLRC
A booklet of prayers.

Little Folk's Nursery Rhymes
4324 LITTLE FOLK'S NURSERY RHYMES
Offset Printing Coy Pty Ltd., Sydney, n.d.
8pp, 3 f/p part col. illus., stiff pic. wrappers, 175x122mm. VMOU

Little Folks Nursery Rhymes
4325 LITTLE FOLKS/NURSERY RHYMES/[drawing]/An Australian Production/Published by/R. P. Dean & co., 178 Rundle Street, Adelaide
Printed by Vardon & Sons Ltd, 95 Grote St, Adelaide, n.d. [194-?]
16pp, 10 f/p col. illus., by M. Brittain, pic. wrappers, 282x214mm. CLRC

Little Folks Nursery Rhymes
4326 LITTLE FOLKS/NURSERY RHYMES
Young's Merchandising Co, 8 Spring St. Sydney, n.d.
Printed by Photogravure, Melbourne
[18]pp, 8pp col. illus. & part col. drawings & rhymes, 350x235mm. KP

The Little Gingerbread Boy
See Gunn, Florence

Little Henry's Records
See Newcombe, Samuel Prout

The Little Gum Tree
4327 THE LITTLE GUM TREE
Whitcombe & Tombs Ltd, Christchurch, N.Z., n.d. [194-?]
See McLaren 157

The Little Kangaroo
4328 THE LITTLE KANGAROO/Illustrations by Giannini/[col. illus. of kangaroo]/[Dean & Son Ltd Colophon]/Published by Dean & Son Ltd, 1969/© by Editions des Deux Coqs d'Or, Paris 1968
24pp, col. illus. throughout, col. pic. wrappers, 205x205mm. KP
Good Night Series.

Little Tommy Train
4329 LITTLE/TOMMY/TRAIN
Photogravure Ltd, Melbourne, n.d. [194-?]
[8]pp (but text begins & ends inside covers, hence 10pp illus. & text), col. illus. throughout, pic. covers, 240x162mm. KP
Printed on light bd. All Australian scenes.

LITTLEJOHN, Agnes
4330 THE/SILVER ROAD/and other Stories/By Agnes Littlejohn/Author of/"The Daughter of a Soldier", "A Lapse of/Memory", "Mirage of the Desert",/"The Breath of India", and "Lyrical Poems"/Sydney/Printed by Harry Gorton/At the Kingston Press, 38–42 Oxford Street/1915
223pp, unillus., wrappers, 235x130mm. ANL
Fairy stories with a few poems.

4331 STAR DUST AND/SEA SPRAY/[vignette]/By/Agnes Littlejohn/Edwards, Dunlop & Co. Ltd./Sydney & Brisbane/1918
82pp, part-col. frontis. & b/w illus. by S. Ure Smith & Percy Leason, dec. bd., 240x230mm. NSL:M

4332 RAINBOW DREAMS/[decoration]/By Agnes Littlejohn/Illustrated by Alek Sass/Frontispiece by Albert Collins/Edwards, Dunlop & Co. Ltd./Sydney and Brisbane/1919
78pp, 1p dedicatory verse, col. frontis., b/w drawings & decorated initials at beginning of each story, bd., 240x220mm. KMM
Includes some verses.

4333 THE/SLEEPING/SEA-NYMPH/[decoration]/by/Agnes Littlejohn/Illustrated by Albert Collins & Olive Crane/Edwards Dunlop & Co. Ltd./Sydney & Brisbane n.d. [1924]
56pp, col. frontis. & 1 col. illus., b/w illus. & decorations in text, bd. (with col. illus. reproduced on front cover), 220x175mm. KMM

4334 THE LOST EMERALD/and Other Stories/By/Agnes Littlejohn/Illustrated by/Pixie O'Harris/Artistic Designs by/Smith & Julius/Edwards, Dunlop & Co. Ltd./Sydney and Brisbane/1924
79pp, b/w frontis. & b/w drawings throughout, dec. bd., 240x210mm. ANL

LITTLEJOHN, Peggy
4335 FAIRIES/By/Peggy Littlejohn/Decorated by/Florence Swinbourne/[drawing]/Sydney 1942
Set up, printed & bound in Australia by New Century Press Pty Ltd, 3 North York St, Sydney
62pp, t.p. printed in 2 cols., 6 f/p col. illus., pic. bd., 245x178mm. NSL:M
Verse & stories.

4336 THE MAGIC SKATES/and other stories/by Peggy Littlejohn/Decorated by/Florence Swinbourne/[drawing]/Sydney 1944
New Century Press Pty Ltd
62pp, 2 f/p col. illus. & 2 f/p b/w illus., b/w drawings in text, pic. bd., 240x185mm. KMM

4337 SEASIDE/FAIRYTALE/By/Peggy Littlejohn/Decorated by Florence Swinbourne
n.p., n.d. [194-?]
23pp, 6 col. plates, paper bd. with col. panel pasted on front cover, 210x180mm. KMM

4338 TALES FROM/FAIRYLAND/By/Peggy Littlejohn/Decorated by/Florence Swinbourne/[drawing]/Sydney 1950
Printed by Winn & Co, Sydney
75pp (inc. 1p dedication), 10 f/p col. plates, pic. bd., clo. spine, 240x180mm. VMOU
Contains stories & verses. Some of the contents rpt from *The Magic Skates.*

4339 MAGIC IN THE POOL/by Peggy Littlejohn/Decorated by/Jane King/Sydney—1951
Winn & Co., Balfour Street, Sydney
n.d.
25pp, 6 f/p col. illus., 2 f/p b/w illus. & drawings in text, bd., with col. illus. pasted on front cover, 206x184mm. KMM

LITTLEJOHNS, R. T. & LAWRENCE, S. A.
4340 BIRDS OF/OUR BUSH/or/Photography for Nature-Lovers/By/R. T. Littlejohns and/S. A. Lawrence/Members of the Royal Australasian Ornithologists' Union/and/Nature Photographers' Club of Australia/with an Introduction by/J. A. Leach, D. Sc./Colonial Member British Ornithologists' Union and/Vice-president Royal Australasian Ornithologists' Union/Illustrated from Photographs/By the Authors./[device]/Melbourne/Auckland, Christchurch, Dunedin and Wellington, N.Z./and London./Whitcombe & Tombs Limited.
n.d. [1920]
208pp (inc. 4pp introduction, 2pp preface, 4pp indices), b/w photographic frontis. & 66 f/p b/w plates, pic. clo., 220x137mm. HBM

LITTLEWOOD, Jean
4341 THE ADVENTURES/OF BREN/By Jean Littlewood/Illustrated by Ivan G. Pagett/Copyright Alpha Printing Co., Melbourne 1947

16pp, col. illus. throughout, pic. bd., dec. e/p, 145x135mm. ANL
Verse.

Lives and Voyages of Drake, Cavendish and Dampier
4342 LIVES AND VOYAGES/OF/DRAKE, CAVENDISH, AND DAMPIER:/including a view of the/History of the Buccaneers./with three portraits engraved by Horsburgh./Third edition./Edinburgh:/ Oliver & Boyd, Tweeddale Court;/and Simpkin, Marshall, & Co., London./MDCCCXXXVII
432pp (inc. 2pp preface & 6pp index), frontis. & 2 other engraved portraits, copy seen re-bound, 164x100mm. SSL
Dampier & the Buccaneers of America pp182–426 of which A Voyage to New Holland occupies the last 42pp. From preface: 'If the first aspiring thoughts of British youth are inseparably connected with maritime enterprise. . . this work cannot want interest'. Other words imply the book was considered suitable for youth.

The Lizards Picnic Story-Book
4343 THE LIZARDS PICNIC/STORY-BOOK
Whitcombe & Tombs Pty Ltd, Melbourne, n.d. [1944]
35pp, 16 f/p col. illus., stiff dec. wrappers, cover title, 160x185mm. ANL
Stories about insects.

LLOYD, Charlotte J.
4344 THE HOUSE/OF/JUST FANCY!/[drawing]/ Pictures and Verses/By/Charlotte J. Lloyd/The Judd Publishing Company/The Best Book Shop: 361 Pitt Street, Sydney
n.d. [1921]
38pp, 6 col. illus. & b/w drawings in text thoughout, bd. (with col. illus. on front cover), 240x190mm. VSL

LLOYD, Christopher
4345 WILLIAM DAMPIER/Christopher Lloyd/Faber and Faber/24 Russell Square/London
1966
165pp, f/p b/w frontis., 4 f/p b/w plates, 4 b/w maps & 1 b/w text illus., clo. KMM

Sam Lloyd's Puzzles
4346 SAM LLOYD'S PUZZLES. A Book for Children, Melville & Mullen Pty Ltd, Melbourne
n.d. [printed in America, 1912] Not Australian. Grant

LLOYD, T.
A BOY'S PRAYER *See* Moy, J. , A LITTLE CHILD SHALL LEAD THEM

LO, Hui-Min
4347 THE STORY OF CHINA/Lo Hui-Min/Illustrated by Elaine Haxton/Angus and Robertson
Sydney 1970; rpt 1971
82pp, 16pp col. illus., b/w illus. throughout, pic. bd., dec. e/p, 220x275mm. KMM

LOAM, Arthur S.
4348 Imperial Edition No. 1004/PLAYHOUR PIECES/ Piano Pieces for Little Hands/with big notes/by/ Arthur S. Loam/[11 songs listed]/Allans Music (Australia) Pty. Ltd./Melbourne, Adelaide Geelong, Bendigo, Hobart, Launceston./Printed in Australia
copyright 1951
24pp, b/w drawings (signed LAM), col. dec. wrappers, 305x235mm. KP

LOCKE, Elsie
4349 Elsie Locke/THE RUNAWAY SETTLERS/An historical novel for children/Illustrated by Antony Maitland/[device]/Jonathan Cape/Thirty Bedford Square/London
1965
191pp (inc. 2pp note), b/w frontis. & 5 f/p b/w illus., b/w chapter headings throughout, b/w map e/p, clo., 195x125mm. BBC
Pioneering story of New Zealand, based on fact, with the first 35 pages devoted to Australia.
4350 Elsie Locke/THE RUNAWAY SETTLERS/An historical novel for children/Illustrated by Antony Maitland/The Children's Book Club/121 Charing Cross Road/London W.C.2
1965
Details as above. KP
4351 Elsie Locke/THE RUNAWAY SETTLERS/ Illustrated by Antony Maitland/Penguin Books Harmondsworth, Middlesex, England, 1971
176pp (inc. 2pp historical note), 2 b/w maps, b/w frontis. & 5 f/p b/w illus., b/w chapter headings, pic. wrappers, 180x110mm. Puffin Books. KMM

LOCKER, Arthur
4352 STEPHEN SCUDAMORE/THE YOUNGER;/or, The Fifteen-Year Olds./By/Arthur Locker./With illustrations./London:/George Routledge & Sons,/The Broadway, Ludgate:/New York: 416, Broome Street, 1871
339pp, 12pp adv., b/w frontis. & 5 f/p b/w illus., dec. clo., 180x120mm. CLRC
Boys' adventure story set mainly at the Victorian gold diggings. Small platypus in gilt on front cover under decorative title, & boy & kangaroo in gilt on spine.

LOCKEYEAR, J. R.
4353 Story for the Young./by/J. R. L./OLD/BUNYIP,/ The Australian River/Monster./[vignette]/ Collingwood/Printed by Henry S. Dawson, Derby Street/1871
16pp, b/w engravings, wrappers, 155x120mm. VSL

4354 "MR. BUNYIP":/or,/Mary Somerville's/Ramble/A Story for Children/By/J. R. Lockeyear/Fitzroy/ Collingwood/Printed by Henry S. Dawson, Derby Street/1871
16pp, unillus., wrappers, 155x115mm. NSL:M
4355 "MR. BUNYIP";/or,/Mary Somerville's Ramble/ An Australian Story for Children/By/J. R. Lockeyear/ Author of "Goulburn Mary", "Little Mother", "The/ Bush Wedding" etc. etc./Price, 6d./Melbourne:/ Spectator Publishing Co. Limited/270 Post Office Place/1891
24pp, unillus., wrappers, 190x130mm. NSL:M
4356 "MR. BUNYIP";/or/Mary Somerville's Ramble,/ An Australian Story for Children,/By/J. R. Lockeyear/ Author of "Goulburn Mary", "Little Mother", "The/ Story of a Rose", "The Bush Wedding", "Wooing/for Wealth" "Bachelor's Hall", "Katie, or The/Thorn in the Flesh", "George the Foundryman" or/"The Flaw in the Diamond", "Christmas in our/Bark Hut", &c. &c./Price 6d./Mount Gambier/Laurie & Watson, Plain and Ornamental Printers/1894
24pp (inc. 1p reviews), wrappers, 180x115mm. CLRC

4357 An/Australian/Tale/By/J. R. Lockeyear/[vignette]/ [diagonally across page] "GOULBURN MARY,"/ Author/of/"Mr. Bunyip;/or/Mary Sommerville's [*sic*] /Ramble"./Rider & Mercer, Ballarat./Tyrrell's Bookshop, Gawler Place. [Adelaide]
Printed by The Sun Printing and Publishing Co., Post Office Place, Melbourne, n.d. [1894]
128pp, 180x115mm. ANL

LOCKHART, Margaret D. & BROWN, Rhoda E.
4358 GOUROU/Texte par/Margaret D. Lockhart/[4 lines]/et/Rhoda E. Brown/[3 lines]/Longmans Green and Co./London Melbourne New York
1950
32pp (last blank) & acknowledgements, foreword, notes & 8pp vocabulary, pic. wrappers, 182x120mm. KP
French story for school children written by two French teachers at Melbourne's P.L.C.
• Rpt as above, 1953. MK

LOCKWOOD, Douglas
4359 I, THE ABORIGINAL/by/Douglas Lockwood/ Rigby [device] Limited/Adelaide
School ed. October 1966
240pp (inc. 1p note & 1p dedicaton), unillus., limp clo., dec. e/p, 213x135mm. KMM

LOGAN, Anna & others
4360 THE GHOST OF/NORTHMEADE COLLEGE/by Anna Logan/and/Other Stories for Girls/[drawing]/ Wholly set up and published by the Offset Printing Coy. Pty. Limited, Sydney/(All rights reserved)
n.d. [194-?]
32pp, 2 f/p & other part. col. illus., pic. wrappers, 270x210mm. Storytime Series. KMM
Includes the title story, and two girls' school stories , none with any Australian content.
Uniform titles:
THE GREAT WHITE BEAR. TG
KING OF THE JUNGLE
THE SEVEN RAVENS, unseen

LOGUE, Gertrude Elsie
4361 MEET THE LEES/An Australian Story for Boys and Girls/By/G. E. Logue/Geoffrey Cumberlege/Oxford University Press/Leighton House, Melbourne
1946
184pp, unillus., bd., 180x115mm. KMM

LOGUE, W. P. & others
4362 AUSTRALIA'S HERITAGE/W. P. Logue, B.A./Sister M. Anne McLay, B.A., M. Ed./J. E. R. Pearson, B.A., Dip. Ed./J. A. Sparkes, B.A., Dip. Ed./ [drawing]/The Jacaranda Press
Brisbane 1964; rpt 1964
282pp (inc. 3pp introduction, 4pp index, etc.), b/w & part. col. drawings in text, illus. by B. Dean, dec. clo., dec. e/p, 210x140mm. BBC
Background social studies book for schools.

LOHSE, Charlotte & SEATON, Judith
4363 THE/MYSTERIOUS CONTINENT/The Story of the Adventurous Sailors who/Discovered the South Pacific Islands/by/Charlotte Lohse and Judith Seaton/ Maps and illustrations by/W. R. Lohse/[drawing]/The Bobbs Merrill Company/Publishers/Indianapolis New York
n.d. [1944]
165pp (inc. 7pp index), b/w frontis., 10 f/p b/w illus., drawings in text, 8 double-spread maps, clo., 220x140mm. NSL:M

LONDON, Frank
4364 HEROES/OF THE/SOUTH POLE/By Frank London/London:/John F. Shaw & Co., Ltd./3, Pilgrim Street, E.C.
n.d. [191-?]
253pp, col. frontis. & 3 f/p col. illus. by E. S. Hardy, clo., 180x120mm. KMM
The story of the discovery of Antarctica up to the end of Scott's expedition in 1912.
HEROES OF/THE SOUTH POLE
4365 As above, n.d., but earlier bdg. Title in gilt panel on front cover & spine & author's name in gilt. KP

LONG, Charles R.
4366 STORIES OF AUSTRALIAN EXPLORATION, Whitcombe & Tombs, Melbourne, n.d. [1903?] CLRC
A school history reader, & therefore not considered within the scope of this bibliography, as are also C. R. Long & G. M. Wallace's *Notable Deeds of Famous Men and Women* (Robertson & Mullens, Melbourne) & *British Worthies on Sea and Land* (Robertson & Mullens, Melbourne).

4367 NOTABLE DEEDS/IN MYTH AND HISTORY/ Myths and World Stories/For Grade III, Victoria— /Children aged 8 to 9/By/Charles R. Long, M.A./Shakespeare Scholar of the University of Melbourne,/Formerly a Senior Inspector of Schools, Education Department,/Victoria, and Editor of the Department's Publications; Author/of "British Worthies and Other Men of Might", etc./17 illustrations/ Robertson & Mullens Limited/Melbourne
1934. [First publ. 1912]
174pp (inc. 11 appendix), b/w illus. in text, wrappers, 183x120mm. VSL
School book also of general interest.

LONG, E. G.
4368 SANDY & CO./[woodcut]/By/E. G. Long
Printed by Brown Prior & Co. Pty Ltd, 430 Little Bourke St., Melbourne C.1
n.d. [191-?]
16pp, wrappers, 215x140mm. NSL:M

Long Ago
4369 LONG AGO/Wholly Designed in Australia by Renwick Pride Pty Ltd.
Printed by Photogravure
[16]pp (inc. covers), col. illus. throughout, printed on bd., cover title, 310x220mm. JH

LONGMORE, Lydia
4370 A CHILD'S BOOKLET/HOW THE/WATTLE BLOSSOM CAME/by Lydia Longmore
Rigby Ltd, Adelaide, n.d. [1934]
12pp, map & 4 b/w drawings, dec. wrappers, 150x100mm. CLRC
Illustrations signed 'P.O.H.' (1) & 'R.N.B.' (2).

LORD, Beman
THE DAY THE SPACESHIP LANDED
THE SPACESHIP RETURNS
Bay Books, Sydney 1970; reprints of books first published in New York, not Australian

LORD, Florence E.
4371 KANGAROO KINGDOM/By Florence E. Lord/ "Wilga"/Author of "The Kangaroo Fete", "Life in the/ Australian Bush", etc./Brisbane/William Brooks & Co. Ltd., Elizabeth Street/1914
44pp, 1p preface, b/w frontis. & 2 b/w illus., limp clo., 180x120mm. NSL:M

LORD, Fred
4372 LOOK WHO'S/TALKING/By Fred Lord/ [drawing]/A Colorgravure Publication
n.d. [195-?]
111pp, 1 f/p b/w illus., numerous b/w text illus., clo., 212x136mm. J.McG
Foreword (1p) by Crosbie Morrison. Natural history sketches written humorously & intended to amuse children & others.

The Lost Children in the Wood
4373 THE/LOST/CHILDREN/IN THE/WOOD/
London/Sold by the/Booksellers
n.p., n.d. [inscribed 1880]
[16]pp, 6 f/p col. illus., pic. wrappers, cover title, 295x240mm. MAC
The book consists of 6pp illustrations, 8pp blank & 2pp rhyming text. Possibly two pages are missing as there appears to be a hiatus in the narrative, which is in the form of 8-line stanzas, the first text page ending with the children asking to go off & play in the woods, & the next page of text beginning:
'At length the anxious father thought
To try the wild men of the wood,
Whose wondrous instinct might be brought
To track them out as none else could...'
Probably based on the search for the Duff children in 1864.

Lots of Fun Cut Out Book
See The Allied Forces Cut-Out Book

Lots of Things
4374 LOTS/OF THINGS
Photogravures Pty Ltd [Melbourne?, n.d. [194-?]
12pp, col. illus. throughout, pic. bd., cover title, 237x184mm. KP
Light bd. booklet with familiar objects depicted & the names below; illus. signed 'Delma'.

LOTT, L.
4375 BUNNYKINS/Pictures by/E. Donovan/Verses by/L. Lott/F. W. Cheshire Pty. Ltd./Melbourne
n.d. [1945]
31pp, dec. t.p., 16 col. illus., stiff dec. wrappers 155x190mm. ANL

LOVE, J. R. B.
4376 OUR AUSTRALIAN BLACKS/By/J. R. B. Love, B.A., MC., D.C.M./[photograph caption—"Christian Aboriginal Family"]/Price ninepence/Third Edition/Obtainable at the RWMU Depot./156 Collins Street, Melbourne./1923
Printed by Brown, Prior & Co. Pty Ltd, 167 Queen St, Melbourne
36pp & 4pp corrections & list of missionaries &c, b/w photographic illus., wrappers, 214x138mm. CLRC
Mission life written for children.

LOVELL, Muriel
4377 DINNER IN THE MOON/[drawing]/by Muriel Lovell
Reliance Printing Co. Adelaide, n.d. [1950?]
8pp, 2 f/p b/w illus., wrappers, cover title, 240x185mm. KMM

4378 BENNY/AND THE MOON BOY/Sequel to/"Dinner in the Moon"/By/Muriel Lovell/Drawings by Judith Thornquest/Thornquest Press Limited/Adelaide/1952
32pp, 7 f/p b/w illus. & b/w drawings, bd., 185x120mm. KMM

LOW, Charles Rathbone (ed.)
4379 CAPTAIN COOK'S/Three voyages round/the world/with a sketch of his life/Edited by/Lieutenant Charles R. Low/(Late) H.M. Indian Navy, Fellow of the Royal Geographical Society, and/Member of the Royal United Services Institution/London and New York/George Routledge and Sons/1876
512 & 32pp, col. chromolithographic frontis. (native in headdress dancing) & 5 col. plates, dec. clo. with lettering & dec. in gilt on front cover & spine, 170x108mm. KP

4380 Another copy the same, but 1878 with variant frontis. & 1 other plate. KP
4381 Another copy the same, but 1879 with 2 col. plates only bound before t.p., 165x110mm. KP
4382 Another copy the same, but 1880.
London/George Routledge and Sons/Broadway, Ludgate Hill/New York; 416 Broome Street/1880
As above, but col. frontis. only. 170x115mm. RM
4383 Another copy as above to 'London' then, /George Routledge and Sons/Broadway, Ludgate Hill/New York: 8 Lafayette Place
n.d. [school prize 1887]
512pp (inc. 16pp introduction), col. frontis. only, dec. clo., 180x120mm. HBM
4384 CAPTAIN COOK'S/THREE VOYAGES ROUND/THE WORLD/With a Sketch of his life/Edited by/Lieutenant Charles R. Low/Late H.M. Indian Navy, Fellow of the Royal Geographical Society, and/Member of the Royal United Service Institution/London/George Routledge and Sons, Limited/Broadway, Ludgate Hill/Manchester and New York
n.d. [1892?]
512pp, col. lithographic frontis. & 11 f/p col. illus., 27 f/p b/w engravings, pic. clo., 205x135mm. ANL
4385 CAPTAIN COOK'S/THREE VOYAGES ROUND/THE WORLD/with a sketch of his life/edited by/Lieutenant Charles R. Low/(Late) H.M. Indian Navy, Fellow of the Geographical Society, and/Member of the Royal United Service Institution/London/George Routledge and Sons, Limited/Broadway, Ludgate Hill
n.d. [1897?]
512pp, 27 f/p b/w engravings, clo., 220x140mm. Grant
4386 CAPTAIN COOK'S/THREE VOYAGES ROUND/THE WORLD/with a sketch of his life/Edited by/Lieutenant Charles R. Low/(late) H.M. Indian Navy, Fellow of the Royal Geographical Society, and/Member of the Royal United Service Institution/[device]/London/George Routledge and Sons, Limited/Broadway, Ludgate Hill
n.d.
512pp (inc. 16pp introduction), col. frontis. & 11 f/p col. illus., 27 f/p b/w engravings, 1 b/w illus. in text, pic. clo., 205x140mm. HBM
On front cover: 'Captain/Cook's/Voyages/Illustrated'.
4387 CAPTAIN COOK'S/THREE VOYAGES ROUND/THE WORLD/with a sketch of his life/Edited by/Lieutenant Charles R. Low/(late) H.M. Indian Navy, Fellow of the Royal Geographical Society, and/Member of the Royal United Service Institution/[device]/London/George Routledge & Sons, Limited/New York: E. P. Dutton & Co.
n.d. [inscribed 1911]
512pp (inc. 16pp introduction), col. frontis. & 3 f/p col. illus., 27 f/p b/w illus., dec. clo., 195x120mm. HBM
4388 Sir John Lubbock's Hundred Books/19/Captain Cook's/THREE VOYAGES ROUND/THE WORLD/with a sketch of his life/Edited by/Lieutenant Charles R. Low/[2 lines]/London/George Routledge & Sons Limited/Broadway, Ludgate Hill/Glasgow, Manchester, and New York/1892
512pp, b/w frontis. 'Death of Cook', b/w engravings, dec. clo. with gold medallion of 3 boys, 186x124mm. KP
4389 Another copy the same, but undated & frontis. tinted & no other illus. KP
CAPTAIN COOK'S/THREE VOYAGES ROUND/THE WORLD
Various ed. were publ. by other publ., some unillus. & not intended for children, though sometimes seen with prize label, for example:

London:/Miles & Miles/Foresters' Hall Place, Clerkenwell Road, E.C.
n.d. [prize 1900]
512pp, unillus., dec. clo., 196x134mm. KP

4390 Another copy as above, but
London: the Standard Library Company./15 Clerkenwell Rd, E.C.
n.d.
512pp, unillus., clo., 177x114mm. KP

4391 Another copy:
"George Robertson & Co./(Proprietary, Limited)/Melbourne, Sydney, Adelaide, and Brisbane
n.d. [prize 1912], 512pp, col. frontis. only, dec. clo., 185x118mm. KP
Also published in 'Burt's Home Library' but not a children's edition.

LOWNDES, Rosemary & KAILER, Claude

4392 MAKE YOUR OWN/WORLD OF/CHRISTMAS/[col. extended frontis.]/Written and designed by Rosemary Lowndes & Claud Kaiter/for Angus & Robertson Publishers
First publ. in UK by Angus & Robertson (UK) Ltd 1972, 1979, this ed. 1981
Doubtful Australian. CLRC

LUBECK, P. H.

4393 CRAZY RHYMES/by/P. H. Lubeck/Arthur H. Stockwell Limited/Ilfracombe Devon
n.d.
44pp, illus., clo., 190x125mm. MD

Lucky Dip

4394 LUCKY DIP/Kindergarten Stories and Verses/Illustrated by Claire Simpson/[drawing]/Angus and Robertson
Sydney 1970
153pp, line drawings throughout (printed in red), clo., 235x145mm. BBC
Stories & verses by various authors, including Jean Chapman, Elisabeth MacIntyre, Barbara Ker Wilson, Jean Galbraith, etc.

'LUCKY DOOLAN'

4395 48 Full Page Comic. 6d./KELLY GANG/RIDES/also/Thunder/King of the Gorilla Empire/Blitzie Bessie, the Cow/Dickie Lea the Flea/6d.
L. Chapperton, 28 Blanche St., East Brighton, Victoria, n.d. Printed by Wilke & Co, 19–47 Jeffcott St, Melbourne
48pp, b/w comic strips throughout, col. pic. t.p., wrappers, 184x120mm. RM
Ned Kelly comic strip pp1-32.

LUFFMAN, Laura Bogue

4396 WILL AYLMER/A Tale of/the Australian Bush/by/L. Bogue Luffman/London/The Religious Tract Society/4 Bouverie Street and 65 St. Paul's Churchyard
n.d. [Morris Miller gives date 1909]
240pp, col. frontis. & 1 col. plate, clo., 185x115mm. KMM
Boys' story of bush life in Gippsland.

4397 WILL AYLMER/A Tale of/The Australian Bush/by/L. Bogue Luffman/With coloured illustrations/London/The Religious Tract Society/4 Bouverie Street and 65 St. Paul's Churchyard
n.d. [school prize 1913]
240pp, 16pp adv., col. frontis. & 1 col.plate, clo. (with col. onlay on front cover), 190x125mm. KMM

LUKE, E. J.

4398 AUSTRALIAN/NATURE STUDIES/AND/NURSERY RHYMES/Pictured by/Rex Code/Rhymed by/E. T. Luke/From the Children's Page of "The Leader"/The Rhyme Printery/229 Little Collins Street, Melbourne/1921
38pp, 29 b/w illus., wrappers, 220x135mm. ANL

LUM, Vivian Veronica

4399 SUGAR LUMPS/For Little Boys and Girls/Words and Music/by/Vivian Lum/aged 9/Drawings by Joan Arthur/Copyright MCMXXXIII by Allan & Vivian Co. Pty. Ltd. Melbourne/Allan & Co., Pty. Ltd./Melbourne Sydney Adelaide Bendigo
16pp, t.p. portrait photographs, line drawings throughout, dec. wrappers, 300x230mm. VSL
Includes the words & music of 12 songs; four editions are said to have been issued in 1933.

4400 Imperial Edition No 363/SUGAR LUMPS/For Little Boys and Girls/Words and Music/by/Vivian Lum/Drawings by Joan Arthur/copyright MCMXXXIII by Allan & Co. Pty Ltd. Melbourne/Allan & Co Pty Ltd/Melbourne Sydney Adelaide Bendigo [portrait of author]
16pp, b/w drawings throughout, dec. wrappers, 300x230mm, KP
Words & music of 12 songs. Front cover reads 'by Vivian Lum/(aged 9)/Price 2/-'
One issue of this ed. has inside front cover blank; later issues contained 'Important Note'. KP
Another copy as above but 'aged 9' omitted from front cover & price 2/6. KP

LUMBERS, Eugene

4401 A TASTE FOR/BLUE RIBBONS/Eugene Lumbers/[drawing]/Illustrated by George Tetlow/Rigby Limited
Adelaide 1969
236pp, b/w chapter headings, clo., 210x155mm. KMM

4402 I, SMOCKER/by/Eugene Lumbers/Illustrations by Robin Goodall/[drawing]/Macmillan
South Melbourne 1971
118pp, b/w drawings in text, clo., 200x125mm. CLRC
Story of a suburban cat, based on an Australian Broadcasting Commission feature for children.

4403 SMOCKER TAKES OFF/by/Eugene Lumbers/Illustrations by Robin Goodall/[drawing]/Macmillan
South Melbourne 1972
179pp, 1p adv., b/w illus. throughout, clo., 200x125mm. CLRC

LURIE, Morris

4404 THE/TWENTY-SEVENTH/ANNUAL AFRICAN/HIPPOPOTAMUS/RACE/Morris Lurie/Illustrated by Richard Sawers/Collins London
1969
[56]pp, col. & part. col. illus. throughout, pic. clo., pic. e/p, 240x190mm. CLRC

4405 ARLO/THE DANDY LION/Morris Lurie/Illustrated by Richard Sawers/Collins/St. James's Place/London
1971
44pp, col. & part. col. illus. throughout, pic. clo., 255x185mm. CLRC

LÜTGEN, Kurt

4406 Kurt Lütgen/DER GROSSE KAPITÄN/Leben und Entdeckungsfahrten/des englischen Seemanns/James Cook/Georg Westermann Verlag
Braunschweig, 1953
v+353pp & 2pp adv., portrait frontis. & b/w drawings in text, clo., dec. map e/p, 205x135mm. NSL:M
Life of James Cook told for children.

4407 Kurt Lütgen/DER GROSSE KAPITÄN/Leben und Entdeckungsfahrten/des englischen Seemanns/James Cook/Georg Westermann Verlag

(Brunswick) Westermann, 1960 rpt.
v+353pp & 2pp adv., b/w portrait frontis., 7 f/p b/w illus. & numerous text drawings, col. map e/p, clo., 204x134mm. KMM
'Gerstäcker-Preis der Stadt Braunschweig fur das Beste Deutsche Jugendbuch.'

LUXFORD, Nola
4408 KERRY KANGAROO/[coloured illustration]/by/ Nola Luxford/pictures by/Oscar Febrés/Whittlesey House/McGraw-Hill Book Company, Inc./New York Toronto London
1957
32pp, extended dec. t.p., col. & b/w illus. throughout, clo., 255x180mm. ANL

LYALL, C. H.
4409 FRANKIE'S PRINCESS/by/C. H. Lyall/Author of "A Week of Birthdays" etc./[drawing]/London/John F. Shaw (1928) & Co. Ltd./3 Pilgrim Street, E.C.
n.d. [inscribed 1939]
185pp, col. frontis., dec. clo., 180x120mm. MK
Only a small part of this moral tale takes place in Australia. The story opens in Sydney where the heroine's father is dying. She is taken to England & returns fleetingly to Australia at the end.

LYNCH, John
4410 THE STORY OF THE/EUREKA STOCKADE/By/ John Lynch/(one of Peter Lalor's Captains)/The Australian Catholic Truth Society,/143–151 a'Beckett St., Melbourne, and/C.U.S.A. House, 175 Elizabeth St., Sydney
n.d. [194-?]
40pp (inc. 2pp foreword), pic. wrappers, 212x135mm. ANL

LYNE, Nairda
4411 [drawing]/TASMANIAN TALES/by/Nairda Lyne/ with/illustrations by the Author/Fuller's Bookshop/ Hobart
1965
36pp, 1p acknowledgements, 10 f/p b/w illus., drawings in text, pic. clo., dec. e/p, 285x215mm. KMM
Stories first published by the Victorian *School Paper*, & the *N.S.W. School Magazine*.

4412 ADVENTURES/AT POWRANNA/More Tasmanian Tales/By/Nairda Lyne/[drawing]/With seventy-six decorations by the author/[device]/Fuller's Bookshop/Hobart
1969
67pp, b/w drawings throughout, dec. bd., dec. e/p, 275x210mm. KMM

'LYNOTT'
4413 BUBBLEGUG/A/Fairy Story/by/Lynott/This story was originally published with illustrations in the/ children's pages of "The Leader" Melbourne. The permission of/the Proprietors of that journal for the publication of the story in/book form, and for the reproduction of the pictures is gratefully/ acknowledged./Lynott
n.p., n.d.
23pp, 8 brown/white illus. (text also printed in brown), col. pic. bd., 240x180mm. KMM

LYON, Carl
4414 PAINT BOOK
Frank Johnson, Sydney 1943
8pp, b/w drawings throughout, wrappers, 320x250mm. Magpie Picture Books. ANL

4415 ELAINE IN THE FOREST
Frank Johnson, Sydney, n.d. [1944]
12pp, b/w illus. throughout, wrappers, cover title, 275x210mm. ANL

4416 TRIGGER/The Tale of a Dog/By/Carl/Lyon
Frank Johnson, Sydney 1945
16pp, col. illus. throughout, wrappers, cover title, 240x180mm. ANL
Picture book with a few lines of text to each page.

LYONS, Jill
4417 THE THREE DROVERS/An Australian/Musical Christmas Play/for Children/Script by/Jill Lyons/With Lyrics and Music from/"The Australian Christmas Carols" by/W. G. James and John Wheeler/Music arranged by/Hal Evans/Price four shillings net...etc./ Published by/Chappell & Co. Ltd./50 New Bond Street, London, W. 1./Chappell & Co. Ltd., 68–70 Clarence Street, Sydney
n.d. [1961]
24pp, 3 b/w illus.,pic. wrappers, 255x170mm. ANL

LYSTER, Annette
4418 BRYAN AND KATIE./By/Annette Lyster,/Author of 'Those Unlucky Twins', etc./Illustrated by Harry Furniss/[device]/Griffith Farrar Okeden & Welsh,/ Newbery House, Charing Cross Road,/London and Sydney
n.d. [1891?]
160pp, b/w frontis., 3 f/p illus. & 6 small text illus., dec. bd., 182x118mm. KMM
A family story with references only to Australia whence several young brothers are taken by an uncle. KMM

4419 MURIEL'S TWO CROSSES/The Cross she rejected/and/The Cross she chose/by/Annette Lyster/ Author of "The White Gypsy" "Alone in Crowds" "Two Old Maids"/"Piano in the Attic"/"North Ward and Sunshine"/Published under the direction of the/ Committee of General Literature and Education, appointed by/The Society for Promoting Christian Knowledge/London/Society for Promoting Christian Knowledge/Northumberland Avenue, Charing Cross W.C./43 Queen Victoria Street E.C./26 St George's Place, Hyde Park Corner, S.W./Brighton: 135 North Street/New York: E. & J. B. Young & Co.
n.d.
320pp & 16pp adv., b/w frontis. & 3 f/p b/w illus., dec. clo., 180x117mm. ANL
Chapter 14 (pp289–307) set in Australian goldfields.

M., A.I.
4420 THE CHILD'S/HISTORY OF AUSTRALIA/By A.I.M./First Part/Sydney:/William Brooks and Co., Limited,/17 Castlereagh Street./1903
31pp (inc. 1p author's note), b/w map e/p, stiffened paper wrappers, 185x125mm. KMM
Published as a school book for parents & teachers; author's note states: '...we hope that to many families in the far off bush the forthcoming series may be of service'. A note at the conclusion reads: 'The next part of this history containing "Voyage of the Tom Thumb", "Arrival of the First Fleet", and other items of interest to Australian Children, is in course of publication'.
On front cover: 'Puplished [*sic*] Price, Sixpence'.

'MAB'
TALES FOR YOUNG AUSTRALIA. *See* Favenc, Ernest

McCABE, Jean A.
4421 WILGA COMES/TO SCHOOL/By/Jean A. McCabe/[drawing]/Printed and Published by/

Patersons Printing Press Ltd./Perth W.A./Price three shillings and sixpence
n.d. [1942]
55pp, b/w drawings, bd., 240x165mm. NSL:M

McCABE, Joan A.

4422 WILGA COMES/TO SCHOOL/By Joan [*sic*] /A. McCabe/[device]/Patersons Printing Press Ltd./Perth W.A.
n.d.
56pp, 6 b/w illus. in text, dec. bd., 240x185mm. KMM
Note change of Christian name of author from that in the edition above.

4423 JOLLY/GOOD/FELLOWS/Jolly Good Fellows by Joan McCabe
Patersons Press Ltd, Perth, W.A., n.d. [copyright 1949]
47pp, col. dec. t.p., col. & b/w illus. throughout, pic. bd., 165x250mm. NSL:M
Pictures & words by Joan A. McCabe; portraits by Shirley Keene.

MacCALLUM, J.

4424 AUSTRALIAN/ANIMALS/[drawing]/Descriptions and Verse/by J. MacCallum/Illustrations by/Walter Dowman
Currawong Publishing Co., Sydney, n.d. [1943]
70pp (inc. 2pp introduction), dec. t.p., wrappers, 240x165mm. NSL:M
A verse, a drawing, & a page of descriptive text about each of 16 Australian animals.

McARDLE, Brian

GRAHAM IS AN ABORIGINAL BOY. *See* Marks, Stan

McCARTER, James William

4425 THE ANIMAL PACK/by/Jim McCarter/Illustrations by/R. L. Nevin
The Worker Newspaper Pty Ltd, Brisbane 1945
63pp (inc. 4pp introduction & verses), 28 f/p part. col. illus., dec. wrappers, 235x180mm. ANL
Verses for small children about animals.

MACARTHUR-ONSLOW, Annette Rosemary

4426 [drawing]/UHU/(Pronounced Yoo-Hoo)/Annette Macarthur-Onslow/Rapp & Whiting—London Ure Smith Sydney
1969
62pp (inc. 1p quotation & 1p foreword), col., part. col. & b/w drawings throughout, illus. by author, clo., dec. e/p, 275x215mm. KMM
Winner CBCA Picture Book Award 1970.

4427 As above, but
[drawing]/UHU/(Pronounced Yoo-Hoo)/Annette Macarthur-Onslow/Ure Smith—Sydney/Rapp & Whiting London
2nd imp. Jan 1970, 3rd imp. July 1970. KP

4428 As above
4th imp. Sept 1970
Children's Book of the Year Award medallion on d/w (with portrait of James Cook). KP
As above
5th imp. April 1971. KP

4429 [drawing]/UHU/Annette Macarthur-Onslow/Alfred A. Knopf: New York
1970
Details as in English/Australian edition, but size 280x205mm. ANL

4430 MINNIE/Annette Macarthur-Onslow/Ure Smith Sydney
1971
64pp, col. frontis., col. & b/w illus. throughout, clo., dec. e/p, 285x210mm. KMM

McCARTHY, Frederick David

4431 ABORIGINAL/TRIBES AND/CUSTOMS/The Sanitarium Children's Library—Volume 4
Sanitarium Health Food Co., Sydney 1950
16pp (inc. foreword), illus. wrappers, cover title, 280x220mm. KMM
Album for series of coloured picture cards; according to the foreword, the 50 picture cards illustrating the book were drawn in co-operation with the author (artist's name not given). Paragraphs of text describe each of the 50 cards which were to be collected by children from packets of cereal. Map of Australia showing tribal boundaries printed on back wrapper.

4432 The Australian Museum/AUSTRALIAN ABORIGINES/[drawing]
The Australian Museum, Sydney, 1953
12pp, each page has 6 b/w illus. with accompanying text, wrappers, 240x153mm. KMM
First publ. in the *NSW School Magazine* Vol. 37, Nos 1–9.

MACAULAY, James

4433 STRANGE YET TRUE:/Interesting and memorable/Stories Retold/By/Dr Macaulay,/Author of/"Luther Anecdotes", "From Middy to Admiral of the Fleet",/etc./London:/James Nisbet & Co., 21 Berners Street./MDCCCXCII
408pp, 32pp adv., b/w frontis. & 11 f/p b/w illus., pic. clo., 185x125mm. KMM
Contents include: 'Thomas Muir and the Scottish Martyrs' (18pp); 'Captain Matthew Flinders, R. N.' (10pp).

4434 TRUE TALES/OF/TRAVEL AND ADVENTURE, VALOUR AND VIRTUE/By/James Macaulay, M.A., M.D./Author of "All True", "Grey Hawk" etc. and/Editor of "The Leisure Hour"./with thirteen illustrations/Ninth thousand/London/Hodder and Stoughton/27, Paternoster Row/MDCCCLXXXIV/(All rights reserved)
404pp, 4pp adv., part-col. t.p., 13 b/w illus. (only one relating to Australia), pic. clo. (title on spine, no medallion), 200x135mm. CLRC
Contents include: 'Captain Dampier and the Buccaneers' (11pp), 'Early Exploring Expeditions in Australia' (7pp), 'Across Australia from Sea to Sea' (9pp), 'The Discovery of Gold in Australia' (4pp), 'How Christianity was introduced into Mangaia' (11pp & 1 illus.).

- Rpt as above, but 1894. HBM
- Rpt as above, 11th Thousand 1904. KP

4435 TRUE TALES/OF/TRAVEL AND ADVENTURE, VALOUR AND VIRTUE/By/James Macaulay, M.A., M.D./Author of "Grey Hawk", "Stirring Stories" etc./New edition/With illustrations in colour/By T. C. Dugdale/London/Henry Frowde/Hodder and Stoughton/1915
404pp, (no adv.), col. frontis. & 5 f/p col. illus. (inc. one of Burke & Wills expedition), clo. (with Burke & Wills illus. pasted on front cover, & title in medallion on spine), 185x120mm. HBM
Contents as in previous edition.

McCLELLAND, Elna

4436 Series No. 1/"BUNTY"/The Naughty Rabbit/By/Elna McClelland/Illustrated and hand-coloured by/Harry McClelland/Published by/Annie McClelland/Flemington/Price One Shilling
n.d. [1917]
24pp, 7 col. illus., col. dec. wrappers, 150x120mm. NSL:M
Outside wrapper entitled 'Australian Kid Stories'.

4437 "BUNTY"/The Naughty Rabbit/By/Elna McClelland/Illustrated/Harry McClelland/Published by/Annie McClelland/Melbourne
Second ed., n.d. Printed by F. J. Lord & Son Printers, Melbourne 4121
24pp, col. frontis., 1 double-spread col. illus. & 4 col. illus. & tailpiece, pic. wrappers, 150x114mm. KP
Title on wrappers 'Australian Kid Stories'.

McCLUNIE, Alister
4438 THE ADVENTURES OF TOBY AND/SPHINX IN FLOWERLAND/By/Alister McClunie/Illustrated by Alice Polson/[drawing]/Whitcombe & Tombs Limited/Auckland Christchurch Dunedin, and Wellington N.Z./Melbourne and London
n.d. [1920?]
119pp, col. frontis. & 3 f/p col. illus., b/w drawings, wrappers, 185x120mm. NSL:M

MACLURE, Captain K.
4439 JERRY GOES TO/SEA/By/Captain K. Maclure/[drawing]/Illustrated by Savile Lumley/Thomas Nelson & Sons Ltd./London Edinburgh New York Toronto & Paris
n.d. [prize 1933]
295pp, col. frontis. & text drawings, pic. clo., dec. e/p, 185x130mm. ANL

4440 JEREMY "DOWN UNDER"/by/Captain K. Maclure/Author of "Red Ramon's Treasure"/"Jerry goes to Sea" etc./[drawing]/Illustrated by Stuart Tresilian/Thomas Nelson and Sons, Ltd./London, Edinburgh, Paris, Melbourne,/Toronto, and New York
First pub. Sept. 1949; rpt 1955
248pp, col. frontis. & 8 f/p b/w illus., 1 b/w chapter heading, clo., 190x125mm. KMM
The hero serves in a naval escort accompanying one of the convict fleets to New South Wales.

McCONNELL, Louise
4441 PLATYPUS JOE/Louise McConnell/with a foreword by/Alan Marshall/[drawing]/Nelson Melbourne 1969
75pp, 2pp foreword, brown/white drawings throughout, pic. bd., col. e/p, 225x150mm. KMM
Artist's name not shown & drawings unsigned.

MacCORMICK, D.
4442 LITTLE LADDIE/AND HIS BUSH-LAND FRIENDS/Verses by/Capt. D. MacCormick/Melbourne. Australia/Illustrations/by/Ida Outhwaite/Glasgow/Alex. Maclaren & Sons/268 Argyle Street, C.2
(verso first ed. 1948)
32pp (last one blank) (no frontis.), 4 f/p & 23 smaller b/w drawings, clo., 215x275mm. Grant

McCORMICK, P. D.
4443 THE/FOUR/SCHOOL/MATES/An Australian Tale of Misfortune/and Success/by P. D. McCormick/Preface by John Fraser, B.A., LL.D./Introduction by Rev. Archd. Gilchrist, M.A., LL.D./[quotation]/Sydney:/Hayes Brothers, 55 and 57 Elizabeth Street/MDCCCXCVI
xvi+219pp, b/w frontis., clo., 184x120mm. KMM
• Rpt 1906, as above. Grant

McCrae, Dorothy Frances [Mrs C. E. Perry]
See Alsop, Marion & McCrae, Dorothy Frances

MACRAE, Herbert
THE FIGHTING FREELANCE. *See* Champion Library

McCRAE, Hugh
4444 THE AUSTRALIAN/ALPHABET/[drawing]/Drawings by Norman Carter/Jingle by Hugh McCrae/Sydney & Melbourne/Angus & Robertson [space] All rights reserved
n.d. [1905]
26pp, b/w illus. on every page, with initials & main letter printed in tan-col. ink, pic. wrappers, 280x220mm. VSL

McCUAIG, Ronald
4445 GANGLES/by Robert McCuaig/Illustrated by Noela Young/Angus and Robertson
Sydney 1972
125pp, b/w drawings in text, clo., 195x180mm. KMM

McCUAIG, Ronald & STUART, Isla
See YOU CAN DRAW A KANGAROO

McCULLOCH, Samuel Clyde
GEORGE GIPPS. *See* Great Australians

McCUTCHEON, A. D.
4446 THE/MAGIC OF/CHRISTMAS/By A. D. McCutcheon
Lush Studios—Printed by Gillingham & Co. Adelaide, n.d. [1948?]
[16]pp, 8 b/w illus., pic. wrappers, cover title, 178x125mm. KMM
Illus. signed L. Macdonald. Stories with religious meaning.

MACDONALD, Alexander
4447 THE/LOST EXPLORERS/A Story of/The Trackless Desert/By/Alexander Macdonald, F.R.G.S./Illustrated by Arthur H. Buckland/Blackie & Son, Limited/London, Glasgow, Dublin, New York/1906
378pp & 2pp adv., b/w frontis. & 7 f/p b/w plates, red pic. clo., 187x125mm. CLRC
4448 THE LOST EXPLORERS/A Story of the Trackless Desert/By/Alexander Macdonald/F.R.G.S., F.R.S.G.S., F.R.C.I./Author of/"In Search of El Dorado"/"The Trail of the Pioneer"/"Pioneering in Klondike"/Illustrated by Arthur H. Buckland/Blackie and Son Limited/London Glasgow Dublin Bombay/1907
380pp, 2pp author's preface, b/w frontis. & 7 b/w plates, pic. clo., 190x135mm. KMM
A tale of gold-digging & exploration.
Another copy as above, with 16pp adv. KMM
4449 THE LOST EXPLORERS/A Story of the Trackless Desert/By/Alexander Macdonald/F.R.G.S., F.R.S.G.S., F.R.C.I./Author of "The Invisible Island", "The Pearl Seekers", &c./Illustrated by Arthur H. Buckland/Blackie and Son Limited/London Glasgow and Bombay
n.d. [inscribed 1925]
380pp, 2pp preface, b/w frontis. & 5 b/w plates, dec. clo., 185x120mm. CLRC
4450 THE LOST EXPLORERS/By/Alexander Macdonald/FRGS, FRSGS, FRCI/Author of 'The Invisible Island' 'The Pearl Seekers' &c/Illustrated by H. Buckland/[device]/Blackie & Son Limited/London and Glasgow
n.d.
379pp, part-col. frontis. & 3 part-col. plates, clo., 180x118mm. KP
4451 Another ed. as above but with b/w frontis. & 3 b/w plates. KP

4452 THE QUEST OF THE/BLACK OPALS/A Story of Adventure in the Heart of/Australia/By/Alexander Macdonald/Author of "The Lost Explorers" "The Pearl Seekers" etc./Illustrated by William Rainey R.I./Blackie and Son Limited/London Glasgow Dublin Bombay/1908

352pp (inc. 2pp author's preface), 16pp adv., b/w frontis. & 5 b/w plates, map, pic. clo., 185x125mm. NSL:M
First edition has title in gilt letters on front cover & spine & addition of blue in cover design.

4453 THE QUEST OF THE/BLACK OPALS/A Tale of Adventure in the Heart of/Australia/by/Alexander Macdonald/Author of "The Lost Explorers"/"The White Trail" etc./Illustrated by William Rainey, R.I./Blackie & Son Limited/London Glasgow and Bombay
n.d.
353pp (inc. 2pp preface), b/w frontis. & 5 f/p b/w plates & map, pic. clo., 185x120mm. RM

4454 As above, but imprint 'London and Glasgow'. Grant

4455 THE PEARL SEEKERS/A Tale of the Southern Seas/By/Alexander Macdonald, F.R.G.S./Author of "The Lost Explorers"/"The Quest of the Black Opals", "In Search of El Dorado", etc./Illustrated by Edward S. Hodgson/Blackie & Son Limited/London Glasgow Dublin Bombay/1908
363pp & 2pp author's preface, 16pp adv., b/w frontis. & 8 b/w plates, 2 maps, pic. clo., 195x165mm. ANL

4456 THE PEARL SEEKERS/A Tale of the Southern Seas/By/Alexander Macdonald,F.R.G.S./Author of "The Lost Explorers"/"The Quest of the Black Opals" "The White Trail" &c/Illustrated by Edward S. Hodgson/Blackie and Son Limited/London Glasgow and Bombay
n.d. [inscribed 1926]
363pp & 2pp author's preface, b/w frontis. & 6 b/w plates, pic. clo., 188x132mm. KP
This edition does not include the maps.

Swedish edition

4457 PÄRLFISKARNA/Berättelse Från Söderhavet/Av/Alexander Macdonald/Från Engelskan/Av/Richard Melander/[device]/Stockholm/C. E. Fritzes Bokförlags Aktiebolag
1st Swedish ed. 1917
315pp, unillus., col. pic. bd. with clo. spine, dec. e/p, 185x120mm. RM

4458 Alexander Macdonald/PÄRLFISKARNA/Berättelse Från Söderhavet/Från Engelskan/Av/Richard Melander/Stockholm/Ab J. Hasselgrens Förlagsbokhandel
'Helsinfors 1944' on verso t.p.
181pp, 6pp adv., unillus., col. pic. bd. with clo. spine, 205x140mm. RM
Printed in Finland.

4459 THE WHITE TRAIL/A Story of the Early Days of Klondike/By/Alexander Macdonald, F.R.G.S./Author of "The Quest of the Black Opals"/"The Lost Explorers" &c./Illustrated by William Rainey, R.I./Blackie and Son Limited/London Glasgow Bombay
n.d. [verso of t.p.: 'Copyright in the U.S.A. 1908/by H. M. Caldwell Co.']
392pp (inc. 1p preface), b/w frontis. & 7 b/w plates, & 1 f/p map, pic. clo., 185x125mm. RM

4460 THE WHITE TRAIL/A Story of the Early Days of Klondike/By/Alexander Macdonald, F.R.G.S./Author of "In the Land of Pearl and Gold" "The Lost Explorers"/"The Pearl Seekers" "The Island Traders" &c/Illustrated by William Rainey, R.I./Blackie and Son Limited/London Glasgow Dublin Bombay 1909
As above but 190x135mm. KMM

4461 THE ISLAND TRADERS/A Tale of the South Seas/By/Alexander Macdonald F.R.G.S./Author of "In Search of El Dorado" "The Lost Explorers"/"The Pearl Seekers" &c./Illustrated by Charles M. Sheldon/Blackie and Son Limited/London Glasgow Dublin Bombay/1909
Published simultaneously in Great Britain and the United States (H. M. Caldwell Co.)
292pp, 16pp adv., b/w frontis. & 5 b/w plates, pic. clo., 185x125mm. NSL:M

4462 THE/ISLAND TRADERS/A Tale of the South Seas/by/Alexander Macdonald, F.R.G.S./Author of "The White Trail", "The Lost Explorers",/"The Pearl Seekers", etc./Illustrated by Charles M. Sheldon/Blackie and Son Limited/London Glasgow and Bombay
n.d.
292pp, b/w frontis. & 5 b/w plates, pic. clo., 185x130mm. KP
• Rpt as above, but 'London and Glasgow', n.d.
292pp, b/w frontis. & 3 b/w plates, pic. clo. (cover design sgd 'Hassall'). KP

4463 THROUGH THE HEART/OF TIBET/By/Alexander Macdonald, F.R.G.S./Author of "In the Land of Pearl and Gold" "The White Trail"/"The Island Traders" "The Pearl Seekers"/"The Lost Explorers" &c./Illustrated by William Rainey, R.I./Blackie and Son Limited/London Glasgow Dublin Bombay/1910
384pp, 16pp adv., part-col. frontis. & 7 part.-col. plates, pic. clo., 185x135mm. KMM

4464 THROUGH THE HEART/OF TIBET/By/Alexander Macdonald, F.R.G.S./Author of "The Quest of the Black Opals" "The White Trail"/"The Island Traders" "The Pearl Seekers"/"The Lost Explorers" &c./Illustrated by William Rainey, R.I./Blackie and Son Limited/London Glasgow and Bombay
n.d.
384pp, b/w frontis. & 5 b/w plates, pic. clo., 190x135mm. RM

4465 THE HIDDEN NUGGET/A Story of the Australian Goldfields/By/Alexander Macdonald/Author of "Through the Heart of Tibet" "The White Trail"/"The Lost Explorers" "The Pearl Seekers" &c./Illustrated by William Rainey R.I./Blackie and Son Limited/London Glasgow Dublin Bombay/1910
284pp, 16pp adv., b/w frontis. & 6 b/w plates, diagram, pic. clo., 185x125mm. NSL:M

4466 THE HIDDEN NUGGET/A Story of the Australian Goldfields/By/Alexander Macdonald/Author of/"The Mystery of Diamond Creek" "Through the Heart of Tibet"/"The White Trail" "The Lost Explorers" &c./Illustrated by William Rainey R.I./Blackie & Son Limited/London and Glasgow
n.d. [192-?]
284pp, b/w frontis. & 3 b/w plates, diagram, clo., 185x125mm. KMM

4467 THE INVISIBLE ISLAND/A Story of the Far North/of Queensland/By/Alexander Macdonald, F.R.G.S./Author of "Through the Heart of Tibet", "The Hidden Nugget",/"The White Trail", "The Island Traders",/"The Pearl Seekers" &c./Illustrated by Charles M. Sheldon,/Blackie and Son Limited/London Glasgow and Bombay/1911
360pp, tinted frontis. & 5 tinted plates, pic. clo., 185x130mm. CLRC

4468 THE INVISIBLE ISLAND/A Story of the Far North/of Queensland/By/Alexander Macdonald, F.R.G.S./Author of "Through the Heart of Tibet", "The White Trail"/"The Island Traders", "The Pearl Seekers", &c./Illustrated by Charles M. Sheldon/Blackie & Sons Limited./London and Glasgow
n.d.

360pp, b/w frontis. & 5 b/w plates, pic. clo., 190x130mm. VSL
• Rpt as above but n.d. & b/w frontis. & 3 plates only & 185x125mm. KP

4469 Also publ. by H. M. Caldwell Co., New York, as above
n.d. [1910?]. Unseen

4470 THE MYSTERY/OF DIAMOND CREEK/by/ Alexander Macdonald/F.R.G.S./Author of "Through the Heart of Tibet"/"The White Trail" "The Lost Explorers"/"The Pearl Seekers" &c./Illustrated by M. Mackinlay/Blackie & Son Limited/London and Glasgow
n.d.
320pp, b/w frontis. & 5 b/w plates, pic. clo., 185x125mm. RM
• Rpt as above, but b/w frontis. & 3 plates only (The Boys' Library). KMM

McDONALD, Babs

4471 PAMELA/FINDS THE/RAINBOW CASTLE/ Written and illustrated/by/Babs McDonald/John Sands Pty. Ltd./Sydney and Melbourne
n.d. [1947]
27pp, dec. col. t.p., col. frontis., col. & b/w illus. throughout, dec. bd., 240x185mm. ANL
2nd imp., n.d. KMM
4th imp., n.d. KP

MACDONALD, Barbara, illustrator

See A NEW BOOK OF OLD RHYMES

MACDONALD, Donald

4472 THE BUSH BOY'S/BOOK/By Donald Macdonald/ Author of/"Gum Boughs and Wattle Bloom",/"How we kept the Flag Flying"/"The Warrigal's Well"/Etc. Etc./Illustrated/Commonwealth of Australia:/Sydney J. Endacott/Melbourne
1911
260pp (inc. author's introduction & 6pp index), 10pp adv., b/w portrait frontis., 50 b/w diagrams, dec. wrappers, 175x110mm. KMM
A compilation from the author's nature notes column in the *Argus*.
Also published in clo. binding.

4473 THE BUSH BOY'S/BOOK/By/Donald Macdonald/ Author of "Gum Boughs and Wattle Bloom", "How we kept/the Flag Flying"/"The Warrigal's Well", "At the End of the/Moonpath", etc./Second Edition, revised and enlarged,/with 46 illustrations/Australia:/ Cornstalk Publishing Company/89 Castlereagh Street, Sydney/1927
329pp, b/w illus., clo., 180x120mm. BBC

4474 THE BUSH BOY'S/BOOK/By/Donald Macdonald/ Author of Gum Boughs and Wattle Bloom, How we kept/the Flag Flying, The Warrigal's Well, At the End of the/Moonpath, etc./third edition/Australia:/ Cornstalk Publishing Company/89 Castlereagh Street, Sydney/1928
329pp, 2pp preface to second edition, b/w diagrams throughout, clo., 170x110mm. BBC
• Rpt 1930, 1933, as above.

4475 AT THE END OF THE/MOONPATH/By/Donald Macdonald/Author of/"How we kept the Flag Flying", "The Bush/Boy's Book", "At [*sic*] the Warrigal's Well" etc./Illustrated by/C. E. James/[publisher's device]/ Melbourne:/Auckland, Christchurch, Dunedin, Wellington/and London/Whitcombe & Tombs Limited.
n.d. [1922]
143pp, 1p adv., b/w frontis. & 10 f/p b/w illus., clo., 180x125mm. KMM

MACDONALD, Donald & EDGAR, John F.

4476 THE/WARRIGAL'S WELL/A North Australian Story/By/Donald Macdonald/Author of 'How we kept the Flag Flying'/and/John F. Edgar/Illustrated by J. Macfarlane/London/Ward, Lock & Co., Limited/New York and Melbourne/1901
307pp (inc. 1p author's note), 4pp & 8pp adv., b/w frontis. & 3 f/p b/w illus., pic. clo., 190x125mm. CLRC
4pp reviews of author's *How we kept the Flag Flying* precede text.

4477 Another copy with the same t.p. printed in red and black, but bound in plain red clo.with title & authors' name in gilt on front cover & spine, 180x120mm. KP

4478 Another copy as above, but with 'and J. F. Edgar' in smaller letters on front cover. KP

McDONALD, E. C.

4479 THE DUNGEON/AT THE FARM/and other stories/by/E. C. McDonald/Arthur H. Stockwell, Ltd:/ Ilfracombe Devon
63pp (inc. 1p foreword by author &c), 6 b/w drawings by author, clo., 184x120mm. NSL:M
Children's stories with an eastern Australian setting.

MACDONALD, Henrietta

4480 "CHILDREN OF THE WIND"/And Other Australian Stories/By/Henrietta Macdonald/ (Copyright)
Sydney. J. Bell & Co., n.d. [195-?]
157pp, 3 f/p b/w illus., pic. wrappers, 200x130mm. NSL:M
Contents, some of which are stories & verses for children, include 'Rainbow Farm', not really children's.

McDONALD, Jo

4481 AUSTRALIA/IN PICTURES/Prepared by Jo McDonald/[photograph of a prize ram with caption]/ Visual/Geography/Series/The Oak Tree Press [device]/London and Melbourne
1966
64pp, b/w photographic illus. throughout, clo., 252x164mm. KP

MacDONALD, Lin

4482 BUD THE MONKEY/And Other Tales of/Soldiers' Pets/Told by Lin MacDonald and/Illustrated by/ Angus MacDonald/With an introduction by/General Sir Ian Hamilton,/G.C.B., G.C.M.G., D.S.O., T.D./Australia/Angus & Robertson Limited/89 Castlereagh Street, Sydney/1932
x, 126pp (inc. 6pp introduction), b/w frontis. & 9 f/p b/w drawings & in text, clo., 205x155mm. KMM

MACDONALD, M. P.

TREFOIL. *See* Parker, Margaret

MACDONALD, Robert M.

4483 THE/GREAT WHITE CHIEF/A Story of Adventure in Unknown/New Guinea/by/Robert M. Macdonald/ Illustrated by W. Rainey, R.I./Blackie & Son, Limited/ London Glasgow Dublin Bombay/1908
viii (inc. 2pp preface), 367pp, 16pp adv., b/w frontis. & 7 b/w plates, double-spread map, pic. clo., 190x140mm. RM

4484 THE/GREAT WHITE CHIEF/A Story of New Guinea/By/Robert M. Macdonald/Illustrated by W. Rainey, R.I./Blackie & Son Limited/London and Glasgow
n.d. [school prize 1928]
367pp, 2pp preface, b/w frontis. & 5 b/w plates, pic. clo., 185x135mm. KMM

4485 Another copy as above, n.d. [192-?]
367pp, b/w frontis. & 3 b/w plates, pic. clo., 180x115mm. KP

4486 CHILLAGOE CHARLIE/By/Robert M. Macdonald/[device]/London: T. Fisher Unwin/Adelphi Terrace. MCMIX
345pp, 6pp adv., col. frontis. & 16 f/p b/w illus., pic. clo., 190x120mm. NSL:M
Frontispiece signed 'Arch Webb'.
4487 Swedish edition 1911. Unseen

4488 THE SECRET OF THE/SARGASSO/By/Robert M. Macdonald/Author of "Chillagoe Charlie"/With 17 illustrations by Arch Webb/London/T. Fisher Unwin/ Adelphi Terrace/MCMIX
368pp, frontis. (missing) & 16 b/w plates, pic. clo., 190x125mm. ANL

4489 THE MOON GOD'S/SECRET/A Tale of the Tropical Pacific/By/Robert M. Macdonald, .F.R.S.G.S./Author of/"Chillagoe Charlie", "The Secret of the Sargasso", etc. etc./With Thirteen illustrations by Arch. Webb/[device]/London: T. Fisher Unwin/ Adelphi Terrace MCMX
319pp, 104pp adv., col. frontis. & 12 b/w plates., pic. clo., 190x125mm. NSL:M

4490 THE/RIVAL TREASURE HUNTERS/A Tale of the Debatable Frontier/of British Guiana/By/Robert M. Macdonald/Author of "The Great White Chief"/Illustrated by Cyrus Cuneo/Blackie and Son Limited/London Glasgow Dublin Bombay/1910
382pp (inc. 2pp preface), 16pp adv., tinted frontis. & 7 tinted plates, pic. clo., 190x135mm. RM
Three of the main characters are Australian.
4491 THE RIVAL/TREASURE HUNTERS/A Tale of British Guiana/by/Robert M. Macdonald/Author of "The Great White Chief"/Illustrated by Cyrus Cuneo/ Blackie and Son Limited/London Glasgow and Bombay
n.d. [prize 1928]
382pp (inc. 2pp preface), b/w frontis. & 5 b/w plates, pic. clo., 190x135mm. RM
4492 THE RIVAL/TREASURE HUNTERS/A Tale of British Guiana/By/Robert M. Macdonald/Author of "The Great White Chief"/Illustrated by Cyrus Cuneo/ Blackie & Son Limited/London and Glasgow
n.d.
viiipp, 382pp & 2pp preface, b/w frontis. & 3 b/w plates, pic. clo., 187x127mm. KMM
Advertisement for 'The Boys' Library' precedes t.p.

4493 THE GOLDSEEKERS; a tale of Adventure, a gold-extracting motor, and the Sahara Desert
T. Fisher Unwin, 1910
360pp with 12 plates by Arch Webb. Unseen

4494 DANGER MOUNTAIN/A Story of Adventure in/ Unexplored New Guinea/By/Robert M. Macdonald, F.R.S.G.S./Author of "The Secret of the Sargasso"/"The Gold-Seekers" etc./With 13 illustrations by Arch. Webb/London/T. Fisher Unwin/ Adelphi Terrace/1911
320pp, col. frontis. & 12 b/w plates, pic. clo., 190x120mm. NSL:M

4495 THE/OPAL HUNTERS/or/The Men of Red Creek Camp/by/Robert M. Macdonald/Author of "The Pearl Lagoons" "The/Moon God's Secret" etc./London/S. W. Partridge & Co. Ltd./Old Bailey
n.d. [1912]
320pp, 32pp adv., part-col. dec. t.p., col. frontis. & 5 b/w plates, clo. (with col. onlays on front cover & spine), 190x135mm. KMM
Illustrations signed 'Holloway'.

4496 THE/PEARL LAGOONS/or/THE LOST CHIEF/ By/Robert Macdonald/London/S. W. Partridge & Co., Ltd./[vignette]
n.d. [1915?] Library copy acquired 1918
320pp, dec. t.p., col. frontis. & 5 b/w plates (unsgd,) pic. clo., 190x125mm. NSL:M
4497 THE/PEARL LAGOONS/or,/The Lost Chief/By/ Robert Macdonald/Author of "The Opal Hunters" etc.etc./London/S.W.Partridge & Co.Ltd./E.C.4
n.d.
320pp, col. frontis. & 3 b/w plates, pic. clo., 188x128mm. KMM

MacDONNELL, J. E.
[*see* 'James Macnell' pseud.]

McFADYEN, Ella
4498 HERE'S FUN/FOR YOU!/Children's Verse for/ Recitation and Group/Speaking/By/Ella McFadyen/ ("Cinderella" of "The Sydney Mail")/Illustrations by/ Edwina Bell/Dymock's Book Arcade Ltd./The "Block"/424–426 George Street/Sydney
54pp, b/w drawings throughout, dec. wrappers, 180x115mm. ANL

4499 PEGMEN/TALES/[drawing]/by/Ella McFadyen/ Illustrated by/Edwina Bell/Angus and Robertson/ Sydney: London/1946
142pp, col. frontis., col. & b/w illus. throughout, bd. (clo. spine), 240x180mm. ANL
4500 The Junior Library of Australian Books/PEGMEN TALES/By/Ella McFadyen/Angus and Robertson/ Sydney—London
1949
154pp, b/w frontis. & 4 f/p b/w illus., bd., 185x120mm. ANL

4501 PEGMEN/GO/WALKABOUT/By/Ella McFadyen/ Illustrated by/Edwina Bell/This Book/is a sequel to/ 'Pegmen Tales'/Angus and Robertson/Sydney: London/1947
273pp, part. col. frontis., 10 f/p b/w illus. & b/w drawings in text, clo., 190x120mm. ANL

4502 LITTLE DRAGONS/OF THE/NEVER NEVER/by/ Ella McFadyen/Illustrated by/Edwina Bell/[device]/ Australasian Publishing Company/Sydney Wellington London
First publ. 1949
96pp, b/w drawings, pic. bd., 184x135mm. KP
The York series.
4503 LITTLE DRAGONS/OF THE/NEVER NEVER/by/ Ella McFadyen/Illustrated by/Edwina Bell/ Australasian Publishing Company/Sydney Wellington London/in association with/George G. Harrap & Co. Ltd.
First pub. 1948; rpt 1950, 1954
96pp, b/w drawings in text throughout, pic. bd., 190x160mm. CLRC

4504 THE/WISHING STAR/by/Ella McFadyen/ Illustrated by Ernst Corvus/Angus and Robertson/ Sydney—London—Melbourne—Wellington
1956
32pp, col. illus. throughout, pic. bd., 245x180mm. BBC

4505 KOOKABURRA/COMEDIES/Junior/Plays/by/Ella McFadyen/Book 1/School Projects Pty. Limited/ Rockdale N.S.W.
n.d. [library copy acquired 1956]

20pp, unillus., wrappers, cover title, 215x140mm. NSL:M
Contents: *The Magpie's Nest, Riding with the Mailman, Pigtails in Peril.*

4506 THE BIG BOOK OF/PEGMEN TALES/by/Ella McFadyen/containing favourite stories from/Pegmen Tales and Pegmen go Walkabout/Illustrated by/ Edwina Bell/Angus and Robertson
Sydney, 1959
viii, 198pp, b/w frontis. & b/w drawings throughout, clo., 235x145mm. KMM

MACFARLANE, Barbara
4507 NAUGHTY/AGAPANTHUS/Story by Barbara Macfarlane/Illustrations by Margaret Lees/Nelson
Thos. Nelson (Australia) Ltd Melbourne 1966 [Printed in Hongkong]
26pp, col. illus. on alternate pages, pic. bd., dec. e/p, 190x270mm. CLRC
Picture book with brief text by two Melbourne women.

4508 AGAPANTHUS/IS LOST/Story by Barbara Macfarlane/Illustrations by Margaret Lees
Bay Books Pty Ltd, Rushcutters Bay, NSW, 1970
[28]pp, col. illus. throughout, pic. bd.,195x280mm. CLRC

4509 QUEEN/AGAPANTHUS/Story by Barbara Macfarlane/Illustrations by Margaret Lees
Bay Books Pty Ltd, Rushcutters Bay, NSW, 1970
[28]pp, col. illus. throughout, pic. bd., 195x275mm. CLRC

4510 ZOP, KING OF THE FIREFLITTERS/Story by Barbara Macfarlane/Illustrations by Margaret Lees/Bay Books Ltd. Sydney
1971
[26]pp, col. & b/w illus. throughout, pic. bd., 230x205mm. CLRC
One page of text & one page of illustrations precede title which is printed on two pages.

McFARLANE, Mary
4511 THE STORY OF/WALLY WALLAROO/By Mary McFarlane
Moderne Publishing Co., Sydney, n.d. [1945]
20pp, col. & b/w illus. throughout, stiff pic. wrappers, cover title, 195x240mm. ANL
Cover design signed 'Clements'.

4512 FARMYARD/STORIES/Illustrated by/A. Dickens
Jons Productions, Sydney, n.d. [1946]
28pp, col. & b/w illus. throughout, bd., cover title, 215x230mm. ANL
Three booklets bound together: *Rosie, The Golden Bantam; Bertie Bunny and Company; The Little Calf called Stalky.*

4513 THE MOUSE WITH THE SILVER/TAIL!/Drawings by Rufus Morris—Story by Mary McFarlane/A Jons Production
Sydney, n.d. [1946]
28pp, col. & b/w illus. throughout, pic. bd., 210x230mm. ANL
4514 Another copy as above but on t.p.'Registered at the GPO Sydney, for transmission by post as a book
n.d. (Lithographed in Australia by Colourtone Pty Ltd for Jons Productions Pty. Ltd., Sydney)
Details as before but printed on better quality paper, with linen-like finish. KP

MacGILLIVRAY, Mona & CROFTS, Rhona Reidy
Trim Rag Book Series
4515 ANIMAL ANTICS
4516 JUNIOR NURSERY RHYMES
Uniform booklets published by Robertson & Mullens Ltd, Melbourne 1948
12pp, simple pictures on stiffened rag, 140x140mm. ANL

MacGREGOR, Charles & others
4517 Royal Edition/No 310/SOME/AUSTRALIAN SONGS/1. The land of the Blue Gum/2. Elizabeth Ann/3. Click Beetle/4. Peter's Ticket/5. When I'm a Man/6. The Pickaninny's *[sic]* Cradle/7. The Magpie Geese/8. Golden Wattle/Words by/Charles MacGregor, Richard Lomas/and Eleanor Wemyes/ Music by/Edith Harrhy/Copyright Price 2/6 net/W. H. Paling & Co. Ltd./Sydney/Brisbane Newcastle/ Toowoomba Rockhampton/Printed in England [all in dec. border]
n.d. [1928]
24pp, unillus., wrappers, 310x240mm. MC

McGREGOR, Emily
See Cotton, Emily Alice

McGUINNESS, Lurline
4518 MUFF/THE CIRCUS MONKEY/by/Lurline McGuinness/Illustrated/by/Galina Herbert/[device]/ Lothian Publishing Co. Pty. Ltd./Melbourne Sydney Auckland
1964
29pp, 4 col. illus. & b/w drawings in text throughout, pic. bd., pic. e/p, 240x180mm. KMM
4519 Another copy Angus and Robertson/London 1965, as above but plain clo. KMM

McGUIRE, Frances Margaret [Mrs Dominic Paul McGuire, née Cheadle]
4520 THREE AND/MA KELPIE/by/Frances Margaret McGuire/illustrated by/Vennetta Brus/[device]/ Longmans
Melbourne 1964
150pp, 1p dedication, 1p author's note, 1p acknowledgements, &c., b/w illus. in text throughout, clo., 185x120mm. KMM

McHENRY, Zoë Rosalind
4521 RHYMES AND RHYTHMS/Simple Songs/for little children;/By/Zoë R. McHenry/Illustrated by/Jocelyn Hughes/Published for the Author by/Whitcombe & Tombs Pty. Ltd./Melbourne and Sydney/Associated House Christchurch, Auckland, Wellington,/Dunedin, Invercargill, London
n.d. [1941]
32pp (inc. 1p author's note), b/w illus. throughout, wrappers, 270x210mm. ANL
Contains 29 songs with music.
4522 Another copy as above [n.d., inscribed 1963], but 28pp, 267x205mm. KP
A number of variations seen, some with 6, some with 7 titles listed inside back cover. All KP
4523 RHYMES & RHYTHMS [& on next page:] Simple Songs/For Little Children/By/Zoe R. McHenry/Illustrated by/Jocelyn Hughes/Whitcombe & Tombs Pty Ltd./Melbourne Sydney Perth
32pp, b/w illus., stiff pic. wrappers, 248x182mm. KP
8 titles listed on p30, last 2pp blank.

4524 MOSTLY RHYTHM/A companion to "Rhymes & Rhythms"/Words & Music/by/Zoë R. McHenry/ Illustrated by/Jocelyn Hughes/(Copyright)/Published for the Author by/Whitcombe & Tombs Pty. Ltd./ Melbourne, Sydney, Perth
n.d. [1944]

28pp (inc. introduction by Anne H. Dreyer), b/w illus. throughout, wrappers, 250x185mm. ANL
• Rpt as above, but 5 other titles by author listed inside back cover. KP
• Rpt as above, but 6 other titles by author listed inside back cover. KP
• Rpt as above, but 7 other titles listed. KP

4525 KINDERGARTEN HOUR/More Rhymes and Rhythms/Words and Music/By/Zoë R. McHenry/(Copyright)/Illustrated by/Jean Brown/Whitcombe & Tombs Pty. Ltd./Melbourne, Sydney, Perth, Geelong
n.d.
28pp, b/w illus. throughout, wrappers, 245x185mm. Grant
KINDERGARTEN HOUR/More Rhymes and Rhythms/Words and Music/by/Zoë R. McHenry/(Copyright)/Published for the Author by/Whitcombe & Tombs Pty. Ltd./Melbourne, Sydney, Perth
n.d.
28pp, b/w drawings, pic. wrappers, 244x186mm. KP
• Rpt as above, but The Kindergarten Song-time Series [4 titles] listed on last page. KP
• Rpt as above, but 6 titles listed on last page. KP
• Rpt as above, but 7 titles listed on last page. KP
• Rpt as above, but 'Registered in Australia for transmission by post as a book' printed above publisher's imprint. As before but 8 titles listed on last page. KP

4526 THREE TO SIX/More Rhymes and Rhythms/Words and Music by/Zoë R. McHenry/(Copyright)/Illustrated by Jean Brown/Cover Design by Jocelyn Hughes/Whitcombe & Tombs Pty. Ltd./Melbourne Sydney Perth Geelong
n.d. [194-?]
28pp, b/w illus. in text, pic. wrappers, 245x185mm. CLRC
Music & words of 24 songs, with drawings at head of some pages
• Rpt as above, n.d., inscribed Dec 1957
Last page lists 7 song titles in series. KP

4527 GIRLS & BOYS/Traditional Nursery Rhymes/very simply arranged by/Zoë R. McHenry/Author of "Rhymes and Rhythms" and/"Mostly Rhythms"/Illustrated by/Jocelyn Hughes/(Copyright)/Published for the Author by/Whitcombe & Tombs Pty. Ltd./Melbourne, Sydney, Perth
n.d. [1944]
28pp, b/w illus. throughout, wrappers, 250x190mm. ANL
• Rpt as above but 6 titles listed inside back wrappers, KP
• Rpt as above but 7 titles listed inside back wrappers, KP

4528 GIRLS & BOYS/Traditional Nursery Rhymes/very simply arranged
As above, but part-col. frontis., stiff pic. wrappers & 8 titles listed inside back wrappers, 246x185mm. KP

4529 PRE-SCHOOL DAYS/More Rhymes and Rhythms/By/Zoë R. McHenry/Illustrated by/Jean Brown/Published for the Author by/Whitcombe & Tombs Pty. Ltd./Melbourne, Sydney, Perth
n.d. [1948]
27pp, 1p adv., b/w illus. throughout, wrappers, 250x185mm. ANL
• Rpt as above, n.d. KP

4530 HEY DIDDLE DIDDLE/Traditional Nursery Rhymes/Very Simply Arranged by/Zoë R. McHenry/Author of "Rhymes and Rhythms" and/"Mostly Rhythm"/Illustrated by/Jocelyn Hughes/(copyright)/Published for the author by/Whitcombe & Tombs Pty. Ltd./Melbourne Sydney Perth
n.d.
28pp, b/w frontis., 1 f/p b/w illus. & b/w drawings in text, pic. wrappers, 248x187mm. KP
6 titles listed inside back wrappers.
• Rpt as above, n.d. KP

4531 HEY DIDDLE DIDDLE/Traditional Nursery Rhymes/Very Simply Arranged by/Zoe R. McHenry/Author of "Rhymes and Rhythms" and/"Mostly Rhythm"/Illustrated by/Jocelyn Hughes/(Copyright)/Whitcombe & Tombs Pty. Ltd./Melbourne, Sydney, Perth, Geelong
n.d.
32pp (last blank), b/w frontis., 1 f/p & numerous b/w illus. in text, stiff dec. wrappers, 245x185mm. KP
7 titles listed on p31

4532 BIBLE STORY TIME/Words and Music by/Zoe R. McHenry/Illustrated by Jean Brown/Cover Design by Jocelyn Hughes
Whitcombe & Tombs Pty Ltd, Melbourne, Sydney, Perth, Geelong, n.d.
28pp (last blank), some small illus., pic. wrappers, 245x180mm. KP

MacILWAINE, Herbert C.

4533 THE WHITE STONE/The Story of a Boy from the Bush/By/Herbert C. MacIlwaine/Author of/"Dinkinbar", "Fate the Fiddler" Etc./Illustrated by G. D. Rowlandson/London/Wells Gardner, Darton & Co./3 Paternoster Buildings
1900
408pp, 2pp adv., b/w frontis. & 17 f/p b/w illus., line drawings in text throughout, pic. clo., 205x145mm. NSL:M

4534 Another edition as above, but /New York/Frederick A. Stokes Company
n.d.
408pp (no adv., t.p. printed in red & black (printed by Richard Clay & Sons Ltd, London and Bungay), b/w frontis. & 17 f/p b/w illus. & line drawings in text throughout, pic. clo., 205x147mm. KMM

MacINTYRE, Elisabeth

4535 AMBROSE KANGAROO/[drawing]/A Story that/Never Ends/Elisabeth MacIntyre
Consolidated Press, Sydney, n.d. [1941]
[36]pp, col. illus. throughout, stiff pic. wrappers, cover title, 185x246mm. KMM
• Rpt as above with note, 'As so many people have asked for "Ambrose Kangaroo" in a more permanent form the 5th edition comes in a cover instead of a box'. CLRC
US edition

4536 AMBROSE KANGAROO/[drawing]/A Story that/Never Ends/Elisabeth MacIntyre
Chas. Scribner's Sons, New York 1942
[32]pp, col. illus. throughout, pic. bd., cover title, 208x254mm. ANL

4537 AMBROSE/KANGAROO/HAS A BUSY DAY/by/Elisabeth MacIntyre/Consolidated Press Ltd./Sydney/1944
30pp, col. illus. throughout, dec. wrappers, 180x240mm. ANL

4538 THE BLACK LAMB/by/Elisabeth MacIntyre/[drawing]
Dawfox Productions, Sydney, n.d. [1944 or 1945]
32pp, col. illus. throughout, dec. bd., 210x230mm. ANL

4539 Another copy, but 'printed in Australia by

Colourtone Pty Ltd for Dawfox Productions, Sydney', 210x230mm. KP

4540 THE BLACK LAMB/By/Elisabeth MacIntyre/[b/w drawing]/[3 lines text]
Printed in Australia by Hollander & Govett Pty Ltd for Jons Productions, Sydney
28pp, 14 f/p col. illus. & b/w illus., wrappers, 210x230mm. KP

4541 THE FORGETFUL/ELEPHANT/by/Elisabeth MacIntyre/[drawing]
Dawfox Productions, Sydney, n.d. [1944 or 1945]
32pp, col. illus. throughout, dec. bd., 213x237mm. ANL

4542 THE FORGETFUL/ELEPHANT/by/Elisabeth MacIntyre/[drawing]/A Jons Production/Lithographed in Australia by...Posters Ltd. for Jons Productions Pty. Ltd., Sydney
n.d. [1950]
[18]pp, 8pp col. illus., b/w illus. on other pages, dec. bd., dec. e/p, 164x155mm. ANL
Does not include all the illustrations in the larger edition.

4543 THE HANDSOME/DUCKLING/by/Elisabeth MacIntyre/[drawing] A Dawfox Production
Sydney, n.d. [1944?]
32pp, col. illus. throughout, dec. bd., 210x230mm. ANL

4544 Another copy, on back page 'Printed in Australia by Colourtone Pty Ltd for Jons Productions'. This edition printed on better quality paper. KP

4545 THE HANDSOME/DUCKLING/by/Elisabeth MacIntyre/[drawing]/A/Jons/Production/Registered at the GPO Sydney for transmission by post as a book. Details as above. KP

4546 Another copy as above but without 'Registered at the GPO &c.' KP

4547 THE WILLING/DONKEY/by/Elisabeth MacIntyre/[drawing]/A Dawfox Production
Sydney, n.d. [1944?]
32pp, col. illus. throughout, dec. bd., 210x230mm. ANL

4548 Copy as above, school prize December 1944 with author's name on pic. board cover printed in yellow. KP

4549 Another copy as above with author's name printed in green, & on back page, 'Lithographed in Australia by Colourtone Pty Ltd for Jons Productions Pty Ltd, Sydney'. KP

4550 THE WILLING DONKEY/by/Elisabeth MacIntyre/[drawing]/Jons Productions Pty Ltd, Sydney/Lithographic plates by Printers Plates Pty Limited/Lithographed by Deaton Spencer Pty Ltd, Sydney Australia
n.d.
16pp, col. & b/w illus., pic. bd. (with pic. d/w), pic. e/p, 165x155mm. KP
Varies greatly from earlier editions with some plates either reduced or enlarged, &c.

4551 Another copy as above but col. illus. throughout, 175x155mm. KP

4552 SUSAN/WHO LIVES IN/AUSTRALIA/by/Elisabeth MacIntyre/[drawing]/1944 Charles Scribner's Sons New York
[32]pp, col. pic. t.p. with dec. border, col. illus. throughout, col. pic. bd., 215x150mm. ANL
Published subsequently in various editions in Australia & England under the title of *Katherine* with variations in illustrations & text.

4553 KATHERINE/by/Elisabeth MacIntyre/Australasian Publishing Company, Pty. Ltd., Sydney
First Australian edition 1946
30pp, t.p. within col. dec. border, col. illus. throughout, dec. bd., 180x240mm. CLRC
Rhyming text.

4554 KATHERINE/by/Elisabeth MacIntyre/London: George G. Harrap and Co. Ltd.
First published 1946
30pp, title within col. dec. border, col. illus. throughout, dec. clo., 184x244mm. ANL

4555 KATHERINE/[drawing]/Elisabeth MacIntyre/Angus & Robertson/Sydney London Melbourne Wellington
1958
32pp, dec. t.p., col. lithographic illus. throughout, dec. bd., 280x220mm. KMM
Illustrations & text differ from earlier editions.

4556 KATHERINE/Elisabeth MacIntyre/Angus and Robertson
Sydney 1963
32pp, dec. t.p., col. lithographic illus. throughout, dec. bd., 250x185mm. KMM
Many small variations occur in the rhyming text, & a number of illustrations have been redrawn, including those on title page & front cover.
- Rpt 1967, unseen
- Rpt 1971, blurb printed on fly; illus. on front cover printed in col. instead of white, & no d/w. KP

4557 WILLIE'S WOOLLIES/The Story of/Australian Wool/by/Elisabeth MacIntyre/[device]/Georgian House/Melbourne
1951
30pp, dec. t.p., col. & b/w illus. throughout, pic.wrappers, 180x250mm. KMM
Much of the material used in this book originally appeared in the Melbourne *Age*. The book was simultaneously issued in pic. bd.

4558 Another edition 1963, as above but pic. bds, 185x250mm. CLRC

4559 MR. KOALA BEAR/[coloured drawing]/by Elisabeth MacIntyre/Charles Scribner's Sons New York
1954
32pp, col. illus. throughout, clo., 255x200mm. NSL:M
Picture book with brief rhyming text.

4560 MR. KOALA BEAR/[coloured drawing]/by Elisabeth MacIntyre/Angus and Robertson
First published 1954 by Charles Scribner's Sons, New York; Sydney 1965 (with illustrations redrawn)
[32]pp, col. illus. throughout, clo., 250x185mm. BBC
- Rpt 1966, 1967. KP

4561 JANE LIKES PICTURES/Elisabeth MacIntyre/[drawing]/London Collins Glasgow
1959
30pp, col. illus. throughout, clo., 250x200mm. KMM

4562 JANE LIKES PICTURES, Charles Scribner's Sons, New York
Unseen: Published at the same time & in the same format as the English edition. IFA

4563 [drawing] AMBROSE/KANGAROO/GOES TO TOWN/Elisabeth MacIntyre/Angus and Robertson
Sydney 1964
32pp, dec. t.p., part. col. illus. throughout, dec. bd., dec. e/p, 245x180mm. KMM

4564 HUGH'S ZOO
First published by Knopf, New York 1964
Unseen: IFA

4565 HUGH'S/ZOO/Written and illustrated by/ Elisabeth MacIntyre/Constable Young Books —London
1964
[34]pp, dec. t.p., part-col. illus. throughout, clo., dec. e/p, 255x195mm. KMM
Second imp. 1965. KP

4566 THE AFFABLE AMIABLE BULLDOZER MAN
First published by Knopf, New York 1965
Unseen: IFA

4567 THE AFFABLE, AMIABLE BULLDOZER MAN/ written and illustrated by/Elisabeth MacIntyre/Angus and Robertson.
Sydney 1965
36pp, extended dec. t.p., col. illus. throughout, pic. bd. (clo. spine), 250x195mm. KMM

4568 NINJI'S MAGIC
New York, Knopf 1966
114pp, illus. by Mamoru Funai, map. 21cm. Unseen: ANB 1967

4569 NINJI'S MAGIC/by Elisabeth MacIntyre/Illustrated by Mamoru Funai/Angus and Robertson
Sydney 1967
114pp, 3pp glossary, 1p biographical note, b/w map, b/w drawings throughout, clo., 200x150mm. CLRC

McINTYRE, Ella L.

4570 PIN MONEY/A Story for Children/By/Ella L. McIntyre/Illustrated by/J. Warren Smith/[publisher's device]/Shakespeare Head Press/310 George St. Sydney/1936
104pp, 6 f/p b/w illus., drawings in text, dec. wrappers, 205x160mm. KMM

4571 For the Young and the not so young age group/ WILD FREEDOM/by Ella L. McIntyre/Author of "Pin Money"
Printed and Bound by Watson Ferguson and Company, 221 Stanley Street, South Brisbane, n.d. [1971?]
82pp, 9 b/w pencil drawings, pic. wrappers, 240x180mm. CLRC
Drawings unsigned. Reviews for *Pin Money* printed on back wrapper; in one review it is mentioned that 'the book is cleverly illustrated by J. Warren-Smith'.

4572 THE/YOUNG/PIONEERS/By Ella L. McIntyre/ Author of 'Pin Money', published by Shakespeare Head/Press, Sydney, and "Wild Freedom", Brisbane
1972
125pp, unillus., clo., 210x135mm. CLRC

MACK, Amy Eleanor [Mrs Launcelot Harrison]

4573 WATERSIDE/STORIES/By/Amy E. Mack/(Mrs. Launcelot Harrison)/Sydney/Angus & Robertson Ltd./ 89–95 Castlereagh Street/1910
112pp, unillus., limp clo., 180x125mm. Australian Story Series. ANL

4574 BIRDLAND/STORIES/By/Amy E. Mack/(Mrs. Launcelot Harrison)/Sydney/Angus & Robertson Ltd./ 89–95 Castlereagh Street/1910
111pp [numbered pp113–224], unillus., limp clo., 180x120mm. ANL
Contains 7 short stories; companion volume to *Waterside Stories.*

4575 BUSHLAND/STORIES/By/Amy E. Mack/(Mrs. Launcelot Harrison)/Sydney/Angus & Robertson Ltd./ 89–95 Castlereagh Street/1910
115pp [numbered 225–336, & t.p., contents &c.], unillus., limp clo., 185x120mm. KMM Australian Story Series.
Apparently continuation of *Waterside Stories* & *Birdland Stories.* Contains 8 stories. KMM

4576 BUSHLAND/STORIES/By/Amy E. Mack/Author of "A Bush Calendar"/With Coloured Illustrations/ Sydney/Angus & Robertson Ltd./89 Castlereagh Street
1910
349pp, 32pp adv. (dated Sept.1910), col. frontis. & 5 col. plates, illus. by Lionel Lindsay, pic. clo., 180x115mm. ANL
Contains 25 stories.

4577 BUSHLAND/STORIES/By/Amy Eleanor Mack/ Author of "A Bush Calendar", "Bush Days",/and "Scribbling Sue"/With coloured illustrations/Sydney/ Angus & Robertson Ltd./89 Castlereagh Street
First published 1910; 2nd ed. from new type, 1914
261pp, 32pp adv., col. frontis. & 4 col. plates (omitting one plate from 1st ed.), illus. by Lionel Lindsay, clo. (with col. illus. on front cover) by Rupert Hale) lettering blocked in gilt panel,180x115mm. KMM
Contains 18 stories.

4578 Another copy as above(prize label 1922) with col. onlay &c. on front cover & spine, but lettering in col. (not gilt) panel. KP

4579 BUSHLAND/STORIES/By/Amy Eleanor Mack/ Author of "A Bush Calendar", "Bush Days", "Scribbling Sue" etc./with 47 illustrations by Joyce Dennys/Australia/Angus and Robertson Ltd./89 Castlereagh Street, Sydney
n.d. [1921?]
183pp, col. frontis. & 7 f/p col. plates, b/w drawings in text, clo., dec. e/p, 245x180mm. ANL
Edition de Luxe (endpapers printed with blue A. & R. device). Contains 25 stories

4580 Another copy
n.d. [1921?]
As above, but with plain endpapers instead of those printed with the A. & R. device, the lettering on the spine printed in black instead of gold, & the A. & R. colophon on the front cover has a design of two scotch thistles, whereas that on the copy previously described comprised sheep & a gum tree. Both are bound in red cloth, & possibly the same sheets were bound up a little later for this variant copy, as internally there is no variation. KMM

4581 BUSHLAND STORIES/By/Amy Eleanor Mack/ Author of "A Bush Calendar", "Scribbling Sue", etc./ With coloured illustrations/Australia:/Angus & Robertson, Ltd./89 Castlereagh Street, Sydney
1923
200pp, col. frontis. & 4 col. plates, illus. by Lionel Lindsay, clo., 175x110mm. KMM
Contains 18 stories.

4582 BUSHLAND STORIES./By/Amy Eleanor Mack/ Author of A Bush Calendar, Scribbling Sue, etc./With coloured illustrations/Australia:/Cornstalk Publishing Company/Arnold Place, Sydney/1924
200pp, 5 f/p b/w illus. by Karna Birmingham only, clo., 175x110mm. Platypus Edition. KMM
Contains 18 stories.

4583 BUSHLAND STORIES/By/Amy Eleanor Mack/ Author of A Bush Calendar, Scribbling Sue, etc./With 5 illustrations/Australia:/Cornstalk Publishing Company/Arnold Place, Sydney/1925
248pp, 5 f/p b/w illus. by Karna Birmingham, clo., 185x120mm. KMM
Contains 18 stories.

4584 BUSHLAND STORIES/By/Amy Eleanor Mack/ Author of A Bush Calendar, Scribbling Sue, etc./ Australia/Cornstalk Publishing Company/89 Castlereagh Street, Sydney/1928
Details as in 1925 edition. ANL

4585 BUSHLAND STORIES/By/Amy Eleanor Mack/Author of A Bush Calendar, Scribbling Sue, etc./Australia/Angus & Robertson Limited/89 Castlereagh Street, Sydney/1935
248pp, unillus., clo., 185x120mm. KMM
Contains 18 stories.

4586 BUSH DAYS/By/Amy E. Mack/(Mrs. Launcelot Harrison)/Author of "A Bush Calendar" and "Bushland Stories"/with illustrations from photographs by/J. Ramsay and L. Harrison/Sydney/Angus & Robertson Ltd./89 Castlereagh Street/1911
132pp, b/w photographs throughout, clo., 170x140mm. CLRC
A compilation of articles on Australian natural history which originally appeared in the *Sydney Morning Herald;* not specifically a children's book.

4587 THE TOM-TIT'S NEST/And Other Stories/by/Amy Eleanor Mack/Author of "Bushland Stories", "A Bush Calendar",/"Bush Days" etc./Sydney/Angus & Robertson Ltd./89 Castlereagh Street
n.d. [1914]
33pp, b/w frontis. & 3 b/w illus., wrappers, 155x120mm. Grant

4588 SCRIBBLING SUE/And other Stories/by/Amy Eleanor Mack/Author of "A Bush Calendar", "Bush Days",/and "Bushland Stories"./With Illustrations/Sydney/Angus & Robertson Ltd./89 Castlereagh Street
n.d. [1914?]
228pp, 31pp adv. (dated July 1914), col. frontis. & 4 b/w plates by May Gibbs, clo. (with col. onlay on front cover), 185x120mm. KMM
Contains 21 stories, some reprinted from the *Sydney Mail.*
As above, but with adv. date Jan 1916. KP
Another copy as above, but with no adv. KP

4589 SCRIBBLING SUE/And Other Stories/By/Amy Eleanor Mack/Author of "A Bush Calendar", "Bush Days"/and "Bushland Stories"/with Illustrations/Sydney/Angus & Robertson Ltd./89 Castlereagh Street
Sticker on verso of t.p. reads 'Wholly set up and printed in Australia by/Eagle Press Ltd. Sydney' (1923 handwritten in ink)
228pp, no adv., col. frontis. & 4 b/w plates, by May Gibbs, col. onlay on front cover & spine but lettering & dec. in col. ink, not gilt, clo., 184x120mm. KP

4590 SCRIBBLING SUE/And Other Stories/By/Amy Eleanor Mack/Author of "A Bush Calendar", "Bush Days",/and "Bushland Stories"./With seven illustrations/Australia/Angus & Robertson Ltd./89 Castlereagh Street
1923
202pp, col. frontis. by May Gibbs & 6 f/p b/w illus. by Karna Birmingham, clo., 175x110mm. Platypus Edition. KMM
Contains 21 stories.

4591 SCRIBBLING SUE/and Other Stories/By/Amy Eleanor Mack/Author of A Bush Calendar, Bush Days,/and Bushland Stories/With seven illustrations/Australia:/Cornstalk Publishing Company/Arnold Place, Sydney/1925
218pp, col. frontis. by May Gibbs & 6 f/p b/w illus. by Karna Birmingham, clo., d/w designed by E. K. Robison, 170x110mm. Second Platypus Edition. KMM
Another copy, Angus & Robertson, Sydney 1925
Details as in previous 1925 edition, but not described as 'Platypus edition' on verso of t.p., blue clo., 185x120mm. KMM

4592 SCRIBBLING SUE/and other Stories/by/Amy Eleanor Mack/For Children aged 8 to 9 years/Australia:/Cornstalk Publishing Company/89 Castlereagh Street, Sydney/1928
69pp, b/w frontis. & 3 f/p b/w illus. by Karna Birmingham, wrappers, 170x110mm. ANL
Contains 5 stories.
• Rpt 1929, as above, but *'The Gumnut Readers'* ed., 183x123mm. ANL

4593 THE WILDERNESS/By/Amy Eleanor Mack/(Mrs. Launcelot Harrison)/Author of "A Bush Calendar" "Bushland/Stories", "Scribbling Sue", etc./Illustrated by John D. Moore/Australia:/Angus & Robertson Ltd./89 Castlereagh Street, Sydney
1922
26pp, col. frontis., b/w drawings throughout in text, wrappers (with col. illus. on front cover), 215x150mm. ANL
The Wilderness first appeared in the *Sydney Morning Herald;* it is a natural history sketch for children.

4594 THE/BIRDS' CONCERT/And other Stories of/Australian Bush Birds/By/Amy Eleanor Mack/For Children aged 8 to 10 years/Australia:/Cornstalk Publishing Company/89 Castlereagh Street, Sydney/1928
74pp, b/w frontis., wrappers, 170x110mm. ANL
Contains 4 short stories reprinted from *Bushland Stories.*
Another edition 1929, the same. KMM

4595 THE/FANTAIL'S HOUSE/And other Australian/Nature Stories/By/Amy Eleanor Mack/For Children aged 8 to 9 years/Australia:/Cornstalk Publishing Company/89 Castlereagh Street, Sydney/1928
62pp, b/w frontis. & 1 b/w illus. by Karna Birmingham, wrappers, 175x115mm. ANL
Contains 8 short stories.

4596 THE/FLOWER FAIRIES/and other stories of/the Australian Bush/By/Amy Eleanor Mack/For Children aged 8 to 10 years/Australia:/Cornstalk Publishing Company/89 Castlereagh Street, Sydney/1928
88pp, b/w frontis. & 2 f/p b/w illus. by Karna Birmingham, wrappers, 180x115mm. KMM
Contains 6 stories reprinted from *Bushland Stories.*
• Rpt 1929, as above. Grant

4597 THE GUM LEAF/THAT FLEW/And Other Stories of/Australian Bushland/By/Amy Eleanor Mack/For children aged 8 to 9 years/Australia;/Cornstalk Publishing Company/89 Castlereagh Street, Sydney/1928
47pp, b/w frontis. by Karna Birmingham, wrappers, 170x110mm. ANL
Contains 4 stories.

4598 THE/LITTLE BLACK DUCK/and other Stories/of Bushland and Sea/By/Amy Eleanor Mack/For Children aged 8 to 10 years/Australia: Cornstalk Publishing Company/89 Castlereagh Street, Sydney/1928
87pp, b/w frontis. & 1 f/p b/w by illus. Karna Birmingham, wrappers, 180x120mm. KMM
Contains 6 short stories reprinted from *Bushland Stories.*
• Rpt as above, 1929. KMM

4599 WHY THE SPINEBILL'S/BEAK IS LONG/And Other Stories of/Australia's Bushland/By/Amy Eleanor Mack/For Children aged 9 to 10 years/Australia:/Cornstalk Publishing Company/89 Castlereagh Street, Sydney/1928
64pp, b/w frontis., wrappers, 170x110mm. ANL
Contains 4 stories.
• Rpt 1929, as above. KMM

MACK, Louise Marie [Mrs Allen I. Leyland, formerly Mrs J. Percy Creed]

4600 TEENS/A Story of Australian Schoolgirls/By/Louise Mack/(Mrs. J. Percy Creed)/With fourteen illustrations by F. P. Mahony/Sydney/Angus and Robertson/1897
266pp, 32pp adv., b/w frontis. & 13 b/w plates, pic. clo., 185x120mm. KMM

4601 TEENS/A Story of Australian Schoolgirls/By/Louise Mack/Author of "Girls Together"/With six illustrations/Australia/Angus & Robertson Ltd./89 Castlereagh Street
First Platypus edition 1923
197pp, b/w frontis. & 5 b/w illus. by Karna Birmingham, clo., 175x110mm. VSL
Abridged by H. G. Hain.

4602 TEENS/A Story of Australian Schoolgirls/by/Louise Mack/Author of "Girls Together"/with six illustrations/Australia/Cornstalk Publishing Company/Arnold Place Sydney/1924
197pp, col. frontis. by Percy Lindsay bound in before half-title & 6 f/p b/w illus. by Karna Birmingham, clo., 175x110mm. Platypus Series. CLRC

4603 TEENS/A Story of Australian Schoolgirls/by/Louise Mack/Author of "Girls Together"/with six illustrations/Australia:/Cornstalk Publishing Company/Arnold Place Sydney/1925
240pp, 6 b/w illus. by Karna Birmingham, clo., 185x120mm. ANL

4604 TEENS/A Story of Australian Schoolgirls/by/Louise Mack/Author of "Girls Together"/with six illustrations/Australia:/Cornstalk Publishing Company/89 Castlereagh Street, Sydney/1927
240pp, 6 f/p b/w illus. by Karna Birmingham, clo., 175x110mm. KMM

4605 TEENS/A Story of Australian Schoolgirls/Abridged by H. G. Hain from the Platypus edition/of Louise Mack's story/For Children aged 10 to 12 years/Australia: Cornstalk Publishing Company/89 Castlereagh Street,Sydney/1928
92pp, b/w frontis. & 2 f/p b/w illus. by Karna Birmingham,wrappers,185x120mm. KMM
• Rpt 1929, as above. CLRC

4606 TEENS/A Story of Australian Schoolgirls/by/Louise Mack/Author of Girls Together/Australia:/Cornstalk Publishing Company/89 Castlereagh Street, Sydney/1929
240pp, b/w frontis. by Edgar A. Holloway only, clo., 174x110mm. TG

4607 TEENS/A Story of Australian Schoolgirls/By/Louise Mack/(Mrs J. Percy Creed)/With illustrations by F. P. Mahony/Printed in Great Britain for/Angus & Robertson Limited/89 Castlereagh Street, Sydney
n.d.
240pp, b/w frontis. & 5 f/p b/w illus., limp clo., 177x124mm. KP
Australian Story Series.

4608 TEENS/A Story of Australian Schoolgirls/By/Louise Mack/(Mrs. J. Percy Creed)/With fourteen illustrations by F. P. Mahony/London:/Andrew Melrose/16 Pilgrim Street, E.C.
n.d. [prize 1904] First English edition
vi+266pp, b/w frontis. & 13 b/w plates, pic. clo., 180x130mm. KMM
Dark blue clo., front cover has title & author in gilt & illus. of girl in pinafore blocked in colour; title in gilt panel on spine & illus. of girl running, and 'Melrose' at base of spine.

4609 Another copy as above, n.d.
viii+266pp, same illus. on spine, but lettering & decoration only on front cover. CLRC

4610 Fourth edition. Details as before, but title printed in red on t.p., lettering in gilt on pic. cover, g.e. & printed on superior quality paper. KP

4611 TEENS/By/Louise Mack/(Mrs J. Percy Creed)/The Pilgrim Press/16 Pilgrim Street, London, E.C.4
n.d [prize label 1934]
240pp & 1p dedication, 7pp adv., b/w frontis. by Savile Lumley, clo., 185x120mm. JMcG
The Prize Library. Illus. on jacket modernized version of Mahony's original illus. 'setting out to see the sunrise'.

4612 GIRLS TOGETHER/By/Louise Mack/(Mrs. J. P. Creed)/With four illustrations by G. W. Lambert/Sydney/Angus and Robertson/1898
226pp & 16pp adv., b/w frontis. & 3 f/p b/w illus., clo., 185x120mm. KMM

4613 GIRLS TOGETHER/By/Louise Mack/(Mrs. J. P. Creed)/With four illustrations by G. W. Lambert/Sydney/Angus & Robertson Ltd./Printed in Great Britain
n.d.
226pp, b/w frontis. & 3 f/p b/w illus., limp clo., 180x120mm. Australian Story Series. KMM

4614 GIRLS TOGETHER/By/Louise Mack/Author of "Teens"/With three illustrations by G. W. Lambert/Australia/Angus & Robertson Ltd./89 Castlereagh Street, Sydney
1923
196pp, b/w frontis. & 2 f/p b/w illus., clo., 175x110mm. VSL

4615 GIRLS TOGETHER/By/Louise Mack/Author of "Teens"/With three illustrations by G. W. Lambert/Australia:/Cornstalk Publishing Company/Arnold Place, Sydney/1924
196pp, col. frontis., 3 b/w illus., clo., 175x110mm. PR
Coloured frontispiece by Percy Lindsay bound in before half-title.

4616 GIRLS TOGETHER/By/Louise Mack/Author of "Teens"/With three illustrations by G. W. Lambert/Australia:/Cornstalk Publishing Company/Arnold Place, Sydney/1925
228pp, b/w frontis. & 2 b/w illus., clo., 183x120mm. CLRC
• Rpt 1927, as above, Platypus series. KP

4617 GIRLS TOGETHER/By/Louise Mack/Author of "Teens"/Australia:/Cornstalk Publishing Company/89 Castlereagh Street, Sydney/1929
228pp, b/w frontis. by Edgar A. Holloway, clo., 170x105mm. Platypus Series. KMM

4618 GIRLS TOGETHER/By/Louise Mack/(Mrs. J. P. Creed)/with four illustrations by G. W. Lambert/London:/Andrew Melrose/16 Pilgrim Street, E.C.
n.d. [1903, but copy seen with adv. dated Oct.1898, & another with adv.1900, both KP)
226pp, 6pp adv., b/w frontis. & 3 f/p b/w illus., pic. clo., 180x130mm.

4619 GIRLS TOGETHER/By/Louise Mack/(Mrs. J. P. Creed)/With four illustrations by G. W. Lambert/Second Edition/London/Andrew Melrose/16 Pilgrim Street, E.C.
n.d.
226pp, 16pp adv., b/w frontis. & 3 f/p b/w illus., pic. clo., 185x120mm. NSL:M

4620 GIRLS TOGETHER/By/Louise Mack/(Mrs. J. P. Creed)/With four illustrations by G. W. Lambert/Third Edition/London:/Andrew Melrose/16 Pilgrim Street, E.C.
n.d.
226pp, b/w frontis. & 3 f/p b/w illus., pic. clo., 180x130mm. KMM

4621 GIRLS TOGETHER/By/Louise Mack/(Mrs. J. Percy Creed)/The Pilgrim Press/16 Pilgrim Street, London, E.C.4
n.d. [1930?]
220pp, b/w frontis., clo., 185x120mm. KMM
Frontispiece signed Savile Lumley. Also serialized in *The Girls' Empire Annual,* Volume 2, n.d.

4622 TEENS TRIUMPHANT/By/Louise Mack/Sydney/ P. R. Stephensen & Co./24 Bond Street
1933
287pp, unillus., clo., 210x130mm. VSL
Louise Mack was also the author of many light romances of a more adult nature, including *The World is Round* (London, Unwin, 1896), *Children of the Sun* (London, Melrose, 1904? & serialized in 'The Girls Empire' Volume 3, n.d.). Her *An Australian Girl in London* (1902) is autobiographical, & not a children's book.

MACK, Phyllis K.
4623 I LIVE/IN GOD'S/WORLD/by Phyllis K. Mack/ Collage pictures by W. M. Rolland
The Joint Board of Christian Education of Australia & NZ, Melbourne, 1970
Kindergarten Take-home Book Year 2
16pp, part-col. illus. throughout, pic. wrappers, 210x130mm. CLRC

MACKANESS, George
See Mackaness, Joan Symons & George, & also Stevens, Bertram & Mackaness, George

MACKANESS, Joan Symons & George (eds.)
4624 FROLIC FAIR/A Book of Australian Verse/for Children under ten/Chosen by/Joan S. Mackaness, B.A./and/George Mackaness, M.A., Litt. D./ [quotation]/Australia/Angus Robertson Limited/89 Castlereagh Street, Sydney/1932
87pp, wrappers, 170x110mm. ANL
4625 Another copy as above, but on verso of t.p.: First ed. August 1932, 2nd ed. Oct. 1932, bd. KP
4626 Another copy, 90pp. wrappers 3rd ed. June 1834; Fourth ed. Nov. 1937. KP
Other copies as above, but bd. or leatherette. CLRC
4627 FROLIC FAIR/A Book of Australian Verse/for Children under Ten/Chosen by/Joan S. Mackaness, B.A./and/George Mackaness, M.A., Litt. D./ Decorations by/Pixie O'Harris/Angus and Robertson/ Sydney London
First edition 1932; revised edition 1950
117pp (inc. 1p index), b/w frontis. & b/w drawings in text throughout, dec. bd., 180x120mm. KMM

4628 THE /WIDE BROWN LAND/ A new Anthology of Australian verse/chosen by/ Joan S. Mackaness, B.A./and/ George Mackaness, M.A.,Litt.D./ [verse]/ Australia/ Angus & Robertson Limited/ 89 CastlereaghStreet Sydney/1934
xii+263pp, unillus, clo.,182x122mm. KMM
4629 THE/WIDE BROWN LAND/Being a revised edition of/Selections from the Australian Poets/chosen by/Joan S. Mackaness, B.A./and/George Mackaness, M.A., Litt.D./[8 lines Dorothea MacKellar]/Angus & Robertson Limited/Sydney and London/1944
263pp, unillus., wrappers, 184x124mm. KMM
Another ed. 1946, as above with dec. wrappers. KMM
4630 THE WIDE BROWN LAND/Selections from the Australian Poets/Chosen by/Joan S. Mackaness, B.A./and/George Mackaness,/M.A., Litt.D./[quotation Dorothea Mackellar]/Angus and Robertson /Sydney London 1951
• Rpt 1959, as above, with variant dec. wrappers. KMM

McKAY, Gwendda
See Rogers, June & McKay, G.

McKAY, Kathleen
4631 SING/A SONG/OF/BUSHLAND/[verse]/Written by/Kathleen McKay/Illustrated by Bill Davies/John Sands Pty. Ltd./Sydney, Melbourne, Brisbane, Adelaide./Perth, Hobart/Registered in Australia for transmission by post as a book
n.d. [1953]
16pp, dec. t.p., col. illus. throughout, dec. bd., 265x205mm. CLRC

MACKENZIE, Donald A.
4632 SONS & DAUGHTERS/OF AUSTRALASIA/By Donald A. Mackenzie/[drawing]/Blackie and Son Limited/London Glasgow Bombay
n.d. [1920?]
70pp [numbered pp147–216], 3 double-spread col. illus. & 5 f/p col. illus., b/w drawings, clo. (with col. illus. pasted on front cover), 255x195mm. Excerpt from Our Glorious Empire. KMM
Coloured illustrations by H. M. Brock & Sydney R. Jones; b/w drawings by various artists.

4633 OUR/GLORIOUS EMPIRE/[medallion]/Blackie and Son Limited/London Glasgow Bombay
n.d. [1920?]
360pp, col. frontis. & 44 f/p col. illus., b/w drawings in text, illus. by Sydney R. Jones, dec. clo., 250x190mm. CLRC
Contains section on Australasia (pp146–216).

MacKENZIE, Geraldine
4634 THE FIRST AUSTRALIAN'S [*sic*] /FIRST BOOK/ By/Geraldine MacKenzie, B.A./Diploma of Education, Melbourne/Missionary since 1925 of the/Australian Presbyterian Church/at Aurukun, N. Queensland, Australia/Illustrated by Roma Thompson/[device]/F. W. Cheshire/Melbourne
1951
26pp, 1p note, 2pp foreword by Prof. F. J. Schonell, b/w illus. throughout, pic. wrappers, front cover design by Frances Derham, 120x180mm. KMM
The first of a series of 6 readers designed for Aboriginal children in the far north, using subject matter with which they would be familiar. The simple sentences become slight stories in the later books of the series, which contain more pages but are otherwise uniform & are not recorded here.

McKEOWN, Keith C.
4635 THE MAGIC SEEDS:/TESSA IN TERMITARIA/ By/Keith C. McKeown/1940/New Century Press Pty. Ltd./3 North York Street/Sydney
169pp, 5pp adv., b/w frontis. & 11 f/p b/w illus., b/w drawings in text, illus. by John Andrews, clo., 185x120mm. NSL:M

MOOGRABAH: An Australian Aboriginal Legend. *See* Blue Wren Books

4636 THE/LAND OF BYAMEE/Australian Wild Life in Legend/and Fact/By/Keith C. McKeown/Australia/ Angus & Robertson Limited/89 Castlereagh Street, Sydney/1938
xviiipp, 229pp (inc. 3pp foreword & 4pp preface), b/w photographic frontis. & 10 b/w plates, clo., 182x120mm. KMM
Foreword by Dame Mary Gilmore; the author in his preface refers to the Langloh Parker Legendary Tales, obviously one of his sources.
4637 THE/LAND OF BYAMEE/Australian Wild Life in Legend/and Fact/By/Keith C. McKeown,

F.R.Z.S./Assistant Curator of Insects/The Australian Museum, Sydney./Australia:/Randle House Publishing Company/3 Randle Street/Sydney
1952
220pp, 5pp foreword by Mary Gilmore, 2pp author's preface, photographic frontis. & 17 b/w photographic illus. in text, wrappers, 180x125mm. Grant

MACKEY, Jan
4638 Written by Jan Mackey Illustrated by Tony Dick/ KOOKABURRA/a bird of many parts/Paul Hamlyn/ London New York Sydney Toronto
1969
[25]pp, col. illus. on every page, col. pic. bd., dec. e/p, 314x230mm. KMM
• Rpt 1971 and 1972, both KP

MACKIE, Elizabeth
4639 KOALAS/Text by Elizabeth Mackie/Ninon Phillips/Nelson
Thomas Nelson (Aust.) Ltd, Melbourne 1969
20pp, col. frontis. & 8 f/p col. illus. by Ninon Phillips, bd., col. dec. e/p, 325x240mm. BBC

McKIE, Graham
See McKie, Robert

MACKIE, John
4640 THE/GREAT ANTARCTICA/A Record of Strange Facts/and Adventures/By/John Mackie/Author of/ "The Heart of the Prairie", "In Search of Smith", "The Rising/of the Red Man", "The Life Adventurous", "Hidden in/Canadian Wilds", "The Treasure Hunters",/"Black Man's Rock", "Canadian/Jack", etc./ [device]/Illustrated by Francis E. Hiley/London/Jarrold & Sons, 10 & 11 Warwick Lane, E.C.
n.d.
287pp (inc. 1p foreword), col. frontis. & 8 f/p b/w illus., pic. clo., pic. e/p, 190x125mm. RM
4641 THE/GREAT ANTARCTICA/A Record of Strange Adventures/By/John Mackie/Author of "The Rising of the Red Man", "The Life Adventurous"/"The Treasure Hunters", etc./Illustrated by Francis E. Hiley/[device]/ Jarrolds/Publishers (London) Ltd.
n.d. [1913]
287pp (inc. 1p foreword), col. frontis. & 4 f/p b/w illus., pic. clo., 185x125mm. RM

4642 IN SEARCH OF/SMITH/By/John Mackie/Author of/"The Heart of the Prairie", "Hidden in Canadian Wilds",/"The Rising of the Red Man", Etc./[device]/ With Twenty-two illustrations by/R. Caton Woodville/ London/Grant Richards Ltd./Publishers
1911
294pp, b/w frontis. & 21 f/p b/w illus., pic. clo., 190x140mm. KMM
Story set in the Northern Territory & Queensland.

4643 THE/TREASURE HUNTERS/A Story of Tropical Sons/[device]/By/John Mackie/Author of "The Man Who Forgot" "The Life Adventurous"/"The Rising of the Red Man" "Hidden in Canadian Wilds,"/"In Search of Smith," "Blackman's Rock," "The Heart of/ The Prairie," etc. etc./Frontispiece by Francis E. Hiley/ Jarrolds,/Publisher (London) Ltd.
n.d. [1911]
268pp (2pp adv. preceding text & also on verso of half-title), col. frontis. only, clo. with col. reproduction of frontis. on front cover, 180.5x120.3mm. KP
Story of Northern Australia, Qld & islands north of Australia.

4644 A BUSH MYSTERY/or/The Lost Explorer/By/John Mackie/Author of "The Heart of the Prairie", "The Rising of the Red Man",/"Hidden in Canadian Wilds", "Black Man's Rock", "In Search/of Smith", "The Treasure Hunters", "The Life/Adventurous", etc etc/ London/James Nisbet & Co., Limited/22 Berners Street, W./1912
320pp, 1p preface, 30pp adv., col. frontis. & 4 f/p sepia plates, pic. clo., top edge gilt, marbled e/p, 190x126mm. NSL:M
The Holiday Library. Based on the disappearance of the explorers Ludwig Leichhardt & party. Illus. Arthur Twidle.
4645 A BUSH MYSTERY/or/The Lost Explorer/By/John Mackie/Austhor of/"The Heart of the Prairie", "Hidden in Canadian Wilds",/"Black Man's Rock", etc/London/James Nisbet & Co., Limited/22 Berners Street, W.
n.d.
viiipp (author's introduction), 320pp, 8pp adv., col. frontis., 4 sepia/white plates, clo. with col. onlay of frontis. pasted on front cover, dec. gilt spine, marbled e/p, 190x125mm. KP

[McKIE, Roberta Emma Madeline & McKIE, Graham Donald]
4646 THE/HOUSE/THAT/WORDS/BUILT
Lanternhouse Educational Publications, Melbourne, n.d. [1947]
16pp (inc. foreword), col. illus. throughout, wrappers, cover title, 280x220mm. ANL
Laugh and Learn Series. Rhyming text.

4647 THE/WATER/THAT/FLEW
As above. KMM

McKINLAY, Jean
4648 SPACE/SONGS/Jean McKinlay/Nelson
Thomas Nelson (Australia) Limited, Melbourne
copyright 1967
14pp, 6 f/p col. illus., by Don Angus. col. pic. wrappers, cover title, 240x184mm. KP

4649 SPACE SONGS/FOR YOUNG CHILDREN/Jean McKinlay/Ilustrated by Don Angus/[contents & notes]/Thomas Nelson (Australia) Limited/597 Little Collins Street, Melbourne C.I./321 Pitt Street, Sydney/ Copyright Thomas Nelson (Australia) Ltd. 1967
16pp, 8pp col. illus. & 8pp music, pic. wrappers, 240x185mm. Grant
Contains words & music of 10 songs. Contents same as above.

4650 PLAY & SING/by/Jean McKinlay/[drawing]/ Whitcombe & Tombs Pty Ltd
Melbourne, n.d.
24pp, b/w illus., dec. wrappers, 246x184mm. CLRC
Words & music of 27 songs.

MACKNESS, Constance
4651 GEM OF THE FLAT/By/Constance Mackness/ With Illustrations/Sydney/Angus & Robertson Ltd./89 Castlereagh Street
n.d. [advertisements dated July 1914]
321pp, 32pp adv., col. frontis. by May Gibbs & 7 b/w photographic plates, clo. (with col. onlay on front cover & spine), 180x115mm. ANL
Another copy as above, but no adv. & no gilt on front cover. KP
4652 GEM OF THE FLAT/By/Constance Mackness/ With illustrations/Australia:/Cornstalk Publishing Company/Arnold Place, Sydney/1924
287pp, 7 b/w photographic plates, clo., 185x120mm. KMM
4653 GEM OF THE FLAT/By/Constance Mackness/with

illustrations/Australia:/Cornstalk Publishing Company/Arnold Place, Sydney/1924
First Platypus Edition
235pp, 7 b/w photographic plates, clo. (with jacket col. illus. reproduced on inside cover), 175x110mm. KMM

4654 GEM OF THE FLAT/By/Constance Mackness/ With Illustrations/Australia:/Cornstalk Publishing Company/Arnold Place, Sydney/1925
287pp, 7 f/p b/w photographic illus., clo., 180x120mm. KMM
Dustwrapper printed in col. from drawing by Percy Lindsay.

4655 GEM OF THE FLAT/By/Constance Mackness/ With illustrations/Australia:/Cornstalk Publishing Company/89 Castlereagh Street, Sydney/1927
1st Platypus ed. 1924; 2nd Platypus ed. Jan. 1927
287pp, 7 b/w photographic plates, clo., 180x115mm. ANL

4656 MISS PICKLE/The Story of an Australian/ Boarding-School/By/Constance Mackness/Author of "Gem of the Flat"/Illustrated by M. D. Johnston/ Humphrey Milford/Oxford University Press/London Edinburgh Glasgow Copenhagen/New York Toronto Melbourne Cape Town/Bombay Calcutta Madras Shanghai
1924
280pp, col. frontis. & 4 b/w plates, 185x120mm. ANL

4657 MISS/PICKLE/By/Constance/Mackness/ Humphrey Milford/Oxford University/Press/London
• Rpt 1930
280pp, col. frontis., col. pic. bd., 185x120mm. CLRC
The New Ensign Series.

4658 MISS PICKLE/The Story of an Australian/ Boarding-School/By/Constance Mackness/Author of "Gem of the Flat"/[device]/Humphrey Milford/Oxford University Press/London Edinburgh Glasgow New York/Toronto Melbourne Cape Town Bombay
1933
280pp, col. frontis. pic. bd., 185x120mm; New Ensign series. JMcG

4659 MISS PICKLE/By/Constance Mackness/Geoffrey Cumberlege/Oxford University Press/Leighton House Melbourne
First Australian edition 1948
191pp, unillus., clo., 190x130mm. ANL

4660 GROWING UP/By/Constance Mackness/Author of "Gem of the Flat" and "Miss Pickle"/Ward, Lock & Co., Limited/London and Melbourne/1926
256pp, b/w frontis., 3 f/p b/w illus., pic. clo., 184x122mm. KP

4661 GROWING UP/By/Constance Mackness/Ward Lock & Co. Limited/London and Melbourne
n.d. [1926]
256pp, col. frontis. by Dewar Mills, clo., 185x120mm. CLRC
• Rpt as above, but b/w frontis. only. KP

4662 GROWING UP/By/Constance Mackness/Author of "The Blossom Children", "Clown of the School",/"The Young Beachcombers", "Daffy-Down Dilly",/etc etc./Ward, Lock & Co., Limited/London and Melbourne
n.d.
256pp, col. frontis. only, patterned clo., 184x120mm. KP
The Sentinel Series.

4663 THE/BLOSSOM CHILDREN/By/Constance Mackness/Author of "Gem of the Flat", "Miss Pickle", "Growing Up"/Ward Lock & Co. Limited/London and Melbourne/1927
256pp, b/w frontis. & 3 b/w plates, by Dewar Mills, clo., 180x120mm. KP

4664 Another copy as above, but n.d.
256pp, col. frontis. only, dec. clo,180x120mm. KMM

4665 THE/BLOSSOM CHILDREN/By/Constance Mackness/Author of "Gem of the Flat", "Miss Pickle", "Growing Up",/Ward, Lock & Co., Limited/London and Melbourne
n.d.
256pp, b/w frontis. & 3 b/w plates, patterned clo., 184x120mm. KP

4666 THE/BLOSSOM CHILDREN/By/Constance Mackness/Ward, Lock & Co.,Limited/London and Melbourne
256pp, col. frontis. only, dec. clo., 180x120mm, The Sentinel Series. KMM

4667 THE/GLAD SCHOOL/By/Constance Mackness/ Author of "Gem of the Flat", "Miss Pickle", etc./ Australia/Cornstalk Publishing Company/89 Castlereagh Street, Sydney/1927
244pp, 2pp preface, 3 b/w plates by Edgar Holloway, clo., 185x120mm. ANL
• Rpt 1928 (Bell Bird Series), as above. KMM

4668 THE/GLAD SCHOOL/By/Constance Mackness/ Author of Gem of the Flat, etc./Australia:/Cornstalk Publishing Company,/89 Castlereagh Street, Sydney/ 1929
244pp, b/w frontis. only, clo.,185x120mm. KP

4669 MISS BILLY/By/Constance Mackness/Author of "Gem of the Flat", "The Blossom Children" etc./ Australia:/Cornstalk Publishing Company/89 Castlereagh Street, Sydney/1928
269pp, b/w frontis. & 3 f/p b/w illus., clo., 185x115mm. NSL:M
Illustrations signed 'E.P.' [? Elizabeth Powell]

4670 DI-DOUBLE-DI/By/Constance Mackness/Author of "Gem of the Flat", "Miss Billy", and/"The Glad School"/Australia/Cornstalk Publishing Company/89 Castlereagh Street, Sydney/1929
299pp, b/w frontis. & 2 b/w illus. by Edgar A. Holloway, clo., 185x120mm. ANL

4671 THE YOUNG/BEACHCOMBERS/By/Constance Mackness/Author of/"The Blossom Children". "Growing Up" etc./Ward, Lock & Co., Limited/ London and Melbourne
1934
256pp, b/w frontis. & 3 f/p b/w illus. by Norman Sutcliffe, clo., 185x120mm. CLRC

4672 CLOWN OF THE SCHOOL/By/Constance Mackness/Author of/"The Blossom Children", "Growing Up"/"The Young Beachcombers"/Ward Lock & Co. Limited/London and Melbourne
n.d. [1935]
254pp, b/w frontis. & 3 b/w plates by Norman Sutcliffe, pic. clo., 190x130mm. ANL

4673 DAFFY-DOWN-DILLY/By/Constance Mackness/ Ward, Lock & Co. Limited/London and Melbourne
1937
254pp, b/w frontis. & 3 b/w plates, by Norman Sutcliffe, pic. clo. (with illus. reproduced on front cover), 185x125mm. The Tower Series, KP

McLACHLAN, Donald (ed.)

4674 AN AUSTRAL GARDEN/An Anthology of/ Australian Prose/Selected and Edited by/Donald McLachlan/George Robertson and Company/Propy. Ltd./Melbourne, Sydney, Adelaide,/and Brisbane
[1922]

viiipp, 296pp (inc. 6pp biographies), unillus., clo., 180x119mm. KMM
Publ. in School Edition, Library Edition with 12 portraits & Presentation Edition in suede.
See also Hansen & McLachlan AN AUSTRAL GARDEN OF VERSE

McLAUGHLIN, A.
THE FRUIT INDUSTRY. *See* This Australia series

[MacLEAN, A. S.]
4675 THE/VICTORY/BOOK/Orders of the British Empire—Rank and/Badges of the Navy, Army and Air Force—/Medals and Decorations—Stories/With Pictures to Color/No. 16 An Australian Production, Copyright/By Gunn and Taylor Pty. Ltd., Melbourne/ Distributors for N.S.W., and Queensland: Hamson & Leonard, 101 York Street, Sydney
n.d. [1942]
20pp, b/w illus. throughout, stiff pic. wrappers, 365x240mm. Grant

MACLEAN, Donald
4676 THE LUCK OF THE/"GOLD MOIDORE"/Being the contents of the original Manuscript written/by Master Andrew Barton, sometime Merchant and/ Shipowner, of Plymouth Town, England, which was/ found in the old log hut on Curdie's River. In which/ MS Master Barton tells of the wild voyages of the "Gold Moidore" and the "White Ship" to the/Great South Land in search of treasure in the years/ 1627–1629, and of the astounding experiences by sea/ and land of the men who sailed in them/By/Donald Maclean/Author of/"The Man from Curdie's Creek"/"John Scarlett"/etc/London: H. R. Allenson, Limited/7 Racquet Court, 114 Fleet Street, E. C.
n.d. [1920]
240pp (inc. 1p author's note), unillus., clo., 185x120mm. KMM
Published serially in England under the title 'The Mahogany Ship'; set near Port Fairy, Victoria.

McLEAN, Donald
4677 Great Stories of Australia/TREASURE/FROM THE EARTH/By/Donald McLean/Stories of the adventurous men who discovered/Australia's mineral wealth/Illustrated by/Frank Beck/Melbourne/ Macmillan & Co. Ltd./1963
165pp, 1p author's foreword, 15 b/w & part. col. illus., diagram, clo., dec. e/p, 215x135mm. KMM

MACLEAN, J. Kennedy
4678 HEROES OF THE/POLAR SEAS/A Record of Exploration in the Arctic and Antarctic Seas/By/J. Kennedy Maclean/With eight illustrations by/W. H. C. Groome/London: 38 Soho Square, W./W. & R. Chambers Limited/Edinburgh: 339 High Street
n.d. [1914?]
404pp, b/w frontis. & 9 f/p b/w illus., 2 folding b/w maps, pic. clo., 195x130mm. KMM
The last 6 chapters (approx. 103pp) deal with Antarctic exploration, including Scott's & Shackleton's expeditions, etc. In addition to Groome's illustrations, there is one photographic plate; & another illustration & the cover design are reproduced from drawings by R. Caton Woodville.
4679 HEROES OF THE/POLAR SEAS
As above, but 1910
382pp, b/w frontis. & 7 b/w plates & 2 folding maps, pic. clo., 193x130mm. KP
Antarctic exploration pp301-82.
4680 HEROES OF THE FARTHEST NORTH/AND FARTHEST SOUTH/Adapted from/J. Kennedy Maclean's/'HEROES OF THE POLAR SEAS'/London: 38 Soho Square, W./W. & A. Chambers, Limited/ Edinburgh: 339 High Street/1913
240pp, portrait frontis. of Capt R. F. Scott, R.N., 10 f/p b/w illus., 2 double-spread b/w maps, pic. clo., 175x115mm. KP
Another copy as above, n.d.
1p contents, 240pp, b/w frontis., 2 maps as before & 10 b/w illus. as before, pic. clo., 175x115mm. KP
Adapted & abridged from *Heroes of the Polar Seas.*

MACLEAN, Meta
THE SINGING SHIP/An Odyssey of Evacuee Children/By/Meta Maclean/Angus and Robertson Ltd./Sydney: London/1941
A book about, rather than for, children. CLRC

McLELLAND, A. D.
4681 1916/THE GREAT WAR/Written for/Young Australians/By/H. D. McLelland, B.A.,/Deputy Chief Inspector of Schools./Issued under the authority of/ Hon. Arthur Griffith, Minister for Education./Sydney: William Applegate Gullick, Government Printer—1916
46pp, unillus., wrappers, 240x163mm. WRT
Includes 10pp verses from various sources.

McLEOD, Frederick John
4682 WOMBA/An Aboriginal Stockboy/in the/Cattle Country/in the/Heart of Australia/By F. J. McLeod/ Georgian House—Melbourne
1951
168pp (inc. 2pp foreword by Dr Charles Duguid), 4pp author's introduction, unillus., clo., 215x135mm. HBM
German edition
4683 F. J. McLeod/WOMBA/UND DIE/ "MAL-MAL"/Erlebnisse eines jungen Austral-Negers bei den "mal-mal", den/weissen Siedlern in der australischen Steppe
H. R. Sauerländer & Co., Aarau & Frankfurt am Main, 1956
175pp, b/w drawings throughout, clo., dec. e/p, 210x145mm. Grant

MacLEOD, Jessie
See Palmer, Helen Gwynneth & MacLeod, Jessie

MACLEOD, Sheila
4684 THE WAYWARD BREEZE/and/Other Stories/By/ Sheila Macleod/Illustrations by Mirren/Published by Dunvegan Publications/Box 4614, GPO Sydney
n.d. [1946]
127pp, col. frontis. & 3 f/p col. illus., b/w drawings, clo., 190x130mm. ANL

MACMILLAN, David Stirling
ENTER THE MERCHANT
IRON AND STEEL
TALL SHIP AND STEAMBOATS.*See* Australian Landmarks

CHARLES NICHOLSON
JOHN DUNMORE LANG
EDGEWORTH DAVID. *See* Great Australians

JOHN McDOUALL STUART. *See* Great People in Australian History

McMILLAN, R. [pseud. 'Gossip']
4685 THE/VOYAGE OF/THE MONSOON/or,/The Adventures of a Stowaway/By/R. McMillan/ ("Gossip")/Illustrations by D. H. Souter/1900/William Brooks & Co./Sydney and Brisbane
167pp (inc. 1p dedication), 8pp adv., b/w frontis. & 2 f/p illus. & 11 b/w drawings in text, clo., 190x130mm. NSL:M

4686 SCIENCE GOSSIP/For Young and Old/(Illustrated)./By "Gossip",/Author of "Australian Gossip and Story", "There and/Back", "The Voyage of the Monsoon", &c. &c./Sydney:/Printed and Published by/The Sydney Stock and Station Journal,/17 Castlereagh Street./1907
182pp (inc. 1p author's preface), 8pp adv., 15 b/w drawings in text, dec. clo., 180x120mm. KMM

4687 THE ORIGIN/OF THE WORLD/By/R. McMillan/("Gossip")/Author of "Science Gossip" "The Voyage of the Monsoon"/"There and/Back" etc. etc./Sydney:/William Brooks & Co., Ltd., Printers, Castlereagh Street./1913
195pp (inc. 1p author's foreword & 5pp introduction), b/w portrait frontis., 11 b/w drawings in text, clo., 210x135mm. KMM

4688 THE ORIGIN OF THE/WORLD/A Book for Children/By/R. McMillan/Author of Science Gossip, The Great Secret, etc. etc./(Issued for the Rationalist Press Association, Limited)/London:/Watts & Co.,/17 Johnson's Court, Fleet Street, E.C./1914
136pp, 4pp introduction by Adams Gowans Whyte, 1p foreword, 1 f/p b/w illus., diagrams in text, clo., 200x125mm. NSL:M

4689 THE ORIGIN OF THE/WORLD/A Book for Children/By/R. McMillan/Author of Science Gossip, The Great Secret, etc. etc./(Issued for the Rationalist Press Association, Limited)/London:/Watts & Co.,/17 Johnson's Court, Fleet Street, E.C.4/1922
139pp, 6pp adv., wrappers, 185x120mm. NSL:M
• Rpt as above 1925. VSL

4690 THE STORY OF A/MICROSCOPE/Told to a boy/By "Gossip"/(R. McMillan)/Author of "There and Back",/"Science Gossip" "The Origin/of the World", "The Voyage/of the Monsoon", &c &c/William Brooks and Company, Limited/Sydney and Brisbane, 1914
127pp (inc. 1p foreword) & 2pp adv. preceding text, b/w frontis. & 13 b/w illus. in text, wrappers, 180x120mm. CLRC

4691 As above but bound in clo. KMM

McNAIR, William Allan

4692 STARLAND OF THE/SOUTH/By/William Allan McNair/M.Com., Dip. Soc. Sc./Illustrated by/William R. Taplin/[device]/Angus and Robertson/Sydney London
1950
xvipp (inc. 1p acknowledgements & 2pp pronunciations. 96pp (inc. 2pp bibliography), 10 plates, 9 printed in blue, black & white of maps of the skies, clo., 216x135mm. KP

4693 STARLAND OF THE/SOUTH/By/William Allan McNair/M. Com, Dip. Soc. Sc./Illustrated by/William R. Taplin/Whitcombe & Tombs Pty. Ltd./Sydney, Melbourne and Perth/and/New Zealand Associated Houses
First pub. 1950; new edition 1952
96pp (inc. preface, bibliography &c.), 9 part-col. illus. & 1 b/w illus., clo., 205x130mm. KMM

4694 Another edition 1959, as above, 220x135mm. BBC
• Rpt as above, 1959, 1961. KP
Highly commended CBCA Award 1951.

McNEIL, Jill

4695 Completely New/AUSTRALIAN/COLOURING BOOK/[drawing]/Tim Spends a holiday in the country [&c for 4 lines]/Compiled by Jill McNeil/Drawn by Australian artist,/Arthur McNeil/Copyright 1964 Arthur McNeil
32pp, b/w illus. throughout, col. pic. wrappers, 305x220mm. KP
True Australia Series; on front cover 'Tim visits a sheep station'.

'MACNELL, James' [pseud. for MACDONNELL, J. E.]

4696 CAPTAIN/METTLE/V.C./by/James Macnell/Constable London
1955
181pp, 2pp adv., 4 f/p b/w illus., clo., 185x120mm. KMM

4697 CAPTAIN/METTLE/V. C./by/James Macnell/The Children's Press/London and Glasgow
n.d. [1960]
188pp, unillus., clo., 180x115mm. KMM

4698 METTLE DIVES/DEEP/by/James Macnell/Constable London
First publ. 1956
232pp, unillus., clo., 184x118mm. KP

4699 METTLE DIVES/DEEP/by/James Macnell/The Children's Press/London and Glasgow
n.d. [1960; First published Constable 1958]
252pp, unillus., clo., 180x115mm. BBC

4700 METTLE AT/WOOMERA/By/James Macnell/Illustrated by/Douglas Hall/Constable London
1957
186pp, 4 f/p b/w illus., clo., 185x120mm. BBC

4701 METTLE AT/WOOMERA/By/James Macnell/The Children's Press/London and Glasgow
[1960 reprint]
188pp, unillus., clo., 180x115mm. KMM

4702 COLT & CO./IN THE/VALLEY OF GOLD/J. E. MacDonnell/London/J. M. Dent & Sons Ltd.
1960
184pp, b/w frontis. by Richard Kennedy, clo., 190x125mm. KMM
Adventure story set in New Guinea.

McNICOL, Rev Alexander

4703 NYANG NURSERY/or/Dewdrops from the Manse [Lacks t.p. Dedication reads: To my/dear Grandchildren at Nyang/This little volume of Practical Poems/is affectionately inscribed/by the author/Dominus vobiscum/The Manse, Moulamein, N.S.W./25th December 1879. Also dedicated to Neil and Agnes Turner, parents of the children]
[1880]
19pp, clo., 185x120mm. VSL
Contains 5 poems, all reprinted in author's later volume *Wreaths of Love*, 1886.

4704 WREATHS OF LOVE/or,/Musings from the Manse./By/The Rev. Alexander McNicol/(Upwards of Thirty Years' Presbyterian Minister in Victoria)./[3 lines quotation—Young's *Night Thoughts*/Melbourne:/M. L. Hutchinson, 15 Collins Street West./1886
viiipp, 328pp, unillus., clo. dec. with title & author in gilt in a decorative wreath on front cover, 190x130mm. VSL

McNUTT, M. E.

4705 SONGS OF BUSHLAND/By/M. E. McNutt/[drawing]/North Sydney/Winn & Co., Printers, Ridge St./1918
95pp, 1 b/w drawing, bd., with b/w pic. front cover, 183x120mm. ANL
Front cover reads 'Songs of Bushland by Mollie the Nutt'. Verse with 13pp section 'For the Little Ones'.

McPHEAT, W. Scott

JOHN FLYNN. *See* Great Australians

[McPHEE, Edward Tannock]
4706 MARGARET/PILGRIM'S/RHYME/BOOK
J. Walch & Sons, Hobart, n.d. [1935] [According to Morris Miller published by the author, Canberra 1935]
11pp, unillus., wrappers, cover title, 190x150mm. ANL
Children's verses.

MACPHERSON, Bruce & June
TRUE AUSTRALIAN Series
Format example:
4707 THE LOST KOALA/an adventure with/Jenny and Sue/in the Australian Bush/Photographs & Story by/Bruce & June Macpherson
Copyright 1962, Kingsway Press Pty Ltd, Caringbah, NSW
[24]pp, col. & b/w photographic illus. throughout, pic. bd., 245x185mm. KMM
Col. & b/w photographs of dolls posed among Australian native animals & flora; factual information printed on back pastedown.
Others in series (reprinted many times; also published as *Young Australian Books*)
4708 THE BLUE OPAL (Caringbah, NSW, n.d.)
4709 THE MAGIC BOOMERANG(later rpt 28pp)
4710 THE SEA URCHIN
4711 THE WHITE WALLABY

4712 THE HAPPY HOLIDAY/with the little Sea Urchin/an adventure with Jenny and Sue/on an Australian Beach/Photographs and story by Bruce and June Macpherson/Seymour doll created by Merla Ratcliffe.
Horwitz Group Books, North Sydney, n.d.
24pp & 1 p facts about Australian coast, col. & b/w photographs, col. pic. bd., 238x180mm. KP

4713 JOURNEY TO THE/RED ROCK/a story of Central Australia by/Bruce and June Macpherson/Collins St. James's Place, London, 1965
48pp, 23pp col. photographs, b/w photographs on other pages, col. photographic bd., col. e/p, 290x210mm. CLRC
A picture book of a girl's visit to Ayer's Rock, with brief accompanying text.

MACPHERSON, June
4714 THE JOLLY SWAGMAN/Photographs and Story/by June Macpherson
Published by Jack de Lissa (Aust.) Pty Ltd, Sydney, n.d. [196-?]
[26]pp, col. & b/w photographs throughout, col. pic. bd., 240x175mm. KMM
True Australian Series. Photographs of dolls, Australian animals, etc.
• Rpt by Horwitz Group Books, [1970] as above, but 26 pp. KP

4715 JOYRIDES/[coloured illustration] June Macpherson
Horwitz, North Sydney, n.d. [1971?]
[10]pp, col. photographic illus. throughout, bd., cover title, 255x165mm. KMM
Board book with brief rhyming stanza to each page opening.

TOPPAN'S FOTO BOOKS series
Format example:
4716 Toppan's Foto Books/THE KANGAROO/AND HIS FRIENDS/Photographed in Australia by June Macpherson
Froebel-Kan Co, Ltd., Tokyo, Japan 1967
[16]pp, col. photographic pictures printed on bd., cover title, 264x184mm. KP
(pagination includes both covers)
In same series
4717 ANIMAL PLAYMATES. WRT
4718 LITTLE KOALA AND HIS FRIENDS. WRT
4719 LOVELY PETS. KMM
Later 6 titles published by Golden Press in same format and varied illus; later still Toppan's Peewee series of 8 pp slightly smaller was produced. KP

MACPHERSON, Margaret L. [Mrs M. L. Albert]
4720 AUSTRALIA CALLING/By/Margaret L. Macpherson/Illustrated by/Kurt Wiese/[vignette]/Dodd, Mead & Company/New York 1946
199pp, b/w drawings in text throughout, clo., 195x135mm. NSL:M
Travels of two American children in Australia with an Australian flying doctor.

MacROBERTSON
4721 MacRobertson/takes pride in presenting/THE STORY OF CHOCOLATE/AND CONFECTIONERY/[2 lines text]
Melbourne, 7th ed. 1962
16pp, col. & b/w photographic illus. & diagrams, pic. wrappers, 204x250mm. KP
Promoting the well-known chocolate manufacturer

MacVICAR, Angus
THE LOST PLANET
RETURN TO THE LOST PLANET, 1953 and many rpt. KP
Narrator purports to have been born in Australia, but insufficient Australian content for inclusion. The author is Scottish.

MADER, Fr. W.
4722 Friedr. Wilh. Mader/IM WELTMEER VERIRRT/Seltsame Abenteuer/in der Südsee/Mit 6 Londrückbildern und 15 Textzeichnungen/von Hans Anton Aschenborn Sowie einer Karte/[device]/Union Deutsche Verlagsgesellschaft/Stuttgart/Berlin/Leipzig
Dritte Auflage [copy acquired 1945; preface dated 1929]
268pp (inc. 2pp preface & 7pp index), 4pp adv., b/w frontis. & 4 f/p b/w illus., drawings in text, clo., 190x140mm. NSL:M
4723 4th ed. as above, n.d.
268pp,1p map, 3pp adv. b/w frontis. & 5 plates & text drawings, t.p. printed in 2 cols., dec.clo. 190x140mm. SUA

MADIGAN, Frank
4724 [b/w illus.]/THE/DANGEROUS/DESERT/Frank Madigan/Ward Lock and Co Limited/London and Melbourne
1966
164pp, b/w frontis. & t.p., b/w illus. throughout, clo., 200x128mm. KP
Illus. Dora Schackell. Boys' adventure story set in NW Australia.

'The Magic Charm' and other stories
4725 "THE/MAGIC CHARM"/AND OTHER STORIES
n.p., n.d. [Sydney?1920-?]
[24]pp, 4pp adv., 4 f/p b/w drawings & 9 smaller drawings in text, col. pic. wrappers, cover title, 180x120mm. RM
Contains 4 stories with Australian background, written to advertise 'Clement's Tonic'.

The Magic Skipping-Rope
4726 THE MAGIC SKIPPING-ROPE (for the sixes)
Whitcombe & Tombs, Auckland, n.d. [1926]
16pp, frontis., 182mm. VSL
See McLaren 3

The Magic World of Photography
4727 THE MAGIC WORLD/OF/PHOTOGRAPHY/
Photography for Young People

Kodak (Australasia) Pty Ltd., n.p., n.d. [1950-?]
32pp (inc. covers), b/w photographs on every page, pic. wrappers, cover title, 217x140mm. KMM

MAHER, A. L.
4728 MAHER'S V.E.M./TOY/MAKING/Supplement/for the/Senior Pupils/Editor:/Victorian Educational Monthly/A. L. Maher
Publ. by P. H. O'Donoghue & printed by the Ruskin Press Pty Ltd, 123 Latrobe St, Melbourne, n.d. [prize 1965] [prices before decimal currency]
22pp, b/w diagrams, wrappers, 243x180mm. KP
Patterns for toys made of wood &c.

MAHOOD, Margot
4729 THE/WHISPERING/STONE/An Australian/Nature Fantasy/Story and Pictures/by Margot Mahood
The author, Melbourne, n.d. [1944]
31pp, t.p., & 7 other pp. illus in col., b/w drawings in text by author, pic. bd., 180x235mm. ANL

4730 DRAWING/AUSTRALIAN/ANIMALS/by/Margo [*sic*]/Mahood/[device]/
Whitcombe & Tombs Pty. Ltd./Melbourne Sydney Perth
32pp, b/w illus., pic. wrappers, 246x186mm. KMM

MAHUZIER, Philippe
4731 Philippe Mahuzier/Illustrations de Raoul Auger/LES MAHUZIER/EN AUSTRALIE/[device]/Éditions G.P., 80, Rue Sainte-Lazare, Paris 9c/©1962 Éditions G.P., Paris
187pp & 1p adv., col. frontis. map, col. & b/w illus. throughout, bd., 200x142mm. RC
A French family visits Australia.

MAIDIERES, Pierre
4732 Pierre Maidières/LE DESTIN TRAGIQUE/DE JAMES COOK/Éditions Jules Tallandier/(Section Bleue)/75, Rue Dareau, Paris (XIV)
1932
124pp, 7 f/p b/w illus. & 1 b/w chapter heading, pic. wrappers, 240x160mm. NSL:M

Make and Paint/A Cut-out and Colouring Book
4733 MAKE AND PAINT/A CUT-OUT AND/COLOURING BOOK/[illus.]/John Sands Pty Ltd. Sydney, n.d.
[24]pp, b/w & col. illus. throughout, pic. wrappers, 240x185mm. KP
Sandman Series.

Make Colourful Pictures from Scraps of Material
4734 MAKE COLOURFUL PICTURES FROM SCRAPS OF MATERIAL/for children from 4 to 12/Kite's Publishing Co. Melbourne N 21 Series 531-1
n.d.
Folder containing 6 cards with bold pic. printed in b/w to which materials could be pasted, 228x228mm. ANL

MALAN, Rev. Arthur Noel
4735 THE WALLABY MAN/By the Rev./A. N. Malan, D.D., F.G.S./Author of/"Schooldays at Highfield House", "Uncle Towser" etc./With illustrations by/J. Macfarlane/London/The Religious Tract Society/4 Bouverie Street and 65 St. Paul's Churchyard
n.d. [inscribed 1908]
257pp, 2 pp adv., b/w frontis & 6 b/w plates, pic. clo., 195x130mm. KP
A boys' school story set in England, the only Australian connection being the man of the title, who kept a tame wallaby.
• Rpt n.d.[prize 1916]
257pp 2 pp adv., part-col. t.p., col. frontis. & 2 col. plates, clo., 195x130mm. KMM

MALAN, C. F. de M.
4736 ERIC AND CONNIE'S/CRUISE IN THE SOUTH PACIFIC/By/C. F. de M. Malan, R.N./With Illustrations/London/Sampson Low, Marston, Searle & Rivington, Ltd./St. Dunstan's House/Fetter Lane, Fleet Street, E.C./1889/(All rights reserved).
339pp, 1p preface, 32pp adv., b/w frontis. & 6 f/p b/w illus., pic. clo., 180x120mm. KMM
The adventures of two Australian children & their uncle on a cruise in the south-west Pacific; the first & last chapters are set in Sydney.

MALCOLM, Penelope
4737 A/HOLIDAY AT THE/SEASIDE./By Penelope Malcolm
The Valentine Publishing Co. [Melbourne?] n.d. [copyright 1946]
17pp, col. illus. throughout by Jay Ellen, stiff dec. wrappers, cover title, 310x205mm. NSL:M

MALIN, Lin
4738 STORIES OF/FAERIELAND/By/Lyn Malin/Illustrated by May Voke/Adelaide: At the Hassell Press/1931
37pp, b/w frontis. & 2 f/p b/w illus., drawings throughout, wrappers, 240x170mm. NSL:M
4739 STORIES OF/FAERIELAND/By Lyn Malin/Illustrated by May Voke/Second Edition/Adelaide: At the Hassell Press/1931
Details as above. ANL

MALLINSON, Mavis
4740 THE/MAGIC/KANGAROO/By/Mavis Mallinson/[drawing]/The/Adventures/of/Dicky/and/Nooroo/Sandman Series published by John Sands Pty. Ltd. Sydney, n.d. [1944]
64pp, dec. t.p., part-col. illus. throughout by author, col. stiff pic. wrappers, 235x175mm. KMM
Story told in comic-strip form.
• Rpt as above, n.d. (inscribed 1947) 240x175mm. KP

MALLORY, Clare
A New Zealand writer whose girls' story books, published in Melbourne between 1947 and 1951, are not Australian in subject matter.

MALONE, H. L'Estrange
4741 ELLEY AND KANGY/An Animal Story for Children/By/H. L'Estrange Malone/Author of/"The Children's King",/"Shaggy the Great" "Nipping Bear",/"Winfred: [*sic*] A Romance of Rumayne," /&c &c./London/The Epworth Press/J. Alfred Sharp n.d. [192-?]
Story set in Africa about a friendship between an elephant & a kangaroo. Not Australian. KP

MALTBY, G. B. [Peg]
4742 PEGS/FAIRY/BOOK/Written & Illustrated/by Peg Maltby
Murfett Pty Ltd [Melbourne], n.d. [1944]
[50]pp, col. frontis. & 14 col. plates & drawings in text on every page, illus. t.p., pic. bd., clo. spine, 317x234mm. KP
Printed throughout in sepia. The unnumbered plates are counted separately (i.e. 80pp in all)
No apostrophe in title
4743 PEGS/FAIRY/BOOK/Written & Illustrated by/Peg Maltby
Murfett Pty Ltd, Melbourne, 2nd ed. 1945
[50]pp & 15 f/p col. plates, drawing in text throughout (no frontis. but plate in text), pic. bd., clo. spine, 320x235mm. KP
Printed throughout in sepia.

4744 PEGS/FAIRY/BOOK
3rd ed. as above
Murfett Pty Ltd, Melbourne, n.d. [1946]. Printed by Queen City Printers for Murfett Pty Ltd.
50pp & 15 f/p plates, 320x235mm. KP
Printed in sepia.

4745 PEGS/FAIRY/BOOK/Written & Illustrated/by Peg Maltby
n.d.
On back cover [device—Fama, Goddess of Fame] A Murfett Production Queen City Printers for Murfett Pty Ltd 364 Lonsdale St Melb.
Details as above, pic. bd., clo. spine, 320x235mm. KP

4746 PEG'S/FAIRY/BOOK/Written and illustrated by Peg Maltby
P. C. Grosser & Co. Ltd, Moorabbin, Victoria [1961]
64pp, dec. t.p. varying from that of other ed., 15 col. illus., b/w illus. throughout, book printed throughout in b/w, text printed on back of col. illus., col. pic. bd. (1 col. illus. rpt on front cover), clo. spine, 317x230mm. KP
The b/w illus. vary from those of other ed. & are not as copious.

4747 PIP AND PEPITA/IN GOBLINLAND/[drawing]/ Illustrations by Peg Maltby/Story by G. B. Maltby
Murfett Pty. Ltd., Melbourne, n.d. [1945]
32pp, 8 f/p col. illus. & b/w drawings throughout, pic. bd., 240x180mm. ANL

4748 NUTCHEN/OF THE/FOREST/Written and/ Illustrated by/P. Maltby
Murfett Pty Ltd, Melbourne, n.d. [1945]
32pp, dec. t.p., 8 f/p col. illus. & b/w drawings throughout, bd., 240x180mm. ANL

4749 PEPITA'S PARTY/Illustrations/and/Story by/P. Maltby/A Murfett/Production
Melbourne, n.d. [1945]
32pp, dec. t.p., 8 f/p col. illus. & b/w drawings throughout, pic. bd., 240x180mm. ANL

4750 PIP & PEPITA'S/NEW HOME/[drawing]/Written and/Illustrated by/P. Maltby
Murfett Pty Ltd, Melbourne, n.d. [1945]
32pp, 8 f/p col. illus. & b/w drawings throughout, dec. bd., 245x180mm. ANL
See also Newberry, Agnes for others in series

4751 PIP & PEPITA'S/NEW HOME/[drawing]/Written and Illustrated by/P. Maltby/Printed in Australia by Queen City Printers Pty Ltd., Melbourne, for the/ Publishers, Murfett Pty Ltd, 118 Queen Street, Melbourne
n.d. [inscribed 11/5/1945]
Details as above. KP

4752 BEN AND BELLA
4753 BEN AND BELLA DOWN ON THE FARM
4754 BEN AND BELLA IN THE CLOUDS
4755 BEN AND BELLA IN THE HILLS
Uniform booklets published by Murfett Pty Ltd, Melbourne, n.d. [1947]
16pp, 8 f/p col. illus. & b/w drawings throughout, dec. wrappers, cover title, 360x250mm. NSL:M
BEN AND BELLA [rpt 1961]
BEN AND BELLA IN THE CLOUDS [rpt 1961]
P. C. Grosser & Co. Ltd, Moorabbin, Victoria, n.d.
16pp, 8 f/p col. illus. & b/w drawings throughout, dec. wrappers, cover title, 295x200mm. NSL:M

4756 MEET/MR. COBBLEDICK!/Illustrations and/Story by/P. Maltby
Murfett Pty Ltd, Melbourne, n.d. [1948]
32pp, dec. t.p., 9 f/p col. illus. & b/w drawings throughout, bd., 245x245mm. ANL

4757 NUTCHEN/AND THE/GOLDEN KEY/[25-line foreword]/Story and Pictures/by/P. Maltby
Murfett Pty Ltd, Melbourne, n.d. [1948]
32pp, 9 f/p col. illus. & b/w drawings throughout, bd., 245x245mm. ANL

4758 NURSERY RHYMES/By/P. Maltby/Murfett Pty Ltd.
Murfett Pty Ltd, Melbourne
16pp, col. & b/w illus. on alternate page openings, pic. wrappers, 360x250mm. KP
Mother Goose riding her goose on blue background on front cover.

4759 NURSERY/RHYMES/Illustrated by/Peg Maltby
Murfett Pty Ltd, Melbourne, n.d. [1948]
Details as above. KMM

4760 NURSERY RHYMES/Illustrated by/Peg Maltby
Murfett Pty Ltd, 364 Lonsdale St, Melbourne
16pp, col. & b/w illus. on alternate page openings, col. pic. wrappers, 365x252mm. KP
Yellow border to covers; a rabbit & an elf dancing beneath a bough covered with reddish plums? Back cover shows a fairy swinging on a poppy stem. Contents totally different from those in blue covers *Nursery Rhymes* & much less attractive work in the yellow book.

4761 BEN AND BELLA/AND THE/APPLE TREE
Printed in Australia by Queen City Printers, Melbourne for Murfett Pty Ltd, 364 Lonsdale St, Melbourne, [1949]
16pp, 8 f/p col. illus., pic. wrappers, cover title, 367x250mm. KP
Uniform with above:
4762 BEN AND BELLA/AT THE BEACH. KP
4763 BEN/AND/BELLA/IN THE GARDENS/Peg Maltby [1951]. KP

4764 FOREVER/CUCKOO!/By/P. Maltby
Murfett Pty Ltd, Melbourne, [1950]. Queen City Printers
16pp, col. & b/w illus. on alternate page openings, pic. wrappers, 365x260mm. KP

4765 LITTLE RED RIDING HOOD/Retold by/Peg Maltby
Murfett Pty Ltd, Melbourne, n.d. [1950]
16pp, 8 f/p col. illus. & b/w drawings in text, stiff paper wrappers, cover title, 180x240mm. KMM

4766 GOLDILOCKS/AND/THE THREE BEARS/Retold/ by/Peg Maltby
Murfett Pty Ltd, Melbourne, n.d. [1950]
16pp, 8 f/p col. illus. & b/w drawings, wrappers, cover title, 180x240mm. ANL

4767 THE/SLEEPING/BEAUTY/Retold by/Peg Maltby
Murfett Pty Ltd, Melbourne, n.d. [1951]
16pp, 8 f/p col. illus. & b/w drawings, wrappers, cover title, 185x250mm. ANL

4768 LITTLE THUMBELINE/Pictures by Peg Maltby
Murfett Pty Ltd, Melbourne, n.d. [1951]
16pp, 8 f/p col. illus. & b/w drawings throughout, dec. wrappers, cover title, 185x250mm. ANL

4769 WINKIE'S/MAGIC/PEPPER POT./Peg/Maltby
Peg Maltby Productions, Olinda, Victoria. Printed by Sands & Macdougalls
16pp, col. & b/w illus. on alternate page openings, pic. wrappers, 360x242mm. KP
Story and pictures by Peg Maltby.

Malties Bird Album
4770 MALTIES/[drawing]/BIRD ALBUM
Malties Pty Ltd, East Brunswick, Victoria, n.d.
8pp, printed on bd. & folding together, 40 spaces for cards to be collected & pasted in, information printed on back of sheets, pic. bd., 320x188mm. KP

'MALVERN, Pat' [pseud. SKRINE, Cynthia M.]
4771 SECRET GOLD/A Story of Two Boys who found/wealth in the heart of the/Australian Desert/By/Pat Malvern/London/The Sheldon Press/Northumberland Avenue, W.C.2
n.d. [1934]
192pp & 15pp adv., col. frontis. only, clo., 190x124mm. NSL:M

MANNING, Katherine
4772 AUSTRALIAN/KINDERGARTEN/TIME/by/Katherine Manning/Colour Photography by/Douglass [*sic*] Baglin/Readabout Books
Readabout Books, Crow's Nest, NSW, 1964
16pp, col. photographs throughout, stiff dec. wrappers, cover title, 205x275mm. BBC
Book of photographs of children at kindergarten, with brief accompanying text.

MANNING-SAUNDERS, Ruth
4773 Ruth Manning-Saunders/THE/EXTRAORDINARY/MARGARET/CATCHPOLE/[device]/Heinemann London
1966
222pp (inc. 1p author's note), unillus., clo., 195x125mm. KMM

MANSFIELD, John
4774 HASSAN/the little Arabian/by John Mansfield/Illustrated by Joan Martin May/[drawing]/Nelson London, second impression 1967
24pp, b/w drawings, pic. bd., 200x150mm. MD

4775 KIRAN/the little Indian/by John Mansfield/Illustrated by Joan Martin May/[drawing]/Nelson London, second impression 1967
24pp, b/w drawings, pic. bd., 200x150mm. MD

4776 TOPA/the little Peruvian/by John Mansfield/Illustrated by Brownie Downing/[drawing]/Nelson London, second impression 1967
24pp, b/w drawings, pic. bd., 200x150mm. MD
Australian author
See also DOWNING, Brownie and MANSFIELD, John

MANSON, Cecil & Celia
4777 THE ADVENTURES OF/JOHNNY VAN BART/Cecil and Celia Manson/Illustrated by/Ian Armour-Chelu/London/Epworth Press
1965
202pp, 11 f/p b/w illus., clo., 197x130mm. ANL

MANT, Gilbert
4778 BUTTERCUP/By/Gilbert Mant
Publ. by Wendy Rene Pty Ltd, Barraba, NSW, 1969
42pp, 6 f/p b/w illus., by Smee Morris, bd., 185x120mm. KP

MARC, Elizabeth
4779 TWO IN THE BUSH/A Story of Adventure/in Australia/By/Elizabeth Marc/Author of "Lost in the Arctic" etc./With four illustrations in/Colour and Black-and-White/by John de Walton/Cassell and Company Ltd./London, Toronto, Melbourne and Sydney
1929
216pp, col. frontis. & 3 b/w plates, clo., 190x125mm. ANL

4780 TWO YOUNG/ADVENTURERS/A Tale of/The Australian Bush/By/E. Marc/Author of "A Man Hunt in the Arctic", etc./Illustrated/in Colour and Black/and White by/John de Walton/[device]/Cassell/and Company, Limited/London, Toronto, Melbourne/and Sydney
1934
252pp, col. frontis. & 3 b/w plates, clo., 180x120mm. KMM
Children's story located in New South Wales & Central Australia.
Note This book consists of the story *Two in the Bush,* with an additional 13 chapters; one of the illus. is the same as in *Two in the Bush.*

4781 BUSH/RAGAMUFFINS/By Elizabeth Marc/Illustrated by H. Radcliffe Wilson/1935/Methuen & Co. Ltd. London
200pp, 6 f/p b/w illus. & drawings in text, clo., 205x155mm. NSL:M

Australian writer also author of the foll.
LOST IN THE ARCTIC, illus. Archibald Webb, Cassell & Co. Ltd, London, 1926, 212pp.

WITH PUCKER TO THE ARCTIC/A story for Young Readers, illus. E. Brier, Thomas Nelson & Son Ltd, London, n.d. [1927?] 264pp.

A MAN HUNT IN THE ARCTIC, Cassell & Co Ltd., London, 1932, 191pp, frontis. only. KP

MARCET, Eduardo
4782 EN FÄRD/I DET INRE AF AUSTRALIEN/af/Eduardo Marcet/ofversättning från franskau./Stockholm, Sigfrid Flodins förlag
1870
125pp, unillus. NSL:M

MARCHANT, Bessie
4783 A BRAVE LITTLE COUSIN/By/Bessie Marchant/(Mrs J. A. Comfort)/Author of 'The House of Brambling Minster'/'The Ghost of Rock Grange', etc/Illustrated by W. S. Stacey/Published under the direction of the general/literature committee/London:/Society for Promoting Christian Knowledge,/Northumberland Avenue, W.C./43 Queen Victoria Street, E.C./Brighton: 129 North Street,/New York: E & J. B. Young & Co.
n.d.
[prize 1905]
254pp & 16pp adv., b/w frontis. & 2 b/w plates, pic. clo., 190x125mm. ANL
Story set in outback Qld.
• Rpt as above, but
Northumberland Avenue W.C./43, Queen Victoria Street, E.C./Brighton: 129, North Street
[inscribed 1914]
254pp, 1p adv, b/w frontis. & 2 plates, pic. clo., 190x125mm. KMM
• Rpt as above, but
New York: E. S. Gorham
n.d.
Details as before. KP

4784 A BRAVE LITTLE/COUSIN/By/Bessie Marchant/Author of 'The Deputy Boss', 'Redwood Randi', etc./Illustrated by George Baker/London/The Sheldon Press/Northumberland Avenue, W.C.2/New York and Toronto: The Macmillan Co.
254pp & 16pp adv., 1 illus. only, pic. clo., 190x120mm. ANL

4785 THE APPLE LADY/By/Bessie Marchant/Author of 'The Girls of Wakensede'/'Juliette, the Mail Carrier',

Etc./Illustrated by/George Soper/London and Glasgow/Collins' Clear-Type Press
London, [1908] [prize 1912]
364pp & 3pp adv., additional col. pic. t.p., col. frontis. & 3 f/p col. plates, dec. clo. with col. pic. onlay, 190x135mm. ANL
Girls' story set in Tasmania.

4786 THE/BLACK COCKATOO/A Story of Western Australia/By/Bessie Marchant/With Coloured Illustrations by/Lancelot Speed/London/The Religious Tract Society/4 Bouverie Street and 65 St. Paul's Churchyard, E.C.
n.d. [1910]
282pp, 6pp adv., col. frontis. & 1 f/p col. illus., pic. clo., 190x125mm. KMM

4787 THE/FERRY HOUSE GIRLS/an Australian Story/By/Bessie Marchant/Author of "A Girl of Distinction" "A Countess from Canada"/"Great's Domain"/"Daughters of the Dominion" &c./Illustrated by W. R. S. Stott/Blackie and Son Limited/London Glasgow and Bombay/1912
283pp, b/w frontis. & 5 f/p sepia/white illus., pic. clo., title & author in gilt on front & spine, 185x125mm. JMcG

4788 THE/FERRY HOUSE GIRLS
As above, but inscribed 1924
Pic. clo. with 2 girls on horseback, more modern d/w by Warwick Reynolds showing a girl on horseback jumping a fence. KP

4789 Another copy as above, but green cloth bdg with design of a collie dog running down steps from a doorway with a girl & other dog watching. KP

4790 SALLY MAKES GOOD/A Story of Tasmania/By/Bessie Marchant/Author of "A Transport Girl in France"/"Norah to the Rescue"/"Cynthia Wins"/Illustrated by Leo Bates/Blackie and Son Limited/London Glasgow Bombay
n.d. [1920]
255pp, col. frontis., 4 f/p plates, pic. clo., 185x120mm. KP

4791 THE/ADVENTUROUS/SEVEN/Their Hazardous Undertaking/By/Bessie Marchant/Author of "The Heroine of the Ranch"/"The Loyalty of Hester Hope" "A Princess of Servia" [*sic*]/"The Youngest Sister"/Illustrated by W. R. S. Stott/Blackie and Son Limited/London Glasgow and Bombay
n.d. [1914]
256pp, col. frontis. & 4 b/w plates, pic. clo., gilt lettering on cover, 185x125mm. ANL
Story has an Australian background

4792 THE/ADVENTUROUS SEVEN/By/Bessie Marchant/Author of "The Heroine of the Ranch"/"The Loyalty of Hester Hope"/"A Princess of Servia"/"The Youngest Sister" &c./Blackie & Son Limited/London and Glasgow
n.d. [first pub. 1914; re-issued 1936]
256pp, b/w frontis. by W. R. S. Stott, clo., 185x120mm. CLRC

Swedish edition

4793 SJU SYSKON PÅ ÅVENTYR/Benättelse för Ungdom/av/Bessie Marchant/Bymyndigad/Översättning/av/Elisabeth Lilljebjörn/[device]/Stockholm/C. E. Fritzers Bokförlags Aktiebolag
1917
205pp, b/w frontis., bd., 160x114mm. ANL
Frontis. illus. from English ed. reproduced reduced & in b/w on front cover. Nytt Bibliotek för Barn och ungdom.

4794 THE/BESSIE MARCHANT/OMNIBUS BOOK/The Gold-marked Charm/Sally Makes Good/Three Girls in Mexico/[device]/Blackie & Son Limited/London and Glasgow
n.d. [1932]
352pp, 255pp, 294pp & 2pp adv., unillus., clo., 196x128mm. ANL
Includes *Sally Makes Good*, a Tasmanian story.

4795 WAIFS OF/WOOLLAMOO/A Story for Girls/By/Bessie Marchant/Frederick Warne & Co. Ltd./London and New York
1938
288pp, col. frontis. only, clo., 195x130mm. CLRC

4796 WAIFS OF/WOOLLAMOO/A Story for Girls/by/Bessie Marchant/Frederick Warne and Co. Ltd./London and New York
n.d.
189pp, unillus., col. pic. wrappers, 179x115mm. KMM

MAREY, Helen

4797 STOLEN/VOYAGE/Helen/Marey/Illustrated by/Astra Lacis Dick/Angus and Robertson
Sydney 1965
166pp, dec. t.p., b/w illus. throughout, clo., 215x135mm. BBC

'MARGARET, Sister M.'

4798 DERRING-DO MARY/The Story of Mary McKillop/An Australian Girl/Who Tried Always to say "Yes" to God/by/Sister M. Margaret/illustrated by/Sister M. Mildred/E. J. Dwyer/Sydney
1965
87pp & 1p foreword, 16 part-col. illus. throughout, clo., 230x150mm. KMM
Foreword by Cardinal Gilroy.

MARK, Annie H.

4799 "HAPPY HEARTS"/Poems for Children/By/Annie H. Mark/Author of/"From Heatherland"/(Digby Long & Co., London)/"Poems of the West"/(Wigg's Perth, Western Australia)/(Author's Copyright)/Price: Two Shillings
Paterson's Printing Press, Perth, n.d. [1939]
61pp, unillus., bd., 180x110mm. VSL

MARKHAM, Clements R.

4800 THE SEA FATHERS:/A Series of/Lives of Great Navigators/of/Former Times./By/Clements R. Markham, C.B., F.R.S./Secretary of the Royal Geographical Society/with frontispiece/Cassell & Company, Limited:/London, Paris & New York./1884/(All rights reserved)
214pp, 7pp appendix, 6pp adv., engraved frontis., dec. clo., 180x117mm. KP
Includes William Dampier pp163-87; Cook, Scoresby & Dance pp188–214.

4801 FAMOUS SAILORS/OF/FORMER TIMES:/The Story of the Sea Fathers./By/Clements R. Markham, C.B., F.R.S./Secretary of the Royal Geographical Society./With frontispiece/second edition/Cassell & Company, Limited:/London, Paris, New York & Melbourne./1886
214pp & 7pp appendix, 18pp adv., engraved frontis only, dec. clo.., 180x117mm. HBM

MARKS, Stan

4802 GRAHAM/IS AN ABORIGINAL BOY/Photographs by/Brian McArdle/Text by/Stan Marks/[photograph] Methuen/in association with/Hicks Smith London and Melbourne 1968
48pp, b/w photographs throughout, b/w map, pic. bd., clo. spine 210x160mm. BBC
• Rpt 1970. WRT.

Another copy the same, with 'Hicks Smith' instead of Methuen on spine. KP
• Rpt 1971 as above. KP
US edition
Hastings House, New York, 1969
Unseen: ANB 1969

4803 ANIMAL/OLYMPICS/Story by Stan Marks/ Illustrated by Jeff Hook/Wren
Wren Publishing Pty Ltd, Melbourne 1972
57pp, col. illus. throughout, pic. clo., 220x265mm. CLRC

4804 ANIMAL/OLYMPICS/Story by Stan Marks/ Illustrated by Jeff Hook/[device] Gold Star Publications/Melbourne
1972
[57]pp (inc. col. frontis.), details as above but bound in pic. wrappers, 220x260mm. KP

MARRYAT, Augusta

4805 LEFT TO THEMSELVES./A Boy's/Adventures in Australia./By/Augusta Marryat./With Original Illustrations./[device]/London:/Frederick Warne and Co.,/Bedford Street, Strand
Preface dated 1878
viiipp, 339pp, engraved frontis. & 5 f/p b/w illus., pic. clo., 178x116mm. CLRC

4806 THE YOUNG LAMBERTS/A Boy's Adventures in Australia/by/Augusta Marryat/Author of "The Reverse of the Shield"/with original illustrations/ London/Frederick Warne and Co./Bedford Street, Strand
n.d. [1878]
339pp, 4pp adv., b/w frontis. & 3 f/p b/w illus. in text, dec. clo., 180x115mm. Grant
Publisher's note: 'This work was originally published under the title of "Left to Themselves" but as that title is claimed as copyright we have altered it to "The Young Lamberts".' [Entered in BMC as 'Left to themselves: A Boy's Adventures in Australia'.]

4807 THE YOUNG LAMBERTS./A Boy's Adventures in Australia./By/Augusta Marryat,/Author of "The Reverse of the Shield."/With Original Illustrations./ [device]/London and New York:/Frederick Warne and Co.
n.d. [inscribed Xmas 1911]
339pp (inc. 1p preface), 4pp adv., b/w frontis. & 5 f/p b/w plates, chapter headings & tailpieces, pic. clo., dec. e/p, 180x120mm. RM

MARRYAT, Emilia

See Norris, Emilia Marryat

MARSH, Honor

4808 GLOW-WORM/LEGEND and/other Songs for Children/[drawing]/Words and Music by/Honor Marsh/Copyright Price 3/6/W. H. Paling & Co. Limited/Sydney Brisbane/And established throughout N.S.W. and Queensland
1959
10pp (last blank), cover title, dec. wrappers, 247x186mm. KMM
Contents include title song & 3 others.

MARSH, John

4809 THE CRUISE/OF THE/CAREFREE/By/John Marsh/Ward, Lock & Co. Limited/London and Melbourne
1955
160pp, b/w frontis. clo., 182x120mm. KP
Another copy as above, but
London Melbourne and Cape Town
n.d.
Herald Library. Otherwise as before. KP

MARSH, Lewis (ed.)

4810 The Rambler Travel Books/The Countries of the World as/described in works of Travel/ AUSTRALASIA/AND MALAYSIA/Edited by Lewis Marsh/[device]/Blackie and Son Limited/50 Old Bailey London/Glasgow and Bombay/1915
80pp (inc. 1p publisher's note), col. frontis. & 3 f/p col. illus., 8 f/p b/w illus. & b/w drawings in text, illus. by R. Talbot Kelly, bd. (with col. illus. pasted on front cover), 180x130mm. KMM
43pp devoted to Australia, 12pp to New Zealand, 15pp to the Pacific Islands, & the remainder to the Malay Archipelago.
Another copy as above but: Blackie & Son Limited/ London and Glasgow
n.d. KP

MARSH, Michael

4811 MAMMALS/by/Michael Marsh, A.B., M.S., Ph.D./(University of California)/Lecturer in Biology/ University of Sydney./[device]/II/Longmans 1965 Melbourne
32pp, part-col. illus. throughout, stiff pic. wrappers, 210x160mm. BBC
Australian Nature Series No. II.

MARSHALL, Alan

4812 PEOPLE OF THE/DREAMTIME/By/Alan Marshall/Illustrated by/Lesbia Thorpe/[device]/F. W. Cheshire/Melbourne
1952
88pp, b/w frontis. & 20 f/p b/w woodcut illus., smaller woodcuts in text, clo., 210x130mm. CLRC
Contains 20 Aboriginal legends.

4813 Alan Marshall/I CAN JUMP PUDDLES/[vignette]/ Illustrated by/Alison Forbes/Melbourne/F. W. Cheshire/1955
225pp, 1p preface, b/w chapter headings, clo., 215x140mm. KMM
This story about childhood, although subsequently published in school editions, was not published originally as a children's book, & I do not consider it to be one, & have therefore not made further entries, except for some foreign editions produced as children's books.
German edition

4814 Alan Marshall/ICH BIN DABEI!/Aus dem Leben/ eines Tapferen Australierbuben/Schweizer Jungend-Verlag/Solothurn
1956
302pp (inc. foreword by translator & by author & 2pp glossary), 2pp adv., unillus., pic. bd., 187x120mm. ANL
Slovak edition

4815 UZ ZASA PRESKAKUJEM KALUZE
1960
Bratislava
270pp. SLCSR

4816 MOJ ZIVOT PATRI TEBE
Bratislava, 1960
211pp. SLCSR
As above

4817 Bratislava, 1964
270pp. SLCSR
Czech edition

4818 UZ ZASA PRESKAKUJEM KALUZE
Prague, 1962, 1963, 1972. SLCSR

4819 WHISPERING/IN THE/WIND/Alan Marshall/ Illustrated by/Jack Newnham/[drawing]/Nelson
Thomas Nelson (Australia) Ltd, Melbourne 1969

165pp, b/w drawings in text, clo., dec. map e/p, 210x130mm. KMM
• Rpt 1969, as above. KMM

4820 Alan Marshall/WHISPERING IN/THE WIND/[drawing]/Illustrated by Jack Newnham/Collins/Armada Lions
London 1971
160pp, 16 f/p b/w illus., pic. wrappers, 180x110mm. KMM

4821 FIGHT FOR LIFE/Alan Marshall/Illustrated by Rae Dale/Cassell Australia
Melbourne 1972
98pp, 8 f/p b/w illus., pic. wrappers, 180x110mm. Patchwork Paperbacks. KMM

MARSHALL, Ann

4822 THE/JUNIOR/CHEF/Ann Marshall/Illustrated by/John Gould/Ure Smith—Sydney London
1969
112pp, b/w drawings throughout, laminated pic. bd., 190x125mm. CLRC

MARSHALL, H. E.

4823 "Our Empire Story" Series/AUSTRALASIA'S STORY/Told to Boys and Girls by/H. E. Marshall/Author of/"Our Island Story," "Scotland's Story",/Etc. Etc./With pictures in colour by/J. R. Skelton and G.W. Lambert/[drawing]/London: T. C. & E. C. Jack/67 Long Acre, W.C./and Edinburgh
n.d. [1911]
118pp, 2 b/w maps, col. frontis. & 7 f/p col. illus., clo. (with col. illus. pasted on front cover), 200x140mm. CLRC
• Rpt as above, but
Thomas Nelson and Sons, Ltd./(incorporating T. C. & E. C. Jack, Ltd.)/London, Edinburgh, New York/Toronto, and Paris.
Contents as before but printed on thicker paper. RM

4824 OUR EMPIRE STORY/Stories of India and/The Greater Colonies/told to Boys and Girls by/H. E. Marshall/Author of/'Our Island Story' 'Scotland's Story'/etc etc/with pictures by/J. R. Skelton/Sixth impression/[vignette]/London: T. C. & E. C. Jack, Ltd./35 Paternoster Row, E.C., & Edinburgh
xviiipp, 493pp (inc. 2pp preface, 2pp List of Rulers, 9pp index), 1p adv., col. frontis. & 19 f/p col. plates & 6 b/w maps, clo. with British emblem in col. on front cover, 230x 160mm. KP
Contains 55pp relating to Australia

4825 OUR EMPIRE STORY/Told to Boys and Girls/By/H. E. Marshall/author of 'Our Island Story', 'Scotland's Story'/etc./With Pictures by J. R. Skelton/Thomas Nelson and Sons Ltd/London Edinburgh Paris Melbourne/Toronto and New York
n.d. [1911?]
493pp (inc. 9pp index), 2pp notes, col. frontis. & 19 f/p col. illus., 6 b/w maps, dec. clo., 225x160mm. RM
Author of numerous other histories for children with no relation to Australia.

'MARSHALL, James Vance'

4826 THE CHILDREN/James Vance Marshall/[device]/London/Michael Joseph
First published May 1959
126pp, unillus., clo., 196x125mm. KP
First published as an adult novel, not a children's book
Second imp. as above August 1959. KP

4827 THE CHILDREN/James/Vance Marshall/Illustrated by/Noela Young/London/Methuen & Co. Ltd./36 Essex Street WC2
This illus. edition first published 1960
135pp, b/w frontis. & b/w drawings throughout, pic. clo., 170x110mm. CLRC
J. V. Marshall, author of *Walkabout* died in 1964. Then & since, by permission of his family, his name has been used for *A River Ran out of Eden,* and *My Boy John That Went to Sea* (translated into 12 languages) and also *A Walk to the Hills of Dreamtime.* These three novels are in no way works of collaboration, although in the last-mentioned, use has been made of Mr Marshall's notes on the Outback, but are wholly original to Donald Payne, their hitherto pseudonymous NZ author who helped Mr Marshall in the last years of his life. (From note on d/w of *A Walk to the Hills of the Dreamtime*)

4828 WALKABOUT/James Vance Marshall/Penguin Books/in association with Michael Joseph
First published as *The Children,* Michael Joseph, London 1959; this edition published Harmondsworth, Middlesex, England, 1963
125pp, 2pp adv., unillus., pic. wrappers, cover design by Richard Kennedy, 180x110mm. Peacock Books. KMM
• Rpt 1967, 1969, 1970, 1971, 1972, details as above, but with different cover design (col. still from film of same name). KMM

4829 WALKABOUT/James Vance Marshall/Michael Joseph London
Revised edition 1971
123pp, unillus., clo., 195x130mm. BBC
First published as *The Children.*

4830 WALKABOUT/James Vance Marshall/New York 1971/William Morrow and Company, Inc
123pp, col. photographic frontis. only, bd. with clo. spine, 210x130mm. NSL:M
Dutch edition

4831 DE VUURDOOP/door/James Vance Marshall/[device]/Amsterdam/Van Hokema & Warendorf N.V.
n.d. (acquired 1966), b/w drawings (N. Young), bd., 200x124mm. NSL:M

4832 MY BOY JOHN/THAT WENT TO SEA/By/James Vance Marshall/Hodder and Stoughton
London, 1966
126pp, b/w map frontis. only, clo., 193x130mm. KMM

4833 James Vance Marshall/MY BOY JOHN/THAT WENT TO SEA/Penguin Books
First published Hodder & Stoughton 1966; this edition published Harmondsworth, Middlesex, England, 1971
119pp (inc. 3pp author's note, etc.), b/w map, otherwise unillus., pic. wrappers, cover design by Ben Wohlberg, 180x110mm. Puffin Books. KMM
Story of whaling in the Antarctic.
US edition
Morrow, 1967;
paperback edition, Ballantine, 1968

4834 [drawing]/A RIVER RAN/OUT OF EDEN/James Vance Marshall/Illustrated by Maurice Wilson/Hodder & Stoughton
First pub.1962; fourth imp. Dec. 1962
117pp, b/w drawings in text throughout, clo., 200x150mm. KMM
Story of a boy and a seal in the Aleutian islands.
• Rpt 2nd imp. Sept 1962. KP
• Rpt 3rd imp. Nov 1962. KP

4835 James Vance Marshall/A RIVER RAN OUT/OF EDEN/Illustrated by Maurice Wilson/Hodder and Stoughton
First printed Sept 1962; fourth impr. Nov 1962, this ed. 1964
126pp, b/w illus. in text, pic. wrappers, 180x110mm. KP

4836 A WALK TO THE/HILLS OF THE/DREAMTIME/ James Vance Marshall/Illustrated by Lydia Rosier/ [drawing]/Hodder and Stoughton
London 1970
158pp (inc. 12pp glossary & notes), b/w chapter headings, clo., 215x140mm. KMM

4837 [drawing]/A WALK/TO THE HILLS/OF THE/ DREAMTIME/by James Vance Marshall/Illustrations by Lydia Rosier/William Morrow and Company, Inc./ New York 1970
150pp (inc. 10pp glossary), b/w chapter headings, clo., 210x136mm. KP

MARSHALL, Marie

4838 TONY TITHERS/The Story of a Scottie/[Drawing]/ By/Marie Marshall/Drawings/by/John Magrath/ Shepherd and Newman Pty. Ltd. Sydney
n.d. [1943]
50pp, col. frontis. & 2 f/p col. illus., b/w drawings throughout, dec. bd., dec. e/p, 265x200mm. KMM
• Rpt 1944, 2nd ed. 10 000 copies
Details as above but 267x200mm. KP

Marshall's Annual

4839 MARSHALL'S/ANNUAL/James Marshall & Co., Ltd,/22 Rundle Street,/Adelaide
n.d. [inscribed Xmas 1925]. Printed by John Drew Printers, Aldershot. 9069B
[192]pp, col. frontis. & 7 col. plates, b/w illus., pic. bd., 244x184mm. CLRC
Various contributions. No Australian content, apart from the SA draper's imprint on title page.

MARSON, Charles L.

4840 FAERY: STORIES/By Charles L. Marson/E.A. Petherick & Co./Adelaide, Melbourne, and Sydney/ (All rights reserved)
n.d. [inscribed 1891]
98pp, unillus, clo., 165x110mm. KMM
Contains 9 stories.

MARSTON, Hilda

4841 THE LITTLE/PAPER MAN/By/Hilda Marston/ Graduate Sydney Kindergarten Training/College/ Illustrated by Yvonne Francart/Copyright/William Brooks & Co. Limited/The Educational Publishers of Australia/99 Pitt Street Sydney/299 Queen Street Brisbane
n.d. [Copyright 1949]
19pp, 6 b/w drawings, wrappers, 180x120mm. NSL:M

MARTIN, A. Patchett (ed.)

4842 OVER THE SEA/Stories of Two Worlds/by/Mrs. Campbell Praed/Countess de la Warr/ "Tasma"/Frederic E. Weatherly/Mrs. Patchett Martin/ Hume Nisbet/Miss M. Senior Clark/H. B. Marriott Watson/Edited by/A. Patchett Martin/Illustrated in Colour by/H. J. Johnstone, T. J. Hughes & R. Carrick, R.I.M./and in Black and White by/Emily J. Harding Marcella Walker/A. W. Wall/Engravings by/Ch. Guillaume & Co./London/Griffith Farran Okeden & Welsh/Newbery House, Charing Cross Road/and Sydney
n.d. [inscribed Nov. 1890]
48pp, dec. t.p., col. frontis. & 8 col. plates, 34 b/w illus., pic. bd., dec. col. e/p, 245x190mm. CLRC

4843 TRUE STORIES/FROM/AUSTRALASIAN HISTORY/By/A. Patchett Martin/Author of/"The Life and Letters of Robert Lowe, Viscount Sherbrooke"/etc. etc./Illustrated/[device]/London/Griffith, Farran & Co./Newbery House, 39 Charing Cross Road/1893
320pp (inc. 4pp preface), 48pp adv., engraved frontis. & 31 engravings, pic. clo., dec. e/p, 180x125mm. NSL:M
Another copy as above
1893 with 31 engravings but no frontis. & does not appear to have had one. KMM
Another copy
n.d.[prize 1901]
No adv., frontis. portrait of Cook & 31 engravings, plain e/p. KP

MARTIN, A. W.

HENRY PARKES. *See* Great Australians

MARTIN, Bernard

4844 Bernard Martin/THE WALKABOUT PLOT/ Illustrated by/Nan Fullarton/Heinemann/Melbourne London Toronto
London 1958
253pp, b/w frontis. & line drawings throughout, clo., 185x115mm. KMM

MARTIN, Beryl

4845 Beryl Martin/BATIK/FOR BEGINNERS/Angus and Robertson
Sydney 1971
44pp (inc. 8pp col. plates), b/w photographic illus. in text, clo., 220x180mm. CLRC

MARTIN, David

4846 SPIEGEL/THE CAT/A Story-poem by David Martin/based on a tale by Gottfried Keller/Illustrated by Roderick Shaw/[device] F. W. Cheshire Melbourne Canberra Sydney
1961
70pp & 1p author's note, part-col. frontis., 16 b/w drawings, clo., 246x178mm. KMM
Doubtful children's.

4847 SPIEGEL/THE CAT/A Story-Poem/By David Martin/Based on a Tale by/Gottfried Keller/Cassell London
First publ. 1961, first publ. in Great Britain 1969
58pp (inc. 2pp postcript), unillus., clo., 204x140mm. KP

4848 HUGHIE/David Martin/Illustrated by/Ron Brookes [*sic*]/Nelson Thomas Nelson (Australia) Ltd, 1971
165pp, 1p dedicatory verse, b/w frontis. & b/w drawings in text, clo., 215x135mm. KMM
• Rpt 1972. KP

4849 GARY/David Martin/Illustrated by Con Aslanis/ Cassell Australia
Melbourne 1972
100pp, 8 b/w illus., pic. wrappers, 180x110mm. Patchwork Paperbacks. CLRC

4850 FRANK/&/FRANCESCA/David Martin/Nelson Thomas Nelson(Australia) Ltd, Melbourne 1972
152pp, 2 b/w double-spread maps, illus., clo., d/w designed by Elizabeth Lord, 210x135mm. CLRC

[MARTIN, George W.]

4851 THE SENTRY AND/THE/SHELL FAIRY
Printed by Anderson, Gowan Pty Ltd, Melbourne, for The British Imperial Oil Co. Ltd, n.d. [1924]
16pp, 6 f/p col. illus. & b/w tailpieces, illus. by Ida Rentoul Outhwaite, wrappers, cover title, 240x175mm. KMM
Publication issued to advertise Shell Motor Oil &c.
See also JEAN AND THE SHELL FAIRY

MARTIN, J. H. & W. D.

4852 THE AUSTRALIAN BOOK OF/TRAINS/ [photograph]/J. H. and W. D. Martin/Angus & Robertson/Sydney London/1947

248pp (inc. 1p dedication & 1p acknowledgements), col. frontis. & 5 f/p col. photographic illus. & one (listed in index) on d/w only, b/w photographic illus. throughout, map e/p, clo, 245x185mm. KMM

4853 AIRCRAFT/OF TODAY AND TOMORROW/By J. H. and W. D. Martin/[photograph]/Angus and Robertson/Sydney—London
n.d. [1953]
240pp, 1p author's foreword, b/w photographic illus. on almost every page, ?clo. (copy seen rebound) 245x180mm. CLRC
Joint winner CBCA Award 1953.

MARTIN, Marianne
4854 BUSHLAND TALES/[photograph of George Edwards]/Mr. George Edwards has pleasure in presenting a/further series of aboriginal stories of the younger folk./[photograph of author]/This book is the work of Miss Marianne Martin/Printed and Published by Winn & Co. Printers,/Balfour Street, Sydney/1945
40pp, 3 f/p col. illus. & b/w drawings throughout, dec. wrappers, 240x185mm. KMM
See also Edwards, George

MARTIN, Moyra
See Morell, Musette

MARTIN, W. D.
See Martin, J. H. & W. D.

MARTON, Gregory
4855 Illustrations by Brian Wildsmith/Gregory Marton/THE BOY/AND HIS FRIEND/THE BLIZZARD/Jonathan Cape Thirty Bedford Square
1962
126pp, extended dec. t.p., part. col. illus. throughout, dec. clo., dec. e/p, 190x120mm. ANL
Publisher's 'blurb' states that the author, born in Budapest in 1924, emigrated to Australia in 1949 & now lives in NSW. The contents of the book are not Australian.

MARTYR, Ethel
4856 Imperial Edition No. 307/SONGS FOR CHILDREN/Contents/[9 songs listed]/Words by Ethel Martyr/Music by Margaret Sutherland./Allan & Co., Melb. Syd. Ade. Bendigo Launceston
1929
26pp, col.illus. wrappers, by Alice H. Farr, 230x306mm. VSL.

Marvels of the Great Barrier Reef
4857 MARVELS OF THE/GREAT BARRIER/REEF/A Pictorial Record of/Australia's Marine Wonderland
The Sanitarium Health Food Co, Sydney, n.d. [195-?]
14pp (with spaces left for col. cards to be pasted in), pic. wrappers, cover title, 175x215mm. CLRC

Mary goes to Wonderland
4858 MARY GOES TO WONDERLAND
Ayers & James Pty Ltd, Sydney, n.d. [1949]
14pp, col. illus. throughout, pic. wrappers, cover title, 280x125mm. NSL:M

MÄRZ, Johannes
4859 COOK/DER WELTUMSEGLER/Leben, Reisen und Ende des Kapitäns James Cook/für Jugend und Volk erzählt/von/Johannes März/Zweite auflage/mit 68 textabildungen/[device]/Leipzig/Verlag von Otto Spamer
n.d. [1905?]
261pp, 11pp adv. 20 f/p b/w illus. & numerous engravings in text, pic. clo., dec. e/p, 220x150mm. NSL:M

MARZIALS, Ada M.
4860 STORIES OF ADVENTURE/AND DISCOVERY/For the Story Hour/By/Ada M. Marzials/Author of/"Stories for the Story Hour" etc./Illustrated/[device]/George G. Harrap & Company Ltd./London Bombay Sydney
n.d. [1928]
249pp, 8pp map & appendix, etc., b/w frontis. & 8 f/p b/w illus. by various artists, dec. clo., 190x125mm. PR
Contents include: 'A Midshipman's Adventures' (Bass and Flinders); 'A Bitter Disappointment' (Burke and Wills).

MASCORD, Ramon
4861 OUR/FEATHERED FRIENDS/Written and Illustrated/by/Ramon Mascord/1947/New Century Press Pty. Ltd./3–5 North York Street/Sydney
19pp, 16 f/p col. illus., dec. bd., 235x185mm. ANL
Rhyming text.

MASON, Cyrus
4862 THE/AUSTRALIAN/CHRISTMAS STORY BOOK/by/Cyrus Mason/With Coloured Illustrations by the Author/Melbourne/George Robertson, 69 Elizabeth Street/1871
48pp, 1p preface, col. frontis. & 3 col. illus., wrappers, 180x140mm. NSL:M
Contains 4 stories.

4863 THE/AUSTRALIAN/STORYBOOK/By/Cyrus Mason/with Coloured Illustrations by the author/Second Edition/Melbourne/George Robertson, 69 Elizabeth Street/1872
48pp, 1p preface, contents & details the same as first edition. ANL
The second edition has a new preface. One of the earliest children's books published in Australia with coloured illustrations.

MASON, George F.
4864 ANIMAL TOOLS/By/George F. Mason/William Morrow & Company/New York 1951
94pp (inc. 2pp index), b/w illus. throughout, clo., 205x120mm. NSL:M
Book of natural history with some reference to Australian marsupials & other native animals.

MASON, Michael
4865 by Michael Mason/THE BOOK THAT JASON WROTE/illustrated by Don Bolognese/Funk & Wagnall New York
1968
32pp, col. & b/w illus. throughout, clo., pic. e/p, 254x202mm. KP
Fantasy about a boy who fell overboard & was marooned on an island on the way to Australia.

MASON, Olive L.
4866 QUIPPY/by/Olive L. Mason/1946/Pictured by Walter Cunningham
John Sands Pty Ltd, Sydney, n.d. [1946]
62pp, 30 col. illus., dec. bd., 120x140mm. NSL:M
John Sands pre-school & kindergarten series.

4867 PETER PORTER/[coloured drawing]/Story by/Olive L. Mason/Illustrations by/Esme E. Bell/John Sands Pty. Ltd./Sydney, Melbourne, Brisbane, Adelaide, Perth and Hobart/Registered in Australia for transmission by post as a book
n.d. [1952]
38pp, col. illus. on alternate pages, dec. bd., 135x205mm. KMM

4868 QUIPPY AND SOOT/by Olive Mason/Sketches by Jimmy Winter
John Sands Pty Ltd, Sydney, n.d. [1953]
60pp, col. illus. on alternate pages, dec. bd., 115x140mm. KMM

MASON, Theodore K.
4869 ALL ABOUT THE FROZEN CONTINENT/ANTARCTICA/Theodore K. Mason/Paul Hamlyn Sydney London New York Toronto
Dee Why West, NSW, 1972
79pp (inc. 2pp index), col. & part-col. illus. throughout, extended illus. t.p., pic. bd., 270x200mm. CLRC

MASON, Walter George
4870 THE/AUSTRALIAN/PICTURE/PLEASURE BOOK/Illustrating the/Scenery, Architecture, Historical Events, Natural History/Public Characters, &c./ of Australia./Engraved, selected and arranged by Walter G. Mason,/Sydney;/J. R. Clarke, Publisher,/205/George Street/1857
62pp & f/p b/w frontis. ('Ceremony of Opening the Paris Exhibition at the Museum, Sydney, 1854.'), b/w illus. throughout, illus. bd. cover with title as follows: 'The Australian/Picture Pleasure Book/[engraving—View in George Street, Sydney, New South Wales]/200 Illustrations/Sydney/J. R. Clarke, Publisher, 205, George Street.' 355x260mm. CLRC

MASS, Celeste
4871 LITTLE MISS SNIPIT/by/Celeste Mass/[decoration]/Consolidated Press/1945
[Sydney]
22pp, 9 f/p col. illus. & b/w drawings, dec. wrappers, 270x205mm. ANL

MASS, Nuri
4872 Shakespeare Head Publication/AUSTRALIAN/WILD-FLOWER FAIRIES/by/Nuri Mass/Botanical/Illustrations/by/Nuri Mass/Fairy/Illustrations/by/Celeste Mass/[drawing]/Shakespeare Head Press/310 George St., Sydney/1937
132pp (inc. 1p preface by E. Breakwell, Inspector of Schools & 2pp author's introduction), 8 f/p b/w illus., b/w drawings, dec. wrappers, 225x130mm. KMM
Fairy stories & verse, with botanical notes.

4873 AUSTRALIAN/WILD-FLOWER FAIRIES/by/Nuri Mass/Botanical/illustrations/by/Nuri Mass/Fairy/Illustrations/by/Celeste Mass/[drawing]/Consolidated Press Ltd./Sydney/1945
Details as above, but 220x130mm. KMM

4874 THE LITTLE GRAMMAR/PEOPLE/By/Nuri Mass/Illustrated by/Celeste Mass/[drawing]/Angus and Robertson Ltd./Sydney: London/1942
104pp, col. frontis. & 3 f/p b/w illus., b/w drawings throughout, dec. bd., 240x180mm. NSL:M
• Rpt 1943, with plain e/p. KP

4875 MAGIC AUSTRALIA/By/Nuri Mass/Decorated by/Celeste Mass/Angus and Robertson Limited/Sydney: London/1943
164pp (1p verse & b/w drawing preceding text), col. frontis. & 3 f/p col. illus., 4 f/p b/w illus. & b/w drawings in text, bd., map e/p, 240x180mm. KMM
• Rpt as above, 1947. KMM

4876 THE WIZARD/OF JENOLAN/by/Nuri Mass/Drawings by/Celeste Mass/Angus & Robertson Limited/89 Castlereagh Street/Sydney/1946
93pp (1p verses & b/w drawing preceding text), col. frontis. & 3 f/p col. illus., 4 f/p b/w illus. & b/w drawings in text, dec. bd., 240x185mm. KMM

4877 THE/SILVER CANDLESTICK/Nuri Mass/Decorated by/Celeste Mass/[drawing]/The Writers' Press/Sydney
Handset & printed by the author; inscription states that this is the very first Writers' Press publication, n.d. [1956]
[16]pp, numerous blue/white illus. in text, pic. wrappers, 185x125mm. Grant

4878 WHERE/THE INCAS TROD/By/Nuri Mass/Illustrated with Line-Drawings by/Celeste Mass/24 Photographs, and a Map/[device]/The Writers' Press/Sydney
1956
223pp, b/w photographic illus. & drawings, clo., 215x135mm. NSL:M

4879 THE WONDERLAND/OF NATURE/by/Nuri Mass, M.A./[device]/The Writers' Press/Sydney Australia
n.d. [1964]
171pp, 1p acknowledgements, b/w portrait photograph, b/w drawings & diagrams in text, dec. clo., dec. e/p, 240x170mm. KMM

4880 THE WONDERLAND/OF NATURE/Written and illustrated/by Nuri Mass, M.A./[device]/The Writers' Press/81 Prospect Road/Summer Hill, N.S.W.—Australia
1st ed. Feb. 1964; 2nd imp. (revised) June 1964; 2nd ed. (enlarged) May 1965; rpt May 1966
284pp (inc. 4pp index), 1p acknowledgements, b/w portrait photograph, b/w drawings & diagrams in text, dec. clo., dec. e/p, 240x170mm. BBC
The contents are the same as the first edition with the addition of one chapter 'Opal—and Other Treasures in Australia' (7pp).
• Rpt as above, 1968. BBC

4881 MANY PATHS—/ONE HEAVEN/by/Nuri Mass, M.A./Drawings by/Celeste and Nuri Mass/The Writers' Press/81 Prospect Road, Summer Hill, N.S.W./Australia
1st ed. May 1965; 2nd ed. (revised) Sept. 1965
128pp (inc. 3pp index), b/w & sepia/white drawings throughout, dec. clo., dec. e/p, 240x170mm. KMM
Book on various world religions intended for use in schools.
Another copy as above, but n.d. KMM

4882 AUSTRALIAN/WILDFLOWER/MAGIC/Illustrated by the Author/Nuri Mass, M.A./The Writers' Press/81 Prospect Road/Summer Hill, N.S.W., Australia
First published June 1967; second edition (revised) Dec. 1967
304pp, b/w drawings throughout, dec. clo., dec. e/p, 235x170mm. BBC
Descriptions, with botanical drawings, of Australian wildflowers.

4883 CHINA—/THE WAKING GIANT/by/Nuri Mass, M.A./Illustrated by her daughter Tess (13 years)/The Writers' Press/81 Prospect Road, Summer Hill/N.S.W., Australia
n.d. [1969?]
104pp (inc. 4pp chronological table, 6pp index), b/w drawings in text, pic. clo., map e/p, 180x115mm. BBC

MASTERS, Molly
4884 Imperial Edition No. 474/LITTLE GIPSY GAY/A Juvenile Operetta/(Duration: about 60 minutes)/Dialogue and Lyrics by/Molly Masters/Music by/Evelyn Wales/Musical Contents/[12 items listed]/Copyright 1939/Allan & Co. Pty. Ltd./Melbourne Sydney Adelaide Bendigo
40pp, pic. wrappers, 250x180mm. VSL

Matches make Models

4885 MATCHES/MAKE MODELS/A Documentary Booklet/for/Children and Adults/Wholly set up, printed and published by/E. L. Bell & Co. Pty. Ltd., 182 Stawell St., Burnley/Victoria Australia
1960
55pp, b/w & part-col. illus. & diagrams, pic. wrappers, 230x170mm. CLRC
Includes article on model-making & photographs of actual models.

4886 MATCHES/MAKE/MODELS/A Documentary/Booklet/for children and adults/A Brymay Publication
Bryant & May, Richmond, Victoria, copyright 1960. Fourth ed.
58pp, diagrams, photographic illus. & sketches, pic. wrappers, 232x169mm. KP
Includes a short history of matches.
• Rpt as above fifth ed. 1960. KP

[MATHEWS, Julia A.]

4887 "THY KINGDOM COME."/A Tale for Boys and Girls./By the Author of/"Little Snowdrop and her Golden Casket" "The Guiding Pillar"/&c &c [device]/London:/T. Nelson and Sons, Paternoster Row./Edinburgh: and New York./1886
144pp, b/w frontis. & additional illus. t.p., dec. clo., 180x117mm. CLRC
On front cover: 'The Little Hazel Series' 'By the Author of Little Hazel'. Set partly in Australia.

MATHEWS, N. L.

4888 BUNTIPIT/AND THE WILLOW TREE/by N. L. Mathews
T. V. Boardman & Co. Ltd, London, by courtesy of the *Christian Science Monitor*, n.d.
[24]pp, 12 f/p col. illus. & 1 double-spread, b/w drawings in text, illus. by Richard Ogle, pic. wrappers, 180x120mm. KMM
Front cover reads: 'Buntipit/and the/Willow Tree/Australian Bush Tales'. Advertisement on back cover for *The Beginnings of the Bush*.

MATHIESON, J.

ROADS. *See* Life in Australia

MATTHEUS, Peter

4889 Peter Mattheus/MICK I AUSTRALIEN/Till Svenska Av/Hugo Hultenberg/[drawing]/A/B Ljus Förlag—Stockholm
1942
113pp, 2pp adv., 3 f/p b/w illus., 2 half page b/w illus., col. pic. bd., clo. backstrip, 185x120mm. RM

4890 Peter Mattheus/MINNEWITT/UND KNISTERBUSCH/Lustige und abendeuerliche Erlebnisse/in dem "sonderbaren Land Australien"/[drawing]/Franz Schneider Verlag
Augsburg 1951
112pp, 3 f/p & other b/w drawings in text, illus. & cover design by Fritz Eichenberg, pic. bd., 185x125mm. KMM
'Happy and adventurous experiences in the strange land of Australia.'

"MATTIE and AMBROSE"

THE CIRCUS. *See* Barry Books

MATTINGLEY, Christobel

4891 Christobel Mattingley/THE PICNIC DOG/Illustrated by/Carolyn Dinan/[drawing]/Hamish Hamilton/London
1970
48pp, part-col. illus. throughout, pic. clo., 180x120mm. Gazelle Books. KMM

4892 Christobel Mattingley/THE [*sic*] WINDMILL/AT MAGPIE CREEK/Illustrated by Gavin Rowe/Brockhampton Press
Leicester, England, 1971
88pp, b/w frontis. & 17 b/w illus., clo., 185x125mm. KMM
Highly commended CBCA Award 1972.

4893 Christobel Mattingley/WINDMILL/AT MAGPIE CREEK/Illustrated by Gavin Rowe/Brockhampton Press
Second impression 1972
Details as in first edition. BBC

4894 Christobel Mattingley/WORM WEATHER/Illustrated by/Carolyn Dinan/[drawing]/Hamish Hamilton/London
1971
48pp, part-col. drawings throughout, pic. clo., 180x120mm. Gazelle Books. KMM

4895 EMU KITE/Christobel Mattingley/[drawing]/Illustrated by/Gavin Rowe/Hamish Hamilton
London 1972
88pp, b/w drawings throughout, pic. clo., 185x120mm. Antelope Books. KMM

MATTINGLEY, David

MATTHEW FLINDERS AND GEORGE BASS. *See* Australian Explorers

'MAURICE, Furnley' [pseud. Frank Wilmot]

4896 THE/BAY AND PADIE/BOOK/Kiddie Songs/By/Furnley Maurice/Illustrations by/Vera Hamilton/and/Cyril Dobbs/Commonwealth of Australia/Sydney J. Endacott/Melbourne/1917
28pp, 6pp preceding text, part-col. line drawings throughout, dec. wrappers (with illus. label pasted on front cover), 240x180mm. NSL:M
Includes 31 verses. NSL:M

4897 THE/BAY AND PADIE/BOOK/Kiddie Songs/by/Furnley Maurice/Illustrations by/Vera Hamilton/and/Cyril Dobbs/Commonwealth of Australia/Sydney J. Endacott/Melbourne/1917
On verso of t.p.: 'First ed. Nov. 1917; Second Edition February 1918', contents as in first edition, but dec. bd.. KMM

4898 THE BAY AND PADIE BOOK/Kiddie Songs/by/Furnley Maurice/Third Edition/Commonwealth of Australia/Sydney J. Endacott/Melbourne
September 1926
55pp, unillus., bd., 190x120mm. NSL:M
Includes 41 verses & preliminary verse 'Nonsense Immortal', with eleven additional poems.

4899 THE BAY AND PADIE BOOK/Child Poems/by/Furnley Maurice/Third Edition/[device]/Melbourne University Press/in association with/Oxford University Press/Melbourne London Edinburgh Capetown/Bombay Toronto Etc./1937
Contents the same as the 1926 edition, but with different t.p., bd., 185x120mm. NSL:M
Note on verso of title page reads: 'Third Edition Sept. 1926 Transferred to Melbourne University Press From The Galleon Press, August 1937'.

4900 THE BAY AND PADIE BOOK/Child Poems/by/Furnley Maurice/Melbourne University Press/in association with/Oxford University Press
• Rpt October 1943
55pp, unillus., dec. bd., 185x115mm. KMM
• Rpt 1944, as above. KMM

MAVOR, William Fordyce

4901 HISTORICAL ACCOUNT/OF THE MOST CELEBRATED/VOYAGES,/TRAVELS AND

DISCOVERIES,/from the/Time of Columbus/to the/Present Period/[quotation]/By William Mavor, LL.D./Vol.1/London:/Printed for E. Newbery,/St Paul's Church-yard./1796
Published in 20 vols, each with engraved frontis. & 2 engraved plates, three-quarter leather & marbled bd., 140x85mm. CLRC
Contents:
vol.1. 288pp Voyages of "Vasquez de Gama"[*sic*], Magellan
vol.2. 290pp Voyages of Drake, Schouten and La Maire
vol.3. 263pp includes Dampier (pp61-157)
vol.4. 297pp " Roggewein, for the Discovery of a Southern Continent (pp20) & Voyage of Commodore Anson round the world (pp84)
vol.5. 284pp Hon Commodore Byron(pp34), Captain Wallis (pp40), Voyage of Carteret (pp28), Voyage of Bougainville (pp104)
Vol.6. 319pp First and 2nd Voyages of Cook, with folding map frontis.
Vol.7. 292pp Third Voyage of Cook, with folding engraving of the death of Cook.
Vol.8. 292pp(1797) Andrew Sparrman, Cape of Good Hope and Round the World; Thomas Forrest from Balam Bangan to New Guinea
vol.9. 311pp (1797) Captain Wilson's shipwreck on the Pelew islands; Voyage of Gov. Phillip to Botany Bay(pp46), Discovery by Lt. Shortland (pp12),Voyage of Capt. Marshall from Pt. Jackson to China; Voyage of Lt. Watts to Otaheite & China, Voyage of Capt. Bligh to the South Seas (pp61)
Introduction to volume 10 (which has no Australian content) states that the first 10 vols complete the set. The second 10 vols dated 1797 do not contain any material relevant to this region apart from vol.15 (284pp.) which includes the Voyage of M. de Pages towards the South Pole in 1773 & 1774 .

4902 AN/HISTORICAL ACCOUNT/OF THE/VOYAGES/OF/CAPTAIN JAMES COOK/TO THE/SOUTHERN AND NORTHERN/HEMISPHERES/By William Mavor, LL.D./In Two volumes/Vol. 1/London/Printed for J. Harris, Successor to E. Newbery, Corner of/St. Paul's Church-Yard; H. D. Symonds No. 20,/Paternoster Row; and Vernor and/Hood, in the Poultry/1805
319pp, frontis., folding map, 2 b/w woodcuts, bd., 145x90mm. Grant
Vol. 2: t.p. the same; 340pp, frontis., folding b/w woodcut & 2 b/w woodcuts (dated 21st Jan. 1797) bd., 145x90mm. Grant
These are volumes 6 & 7 of the above, rpt 1805.

4903 A/GENERAL/COLLECTION/OF/VOYAGES/AND/TRAVELS,/FROM/THE DISCOVERY OF AMERICA/TO THE/COMMENCEMENT OF THE NINETEENTH CENTURY./In twenty-eight volumes,/Vol.1/London:/Printed for Richard Phillips,/Bridge Street, Blackfriars./1810
vol.1. xxiv+348, 2 folding maps, calf,152x94mm. Contents include Columbus, Da Gama, Magellan, Drake, &c.
vol.2. 356pp Anson's Voyage round the world, &c.
vol.3. 404pp.Voyages round the World by Byron, Wallis, Carteret.
vol.4 373pp(1809) frontis. James Cook, First Voyage of Cook, 1 folding map & 5 folding engravings.
vol.5. 354ppVoyage of Cook (to the end), 2 folding engravings.
vol.6. 348pp Second Voyage of Cook, 5 folding plates.
vol.7. 262pp Second Voyage of Cook, 3 folding engravings, , & Vocab. of the Language of the Society Isles(32pp & folding table of specimens of different languages spoken in the South Seas)
vol.8. lxviii+438pp Cook's Third Voyage, first vol., folding map of the Pacific, lxviii+438pp and 2 plates
vol.9. 504pp Cook's Third Voyage, 5 folding plates
vol.10. 442pp Conclusion of Cook's Third Voyage, folding frontis. of 'Karakakooa in Owyhee', 30pp appendix 'Vocab. of the language of the Friendly Isles, May 1777'
vol.11. 372pp Voyage of Capt. Thos. Forrest to New Guinea & the Moluccas; Capt., Henry Wilson to Pelew Islands, Gov. Phillip to Botany Bay. &c, 372pp & 1 folding plate
vol.13. 271pp Bligh's Voyage to the South Seas (pp23 to 84) sundry other voyages, and general index to 13 vols. of voyages, 76pp.
vol.12, and vols.14-28 do not include material relevant to this bibliography. SSL
Other editions of Mavor's *Voyages* include two further sets each of 25 vols, published by
E. Newbery, London 1796–1801 and 1796–1802; other sets by Samuel Bradford, Philadelphia 1892, 25 vols, and William V. Morse, Newhaven, 1802–3, 24 vols. Another set published by Sherwood, Neely & Jones, 1812–13, 28 vols. Unseen, information from BMC and NUC
William Mavor also published THE BRITISH NEPOS;/or/Youth's Mirror:/Being /Select Lives/of/Illustrious Britons.1798, and many times reprinted. This 464-page volume contains a 6pp section on James Cook but is of insufficient interest for further inclusion.

MAXTON, G. S. (ed.)

4904 Visits to Storyland—No. E3/ General Editor—Dr G. S. Maxton/TALES OF EXPLORATION/AND ADVENTURE/Book Two/Illustrations by/Phillips Paterson/McDougall's Educational Co. Ltd./London and Edinburgh
n.d.
63pp, map frontis., 13 b/w illus., wrappers, 197x135mm. KMM
Includes 'Faithful Jacky' from Kennedy's Expedition pp41–56.

MAXWELL, Arthur S.

4905 UNCLE ARTHUR'S BEDTIME STORIES—Signs Publishing Company Warburton, Victoria (Eighteenth series 1944)
The author is an American Seventh Day Adventist whose books were rpt in Australia, but do not have much Australian content.

4906 UNCLE ARTHUR'S/BEDTIME/STORIES/by/Arthur S. Maxwell/Series 41/Printed and Published by/Signs Publishing Company/(Australasian Conference Association/Limited, Proprietors)/Warburton Victoria Australia
n.d. [1967]
93pp, col. illus. throughout, col. pic. bd., col. pic. pastedowns, 190x130mm. KP
Evangelical publication written in California, though some stories set in Australia, by the American Seventh Day Adventists.

MAYNE, William S.

4907 MURIEL/VERNON/A Story for/Young Folk/By Wm. Mayne/Mildura Cultivator/1917
11pp, unillus., wrappers, cover title, 202x135mm. NSL:M
The action takes place in St Malo, France, without any reference to Australia. NSL:M

MAZET, Horace S.

4908 SHARK FISHING OFF THE/GREAT BARRIER

REEF/by Horace S. Mazet/Illustrated by Russell Peterson/Ariel Books/Farrar, Straus and Cudahy/New York
1957 [published simultaneously in Canada by Ambassador Books Ltd, Toronto]
215pp, 8pp illus., clo., 210x130mm. ANL

MAZURE, A.
4909 LE/PORTEFEUILLE/DU/JEUNE AMATEUR/de la Nature, de l'Histoire/et de l'Art;/ou/Description Méthodique/des Sites et des Monuments les plus remarquables/dans les Cinq Parties du Monde./Par A. Mazure/Amerique et Océanie/avec gravures/Paris 1839/Lehuby/Rue de Seine No. 48
336pp, dec. t.p. (title within dec. border), engraved frontis. & 2 other engraved plates, morocco, 170x100mm. NSL:M

MEAD, Stella
4910 THROUGH THE/BRITISH COMMONWEALTH/AUSTRALIA AND/TASMANIA/By Stella Mead/Cover and Sketches by Eulalie
24pp, col. & b/w illus. throughout, 1 col. map, col. pic. wrappers, cover title, 225x175mm. KMM
A series in 12 parts, Part VI concerning Australia & Tasmania, & Part VII New Zealand, New Guinea, Papua & Hong Kong.

4911 WID WAD WOO/by Stella Mead/Eulalie
Ayers & James, Sydney, n.d. [1948]
16pp, col. illus. throughout, dec. wrappers, cover title, 320x250mm. NSL:M
Song with music by Joan Turnley Hill on back cover.
Story of a family of kangaroos dressed as humans.

4912 HOPPING/TIMOTHY/By/Stella Mead/Pictures by Eulalie
Ayers & James, Sydney, n.d. [1949]
16pp, col. illus. throughout, dec. wrappers, cover title, 320x240mm. NSL:M
Song with music by Joan Turnley Hill on back cover.

MEADE, L. T.
4913 THE/LADY OF THE FOREST/By/L. T. Meade/Author of/"Scamp and I", "Sweet Nancy", "The LIttle Princess of Tower Hill",/etc etc/[quote]/New Edition/London/S. W. Partridge and Co/8 & 9 Paternoster Row/1898
318pp & 24pp adv., b/w frontis. & 14 f/p b/w illus. (signed J. B. Yeats), chapter headings, pic. clo., 185x125mm. CLRC
Story about different children claiming the inheritance of the Avonsyde estate. The successful heir comes from Australia & 2 chapters are set in Australia.

4914 A/VERY NAUGHTY GIRL/By/L. T. Meade/Author of/"Miss Nonentity" "The Odds and the Evens" "Light o' the Morning"/"The Girls of St Wodes" etc./with eight illustrations/by/W. Rainey/W. & R. Chambers, Limited/London and Edinburgh
n.d. [copy inscribed Xmas 1903]
371pp, frontis. & 7 f/p illus., clo., 185x125mm. JMcG
School story set in England about a girl born & brought up in Tasmania.

MEADOWS, Maureen Clare
4915 COBBLER'S PEGS/By/Maureen C. Meadows/Illustrated by Berenice C. Eklund/Brisbane/Watson, Ferguson & Co.,/1944
31pp, b/w drawings throughout, dec. bd. (clo. spine), 280x215mm. ANL
Children's verse.
Second edition 1945, as above. KMM

4916 BILLI-BILLI'S/WALKABOUT/By/Maureen C. Meadows/Author of "Cobbler's Pegs"/Illustrated by Berenice C. Eklund/Brisbane/Watson Ferguson & Co./1945/Registered at the General Post Office, Brisbane for transmission/through the post as a book.
88pp, b/w illus. throughout, bd., dec. e/p, 240x180mm. ANL

4917 LITTLE WORDS TO GOD/by/Maureen C. Meadows/Illustrations by/Winifred Towers/Published by:/George M. Dash/Chartres House, 309 George Street,/Sydney, N.S.W., Australia
1949
36pp (inc. 1p foreword by Dr Paul White), col. frontis.& 5 f/p col. illus., b/w drawings throughout, dec. wrappers, 205x170mm. NSL:M
Children's prayers.

MEAGHER, Alice
4918 TEN ORIGINAL LITTLE/PLAYS/FOR/AUSTRALIAN CHILDREN/By/Alice Meagher/Melbourne/(Contributor to Victorian Education Department's School Paper...etc.)/Sole Publishers and Distributors:/The Scholastic Supply Pty. Ltd./4th Floor, Rickard's Building (opp. Victoria Palace)/226 Little Collins Street, Melbourne
n.d.
40pp, unillus., wrappers, 220x140mm. ANL

MEE, Arthur
4919 Arthur Mee/HEROES/OF THE/FLAG/Hodder and Stoughton [copy seen lacks t.p.]
London, n.d. [193-?]
160pp, 5 f/p illus. (printed in blue), clo., 200x135mm. KMM
Contents include: 'Captain James Cook' (13pp); 'The Men of Anzac' (4pp); 'Alfred Deakin' (1p).

4920 THEY NEVER/CAME BACK/By/Arthur Mee/Editor of The Children's Newspaper/London:Hodder and Stoughton [within dec. border]
1936
ix+191pp, frontis. & 7 plates (printed in blue & white), bd., 200x136mm. ANL
Includes chapters on Captain Robert Scott (11pp), Sir John Franklin (7pp), La Perouse (12pp), Captain Cook (12pp), Balboa (8pp), Burke & Wills (6pp), Leichhardt (7pp), Magellan (12pp) & Amundsen (8pp).

MEEKING, Charles
4921 Charles Meeking/SNOWY MOUNTAINS/CONQUEST/Harnessing the Waters of/Australia's Highest Mountains/[device]/Hutchinson of London
1968
192pp (inc. 1p foreword, 8pp appendices, index, etc.), 12pp b/w photographic illus., clo., map e/p, 195x120mm. Men in Action Series CLRC
Foreword by Rt Hon. Harold Holt, written just before his death.

MEILLON, Claire
4922 ADVENTURE/DOWN UNDER/By/Claire Meillon/The Australasian Publishing Co. Pty. Ltd./Sydney, N.S.W.
1947
254pp, b/w frontis., clo., 185x125mm. ANL
Story of an American boy in outback Australia.

4923 THE/NEW SURF CLUB/by/Claire Meillon/Author of "Adventure Down Under"/Illustrated by Jennifer Murray/Angus and Robertson
Sydney 1959
202pp, b/w frontis. & b/w drawings throughout, clo., dec. e/p, 200x125mm. BBC

MEILLON, Jill

4924 ROBBIT RABBIT FINDS OUT/[drawing]/By Jill Meillon/Drawings by Adye [pseud.]/Caslon House/
1945
Sydney
21pp, b/w drawings throughout, wrappers, map e/p, 115x180mm. ANL

4925 THE/DUCKS WHO/DIDN'T/By/Jill Meillon/The Currawong Publishing Company,/32 Jamieson Street,/Sydney
n.d. [1946]
16pp, b/w drawings throughout, illus. by 'Percival', illus. wrappers, 210x150mm. ANL

4926 PERCIVAL!/POLLY!/AND PIP!/By/Jill Meillon/The Currawong Publishing Company,/32 Jamieson Street,/Sydney
n.d. [1946]
15pp, b/w drawings throughout, dec. wrappers, 205x160mm. ANL

THE JEWEL CASKET. *See* Australian Youth Plays

4927 THE QUEEN CAME BY/Written by Jill Meillon/Illustrated by Noela Young/[drawing]/Ure Smith—Sydney
1954
34pp, dec. t.p., 7 f/p col. illus., 2 col. illus. in text & b/w drawings throughout, dec. bd., 255x185mm. KMM

4928 [drawing] WHY?/by/Jill Meillon/drawings by/Adye Adams/Angus and Robertson/Sydney London Melbourne Wellington
1956
32pp, b/w drawings throughout, wrappers, 150x235mm. KMM
Simple story explaining origin of young animals & babies to young children. Subtitled: 'A Story of Wonderful Things'.

4929 Build a Book Series/Social Studies for the Infant's School/Book 2/DOWN THE WIDE ROAD/[drawing]/by/Jill Meillon/Illustrated by Adye Adams/Angus and Robertson/Sydney London Melbourne Wellington
n.d.
32pp, b/w drawings, stiff pic. wrappers, 250x185mm. BBC
Social Studies textbook; others in series: *Out of My Window, Across the Sea, Let's Travel On, Sea, Sight and Sound.*

MEILLON, Jill & 'ADYE' [pseud.]

4930 THE CHILDREN'S/GARDEN/[drawing]/By Jill Meillon and Adye/With the help of the three Bears/Australasian Publishing Company Pty. Ltd., Sydney
1947
64pp, col. illus. throughout, dec. bd., dec. e/p, 180x245mm. NSL:M
Verses, stories, games, &c. Commended CBCA1947.

MEISSNER, H.

4931 JAMES COOK/oder/DREIMAL UM DIE ERDE/Ein Lebensbild für die reifere Jugend/Von/H. Meissner/Lehrer an der I. Bürgerschule zu Gera/mit drei Karten nach Zeichnungen des Verfassers,/sechs farbdrukbildern und zahlreichen Text-Illustrationen/von Fritz Bergen./Stuttgart./Druck und Verlag von Gebrüder Kröner.
1886
286pp, 2pp adv., 3 double-spread b/w maps, col. frontis. & 5 f/p col. illus., b/w drawings in text, pic. clo., 215x145mm. NSL:M

4932 Another edition, n.d. [191-?] Stuttgart, Union Deutsche Verlagsgesellschaft
307pp, illus., maps, unseen

MEISZNER, H.

4933 JORDEN RUNDT/TRENNE GANGER./Berättelse För Den Mognare Ungdomen/Af/H. Meiszner [*sic*]/Fri Ofversattening/Af/S.../Med Planscher./Stockholm Oscar L. Lamms Förlag
1887
294pp, 6pp adv., col. frontis. & 3 f/p col. illus., bd. (with adv. verso back cover), clo. backstrip, 200x140mm. RM
This is the first Swedish translation of H. Meissner's version of Cook's Voyages for children.

4934 P. A. Norstedt & Söners ungdomsböcker Nr. 18/JAMES COOK/eller/Jorden rundt tre Ganger/Bearbetning från Tyskan/af/D. S. Hector/Stockholm/P. A. Norstedt & Söners Förlag
1894
296pp (inc. 2pp index), b/w drawings in text throughout, pic. clo., 185x120mm. NSL:M

MELLOR, Dorothy

4935 MICKLES/AND/MUCKLES/Gift Book/of the Commonwealth Savings Bank of Australia
Printed by Simmons Ltd, Sydney, n.d. [1925?]
[16]pp (printed inside both covers), 25 part-col. illus. by Dorothy Wall, pic. wrappers, cover title, 210x135mm. NSL:M

4936 ENCHANTING ISLES/By/Dorothy Mellor/Illustrated by/Ida Rentoul Outhwaite/Sydney/Howard, Whyte & Coy./1934
112pp, b/w illus. throughout, bd., 185x125mm. NSL:M
Story set in the New Hebrides & other islands of the Pacific.

MELLOR, Kathleen

Series of Kindergarten Picture Books

4937 GEE/UP/BONNY/Made for the children at the/Lady Gowrie Child Centre/Adelaide/by/Kathleen Mellor
Georgian House, Melbourne, n.d. [1945]
24pp, col. illus. throughout, pic. wrappers, 170x185mm. ANL
Picture book with simple rhyming text.

4938 THE STORY/OF/BIM/Written for 3 year old/Charlotte/by/Kathleen Mellor/[drawing]
Georgian House, Melbourne, n.d. [1945]
25pp, col. illus. throughout, stiff pic. wrappers, cover title reads 'Bim', 165x180mm. KMM

4939 LET'S GO/TO THE/BEACH/Story by Kathleen Mellor/Illustrations by Marjorie Hann/This is a/story/About—[drawing]/Georgian House/Melbourne
n.d. [1947]
24pp, col. illus. throughout (flap concealing drawing on bottom right hand corner of each double-spread), pic. wrappers, 185x145mm. KMM
Uniform with above [1947]

4940 NOW/I'M/READY. KMM

4941 SPLISH-SPLASH/RAINY DAY. KMM

4942 GOLDY/By Kathleen Mellor/Drawings by Harold Freedman/Published in Melbourne by Georgian House
n.d. [1952]
24pp, col. illus. throughout, pic. wrappers, 165x180mm. KMM
Uniform with above [1952]

4943 OVER THE HILL. KMM

4944 PINE FARM. KMM

4945 HOW IT/HAPPENED/Told to Kindergarten Children/in South Australia/By/Kathleen Mellor/For/ The Kindergarten Union of S.A. Jubilee Year/1955
24pp, 1p foreword by Lillian de Lissa (founder of the movement), part. col. illus. throughout, dec. wrappers, 170x190mm. KMM
Story of establishment of kindergartens in South Australia told simply for pre-school children.

MELLOR, Kathleen & FISHER, Marjorie
4946 [drawing] STOP/LOOK/[drawing]/LISTEN/ [drawing]
Georgian House, Melbourne, n.d. [1945]
23pp, dec. t.p., col. illus. throughout (with flaps & other devices for concealed drawings), dec. wrappers, 160x180mm. KMM

MELLOR, Kathleen & MORRIS, Vivienne
4947 THE TRAFFIC/LIGHTS
Georgian House, Melbourne, n.d. [1945]
21pp, col. illus. throughout, dec. wrappers, cover title, 165x180mm. KMM
Foreword by C. M. Heinig, Federal Educational Officer, Australian Association for Pre-school Development.

[MELVILLE, Harden S.]
4948 THE ADVENTURES OF/A GRIFFIN/On a Voyage of Discovery./Written by Himself/[drawing]/London:/ Bell and Daldy, York Street, Covent Garden,/and 186, Fleet Street,/1867/(The right of translation and reproduction is reserved)
248pp, engraved frontis. & 28 engravings, illus. by author, dec. clo., 190x125mm. Grant

4949 A/BOY'S TRAVELS/ROUND THE WORLD,/or the/Adventures of a Griffin/On a Voyage to/Madeira, The Cape of Good Hope, Van Dieman's Laud [sic.],/Percy Islands, Cape Upstart, Gould Islands,/Java, Madiera, Singapore, and Malacca./Related by Himself./Illustrated by H. S. Melville,/with thirty very fine wood engravings, from/Drawings taken on the Spot./London: Bell and Daldy,/4, 5, & 6, York Street, Covent Garden./(The right of Translation is reserved.)
n.d. [inscribed midsummer 1871]
248pp, engraved frontis. & 28 engravings, dec. clo.gilt, g.e., 187x125mm. KMM
French edition
4950 MON PREMIER VOYAGE/EN/MER.Traduit et adapté de l'Anglais/[vignette]/Illustré par/H. S. M. et A. Marie/Paris/Bibliothèque/d'/Education et de Récréation/J. Hetzel et Cie, 18, Rue Jacob/Tous droits de traduction et de reproduction réservés
n.d. [1875?]
313pp (inc. 3pp table), f/p b/w frontis., 8 f/p b/w plates & 36 b/w illus. in text, 1 double-spread map, full morocco, 235x155mm. RM
4951 Another copy as above but bound in cloth, heavily dec. in gilt on front cover & spine & gilt edges with lettering on front cover & spine:
Thoulet/Mon Premier Voyage/en Mer
Thoulet was the translator & adaptor. The plates (signed A.M.) appear only in the French ed. & are presumably by A. Marie. KMM

MEMLING, Carl
4952 C. B. S. Television's/CAPTAIN KANGAROO/and his Animal Friends/By Carl Memling—Pictures by Marie Nonnast/Golden Press—New York/Copyright 1959
28pp, dec. t.p., col. & b/w illus. throughout, dec. bd., dec. e/p, 280x205mm. NSL:M
Australian in title only. [also author 'ABC Rhymes', Golden Press, Sydney 1972, but doubtful Australian author]

Men of Stamina
4953 [device printed in orange & black]/MEN OF STAMINA/With the Compliments of/The Makers of Stamina Clothes
Printed by Websdale Shoosmith, Sydney, n.d.
[32]pp (inc. 1p foreword), col. frontis. & col. illus. (Walter Jardine), adv. on last page, 26 part-col. illus., wrappers, 166x245mm. KP
Each page devoted to different occupations with illus.
A series of loose part-col. illus. pages also issued as advertising material, 125x220mm. KP
Sir Richard Grenville; Rev John Flynn; David Livingstone; Christopher Columbus; T. S. Mort; Lord Shaftesbury.
Another series of 16 cards advertising Crusader Cloth & illus. the processes from the sheep bearing the fleece to the bolt of cloth in the tailor's hands. Each card illus. in col. by Walter Jardine & a written description of the process on the back. 110x134mm. KP
4954 [device]/AUSTRALIAN MEN OF STAMINA/[7 lines of text & quotation from Longfellow]/Published and presented with the compliments of/Stamina Clothing Company Pty Limited/Sydney NSW
n.d. [no further imprint]
44pp (inc. 1p introduction), col. frontis. & 19 f/p col. illus. (Walter Jardine) & part col. portraits of 18 men with accompanying biographies, wrappers, 174x240mm. KMM
Subjects of articles: Cook, Phillip, John Macarthur, Flinders, Mitchell, Wentworth, Sturt, Stuart, Sir Henry Parkes, T. S. Mort, Farrer, Forrest, Lawrence Hargrave, Alfred Deakin, the Longworth family, John Monash, Herbert Hinkler, Mawson, Kingsford Smith.
4955 MEN OF/STAMINA/[drawing]/Stamina Clothes/ With the Compliments of/The Makers of Stamina Clothes/Sydney/NSW
Stamina Clothing Co Pty Ltd, Sydney, n.d.
60pp, f/p col. frontis. & 52 f/p tinted portraits with captions (Walter Jardine), stiffened dec. wrappers, 243x160mm. RM
4956 [device]/MEN OF STAMINA/The World's Great Men/[11 lines text]/with the compliments of the/ Stamina Clothing Company/Sydney/N.S.W.
Sydney, n.d.
[80]pp & 1p adv., col. frontis., part-col. illus. throughout (Walter Jardine), bd., 240x160mm. KMM
Col. frontis. portrait of James Cook, portraits & biographical notes of 78 other famous men, inc. Kingsford Smith, Phillip, Macquarie, Macarthur, Flinders, Mitchell, Wentworth, Sturt.

MENDOZA, Dot
4957 THE TAIL IS FAMILIAR/Stories by/Dot Mendoza/ Sketches by June Mendoza/[drawing]/The National Press Pty. Ltd./Melbourne.
n.d. [inscribed 1950]
59pp (inc. 1p dedication & 1p foreword by Peter Mendoza), 8 f/p brown/sepia illus. & drawings in text, pic. bd., 240x185mm. KP

MENPES, Constance
4958 THE/FAIRY/BOOK/By/Constance Menpes
C. H. Pitman, Perth, n.d.
20pp, line drawings throughout (printed in blue), pic. bd., cover title, 250x185mm. IMcG
Appears to have been illustrated by author.

MERCER, Diana
4959 COWS CAN'T EAT/CEDAR/by/Diana Mercer/

Longmans, Green and Co./London Melbourne New York
1957
138pp, b/w drawings throughout, illus. by Margaret R. Dods, map frontis., clo., 185x120mm. BBC

MERCIER, Emile

4960 THE COMIC/CHALK-COLOURING/BOOK/ [drawing]/by/Emile Mercier/A Frank Johnson Magpie picture book
Sydney 1943
8pp, 6 b/w illus. [to colour], wrappers, 300x240mm. ANL

Other uniform booklets by same artist/author, all published by Frank Johnson, Sydney 1944:
4961 OSKAR
4962 PIPPY
4963 TIBBY TIMES
16pp, illus. throughout, wrappers, 240x180mm. NSL:M

4964 MUDRAKE/AND THE PLOTTERS OF SKROOMANIA/ Emile/Mercier/ A/ Frank/ Johnson/ Publication/6d.
Sydney, n.d. [copyright 1945]
36pp, wrappers, cover title, 180x120mm. NSL:M
Whole book produced in b/w comic-strip form.

4965 SUPA DUPA/MAN/The Big/Curl/By/Emile/ Mercier/A/Frank/Johnson/Publication/6d
Sydney, n.d. [194-?]
36pp, b/w ilus., wrappers, cover title, 240x180mm. MCa

4966 TRIPALONG/HOPPITY/The Fearless/Texas Ranger/By Emile Mercier/A/Frank Johnson/ Publication/6d.
Sydney, n.d. [194-?]
36pp, b/w illus., wrappers, cover title, 240x180mm. MCa

4967 WOCKO/THE BEAUT/By/Emile/Mercier/The/ Smugglers/of Bindy Eye Bay/A/Frank/Johnson/ Publication/6d
Sydney, n.d. [194-?]
36pp, b/w illus., wrappers, cover title, 240x180mm. MCa

MERCIER, Emile & Flora

4968 THE GARDEN/ALPHABET/By Emile & Flora Mercier/A Frank Johnson Publication
Sydney 1944
16pp, illus.,wrappers, cover title,240x180mm. NSL:M

4969 PLAYTIME/ALPHABET/By/Emile/& Flora/ Mercier/A Frank Johnson/Publication
Sydney 1945
16pp, illus. throughout, wrappers, cover title, 240x180mm.
Picture books with brief text. NSL:M

MEREDITH, Louisa Anne [Mrs Charles, née Twamley]

4970 SOME/OF/MY BUSH FRIENDS/IN/TASMANIA/ Native Flowers, Berries and Insects/drawn from life, illustrated in verse/and briefly described/by/Louisa Anne Meredith/Author of "Our Wild Flowers" (English)/"Romance of Nature" "Notes and Sketches of/New South Wales" "My Home in Tasmania" &c./London. Published 1860./By Day & Son, Lithographers to the Queen,/6 Gate Street Lincoln's Inn Fields
vi + 106pp, 11 numbered col. litho. plates, sep. col. dec. t.p. & 3pp with col. decs (inc. author's monogram), printed throughout in sepia with intricate pic. borders as t.p. to each poem, clo., elaborately ornamented in gilt with title, date & author's monogram on front cover, g.e., 370x270mm. KMM

4971 LOVED AND LOST, London, Day & Son n.d. [1860] unseen

4972 LOVED, AND LOST!/The True Story of a Short Life./Told in Gossip Verse,/and/Illustrated,/by/Louisa Anne Meredith,/Author of "Some of my Bush Friends in Tasmania", "My Home in Tasmania",/Our Wild Flowers" (English), &c. &c./London:/Day and Son, Lithographers to the Queen./George Robertson, Melbourne and Sydney./W. C. Rigby, Adelaide, Walch & Sons, Hobart and Launceston
n.d. [1869?]
96pp (inc. 8pp notes & 10pp introduction), 16 b/w lithographed illus. & b/w drawings, dec. clo., 210x140mm. CLRC
Verses for children about flowers, birds &c.

4973 CHILDREN'S SONG OF WELCOME TO PRINCE ALFRED/To the Queen/this/Choral March/arranged at the desire of/Mrs Gore Browne/and sung by/Five Thousand children/on the arrival of/His Royal Highness/the Duke of Edinburgh/in/Tasmania/is/ respectfully dedicated/by/Her Majesty's faithful subjects/Louisa A. Meredith/and/Frederick A. Packer/ Published by Walch & Sons/Hobart Town & Launceston
H. Henn Litho., 1867
4pp, unillus., 350x215mm. TSL

4974 GRANDMAMMA'S/VERSE BOOK/for/Young Australia/Part 1/By Mrs. Meredith/Author of "My Home in Tasmania", "Some of My Bush/Friends in Tasmania", &c. &c./Tasmania:/Printed for the author by W. Fletcher;/and sold also by/J. Walch & Sons, Hobart Town;/Walch Brothers & Birchall, Launceston;/and/Geo. Robertson, Melbourne & Sydney/1878/All rights reserved
56pp (inc. 4pp notes), 1p dedication, 1p author's preface, unillus., bd., 180x120mm. TSL

4975 TASMANIAN FRIENDS AND FOES/Feathered, Furred, and Finned/A Family Chronicle of Country Life, Natural/History, and Veritable Adventure/By/ Louisa Anne Meredith/Author of "My Home in Tasmania" "Some of My Bush Friends in Tasmania",/"Our Island Home: A Tasmanian Sketch-book", &c. &c./With Coloured Plates, from Drawings by the Author/and other illustrations/ [quotation—Longfellow]/London:/Marcus Ward & Co., 67 & 68, Chandos Street/and Royal Ulster Works, Belfast/1880
259pp (inc. 1p 'In Memoriam' note, 4pp preface, 2pp 'List of Algae' & 3pp index), col. frontis. & 7 f/p col. illus., many b/w drawings in text, green pic. clo., dec. e/p, g.e., 220x165mm. KMM

4976 Another copy as above but with variant imprint /Sole Publishers for Australia:/J. Walch & Sons, Hobart Town/Walch, Brothers, & Birchall, Launceston/ London: Marcus Ward & Co./1880
Details as before, but this edition does not appear to have a frontispiece, but the same number of coloured plates are arranged throughout the book. KMM

4977 As above but
/Second Edition/London: Marcus Ward & Co. 67 & 68, Chandos Street/and Royal Ulster Works Belfast/ 1881
Details as in first edition. CLRC

4978 WARATAH RHYMES/FOR YOUNG AUSTRALIA/ By/Louisa A. Meredith/with photo-etched illustrations/by/Mrs. E. M. Boyd, Mr. R. André, and

the Author/London:/Vincent Brooks, Day & Son,/Gate Street, Lincoln's Inn Fields
n.d. [1891] [Preface by author dated 1878 reprinted from *Grandmamma's Verse Book*, & additional preface by author dated 1891]
64pp, b/w frontis. & b/w drawings throughout, dec. bd., dec. e/p, 240x180mm. CLRC
Largely a reprint of *Grandmamma's Verse Book*.

4979 Last Series./BUSH FRIENDS/IN/TASMANIA,/ Native Flowers, Fruits and Insects, Drawn from Nature,/with/prose descriptions and illustrations in verse,/by/Louisa A. Meredith[7 lines]/Macmillan & Co./London and New York./Executed by Vincent Brooks, Day and Son,/Gate Street, Lincoln's Inn Fields,/London
n.d. [1891]
xvi + 76pp + vii pp, 12 numbered col. litho. plates & 3 additional f/p col. illus., sepia drawings throughout, clo. elaborately ornamented, uniform with *Some of My Bush Friends*, 370x270mm. KMM
The contents pages include a list of the details of plates in that volume, as well as in the present volume. Edition limited to 700 copies. Author acknowledges the help of Edward La Trobe Bateman in the design of the poem titles & cover design.

MERIVALE, Fred.
4980 THE GOBURRA'S/REWARDS/By/Fred. Merivale/ Bombala Edition 1908/Price—One Shilling, by Post or Otherwise/Sydney/The "World" Printing and Publishing House,/275 Clarence Street/1909
48pp, 1p preface, unillus., wrappers, 185x120mm. NSL:M
On front wrapper: 'Bombala Edition 1908'.

MERIVALE, J.
4981 The Boys' Torch Adventure Library/No. 85/THE SUNDOWNER'S/GOLD/By/J. Merivale/Author of/ "Leo the Lazy" "Rendall Rises"/"Black Jim Pays" etc./ London/Edinburgh House Press/2 Eaton Gate, S.W.1/1936
29pp & 3pp adv., pic. wrappers, 180x124mm. KP

MERRETT, John
4982 THE TRUE BOOK ABOUT/CAPTAIN COOK/by/ John Merrett/Illustrated by/F. Stocks May/Frederick Muller Ltd./London
1954
140pp, 2pp maps, b/w frontis. & 18 b/w illus., clo., 185x120mm. ANL
4983 True Books/Editor: Vernon Knowles/THE TRUE BOOK ABOUT/CAPTAIN COOK/by/John Merrett/ Illustrated by/F. Stocks May/Frederick Muller Limited/London
1954; rpt 1955, 1957, 1959, 1963
140pp, 2pp adv., 2pp maps, b/w portrait frontis. & 18 b/w illus., clo., 185x120mm. BBC

4984 CAPTAIN/JAMES COOK/John Merrett/Illustrated by H. Lawrence Hoffman/Criterion Books New York
1957
192pp, b/w double-spread frontis. map, 7 f/p b/w illus. & drawings in text, clo., 210x135mm. ANL

MERRY, Andrew
4985 "THE CHINCHA"/and other Poems for Children/ by/Andrew Merry/Illustrations by Ninon Phillips
The author, Maryborough, Victoria, 1944 [printed by John Fraser & Sons, Ballarat].
37pp, b/w drawings, wrappers, 180x120mm. ANL

The Merry-go-Round Book
4986 THE MERRY-GO-ROUND BOOK: Pictures by Dorothy
Ayers & James Pty Ltd, Sydney, n.d. [1949]
16pp, col. illus. throughout, pic. wrappers, cover title, 275x210mm. NSL:M

MERYON, Edward
4987 AT HOLLAND'S TANK/By/Edward Meryon/ Illustrations by Percy Lindsay/All Rights Reserved/ N.S.W. Bookstall Co., Ltd.,/Sydney/1922
189pp, 3pp adv., b/w illus., clo. PH

MESSENT, Esther M.
4988 SCRUBLAND SONGS/By/Esther M. Messent/ Illustrations by Nell Uncle and Esther M. Messent/ Contents [list of contents & decoration]
The Hassell Press, Adelaide 1922
14pp, b/w frontis., b/w drawings, wrappers, 245x185mm. KMM

'METCALFE, William Charles' [pseud. C. Lawrence]
4989 FRANK WEATHERALL/or/Life in the Merchant Marine/A Sea Story for Youth/by/William C. Metcalfe/Author of "Aboveboard" "Steady your Helm", etc./London/James Nisbet & Co., 21 Berners St.
n.d. [school prize 1898; first pub. J. & R. Maxwell, 1886]
352pp, 16pp adv., b/w frontis. & 2 f/p b/w illus., clo. (replica of frontis. stamped in black below title), 180x120mm. Grant
Contains 10 chapters on Australia.
4990 FRANK WEATHERALL/A Sea Story for Boys/By/ William C. Metcalfe/Author of/"Above Board", "Steady your Helm", etc./London/James Nisbet & Co., Limited/21 Berners Street
n.d. [school prize 1906]
As above with 16pp adv. KMM
Although a frontis. & 2 plates are listed there has been a fourth plate in 3 copies I have examined, though not listed. It appears opposite p351 & is entitled 'Frank's Homecoming'.
4991 Another copy with same t.p.
[1906?]
352pp & 32pp adv., 2 b/w illus. & frontis. missing, pic. clo., lettering in black & an illus. of a schoolboy seated on a chair reading with bat & ball beside him, 184x122mm. KP

4992 NAILING THE COLOURS/or/The Light that Shines/By/William Charles Metcalfe/Author of "Rogue's Island",/"Steady your Helm", "Aboveboard"[*sic*] etc./Illustrated by G. Grenville Manton/[quotation]/London/Jarrold & Sons, 10 & 11 Warwick Lane, E.C./(All rights reserved)/1895
360pp, 8pp adv., b/w frontis. & 5 b/w plates, pic. clo., 185x120mm. KMM
Temperance tale of a boy apprentice on a voyage to Sydney & back from England; pp249–346 deal with life in Sydney.
4993 NAILING/THE COLOURS/or/The Light that Shines/By/William Charles Metcalfe/Author of "Rogue's Island", "Steady your Helm",/"Aboveboard"[*sic*] etc./[8 line quotation]/ device]/Illustrated by G. Grenville Manton/London/ Jarrold & Sons, Publishers, E.C./(All rights reserved)
n.d. [school prize 1915]
360pp, 1p adv., col. frontis. & 6 b/w plates, pic. clo., pic. e/p, 185x120mm. RM
The front cover uses the same illustration as used in the edition above but in a variant design.

4994 THE BOY SKIPPER/by/William Charles Metcalfe/

Author of/"Nailing the Colours", "Rogue's Island", "Steady Your Helm", "Aboveboard"[*sic*] etc. etc./ Frontispiece by Neville Lumley/Jarrolds (Publishers) London Limited,/1 & 2 Pleydell Court, 55 Fleet Street, E.C.4.
n.d. [1895]
251pp (inc. 3pp dedication, preface etc.), 4pp adv., col. frontis., clo., 180x120mm. MK
The story of William Shotton who navigated the ship *Trafalgar* from Java to Melbourne in the 1890s, & received an award from Lloyds of London.

4995 THE BOY SKIPPER/by/William Charles Metcalfe/ Author of "Junk Ahoy!" "Tom Bolt", etc./Illustrated by Charles Norman/[device]/London/Jarrold & Sons, 10 & 11 Warwick Lane, E.C.
n.d. [inscribed 1916]
264pp (inc. 12pp reviews), col. frontis. & 4 b/w photographic illus., dec. e/p, pic. clo., 185x120mm. Grant

4996 BILLOWS & BERGS/By/W. Charles Metcalfe/ Author of "The Boy Skipper", "On the Face of the Deep"/"Rogues Island", "Nailing the Colours", Etc./ With Original Illustrations by/Chas. J. De Lacy/ [device]/London/Frederick Warne and Co./and New York/1902/(All rights reserved).
399pp, b/w frontis., 7 f/p b/w illus., pic. clo., 195x135mm. RM
The first 16 chapters tell of the voyage of the ship *Parramatta* to Sydney; Chapters 17 & 18 are set in Sydney, & Chapters 19–45 are set in & around Antarctica.

4997 THE VOYAGE OF THE/STORMY PETREL/By/W. C. Metcalfe/Author of 'Nailing the Colours', 'On the Face of the Deep', etc./With three illustrations by Lancelot Speed/London/The Religious Tract Society/4 Bouverie Street and 65 St Paul's Churchyard, E.C.
n.d. [inscribed Xmas 1906] [1st publ. 1905]
320pp & 16pp adv., b/w frontis. & 2 b/w plates, pic. clo., title in gilt on front cover & spine, 194x133mm. KP

4998 THE VOYAGE OF THE/STORMY PETREL/by/W. C. Metcalfe/Author of "Nailing the Colours", "On the Face of the Deep",/With coloured and other illustrations/by Lancelot Speed/London/The Religious Tract Society/4 Bouverie Street and 65 St. Paul's Churchyard
n.d. [inscribed 1917]
320pp, 16pp adv., col. frontis. & 2 b/w plates, pic. clo., 190x130mm. Grant

4999 GRIT AND PLUCK/or/The Young Commander/ By/W. Chas Metcalfe/Illustrated by Harold Piffard/ Published under the direction of the general/Literature Committee/London/Society for Promoting Christian Knowledge/Northumberland Avenue, W.C; 43 Queen Victoria Street, E.C./Brighton: 129 North Street/New York: E. S. Gorham
n.d. [1906]
vipp, 354pp, 10pp adv., col. frontis. & 3 f/p col. plates, pic. clo., 192x122mm. KMM
Title 'Grit and Go' printed above chapter one & and as a running title on heading of verso pages throughout. Action takes place on a vessel bound for Sydney; after many mishaps including a violent storm, they put in at Kerguelen Island to make some necessary repairs & after further adventures reach Sydney safely & then return to England.

METHLEY, A. A.

5000 BUSHRANGERS'/GOLD/by/A. A. Methley/ Author of/Jock of the Scots Brigade, etc./[drawing]/A. & C. Black, Ltd./4, 5 & 6 Soho Square, London, W.1. 1930
248pp, col. frontis. by J. H. Hartley, clo., 185x120mm. Black's Boys' Library. NSL:M

METHLEY, Violet M.

5001 COCKY & Co./and their Adventures/By/Violet M. Methley/Illustrated by/T. Cuneo/Raphael Tuck & Sons Ltd./London Paris New York/Printed in England/Copyright
n.d.
184pp & 8pp adv., dec. t.p., col. frontis. & 1 col. plate & text drawings (T. Cuneo), pic. bd., 225x170mm. KMM
First 30pp in Australia, the rest on an eventful voyage to England.

5002 SEEING THE EMPIRE/The Adventurous Tour/of Steven and Sallie/By/Violet M. Methley/With/Colour Illustrations by/C. E. Brock, R.I./Raphael Tuck & Sons Ltd./Publishers to Their Majesties the King & Queen/ and to HRH The Prince of Wales./London Paris New York/Printed in England/copyright
n.d.
184pp & 8pp adv., dec. t.p., col. frontis. & 1 col. plate, b/w drawings throughout, col. pic. bd., clo. spine, 220x170mm. ANL
Section on Australasia pp45–53. The Treasure Trove Library.

5003 MISS QUIXOTE/By/Violet M. Methley/with four illustrations in colour by/Stanley Davis/Cassell and Company, Ltd/London, New York, Toronto and Melbourne
London, 1916
295pp, col. frontis. & 3 f/p col. illus., clo. with medallion in col. on front cover, 205x145mm. JMcG

5004 THE/BUNYIP PATROL/The Story of an Australian/Girls' School/By/Violet M. Methley/ [device]/The Pilgrim Press/16, Pilgrim Street, London, E.C.4
n.d. [1926]
192pp, col. frontis. only, clo., 180x120mm. KMM

5005 DRAGON ISLAND/An Adventure Story/for Girls/ By/Violet M. Methley/Illustrated by/Stella Schmolle/ [device]/Oxford University Press/London: Humphrey Milford
1938
255pp, col. frontis. & 6 f/p b/w illus., clo., 180x120mm. KMM
Adventure story of three girls shipwrecked off the Queensland coast.

5006 DERRY DOWN/UNDER/A Story of Adventure in Australia/by/Violet M. Methley/Illustrated by L. F. Lupton/[device]/Frederick Warne & Co., Ltd./London and New York
1943
236pp, b/w frontis., clo., 180x120mm. KMM

5007 TWO IN THE BUSH/by/Violet Methley/ Illustrations by/Isabel Veevers/Oxford University Press/London New York Toronto
1945
182pp, col. frontis. & 4 f/p b/w illus., clo., 185x120mm. CLRC

5008 THE QUEER ISLAND/By/Violet M. Methley/ Author of "The Windmill Guides" "Ensign Lydia Gaff" &c/Illustrated by D. L. Mays/Blackie & Son Limited/ London and Glasgow
n.d. [prize 1960]

224pp, b/w frontis. & 2 b/w plates, clo., 184x120mm. KP
Story set on coast north of Sydney.

5009 THE QUEER ISLAND/Violet M. Methley/with frontispiece by Terence Freeman/Blackie & Son Limited/London and Glasgow
n.d. [inscribed 1958]
224pp, b/w frontis., clo., 185x120mm. KMM
The Tower Library.

Michael & Mary Anne's Adventure

5010 MICHAEL & MARY ANNE'S/ADVENTURE/[drawing]
Consolidated Merchandising Co., 325 Bourke St., Melbourne, n.d. [194-?]
20pp, dec. t.p., col. illus. throughout, bd., 245x185mm. ANL

MICHELL, Barbara Ann & BROWN, David

5011 Barbara Ann Michell and David Brown/SINBAD/THE DOLPHIN/Photography by John Reynolds/The Jacaranda Press
Brisbane, 1971
[21]pp, col. photographic illus. throughout, extended col. illus. t.p., pic. bd., pic. e/p, 310x225mm. BBC

MICKLE, Alan Durward

5012 PEMMICAN PETE/and other Verses/For Children of all Ages/by Alan D. Mickle/With drawings by James Cook/[drawing]/Hodder & Stoughton/Limited London/1934
112pp, b/w drawings throughout, clo., 185x120mm. VSL

5013 THE/TRIO/FROM/RIO/And other Quaint Folk.../By/Alan D. Mickle/Illustrated by/Armstrong/Robertson & Mullens Limited, Melbourne
1942
119pp, b/w frontis. & 19 b/w drawings, clo., dec. e/p, 225x145mm. NSL:M
Also a signed & numbered edition of 50 copies of first edition, as above with variation in binding. KMM
2nd ed. 1942 as above. KP
4th ed. 1943 as above. KP
5th ed. 1943 as above. KP

5014 THE TRIO FROM/RIO/by/Alan D. MEIKLE [*sic*]/A Book which the Author &c [4 lines]/Collins/London and Glasgow
1946
196pp, col. frontis. & 23 f/p b/w illus., clo., 180x120mm. KP

5015 THE TRIO FROM/RIO/by/Alan D. Mickle/Illustrated by Bovey/A Book which the Author cannot make up his mind/whether to describe as a Grown-up's Book/for Children or a Children's/Book for Grown-ups./Collins/London and Glasgow
Copyright 1946, rpt 1947
192pp, col. frontis. & 23 f/p b/w illus., drawings in text, bd., 180x120mm. CLRC

5016 [Verse from The Trio from Rio]/THE TREASURE/OF CAPTAIN/CARBUNCLE/By/Alan D. Mickle/Illustrated by/Alan McCulloch/The National Press Pty. Ltd./34 Lonsdale Street, Melbourne
n.d.
Front cover reads:
Rhythmy/Rhymes/by/Alan D. Mickle/illustrated by/Alan McCulloch/No. 2/The Treasure of/Capt. Carbuncle
[16]pp, b/w drawings throughout, pic. wrappers, 180x120mm. VMOU

MIDDLETON, H. T. M.

THE HAPPY REVOLUTION. *See* Australian Youth Plays

MIDGLEY, Frederick

5017 CHILDREN'S/SHIRE HISTORY/The Story of Sutherland Shire/in word and picture/[drawing]/by F. Midgley
Sutherland Historical Press, Sutherland, NSW, 1969
39pp (inc. 1p foreword & acknowledgements), b/w drawings in text, pic. wrappers, 255x200mm. ANL
The area covered lies between Botany Bay & Port Hacking.

MILES, Alfred H. (ed.)

5018 FIFTY-TWO STORIES/OF THE/BRITISH EMPIRE./By/B. L. Farjeon, Marcus Clarke, C. Haddon Chambers,/Robert Overton, H. Hervey, David Ker,/C. G. D. Roberts, Alice F. Jackson,/and other writers/Edited by Alfred H. Miles./Illustrated./London:/Hutchinson & Co.,/34 Paternoster Row.
n.d. [inscribed 1902]
470pp (inc. 2pp author's preface) & 2pp adv., b/w frontis. & 4 f/p b/w plates, dec. clo., 192x130mm. CLRC
144pp of Australia, inc. Marcus Clarke, B. L. Farjeon, C. Haddon Chambers &c.

5019 FIFTY-TWO STORIES/OF/GREATER BRITAIN./By/Geo Manville Fenn/Marcus Clarke, Robert Overton,/H. Hervey,/Alice F. Jackson,/L. T. Meade,/Stinson Jarvis, Charles G. D. Roberts,/R. Choate Williamson,/and other writers./Edited by/Alfred H. Miles/Illustrated/London:/Hutchinson & Co.,/34 Paternoster Row.
464pp (inc. 2pp preface dated 1901), 4 b/w plates (?more), pic. clo., 193x130mm. ANL
Contains Australian section pp13-90 with bushranger & convict stories (inc. four by Marcus Clarke) & an account of the 'Rum Rebellion'.

MILES, J. A. (ed.)

5020 Australian Council for Educational Research/BRAVE YOUNG/SINGERS/An Anthology of Child Verse Com-/piled from the work of pupils of/the Correspondence Classes of/Western Australia/Edited by J. A. Miles, B.A./Melbourne University Press/in association with/Oxford University Press/Melbourne London Edinburgh New York/Capetown Bombay Toronto Etc./1938
88pp (inc. 3pp foreword), b/w map frontis. & 4pp b/w photographs of contributors, bd., 215x135mm. KMM

MILES, Thomas A.

5021 THE/ANZAC/STORY/FOR/BOYS & GIRLS/by T. A. Miles/Illustrated by John L. Curtis/Shakespeare Head Press/Sydney/1957
47pp (inc. 1p foreword by Lt-Gen. Sir Iven Mackay), b/w drawings throughout, dec. bd., map e/p, 235x175mm. ANL

Military Decorations and Medals

5022 MILITARY/DECORATIONS/AND MEDALS/A/Vita-Brits/Card Series/20c
Nabisco Pty Ltd, Melbourne, n.d. (post 1966, date mentioned in text)
[16]pp, spaces left for cards to be pasted in, stiff pic. covers, cover title, 240x180mm. KP

The Milky Way

5023 THE/MILKY/WAY
Printed & issued by the Milk Board, Victoria, Domville Avenue, Hawthorn 3122, n.d.
[12]pp & 2 centre pp cut-outs [equals 4pp], col. & b/w illus. throughout, pic. wrappers, 236x180mm. KP

5024 Another copy printed in sepia
[12]pp & 1 double-page centre cut-out, pp 7 & 8 list points about value of milk as food while in other (?later) editions seen, these pages describe with the aid of col. diagrams how cows make milk. KP

MILLAR, Rev. David
5025 THE SPIDER'S TELEPHONE/WIRE/and other talks with Boys and Girls/By the Rev./David Millar,/ Armadale, Melbourne, Victoria/with thirty-seven illustrations in colour and monochrome/By Mrs./ Otway Falkiner,/Boonoke N., Widgiewa,/N.S.W./[col. illus.]/London: H. R. Allenson, Limited/7 Racquet Court, 114 Fleet Street, E.C.4
n.d. [1929]
70pp & 2pp adv., col. frontis. & 13 col. illus., b/w plates, some photographic illus. & drawings in text, col. pic. bd. with clo. spine, 247x188mm. KMM

5026 THE/GARDEN OF LIFE/Stories by/The Reverend David Millar/Illustrations by Una Falkiner/Published by/Alexander Henderson/Melbourne/Registered in Australia for transmission by post as a book
n.d. [1944]
80pp (inc. 1p foreword by Lady Gowrie), dec. col. t.p., b/w frontis., 7 col. & 4 b/w f/p illus., dec. bd., 245x185mm. ANL

MILLEN, Bernard
5027 DISCOVERING/MODERN/AUSTRALIA/Bernard Millen/With illustrations by/Bonar Dunlop/Maps by Edgar Holloway/University of London Press Ltd./ Warwick Square, London E.C.4.
1963
112pp (inc. 8pp foreword, index, bibliography &c.), b/w photographic frontis. & 10pp b/w photographs, 3 b/w maps & line drawings in text, clo., 195x135mm. BBC The Discovery Reference Books.

MILLER, Basil
5028 KEN'S MERCY FLIGHT TO AUSTRALIA/by/Basil Miller/Zondervan Publishing House/Grand Rapids, Michigan
n.d. [1944]
64pp, unillus., clo., 195x130mm. NSL:M
Second edition 1945, as above. RM

MILLER, Ian
5029 THE/LOST REEF/By/Ian Miller/[device]/Oxford University Press/London: Humphrey Milford
1940
96pp, col. frontis., 2 text maps, pic. bd., 185x120mm. CLRC
The search for Lasseter's Reef.

MILLER, Patricia K. and SELIGMAN, Iran [*sic*] L.
5029a JOEY KANGAROO/by Patricia K. Miller and Iran L. Seligman/A Little Owl Book [device] Holt, Rinehart and Winston, Inc. New York/Illustrations by Ed Renfro/Copyright 1963 [& etc. 3 lines]
[26]pp, col. dec. t.p., col. illus. throughout, pic. bd., pic e/p, 230x145mm. VMOU

French edition
5029b LE/KANGOUROU/par Robert Gurik/Illustrations de Ed Renfro/Adapté de "Joey Kangaroo" par/Patricia K. Miller et Iran [*sic*] L. Seligman
Holt, Rinehart et Winston Ltée, Montréal et Toronto, 1967
Copyright 1963 Holt, Rinehart & Winston Inc.
[26]pp, col. dec. t.p., col. illus. throughout, pic. bd., pic. e/p, 230x145mm. KMM

MILLER, Rosalind
5030 ADVENTURES OF/MARGERY PYM/by/Rosalind Miller/Illustrated by/Jean Elder/London/Hutchinson & Co./(Publishers), Ltd.
n.d. [1939?]
272pp, col. frontis., 1 b/w plate, b/w drawings in text, clo., 185x130mm. KMM
Cover reads: 'Margery Pym'. From the text this story appears to precede *The Pyms at Yarrambeat* (1940).

5031 THE PYMS/AT YARRAMBEAT/by/Rosalind Miller/Illustrations and wrapper/by Kiddell Monroe/ Hutchinson & Co. (Publishers) Ltd./Paternoster Row, London; and Melbourne
n.d. [1940]
264pp, b/w frontis. & 2 b/w plates, clo., 185x120mm. ANL

MILLER, Sydney
5032 ALPHABET BOOK/by/Syd Miller
5033 PENNY/THE PUPPY/by/Syd Miller
5034 THE FOUR/BEARS/Syd Miller
Uniform picture books published by Frank Johnson, 350 George St, Sydney, n.d. [1941]
16pp, col. illus. throughout, wrappers, cover title, 240x180mm. NSL:M

MILLER, W. H. B.
5035 UNCLE BEN'S/MEADOW/BROOK/Temperance Stories/for Boys and Girls/First Book/By W. H. B. Miller/Author of Uncle Ben's Cobblestones/Uncle Ben's Cloverfield/Illustrated by Percy Lindsay/Signs Publishing Company/(A.C.A. Ltd. Proprietors)/Warburton, Victoria, Australia
1926 [copyright 1912]
104pp, dec. t.p., b/w drawings in text, dec. wrappers, 200x125mm. NSL:M

5036 UNCLE BEN'S/SUNSHINE STORIES/Temperance Tales for/Boys and Girls/(A Companion to "Uncle Ben's/Meadow Brook")/By W. H. B. Miller/Author of "Uncle Ben's Cobblestones"/and "Uncle Ben's Cloverfield"/Illustrated by Percy Lindsay/Signs Publishing Company/(A.C.A. Ltd. Proprietors)/Warburton, Victoria, Australia/Wholly set up and printed in Australia. 1926/Registered by The Postmaster-General for/Transmission through the post as a book
101pp & 2pp adv., dec. t.p., b/w drawings in text throughout, pic. wrappers, 205x134mm. KMM
Seventh Day Adventist propaganda.

MILLS, Frederick J. ["The Twinkler"]
5037 A DAY IN THE LIFE OF/JACK SUNDOWNER/ Written by/"The Twinkler" (F. J. Mills), Adelaide/ [photograph of kookaburras] Greeting
Cole's Book Arcade, 14 Rundle Street Adelaide, n.d. [1924]
16pp, photographs & other b/w illus. throughout, pic. wrappers, 225x150mm. NSL:M
5038 A DAY IN THE LIFE OF/JACK SUNDOWNER/ Written by/"The Twinkler" (F. J. Mills), Adelaide/ [photograph of kookaburras]/Greeting
J. B. Siddall & Son, Adelaide, n.d. [copy inscribed Dec '25]
16pp, 6 f/p sepia/white plates & 2 f/p photographs, pic. wrappers, 228x158mm. KMM
Col. cover illus. & the sepia/white illus. signed 'Otho Hewett', drawing of a 'sundowner' inside front cover.

5039 SAM SCOOTER;/also/Jimmy Sniggles and Jonesy/ and/Smoodger the Dog/By The Twinkler/(Frederick J. Mills)/Author of "Dinkum Oil", "Square Dinkum", "Cheer-up"/"Happy Days" etc./Copyright/Wholly set up and printed by W. K. Thomas & Co. Printers/ Grenfell Street Adelaide/1928

126pp (inc. 1p author's note), portrait frontis., wrappers, 180x115mm. CLRC
Frontispiece caricature of author by Kerwin Maegraith. Series of humorous sketches about boys.

MILNE, Jonathon
5040 ABC WITH PEOPLE/by Jonathan Milne/ Macmillan
Macmillan Co. of Aust. Pty Ltd, South Melbourne 1971
[27]pp, col. illus. throughout, pic. bd., 255x265mm. CLRC

MILOTTE, Alfred G.
5041 THE STORY OF THE/PLATYPUS/By/Alfred G. Milotte/Illustrated by Helen Damrosch Tee-van/Angus and Robertson/London Melbourne Sydney
1966 [First published in the United States 1964]
116pp, 2pp preface, 33 b/w illus., clo., 205x150mm. CLRC
• Rpt as above but 1965. KP

'MILTAREE'
5042 MILTAREE'S/STORIES FOR LITTLE FOLK/ [device]/Adelaide:/Hussey and Gillingham, Printers, Waymouth Street/1893
36pp (inc. 1p preface), unillus., wrappers, 140x90mm. KMM
Six short stories written by an eight-year-old girl, published when the author was almost ten.

MINCHAM, Hans
5043 VANISHED/GIANTS/OF/AUSTRALIA/Illustrated by Terry Houston/Rigby Ltd, Adelaide 1966
84pp (inc. 2pp index), b/w illus. throughout, col. pic. clo., 212x160mm. KMM

5044 PREHISTORIC/AUSTRALIA/Hans Mincham/ Illustrated by Rich Richardson/Golden Press Sydney 1971
63pp (i.e. 62pp with illustration, index, etc. inside front & back covers), col. illus. throughout, dec. bd., 325x240mm. BBC

The "Minties" Magic Drawing Book
5045 THE/"MINTIES"/MAGIC DRAWING/BOOK/ Directions/[4 lines]/Published by/James Stedman-Henderson's Sweets Ltd./Sweetacres, Rosebery, Sydney
14pp, b/w illus. (signed Percy Lindsay), pic. wrappers, 140x135mm. KP
Adv. for the confectionery.

'MIRIAM, Agatha'
See Le Breton, Agatha

'MIRRIAM'
See Hart, Marion H.

MIRVALD, Karel
5046 CELYM SVETEM (Through the Whole World) Orbis, Prague 1936
384pp. Unseen: SLCSR

The Misdoings of Mickey and Mack
See Joy Series

MISSINGHAM, Hal
5047 AUSTRALIAN/ALPHABET/By/Hal Missingham/ Consolidated Press Limited, Sydney
n.d. [1942]
26pp, wrappers, 250x185mm. ANL
Drawings of Australian animals & birds with brief descriptive text beneath each drawing.
Also author of *An Animal Anthology*, Shepherd Press, Sydney 1948, which is not a children's book.

MITCHELL, Anne
5048 Imperial Edition NO. 726/YOUTHFUL FANCIES/ 20 Songs for Children/Words by/Anne Mitchell/Music by/Christian Helleman/]list of songs]/Allan & Co. Pty Ltd./Melbourne Adelaide Bendigo/Printed in Australia Copyright 1957
36pp, unillus., dec. wrappers, 245x180mm. KMM

MITCHELL, Elyne
5049 Elyne Mitchell/THE SILVER BRUMBY/Drawings by/Ralph Thompson/Hutchinson of London 1958
192pp (inc. glossary), b/w photographic frontis. & 4pp b/w photographic illus., map, b/w chapter headings, clo., 200x125mm. BBC
5050 Elyne Mitchell/THE SILVER BRUMBY/Drawing by/Ralph Thompson/[device]/Hutchinson of London
First pub. Aug. 1958; 2nd imp. Oct. 1958; 3rd imp. Nov. 1958; 4th imp. Jan. 1959; 5th imp. Nov. 1960; 6th imp. Oct. 1961
192pp (inc. 2pp glossary), b/w photographic frontis. & 4pp b/w photographic illus., map, 1 f/p b/w illus. & b/w chapter headings, clo., 195x125mm. BBC
• Rpt as above, 1962, 1965, 1966, 1969, 1971. BBC
5051 Elyne Mitchell/THE SILVER BRUMBY/Drawings by/Ralph Thompson/Jacket-Frontispiece by Sam Savitt/New York/E. P. Dutton and Co., Inc./1959
190pp, col. frontis. & b/w illus. as in English edition, clo., 20cm. Unseen: IFA
5052 THE SILVER BRUMBY/Elyne Mitchell/Cover illustrations/By Peter Archer/Text illustrations/By Ralph Thompson/[device]
Atlantic Book Publishing Co. Ltd, London 1968
157pp (inc. 2pp glossary), 3pp adv., b/w map, b/w chapter headings, pic. wrappers, 180x110mm. Dragon Books. KMM
German editions
5053 Elyne Mitchell/DER SILBERHENGST/Illustriert von Monica Wüest/Rascher Verlag/Zürich und Stuttgart
n.d. [1964]
187pp, b/w drawings, clo., 205x135mm.
Translated by Eva Grünert. Unseen: IFA
5054 Elyne Mitchell/DER SILBERHENGST/Illustriert von Monica Wüest/Benziger Verlag
Zürich and Köln
189pp, 1p glossary, b/w illus., clo., 195x125mm. Unseen: IFA
5055 Elyne Mitchell/DER SILBERHENGST/Illustriert von Monica Wüest/Buchclub ex libris
Zürich 1969
194pp, 2pp glossary, b/w drawings, wrappers. Unseen: IFA
Swedish edition (abridged)
5056 Elyne Mitchell/WINDY/LEDAR HINGSTON/B. Wahlstrom Bokforlag
1972
157pp, 2pp adv., 8 f/p b/w illus. by B. O. Wennerberg, pic. bd., clo. spine, 200x130mm. Unseen: IFA
Spanish edition
5057 Elyne Mitchell/THOWRA/CABALLO SALVAJE/ Editorial/Molina
1960
223pp, b/w illus. as in English edition, pic. bd., 19.5cm.
Translated by Ramon Margalef Llambrich. Unseen: IFA
Finnish edition
5058 Elyne Mitchell/SØLVHINGSTEN/Tegninger af/ Ralph Thompson/Det Schønbergske Forlag/Købrnhsbn
1960

196pp, b/w illus. as in English edition, paper wrappers, 21cm. Unseen: IFA

5059 Elyne Mitchell/SILVER BRUMBY'S DAUGHTER/ Drawings by/Grace Huxtable/Hutchinson of London 1960
239pp, b/w photographic frontis. & 3 b/w photographic illus., map, b/w drawings in text, clo., 190x125mm. KMM

5060 Elyne Mitchell/SILVER BRUMBY'S DAUGHTER/ Drawings by/Grace Huxtable/[device]/Hutchinson of London
First published June 1960; 2nd imp. 1961; 3rd imp. 1962; 4th imp. 1966; 5th imp. 1970
Details as in first impression, but without photographic illus., 195x125mm. BBC

Spanish edition

5061 Elyne Mitchell/KUNAMA/HIJA DE THOWRA/ Editorial/Molina
Barcelona 1962
207pp, b/w drawings as in English edition, pic. bd., 195x132mm. LRA
Translated by Carlos Sempau Sopena; cover design by Roque Riera Rojas.

American edition

5062 Elyne Mitchell/THE SNOW FILLY/[drawing]/ Drawings by Grace Huxtable/New York/E. P. Dutton & Co., Inc./1961
192pp, b/w illus. (as in English edition), clo., 20cm. Unseen: IFA

5063 SILVER BRUMBY'S/DAUGHTER/Elyne Mitchell/ Cover illustration/By Peter Archer/Text illustrations/ By Grace Huxtable/[device]
Atlantic Publishing Co., London 1968
157pp, 3pp adv., b/w map, drawings in text, pic. wrappers, 180x110mm. Dragon Books. KMM

German editions

5064 Elyne Mitchell/KUNAMA DAS SILBERFOHLEN/ Illustriert von Monica Wüest/Benziger Verlag
Zürich and Köln 1972
187pp, 2pp glossary. Unseen: IFA

5065 Elyne Mitchell/KUNAMA/DAS SILBERFOHLEN/ Illustriert von Monica Wüest/1965/Rascher Verlag/ Zürich und Stuttgart
182pp, extended t.p., b/w drawings throughout, clo., 200x135mm.
Translated by Eva Grünert. Unseen: IFA

5066 Elyne Mitchell/KINGFISHER FEATHER/ [drawing]/Illustrated by Grace Huxtable/Hutchinson of London
1962
224pp, b/w chapter headings & some tailpieces, clo., 195x125mm. KMM

5067 WINGED SKIS/Elyne Mitchell/illustrations by/ Annette Macarthur-Onslow/[drawing]/Hutchinson/of London
1964
247pp (inc. 1p glossary), b/w part. col. map frontis., 2 f/p b/w illus. & b/w drawings in text throughout, clo., dec. e/p, 195x125mm. KMM

5068 SILVER BRUMBIES/OF THE SOUTH/Elyne Mitchell/Illustrated by/Annette Macarthur-Onslow/ [drawing]/Hutchinson of London
1965
240pp (inc. 2pp glossary), b/w map frontis. & 2 f/p b/w illus., b/w drawings in text, clo., 200x130mm. CLRC
Second impression as above, 1966. BBC

5069 SILVER BRUMBIES/OF THE SOUTH/Elyne Mitchell/Cover illustration/By Peter Archer/Text illustrations/By Annette Macarthur-Onslow/[device]
Atlantic Publishing Co., London 1968
156pp, 3pp adv., b/w map, b/w drawings, pic. wrappers, 180x110mm. KMM

5070 Elyne Mitchell/SILVER BRUMBY KINGDOM/ Illustrated by/Annette Macarthur-Onslow/[drawing]/ Hutchinson of London
1966
189pp (inc. 1p glossary), b/w chapter headings & drawings in text, clo., 195x120mm. KMM

5071 SILVER BRUMBY/KINGDOM/Elyne Mitchell/ Cover illustration/by Peter Archer/Text illustrations/ By Annette Macarthur-Onslow
Atlantic Book Publishing Co. Ltd. London 1968
139pp & 1p adv. & inside back cover, b/w drawings in text, pic. wrappers, 180x110mm. KP

5072 Elyne Mitchell/MOON FILLY/Illustrated by Robert Hales/Hutchinson of Australia
Richmond, Victoria, 1968
167pp, b/w illus. t.p., map & chapter headings, clo., 195x125mm. KMM

5073 Elyne Mitchell/MOON FILLY/Illustrated by Robert Hales/The Children's Book Club/121 Charing Cross Road/London W.C.3
1969
167pp, b/w illus. t.p., map & chapter headings, clo., 180x115mm. Unseen: IFA

5074 Elyne Mitchell/JINKI/DINGO OF THE SNOWS/ Illustrated by Michael Cole/Hutchinson of Australia
1970
168pp (inc. 1p note), 6 f/p b/w illus., b/w drawings in text, clo., 195x120mm. KMM
Second impression 1970. KP

5075 JINKI,/DINGO OF THE SNOWS/Elyne Mitchell/ Illustrated by Michael Cole/[device]/Armada
William Collins, London 1971
128pp, 6 f/p b/w illus., b/w drawings in text, pic. wrappers, 180x105mm. KMM

5076 Elyne Mitchell/LIGHT HORSE TO DAMASCUS/ Illustrated by Victor Ambrus/[drawing]/Hutchinson of Australia
Melbourne 1971
192pp, b/w map, 17 b/w drawings, clo., 215x135mm. CLRC

MOLDOFF, Sheldon

5077 MARCO/POLO/Junior/By Sea to Xanadu/from the animated feature film/story by/Sheldon Moldoff/ artwork by/Eric Porter/book adaptation by/Stuart Glover/Paul Hamlyn/Sydney London New York
Toronto 1972
60pp, col. illus. throughout, col. pic. bd. & e/p, 280x215mm. KP

Monarchs of Ocean

5078 MONARCHS OF OCEAN:/Columbus and Cook/ Two Narratives of Maritime Discovery./[quotation]/ Edinburgh;/William P. Nimmo
n.d. [first pub. Simpkin, 1866]
227pp (inc. 2pp preface), 24pp adv. (advertising 'The Poems of Robert Burns' in preparation for Christmas 1867) b/w frontis. only., clo. (with gilt decorations & gilt edges), 160x100mm. CLRC
Section on Cook pp123–227.(an abridgement of James Cook's first voyage from John Hawkesworth's 'An account of the voyages undertaken for making discoveries in the Southern Hemisphere', London 1773)

5079 Another copy as above, n.d., t.p. printed in red &

black inside a red ruled border; b/w frontis., 4 plates, dec. clo., with gilt border, g.e.,160x110mm. KP
'New gift books for 1870' listed on last page of adv.
5080 Another copy as first entry, but 1883
227pp & 4pp adv., b.w frontis & 3 plates, dec. clo., 160x100mm. KP
5081 MONARCHS OF OCEAN:/Columbus and Cook./ Two Narratives of Maritime Discovery./[quotation]/ Edinburgh:/William P. Nimmo, Hay, & Mitchell. 1886
227pp (inc. 2pp preface), 16pp adv., b/w frontis. & 3 f/p b/w illus., pic. clo., 175x120mm. KP
• Rpt as above, but 1889. RM
• Rpt as above, but 1891, 16pp adv. RM

MONRO, Ronald K.
5082 AUSTRALIAN/NATURE STORIES/Written and Illustrated/by/Ronald/K. Monro/Robertson and Mullens/Melbourne
1944
116pp (inc. 1p author's note, 1p introduction by Charles Barrett & 1p glossary), b/w photographic illus. throughout, bd. (clo. spine), dec. e/p, 235x170mm. CLRC
Second edition as above, 1947
Third edition as above, 1953, both KP

MONSARRAT, Nicholas (ed.)
5083 THE BOYS' BOOK/OF THE SEA/Edited by/ Nicholas Monsarrat/(author of *The Cruel Sea*)/with 15 illustrations by/James Holland/[device]/Cassell and Company Ltd./London
1954
196pp, 2pp author's foreword, 1p acknowledgements, 9 f/p & 6 smaller b/w illus., clo., 210x132mm. HBM
2nd ed. Nov 1954; 3rd ed. March 1960. KP
5084 Piccolo True Adventures/THE BOYS' BOOK OF/ THE SEA/Edited by Nicholas Monsarrat/(Author of The Cruel Sea)/Cover illustrations by Gary Long/Text illustrations by James Holland/[device]/A Piccolo Book/Pan Books Ltd./London
First publ. 1954 by Cassell and Co. Ltd. This abridged ed. publ. 1972 by Pan Books Ltd. London 2nd printing 1972
xiii+145pp & 3 pp adv., 11 f/p b/w illus., pic. wrappers, 178x110mm. HBM
Includes: 'Captain Bligh's Voyage to Timor' from *The Wake of the Bounty* by C. S. Wilkinson 6pp; 'Running the Easting Down' from *White Sails and Spindrift* by Capt F. H. Shaw (outward bound for Australia) 7pp; 'Return from the Pole' from Capt R. F. Scott's *Scott's Last Expedition* 10pp.

5085 THE BOYS' BOOK/OF THE/COMMONWEALTH/ Edited by/Nicholas Monsarrat/(Author of *The Cruel Sea*)/With 15 illustrations by/H. A. Simmons/[device]/ Cassell & Company Ltd/London
1957
193pp & 3pp foreword, acknowledgements &c, b/w illus., clo., 213x138mm. WRT
Includes Australian section of 38pp, comprising extracts from Kylie Tennant's *Australia: Her Story*; Ernestine Hill's *Flying Doctor Calling* & Rolf Boldrewood's *Robbery Under Arms*.

MONTENGON, Eva
5086 THE STORY OF A/LITTLE KANGAROO/Story and illustrations of/Ramon Sabates/Text of Eva Montengon/1965. Editrice Piccoli Milan/Publishers Piccoli Milan
[20]pp, col. frontis., col. & b/w illus. in text, dec. bd., dec. e/p, 225x175mm. Grant

MONTGOMERY, Richard R.
See Pluck and Luck series

MONTGOMERY, Rutherford G.
KING OF THE CASTLE/The Story of a Kangaroo Rat
Background Arizona not Australia. NSL:M

MONTI, Jolanda Colombini
5087 Jolanda Colombini Monti/WHY ARE YOU/ CRYING, KANGAROO?/Copyright 1956 by Casa Editrice "Piccoli"/Illustrations by/Mariapia/Publishers Piccoli Milan
16pp, col. dec. t.p., col. illus. throughout, pic. bd., 300x225mm. KMM
5088 Jolanda Colombini Monti/WHY ARE YOU/ CRYING, KANGAROO?/Illustrations by Mariapia/ ©1956 by Casa Editrice "Piccoli"/Printed in Great Britain/Dean & Son Ltd./[device]/41/43 Ludgate Hill, London E.C.4/Trade Mark
Variant ed. RC

MONYPENNY, Kathleen
5089 FROM FOOTPATH/TO/BULLOCK TRACK/ Exploration and Settlement/in Early Australia/by/ Kathleen Monypenny/To My Mother,/Herself of/Port Phillipian Descent/London/Sir Isaac Pitman & Sons, Ltd./Pitman House, Parker St., Kingsway W.C.2/Bath Melbourne
n.d. [1938]
128pp, 2pp adv., 1p acknowledgements, 1p foreword by Hugh McCrae & 2pp introduction, b/w photographic frontis., b/w drawings & photographic illus., dec. bd., dec. map e/p, 185x120mm. KP

5090 THE/KITES THAT FLEW/INTO THE MOON/ And/Other Chinese Stories/by/Kathleen Monypenny/ Illustrated by/Kathleen M. Blair/London/Sir Isaac Pitman & Sons Ltd.
1938
84pp, col. frontis. & 5 b/w drawings, clo., 195x135mm. NSL:M

5091 FROM/WHALING STATION/TO SHEEP RUN/ Beginnings in New Zealand/By/Kathleen Monypenny/ (Author of 'From Footpath to Bullock Track';/'The Kites that Flew into the Moon'.)/London/Sir Isaac Pitman & Sons, Ltd./Pitman House, Parker St., Kingsway, W.C.2/Bath [space] Melbourne
n.d. [1938]
xipp (prologue &c), 108pp, b/w photographic frontis., 12 f/p b/w photographic illus., map e/p, pic. clo., 185x120mm. KMM

5092 THE/YOUNG TRAVELLER IN/AUSTRALIA/by Kathleen Monypenny/[device]/Phoenix House London
1948
160pp (inc. 6pp index), double-spread b/w map & 16pp b/w photographic illus., clo., 180x110mm. NSL:M
• Rpt 1951. KP
5093 THE YOUNG TRAVELLER IN/AUSTRALIA/ Kathleen Monypenny/Phoenix House London
First published in Great Britain 1948; 6th imp. 1956
154pp, 6pp index, col. frontis., map, 16pp b/w photographic illus., clo., 185x120mm. BBC
5094 THE YOUNG TRAVELLER IN/AUSTRALIA/by Kathleen Monypenny/Illustrated with Photographs and Map/Sketches by Henry C. Pitz/Edited by Margaret Hodges/[drawing]/E. P. Dutton & Company, Inc./New York, 1954
First American edition
223pp (inc. 7pp index), b/w frontis., extended b/w map, 25 b/w photographic illus., clo., 205x130mm. Fuller's Bookshop, Hobart

Japanese edition
5095 THE YOUNG TRAVELLER IN AUSTRALIA/by/ Kathleen Monypenny/Translated in Japan/by Masami Kato/Copyright 1948 in England/by Phoenix House Ltd/Japanese Translation Published 1958/by Hoikusha Co. Ltd/arranged through/Charles E. Tuttle Co. Tokyo
220pp, b/w photographic illus. & b/w drawings, bd., col. pic. e/p, 210x150mm. NSL:M

5096 THE CHILDREN/WENT TOO/Horse and Waggon Days/By Kathleen Monypenny/Illustrated by Irene Maher/Angus and Robertson/Sydney London Melbourne Wellington
1954
169pp, 1p acknowledgements, dec. t.p., extended frontis., 7 f/p b/w & part-col. illus., drawings in text, clo., 220x140mm. KMM
Parts of this book were published in 1938 under the title *From footpath to bullock track.*

MOON, Elaine [compiler]
5097 STORIES OF ADVENTURE. [compiled by] Elaine Moon [and] Kenneth Moon
[Sydney, Brooks, 1966]
64pp, illus., 20cm. cover title
Stories first published in the School Magazine of the NSW Department of Education. Unseen: ANB 1967

MOON, Kenneth
5098 THE FIRE SERPENT/MYSTERY/Kenneth Moon/ Illustrated by/B. Biro/[device]/Ernest Benn Limited/ London
1963
121pp, 12 f/p b/w illus., clo., 180x120mm. BBC
Another copy as above, but bound together with 2 non-Australian books: W. Mantle's *Sandy Smith,* and R. Martin's *Tony and the Champ.* KP

JOHN FLYNN AND THE FLYING DOCTOR SERVICE *See* Great People in Australian History

MOON, Kenneth & Elaine
NEW AUSTRALIANS. *See* Life in Australia

CHARLES KINGSFORD SMITH. *See* Great People in Australian History

'MOONBEAM SERIES'
5099 DICK WHITTINGTON
5100 THE GOLDEN GOOSE
5101 THE HOUSE THAT JACK BUILT
5102 JACK AND THE BEANSTALK
5103 NOAH'S ARK NONSENSE (illus. D. H. Gilmore)
5104 NURSERY RHYMES
5105 PIG WON'T GET OVER STILE (illus. D. H. Gilmore)
5106 THE PRINCE WHO WAS AFRAID OF NOTHING (illus. Rhys Williams)
5107 PUSS IN BOOTS
5108 ROBIN HOOD
5109 THE SLEEPING BEAUTY
5110 STRONG HANS
Uniform booklets published by W. H. Honey Publishing Co., Sydney, n.d. [1943]
[16]pp, b/w drawings in text, stiff dec. wrappers, cover title, 245x185mm. NSL:M

MOORE, F. Frankfort
5111 UNDER HATCHES:/or/Ned Woodthorpe's Adventures./By/F. Frankfort Moore,/Author of "The Great Orion", "Will's Voyages", "Mate of the Jessica", &c./with eight full-page illustrations/By A. Forestier/ [device]/London:/Blackie & Son, 49 & 50 Old Bailey, E.C./Glasgow, Edinburgh, and Dublin/1889
352pp & 32pp adv., b/w frontis. & 7 b/w plates, pic. clo., 185x120mm. CLRC

5112 UNDER HATCHES/or/Ned Woodthorpe's Adventures/By/F. Frankfort Moore/Author of "Highways and High Seas" "I forbid the Banns" "The Great Orion" &c./With six page Illustrations by A. Forestier/[device]/London/Blackie & Son, Limited, 50 Old Bailey, E.C/Glasgow and Dublin
n.d. [inscribed 1898]
352pp, 32pp adv., b/w frontis. & 5 b/w plates, dec. clo., 180x125mm. RM

5113 UNDER HATCHES or, Ned Woodthorpe's Adventures/By/F. Frankfort Moore/Author of "Highways and High Seas" "I Forbid the Banns"/"A Gray Eye or So" &c./with six page illustrations by A. Forestier/Blackie and Son Limited/London Glasgow and Dublin
n.d.
352pp, 32pp adv., b/w frontis. & 5 b/w plates, dec. clo., 175x120mm. KMM
Adventure on the convict ship *Southern Cross.*
Another copy with 16pp adv. KP

5114 THE ICE PRISON./By/F. Frankfort Moore,/Author of "Tre, Pol, and Pen," "Will's Voyages,"/"Coral and Cocoa-nut," etc./Illustrated by W. H. Overend./ Published under the direction of the Committee/of General Literature and Education appointed by the/ Society for Promoting Christian Knowledge/Society for Promoting Christian Knowledge/London: Northumberland Avenue, WC;/43 Queen Victoria Street, E.C./Brighton: 135, North Street./New York: E. & J. B. Young & Co./1891
319pp & 8pp adv., b/w frontis. & 8 b/w plates, pic. clo., bevelled edges, dec. e/p, 180x120mm. ANL
Antarctic setting for part of book.

5115 FROM THE/BUSH TO THE BREAKERS/by/ F. Frankfort Moore,/Author of/"Sailing and Sealing", "The Ice Prison", "Will's Voyage", Etc./Illustrated by W. H. Overend/Published under the Direction of the General Literature Committee./London:/Society for Promoting Christian Knowledge./Northumberland Avenue, W.C.,/43, Queen Victoria Street, E.C./Brighton: 135, North Street./New York: E. & J. B. Young and Co.
n.d. [school prize 1901]
378pp, 5pp adv., b/w frontis. & 3 f/p b/w illus., pic. clo., 180x120mm. RM
Story of adventure with bushrangers, etc. set partly in Australia, the action of the latter part of the story taking place aboard a schooner in the Pacific.
Two copies as above with variation in pic. clo. bdg and e/p. KP

5116 THE TWO CLIPPERS./by/F. Frankfort Moore,/ Author of/"From the Bush to the Breakers", "Coral and Cocoa-nut",/"The Ice Prison", Etc. Etc./Illustrated by W. H. Overend./Published under the Direction of the General Literature/Committee./London:/Society for Promoting Christian Knowledge/Northumberland Avenue, Charing Cross, W.C.;/43 Queen Victoria Street, E.C./New York: E. & J. Young & Co.
n.d. [prize 1904]
366pp, 1p list of books by same author, 16pp adv., b/w frontis. & 3 f/p b/w illus., clo., 180x120mm. Grant
Set in NSW & then the South Pacific.
Also author of TWO IN THE BUSH, a collection of stories, the first only of Australian interest, but not children's. KP

MOORE, Henry Byron

5117 HOW THE CRUEL/IMP BECAME A GOOD/FAIRY/And Other Stories/(With 30 illustrations)/By H. Byron Moore/Illustrated by/Frederick S. Sheldon/George J. S. Ross/T. G. Moore/and/H. Winkelmann/Melbourne/Published by/Melville & Mullen
1900
103pp (inc. prologue, acknowledgements, &c., & 11pp adv.), b/w illus., pic. bd., 200x170mm. NSL:M
Published to assist the Children's Hospital fund, 2000 copies having been given to the Institution by the author.

5118 Dedicated by kind permission to/The Lady Tennyson/HER ROYAL HIGHNESS/QUEEN BEE/A Story of fact and fancy/and other Stories/By/H. Byron Moore/Copiously illustrated by/Miss Hope S. Evershed of Launceston/Published by Melville and Mullen
Melbourne, n.d. [1905]
118pp (inc. 3pp preface), 9pp & 21pp adv., b/w drawings throughout, clo., 205x165mm. CLRC

MOORE, Henry Charles

5119 NOBLE DEEDS OF THE/WORLD'S HEROINES/by/Henry Charles Moore/Author of "Through Flood and Flame", "Brave Sons of Empire"/With fifteen page illustrations/London/The Religious Tract Society/4 Bouverie Street and 65 St. Paul's Churchyard, E.C.
n.d. [1903]
286pp (inc. 1p preface), 2pp adv., b/w frontis. & 14 b/w plates, pic. clo., 195x130mm. KP
Includes one chapter (5pp) on Grace Bussell & the wreck of the *Georgette* off the south-west coast of Western Australia; also one chapter (10pp) on Jane Chalmers, 'Alone Amongst Cannibals' (Rarotonga).
Another copy as above, but 'Second impression'

5120 BRAVE SONS/OF THE EMPIRE/by/Henry Charles Moore/Author of "Noble Deeds of the World's Heroines",/"Through Flood and Flame"/with seven coloured illustrations/by Arthur Twidle/London/The Religious Tract Society/4 Bouverie Street & St. Paul's Churchyard
n.d. [1910]
251pp, 4pp adv. ('The Boy's Own Series') col. frontis. & 6 col. plates, pic. clo., 195x135mm. Brave Deeds Series KMM
Contents include: 'A Pioneer of the Cross'—Chalmers of New Guinea (27pp); 'An Antarctic Hero'—Sir James Ross (13pp); 'Death in the Desert'—Burke and Wills and the crossing of Australia (17pp).
Several copies seen as above with prize labels from 1913 (copy with gilt lettering on cover) to 1920.
Another undated copy has t.p. printed only in blue & red on white paper without the yellow background of earlier ed. KP

MOORE, Patrick

5121 MISSION TO MARS [copy seen lacks t.p.]
Burke, London, n.d.
158pp, unillus., clo., 185x120mm. Falcon Library
Science fiction story beginning at Woomera, South Australia. KMM
• Rpt as above, 1958. KP

5122 THE DOMES OF MARS/Patrick Moore/London/Burke
First published 1956; rpt 1959
160pp, unillus., clo., d/w by Patricia Cullen, 185x120mm. CLRC
'Maurice Gray, grown up since 'Mission to Mars' is now a young man of twenty and a fully qualified radar engineer at the Australian rocket range of Woomera. Maurice is to become one of the small permanent colony which now inhabits Mars...' (from publisher's 'blurb')

5123 Patrick Moore/THE VOICES/OF MARS/Burke
1st publ. 1957. This ed. Oct 1960
160pp, unillus., clo., 182x120mm. ANL
Set partly in Woomera

PERIL ON MARS
No Australian content

MOORE, T. Inglis

ROLF BOLDREWOOD. *See* Great Australians

MOORE, W. G.

5124 MARTIN/MUSTERS THE SHEEP/by/W. G. Moore/Illustrated by/Teresa Freeman/More children far and near/series/[device]/Hutton Educational Publications
London, 1965
31pp, alternate page opening illus. in col. & b/w, pic. wrappers, 205x135mm. VMOU

MOOREHEAD, Alan McCrae

5125 THE BLUE NILE/By/Alan Moorehead/Junior Edition/[device]/Hamish Hamilton/London
First published in 1962; first published in The Heron Series 1965 (abridged by Lucy Moorehead)
155pp, 2 b/w maps, pic. clo., cover design by Roger Payne, 210x130mm. CLRC

5126 COOPER'S CREEK/By/Alan Moorehead/Junior Edition/abridged by/Lucy Moorehead/[device]/Hamish Hamilton/London
First published in Great Britain 1963; first published in the Heron Series 1968
148pp, b/w map, pic. clo., cover designed by Gillian Willet, 205x135mm. CLRC
The story of Burke & Wills.

5127 NO ROOM IN/THE ARK/By/Alan Moorehead/Junior Edition/[device]/Hamish Hamilton/London
First publ. in The Heron Series 1965
160pp, 4 plates, b/w chapter headings & tailpieces, pic. clo., map e/p, 210x137mm. ANL

5128 THE WHITE NILE/By/Alan Moorehead/Junior Edition/abridged by/Lucy Moorehead/[device]/Hamish Hamilton/London
First publ. in this abridged ed. 1966
154pp, unillus., clo., 210x140mm. WRT

5129 THE FATAL IMPACT/Alan Moorehead/Junior Edition/abridged by/Lucy Moorehead/[device]/Hamish Hamilton/London
1969
147pp, 1p author's note, 2 b/w maps (1 f/p & 1 double-spread), 8pp b/w photographic illus., pic. clo., 210x135mm. CLRC

MORAN, H. T. [ed.]

5130 THE PLAY GOES ON/Nine Short Plays/Selected by/H. T. Moran/F. W. Cheshire/Melbourne
173pp, unillus., clo., 185x130mm. ANL
Intended for pupils in secondary schools. Only two of the plays are of Australian content or origin: *The Blind God,* adapted by H. T. Moran from the short story of H. E. Riemann, & *To Pay Paul,* adapted by editor from the short story of Randolph Bedford.

MORANT, H. C. F.

5131 WHIRLAWAY/Written by/H. C. F. Morant/Illustrated by Jean Elder/A Story/of the/Ages/Hutchinson/London
1937

237pp (inc. 2pp author's preface, 1p acknowledgements, 1p introduction by Frank Tate & notes), dec. t.p., col. frontis. & 8 col. illus., b/w drawings, clo., 200x160mm. CLRC
Some copies with pic. e/p & pic. clo.

More Australian Verse for Children
5132 MORE/AUSTRALIAN VERSE/FOR/CHILDREN/ Education Department of Victoria/By Authority: W. M. Houston, Government Printer
n.d. [inscribed on e/p, Xmas 1955]
166pp, 2pp foreword by Alan Ramsay, Director of Education, b/w illus. throughout, bd., 210x130mm. Grant
Illustrated by Marjorie Howden, Pixie O'Harris, Betty Patterson, D. Ovenden & others.

'MORELL, Musette' [pseud. Moyra Martin]
5133 THE ANTICS OF/ALGY/[drawing]/By/Musette Morell/Illustrated by/Hartmut Lahm/Angus and Robertson/Sydney: London/1946
69pp, col. frontis. & 3 f/p col. illus., drawings in text, bd., 255x180mm. ANL

5134 PLAYS FOR CHILDREN/Book one/Selected by the Department/of Education; with Foreword/by L. F. Keller, and Edited/by Musette Morell/Sydney/ Currawong Publishing Co./Pty. Ltd./3 Castlereagh Street
First pub. 1947; rpt (revised) 1950
112pp, 2pp foreword, 3pp editor's introduction, 10pp notes, illus. by Edwina Bell, bd., 185x115mm. ANL
Contains 5 plays by Australian authors: *Magpie Gully*, by Catherine Shepherd; *King Cole and the Birthday Cake*, by Charles Swain; *A Hundred Thousand Monkeys*, by Helene Barclay; *If Animals had their Way*, by Musette Morell; *The Emperor's New Clothes*, by Rosemarie Benjamin.

5135 BUSH COBBERS/by/Musette Morell/Illustrated by/Edwina Bell/Australasian Publishing Company/ Sydney Wellington London
1948
96pp, b/w drawings throughout, dec. bd., 190x135mm. York Series. NSL:M
• Rpt as above but
/in association with/George G. Harrap & Co. Ltd.
First pub. 1948; rpt 1950, 1954. KMM

PRESENTED WITHOUT COURTESY. *See* Australian Youth Plays

5136 TEN PUPPET PLAYS/(and production notes)/graded for/lower junior to senior classes/By/ Musette Morell/Sydney/Currawong Publishing Co./ Pty. Ltd./3 Castlereagh Street
1950
116pp, 11 b/w illus., wrappers, 185x125mm. ANL

MORES, Sarah
5137 PRETTY POLLY/or/THE HISTORY OF A COCKATOO/by/Sarah Mores/Author of "Homely Tales" etc./Profusely illustrated by/E. Piroden./ London/Hutchinson & Co./25, Paternoster Square/ 1890
138pp, 22 f/p illus., pic. clo., 210x165mm. KMM

MORESBY, E. I.
5138 THE/LUCKY DOZEN/Real Life Stories/for/Boys and Girls/by/E. I. Moresby
Verona Press Pty Ltd, 26–30 Flinders Street, Melbourne, n.d. [194-?]
47pp, b/w drawings, dec. bd., 245x175mm. KMM
Includes 12 adventure stories.

MOREY, Geoffrey
5139 THE/LINCOLN/KANGAROOS/Geoffrey Morey/ Hodder & Stoughton/London
1962
78pp, b/w photographic frontis. & illus. throughout, bd., pic. e/p, 210x156mm. CLRC

MORGAN, Diana
5140 7 SONGS/FOR CHILDREN/music by/Marjorie Hesse/words by/Diana Morgan/[list of songs]/Leeds Music Pty Limited/Griff House, 324 Pitt St, Sydney, N.S.W./Price/6/-
n.d. (pre-decimal currency)
16pp, unillus., pic. wrappers, 268x212mm. WJSB
Dedication to the author who is blind.

MORGAN, Joyce [ed.]
5141 IT'S FUN TO SING/Lothian Publishing Co. Pty Ltd./Aust N.Z.
n.d. [1954]
32pp, b/w illus., pic. wrappers, 272x215mm. VSL
Songs, illus. & cover are the work of the Wellington Free Kindergarten, N.Z.

'MORGAN, Scud'
See Trend Books

'MORGAN, W. Ingram' [pseud. R. G. Campbell]
5142 COLOSSAL/CORCORAN/ON/SMOKE ISLAND/ by/W. Ingram Morgan/Illustrated by/Wally Driscoll/ E. W. Cole/[device]/Melbourne
1952
94pp, 1p adv., 5 f/p b/w illus., bd., 180x120mm. KMM
According to the publisher, R. G. Campbell also wrote under the name of 'Rex Grayson'. The series of six books was brought out simultaneously in an attempt to compete, in Australia at least, with the 'Biggles' books. The venture was a complete failure.

5143 COLOSSAL/CORCORAN/IN/CENTRAL AFRICA/by/W. Ingram Morgan/Illustrated by/Wally Driscoll/E. W. Cole/[device]/Melbourne
1952
109pp, 1p adv., 6 f/p b/w illus., clo., 180x120mm. KMM

5144 COLOSSAL/CORCORAN/ON/SKULL ATOLL/by W. Ingram Morgan/[drawing]/Illustrated by/Wally Driscoll/E. W. Cole/[device]/Melbourne
1952
96pp, 1p adv., 4 b/w illus., clo., 180x120mm. KMM

5145 COLOSSAL/CORCORAN/IN THE/CARIBBEAN SEA/by W. Ingram Morgan/[vignette]/Illustrated by/ Wally Driscoll/E. W. Cole [device]/Melbourne
95pp, 1p adv., 5 f/p b/w illus., clo., 180x120mm. KMM

5146 COLOSSAL/CORCORAN/IN/MYSTERY VALLEY/by W. Ingram Morgan/[drawing]/Illustrated by Wally Driscoll/E. W. Cole/[device]/Melbourne
1952
111pp, 1p adv., 5 b/w illus., clo., 180x120mm. KMM

5147 COLOSSAL/CORCORAN/IN THE/HINDU KUSH/MOUNTAINS/by W. Ingram Morgan/ [vignette]/Illustrated by/Wally Driscoll/E. W. Cole/ [device]/Melbourne
1952
95pp, 1p adv., 5 f/p b/w illus., clo., 180x120mm. KMM

MORGENSTERN, Judith
5148 BUNTY GOES/EXPLORING/Judith Morgenstern/

Illustrated by Sally Michel/[drawing]/Lutterworth Press/London
First impression 1961; second impression 1965
64pp, col. frontis. & b/w drawings, clo., 195x130mm. MD
Contains 4 stories about a koala.

MORNEMENT, Ina
5149 To Jennifer Tait/Imperial Edition NO. 371/ODDS & ENDS/(for Little Friends)/Songs for Children/ Words and Music/by/Ina Mornement/contents/[13 songs listed]/Copyright Price 1/6 net/Allan & Co Prop. Ltd./Melbourne Sydney Adelaide Bendigo
1935
16pp, unillus., wrappers, 254x177mm. VSL

MORPHETT, Hazel E.
5150 THE/MAGIC RING/An Instructive Story to Bring the/Child in Closer Touch with/Nature and the/ Creator/By/Hazel E. Morphett/Copyright/Rigby Limited/Adelaide, South Australia/1938
58pp(inc. 1p author's foreword), b/w frontis. & 7 b/w drawings, wrappers, 245x185mm. NSL:M

MORRIS, Alice Talwin
5151 MY BOOK ABOUT/AUSTRALIA/By Alice Talwin Morris/[drawing]/Illustrated by Charles Robinson/ Blackie and Son Limited/London Glasgow and Bombay
1912
[28]pp, t.p. printed in red & black, 6 f/p col. illus., 5 f/p b/w illus. & drawings in text, bd. with col. illus. on front cover & clo. spine, 257x200mm. KP

MORRIS, Erica
See Connell, Mary & Morris, Erica

MORRIS, Ethel Jackson
5152 ALL AMONG THE FAIRIES/[uneven lines]/by Ethel Jackson Morris/Melbourne:/Published by John Wyatt/313–315 Little Collins Street/Printed by Arbuckle, Waddell & Fawckner/20 McKillop St.
[1909]
47pp, dec. t.p., b/w drawings throughout, pic. wrappers, 180x235mm. KMM
Contains 4 stories & 1 verse.

5153 THE/WHITE BUTTERFLY/and/Other Fairy Tales/ Written and Illustrated/By/Ethel Jackson Morris/ [decorative device]/C. J. De Garis Publishing House/ Melbourne/1921
107pp, col. frontis. & 7 col. plates, 3 b/w plates & drawings in text, clo., 270x220mm. KMM

MORRIS, Jill
5154 BOBUCK/The Mountain Possum/Written by Jill Morris/illustrated by Rich Richardson/Golden Press Sydney 1971
[46]pp, col. illus. throughout, col. pic. bd., 235x210mm. CLRC
Also uniform with above,
5155 HARRY THE HAIRY-NOSED WOMBAT. CLRC

5156 RUFUS THE RED KANGAROO. CLRC
Golden Press Sydney 1970

5157 KOLO THE BUSH KOALA. KMM

5158 PERCY THE PEACEFUL PLATYPUS. CLRC

5159 RUSTY THE NIMBLE NUMBAT. KMM
All Golden Press, Sydney, 1971

MORRIS, Katherine
5160 THE FROG/An Aboriginal Legend/Retold and illustrated/for young children/by Katherine Morris Whitcombe & Tombs Pty Ltd, Sydney 1968
40pp, part. col. illus. throughout, pic. clo., 240x175mm. KMM

DOWN BY THE RIVER. *See also* Laird, Eveline & Morris, Katherine

MORRIS, Myra
5161 US FIVE/By Myra Morris/Illustrated by Myrtle Kaighin/and the Author/Melbourne Publishing Company/"Rialto" 497 Collins Street, Melbourne
n.d. [1922]
253pp, b/w drawings in text, clo., 180x115mm. KMM
This story was first published in the *Weekly Times* under the title 'The Other Side of the Hill'.

MORRIS, Rufus
5162 THE BOOK OF FABLES/Illustrated by/Rufus/ Morris
Dawfox Productions, Sydney, n.d. [inscribed 1945]
32pp, 16 f/p b/w illus., bd., 210x230mm. Grant
Illustrations printed on various coloured paper.

5163 FLUFF/AND/FLOPPY/Written—Drawn by/Rufus Morris/A Jons Production/Registered at the G.P.O. Sydney for transmission by post as a book
n.d. [1947]
27pp, col. & b/w illus. throughout, dec. bd., 215x230mm. ANL

5164 THE/LITTLE/RED HEN/[drawing]/Illustrated by/ Rufus Morris
O.P.C. Distributors Pty Ltd, Sydney 1948
25pp, part-col. illus. throughout, dec. bd., 175x115mm. NSL:M

5165 THREE/LITTLE KITTENS/[drawing]/Illustrated by/Rufus Morris
O.P.C. Distributors Pty Ltd, Sydney 1949
25pp, part-col. illus. throughout, dec. bd., 175x115mm. NSL:M
Picture book with very slight text.

Picture Books as follows:
5166 BABES OF THE FOREST

5167 LITTLE ANIMALS

5168 THE JOLLY NURSERY RHYMES (text by Franklin Bennett)

5169 "OUPS-A-DAISY" NURSERY RHYMES (text by Franklin Bennett)
Offset Publishing Co., Sydney 1949
Each contain 16pp, illus. throughout in col. & b/w, pictorial wrappers, 270x205mm. ANL

5170 TWINKLE-TWINKLE/NURSERY RHYMES/ Illustrations by Rufus Morris
Jons Productions Pty Ltd, Sydney, n.d. [194-?]
60pp, dec. t.p., 8 f/p col. illus., part-col. illus. in text throughout, dec. bd. (clo. spine), dec. e/p, 270x210mm. VSL
The text is of the conventional nursery rhymes.

5171 TWINKLE-TWINKLE/NURSERY RHYMES/ Illustrations by Rufus Morris
Jons Productions, Sydney, n.d. [inscribed 1954]
[48]pp, 4 f/p col. illus., part-col. illus. throughout, part-col. dec. t.p., col. pic. bd., clo. spine, 272x210mm. KP
5172 Another copy as above but cover illus. only in part-col. (replica of t.p.) instead of full col. illus., clo. spine, 265x210mm. KP

5173 NURSERY/RHYMES/[drawing]/Illustrated by/ Rufus/Morris/Registered at the G.P.O. Sydney for transmission by post as a book

A Jons production, n.d. [194-?]
56pp (inc. 2pp index), 7 f/p col. illus., col. & b/w drawings in text, pic. bd., 124x100mm. KP

5174 THE/TALE OF A MOUSE/Drawings by Rufus Morris/Sers 8.41[series no.?]
Offset Printing Coy Pty Ltd, Sydney, n.d. [194-?]
16pp, no words, f/p b/w drawings, col. pic. wrappers, 264x214mm. KP
Colouring book.

5175 TODDLER'S/PICTURE/BOOK/[drawing]/ Illustrated by/Rufus/Morris/A Dawfox/Production Sydney, n.d.
10pp (inc. 3pp col. illus & illus. printed in blue & white), col. pic. wrappers, 360x240mm. KP
Rufus Morris Series (listed on back cover)
1 Three Blind Mice
2 Jungle Jingles
3 Toddlers Picture Book
4 Playtime.

MORRIS, Ruth
5176 THE RUNAWAY/By Ruth Morris/[device]/Rigby Limited/Adelaide
First published in association with Michael Joseph, London 1961
173pp, unillus., clo., 180x120mm. KMM
5177 Ruth Morris/THE RUNAWAY/Penguin Books/In association with Michael Joseph
First published by Michael Joseph 1961; Published by Penguin Books, Harmondsworth, Middlesex, England, 1964
138pp, 5pp adv., unillus., pic. wrappers, cover design by Richard Kennedy, 180x110mm. KMM
Although not originally published as a children's book, this story is of interest to older children, & the Penguin edition is produced in the 'Peacock Book' series, designed for older children.

MORRIS, Vivienne
See Mellor, Kathleen & Morris, Vivienne

MORRISH, Hannah
5178 THE ANIMALS'/PARTY/by/Hannah/Morrish/ Pictures by/Jack/Quayle
Frank Johnson, Sydney, n.d. [1944]
16pp, col. illus. throughout, pic. wrappers, cover title, 240x180mm. ANL
Rhyming text.

MORRISON, Crosbie
5179 NATURE/STUDIES/1956/Prepared and Broadcast/by/Crosbie Morrison, M.Sc./of "The Argus" Melbourne/Published by/The Australian Broadcasting Commission/Youth Education Department
1956
36pp, b/w photographs throughout, wrappers, 180x240mm. KMM
This booklet was prepared originally to illustrate a series of broadcasts to schools by Crosbie Morrison of the *Argus*, Melbourne.

5180 Crosbie Morrison/THE JUNIOR/NATURALIST/ Illustrated by Nancy Adams/[drawing]/Whitcombe & Tombs Ltd.
Christchurch, NZ, 1966
111pp (inc. 1p note), b/w drawings in text throughout, clo., 210x140mm. KMM
Book compiled by the author's widow, Mrs Lucy Crosbie Morrison, from 'The Junior Naturalist', a popular children's programme broadcast throughout Australia & New Zealand.

MORRISON, John W.
5181 Morrison's/Sensational Series/Copyright 1881 by John W. Morrison. (entered at the Post Office, New York, as second class matter.) Nov. 12, 1881./Vol. 1 No. 13/$2.50 per year. John W. Morrison, Publisher 13 and 15 Vanderwater St. N.Y. 6 months $1.25. (Price 5 cents.)/ROSE CASEY, THE FEMALE BUSHRANGER./ [illus.] [caption]
15pp, adv. verso back wrapper, unillus., b/w pic. t.p., wrappers, 290x210mm. RM
Title over chapter 1: 'Rose Casey,/The Female Bushranger of Australia'.

MORRISON, W. A.
ERNEST MORRISON. *See* Great Australians

MORROW, Marjorie
5182 WATER/Book One/by/Marjorie Morrow, B.Sc., Dip. Ed./Lecturer in Biology/Balmain Teachers' College/Sydney/Illustrated by/Margaret Senior/ [device]/6/Longmans 1965
Melbourne
32pp (inc. bibliography), part-col. illus. throughout, stiff pic. wrappers, 210x155mm. Australian Nature Series No. 6. BBC

5183 WATER. Book two, as above. Australian Nature Series No. 12. BBC

MORT, Eirene
5184 COUNTRY/COUSINS/Presented in/Picture and/ Rhyme by/Eirene Mort
n.d. [illus. dated 1904]. Printed by G. B. Philip & Son, 451 Pitt St, Sydney
[38]pp, 16 f/p b/w illus., with rhymes, wrappers, 254x184mm. KMM

5185 THE STORY OF ARCHITECTURE/retold by Eirene Mort/Consolidated Press Ltd./Sydney 1942
108pp, 29 b/w photographic plates, clo., 215x140mm. Grant
5186 THE STORY OF/ARCHITECTURE/retold by/ Eirene Mort/The Shakespeare Head/London New York Sydney Durban Paris/1946
108pp (inc. 4pp glossary), 29pp b/w illus. (some photographic & some drawings), clo., 212x140mm. KP

MORTENSEN, William C.
5187 A/JUNGLE/WEDDING/By/William C. Mortensen
The author, Sydney, n.d. [copyright 1935]
10pp (inc. 1p foreword & 1p author's note at end of text), unillus., wrappers, 145x115mm. NSL:M

ANON [Mortimer, Mrs M., Favell Lee Mortimer, née Bevan]
5188 FAR OFF;/or,/Asia and Australia described./with anecdotes/and/numerous Illustrations/By/The Author of "The Peep of Day",/&c &c/London:/T. Hatchard, 187, Piccadilly./Simpkin, Marshall, & Co., Stationers' Hall Court/1852
xvipp, 316pp & 36pp adv., b/w engraved frontis., engravings in text, folding map, dec clo., 170x105mm. CLRC
Pp278–316 relate to Australia with 1 illus. (Wylie).
5189 FAR OFF;/or,/ASIA AND AUSTRALIA DESCRIBED./With Anecdotes/and/Numerous Illustrations/Part 1/By/The Author of "The Peep of Day",/&c. &c./Eleventh Thousand/London:/T. Hatchard, 187, Piccadilly./Simpkin Marshall, & Co., Stationers' Hall Court./1856
xvi+334pp, 2pp 'Works by the same author', 36pp adv. (dated May. 1856), 1p explanatory note & 4pp preface, b/w frontis., folding map, 43 b/w illus., dec. clo., 170x105mm. CLRC

Only the last 38 pages & one illustrations relate to Australia, & include a description of Eyre's experiences on his overland expedition.
• Rpt as above, fourteenth thousand, 1856 (adv. dated Dec.1857) KMM

5190 FAR OFF;/or,/Australia, Africa and America/ Described/with/Anecdotes and Numerous Illustrations./Part II./By/The Author of "The Peep of Day",/Etc. etc./Eleventh Thousand./London:/ Hatchard & Co. 187 Piccadilly./Simpkin, Marshall, and Co./1860
xvi+416pp & 1p adv. (preceding t.p.), engraved frontis. & engravings in text throughout, 1 folding map, blind-stamped clo., gilt dec., 170x105mm. KMM
The Australian content of Part II is an expanded version of the section appearing in Part I extending to 60pp whereas in Part I it covered only 39pp.
Sixteenth thousand, as above. KP

5191 FAR OFF;/or,/AUSTRALIA, AFRICA, AND AMERICA/Described/with/Anecdotes and Numerous Illustrations/Part II/By/The Author of. . . &c Nineteenth thousand/London:/Hatchard & Co. 187 Piccadilly./Booksellers to H.R.H. The Princess of Wales./Simpkin, Marshall, and Co./1864
Details as above. RM

5192 FAR OFF./Part II./Oceania, Africa, and America/ Described./with anecdotes and two hundred illustrations./by/The author of 'The Peep of Day',/etc etc./Third and corrected issue of/New Edition,/with small maps of Africa and South America./London:/ Longmans, Green, and Co./and New York: 15 East 16th Street./1893
xxivpp, 744pp, 2pp adv., col. frontis., 5 col. & 2 b/w folding maps, b/w engravings, dec clo., gilt kangaroo on spine, 160x100mm. KP
Australia 109pp, NZ 37pp, Papua New Guinea 20pp, Melanesia & Polynesia 77pp.

5193 FAR OFF./Part II./Oceania, Africa, and America/ Described/with anecdotes and illustrations./By/The author of 'The Peep of Day',/etc etc/New and revised edition./Longmans, Green and Co./39 Paternoster Row, London./New York and Bombay./1901
xxiipp, 648pp, col. frontis. & 1 col. plate & numerous engravings, 5 col. & 2 b/w folding maps, dec. clo., 165x100mm. KP
Australia 97pp, NZ 35pp, Papua New Guinea 17pp, Melanesia and Polynesia 48pp.

MORTON, Frank

5194 VERSES FOR MARJORIE/and Some Others/By/ Frank Morton/Author of "Laughter and Tears"/[quotation]/The Lothian Book Publishing Company/Proprietary Limited/Melbourne and Sydney/Printed in England
1916
173pp, 16pp adv., b/w portrait frontis., clo., 185x120mm. NSL:M
The first 25 pages only are addressed to a child.

MORTON, Jean

5195 Jean Morton's/TINGHA/AND/TUCKER/Bedside Book
Jean Morton Enterprises Ltd, 1967, World Distributors Manchester Ltd.
45pp, col. illus. throughout, pic. bd., pic. e/p, 265x195mm. KP

MOSES, Howell G.

5196 THE KANGAROOS/OF AUSTRALIA/Animals of Many Lands/Howell G. Moses/design and pictures by Frank Bird/Geoffrey Chapman/London Dublin Melbourne 1969
32pp, col. illus. on alternate pages, col. pic. wrappers, 140x178mm. KP

MOSLEY, Helen

5197 FOLLOW THE FLUTE/Poems by/Helen Mosley/ Illustrated by/Helen Vincent/Georgian House/ Melbourne
1948
28pp, col. illus. throughout, clo., dec. e/p, 240x180mm. VSL
Another copy, pic. wrappers. KP

MOSELY, J. G

See Life in Australia

MOSS, Franklin

5198 THE VAIN RED FOX/Written by Franklin Moss Pictures by Elaine Haxton/John Sands Pty. Limited/ Sydney and Melbourne
n.d. [1947]
40pp, extended dec. t.p., col. illus. throughout, dec. bd., dec. e/p, 240x180mm. KMM
Contains title story & 7 other stories.

5199 THE/DOVE AND THE EAGLE/By Franklin Moss/ With drawings by Walter Cunningham/John Sands Pty. Ltd./[drawing]/Sydney, Melbourne, Brisbane, Adelaide, Perth, Hobart
n.d. [1956]
30pp, col. illus. throughout, dec. bd., 180x240mm. KMM

'MOSS, Dr I.'

5200 THE JOURNEY TO NEVERCOLD/a fascinating Fairy Story/by Dr. I. Moss [dedicatory &c.]
A. W. Allen Ltd, Melbourne, n.d. [1930]
16pp, 1p riddles, part-col. illus. throughout, dec. wrappers, 180x120mm. NSL:M
Advertisement for 'Irish Moss Gum Jubes' &c.

MOSSENSON, David

JOHN FORREST. *See* Australian Explorers

MOSSMAN, Samuel

5201 HEROES OF DISCOVERY/Magellan, Cook, Park, Franklin,/Livingstone./By Samuel Mossman/Author of 'Our Australian Colonies',/'China: its inhabitants and their institutions',/etc. etc./Edinburgh/Edmonton and Douglas/1868
347pp, 7pp introduction, 24pp adv., engraved portrait frontis. & 4 other portrait engravings, clo., 185x125mm. KMM

5202 HEROES OF DISCOVERY:/Livingston, Park, Franklin,/Cook, Magellan./By Samuel Mossman./ Author of/'Our Australian Colonies,' 'China: its inhabitants and their institutions,'/'New Japan: the Land of the Rising Sun,' etc. etc./New edition, with portraits/Edinburgh:/William Oliphant & Co./1877
First publ. Edinburgh 1868 [1867]
349pp & 1p preface to new edition dated 1877, portrait frontis. & 4 portraits, bevelled dec. bd., 192x130mm. KP

5203 Another copy as above, but with variant imprint: Edinburgh & London/Oliphant Anderson & Ferrier
n.d.
349pp, portrait frontis. & 4 b/w portraits, dec. clo., 204x140mm. CLRC

MOTE, Jerrine

5204 AUSTRALIA/By/Jerrine Mote/Illustrated by/Nell Reppy/1944/Allyn and Bacon/Boston New York Chicago/Atlanta San Francisco Dallas
44pp, dec. t.p., col. illus. throughout, clo., 195x140mm. NSL:M
Another copy as above, 1945. KMM

A Mother's Offering to her Children
See [Barton, Charlotte]

MOUNTEVANS, Lord
See Evans, E. R. G. R., first Baron Mountevans

MOUNTFORD, Charles P.
5205 BROWN MEN/AND RED SAND/Wanderings through wild Australia/by/Charles P. Mountford/ F.R.A.I., F.R.G.S./School Edition Adapted/Robertson & Mullens Ltd./Melbourne
1952
76pp (inc. 2pp glossary), b/w photographic frontis. & 1 diagram in text, wrappers, 180x120mm. HBM
An abridgement of a book written for adults.
5206 BROWN MEN/AND RED SAND/Journeyings in Wild Australia by/Charles P. Mountford/O.B.E., M.A. (Adel.), Dip. Anthrop. (Cantab.)/(Abridged School Edition)/Angus and Robertson
Sydney; first published 1950; this school edition first published 1968
151pp, double-spread b/w map, 16pp b/w photographic illus., pic. wrappers, 180x110mm. KMM

MOUROT, Suzanne
5207 UN AN À NOUMÉA/By/Suzanne Mourot/With a Foreword by/Charles Schindler/Licencié en droit (Paris), M.A./Lecturer in French, University of Queensland/with illustrations/Longman, Green and Co. Ltd./of Paternoster Row, London New York Toronto
1st publ. in England 1939; publ. in Australia 1941
95pp (inc. 3pp foreword) & 12pp index &c, b/w photographic illus., clo., 176x116mm. ANL

5208 UN AN EN AUSTRALIE/By/Suzanne Mourot/ With Illustrations/Longmans, Green and Co. Ltd./of Paternoster Row/London: New York: Toronto
First published 1941; rpt 1944, 1947
86pp (inc. 15pp vocabulary, etc.), 1p note, 1p quotation, 19 b/w photographic illus., limp clo., 185x125mm. KMM
Diary of a visit to Australia written as a school text.

MOXON, Keith
5209 Keith Moxon/CHARLIE/COCKATOO/VISITS THE/INSECT WORLD/The/astonishing/adventures/ of a/very/talkative/bird/Beacon Hill Press/Kansas City, Missouri
1959
95pp, b/w illus. t.p., b/w illus. in text, pic. clo., 190x130mm. NSL:M
Short stories written by a Sydney high school teacher; most of the stories relate to Charlie Cockatoo's adventures in Australia.

MOY, Josie
5210 I/"A LITTLE CHILD SHALL/LEAD THEM"/(A Story founded on fact)/By Josie Moy/II/A BOY'S PRAYER/By T. Lloyd/Melbourne:/Australian Catholic Truth Society./312 Lonsdale St./1915/No. 227 One Penny
16pp, unillus., printed wrappers, 175x120mm. NSL:M

Mrs Possum's Adventure
5211 MRS POSSUM'S ADVENTURE n.d., n.p.
[14]pp inc. cover (possibly one leaf missing), col. illus. on each page & one line text, stiff paper cover title, 317x266mm. KMM
See also STEELE, John V., who appears to have drawn the illus. which are not signed; on front cover 'Printed in Japan, Australian copyright no.6596', same as on cover of 'The Bush Pets' Party'.

MUDIE, Ian
5212 Australian/White Children &/Little Aborigines/All Mainland States/and Tasmania/A/Frank Cork/ Publication/THE/CHRISTMAS KANGAROO/By Ian Mudie
Adelaide 1946
66pp, extended dec. t.p., b/w illus. throughout, illus. Trevor Clare, clo., 215x140mm. KMM

5213 Today Series/TS/AUSTRALIA TODAY/by Ian Mudie/Kaye & Ward Ltd, London/in association with/ Hicks, Smith & Sons/Australia and New Zealand
London, 1970
96pp, b/w photographic frontis. & b/w photographic illus. throughout, bd., 214x175mm. KP
See also Thiele, Colin & Mudie Ian

MUIR, Marcie, (ed.)
5214 STRIKE-A-LIGHT/THE BUSHRANGER/and Other Australian Tales/Edited by/Marcie Muir/Hamish Hamilton—London/Thomas Nelson—Melbourne
1972
151pp (inc. 2pp introduction, 1p acknowledgements), unillus., clo., dustjacket designed by Peter Bate, 235x150mm. KMM
Collection of stories & extracts from early as well as contemporary children's books with an Australian setting.

[MÜLLER, Karl]
5215 AUF FREM DER ERDE./Zwei Erzählungen für die reifere Jugend./von/Offr: Mylius/Inhalt:/JAMES COOK, DER WELTUMSEGLER/oder/was aus einem Schiffsjungen werden Kann;/DER GORILLA-JÄGER./ Erlebnisse und Abenteuer eines jungen Deutschen/in Westafrika./[device]/Mülheim a.d. Ruhr./Verlag von Julius Bagel
n.d. [1881?]
2 books bound together, 128pp, 144pp, col. frontis. & 1 col. plate to each vol., col. pic. bd., with clo. spine, 172x120mm. ATL
The first book relates to James Cook, the second is set in West Africa.

MUMFORD, N. E.
5216 CHIPS
Photogravure, Melbourne, n.d. [1951?]
12pp, stiff pages, col illus. with brief text, pic. wrappers, cover illus. signed N. E. Mumford, 237x176mm. KP
Picture book of small dog among farm animals in gumtree setting with kookaburra on branch of tree, etc.

MUNDELL, Frank
5217 CAPTAIN COOK/The Prince of Navigation/By/ Frank Mundell/Author of/"James A. Garfield", "Stories of the Fire Brigade"/Etc. Etc./With Eight Coloured Plates/London./Andrew Melrose/16 Pilgrim Street, E.C.
n.d. [illustrations dated 1907]
120pp, col. frontis. & 7 f/p col. plates (sgd.'Watson Charlton'), pic. clo., 160x110mm. RM
The World's Heroes Series
Author of *Stories of Travel Adventure*, Sunday School Union (1899), 159pp, containing chapter on Burke & Wills (12pp) and one (11pp) on the Solomon Islands; also
Heroines of Mercy, Sunday School Union, London (1896), 159pp, containing 'The Emigrants Friend' (Caroline Chisholm); and
Stories of the Royal Humane Society, Sunday School

Union (1896), 160pp, containing 'An Australian Grace Darling' (5pp) (Grace Bussell). WRT

The Murder at Rocky Reef
5218 No 314 Vol XXXII/boys' Weekly-Reader/Novelette/A Complete Story Weekly/THE MURDER AT ROCKY REEF/[illus. with caption 'Lynch him! Lynch the murderous wretch!' cried the men]
Publ. between 1861 and 1870
24pp, unillus., pic. wrappers, 210x138mm. CLRC [facsimile]

MURDOCH, Walter Logie Forbes
5219 ANNE'S ANIMALS/Verses/By/Walter Murdoch/Illustrations/By/Mrs. Arthur Streeton/Commonwealth of Australia/Sydney J. Endacott/Melbourne/1921
34pp, b/w drawings throughout, illus. wrappers, 210x140mm. Grant
Second edition 1922, as above. KMM

MURPHY, Elizabeth G.
5220 THE FAIRY TREE/by/Elizabeth G. Murphy/[drawing]/Published for the author by/Whitcombe & Tombs Pty. Ltd./Melbourne Sydney Perth
nd. [1949]
33pp, b/w frontis. & 4 b/w drawings, dec. wrappers, 180x120mm. ANL

MURPHY, Sutton
5221 BERTIE KANGAROO/By/Sutton Murphy/Pictures by/Eve Rockwell
Rand McNally, Chicago, n.d. [196-?]
28pp, numerous col. illus., col. pic. bd., 140x110mm. KP

[MURRAY, Andrew]
THE BLACK OPAL MINE. *See* The Sexton Blake Library

MURRAY, E. R.
5222 TO A CHILD/and other Verses/By/E. R. Murray/[decoration]/Illustrations by/Ian McBain/W. R. Smith & Paterson Pty. Ltd./Marshall St., The Valley, Brisbane/[7 lines acknowledgements]
n.d. [1936]
23pp, col. frontis. & marginal drawings, dec. wrappers, 220x180mm. ANL

MURRAY, Kit
5223 AUSTRALIAN STORIES/FOR CHILDREN/By/Kit Murray/Illustrated by/Edward Scott-Snell/London/Houghton & Scott-Snell/Regent House, Regent Street, W.1.
n.d. [1935]
62pp, col. frontis. & 1 col. illus., 4 b/w illus., clo., 205x145mm. NSL:M

MURRAY, Mary Beth
MY CHILDHOOD AUTOBIOGRAPHY/True Reminiscences of My Happy Childhood/by/Mary Beth Murray, Blind Novelist/[verse]
Adelaide, n.d. [1944]
Not a children's book; simple reminiscences of childhood.

MUSICAL NURSERY RHYMES PICTURE BOOK
See Outhwaite, Ida Rentoul

MUSMAN, Richard
5224 CAPTAIN COOK/Richard Musman/[b/w portrait]/Illustrated by Biro/Maps by Kathleen Dance/[device]/Hutchinson Educational
London 1967
95pp & 1p book list, 5 f/p b/w illus., 1 diagram & b/w drawings in text, clo., map e/p, 180x115mm. KMM

Swedish edition
5225 Richard Musman/[vignette]/JAMES COOK/UPPTÄCKTSRESANDE/Natur och Kultur—Stockholm 1969
136pp (inc. 1p list of dates), 1 f/p b/w illus., 20 b/w drawings, diagrams, maps, etc., col. pic. bd., 185x110mm. RM

Mxxxx, Le Baron de
5226 PETITS/VOYAGES PITTORESQUES/Dans L'Asie,/L'Afrique, L'Amérique,/La Polynésie/Et Les Terres Australes;/Contenant/La Description des principaux pays de ces/parties du monde, et celle de leurs habitants,/Avec trente-deux planches colriées soigneusement,/représentant les costumes de tous ces peuples./Par M. Le Baron de Mxxxx/Tome Premier/A Paris,/Chez Saintain, Libraire de S. M. L'Impératrice,/rue du Foin-Saint-Jacques, No 11/1813
2 vols: vol. 1 iv +107 +95pp ('interesting anecdotes'), col. frontis. & 16 col. engravings, embossed morocco, 118x93mm; vol. 2 iv + 106 +94pp ('interesting facts'), col. frontis. & 13 col. engravings, embossed morocco, 118x93mm. ANL

My ABC
5227 MY/ABC
Edward Fahey, Educational Publications, Bridge St, Sydney, n.d. [195-?]
32pp, col. illus. & letters, col. illus. wrappers, 135x205mm. KP

My ABC of Puppy Dogs
5228 MY/ABC/OF PUPPY DOGS
Australian Universities Press Pty Ltd., 1971. Printed in Hong Kong
[26]pp, col. photographic illus. throughout, col. pic. bd., cover title, 305x243mm
Playtime Series. KMM

My Book of Heroism
5229 The Children's Favourite Series/MY BOOK/OF/HEROISM/[device]/London/Edward Arnold/37, Bedford Street, Strand, W.C./(All rights reserved)
n.d. [189-?]
192pp, b/w frontis. & b/w engraving in text, pic. clo., 185x135mm. CLRC
Contains 'An Australian Heroine' (Grace Bussell & the wreck of the *Georgette* off the WA coast (6pp).

My Book of Playtime and Rhyme
5230 MY BOOK OF/PLAYTIME/AND RHYME
Georgian House, Melbourne, n.d.
8pp, col. illus. throughout, pic. covers, cover title, bd., 150x115mm. KP

My Book of Farmyard Friends
5230a MY BOOK OF/FARMYARD FRIENDS
n.p., n.d.
Uniform with above. KP

My Book of Speed
5231 MY BOOK OF SPEED
Georgian House, Melbourne, n.d. [194-?]
10pp of illus., dec. bd., all printed on bd., cover title, 150x116mm. ANL

My Day at the Zoo Book
5232 MY/DAY AT THE ZOO/BOOK
Hikarinokuni Showa Pub. Co. Ltd, n.d. Printed in Japan
12pp (inc. covers), col. photographic illus. printed on bd., cover title, 256x180mm. KP
Front cover illus. of koalas, 2pp kangaroos, 1p penguins.

'My Farm Pals'
5233 "MY FARM PALS"
Bridge Printery, 117 Reservoir Street, Sydney, n.d. [1950?]
[16]pp, illus. throughout, b/w & part-col. & with col. double-spread, light card wrappers, col. illus., 238x180mm. MC
Verses & illus. throughout. Also listed 'My Pals' Dolls, My Zoo Pals, My Pals' Pussies.'

My First Story Book
5234 MY FIRST/STORY BOOK
Hackett's, London, Sydney, n.d. Printed in the Netherlands
57pp, part col. illus. throughout, col. pic. bd., dec e/p, 242x185mm
'Hillside Series'. One story by John Tombs, Gay Gordon, F. S. Raeburn, Sheila Faen. Cover design & some illus. Pixie O'Harris. KP

My Happy Nursery Rhymes
5235 MY HAPPY/NURSERY RHYMES
Barker & Co., Melbourne, n.d. [1941]
[16]pp, col. illus. throughout, pic. wrappers, cover title, 286x216mm. KMM

My Magic Garden
5236 MY/MAGIC/GARDEN
An 'O'Possum' Australian Production, Sydney, n.d. [1946?]
16pp, col. illus. throughout, dec. wrappers, cover title, 240x185mm. ANL
Verses, puzzles, stories &c.

My Nursery Rhymes
5237 MY NURSERY RHYMES
Offset Printing Coy Pty Ltd, Sydney, n.d.
16pp (inc. covers), col. illus. (Anne Drew) on alternate pages, pic. wrappers, 250x185mm. VMOU

My Pals' Dogs
5238 MY PALS' DOGS
Standard Publishing House, 69 Nelson Street, Rozelle, NSW, n.d. [195-?]
16pp, b/w & part-col. illus. throughout, col. pic. covers, cover title, 235x182mm. KP
Verses about different breeds of dogs & a page of hints on dog care.

My Rhyme Book
5239 MY RHYME BOOK
W. H. Honey Pub Co., 31 Cunningham St., Sydney
8pp (inc. covers), 4 col. illus. & others printed in blue/white, pic. covers, cover title, 200x123mm. KP
Printed on light bd. Illus. signed 'Jordan'.

My Transport Book
5240 MY TRANSPORT/BOOK/Series 7-6
Printed & publ. by Allied Enterprises, Sydney, n.d.
8pp, col. illus. throughout, col. pic. wrappers, cover title, 268x214mm. KMM

'MYLIUS, Offr.'
AUF FREM DER ERDE. *See* [Müller, Karl]

MYLNE, Kathleen A.
See Challands, Mary Ethel & Mylne, Kathleen

'MYSTERY, John' [pseud. Lester Sinclair]
5241 John Mystery's/FAERIE/BLUE MOUNTAINS/A Fantasy for children of to-day and to-morrow/from the land of must be/[quotation]
n.d. [1954]
88pp (inc. 1p dedication to the Queen & 7pp poems & quotations &c), unillus., full blue morocco covers, pic. e/p, 280x214mm. RM
Short stories & poems about Australia featuring the two sisters Pearl and Plain. Book was written, publ. & bound especially to be presented to The Queen during her tour of the Blue Mountains on the Royal Visit of 1954.

5242 John Mystery's/ADVENTURE/TALES/[8 lines verse]/Publicity Press (1938) Pty Ltd./Regent Street, Sydney
[96]pp (inc. 3pp adv.), b/w illus., col. pic. wrappers, 282x210mm. JH
Also listed in this series:
Adventure Tales
Baby Bunting's Big Book
Captain Kidd's Good Book
Sweethearts Good Book, all unseen

5243 THE/ADVENTURES/OF/[illus.]/THE/WOOLLY SISTERS/PEARL AND PLAIN JANE
Publicity Press (1938) Pty Ltd, Sydney, n.d. [194-?]
96pp (inc. 9pp introduction &c), 11 f/p black & yellow illus. & b/w drawings throughout, pic. wrappers, 280x200mm. CLRC
Adv. inside front cover & both sides back cover.

5244 John Mystery's/BLUE/SUNSHINE/[illus.]/—Again The Woolly Sisters/PEARL AND PLAIN
Publicity Press (1938) Pty Ltd, Sydney, n.d. [194-?]
96pp (inc. 11pp introduction &c), black & yellow frontis. & b/w drawings throughout, printed on yellow paper, pic. wrappers, 280x200mm. CLRC

5245 John Mystery presents/again PEARL AND PLAIN/IN/GREEN WATERS/[8 lines verse]/Printed and Published by/Publicity Press (1938) Pty Ltd./71–75 Regent St. Sydney
n.d.
96pp, b/w illus. throughout, pic. card cover, 276x207mm. JH

5246 John Mystery's/BIG/PARADE/[verse]/Printed and Published by/Publicity Press (1938) Pty Ltd./Regent Street/Sydney
n.d.
311pp & 9pp adv. &c, b/w illus. throughout, pic. bd., 270x205mm. JH

5247 JOHN MYSTERY'S/BOY'S/STORY/TIME/TO. . . /From . . .
Publicity Press (1938) Pty Ltd, 71–75 Regent St, Sydney
75pp (inc. front & back pastedowns), 7 f/p b/w illus. & 1 part-col. & drawings in text, pic. bd., 248x186mm. KMM
Some illus. signed Walter Bowman. Anonymous re-telling of traditional & other tales with no reference to Australia except in the editor's letter at end of book (adv. the series).

5248 John Mystery's/BOYS'/BUMPER/BOOK/[8 lines verse]/Publicity Press (1938) Pty Ltd/Particular Printers and Publishers/71–75 Regent Street, Sydney
96pp (inc. 3pp adv.), b/w illus., col. pic. card wrappers, 280x205mm. JH

5249 A John Mystery Book/BUMPER BOOK/FOR GIRLS/[drawing]/Other John Mystery Books [3 columns]/Lonsdale & Bartholomew/Art Publishers/Sydney
n.d. [inscribed 1943]
128pp, b/w illus., col. pic. wrappers, 280x200. CLRC

5250 John Mystery's/GIRLS'/BUMPER BOOK/[verse]/Publicity Press (1938) Pty Ltd./Particular Printers and Publishers,/71–75 Regent Street, Sydney

93pp (inc. 3pp adv.), b/w illus. throughout, pic. wrappers, 284x204mm. JH

5251 John Mystery's/BURIED TREASURE/[8 lines verse]/Publicity Press (1938) Pty Ltd./Particular Printers and Publishers/Regent Street, Sydney
94pp & 2pp adv., b/w illus. throughout, col. pic. wrappers, 276x205mm. JH
Also listed in this series:
5252 COWBOYS
5253 DETECTIVES
5254 GHOSTS all unseen

5255 John Mystery's BUTTON BUNNIES/HOPEFUL HEARTS
Sydney, n.d.
12pp b/w illus., 4pp col. illus., col. pic. wrappers, 366x246mm. KP
Australian animals included. *Button Bunny Books*: Home Sweet Home; Faithful Friends; Hopeful Hearts; Joy Bells.

5256 John Mystery's/CAMP/FIRE/HOUR/[8 lines verse]/Printed and Published by/Publicity Press (1938) Pty Ltd/Regent Street, Sydney
64pp, b/w illus., col. pic. wrappers, 275x205mm. CLRC
Some illus. signed 'J. Butler'.
Also listed in this series:
5257 PILGRIM'S PROGRESS
5258 ROMANTIC HOUR
5259 THRILL TIME

5260 A John Mystery Book/'COBBERS'/AUSTRALIAN/CHILDREN'S/ANNUAL/Other John Mystery Books/"Story-Time" Series [6 listed]/"Little People" Series [4 listed]/"Colour Book" Series [4 listed]/Lonsdale & Bartholomew/(Aust) Pty Ltd./Art Publishers/Sydney
128pp, b/w illus. throughout, col. pic. wrappers, 285x205mm. JH

5261 John Mystery's/COBBERS'/ANNUAL/[8 lines verse]/John Mystery/Publicity Press (1938) Pty Ltd./Particular Printers and Publishers,/71–75 Regent Street, Sydney
96pp (inc. 3pp adv.), b/w drawings in text, pic. wrappers, 284x210mm. KMM
Miscellaneous stories, verses, articles, all anonymous.

5262 JOHN MYSTERY'S/DEEDLEDUMS/ANIMALS
John Mystery's Productions Ltd, Sydney
10pp, col. illus. on every page (Betty Lou), pic. wrappers, 240x140mm. TG

5263 JOHN MYSTERY'S DEEDLEDUM'S/DOG/LAND
John Mystery's Productions Pty Ltd, 71–75 Regent St, Sydney, n.d. [inscribed 1949]
10pp, col. illus. throughout, col. illus. wrappers, cover title, 237x175mm. TG

5264 JOHN MYSTERY'S/DEEDLEDUM'S/TEDDY/BEARS
John Mystery's Productions Pty Ltd., Sydney
[12]pp (inc. card covers), col. illus. on every page, col. pic. cover, cover title, 225x175mm. JH

5265 JOHN MYSTERY'S/DEEDLEDUM'S/BEACH BOOK
As above. JH

5266 John Mystery's/EXCITING/TALES/[verse]/Printed and Published by/Publicity Press (1938) Pty Ltd./71–75 Regent St. Sydney
n.d.
96pp, b/w illus. throughout, col. pic. stiff wrapper, 284x212mm. CLRC

5267 Read and Colour/John Mystery's/FAIRY/FROLICS
Lonsdale & Bartholomew Pty Ltd, Sydney, n.d.
[10]pp, col. & b/w illus., pic. wrappers, cover title, 233x188mm. KMM

5268 JOHN MYSTERY'S FAMOUS GIANTS
Publicity Press (1938) Pty Ltd, Regent St, Sydney
64pp, b/w illus. throughout, pic. cover title, 275x205mm. Dromkeen

5269 John Mystery's/FAMOUS/ROBBERS/[8 lines verse]/Printed and Published by/Publicity Press (1938) Pty Ltd.,/71–75 Regent St, Sydney
n.d.
64pp, b/w drawings throughout, pic. wrappers, 280x208mm. KMM

5270 John Mystery's/FUN OF THE FAIR/TO/COLOUR
John Mystery Productions Pty Ltd., Sydney
[12]pp, b/w illus. & 4pp in part-col., col. pic. wrappers, cover title, 240x178mm. JH

5271 John Mystery's/GET-WELL/BOOK/By/Pearl and Plain/500 other John Mystery Books/for children of all ages/[verse]/Printed and Published by/Publicity Press (1938) Pty Ltd./71–75 Regent Street, Sydney
n.d.
48pp, b/w illus. throughout, pic. wrappers, 276x210mm. KMM
Some illus. signed 'Matt'.

5272 John Mystery presents/GIPSY BOY IN/TORTURE/TOWN/[8 lines verse]/Printed and Published by/Publicity Press (1938) Pty. Ltd./Regent Street, Sydney
64pp (inc. 4pp adv.), b/w illus., col. pic. card covers, 278x208mm. JH
In this series: Gipsy Boy in Ghost Island.

5273 John Mystery's/GIRLS/GET WELL/BOOK/[8 lines verse]/Printed and Published by/Publicity Press (1938) Pty Ltd./Regent Street, Sydney
48pp, b/w illus. throughout (J. Butler), col. light bd., pic. covers, 275x205mm. JH

5274 John Mystery's/GIRLS' STORY/BOOK
Publicity Press, Sydney, n.d.
75pp (inc. back pastedown & 2pp adv.), col. frontis. & b/w illus., col. pic. bd. (4pp printed on light card), cover title, 244x184mm. JH

5275 John Mystery's/IN BLINKY LAND/WITH FAIRY/BEAUTY/[8 lines verse]/Publicity Press (1938) Pty Ltd./Particular Printers and Publishers/Regent Street/Sydney
[64]pp (last 2pp adv.), b/w illus., col. pic. card wrappers, 280x208mm. JH

5276 A John Mystery Book/IN BLINKY LAND/With/The/Brothers/Grimm/Other John Mystery Books/[lists in 3 columns follow]Lonsdale & Bartholomew/(Aust) Pty Ltd/Art Publishers/Sydney
[64]pp, b/w illus. throughout, stiff pic. wrappers, 280x200mm. Dromkeen
Listed in same series: In Blinky Land with Hans Andersen.

5277 John Mystery's/IN BLINKYLAND/WITH/MOTHER GOOSE/[verse]/Printed and Published by/Publicity Press (1938) Pty Ltd/71–75 Regent St Sydney
[60]pp, b/w illus. in text, pic. wrappers, 278x206mm. WRT
Illus. signed 'Betty van der Pot'.

5278 John Mystery's/LOVELY/TALES/[8 lines verse]/Printed and Published by/Publicity Press (1938) Pty Ltd/Regent Street, Sydney

96pp (inc. 3pp adv.), b/w illus., col. pic. card covers, 275x205mm. JH

5279 John Mystery's/MAGIC/LAND/WITH/THE WOOLLY SISTERS/Pearl and Plain Jane/[drawing]/ Lonsdale & Bartholomew/(Aust) Pty Ltd./Art Publishers/Sydney
n.d. [inscr. 1943]
[48]pp, b/w illus., col. pic. light card covers, 275x205mm. JH

5280 John Mystery's/MONEY BOOK/'PINK PIG'
Publicity Press Pty Ltd, Sydney, n.d.
[6]pp, b/w illus., col. pic. card covers, cover title, 88x120mm. KMM
Instructions to make a 'Pink Pig' money box from a condensed milk tin.

5281 A John Mystery Book/MOTHER GOOSE/ BED-TIME/TALES/Other John Mystery Books [various series listed]/Lonsdale & Bartholomew/(Aust.) Pty Ltd./Art Publishers/Sydney
n.d.
[32]pp, b/w illus., col. pic. wrappers, 280x204mm. JH
Front cover signed 'Matt.'

5282 MOTHER GOOSE RHYME AND STORY BOOK
[80]pp, b/w illus., cover missing, 283x206mm. JH
Exciting Series.

5283 Tiny Tots/Everynight/Series/John Mystery/ Present/"MOTHER'S/GO-TO-BED/TALES"
Lonsdale & Bartholomew, n.d. [inscribed 1942]
10pp (inc. insides of front & back wrappers), b/w illus. throughout, col. pic. wrappers, cover title, 187x240mm. CLRC

5284 A John Mystery Book/MY BEST/FAIRY/TALES/ [drawing]/Other John Mystery Books [list follows]/ Lonsdale & Bartholomew/(Aust.) Pty ltd./Art Publishers/Sydney
n.d.
32pp, b/w drawings in text, pic. wrappers, 285x205mm. CLRC
Traditional fairy tales.

5285 MY BIG BOOK OF SHIPS/John Mystery
Publicity Press (1938) Pty Ltd.
12pp (inc. 6 f/p col. illus.), b/w illus. in text, col. pic. light card wrappers, cover title, 370x243mm. JH
Listed inside front cover:
5286 My Big ABC Book
5287 My Big Book of Aeroplanes
5288 My Big Book of Horses
5289 My Big Book of Ships
5290 My Big Book of Speed
5291 My Big Book of Trains
all unseen

5292 MY/LITTLE SAILOR'S/BOOK
Publicity Press, Sydney, n.d.
[12]pp, 6pp col. illus. & b/w illus. on others, pic. wrappers, cover title, 274x210mm. KMM

5293 MY/LITTLE SOLDIER'S/BOOK
n.d. [1942?]
[8]pp, 4pp col. illus. & b/w illus. in text, pic. wrappers, cover title, 280x206mm. Dromkeen

5294 A John Mystery Book/OMNIBUS/FOR/ EVERYONE/[drawing]/[adv. for other John Mystery Books] Lonsdale & Bartholomew/(Aust) Pty Ltd/Art Publishers/Sydney
n.d.
[62]pp, b/w illus. throughout, pic. wrappers, 280x204mm. TG

5295 A John Mystery Book/Simplified version of/ PILGRIM'S/PROGRESS/By John Bunyan/Other John Mystery Books/[series listed]/Lonsdale & Bartholomew/(Aust) Pty Ltd./Art Publishers/Sydney
n.d.
[64]pp (inc. 4pp introduction), b/w illus. throughout (sgd 'Matt'), 26 f/p b/w illus. & drawings in text, pic. wrappers, 285x210mm. CLRC

5296 John Mystery/Presents/His Little Dog/THE CRANKY PRANKS/OF/PUPPY SMUT/BUNNY'S TALE
Publicity Press, Sydney
[12]pp (inc. covers), b/w illus. throughout, col. pic. front cover, cover title 185x243mm. JH
Twelve Puppy Smut titles listed in series, unseen.

5297 John Mystery's/ROMANTIC/HOUR/[verse]/ Publicity Press (1938) Pty. Ltd./Particular Printers and Publishers, 71–75 Regent St., Sydney
[61]pp & 2pp adv., b/w illus. throughout, pic. wrappers, 285x210mm. TG

5298 A John Mystery Book/ROMANTIC/HOUR/FOR GIRLS/[drawing] Other John Mystery Books/[3 series listed]/Lonsdale & Bartholomew/(Aust) Pty Ltd./Art Publishers/Sydney
[64]pp, b/w illus., pic. wrappers, 284x204mm. JH

5299 John Mystery's/SWEETHEART'S/GOOD BOOK/ [verse]/Printed and Published by/Publicity Press(1938) Pty Ltd/Regent Street, Sydney
93pp & 3pp adv., b/w illus., pic. wrappers, 280x214mm. TG
Stories, verse &c.

5300 John Mystery's Tiny Teachers/SLEEPING/BEAUTY
8pp, b/w illus., col. pic. wrappers, cover title, 156x127mm. CLRC
Story told in form of alphabet & printed inside both wrappers. 16 titles in series (from adv.).

5301 John Mystery's/THE TOOBOOTY TWINS/"FIND A MOTHER"/To our Happy Home
John Mystery's Productions Pyt Ltd., Sydney
[16]pp, sepia illus. on 12pp & 4pp printed in col., pic. wrappers, cover title, 254x194mm. JH
Front cover signed 'Betty van der Pot'. JH

5302 A John Mystery Book/THRILL TIME/FOR BOYS/ [drawing]/Other John Mystery Books/Story Time Series [list of titles]/"Little People" Series [list of titles]/"Colour Book" Series [list of titles]/Lonsdale & Bartholomew/(Aust) Pty Ltd./Art Publishers/Sydney
[64]pp, b/w illus. throughout, col. pic. wrappers, 285x205mm. JH

5303 John Mystery's/ THRILL TIME/[8 lines verse sgd.'John Mystery']Publicity Press (1938) Pty Ltd/ Particular Printers and Publishers/ 71–75 Regent St.,Sydney
n.d.
[64]pp [last 2 pp adv.], b/w illus. throughout, col. pic. wrappers, 285x205mm. KMM

5304 JOHN MYSTERY'S WHY/HORSES/NEIGH/Laugh and Learn/with Bookie Worm
Publicity Press (1938), 71–75 Regent St, Sydney
[12]pp, b/w illus., 2pp col. illus., col. pic. card covers, cover title, 235x180mm. JH

5305 Laugh and Learn/with/Bookie Worm/John Mystery's/WHY KOALAS/CRY
Publicity Press (1938) Pty Ltd, Sydney, n.d.
[12]pp, 1 col. double-spread illus., b/w illus. throughout, stiff pic. wrappers, 240x180mm. KMM

5306 John Mystery/Adventures of Rosie No. 1/WHY/COWS/MOO/[drawing]/Other John Mystery Books/[series listed] Lonsdale & Bartholomew/(Aust) Pty. Ltd./Art Publishers/Sydney
[32]pp, b/w illus. throughout (signed 'Matt Heriot'), col. pic. wrappers, 290x205mm. CLRC

5307 John Mystery/Adventures of Rosie No 2/WHY/FROGS/CROAK/Other John Mystery Books/[numerous titles listed]/Lonsdale & Bartholomew/(Aust) Pty Ltd./Art Publishers/Sydney
n.d. [194-?]
[32]pp, b/w illus. throughout (inc. on t.p.), pic. paper wrappers, 290x204mm. KMM
Illus. signed 'Matt'.
John Mystery Pocket Books. Rpt of classics
A Christmas Carol
The Heroes
The Old Curiosity Shop
What Katy Did
What Katy Did at School
All rpts of overseas books and so not of Australian interest. JH

N., A.V.E.
5308 LOST IN THE BUSH:/A True Tale./and/THE IDIOT./By A.V.E.N./[device]/The Profits...etc. [3 lines]/Tenth Edition./London:/Saunders, Otley, & Co., 66, Brook Street, W.1/Reigate: W. Allingham, Market Place./1865/(All rights reserved)
31pp, unillus., wrappers, 180x120mm. NSL:M
There is a 2pp preface which describes the story of the Duff children on which the first poem is based.

NANKIVELL, Joice [Mrs J. M. Loch]
5309 THE/COBWEB LADDER/By/Joice Nankivell/Illustrated by Edith Alsop/The Lothian Book Publishing Company/Proprietary Limited/Melbourne and Sydney/Printed in England
First published September 1916
61pp, 7 f/p b/w illus. & b/w drawings in text throughout, pic. bd., pic. e/p, 280x205mm. NSL:M

NAPIER, S. Elliott
5310 ON THE/BARRIER REEF/A Story of Australia's Coral Wonderland/Abridged for use in Schools/by/S. Elliott Napier/For Children aged 12 to 14 years/Australia:/Cornstalk Publishing Company/89 Castlereagh Street, Sydney/1928
105pp, b/w frontis., b/w photographic illus. & maps, wrappers, 185x130mm. NSL:M
- Rpt 1929 as above. Grant
- Rpt 1932 but 'Angus & Robertson Limited.' CLRC
- Rpt 5th ed, 1933
- Rpt 6th ed 1934, both unseen

NATHAN, Isaac
5311 HEY-DIDDLE-DIDDLE!/Composed by I. Nathan/Ent. Sta. Hall—Price 3 shillings./[music and words—for Soprano Primo, Soprano Secondo, Alto tenore/Basso primo e secondo./Pianoforte/]Sydney—Published for the composer, Byron Lodge, Randwick
n.d. [prior to author's death in 1864 as copy inscribed by author]
8pp, unillus., music & words, paper cover, 322x257mm. KMM
Adv. lower half of back wrapper. Also adv. 'Preparing for Press, composed and arranged by I. Nathan, for Voice and chorus, "Jack and Jill" '.

NATT, Hilaire
5312 QUENTIN/A Story of a Little Quokka/I can read books/Written by/Hilaire Natt, B.A., Dip. Ed./Illustrations Amahk
Printed by Muhlings Pty Ltd, for 'I Can Read Books' 596–598 Hay Street, Perth, WA, 1965
16pp, b/w illus. throughout, wrappers, cover title, 185x250mm. KMM

5313 Another copy as above, but imprint on back cover: "I can Read Books",/c/- Marshall and Marshall/168 St George's Terrace, Perth,/Western Australia
[1965?]
Slip inside front wrapper with some information concerning quokkas & announcing future books. KP

5314 Another copy as before with above information printed inside front wrapper. Imprint:
Produced by Murray Views Pty Ltd./Gympie, Q. Australia
This copy is printed with a different type & a few minor changes in layout. KP

Naughty Maggie
See Shaped Books

NEAL, Laura
SNOW COUNTRY. *See* Life in Australia

Ned Kelly: The Iron-clad Australian Bushranger
See Borlase, James Skipp

Ned Kelly the Ironclad Australian Bushranger
5315 NED KELLY/THE/IRONCLAD/AUSTRALIAN BUSHRANGER/[illus.]
n.p., n.d.
47pp, unillus., back wrapper blank, cover title, 270x210mm. CLRC
Inside front cover illus. of Ned Kelly holding up a coach with the title
'Ned Kelly the King/of Australian Bushrangers'./Wholesale from D. R. Burnside, 79 Frederick Street, Glasgow

Ned Nimble amongst the Bushrangers of Australia
5316 NED NIMBLE/AMONGST THE/BUSHRANGERS OF AUSTRALIA./Complete./Beautifully Illustrated./London./Harkaway House, 6, West Harding Street, Fetter Lane./Fleet Street, E.C., and all Booksellers
n.d.
264pp, 8pp adv., b/w frontis., 16 f/p b/w illus. & 1 f/p col. illus. (loosely inserted), pic. wrappers (with adv. verso back wrapper), 255x180mm. RM
As advertised in others of the same publisher's series, the coloured illustration was probably given away with one of the parts. There is a separate title page, & the front cover has on it 'Price 6d.'.

Needles Hooks to Yarns
5317 NEEDLES/HOOKS to/YARNS/A Beginner's Guide to/Knitting & Crocheting/by/Villawool/[illus. of a girl sitting cross-legged, knitting]/50 cents
Villawood [*sic*] Textile Company, 255 George Street, Sydney
n.d. [197-?]
34pp (inc. inside front cover & both sides back cover), col. & b/w illus. throughout, col. pic. wrappers, cover title, 272x200mm. KP

'NEELIA'
See Burrow, Aileen L.

NESDALE, Ira
5318 RIVERBEND BRICKY/Ira Nesdale/[drawing]/Illustrated by Charles Keeping/Blackie & Son Limited/London and Glasgow
1960
96pp, b/w & part. col. illus. throughout, clo., 195x130mm. BBC

5319 BRICKY/AND THE HOBO/Ira Nesdale/[drawing]/

Illustrated by Charles Keeping/Blackie/London and Glasgow
1964
78pp, 14 drawings in text, bd., 198x130mm. CLRC
Some drawings printed in two col. Set in small town on the river Murray.

NEVILLE, Kenneth de L.
5320 IT BEGAN WITH/DALTON THE DOLPHIN/by/Kenneth de L. Neville/Illustrations by/Joan de L. Neville
N.S.W. Bookstall, Sydney, n.d. [1944]
107pp, 4 f/p col. illus. & b/w drawings throughout, stiff pic. wrappers, 235x180mm. NSL:M

NEW, Anne
5321 MY NATIVE PLACE/and other Songs/Music by Illay Lee/English by Anne New/Illustrated by Esmond New/Masan Korea/1938
36pp, title in border in b/w dec., b/w illus. throughout, pic. wrappers, 265x195mm. KP
21 songs with music & words in both Korean & English. Preface in Korean by Eunsang Lee, Korean poet, & in English by Dr Alice R. Appenzellar. Anne New (d. 1968), born in Australia, was the wife of Rev. Esmond New, Victorian Presbyterian church minister, missionary to Korea, 1936–41, 1949–55.

NEW, Esmond
5322 LET'S GO TO KOREA/An Introduction to Korea and/the Koreans/[drawing]/Issued by the Australian Presbyterian Board of Missions,/Margaret Street, Sydney, New South Wales/Price 2/-
n.d.
60pp, maps inside covers, b/w illus. throughout, pic. wrappers, 218x140mm. ANL

5323 THE TAME/DRAGON/A Story of Korea for the children/Written and illustrated by E. W. New
Aust. Presbyterian Mission, Kyumasan, Korea, n.d.
14pp, 6 f/p & 1 double-spread col. illus., col. pic. wrappers, 270x190mm. KP

New Australian Fairy Tales
5324 NEW AUSTRALIAN/FAIRY TALES/Illustrated by/A. J. Shackel/Blocks by/Prebble &/James/109 Flinders Lane/Melbourne/Published by/George Breston Pty. Ltd./127 Queen St. Melbourne C.1.
n.d. [1933]
44pp, dec. t.p., part-col. illus. throughout, bd., 245x185mm. ANL Series No.1
Contains: 'Bunyip and the Haunted Hills', 'Koala and the Mayor of Mt. Dandendong', 'Kanga and Kooka', & others

A New Book of Old Rhymes
5325 A NEW BOOK OF OLD RHYMES/Illustrated by Barbara Macdonald/[biographical note on artist]/Art in Australia Limited/24 Bond Street/Sydney.
n.d. [drawings dated 1920]
13 loose sheets in addition to t.p., with stylized drawings in full colour, each illustrating a traditional nursery rhyme, the text of which is also printed alongside. All enclosed in a portfolio cover. 285x295mm. KMM

NEWBERRY, Agnes
5326 INTRODUCING/PIP/AND/PEPITA/Agnes Newberry
Murfett Pty. Ltd, Melbourne, n.d. [1944]
16pp, 7 f/p col. illus., dec. wrappers, cover title, 240x180mm. ANL

5327 PEPITA'S/BABY/Agnes Newberry
Murfett Pty Ltd, Melbourne, n.d. [1944]
16pp, 7 f/p col. illus., dec. wrappers, cover title, 240x180mm. ANL
See also Maltby, Peg for others in series

NEWBOLT, Henry
5328 THE BOOK OF/THE LONG TRAIL/By/Henry Newbolt/Author of 'Submarine and Anti-submarine Tales of the Great War' etc./with a coloured frontispiece and/thirty other illustrations/By Stanley L. Wood/Tenth impression/Longmans, Green and Co. Ltd./39 Paternoster Row London E.C.4/New York Toronto/Bombay Calcutta and Madras/1926/All rights reserved
First published Oct. 1919; rpt 1919, 1921, 1922 (twice), 1923, 1924 (twice), 1925
312pp, col. frontis. & 30 b/w illus., clo., 190x130mm. PR
Contents include section on Burke & Wills, & on Wollaston of Papua

5329 THE BOOK OF/THE LONG TRAIL/By/Henry Newbolt/With a coloured frontispiece and thirty other illustrations/By Stanley L. Wood/Longmans Green and Co./London, New York Toronto/1931
312pp, 12pp introduction, etc., col. frontis. & 30 b/w illus., clo., 185x125mm. PR
On front cover: 'The Venture Library'.

[NEWCOMBE, Samuel Prout]
5330 LITTLE HENRY'S/RECORDS/OF HIS LIFE-TIME./By the author of "Pleasant Pages"/OLD/EIGHTEEN-FIFTY-TWO;/A Tale for Any Day/in/1853./Being the Second Annual Volume of the/History of the Present/Half-Century./London:/Houlston and Stoneman; and all Book Sellers.
n.d. [inscribed Christmas 1852]
116pp & 4pp adv. & adv. inside both covers ("Pleasant Pages, a Journal of Instruction for Families and Schools"), b/w frontis. (The Duke of Wellington), dec. t.p., 4 f/p illus. (of Australian subjects) & 4pp other illus., dec. clo., 135x105mm. CLRC
Old Eighteen fifty two consists of 4 parts:
1 Introduction—The Colonist from Australia
2 News from the Colonies—How Australia became known; Description of Australia; How Australia became important [Australian content first 50pp.]
3 The News from England—The Duke of Wellington &c
4 The News from Foreign Countries

NEWELL, Averil
5331 THE/ENCHANTED SEAS/by Averil Newell/with four illustrations/in colour by/Ida Rentoul Outhwaite/A. & C. Black Ltd./4, 5 & 6 Soho Square, London, W.1
1937
64pp, col. frontis. & 3 f/p col. illus., clo., 180x120mm. KMM
Doubtful whether author was Australian.
• Rpt 1942. Grant

5332 THE/RED WITCH/By/Averil Newell/with four illustrations/in colour by/Ida Rentoul Outhwaite/A & C Black Ltd/4 5 & 6 Soho Square, London, W.1
1937
64pp, 4 col. plates (signed 'IRO'), blue clo. cover, 180x120mm. KMM

NEWELL, Crosby & LEAVENS, George
5333 KIPPY/THE KOALA/Pictures by George Leavens/Words by Crosby Newell/Designed by Luc Bouchage/Harper & Brothers Publishers New York/To Kay and Mike/Kippy the Koala/[copyright information 1960]
[32]pp, b/w photographic illus. throughout, pic. bd., 275x215mm. CLRC

Picture book with slight text. The photographer is Australian.

NEWMAN, Hans

5334 EVERYBODY'S/DOG BOOK/Written and illustrated by/Hans Newman
Children's Press, 141 York Street, Sydney, n.d. [inscribed 1952]
16pp, b/w drawings throughout, pic. wrappers, cover title, 275x210mm. KMM
Contains drawings & descriptions of dogs.

[NEWMAN, William]

5335 THE HISTORY OF A/GOLDEN SOVEREIGN/in Rhymes and Pictures/London. Griffith & Farran, St Pauls Ch. Yd.
n.d.[1860]
[20]pp (numbered 1–10, last blank), hand-coloured engravings by author, with verse on every alternate page, other pp blank, col. pic. wrappers, cover title, 135x90mm. CLRC
The only definite reference to Australia occurs in first line. Bound together with several uniform booklets, 'The History of a pound of sugar' &c.

NEWSTEAD, Margaret

5336 IN GOOD HANDS/by/Margaret Newstead/Illustrated by/Romola Clifton/Rigby Limited/Adelaide
Published in association with George G. Harrap & Co. Ltd, London, 1962
166pp, b/w frontis. & 8 other f/p b/w illus., clo., 200x130mm. CLRC

NEWTON, D. & SMITH, D.

5337 They were First: 5/FLINDERS/BURKE & WILLS/D. Newton/D. Smith/illustrated by/D. E. Brookfield
Oliver & Boyd, Edinburgh, first published 1969; rpt 1971
16pp, 6 col. illus. & 4 b/w illus., pic. wrappers, cover title, 215x155mm. KMM
A background reader for primary schools.

NEY, Marie

5338 Price—Sixpence/A FAIRY STORY/By Marie Ney/(of the Palace Theatre, Sydney)/[drawing]/Proceeds in aid of/Royal Society for the Welfare of/Mothers and Babies
n.d. [NSL:M Catalogue 1919?]
3pp leaflet, 210x135mm. NSL:M

NICHOLLS, Brooke

5339 JACKO—/THE BROADCASTING KOOKABURRA/His Life and Adventures./By/Brook Nicholls/Decorated by/Dorothy Wall./[drawing]/Angus and Robertson Limited./89 Castlereagh St./Sydney/1933
106pp, 2pp foreword by J. McRae, Department of Education & 1p author's note, 12 f/p b/w illus., b/w chapter headings & drawings in text throughout, bd., 240x180mm. KMM
Author's note reads: 'This is the true story of Jacko, the Broadcasting Kookaburra, that so many of his fellow Australians have heard laughing over the air from the wireless stations of Melbourne, Sydney, and Brisbane &c.'

5340 Another copy, second edition November 1933, as above, but 96pp. SLV

5341 THE AMAZING ADVENTURES/OF/BILLY PENGUIN/By Brooke Nicholls/Decorated by/Dorothy Wall/[drawing]/Angus and Robertson Limited/89 Castlereagh St.,/Sydney/1934
79pp, 2pp author's note & 1p foreword, 13 f/p b/w illus. & drawings in text, bd., 240x185mm. CLRC

NICHOLLS, Sydney Wentworth

5342 THE FATTY FINN/BOOK/From the Series of Comics by Syd Nicholls/Appearing in/"The Sunday News"/Price 2/-/Wholly set up and printed in/Australia, 1928, by the Artcraft/Printing Company, 18 Albion St.,/Sydney, for Publications Ltd.,/168 Castlereagh Street, Sydney
32pp, full col. comic-strip pictures, stiff pic. wrappers, cover title, 305x250mm. ANL

5343 THE/FATTY FINN/BOOK/No 2/From the series of comics by Syd Nicholls appearing in/"The Sunday News"/Wholly set up and printed in Australia 1929 by the Artcraft Printing Company,/18 Albion Street, Sydney, for Publication Ltd., 168 Castlereagh Street, Sydney./Registered by the Postmaster-General for transmission through the post as a book
32pp (inc. 28pp comics), illus. in col. throughout, pic. wrappers, 310x248mm. ANL

5344 THE/FATTY FINN/BOOK/No. 3/From the Series of/Cartoons by Syd Nicholls/Appearing in/the Sunday Guardian/Wholly set up and printed in Australia, by Messrs Waite & Bull, 81 Campbell Street, Sydney,/for the proprietors of the "Sunday Guardian" 191–193 Elizabeth Street, Sydney/Registered by the Postmaster-General for transmission through the post as a book/Price 2/-
32pp, col. comic-strips throughout, col. pic. wrappers, 310x248mm. ANL

5345 MIDDY MALONE, A Book of Pirates/By Syd. Nicholls/[dedication]/[verses]/Registered at the G.P.O./Sydney, for transmission/through the Post as a/book. 1941
24pp, col. pic. t.p., col. illus. throughout, stiff pic. wrappers, 350x250mm. ANL
Story told in comic-strip form. On front cover: 'By Syd. Nicholls, Author of "The Phantom Pirate" '.

5346 MIDDY MALONE/AND THE SOUTH SEA PIRATES/By Syd Nicholls
[1942] Printed by Supertone Co, Sydney for the author, n.d.
[20]pp, col. illus. throughout, stiff pic. wrappers, cover title, 358x238mm. KMM

5347 THE FURTHER ADVENTURES OF/MIDDY MALONE/A Book of/Pirates/By Syd Nicholls
Printed by Supertone Co., 200 Chalmers St, Sydney for the author, 1943
24pp, col. illus. throughout, stiff pic. wrappers, cover title, 355x240mm. ANL
Comic strip.

5348 THE/PHANTOM/PIRATE/by/Syd Nicholls/[verse]/Registered at the G.P.O. Sydney, for transmission through the post as a book.
1943/2484C—Supertone Co.—Registered at [etc.]
Published by the author
[24]pp, col. illus. t.p., col. illus. throughout, pic. wrappers, dec. e/p, 360x240mm. KMM
Story written in comic-strip form throughout. Based on William Dampier.

5349 MIDDY MALONE IN THE LOST WORLD
Publ. by author [1946]. Printed by Deaton & Spencer, Sydney
20pp, col. illus. throughout, stiff pic. wrappers, cover title, 360x240mm. JR
Full col. comic strips; interior of cover patterned in blue & white.

5350 ABOUT SHIPS/From the Egyptian Galley to the Queen Elizabeth/Illustrations and Story by/Syd. Nicholls/[dedication—10 lines text]/[drawing]/

[acknowledgement—12 lines text signed by author]/ Published by the author/at 166 Phillip St., Sydney/ Australia/Wholly set up and printed in Australia by Deaton & Spencer Pty. Ltd., and/Posters Pty. Ltd. for the publisher, Syd. Nicholls, 166 Phillip Street, Sydney./Registered at the General Post Office, Sydney,/for transmission through the Post as a book.
n.d. [1947]
48pp, 16pp f/p col. illus., 16pp b/w illus., 16pp text, pic. bd., dec. e/p, 340x230mm. NSL:M

5351 A BIG BOOK OF/AUSTRALIAN/ADVENTURE/ by Syd. Nicholls
Printed by the Supertone Co., Sydney for the Publisher, Syd. Nicholls, Sydney, n.d.
[12]pp, 4 f/p col. illus., 1 f/p b/w illus. & 10 half-page b/w illus., stiff pic. wrappers, cover title, 355x240mm. KMM
Story begins & ends on insides of covers. An imaginary journey through Australian history.

5352 THE MAGIC/BOOMERANG/An Australian Fairy Story/by Syd. Nicholls
No printer's imprint or date [194-?]
[12]pp, 4 f/p col. illus., 2 f/p b/w illus. & 6 half-page b/w illus., stiff paper pic. wrappers, cover title, 355x240mm. Grant
Story begins & ends on insides of covers.

5353 SEA ADVENTURE
Wholly set up and printed in Australia by the Supertone Co., 20 Chalmers Street/Sydney, for the Publisher, Syd. Nicholls, 34 Martin Place, Sydney, n.d. [194-?]
[12]pp, 4 f/p col. illus. & b/w illus. throughout, stiff pic. wrappers, cover title, 350x240mm. KMM

5354 A BOOK OF/FAMOUS SHIPS/By Syd Nicholls
Supertone Co., for Syd Nicholls, 34 Martin Place, Sydney, n.d.[194-?]
8pp, 4pp col. illus., col. & b/w drawings throughout (inc. both sides of stiff pic. wrappers), cover title, 357x234mm. NSL:M

5355 A BOOK OF PLANES, TRAINS AND CARS
Sydney, n.d. Printed by Supertone Co. for the author
12pp (inc. wrappers), illus. wrappers, 240x350mm. JR

MIDDY MALONE'S BUMPER BOOK
192pp, b/w illus. only, 270x195mm. ANL
Comprised of bound copies of *Middy Malone's Magazine*.

NICHOLS, Freda

5356 SHIPPED TO/BOTANY BAY/By/Freda P. Nichols/Illustrated by/John Sergeant/Ginn and Company Ltd./18 Bedford Row London W.C.1
1967
vipp, 186pp (inc. 2pp introduction & acknowledgements), 15pp notes, b/w text illus. throughout, map & diagrams on e/p, dec. clo., 178x122mm. CLRC

NICHOLSON, Joyce [née Thorpe]

5357 YOU CAN RUN/A LIBRARY/by/Joyce Nicholson, B.A./[device]/Australian Red Cross Society/Founded in 1914, Incorporated by Royal Charter, 1941
n.d. [1948]
56pp, part-col. frontis., 33 b/w & part. col. illus. & diagrams, pic. wrappers, 180x115mm. Grant

5358 150/GAMES AND/COMPETITIONS/Compiled by/Joyce Nicholson, B.A./All rights Reserved/ Registered at the General Post/Office [3 lines]/ Wholesale Distributors in Australia and New Zealand/ Gordon and Gotch (A/sia) Ltd./Melbourne, Sydney, Brisbane, Adelaide, Perth, Launceston
n.d. Rev. & enlarged ed. of *100 New Games and Competitions* (before1966 as price given on cover as 2/6)
64pp, unillus., wrappers, 202x136mm. KP
Adv. by same author: *The Children's Party and Games Book.*

5359 THE/CHILDREN'S/PARTY AND/GAMES BOOK/ 120 Different Games to Play/By Joyce Thorpe, B.A./Author of/"Successful Parties and Social Evenings," and "100 New Games/and Competitions."/Wholesale Distributors:/Gordon and Gotch (Australasia) Ltd./Melbourne Sydney Brisbane Adelaide Perth/Launceston Wellington Auckland Christchurch/and Dunedin
n.d.
43pp, unillus., wrappers, 210x135mm. KP

5360 THE/CHILDREN'S/PARTY AND/GAMES BOOK/ 120 Different Games to Play/By/Joyce Nicholson/ Author of/'Successful Parties and Social Evenings' and '100 New Games/and Competitions'/Wholesale Distributors:/Gordon and Gotch (Australia) Ltd./ Melbourne Sydney Brisbane Adelaide Perth/ Launceston Wellington Auckland Christchurch/and Dunedin
n.d.
63pp, unillus., stiff wrappers, 205x135mm. KMM

5361 GAMES/FOR THE FAMILY/by/Joyce Nicholson, B.A./Illustrated/by [drawing of four heads with names below]/as drawn by themselves/This is a book to help boys and girls to do things for themselves./All the drawings have therefore been done by the Nicholson children
Printed by Wilke & Co., Ltd, Melbourne; distributed by Gordon & Gotch (A/sia) Ltd, n.d.
61pp, 3pp adv., b/w diagrams & drawings in text, wrappers, 200x135mm. KMM

5362 THE/LITTLE BLUE CAR/By/Joyce Nicholson/ Published by The Little Books Publishing House/ Illustrated by Max B. Miller
[Hawthorn, Victoria, 1950]
24pp, col. & b/w illus. throughout, dec. bd., 185x125mm. ANL

5363 THE/LITTLE GREEN/TRACTOR/[drawing]/By Joyce Nicholson
The Little Books Publishing House, Hawthorn, Victoria, n.d. [1950]
24pp, col. & b/w illus. throughout, illus. by Max B. Miller, dec. bd., 185x125mm. ANL

5364 AN/ABC/OF/SHIPS AND/THE SEA/by/Joyce Nicholson/Illustrated by Max B. Miller/Published by The Little Books Publishing House, Joyce Nicholson [Melbourne] 1950
24pp, 12 col. illus. & 12pp b/w illus., stiff bd., 180x120mm. ANL

5365 THE AEROPLANE/THAT COULD NOT FLY/ [drawing]/By/Joyce Nicholson/Illustrations by/Max B. Miller/Published by the/Little Books Publishing House/P.O. Box 31, Hawthorn, Vic.
n.d. [1951]
[24]pp, col. & b/w illus. on alternate page openings, dec. bd., 185x120mm. KMM

5366 ADVENTURE AT/GULLS' POINT/by/Joyce Nicholson/London: The Epworth Press
1955
170pp, map frontis., clo., 185x120mm. KMM

5367 OUR/FIRST OVERLANDER/By/Joyce Nicholson, B.A./A Background of Australia Book/Shakespeare Head Press/Sydney/1956
128pp, b/w map frontis., b/w drawings, illus. M. Penglase, dec. bd., map e/p, 210x135mm. KMM
The story of the explorers Hume & Hovell, with maps of early New South Wales & the 1824 overland expedition from Lake George to Port Phillip.

5368 GULLS' POINT/AND PINEAPPLE/by/Joyce Nicholson/London: the Epworth Press
1957
152pp, map frontis., clo., 185x120mm. KMM
Also published simultaneously in p/b ed, 'Koala Series'. KP

5369 MAN AGAINST/MUTINY/The Story of Vice-Admiral William Bligh/Joyce Nicholson/ Lutterworth Press/London
1961
95pp, col. portrait frontis. & 2pp b/w map, clo., 180x120mm. HBM

5370 [5 lines acknowledgements] KERRI AND HONEY/ Story by/Joyce Nicholson/Photography by/Gordon De' Lisle [*sic*]/Lansdowne Melbourne 1962
Printed in Japan by Toppan Printing Co. Ltd, Tokyo
32pp, extended illus. t.p. (with 2 b/w photographs), b/w photographs on alternate pages, pic. bd., 255x185mm. KMM
Slight story of two koalas.
• Rpt 1964, KMM, 1965. KP

5371 [8 lines acknowledgement]/CRANKY/THE BABY AUSTRALIAN CAMEL/Story by/Joyce Nicholson/ Photography by/Gordon De'Lisle/Lansdowne/ Melbourne/1963
32pp, extended illus. t.p. (with 2 b/w photographs), b/w photographic illus. on alternate pages, dec. bd., 255x185mm. KMM
• Rpt as above 1965. KMM

5372 Joyce Nicholson/A MORTAR-BOARD/FOR PRISCILLA/Melbourne/F. W. Cheshire/Canberra Sydney
1963
120pp, dec. t.p., dec. chapter headings, otherwise unillus., clo., cover design by Alison Forbes, dec. e/p, 215x135mm. KMM

5373 Joyce Nicholson/A MORTAR-BOARD/FOR PRISCILLA/Children's Library Guild/of Australia/ Melbourne Canberra Sydney
1963
121pp, unillus., clo. pic. e/p., 212x137mm. KP

5374 ANDY'S/KANGAROO/Story by Joyce Nicholson/ Photography by Gordon De'Lisle/Lansdowne/ Melbourne and Sydney/1964
32pp, b/w photographic frontis., b/w photographs on alternate pages, b/w pic. bd., 245x185mm. KMM
Slight text accompanying photographs.

5375 RINGTAIL/THE/POSSUM/Story by Joyce Nicholson/Photography by Gordon De'Lisle/ Lansdowne 1965
Melbourne
32pp, b/w photographs on alternate pages, pic. bd., 245x180mm. KMM
Brief text accompanying photographs.

5376 SIR/CHARLES/AND THE/LYREBIRD/Story by Joyce Nicholson/Photography by Brian McArdle/ Lansdowne 1966
Melbourne [Printed in Japan]
[32]pp, b/w photographs on alternate pages, pic. bd., 245x180mm. KMM
Slight story accompanies photographs.

5377 Publ. as above, Angus and Robertson, London, 1967.

5378 YAP THE PENGUIN/Story by Joyce Nicholson/ Photography by L. H. Smith/Lansdowne 1967 Melbourne
32pp, b/w photographic illus. throughout, pic. bd., 245x180mm. KMM
Pictures & story of a fairy penguin from Phillip Island, Victoria.

5379 WOOP THE WOMBAT/story by Joyce Nicholson/ photography by L. H. Smith/Lansdowne Melbourne 1968
[32]pp, extended pic. t.p., b/w photographic illus. throughout, col. pic. bd., 250x180mm. KMM

A GOLDSEEKER. *See* Early Australians

NICKELS, Sylvie

5380 SCOTT & THE/DISCOVERY/OF THE/ ANTARCTIC/compiled by Sylvie Nickels
Jackdaw Publications Ltd, 30 Bedford Square, London, 1927
8 listed documents, maps, illus. & picture strips & 4 broadsheets with explanatory booklet by author enclosed in illus. envelope, 225x345mm. Jackdaw No. 123. KMM

NICOL, W. D. & E. C. [eds]

5381 ABORIGINAL/CHILDREN'S/STORIES
by Aboriginal Teaching Assistants, Kormilda College, Darwin. Produced for Welfare Branch, Education Section, N.T. Admin. Illus. adapted from students' drawings by Jennifer Nicol. Printed by N.T. News Services Ltd, 46 Mitchell St, Darwin, n.d.
35pp, 1p foreword by H. C. Giese, Director Social Welfare, Darwin, b/w drawings in text throughout, pic. wrappers, 185x240mm. KMM
Another copy printed by N.T. News Services, 28 Mitchell Street, Darwin. KP
New ed. 1970, rpt 1970. KW

NICOLL, Fred J.

5382 TEDDY/COUNTS/HIS/POTS/By/Fred J. Nicoll/ Pretty Pat and/Troublesome Teddy/Series No. 1
Ramsay Ware Publishing Pty Ltd, Melbourne, n.d. [Library copy acquired 1943]
16pp, part-col. illus. throughout, stiff dec. wrappers, cover title, 280x215mm. NSL:M
Another copy as above, but this book & others in the series were originally produced with one page of cutouts, perforated along the top & hinged on the verso of front cover.

5383 TEDDY/AT THE/CIRCUS/By/Fred J. Nicoll/ Pretty Pat and/Troublesome Teddy/Series No. 2
Ramsay Ware Publishing Pty. Ltd., Melbourne, n.d. [Library copy acquired 1943]
16pp, part-col. illus. throughout, stiff dec. wrappers, cover title, 280x215mm. NSL:M

5384 TEDDY JOINS THE/NAVY
Ramsay Ware Publishing Pty Ltd, Melbourne, n.d. [1943]
16pp, part-col. illus. throughout, stiff dec. wrappers, cover title, 280x215mm. Grant
Pretty Pat and Troublesome Teddy series

5385 TEDDY IN/FAIRYLAND/By/Fred J. Nicoll/Pretty Pat and/Troublesome Teddy/Series No 4
Ramsay Ware Publishing Pty Ltd, Melbourne, 1943

16pp, part-col. illus. throughout, col. stiff pic. wrappers, 278x214mm. KP
Includes sheet pasted inside front cover with 7 figures to be cut out & folded so as to stand out.

Uniform titles listed as in series but unseen
TEDDY GIVES A PARTY
TEDDY GOES TO SCHOOL

NICOLSON, T.
5386 CASKIE WOODS/By/T. Nicolson/Decorations by Harold Freedman/Georgian House/Melbourne
1948
131pp, 6 f/p part-col. illus. & b/w drawings throughout, clo., 210x135mm. VSL

Nineteenth Century Explorers
5387 Collins/New Biographical Series/NINETEENTH/CENTURY/EXPLORERS/With Coloured Illustrations/and/Eight Portraits/London and Glasgow/Collins' Clear-Type Press
n.d.
192 (inc. 2pp preface), col. frontis. & 1 col. plate & 8 sepia/white portraits, clo., 155x100mm. HBM
Contains John McDouall Stuart [23pp]

NISBET, Hume
5388 EIGHT BELLS/A Tale of the Sea and of the/Cannibals of New Guinea/By/Hume Nisbet/Author of "Dr Bernard St Vincent", "The Land of the Hibiscus Blossom", etc/[vignette]/Illustrated by the author/Ward and Downey,/12 York Street, Covent Garden, London/1889
334pp, b/w frontis. & 9 f/p b/w illus., pic. clo. with title & author in gilt on frontis. & spine, bevelled edges, 190x140mm. NSL:M
Adventure story about 2 boys on a voyage to Australia & the Pacific but not specifically a boys' book.

5389 THE DIVERS/A Romance of Oceania/By/Hume Nisbet/Author of "Bail Up", "The Bushranger's Sweetheart"/"The Jolly Roger", etc. etc./[drawing]/London/Adam and Charles Black/1892
395pp (inc. 2pp preface), 8pp adv., b/w frontis. only, dec. clo., 180x120mm. ANL
5390 THE DIVERS/A Romance of Oceania/By/Hume Nisbet/Author of "Bail Up", "The Bushranger's Sweetheart",/"The Jolly Roger", etc. etc./[vignette]/Cheap Edition/London/Adam and Charles Black/1894
395pp (inc. 2pp preface), 8pp adv., b/w frontis. & 6 f/p b/w illus., pic. clo., dec. e/p, 185x120mm. RM
5391 THE DIVERS/By/Hume Nisbet/With Eight Illustrations in Colour by/The Author/London/Adam and Charles Black/1904
395pp (inc. 2pp preface), 4 adv., col. frontis. & 7 f/p col. plates, pic. clo., 197x134mm. KMM

5392 KINGS OF THE SEA/A Story of the Spanish Main/By/Hume Nisbet/Author of/'Bail Up' 'The Jolly Roger', 'A Desert Bride',/'Valdmer the Viking' Etc. Etc./Etc/[vignette with caption]/Illustrated by J. B. Greene/With vignette by The Author/London/F. V. White & Co./14 Bedford Street, Strand, W.C./1896
[x] + 282pp & 16pp adv., frontis. & 5 b/w plates, pic. clo. g.e., 192x128mm. NSL:M
No Australian references.

'NIWRAD, William' [pseud. William Darwin]
5393 MAJOR BILLS'/A PRINCE OF PUPS/and eleven other stories/by William Nirwad/F.R.G.S./1949/Melbourne
Printed by National Press Pty Ltd, Melbourne
133pp, 18 b/w illus., bd., 180x120mm. NSL:M

Another copy as above, but with a new dustjacket with photograph of Prince Charles & Princess Anne reproduced. The author has inscribed the copy on the t.p., altering the publication date to 1954. KP

NIXON-ROULET, Mary E.
5394 OUR LITTLE/AUSTRALIAN COUSIN/By/Mary F. Nixon-Roulet/Author of "God, the King, My Brother", "Our/Little Spanish Cousin", "Our Little Alaskan/Cousin," "Our Little Grecian Cousin",/"Our Little Brazilian Cousin", etc./Illustrated by/Diantha W. Horne/[device]/Boston/L. C. Page & Company/MDCCCCVIII
131pp & 16pp adv., half-tone frontis. & 5 plates, pic. clo., 190x130mm. KMM
'Little Cousin' series

Noah's Ark Cut-out Book
5395 Series A204/NOAH'S/ARK/CUT-OUT/BOOK. *See* Offset Publishing Cut-Out Books

NOAKES, Helen
5396 MOON MAGIC/Written and Illustrated by/Helen Noakes/[drawing]/Australasian Publishing Co. Pty. Ltd./Sydney
First Australian edition 1942
60pp (inc. 2pp foreword), col. frontis. & 3 f/p col. illus., b/w drawings in text, dec. bd., 230x170mm. Grant
Story set in the sugar cane country of Queensland & New South Wales.
Second edition 1943, as above. KMM

5397 LITTLE/SONGS/THAT/GRANDPA SINGS/Words and Illustration/by Helen Noakes/Music by/Mildred Bell/Copyright Paling 3/-
W. H. Paling, Sydney, [1946]
[24]pp (inc. covers), dec. contents page (9 songs), drawings throughout, pic. wrappers, 305x240mm. ANL
Printed throughout in blue.

5398 Imperial Edition 729./PERCY PLATYPUS/And Other Songs/For Children/Words by/Helen Noakes/Music by O. G. Campbell Egan/[list of songs] 1954
Allan & Co. Pty Ltd./Melbourne—Adelaide—Bendigo/Printed in Australia
20pp, unillus. wrappers, 245x180mm. CLRC
Contains 9 songs.

NOBLE, Edward
5399 THE SEA OF THE/SUNKEN LANDS/by/Edward Noble/With Frontispiece and Map Drawing by/Drake Brookshaw/Thomas Nelson and Sons, Ltd./London, Edinburgh, Paris, Melbourne/Toronto, and New York
1949
254pp, col. frontis. & b/w map, clo., 187x130mm. KMM
An adventure story of a search for treasure in the islands north of Australia begins & ends in Sydney.
German edition
5400 DIE VERSUNKEN INSEL. Eine abenteuerliche Erzählung mit 21 Zeichnungen von Kurt Wendtlandt
Vienna—Heidelberg, Ueberreuter, [1954]
319pp, illus., pic. bd., clo. spine. Unseen [Serendipity Books Cat.139, 1984]

NOBLE, Captain John
AUSTRALIAN LIGHTHOUSES. *See* Around Australia Program

NOBS, Dr Max
5401 Schweizer Real bogen/Herausgegeben von/Emil Wyman/Schul-inspektor/Dr. H. Kleinert/Gymnasiallehrer/DER AUSTRALISCHE BUSCH/von/Dr. Max Nobs/Verlag Paul Haupt, Bern 1928

35pp, 1p adv., 2pp b/w illus., wrappers, 225x155mm. NSL:M
German extracts from books on Australia, with list of children's books in German.

NOLDT, Beverly
5402 JOCK/An Australian Fantasy/By/Beverley Noldt/Illustrated by Marjorie Draper
Australasian Medical Publishing Co. Ltd, Glebe, NSW, 1947
69pp, b/w frontis. & 7 f/p b/w illus., bd., 180x110mm. VSL

'NONAME'
See Pluck and Luck series and Enton, Harry

NOONAN, Michael
5403 IN/THE LAND/OF THE/TALKING/TREES/A Fantasy/by Michael Noonan/Illustrated by D. H. Gilmore/Angus & Robertson/Sydney: London/1946
89pp, col. frontis. & 13 f/p col. illus., b/w drawings, bd., 245x180mm. KMM
The author is a New Zealander by birth.

5404 THE GOLDEN/FOREST/The Story of Oonah the Platypus/By/Michael Noonan/[drawing]/Illustrated by/Douglas Albion/Angus and Robertson/Sydney: London/1947
186pp, col. frontis. & 3 f/p col. illus., b/w drawings, clo., 185x120mm. VSL

5405 [drawing]/FLYING DOCTOR/by/Michael Noonan/Illustrated/by/R. E. Hicks/London/Hodder and Stoughton
1961
192pp, 6 f/p b/w illus., clo., 210x135mm. KMM
Dedicated to the Royal Flying Doctor Service of Australia.
2nd impression, as above, 1962. CLRC
Dutch edition
5406 DE VLIEGENDE DOKTER—Junior Pocket 230
Spectrum, Utrecht, Holland, 1963
192pp, 8 b/w illus. (as in English edition), paper binding, 180x105mm. Unseen: IFP

5407 FLYING DOCTOR/AND/THE SECRET OF THE PEARLS/by/Michael Noonan/London/Hodder & Stoughton
1962
160pp, 6 f/p b/w illus. by R. E. Hicks, clo., 220x135mm. KMM
5408 Another copy as above, but Brockhampton Press [London] as above but unillus. 210x130mm. KP

5409 FLYING DOCTOR/ON THE/GREAT BARRIER REEF/by/Michael Noonan/Illustrated by R. E. Hicks/London/Hodder & Stoughton
1962
190pp, 4 f/p b/w illus., clo., 210x135mm. CLRC

5410 FLYING DOCTOR/SHADOWS THE MOB/by/Michael Noonan/Illustrated by R. E. Hicks/[device]/Hodder and Stoughton
London 1964
160pp, 6 f/p b/w illus., clo., 220x135mm. CLRC

5411 FLYING DOCTOR/HITS THE HEADLINES/by/Michael Noonan/[device]/Hodder and Stoughton
London 1965
158pp, unillus., clo., d/w designed by R. E. Hicks, 215x135mm. KMM

5412 Michael Noonan/AIR TAXI/Illustrated by Barry Rowe/[drawing]/Brockhampton Press
Leicester, England, 1967
120pp (inc. 1p glossary), double-spread map, b/w frontis., b/w drawings & diagrams in text, clo., 215x135mm. KMM

5413 Michael Noonan/FLYING DOCTOR/UNDER THE DESERT/Brockhampton Press
Leicester, England, 1969
152pp, extended b/w frontis. only, illus. & d/w by Roger Payne, clo., 210x135mm. CLRC
Also the author of *The December Boys* & *The Patchwork Hero*, neither of which was intended for children.

NORDHOFF, Charles
5414 THE/MERCHANT VESSEL:/A/Sailor Boy's Voyages/To see the World./By the author of "Man-of-War Life"./Cincinnati:/Moore, Wilstach, Keys & Co./New York: Miller, Orton & Mulligan./Boston: Whittemore, Niles & Hall./Phila. J. B. Lippincott & Co./1856
viiipp, 288pp, engraved frontis. & 4 plates & engravings in text, clo., 168x110mm. ANL
Pp162–214, Sails for Sydney, New Guinea, Lombok, sandalwood hunting, tending cattle in NSW.

5415 SEEING THE WORLD:/A Young Sailor's own Story./By/Charles Nordhoff/Author of 'The Young Man-of-wars-Man'/William P. Nimmo;/London: King William Street, Strand;/and Edinburgh./1876
224pp, frontis. & 3 f/p engravings, copy re-bound, 163x105mm. ANL
Sections on Papua, Sydney, Pitcairn Island, sandalwood trading &c.

NORDHOFF, Charles & HALL, James Norman
5416 MYTERIET/PÅ BOUNTY/[drawing with brief résumé of plot in panel]/Av Charles Nordhoff/James Norman Hall/This edition of Mutiny on the Bounty is reprinted by arrangement with Little, Brown & Company, Boston, by whom/the work is published in association with the Atlantic Monthly Press.
'Illustrerade Klassiker' NO 9. Printed by Dyva & Jeppesens Trykkeri Aktieselskab, Kobenhavn, n.d.
43pp, 5pp adv., col. illus. throughout, pic. wrappers, 250x175mm. HBM
Story told in comic-strip form, but artist's name not given.

NORLEDGE, Mildred [ed.]
5417 ABORIGINAL LEGENDS/FROM/EASTERN AUSTRALIA/The Richmond-Mary River Region/Compiled by/Mildred Norledge/illustrated by Denis Burton/A. H. & A. W. Reed/Sydney Wellington Auckland
First published 1968; rpt 1968
62pp (inc. 3pp foreword, acknowledgements, etc.), b/w drawings in text, bd., 240x180mm. CLRC
Foreword by Professor A. P. Elkin; 'drawings prepared from original sketches by an aboriginal artist, Mr. Denis Burton of Kyogle'. D/w design by D. W. Sinclair.

NORMAN, Lilith
5418 CLIMB A/LONELY HILL/Lilith Norman/Collins/London & Sydney
1970
160pp, unillus., clo., d/w designed by Jillian Willett, 210x135mm. KMM
• Rpt 1971. KP
5419 CLIMB A/LONELY HILL/Lilith Norman/Collins/London & Sydney
Special Australian Edition 1971
160pp, unillus., pic. limp clo., 180x120mm. KW
5420 CLIMB A/LONELY HILL/Lilith Norman/[device]Collins/Armada Lions
1972

127pp & 1p adv., unillus., pic. wrappers, 180x107mm. KP
5421 American edition
Henry Z. Walck, New York 1972
159pp, 22cm. Unseen: ANB 1972

5422 THE SHAPE OF/THREE/Lilith Norman/Collins/London & Sydney
1971
192pp, unillus., clo., d/w designed by Gavin Rowe, 210x135mm. KMM

NORRIS, Emilia Marryat
5423 THE/EARLY START IN LIFE/By/Emilia Marryat Norris/(Daughter of the late Captain Marryat)/Author of "What became of Tommy"; "A Week by Themselves";/"Harry at School"; "Long Evenings" etc./with illustrations by J. Lawson/[publisher's device]/Griffith & Farran/(Successors to Newbery and Harris)/West Corner St Paul's Churchyard, London/E. P. Dutton & Co., New York
[1867]
373pp, b/w engraved frontis. & 5 f/p engravings, half leather (re-bound), 180x120mm. NSL:M
5424 Another copy as above
n.d. [inscribed 1889]
372pp & 16pp adv., b/w frontis. & 5 f/p engravings, dec. clo. with gilt panel & all edges gilt, 180x120mm. KP
5425 THE/EARLY START IN LIFE/by/Emilia Marryat Norris/(Daughter of the late Captain Marryat)/Author of "What became of Tommy?" "A Week by Themselves";/"Harry at School"; "Long Evenings"; Etc./With illustrations by J. Lawson/[device]/London/Griffith Farran Okeden & Welsh/Newbery House, Charing Cross Road/and at Sydney
1890
372pp, b/w engraved frontis. & 5 f/p engravings, clo., 180x120mm. Grant

5426 JACK STANLEY/or/The Young Adventurers/By/Emilia Marryat (Mrs. Norris)/With original illustrations/London/Frederick Warne and Co./Bedford Street Strand
n.d. [1882?]
366pp, 8pp adv., b/w frontis. & 3 f/p b/w illus., dec. clo., 180x120mm. PR
Frontispiece signed 'Gunston'.
The story, which takes place in New Zealand, contains one chapter entitled 'A Reminiscence of a Kangaroo Hunt in Australia' (pp248–57). Published London 1874 as '*Amongst the Maoris*'.

NORRY, Roy
5427 ANTARCTIC/EXPLORER/The Story of Dr. Phillip Law/Roy Norry/Illustrations by/Don Angus/Nelson Thomas Nelson (Australia) Ltd, Melbourne 1966
28pp, col. illus. t.p., map, col. illus. throughout, pic. bd., 170x190mm. KMM
Lyrebird Books. Designed by Nola Bearlin.
Uniform books in same series, same date &c., all KMM

5428 AUSTRALIAN/SNAKE MAN/The Story of Eric Worrell/Roy Norry/Illustrations by/Michael Hutchards/Nelson

5429 SKY SEARCHER/IN AUSTRALIA/The Story of Dr. E. Bowen/Roy Norry/Illustrations by/Charles Billich/Nelson

5430 VIRUS HUNTER/IN AUSTRALIA/The Story of Sir Macfarlane Burnet/Roy Norry/Illustrations by/Don Angus/Nelson

NORTH, Dorothy
5431 VERSES/FOR THE VERY YOUNG/by/Dorothy North/[drawing]/Illustrations by/Clyde Rosman The author, Melbourne, n.d. [1961]
[51]pp (printed on alternate pages only), b/w drawings throughout, clo. (with dec. title pasted on front cover), 185x120mm. ANL

NORTON, C. B.
5432 IT'S A FACT/Truth Stranger than Fiction/Fully illustrated in/Pictures and Stories/by C. B. Norton/Acknowledgement [5 lines by author]/Printed and Published by Offset Printing Coy. Pty. Limited, 169 Phillip St. Waterloo. (All rights reserved.)
n.d. [1940?]
[64]pp, b/w illus. on alternate pages, pic. wrappers, 250x176mm. KP
Paragraphs that originally appeared in *PIX* with accompanying drawings.

NORTON, Frank
5433 FIGHTING SHIPS/OF AUSTRALIA/& NEW ZEALAND/by/Frank Norton/Lieutenant-Commander (Sp.), R.A.N.V.R./Official Naval War Artist 1941–5, 1952/With a Foreword by Vice-Admiral Sir John Collins, K.B.E., C.B., R.A.N./Angus and Robertson/Sydney—London/1953
96pp (inc. 1p foreword & 1p abbreviations &c.), dec. t.p., col. frontis. & 9 col. illus., b/w illus., plans, diagrams &c. throughout, dec. bd., 185x250mm. KMM
Factual & detailed account of various naval craft, &c.

5434 AUSTRALIAN AND NEW ZEALAND/SHIPS OF TODAY/Frank Norton/[illustration]/Angus & Robertson/Sydney London Melbourne Wellington
1958
96pp, col. & b/w lithographic diagrams, drawings & maps throughout, dec. bd., 185x245mm. KMM

NORWOOD, Edwin P.
5435 IN THE LAND OF/DIGGELDY DAN/By/Edwin P. Norwood/with illustrations by/A. Conway Peyton/Boston/Little, Brown, and Company/1923
226pp, col. frontis. & 7 f/p col. illus., clo. (with col. onlay), 200x135mm. KMM
A fantasy featuring a kangaroo as one of the main characters. Several of the 8 col. plates feature the kangaroo, including that which is reproduced on the front cover.

NORWOOD, F. W.
5436 SUNSHINE/AND/WATTLEGOLD/By/F. W. Norwood/Lothian Book Publishing Company Pty Ltd/Melbourne Sydney/Printed in England
[1915?]
256pp & 12pp adv., unillus., clo., 195x125mm. KP
5437 SUNSHINE/AND/WATTLEGOLD/By/F. W. Norwood, D.D./Minister of the City Temple, London/London: H. R. Allenson, Limited/7 Racquet Court, 114 Fleet Street, E.C.
n.d.
244pp & 12pp adv., unillus., clo., 183x120mm. KP
Publ. in a series 'Capital Addresses to Children'.
Foreword says 'intended for young folk'.

'NORWOOD, John' [pseud. Donald Norwood Veron]
5438 THE AUSTRALIA BOOK/FOR/ENGLISH BOYS & GIRLS/(And their Parents)/By/John Norwood/(The pseudonym of an Australian Officer of high rank, author of "Stony Ground"/Photos supplied by:/Australian News and Information Bureau/Australia House, Strand, London, W.C.2/Dorothy Crisp & Co. Ltd./Lansdowne Row,/London, W.1.
n.d. [1947]

19pp, portrait frontis. [H.M. King George VI & Queen Elizabeth], 24pp photographic illus. & map, clo., 245x180mm. NSL:M

NOSKE, Rob
See Trend Books

Nothing at all Rhymes
5439 NOTHING AT ALL RHYMES/illustrated by Allan Stomann/Paul Hamlyn/London New York Sydney Toronto
Dee Why West, NSW, 1969
[26]pp, col. illus. throughout, pic. bd., 310x225mm. BBC
Conventional nursery rhymes

NOYLE, George
See Elliott, Lydia Susanna & Noyle, George

Nursery Days Cut-out Book
See Offset Publishing Cut-Out Books

Nursery Rhymes
5439a NURSERY RHYMES
Publ. in Australia by Ayers & James Pty Ltd, Sydney, Photogravures Pty Ltd, n.d. [194-?]
10pp, col. illus. throughout, printed throughout on light card, pic. wrappers, 180x154mm. KMM

Nursery Rhymes
5440 NURSERY/RHYMES
Series 1204, Dawfox Productions, Sydney, n.d. [194-?]
18pp (inc. 8pp printed in col.) & b/w illus., col. pic. wrappers, 360x240mm. KP

Nursery Rhymes
5441 NURSERY/RHYMES
Jons Productions, Sydney, n.d. [194-?]
16pp, col. & b/w illus. on alternate pages, pic. wrappers, 360x240mm. KMM
Anonymous illus.

Nursery Rhymes
5442 NURSERY/RHYMES/Little Polly Flinders/Henry H. L. Jenks
Marketgravure, Australia, n.d. [194-?]
12pp, col. pic. book with slight text, pic. wrappers, cover title, 294x228mm. KMM

Nursery Rhymes
5443 NURSERY RHYMES
Wholly set up & printed in Australia by the H. & H. Printing Co., Carlton, Victoria
8pp, wrappers, unillus., 220x140mm. KP
Front cover with a col. illus. with caption 'Twinkle, twinkle little star'.

Nursery Rhymes
5444 NURSERY/RHYMES/Photogravures Pty Ltd.
n.p., n.d.
18pp, col. pic. covers, 3/4 page-illus., alternately col. & b/w, cover title, 240x180mm. KP

Nursery Rhymes
5445 NURSERY RHYMES/[col. drawing & verse]/BUY! War Savings Certificates/and 6d. War Savings Stamps
Commonwealth Government [Sydney], n.d. [194?]
8pp, col. illus. on every page, col. pic. wrappers, 120x90mm. CLRC
Modified nursery rhyme verses. Illus. unsigned.

Nursery Rhymes
5446 NURSERY/RHYMES/W. H. Honey Publishing Co. Sydney
n.d. [copyright 1943]
64pp, b/w illus. throughout, pic. bd., cover designed by Rhys Williams, cover title, 245x175mm. NSL:M

Nursery Rhymes
5446a NURSERY/RHYMES/With bright coloured pages/Illustrated/by/Marna Fitchett/and Ruth Iggsten.
See Gunn and Taylor

Nursery Rhymes for Rainy Days
5447 NURSERY RHYMES/FOR/RAINY/DAYS/[b/w drawings]/Printed and Published by Offset Printing Coy. Pty Ltd. 169 Phillip St. Waterloo Sydney (All Rights Reserved)
n.d. [195-?]
16pp, inc. 4pp f/p col. illus., b/w illus. in text, col. pic. wrappers, 276x214mm. CLRC
Illus. signed Franklin Bennett. Series A197.
See also 'Oops-A-Daisy' Nursery Rhymes.

Nursery Stories
5448 NURSERY STORIES
W. H. Honey Publishing Co., Sydney, n.d. [copyright 1943]
96pp, b/w illus. throughout, dec. bd., cover title, 245x175mm. NSL:M
Traditional stories.

Nursery Stories and Rhymes for Boys and Girls
See Gunn & Taylor

Nursery Times
5449 NURSERY/TIMES
Babies Home, Walkerville (SA) Incorporated [1944?]
Printed by Sharples Printers Ltd, 98 Hindley Street, Adelaide
[24]pp, b/w photographs of babies with re-written nursery rhymes, wrappers, cover title, 140x225mm. KMM
Foreword by Eleanor K. Barker explaining the purpose of the booklet, to raise funds for the establishment of a Mothercraft Training Centre.

OAKLEY, Eva Bessie Isabel
5450 FAIRY POEMS/by Eva Oakley
Austral Publishing Co., Melbourne, n.d. [1945]
8pp, unillus., dec. wrappers, cover title, 180x120mm. ANL

5451 REAL/AUSTRALIAN/FAIRY STORIES/By/Eva Oakley
Austral Printing & Publishing Co., Melbourne, n.d. [1945]
16pp, b/w drawings, wrappers, cover title, 185x120mm. First Series. ANL

5452 REAL AUSTRALIAN/FAIRY STORIES/[drawing]/ By Eva Oakley
Austral Printing & Publishing Co., Melbourne, n.d. [1950?]
16pp, b/w drawings, wrappers, cover title, 185x120mm. Second Series. ANL
Includes some verses.

5453 ROBBIE AND SPADGIE/MASTER TOM CAT AND/MISS POMERANIAN/AND/WEDDING BELLS IN FAIRYLAND/[drawing signed Nelson White]/ Copyright/By Eva Oakley
The author, Melbourne, n.d. [1949]
16pp, b/w drawings, wrappers, cover title, 180x120mm. ANL
Verses.

5454 WILLIE WAGTAIL/Two Little Romances/and/ Other Verses/By/Eva Oakley/Copyright
Austral Printing & Publishing Co., Melbourne, n.d. [1950]
15pp, b/w illus., wrappers, cover title, 180x120mm. ANL

OAKLEY, E. D.

5455 JIMMY/OF/"MURRUMBAR":/A Story of the Amazing/Ability & Fidelity of an/Australian Black Tracker/By/E. D. Oakley/Australia:/Osboldstone & Co. Pty. Ltd./Melbourne
[1938]
181pp (inc. foreword & 1p appreciation), frontis. (reproducing cover illus.), bd., 180x120mm. ANL
Foreword by C. W. S. Anderson, Chief Commissioner, Boy Scouts Association, Victorian Branch; appreciation by J. H. Sexton, Secretary, Aborigines Friends' Association; cover design by Val Hickman.

OATS, W. N.

5456 MAKING THEM LIVE./New and Old Testament Plays designed/to be acted & discussed by children/By/W. N. Oats, B.A., Dip. Ed./In two Parts:/The Boyhood of Jesus/From Noah to Moses/Australasian Publishing Company/Sydney Wellington London
1952
199pp (inc. 9pp foreword &c), unillus., limp clo., 180x124mm. ANL

Ocean Scenes

5457 OCEAN SCENES,/or,/the Perils and Beauties of/the Deep;/being/interesting, instructive, and graphic accounts/of the/most popular voyages on record,/remarkable shipwrecks, hair-breadth escapes, naval adven-/tures, the whale fishery, etc, etc,/—/Dublin:/Published by James M'Glashan,/21, D'Olier Street./—/MDCCCXLIX.
xvipp, [17]pp, 326pp, [2]pp (W. Tegg's list of books), frontis. (Brig under sail) & 7 text illus., black blind-stamped clo. bd.,165x101mm. ANL
on spine in gold lettering: Ocean/Scenes/Standard/Series. Tegg's list (ivpp.) precedes t.p.
Contains, *inter alia*, short accounts of Dampier (1p), De Bougainville (pp82-7), La Pérouse, (pp197-219) & D'Entrecasteaux (pp277-82).

L'Océanie

5458 L'OCÉANIE/d'Après Les Voyageurs Les Plus Célèbres/Par un homme de lettres./2e Édition./[drawing]/Lille/L. Lefort, Imprimeur-Libraire/1851.
xvipp (inc. introduction, t.p. & frontis.), 201pp (inc. 3pp table of contents), 1p adv. (preceding t.p.), f/p engraved frontis. only, dec. bd., with col. illus. pasted in oval panel on front cover, 180x110mm. RM
Divided into 4 parts, 'La Melanesie' pp46–83 relating to Australia, & remainder of book to islands of the Pacific & to the north of Australia. Famous French explorers of the Pacific often mentioned.

O'CONNER, Elizabeth

5459 THE CHINEE/BIRD/by Elizabeth O'Conner/illustrated by Astra/Ure Smith—Sydney
1966
159pp, 4 f/p b/w illus. & drawings in text, clo., 215x135mm. CLRC

O'DEA, Marjory

5460 SIX DAYS/BETWEEN/A SECOND/Marjory O'Dea/River House
Heinemann Educational Australia Pty Ltd, South Yarra, Victoria 1969
120pp, 1p verse, b/w illus. throughout, illus. by Jonathon Waud, dec. e/p, maps, clo., 210x135mm. BBC

ODELL, Carol [Carol Foote]

5461 JOHNNY'S HUNGER STRIKE/by Carol Odell/[drawing]/Illustrated by Alan Howard/Faber and Faber Limited/24 Russell Square London
1960
31pp, col. t.p., col. illus. throughout, dec. bd., 200x140mm. KMM

5462 LATE FOR SCHOOL/by/Carol Odell/illustrated by/Leslie Wood/Faber and Faber Limited/24 Russell Square/London
1960
32pp, col. lithographic illus. throughout, dec. bd., 200x140mm. KMM

5463 THE HOUSE NEXT DOOR/by/Carol Odell/illustrated by/Leslie Wood/[drawing]/Faber and Faber Limited/24 Russell Square/London
1961
32pp, b/w & col. illus. on alternate pages, dec. bd., 200x140mm. KMM

5464 THE/GETTING BETTER/BOOK/by/Carol Odell/Illustrated by/Sally Michel/London/Evans Brothers Limited
1961
96pp, 33 b/w illus., bd., 210x155mm. BBC

5465 MARK/AND HIS/PICTURES/Story by/Carol Odell/Pictures by/Gerald Rose/Faber and Faber/London
1962
32pp, dec. t.p., col. illus. throughout, dec. bd., 240x180mm. KMM

5466 [drawing]/FIRES/AND/FIREMEN/by/Carol Odell/[device]/Angus and Robertson
Sydney 1963
64pp, b/w photographic illus. throughout, dec. clo., 250x185mm. KMM

5467 A DAY AT THE/ZOO Carol Odell/[photograph]/Angus and Robertson
Sydney 1964
64pp, b/w photographic frontis. & b/w photographs on almost every page, clo., dec. e/p, 250x190mm. CLRC

5468 JIMMY/HURLEY/TO THE/RESCUE/Carol Odell/[drawing]/illustrated by Astra Lacis/Angus and Robertson
Sydney 1964
108pp, 13 b/w drawings in text, clo., 215x135mm. KMM

5469 KATE AND THE/BUNYIP/By Carol Odell/Illustrated by Molly G. Johnson/[coloured drawing]/Readabout Books
Crow's Nest, NSW, 1964
24pp, col. & part-col. illus. throughout, stiff dec. wrappers, 215x180mm. KMM

5470 THE/KOOKABURRAS/WHO WOULDN'T/LAUGH/by/Carol Odell/Illustrated by/Emilie Beuth
Readabout Publishers Pty Ltd, Crow's Nest, NSW, 1964
24pp, col. & part-col. illus. throughout, stiff dec. wrappers, 215x180mm. BBC

5471 POLICE TO THE/RESCUE/Carol Odell/[photograph]/Angus and Robertson
Sydney 1965
64pp, b/w photographic illus., clo., photographic e/p, 250x185mm. KMM
Book comprised mainly of photographs of police rescue work, with short text, including a variety of safety hints from the Police Rescue Squad.

5472 WAKE UP!/IT'S NIGHT/By Carol Odell/Pictures by/Penelope Janic/Angus and Robertson
Sydney 1966

[31]pp, dec. t.p., col. illus. throughout, pic. clo., dec. e/p, 250x170mm. CLRC

5473 [photograph]/WORKING DOGS/by Carol Odell/ Sheep-dogs/Guide Dogs/Husky Dogs/[two photographs]
[Angus and Robertson] Sydney 1966
51pp, b/w photographic illus. throughout, clo., 245x180mm. CLRC

5474 A LINER GOES TO SEA/by Carol Odell/Angus and Robertson
Sydney 1968
63pp, b/w photographic frontis. & b/w photographic illus. throughout, clo., 245x180mm. KMM
Factual account of a liner's voyage from Sydney to Britain; photographs taken aboard S.S. *Canberra.*

ODELL, Carol [ed.]
5475 THE/MAGIC/OF/VERSE/Australian Poetry selected by Carol Odell/from *Chosen for Children* by Joyce Saxby/Illustrated by Noela Young/Angus and Robertson
Sydney 1970
[26]pp, col. illus. throughout, pic. bd., 290x235mm. *Young Australia Series.* KMM
See also Wall, Dorothy & Odell, Carol

'ODELL, Gill' [pseud. Carol Foote & Gill Traviss]
5476 MR. OZZLE/OF/WITHERY WOOD/by/Gill Odell/With illustrations by/J. S. Goodall/Angus & Robertson
London 1959
160pp, 11 b/w drawings in text, clo., 190x125mm. KMM
Children's detective story with woodland animals as characters.

[OERTEL, Philipp Friedrich W.]
JAMES COOK. *See* Horn, W. O. von

[O'FERRALL, Ernest, pseud. 'Kodak']
5477 THE ADVENTURES/OF/"CHUNDER LOO"/Published by/Blyth & Platt (Australia) Ltd.,/Proprietors of/"COBRA". *The* Boot Polish
Sydney, n.d. [1917]
[54]pp, 52pp b/w illus. by Lionel Lindsay, stiff paper cover (with col. illus.), 280x215mm. CLRC
Each page comprises a b/w illustration with a verse beneath. Sir Lionel Lindsay in his autobiography, *Comedy of Life* (Angus & Robertson, Sydney, 1968), tells how he illustrated O'Ferrall's verses of 'Chunder Loo' for a series of advertisements which appeared in the Sydney *Bulletin* some time after 1903, & that the 'blacking' company later printed a book from these advertisements & 'gave me nothing'.

OFFSET PUBLISHING CUT-OUT BOOKS
5478 Series A 204/NOAH'S/ARK/CUT-OUT/BOOK/ Complete with/All the Animals in Colour to/cut out and make up/Printed and Published by Offset Printing Coy Pty Ltd 169 Phillip St, Waterloo. Sydney (All Rights reserved) OPC Publication
8pp, col. illus., stiff col. pic. wrappers, cover title, 370x250mm. MCa
5478a NURSERY DAYS/CUT-OUT/BOOK/OPC/Series A 200
As above but 9pp, comprising The House that Jack Built, Nursery Time, Nursery Days, 240x240mm. KP
5479 OUR FARMYARD PETS CUT-OUT BOOK
Offset Publishing Co, Sydney, n.d.
6pp, col. illus. card, 238x240mm. MAC
5480 RHYMELAND Series No E22
As above. Unseen

Uniform with above:
5481 THE HOLIDAY CUT OUT BOOK
16 pp (printed one side only & inc. covers), 370x255mm. MAC
5482 DOWN ON THE FARM CUT OUT BOOK
16pp (printed one side only & inc. covers), 255x360mm. MAC

Og
5483 OG 1/Og's First Story/Concerning the Manner in Which he Met Oliver the Ostrich/A Story Book that Unfolds to Make a Wall Mural 6 1/2 Feet Long (Jigsaw Pty Ltd.)
1971
8pp-fold single sheet, col. illus. throughout, col. dec. wrappers, cover title, 255x255mm. MCa

5484 OG 2/Og's Second/Story in Which/He Travels to the City to Obtain New/Eyeglasses (Jigsaw Pty Ltd)
1971
As above. MCa
5485 OG 3/A Visit to Og's Palace, and Some General Information About Giants/Og's Third Story (Jigsaw Pty Ltd)
1971
As above. MCa

O'HANLON, M. A.
5486 CHRIS OF COORABEEN/By M. A. O'Hanlon/The Bruce Publishing Company/Milwaukee [USA]
1955
234pp, unillus., clo., 205x135mm. CLRC
Story set in Australia prior to the First World War.

5487 COORABEEN/By/M. A. O'Hanlon/Pellegrini & Co. Pty. Ltd./Sydney Melbourne Brisbane/Adelaide Perth
1957
270pp, unillus., clo., 200x135mm. KMM

'O'HARRIS, Pixie' [pseud. Rona Olive Pratt]
5488 THE/"PIXIE O. HARRIS FAIRY BOOK"/Stories and Verse/By/Lynette Yardley/Eva Lawton/Gwen M. Cock/Pixie O. Harris/Illustrations/in/Color, Half-tone and Line/By/Pixie O. Harris/Price: five shillings/ Copyright/Rigby Limited/Publishers/Imperial Place/ Adelaide.
n.d. [1925]
63pp, col. frontis. & 1 f/p col. illus., 13 f/p b/w & part. col. illus., b/w drawings throughout, wrappers (with col. frontis. reproduced on front cover), 265x200mm. KMM
Dedication, verses & stories.

5489 PEARL PINKIE.../AND SEA GREENIE/The Story of Two Little Rock Sprites/Told and Decorated/by/ Pixie O'Harris/[drawing]/Angus and Robertson Limited/89 Castlereagh Street, Sydney/1935
64pp, col. frontis. & 3 f/p col. illus., b/w drawings throughout, bd., 240x180mm. NSL:M
5490 PEARL PINKIE AND SEA GREENIE/The Story of Two Little Rock Sprites/Told and Decorated by Pixie O'Harris
Angus and Robertson Ltd., Sydney, London, 1940
2nd ed. 245x180mm. JBP
• Rpt 1942. Unseen

5491 PIXIE O'HARRIS/STORY BOOK/[drawing]/ Illustrated by the author/Angus and Robertson Limited/89 Castlereagh Street, Sydney/1940
160pp, col. frontis. & b/w illus. throughout, bd., 240x180mm. ANL
5492 THE/PIXIE O'HARRIS/STORY BOOK/[drawing]/

Illustrated by the author/Angus and Robertson/
Sydney London
First pub. 1940; New & revised ed. 1948
168pp, col. frontis. & 1 f/p col. illus., part-col. illus. throughout, clo., 245x160mm. ANL
Contents vary considerably from 1940 edition.

5493 THE/PIXIE O'HARRIS/STORY BOOK/Angus and Robertson/Sydney London Melbourne Wellington
New & revised edition 1956
152pp, part-col. extended t.p., 2 f/p col. illus., part. col. & b/w illus. throughout, clo., dec. e/p, 235x155mm. KMM
Omits 5 stories from 1948 edition.

5494 PIXIE O'HARRIS/SONGS FOR CHILDREN/[drawing]/Lyrics and Illustrations by/Pixie O'Harris/(with acknowledgments to NSW & Victorian/Education Departments)/Special Musical Arrangements by/Dorothy R. Mathlin/Published by D. Davis & Co. Pty Ltd./250 Pitt St, Sydney
n.d. [1940?]
25pp, b/w drawings inside front cover & on t.p. & on some pages, words & music of 12 songs, col. pic. wrappers with drawing of 3 children printed in col. on a dark blue background & price 3/- on front cover & another drawing on back cover, 275x218mm. KP

5495 Another copy as above, but
D. Davis & Co. Pty Ltd. 250 Pitt Street, Sydney
Details as above, but figures on front & back covers printed in b/w, & 4/- and publisher's address on front cover, 280x220mm. KP

5496 'Imperial Edition 927'/PIXIE O'HARRIS/SONGS FOR CHILDREN/[drawing]/Lyrics and Illustrations by/Pixie O'Harris/(With acknowledgements to N.S.W. & Victorian/Education Departments)/Special Musical Arrangements by/Dorothy R. Mathlin/[device]/4/6/Published by/D. Davis & Co. Pty. Ltd. 250 Pitt Street—Sydney 1945
24pp [back cover numbered 25, continuing last song], 12 b/w song headings, wrappers, cover title, 280x220mm. Grant

5497 THE BABES/IN THE WOOD/1941/Copyright/New Century Press Pty. Ltd./3 North York Street/Sydney Australia
28pp col. & b/w illus. throughout, dec. wrappers, 235x180mm. ANL
According to the author the story was re-written to exclude horror.

5498 CINDERELLA/1941/Copyright/New Century Press Pty. Ltd./3 North Street/Sydney Australia
29pp, col. & b/w illus. throughout, dec. wrappers, 235x180mm. ANL

5499 LITTLE RED/RIDING HOOD/1941/Copyright/New Century Press Pty. Ltd./3 North York Street/Sydney Australia
29pp, col. & part-col. illus. throughout, dec. wrappers, 235x175mm. NSL:M
The familiar story retold & illustrated by Pixie O'Harris.

5500 FORTUNES OF/POPPY TRELOAR/By/Pixie O'Harris/Angus and Robertson Ltd./Sydney: London/1941
253pp, b/w frontis. by author, clo., 185x120mm. VSL
• Rpt as above, 1946. KMM
• Rpt as above, 1947. KP
• Rpt as above, 1948. KMM

5501 THE/FORTUNES/OF/POPPY/TRELOAR/by Pixie O'Harris/Paul Hamlyn/London New York Sydney Toronto
Sydney 1969
432pp, b/w frontis. by author, clo., 245x170mm. BBC
Comprises: *The Fortunes of Poppy Treloar; Poppy and the Gems; Poppy Faces the World; Poppy at Wildacres* (102pp, first published in this volume).

5502 MARMADUKE/THE POSSUM/By/Pixie O'Harris/[drawing]/Angus and Robertson Ltd./Sydney: London/1942
165pp, col. frontis., 6 f/p b/w illus. & b/w drawings throughout, bd., 240x180mm. KMM
• Rpt 1947, as above. ANL
• Rpt 1950, as above. ANL

5503 MARMADUKE/THE POSSUM/By/Pixie O'Harris/[drawing]/Angus and Robertson/Sydney London
First publ. 1943, rpt. 1947, rpt. 1950 [This is incorrect as the book was first publ. 1942]
165pp, col. frontis., 15 f/p sepia/white illus. & drawings in text, illus. bd., 240x180mm. KP

5504 GOOLARA/By/Pixie O'Harris/The Currawong Publishing Company,/32 Jamieson Street,/Sydney
n.d. [1943]
48pp, dec. t.p., 10 b/w illus. by Joyce Abbott, dec. wrappers, 135x210mm. ANL
Children's stories of the Aborigines; also includes 'Daughters of the Billabong'.

5505 RONDEL, THE FAIR/by/Pixie O'Harris/The Currawong Publishing Co./32 Jamieson Street,/Sydney
n.d. [1943]
48pp, b/w frontis. & 3 f/p b/w illus., b/w drawings in text, dec. wrappers, 135x210mm. CLRC
Includes also 'Bird of Flame and Bird of Snow'.

5506 POPPY AND THE GEMS/by/Pixie O'Harris/[drawing]/The Currawong Publishing Company/32 Jamieson Street, Sydney
n.d. [1944]
192pp, unillus., bd., 215x140mm. ANL
Sequel to *The Fortunes of Poppy Treloar.*

5507 POPPY AND THE GEMS/by/Pixie O'Harris/[drawing]/Currawong Publishing Company Pty. Ltd./3, Castlereagh Street, Sydney
n.d.
192pp, unillus., clo., 195x130mm. KMM

5508 ROCKS OF HAN/A Fairy Story/Written and Illustrated/by/Pixie O'Harris/The Currawong Publishing Company/32 Jamieson Street, Sydney
n.d. [1944]
61pp, 1p adv., b/w frontis. & 11 b/w illus., dec. wrappers, 180x120mm. ANL

5509 PRINCESS OF CHINA/by/Pixie O'Harris/The Currawong Publishing Company,/32 Jamieson Street,/Sydney
n.d. [1946?]
48pp (no frontis.), 4 f/p & 4 half-page b/w illus., pic. wrappers, 135x215mm. CLRC
Date surmised from the fact that *Goolara*, & *Rondel, the Fair* by the same author are among the books advertised.

5510 POPPY FACES THE/WORLD/By/Pixie O'Harris/Angus and Robertson/Sydney: London/1947
250pp, unillus., clo., 180x120mm. VSL
Sequel to *Poppy and the Gems.*
• Rpt as above, 1948. KMM

5511 THE FAIRY/WHO WOULDN'T FLY/told & pictured by/Pixie O'Harris
Marchant & Co. Pty Ltd, Sydney, n.d. [1947, according to the author]
[56]pp, dec. t.p., col. frontis. & 5 f/p col. illus., 10 f/p

b/w illus. & b/w drawings throughout, dec. bd., 230x170mm. KMM
5512 Second ed., as above, 1948. KP

5513 MARMADUKE/AND/MARGARET/by/Pixie O'Harris/Angus and Robertson/Sydney—London 1953
132pp, col. frontis. &1 f/p col. illus., b/w drawings throughout, illus. by author, clo., 215x135mm. KMM

5514 PIXIE O'HARRIS/GIFT BOOK/Stories and Poems written and illustrated/by Australia's best beloved writer/for the Not-so-old/[drawing]/Dymock's Book Arcade Limited/Sydney
n.d. [1953]
128pp, 64 b/w illus., bd., 250x185mm. VSL
Includes *Rondel the Fair*, & also verses.

5515 THE/TOWN OF FLOWERS/Pixie O'Harris/ 1957/Arthur H. Stockwell Limited/Elms Court, Ilfracombe/Devon [England]
n.d.
31pp, unillus., wrappers, 180x120mm. ANL
Verses.

5516 THE/MAGIC CLOAKS/and the Tale of/THE/ CURIOUS PIPE/[drawing]/Printed by Morris & Walker, Melbourne,/for the publishers, Offset Printing Co Pty Limited, Sydney
n.d.
16pp, 11 drawings (Pixie O'Harris) & many smaller part-col. illus., col. pic. wrappers, 240x175mm. ANL

The Oil Industry
5517 The Student's Guide Book to THE/OIL/ INDUSTRY
Shell Co. of Aust. Ltd, Melbourne, 1954
46pp, col. diagrams, maps & col. & b/w photographs, pic. wrappers, spirax bdg, 270x205mm. KP
• Rpt as above, Melbourne 1957. KP

The O.K. Fairy Book
5518 THE/O.K./FAIRY/BOOK/New Rhymes and Pictures/For Kiddies Only
Booklet publ. to advertise O.K. jams & sauces, designed by the Weston Company Limited, cnr George & Grosvenor Strs, Sydney, n.d. [illus. dated 1923]
16pp (inc. 12pp of verses printed inside a col. pic. border depicting fairies & gnomes &c repeated on each double-page spread), col. pic. wrappers with illus. inside printed in blue & white, 185x125mm. KP
Illus. throughout by Pixie O'Harris.

O'KEEFE, Dan
5519 THE VOYAGES/OF/CAPTAIN COOK/by Dan O'Keefe/Illustrated by Richard Gregory/Paul Hamlyn/ London New York Sydney Toronto
1969
64pp (inc. 2pp index), col. illus. throughout, col. extended frontis., col. extended map, pic. bd., 310x225mm. BBC
• Rpt 1969, 1970. KP

'OLD BOOMERANG'
See Houlding, John Richard

Old Broadbrim
5520 Old Broadbrim Weekly (More reading matter than any/five cent detective library published)/Five Cents/ OLD BROADBRIM/No. 32/INTO THE HEART OF AUSTRALIA/[col. illus. with caption]/By the author of/'Old Broadbrim'
Street & Smith, 238 William St, New York, 1903
32pp, unillus, col. pic. wrappers (adv. verso back wrapper), cover title, 270x210mm. RM
On first text page title given as 'Old Broadbrim into the Heart of Australia; or, A Strange Bargain and its consequences.'

Old Mother Hubbard
The Old Woman & her Pig
5521 OLD/MOTHER HUBBARD
5522 THE OLD WOMAN/& HER PIG
Uniform picture books published by Georgian House, Melbourne, n.d. [1944]
16pp, 8 f/p col. illus. (sgd. 'J.H.'), dec. wrappers, 250x195mm. NSL:M

The Old Navigators
5523 Collins' New Biographical Series/THE/OLD NAVIGATORS/Coloured Illustrations/and/Eight Portraits and Pictures/London and Glasgow/Collins' Clear-type Press
n.d. [1909]
190pp & 2pp notes, col. frontis. & col. plate & 8 sepia/ white plates, clo., 154x100mm. ANL
Contains: Dampier pp79-89; Cook pp116-55; La Pérouse pp156-73.

Old Tales in New Rhyme
5524 OLD TALES/IN/NEW RHYME
Hicks Smith & Wright, Melbourne, n.d. [194-?]
8pp (inc. covers), part col. illus., pic. wrappers, cover title, 150x115mm. KP

OLDFIELD, Audrey
5525 DAUGHTER/OF TWO/WORLDS/Audrey Oldfield/Rigby
Adelaide 1970
155pp, 11 b/w illus. & d/w by Jean Elder, clo., 210x130mm. KMM

OLDHAM, Wilfrid
5526 LONDON ON THE/THAMES/A Story for Boys and Girls/by/Wilfrid Oldham Ph.D., M.A./Lecturer in History, University of Adelaide/Oxford University Press/Cathedral Buildings, Melbourne/London, Edinburgh, New York, Toronto/Capetown Bombay and Madras/1935
32pp, frontis. map & 1 map in text, wrappers, 185x125mm. KMM
Introduction by G. V. Portus.
• Rpt 1935. CLRC

OLIPHANT, Sir Marcus Laurence Elwin
5527 THE STORY/OF ATOMIC/ENERGY
Australian Atomic Energy Commission Sydney 1961
[First published 1958; rpt 1961]
11pp, diagrams, wrappers, cover title, 245x185mm. ANL
Text of talks to schoolchildren.

OLIVER, Arthur
5528 TRUTH/IN THE ARENA/by Arthur Oliver
A Modern Morality Play—specially written for the National Christian Youth Convention, Sydney, 1955
16pp, unillus, dec. wrappers, 215x140mm. ANL

OLIVIER, Jean
5529 Jean Olivier/TONY/AND THE KANGAROO/ Illustrations by Clauss
Oliver & Boyd, Edinburgh & London [original French edition copyright 1961, Dargaud-Mame; translation copyright 1962, Oliver and Boyd]
[Printed in Italy]
18pp, col. illus. throughout, dec. bd., dec. e/p, 230x170mm. Round the World Series. CLRC

OLYOTT, Muriel
5530 COME TO THE FAIR/IN NURSERY

RHYMELAND/a story by/Muriel Olyott/decorations by/Walter Cunningham/an Alpha Production/ Published by the Commonwealth Trades Alphabet/142 Phillip Street, Sydney/Copyright
n.d. [1944]
32pp, col. & part-col. illus. throughout, wrappers, 180x245mm. ANL

5531 WONDERCAP ADVENTURES/WITH THE SANDMAN/Written by Muriel Olyott & pictured by Walter Cunningham/[coloured drawing]/John Sands Pty. Ltd./Sydney & Melbourne/Registered in Australia for transmission by Post as a book
n.d. [1946]
40pp, 4 f/p col. illus. & col. or b/w drawings throughout, stiff dec. wrappers, 245x245mm. KMM

OMMANNEY, F. D.
5532 A Bodley Head Natural Science Picture Book/ Scientific Adviser: Dr. Gwynne Vevers/ANIMAL LIFE/ IN THE PACIFIC/F. D. Ommanney/Illustrated by/ Robert Gillmor/[device]/The Bodley Head, London Sydney Toronto
1969
32pp, b/w & col. illus. on alternate page openings, pic. bd., dec. e/p, 195x250mm. KMM

5533 A Bodley Head Natural Science Picture Book/ Scientific Adviser: Dr Gwynne Vevers/ANIMAL LIFE/ IN THE ANTARCTIC/F. D. Ommanney/Illustrated by/Robert Gillmor/[device]/The Bodley Head/London Sydney Toronto
1969
32pp, illus. throughout alternately in col. & b/w, pic. bd., dec. e/p, 195x125mm. KP

On the Farm/A Johnny, Jane and Jason Book
See AT THE CIRCUS WITH JOHNNY, JANE AND JASON

Once a Jolly Swagman
5534 ONCE A JOLLY SWAGMAN
n.p., n.d.
24pp (inc. covers), col. illus. throughout, pic. wrappers, 160x220mm. KP
Tourist promotional brochure using the poem *Waltzing Matilda* which is illus. throughout by photographs of a modern re-enactment of the verse.

Once I saw a Little Bird
5535 ONCE I SAW A LITTLE BIRD/and other Nursery Rhymes/illustrated/by/Stan Clements
Printed by Mastercraft and Publishing Co., 790 and 796 George/Street, Sydney, for the publishers, The Clarendon Pub. Co., Sydney, n.d. [194-?]
[12]pp, 1 f/p col. illus. & 10 smaller col. illus., pic. wrappers, 240x185mm. Grant
'The Claro Series'

Once Upon a Time
5536 ONCE UPON A TIME:/or, The Boy's Book of Adventures./[decoration]/London:/The Religious Tract Society./56 Paternoster Row; 65, St. Paul's Churchyard/and 164, Piccadilly.
n.d. [1878]
288 (inc. 2pp introduction), 11 f/p b/w illus. & b/w decorations in text, pic. clo. (gilt dec.), 180x130mm. KMM
A collection of anonymous adventure stories which first appeared in the *Leisure Hour.* Contents include: 'Melbourne and the Diggings' (14pp); 'Wreck of the *Admella*' (off the South Australian coast, 9pp); 'Strange Signals' (set in the Marquesas, 31pp); 'Among South Sea Cannibals' (in New Caledonia, 24pp).

5537 ONCE UPON A TIME/or/The Boy's Book of Adventures/[decoration]/London/The Religious Tract Society/56 Paternoster Row, 65 St. Paul's Churchyard/ and 164 Piccadilly
n.d. [1897?]
383pp (inc. 2pp introduction), b/w frontis. & 8 f/p b/w illus., dec. clo. (title printed in black on gilt panel on cover & spine), 180x115mm. Grant

5538 ONCE UPON/A TIME/or/The Boy's Book of Adventures/With fifteen illustrations/London/The Religious Tract Society/56 Paternoster Row and 65 St. Paul's Churchyard
n.d. [1900?]
319pp (inc. 2pp introduction), 16pp adv., b/w frontis. & 14 f/p b/w illus., pic. clo., 195x125mm. KMM
Another copy as above, n.d., but publisher's address '4 Bouverie Street and 65 St Paul's Churchyard'. KMM

5539 ONCE UPON/A TIME/or,/The Boy's Book/of Adventures/With coloured/and other Illustrations/ London/The Religious Tract Society/4 Bouverie Street & 65 St. Paul's Churchyard
n.d. [school prize 1915]
319pp (inc. 2pp introduction), 16pp adv., col. frontis. & col. t.p., 2 f/p col. plates & 8 f/p b/w plates, pic. clo., 195x133mm. KP

Once upon a Time
5540 ONCE UPON A TIME/[illus.]/Stories
Thomas Tennant Chatswood, NSW, [1944?]
34pp & poem & illus. inside back cover, b/w & part-col. illus., stiff pic. wrappers, cover title, 247x178mm. ANL

Once upon a Time: Easy to read slumberland stories
Ayers & James Pty Ltd, Sydney, n.d. [1949]
Not Australian in content. NSL:M

O'NEILL, Sally
GEORGE FIFE ANGAS. *See* Great Australians

O'NEILL, W. J.
5541 BUDGEREE BILL/An Australian Story/for Little Australians/By/W. J. O'Neill/Illustrated by B. E. Minns/[drawing]/Australia:/Cornstalk Publishing Company/89 Castlereagh Street, Sydney
1926
42pp, 6 f/p b/w illus., marginal drawing & drawings in text throughout, clo., 230x185mm. KMM

'Oops-a-Daisy' Nursery Rhymes
5542 "OOPS-A-DAISY"/NURSERY RHYMES/[col. illus.]/Series E 204
Offset Printing Coy Pty Ltd./169 Phillip St, Waterloo, Sydney, n.d.
14pp (inc. 3 f/p col. illus.), b/w illus. in text (by Franklin Bennett) col. pic. wrappers(sgd Rufus Morris) 270x218mm. CLRC
Contents repeated from *Nursery Rhymes for Rainy Days.*

ORD, Marion
5543 DONOVAN/AND THE LOST BIRTHDAY/Marion Ord Illustrated by Penelope Janic/Heinemann Melbourne London
1968
[29]pp, col. illus. throughout, pic. clo., dec. e/p, 235x230mm. CLRC

5544 DONOVAN/SAVES THE SKATES/Marion Ord/ [*sic* —a slanting stroke]
Illustrated by Penelope Janic/Heinemann Melbourne
1970
32pp, col. illus. throughout, pic. clo., dec. e/p, 233x233mm. CLRC

O'REILLY, Bernard

5545 WILD RIVER/By/Bernard O'Reilly/Cassell & Co. Ltd./London, Toronto, Melbourne, Sydney/Wellington
n.d. [1949]
159pp, b/w photographic frontis. & 3 photographic illus., 4 f/p b/w drawings sgd 'Browning', 200x135mm. VSL

5546 WILD RIVER/By/Bernard O'Reilly/Cassell & Co. Ltd./London Toronto Melbourne Sydney Wellington
First Australian edition 1949; second Australian edition 1952
159pp, unillus., limp clo., 180x120mm. KMM
Edition produced as a school reader.
- Rpt as above, 3rd Australian ed. 1956 KP
- Rpt as above 1961, 1965, 1967 (soft board bdg), all KP

[ORR, Mrs Andrew]

5547 SUNNY AUSTRALIA/[drawing, 'Christmas Bush']/ FOR/AUSTRALIA'S CHILDREN/W. M. Maclardy, lith. Sydney
n.d. [189-?]
16pp (1st page dedication, 7pp text with drawings, other pages blank), b/w drawings throughout, b/w pic. wrappers, 280x220mm. NSL:M
Verses for children about Australian wildflowers illus. with b/w drawings.

O'RYAN, Barbara

5548 BUSY HANDS/by/Barbara O'Ryan/[drawing]/ Whitcombe and Tombs Pty. Ltd.
Sydney 1965
44pp, pic. wrappers, 230x175mm. Grant
Instructional booklet on how to make things.

OS, P. van

5549 REIS/naar/NIEUW-ZUID-WALLIS,/Uit het Dagboek van een Scheepsdoctor./Voor de Jeugd Bewerkt./Door/P. VAN OS/mit vier plaatjes./Te Sneek, Bij/van Druten & Blecker
[1853?]
ivpp, 188pp & 4pp adv., engraved frontis. & 3 plates, clo. with vignette in gilt on front cover, 166x100mm. ANL

OSBORN, Mrs Annie Rattray [née Annie O'Neill, 'Cinderella' of the *Leader*]

5550 The Willie Winkie Zoo Books/FUZZY, WUZZY, and BUZZY/Written by/Mrs. A. R. Osborn/Pictured by/Ida Rentoul Outhwaite/Whitcombe & Tombs Limited/Melbourne/Auckland Christchurch Dunedin and Wellington N.Z./and London
n.d. [library stamp 1918]
44pp, 6 f/p b/w illus., b/w drawings in text, wrappers (with col. illus. on frontis. cover), 180x135mm. ANL
Uniform with the above

5551 THE GUINEA PIG THAT WANTED A TAIL (Also in Whitcombe's Story Books. *See* McLaren 315)

5552 THE NAUGHTY BABY MONKEY*

5553 PETER'S PEACH

5554 THE QUARREL OF THE BABY LIONS

5555 TEDDY BEAR'S BIRTHDAY PARTY (Also in Whitcombe's Story Books. *See* McLaren 313)
All ANL

* not reprinted in Whitcombe's Story Books, but withdrawn from series because of its contents

5556 Australian Nature Story Readers/FUZZY, WUZZY, and BUZZY/by/Mrs. A. R. Osborn/for children ages 7 to 8 years/Whitcombe & Tombs Limited/Melbourne/ Auckland Christchurch Dunedin and Wellington N.Z./and London
n.d.
32pp, b/w frontis. & 2 f/p b/w illus., b/w drawings by Ida Rentoul Outhwaite, wrappers (with b/w illus.), (Willie Winkie Preface inside front cover), 180x125mm. KMM
See also McLaren—'Whitcombe's Story Books' 314, which lists many reprints & records that 8 ed. totalling 46 627 copies had been bound to February 1939, & further ed. were issued up to 1954.

5557 Cassell's/Commonwealth Story Readers/THE FOUR BEARS/For Children aged/7 to 10 years/ [drawing]/By Mrs A. R. Osborn/Author of/"Almost Human", "Willie Winkie/Zoo Books", "Mollie at/the Zoo" etc./Cassell & Company Limited/Melbourne, Sydney, Brisbane/New York, Toronto, and London
n.d. [library acquired copy 1923]
24pp, 3 f/p b/w illus., b/w drawings in text, wrappers, 180x110mm. VSL

5558 Cassell's/Commonwealth Story Readers/THE FOUR BEARS/By Mrs A. R. Osborn/Author of/ "Almost Human", "Willie Winkie/Zoo Books", "Mollie at/the Zoo" etc./For children aged/7 to 10 years/ Cassell & Company Limited/Melbourne, Sydney, Brisbane, New York, Toronto and London/Wholly set up and printed in Australia. Registered by/the Postmaster General for transmission through the/post as a book. 1923
24pp, b/w frontis., 2 f/p b/w illus., 4 b/w illus. in text, wrappers (with adv. on both sides of back cover), 180x120mm. CLRC

5559 Cassell's/Commonwealth Story Readers/MOLLIE AT THE ZOO/By Mrs A. R. Osborn/Author of/"The Four Bears", "The Willie Winkie/Zoo Books", &c./Cassell & Company Limited/Melbourne Sydney Brisbane/New York, Toronto, and London
n.d.
46pp, 2pp adv., b/w drawings in text throughout, wrappers (with adv. on both sides of back wrapper), 180x110mm. VSL

OSBORNE, Mrs F.

5560 A MODERN BLUEBEARD/AND/A SCRAP OF PAPER/[Allied Flags]/[patriotic quotation]/By Mrs. F. Osborne/Price Sixpence/In Aid of Australian Wounded/and Belgian Funds
The author, Manly, NSW, n.d. [NSL:M copy 1915]
4pp, unillus., wrappers, 225x130mm. NSL:M
Patriotic account written for children of the beginning of World War I.

OSMOND, Edward

KANGAROOS. *See* Life in Australia

5561 Animals of the World/KANGAROOS/By Edward Osmond/Oxford University Press
n.d. [1960?]. Printed in England
32pp, b/w illus. in text, stiff wrappers, cover title, 194x154mm. WRT
Illus. by author. Contents the same as *Kangaroos* in the 'Life in Australia' series.

OSMOND, Sophie

5562 By/Sophie/Osmond./The FOOT OF THE RAINBOW./Price:/One Shilling
J. W. Knapton and Co., Printers, 290a Little Collins St., Melbourne
80pp, unillus., wrappers, cover title, 176x116mm. ANL
Dedicated 'To My dear Friend—Mrs T. N. Whyte'.
Fantasy about children but not intended for them.

5563 THE WATTLE BLOSSOM
8pp, bound together with *The Foot of the Rainbow*, no t.p. but with separate pagination

An Aboriginal legend about the coming of the wattle, dedicated to the Mentone Wattle Club. Doubtful children's. ANL

O'SULLIVAN, Joan

5564 Mullens' Stories for Children/No. 103/BUMP-AH/ By/Joan O'Sullivan/(For Ages 7 to 8)/[drawing]/ Robertson & Mullens Ltd./Melbourne
1952
32pp, b/w frontis. & 2 f/p b/w illus. (sgd. 'Rolland'), wrappers (with adv. on both sides of back wrapper), 180x115mm. ANL

OSWIN, Jennifer

5565 AUSTRALIAN ANIMALS/Illustrated by John Richards/Text by Jennifer Oswin/Paul Hamlyn/ London New York Sydney Toronto
1970
61pp (inc. covers), col. illus. throughout, pic. bd., pic. e/p, 310x230mm. CLRC
Coloured illustrations of animals, birds, insects, fish, etc. with brief test beside each illustration.

OTTLEY, Reginald

5566 [drawing] BY THE SANDHILLS OF YAMBOORAH/Reginald Ottley/Illustrated by Clyde Pearson/[device]/André Deutsch
London 1965
174pp, extended t.p., 6 f/p b/w illus. & line drawings in text, clo., 195x125mm. KMM
Second impression July 1966, as above, but variant d/w reproducing illus. facing p62. BBC
3rd impression 1969. KP

5567 Reginald Ottley/BY THE SANDHILLS/OF YAMBOORAH/[drawing]/Illustrated by Clyde Pearson/Collins/Armada Lions
London 1971
157pp, 1p note, 3pp adv., 6 f/p b/w illus., b/w drawings in text, pic. wrappers, 180x110mm. KMM

5568 BOY ALONE/[drawing]/Reginald Ottley/ Illustrated by Clyde Pearson/Harcourt, Brace & World, Inc., New York
1965
191pp, b/w drawings, clo., 202x134mm. SCAE
This American edition received the following US awards: New York Herald Tribune Spring Book Festival Award 1966; Thomas Alva Edison Mass Media Award 1967; Lewis Carroll Shelf Award, Gold Cheshire Cat Seal 1971.
Yugoslav edition

5569 IZDAVAC"KO KNJIZ"ARSKO PODUZEC"E MLADOST
Zagreb 1968
132pp (inc. 3pp author's note), unillus., 200x140mm. Unseen: IFA
Afrikaans edition

5570 Tafelberg-Uitgewers (Edms) Beperk, Cape Town
1969
143pp (inc. 3pp author's note), 6 f/p b/w illus., clo., 220x140mm. Unseen: IFA

5571 THE ROAN COLT/OF YAMBOORAH/Reginald Ottley/Illustrated by David Parry/[device]/André Deutsch
1966
127pp (inc. 3pp author's note), 10 b/w illus., clo., 200x130mm. KMM
2nd impression 1967. KP

5572 Reginald Ottley/THE ROAN COLT OF/ YAMBOORAH/[drawing]/Illustrated by David Parry/ Collins/Armada Lions
London 1971
124pp (inc. 3pp author's note, 1p note), 4pp adv., 10 f/p b/w illus., pic. wrappers, 180x110mm. KMM
American edition

5573 Harcourt, Brace & World, New York 1967
159pp, illus., 21cm. Unseen: ANB 1967
Afrikaans edition

5574 Reginald Ottley/DIE SKIMMEL-HINGS VAN/ YAMBOORAH/Tafelberg-Uitgewers 1969
119pp (inc. 3pp note by author), b/w illus. [David Parry], clo., 212x135mm. LRA

5575 RAIN COMES TO/YAMBOORAH/Reginald Ottley/Illustrated by Robert Hales/[device]/André Deutsch
London 1967
128pp (inc. 1p author's note), 10 b/w illus., clo., d/w designed by Jillian Willett, 195x125mm. KMM
2nd impression 1969. KP
American edition

5576 Harcourt, Brace & World, New York 1968
159pp (inc. 2pp author's note), 4 f/p b/w illus., b/w drawings in text, clo., 210x140mm. Unseen: IFA
Afrikaans edition

5577 Tafelberg-Uitgewers (Edms) Beperk, Cape Town
1971
122pp, 1 f/p b/w illus., clo., 220x140mm. Unseen: IFA

5578 GISELLE/Reginald Ottley/Collins/St. James's Place/London 1968
160pp (inc. 2pp author's note), unillus., clo., d/w by Victor Ambrus, 200x135mm. KMM
Story set in New Caledonia.

5579 GISELLE/Reginald Ottley/Harcourt, Brace & World Inc./New York
1968
159pp (inc. 2pp author's note), unillus., clo., 200x170mm. KMM

5580 THE/BATES FAMILY/by/Reginald Ottley/ Collins/London Sydney/1969
160pp (inc. 1p author's note), unillus., clo., d/w designed by Betty Maxey, 195x125mm. CLRC
American edition

5581 Harcourt, Brace & World, New York 1969
175pp (inc. 1p author's note), unillus., clo., 210x145mm. Unseen: IFA

5582 BRUMBIE DUST/A Selection of Stories by/ Reginald Ottley/illustrated by/Douglas Phillips/ Collins/London and Sydney
1969
127pp (inc. 2pp author's note), b/w drawings in text, clo., 195x125mm. KMM
American edition

5583 Harcourt, Brace & World, New York 1969
143pp (inc. 2pp author's note), unillus., clo., 210x140mm. Unseen: IFA

5584 JIM GREY OF/MOONBAH/Reginald Ottley/ Collins/London & Sydney
1970
159pp (inc. 1p author's note), unillus., clo., d/w designed by Victor Mays, 195x125mm. KMM

5585 JIM GREY OF MOONBAH/By Reginald Ottley/ Harcourt, Brace & World, Inc., New York
1970
159pp (inc. 2pp author's note), unillus., clo., 204x134mm. KP

5586 THE WAR ON/WILLIAM STREET/Reginald Ottley/Collins/London & Sydney
1971
160pp (inc. 1p author's note), unillus., clo., 205x135mm. CLRC

5587 Reginald Ottley/NO MORE TOMORROW/Harcourt, Brace & World/New York
1971
107pp (inc. 1p author's note), unillus., clo., 210x145mm. Unseen: IFA

5588 NO MORE/TOMORROW/Reginald Ottley/Collins/London and Sydney
1972
126pp (inc. 1p author's note), unillus., clo., 195x125mm. CLRC

Our Baby's Story Year by Year

5589 OUR BABY'S/STORY/YEAR BY/YEAR/From Birth to the Age of Seven/Made in Australia
n.p., n.d.
18pp (inc. frontis. & back pastedowns), headings & col. dec., dec. bd., cover title, 240x196mm. KP

Our Digger Prince with the Australian Kiddies

5590 OUR DIGGER PRINCE WITH THE AUSTRALIAN KIDDIES/2/6 Nett/Published by John L. Bennett, 16 Tooks Court, Chancery Lane, London, E.C.4
1921.
20pp & introduction inside front cover, 10 f/p col. illus., 11 monochrome illus., col. pic. bd. (illus. front & back), cover title, printed throughout in sepia, 280x330mm. MAC
Illus. A. Gladys Holiman.

Our Farmyard Pets/Cut-Out Book

See Offset Publishing

Our Pets Picture Book

5591 OUR/PETS/PICTURE/BOOK/The Sandman Series John Sands Pty Ltd, Sydney, n.d. [194-?]
[16]pp (inc. covers, col. & b/w illus. throughout, pic. wrappers, cover title, 296x250mm
Series 1 No. 3. Printed on stiff paper. KP
See also Steele, John V.

OUTHWAITE, Ida Rentoul [Ida Sherbourne Outhwaite, née Rentoul, Mrs A. G. Outhwaite] & RENTOUL, Annie Rattray

5592 ELVES & FAIRIES/of Ida Rentoul Outhwaite/Verses by Annie R. Rentoul/Edited by Grenbry Outhwaite/[drawing]/Melbourne & Sydney/The Lothian Book Publishing Coy. Pty. Ltd.
First edition (limited to 1500 copies) 1916
118pp (inc. 2pp foreword by Archibald T. Strong), 9pp list of subscribers, 15 col. plates , 30 b/w plates. & b/w drawings in text, clo., dec. e/p, 370x255mm. KMM

5593 ELVES AND FAIRIES/of/Ida Rentoul Outhwaite/Verses by/Annie R. Rentoul/Edited by/Grenbry Outhwaite/[drawing]/Melbourne & Sydney/Lothian Book Publishing Co. Pty. Ltd.
Selected edition 1919
88pp (inc. 2pp foreword by Archibald T. Strong), 6 f/p col. illus., 15 f/p b/w illus. & b/w drawings in text, bd., 240x180mm. KMM

5594 [drawing]/For our Little Friends/Copyright/THIS IS A STORY/OF/ACKMAN'S/Genuine ALWAYS Genuine
Publ. by Ackman's, Complete Home Furnishers, 243–255 Smith Street, Fitzroy, Victoria, 1918
[16]pp, 10 col. illus., wrappers, 244x185mm. KP

5595 THE/ENCHANTED FOREST/By/Ida Rentoul Outhwaite/and/Grenbry Outhwaite/[drawing]/A. & C. Black, Ltd./4, 5 & 6 Soho Square, London, W.1/1921
Edition limited to 500 copies
93pp, 2pp adv., col. frontis. & 15 col. plates, 15 b/w plates, dec. clo., dec. e/p, 265x200mm. NSL:M

5596 THE ENCHANTED FOREST. The ordinary first ed. Details as those for the limited ed. except for the bdg. This ed. has dec. paper-covered bd. with clo. spine & an onlay with title, author and b/w drawing pasted on front cover. KMM

5597 Second ed., 1925, as above. KMM

5598 THE/LITTLE FAIRY/SISTER/by/Ida Rentoul Outhwaite/and/Grenbry Outhwaite/[drawing]/A. & C. Black Ltd./4, 5 & 6, Soho Square, London, W.1./1923
91pp, 4pp adv., col. frontis. & 7 col. plates , 8 b/w plates & 2 b/w drawings, dec. bd. (clo. spine), dec. e/p, 265x200mm. KMM

5599 New ed., 1929, as above, but bound in blue clo. KMM

5600 FAIRYLAND/of Ida Rentoul Outhwaite/Verses by Annie R. Rentoul/Stories by/Grenbry Outhwaite/and Annie R. Rentoul/[drawing]/Ramsay Publishing Pty. Ltd./Melbourne/1926
Edition de luxe, 23rd August 1926, limited to 1,000 copies, signed by Ida Rentoul Outhwaite
160pp, 4pp list of subscribers, col. frontis. & 18 col. plates, 32 b/w plates & b/w drawings in text, clo., dec. e/p, 370x265mm. KMM
Note: Some copies of the above edition have been seen, unsigned, and bound in a cheaper binding with col. instead of gilt lettering &c., suggesting that they may have been bound up later and sold as remainders.

5601 FAIRYLAND/of Ida Rentoul Outhwaite/Verses by Annie R. Rentoul/Stories by/Grenbry Outhwaite and Annie R. Rentoul/[drawing]/Frederick A. Stokes Company/New York MCMXXIX
126pp col. frontis. & 18 f/p col. plates, 32 f/p b/w plates & b/w drawings in text, clo. with reproduction of one col. plate pasted on front cover, 333x252mm. KMM
In the original ed. the plates are tipped in, mounted on pages of superior paper & protected by tissue guards, whereas in this ed. they are printed on text-paper. The plate on p18 (Fairy Frolic) has been transposed with 'Tossing the Rainbow Bubbles.'

5602 FAIRYLAND/of Ida Rentoul Outhwaite/Verses by Annie R. Rentoul/Stories by Grenbry Outhwaite/and Annie R. Rentoul/[drawing]/A. & C. Black, Ltd./4, 5 & 6 Soho Square, London, W.1.
1931
128pp, col. frontis. & 15 col. plates, 31 b/w plates & drawings in text, clo., dec. e/p, 320x245mm. CLRC

5603 [illustration] WHEN WINTER COMES. Ida Rentoul Outhwaite
Wholly set up and printed in Australia by Ramsay Publishing Co. Pty. Ltd.
197–207 King St., Melbourne and published/by them in conjunction with A. G. Outhwaite for the Glaciarium
n.d. [192-?]
16pp, 3 f/p b/w illus. & 7 b/w drawings, illus. wrappers, cover title, 245x185mm. Grant

5604 BLOSSOM/A Fairy Story/Written & Illustrated/By/Ida Rentoul Outhwaite/[vignette]/A. & C. Black Ltd./4, 5 & 6 Soho Square, London, W.1.
1928
94pp, 2pp adv., col. frontis. & 7 col. plates 8 b/w plates & b/w drawings, bd. (clo. spine) (illus. on front cover), dec. e/p, 265x200mm. KMM

5605 BUNNY & BROWNIE/The Adventures of/George & Wiggle/Written & Illustrated/by/Ida Rentoul

Outhwaite/[vignette]/A. & C. Black Ltd./4, 5 & 6 Soho Square, London, W.1.
1930
99pp, 4pp adv., col. frontis. & 7 col. plates, 8 b/w plates & b/w drawings in text, bd. (clo. spine), dec. e/p, 270x200mm. ANL

5606 A BUNCH OF/WILD FLOWERS/Verse and Illustrations/By/Ida Rentoul Outhwaite/[decoration]/Australia/Angus & Robertson Limited/89 Castlereagh Street, Sydney/1933
50pp, 6 col. plates, 15 f/p b/w illus. & b/w drawings in text throughout, bd., 235x180mm. ANL
• Rpt as above, 1934. CLRC

5607 A BUNCH OF/WILD FLOWERS/Verses and Illustrations/by/Ida Rentoul Outhwaite/Angus and Robertson Ltd./Sydney London/1940
50pp, 6 col. & 15 b/w plates, b/w illus. in text, col. pic. bd., 240x187mm. KP

5608 A BUNCH OF/WILD FLOWERS/Verse and Illustrations/By/Ida Rentoul Outhwaite/Angus and Robertson/Sydney: London/1948
50pp, col. frontis. & 21 col. plates., b/w drawings, clo., 235x180mm. ANL
Some of the illustrations redrawn for this edition.

5609 SIXPENCE TO SPEND/Story and Illustrations/by/Ida Rentoul Outhwaite/Author of "A Bunch of Wild Flowers"/Angus and Robertson Limited/89 Castlereagh Street, Sydney/1935
92pp, col. frontis. & 4 col.plates , b/w drawings throughout, pic. bd., 240x180mm. VSL

5610 MUSICAL/NURSERY/RHYMES/PICTURE BOOK/To Sing &/Play with the/Watcher/Bird/[contents listed] Illustrated by/Ida Rentoul Outhwaite/Published by Murfett Pty Ltd
1945
16pp, 8 f/p col. illus.by Ida Rentoul Outhwaite, music & words of 8 songs, pic. bd., spirax bdg, cover title, 290x217mm. KP
'De Luxe Edition'.

5611 NURSERY/RHYMES/Illustrations/by/Ida Rentoul Outhwaite/[drawing]
Murfett & Co., Melbourne 1948
32pp, 14 f/p col. illus. & b/w drawings throughout, stiff col. pic. wrappers, 290x225mm. NSL:M

5612 CINDERELLA'S/DREAM/[illus.]/and what it taught her
Publ. for J. J. Kitchen & Sons by Farrow Falcon Press, 225–230 Little Lonsdale St., Melbourne, n.d. [193-?]
16pp, b/w illus. on every page, wrappers, cover title, 62x120mm. KP
Verses adv. various soap products with a b/w illus on every page. Illus initialled 'IRO.'

THE LITTLE GREEN ROAD TO FAIRYLAND. *See* Rentoul, Annie Rattray

Ida Rentoul Outhwaite illustrated many children's books, including *Mollie's Staircase* by her mother, Annie Isobel Rentoul, under her maiden name of I. S. Rentoul. Also under this name she collaborated with her sister, Annie Rattray Rentoul, & this & other relevant entries will be found under Rentoul.

OVENDEN, Dick

5613 ROUND THE WORLD/WITH/BILLY BEAR/Sketches by/Dick Ovenden/Jingles by/W. L. Williams/and/J. R. Lyall/[drawing]/Melbourne/Robertson & Mullens Limited
n.d. [1938?]
40pp, b/w illus., illus. wrappers, 230x170mm. NSL:M
Educational story presented in comic-strip form.

OVER, Elsie Maud

5614 WIM-WAM TALES/By/Elsie M. Over/(Copyright)/[drawing]/Illustrations: Frank Over/Revised and printed by the kind/permission of "The Western Mail"/Paterson's Printing Press Ltd./65 Murray Street, Perth
n.d. [1945]
36pp, b/w frontis. & 5 f/p b/w illus., bd., 240x180mm. VSL

5615 THE GREEN DRAGON/OF THE PORONGORUPS/(Copyright)/by Elsie M. Over/(Author of "Wim-Wam Tales")/[drawing]/Illustrations:/Frank Over/Printed and Published by/Paterson's Printing Press Ltd./65 Murray Street Perth/Price 6/6
n.d. [1944]
22pp, 7 col. illus., b/w drawings, dec. bd., 240x180mm. ANL

OVERTON, Robert

5616 THE KING'S PARDON!/or/The Boy who saved his Father/A Story of Land and Sea/By/Robert Overton/Author of "After School", "Queer Fish", "The Overton Reciter",/"A Round Dozen", "Ten Minutes", "Lights Out", etc./Illustrations by W. H. Margetson/London/Jarrold & Sons, 10 & 11, Warwick Lane, E.C./[All rights reserved]/1895
263pp, 9pp adv., b/w frontis. & 11 f/p b/w illus., pic. clo., 185x120mm. KMM
The adventures of Bart Arben who set out to find his father who had been wrongly convicted & sent to Botany Bay, then believed dead. After adventures in the Pacific all is happily resolved.

5617 FAR FROM HOME!/or/The Fights and Adventures of/A Runaway/By/Robert Overton/Author of "The King's Pardon", "After School", "Lights Out!"/"The Overton Reciter", "Water-works!" &c./Illustrated by Enoch Ward/[device]/Second Edition/London/Jarrold & Sons, 10 & 11, Warwick Lane, E.C./(All rights reserved)
[1896, this copy prize 1903]
271pp, 16pp adv., b/w frontis. & 6 plates, pic. clo., 180x120mm. KP
Story tells of the hero who stows away on a ship bound for Sydney. Two chapters are set in NSW & the remainder of the book tells of the voyage home, including a shipwreck & adventure on the Kermadec group of islands in SW Pacific.

5618 FAR FROM HOME/or/The Fights and Adventures/of a Runaway/By/Robert Overton/Author of "After School", "The King's Pardon", "Lights Out!", "The Orphan of Tor College", "Friend or Fortune?"/"The Son of the School", "A Chase Round the World",/"Decoyed across the Seas", "Dangerous Days",/"Saturday Island", etc/[device]/with illustrations by Enoch Ward/London/Jarrold & Sons, Warwick Lane, E.C.
n.d. [1st publ. 1896, this copy 191-?]
271pp, col. frontis & 6 b/w plates, pic. clo., 185x120mm. KMM

5619 THE SON OF A HUNDRED/FATHERS/or/Daring Deeds in Dangerous Days/By/Robert Overton/Author of "The King's Pardon", "Lights Out",/"After School", etc/with thirty four illustrations by J. B. Greene/[vignette]/London/Jarrold & Sons, 10 & 11 Warwick Lane, E.C./[All rights reserved]/1899
356pp & 12pp adv., b/w frontis. & text illus. throughout, pic. clo., bevelled edges, 190x130mm. ANL

Voyage to Hobart (189pp). Rescue of an escaped convict. Pirate attacks. Return to Sydney.

5620 A CHASE ROUND THE WORLD/The Following-up of a chain of mystery/By/Robert Overton/Author of "Friend of Fortune", "After School", "Lights Out"/"The King's Pardon", "Far from Home", etc/with original illustrations/By A. Monro/[device]/London/Frederick Warne and Co./and New York/1900/(All rights reserved)
299 pp & 20pp adv., b/w frontis. & 16 b/w illus., pic. clo., 195x130mm. KP
Adventure story set on an Australia-bound steamer & some action takes place in Tasmania & on homeward voyage.

5621 DECOYED ACROSS/THE SEAS/A Tale of a Tangle/By/Robert Overton/Author of "A Chase round the World"/"After School" etc etc./with original illustrations/by/Paul Hardy/[device]/London/Frederick Warne and Co./and New York/(All rights reserved.)
[1907]
324pp, b/w frontis., b/w drawings in text, pic. clo., 195x130mm. KP

OWEN, Harrison
5622 TOMMYROT RHYMES/(For Children and Grown-ups who/Ought to know Better)/By/Harrison Owen/Pubished by Alexander McCubbin/9 Queen Street, Melbourne
n.d. [1923]
22pp, wrappers, 180x115mm. ANL

OWEN, Norman
THE GOLDEN CREEK. *See* Boys' Friend Library

OWEN, Russell
5623 THE CONQUEST/OF THE/NORTH AND SOUTH/POLES/Adventures of the Peary/and Byrd Expeditions/By Russell Owen/Illustrated by Lynd Ward/[device]/Random House/New York
ixpp (inc. 3pp author's foreword), 181pp (inc. 5pp index), numerous illus printed in b/w with the addition of blue, clo., dec. e/p, 208x140mm. KMM
Landmark Books

OWNER, Faye
NATURE PROJECT BOOKS
Format example:
5624 Nature Project Book 1/MAMMALS/OF AUSTRALIA AND/NEW ZEALAND/By Faye Owner/Foreword by Eric Worrell
Angus and Robertson Ltd, Sydney, 1970
32pp, b/w drawings on 30 pages, stiff pic. paper wrappers, 136x217mm. KP
Original drawings by Faye Owner.
Others in series as above by same author, all KP
5625 2 REPTILES
5626 3 BIRDS
5627 4 INSECTS

PABST, Johan Georg Friedrich
5628 DIE/ENTDECKUNGEN/DES/FÜNFTEN WELTTHEILS;/oder/Reisen um die Welt/Ein/Lesebuch für die Jugend/von/Johan Georg Friedrich Pabst/ausserordentlichen Lehrer der Weltweissheit/zu Erlangen/Zweiter Band/Mit des ältern herrn Forsters Bildnisse/Nürnberg/in der Felsseckerische Buchhandlung
Volume 2 of 2 vols, 1784
324pp, engraved portrait frontis., wrappers, 180x120mm. ANL
Story told in dialogue form; Cook's Voyages are described in this volume.

5629 DIE/ENTDECKUNGEN/DES/FÜNFTEN WELTTHEILS;/oder/Reisen um die Welt/Ein/Lesebuch für die Jugend/von/Johan Georg/Friedrich Pabst/Professor auf der Friedrich-Alexanders Univer-/sitat zu Erlangen/[vignette]/Zwote und verbesserte Auflage/Nürnberg,/in der Felsseckerische Buchhandlung, 1788
Four volumes in two, the second only dealing with Cook's Voyages
412pp. ,unillus. wrappers, 180x120mm. ANL

PACEY, William Harman
5630 BOBBY/IN/GOBLIN LAND/Introducing/King Kobar and Safety First/By/Constable Pacey/School Lecturer/New South Wales/Police Department/William Brooks & Co. Limited/The Educational Publishers of Australia/99 Pitt Street Sydney/299 Queen Street Brisbane
1948
59pp (inc. 1p foreword), 6 b/w illus., wrappers, 185x120mm. King Kobar Series Book 1. NSL:M

5631 OFF TO/FAIRY CITY/introducing/King Kobar and Safety First/By/Constable Pacey/School Lecturer/New South Wales/Police Department/William Brooks & Co. Limited/The Educational Publishers of Australia/99 Pitt Street Sydney/299 Queen Street Brisbane
1948
60pp, b/w drawings throughout, wrappers, 180x115mm. King Kobar Series Book 2. NSL:M

5632 THE ADVENTURES/OF/KING KOBAR/By/William Pacey/Late Safety Lecturer, New South Wales/Police Department/Illustrated/by/"Mahdi"/King Kobar Enterprises/Sydney, N.S.W./1954
134pp (inc. 1p foreword by H. E. Snowden, Superintendent of Traffic, NSW), b/w illus. throughout, clo., 180x120mm. ANL
Stories to illustrate traffic safety rules for children.

The Pacific Ocean Colouring Book
5633 THE PACIFIC/OCEAN/COLOURING BOOK/H. E. C. Robinson Pty Ltd
Sydney, n.d.
16pp (and col. flap inside front cover with col. guide), wrappers. MAC

The Pacific Ocean of Captain Cook
5634 [portrait] THE PACIFIC OCEAN/OF CAPTAIN COOK
Printed and published in Australia by W. C. Penfold & Co. Pty. Ltd, 88 Pitt Street, Sydney 1969
8pp, col. illus. & b/w map & drawings, wrappers, cover title, 285x245mm. Grant
Contains 'Captain Cook Reference Dictionary' with 11 press-out pictures & 2pp where pictures can be pasted to complete dictionary.

PACINI, John
5635 Imperial Edition NO. 482/OUR OWN/SONG/BOOK/Words and Music/by/John Pacini/Allan & Co. Pty Ltd,/Melbourne Adelaide Bendigo/Price 1/- net
Allan & Co, 1940
12pp, 12 songs, col. pic. wrappers, 253x178mm. VSL

PAGE, Brenda
5636 SCHOOLGIRL RIVALS/By/Brenda Page/With Frontispiece in Colour and/Three Black and White Illustrations/By P. B. Hickling/[device]/Cassell and

Company, Limited/London, Toronto, Melbourne, and Sydney
1927
218pp, col. frontis. & 3 f/p b/w illus., clo. with col. onlay reproducing frontis., 190x125mm. JMcG
The story of an Australian girl at school in England. Author probably not Australian.

A Pageant of the Years
5637 A PAGEANT OF THE YEARS/[text]/issued by/The Sanitarium Health Food Company/118 Union Street, Prahran, 43 Elizabeth Street, Hobart, Tas.
1942
12pp text (spaces for 60 col. illus. to be collected & pasted in), wrappers, 220x285mm. Grant
Cover title: 'Advance Australia/A Pageant of the Years'.

PAICE, Margaret [Mrs Wilfrid Harris, formerly Mrs Hubert Paice]
5638 [drawing] MIRRAM/Written and Illustrated by/Margaret Paice/Angus and Robertson/Sydney London Melbourne Wellington
1955
32pp, b/w drawings throughout, wrappers, 240x180mm. BBC
• Rpt 1956, as above. KMM

5639 NAMITJA/Written and Illustrated by/Margaret Paice/[drawing]/Angus and Robertson/Sydney London Melbourne Wellington
1956
32pp, b/w frontis. & 3 other f/p b/w illus., wrappers, 240x185mm. KMM

5640 VALLEY IN THE NORTH/By/Margaret Paice/Author of 'Mirram', 'Namitja'/With illustrations by the author/Angus and Robertson/Sydney London Melbourne Wellington
1957
123pp, b/w frontis. & b/w drawings throughout, clo., 200x125mm. KMM

5641 VALLEY IN THE NORTH/By/Margaret Paice/Author of 'Mirram', 'Namitja'. 'The Lucky Fall'/With illustrations by the author/[device]/Angus and Robertson
First school edition 1958, rpt 1960
123pp, details as above but limp clo. bdg with illus. printed on front cover 195x128mm. KMM

5642 THE LUCKY FALL/Written and Illustrated/by/Margaret Paice/Author of/"Valley in the North"/"Namitja"/"Mirram"/Angus and Robertson Sydney 1958
140pp, b/w frontis. & 8 b/w illus., clo., dec. e/p, 200x125mm. KMM

5643 School edition as above (but without 'Sydney 1958'), 1960
140pp, b/w frontis., 7 f/p b/w illus., limp clo., 197x129mm. KMM

5644 A JOEY/FOR CHRISTMAS/Written and Illustrated by/Margaret Paice/Angus and Robertson/Sydney—London—Melbourne.
1960 [Author states that although set up 1960, publication was delayed & book actually appeared 1961]
55pp, extended frontis., part-col. & b/w illus. throughout, dec. bd., dec. e/p, 235x155mm. KMM

5645 First school edition 1962, as above
56 pp, extended frontis., line drawings throughout, some printed in two cols, pic. limp clo., 184x120mm. KMM

5646 THE SECRET OF/GREYCLIFFS/A Sequel to/The Lucky Fall/by/Margaret Paice/Illustrated by/the Author/[drawing]/Angus and Robertson
Sydney 1961
147pp, extended dec. t.p., b/w frontis. & 15 b/w drawings in text, clo., dec. e/p, 195x125mm. CLRC

5647 OVER/THE/MOUNTAIN/Margaret Paice/with illustrations/by the author/Angus and Robertson
Sydney 1964
111pp, extended dec. t.p., b/w drawings in text throughout, clo., col. e/p, 215x135mm. CLRC

5648 THE BENSENS/By Margaret Paice/Illustrated by the author/Collins/London & Sydney/1968
160pp, extended b/w frontis., b/w drawings in text, clo., 200x135mm. KMM

5649 THEY DROWNED/A VALLEY/Margaret Paice/Illustrated by the author/[drawing]/Collins/London & Sydney/1969
192pp, b/w drawings in text, clo., d/w designed by Margery Gill, 195x125mm. KMM
2nd impression 1970. KP

5650 Margaret Paice/THE MORNING GLORY/Collins/London and Sydney
1971
160pp, unillus., clo., d/w designed by Eileen Walton, 210x135mm. KMM

5651 RUN TO THE MOUNTAINS/Margaret Paice/Collins/Sydney London
1972
151pp, 3 f/p b/w illus., clo., 210x130mm. KMM
Artist unnamed, presumably the author.

Painter Pete & Other Pictures
See DAWFOX PRODUCTIONS

Painting Book and Rhymes for Little Children
See HAPPY AND SUNNY

PALK, Arthur J.
THE CALL OF THE DRAGON. *See* Sexton Blake in Australia

PALLOT, E. C.
5652 THE GOLDEN WEB/By/E. C. Pallot, M.A., B.D./The Epworth Press/(Edgar C. Barton)/25–35 City Road, London, E.C.1
1937
126pp, unillus., clo., 185x120mm. KMM
Foreword by Eric S. Waterhouse. Preface by author. Religious addresses to young people by an Australian author.

5653 THE YOUNG/METHODIST/A Simple and Brief Introduction/to the History, Beliefs, and/Enterprises of the People called/Methodists. Specially written for/young people, for group study,/and private reading./By E. C. Pallot,/M.A., B.D., Ph.D./Published by the Youth Committee of the General/Conference of the Methodist Church of Australasia./Registered &c [2 lines]/Wholly set up and printed in Australia by/Spectator Publishing Co. Pty. Ltd./134a Little Collins Street, Melbourne, C.1/1938
87pp, b/w frontis. portrait John Wesley, some b/w illus. in text, wrappers, 180x123mm. KP

5654 The same, but
Methodist Book Depot, Melbourne 1950, 4th ed.
92pp (inc. 2pp assignments). KP

5655 The Slip-rail Series, No. 4/THE GOD OF THE/BIBLE/E. C. Pallot, M.A., B.D., Ph.D./For the use of Young People/Teachers and Leaders of Youth/The Book Depot,/Melbourne./1944

20pp (inc. 1p author's preface), unillus., wrappers, 136x102mm. CLRC

PALMER, Helen Gwynneth
5656 Australia at work/OUR SUGAR/By/Helen G. Palmer, B.A. (hons), Dip.Ed./Longmans Green & Co./ London Melbourne New York
1949
64pp, b/w photographic illus. & diagrams, maps &c, wrappers (copy seen re-bound), 214x164mm. CLRC

5657 BENEATH THE SOUTHERN CROSS/By/Helen Palmer/Illustrated by/Evelyn Walters/F. W. Cheshire/ Melbourne.
1954
104pp, b/w drawings throughout, clo., 180x120mm. KMM
Story of life on Ballarat goldfields at the time of the Eureka stockade.

5658 THE/FIRST/HUNDRED/YEARS/By/Helen G. Palmer/and Jessie MacLeod/Illustrated by/Harold Freedman/[drawing]/Longmans Green & Co./London Melbourne New York
1954
176pp (inc. 12pp notes &c.), 2pp foreword, b/w drawings throughout, clo., 215x135mm. KMM
• Rpt 1956, as above. BBC
5659 THE/FIRST/HUNDRED/YEARS/By/Helen G. Palmer/and Jessie MacLeod/Illustrated by/Harold Freedman/[drawing]/Longmans
Melbourne 1954; rpt 1956, 1959
176pp (inc. 12pp notes, &c.), b/w drawings in text, clo., 215x135mm. KMM
• Rpt 1962, 1964, 1966. KP

5660 MAKERS OF THE/FIRST HUNDRED YEARS/by/ Helen G. Palmer/and Jessie MacLeod/Illustrated by/ Pamela Lindsay/Longmans, Green & Co./London, Melbourne, New York.
1956
149pp, b/w drawings throughout, clo., 185x120mm. KMM
Also soft cover edition. KP

5661 AFTER/THE FIRST/HUNDRED/YEARS/By/ Helen G. Palmer/and Jessie MacLeod/Illustrated by/ Mary MacQueen/Longmans
Melbourne 1961
203pp (inc. 7pp notes, sources, & acknowledgements), dec. t.p., 11 b/w illus., clo., 215x135mm. KMM
Social history from 1900 to mid-twentieth century.

FENCING AUSTRALIA

W. G. SPENCE AND THE RISE OF THE TRADE UNIONS. *See* Australian Landmarks

'BANJO' PATERSON. *See* Great People in Australian History

PALMER, P. J.
5662 P. J. Palmer/The Age in which we live/THE/ TWENTIETH CENTURY/F. W. Cheshire Melbourne Canberra Sydney
1965
126pp, dec. t.p. on 2 pages, b/w photographic illus., maps & diagrams, pic. clo., map e/p, 235x152mm. KP

PALMER, Robin
5663 THE GIANT'S/TOOTH/By/Robin Palmer/And other/Popular Stories
Ayers & James Pty Ltd, Sydney, n.d. [194-?]
14pp, 4pp col. illus., b/w illus. throughout, col. pic. wrappers, cover title, 368x240mm. KMM

PALMER, Vance
5664 THE/RAINBOW-BIRD/and Other Stories by/ Vance Palmer/Selected by/Allan Edwards/Professor of English Literature/University of Western Australia/ Angus and Robertson/Sydney London Melbourne Wellington
1957
xvipp (inc. 9pp editor's preface) & 125pp (inc. 7pp appendices by Vance Palmer), unillus., limp dec. clo., 183x122mm. KP
A selection for children of Palmer's short stories, publ. as a school text.

Pals in Peril
See Diamond Library

Pam and Peter go to School
5665 PAM AND PETER/GO TO SCHOOL/Railway Lines for Engines/Boats sail on the Sea/Cars go Whizzing down the road/The footpath is for me/A Gift to Mark my First Day at School.
Issued by the Australian Road Safety Council, n.d. [195-?]
Leaflet with 2 front pages folded over to meet in front making an 8pp booklet, col. illus. & covers, 230x205mm. KP

Pantomime Favourites
5666 PANTOMIME/FAVOURITES
Photogravures Pty Ltd, Melbourne, n.d. [195-?]
[12]pp (inc. covers), printed throughout in col. on light card, illus. of pantomime characters with captions, cover title, 310x244mm. CLRC

PAPALLO, George
5667 HOW IT WORKS/Text: George Papallo, Dip. Tech./Technical illustrations: Graham Forsaith/Paul Hamlyn/Sydney London New York Toronto
1972
76pp, col. & part-col. diagrams & illus. throughout, pic. bd., 270x200mm. CLRC

PAPPAS, George & LEWIS, Brett
5668 IMAGES/Compiled by George Pappas and Brett Lewis/Photographs by Rob Middenway/[colophon]/ Longman
Victoria, 1971
120pp, b/w photographs throughout, dec. bd., 207x160mm. CLRC
Anthology of verse for children.

PARK, Ruth
THE UNINVITED GUEST. *See* Australian Youth Plays

5669 THE HOLE/IN THE HILL/[drawing]/by Ruth Park/Illustrated by Jennifer Murray/Ure Smith Sydney.
1961
144pp, part-col. t.p. & part-col. chapter headings throughout, dec. clo., dec. e/p, 215x135mm. CLRC
A shorter version of this story appeared in 1961 in the NSW *School Magazine*, published by the NSW Department of Education.

5670 THE HOLE IN THE HILL
Macmillan, London 1962; New edition 1963
Unseen: Information from publisher's catalogue, in which it was also mentioned that the book was about to be reprinted in the US by Doubleday, New York
5671 SECRET OF THE MAORI CAVE
Doubleday, Garden City, New York [1964]
168pp, illus. by Michael A. Hampshire, 22cm.
US edition of *The Hole in the Hill.* Unseen: NUC
5672 THE HOLE/IN THE HILL/Ruth Park/A Piccolo Book/Pan Books Ltd./London

First published in Great Britain 1962; this edition 1971
127pp, unillus., pic. wrappers, 175x110mm. KMM

5673 Tales of the South 1/THE/SHIP'S CAT/by/Ruth Park/[drawing]/Illustrated by Richard Kennedy/London/Macmillan & Co. Ltd./New York—St. Martin's Press/1961.
64pp (inc. 2pp questions), 20 b/w illus. in text, illus. wrappers, 190x135mm. KMM
School reader with NZ historical background.

5674 Tales of the South 2/UNCLE MATT'S/MOUNTAIN/by/Ruth Park/[drawing]/Illustrated by Laurence Broderick/London/Macmillan & Co. Ltd./New York—St. Martin's Press/1962.
64pp (inc. 2pp questions), b/w drawings in text throughout, illus. wrappers, 190x135mm. CLRC
School reader with NZ historical background.

5675 Tales of the South 3/THE ROAD/TO CHRISTMAS/by/Ruth Park/[drawing]/Illustrated by Noela Young/London/Macmillan & Co. Ltd./New York—St. Martin's Press/1962.
64pp (inc. 1p exercises), b/w illus. throughout, stiff illus. wrappers, 190x135mm. CLRC
Story intended as school reader.

5676 THE ROAD/UNDER THE SEA/[drawing]/by Ruth Park/Illustrated by Jennifer Murray/Ure Smith—Sydney.
1962
125pp, 11 b/w illus., b/w chapter headings, dec. clo., dec. e/p, 220x135mm. CLRC

5677 THE ROAD/UNDER THE SEA/[drawing]/by Ruth Park/illustrated by Jennifer Murray/London/Macmillan Co. Ltd./1963
First U.K. edition as above, 217x137mm. KP

French edition

5677a Ruth Park/LE CHEMIN/SOUS LA MER/(The Road Under the Sea)/Publié par MacMillan [*sic*] and Co. Ltd London)/Traduit de l'anglais par Yvonne Girault/Illustrations de G. Pichard/1964/Éditions Gautier—Languercan/18, Rue Jacob, Paris VI
121pp, 2pp advs, 4 col. & f/p b/w illus., text drawings, col. pic. bd, 172x120mm. CLRC

5678 THE/SHAKY ISLAND/by Ruth Park and/illustrated by Iris Millington/Constable and Co. Ltd. London
1962
32pp, extended dec. t.p., sepia/white illus. throughout, clo., 250x185mm. KMM

5679 THE/SHAKY ISLAND/by Ruth Park and/illustrated by Iris Millington/David McKay Company Inc., New York
1962, details as above. ANL

5680 THE/MUDDLE-HEADED/WOMBAT/Ruth Park/[drawing]/Illustrated by/Noela Young/The Educational Press
Sydney 1962
67pp, part-col. frontis. & part-col. illus. dec. bd., 235x155mm. BBC
• Rpt 1963. CLRC

5681 THE/MUDDLE-HEADED/WOMBAT/Ruth Park/[drawing]/Illustrated by/Noela Young/Angus and Robertson
Publ. in Great Britain 1963
67pp, 1p adv., part-col. frontis., part-col. illus. throughout, clo., 234x150mm. KP
As above, but with pic. bd.
• Rpt The Educational Press, Sydney, 1967. KP
• Rpt The Educational Press, Sydney, 1968. KP
• Rpt The Educational Press, Sydney, 1969. KP
• Rpt The Educational Press, Sydney, 1971. KP
New ed. as above, Angus & Robertson, 1971. KP

5682 THE/MUDDLE-HEADED/WOMBAT/Ruth Park/[drawing]/Illustrated by/Noela Young/The Educational Press
Sydney, first school ed., 1966
67pp, 1p adv., b/w frontis. & b/w illus. throughout, limp clo. with b/w illus. on front cover, 235x153mm. KP

German edition

5683 Ruth Park/KLEINER DUMMER/WOMBI/[drawing]/Cecilie Dressler Verlag Berlin
1962
93pp, 2pp adv., b/w illus., pic. bd., 216x140mm. CLRC

Danish edition

5684 Ruth Park/VOMBAT/illustreret af Noela Young
Alle Børns Bogklub, Copenhagen 1972
83pp, b/w illus. throughout, pic. bd., 215x140mm. CLRC
Translated by Hanne Stouby.
Another edition published by Forlaget Palbe, Copenhagen, 1972, details as before. CLRC

5685 THE/MUDDLE-HEADED WOMBAT/ON HOLIDAY/Ruth Park/Illustrated by/Noela Young/The Educational Press
Sydney 1964
67pp, part. col. frontis., 8 f/p col. illus., part-col. illus. in text, dec. bd., 235x155mm. BBC
• Rpt 1967, 1969. KP

German edition

5686 Ruth Park WOMBI,/LU UND MAUS/Cecile Dressler Verlag Berlin
1964
96pp, b/w frontis. extended on t.p., b/w illus., pic. bd., 216x140mm. CLRC

5687 AIRLIFT FOR/GRANDEE/Ruth Park/[drawing]/Illustrated by/Sheila Hawkins/London: Macmillan & Co. Ltd./New York: St. Martin's Press/1964
94pp, extended t.p., 6 f/p b/w illus. & drawings in text, clo. (with b/w illus. printed on front cover), 195x130mm. Crown Books. KMM

5688 AIRLIFT FOR/GRANDEE/Ruth Park/[drawing]/Illustrated by/Sheila Hawkins/Melbourne: Macmillan/1967
As above, but with limp clo. covers. KW

5689 THE/MUDDLE-HEADED WOMBAT/IN THE TREETOPS/Ruth Park/Illustrated by/Noela Young/The Educational Press
Sydney 1965
67pp, part-col. t.p., extended frontis., 4 f/p part-col. illus., part-col. drawings in text, pic. bd., 235x155mm. KMM
• Rpt 1969 as above. KP

German edition

5690 Ruth Park WOMBI/UND DAS BAUMHAUS/Cecilie Dreslen Verlag Berlin
1965
95pp & 1p adv., extended frontis., b/w illus., pic. bd., 215x140mm. CLRC

5691 THE/MUDDLE-HEADED WOMBAT/AT SCHOOL/Ruth Park/[drawing]/Illustrated by/Noela Young/The Educational Press
Sydney 1966
67pp, part. col. extended frontis., 2 f/p part-col. illus., part-col. drawings in text, pic. bd., 235x155mm. CLRC
• Rpt as above, 1968. KP

5692 THE/MUDDLE-HEADED/WOMBAT/AT SCHOOL/Ruth Park/Illustrated by Noela Young/[drawing]/Angus and Robertson. Publishers
1st publ. 1966, rpt. 1968, 1970. New ed. 1972

67pp, b/w illus. throughout, pic. bd., 234x150mm. CLRC
Different col. illus. printed on front cover.

5693 THE/MUDDLE-HEADED WOMBAT/IN THE SNOW/Ruth Park/Illustrated by/Noela Young/The Educational Press
Sydney 1966
67pp, part-col. t.p., part-col. frontis., 5 f/p part. col. illus., part-col. drawings in text, pic. bd., 230x155mm. CLRC
• Rpt as above 1968, 1970. KP

5694 [drawing]/RING FOR THE SORCERER/by Ruth Park/illustrations by William Stobbs/a Horwitz-Martin publication
Sydney 1967
40pp, 6 f/p b/w illus., b/w drawings in text, dec. wrappers, 195x150mm. KMM

5695 THE/SIXPENNY/ISLAND/[drawing]/Ruth Park/Illustrated by David Cox/Ure Smith Sydney
1968
126pp, 6 f/p b/w illus. & b/w drawings in text, clo., dec. map e/p, 215x135mm. KMM
English edition
Macmillan, London 1968
Details as above. Unseen: ANB 1969
American edition
5696 TEN CENT ISLAND/Ruth Park/illustrated by Robert Frankenburg/Doubleday Garden City, New York
1968
189pp, 10 f/p b/w illus., 215x145mm. Unseen: IFA
Prebound edition, Doubleday
Details as above, but cover title (as t.p. above), no separate wrapper. IFA
German edition
5697 Ruth Park/DIE FÜNFGROSCHENINSEL/Eine Erzählung für die Jugend/Albert Müller/Ruschlikon—Zürich—Stuttgart—Wien
1972
168pp, unillus., pic. wrappers, 210x130mm. Unseen: IFA

5698 THE/MUDDLE-HEADED WOMBAT/ON A RAINY DAY/Ruth Park/Illustrated by/Noela Young/The Educational Press
Sydney 1969
67pp, part-col. frontis., b/w & part-col. illus. throughout, pic. bd., 235x150mm. KMM
5699 The same, Angus & Robertson, London 1970, unseen

5700 NUKI/AND THE/SEA SERPENT/[drawing]/A Maori story/By/Ruth Park/Illustrated by Zelma Blakely/Longmans Young Books Ltd/Text copyright 1969 by Ruth Park/Illustrations Copyright 1969 by Zelma Blakely/SBN: 582 15255 0/Printed in Great Britain by W. S. Cowell Ltd. at the Butter Market, Ipswich
32pp, part-col. illus. throughout, pic. bd., 245x185mm. KMM

5701 THE/RUNAWAY/BUS/Story by/Ruth Park/Illustrated by/Peter Tierney/Hodder & Stoughton
Sydney 1969
[32]pp, b/w & part-col. illus. throughout, dec. bd., 240x180mm. KMM

5702 THE/MUDDLE-HEADED WOMBAT/IN THE/SPRINGTIME/Ruth Park/Illustrated by/Noela Young/The Educational Press
Sydney 1970
67pp, part-col. frontis., part-col. dec. t.p., part-col. drawings throughout, pic. bd., 235x150mm. KMM
5702a The same, Angus & Robertson, London 1970, unseen

5703 THE/MUDDLE-HEADED WOMBAT/ON THE RIVER/Ruth Park/Illustrated by/Noela Young/The Educational Press
Sydney 1970
67pp, part-col. illus. throughout, pic. bd., 235x150mm. CLRC
5704 The same, Angus & Robertson, London 1971, unseen

PARKE, Margaret B.
5705 GETTING TO KNOW/AUSTRALIA/by Margaret B. Parke/Illustrated by Claudine Nankivel/Coward-McCann, Inc. New York
1962
64pp (inc. 2pp notes & 1p index), 1p adv., extended map frontis., b/w & part. col. drawings throughout, clo., dec. e/p, 215x155mm. The Getting to Know Books. ANL
5706 GETTING TO KNOW AUSTRALIA
As above, but Frederick Muller Limited London
1965, Rpt 1966
As above but maps & e/p printed in tan, this colour also added to many of the b/w drawings, clo., 215x160 mm. KP

PARKER, B.
5707 THE HISTORY OF/THE HOPPERS/[drawing]/Verses by/B. Parker/Illustrated by/N. Parker/W. & R. Chambers, Limited, 38 Soho Square, London, & 339 High Street, Edinburgh
n.d. [1912]
[53]pp, 12 f/p part-col. illus., sepia/white line drawings throughout, col. pic. bd., 295x230mm. CLRC
Comprises 12 stories in verse, with marginal drawings &c., in which all the characters are kangaroos.

PARKER, Catherine Somerville
See Parker, K. Langloh

PARKER, David
5708 TERRANCE/by/David Parker/Macmillan of Australia/1969
Melbourne
15pp, b/w photographic illus. throughout, pic. bd., 315x250mm. ANL

PARKER, Mrs K. Langloh [Catherine Somerville, née Field, later Mrs P. R. Stow]
5709 AUSTRALIAN/LEGENDARY TALES/Folk-lore of the Noongahburrahs/as told to the Piccaninnies/collected by/Mrs. K. Langloh Parker/With introduction by/Andrew Lang, M.A./Illustrations by a native artist [Tommy MacCrae], and a specimen/of the native text./London/David Nutt, 270–271 Strand./Melbourne/Melville, Mullen & Slade/1896.
viii, 132pp text (inc. 3pp appendix & 4pp glossary), 12pp adv., 12 b/w drawings in text, dec. clo., 205x140mm. HBM
Contains 31 stories.
Another copy as above, but without adv. & with uncut, instead of g.e., & with 'D. Nutt' on base of spine, 210x150mm. HBM
5710 Second edition as above, 1897
xvi, 132 pp & 12pp adv., 12 b/w drawings, pic. clo., 205x148mm. HBM
The 1897 edition appeared both with and without 'second edition' appearing on the t.p. Some copies were bound separately and others bound together with *More Legendary Tales*.
5711 AUSTRALIAN/LEGENDARY TALES/Folk-lore of

the Noongahburrahs/as told to the Piccaninnies/ Collected by/Mrs. K. Langloh Parker/With introduction by/Andrew Lang, M.A./Illustrations by a native artist, and a specimen of the native text/Second Edition/London/David Nutt, 270–271, Strand/ Melbourne/Melville, Mullen & Slade/1897/[All rights reserved]
viii, 132pp, *bound together with:*
MORE AUSTRALIAN/LEGENDARY TALES/Collected from various tribes by/Mrs. K. Langloh Parker/Author of/Australian Legendary Tales/with introduction by/ Andrew Lang, M.A./with illustrations by a native artist/London/David Nutt, 270–271, Strand/ Melbourne/Melville, Mullen & Slade/1898.
xv, 104pp (inc. 4pp glossary), 16pp adv., 5 b/w illus., dec. gilt clo., 200x135mm. HBM
Contains 23 tales. The decorations on the front cover & spine of this edition are the same as those on the first & second editions of *Australian Legendary Tales,* but are printed in gilt on dark blue cloth, whereas those in the other editions are printed in dark green on light green cloth. The title on front cover & spine is still 'Australian/Legendary/Tales'.
Another copy as above, but without adv. & with uncut instead of gilt edges, & with 'D. Nutt' on base of spine, size 210x150mm. HBM

5712 MORE AUSTRALIAN/LEGENDARY TALES/ Collected from various tribes by/Mrs. K. Langloh Parker/Author of/Australian Legendary Tales/With Introduction by/Andrew Lang, M.A./With Illustrations by a Native Artist/London/David Nutt, 270–271 Strand/Melbourne/Melville, Mullen & Slade/1898
xv, 104pp (inc. 4pp glossary), 16pp adv., b/w illus., dec. clo. (light green, with different cover design from *Australian Legendary Tales*), 205x145mm. HBM

5713 AUSTRALIAN/LEGENDARY TALES/Collected by/K. Langloh Parker/Selected and Edited by/H. Drake-Brockman/Illustrated by/Elizabeth Durack/ Angus and Robertson/Sydney London
First published 1953
vii, 237pp text (inc. 52pp notes, glossary & bibliography), extended sepia frontis. & 15 f/p sepia/ white & b/w illus., line drawings in text throughout, clo., dec. e/p, 235x150mm. KMM
Introduction by H. Drake-Brockman; notes on illustrations by Elizabeth Durack. Selected from the original edition of *Australian Legendary Tales, & More Australian Legendary Tales.* Illustrated after the style of Aboriginal drawings.
Winner CBCA Award 1954.
AUSTRALIAN/LEGENDARY TALES/Collected by/K. Langloh Parker Angus and Robertson/Sydney London
• Rpt 1954. KP
• Rpt 1955—Imprint: Angus and Robertson/Sydney London Melbourne Wellington. KP
• Rpt 1957, as above. KP
AUSTRALIAN/LEGENDARY TALES/Collected by/K. Langloh Parker/Selected and Edited by/H. Drake-Brockman/Illustrated by/Elizabeth Durack/ Angus and Robertson
Reprinted 1954, 1955, 1957, 1959, 1963, 1965
Details as in 1953 edition. BBC
• Rpt 1967, as above. KMM
• Rpt 1970, as above. KMM
(In the 1967 and 1970 eds lines 2 & 3 are transposed on p 77.)

5714 AUSTRALIAN/LEGENDARY TALES/By/ K. Langloh Parker/Illustrated by/Elizabeth Durack/ Angus and Robertson/Sydney London Melbourne Wellington.
First published 1953; rpt 1954; First school edition 1955
96pp, b/w frontis. & 7 f/p b/w illus., limp clo., 185x125mm. ANL

Russian edition

5715 MIFY I SKAZKI AUSTRALII, sobrany K. Lanlo-Parker perevod s angliisko S. A. Liubimova i I. F. Kurdiukova Otvetstvennyi Redaktor i avtor Predisloviia E. M. Meletinskii. Moskva, Izdatellstvo "Nauka" Glauvnaiia Redaktsiia Vostochnoi Literatury, 1965
166pp, illus., 20cm. Unseen: ANB May 1966

5716 AUSTRALIAN LEGENDARY/TALES/Collected by/K.Langloh Parker/Selected and Edited by/H. Drake Brockman/The Viking Press New York
1966
255pp (inc. notes, appendixes and glossary), b/w frontis.,15 f.p. b/w illus. & illus. throughout (by Elizabeth Durack) plain e/p., blind stamped clo. (using illus. opp. p63), with variant d/w designed by Mel Williamson; larger type & differing dec. on t.p. 235x150mm. KP

5717 AUSTRALIAN/LEGENDARY/TALES/Collected by/K. Langloh Parker/Selected and edited by/H. Drake-Brockman/The Viking Press New York
Publ. 1966 & simultaneously in Canada by The Macmillan Coy of Canada Ltd; second printing 1968
This ed. printed on white paper whereas first American ed. printed on cream paper. Instead of the ivory blind-stamped clo. bdg with brown lettering on spine this copy has the Durack illus. from p232 inverted & printed in black with the addition of plum & pink shapes alongside.
The jacket design is repeated on clo. cover. KP

5718 AUSTRALIAN/LEGENDARY/TALES/Selected from the collection of/K. Langloh Parker/Edited by H. Drake-Brockman/Illustrated by Cecily Trueman/ [device]/Brolga Books Pty. Ltd./Adelaide, South Australia
1969
127pp (inc. 3pp biographical note, 13pp glossary), 1p adv., 3 f/p b/w illus., b/w drawings in text, pic. wrappers, 180x110mm. KMM

5719 TALES FROM THE DREAMTIME/A Collection of Aboriginal Legends/Adapted by J. W. Allan/from/ *Australian Legendary Tales*/by/K. Langloh Parker./ Greek translations by A. Georges./[drawing]/for use in Bilingual Education Project only
n.p., n.d.
41pp, 19 b/w illus., wrappers, 338x198mm. KMM
Processed, parallel Greek/English text.
See also Howard, Peter & Levy, Wayne, eds AUSTRALIAN STORY SAMPLER

5720 THE WALKABOUTS/OF WUR-RUN-NAH/ Compiled by/Catherine Stow/from the published and unpublished legends/collected by/K. Langloh-Parker/ Illustrated by Marion Hart/Adelaide: G. Hassell & Son/1918
33pp, b/w drawings in text, dec. wrappers, 215x130mm. HBM
Cover reads: 'The Walk Abouts/of Wur-run-nah'. First page of text headed: 'Wur-run-nah's/Walkabouts'.

5721 WOGGHEEGUY/Australian Aboriginal Legends/ Collected by/Catherine Stow/(K. Langloh Parker)/Illustrated by Nora Heysen/Adelaide/F. W. Preece & Sons/1930
98pp (inc. 2pp glossary), 2pp author's foreword, b/w frontis. & 7 f/p b/w illus., drawings in text, dec. bd., dec. e/p, 240x175mm. HBM
Text comprising 26 tales, different from those in the two collected editions.

MY BEST BOY and MY BOY-IN-LAW. and "BOBBITY" a Bush Baby, Dymocks, Sydney 1901. Title on cover reads: Sketches/of Children/from Life
These are in fact sketches of children, & not written for children.

PARKER, Lee David

5722 DREAMTIME/poems for children by/Lee David Parker/illustrations by/Susan Boyd/[drawing]/ 1972/printed in South Australia at The Griffin Press, Adelaide
16pp, b/w illus. in text, stiff illus. wrappers, 175x246mm. CLRC

PARKER, Margaret [Margaret MacDonald]

5723 FOR THE SAKE OF A FRIEND/A Story of School Life/By/Margaret Parker/Author of "Ida Cameron"/With four illustrations by/G. Demain Hammond/[device] London/Blackie & Son, Limited, 50 Old Bailey, E.C./Glasgow and Dublin/1896
224pp & 32pp adv., b/w frontis. & 3 f/p b/w illus., dec. clo., 176x116mm. KMM
Girls' school story set in Melbourne.

5724 FOR THE SAKE OF A FRIEND/A Story of School Life/By/Margaret Parker/Author of "Ida Cameron"/Illustrated by G. Demain Hammond/ Blackie and Son Limited/London Glasgow and Dublin n.d.
224pp & adv., 24pp, b/w frontis. & 3 f/p b/w illus., pic. clo., 180x120mm. KMM
Variant binding

5725 TREFOIL/THE STORY OF A GIRLS' SOCIETY/ By/M. P. Macdonald/With Six Illustrations by W. H. Margetson/Thomas Nelson and Sons/London, Edinburgh, and New York/1900
364pp & 4pp adv., b/w frontis. & 5 b/w plates, pic. clo. with vignette of the 3 girls in gilt-framed oval on front cover, 190x125mm. KMM
Continues the story of three girls at 'Stormont House' told in *For the Sake of a Friend*, the author here writing under her maiden name.

PARKER, Nancy

5726 Nancy Parker/MYSTERY/ABOARD THE MURRABIT/Illustrated by the Author/[device]/F. W. Cheshire/Melbourne Canberra Sydney 1964
132pp, b/w drawings in text throughout, dec. clo., dec. e/p, 210x135mm. KMM

PARKER, Richard

5727 THE PENGUIN/GOES HOME/[drawing]/Richard Parker/with illustrations by/Biro/1951/Chatto and Windus/London
144pp, b/w illus. in text, clo., 185x120mm. Grant
The story of an expedition to the South Pole made by some animals who have escaped from a zoo.

5728 NEW HOME SOUTH/Richard Parker/Illustrated by Prudence Seward/Brockhampton Press
Leicester, England, 1961
128pp, b/w frontis. & 22 b/w drawings in text, clo., 185x130mm. KMM
American edition

5729 VOYAGE TO TASMANIA/Richard Parker/ Illustrated by Prudence Seward/The Bobbs-Merrill Company, Inc./A Subsidiary of Howard W. Sams & Co., Inc./Publishers—Indianapolis—New York 1961
127pp, b/w frontis. & 22 b/w illus. in text, clo., 210x135mm. ANL

5730 A VALLEY FULL OF PIPERS/by Richard Parker/ illustrated by Richard Kennedy/
London—Victor Gollancz Ltd. 1962.
159pp, dec. t.p., b/w frontis. & 13 b/w illus., clo., 200x125mm. KMM

5731 A VALLEY FULL OF PIPERS, Illus. by Richard Kennedy, Indianapolis, Bobbs-Merrill [1963]
156p., illus., 22cm. Unseen: ANB 1963

5732 A VALLEY FULL OF PIPERS/Richard Parker/ [drawing]/Illustrated by Richard Kennedy/Penguin Books
Harmondsworth, Middlesex, England; First Published in Puffin Books 1965
138pp, 1p biographical note, 3pp adv., b/w extended frontis., b/w drawings in text, pic. wrappers, 180x110mm. KMM

5733 Richard Parker/THE HOUSE THAT GUILDA DREW/Illustrated by Prudence Seward/[drawing]/ Brockhampton Press
Leicester, England, 1963
120pp, extended dec. t.p., b/w drawings in text throughout, clo., 185x130mm. BBC

5734 Richard Parker/THE HOUSE/THAT GUILDA DREW/Illustrated by Prudence Seward/Knight Books
London 1967
127pp, 1p author's note, b/w drawings throughout, pic. wrappers, 180x110mm. Grant
American edition
Bobbs Merrill, 1964

5735 PERVERSITY OF PIPERS/by/Richard Parker/ Illustrated by/Richard Kennedy/London/Victor Gollancz Ltd./1964
160pp, b/w frontis. & 7 f/p b/w illus., b/w drawings in text, clo., 195x125mm. KMM

5736 PERVERSITY OF PIPERS
Van Nostrand, Princeton, N.J. [1964]
159pp, illus. by Richard Kennedy, 21cm. Unseen: NUC

5737 PERVERSITY/Richard Parker/OF PIPERS/ Illustrated by/Richard Kennedy/Penguin Books
Harmondsworth, Middlesex, England, 1972
126pp, b/w frontis., b/w drawings throughout, pic. wrappers, 180x110mm. KMM

PARKES, Varney

5738 PACIE/A Fairy Tale of the "Illawarra Undersea"/Written for the children of the District/by Varney Parkes.
Newspaper cuttings from The Times, Melton, Feb. 1932 pasted into book. NSL:M

PARKMAN, Sydney

5739 THE/REEF PEARLERS/By/Sydney Parkman/with illustrations/by C. J. Ambler/University of London Press, Ltd/War-time address:/St. Hugh's School, Bickley, Kent/1943
144pp (inc. 5pp exercises headed "Afterthoughts"), b/w frontis. & 11 f/p b/w illus. & b/w drawings in text, limp clo. wrappers, 180x135mm. KMM
The London Supplementary Readers. Pearling adventure story set round Thursday Island.
Another copy as above, but n.d. KP

[PARKS, Hal]
See Edwards, George

'PARLEY, Peter' pseud.
See [Goodrich, Samuel Griswold]

PARNELL, Douglas & ANDREW, Bruce

5740 AUSTRALIAN FOOTBALL/HINTS AND ADVICE/Compiled by/Douglas Parnell/(former South Australian League Player)/and/Bruce Andrew/(Former

Victorian League Player)/For/The Australian Naitonal Football Council/A Text Book on how to/play the Australian National/Game of Football/Edited by/Bruce Andrew
Adelaide, n.d. [1959?]
50pp (last blank), b/w photographic illus., b/w pic. wrappers, 205x135mm. CLRC

PARR, Letitia

5741 [drawing]/GREEN IS FOR GROWING/written by/ Letitia Parr/with drawings by/John Watts
Angus & Robertson, Sydney 1968
[32]pp, part-col. drawings throughout, pic. clo., col. e/p, 245x180mm. KMM

5742 SEAGULL/written by/Letitia Parr/with photographs by/Geoffrey Parr/Angus and Robertson
Sydney 1970
[32]pp, b/w photographic illus., clo., 180x240mm. CLRC
Slight text accompanies photographs.

5743 WHEN SEA AND SKY ARE BLUE/written by/ Letitia Parr/with drawings by/John Watts/Angus and Robertson
Sydney 1970
[32]pp, part-col. illus. throughout, pic. clo., 240x175mm. KMM

5744 DOLPHINS ARE DIFFERENT!/Written by Letitia Parr/Illustrated by Patricia Mullins/Angus and Robertson
Sydney 1972
[32]pp, col. & part-col. illus. throughout, clo., col. e/p, 240x180mm. KMM

PARROTT, J. Edward

5745 BRITAIN/OVERSEAS/The Empire in Picture/and Story/[device]/By J. Edward Parrott, M.A., LL.D./Thomas Nelson and Sons/London, Edinburgh, and Dublin
n.d. [1908]
320pp, col. frontis. by Seymour Lucas & 20 f/p col. illus., b/w photographic illus. throughout, marginal drawings, illus. by various artists, dec. clo., 235x160mm. KMM
Young Folks' Bookshelf No. 1. Elaborately gilt decorated cloth with gilt edges & decorated endpapers. Includes section on Australia (38pp).

PARRY, Seff

5746 FOOTBALL/Illustrated Text Book/The Australian Game/by Seff Parry/Fitzroy, West Adelaide and East Perth Rover
n.p., n.d.
35pp, b/w photographs, col. dec. wrappers, cover title, 210x136mm. CLRC
Daniels Print adv. on back page & back cover. Lacks t.p.

PASCOE, J. H., Jun.

CRUSHED HOPES: A Story of Australian Life, Adelaide, 1905
Not a children's book.

PATCHETT, Mary Elwyn

5747 AJAX THE WARRIOR/by/Mary Elwyn Patchett/ Illustrated by/Eric Tansley/Lutterworth Press/London. 1953
183pp, col. frontis. & 8 f/p b/w illus., clo., 185x115mm. CLRC
• Rpt 2nd imp. 1955 as above CLRC
• Rpt 3rd imp. 1960; 4th imp. 1963, as above. CLRC
• Rpt 9th imp. 1968. CLRC

Austrian edition
5748 MEIN FREUND AJAX
Wiener Verlag, Vienna, n.d.
152pp, 38 b/w illus. by Adalbert Pilch, 200x140mm. unseen, IFA
French edition
5749 Omnibus edition comprising 4 books: *Ajax, Chien sans Peur, Tam l'indompte, Le Tresor de la Grande Barrière, Mary et ses Amis [Ajax, Tam the Untamed, Treasure of the Reef, Return to the Reef]*
Robert Laffont, Printed in Belgium 1958
539pp, b/w illus., 200x145mm.
Translated by Anne Bernandon. Unseen: IFA

5750 AJAX/Golden Dog of the Australian Bush/by/ Mary Elwyn Patchett/[drawing]/Illustrated by/Eric Tansley/The Bobbs-Merrill Company, Inc./Publishers/ Indianapolis/New York.
First American edition 1953
172pp, 7 f/p b/w illus., clo., 210x140mm. ANL
Norwegian edition
5751 AJAX DEN DRISTIGE; H. Aschehoug & Co. 1956, Oslo
134pp, picture jacket by G. K. Malmstrom, 190x130mm. Unseen: IFA
Swedish edition
5752 AJAX OCH JAG, Stockholm 1956
182pp, b/w illus. Sven Bjornson, illus. cover, clo., 190x130mm. Unseen: IFA
German edition
5753 AJAX MEIN LEBENSTRETTER, Erika Klopp Verlag, 1953
174pp, b/w illus. H. Born, stiff back, illus. jacket, 190x130mm.
Second edition as above, 1960, 188pp, b/w illus. by Adalbert Pilch. Unseen: IFA
5754 AJAX MEIN LEBENSTRETTER [von] Mary Patchett Erika Klopp [1968] 3rd edition
188pp, illus., 19cm. Unseen: ANL catalogue
Polish edition
5755 AJAKS WALECZNY; Publisher Nasza Ksiegarnia, Warsaw 1958
173pp, illus. Janusz Grabianski, 190x120mm. Unseen: IFA
Dutch editions
5756 ALEX DE VECHTERBAAS [Nederlands van J. P. D. Baas van Dijk. Illustraties van Eric Tansley]
Prisma-Boeken, Utrecht [1961]
187pp, illus., 18cm. (Prisma Juniores). Unseen: ANL Catalogue
5757 ALEX DE VECHTERBAAS—Junior Pocket 159
Spectrum, Utrecht, Holland, 1961
192pp, 8 b/w illus. by Eric Tansley, paper wrappers, 180x105mm. Unseen: IFA
French edition
45758 4[QUATRE] AVENTURES DE AJAX, le chien sans peur
661pp. Unseen: ANL Catalogue
Finnish edition
5759 MINÄ JA KOIRAT: Nuorisonromaani. Suomentanut: Aila Nissinen
Kustannusosakeyhtiö Otava, Helsingissä [Helsinki] [1965]
178pp, 19cm. Unseen: ANL Catalogue
5760 AJAX/Mary Elwyn Patchett/THE/WARRIOR/ Illustrated by/Eric Tansley/Penguin Books
First published 1953; this edition published Harmondsworth, Middlesex, England, 1972
144pp, 8 f/p illus., pic. wrappers, 180x110mm. Puffin Books. KMM
This title also published in a paperback edition by US Scholastic Book Services, & in Danish & Finnish

editions according to the author, who unfortunately was unable to give any further details of these editions.

5761 KIDNAPPERS/OF SPACE/the Story of two boys in a spaceship/abducted by the golden men of Mars/ by/M. E. Patchett/[publisher's device]/Lutterworth Press/London.
1953
208pp, col. frontis. map, clo., 190x125mm. CLRC

5762 SPACE CAPTIVES/OF THE/GOLDEN MEN/by/ M. E. Patchett/The Bobbs-Merrill Company, Inc./ Indianapolis Publishers New York.
1953 [First American edition of *Kidnappers of Space*]
222pp, unillus., clo., 200x140mm. ANL
Dutch edition
5763 RUIMTE-PIRATEN/Vertaling: Mr. W. Joosten/ Tekeningen: Rein van Looy/N. V. Uitgeverij de Verkenner-Baarn.
n.d.
188pp, 6 b/w illus., wrappers, 110x90mm. ANL

5764 THE LEE TWINS:/Beauty Students/Mary Elwyn Patchett/The Bodley Head
London, first published 1953; rpt 1953, 1955
191pp, 1p adv., unillus., clo., 185x120mm. CLRC
• Rpt 1957. KP
Finnish edition
5765 KAUNENSALONGIN OPPILAAT. Suomentanut: Maija Hahl Kustannusosakeyhtiö Otava, Helsingissä [Helsinki] [1963]
200pp, 19cm. Unseen: ANL Catalogue

5766 TAM THE UNTAMED/by/Mary Elwyn Patchett/ Illustrated by/Kiddell-Monroe/Lutterworth Press/ London.
1954
176pp, b/w frontis. & 6 f/p b/w illus., b/w chapter headings, clo., 185x120mm. ANL
2nd imp. 1955, 4th imp. 1963, 5th imp. 1967, as above. KP
5767 TAM THE UNTAMED/by/Mary Elwyn Patchett/ author of/Ajax, Golden Dog of the Australian Bush/ Illustrated by Gerald McCann/The Bobbs-Merrill Company Inc./Publishers/Indianpolis—New York.
1955
186pp, b/w illus. throughout, clo., 205x140mm. ANL
Included in French omnibus edition, Robert Laffont, Belgium 1958. Unseen: IFA
Norwegian edition
5768 HESTON SOM IKKE VILLE TEMMES
H. Aschehoug & Co., 1957
139pp, 190x125mm. Unseen: IFA
German edition
5769 MEIN SILBERHENGST, Erika Klopp Verlag, 1955, illus. Kiddell-Monroe
191pp, clo., 190x125mm. Unseen: IFA
Polish edition
5770 TAM NIEPOSKROMIONY, 1959
173pp, illus. Januscz Grabianski, b/w illus., stiff cover, 190x120mm. Unseen: IFA
Swedish edition
Unseen: Stated by author to have been translated into Swedish & published in Sweden, but no details given.

5771 WILD BROTHER/by/Mary Patchett/[drawing]/ With drawings by/John Rose/Collins/St. James's Place London/1954.
256pp, map & b/w illus. throughout, clo., 195x135mm. CLRC
5772 WILD BROTHER/Mary Patchett/Collins/Fontana Books
1957
191pp, b/w map frontis., wrappers, 180x110mm. ANL
5773 WILD BROTHER/Mary Patchett/[device]/Armada Armada Books. London 1971
157pp, 1p author's note, 1p adv., unillus., pic. wrappers, 180x110mm. KMM
French edition
5774 FRERE SAUVAGE [par] Mary Patchett. Traduction de Jérome Harrap. Illustrations de Henri Dimpre [Paris] Hachette [1956]
190pp, illus., 17cm. (Bibliothèque verte). Unseen: ANL Catalogue
German edition
5775 MEIN WILDER BRUDER, Erika Klopp Verlag 1956, 236pp, clo., e/p maps, 190x140mm. Unseen: IFA
Dutch edition
5776 SHULA, Nieuwe Wicken N.V. Eng.
239pp, illus., clo., 210x145mm. Unseen: IFA

5777 ADAM TROY,/ASTROMAN/The Exciting Story of How a/Great Space-Pilot saved the/World from Radiation Beasts/by/M. E. Patchett/Lutterworth Press/London.
1954
189pp, col. frontis. only, clo., 190x130mm. KMM

5778 LOST/ON VENUS/The Thrilling Story of two Boys/who land on the Planet/and Explore a Fantastic World/by/M. E. Patchett/Lutterworth Press/London.
1954
192pp, col. frontis., clo., 190x130mm. ANL
Dutch edition
5779 NOODLANDING OP VENUS [van] M. E. Patchett. Vertaling: J. Stevens. Tekeningen: Karel Thole. Baarn, N. V. Uitgeverij de Verkenner [196-?]
191pp, illus., 12cm. (Junior—jongensboekenserie, no. 68). Unseen: ANL Catalogue
US edition
5780 FLIGHT/TO THE/MISTY PLANET/by/M. E. Patchett/The Bobbs-Merrill Company, Inc./ Indianapolis, Publishers New York
n.d.
236pp, unillus., clo. (copy seen re-bound), 200x130mm. CLRC

5781 EVENING STAR/Mary Elwyn Patchett/Illustrated by/Olga Lehmann/Lutterworth Press/London
1954
176pp, b/w frontis. & 7 f/p b/w illus., clo., 195x125mm. KMM

5782 YOUR CALL,/MISS GAYNOR"/Mary Elwyn Patchett/Illustrated by/Bill Martin/Lutterworth Press/ London
1955
222pp, b/w frontis. & 7 f/p b/w illus., clo., 195x125mm. KMM

5783 TREASURE/OF THE REEF/An Ajax Book/Mary Elwyn Patchett/Illustrated by/Joan Kiddell-Monroe/ Lutterworth Press/London.
1955
203pp, b/w map frontis., b/w illus. throughout, clo., 185x120mm. KMM
Norwegian edition
5784 KORALLREVETS HEMMLIGHET, H. Aschehoug, Oslo, 1958.
158pp. Unseen: IFA
Included in French omnibus edition, Robert Laffont, Belgium 1958. Unseen: IFA
US edition
5785 THE GREAT BARRIER REEF, Bobbs Merrill Inc., 211pp, illus. Kiddell-Monroe 1955. Unseen: IFA
Swedish edition
5786 AJAX OCH JAG BLIR SKATT SÖKARE. Illustrerad av Sven Björnson [Översättning av Ulla Lundberg]

Eklund Tidea, Stockholm [1957]. Unseen: ANL Catalogue
Polish edition
5787 SKARBY RAFY KORALOWEJ. Przetozyta Ewa Kotaczkowsa Nasza Ksiegarnia, Warszawa 1962
221pp, 20cm. Unseen: ANL Catalogue

5788 UNDERSEA/TREASURE HUNTERS/by/Mary Elwyn Patchett/Illustrated by/Kiddell-Monroe/ Lutterworth Press/London.
1955
180pp, b/w frontis. & 5 f/p b/w illus., clo., 195x125mm. KMM
US edition
5789 THE CHANCE OF TREASURE. Bobbs-Merrill & Co., 1957, 220pp, illus. Tom Hickey, 215x140mm. Unseen: IFA
German edition
5790 CHICKOWEE BUCH, Erika Klopp Verlag, 1957, 221pp, b/w illus., 190x140mm. Unseen: IFA

5791 RETURN/TO THE REEF/An Ajax Book/Mary Elwyn Patchett/Illustrated by/Kiddell-Monroe/ Lutterworth Press/London.
1956
171pp, dec. map frontis. & 6 f/p b/w illus., clo., 185x120mm. KMM
Included in French omnibus edition, Robert Laffont, Belgium 1958. Unseen: IFA
Norwegian edition
5792 TILBAKE TIL KORALLEVET
H. Aschehoug & Co., 1959
118pp, unillus., map e/p, 190x125mm. Unseen: IFA

5793 SEND FOR/JOHNNY DANGER/The amazing adventures of/the Ace Pilot, Captain Danger,/and his Crew on the Moon/by/M. E. Patchett/Lutterworth Press/London.
1956
174pp, col. frontis. only, clo., 185x120mm. KMM
US edition
Whittesley House, USA, 1958, clo., 190x125mm. Unseen: IFA
Japanese edition
(Publisher's name &c. in Japanese lettering) 1961, line illus. on every page, in laminated container, 190x125mm. Unseen: IFA

5794 SALLY'S/ZOO/Mary Patchett/[drawing]/ Illustrated by/Pat Marriott/Hamish Hamilton/London.
1957; rpt 1959
91pp, 4pp adv., 14 f/p b/w illus. & b/w drawings in text, clo.,185x120mm. Antelope Book BBC

5795 CARIBBEAN/ADVENTURERS/Mary Elwyn Patchett/Illustrated by/William Stobbs/[vignette]/ Lutterworth Press/London
1957
175pp, b/w frontis. & 5 f/p b/w illus., b/w drawings in text, clo., 185x120mm. KMM
German edition
5796 MIT ONKEL PORTY AUF TRINIDAD. Erika Klopp Verlag, 1958, 189pp, 190x140mm. Unseen: IFA
Also published in a paperback edition by Otto Maier Verlag. Unseen: IFA (who gives no further details)

5797 OUTBACK/ADVENTURE/An Ajax Book/Mary Elwyn Patchett/Illustrated by/Kiddell-Monroe/ Lutterworth Press/London.
1957
176pp, b/w frontis. & 6 f/p b/w illus., clo., 185x120mm. CLRC
Polish edition
Published by Nasza Ksiegarnia. Unseen: IFA (who gives no further details)

5798 THE BRUMBY/Mary Elwyn Patchett/Illustrated by/Juliet McLeod/Lutterworth Press/London.
1958
220pp, b/w frontis. & 2 b/w illus., clo., 185x120mm. BBC
2nd imp. 1959, 3rd imp. 1960, 4th imp. 1963, all as above. KP
US edition
5799 Bobbs-Merrill, Indianapolis, New York 1959
224pp, b/w illus. by Gerald McCann, clo. Unseen: IFA
5800 [drawing]/Mary Elwyn Patchett/THE BRUMBY/ Illustrated by Juliet McLeod/Penguin Books [England] 1964
191pp, 2 f/p b/w illus., dec. wrappers, cover design by Barrie Driscoll, 185x110mm. Puffin Books. KMM
• Rpt 1965, 1967, 1971. KP
Norwegian edition
5801 VILLHESTEN. Oversatt av Liv Malling
H. Aschehoug, Oslo 1962
145pp, 19cm. Unseen: ANL Catalogue
Swedish edition
Published by Eklund Tidens, Stockholm. Unseen: IFA (who gives no further details)
Polish edition
5802 BRUMBY, PRZETOZYTA EWA KOTACZKOWSA. Ilustrowat Ludwik Maciag. Warszawa. Nasza Ksiegarnia 1965
205pp, illus., 20cm. Unseen: ANL Catalogue

5803 THE/MYSTERIOUS POOL/Mary Patchett/ [drawing]/Illustrated by/Pat Marriott/Hamish Hamilton/London
1958
89pp, 4pp adv., b/w drawings in text, clo., 185x115mm. Antelope Books. CLRC
• Rpt 1960, 1963. KP; 1965. CLRC
Dutch edition
5804 HET GEHEIM VAN DE BOEMBOEM. Kinderpocket 23
Spectrum, Utrecht, Holland, 1963
96pp, 8 b/w illus. by Pat Marriott, paper wrappers, 180x105mm. Unseen: IFA
Afrikaans edition
5805 AROO [by] Mary Patchett. Vertaal deur J. P. Smuts en Ria van Rensburg [Illustrasies deur Pat Marriott] John Malherbe, Kaapstad [South Africa] 1963
68pp, illus., 19cm. Unseen: ANL Catalog

5806 THE CALL OF/THE BUSH/Mary Elwyn Patchett/ Illustrated by/Wildsmith/Lutterworth Press/London
1959
179pp, b/w frontis. & 5 f/p b/w illus., clo., 185x125mm. CLRC
Norwegian edition
5807 OPPDANGERFERD MED AJAX, H. Aschehoug, Oslo, 1960, 141pp, cover illus. Liv Malling (uniform with other Norwegian editions). Unseen: IFA
French edition
5808 L'ENFANT DU DÉSERT [par] M. E. Patchett, traduit de l'anglais par J. F. Gravrand. Illustrations de Michel Gourlier
Les Presses de la Cité, Paris [1967?]
187pp, illus., 20cm. Unseen: ANL Catalogue

5809 Mary Patchett/THE PROUD EAGLES/With pictures by/Maurice Wilson/[publisher's colophon]/ Heinemann/London Melbourne Toronto
1960
215pp, b/w drawings throughout, clo., 190x120mm. BBC
Not a children's book, but of interest to some.

US edition
The World Publishing Co., 1961
Uniform with above. Unseen: IFA
German edition
5810 AQUILA IN DEN LÜFTEN [von] Mary Patchett [Übertragen von Irma Silzer] Bern, Switzerland, Scherz [1965]
199pp, 20cm. ANL Catalogue

5811 THE/QUEST/OF/ATI MANU/M. E. Patchett/ Illustrated by/Stuart Tresilian/[drawing]/Lutterworth Press/London.
1960
174pp, b/w drawings throughout, clo., 180x120mm. CLRC
Boys' adventure story, set in North Queensland.
US edition
5812 THE QUEST OF/ATI MANU/Mary Elwyn Patchett/Illustrated by Stuart Tresilian/[drawing]/The Bobbs-Merrill Company, Inc./A subsidiary of Howard W. Sams & Co. Inc./Publishers—Indianapolis—New York
First American ed. 1962
188pp, 4 f/p b/w illus. & drawings in text, clo., 210x138mm. KP
Swedish edition
5813 ATI MANU, DEN GÖMDA SKATTEN: M. E. Patchett [Översättning: Celine-Marie och Walter Dickson. Illustrationer: Tord Sundquist]
Tidens Förlag, Stockholm [1962]
Unseen: ANL Catalogue

5814 COME HOME,/BRUMBY/by/Mary Elwyn Patchett/Illustrated by/Stuart Tresilian/Lutterworth Press/London.
1961
192pp, b/w frontis. & 8 f/p b/w illus., clo., 185x120mm. KMM
Sequel to *The Brumby.*
2nd imp. 1962. KP
5815 COME HOME,/BRUMBY/by/Mary Elwyn Patchett/Illustrated by/Stuart Tresilian/[device]/ Lutterworth Press/London
New Ed. 1969
192pp, b/w frontis. & 8 f/p b/w illus., clo., 204x134mm. KP
US edition
Published by Bobbs-Merrill
Unseen: IFA (who gave no further details)
5816 Mary Elwyn Patchett/COME HOME,/BRUMBY/ Illustrated by/Stuart Tresilian/[device]/Penguin Books Harmondsworth, Middlesex, England, 1972
175pp, b/w frontis. & 8 f/p b/w illus., pic. wrappers, cover design by David Carl Forbes, 180x110mm. KMM
Norwegian edition
5817 VILLHESTEN KOMMER HJEW. Oversatt av Liv Malling
H. Aschehoug, Oslo 1964
119pp, 19cm. Unseen: ANL Catalogue

5818 THE END/OF THE OUTLAWS/Mary Elwyn Patchett/Illustrated by/Roger Payne/Lutterworth Press/London.
1961
159pp (inc. 2pp author's note), col. frontis. & 5 f/p b/w illus., clo., 185x120mm. KMM
An *Ajax* Book.
US edition
5819 THE END OF THE OUTLAWS. Illustrated by Roger Payne, Indianapolis Bobbs-Merrill [1963]
157pp, illus., 22cm. Unseen: ANB 1964

German edition
5820 MEINE HEIMAT IST DER BUSCH [Übertragen von Lena Stepath]
Erika Klopp Verlag, Berlin 1962
155pp, illus., 19cm. Unseen: ANL Catalogue

5821 WARRIMOO/M. E. Patchett/[drawing]/Illustrated by Roger Payne/Brockhampton Press
London 1961
187pp, b/w drawings throughout, clo., 205x135mm. CLRC
First part of the book has an Australian setting; the second the South American jungle.

5822 CIRCUS BRUMBY/by/Mary Elwyn Patchett/ Illustrated by/Stuart Tresilian/[device]/Lutterworth Press/London
1962
190pp, b/w frontis. & 7 f/p b/w illus., clo., 180x120mm. KMM
Sequel to *The Brumby, & Come Home Brumby.*

5823 M. E. Patchett/DANGEROUS ASSIGNMENT/ Illustrated by Roger Payne/[drawing]/Brockhampton Press/Leicester
1962
182pp, b/w frontis. & 23 b/w drawings, clo., 220x135mm. CLRC
A sequel to *Warrimoo.*
US edition
5824 DANGEROUS ASSIGNMENT
Indianapolis, Bobbs-Merrill 1964. Unseen: ANB 1964

5825 IN A WILDERNESS/by/Mary Patchett/London/ Hodder & Stoughton London
First publ. 1962
156pp, unillus., clo., 204x137mm. KP
This story of a boy's obsession with a wild dingo has a strong appeal to nature lovers but is not produced as a children's book.

5826 THE GOLDEN/WOLF/Mary Elwyn Patchett/ Illustrated by/Roger Payne/Lutterworth Press/London.
1962
174pp, col. frontis. & 7 b/w illus., clo., 185x120mm. KMM
German edition
5827 DER GOLDENE WOLF [von] Mary Patchett. Übertragen von Lena Stepath
Berlin, Erika Klopp Verlag [1967]
144pp, illus., 19cm. Unseen: ANL Catalogue

5828 AJAX/AND THE/HAUNTED MOUNTAIN/Mary Elwyn Patchett Illustrated by/Roger Payne/[device]/ Lutterworth Press/London
1963
143pp, col. frontis., 4 f/p b/w illus. & b/w drawings, clo., 185x115mm. KMM
US edition
5829 AJAX AND THE HAUNTED MOUNTAIN
Indianapolis, Bobbs-Merrill [1966]
135pp, 22cm. Unseen: ANB 1966
Finnish edition
5830 AJAX JA AAVENVUORI. suom. Aila Nissinen
Helsinki: Otava 1972 (Keuruu) 147s. LRA

5831 M. E. Patchett/THE VENUS PROJECT/Illustrated by Roger Payne/Brockhampton Press
Leicester, England, 1963
160pp, b/w frontis. & b/w drawings in text, clo., 220x135mm. CLRC
Sequel to *Warrimoo, & Dangerous Assignment.*

PATCHETT, Mary Elwyn

5832 AJAX/AND THE/DROVERS/Mary Elwyn Patchett/Illustrated by/Roger Payne/[device]/ Lutterworth Press/London
1964
143pp, col. frontis., 2 double-spread, 3 f/p & 2 small b/w illus., clo., 185x120mm. CLRC
Finnish edition
5833 AJAX JA SAVANNIN KAVJALAUMA. Suomentanut [trans.] Aila Nissinen
Kustannusosakeyhtiö Otava, Helsingissä [Helsinki] [1968]
160pp, 19cm. Unseen: ANL Catalogue

5834 M. E. Patchett/TIGER IN THE DARK/Illustrated by Roger Payne/Brockhampton Press
Leicester, England, 1964
153pp (inc. 5pp prologue & 2pp epilogue), extended b/w frontis. & 2 f/p b/w illus., b/w drawings in text, 215x135mm. CLRC
The fourth book in the *Warrimoo* series.
5835 TIGER IN THE DARK/Mary Elwyn Patchett/ [extended frontispiece illustration]/Illustrations by Roger Payne
Puffin Books, Harmondsworth, Middlesex, England, 1966
158pp, 1p biographical note, 1p adv., pic. wrappers, 180x110mm. KMM
Dutch edition
5836 DE GEHEIMZINNIGE TIJGER [van] M. E. Patchett/Vertaald door William Plover. Illustraties van Roger Payne/[Neth.]/Uitgeverij G. F. Callenbach/1964 Nijkerk
158pp, illus., 22cm. Unseen: ANL Catalogue
US edition
5837 TIGER IN THE DARK/[drawing]/Mary Elwyn Patchett/Illustrated by Roger Payne/Duell, Sloane and Pearce New York
[1966]
166pp, extended b/w frontis., b/w illus. in text, 202x134mm. KP
Afrikaans edition
5838 M. E. Patchett/TIER VAN DIE NAG/John Malherbe Edms Bpk/Posbus 1207—Kaapstad/1967
146pp, extended b/w frontis. & b/w drawings in text (as in original edition), clo., 210x140mm. KMM
French edition
5839 L'ENFANT DU DÉSERT
Published by Les Presses de la Cité 1967
Unseen: IFA (who gives no further details)
German edition
5840 TIGER IM DUNKEL [von] Mary Patchett. Übertragen von Lena Stepath, Berlin Erika Klopp Verlag 1968
176pp, 19cm. Unseen: ANL Catalogue

5841 STRANGER/IN THE HERD/A Brumby Book/by/ Mary Elwyn Patchett/Illustrated by/Stuart Tresilian/ [device]/Lutterworth Press/London
1964
160pp, b/w frontis. & 7 b/w illus., clo., 185x115mm. CLRC

5842 A BUDGIE CALLED FRED/by/Mary Patchett/ With photographs by/Stuart Gore/Arthur Barker Limited/20 New Bond Street London W.1.
1964
63pp (inc. 1p prologue), 6pp b/w photographic illus., clo., 180x120mm. CLRC
Not expressly intended for children.

5843 THE WHITE DINGO/By/Mary Elwyn Patchett/ Illustrated by/Peter Kesteven/[device]/Lutterworth Press/London
1965
140pp, b/w frontis. & 5 f/p b/w illus., b/w drawings in text, clo., 195x125mm. KMM

CRY OF THE HEART, London, Collins 1956
Not a children's book.
French edition abridged for children
5844 MAMOU, Bibliothèque Verte, trans. Jean Murray, Hachette Paris
189pp, b/w illus. by Paul Durand, hardback, 170x120mm. Unseen: IFA

5845 BRUMBY FOAL/Mary Elwyn Patchett/Illustrated by/Victor G. Ambrus[device]/Lutterworth Press/ London
1965
124pp, b/w frontis. & 5 f/p b/w illus., b/w drawings in text, clo., 205x130mm. BBC
Second ed. 1969. KMM
US edition
5846 Published by Duell, Sloane & Pearce, USA
Norwegian edition
5847 Published by Aschehoug, Oslo. Unseen: IFA (who gives no further details)

5848 SUMMER ON/WILD HORSE ISLAND/Mary E. Patchett/Illustrated by Roger Payne/Brockhampton Press
Leicester, England, 1965
120pp, b/w frontis. & b/w drawings in text, clo., 185x130mm. CLRC
2nd imp. 1969. KP
US edition
5849 SUMMER ON WILD HORSE ISLAND
New York, Meredith Press [1967]
116pp, illus. Roger Payne, 21cm. Unseen ANB 1967

5850 THE TERROR OF/MANOOKA/Mary Elwyn Patchett/Illustrated by/Roger Payne/[device]/ Lutterworth Press/London
1966
160pp, b/w frontis. & 7 b/w drawings in text, clo., 195x125mm. KMM

5851 Mary E. Patchett/SUMMER ON/BOOMERANG BEACH/Illustrated by Roger Payne/Brockhampton Press
Leicester, England, 1967
120pp, b/w frontis. & b/w drawings in text, clo., 185x130mm. ANL

5852 Mary E. Patchett/FESTIVAL/OF JEWELS/ Illustrated by Roger Payne/[illustration]/Brockhampton Press
London 1968
120pp, b/w illus. in text, clo., 180x130mm. KMM

5853 FARM BENEATH THE SEA/by/Mary Patchett/ Illustrated by/H. Johns/George G. Harrap & Co. Ltd./ London Toronto Wellington Sydney
1969
173pp, b/w frontis. & 6 f/p b/w illus., clo., 195x130mm. KMM

5854 THE LONG RIDE/A Brumby Book/Mary Elwyn Patchett/Illustrated by/Mike Charlton/Lutterworth Press London
1970
140pp, b/w frontis. & 5 f/p b/w illus., 1 b/w map, clo., 195x125mm. KMM

5855 QUARTER/HORSE BOY/by Mary Patchett/

illustrated by Roger Payne/[drawing]/George G. Harrap & Co. Ltd./London Toronto Wellington Sydney
1970
159pp, 5 f/p b/w illus., 1 b/w drawing in text, clo., 195x125mm. CLRC

5856 REBEL BRUMBY/Mary Elwyn Patchett/[device]/ Lutterworth Press. Guildford and London
1972
158pp, b/w map, 9 b/w drawings in text, illus. by Roger Payne, clo., 195x130mm. BBC

PATEN, May Lillian

5857 THE ADVENTUROUS ELVES/An Authoritative Fairy Story/By/May Lillian Paten/Author of/'Frances of the Farm'/Illustrated by/Christian Yandell/ Commonwealth of Australia/Edward A. Vidler/178 Collins Street/Melbourne
1926
54pp, 4 f/p b/w illus., bd. (with col. illus. pasted on front cover), 195x140mm. VSL

PATERSON, Andrew Barton

5858 THE ANIMALS/NOAH/FORGOT/by A. B. Paterson ("Banjo")/Illustrated by Norman Lindsay/ Published by The Endeavour Press/Bulletin Buildings, 252 George Street, Sydney, N.S.W.
March 1933
64pp (inc. photographic portrait frontis.), 1p verse, 4pp foreword, dec. t.p., 24 b/w drawings, bd., 212x137mm. HBM
Verses.
• Rpt April 1933, as above. HBM
Third printing 1933, as above. KP

5859 THE/ANIMALS/NOAH/FORGOT/by A. B. Paterson ("Banjo")/illustrated by Norman Lindsay/ Lansdowne Press
First published 1933; this edition published Melbourne 1970
71pp, dec. t.p., b/w portrait of author, line drawings, clo., 240x150mm. KMM

5860 BANJO PATERSON'S/HORSES/The Man from Snowy River/Father Riley's Horse/Story of Mongrel Grey/by A. B. Paterson/Illustrated by Walter Stackpool/Angus and Robertson
Sydney 1970
[26]pp (inc. 1p biographical note & portrait sketch), col. illus. throughout, pic. bd., pic. e/p, 290x225mm. *Young Australia Series.* KMM
• Rpt 1971. KP

5861 WALTZING MATILDA/Poem by/A. B. Paterson/ Illustrations by/Desmond Digby/Collins Sydney London
1970
34pp, 1p glossary, col. illus. throughout, pic. bd., col. e/p, 210x255mm. CLRC
Won CBCA Picture Book Award 1971
US edition

5862 Holt, Rinehart & Winston, New York [1972]
[36]pp, col. illus., 220x260mm. Unseen: ANL Catalogue

5863 BENJAMIN/BANDICOOT/A. B. 'Banjo' Paterson/ Illustrated by Rich Richardson/[drawing]/Lansdowne Press
Melbourne 1971
[20]pp (printed on inside front cover & fly-leaf), col. illus. throughout, pic. bd., col. e/p, 275x210mm. BBC
From *The Animals Noah Forgot,*.

5864 WEARY WILL/THE WOMBAT/A. B. Paterson/ Illustrated by Rich Richardson/Lansdowne Press
Melbourne 1971
[22]pp (printed inside front & back covers & on e/p), col. illus. throughout, pic. bd., 275x210mm. CLRC
From *The Animals Noah Forgot*, with a note relating to A. B. Paterson, & to wombats.

PATERSON, Betty

5865 BABY RHYMES/By/Blue Ribbon/(Betty Paterson, Brisbane)/[drawing]/Printed for Private Circulation by/ Jackson, Wylie & Co./Glasgow 1934
37pp, unillus., clo., 168x105mm. NSL:M
Verses by well-known illustrator

5866 BETTY PATERSON'S/WORLD/OF/BABIES/ Nelson
Melbourne 1968
64pp, col. & b/w drawings throughout, 3pp biographical note by the artist, dec. clo., pic. e/p, 270x202mm. KP

5867 BABY'S BOOK/OF/HAPPY EVENTS
A. H. Massina & Co Pty Ltd, Melbourne, n.d.[193-?]
16pp, col. illus. on front cover, cover title, pic. wrappers, 150x116mm. KP
Blank pages with col. illus. of babies with spaces for a record to be kept. Last page note for the opening of a Savings Bank Account. Inside back cover printed page showing Savings Bank interest on a child's account, opening at the State Savings Bank of Victoria. General Manager J. Thornton James (overstamped N. R. Williams).

"BINKIE THE BOTHER" by Betty Paterson
Printed in col. & b/w, bound with silk cord, 6ins x 5ins [i.e. 153x128mm] words & pic. by Betty Paterson, price 2/6. Unseen.
'... verses & pictures of the amusing adventures of a very naughty baby called Binkie. It is beautifully printed on the best art boards ... enveloped in a dainty envelope.'
Advertised on back of *Southern Seas Story Book* along with *Me* by Esther Paterson, 'A Story of a Flapper's Adventures'.
Probably not for children.

PATERSON, Betty & GILL, G. Hermon

5868 THE/ENCHANTED/EVENING/By/Betty Paterson/and/G. Hermon Gill/Melbourne:/ Osboldstone & Co. Pty Ltd/Printers and Publishers
n.d. [1920?]
32pp, 8 f/p part-col. illus., b/w drawings in text, wrappers (with separate pic. wrappers), cover title, 245x185mm. CLRC
Story with dedicatory verse.

PATERSON, Beverley

5869 MORE/THOUGHTS OF CHILDHOOD/by/ Beverley Paterson/(aged 11 years)/Some of these verses have appeared in the/"Young Folk's Page" of "The Australasian",/and some in "Somerville House Magazine",/and are reprinted with kind permission.
The author, Brisbane, n.d. [copyright 1936]
31pp, 1p foreword, dec. wrappers, 125x95mm. ANL

5870 THOUGHTS OF GIRLHOOD/by/Beverley Paterson/Some of these poems have appeared in Clayfield College/Magazine and Somerville House Magazine, also in the Young/Folks' Page of the Australasian and The B.P. Magazine, and are reprinted with kind permission
The author, Brisbane, n.d. [1941] [Printed by Dalton & Gilpin]
31pp (inc. 1p introduction), dec. wrappers, 135x100mm. ANL

5871 MUSICAL THOUGHTS/OF CHILDHOOD/Words

by/Beverley Paterson/(aged 8 years)/Music by/Gwen Timbury/Contents [8 songs listed]/Price 3/- net/ Copyright MCMXXXIV by Beverley Paterson & Gwen Timbury/Clayfield Brisbane Queensland/Assigned to W. H. Paling & Co Ltd, 1952
16pp, unillus., pic. wrappers, 248x176mm. CLRC

PATON, Hugh
5872 TALKS/TO/YOUNG PEOPLE/By/Hugh Paton/ The Grown-ups will like them too!/Price: Sixpence
Robert Dey Sons & Co., Sydney 1931
32pp, unillus., wrappers, 186x125mm. NSL:M
Religious instruction.

[PATON, J.]
See Billabong Readers

PATON, James
5873 THE/STORY OF JOHN G. PATON/Told for Young Folks/or/Thirty Years among South Sea Cannibals/By The Rev. James Paton, B.A./With Forty-Five Full-Page Illustrations/By James Finnemore/ London/Hodder and Stoughton/27 Paternoster Row/ MDCCCXCII
397pp, 32pp adv., b/w frontis. & f/p b/w map, 44 f/p b/w illus. in text, dec. clo., 200x135mm. CLRC
Contains much Australian material.
5874 THE/STORY OF JOHN G. PATON/Told for Young Folks/or/Thirty Years among South Sea Cannibals/Re-arranged and Edited/By The Rev. James Paton, B.A./Fourth Edition/completing twenty-third thousand/London/Hodder and Stoughton/27 Paternoster Row/MDCCCXCVII
304pp, 16pp adv., b/w portrait frontis., b/w map, 44 f/p b/w illus., pic. clo., 195x135mm. KMM
5875 THE/STORY OF JOHN G. PATON/Told for Young Folks...
Fifth edition completing thirty-fifth thousand...London MDCCCXCVIII
304pp &12 pp adv., portrait, map, 6 plates & 3 text illus., pic. clo.,198x134mm. KP
Sixth edition completing 38th thousand 1898, as above. KP
Seventh edition completing 43rd " 1899 as above. KP
Ninth edition " 58th " 1900 as above. KP
Tenth " 1901; 12th ed 1904; 13th ed 1904; 14th ed. 1907; 15th ed 1909, 16th ed, re-arranged 1911, completing 92nd thousand, all KP
5876 THE/STORY OF JOHN G. PATON/Told for Young Folks/or,/Thirty Years among South Sea Cannibals/By the Rev. James Paton, B.A./New Copyright edition, with two new chapters/and forty-five full-page illustrations/By James Finnemore/ Fifteenth thousand/New York:/American Tract Society/10 East 23rd Street./1898/(All rights reserved)
404pp (inc. preface to 1892 ed. & additional note), b/w frontis. & 44 f/p b/w illus., pic. clo., 198x130mm. KMM
The two new chapters continue Paton's story from 1885 when he returned to Victoria. During this time he visited other Australian colonies, and in 1892 set out on a world tour attending a Pan-Presbyterian conference in Toronto, and travelling widely in N. America before sailing to Liverpool. He addressed meetings in many parts of Britain to raise funds for the missions before returning to Victoria in 1894. This edition first published in New York by American Tract Society in 1893.

PATTERSON, K. A.
5877 GUIDING/STARS/by/K. A. Patterson B.A./Foreword by/Dr F. Loewe
Austral Printing & Publishing Co. Ltd, 524 Elizabeth St, Melbourne, n.d.
32pp, b/w diagrams, wrappers, 185x124mm. KP
Astronomy for children.

PAUL, Amery
5878 IT COULD BE SO/Verses by Amery Paul/ Drawings by Douglas Annand/Georgian House/ Melbourne/1944
26pp, b/w drawings throughout, dec. bd., 245x180mm. VSL

5879 PEGGY/By Amery Paul/Pictures by/Syd Miller/ Georgian House/Melbourne/1944
25pp, dec. t.p., col. illus. throughout, bd., dec. e/p, 230x190mm.
Story in rhyme. VSL

5880 TEA PARTY/FOR/POFFINELLA/Story/Amery Paul/Pictures/Syd. Miller/Georgian House/ Melbourne/1945
27pp, col. illus. throughout, dec. bd., 240x180mm. VSL
Children's verse.

Paul and Marie
5881 PAUL AND MARIE,/The Orphans of Auvergne,/ and other Tales/Thomson & Niven,/Publishers,/ Melbourne, Sydney and Adelaide/1885
312pp, b/w frontis. & b/w drawings throughout, dec. clo., 165x105mm. CLRC
Contains: 'A Peep at an Australian Goldfield', by 'Uncle Godfrey' (6pp).

PAXTON, Peter
5882 BUSH AND BILLABONG/Australian Tales of Long Ago/By/Peter Paxton/With a Foreword by The Hon. Dr. A. Louis Bussau/London/Alliance Press Limited/ King William St. House, Arthur St., E.C.4.
n.d. [NSL:M copy acquired 1945]
93pp (inc. 1p foreword & 8pp glossary), 3pp adv., 15 f/p part. col. illus. by Hedi Schick, clo., 185x120mm. NSL:M
5883 New edition as above, n.d. but 'Foreword by the Hon. Sir A. Louis Bussau/[device]' KMM

PAYNE, Donald Gordon
See 'Marshall, James Vance'

PAYNE, [Rev.] G. Warren
5884 THREE BOYS/IN ANTARCTICA/A Story for Boys/By/G. Warren Payne/Illustrated by Arthur Twidle/London/Charles H. Kelly/25–35 City Road, & 26 Paternoster Row, E.C.
n.d. [1912]
210pp, 6pp adv., b/w frontis. & 3 f/p b/w illus., pic. clo., 190x120mm. NSL:M
Also author of *The Backblocks' Parson, A Story of Australian Life*, by 'Tom Bluegum' (Charles H. Kelly, London 1899), which though not a children's book is a story of outback experiences & adventure.

PAYNE, Roma
5885 SHIRLEY AND JANET:/A Play for Junior Children/Written by/Roma Payne/1948
Imperial Printing Co., 520 Kent St., Sydney
8pp, unillus., wrappers, 205x122mm. MAC

PAYNE-SCOTT, Valerie & CAMPBELL, Marion
5886 Australian Nature Story Readers/WATTLE GOLD/ and Other Stories/By/Valerie Scott/and/Marion Campbell/Illustrated by Mary Genevieve Courtney/For Children aged 8 to 9 years/[device] Melbourne/ Auckland Christchurch Dunedin/Wellington N.Z., and London/Whitcombe & Tombs Limited

64pp, 6 f/p b/w illus. & dec. headings, pic. wrappers, 180x120mm. KP
Contains 6 stories. *See* McLaren 316

PEACH, L. du Garde

5887 An Adventure from History/THE STORY OF/ CAPTAIN COOK/[drawing]/Written by L. du Garde Peach/Illustrated by/John Kenney/Publishers: Wills & Hepworth Ltd., Loughborough/First published 1958—Printed in England
51pp, 24 f/p col. illus., dec. bd., 175x110mm. A Ladybird Book. KMM

5888 An Adventure from History/THE STORY OF CAPTAIN COOK
Many varied eds with patterned e/p, 'A Ladybird History Book' on front cover; later ed. has map e/p but with col. d/w with picture of a seaman raising the Union Jack & 'price 4/6, Aust. 45c.' KP
In later eds the d/w is discarded and the picture printed directly on to the bd.; others have the same design with a col. ladybird in bottom R/H corner or on top R/H corner. KP

5889 A later copy shows a be-wigged younger naval officer unrolling a map. Internally the front e/p have a coloured map and the back e/p & pastedown contains an index. KP

5890 An Adventure from History/CAPTAIN SCOTT/ [drawing]/by/L. du Garde Peach/with illustrations by/ John Kenney/Publishers: Wills & Hepworth Ltd., Loughborough/First published 1963—Printed in England
51pp, 24 f/p col. illus., bd., dec. map e/p, 170x110mm. KMM
'A Ladybird History Book' Series 561. Tells of Captain Scott's journey to the South Pole.

PEACOCKE, Isabel Maud

5891 MY FRIEND/PHIL/By/Isabel Maud Peacocke/with coloured plates by/Margaret W. Tarrant/Ward, Lock & Co., Limited/London Melbourne and Toronto
n.d. [1915]
320pp, 16pp adv., col. frontis. & 5 col. plates, dec. clo. col. onlay on front, 185x117mm. CLRC
Story set in Sydney.

5892 MY FRIEND/PHIL/By/Isabel Maud Peacocke/ Ward, Lock & Co., Limited/London and Melbourne
n.d.
As above, but b/w instead of col. plates. KMM

5893 THE MISDOINGS OF/MICKY AND MAC/By/ Isabel M. Peacocke/Author of "My Friend Phil" "Patricia Pat"/"Dicky, Night-Errant," etc./Illustrated by Harold Copping/Ward, Lock & Co., Limited/ London, Melbourne and Toronto/1919
304pp & 16pp adv., b/w frontis. & 5 plates, clo., with onlay reproducing frontis. on front cover, 185x120mm. CLRC
Another copy as above, but
London and Melbourne
n.d.
Details as above. CLRC

PEARCE, Andrew J.

5894 BROWN BOYS AND BOOMERANGS/and other stories for boys and girls of all ages/by/Andrew Pearce/(Uncle Andrew of NEW LIFE)/U.A.M. Missionary, Finniss Springs South Australia/Price 1/3/Published for the/United Aborigines Mission/66 Pirie Street, Adelaide, S.A.
n.d. [194-?]
32pp (inc. 1p prologue), 4pp b/w photographs, dec. wrappers, 215x140mm. KMM

5895 THE LAND OF/SUNBURNT/BABIES/by/Mr. Andrew Pearce/(Uncle Andrew)/U.A.M. Missionary, Finniss Springs/Published for the/United Aborigines Mission/(S.A. Incorporated)/66 Pirie St., Adelaide/by/ Lush Studios, Box 1219 K, G.P.O., Adelaide, S.A.
n.d. [inscribed 1946]
36pp (inc. 1p foreword & 1p author's introduction), photographic portrait frontis., dec. chapter headings, wrappers, 215x140mm. KP
14 simple stories of outback experiences.

PEARCE, C. E.

5896 NED/KELLY/THE/BUSHRANGER/By/C. E. Pearce/[illus.]/Lloyd's/Boys Adventures Series No. 17/4d.
United Newspapers (1918) Ltd., London, n.d. [1918]. Printed Fleetway Press Ltd.
82pp (inc. editor's note & 1p adv.), unillus., col. pic. wrappers (signed Broderick Parker), cover title, 160x110mm. RM

PEARCE, Moira Margaret

5897 THE FLOWER/FAIRIES SECRETS/by/Moira M. Pearce/Arthur H. Stockwell Ltd./Ilfracombe Devon [England]
n.d. [1963]
96pp, unillus., clo., 175x115mm. KP

PEARCE, Cyril

5898 ANZAC NEWSREEL/[photograph]/A Picture History of Gallipoli by Cyril Pearl/1963/Ure Smith: Sydney/Printed in Australia at the Griffin Press, Adelaide, for Ure Smith Pty. Ltd., 166 Phillip St., Sydney. [acknowledgements]/Registered in Australia for transmission by post as a book./All rights reserved.
49pp, b/w photographs throughout, dec. clo., dec. e/p, 180x220mm. BBC
Does not appear to have been produced as a book specifically for children though of interest to them.

PEARSON, Elsie

THE SQUEAKING POWDER. *See* Australian Youth Plays

PEARSON, Katherine

5899 HUGH ROYSTON/By/Katherine Pearson/ Australia/Cornstalk Publishing CompanyArnold Place, Sydney/1924
288pp, unillus., clo., 185x120mm. ANL
Family story set in England.

PEARSON, Margaret Mary

5900 POPPET AND/PETE/Written and Illustrated by/ Margaret M. Pearson/Australasian Publishing Company Pty. Ltd. Sydney
1943
46pp (inc. 10pp illus. glossary), dec. t.p., col. illus. throughout, dec. bd., 195x240mm. KMM

5901 FIRE! FIRE!
National Safety Council of Australia, Melbourne, n.d. [1944?]
17pp, numerous illus., dec. wrappers, cover title, 245x177mm. KMM
Based on prize-winning project book prepared by 4th, 5th & 6th grades Smythesdale State School, Victoria, reproduced for printing by *Margaret Mary Pearson.* 17pp have been written & illus. by lithograpy in col.

5902 PUDDLES/and/other/rhymes/Written and drawn/by/Margaret/Mary/Pearson
Australasian Publishing Co., Sydney 1945
24pp, dec. t.p., col. illus. on alternate pages, dec. bd., dec. e/p, 185x135mm. ANL

5903 THE STORY OF/AUSTRALIA/Written/and/ Illustrated/By/Margaret/Mary /Pearson/Australasian Publishing Company Pty. Ltd. Sydney
1946
85pp, dec. t.p., col. illus. throughout, dec. bd., dec. e/p, 180x245mm. KMM

5904 MIRANDA/WITH THE/MOUSE/Written and/ Illustrated by/Margaret M. Pearson/Author of/ "Poppet and Pete"/"Puddles"/"Story of Australia"/Australasian Publishing Company Pty. Ltd. Sydney
1947
58pp, dec. t.p., col. illus. throughout, dec. bd., dec. e/p, 180x235mm. KMM

5905 LONDON ADVENTURE. A story-book and guide for children of all ages, with illustrations by author
George G. Harrap & Co., London 1951
156pp. Unseen: BMC

PECH, Émile

5906 Émile Pech/UN/ONCLE D'AUSTRALIE/Ouvrage illustré de 73 gravures/d'après les dessins de Liège/ [device]/Paris/Librairie Furne/Jouvet & Cie, Éditeurs/ 5.Rue Palatine, 5/Tous droits réservés
n.d. [1879]
286pp (inc. 2pp epilogue),18 f/p engravings & smaller engravings & tailpieces throughout, dec. clo., 280x190mm. RM
On front cover: 'Ville de Paris/Prix d'Honneur' with title on spine.
The young hero, orphaned when his parents are shipwrecked, is sent to Victoria for adoption.

PECK, Charles William

5907 AUSTRALIAN LEGENDS/Tales Handed down from/the remotest times by/The autocthonous inhab-/itants of our land/[vignette]/Parts 1 and 2/By/ C. W. Peck/Stafford & Co. Ltd., Printers and Publishers/21–23 Wellington St., Sydney/1925
211pp, 1p notes, b/w frontis. & 4 f/p b/w illus., b/w drawings in text, dec. wrappers, 180x115mm. NSL:M
Some of the legends were originally published in the *Sydney Mail;* not specifically a children's book.

5908 AUSTRALIAN LEGENDS/Tales/Handed down/ from the remotest/Times by the autocthonous/ inhabitants of our land/C. W. Peck/[drawing]/ Illustrated by Geo. Pownall/Australia:/The Lothian Publishing Co. Pty. Ltd./Fleming Place, Melbourne.
1933
234pp (inc. 2pp verse), b/w frontis. , dec. half-title page & 7 b/w illus., clo., 180x120mm. ANL

5909 Another copy as above,
November 1938
234pp (inc. 2pp verses), b/w frontis. & f/p illus. with dec. border of waratahs with verse 'Australian Legends' precedes t.p., b/w illus. in text, clo., 180x124mm. KP

PEDERSON, Audrey & others

5910 THE/SECRET TUNNEL/AND OTHER/STORIES FOR GIRLS/[drawing]/Printed and Published by Offset Printing Coy. Pty Limited/169 Phillip Street, Waterloo, Sydney
n.d. [194-?]
32pp, part col. illus., col. pic. wrappers, 240x175mm. ANL
Wattle series

PEDERSON-KRAG, G.

5911 ALL ABOARD FOR/ENGLAND!/By/G. Pederson-Krag/Illustrated by Jack Matthew/ [publisher's device]/William Heinemann Ltd./London Toronto
1940
193pp, b/w frontis. & 3 f/p b/w illus., b/w drawings in text, dec. clo., 195x125mm. KMM
The adventures of an Australian family in the 1850s on a voyage to England.

Pedigree Dogs

5912 PEDIGREE/DOGS/Golden Fleece Swap Card Album/price 15 cents
Golden Fleece, n.d.
12pp, text & spaces for 36 cards to be pasted in, col. pic. wrappers, 180x245mm. KP

PEDLEY, Ethel C.

5913 DOT AND THE KANGAROO/By/Ethel C. Pedley/With twenty illustrations by Frank P. Mahony/ London/Thomas Burleigh/1899
109pp, 1p dedication, 1p publisher's note, 2pp adv., portrait frontis., & 19 f/p b/w illus., clo., dec. e/p, 245x185mm. KMM
Posthumously published; the book, though printed & published in England was 'entirely produced in Australia' (editor's note).

5914 DOT AND THE KANGAROO/by/Ethel C. Pedley/With twenty illustrations by Frank P. Mahony/ Second edition/London/Thomas Burleigh/1900
Details as in first edition, but red clo. binding with pic. front cover, with title & drawing of Dot & the bird in gilt, the leaves in green & the fence & the men printed in black. Grant

5915 DOT AND THE KANGAROO/By/Ethel C. Pedley/With six illustrations by Frank P. Mahony/ Sydney/Angus and Robertson/89 Castlereagh Street/ 1906
206pp, 32pp adv. (dated November 1906), b/w frontis. & 5 b/w plates, red clo. (with col. illus. on front cover & small gilt kangaroo on spine), 185x120mm. NSL:M

5916 DOT AND THE KANGAROO/By/Ethel C. Pedley/Illustrated by Frank P. Mahony/London/ Angus and Robertson, Ltd./1913
206pp, 30pp adv. (dated July 1914), b/w frontis. & 5 b/w plates, clo. (with col. onlay by J. Muir Auld on front cover & on spine), 185x120mm. KMM

5917 DOT AND THE KANGAROO/By/Ethel C. Pedley/Illustrated by Frank P. Mahony/Sydney/Angus and Robertson, Ltd./89 Castlereagh Street
n.d. [copy inscribed 1916]
206pp, 4pp adv., b/w frontis. & 5 f/p b/w illus., limp clo., 180x120mm. KP
On front cover: 'Australian Story Series/Dot/and the/ Kangaroo/by/Ethel C. Pedley/Sydney/Angus & Robertson Ltd.'

5918 DOT AND THE KANGAROO/By/Ethel C. Pedley/With 19 illustrations by Frank P. Mahony/ Australia/Angus & Robertson Ltd./89 Castlereagh Street, Sydney/1920
81pp, col. frontis. & 18 f/p b/w illus., dec. bd., 245x185mm. VSL

5919 DOT AND/THE KANGAROO/By/Ethel C. Pedley/With 8 illustrations/Australia:/Angus & Robertson, Ltd./89 Castlereagh Street, Sydney
1923
158pp, col. frontis. & 7 b/w illus. by Frank Mahony, clo., 175x110mm. Platypus series. KMM

5920 DOT AND/THE KANGAROO/by/Ethel C. Pedley/with 8 illustrations/Australia:/Cornstalk Publishing Company/Arnold Place, Sydney/1924
On verso of t.p.: 1st Platypus ed. 20th Nov. 1923, 5000 copies; 2nd Platypus ed. 20th Aug. 1924, 3000 copies
158pp, col. frontis. & 7 f/p b/w illus., clo., col. illus. e/p, 170x105mm. KP
Frontispiece signed Frank Mahony; endpaper illustration (of Dot and the Kangaroo) signed Percy Lindsay.

5921 DOT AND/THE KANGAROO/By/Ethel C. Pedley/With 8 Illustrations/Australia:/Cornstalk Publishing Company/Arnold Place, Sydney/1925
204pp, col. frontis. & 7 f/p b/w illus. by Frank Mahony, red clo., col. e/p (reproducing frontis. illus.), 175x105mm. Platypus series. KMM

5922 DOT AND/THE KANGAROO/By/Ethel C. Pedley/With 7 illustrations/Australia/Cornstalk Publishing Company/Arnold Place, Sydney/1925
204pp, 7 f/p b/w illus. by Frank Mahony, blue clo., 180x120mm. KMM

5923 DOT AND/THE KANGAROO/By/Ethel C. Pedley/For Children aged 9 to 10 years/Australia/Cornstalk Publishing Company/89 Castlereagh Street, Sydney/1928
111pp, b/w frontis. by Frank Mahony, wrappers, 175x110mm. ANL

5924 DOT AND/THE KANGAROO/By/Ethel C. Pedley/For Children aged 9 to 10 years/Australia:/Angus & Robertson Ltd./89 Castlereagh Street, Sydney/1929
111pp, b/w frontis., wrappers, 185x125mm. KMM
Advertisement list of 'Gumnut Readers' on back cover.

5925 DOT AND/THE KANGAROO/by/Ethel C. Pedley/Eighty-second thousand/Australia: Cornstalk Publishing Company, 89 Castlereagh Street, Sydney/1929
203pp, 7 f/p b/w illus., clo., 175x110mm. Grant
There appears to be no frontispiece & the 7 illustrations are unsigned.

5926 DOT AND/THE KANGAROO/by/Ethel C. Pedley/Eighty-Fifth thousand/Australia/Angus & Robertson Limited/89 Castlereagh Street, Sydney/1933
204pp, 7 b/w illus., clo., 174x108mm. KP

5927 DOT AND/THE KANGAROO/by/Ethel C. Pedley/Illustrated by Frank P. Mahony/Australia/Angus & Robertson Limited/89 Castlereagh Street, Sydney/1934
104pp, col. frontis. & 12 f/p b/w plates, bd., 240x180mm. Grant

5928 DOT AND/THE KANGAROO/By/Ethel C. Pedley/Illustrated by Frank P. Mahony/Angus & Robertson Limited/Sydney and London/1938
Details as above. KMM

5929 DOT AND/THE KANGAROO/By/Ethel C. Pedley/Angus & Robertson Limited/Sydney and London/1940
110pp, col. frontis., 6 f/p b/w illus. (printed on text paper), pic. bd., 240x184mm. TG

5930 DOT AND/THE KANGAROO/By/Ethel C. Pedley/Angus & Robertson Limited/Sydney and London/1941
110pp, col. frontis., 6 f/p b/w illus., dec. cardboard wrappers, 245x185mm. CLRC
The illustrations are by F. P. Mahony crudely reproduced on wartime paper; the coloured frontispiece, reproduced on the front cover is better, being printed on art paper.

5931 The Junior Library of Australian Books/DOT AND/THE KANGAROO/By/Ethel C. Pedley/Angus and Robertson/Sydney London
First published in this edition 1949
153pp, b/w frontis. & 6 b/w illus., bd., 180x120mm. CLRC
The illustrations, which are unsigned, are adapted from the original Mahony drawings.
The Junior Library of Australian Books/DOT AND/THE KANGAROO/By/Ethel C. Pedley/Angus and Robertson/Sydney London
Reprinted in the Junior Library series 1951
153pp, b/w frontis. & 6 b/w illus. (as in previous Junior Library edition), bd., 185x125mm. KMM

5932 DOT/AND THE/KANGAROO/by/Ethel Pedley/illustrated by/Frank Mahony/[device]/Angus and Robertson Limited
Sydney 1965
109pp, part-col. frontis. & 18 f/p part-col. illus., clo., 250x185mm. KMM
• Rpt 1967, 1970, 1972. KP

5933 DOT/AND THE/KANGAROO/by Ethel Pedley/illustrated by/Frank Mahony/Angus and Robertson
This edition Sydney 1965, rpt 1967, 1970, 1972
109pp, frontis. & 18 f/p illus. (printed in green ink), laminated pic. bd., 250x185mm. KMM

5934 An Australian Play for Australian Children/DOT AND/THE KANGAROO/By/Ethel C. Pedley/Adapted for stage representation by/Stella Chapman and Douglas Ancelon/With 4 plates in colour by Clint/Australia:/Angus & Robertson, Ltd./89 Castlereagh Street, Sydney/1924
74pp (inc. 2pp notes), 4 f/p col. illus. by Alfred T. Clint from sketches by Stella Chapman, clo., 180x120mm. KMM

PEEL, Hazel M.

5935 FURY, SON OF THE WILDS/by/Hazel M. Peel/illustrated by/Joan Kiddell Monroe/George G. Harrap & Co. Ltd./London Toronto Wellington Sydney
1959
152pp, b/w frontis. & 3 f/p b/w illus., clo., 200x130mm. CLRC
• Rpt 1959. CLRC

5936 FURY, SON OF THE WILDS/by/Hazel M. Peel/illustrated by Joan Kiddell Monroe/Sydney/Australasian Publishing Company/in association with/George G. Harrap & Co. Ltd./London
First Australian edition 1961
128pp, b/w frontis. & 3 f/p b/w illus., limp clo., 180x125mm. CLRC

5937 JAGO/by/Hazel M. Peel/illustrated by/Sheila Rose/[device]/George G. Harrap & Co. Ltd./London Toronto Wellington Sydney
1966
140pp, 4 f/p b/w illus., clo., 195x130mm. BBC

5938 UNTAMED!/Hazel M. Peel/Author of "Fury, Son of the Wilds"/"Pilot the Hunter" "Pilot the Chaser"/"Easter the Show Jumper" "Jago"/"Night Storm the Flat-racer"/"Dido and Rogue" "Gay Darius"/Illustrated by/Mortelmans/[device] George G. Harrap & Co. Ltd./London Toronto Wellington Sydney
London 1969
133pp (inc. 1p 'Some words explained', 1p quotation), b/w frontis. & 7 f/p b/w illus., clo., 195x125mm. BBC

PEEL, Noel

5939 THE FIRST ADVENTURES OF/WOOLIE/WINKLE/with Sintho the Giant/World Copyright reserved/by Noel Peel/British Empire Copyright No. 7108/United States of America Copyright/Class G. Unp., No. 43642/Printed in Australia by Queen City/Printers Pty. Ltd., Melbourne, for the/Publishers, Murfett Pty. Ltd./118 Queen Street Melbourne.
n.d. [1945]
24pp, col. illus. throughout, bd., 180x235mm. ANL

5940 FREIGHTER/MY/PARTNER/By Noel Peel/W. H. McKechnie,/Publisher,/262 Queen Street, Melbourne,/Australia 1946
190pp, unillus., clo., 180x120mm. ANL

PENDER, Lydia

5941 MARBLES/IN MY POCKET/Illustrated by/Pixie O'Harris/[drawing]/The Writers' Press/Sydney
n.d. [1958]

64pp (inc. acknowledgements), b/w frontis. & drawings throughout, clo., 165x120mm. NSL:M
Children's verses.

5942 BARNABY AND THE HORSES/by Lydia Pender/pictures by Alie Evers/Abelard-Schuman/London New York Toronto/Copyright 1961 by Lydia Pender Library of Congress Catalog Card Number 61:6683 Printed in Holland.
42pp, extended illus. t.p., col. lithographic illus. throughout, clo., dec. e/p, 255x175mm. KMM
Written in free verse.

5943 DAN/McDOUGALL/AND THE/BULLDOZER/By Lydia Pender/Pictures by Gerald Rose/Abelard-Schuman/Copyright 1963 by Lydia Pender Library of Congress Catalog Card Number 63—8107 Printed in the United States of America
[42]pp, dec. t.p., col. decorations throughout, clo., dec. e/p, 250x175mm. KMM

5944 SHARPUR/THE CARPET SNAKE/by/Lydia Pender/pictures by/Virginia Smith/Abelard-Schuman/London New York Toronto/Copyright 1967 by Lydia Pender/Library of Congress Catalog Card Number: 67—13608/Standard Book Number: 200.71499.6/Printed in the United States of America
[41]pp, extended dec. t.p., col. & part-col. & b/w illus. on alternate pages throughout, clo., dec. e/p, 250x175mm. KMM
Both author & illustrator are Australian.

5945 BROWN PAPER/LEAVES/By Lydia Pender/[drawing]/Illustrated by Anne Clarke
Wentworth Press, Sydney 1971
32pp, b/w drawings throughout, pic. bd., 195x250mm. KMM
Verses originally published in the school magazines of the Education Departments of New South Wales, Victoria & Queensland.

5946 BARNABY/AND THE/ROCKET/Story by/Lydia Pender/Illustrations by/Judy Cowell/Collins/Sydney London
1972
[37]pp, col. illus. throughout, pic. bd., 250x190mm. KMM
See also Gilmore, Mary & Pender, Lydia

Penguins
5947 PENGUINS/A Charming Tale/for Every Girl and Boy/[drawing]/Designed and Published by/P. M. Productions Ltd/London & Letchworth
n.d. [prize label 1949]
44pp, 16 col. plates & b/w illus., pic. bd., 244x180mm. KP

PENNEY, R. L.
5948 THE PENGUINS/ARE COMING!/by R. L. Penney/[drawing]/Pictures by Tom Eaton/A Science I can Read Book/No 65/A World's Work Children's Book
1969
64pp (inc. 1p biography), part-col. illus. throughout, pic. bd., 215x145mm. KP

The "Pennant Fairies"
5949 THE/"PENNANT FAIRIES"
The British Imperial Oil Company Limited, throughout Australia and NZ, n.d. [1923?]. Printed by Anderson Gowan Pty Ltd, 552–4 Lonsdale St, Melbourne
16pp, 6 part-col. illus. (printed in black, grey & blue), 9 drawings in text, pic. wrappers, cover title, 238x176mm. VMOU

Peppo the Pony
See Joy Publications

Perce Parrot and Others
See Dawfox Productions

PERCIVAL, C. H. [illustrator]
5950 HAPPY HOLIDAYS/Stories and pictures/for children/Colour Illustrations by/C. H. Percival/Printed and Published by Offset Printing Coy. Pty. Limited, 169 Phillip Street, Waterloo (All rights reserved)
n.d. [1947]
20pp, 8 f/p col. illus., dec. wrappers, 270x215mm. ANL

'THE PERFESSER & ALTER EGO, Esquire' [pseud. Lancelot Harrison]
5951 TAILS—AND/TARRADIDDLES/An Australian/Book of Birds and Beasts/By The Perfesser/and Alter Ego, Esquire/[drawing]/Australia/Cornstalk Publishing Company/Arnold Place, Sydney/1925
108pp (inc. 2pp preface & 2pp glossary), b/w frontis. & 76 b/w drawings, illus. by author, clo., 185x145mm. KMM
Verses. Professor Launcelot Harrison was the husband of Amy Eleanor Mack.
5952 Imperial Edition No. 476/Songs from/TALES/AND/TARADIDDLES/Words by/"The Perfesser & Alter Ego Esq."/Music by/Arthur S. Loam/Contents/[11 songs listed]/Copyright Price 2/- net./Allan & Co. Pty. Ltd./Melbourne Sydney Adelaide Bendigo
n.d. [1939]
36pp (inc. 1p glossary & 1p explanation) 12 b/w illus., dec. wrappers (with adv. inside front cover & on both sides of back cover), 245x175mm. KMM
Illustrations & verses reproduced from the book *Tails and Tarradiddles*. Notice different spelling of the word 'Tales' on title page & front cover of this item.

PERKINS, Charles Ernest
5953 Mallee Children's Poems/PINK SALT AND COPI/by/Chas. E. Perkins/Copyright
Ronald Press, South Melbourne, n.d. [1949]
8pp, wrappers, cover title, 155x100mm. ANL

PERRIE, George & GUY, Rita
5954 NUMBER/FUN/by/George Perrie/&/Rita Guy
Victory Publicity, Melbourne, n.d. [1946]
12pp, dec. t.p., col. illus. throughout, dec. wrappers, 280x215mm. ANL

PERRY, Mrs C. E. [Dorothy Frances McCrae]
See Alsop, Marion & McCrae, Dorothy Frances

PERSSE, Michael de B. Collins
W. C. WENTWORTH. *See* Great Australians

5955 THEIR SUCCEEDING/RACE/By/Michael Persse/A Pageant-Play performed by/Geelong Church of England Grammar School/in the Centenary Year. 1957/[device]/F. W. Cheshire/Melbourne
1958
104pp, b/w drawings in text, dec. clo., 215x137mm. KMM

PESCOTT, Richard Thomas Martin
POSSUMS
KOALAS. *See* Life in Australia

PETERS, Dorothy M.
5956 Dorothy M. Peters/THE CHINA DOG/&/OLD CREAKY/Illustrated by/Bernard Brett/London/J. M. Dent & Sons Ltd.
1960
72pp, b/w frontis. & 16 b/w drawings, clo., 180x135mm. KMM

Peter's Puzzle Book
See SPOTTY AT THE CIRCUS

PETIGNY, Clara Filleul de
5957 LE/DUMONT-DURVILLE de/La Jeunesse/[vignette]/Paris/Chez Maugars, Librairie,/Rue Ste-Croix de la Bretonnerie, 32/1845
208pp (inc. 6pp on d'Urville's life), 2 engravings on frontis. page & 1 on t.p., dec. bd., 174x102mm. ANL

Le Petit Messager
5958 LE PETIT/MESSAGER/des/Missions Evangéliques/Dédié à la jeunesse/Première Année/Paris/Chez L.R.Delay/2 Rue Tronchet/1846 Troisième
1844–1847
4 vols, 380, 384, 384, 388pp, ea. vol. contains numerous engravings in text, marbled bd., half leather, 115x72mm. CLRC
Contents (in vol. 3) include 'Mickey, ou le petit garçon de l'Australie du Sud' & other sections on Pacific areas &c.
See also The Child's Companion and Juvenile Instructor

PETRIE, Marion
AUSTRALIAN BIRDS. *See* Golden Stamp Books

'PHILBERT, W. S.' [pseud. Hector Wilshire]
5959 BABBER-BALLADS/by/W. S. Philbert/Illustrated by Margaret Horder/Sydney/W. C. Penfold & Co. Ltd./88 Pitt Street/1924/copyright
Humorous verses, but not intended for children. KMM

Philip the Frog
5960 PHILIP/THE FROG/[drawing]/Published by/Barker & Company/476–90 Little Lonsdale Street, Melbourne/and at 37–43 Bay Street. Glebe, Sydney/Copyright
n.d. [1941]
12pp, part-col. illus. throughout, stiff wrappers, 280x215mm. NSL:M
5961 Joy series No. 3/PHILIP/THE FROG/[drawing]/Produced by/[publisher's colophon]/The House of Barker/Melbourne and Sydney/Australia
n.d.
12pp, details as above. KMM
See Joy series

[PHILLIP, Arthur]
5962 THE/VOYAGE /OF/GOVERNOR PHILLIP/TO/BOTANY BAY/with an/Account of its/Origin and Present State./London:/Printed by T. Maiden, Sherbourn-Lane/For Ann Lemoine, White Rose Court, Coleman-Street,/And J. Roe, No.90, Houndsditch./Sold by all the Booksellers in/The United Kingdom
1807
ii+58pp, engraved frontis. wrappers, 150x95mm. ANL
See also 'The Pocket Navigator'; in which this chapbook is included.
5963 THE/VOYAGE/OF/GOVERNOR PHILLIP/to/Botany Bay,/with an/Account/of its origin and Present State/[engraving]/London/Printed for, and published by/J. Arliss,/Juvenile Library/No.38 Newgate Street.
1807
ii+58, engraved frontis., wrappers, 150 x 95mm. QSL
Unseen, ?re-issue (Ferguson 797a).

PHILLIPS, Jessie
THE STORY OF WANGO; ADVENTURES OF BRIGHT-EYES. *See* Books for the Bairns

5964 RONNIE AND THE KANGAROO, illus. by B. Le Fanu
Books for the Bairns; New Series No 4, Feb 1920
b/w illus. & wrappers
Info. from S. Wood, *W. T. Stead and his Books for the Bairns*

PHILLIPS, Ninon [illustrator]
KOALAS. *See* Mackie, Elizabeth

PHILP, Ruth
5965 THE HAPPY THREE/by Ruth Philp/Illustrations by Winifred M. Towers/A Ruth Philp Production
Samuel Lee & Co. Pty. Ltd, Stanthorpe, Queensland, 1961
44pp, 3 col. illus., 1 f/p, b/w illus. & b/w drawings in text, illus. wrappers, cover title, 245x185mm. ANL
5966 THE /HAPPY/THREE/By/ Ruth Philp [Note on verso of t.p.'1st ed. 1960, 2nd ed. 1961']
Samuel Lee & Co. Pty Ltd, Stanthorpe, Q.
Details as in previous ed., but pic. boards, 240x180mm. KMM

PHIPSON, Joan Margaret [Mrs C. H. Fitzhardinge]
CHRISTMAS IN THE SUN. *See* Blue Wren Books

5967 GOOD LUCK/TO THE RIDER/by Joan Phipson/Illustrated by/Margaret Horder/Angus and Robertson/Sydney London
First published 1953
149pp, dec. t.p., b/w & part-col. illus. throughout, clo., dec. e/p, 215x135mm. KMM
Winner CBCA award for 1953
• Rpt as above 1954, 1955, 1958. BBC
5968 GOOD LUCK TO THE RIDER/[drawing]/Joan Phipson/Illustrated by Margaret Horder/Harcourt, Brace & World, Inc., New York
1968
186pp, b/w illus., clo., 200x140mm. Unseen: IFA
5969 GOOD LUCK/TO THE RIDER/by Joan Phipson/Illustrated by/Margaret Horder/Angus and Robertson/Sydney London/Melbourne Wellington
• Rpt as above 1959. KMM
• Rpt as above 1963. CLRC
5970 Upper Primary Library/For Students aged 11–14/GOOD LUCK TO/THE RIDER/by Joan Phipson/Illustrated by/Margaret Horder/Angus and Robertson/Sydney London
1954
128pp, 10 b/w illus., soft clo., 175x120mm. KP
Swedish edition
5971 Joan Phipson/LYCKA TILL, RYTTARE/Stockholm/Albert Bonniers Fürlag
1956
172pp, unillus., hard clo. (no d/w), 185x120mm. Unseen: IFA

5972 SIX AND/SILVER/by Joan Phipson/Angus and Robertson/Sydney London Melbourne Wellington
1954
147pp, extended b/w frontis., 11 b/w drawings, & decorations in text, illus. by Margaret Horder, clo., dec. e/p, 215x135mm. KMM
• Rpt as above 1957, 1958. KP
School edition
5973 Upper Primary Library/For Students Aged 11–14/SIX AND SILVER/By Joan Phipson/Illustrated by/Margaret Horder/Angus and Robertson/Sydney London Melbourne Wellington
First school edition 1955
125pp, b/w frontis. & 10 b/w drawings, limp clo., 185x125mm. ANL
5974 SIX AND SILVER/Joan Phipson/Illustrated by/Margaret Horder/Harcourt Brace Jovanovich, Inc./New York
1971
190pp, extended illus. t.p., b/w illus. in text, clo., 200x130mm. ANL

5975 Joan Phipson/IT/HAPPENED/ONE SUMMER/ Illustrated by/Margaret Horder/Angus and Robertson/ Sydney London Melbourne Wellington
1957
71pp, extended sepia/white frontis., part-col. drawings throughout, clo., dec. e/p, 235x155mm. KMM
Author's note: 'The first three chapters of this story appeared in a shortened version as *Christmas in the Sun* in the Blue Wren Series...now out of print'.
• Rpt as above 1959. BBC

5976 IT HAPPENED/ONE SUMMER/Joan Phipson/ Illustrated by/Margaret Horder/Hamish Hamilton/ London
First published by Angus & Robertson 1959; First published in Great Britain 1964
94pp, extended b/w frontis., b/w drawings in text throughout, pic. clo., 180x120mm. KMM Antelope Books.
Second imp. 1966 as above. KP
• Rpt 1968 as above. KP

5977 [drawing]/THE BOUNDARY RIDERS/by/Joan Phipson/Illustrated by Margaret Horder/Constable and Co. Ltd./and Angus and Robertson
London and Sydney 1962
184pp, 3 f/p b/w illus. & b/w drawings in text, clo., 200x130mm. KMM
• Rpt 1968 as above. KP

5978 [drawing]/THE/BOUNDARY/RIDERS/Joan Phipson/Illustrated by Margaret Horder/Harcourt, Brace & World, Inc., New York
First American ed. 1963
189pp, b/w drawings throughout, pic. clo., 204x136mm. KMM

5979 THE BOUNDARY/RIDERS/by Joan Phipson/ Illustrated by Margaret Horder/Penguin Books [England] First published in Puffin Books 1965
160pp, extended illus. t.p., 4 f/p b/w drawings & b/w illus. in text throughout, dec. wrappers, 180x110mm. KMM

Swedish edition

5980 Joan Phipson/GRÄNSRYTTARNA/Albert Bonniers Förlag Stockholm
1967
150pp, unillus., bd., 190x125mm. Unseen: IFA

5981 Joan Phipson/THE/FAMILY CONSPIRACY/ [vignette]/Illustrated by/Margaret Horder/Constable and Co. Ltd./and Angus and Robertson Ltd.
1962
188pp, b/w chapter headings & drawings in text throughout, clo., 220x135mm. KMM
Winner CBCA award 1963
• Rpt as above 1968 but with vignette & title on cover blocked in gilt. KP

5982 THE FAMILY CONSPIRACY/Joan Phipson/ [drawing]/Illustrated by Margaret Horder/Harcourt, Brace & World, Inc., New York
1964
224pp, b/w illus. throughout, clo., 205x140mm. Unseen: IFA

5983 THE FAMILY CONSPIRACY/Joan Phipson/ [drawing]/Illustrated by Margaret Horder/[colophon]/ A Voyager Book/Harcourt, Brace & World, Inc., New York/1966
224pp, b/w illus., wrappers, 190x130mm. Unseen: IFA

Danish edition

5984 Joan Phipson/ FAMILIE-SAMMENSVAERGELSEN/oversat af Inger Bang/[colophon]/Jespersen og Pios Forlag/København
1965
141pp, bd., 210x140mm. Unseen: IFA

5985 THREAT/TO THE BARKERS/[drawing]/Joan Phipson/Illustrated by/Margaret Horder/Constable Young Books Ltd./and Angus and Robertson Ltd.
London 1963
189pp, b/w drawings in text throughout, clo., 215x135mm. KMM
2nd imp. 1964. KP

5986 THREAT TO THE BARKERS/[drawing]/Joan Phipson/Illustrated by Margaret Horder/Harcourt, Brace & World, Inc., New York
1965
219pp, b/w illus. throughout, clo., 210x140mm. Unseen: IFA

5987 BIRKIN/Joan Phipson/[drawing]/Illustrated by/ Margaret Horder/Lothian Publishing Co., Pty. Ltd./ Constable Young Books Ltd./Longmans Canada Ltd.
Melbourne 1965
189pp, b/w illus. throughout, dec. clo., 215x135mm. KMM

German edition

5988 Joan Phipson/WOHIN MIT ODIN?/Erika Klopp Verlag Berlin/[publisher's colophon]
1967
175pp, b/w drawings throughout, illus. by Kurt Schmischke, illus. e/p, clo. Unseen: IFA

5989 A LAMB IN THE FAMILY/Joan Phipson/ illustrated by/Lynette Hemmant/[drawing]/Hamish Hamilton/London
1966
95pp, b/w drawings in text, clo., 185x120mm. KMM
• Rpt 1967 as above but pic. wrappers, 184x110mm. KW

5990 THE CREW OF/THE MERLIN/by/Joan Phipson/ [drawing]/Illustrated by/Janet Duchesne/London: Constable Young Books Ltd./Sydney: Angus and Robertson Ltd./Longmans Canada Ltd.
1966
159pp, b/w map, b/w chapter headings & drawings in text, clo., 215x135mm. KMM

US edition

5991 CROSS CURRENT
New York, Harcourt Brace & World [1967]
192pp, illus. by Janet Duchesne, 21cm. Unseen: ANB
1967

German edition

5992 Joan Phipson/ZULETZT GESEHEN IN BROKEN BAY/Englebert-Verlag Balve Westfalen
1970
175pp, unillus., clo., 200x135mm. Unseen: IFA

5993 PETER AND BUTCH/Joan Phipson/Longmans of Australia Pty. Ltd.
Croydon, Victoria, 1969
173pp, unillus., clo., d/w designed by Peter Edwards, 215x135mm. KMM

5994 PETER/AND/BUTCH/Harcourt, Brace & World, Inc./New York
1969
222pp, unillus., clo., 210x135mm. Unseen: IFA

5995 PETER AND BUTCH/Longmans Young Books Ltd London and Harlow, 1969
173pp, unillus., clo., 214x138mm. KP

5996 THE HAUNTED NIGHT/Joan Phipson/Macmillan of Australia/1970
159pp, unillus., clo., 200x120mm. CLRC

5997 THE/HAUNTED/NIGHT/Joan Phipson/Harcourt, Brace & World, Inc./New York
1970
187pp, 2 b/w plans, clo., 200x130mm. Unseen: IFA

5998 BASS/&/BILLY MARTIN/Illustrated by/Ron Brooks/[drawing]/Macmillan
Melbourne 1972
241pp (inc. 7pp notes), 2pp author's note, 2pp b/w maps, b/w frontis. & 14 f/p b/w illus., b/w drawings in text, clo., dec. e/p, 205x125mm. KMM

The Pick-me-up Nursery Rhyme Book
5999 THE/PICK-ME-UP/NURSERY RHYME/BOOK
Pick-Me-Up Condiment Co Ltd, Newtown Sydney, 1923
32pp (inc. 8pp f/p col. illus.), b/w illus. throughout, col. pic. wrappers, cover title, 214x134mm. KP
Little Bo-Peep, Mary had a Little Lamb, Little Miss Muffett, Red Riding Hood, Little Betty Blue. Appears to comprise the five Weston Cut-Out Nursery Rhyme Booklets. with ills by Harry J. Weston.
See also Weston, Harry J.

The Pictorial Tour of the World
6000 THE/PICTORIAL/TOUR OF THE WORLD/ containing pen and pencil sketches of/Travel, Incident, Adventure, and Scenery;/in all parts of the Globe/ London/Frederick Warne and Co./and New York
1st ed., n.d. [188-?]
312pp, col. pic. t.p. with dec. border, col. frontis., numerous b/w engravings, pic. clo., 242x170mm. ANL
'Yarding Wild Horses in Australia' pp44–7; 'The Pitcairn Islanders' pp124–6; 'Submarine Caves (Tonga)' pp145–6; &c.

Pictorial World Atlas
6001 PICTORIAL/WORLD ATLAS/Nestlé's
Nestle, Sydney, [copy inscribed May 1939]
32pp, col. maps with description of the country on opposite page & spaces left for cards to be pasted in, stiff pic. covers, cover title, 264x210mm. KP

Picture Stamp Album
6002 NESTLÉ'S/PICTURE STAMP ALBUM/When/ How/Why /[9 lines text]
Nestlé and Anglo-Swiss Condensed Milk Co. (Australasia) Ltd, Sydney, n.d.
24pp (with loose sheet of instructions to collectors inserted), information relating to the 144 cards to be collected & pasted in the book in spaces provided, col. pic. wrappers, 258x208mm. KP

Pictures of Australian Birds
See Calvert, W.

'PIERS' [pseud. Senior, Margaret]
See Bracken, Anne & 'Piers'

PIGGOTT, Juliet
6003 THE STORY OF JAPAN/Julie Piggott/illustrated by Wolfgang Grässe/Angus and Robertson
Sydney 1971
96pp (inc. 1p index), 12 f/p col. illus., smaller col. & b/w illus. in text, laminated pic. bd., 215x275mm. KMM

PIKE, Douglas
JOHN McDOUALL STUART. *See* Australian Explorers
CHARLES HAWKER. *See* Great Australians

PIKE, Geoff
6004 AROUND THE WORLD/WITH/UNBEARABLE BEAR/This little book is based on Australia's/first Television Cartoon Series/"Unbearable Bear/in/T.V. Tours"/[drawing]/Created and Written/by Geoff Pike/ For Artransa Park/Television Pty Ltd.,/Sydney, Australia./Adapted by/Laurie/Sharpe/Copyright 1964 by Artransa Park Television Pty Ltd. All rights reserved throughout the world. Printed/and published by Sungravure Pty Limited...etc. [2 lines]
23pp, col. illus. throughout, bd., 195x155mm. Grant
Advertisement inside back cover for 'Unbearable Bear in T.V. Tours' lists 13 titles.

6005 UNBEARABLE BEAR/IN/BOY MEETS BEAR
Artransa Park Television Pty Ltd, Sydney 1964
Uniform with *Around the World with Unbearable Bear.*
Grant

6006 AROUND THE WORLD/WITH/UNBEARABLE BEAR...etc.
Artransa Park Television Pty Ltd, Rosebery, NSW, 1964
[24]pp, col. illus. throughout, pic. bd., 195x155mm. KMM
Cover title: 'UNBEARABLE BEAR/in/LONDON/ Another T.V. Tours Book'.

6007 UNBEARABLE BEAR/IN/SCOTLAND/Another T.V. Tours Book
Artransa Park Television Pty Ltd, Rosebery, NSW, 1964
[24]pp, col. illus. throughout, pic. bd., cover title, 200x160mm. KMM
25 titles in series listed on back cover.

PINKERTON, John
Cassell's National Library/EARLY/AUSTRALIAN VOYAGES/
Cassell & Co., 1886
Abridged from Pinkerton's 'General Collection of Voyages and Travels'. Although this small booklet at first seems from its size (140x95mm) to have been intended for children it is in fact meant for the general reader. KMM

PIRANI, Leila
6008 Imperial Edition No. 380/OLD Mr SUNDOWN/IN FAIRYLAND/Children's Cantata/Words by/Leila Pirani/Music by/Mirrie Hill/Copyright/Allan & Co.,/Proprietary Limited/Melbourne, Sydney, Adelaide, Bendigo
1935
32pp (last page blank), pic. wrappers, 250x175mm. MAC
Music & words of 15 songs. The unsigned cover (printed in sepia) depicting a reclining tramp surrounded by fairies appears to be by Ida Rentoul Outhwaite though there are no initials.
Various reprints, some with adv. on last page & back cover, some with price (e.g. 3/-) on front cover. KP

6009 Imperial Edition No. 409/PLAY DAY IN/HAPPY HOLLAND/A Juvenile Operetta/(Duration: About 45 minutes)/Verses and Dialogue by/Leila Pirani/Music by/Ethel Harrhy/[list of musical contents, songs &c.] Copyright Price 2/6 net/Allan & Co. Prop. Ltd./ Melbourne Sydney Adelaide Bendigo
n.d. [copyright 1937]
30pp, pic. wrappers (with story of operetta on verso & adv. on both sides of back cover), cover title, 255x180mm. Grant

6010 Imperial Edition No. 416/COWBOYS AND INDIANS/or/The Story of Grey Eagle and The Palefaces./A Juvenile Operetta/(Duration; About 45 minutes)/Words by/Leila Pirani/Music by/Alfred Wheeler/Allan & Co. Pty Ltd./Melbourne, Sydney, Adelaide, Bendigo.
1937

28pp (inc. 3pp story, cast &c), pic. wrappers, 250x175mm. Grant
Illus. on wrapper signed 'Fildes'.

6011 I/MET/THEM/IN/CHINA/by Leila Pirani/ Illustrated by Ruth Shackel/Robertson/& Mullens/ Melbourne
n.d. [1944]
32pp, part-col. illus. throughout, wrappers, 290x180mm. KMM
Verses.

6012 A Saga of the River Murray/THE/OLD/MAN/ RIVER/OF AUSTRALIA/by/Leila Pirani/Illustrated by/Walter Cunningham/Copyright 1945/John Sands Pty. Ltd., Publishers/Sydney and Melbourne
39pp (inc. 1p foreword by L. R. East, Commissioner, River Murray Commission), map frontis., marginal drawings & tailpieces throughout, bd., 240x180mm. CLRC

6013 A Saga of the River Murray/THE/OLD/MAN/ RIVER/OF AUSTRALIA/By/Leila Pirani/Illustrated by/Walter Cunningham/John Sands Pty. Ltd., Publishers/Sydney Melbourne Brisbane Adelaide Perth Hobart
Second edition [1955], details as in first edition. NSL:M

6014 LAZY THE PIG/AND HIS CHINESE ADVENTURES/By Leila Pirani/Drawings by/Joyce Janes/[drawing]
Ramsay Ware Publishing Co., Melbourne, n.d. [1945]
32pp, part-col. drawings throughout, stiff wrappers, 240x180mm. ANL

6015 LITTLE HANS/OF HOLLAND/by/Leila Pirani
Ramsay Ware Publishing Coy, Melbourne, n.d. [1945]
32pp, part-col. drawings throughout, stiff dec. wrappers, 240x180mm. ANL

6016 THE PRINCESS OF THE/WATER-LILIES/by/Leila Pirani/Illustrated by/Betty & Esther/Paterson
H. I. McKechnie, Melbourne, n.d. [1946]
30pp, col. frontis. & 6 col. illus., bd., cover title, 240x180mm. ANL

6017 DANDELION/DICK/and other stories/by/Leila Pirani/Drawings by/Joyce Janes/A Ramsay Ware Production
Melbourne, n.d. [195-?]
[16]pp, line drawings, alternate pages printed in blue & black with the illus. on the recto printed on either a blue or yellow background, pic. wrappers, cover title, 270x215mm. KMM

PIRANI, Leila & DAVIES, Norman

6018 MRS./HEN/COUNTS/HER/CHICKENS/ [drawing]/Angus and Robertson/Sydney, London/ 1949
30pp, col. illus. t.p., 11 f/p col. illus., dec. wrappers, 235x175mm. ANL

The Pirate Penguin

6019 THE/PIRATE PENGUIN
Young World Productions, London, 1972
20pp, col. illus. throughout, pic. bd., cover title, 190x157mm. KP

[PITMAN, Arthur]

6020 CHIPPY CHICKS
6021 DELIGHTFUL DUCKLINGS
6022 FRISKY PUPPIES
6023 PALLY PIGGIES
Uniform picture books published by Offset Printing Co. Pty Ltd, Sydney, n.d. [1948?]
8pp, col. illus. throughout, dec. wrappers, cover title, 275x215mm. ANL

6024 FRISKY PUPPIES/AND/DELIGHTFUL DUCKLINGS/Series B44
OPC Distributors, Sydney, n.d. [1948]
32pp, col. illus. throughout, col. pic. bd., dec. e/p, 270x215mm
Combines 2 of above paperback books. KP
Another copy as above, but
'Playtime series', Australian Universities Press, n.p., 1971. KP

6025 PALLY PIGGIES/AND/CHIPPY CHICKS
Offset Printing Coy, Sydney, n.d. [1948]
32pp, col. pic. throughout, col. pic. bd., dec. e/p, 270x215mm. KP
'Series B43' on front cover. Combines 2 of above paperback books .

6026 PLAYFUL PUSSIES/Series E249
Printed in Australia for OPC Distributors Pty Ltd., n.d. [1948]
8pp (i.e. 4 sheets of board with illus. each side & attached on a spirax spine), 264x212mm. KP

PITMAN, Mrs Emma Raymond

6027 "The Woman of all Lands for Jesus"/HEROINES/ OF THE MISSION FIELD./Biographical Sketches/of/ female missionaries who have laboured in various/ lands among the heathen/By/Mrs Emma Raymond Pitman,/Authoress of "Vestina's Martyrdom" "Profit and Loss" "Margaret Mervyn's/Cross"/London Missionary Society's Edition./—/Cassell, Petter Galpin & Co./London, Paris & New York
vipp, 278pp, 16pp adv., engraved frontis. & engravings in text throughout, dec. clo. with pic. onlay, 180x120mm. ANL
Includes 'Mrs Mary Williams of the South Seas' pp121–39, 'Mrs Mary Ellis of the South Seas pp160–74, 'Mary James Chalmers of Rarotonga and New Guinea' pp186–97.

6028 FLORENCE GODFREY'S FAITH/A Story of Australian Life/By/Emma Raymond Pitman/Author of "Garnered Sheaves," "My Governess Life," "Life's Daily Ministry," &c./With four illustrations by Paul Hardy/New Edition /[device]/London/Blackie & Son, Limited, 50 Old Bailey, E.C./Glasgow and Dublin/ 1898 [first pub. 1882]
309pp & 32pp adv., b/w frontis. & 3 f/p illus., dec. clo., 180x120mm. CLRC
The story of the emigration to Australia of a family in the 1860s after the collapse of some of the Manchester cotton mills. The advertisements are all for books for boys & girls.

6029 FLORENCE GODREY'S FAITH/A Story of Australian Life/By/Emma Raymond Pitman/Author of "Garnered Sheaves", "Life's Daily Ministry"/"My Governess Life", &c./With illustrations by Paul Hardy/ Blackie & Son Limited/London Glasgow Dublin Bombay
n.d. [prize 1909]
309pp, 16pp adv., col. frontis. & 3 f/p b/w illus., dec. clo., 185x125mm. KMM
Copies with variant col. clo. bindings with prize labels 1912, 1916. KP
Author of *One of the Last, and Ray Elliot's Deliverer* a book of 2 long stories, the last with an Australian setting but not intended for children. NSL:M

PITTS, Herbert

6030 CHILDREN OF/WILD AUSTRALIA/By/Herbert Pitts/Author of/"The Australian Aboriginal and the

Christian Church"/with eight coloured illustrations/ Edinburgh and London/Oliphant, Anderson & Ferrier n.d. [1914?]
90pp (inc. 2pp author's introduction), 4pp adv., col. frontis. & 7 f/p col. illus. signed 'W. H.', clo. (with col. illus. reproduced on front cover), 190x125mm. KMM
Factual book with mission background.

6031 Another copy as above, but /[device]/Fleming H. Revell Company/New York Chicago Toronto
n.d.
Details as above. KP
Another variant copy having an additional 16pp of publisher's adv. & lettering on spine blocked in gilt. KP

PIZZEY, Graham

LYREBIRDS. *See* Life in Australia

PLACE, Marion

6032 GOLD/DOWN/UNDER/The Story of the/ Australian Gold Rush/Marion T. Place/Crowell-Collier Press/Collier-Macmillan Limited, London
1969
169pp (inc. 2pp bibliography, 3pp index), b/w frontis. & b/w reproductions of contemporary drawings, etc., pic. clo., 210x140mm. World in the Making Series. ANL

Planes Ships and Trains

6033 PLANES/SHIPS/and/TRAINS
Photogravures Pty Ltd, Melbourne, n.d. [inscribed 1944]
12pp, photographs in part col. with caption, stiff pic. wrappers, 300x245mm. KP
Includes photograph of 'Australia's Pride', 'The Spirit of Progress'.

Playful Pets

6034 PLAYFUL PETS
Offset Publishing Co., Sydney, n.d. [1947]
16pp, 8 f/p col. illus. & b/w illus. throughout, dec. wrappers, cover title, 205x260mm. ANL

Playful Pussies

6035 PLAYFUL PUSSIES
Offset (O.P.C. Distributors), Sydney, n.d. [1950]
8pp, col. illus. throughout, printed on bd., cover title, 270x210mm. NSL:M
Brief rhyming text.

Playtime/ABC

E. C. Harry, Melbourne
Not Australian. Published by Dean & Son, London. ANL

PLUCK AND LUCK Series

Format example:

6036 Pluck and Luck/Complete Stories of Adventure/ Issued Weekly—By Subscription $2.50 per year. Entered as Second Class Matter at the New York Post Office, November 7, 1898 by Frank Tousey/No. 162 New York, July 10 1901. Price 5 cents./THE LAND OF GOLD;/or/Yankee Jack's Adventures in early Australia./By Rich'd R. Montgomery./[col. illus./ caption]
32pp (inc. 2pp adv. & adv. outside back cover), unillus., col. pic. wrappers, cover title, 285x205mm. CLRC
Other titles in series as above:

6037 No. 63 LOST AT THE SOUTH POLE by Capt. Thos. H. Wilson. Unseen

6038 DOUBLE QUICK THE KING HARPOONER, by Capt. Thos. H. Wilson, 1898. Unseen

6039 No. 226 JACK WRIGHT AND HIS PRAIRIE ENGINE! or, Among the Bushmen of Australia, 1902 by 'Noname'. CLRC

6040
• Rpt 1918 by Harry E. Wolff, New York, Pluck & Luck No. 1027, 31pp (inc. 2pp adv. & 10pp extraneous material). RM
See also Aldine Romances for English ed.

The Pocket Navigator

6041 THE/ POCKET NAVIGATOR,/consisting of/A collection/of the most/Select Voyages/vol. III/ Containing the Voyages, etc./of/Commodore Anson./ Biron's [*sic*] Narrative/Captain Wallis. /Captain Carteret./Captain Wilson/Governor Phillip/ London:/Printed by T. Maiden, Sherbourn—Lane,/For Ann Lemoine, White Rose Court, Coleman Street,/And J. Roe, No. 90, Houndsditch./Sold by all the Booksellers in/The United Kingdom.
n.d.[1808?]
Consists of 5 chapbooks with sep. pagination bound together with engraved frontis. & pic. t.p., clo., 150x92mm. CLRC
The fifth chapbook as follows:
THE/VOYAGE/OF/GOVERNOR PHILLIP/TO/ BOTANY BAY;/with an/Account /of its/Origin and Present State./London:/Printed by T. Maiden, Sherbourn—Lane,/For Ann Lemoine, White Rose Court, Coleman Street,/And J. Roe, No. 90, Houndsditch./Sold by all the Booksellers in/The United Kingdom
58pp; the Voyage being 29pp. and the Account of Botany Bay being the second part.
Vol. 4 of this series consists of The Voyages of Captain James Cook round the World.
As the Voyage seems based on Mavor's Account it was presumably intended for children; also published separately, *see* Phillip, Arthur.

POIGNANT, Axel

6042 PICCANINNY/WALKABOUT/A Story of Two Aboriginal Children/By/Axel Poignant/Angus and Robertson/Sydney London Melbourne Wellington
First published 1957
49pp, 1p acknowledgements, 1p author's note, 5pp author's preface, b/w photographs throughout, clo., 245x185mm. KMM
Winner CBCA Picture Book award 1958
• Rpt June 1958, Sept. 1958. KP

6043 PICCANINNY/WALKABOUT/A Story of Two Aboriginal Children/By/Axel Poignant/Angus and Robertson [Sydney]
First pub. 1957; rpt June 1958; September 1958; July 1959, as above. KMM
• Rpt 1961, 1963, 1964, 1968. KP

6044 BUSH WALKABOUT/Axel Poignant/Angus & Robertson
Formerly published as *Piccaninny Walkabout,* first published 1957, rpt 1958 (twice), 1959, 1961, 1963, 1964, 1965; this edition published Sydney 1972
[64]pp (inc. 3pp introduction), b/w photographic illus. throughout, clo., map e/p, 255x235mm. CLRC

POIGNANT, Axel & Roslyn

6045 KALEKU/Axel & Roslyn Poignant/Angus and/ Robertson/[coloured illustration]
Sydney 1972
[48]pp (inc. 1p acknowledgements), col. & b/w photographic illus. on alternate page openings, clo., map e/p, 255x240mm. KMM
Story set in the Chimbu district of the New Guinea Highlands.

POLLARD, Jack (ed.)

6046 CRICKET/THE AUSTRALIAN WAY/edited by/Jack Pollard/[publisher's device]/Lansdowne Press/Melbourne
1st ed. June 1961; 2nd ed. Jan. 1962; 2nd imp. Nov. 1962
127pp (inc. 1p acknowledgements & 3pp foreword by Sir Donald Bradman), b/w photographic frontis. & b/w photographic illus. throughout, clo., 230x180mm. CLRC
Contributions by various well-known Australian cricketers, &c.

6047 edited by/Jack Pollard/CRICKET THE AUSTRALIAN WAY/Lansdowne/Press/Melbourne/[photograph]
First published 1961, rpt 1962 (twice); revised & enlarged edition 1968, rpt 1970, 1971, 1972
197pp, 1p acknowledgements, 2pp foreword by Sir Donald Bradman, 1p introduction, b/w photographic illus. throughout, clo., 285x205mm. BBC

6048 THIS IS/RUGBY LEAGUE/edited by/Jack Pollard/[device]/Lansdowne Press/Melbourne
1962
126pp (inc. 1p acknowledgements, 1p foreword by H.R.H. The Duke of Edinburgh & 1p introduction by W. C. Buckley, Chairman, Australian Rugby League Board of Control), b/w photographic frontis. & b/w photographic illus. throughout, clo., 230x180mm. CLRC
Contains contributions by various international players.

6049 LAWN TENNIS/THE AUSTRALIAN WAY/edited by/Jack Pollard/Drawings by Will Mahony/With special photographs on how each stroke is played by world famous tennis/"twins" Lew Hoad and Ken Rosewall/Lansdowne Press/Melbourne
First published September 1963
143pp (inc. 1p foreword by Sir Norman Brookes), b/w photographic frontis. & b/w photographic illus. throughout, clo., 235x180mm. BBC
Contributions by various well-known experts on the game, but not intended chiefly as a children's book.

6050 SWIMMING/Australian Style/edited by/Jack Pollard/[device]/Lansdowne Press/Melbourne
1963
142pp (inc. 1p acknowledgements & 2pp foreword by Mr Justice Herron, President, NSW Swimming Union), b/w photographic frontis. & b/w photographic illus. throughout, clo., 230x180mm. CLRC

6051 THE AUSTRALIAN/SURFRIDER/Compiled by/Jack Pollard/Murray: Sydney
K. G. Murray Publishing Co., 1st imp. 1963; 2nd imp. 1963
144pp (inc. 1p foreword by Duke Kahanamoku), b/w photographic frontis. & b/w photographs throughout, clo., 245x175mm. BBC
Contributions on the sport by various experts, & not intended as a children's book.

6052 HIGH MARK/The Complete Book on Australian Football/Edited By/Jack Pollard/Murray: Sydney & Melbourne
n.d.
160pp, b/w photographic illus., clo., 244x180mm. KP

POLLARD, James Theodore Harvey

6053 NATURE'S STORY BOOK/Nature Stories at School/in Town and in Bushland./A Reader for Classes III & IV/By James Pollard/With a Foreword by/Mr. E. A. Coleman/Senior Inspector of Schools in the/Education Department of Western Australia/Illustrated by Mr. R. Heywood/Publishers/E. B. Bayliss Print/13 Pier St., Perth/Western Australia
1936
109pp (inc. 1p foreword &c.), 3 f/p b/w illus., clo., 205x135mm. ANL

6054 OFO/MATE OF THE RIVERSIDE/By/James Pollard/[drawing]/Copyrighted by the Author/Printed and Published by/Patersons Printing Press Ltd./65 Murray Street, Perth/Price 4/-
n.d. [1944]
24pp, 6 col. illus. & b/w drawings in text, dec. bd., 245x175mm. VSL
• Rpt 1947 as above. KMM

6055 CHENO—A/TALE OF THE BLACK SWAN/[drawing]/By James Pollard/Illustrated by John Lunghi/Printed and Published by/Patersons Printing Press Ltd./65 Murray Street, Perth W.A.
n.d. [1945]
59pp, 7 col. illus. & b/w drawings, bd., 240x180mm. ANL

6056 THE/CHRISTMAS STORY/by James Pollard/Paterson Brokensha Pty. Ltd./Printers and Publishers—65 Murray Street, Perth, W.A.
n.d. [1953]
12pp, unillus., dec. wrappers, 240x180mm. KMM

6057 ON TIMELESS WINGS/Tales and Legends of Bible Birds/by/James Pollard/Paterson Brokensha Pty. Ltd./65 Murray Street—Perth Western Australia
n.d. [1959]
116pp, b/w frontis. only, clo., 215x135mm. ANL
Some verses included in text.
Also published with pic. wrappers. Author of *The Bushland Man* (Hodder & Stoughton, London 1926), which is not a children's book.

POLLOCK, James Martin

6058 THE/ADVENTURES OF JOSEPH/by/James Martin Pollock/Newnes: London
Copyright 1936
[75]pp, col. frontis., 5 col. illus. & 1 col. double-spread, 14 sepia & white f/p illus., book printed throughout in brown, col. illus., litho., green, red & black bd. with frontis. reproduced in col. on front cover, 278x210mm. VSL
Story about a koala.

"POLLYANNA"

6059 VERSES TO BLESS/Proverbs and Precepts/[drawing]/Copyright reserved/1958/by "Pollyanna"/(Jess)
Melbourne
23pp, unillus., wrappers, 204x125mm. KP

Pompy the Panda

6060 POMPY/THE PANDA
John Morrisey, Melbourne, n.d. [195-?]
12pp, col. & b/w illus. on alternate page openings, pic. wrappers, cover title, 240x180mm
A 'Little Treasure Book', illus. John Morrisey. KP

Popular Film Stars

6061 Album of/POPULAR FILM STARS/This album contains spaces for the series of 50 "Popular Film Stars" cards.[8 lines]
Vita-brits, n.p., n.d.
12pp, b/w photographs & pen-sketches of film stars & spaces for cards to be pasted in, col. pic. wrappers, 210x275mm. KP

PORNETT, Muriel

6062 MIA MIA MITES/Drawn for and told to/"Lyttlee"

"Pattypan" and "Doddie"/By/Muriel Pornett/Melville and Mullen Pty. Ltd./Melbourne
n.d. [1919]
16pp, 7 f/p col. illus. & b/w drawings, dec. bd., 255x190mm. NSL:M

PORTEOUS, Richard Sydney [pseud. 'Standby']

6063 TAMBAI ISLAND/By/R. S. Porteous/Angus and Robertson/Sydney London Melbourne Wellington
1955
178pp, b/w frontis. & b/w drawings in text, clo., 205x130mm. ANL

6064 THE TAMBAI/TREASURE/By/R. S. Porteous/ Illustrated by/Wal Stackpool/Angus and Robertson/ Sydney London Melbourne Wellington
1958
169pp, b/w frontis. & b/w drawings in text, clo., 195x120mm. KMM
Sequel to *Tambai Island.*

6065 THE /SILENT ISLES/R. S. Porteous/Illustrated by/Wal Stackpool/[drawing]/Angus and Robertson Sydney 1963
160pp, b/w drawings in text, clo., 215x135mm. KMM

PORTER, Eric

6066 [drawing]/WILLIE WOMBAT/IN/WASTE NOT WANT NOT/Featuring All Australian Animals/ Illustrated and Prepared by/Eric Porter/All rights reserved
Publicity Press, Sydney, n.d. [1937?]
24pp, b/w & part. col. illus. throughout, pic. wrappers, 280x220mm. ANL

6067 The All-Australian Novelty Song Success!/"I'M WILLIE THE WOMBAT"/Foxtrot/by/Lance Warlinson/[col. illus.]/The theme song from Australia's first/All-coloured animated cartoon/"Waste not—want not"/from Eric Porter Studios/Copyright Nicholson's Pty Ltd/
416–418 George Street, Sydney 2/- Net
1939
6pp (inc. covers), pic. wrappers, 310x236mm. MAC

6068 ABC
6069 THE BIRDS AT HOME
6070 THE CONTENTED BEARS
6071 DINKY-DI & KOALA
Uniform booklets published by Frank Johnson, Sydney
1943
16pp [*ABC:* 12pp], col. illus. throughout, dec. wrappers, cover title, 240x180mm. [*ABC:* 280x220mm]. NSL:M

6072 THE/GIPSY/STORY/by/Eric Porter
Frank Johnson, Sydney, n.d. [1944]
12pp, b/w illus. throughout, dec. wrappers, cover title, 280x210mm. NSL:M

6073 THE/TREASURE/CHEST/Eric Porter [drawing]
Frank Johnson, Sydney, n.d. [1944]
Details as above, part-col. cover illus. NSL:M

6074 SANTA/CLAUS/By/Eric Porter
Frank Johnson, Sydney, n.d. [1945]
32pp, 14pp col. illus., pic. wrappers, cover title, 240x185mm. ANL

6075 THE/COWARDLY/FAWN/Eric Porter
Frank Johnson, Sydney, n.d. [1946]
16pp, col. illus. throughout, pic. wrappers, cover title, 240x185mm. ANL

PORTER, J. A. [pseud. 'Spinifex']

6076 Pioneer Library/ROLL THE/SUMMERS BACK/J. A. Porter/The Jacaranda Press
First published Brisbane 1961, rpt 1969
250pp, b/w drawings in text, clo., 210x130mm. BBC
Outback reminiscences of an old pioneer, including his experiences with the Bushmen's Contingent in South Africa during the Boer War, not expressly written for children. Author wrote for the *Bulletin* under the pseudonym 'Spinifex'.

[PORTER, Sarah Ricardo]

6077 ALFRED DUDLEY,/or/The Australian Settlers/ [verse]/London/Printed for Harvey and Darton./ Gracechurch Street./MDCCCXXX
vii+193pp (inc. 1p glossary), engraved frontis, & 3 f/p engraved illus. (each illus. comprising 2 vignettes within a dec. border), clo. with gilt title on spine, 180x100mm. HBM

6078 ALFRED DUDLEY,/or,/The Australian Settlers./ [verse]/Second Edition/London./Harvey and Darton, Gracechurch Street.
iv+196pp (inc. 2pp glossary) & 24pp advs, engraved frontis.(not in first edition), 8 f.p. engravings, morocco embossed with gilt, 132 x104mm. CLRC
The engravings are the same as in the first edition, though printed on separate pages with no border. Ferguson quotes only 3 plates for the first edition though there are four.

6079 ALFRED DUDLEY, Second Edition, variant issue
t.p. as before, but with illus. opp. p29 in original second edition here used as frontis. & 6 other b/w illus. (probably one missing in this copy).
iv+196pp+16pp adv., blind-stamped clo., 135x107mm. KMM
The adv. are dated October 1859 & consist of 'a catalogue of instructive & amusing works for the young, including those formerly published by Clarke & Co. (late Darton & Harvey). This catalogue is produced by Arthur Hall, Virtue & Co., 25 Paternoster Row'. This appears to be Ferguson's re-issue (3342 and note, IV p662)

Possum Bother

6080 POSSUM/BOTHER/[device]/Produced and Published by/E. W. Kaye/Sydney/Printed by/ Hollander & Govett Pty. Limited/Sydney
n.d.
16pp, part-col. illus. throughout, dec. wrappers, 240x180mm. KMM
Verse.

POTTER, Dora Joan

6081 WITH WENDY/AT/WINTERTON SCHOOL/By/ Dora Joan Potter/Oxford University Press/Leighton House, Melbourne/London: Humphrey Milford
1945
128pp, unillus., bd., 180x120mm. CLRC

6082 WITH WENDY/AT/WINTERTON SCHOOL/By/ Dora Joan Potter/Geoffrey Cumberlege/Oxford University Press/Melbourne Wellington
First published 1945; rpt 1947, 1948, 1949, 1950
128pp, unillus., bd., 180x120mm. CLRC

6083 PAM/PAYS HER DEBT/By/Dora Joan Potter/ Oxford University Press/Leighton House, Melbourne/ London Humphrey Milford
1945
135pp, unillus., bd., 180x120mm. KMM

6084 THOSE/SUMMER HOLIDAYS/By/Dora Joan Potter/Geoffrey Cumberlege/Oxford University Press/ Leighton House Melbourne
1946
156pp, unillus., bd., 185x120mm. KMM
• Rpt 1947. KMM

6085 MARGARET'S/DECISION/By/Dora Joan Potter/Geoffrey Cumberlege/Oxford University Press/Leighton House Melbourne
1947
149pp, unillus., bd., 185x120mm. KMM

6086 WENDY/MOVES UP/Dora Joan Potter/Geoffrey Cumberlege/Oxford University Press/Melbourne Wellington
1947
189pp, unillus., bd., 185x120mm. BBC
• Rpt 1949. KMM

6087 WENDY/MOVES UP/By/Dora Joan Potter/Geoffrey Cumberlege/Oxford University Press/Leighton House Melbourne
• Rpt 1949, 1950
Details as in 1st edition. KMM

6088 WENDY IN CHARGE/By/Dora Joan Potter/Geoffrey Cumberlege/Oxford University Press/Leighton House Melbourne
First published 1947, rpt 1949
189pp, unillus., bd., 180x115mm. KMM

6089 ALTHEA'S TERM/AT WINTERTON/By/Dora Joan Potter/Geoffrey Cumberlege/Oxford University Press/Leighton House Melbourne
1948 [Annual Catalogue of Australian Publications gives publication date as 1948, i.e. 1949]
152pp, unillus., bd., 180x120mm. KMM

6090 WINTERTON/HOLIDAY CRUISE/By/Dora Joan Potter/Geoffrey Cumberlege/Oxford University Press/Leighton House Melbourne
1949
128pp, unillus., bd., 185x120mm. KMM

6091 HELEN'S/INHERITANCE/Dora Joan Potter/Geoffrey Cumberlege/Oxford University Press/Melbourne Wellington
First published 1950
109pp, unillus., bd., 185x120mm. KMM

6092 A NEW GIRL/FOR WINTERTON/By/Dora Joan Potter/Geoffrey Cumberlege/Oxford University Press/Melbourne Wellington
1950
122pp, unillus., bd., 185x120mm. KMM

POWELL, Elizabeth [Mrs Sandery]

6093 THE BEEHIVE/By/Elizabeth Powell/("Kirkcaldy")/with 9 illustrations by the Author/Australia/Cornstalk Publishing Company/89 Castlereagh Street, Sydney/1928
338pp, b/w frontis. & 8 f/p b/w illus., clo., dec. e/p, 180x120mm. KMM
• Rpt as above
On verso of t.p.: 'First Australian edition October 1928, 2000 copies; second Australian edition December 1928, 2000 copies'
Details as in previous entry. Grant

6094 THE BEEHIVE/By/Elizabeth Powell/("Patricia Ann") Angus and Robertson/Sydney: London/1947
287pp, b/w frontis. only, clo., 185x120mm. KMM

6095 MR. JIGSAW/Elizabeth Powell/Author of The Beehive/[coloured drawing]/Australia/Cornstalk Publishing Company/89 Castlereagh Street Sydney/1928
24pp, col. illus. throughout by author, dec. bd., dec. e/p, 185x145mm. ANL

6096 SUNSET HILL/By/Elizabeth Powell/Author of The Beehive/Australia:/Cornstalk Publishing Company/89 Castlereagh Street, Sydney/1929
350pp, unillus., clo., dec. e/p signed 'E.P.', 180x115mm. CLRC

6097 THE OLD/BROWN HOUSE/By/Elizabeth Powell/Angus and Robertson Ltd./Sydney: London/1942
243pp, unillus., clo., 180x120mm. KMM
• Rpt 1946, as above.
• Rpt 1948, as above. Both KMM

POWELL, Gordon

6098 Gordon Powell/THE SECRET/OF BETHLEHEM/Illustrated by George Browning/London: Peter Davies
1963
31pp, part-col. frontis., 10 f/p part-col. illus., pic. bd., 165x130mm. CLRC

POWELL, Leslie Cameron

6099 TURI/THE STORY OF/A LITTLE BOY/Lesley/Cameron/Powell/Pictures by Pius Blank/Angus and Robertson
Sydney 1964
56pp (inc. 1p glossary), extended illus. t.p., b/w photographic illus. throughout, pic. clo., 245x150mm. BBC
The story of a Maori boy. Not known if author is Australian.

POWER, M. Danvers

6100 LITTLE BROTHERS/By/M. Danvers Power
The Beacon Press, Sydney, 1931
Ed. limited to 150 copies
61pp, printed on sections of different col. paper, drawings in text, bd., 225x150mm. NSL:M
Natural history stories.

POWER, M. F.

6101 LITTLE/BROTHERS/written and illustrated by/M. F. Power/Korman Press Sydney
n.d.
48pp, wrappers, cover title, 185x120mm. Grant
Contents include 9 nature stories, each preceded by a b/w sketch of an insect. The book is dedicated to the Wolf Clubs of the world.

POWER, Phyllis Mary [née Clarke]

TWO STORIES/By/Phyllis M. Clarke/of Rupertswood/Melbourne:/McCarron, Bird & Co., 479 Collins Street/1906
Not a children's book. NSL:M

6102 THE TALE OF/BILLY FLEA'S EXPERIENCES/By/Phyllis M. Clarke/Illustrated by/Beatrice A. Robertson/Melbourne/Melville & Mullen Propty. Ltd./262 Collins Street/1912/(All rights reserved)
79pp, col. frontis. & 17 f/p col. illus., bd. (with small medallion of one col. illus. pasted on front cover), marbled e/p, 140x105mm. VSL
Produced in a very similar format to the Beatrix Potter books.

6103 FIVE STORIES/FOR/MARGRETTE ANNE/By/Phyllis M. Power, Proceeds in aid of Children's Hospital Funds/1944/McCarron, Bird & Co./Printers, 479 Collins Street, Melbourne
36pp, unillus., pic. wrappers, 210x135mm. KMM
Coloured drawing on front cover with title: '5/STORIES/FOR/MARGRETTE/ANNE/by/Phyllis M. Power'.

6104 STORIES/FOR/MARGRET[*sic*] ANNE/By/Phyllis M. Power/1945/McCarron, Bird & Co., Printers, 479 Collins Street, Melbourne
36pp, 4 b/w illus., illus. wrappers, 210x135mm. ANL
Published in aid of Children's Hospital.

6105 FAIRY/CHATTER BOOK/by/Phyllis M. Power

The author, 1950. Printed at McKellan Press, Malvern, Victoria
[40]pp, unillus., wrappers, 217x140mm. VSL

6106 SOMETHING/TO READ FOR/TEEN-AGERS/by/Phyllis M. Power
McKellar Press, Malvern, Victoria, n.d. [1951]
64pp, unillus., wrappers, 210x135mm. ANL
Short stories.

6107 Mullens' Stories for Children/No. 403/MICHAEL FLANNIGAN/AND HIS COW/by/Phyllis M. Power/(for ages 10 to 12)/[drawing]/Robertson & Mullens Ltd./Melbourne
1952
94pp, 2 f/p b/w illus. by Marjorie Howden, wrappers, 180x120mm. ANL

6108 Mullens' Stories for Children/No. 402/THE STORY OF A/CARPET BAG/by/Phyllis M. Power/(For Ages 10 to 12)/[drawing]/Robertson & Mullens Ltd./Melbourne
1952
85pp, b/w frontis. & 1 other b/w illus. by Marjorie Howden, pic. wrappers, 180x120mm. VSL

6109 LOST/IN THE OUTBACK/Phyllis M. Power/Illustrated by/Will Nickless/Blackie & Son Limited/London and Glasgow
n.d. [1954]
253pp, b/w frontis. & 3 f/p b/w illus., clo., 185x120mm. KMM

6110 UNDER/AUSTRALIAN/SKIES/by/Phyllis M. Power/Illustrated by Dobson Broadhead, R.I./Blackie & Son Limited/London and Glasgow
1955
206pp, b/w frontis. & 2 f/p b/w illus., clo., 185x120mm. KMM
• Rpt 1956. KP; 1957. TG; 1958. KMM

6111 UNDER/AUSTRALIAN/SKIES/by/Phyllis M. Power/Peal Press
London, n.d. [1964]
206pp, unillus., bd., 185x120mm. Reward Library. CLRC

6112 UNDER/AUSTRALIAN/SKIES/by/Phyllis M. Power/[device]/Abbey Rewards/Cresta House, London
n.d.
[198]pp, unillus., pic. bd., pic. e/p, 195x124mm. KP
French edition

6113 SEPT FILLES DANS LA BROUSSE, Edition Fleurus, 31 Rue de Fleurus, Paris, n.d.
126pp, translated by D'Alaine Valière, 9 b/w illus. by J. Giraud, hard covers, 17.5cm. Unseen: IFA

6114 ADVENTURE/IN THE OUTBACK/Phyllis M. Power/With Illustrations by/Helen Harvie/London: J. M. Dent & Sons Ltd.
1957
157pp, b/w frontis. & b/w drawings in text, clo., 195x125mm. CLRC

6115 Phyllis M. Power/LEGENDS FROM/THE OUTBACK/Illustrated by Ida Outhwaite/London: J. M. Dent & Sons Ltd.
1958
127pp, col. frontis. & b/w drawings throughout, clo., 185x135mm. KMM

6116 Phyllis M. Power/LEGENDS FROM/THE OUTBACK/Illustrated by/Ida Outhwaite/[device]/Dent/Pennant Books
London; First published 1958; First published in this edition 1965
127pp, b/w frontis. (repeated on p88) & 2 other f/p b/w illus., b/w drawings in text throughout, clo., 180x120mm. KMM

6117 NURSING/IN THE OUTBACK/Phyllis M. Power/Illustrated by Will Nickless/Blackie/London and Glasgow
1959
190pp, b/w frontis. & 2 f/p b/w illus., clo., 185x115mm. KMM
Sequel to *Lost in the Outback*.
• Rpt 1960. KP

6118 NURSING/IN THE OUTBACK/Phyllis M. Power/Illustrated by Will Nickless/Peal Press
London n.d. [1965]
190pp, b/w frontis. & 2 f/p b/w illus., bd., 185x120mm. KMM

6119 NURSING/IN THE OUTBACK/Phyllis M. Power/Illustrated by Will Nickless/[device]/Abbey Rewards/Cresta House, London
n.d.
[184]pp, 3 f/p b/w illus., pic. bd., pic. e/p, 195x125mm. KMM

6120 THE/SAMMY/STORIES/Being the Adventures/of a Black Doll/By/Phyllis M. Power/Illustrated by/Claire Kelly/London/J. M. Dent & Sons Ltd.
1960
125pp, col. frontis. & b/w drawings throughout, clo., 180x135mm. KMM
Contents include: 'Sammy in England', 'Sammy at Sea', 'Sammy in Australia'.

6121 KANGAROO COUNTRY/Phyllis M. Power/Illustrated by Ian Ribbons/Blackie: London and Glasgow
1961
189pp, 8 b/w drawings, clo., 185x120mm. KMM

6122 Phyllis M. Power/SABOTAGE IN THE/SNOWY MOUNTAINS/with drawings by/Gustav King/London/J. M. Dent & Sons Ltd.
1961
152pp, b/w frontis., 2pp b/w map, chapter headings throughout, clo., 190x120mm. KMM

6123 FROM THE FIG TREE/The Adventures of Two Boys from the/Swan River in Western Australia/One Hundred Years Ago/by/Phyllis M. Power/Pageant Press, Inc. New York
1968
viii, 146pp, unillus., clo., 200x135mm. KP

THE FIGUREHEAD. *See* Gunn & Taylor, no. 92, The Junior Library no. 2

POWIS, Fred

6124 BILLIE/THE/BEETLE/Written & illustrated/by/Fred Powis/Published by/Invincible Press/Sydney Melbourne Brisbane Adelaide
n.d. [copyright 1946]
32pp, dec. t.p., 16 col. illus. & b/w drawings, stiff dec. wrappers, 240x180mm.
On front cover: 'The Story of/the Adventures/of an Australian/Christmas/Beetle'. NSL:M

POWNALL, Eve [Marjorie Evelyn Pownall]

6125 NURSERY RHYMES/TOLD ANEW/By/Eve Pownall/The Author and the Artist are very grateful/to a wise old lady named/Mother Goose,/for without her this book might never/have happened./[drawing]/Registered at G.P.O. Sydney for transmission by post as a book
Wirraway Publishing Company, Sydney, n.d.[1945]

[24]pp, b/w drawings in text, col. pic. wrappers, 245x185mm. KMM
Some illustrations signed 'Powis'.

6126 THE STORY OF A BABY/[drawing]/by Eve Pownall/Illustrated by Dorothea Johnston/Published by/The F. H. Johnston Publishing Co. Pty. Limited/34 Jamieson Street, Sydney/Not registered in Australia for transmission through the Post as a book [*sic*]
n.d. [copyright 1948]
26pp, 1p verses, col. illus. throughout, dec. bd., 240x180mm. NSL:M
Album with slight text & spaces to be filled in by owner.

6127 SQUIK THE SQUIRREL POSSUM, first edition 1949, unseen

6128 SQUIK/THE SQUIRREL POSSUM/by Eve Pownall/Pictured by Raymond Johnson
John Sands Pty Ltd, Sydney, n.d. [1955]
64pp, col. illus. on alternate pages, dec. bd., 120x145mm. KMM

6129 COUSINS-COME-LATELY/Adventures in Old Sydney Town/by/Eve Pownall/Illustrated by/Margaret Senior/Sydney/Shakespeare Head Press/
1952
102pp, b/w drawings throughout, dec. bd., dec. map e/p, 245x185mm. KMM

6130 COUSINS-COME-LATELY/Adventures in Old Sydney Town/by/Eve Pownall/Illustrated by/Margaret Senior/1955/Shakespeare Head Press/Sydney
127pp, 9 b/w drawings in text, dec. bd., 185x125mm. KMM
Another copy as above but bound in limp clo. (school reader),180x120mm. KMM

6131 [Coat of arms]/THE AUSTRALIA BOOK/Written by Eve Pownall/Illustrated by Margaret Senior/Printed & Published by The House of John Sands
Sydney, n.d. [1952]
46pp, dec. col. t.p., col. illus. throughout, dec. bd., dec. e/p, 345x240mm. KMM
Winner of CBCA award 1952
Third ed. as above, n.d. KP
Another copy as above, but fourth edition, n.d. Publisher's blurb states that the book was edited by Maurice Cadsky, & that 'It has already been published in Great Britain and is now in its fourth and revised Australian edition'. BBC

6132 Fifth ed., Sydney, n.d. [after 1961 as Larry the Seagull listed on flap of d/w, after 1964 as Russ the Tree Kangaroo listed on flap of d/w]
46pp, col. illus. throughout, col. pic. bd., 298x220mm. KP
Retail price 22/6. This ed. as well as smaller is printed in much stronger col. on white instead of cream paper & has a glossy dustjacket & glossy paper bd. KP
Another copy as above but un-numbered & undated, printed on pebble-grained white paper. KP

6133 FIVE BUSY/MERRY-MAKERS/Written by/Eve Pownall/Illustrated by/Bill Layne/[coloured drawing]/John Sands Pty. Ltd./Sydney, Melbourne, Brisbane, Adelaide, Perth, Hobart
n.d. [1953]
23pp, 7 col. illus. & b/w drawings in text, dec. bd., 240x240mm. ANL

6134 BINTY/THE BANDICOOT/Written by Eve Pownall/Pictures by Bob Booth/[drawing]/Published by John Sands Pty. Ltd./Sydney, Melbourne, Brisbane, Adelaide, Perth, Hobart
n.d. [1957]
60pp, col. illus. throughout, dec. bd., 115x135mm. KMM
Pre-school & kindergarten series.

6135 Methuen's [publisher's device] Outlines/EXPLORING/AUSTRALIA/By/Eve Pownall/illustrated by/Noela Young/Methuen & Co. Ltd./36 Essex Street, Strand, London, W.C.2.
1958
74pp, 3pp index, 2pp bibliography, b/w dec. map frontis., maps & b/w drawings in text, clo., 210x170mm. KMM

6136 Methuen's [publisher's device] Outlines/EXPLORING/AUSTRALIA/by/Eve Pownall/Illustrated by/Noela Young/Methuen & Co. Ltd./11 New Fetter Lane London E.C.4.
First published May 1958; rpt with minor corrections 1959, rpt twice [*sic*] rpt 1966
74pp, 3pp index, 2pp bibliography, dec. map frontis., maps & b/w drawings in text, pic. bd., 205x165mm. KMM

6137 EXPLORING/AUSTRALIA/Eve Pownall/Illustrated by/Noela Young/Lond: Methuen & Co Ltd/New York: Roy Publishers Inc
1970
74pp, b/w maps & drawings in text, pic. bd., 210x166mm. KP

6138 THEY LIVE/IN/AUSTRALIA/by/Eve Pownall/with drawings by/Walter Cunningham/Shakespeare Head Press/Sydney
n.d. [1966]
72pp, 6 f/p col. illus., alternate b/w & col. marginal drawings throughout, pic. bd., pic. e/p, 275x200mm. CLRC

6139 Eve Pownall/THE THIRSTY LAND/Harnessing Australia's water resources/Illustrated with photographs, maps/and reproductions of old prints/Methuen & Co. Ltd./11 Fetter Lane—London E.C.4/Hicks Smith & Sons Pty. Ltd./Sydney Melbourne Brisbane
1967
158pp (inc. 2pp acknowledgements, 2pp bibliography & 4pp index), b/w photographic frontis., b/w photographic illus., map e/p, clo., 215x150m. CLRC
'The World we are Making' series

A PIONEER DAUGHTER
A DROVER. *See* Early Australians

THE GREAT SOUTH LAND. *See* Australia Past and Present

POYNTER, James

6140 THE/SEARCH IN SUMMER/by/James Poynter/Illustrated by Max Angus/[device]/Angus and Robertson
Sydney 1965
95pp, b/w frontis. & b/w drawings in text, clo., map e/p, 215x135mm. CLRC

PRATT, Bruce W.

THE SNOWY MOUNTAINS SCHEME. *See* Around Australia Program

PRATT, Edwin A.

6141 NOTABLE/MASTERS OF MEN/Modern Example of/Successful Lives/By/Edwin A Pratt/Author of "Pioneer Women in Victoria's Reign"/"Leading Points in South African History"/etc. etc./London:/The Pilgrim Press/57 and 59 Ludgate Hill, E.C.
n.d. [school prize label dated 16/12/1912]

320pp, b/w photographic frontis. & 7 f/p b/w plates, dec. clo., 196x140mm. WRT
Contains chapters on Sir Henry Parkes, James Tyson, James Chalmers, J. G. Paton.

PRATT, Mara L.
6142 PEOPLE AND PLACES./Here and there./Volume 1/AUSTRALASIA/By Mara L. Pratt/Author of "American History Stories," "Young Folk's Library of American/History,"—Etc./Educational Publishing Company/Boston/New York Chicago San Francisco 1892
220pp & 2pp adv., 44 f/p & numerous b/w illus., bd., 170x125mm. KMM
Second half of book deals with New Zealand & various South Pacific islands. Many of the illus. have been publ. in earlier vol. & included is one map of Victoria. Of educational & general interest.

PRATT, Rona Olive
See 'O'Harris, Pixie'

'PRATTLE, Peter'
6143 AMUSING AND INSTRUCTIVE TALES/by/Peter Prattle/Embellished with neat coloured Engravings/ London/T. H. Munday, 9, Fore Street
n.d. [NSL:M copy inscribed 1832]
26pp, 5 col. engravings, bd., 170x270mm.
Second story (7pp) entitled 'The Happy Grandmother, and her Grandchildren who went toAustralia'. NSL:M
Numerous editions & other collections containing this one story relative to Australia.
6144 As above 14pp, wrappers. ANL
6145 As above, 90pp, 20 hand-coloured engravings, blind-stamped clo., title on front cover, 'Instructive Tales', 184x280mm.
'The Happy Grandmother' is illustrated with 2 col. engravings. CLRC
Also published in:
6146 CHEERFUL TALES [18pp]. ANL
6147 THE KEEPSAKE [18pp]. ANL
6148 TALES IN PROSE AND VERSE
18pp, 4 col. engravings, wrappers.
Two variant copies. ANL

Presents for the Koala Bears
6149 PRESENTS FOR/THE KOALA BEARS
Brimax Books, Cambridge, England. Series 1450, n.d.
12pp, col. illus. throughout, pic. wrappers, cover title, 240x215mm. WRT

PREST, Jean
HAMILTON HUME AND WILLIAM HOVELL. *See* Australian Explorers

PRESTON, James
6150 THE/RING/OF/THE AXE/James Preston/ Lansdowne
Lansdowne Press Pty Ltd, Melbourne 1968
154pp, unillus., clo., 210x135mm. CLRC
6151 THE/RING/OF/THE AXE/James Preston/[device]
Geoffrey Chapman/London Dublin Melbourne 1971
154pp, unillus., clo., 215x137mm. KP
6152 JEEDARRA/COUNTRY/James Preston/Illustrated by Helen Sallis/Rigby Limited
Adelaide 1971
187pp, 10 f/p b/w illus., clo., 210x135mm. KMM
The story of the search for two children lost on the Nullarbor Plain.
6153 JEEDARRA/COUNTRY/James Preston/Illustrated by Helen Sallis/John Gifford Limited
London 1972
Details as in Australian edition. KMM

Pretty Pollie Pillicote
See Blue Wren Books

PRICE, Marcelle
6154 BRUCE FINDS A FRIEND/Marcelle Price/[device]/ Pickering & Inglis Ltd./1962
London
64pp, unillus., clo., 190x125mm. MD
Story set in a Melbourne boys' boarding school & in the Grampians.
Another copy, as above, but with col. frontis. MK

PRICE, Willard
6155 Willard Price/DIVING ADVENTURE/Illustrated by Pat Marriott/Knight Books/the paperback division of Brockhampton Press
1st publ. 1969. This ed. 1972
191pp, 5 f/p b/w illus., & text illus. pic. wrappers, 180x110mm. KP
Barrier Reef setting.

PRICHARD, Katharine Susannah
6156 THE WILD OATS/OF HAN/By/Katharine Susannah Prichard/Australia:/Angus & Robertson Limited/89 Castlereagh Street, Sydney/1928
215pp, 2pp author's foreword, b/w frontis. by Enid Dickson & 12 f/p b/w illus., marginal drawings in text by Elizabeth Powell, clo., 190x130mm. KMM
Sketches about childhood, first published in *The Home*, Sydney, Aug-Dec 1926; Jan-May 1927, Illus. by Raymond McGrath
6157 THE/WILD OATS/OF HAN/By/Katharine Susannah Prichard/Illustrated by/Genevieve Melrose/ Lansdowne
Lansdowne Press Pty Ltd, Melbourne; first published 1928, revised edition 1968
160pp, 1p author's foreword, b/w frontis. & 10 f/p b/w illus., clo., 215x135mm. KMM
6158 MOGGIE/AND HER/CIRCUS PONY/by Katharine Susannah Prichard/Illustrations by Elaine Haxton/F. W. Cheshire Melbourne Canberra Sydney 1967
34pp, col. dec. t.p., col. illus. throughout, clo., dec. e/p, 275x210mm. KMM

PRIMER, W.
6159 V AUSTRALSKYCH HOUSTINACH (In the Australian Bush)
E. Solc, Prague 1916
35pp. Unseen: SLCSR

'PRIMROSE', Jane' [Mrs Winifred J. P. Curry]
6160 THE THREE FLAMES/By/Jane Primrose/(Mrs. Winifred J. P. Curry)/Author of "In the Net"/Australia:/Cornstalk Publishing Company/89 Castlereagh Street, Sydney/1928
280pp, unillus., clo., 185x115mm. NSL:M

The Prince who was afraid of Nothing
6161 THE PRINCE WHO/WAS/AFRAID OF/ NOTHING/"Moonbeam" Series/Published by/The W. H. Honey Publishing Co./31 Cunningham Street, Sydney
n.d.
16pp, b/w illus. inside both covers, 6 b/w illus. in text signed 'Rhys Williams', dec. bd., cover title, 245x185mm. Grant

PRINCE, Lyn
6162 MARK AND WOOFY ON A/SURFING/ HOLIDAY/written and/illustrated by Lyn Prince/ Golden Press Sydney
1971

[18]pp, col. illus. throughout, pic. bd., pic. e/p, 280x210mm. CLRC

PRIOR, Enid

6163 BUSHLAND/BROADCAST/Stories and Verse/by/Enid Prior/Illustrations/by/Florence Camm/1933/Robertson & Mullens Limited/107–113 Elizabeth Street/Melbourne
78pp, col. front & 3 f/p col. illus., b/w drawings in text, clo., 245x180mm. VSL

PROWSE, J. J.

6164 CARLO AND BILL/Written by J. J. Prowse/Illustrated by Judi Wynn
Whitcombe & Tombs Pty Ltd, Sydney 1971
19pp, col. illus. throughout, stiff pic. wrappers, 200x135mm. CLRC
Original story published as a school reader.

In same series, & uniform with the above:
6165 CARLO AND BILL AND THE BLUE SPEED BOAT
6166 CARLO AND BILL AND THE LITTLE OLD LADY
6167 CARLO AND BILL AND THE SHINY RED RACING CAR. CLRC

6168 GOLDIE/The Story of a Guide Dog/J. J. Prowse/Illustrated by Jonathon Waud/With an introduction by/J. K. Holdsworth, Director,/Royal Guide Dogs for the Blind/Association of Australia/[device]
Heinemann Educational Australia Pty Ltd, South Yarra, Victoria, 1969
96pp (inc. 1p introduction), b/w frontis. & 9 f/p b/w illus., b/w drawings in text, pic. clo., 210x135mm. KMM

6169 GUIDE DOG NALDA/a read and do book/[photographic illustration]/by/J. J. Prowse
Published by the author, Victoria 1971
40pp, b/w drawings, wrappers, cover title, 240x180mm. KMM
Pictures to colour by Jim Williamson.
Puzzles, stories, etc.

PUCKRIDGE, Doreen K.

6170 KING'S CASTLE/By/Doreen K. Puckridge/Australia/Angus & Robertson Ltd./89 Castlereagh Street, Sydney/1931
221pp, 18pp adv., unillus., clo., 185x115mm. KMM

PULLAN, Rupert Desmond

6171 THE/STORYTELLER/Series 1/by/Ru Pullan/Illustrated by/I. M. Hill/1949/The National Press Pty. Ltd./Melbourne
71pp, 4 col. illus. & b/w drawings in text, bd., 215x135mm. ANL

6172 THE TIMID TRAIN/&/THE MAKER OF MUSIC/by Ru Pullan/Whitcombe & Tombs Pty. Ltd./Melbourne Sydney Perth Geelong
n.d. [1953]
23pp, 8 part-col. illus. signed 'Hudson', wrappers, 185x120mm. ANL
Published in conjunction with Spotlight Varieties 'Animated Stories', recordings of these two stories.

PULVER, Louis

6173 FIRST/BIBLE STORIES/FOR/LITTLE PEOPLE/The History of the Earlier Portions of the Bible/Narrated in the language of childhood/by/Louis Pulver/[quotation]/Melbourne/George Robertson and Company/390 Little Collins Street/1889
xii, 236pp, unillus., clo., title on front cover in dec. gilt lettering, 136x90mm. CLRC

Pupils' Danger Patrol Companion

6174 PUPILS'/DANGER PATROL/COMPANION/Jacaranda Press/1955/Printed in Linotype Times Roman by H. Pole & Co. Pty. Limited Brisbane,/for The Publishers, Jacaranda Press, 73 Elizabeth Street, Brisbane
1955
43pp, map frontis., wrappers, 210x135mm. ANL
Notes for schoolchildren on *Danger Patrol* by Leslie Rees, with paragraph about the author.

Puppy Days

6175 PUPPY/DAYS/A Story for Children/in Rhyme and Picture/[coloured illustration]/John Sands Pty. Ltd./Registered in Australia for transmission by post as a book
Sydney, n.d.
22pp, col. drawings on alternate pages, bd., 195x210mm. KMM

PURSE, A. L.

6176 THE/ISLE OF WIRRAWOO/An Australian Fairy Tale/By/A. L. Purse/Illustrated by/Alan Wright and Anne Anderson/[publisher's device]/Humphrey Milford/Oxford University Press/London Edinburgh Glasgow/Toronto Melbourne Cape Town Bombay
First published 1923; rpt 1924, 1926
79pp, col. frontis. & 4 f/p b/w illus., clo., 160x115mm. KMM
Another copy as above, but
1926 with dec. clo. & d/w reproducing frontis. & 'The Oxford Books for Children' printed on band. The 'Golden Rule' series. KP
Another copy the same
• Rpt 1933, clo. binding. The 'Golden Rule' series. KP
Another copy the same
• Rpt 1933, pic. bd. with cover illus. identical with d/w on 1926 ed. KP

PURSLOVE, Amy

6177 I LOVE MY QUEEN/and other Poems/by/Amy Purslove/Arthur H. Stockwell, Ltd./Ilfracombe, Devon
n.d. [1960]
31pp, unillus., wrappers, 180x120mm. ANL

6178 DOWN UNDER/Stories for Little/Folk/by/Amy Purslove/1961/Arthur H. Stockwell Limited/Elms Court/Ilfracombe/Devon [England]
78pp, 7 f/p b/w illus., clo., 185x120mm. KMM

PURTON, Rowland W.

6179 Star [device] Book/MAN IN/ANTARCTICA/By Rowland W. Purton/Pictures by Neil Kitson/Hamish Hamilton/London
First published in Great Britain 1964
32pp (inc. 1p index), part. col. & b/w illus. throughout, dec. bd., 200x150mm. BBC
Contains simple information about history and the geography of this region in textbook form for young children.

6180 Star [device] Book/MAN IN/AUSTRALIA/By Rowland W. Purton/Pictures by B. Biro/Hamish Hamilton/London
First published in Great Britain 1964
32pp (inc. 1p index), part-col. & b/w illus. throughout, dec. bd., 200x150mm. KMM
As above, relating to Australia.

PURVES, David Laing & COCHRANE, R.

6181 THE/ENGLISH CIRCUMNAVIGATORS:/The/Most Remarkable Voyages/round the world/By/English sailors/with a Preliminary Sketch of their lives and Discoveries/Edited with Notes, etc. etc. etc./By/David Laing Purves and R. Cochrane./William P.

Nimmo/London: 14 King William Street, Strand,/and Edinburgh./1876 [first pub. 1874]
831pp (inc. 8pp index, 15pp introduction), text begins p34, 16pp adv., folding part col. map frontis., engraved frontis. & dec. t.p. (additional) & 3 folding part col. maps, dec. clo., 180x120mm. HBM

PURVES, James L.

6182 A/YOUNG AUSTRALIAN'S LOG;/Being the Narrative of a/Voyage/from Melbourne to London,/in/The Steamship "The Pacific", Capt. Thomson,/April to August, 1855/By/James L. Purves./London:/Printed by George Barclay/Castle Street, Leicester Square./1856
32pp, unillus., paper wrappers, 165x100mm. NSL:M
The journal of a very mature young man—the author being a boy on his way to school in England. On his arrival he spent eight months with friends awaiting the arrival of his mother & brothers & sisters. Although written by a schoolboy does not seem intended for children.

[PYE, Moira P.]

6183 BRATLING/CHATTER/[drawing]/By Miss Doublecleff
Hawthorn Press, Melbourne, n.d. [1946]
27pp, b/w drawings, wrappers, cover title, 215x140mm. ANL
Humorous verses.

PYKE, Emma

6184 OLD MYTH STORIES/SIMPLY TOLD/FOR/LITTLE AUSTRALIANS/By Emma Pyke/First I.M.C. Education Department/Melbourne/Melbourne:/Fraser and Jenkinson, Printers, Bookbinders, etc./420 Bourke Street/1906
86pp, 1p author's preface, unillus., wrappers (missing from copy seen), 185x115mm. KMM
Greek myths retold in simple language for the use of children in schools.

6185 OLD MYTH STORIES/SIMPLY TOLD/FOR/LITTLE AUSTRALIANS/by Emma Pyke/First I.M.C. Education Department/Melbourne/Melbourne:/Fraser and Jenkinson, Printers, Bookbinders, etc./343–5 Queen Street/1908
As above, with 2pp adv. & wrappers (with adv. inside front cover & on both sides back cover). KMM

PYKE, Lillian Maxwell [Mrs R. D. Pyke, née Heath]

6186 MAX/THE SPORT/By/Lilian [*sic*] M. Pyke/Ward Lock & Co. Limited/London Melbourne and Toronto/1916
250pp, 6pp adv., b/w frontis. & 7 f/p b/w plates by J. Macfarlane, clo., 180x120mm. KMM
• Rpt as above 1917. MK

6187 JACK/OF ST. VIRGIL'S/By/Lillian M. Pyke/Author of "Max the Sport"/Ward Lock & Co., Limited/London Melbourne and Toronto/1917
319pp, 16pp adv., b/w frontis. & 7 f/p b/w plates by J. Macfarlane, clo., 185x120mm. KMM
• Rpt as above, n.d. KP

6188 PHYL OF THE/CAMP/By/Lillian M. Pyke/Author of "Max the Sport", "Jack of St. Virgil's"/etc. etc./Ward Lock & Co. Limited/London, Melbourne and Toronto/1918
303pp, 16pp adv., b/w frontis. & 7 b/w plates by J. Macfarlane, clo., 180x125mm. KMM
• Rpt as above n.d., 'London and Melbourne' & with sepia onlay on front cover. KMM

6189 A PRINCE AT/SCHOOL/By/Lillian M. Pyke/Author of "Max the Sport", "Jack of St. Virgil's","Phyl of the Camp", etc./Illustrated by J. Macfarlane/Ward Lock & Co., Limited/London, Melbourne and Toronto/1919
252pp, 4pp adv., b/w frontis. & 7 f/p b/w plates, clo., 185x120mm. KMM

6190 CAMP KIDDIES/By/Lillian M. Pyke/A Story of Life on Railway/Construction/With Original Photographs/Melbourne/The Speciality Press Pty. Ltd./189 Little Collins Street
n.d. [1919]
208pp, b/w photographic frontis. & 15pp photographic illus., clo., 180x120mm. KMM

6191 CAMP KIDDIES/abridged from the original by the author/Lillian M. Pyke/Author of "Phil of the Camp"/"A Twin in Paradise" etc./with Eight Original Photographs/Cassell & Company Limited/Melbourne Sydney Brisbane London
n.d. [1923?]
92pp, photographic illus., wrappers (with adv. inside front & back covers), 175x120mm. Grant

6192 Cassell's/Commonwealth Story Readers/CAMP KIDDIES/Abridged from the original by the author/Lillian M. Pyke/Author of "Phil of the Camp,"/"A Twin in Paradise," etc./With Eight Original Photographs/[device]/Cassell & Company Limited/Melbourne, Sydney, Brisbane/New York, Toronto and London
1923
94pp, b/w frontis. & 7 f/p b/w photographic illus.,dec. wrappers, 180x120mm. KMM
Publisher's adv. inside front wrapper & on both sides back wrapper.

6193 BRUCE AT/BOONDERONG/CAMP/By/Lillian M. Pyke/Ward Lock & Co. Limited/London and Melbourne/1920
256pp, b/w frontis. & 7 f/p b/w plates by J. Macfarlane, clo., 180x120mm. KMM

6194 Whitcombe's Story Books/SQUIRMY AND BUBBLES/A School Story for Girls/by/Lillian M. Pyke/Author of "Phyl of the Camp", "Sheila the Prefect" etc./Whitcombe & Tombs Pty. Ltd./Melbourne, Sydney, Perth/Associated Houses:/Christchurch Auckland Wellington Dunedin/Invercargill and London
n.d.
164pp, 2pp adv., b/w frontis. & 3 f/p b/w illus. by Perce Clark, pic. wrappers (with adv. on back cover) 180x120mm. KMM
See McLaren 617

6195 THE BEST SCHOOL/OF ALL/By/Lillian M. Pyke/with illustrations by J. Macfarlane/Ward, Lock & Co. Limited/London and Melbourne/1921
256pp, b/w frontis. & 5 b/w plates, clo., 185x120mm. PR

6196 Cassell's/Commonwealth Story Readers/SATURDAY ISLAND/By/Lillian M. Pyke/Author of/"Camp Kiddies" &c./Cassell & Company Limited/Melbourne, Sydney, Brisbane/New York, Toronto and London/Wholly set up and printed in Australia. Registered by/the Postmaster General for transmission through the/post as a book. 1923
37pp, 3pp adv., b/w frontis. & 3 f/p b/w illus. by Claire Scott, wrappers (with adv. inside front wrapper & on both sides of back wrapper), 180x120mm. KMM

6197 SHEILA/AT HAPPY HILLS/By/Lillian M. Pyke/Ward, Lock & Co., Limited/London and Melbourne/1922

256pp, b/w frontis. & 5 b/w plates by J. Macfarlane, clo., 185x125mm. KMM
Another copy as above, 1923. VSL

6198 SHEILA THE/PREFECT/By/Lillian M. Pyke/ Ward, Lock & Co., Limited/London and Melbourne/ 1923
255pp, b/w frontis. & 3 b/w plates by J. Dewar Mills, clo., 180x125mm. KMM

6199 BROTHERS/OF THE FLEET/By/Lillian M. Pyke/ Illustrated/Ward, Lock & Co. Limited/London and Melbourne/1924
256pp (inc. 1p author's note), b/w frontis. & 3 b/w plates by Norman Sutcliffe, clo., 180x120mm. KMM

6200 THE LONE GUIDE/OF MERFIELD/By/Lillian M. Pyke/Illustrated/Ward, Lock & Co. Limited/London and Melbourne/1925
256pp, b/w frontis. & 3 b/w plates, by J. Dewar Mills, clo., 180x125mm. VSL

6201 THREE/BATCHELOR GIRLS/By/Lillian M. Pyke/ Ward, Lock & Co., Limited/London and Melbourne/ 1926
255pp, b/w frontis. & 3 b/w plates, illus. by W. P. Wightman, clo., 180x125mm. KMM

6202 THE SECRET OF/WALLABY ROCK/By/Lillian M. Pyke/Ward, Lock & Co., Limited/London and Melbourne/1927
255pp, b/w frontis. & 3 b/w plates, illus. by W. P. Wightman, clo., 180x125mm. VSL

PYKE, Lillian Maxwell (ed.)
6203 SOUTHERN SEAS STORY BOOK/General Editor—Henry Stead/Edited by Lilian [*sic*] M. Pyke/ Author of/"Sheila at Happy Hills"/"Camp Kiddies"/"Max the Sport" etc./Published by Alexander McCubbin/152 Elizabeth Street, Melbourne
n.d. [1920]
72pp, 4 f/p col. illus. & b/w drawings, bd., 245x180mm. VSL

COLE'S HAPPY TIME PICTURE AND NURSERY RHYME BOOK. *See* Cole, E. W.

COLE'S HOLIDAY BOOK FOR BOYS AND GIRLS. *See* Cole, E. W. (publisher)

QUICK, Mollie [illustrator]
6204 TEN LITTLE NIGGER BOYS/[drawing]/Drawings by Mollie Quick/A Pyramid Publication
Sydney, n.d. [1947]
16pp, col. illus. throughout, dec. bd., 180x240mm. ANL

6205 JUDY ANNE/AND THE/LITTLE BROWN PUPPY/[drawing]/by Mollie Quick
Pyramid Publications, Sydney, n.d. [1948]
16pp, col. illus. throughout, dec. bd., 240x180mm. ANL

6206 MOTHER GOOSE'S/BABIES/A Nursery Rhyme Book/A Pyramid Publication
Sydney, n.d. [1948]
16pp, col. dec. t.p., col. illus. throughout, dec. bd., 245x180mm. ANL
See also THE HOUSE THAT JACK BUILT

Quilici, Folco
6207 FOLCO QUILICI SUI MARI DEL CAPITANO COOK/[4 line quote]/Vallecchi Editori
Florence, 1965
198pp, illus. in col. & b/w, clo., 276x210mm. NSL:M
Book mostly comprises photographs both in col. & b/w of places Cook visited on his three expeditions especially taken for this book & reproduction of historic illus. from earlier publications & drawings.

QUIN, Tarella
See Daskein, Tarella Quin

QUINLAN, Lucille M.
A POSTBOY. *See* Early Australians

QUIRK, Lorna [illustrator]
6208 A DAY AT THE BEACH
6209 OUR PETS
6210 PLANES, TRAINS AND BOATS
6211 PLAY TIME
6212 SPEED
Uniform picture books published by Georgian House, Melbourne 1946
10pp (inc. front & back covers), board books, col. illus. throughout, 150x120mm. ANL
Brief text, consisting of captions only.

6213 [drawing]/POOBAH/THE/PEKINGESE PUP/by/ Lorna Quirk/Georgian House/Melbourne
1947
32pp, 8 f/p col. illus., dec. bd., 240x180mm. VSL

R., L. N. [Ranyard, Ellen Henrietta]
6214 THE BOOK/AND ITS STORY;/A Narrative for the Young:/on occasion of the/Jubilee of the British and Foreign Bible Society:/with an introductory Preface, by the Rev. T. Phillips,/Jubilee Secretary./By/L. N. R./Thirty-seventh thousand/Eighth Edition, with additions, [device]/London:/Samuel Bagster and Sons,/15 Paternoster Row:/Thomas Hatchard, Piccadilly./MDCCCLV
viiipp (preface & author's preface) 508pp (inc. 8pp index), 16pp adv., engraved frontis. engravings in text, bd., 180x120mm. CLRC
This exceedingly popular Victorian account of the story of the writing & circulating of the Bible & its distribution throughout the world contains slight references to Australia & the Pacific.
6215 Another copy as above, but
Ninety-Second Thousand./Twenty-Third edition./ London: W. Kent and Co., Paternoster Row./Hatchard and Co., Piccadilly./MDCCCLXXIII
Details as above. KMM

RABLING, Harold
6216 THE STORY OF THE PACIFIC/Explorers of the Earth's/Mightiest Ocean/by Harold Rabling/[illus.]/W. W. Norton & Company Inc./[device]/New York
1965
191pp (inc. 3pp index) & 1p biographical note, extended t.p. with photograph of a model of a fifteenth-century caravel, frontis. with caption, b/w photographic illus., pic. clo., 202x130mm. KP
Reinforced library ed.

6217 PIONEERS OF THE PACIFIC/The Story of the South Seas/by Harold Rabling/Angus and Robertson
First published 1965 by W. W. Norton & Co. Inc. New York [under the title *The Story of the Pacific: Explorers of the Earth's Mightiest Ocean*]; this edition published 1966 by Angus & Robertson, Sydney
147pp (inc. 3pp index), 2pp acknowledgements, 1p foreword, extended illus. t.p., 24 b/w illus. & map, dec. clo., 215x130mm. BBC
The author is Australian by birth, but now resident in the USA.

RABLING, Harold & HAMILTON, Patrick
6218 UNDER THE/SOUTHERN CROSS/The Story of Australia/by Harold Rabling/and Patrick Hamilton/

London: Macmillan & Co. Ltd./New York: St. Martin's Press/1961
114pp (inc. 2pp preface & 1p acknowledgements), b/w map frontis. & 5 other f/p maps in text, b/w photographic illus. throughout, clo., 205x150mm. BBC History & general factual book.
• Rpt 1962. KP

RACE, Donald
6219 DANGER QUEST/By/Donald Race/Copyright/ Published by W. J. Nesbit/124 Liverpool Street, Sydney
n.d.
128pp, b/w illus. throughout, col. pic. wrappers, 100x130mm. NSL:M

RACKIN, Martin
LONG JOHN SILVER. *See* Tennant, Kylie

RADCLIFFE, James T.
6220 THE YOUNG PATHFINDER'S BOOK OF THE POLAR REGIONS/[illus.]/By James T. Radcliffe/ Edited by David Halfen/Illustrated by Hilda Simon/ Frederick Muller Limited. London
First publ. in Great Britain 1965; copyright 1962 by Hart Publishing Company Inc.
128pp (inc. 3pp index), extended t.p., b/w & part col. illus. throughout, clo., 230x174mm. KP

RADCLIFFE, Margery
6221 BOLDTOES/Being the Adventures of/Littletoes, Bigtoe/and/Bubblybold/and/The Songs they heard in the Wood/by/Margery Radcliffe/Dedicated to all children/whether they have big or/little toes/ [publisher's device]/The Peter Maurice Music Co. Ltd. London n.d. [book acquired by library 1935]
44pp, col. frontis., b/w drawings throughout signed 'Marian Cotten-Cohen', dec. bd., 240x280m. NSL:M
Words & music of 8 songs included in text.

RAINE, Henry B.
6222 THE/LURE OF THE BUSH/No 1/[col. illus. of 2 kookaburras]/Australian Birds
Wirraway Publishing Company, Sydney, 1944
24pp, b/w illus. (Fred Powis) of bird on every page, pic. wrappers, cover title, 240x180mm. Dromkeen

6223 The Lure of the Sea/AUSTRALIAN FISHES/No. 1/Foreword [15 lines]/Contents [23 headings]/ Registered at GPO Sydney for Transmission by Post as a Book
The Taro Publishing Co., Sydney, 1945
24pp, 23 part-col. illus. (Fred Powis) with text, stiff pic. wrappers, 240x180mm. KP

RAINSFORD, Arthur
HUME AND HOVELL. *See* Famous Australians

RALPH, Edith
6224 EMPIRE BUILDERS IN/AUSTRALIA/Early Days in New South Wales,/Victoria, and South Australia/ By/Edith Ralph/with a map/T. Fisher Unwin/ London/Adelphi Terrace./Leipsic [*sic*] Inselstrasse 20/1911
252pp (inc. 4pp index, 1p bibliography), 2pp introduction, tinted map frontis., clo., 185x120mm. KMM

'RAMBLE, Reuben' [pseud. Samuel Clark]
6225 THE/WORLD/& its inhabitants/or the/Travels & Adventures/of Reuben Ramble. [title with dec. border of inhabitants of various countries] London. Darton & Clark
n.d. [1840?]
[28]pp, 8 maps with hand-col. border of scene of animals & people &c, stiff wrappers with b/w illus. & col. illus. inside covers; inside back cover a col. map of Australia & NZ surrounded by 4 colonial scenes, 210x170mm. ANL

RAMSAY, E. M. Hamilton (Mrs)
6226 HISTORY OF A COCKATOO/As told by Himself/ [b/w drawing of a cockatoo]
The Carlyle Press, 52 Park Row, Bristol, n.d.
81pp, 2 f/p b/w drawings, green clo., 183x115mm. AMcC
Mr John Bonar Peter Hamilton Ramsay was Commissioner of the Gold Fields in North Qld. The drawings show 'The Commissioner' and 'The Mistress'. Giorgio the cockatoo was taken to England by Mr & Mrs Hamilton Ramsay & given to their 2 nieces Alicia & Muffelina. The cockatoo purports to tell the story of his life & adventures in & around Westwood near Rockhampton, his life, adventures with Aborigines and so on.

RAMSDEN, Maude
6227 AUSTRALIAN BUSH/PARABLES/By/Maude Ramsden/Morgan & Scott Ltd./(Office of "The Christian")/12 Paternoster Buildings/London E.C.4/Printed in Scotland.
n.d. [1923]
117pp, col. frontis., wrappers, 180x120mm. ANL
Simple natural history tales.

RAND, Edward A.
6228 ALL ABOARD/FOR SUNRISE LANDS./A Trip through California across the Pacific to/Japan, China and Australia./By/Edward A. Rand./Author of "Pushing Ahead", "Roy's Dory", "Bark Cabin", "Tent in the Notch"/etc. etc. etc./Illustrated/M. A. Donohue & Company,/407–429 Dearborn St./Chicago
n.d. [189-?]
384pp (inc. 1p preface), b/w frontis. & copious b/w illus., pic. bd., 215x170mm. CLRC
Pp 291–361 relate to Australia & New Zealand.
6229 Another copy, published by Pennsylvania Pub. Coy, Harrisburg (1885) Unseen

RANDALL, Anne
6230 CURLY TOP AND THE/NORTH WIND/By/Anne Randall/Drawings by/Joyce Janes
Ramsay Ware Publishing Pty Ltd, 117 King St, Melbourne, n.d.
[16]pp, part-col. illus. throughout, pic. wrappers, 278x216mm. KMM

RANDELL, Laurel E.
6231 "WHEN I AM A/BIG MAN"/and other verse/By/ Laurel E. Randell
Printed by Thornquest Press, Adelaide, n.d. [Annual Catalogue of Australian Publications gives publisher as Whitcombe & Tombs, Melbourne, 1948]
20pp, b/w illus., wrappers, cover title, 180x115mm. ANL

RANDOLPH, Richard
THE LAST CHOICE. *See* The Boys' Friend Library 624

YOUNG YARDLEY. *See* The Boys' Friend Library 625

RANKINE, David & HOOK, Geoffrey
6232 KANGAPOSSUM/& CROCOROO/Illustrated by Geoff Hook/With verses by David Rankine/ Heinemann Melbourne London
1969
[32]pp, col. illus. throughout, pic. wrappers, 235x230mm. KMM
Verses with pages of illustrations bisected horizontally, so that the top half of one drawing coincides with

bottom half of any other, the accompanying rhymes having a similar comical effect.

RANSOM, Wilma J.

6233 THE/WISHING/TREE/Wilma J. Ransom/ Illustrated by Maureen Pritchard/Rigby
Adelaide 1969
94pp, b/w illus. in text throughout, clo., 210x135mm. KMM

RARICK, Carrie

6234 LITTLE/PENGUIN/By Carrie Rarick/Illustrated by/Vivienne Blake De Muth/[drawing]/Rand McNally & Company Chicago/Established 1856/Copyright MCMLX [3 lines]
27pp (text printed inside back cover), col. illus. throughout, pic. bd., 157x117mm. KP

RAYMENT, Tarlton

6235 Australian Nature Story Readers/GOLDWING/The Life Story of the Queen Bee/By/Tarlton Rayment/ Author of/Money in Bees in Australasia/Profitable Honey Plants, etc./For Children aged 8 to 9 years/ [drawing]/Melbourne/Auckland Christchurch Dunedin Wellington/and London/Whitcombe & Tombs Limited.
n.d. [192-?]
32pp, 4 b/w photographic illus. & b/w drawings in text, dec. wrappers, 180x115mm. KMM

6236 THE PRINCE OF THE/TOTEM/A/Simple Black Tale for/Clever White Children/By/Tarlton Rayment/ President Entomologists' Club of Victoria, 1930–1931/Author of 'Bees in Australasia' 'Australian Honey-Plants' etc./and the Film-picture 'The Cliff-dwellers'/Illustrated from/Crayon Drawings/By the Author/Melbourne/Robertson and Mullens Limited/1933
132pp (inc. 2 separate 1p prefaces by author), b/w frontis. & 27 b/w illus., dec. wrappers, 215x140mm. KMM
Also published as above in clo. binding, 210x133mm. KMM
• Rpt 1935, as above. KMM
First broadcast by the Children's Corner, 3LO Melbourne, 1932.
See also Gunn, Jeannie & others. THE AUSTRALIAN WONDER BOOK (1935), in which *The Prince of the Totem* is included.

6237 Whitcombe's Story Books/THE/VALLEY OF THE SKY/Abridged from the Australian Pioneering Story/ by/Tarlton Rayment/For ages 12 to 14 years/[drawing & caption] Whitcombe and Tombs Pty. Ltd./Melbourne and Sydney/Associated Houses/Christchurch Auckland Wellington Dunedin Invercargill/and London
1942
143pp, 6pp notes, 1p adv., b/w map frontis. & b/w drawings in text, wrappers, 185x125mm. ANL
Abridged from the adult novel, published in 1937, which is based on the discovery of Gippsland.
See McLaren 661

RAYMOND, Moore

6238 SMILEY/A Novel By/Moore Raymond/[device]/ Sylvan Press/24–25 Museum Street, London, W.C.1.
First published 1945;
183pp, unillus., clo., 185x120mm. KMM
Adventures of a boy in western Queensland.
• Rpt as above, 1945. VSL

6239 SMILEY/A Novel by/Moore Raymond/Ponsford Newman & Benson Pty Ltd./Melbourne and Sydney/ Sylvan Press/London
Printed by Offset Printing Coy. Pty Ltd, Sydney, but with colophon on last page of Welbecson Press, London; first Australian edition 1946
183pp, unillus., clo., 180x120mm. Grant
Swedish edition

6240 PAWIK I/MURRUMBILLA/Stockholm/Albert Bonniers Forlag
1949
224pp, unillus., pic. bd., clo. spine, 183x120mm. ANL
Cover by Nils Möller.

6241 SMILEY GETS/A GUN/A novel by/Moore Raymond/Sylvan Press London
1947
248pp, unillus., clo., 185x125mm. NSL:M

6242 SMILEY ROAMS THE ROAD/by/Moore Raymond/illustrated by/Pat Nevin/A Swift Novel/ Hulton Press Ltd./London
1959
224pp, b/w frontis. & 8 f/p b/w illus., b/w drawings in text, clo., 200x130mm. KMM

RAYNAL, F. Édouard

6243 LES NAUFRAGÉS/ou/Vingt Mois sur un récif/des îles Auckland/Récit authentique/par F. E. Raynal/ illustré/de 40 gravures sur bois désinées par A. de Neuville/et accompagné d'une carte/Paris/Librairie de L. Hachette et Cie./Boulevard Saint-Germain, No. 77/1870/Droits de traduction et de réproduction réservés.
374pp (inc. 41pp appendices, etc.), engraved portrait frontis., 2 f/p b/w maps, 39 f/p engravings, morocco, 260x165mm. NSL:M

6244 Another copy as above, but
Ouvrage couronné par L'Académie Française/ Cinquième Édition/Paris/Librairie Hachette et Cie./79, Boulevard Saint-Germain, 79/1882 Droits de propriété et de traduction réservés.
374pp & 2pp dedication &c, engraved portrait frontis. & 40 f/p engravings, folding b/w map, morocco bdg, g.e., 260x170mm. CLRC

6245 WRECKED ON A REEF;/or,/Twenty Months among the Auckland Isles,/A True Story./From the French of F. E. Raynal/With forty engravings by Alfred de Neuville/[6 line quotation]/London:/T. Nelson and Sons, Paternoster Row:/Edinburgh; and New York./
1874
350pp, additional engraved t.p., engraved frontis. & 39 f/p illus., pic. clo., 185x120mm. KP
Introductory chapters mention the author's eleven years residence in Australia before setting sail for Campbell Island, south of New Zealand. The survivors from the wreck were eventually returned to Melbourne.
Variant bdg. One copy is bound in olive green clo. with a circular vignette & the letters 'W' & 'R' of title blocked in gold on a rust red background & title on a gilt panel on spine. The other has the same design on a plain brown clo. with title, author & vignette of a man clubbing a seal on spine. KP
• Rpt as above, 1875. KMM

6246 WRECKED ON A REEF;/or/Twenty months in the/Auckland Isles./A True Story/of/Shipwreck, Adventure and Suffering./With forty illustrations/ /London:/T. Nelson and Sons, Paternoster Row./ Edinburgh; and New York./1880
350pp, additional engraved t.p., engraved frontis. & 39 f/p engravings, pic. clo. 175x120mm. ANL
• Rpt as above, 1882. ANL
• Rpt as above, 1885. ANL
• Rpt as above, 1889. HBM
• Rpt as above 1892, pic. clo., dec. e/p, 180x125mm. NSL:M

RAYNER, Joan & Betty

6247 AUSTRALIAN CHILDREN'S THEATRE/ STORY-SONGS/Book One/Liza and Geordie—German/Frog and Mouse English/Il était une 'Bergère (The Shepherdess) French/High Barbaree English/ There came three dukes A-Riding English/Le Roi de Sardaigne (The King of Sardinia) French/The Little Woman and the Pedlar English/Directions for making masks/Acting suggestions are printed beside each song/Dramatizations by Joan and Betty Rayner/ Accompaniments by Barbara Carroll/[publisher's device]/Illustrations by Ingrid Ackland/Georgian House/Melbourne
1961
16pp (inc. authors' foreword), b/w decorations, dec. wrappers, 220x290mm. KMM
Words, music & directions for acting the 7 songs listed above.

6248 AUSTRALIAN CHILDREN'S THEATRE/Song Book Two/[9 titles listed]/Acting suggestions are printed beside each song/Dramatizations by Joan and Betty Rayner/Accompaniments by Barbara Carroll [device] Illustrations by Ingrid Ackland/Georgian House/Melbourne
[1964]
16pp, b/w illus., dec. wrappers, 220x290mm. KP

6249 MANKA AND THE KING/By/Joan and Betty Rayner/A play based on a Czechoslovak folktale/ Playing time: 30 to 40 minutes/Copyright Joan and Betty Rayner 1969/[8 lines]/English Theatre Guild Ltd./Ascot House, 52, Dean Street,/London, W.1
20pp, unillus., wrappers, 185x120mm. ANL

6250 THE TALKING BURRO/(The Talking Donkey)/by/Joan and Betty Rayner/A Play based on a Mexican folktale/Copyright Joan and Betty Rayner, 1969/[9 lines]/English Theatre Guild Ltd./Ascot House, 52, Dean Street, London, W.1
20pp, unillus., wrappers, 185x120mm. ANL

6251 FOUR SHORT PLAYS/by/Joan and Betty Rayner/ Directors of the Australian Children's Theatre/Tale of the Ox, a French legend/Cache-cache, adapted from Decamaron [*sic*] Nights/A Devil sells Out, a Modern Morality/Hats for Cats, a comic fantasy/Copyright Joan and Betty Rayner, 1970/[9 lines concerning performing rights]/English Theatre Guild Ltd./Ascot House, 52 Dean Street/London, WIV 6BJ
24pp (last blank), unillus., wrappers, 183x123mm. KMM

6252 Two Plays/by/Joan and Betty Rayner/THE TONGUE-CUT SPARROW/A play based on a Japanese folktale/THE GIRL WHO BECAME A BIRD/ A play for puppets or actors—based on an Australian Aboriginal myth/Copyright Joan and Betty Rayner, 1970/[10 lines text]/English Theatre Guild Ltd./Ascot House, 52 Dean Street/London, WIV 6BJ
20pp (last blank), unillus., wrappers, 185x125mm. ANL

RAYNER, T. H. [illustrator]

6253 ANIMALS/OF THE/WILD/Descriptive Stories and Pictures of well known Wild Animals/[drawing]/ Illustrated by T. H. Rayner/The House of Offset/ Quality Productions/[section of text follows]/Printed and Published by Offset Printing Coy. Pty. Limited, 169 Phillip St., Waterloo, Sydney—Series E 11/(All rights reserved)
n.d. [1945]
16pp, 8 f/p col. illus. & b/w drawings, illus. wrappers, 340x240mm. ANL

READING, Jacqueline

6254 CHILITOES/Written and illustrated by/Jacqueline Reading
Jons Productions, Sydney, n.d. [1945]
28pp, 12 f/p col. illus., pic. bd., cover title, 215x230mm. ANL
Story for young children, about a penguin.

6255 TAFFETY/AND/PIP/by/Jacqueline Reading/A Jons Production
Sydney, n.d. [1945]
28pp, 12 f/p col. illus., pic. bd., 215x225mm. ANL
Young children's story about a pigeon & a blue wren.

A Real Live Fairy Story for the Children and for Men of Ambition too!

6256 A REAL/LIVE FAIRY/STORY FOR/THE CHILDREN/AND FOR/MEN OF AMBITION/ TOO!/Tropical Traders Limited
863–9 Wellington Street, Perth, n.d. [1950?] (Printed by Daniels Print)
8pp, unillus., wrappers, cover title, 185x125mm. CLRC
An advertising brochure describing the establishment of the import business in bananas, & the fruit trade between Western Australia & Indonesia.

Real Stories

6257 REAL STORIES:/Taken from the Narratives/of/ Various Travellers./[2 line quote: Cowper] London:/ Printed for Harvey and Darton,/Gracechurch-Street./ 1827
ivpp, 204pp, engraved frontis., marbled bd., half leather, 140x87mm. CLRC
Contains 2 chapters of 61pp 'Particularly relative to the South-sea Islands at the time they were visited by Captain Cook' & on 'the present state of the inhabitants of the South-sea Islands'. Written in the form of dialogue between a mother & her children. Book also relates some of Mungo Park's travels in Africa.

REBOUL, Helen

6258 THE/WRENS/by/Helen Reboul/Illustrated by/ Gwen Barr/Sydney/1946
Printed and published by Jno. Evans & Son Printing Co., 486–88 Kent Street, Sydney
63pp, frontis., 7 f/p illus. & 25 drawings in text (printed in brown & white), pic. bd., 240x180mm. KMM

RECORD, Robert

6259 [drawing]/WHITESPOT/The Dingo Puppy who would/not eat meat/A Story for Children
Currawong Publishing Co., Sydney, n.d. [1944]
31pp, 2 b/w drawings, illus. John Andrews, wrappers, 110x135mm. ANL

Red Poppy and Other Stories

6260 RED POPPY/AND/OTHER STORIES/For Use in Schools/Illustrated by Percy Leason/Published by J. Wyatt/313–5 Little Collins Street, Melbourne/By Arrangement with the/McDougall's Educational Co. Ltd.
n.d.
86pp, 4 f/p b/w illus., wrappers, 180x120mm. Grant
Not known whether contents are Australian.

REDE, Geraldine

LITTLE BOOK OF AUSTRALIAN TREES
The author, Melbourne 1909
This booklet of handprinted woodcuts, like the same artist's collaboration with Violet Teague, *Night Fall in the Ti-Tree*, is a fine arts production inspired by the

artist's love of beauty, & not intended for children. CLRC

REDENBACHER, Wilhelm

6261 DES/ENGLISCHEN KAPITANS KOOK/ BERÜHMTE/DREI REISEN UM DIE WELT./Für die liebe Jugend/wieder ans Licht gestellt/von/Wilhelm Redenbacher./Drei Theile in einem Band./Mit Sieben Stahlradirungen./Dritte Auflage./Nürnberg,/Verlag der Joh. Phil. Raw'schen Buchhandlung./(E. A. Braun.)
n.d. [awarded as prize 1861]
viii, 313pp (separate pagination for each part, with 2pp contents to each part, 84pp, 111pp, 114pp), tinted engraved frontis. & 6 f/p b/w engravings, bd. (with frontis. pasted on front cover), 150x110mm. RM
English translation of title page: The/Englishman Captain Cook's/Famous/Three Voyages Around the World./For the beloved youth/brought to light/by/ Wilhelm Redenbacher./Three parts in one book./With seven steel engravings./Third edition./Nuremberg,/ Published by etc.
The Foreword states that certain chapters are not suitable for very young children because of various gruesome events—showing perhaps a more protective attitude towards the young than was common with English 19th-century publishers.

6262 DES ENGLISCHEN KAPITÄNS COOK /BERÜHMTE/DREI REISEN UM DIE WELT./Für die Jugend/von Wilhelm Redenbacher./Sechte Auflage/ [vignette]/Esslingen/Verlag von J. F. Schreiber
viii & 312pp, engraved frontis. & 4 engravings, clo., 146x106mm. NSL:M

6263 DES/ENGLISCHEN KAPITÄNS COOK/ BERÜHMTE/DREI REISEN UM DIE WELT./Für die Jugend/von/Wilhelm Redenbacher/Siebente Auflage/ [vignette]/Esslingen/Verlag von J. F. Schreiber
Seventh edition [inscribed 1888]
218pp, 5pp adv., engraved frontis., 5 b/w illus. in text, pic. bd. (with adv. on e/p & inside covers), 190x125mm. CLRC

REDGRAVE, Leslie Alfred

6264 FEATHERED FAVOURITES/A Booklet of Bird-Verse for the Children,/With illustrations and brief descriptions/By/Leslie Alfred Redgrave/Sydney/ MCMXXXII
Published by the author
32pp (inc. 1p author's foreword), 9 col. illus. & 4 b/w illus., dec. bd., 210x165mm. ANL
• Rpt second edition as above, 1932. Grant

6265 SCRATCH/COCKY!/A Booklet of the Bright/Birds of our Bushland/Pictured in Colour and/Rhymes for the Children/By/Leslie Alfred Redgrave/Author of "Feathered Favourites"/Sydney Australia/1933
Published by the author
32pp, 3pp adv., 12 small col. illus., bd., 215x170mm. NSL:M

'RED-GUM BLOSSOM'

6266 A LITTLE BIT OF/LAUGHTER AND LIFE/FOR THE YOUNG/By/"Red-Gum Blossom"/Adelaide:/ Hussey & Gillingham Limited, Printers and Publishers,/106 and 108 Currie Street,/1912.
106pp, b/w frontis. & b/w drawings in text, illus. by Tom Ferry, dec. bd., 185x225mm. KMM

REDSHAW, Joan

BALLET DANCERS. *See* Australian People
THE COAL MINER
THE MILKMAN
THE NURSE
PILOT AND AIR HOSTESS. *See* Australian People

REED, Alexander Wyclif

6267 ABORIGINAL/FABLES/AND LEGENDARY TALES/by/A. W. Reed/Author of Myths and Legends of Australia/illustrated by/E. H. Papps/A. H. & A. W. Reed/Sydney Wellington Auckland
1965
144pp (inc. 2pp author's introduction), b/w frontis., b/w drawings in text, dec. clo., 185x120mm. KMM

6268 MYTHS AND LEGENDS/OF AUSTRALIA/by/ A. W. Reed/Illustrated by/Roger Hart/[device]/A. H. & A. W. Reed/Sydney Melbourne Wellington Auckland
First published 1965; rpt 1971
256pp (inc. 7pp introduction, glossary, etc.), 30 f/p b/w illus., clo., 205x125mm. CLRC

6269 THE/MISCHIEVOUS/CROW/Stories of the Aborigines/retold by/A. W. Reed/Illustrated by/Max Tilley/A. H. & A. W. Reed/Sydney Melbourne Wellington Auckland
n.d. [1969]
32pp, 8 f/p col. illus., b/w drawings, pic. bd., 280x210mm. CLRC
Text consists of 3 stories.

6270 THE WONDER BOOK OF/AUSTRALIAN ANIMALS/Written by A. W. Reed—Illustrated by Colin Archer/[contents]/First published 1970/A. H. & A.W. Reed/51 Whiting Street, Artarmon, Sydney/[7 lines etc.]
29pp (printed on both e/p), col. illus. throughout, pic. bd., 260x180mm. CLRC

PAGEANT OF THE PACIFIC SERIES
A series of booklets designed for schools divided into 3 sections: The Australian Series, New Zealand Series, & Pacific Series. Only titles in the Australian Series are noted here.
Format example:

6271 Pageant of the Pacific/HOW THE ABORIGINES/ LIVED/by/A. W. Reed/illustrated by/Colin Archer/ [device]/A. H. & A. W. Reed/Sydney Melbourne Wellington Auckland
n.d. [197-?]
24pp, b/w illus. in text, col. pic. wrappers, 246x187mm. KMM
Also, as above, and all KMM

6272 THE DISCOVERY OF AUSTRALIA
6273 THE FIRST SETTLEMENT IN AUSTRALIA
6274 WEATHER AND CLIMATE IN AUSTRALIA

REES, Bob & others
See OUTHWAITE

REES, Coralie [Mrs Leslie Rees, née Clarke]
WAIT TILL WE GROW UP. *See* Australian Youth Plays

6275 WHAT/HAPPENED/AFTER?/Nursery Rhyme Sequels/Written by Coralie Rees. Illustrated by Allan Stomann/Paul Hamlyn/London Sydney New York Toronto
Dee Why West, NSW, 1972
[64]pp, col. illus. throughout, pic. bd., pic. e/p, 315x230mm. CLRC
Prose stories based on familiar nursery rhymes.

REES, George Leslie Clarke

6276 DIGIT DICK/ON THE BARRIER REEF/By/Leslie Rees/[coloured drawing]/Illustrations by Walter Cunningham
On the last page: [coloured illustration]/Copyright 1942 by John Sands Pty. Ltd. All rights reserved. Nothing herein contained to be reproduced without permission of John Sands Pty. Ltd./Printed and

Published in Australia by John Sands Pty. Ltd., Druitt St., Sydney.
[40]pp, alternate col. & part-col. page openings, illus. in text throughout, bd., 240x240mm. KMM
This was the first edition. It has 4 small marginal drawings on pp14, 18, 26 & 36 not reproduced in some later editions. 'Sandman Series' on front cover.

6277 DIGIT DICK/ON THE BARRIER REEF/By/Leslie Rees/[coloured drawing]/Illustrations by Walter Cunningham/Registered in Australia for transmission by post as a book
John Sands Pty Ltd, Sydney, n.d.
[40]pp, pic. t.p., col. illus. throughout, pic. bd., 230x220mm. KMM
(Publishers do not indicate when the book is a reprint, but one copy seen had printed on front cover '65th thousand' and 'copyright 1942' on last page.)

6278 DIGIT DICK ON THE/GREAT BARRIER REEF/by Leslie Rees/illustrated by Hutchings/Paul Hamlyn/London New York Sydney Toronto
First published 1942; this edition published Dee Why West, NSW, 1969
[28]pp, col. illus. throughout, pic. bd., 315x230mm. CLRC

6279 THE STORY OF/SHY/THE PLATYPUS/Written by/Leslie Rees/with illustrations by/W. Cunningham/[device]/John Sands Pty. Ltd.,/Sydney and Melbourne/1944
48pp, 9 f/p col. illus., marginal drawings printed in reddish-brown throughout & col. illus. on pages preceding & following text, bd. with title, author & illustrator printed in 2 col., pic. wrappers, 250x180mm. KMM
This is the first ed. of the first of the Leslie Rees/Walter Cunningham Nature Books. Like all the early ed. the book had a col. pic. wrapper with information about the natural history of the animal or bird concerned printed inside the front flap.
Another ed. as above, but with 'Third Edition' printed on d/w. KMM

6280 THE STORY OF/SHY/THE PLATYPUS/Written by/Leslie Rees/with illustrations by/W. Cunningham/John Sands Pty. Ltd.,/Sydney and Melbourne/1946
Second ed.
Details as above, but covers are plain bd. with pic. d/w, 248x180mm. WRT

6281 THE STORY OF/SHY/THE PLATYPUS/Written by/Leslie Rees/with illustrations by/W. Cunningham/John Sands Pty. Ltd./Sydney, Melbourne, Brisbane, Adelaide, Perth, Hobart
n.d. [1970]
48pp, col. illus. (of platypus on half title & repeated on page at end), 9 f/p illus., marginal drawings printed in green, pic. bd., 240x182mm. ANL

6282 GECKO/The Lizard who lost his Tail/[drawing]/A Story by/Leslie Rees/illustrated by/Walter Cunningham/John Sands Pty. Ltd./Sydney Melbourne Brisbane Adelaide/Perth Hobart/Registered in Australia for transmission by Post as a Book
n.d. [1944?]
[32]pp, alternate col. & sepia illus., pic. bd., 180x235mm. KMM

6283 GECKO/The Lizard who lost his Tail/[col. drawing]/a story by/Leslie Rees/illustrated by/Walter Cunningham/[device]/John Sands Pty. Ltd.
Sydney 1946 [copyright 1943 on back page]
Details as above, but with col. pic. e/p. KMM

6284 *Russian edition*
Published in *Murzilka* Magazine, Moscow, No. 7, 1957.
Unseen: IFA

6285 GECKO/The Lizard who lost his Tail/[drawing]/written by Leslie Rees/Illustrated by Tony Oliver/Paul Hamlyn/London New York Sydney Toronto
1970
[28]pp, col. illus. throughout, col. pic. bd., pic. e/p, 310x230mm. KMM
New edition (with several revisions) with illustrations by a different artist.
• Rpt as above 1972. KMM

6286 Further Adventures of a Wide-eyed Young Australian/DIGIT DICK/AND THE TASMANIAN DEVIL/[coloured drawing]/by Leslie Rees/With illustrations by Walter Cunningham/John Sands Pty. Ltd./Sydney & Melbourne/Registered in Australia for transmission by Post as a book.
n.d. [inscribed 1946]
[40]pp, col. & b/w illus. throughout, pic. bd., 235x235mm. KMM

6287 DIGIT DICK/AND THE/TASMANIAN/DEVIL/By Leslie Rees/Illustrated by Hutchings/Paul Hamlyn/Sydney London New York Toronto
1972
27pp, col. illus. throughout, col. pic. bd., pic. e/p, 315x232mm. KP

6288 THE STORY OF/KARRAWINGI/THE EMU/Written by/Leslie Rees/with illustrations by/Walter Cunningham/[device]/John Sands Pty. Ltd., Sydney and Melbourne
n.d. [1946?]
[44]pp, 6 f/p col. illus., marginal drawings throughout, pic. bd., col. pic. d/w with note on the Emu, 240x175mm. KMM
First winner of CBCA Award 1946.

Russian edition

6289 Russian translation dated 1957
96pp, b/w illus. throughout by Russian artist, dec. bd., dec. e/p, 215x160mm.
Edition of 115 000 copies. Unseen: IFA

Armenian edition

6290 QARROUNGI EMOUI Patmouthyoune, Yerevan, Haypethrat, 1963
66pp, illus., 23cm. Unseen: ANB 1964

6291 THE STORY OF/SARLI/THE BARRIER REEF/TURTLE/Written by/Leslie Rees/illustrated by/Walter Cunningham,/[device]/John Sands Pty. Ltd./Sydney and Melbourne
n.d. [1947]
44pp, 6 f/p col. illus., 3 smaller col. illus. & marginal drawings, pic. bd., pic. d/w with note on the turtle, 240x180mm. KMM

6292 Another copy rpt as above, but: John Sands Pty. Ltd./Sydney, Melbourne, Brisbane/Adelaide, Perth, Hobart
n.d. [1966?]
Details as above, but 235x175mm. KMM

6293 THE STORY OF/SARLI/THE BARRIER REEF/TURTLE/Written by/Leslie Rees/illustrated by/Walter Cunningham/John Sands Pty Ltd/Sydney, Melbourne, Brisbane/Adelaide, Perth, Hobart
n.d. [1967?]
44pp, 6 f/p col. illus., 3 smaller col. illus., col. marginal drawings, pic. bd., 235x175mm. BBC

6294 MATES OF THE/KURLALONG/by/Leslie Rees/Illustrated by/Alfred Wood/[drawing]/John Sands Pty. Ltd./Sydney, Melbourne and Brisbane
n.d. [1948]
255pp (inc. 2pp author's foreword), 12 f/p b/w drawings & drawings in text throughout, clo., dec. map e/p, 185x125mm. KMM

6295 THE STORY OF/SHADOW/THE/ROCK WALLABY/Written by/Leslie Rees/With illustrations by/Walter Cunningham/[device]/John Sands/Pty. Ltd./Sydney, Melbourne/and Brisbane.
n.d. [1948]
44pp, 7 f/p col. illus. & marginal drawings, col. illus. on front fly & back e/p & on pic. d/w, bd., 240x175mm. KMM

6296 BLUECAP/AND BIMBI/[irregular lines]/The Blue Wrens/Written by/Leslie Rees/Pictured by/Walter Cunningham/[coloured drawing]/Trinity House, Sydney
First published 1948 [actually did not appear till 1950]
[32]pp (inc. 1p foreword by J. R. Skemp), 4 f/p col. illus. & col. illus. in text throughout, pic. bd., dec. e/p, 240x180mm. KMM

6297 THE STORY OF/KURRI KURRI/THE KOOKABURRA/[drawing]/Written by Leslie Rees/ Illustrated by Margaret Senior/Published by John Sands Pty. Ltd.
Sydney n.d. [1950]
43pp, 8 f/p col. illus. & drawings in text throughout, dec. bd. (with author, title & small drawing of a kookaburra printed in 2 colours), col. pic. d/w (with publisher's blurb describing the natural history of the kookaburra), col. pic. e/p, 240x180mm. KMM

6298 THE STORY OF/KURRI KURRI/THE KOOKABURRA/Written by Leslie Rees/Illustrated by Margaret Senior/Published by John Sands Pty. Ltd. Registered in Australia for transmission through the post &c
n.d. [1970]
43pp, double-spread t.p. printed in 2 col. with drawing of a kookaburra, 8 col. illus. & drawings, col. pic. bd., col. dec. map e/p, 237x180mm. NSL:M

6299 QUOKKA/ISLAND/By/Leslie Rees/With drawings by/Arthur Horowicz/Collins/St. James's Place, London/1951
254pp, 1p adv., b/w frontis. & 10 b/w illus., clo., dec. e/p, 190x125mm. ANL

6300 QUOKKA ISLAND/By/Leslie Rees/Collins/ London—Sydney
n.d. [1957]
254pp, b/w frontis. & 10 b/w illus., clo., dec. e/p, 190x125mm. KMM

6301 Leslie Rees/QUOKKA ISLAND/Collins/St James's Place/London
First publ. 1950; first issued in this ed. 1966
192pp (inc 1p author's note), b/w drawings in text, clo., 196x128mm. KMM

6302 Leslie Rees/QUOKKA ISLAND/School Edition/ Collins/Sydney London
Sydney, 1967
192pp (inc. 1p author's note), b/w drawings, limp clo., 184x120mm. KMM
The Evergreen Library

6303 DIGIT DICK/IN BLACK SWAN LAND/Written by Leslie Rees/[coloured drawing]/illustrated by Walter Cunningham/John Sands Pty. Ltd.—Sydney Melbourne/Registered in Australia for transmission by post as a book
n.d. [1952]
40pp, col. illus. throughout, pic. bd., 240x230mm. KMM

6304 DIGIT DICK/IN BLACK SWAN LAND/written by Leslie Rees/illustrated by Hutchings/Paul Hamlyn/ Sydney London/New York Toronto
1972
[28]pp, col. illus. throughout, pic. bd., pic. e/p, 310x230mm. KMM
Revised edition of book first published in 1952, with illustrations by a different artist.

6305 THE STORY OF/AROORA/THE RED KANGAROO/[drawing]/Written by/Leslie Rees/ Illustrated by/John Singleton/Published by/John Sands Pty. Ltd.
Sydney, n.d. [1952]
44pp, 7 f/p col. illus. & marginal drawings throughout, bd., pic. d/w, 235x170mm. CLRC

6306 THE STORY OF/AROORA/THE RED KANGAROO/[drawing]/written by/Leslie Rees/ Illustrated by/John Singleton/Published by/John Sands Pty. Ltd.
Published in association with Ure Smith, Sydney, n.d. [1970] [first published 1952]
44pp, col. illus. throughout, bd. (with pic. d/w.), 240x180mm. BBC

6307 TWO-THUMBS/THE STORY OF A KOALA by Leslie Rees/Illustrated by Margaret Senior/[drawing]/ Published by John Sands Pty. Ltd.
Sydney, n.d. [1953]
43pp, 9 f/p col. illus. & part-col. drawings throughout, dec. bd., col. pic. d/w, plain e/p, 240x175mm. KMM
Title printed in black on front cover & small drawing of koala, repeated on t.p. B/w drawing of gum-tree on half-title.

6308 TWO-THUMBS/THE STORY OF A KOALA by Leslie Rees/Illustrated by Margaret Senior/[drawing]/ Published by John Sands Pty Ltd.
Sydney, n.d. [inscribed 1968]
The blurb on the d/w has been slightly re-written. This copy has d/w identical with first ed. & illus. repeated on bd. covers. KMM

Russian edition

6309 Combined Russian ed. of Two Thumbs, Shy, Sarli & Karrawingi—Moscow 1972, b/w illus., ed. of 100 000. Unseen: IFA

6310 DANGER PATROL/A Young Patrol Officer's Adventures/in New Guinea/By/Leslie Rees/Collins/ London—Sydney/1954
255pp, unillus., clo., 185x125mm. KMM

6311 DANGER PATROL/A Young Patrol Officer's Adventures/in New Guinea/by/Leslie Rees/Illustrated by/George W. Brooke/Collins/London—Sydney/1955
255pp, 7 b/w illus., clo., 180x120mm. Grant School edition.
See also PUPIL'S DANGER PATROL COMPANION (Notes on the school edition of the book)

6312 DIGIT DICK/AND THE/LOST OPALS/Story written by Leslie Rees/Drawings by Walter Cunningham/[coloured drawing]/John Sands Pty. Ltd./Sydney Melbourne Brisbane Adelaide Perth Hobart/Registered in Australia for transmission by post as a book
n.d. [1957]
36pp, col. illus. throughout, dec. bd., 240x240mm. KMM

6313 DIGIT DICK/AND THE LOST OPALS/by Leslie Rees/illustrated by Hutchings/Paul Hamlyn/London Sydney New York Toronto
1971
[28]pp, col. illus. throughout, pic. bd., pic. e/p, 310x230mm. KMM
Revised edition of book first published in 1957, with illustrations by a different artist.

6314 THE STORY OF/KOONAWORRA/THE BLACK

SWAN/Written by Leslie Rees/Illustrated by Margaret Senior/[drawing]/John Sands Pty. Ltd./Sydney Melbourne Brisbane Adelaide Perth Hobart
Sydney, n.d. [1957]
42pp, col. & part-col. illus. throughout, pic. bd., pic. e/p, 245x175mm. KMM

6315 AUSTRALIAN/NATURE TALES/Shy the Platypus/Aroora the Red Kangaroo/Sarli the Turtle/Written by/Leslie Rees/John Sands/Pty. Ltd./Sydney Melbourne Brisbane/Adelaide Perth Hobart
n.d. [1958]
115pp, 16 b/w illus. (inc. photograph of author), clo., 185x125mm. BBC
Illustrations reproducing colour illustrations by Walter Cunningham & John Singleton to original editions. Omnibus volume of the three books mentioned in title.

6316 THE STORY OF/WY-LAH/THE COCKATOO/Written by/Leslie Rees/Illustrated by/Walter Cunningham/John Sands Pty. Ltd./Sydney Melbourne Brisbane Adelaide Perth Hobart/Registered in Australia for transmission through the Post as a book
n.d. [1960?]
42pp, 9 f/p col. illus., 2 f/p b/w illus. & b/w marginal drawings, pic. bd., dec. e/p, 245x180mm. KMM

6317 THE STORY OF/WY-LAH/THE COCKATOO/Written by/Leslie Rees/Illustrated by/Walter Cunningham/John Sands Pty Ltd./Sydney Melbourne Brisbane Adelaide Perth Hobart/Registered in Australia [&c.]
n.d. [1970]
42pp, 9 f/p col. & numerous b/w illus., col. pic. bd., col. pic. e/p, 240x180mm. NSL:M

6318 THE STORY OF/RUSS/THE AUSTRALIAN TREE KANGAROO/[drawing]/Written by/Leslie Rees/Drawings by/Walter Cunningham/Published by/John Sands Pty. Ltd./Sydney Melbourne Brisbane Adelaide Perth Hobart
n.d. [1964]
42pp, 7 f/p col. illus., col. & part-col. marginal drawings, pic. bd., dec. e/p, 235x180mm. KMM

6319 THE STORY OF/RUSS/THE AUSTRALIAN TREE KANGAROO/[b/w drawing]/Written by/Leslie Rees/Drawings by/Walter Cunningham/Published by/John Sands Pty. Ltd./Sydney Melbourne Brisbane Adelaide Perth Hobart
n.d. [1970]
43pp, 7 f/p col. illus. & smaller drawings, col. pic. bd., dec. e/p, 240x180mm. NSL:M

6320 BOY/LOST ON/TROPIC COAST/Adventure with Dexter Hardy/By Leslie Rees/Illustrated by Frank Beck/[device]/Ure Smith Sydney London
1968
192pp, b/w drawings in text, clo., dec. e/p, 215x135mm. KMM

REES, Lucia

6321 THE TUCKONIE TREE SONG/Song/Words and Music/by/Lucia Rees/3/-/Southern/Music Publishing Co./(A/sia Pty Ltd.)/Sydney, Auckland, Melbourne
n.d. [copyright 1956]
4pp, unillus., wrappers, 280x220mm. KP

REEVE, Laura

6322 TWINS/AT BOUGAN-VILLA [*sic*]/A Tale of Magnetic Island/By/Laura Reeve/Cassell and Company Ltd./London Toronto Melbourne and Sydney 1948
256pp, unillus., clo., 180x115mm. ANL
Barrier Reef setting

REEVES, Wilf

See 'Jarl, Moonie'

REID, Desmond

FLASHPOINT FOR TREASON; SHOWDOWN IN SYDNEY. *See* Sexton Blake in Australia

'REID, Frank' [pseud. Alexander Vindex Vennard]

6323 Whitcombe's/Australian Nature Story Readers/TOILERS OF THE REEF/By/Frank Reid/Illustrated from Photographs supplied by/the Queensland Government Intelligence/and Tourist Bureau/For Children aged 9 to 10 years/Whitcombe & Tombs Limited/Melbourne, Auckland, Christchurch, Dunedin, Wellington/and London
n.d. [1925]
48pp, b/w photographic frontis. & 6 photographic illus., wrappers, 180x115mm. KMM
See McLaren 409

REID, G. R. S.

6324 "BOBBY WILD GOOSE/and his/Ragged REGIMENT."/A Little Historical Play/Written by/G. R. S. Reid, M.A.
n.d. [1931] Printed by G. W. Hall, Chatswood, NSW
16pp (last blank), unillus., wrappers, 154x104mm. ANL
Published with 'the approval and recommendation of the Youth Departments of the Presbyterian and Methodist Churches'. Play intended for Sunday Schools on their founder Robert Raikes.

REID, Captain Thomas Mayne

6325 LOST LENORE;/or,/The Adventures of a Rolling Stone./Edited by/Captain Mayne Reid./London:/C. H. Clarke, 13, Paternoster Row.
n.d. [1865]
392pp (inc. 1p preface), engraved frontis. & 7 f/p engraved plates, clo. (dec. in gilt on front cover & spine), 162x100mm. KMM
First one-vol. edition. (First pub. C. J. Skeet, London, 3 vols. 1864)

6326 LOST LENORE/or the/Adventures of a Rolling Stone/By/Captain Mayne Reid/Author of the "Rifle Rangers" [*sic*] and the "Scalp Hunters" [*sic*]/London/George Routledge and Sons, Limited/Broadway, Ludgate Hill/Manchester and New York
n.d. [1888? inscribed 1900]
392pp, unillus., clo., 185x120mm. Grant

6327 LOST LENORE;/or/The Adventures of a Rolling Stone./Edited by/Captain Mayne Reid,/Author of/"The Tiger Unters"[*sic*] / "The Wood Rangers", "The Cliff Climbers",/"The Maroon", Etc. Etc./London: Ward, Lock, and Tyler,/Warwick House, Paternoster Row
n.d.
392pp, 32pp adv., f/p engraved frontis. & 7 f/p engravings, dec. bd. & spine, 175x105mm. Grant

6328 LOST LENORE/or the/Adventures of a Rolling Stone/by/Captain Mayne Reid/Author of "The Rifle Rangers" and "The Scalp Hunters"/Melbourne/E. W. Cole, Book Arcade/Bourke Street
n.d. [inscribed 1925]
392pp, unillus., clo., 175x115mm. Grant

6329 Another copy E. W. Cole, Melbourne, as above but 185x120mm. Grant
The original author of this book, Charles Beach, approached Reid with his manuscript. Reid re-wrote the ms, turning it into a publishable book, and to help the unknown author, it was published under Reid's name as editor. He helped Beach with other books, including his boy's book, *The Way to Win*, entered here under Beach. (Information from W. H. P. Crewdson, Oxford, England)

REJJE, E. [HYDE, E. E. C.]
A MODERN CRUSOE, or 313 Days on a South Sea Islet
Stockwell, Ilfracombe, Devon, 1958
Unseen: story of a boy shipwrecked on a voyage from Hobart to Sydney, by a New Zealand author. Also author of 'Noel: an Australian Story', doubtful children's book.

Remarkable Adventures from Real Life
6330 REMARKABLE ADVENTURES/FROM/REAL LIFE/with seven illustrations/London/The Religious Tract Society/56 Paternoster Row 65 St. Paul's Churchyard/and 164 Piccadilly
n.d.
384pp, 5 f/p b/w illus., clo., 180x120mm. Grant
Contents include: 'A Narrow Escape from Snake Bite' (3pp); 'A Night in Tasmania' (23pp).
6331 REMARKABLE/ADVENTURES/FROM REAL LIFE/with coloured and other illustrations/by/J. Finnemore, R.I./London/The Religious Tract Society/4 Bouverie Street and 65 St. Paul's Churchyard
n.d. [school prize1871]
380pp, 6pp adv., part. col. dec. t.p., col. frontis. & 3 f/p col. illus., 3 f/p b/w illus., pic. clo., 200x130mm. CLRC

RENNEVILLE, Sophie de
6332 LES ENFANTS DE 15 ANS/Histoires à mes jeunes amis/par Me de Renneville/orné de Gravures/[vignette]/à Limoges/chez Barbou, Imp. Libraire
n.d. [1814?]
204pp, engraved frontis. & 2 (?1 missing) engravings, leather (copy appears to have been re-bound), 170x100mm. ANL
Contains one story 'Antony ou la conscience' pp153–73, 9pp of which relate to Australia. Appears to be the earliest story publ. relative to Australia. The story appeared in other collections.

RENTOUL, Annie Isobel [Mrs J. L. Rentoul, née Rattray] & RENTOUL, Ida Sherbourne
6333 MOLLIE'S STAIRCASE/By A. I. Rentoul and I. S. Rentoul/[drawing]/Published by/M. L. Hutchinson,/Glasgow Book Warehouse,/305–7 Little Collins St., Melbourne
n.d. [1906]
52pp, dec. t.p., 12 verses, 12 f/p b/w illus., alternate page openings blank, wrappers, 190x230mm. ANL
Annie Isobel Rentoul, wife of Professor J. L. Rentoul, was the mother of Ida S. Rentoul (later Outhwaite) & Annie Rattray Rentoul.

RENTOUL, Annie Rattray & Ida Sherbourne
6334 MOLLIE'S BUNYIP/By/A. R. Rentoul and I. S. Rentoul/[drawing]/Robert Jolly—Melbourne/1904
The Atlas Press
[50]pp (some blanks), text printed in script, 12 f/p & other b/w drawings throughout, wrappers,190x215mm. ANL

6335 MOLLIE'S ADVENTURES/By/A. R. and I. S. Rentoul./Containing/Mollie's Bunyip/and /Mollie's Staircase/in one book/Commonwealth of Australia:/E. W. Cole, Book Arcade, Melbourne,/333 and 346 George Street. Sydney,/67 Rundle Street, Adelaide./1908.
Two books *Mollie's Bunyip* & *Mollie's Staircase* bound together with new cover and t.p. Contents as for the 2 vols described above. MAC

6336 AUSTRALIAN SONGS/FOR/YOUNG AND OLD/Words by Annie R. Rentoul/Music by Georgette Peterson/Illustrations by Ida S. Rentoul/George Robertson & Co./Propy. Ltd./Melbourne Sydney Adelaide and/Brisbane
n.d. [1907]
32pp, 9 f/p b/w illus., dec. dedication page, pic. wrappers, 240x290mm. ANL
Contents: 'Gobble Wobbles'; 'A Little Aboriginee'[*sic*]; 'Mother Sea'; 'A Strayed Sunbeam'; 'Catching Birds'; 'Goldilocks'; 'Baby Bear'; 'Autumn Wind'; 'Goodnight'.
6337 Another copy as above, but n.d. [1908] & on front cover: 'Second Edition'. NSL:M
Later editions had 28pp.
6338 AUSTRALIAN SONGS/FOR/YOUNG AND OLD/Words by Annie R. Rentoul/Music by Georgette Peterson/Illustrations by Ida S. Rentoul/George Robertson & Company Propy. Ltd.,/Melbourne, Sydney and Brisbane
n.d. ['Third edition' on cover] [On back cover: 'Printers/B. R. Gowan & Co./Stationers etc./Melbourne.']
28pp (inc. b/w frontis. & 1p dedication), 8 f/p b/w illus., pic. wrappers, 245x300mm. Grant
Another copy as above but with variant bdg. KMM
As adv. in the *Argus*, Melbourne, 26/10/07 'limp wrappers in three colours 2/6, or basket linen style 5/-.'
6339 AUSTRALIAN SONGS/FOR/YOUNG AND OLD/Words by Annie R. Rentoul/Music by Georgette Peterson/Illustrations by Ida S. Rentoul-Outhwaite/Copyright Allan & Co Pty Ltd 3/- net/276–278 Collins Street, Melbourne/Adelaide Bendigo Geelong 3/- [1924]
28pp (inc. b/w frontis. & 1p dedication, 9 f/p b/w illus., pic. wrappers, 235x315mm. MAC
Imperial ed. no. 335 on cover.
6340 Imperial Edition No. 335/AUSTRALIAN SONGS/FOR/YOUNG AND OLD/Words by Annie R. Rentoul/Music by Georgette Peterson/Illustrations by Ida S. Rentoul-Outhwaite/Copyright Allans Music Publishers/2/6 net
n.d.
28pp, b/w frontis. & 8 f/p b/w illus., col. pic. wrappers, 234x310mm. MC
Cover as before but printed in red & black on natural col. page.
Another copy as above price 3/-. MC
6341 Imperial Edition NO. 335/AUSTRALIAN SONGS/FOR YOUNG AND OLD/Words by Annie R. Rentoul/Music by Georgette Peterson/Illustrations by Ida S. Rentoul-Outhwaite/Copyright Allans/[device Music Publishers—Melbourne/Sydney/Adelaide/Bendigo/Ballarat/Geelong] 3/- net
n.d.
28pp, b/w frontis. & pic. dedication, 8 f/p b/w illus., pic. wrappers, 235x315mm. MAC
Cover printed in blue, brown & purplish pink. Words & music of 9 songs.

6342 THE LADY OF/THE BLUE BEADS/Her Book/Being an account of her first/Blue Moon spent on Sun Island/George Robertson & Co./Propy. Ltd./Melbourne Sydney Adelaide and Brisbane.
n.d. [1908]
102pp, 2pp dedicatory verse, 13 f/p b/w illus. & b/w drawings in text, clo., 275x215mm. KMM
The author's name does not appear on t.p., but on front cover; also 'illustrated by Ida S. Rentoul'.
Dedicatory verse addressed to Margaret Darnley Naylor (the Lady of the Blue Beads).
Another copy. Variant binding, this copy having grey cardboard covers with blue rexine backstrip & inside a design of flowers & leaves 'The Lady of/the Blue

Beads/A Fairy Story/by/Annie R. Rentoul/Illustrated by Ida S. Rentoul'. Grant

6343 PETER/PAN/The Boy who wouldn't grow up
J. C. Williamson's Theatrical Souvenir, S. Day, Melbourne 1908
12pp, b/w photographs throughout, pic. wrappers, cover design by Ida S. Rentoul, cover title, 125x160mm. NSL:M
Photographs from theatrical production.

6344 THE STORY OF/PETER PAN/By Annie R. Rentoul/[illustration from the pantomime]/Founded on/J. M. Barrie's Delightful Fairy Play/As Presented by/J. C. Williamson in conjunction with Chas. Frohman
n.d.
20pp (inc. 2 verses), b/w photographic illus., pic. wrappers, cover title, 285x220mm. NSL:M
Photographs from stage production. Text includes 2 verses: 'To enjoy Mr. Barrie's Play thoroughly we must forget we have ever grown up' by T.D., & 'Peter Pan's Spring Song to bring Wendy' by A.R.R.

6345 THE STORY/OF THE/PANTOMIME/HUMPTY DUMPTY/Specially written/for the Little Ones/By/Annie R. Rentoul/Illustrations by/Ida S. Rentoul/Direction/J. C. Williamson
Sydney, n.d. [S. Day, Printer]
24pp, 5 f/p col. illus. & 3 small col. illus., b/w drawings in text, pic. wrappers, 280x220mm. NSL:M

6346 BUSH SONGS OF AUSTRALIA/FOR YOUNG AND OLD./Words by Annie R. Rentoul/Music by Georgette Peterson/Illustrations by Ida Rentoul Outhwaite/George Robertson & Co./Pty. Ltd./Melbourne, Sydney, Adelaide and Brisbane
n.d. [1910]
36pp (inc. 1p adv.), 9 f/p b/w illus. & b/w drawings in text, pic. wrappers, cover design printed in 3 colours, 250x300mm. NSL:M
Words & music to the following 8 songs: 'The Bell Bird'; 'The Little Mia-Mia'; 'Kookooburra'; 'The Moonboat'; 'Billy Tea'; 'Way Back'; 'Kangaroo Song'; 'The Fairy Fleet'.

6347 BUSH SONGS OF AUSTRALIA/For Young and Old/Words by Annie R. Rentoul/Music by Georgette Peterson/Illustrations by Ida Rentoul-Outhwaite/Copyright 3/- net/Allan & Co. Pty. Ltd./276–278 Collins Street, Melbourne/Adelaide Bendigo Geelong
n.d.
36pp (inc. 1p dedicatory verse), 1p adv., 9 f/p b/w illus. & b/w drawings in text, pic. wrappers, 250x300mm. KMM

6348 BUSH SONGS OF AUSTRALIA/FOR YOUNG AND OLD/Words by Annie R. Rentoul/Music By Georgette Peterson/Illustrations by Ida Rentoul-Outhwaite/Copyright 3/- net/Allan & Co./Melbourne Sydney Adelaide Bendigo Geelong
n.d. [inscribed 1935]
36pp (inc. 1p dedicatory verse), adv. verso back wrapper, 9 f/p b/w illus. & b/w drawings throughout, pic. wrappers, 234x303mm. MC
Imperial ed. no. 336. Beige paper printed in black on green background.

6349 MORE/AUSTRALIAN SONGS/For/Young and Old/Words by Annie R. Rentoul/Music by Georgette Peterson/[contents]/Illustrations by Ida S. Rentoul-Outhwaite/George Robertson & Company Propy. Ltd./Melbourne, Sydney, Adelaide and Brisbane
n.d. [1913]
36pp (inc. dedicatory verse), 8 f/p b/w illus. & drawings in text, pic. wrappers, 245x310mm. NSL:M
Contents: 'As I went O'er the Paddocks'; 'Cooee'; 'Possum'; 'Boomerang'; 'Wattle'; 'Corroboree'; 'Among the Ti-tree'; 'The Southern Cross'.
• Rpt as above n.d., but
Allan & Co./Melbourne, Sydney Adelaide
Same cover, but Allan & Co Melbourne &c on front. MC

6350 MORE/AUSTRALIAN SONGS/FOR/YOUNG AND OLD/Words by Annie R. Rentoul Music by Georgette Peterson/[contents]/Illustrations by Ida S. Rentoul-Outhwaite/Allan & Co. Pty. Ltd./Collins Street, Melbourne/Sydney Adelaide Bendigo
n.d. [1924?]
36pp, 8 f/p b/w illus. & drawings in text, pic. wrappers, 250x300mm. NSL:M

ELVES AND FAIRIES. *See* Outhwaite, Ida Rentoul

6351 THE LITTLE GREEN ROAD/TO FAIRYLAND/By/Annie R. Rentoul/and/Ida Rentoul Outhwaite/[vignette]/A. & C. Black Ltd./4, 5 & 6 Soho Square London W.1/1922
103pp (& 2pp preliminary verses), col. frontis. & 7 col. & 8 b/w plates, dec. bd. with clo. spine & pic. title label pasted on front cover, dec. e/p, 260x200mm. KMM

6352 THE LITTLE GREEN ROAD TO FAIRYLAND. A special deluxe edition with details as above but bound in cream buckram was published simultaneously with the ordinary first edition, and was limited to 300 copies signed by author and artist. QSL

6353 THE LITTLE GREEN ROAD/TO FAIRYLAND
Second edition 1925
as above, but b/w illus repro. on text paper, clo. bdg with title, engraving & author's name on panel pasted on front cover, 200x145mm. KMM

6354 THE LITTLE GREEN ROAD/TO FAIRYLAND/By/Annie R. Rentoul/and/Ida Rentoul Outhwaite/[vignette]/A. & C. Black Ltd./4, 5 & 6 Soho Square London W1
First publ. 1922; rpt 1925, 1932
103pp & 1p preliminary verse, col. frontis. & 7 f/p col. plates & 8 f/p b/w plates, drawings in text, dec. e/p, clo., 264x198mm. KMM

6355 THE/LITTLE GREEN ROAD/TO FAIRYLAND/By/Annie R. Rentoul/and/Ida Rentoul Outhwaite/with sixteen plates/eight in colour/by Ida Rentoul Outhwaite/Adam and Charles Black/4, 5 & 6 Soho Square London W.1/1947
94pp, 1p dedicatory verse, 1p preliminary verse, col. frontis. & 7 col. plates, 8 b/w plates, clo., dec. e/p, 265x195mm. ANL

6356 THE/LITTLE GREEN ROAD/TO FAIRYLAND/By/Annie R. Rentoul/and/Ida Rentoul Outhwaite/with sixteen plates/eight in colour/by Ida Rentoul Outhwaite/[vignette]/Adam and Charles Black/4, 5 & 6 Soho Square London W.1
First pub. 1922; rpt 1925, 1932, 1947; First Australian edition 1948 [this edition was printed in Australia]
94pp, 1p dedicatory verse, 1p preliminary verse, col. frontis. & 7 col. plates, 8 b/w plates, clo., dec. e/p, 260x190mm. KMM
THE LITTLE GREEN ROAD TO FAIRYLAND
• Rpt 1954 [printed in Australia]
Details as in 1948 edition. KMM

6357 THE LITTLE GREEN ROAD/TO FAIRYLAND/By/Annie R. Rentoul/and/Ida Rentoul Outhwaite /[vignette]/E. P. Dutton & Company/New York
n.d. [1922?]
viii (inc. prelim. verse) 103pp. Details as in first English ed. (printed by Billing & Sons, Guildford, as was the

first English ed.), mottled boards, clo. spine, with title, author's & illustrator's name on front cover, 260x200mm. MAC

6358 Imperial Edition No. 394/AUSTRALIAN BUSH/ SONGS/A selection of old favourites in new form: The Little Aboriginee [*sic*]/Baby Bear and others from the famous series of books by these/writers, with simplified accompaniments and easy keys./Words by/ Annie R. Rentoul/Music by/Georgette Peterson/Cover design by Ida Rentoul Outhwaite/Contents [17 songs]/ Allan & Co. Prop. Ltd./Melbourne Sydney Adelaide Bendigo
n.d. [1937, copyright 1936]
32pp, unillus., illus. wrappers, 260x180mm. KMM
Words & music of children's songs.
Another copy as above, but after 'contents' Copyright Price 2/- net./Allan & Co. Prop. Ltd &c. This is probably earlier than the ed. previously described which has the price "3/-" incorporated in the Ida Rentoul Outhwaite cover design. KP
Another copy as above, but reprinted many times; copies seen with price varying from 2/- to 45c on front cover. Contents the same on varying shades of cream to orange wrappers. KP
Other copies seen with minor variations in adv. and printed matter inside covers. MC
FAIRYLAND by Ida Rentoul Outhwaite; verses by Annie R. Rentoul. *See* Outhwaite, Ida Rentoul

RENTOUL, Annie Rattray & WHEELER, Alfred
6359 THE/ROSE OF JOY/A Cantata for Children/By/ Annie R. Rentoul/and/Alfred Wheeler/[drawing]/ Copyright/Price 1/-/.../Allan & Co. Prop. Ltd./ 276–278 Collins Street, Melbourne./Adelaide Bendigo Geelong/Printed in England
n.d.
44pp (last page adv.), 2 photographic illus., pic. wrappers (with adv. inside front & back covers), 250x190mm. KP
6360 Imperial Edition No. 62/THE/ROSE OF JOY/A Cantata for Children/By/Annie R. Rentoul/and/Alfred Wheeler/[drawing]/Copyright Price 1/6/Allan & Co., Prop. Ltd./Melbourne Sydney Adelaide Bendigo
n.d.
44pp (last page adv.) pic. wrappers, (with adv. inside front & back covers), 250x180mm. KP

RENTOUL, Ida Sherbourne
See Outhwaite, Ida Rentoul, & also Rentoul, Annie Rattray

[REVOIL, Bénédict-Henry]
6361 VOYAGE/AU/PAYS DES KANGAROUS/adapté de l'Anglais/par/Bénédict-Henry Revoil/[device]/ Tours/Alfred Mame et fils, Éditeurs/MDCCCLXXVI
254pp (inc. 4pp contents), b/w frontis. & 1 f/p engraving, dec. clo., g.e., 240x150mm. ANL
6362 Another copy as above, but MDCCCLXXXI
240pp (inc. 4pp contents), b/w frontis. & 1 f/p engraving, dec. bd., g.e., 240x150mm. ANL
6363 Another copy as above, but MDCCCLXXXV
This ed. has 3 additional illus., 1 f/p and 2 smaller. ANL

'REX' ed. [W. Rex Plaistowe]
6364 SPARKLETS/A selection of Poems and Stories/ wirtten by members of the 2TM/Sparklers Club during the first year of the Club's activities./Compiled and edited by Rex and/arranged for publication by Rosalind/McCandless
Station 2TM, Tamworth, NSW [1945]
96pp (inc. 1p statistics of club), dec. in text, bd., 214x140mm. KP

Rhymeland Picture Book
6365 RHYMELAND/PICTURE BOOK/Brightly colored Board Book
R. P. Dean & Co., Adelaide
[10]pp, col. illus. throughout, col. pic. wrappers, cover title, 290x208mm. KMM
Printed on light bd., illus. signed 'M. Brittain' some initailled 'A.G.E.' Conventional nursery rhymes.

RICE, Esmée
6366 QUACKLE DUCK/Stories by/Esmée Rice/Pictures by/Elizabeth Paterson/Georgian House, Melbourne 1947
24pp, 6 f/p col. illus. & b/w drawings, bd., 190x240mm. VSL

6367 THE SECRET/FAMILY/By/Esmée Rice/Illustrated by/Pixie O'Harris/Angus and Robertson/Sydney: London/1948
263pp, bw/frontis. & 5 f/p b/w illus., clo., 183x120mm. KMM

RICE, Jo
6368 ROBBIE'S MOB/Written by/Jo Rice/Illustrated by Shirley Hughes/[device]/World's Work Ltd/The Windmill Press/Kingswood Tadworth Surrey
1971
151pp, b/w drawings in text, clo., 215x135mm. VSL
Story set in Australia where the author spent some years as a child.

RICHARDSON, John
6369 GENDARME/THE POLICE HORSE/John Richardson/Photography Ian Brown/To Vanessa and Rowland/and/Bett Edson-Brown
Lansdowne Press Pty Ltd, Melbourne 1971
32pp, b/w photographs throughout, clo., 275x215mm. CLRC
• Rpt 1972. KP

6370 SUEY/THE SHEEP-DOG/John Richardson Photography Ian Brown/To Norman and Bett/and Mary
Lansdowne Press Pty Ltd, Melbourne 1972
[32]pp, b/w photographic illus. throughout, pic. bd., 275x210mm. BBC

[RICHARDSON, L. S. (ed.)]
See ADVENTURE IN THE SKY

RICHARDSON, Robert
6371 THE/BOYS OF SPRINGDALE;/or,/The Strength of Patience./By/Robert Richardson, B.A./Ninth thousand/Edinburgh:/William Oliphant & Co.
n.d. [1875]
64pp, unillus., dec. clo., with col. onlay on front cover, 160x105mm. ANL

6372 THE COLD SHOULDER,/or,/A Half-Year at Craiglea./By Robert Richardson, B.A.,/Author of 'The Boys of Springdale,' etc/Edinburgh:/William Oliphant & Co./1876
128pp, col. frontis. & 2 f/p b/w illus., dec. clo. with col. onlay on front cover, 170x114mm
Frontis. of boy playing cricket. School story set in NSW. NLS

6373 THE/CRAIGLEA BOYS/by/Robert Richardson, B.A./Author of/'The Boys of Springdale' Etc./ Edinburgh & London/Oliphant, Anderson & Ferrier
n.d.

128pp, b/w frontis., dec. clo., 172x116mm. MAC
Later ed. of *The Cold Shoulder*

6374 OUR JUNIOR/MATHEMATICAL MASTER./And/ A Perilous Errand./By Robert Richardson,/Author of 'The Boys at Springdale' 'A Half-Year at Craiglea'. etc./ Edinburgh: William Oliphant and Co./1876
95pp & 1p blank & 8pp adv., col. frontis. only, dec clo., 155x103mm. NLS
Contains title story and 'A Perilous Errand.' Second story also school story set in NSW.

6375 THE BOYS OF/WILLOUGHBY SCHOOL/By/ Robert Richardson, B.A./Author of/"the Cold Shoulder" "Our Junior Mathematical Master"/"The Boys of Springdale" etc./London/Sampson Low, Marston & Co. Ltd.
n.d. [1925? first pub. 1877]
143pp, 17pp notes on children's authors & 32pp adv., col. frontis. only, 185x120mm. ANL
Set in Sydney.

6376 BLACK HARRY;/or,/LOST IN THE BUSH/By/ Robert Richardson/Author of/The Cold Shoulder, Our Junior Mathematical Master/The Boys of Springdale etc. etc./Edinburgh/William Oliphant and Co./1877
96pp, col. frontis. & separate col. t.p., clo., 160x100mm. ANL
Book also includes: 'Joe Wilmot's Quarrel' (25pp, not Australian).

6377 As above but /Edinburgh/Oliphant, Anderson & Ferrier
n.d. [pencilled on t.p. 1885]
96pp, 16pp adv., b/w frontis. (different from frontis. to 1877 ed.) & 3 b/w illus., clo., 170x115mm. ANL
Book also includes: 'Joe Wilmot's Quarrel'.

6378 As above, but 'and 24 Old Bailey, London', no adv. MAC

6379 BLACK HARRY/or/Lost in the Bush/By/Robert Richardson/Author of/'The Craiglea Boys' 'Our Junior Mathematical Master'/'The Boys of Springvale'/Etc. Etc./Illustrated/Edinburgh & London/Oliphant Anderson & Ferrier
n.d.
96pp, b/w frontis. & 4 f/p b/w illus., dec. clo., 173x116mm. KP

6380 THE/YOUNG CRAGSMAN,/and other stories./By Robert Richardson, B.A./Author of 'The Cold Shoulder', 'Our Junior Mathematical Master', etc. etc./ [device]/Edinburgh:/William Oliphant and Co./1878
127pp & 16pp adv., b/w frontis. & 1 f/p b/w illus., pic. clo., 172x115mm. NLS
Other stories: How the Fight was stopped; Adam Ransome's Nephy, An Irish Girl. None Australian.

6381 PHIL'S CHAMPION:/An Irish Story./By/Robert Richardson, B.A./Author of 'The Young Cragsman',/'The Cold Shoulder', 'The Boys of Willoughby' [*sic*] , 'Black Harry',/'Our Junior Mathematical Master', etc./Edinburgh:/William Oliphant & Co./1880.
128pp, b/w frontis. & 2 f/p b/w illus., dec. clo., 170x114mm. NLS
Story of a Dublin boot black, and the lost uncle who emigrates to Australia & then NZ. Note: 'The outline of this story is fact. It is founded on a little ballad poem by Lord Southesk, entitled "Frankie" (*The Meda Maiden and other Poems*) which again is based on a short narrative written by Miss Davies in *The Helping Hand* for 1875.'

6382 ALMOST A HERO;/or,/School-Days at Ashcombe./By/Robert Richardson/Author of "The Young Cragsman", "The Boys of Willoughby" [*sic*]/etc. etc./With illustrations/London:/T. Nelson and Sons, Paternoster Row./Edinburgh; and New York./1880.
236pp & 2pp adv., b/w frontis. & 5 f/p b/w illus., dec. clo., 176x116mm. NLS
Boys' school story set in Devon.

6383 BENEATH/THE SOUTHERN CROSS;/A Story./ By/Robert Richardson, B.A./Author of 'Almost a Hero', 'Phil's Champion', Etc etc/[Latin quote]/ Edinburgh:/The Edinburgh Publishing Co./London: Simpkin, Marshall, & Co./1880
194pp & 7pp adv., unillus., pic. bd., 180x120mm. NSL:M

6384 LITTLE FLOTSAM/A Story for Boys and Girls./ and other Tales./By/Robert Richardson, B.A.,/Author of 'Phil's Champion' &c./[vignette]/Cassell, Petter, Galpin & Co./London, Paris & New York.
[1881]
220pp & 4pp adv., b/w frontis. & 12 f/p b/w illus. & small illus. in text, dec. clo., 180x116mm. NLS
These stories originally appeared in *Little Folk*.
Contents: Little Flotsam; How we spent Christmas Day in Australia; Jake the Little Juggler; The Best of Chums.

6385 LITTLE FLOTSAM./A Story for Boys and Girls./ And other Tales./by/Robert Richardson, B.A./Author of 'Phil's Champion' etc./[vignette]/Tenth Thousand./ Cassell & Company, Limited:/London, Paris and Melbourne
n.d. [inscribed 1896]
220pp, 16pp adv., engraved frontis., 13 f/p engraved illus. & engravings in text, dec. clo., 180x115mm. CLRC
The first story *How we spent Christmas Day in Australia*—a child's description of a Christmas dinner picnic at Pearl Bay, Middle Harbour, Sydney written for relatives in England. This is the only Australian story in the collection.

6386 THE BEST OF CHUMS/And other Stories./By/ Robert Richardson, B.A.,/Author of 'Boys of Springdale', 'The Young Cragsman', 'Phil's Champion',/'Beneath the Southern Cross', 'Little Flossam' [*sic*], etc./Edinburgh:/Oliphant, Anderson, & Ferrier/(late William Oliphant & Co.)/1881
127pp, b/w frontis. & 3 f/p b/w illus., dec. clo., 185x118mm. NLS
Contains also Karl, the foster son; Grandfather's Pipe; Going for the Doctor; Ernest's Wonderful Night; Uncle Ben & the Smugglers. The Best of Chums & Going for the Doctor (only Australian story) have appeared in *Little Folks*.

6387 A LIGHTHOUSE KEEPER/FOR A NIGHT./And other Stories./by Robert Richardson, B.A./Author of the 'Young Cragsman', 'Phil's Champion', Etc/ Edinburgh:/Oliphant, Anderson, & Ferrier/(late William Oliphant & Co.)/1881
62pp, col. frontis. only, clo. with col. onlay (of 2 men in a small boat waving to a figure on the lighthouse), 160x100mm. NLS
Title story rpt from *Little Folks*. Book also contains Trapped in an Attic, and A Cornish Lassie. None Australian in subject matter.

6388 THE TWO BROTHERS/by/Robert Richardson,/ Author of 'Almost a Hero', 'Beneath the Southern Cross'/'Phil's Champion', etc./Edinburgh:/Oliphant, Anderson, & Ferrier./1881
62pp, col. frontis. only, dec. clo. with col. onlay (of a fair) on front cover, 160x100mm. NLS
Uniform with *A Lighthouse Keeper*. Street strollers, a

mother & 2 boys are performing as 'Savoyards'. Set in Scotland.

6389 A CORNISH LASSIE;/and/THE TWO BROTHERS./By/Robert Richardson/Author of 'Almost a Hero', 'Beneath the Southern Cross'/'Phil's Champion'/New Edition/Edinbugh:/Oliphant Anderson & Ferrier/and 24 Old Bailey, London
n.d. [inscribed 1894]
92pp & 4pp adv., b/w frontis. & 1 b/w illus., dec. clo., 173x115mm. NLS
A Cornish Lassie 22pp; The Two Brothers 57pp. Neither Australian background.

6390 A LITTLE AUSTRALIAN GIRL/or/The Babes in the Bush;/and/Jim: A Little Nigger./By Robert Richardson, B.A.,/Author of 'Phil's Champion', 'The Young Cragsman', 'Little Flotsam' etc./Edinburgh:/Oliphant, Anderson, & Ferrier/1881
64pp, col. frontis., 2 f/p b/w illus., pic. bd., col. onlay (not reproduced elsewhere) on front cover, 158x102mm. MAC
First story only Australian relating to children lost in the Bush.

6391 A LITTLE AUSTRALIAN GIRL:/or,/The Babes in the Bush,/And Other Stories/By/Robert Richardson, B.A./Author of/'Phil's Champion', 'The Young Cragsman', 'Little Flotsam', etc./Edinburgh:/Oliphant, Anderson, & Ferrier
n.d.
97pp & 1p adv., b/w frontis. only, dec. clo., 164x105mm. CLRC
Contains title story, Jim: A Little Nigger, A Lighthouse Keeper for a Night, and Trapped in an Attic. Last 2 stories earlier publ. in separate vol.

6392 A LITTLE AUSTRALIAN GIRL;/or,/The Babes in the Bush,/And Other Stories./by/Robert Richardson, B.A.:/Author of/"Phil's Champion", "The Young Cragsman", "Little Flotsam", etc./New Edition./Edinburgh:/Oliphant Anderson & Ferrier./and 24 Old Bailey, London
First published 1881; this edition n.d. [inscription 20/12/1899]
98pp (last page adv.), 3 f/p engravings, dec. clo., 170x115mm. CLRC
Book contains, as well as title story, 3 other non-Australian stories.

6393 RALPH'S/YEAR IN RUSSIA./A Story of Travel and Adventure/in Eastern Europe./By/Robert Richardson./Author of 'Almost a Hero' 'The Young Cragsman'/'The Boys of Willoughby School'/etc. etc./With nine engravings/London:/T. Nelson and Sons, Paternoster Row./Edinburgh; and New York./1882
351pp, engraved frontis. & 8 f/p engravings, pic. clo. with some letters & part of illus. blocked in gilt on both front cover & spine, patterned e/p, 177x117mm. ANL

6394 THE HUT IN THE BUSH:/A Tale of Australian Adventure./And other Stories./By/Robert Richardson, B.A.,/Author of 'Beneath the Southern Cross', 'Phil's Champion',/'The Young Cragsman', 'The Best of Chums', 'Ralph's Year in Russia'/etc etc/Edinburgh:/Oliphant, Anderson, & Ferrier/1883
128pp, b/w frontis. & 2 f/p b/w illus., dec. clo. with frontis. illus. printed in gilt on front cover, 170x115mm. NSL:M
Title story & one other with Australian background.

6395 THE HUT IN THE BUSH;/A Tale of Australian Adventure./And other Stories./By/Robert Richardson, B.A./Author of 'Phil's Champion' 'The Young Cragsman'/'The Best of Chums', etc etc./New edition/Oliphant, Anderson, & Ferrier,/Edinburgh/and 24 Old Bailey, London
Details as above, 174x115mm. MAC

6396 ADVENTUROUS/BOAT VOYAGES/by/Robert Richardson,/Author of "Ralph's Year in Russia", "Almost a Hero"/Etc. Etc./With eighteen illustrations/London:/T. Nelson and Sons, Paternoster Row./Edinburgh; and New York./1886
256pp (inc. 4pp author's introduction), b/w frontis. & 18 f/p b/w illus., pic. clo., 180x120mm. HBM
Pp11-43 relate to Bligh's famous voyage in an open boat. Other contents not Australian.

6397 STORY OF THE NIGER/A Record of Travel and Adventure/From the Days of Mungo Park/To the Present Time./By/Robert Richardson,/Author of "Adventurous Boat Voyages", "Almost a Hero",/"Ralph's Year in Russia"/With 51 illustrations./London:/T. Nelson and Sons, Paternoster Row./Edinburgh; and New York./1893
xiipp, 357pp (inc. 2pp preface) & 2pp adv., additional dec. t.p., b/w frontis., 3 maps & illus. throughout, pic. clo., 180x125mm. ANL
Various travels on the Niger.

RICHTER, Friedrich

6398 NEUE BIBLIOTHEK/DER/UNTERRICHTS-LECTÜRE/fur Engänzung des häuslichen und Schulun- terrichts/für/die Jugend beiderlei Geschlechts/in/Geschichte, Geographie und Naturgeschichte,/herausgegeben/von/Dr Friedrich Richter,/von Magdeburg/Zweite verbesserte Auflage/Zweite Abtheilung./Geographie und Ethnographie/4th Band/Magdeburg 1848
334pp. unillus., yellow paper wrappers, 174x110mm. NSL:M
First 92pp Australian

RIDLEY,William

6399 GURRE KAMILAROI;/or/Kamilaroi Sayings/By/William Ridley,/Missionary.The engravings by W. Mason/[2 line quote]/Sydney:/Printed at the Empire General Steam Printing Office,/173 George Street,/1856
[Sydney]
t.p. & 15pp text, 8 b/w engravings on 2 pp and 8 additional (inc. 2 f/p, last 3 of Jesus with his disciples, and on the Cross) bd., clo. spine 182x122mm. CLRC
Includes a 3pp explanation of the translation of the Kamilaroi language of the Namoi River natives, and a key to their speech; then an English translation of the missionary's text attempting to explain briefly and simply the Creation and Jesus's mission.

RIENITS, Rex

JAMES COOK. *See* Australian Explorers

RILEY, Quintin & TAYLOR, Richard

6400 A Puffin Picture Book/DISCOVERY OF THE POLES/Quintin Riley Richard Taylor
Penguin Books, Harmondsworth, Middlesex, England, 1957
30pp, col. & b/w illus. & maps throughout, dec. wrappers, cover title, 180x220mm. KMM
Half the book deals with Antarctica.

Rippard, the Outlaw

See 'Alouette'

RITCHIE, Paul

6401 AUSTRALIA/by Paul Ritchie
The Macmillan Company, New York;
Collier-Macmillan Limited, London 1968
120pp (inc. 4pp index, etc.), b/w photographic frontis.

& b/w photographic illus. throughout, pic. clo., 230x155mm. CLRC

RITTER, Fred

6402 MODERN/NURSERY/RHYMES/By Fred Ritter/ Decorations by/Roma Thompson and I. G. Paggett/ Printed and Published by Fred Ritter
Melbourne 1949
[44]pp, 1p verse, col. dec. t.p., part. col. decorations & b/w drawings throughout, pic. bd., 215x140mm. NSL:M

RITTER, Paul

6403 CHILD'S EYE VIEW/NURSERY RHYMES/By Paul Ritter/Let the Children colour them!/Illustrated by/ Leonora,/Erica/Penny./[3 drawings of children's heads]
The Ritter Press, 7 Magdala Road, Nottingham [WA], 1959
[40]pp text & illus. printed in grey, card cover, 880x141mm. WJSB
Dec. cover reads
Everybody/Silly/Sometimes

RIVERS, A. R.

6404 MENTION' IN 'PATCHES/By/A. R. Rivers/ Cabarlah, Queensland
['Mentioned in Despatches']
n.d. [1920?]
33pp, b/w drawings, bd., 205x165mm. ANL

RIXSON, Marjorie

6405 THEY SAIL AT SUNRISE/By/Marjorie Rixson/ Illustrated by Joan Turner/Georgian House/Melbourne 1946
118pp, 1p verse, 8 f/p b/w illus. & b/w drawings in text, clo., 210x130mm. VSL

ROACH, Eva M.

6406 WHAT THE WIND/WHISPERED/By Eva M. Roach/Drawings by Rosemary Cave
Printed by Harman & Jacka, Adelaide, n.d. [1933]
32pp, b/w drawings throughout, wrappers (with b/w illus. on front cover), cover title, 230x135mm. KMM
Some of the verses appeared in the *Australasian.*

6407 OVER/THE/HILL/Verses by/Eva M. Roach/ Drawings by/Rosemary Cave
Printed by Harman & Jacka, Adelaide, n.d. [1934]
36pp (inc. 1p preface by Catherine Stow (K. Langloh Parker), b/w drawings throughout, wrappers (with col. illus. on front cover), cover title, 230x140mm. KMM
Some of the verses appeared in the *Australasian.*

Road Safety Rules for Children

6408 ROAD SAFETY RULES/FOR CHILDREN/Issued in the Interests of Children's Safety/By Children's Safety Aids.
Melbourne, n.d. Printed by Hedges and Bell, Sutton Road, Maryborough, Vic.
32pp, part-col. illus. throughout, interspersed with pages of b/w adv. material, wrappers, cover title, 175x120mm. KP
Another copy as above with schools of a different area printed inside front cover (printed in a different col.):
No 1 Ocean Grove—Geelong South Primary School
No 2 Clayton South—Sussex Heights Primary School
KP

ROBERTS, B. J.

6409 THE LITTLE OLD MAN/A "Phonics" Story/B. J. Roberts/Third Edition/Lothian Publishing Co. Pty. Ltd./Melbourne and Sydney
34pp, col. frontis., b/w drawings throughout, pic. wrappers, 185x125mm. KP
Educational. Introduction dated 1928

6410 THE LITTLE OLD MAN/A "Phonics" Story/B. J. Roberts/Lothian Publishing Co. Pty. Ltd./Melbourne and Sydney
1930
32pp, 1p col. illus. & 31 b/w illus., pic. wrappers, 185x125mm. TG

6411 THE LITTLE OLD MAN/A "Phonics" Story/B. J. Roberts/Lothian Publishing Co. Pty. Ltd./Melbourne and Sydney
n.d. [1944]
32pp, col. illus. on alternate page openings, b/w drawings, stiff dec. wrappers, 185x120mm. ANL

ROBERTS, Thelma

6412 STORIES/FOR/KINDERGARTEN/by/Thelma Roberts/The National Press Pty. Ltd./Melbourne C.1.
n.d.
32pp, b/w line drawings in text signed 'T.E.R.', wrappers, 185x125mm. Grant

ROBERTS, Victor

6413 "THE STORY/OF/MOTHER GOOSE"/Story by Victor Roberts/from the book by/Percy King/With/ illustrations by/Betty & Esther Paterson/[drawing]/As Related in the Pantomime/"Mother Goose"/Xmas and New Year
Victory Publicity Pty Ltd, 262 Queen Street, Melbourne, n.d. [193-?]
32pp (last blank), 7 f/p col. illus. & b/w illus. in text, pic. wrappers, 244x185mm. KMM
Adv. inside front & back covers & also on back of back cover
'Listen in to 2UW ('The Search for the Golden Boomerang') at 6.13 pm on Tues. Wed. & Thurs. each week'
Mother Goose at the Tivoli Theatre.

ROBERTSON, Andrew

6414 THE/KIDNAPPED SQUATTER/and other Australian Tales/By/Andrew Robertson/London/ Longmans, Green, and Co./and New York: 15 East 16th Street/1891/All rights reserved
227pp, 26pp adv., unillus., clo., 185x120mm. ANL
Contains 3 stories in addition to the title story, & although not intended as a children's book, could have been read by children.

6415 NUGGETS/IN THE/DEVIL'S PUNCH BOWL/And Other Australian Tales/By/Andrew Robertson/Author of "The Kidnapped Squatter" etc./London/Longmans, Green, and Co./and New York: 15 East 16th Street/ Melbourne/Melville, Mullen, and Slade/1894
218pp, 3pp adv., unillus., clo., 185x120mm. ANL
Contains 3 stories in addition to the title story.

ROBERTSON, T. Brailsford

6416 THE UNIVERSE AND THE/MAYONNAISE/and other stories for children/By/T. Brailsford Robertson/ Illustrated by/K. Clausen/London: John Lane: The Bodley Head/New York: John Lane Company/ Toronto: Bell & Cockburn. MCMXIV
125pp, dec. t.p., col. frontis. & 7 f/p col. illus., b/w marginal drawings, tailpieces &c. throughout, dec. clo., dec. e/p, 210x170mm. KMM
Stories about science for children.

ROBINSON, C. N. & LEYLAND, John

6417 IN THE/ QUEEN'S NAVEE/ The Adventures of a Colonial Cadet/ on his way to the 'Britannia"/ By Commander C.N.Robinson, R.N./ and/ John Leyland/ Illustrated by Walter W. Way/[device]/London/ Griffith, Farran & Co./Newbery House, 39 Charing Cross Road
n.d. [advertisement dated 1892–93]

382pp, 40pp adv., b/w frontis. & 12 f/p b/w illus., b/w drawings in text, pic. clo., 190x130mm. Grant
Chapters 1–15 relate to Australia & the Pacific.

6418 IN THE/ QUEEN'S NAVEE/ The Adventures of a Colonial Cadet/ on his way to the 'Britannia'' By Commander C.N.Robinson, R.N./ and/ John Leyland Illustrated by Walter W. Way/ [device]/ Griffith Farran Browne & Co. Limited/ 35 Bow Street, Covent Garden, London
n.d.
382pp, b/w frontis. & 12 f/p b/w illus., pic. clo., 190x133mm. KP

ROBINSON, Michael

6419 THE HARE TRIES AGAIN/by Michael Robinson/ Illustrated by Tony Oliver/[drawing]/Paul Hamlyn/ London/Sydney/New York/Toronto
1971
[26]pp, col. illus. throughout, pic. bd., pic. e/p, 315x230mm. CLRC

6420 TRACTORS, TRUCKS AND OTHER BIG THINGS/Written by Michael Robinson Illustrated by Ted Martin/Paul Hamlyn/Sydney London New York Toronto
Dee Why West, NSW, 1972
64pp, col. illus. throughout, pic. bd., dec. e/p, 310x230mm. CLRC

ROBINSON, Olga Meredith

6421 OLGA'S DREAMS AND/FANCIES/By/Olga Meredith Robinson/Sydney:/Tyrrell's Ltd., 99 Castlereagh Street/1918
[58]pp (inc. dedication & preface, alternate page openings blank, 9pp b/w sketches & 16pp part col., wrappers, 210x280mm. Grant
The front cover reproduces a photograph of Olga at 7 years of age with pen & paper at table.

ROBINSON, Roland [ed.]

6422 WANDJINA/Children of the Dreamtime:/ Aboriginal Myths & Legends/Selected by Roland Robinson/with illustrations by Roderick Shaw/The Jacaranda Press
Milton, Queensland, 1968
112pp (inc. 8pp introduction, etc.), col. frontis., col. & part-col. illus. throughout, pic. clo., 275x200mm. KMM

ROBSON, Jeremy

6423 The Adventure Book Library/DESTINATION/THE POLES/Text by Jeremy Robson/Illustrations by Robert Lumley/Aldus Books
1968
59pp, col. & b/w illus. on alternate page openings, pic. bd., 152x100mm. KP
Contents: Riding the Ice by Fridjof Nansen; Farthest South by Roald Amundsen; In Defeat, Glory by Robert Scott; The New Man by Vivan Fuchs.

ROBSON, L. L.

A CONVICT. *See* Early Australians

Robur Animal Book

6424 ROBUR/[illus.]/ANIMAL BOOK
Robur Tea Co. Ltd, Clarendon St, South Melbourne, n.d. [193-?]. Printed in Australia by Chas. Steele & Co., Melbourne
12pp, sepia/white illus. throughout, pic. wrappers, 183x120mm. KP

'ROBY' [Robert Wolff]

BIRDS AND ANIMALS OF AUSTRALIA. *See* Casley-Smith, J. R.

ROCHE, J. W. [ed.]

6425 Thrilling Fact and Fiction Series/ANTARCTIC ADVENTURERS/Compiled by/J. W. Roche/ Illustrations by R. G. Botting, A.R.C.A./[publisher's device]/Hulton Educational Publications.
1959
216pp (inc. 1p preface, 2pp introduction, 2pp glossary & 8pp questions), b/w drawings in text, limp clo., 185x120mm. BBC

ROCHESTER, Geo E.

BUCKAROO-OUTLAW. *See* Boys' Friend Library

RODD, Lewis Charles

HENRY PARKES. *See* Great People in Australian History

6426 THE BAD BOY FROM/THE MISSISSIPPI/The Story of/Mark Twain/by L. C. Rodd/F. W. Cheshire/ Melbourne Canberra Sydney
1966
28pp (inc. 3pp 'Bookman's guide to reading Mark Twain'), unillus., dec. wrappers, cover design by G. Melrose, 210x140mm. 'Know your Author' series. KMM

Uniform with above, and all KMM

6427 HIS FATHER'S/MATE/The Story of/Henry Lawson

6428 LOUISA, THE/RUNAWAY TOMBOY/The Story of/Louisa M. Alcott

6429 RUDDY/THE BLACK SHEEP/The Story of/ Rudyard Kipling

6430 THE BOY WHO WAS/ ALWAYS SUPPOSING/ The Story of Robert Louis Stevenson

6431 THE YOUNG FUR/TRADER/The Story of/R. M. Ballantyne

ROE, Michael

PHILIP GIDLEY KING. *See* Great Australians

ROGERS, G. Hunter

6432 MY TRIP/by/''Bunty''/Illustrated by/Hunter Rogers/Hall's Book Store Pty Ltd./Melbourne
1964
99pp, bw/drawings throughout, bd., map e/p, 200x135mm. NSL:M
The story of a toy Pomeranian dog who journeyed from Australia to England. NSL:M

ROGERS, J. N.

6433 THEY WENT/TO LOOK AT/THE KING/by/J. N. Rogers/Illustrated by/Harry J. Weston/Published by/ Frank Johnson/350 George Street, Sydney./60 Market Street, Melbourne
n.d. [1946]
32pp, b/w drawings, dec. wrappers, 210x180mm. ANL

ROGERS, June & McKAY, Gwendda (eds)

6434 AWAY/WITH ME/journey no. 1/Stories, Poems, Songs and Activities for Young Children/June Rogers and Gwendda McKay (Eds)/June Epstein (Music)/Ray Bowler, Intercel Australia (Design and Illustration)/Angus and Robertson Education
1972
48pp, part-col. illus. throughout, pic. bd., 247x186mm. ANL

6435 AWAY/WITH ME/JOURNEY NO. 2
1972
Uniform with above. ANL
Preface states that the main material was written by students of the Melbourne Kindergarten Teachers College.

ROGERS, Stanley

6436 FREEBOOTERS OF/THE PACIFIC/By/Stanley Rogers/Author of "The Barbary Pirates" "The Atlantic Buccaneers"/"Modern Pirates" etc./Blackie & Son Limited/London and Glasgow
n.d. [194-?]
224pp, b/w frontis. only, clo., 185x120mm. KMM
Includes one chapter on Dampier (36pp).

ROLAND, Betty

6437 THE/FORBIDDEN BRIDGE/Betty Roland/Illustrated by/Geraldine Spence/[publisher's device]/Acorn Library/The Bodley Head/London
1961
78pp, 10 b/w illus., clo., dec. e/p, 185x135mm. CLRC
• Rpt 1965. KP

6438 THE/FORBIDDEN BRIDGE/Betty Roland/Illustrated by/Geraldine Spence/[device]/Acorn Library/The Bodley Head. London/Collins Publishers Sydney
First Australian ed. 1965
78pp, 10 b/w drawings, pic. wrappers, 180x124mm. KW
Norwegian edition

6439 Betty Roland/DEN FARLIGE/BROEN/Illustrert av/Geraldine Spence/[device DAAM]/N. W. Damm & Son/Oslo
1962
120pp, 3pp adv., 10 b/w illus., bd., 150x120mm.
Unseen: IFA & The Bodley Head Ltd
Afrikaans edition

6440 DIE/VERBODE BRUG/Betty Roland/John Malherbe Edms Beperk/Posbus 1207 Kaapstad/1963
71pp, 10 b/w illus. (as in English edition), clo., 180x135mm. Unseen: Information from The Bodley Head Ltd
Another copy of the Afrikaans edition, as above, but bound in bd. & size 135x190mm is reported to have been received by the Bodley Head in March 1964, & they query whether this is a second edition.
Swedish edition

6441 BETTY ROLAND/DEN FÖRBJUDNA/BRON/[drawing]/Albert Bonniers förlag/Stockholm
Stockholm, Bonnier, 1965
71pp & 1p adv., b/w drawings in text, pic. bd., 229x156mm. ANL
Tr. Rigmor Lindwall. Illus. Stig Södersten.

6442 JAMIE'S DISCOVERY/Betty Roland/Illustrated by/Geraldine Spence/[device]/Acorn Library/The Bodley Head/London
First published 1963
77pp, 7 f/p b/w illus. & 3 smaller b/w illus., clo., dec. e/p, 185x135mm. BBC
• Rpt 1969. KP
Afrikaans edition

6443 DIE GROT/IN DIE KLOOF/Betty Roland/John Malherbe Edms Beperk/Posbus 1207 Kaapstad/1963
78pp, 10 b/w illus. (as in English edition), bd., 180x135mm. Unseen: IFA

6444 JAMIE'S DISCOVERY/Betty Roland/Illustrated by/Geraldine Spence/Scholastic Book Services/New York Toronto London Auckland Sydney Tokyo
n.d. [1970?]
77pp, 10 b/w drawings, pic. wrappers, 184x130mm. ANL

6445 JAMIE'S/SUMMER VISITOR/Betty Roland/Illustrated by/Prudence Seward/[device]/Acorn Library/The Bodley Head/London
1964
75pp, 8 f/p b/w illus., clo., dec. e/p, 185x135mm. KMM
• Rpt 1969. KP

6446 JAMIE'S/SUMMER VISITOR/Betty Roland/Illustrated by/Prudence Seward/McGraw-Hill Book Company/New York San Francisco
First distribution in the United States 1967
73pp, 8 f/p b/w illus., clo., dec. e/p, 180x130mm. CLRC

6447 JAMIE'S/OTHER GRANDMOTHER/Betty Roland/Illustrated by/Prudence Seward/[device]/Acorn Library/The Bodley Head/London Sydney/Toronto
1970
87pp, 12 b/w drawings, clo., dec. e/p, 185x130mm. KMM

6448 JAMIE'S/OTHER GRANDMOTHER/Betty Roland/Illustrated by/Prudence Seward/Scholastic Book Services/New York Toronto London Auckland Sydney Tokyo
1970
82pp, 12 b/w drawings, pic. wrappers, 180x120mm. KW

6449 THE/BUSH/BANDITS/Betty Roland/Illustrated by/Genevieve Melrose/[drawing]/Lansdowne Press Melbourne 1966
147pp, 1p author's note, b/w drawings in text, clo., 210x130mm. KMM

6450 THE/BUSH/BANDITS/Betty Roland/Illustrated by/Genevieve Melrose/[drawing]/Angus and Robertson/London
1967
147pp & 1p author's note, b/w illus. in text, clo., 213x135mm. KP

6451 THE BUSH/BANDITS/Betty Roland/[drawing]/Illustrated by Genevieve Melrose/Follett Publishing Company/Chicago [device] New York
1969
220pp, b/w illus. in text, clo., 216x149mm. KP

[ROLAND, Sarah Anne Charlotte Amy, née Phillips, Mrs W. J. Martell]

6452 Australian Fairy Lore/ROSALIE'S REWARD;/or,/The Fairy Treasure/By Gumsucker/[verse]/Should this first story be favorably received by the little folks for/whom it is written, it is the Author's intention to publish a series of/tales, so that the merry children of the fair South may revel in dreams of their own Fairy Lore./Ballarat:/Published by Wreford and Co., Albert Street./1870
16pp, unillus., (?wrappers, copy seen re-bound), 170x100mm. NSL:M

ROLLAND, W. M.

6453 Whitcombe's Story Books/BENNIE/THE BANDICOOT/(For Ages 8–9 Years)/By/W. M. Rolland/[drawing]/Whitcombe & Tombs Pty. Ltd./Melbourne, Sydney Perth
1946
31pp, 4 part. col. & other b/w illus., illus. wrappers, 180x115mm. ANL
See McLaren 373

ROLLS, Eric C.

6454 SHEAF TOSSER/and other Poems/[vignette]/By/Eric C. Rolls/Angus and Robertson
Sydney, 1967
58pp, unillus., clo., 215x140mm. KP
Pp49–58 of this book contain poems for children.

Romance in the Making

6455 ROMANCE IN THE MAKING/[col. illus.]/The State Savings Bank of Victoria
Melbourne, 1927

16pp, text surrounded by b/w pic. landscape border on each page, pic. wrappers, cover title, 184x120mm. KP

ROOKE, Daphne

6456 THE/AUSTRALIAN/TWINS/by Daphne Rooke/illustrated by Biro/with an Introduction/by Rhoda Power/[drawing]/Jonathan Cape/Thirty Bedford Square, London
First pub. 1954; 2nd imp. 1955
192pp, b/w illus. throughout, clo., 200x130mm. KMM
American edition

6457 [drawing] TWINS IN AUSTRALIA/Daphne Rooke/Illustrated by Gil Miret/1956/Houghton Mifflin Company Boston/The Riverside Press Cambridge
183pp (inc. 10pp glossary & notes), b/w drawings, clo., 200x130mm. ANL

6458 DOUBLE EX!/by Daphne Rooke/Victor Gollancz Ltd/London 1971
191pp, b/w extended frontis., clo., 195x130mm. KMM
The story takes place in post-war Australia. A party of displaced persons from Europe is travelling to a transit hostel in Pindari Bay, among them two Polish orphans, Herman & Jozef, with their uncle & aunt. Herman steals a box; when the boys open it in the train they discover it contains Double Ex, the dog of the title.

6459 Daphne Rooke/DOUBLE EX!/Cover illustration by John Walsh/[device]/A Piccolo Book/Pan Books Ltd./London
1972
159pp & 1p adv., unillus., pic. wrappers, 178x110mm. KP

ROONEY, Robert

6460 SKIPPING RHYMES/A Collection of Australian Skipping Rhymes/Collected and Illustrated by/Robert Rooney/Moonflower Press/Melbourne/1956
Edition limited to 24 copies
16pp, 6 lino-cuts illus., half leather, 240x185mm. ANL

ROSCHOLLER, John N. (comp.)

6461 CHILD POETS ALL/[drawing]/A collection of poems written by children/in the Primary Schools of the Broadmeadows District/Compiled by John N. Roscholler/Illustrated by A. Stirling
Standard Stationers (& Booksellers), Cheltenham, Victoria, Sept 1969
91pp, part-col. & b/w drawings in text throughout, pic. wrappers, 213x140mm. VSL

ROSCOE, G. T.

6462 OUR NEIGHBOURS/IN/NETHERLANDS NEW GUINEA/G. T. Roscoe/Brisbane/The Jacaranda Press/1959
68pp (inc. 2pp index), b/w map frontis., 8 b/w photographic illus., pic. bd., 206x127mm. CLRC

ROSE, A. J.

6463 HOW PEOPLE LIVE IN/AUSTRALIA/A. J. Rose, M.A./Senior Lecturer in Geography/Australian National University/Ward Lock Educational Co. Ltd. London and Melbourne
1959, 2nd ed. 1962, 2nd imp. 1964, 3rd imp. 1967
102pp (inc. 2pp index, 5pp glossary &c), b/w photographic illus. throughout, pic. clo., 210x160mm. KMM

ROSE, Sir Alec

6464 AROUND THE WORLD/WITH/LIVELY LADY/Sir Alec Rose/Edited by Peter Muccini/Illustrations by John C. Smith/Planning and research by Leander Associates Ltd/Geoffrey Chapman/London Dublin Melbourne 1968
46pp, col. & b/w illus. throughout, pic. bd., 242x204mm. WRT
Account for children of lone-handed voyage round the world, including 2pp on visit to Melbourne & section on Pacific.

ROSE, Ronald

NORTHERN TERRITORY; AUSTRALIA'S ISLAND TERRITORIES; PAPUA AND NEW GUINEA. *See* Around Australia Program

6465 NGARI/THE HUNTER/Ronald Rose/A Panorama Book/Collins/London Sydney/1968
46pp, col. photographic illus. throughout, pic. bd., clo. spine, 290x205mm. CLRC
Book based on the daily life of a Central Australian Aboriginal boy.
• Rpt 1972. KP
US edition

6466 NGARI/THE HUNTER/Ronald Rose/Harcourt, Brace & World, Inc./New York
1968
Details as in Collins edition. ANL

'ROSELER, David' [pseud. E. V. Timms]

6467 LAWRENCE/PRINCE OF MECCA/By/David Roseler/Australia:/Cornstalk Publishing Company/89 Castlereagh Street, Sydney/1927
227pp, col. frontis., 3 b/w maps & 3 f/p b/w illus. by Edgar A. Holloway, clo., 185x115mm. CLRC
New edition 1929 as above but different illus., frontis. portrait by James McBeay, & different size, 175x110mm. Platypus series. KMM

6468 LAWRENCE/PRINCE OF MECCA/By/David Roseler/Australia:/Angus & Robertson Ltd./89 Castlereagh Street, Sydney/1930
122pp, 3 f/p b/w maps, bd., portrait of Lawrence by James McBeay reproduced in col. on front cover, 185x120mm. KP
List of children's books printed on back cover.
Publishers claim this ed. was abridged & adapted for young readers.

ROSKOWSKA, Maria

6469 Egendomligheter/i/Främmande Länder./ENFALDIGE HANS/OCH/STRÅFFANGEN./En Skildring Ur Australiska/Nybyggarelifvet/af/Maria Roskowska,/Forf. Till Pa Halligöarne Och Mooniba./Stockholm,/Sigfrid Flodins Förlag.
1862
90pp, 2pp adv., tinted frontis. & 1 tinted illus., pic. bd., 160x115mm. RM
English translation of t.p.: 'Strange Happenings/in/Foreign Lands./FOOLISH HANS/AND/THE CONVICT./A Story of Australian Settlers' Life/By/Maria Roskowska,/Dedicated by the Author to Pa Halligoarne and Mooniba./Stockholm,/Sigfrid Flodins Publishers'.

6470 Egendomligheter/i/Främmande Länder./II/INDIANHÖFDINGEN MOONIBA,/Eller/Unga Herren Och Vallpojken./Äfventyr bland Australiens vildar./Med tontryckta planscher./Stockholm,/Sigfrid Flodins Förlag
1861
122pp, 1p adv., tinted frontis. & 1 tinted illus., pic. bd., 160x120mm. RM
English translation of t.p.: 'Strange happenings in Foreign Lands/II/THE INDIAN CHIEF MOONIBA,/Or/the young Master and the Shepherd Boy;/Adventures among Australian Savages...'

There is a third book in this series, but it does not relate to Australia.

ROSMAN, Alice Grant

6471 JOCK THE SCOT/The Adventures of the Dog of the House/who gave up town life to run/a country estate/By/Alice Grant Rosman/with 6 coloured plates/ Cassell/and Company Limited/London/Toronto, Melbourne, & Sydney
1930
213pp, col. frontis. & 5 col. illus., b/w drawings, illus. by Joan Esley, clo., dec. e/p, 210x130mm. KMM
Doubtful children's book.
Another copy: Cassell/and Company Limited/London
1951
Details as in previous edition, but plain e/p, 220x140mm. KMM

ROSS, C. Stuart

6472 CONQUERED/BY/LOVE/by the/Rev. C. Stuart Ross/Ballarat:/Printed by A. A. Herberte, Printer, &c. Lydiard Street/1892
51pp, b/w frontis. & 2 b/w illus. in text, b/w chapter headings, wrappers, 180x120mm. Grant
Wrappers read
Australian series/Conquered by Love/by the/Rev. C. Stuart Ross/Melbourne/M. L. Hutchinson/Glasgow Book Warehouse/305 & 307 Little Collins St/1892
Religious story set in Tasmania.

ROSS, Margaret Isabel

6473 GREENTREE/DOWNS/By M. I. Ross/[drawing]/ Illustrated by G. M. Richards/Boston and New York/ Houghton Mifflin Company/The Riverside Press Cambridge
1937
197pp & 1p bibliography, b/w frontis. & 10 f/p b/w illus. & b/w tailpieces, map e/p, clo., 205x140mm. RM
The story of four American children who come to live on a Queensland station.

6474 GREENTREE/DOWNS/By M. I. Ross/[drawing]/ Illustrated by G. M. Richards/London/George Routledge & Sons Ltd./Broadway House: 68–74 Carter Lane E.C./1938
197pp, 4pp adv., b/w frontis. & 10 b/w illus., clo., 185x120mm. VSL

6475 GREENTREE DOWNS/By/M. I. Ross/[publisher's device]/Penguin Books/Harmondsworth Middlesex England/245 Fifth Avenue New York U.S.A.
1945
188pp, 4pp adv., b/w tailpieces, pic. wrappers, 180x110mm. KMM

6476 GREENTREE/DOWNS/M. I. Ross/Illustrated by/ Stuart Tresilian/Longmans
London, 1959
232pp, 6 f/p b/w illus., pic. clo., 165x110mm. KP
Heritage of Literatures series.

6477 THE/DAWN HILL BRAND/A Story of Australia/ By/M. I. Ross/with illustrations by Forrest Orr/ [device]/1939/Houghton Mifflin Company, Boston/ The Riverside Press Cambridge
227pp, b/w extended frontis., b/w illus. in text, clo., pic. e/p, 210x145mm. RM

ROSSITER, Marguerite [pseud. 'Granny']

6478 LITTLE NIPPER/And Other Verses/by Granny/ Illustrated by Atholl MacLennan/[drawing]/Paterson's Printing Press Ltd./65 Murray Street, Perth
n.d. [1947]
32pp, b/w drawings, bd. (clo. spine), 205x160mm. ANL

ROTHWELL, Una

6479 WHERE/ARE THE CATTLE/GONE/Una Rothwell/[device]/Angus and Robertson
Sydney 1966
142pp, unillus., clo., 215x135mm. KMM

6480 NORTH/TO THE/ISA/Illustrated by Helen Sallis/ Rigby Limited./Adelaide 1971
175pp, 10 f/p b/w illus., clo., 210x130mm. KMM
English edition

6481 NORTH/TO THE/ISA/Una Rothwell/Illustrated by Helen Sallis/John Gifford Limited
London 1972
Details as in Rigby edition. BBC

ROUGHLEY, Edna

6482 ELLICE/OF AINSLIE/By/Edna Roughley/The Australasian Publishing Co. Pty. Ltd./Sydney N.S.W.
1947
253pp, b/w frontis., clo., 185x125mm. ANL
Girls' school story set partly on an island off the Queensland coast.

6483 OUR SONGS/Music by Mary Moulton/Words by Edna Roughley/[device]/Australasian Publishing Company/Sydney Wellington London
1952
54pp, pic. wrappers, 245x185mm. KMM
18 songs.

ROWAN, Marian Ellis [Mrs F. C. Rowan, née Ryan]

6484 BILL BAILLIE/His Life and Adventures/By/Ellis Rowan/Author of/"A Flower Hunter in Queensland", "With Pen and Pencil through New Zealand", etc. etc./With eight coloured Illustrations by the Author/ and numerous black and white drawings by Jack Sommers/Melbourne/Christchurch, Wellington, Dunedin N.Z. and London/Whitcombe and Tombs Limited
n.d. [1908]
159pp, 1p author's preface, col. frontis. & 7 col. illus., b/w drawings in text, dec. clo., 175x240mm. KMM
Story, set in the Western Australian countryside, of a bilboa (a small native animal).

6485 Whitcombe's Story Readers/BILL BAILLIE/The Story of a Pet Bilboa/By/Ellis Rowan and Winnifred [*sic*] Scott/For Children aged 10 to 12 years/ Whitcombe & Tombs Ltd./Melbourne/Auckland, Christchurch, Dunedin, Wellington/and London
n.d.
64pp (inc. 2pp introduction by 'Winnifred' Scott), b/w frontis. & 8 b/w drawings in text signed Hans Praetorius, pic. wrappers (with adv. inside front cover & on both sides of back cover), 180x120mm. KMM
From the introduction on 'Mrs Ellis Rowan and how *Bill Baillie* was written' it appears that the book was a collaboration. *See* McLaren 504

ROWCROFT, Charles

TALES OF THE COLONIES
German edition

6486 DIE/ANSIEDLER AUF VAN-DIEMENS-LAND/ Eine Erzahlung aus dem australischen Ansiedlerleben/ von/Charles Rowcroft/Fur die Jugend bearbeitet/von/ Julius Hoffman,/Rekton und Sub-Diaconus in Goswig/ Mit vier kupfern/Breslau/Verlag von Trewendt & Granier/1855
188pp, col. frontis. & 3 f/p col. illus., mottled paper bd. with clo. backstrip, dec. in gilt, 185x130mm. ANL
Swedish edition

6487 NYBYGGARNE/PÅ/VAN DIEMENS LAND./En Berättelse från det australiska nybyggarlifvet/Af/ Charles Rowcroft./Öfversatt från den Tyska

bearbetningen for Ungdom/Af/Julius Hoffman./Med färglagda teckningar./Stockholm,/tryckt hos Eric Westrell, 1861
128pp, 1p foreword, col. frontis. & 3 f/p col. illus., paper-covered bd. with dark green leather backstrip, 180x110mm. RM
This is an anonymous Swedish translation of Julius Hoffman's German abridgement for children; the illustrations are signed 'Tr.hos Anderson'.

ROWE, Agnes M.
6488 [Coat of Arms]/National Song of Australia/Sung by Everyone—Everywhere/YOUNG AUSTRALIA/ Words by/Agnes M. Rowe/Music by/Richmond Fleming/Copyright Price 6d. nett/Published by/ Suttons Pty. Ltd./290–292 Bourke Street, Melbourne/ Ballarat Bendigo Geelong
n.d. [World War I?]
8pp (inc. covers), 1p verse & 3pp music, dec. wrappers, 360x250mm. ANL

ROWE, Jennifer [ed.]
6489 MORE POEMS TO READ TO/YOUNG AUSTRALIANS/By C. J. Dennis Banjo Patterson [*sic*] Pixie O'Harris Lydia Pender/Jeanette Lingard Joan Mellings./Illustrated by Tony Oliver. Selected by Jennifer Rowe/[coloured illustration]/Paul Hamlyn, Sydney London New York Toronto
Dee Why West, NSW, 1971
[25]pp, col. illus. throughout, col. pic. bd., pic. e/p, 315x230mm. KMM
• Rpt 1972. KP

ROWE, John G.
6490 CAPTAIN COOK/EXPLORER AND NAVIGATOR/By/John G. Rowe/Author of/The Island Mine; Queen Alexandra the Beloved; John Howard,/A Popular History of the Great War;/&c. &c./London/The Epworth Press/J. Alfred Sharp
1928
128pp, b/w portrait frontis. & 1 b/w illus., clo., 185x115mm. NSL:M

6491 'BULLY' HAYES,/SLAVE TRADER/By/John G. Rowe/Author of/'The White Prince of the Incas', 'The Boy Orchid Hunters'/'For Honour and Freedom', 'Proving his Mettle', 'The Island Mine'/'Yachting Schoolboys', 'Captain Cook', &c./London/The Epworth Press/J. Alfred Sharp
1929
272pp, col. frontis. only, clo., 187x120mm. ANL

ROWE, John G. & others
6492 SUNKEN GOLD/Australian & other stories of/ Adventure and School/Life London/The Epworth Press/25–35 City Road, E.C.1 1932
192pp, col. frontis. & numerous b/w illus., pic. bd., 215x140mm. KP

ROWE, Minnie I.
6493 THE/WAND OF DAWN/By/Minnie I. Rowe/ Illustrations by the Author/Melbourne Publishing Company/Cromwell Buildings/Melbourne.
n.d. [1918?]
64pp, col. frontis. & 3 f/p col. plates, b/w drawings in text, bd. with col. onlay, 260x205mm. VSL

6494 GULLY FOLK/By/Minnie I. Rowe/Author of/"The Wand of Dawn"/Illustrations by the Author/ Melbourne Publishing Company/Cromwell Buildings/ Melbourne.
n.d.[1919?]
77pp, col. frontis. & 5 f/p col. plates, b/w drawings in text, bd. (with col. illus. pasted on front cover), 210x155mm. KMM

ROWE, Richard [pseud. 'Edward Howe']
6495 THE BOY IN/THE BUSH/by/Edward Howe/ Illustrated by/Zweeker, Fraser, Mahoney, and Dalziel/ London:/Bell & Daldy, York Street/Covent Garden/ 1869
231pp, engraved frontis. & 10 f/p engravings, dec. clo., 170x120mm. CLRC

6496 THE BOY IN/THE BUSH/By Edward Howe/ Illustrated by/Zweeker, Fraser, Mahoney, and Dalziel/ [publisher's device]/Strahan & Co., Publishers/56 Ludgate Hill, London/1872
231pp, b/w frontis. & 10 f/p engravings, dec. clo., 165x115mm. ANL
Serialized in *Good Words* 1869 under the pseudonym of Edward Howe; First edition (Anon) Pub. by Bell & Daldy, 1869, 3 vols.

6497 THE BOY IN THE BUSH/A Tale of Australian Life/By the late/Richard Rowe,/Author of "Roughing it" "The Deserted Ship"/"A Haven of Rest" etc./ Illustrated by/Zweeker, Fraser, Mahoney, and Dalziel/ London: Hodder and Stoughton/27 Paternoster Row/ MDCCCLXXXV/All rights reserved.
231pp, 32pp adv., b/w frontis. & 10 b/w engravings, pic. clo., 180x120mm. VSL

6498 THE/TOWER ON THE TOR/A Tale for Boys/By Richard Rowe/Author of/"Episodes in an Obscure Life" "Jack Afloat and Ashore"/The Boys of Axleford" "The Boy in the Bush"/"A Child's Corner Book", etc/ with illustrations/William P. Nimmo/London: 14 King William Street, Strand/and Edinburgh/1876
ivpp ("To my readers" written for "Good Things"), 314pp & 16pp adv., pic. presentation page, b/w frontis. & 5 f/p engravings, dec. clo., g.e., 174x112mm. KP
Not Australian in content.

6499 A CHILD'S CORNER BOOK/Stories for Boys and Girls,/By Richard Rowe/Author of "Episodes in an Obscure Life", "Jack Afloat and/Ashore", "Hoity Toity", "The Boys of Axle Ford",/"The Tower on the Tor", etc./With illustrations/William P. Nimmo/ London: 14 King William Street, Strand;/and Edinburgh/1876
224pp & 16pp adv., b/w engraved frontis. & 3 f/p illus., dec. clo., title in gilt, col. dec. presentation page, g.e., 164x104mm. RH
Contains Australian story: The Bunyip 7pp.

6500 THE LUCKY BAG/Stories for the Young./By Richard Rowe/Author of "Episodes in an Obscure Life", "Jack Afloat and/Ashore", "Hoity Toity", "The Tower on the Tor"/"The Child's Corner Book", etc./ with illustrations./William P. Nimmo./London: 14 King William Street, Strand;/and Edinburgh./1876
224pp & 16pp adv., col. pic. presentation page, b/w frontis. & 3 f/p engravings, dec. clo. with gilt & all edges gilt, 164x100mm. KP
Contains The Wedge-tailed Eagle pp7-18, The Iguana's Eyes pp102-9, Good for Evil pp223-4, all Australian in content.

6501 A HOLIDAY BOOK/Stories for the Young/By/ Richard Rowe/Author of "Episode in an Obscure Life" "The Tower on the Tor"/"A Child's Corner Book" "The Lucky Bag" etc/With Illustrations/William P. Nimmo/London and Edinburgh/1877
viiipp, 288pp, engraved frontis. & 5 b/w engravings, dec. clo. with title in gilt panel, col. dec. presentation page, g.e., 170x115mm. RH
Contains The Southern Cross and Charles's Wain 54p.

6502 THE/HISTORY OF A LIFEBOAT./By/Richard Rowe,/author of/"Episodes in an Obscure Life" "A

Holiday Book" "The Tower on the Tor"/"A Child's Corner Book" "The Lucky Bag", &c &c/William P. Nimmo,/London and Edinburgh./1878
123pp, col. frontis. only, col. onlay pasted on front cover, dec. clo., 165x100mm. KP
Contains also 'The Rescue from the "Earl of Eldon" ', neither of Australian content.

6503 ROUGHING IT IN VAN/DIEMEN'S LAND/Etc./By the Author of/"The Boy in the Bush"/Strahan and Company Limited/34 Paternoster Row, London/All rights reserved
n.d. [1880]
351pp, unillus., dec. clo., 170x110mm. ANL
The author's name appears as 'Edward Howe' on front cover & spine.
The title story consists of the first 130 pages, then follows 'The Adventures of Harry Delane', but pagination continues; only small part of the action of this second story takes place in Australia.

6504 ROUGHING IT IN VAN/DIEMEN'S LAND/etc./By the author of/"The Boy in the Bush"/[device]/Strahan and Company Limited/34 Paternoster Row, London/All rights reserved
n.d.
351pp, unillus., clo., 165x115mm. Grant
Title & 'Richard Rowe' in gilt on front cover & spine.

6505 ROUGHING IT/IN/VAN DIEMEN'S LAND/By the author of "The Boy in the Bush"/Second Edition/London/W. Swan Sonnenschein & Co./Paternoster Square/1884
351pp, unillus., clo., 160x100mm. CLRC
Another copy, as above, but clo. with cover design in black, & title in gilt on spine, 175x120mm. Grant

6506 FRED LEICESTER;/or,/The Southern Cross and/Charles's Wain./And other Stories./By/Richard Rowe,/Author of 'Jack Afloat and Ashore', etc./Edinburgh:/W. P. Nimmo, Hay, & Mitchell,/1889
126pp, 16pp adv., unillus., dec. clo., 170x110mm. CLRC
Title story only of Australian content (56pp).

6507 THE/GOLD DIGGERS/By/Richard Rowe/Author of "Jack Afloat and Ashore" etc./[device]/London/Sampson Low, Marston & Co., Ltd.
n.d. [192-?]
126pp, 2pp adv., col. frontis. only, clo., 180x120mm. CLRC
Frontis. signed 'M.L.P.'
Contents: 'Fred Leicester; or, The Southern Cross and Charles's Wain' (56pp); 'John Bulb, the Barber' (32pp, not Australian); ' "Dark Denim" and his Grandson' (31pp, not Australian).
Also author of *Peter Possum's Portfolio* (Sydney 1858), which is not a children's book, and *Picked up in the Streets* (1880), which is not Australian and not a children's book.

The Royal Visit Souvenir Cut-Out Book of Framed Portraits

6508 THE/ROYAL VISIT/SOUVENIR CUT-OUT BOOK OF/FRAMED PORTRAITS/with a pictorial itinerary of the Royal Tour in Color/[portrait of Royal pair]/Her Majesty Queen Elizabeth the Second/and/His Royal Highness the Duke of Edinburgh.
n.p., n.d. [1954]
8pp & 2pp inset of cut-out portraits, pic. bd., cover title, 350x240mm. KP
Back cover a col. map of Australia showing itinerary.

The Royal Visit to Australia 1954

6509 This Souvenir/of/THE ROYAL VISIT/TO AUSTRALIA/1954/is presented to/[blank line]/of [blank] School/by/The Commonwealth Government of Australia
16pp, t.p. surrounded by dec. coat of arms printed in black & red, text & part-col. photographic illus. & dec., map of Australia & itinerary, dec. wrappers, 120x175mm. KP

RUDDUCK, Loma

6510 NOW/I'M A BROTHER/[drawing]/by/Loma Ruddock/Illustrated by/Nancy Parker/Georgian House/Melbourne
n.d. [195-?]
24pp, b/w drawings throughout, dec. wrappers. KMM

RUHEN, Olaf

6511 CORCORAN'S/THE/NAME/Angus and Robertson Sydney; Copyright 1956, 1957, 1959, 1964, 1965, 1967
160pp, extended illus. t.p., illus. by Jennifer Tuckwell, clo., 215x135mm. KMM
Story of a sixteen-year-old boy cattle-drover in northern Australia. Chapters of the book have appeared in various periodicals, including *Saturday Evening Post, Squire, Man*, &c.

US edition

6512 CORCORAN'S THE NAME/Olaf Ruhen/An Ariel Book/Farrar, Straus and Giroux, New York
1968
150pp, extended illus. t.p., otherwise unillus., clo., 205x135mm. ANL

RULE, Gordon A.

6513 HUMPHREY/LEARNS/TO SKATE/Gordon A. Rule/Rigby
Adelaide 1969
[18]pp (printed on both e/p), col. illus. throughout, pic. clo., 250x185mm. WRT

6514 HUMPHREY BEAR/AND CONSTABLE/SNIFTER/Gordon A. Rule/Rigby
Adelaide 1970
[18]pp, col. illus. throughout, pic. clo., 250x185mm. KMM
• Rpt as above 1971. KMM
Uniform with the above, all Rigby, 1970:
6515 HUMPHREY GOES FISHING. CLRC
6516 WILBUR'S NARROW ESCAPE. CLRC

6517 HUMPHREY/AND/THE BEES/Gordon A. Rule/Rigby/Opal Books
Adelaide 1972
[18]pp (printed on both e/p), col. illus. throughout, col. illus. e/p, pic. bd., 255x190mm. BBC
As above:
6518 HUMPHREY AND THE CATS
6519 HUMPHREY'S VISIT TO HOSPITAL
6520 HUMPHREY'S VISIT TO THE ZOO

6521 HUMPHREY BEAR'S/FUN BOOK/Written and Illustrated by/Humphrey B. Bear/assisted by/Virginia Fallon, Michael Lodge and Kit Keane/Octopus Books
Sydney, 1972
191pp, col. illus. t.p. & frontis., col. illus. throughout, pic. bd., pic. e/p, 283x203mm. CLRC

RUPERT THE RABBIT

See Joy series

RUSH, Philip

6522 HE SAILED/WITH DAMPIER/Philip Rush/Illustrated by/Richard Ogle/London New York/T.V. Boardman and Company Limited/14 Cockspur Street, SW1
First publ. 1947
192pp, col. frontis. & 3 col. plates, 10 b/w illus., clo., dec. map e/p, 183x117mm. KP

6523 HE WENT WITH/DAMPIER/by/Philip Rush/ illustrated by/P. A. Jobson/[device]/George G. Harrap & Co. Ltd./London Toronto Wellington Sydney
First publ. in Great Britain 1957, rpt 1958
184pp (inc. 1p author's note), b/w frontis. & drawings in text, clo., 198x130mm. KP

'RUSSELL, Arthur' [pseud. Arthur Russell Goode]

6524 DREAM ISLE/An Australian Story/By/Arthur Russell/With illustrations by/R. B. Ogle/[vignette]/ London/The "Boy's Own Paper" Office/4 Bouverie St. and 65 St. Paul's Churchyard, E.C.
n.d. [first edition 1926]
149pp, 2pp adv. (The Garland Library, R.T.S.), col. frontis. & 2 b/w illus., pic. clo., 185x120mm. KMM

6525 DREAM ISLE/An Australian Story/By/Arthur Russell/With illustrations by/R. B. Ogle/London/The 'Boy's Own Paper' Office/4 Bouverie St. E.C.4.
n.d. [1931]
149pp, col. frontis. & 2 b/w illus., clo., 180x115mm. VSL

6526 BUNGOONA/An Australian Story/By/Arthur Russell/Author of "Dream Isle"/With illustrations by/ R. B. Ogle/London/The "Boy's Own Paper" Office/4 Bouverie Street, E.C.4.
n.d. [1928]
192pp, 1p adv. (preceding t.p.), col. frontis. & 2 f/p b/w illus., clo., 180x115mm. ANL

6527 Whitcombe's Story Books/GINGER FOR PLUCK/ by Arthur Russell/(Author of "Dream Island", "Bungoona", "The Woman of/Mystery", "Cleansing Fires", etc. etc.)/[drawing]/(For Ages 8 to 10 years)/Whitcombe & Tombs Limited/Christchurch, Auckland, Wellington, Dunedin, Invercargill, N.Z.,/London, Melbourne, Sydney
n.d. [1929]
47pp, 1p adv., b/w frontis. & 2 b/w illus., pic. wrappers (with adv. on covers), 180x120mm. Grant
Story of a 13-year-old boy on the River Murray.
See McLaren 339

6528 TONY D'ALTON'S/WIRELESS/By/Arthur Russell/Author of "Dream Isle", "Bungoona"/"Twenty-six Radio Stories", etc./ Coloured frontispiece by/C. P. Shilton/London/The "Boy's Own Paper" Office/4, Bouverie Street, E.C.4.
n.d. [1931]
183pp, col. frontis., clo., title, author & publisher in gilt on spine, 180x115mm. ANL
Another undated rpt with black lettering, as above. KP

6529 TWENTY-SIX/RADIO STORIES/By/Arthur Russell/Author of "Bungoona", "Dream Isle", "Tony/ D'Alton's Wireless", etc./Illustrated by/Vernon Soper/ London/The "Boy's Own Paper" Office/4, Bouverie Street, E.C.4
n.d. [1931]
288pp, col. frontis., 4 f/p b/w illus., clo., 215x140mm. KMM

6530 SNOWY FOR LUCK/By/Arthur Russell/Pictures by/Kurt Wiese/A Junior Press Book/Albert Whitman/ & Co./Chicago/1934
128pp, b/w illus., clo., 210x150mm. VSL

6531 TWENTY-SIX/AUSTRALIAN STORIES/by/Arthur Russell/Author of "Dream Isle", "Bungoona", "Tony/ D'Alton's Wireless" "Twenty-six/Radio Stories" etc. etc./London/The "Boy's Own Paper" Office/4 Bouverie Street, E.C.4
n.d. [1934]
256pp, col. frontis. & 4 f/p b/w illus. by J. F. Campbell, clo., 215x135mm. NSL:M

6532 THE/CAVES OF BARAKEE/by/Arthur Russell/ Author of "Bungoona" "Dream Isle", "Tony/D'Alton's Wireless", "Twenty-Six Radio Stories",/"Twenty-Six Australian Stories", etc./London/The Boy's Own Paper Office/Bouverie Street, E.C.4
n.d. [1936]
157pp, col. frontis. only, clo., 180x120mm. KP

6533 TWENTY-SIX/SOUTHSEA STORIES/By/Arthur Russell/Author of "Bungoona", "Dream Isle", "Tony/ D'Alton's Wireless", "Twenty-Six Radio Stories",/"Twenty-Six Australian Stories"/London/ The "Boy's Own Paper" Office/Bouverie Street, E.C.4.
n.d. [1937?]
252pp, 1p adv., col. frontis. & 4 b/w f/p illus., clo., 210x135mm. ANL

6534 THE SKY PIRATES/by/Arthur Russell/[publisher's device]/Cassell & Company Ltd./London, Toronto, Melbourne/and Sydney
1946
240pp, 5 b/w illus. by Bruce Crampton, clo., 180x115mm. ANL
Second edition as above September 1947. KMM

6535 MASON'S CIRCUS/by Arthur Russell/Illustrated by/Edith B. Bowden/F. W. Cheshire Pty. Ltd./ Melbourne and London
n.d. [on verso of t.p. 1957]
214pp, b/w frontis. & b/w drawings in text, clo., 180x115mm. VSL

RUSSELL, B. E.

6536 RABBIT'S BANE/or/A Ferret's Tale/A True Story/ [drawing]/By B. E. Russell/G. T. Foulis & Co./ London/Lothian Publishing Co. Pty. Ltd./Melbourne and Sydney.
n.d. [1940]
78pp, 5 f/p b/w photographic illus., b/w drawings, 185x125mm. VSL

6537 "GEOFFREY"/or a Cat's Tale/By/B. E. Russell/ Author of/Rabbit's Bane or a Ferret's Tale/Lothian Publishing Company Pty. Ltd./Melbourne and Sydney
March 1941
63pp, 11pp adv., 4 f/p b/w photographic illus., b/w drawings, wrappers, 175x120mm. VSL

RUSSELL, Countess Mary Annette

THE APRIL BABY'S BOOK OF TUNES. *See* [Arnhim, Countess Mary Annette von]

RUSSELL, Nancy

6538 SEVEN/LITTLE STORIES/By/Nancy Russell./ (Aged 8¾)./Second Edition./Profits go to the Children's Home./Printed at/"The Bunbury Herald" Office/Bunbury
[1917] [Preface dated November 1917, Western Australia]
15pp (inc. 2pp preface), unillus., pink paper wrappers with title &c printed in black, 136x93mm. RM
Contains 6 stories & the preface which is in the form of a letter explaining that the booklet was produced as a Christmas letter & was 'a little belated because the first lot printed were mislaid, and they had to be done again'. This apparently is the reason for the 'second edition'. Appears to have been the first children's book publ. in WA.

RUST, Doris

6539 TALES FROM THE/AUSTRALIAN BUSH/by/

Doris Rust/illustrated by/Cecil Elgee/Faber and Faber/24 Russell Square/London
1968
56pp, 8 f/p b/w illus., b/w drawings in text, pic. bd., 210x150mm. KMM

RUTHERFORD, Meg
6540 THE BEAUTIFUL ISLAND/Meg Rutherford/ [illustration]/London—George Allen and Unwin Ltd
1969
63pp, b/w illus. on alternate pages. pic. clo., 185x245mm. CLRC
An architectural fantasy created by the use of collage. The author/illustrator is Australian.

RUTLEY, C. Bernard
6541 WILD LIFE IN THE/ICE AND SNOW/By/C. Bernard Rutley/illustrated by Stuart Tresilian/London/ Macmillan and Co. Ltd./1943
62pp, 62pp, 63pp, b/w illus., clo., 190x130mm. KP
3 stories bound together, inc. *Gogo the Penguin* 6pp.

6542 BULLION/ISLAND/By/C. Bernard Rutley/ London/George Newnes Limited/Tower House, Southampton Street/Strand, W.C.2
1949
256pp, unillus., clo., 185x120mm. KMM

6543 THE/PERIL OF THE BUSH/By/C. Bernard Rutley/London/George Newnes Limited/Tower House, Southampton Street/Strand W.C.2
1950
224pp, unillus., clo., 180x120mm. ANL
The hero of this boys' adventure story runs away to sea on a ship bound for Australia. He settles in Victoria where he has adventures at the Ballarat gold diggings, and with bushrangers, &c.

6544 GOGO/THE PENGUIN
Macmillan & Co Ltd, London, 1965
64pp, b/w illus. (Stuart Tresilian) in text, pic. wrappers, cover title, 190x132mm. KP
Wild Life Story Readers

6545 ISLAND OF SECRETS/By/C. Bernard Rutley/Peal Press
London, n.d. [1966]
168pp, 2 f/p b/w illus., bd., 184x120mm. ANL

RYAN, E. Lee
6546 FIVE LITTLE/BUSH/GIRLS/By/E. Lee Ryan/ Illustrated by Betty Paterson/Australasian Author's Agency/237 Collins Street, Melbourne
October 1918
235pp, b/w frontis. & 2 f/p b/w illus., clo., 190x120mm. VSL
Children's story relating to Sydney & station life in New South Wales.

RYAN, Peter
REDMOND BARRY. *See* Great Australians

RYLAH, Ann Flora Flashman [pseud. 'John Wotherspoon']
6547 WHERE THE/EAGLES NESTED/[drawing]/Ann F. Rylah
The author, n.d. [inscribed 1956]. Printed by Specialty Press
16pp, t.p. printed in 2 col., 4 line drawings printed in brown ink, pic. wrappers, 175x120mm. ANL

6548 AUSTRALIAN/ADVENTURE/Girl Guiding Under the Southern Cross/by/Ann Rylah/[device]/ Lansdowne Press
Melbourne 1963
136pp, 1p foreword by Lady Baden Powell, b/w photographic frontis. & b/w photographic illus. throughout, clo., 245x180mm. KMM

RYLAND, Tui
6549 FAIRY/WAXFLOWER/Tui Ryland
The Cambridge Press, 214 Hargrave Street, Bendigo
1940
8pp, b/w frontis., wrappers (stapled), cover title, 220x140mm. Grant

S., S. E. [Sarah Elizabeth Smith]
6550 POEMS FOR CHILDREN/By/S. E. S./Wholly set up and printed in Australia by/Hunkin, Ellis & King Ltd., 113 Pirie Street, Adelaide
n.d. [1944]
59pp, wrappers, 150x115mm. KMM

6551 NEBBY AND NED/AND/OTHER POEMS/By/ S. E. S./Author of "Poems for Children"
Hunkin, Ellis & King Ltd, Printers, Adelaide, n.d. [1948]
31pp, illus. wrappers, 185x120mm. KMM

SABEY, Ian
MELODIE'S YEAR
Not children's

SABINE, Jo
6552 [decoration]/THE PILLOW PAT/POEMS/By/Jo Sabine/Dedication/For Daddy and me (Nic'las)/Our Book/from/Mummy
The author, Grafton, NSW, n.d. [1941] [Printed by New Century Press, Sydney]
60pp, b/w drawings in text, illus. by Pixie O'Harris, dec. bd., 185x125mm. CLRC

SACRE, Grace Laurel
6553 ROBBY/RABBIT/[drawing]/G. L. Sacre
Deaton & Spencer, Printers, Sydney, n.d. [1944]
27pp, 2 f/p col. illus. & 12 f/p b/w illus., dec. bd., 180x235mm. ANL
Verse.

6554 THE PENGUIN'S ADVENTURES/A Story in Verse/with coloured illustrations/[drawing]/by Grace L. Sacre
Deaton & Spencer, Printers, Sydney, n.d. [1945]
27pp, 8 col. illus. & b/w drawings, dec. bd. (clo. spine), 180x235mm. ANL

SAGON, Amyot
6555 DICK DASHWOOD/The Boy Squatter/By/Amyot Sagon/Author of "When George III was King", "A Fair Palmist", Etc./Illustrated by Warwick Goble/London/ Ward, Lock & Co. Limited/New York and Melbourne
n.d. [1902]
285pp, 2pp adv., b/w frontis. & 3 b/w plates, pic. clo., 190x125mm. KMM

6556 Whitcombe's Historical Story Books/SAILING WITH/TASMAN/(For ages 10 to 12 years)/[vignette]/ Whitcombe and Tombs Limited/Christchurch, Auckland, Wellington, Dunedin, Invercargill N.Z./London, Melbourne, Sydney.
n.d.
100pp (inc. covers, & 11pp appendices & notes), b/w frontis. & 2 f/p b/w illus., 4 b/w illus. in text signed 'M. Matthews', stiff pic. wrappers, 180x120mm. KMM
Contains appendices on Tasman's life & works, & notes on his voyage of 1642–43.
See McLaren 538

SAINSBURY, Noel, Jr
6557 The Great Ace Series/BILLY SMITH/EXPLORING ACE/or/By Airplane to New Guinea/By/Noel

Sainsbury, Jr./[drawing]/Cupples & Leon Company/Publishers. New York
Copyright 1928 by Robert M. Mcbride & Company
247pp, 3pp adv., 1 f/p b/w illus. only, dec. clo., pic. e/p, 185x125mm. RM
Action begins in Sydney & takes place mainly in New Guinea.

ST JOHNSTON, Alfred

6558 IN QUEST OF GOLD;/or,/Under the Whanga Falls./By/Alfred St. Johnston,/Author of "Camping Among Cannibals", "Charlie Asgarde", etc./With Eight Original Illustrations by Gordon Browne./Cassell & Company, Limited:/London, Paris, New York & Melbourne./1885/(All Rights Reserved)
280pp, 16pp adv., b/w frontis. & 7 f/p b/w illus., pic. clo., 185x120mm. NSL:M
A boy's adventure story set in Queensland.
• Rpt as above 1887 (second edition). KP
• Rpt as above, seventh thousand, 1892. NSL:M
Swedish edition

6559 ÄFVENTYR I AUSTRALIEN/Under jagt efter guld/af/Alfred S:t Johnston/Med Illustrationer/öfversättning af Jenny R-R/Stockholm/Oscar L. Lamms Forlag
Verso of t.p.: 'Stockholm/Isaac Marcus' Boktryckeri-Aktiebolag/1889'
228pp, 7 f/p b/w illus. signed 'J. C. Foto', pic. bd., clo. backstrip, 200x140mm. RM

ST VINCENT, Isobel

6560 WINNIE WOMBAT/Written by/Isobel St. Vincent/Illustrated by/Helen Haywood/Hutchinson's Books for Young People/10 Great Queen Street/London W.C.2
n.d. [1953?]
54pp, 5 f/p col. illus. & b/w drawings in text, pic. bd., 170x215mm. CLRC

Sally and John

6561 SALLY AND JOHN
Photogravures Pty Ltd (? Melbourne), n.d. [194-?]
[12]pp, col. illus. throughout, wrappers, cover title, 240x182mm. KMM

SALMON, Michael

6562 "THE MONSTER/THAT ATE/CANBERRA"./A Book for the Younger/Generations of/Canberra./By Michael Salmon,/Photos by Peter McKee
Summit Press, Canberra, n.d. [1972]
29pp, dec. t.p., b/w illus. throughout, pic. wrappers, 216x240mm. CLRC
Some pages have an additional col.
• Rpt Nov 1972, as above. ANL

SALMON, Ross

6563 THE TRUE BOOK ABOUT/COWBOYS/by/Ross Salmon/Illustrated by/De Marco/Shakespeare Head/London New York Sydney Paris
First published 1956
141pp, b/w illus. in text, clo., 180x115mm. NSL:M
Includes one chapter on 'Stockmen of Australia' (5pp).

SALNAJS, Charlotte

6564 BENNY IN BUNYIPLAND/by/Charlotte/Salnajs/1961/Arthur H. Stockwell Limited/Elms Court, Ilfracombe/Devon [England]
46pp (inc. 1p author's preface), dec. wrappers, 185x120mm. KMM

SAMMON, Stella

6565 Stella Sammon/THE LUCKY STONE/Illustrated by Margaret Paice/Methuen & Co. Ltd./11 New Fetter Lane London E.C.4
1969
142pp, b/w frontis. & 2 f/p b/w illus., b/w drawings in text, clo., 180x120mm. KMM A Pied Piper Book.
Story of an Aboriginal girl.

Sammy Sprocket Says

6566 SAMMY SPROCKET/SAYS/Issued by: Victorian Road Safety Division/National Safety Council of Australia/321 William Street, Melbourne 3000—Telephone: 30 1951
24pp (inc. covers), photographic & line drawings throughout, wrappers, cover title, 160x92mm. KMM
Adv. throughout: With Acknowledgements to the National Safety Council, Chicago, USA. Safety rules for child cyclists.

SAMPSON, Alf & Shirley

6567 DISCOVERERS/OF/AUSTRALIA/Alf & Shirley Sampson/Golden Press Sydney
1971
60pp, col & b/w reproductions of photographic & other early illus., col. illus. t.p., col. pic. bd., col. illus. e/p, 325x240mm. CLRC

SAMPSON, John Walter

See COLE'S FUNNY DRAWING BOOK

SAMPSON, W. J. C.

6568 JOHNNIE'S LETTERS/FROM HIS DADDY/by/W. J. C. Sampson/Being a Series of Letters written/by a soldier on Active Service/to his Young Son, Johnnie/Printed and Published by:/Paterson's Printing Press Ltd./65 Murray Street, Perth, W.A.
n.d. [1947]
23pp, b/w drawings in text, bd., 245x180mm. ANL

SAMUEL, Getsie R.

6569 THE TWINS/GO TO AUSTRALIA/Getsie R. Samuel, B.A., L.T., M.A.(Redlands)/M.S.(Calif.), T.D.(Sally Oak, Eng.)/Principal, St Christopher's Training College, Madras/[device]/The Christian Literature Society
First printed Dec. 1966; rev. May 1967
99pp (inc. 3pp glossary), 1p preface &c, 12 b/w illus., pic. wrappers, 184x120mm. VMOU
The story is written in the form of a school reader with questions at the end of each chapter.

SAMUEL, Helen Jo

6570 A/SADDLE/AT/BONTHARAMBO/H. J. Samuel/Illustrations by/Cordelle Samuel/Longmans, Green and Co./London Melbourne New York
Melbourne 1950
157pp (inc. 1p preface), b/w drawings throughout, clo., dec. map e/p, 185x120mm. KMM
School edition as above, but limp clo. KP

6571 The Heritage Story Books/General Editor: A. C. Hughes, B.Sc., Ph.D., M. Ed./THE NEW/AUSTRALIANS/By/H. J. Samuel/Pictures by H. C. Gaffron/[drawing]/Longmans
London 1958
64pp (inc. 2pp questions), part. col. illus. throughout, stiff wrappers, 185x120mm. ANL

6572 WILD FLOWER/HUNTER/[drawing]/The Story of Ellis Rowan/By H. J. Samuel/Illustrated by Maie Casey/London/Constable and Co. Ltd.
1961
151pp (inc. 3pp foreword by Maie Casey & 1p bibliography), col. frontis. by Ellis Rowan, 6 f/p b/w illus. & map, b/w drawings in text by Maie Casey, clo., 230x150mm. KMM

SAMUEL, Helen Jo & HEDDLE, Enid Moodie

6573 BOY ON A HORSE/The Story of/Adam Lindsay

Gordon/H. J. Samuel &/Enid Moodie Heddle/[vignette]/Drawings by Alison Forbes/F. W. Cheshire/Melbourne
1957
160pp (inc. 1p. authors' preface), b/w drawings throughout, clo., 215x140mm. KMM

SANDERS, Dorothy Lucie
6574 THE RANDY/The Story of a Mystery Ship/by/Dorothy Lucie Sanders/Australasian Publishing Company/[device]/Sydney Wellington London
1948
109pp, b/w frontis., clo., 185x120mm. KMM
Part of the book originally appeared in the *Bulletin* under the title of 'Jeem'.

SANDERS, Ruth Manning
See Manning-Sanders, Ruth

SANDERSON, Edgar
6575 HEROES OF PIONEERING/True Stories of the Intrepid Bravery and/Stirring adventures of pioneers with/uncivilized man, wild beasts, and/the forces of nature, in all/parts of the world./By/Edgar Sanderson, M.A./Sometime scholar of Clare College, Cambridge/author of/"Great Britain in Modern Africa", "A History of England and the/British Empire", etc. etc./with sixteen illustrations./London/Seeley and Co. Limited/38 Great Russell Street/1908
352pp, 16pp adv., b/w frontis. & 15 f/p b/w illus. by various artists, pic. clo., 195x130mm. PR
Contents include: 'Pioneer Work in South Australia' (pp179–91).
Later pub. as 'Daring Deeds of Great Pathfinders'.

SANDS, LTD, John [publishers]
See Sunny South series

SANFORD, J. C.
6576 THE/WONDERLAND/OF SCIENCE/[drawing]/By/J. C. Sanford/A.S.T.C., A.A.C.I., Dip. Ind. Chem./M.S.A.E./Illustrated by B. E. Pike/Smith, Woods Pty Ltd./50 Prince Albert Street,/Mosman, N.S.W./Australia/1945/Registered at the G.P.O. Sydney for transmission through the post as a book
204pp (inc. 7pp indices, 1p foreword &c), col. frontis., col. & b/w illus. & diagrams throughout, pic. bd., 220x165mm. KP

The Sanitarium Children's Abbreviated Australian Encyclopaedia
6577 THE/SANITARIUM/CHILDREN'S/ABBREVIATED/AUSTRALIAN ENCYCLOPAEDIA/[map of Australia]
Sanitarium Health Food Co., Sydney, n.d. [1946]
72pp, 1p preface, b/w drawings in text (with spaces for 60 col. pictures to be collected & pasted in), wrappers, col. half-page frontis., cover title, 275x205mm. NSL:M
6578 SANITARIUM/CHILDREN'S/AUSTRALIAN/ABBREVIATED ENCYCLOPAEDIA/Revised Edition/Vol. 6 of The Sanitarium Children's Library
Sanitarium Health Food Co, Sydney, n.d. (second ed. rev.)
73pp, 1p preface, b/w drawings in text (with space for 60 col. pictures to be collected & pasted in), pic. wrappers, 275x205mm. WRT

Santa's Visit
6579 SANTA'S VISIT
A 'C.M.C.' Production, Pantheon Publications, 20 Queen St, Melbourne, n.d. [library copy acquired 1947]
14pp, col. illus. throughout, pic. bd., cover title, 350x235mm. NSL:M

SARGENT, Eric
6580 AERIAL STOWAWAY/London/Sampson Low, Marston & Co., Ltd.
n.d. [194-?]
vipp, 250pp, b/w frontis., clo., 197x127mm. ANL

SARGENT, George Etell
6581 FRANK LAYTON;/An Australian Story/By G. E. Sargent/Author of 'Story of a City Arab', etc./with an introduction/by Samuel Mossman/Author of Article "Australia" in the "Encyclopaedia Britannica", etc. etc./London:/Published at the Leisure Hour Office:/56, Paternoster Row, and 164, Piccadilly./Sold at Railway Stations and by the Booksellers
n.d. [first edition, 1865]
286pp (inc. 18pp introduction), 1p adv. (for The Leisure Hour Library), engraved frontis. & 5 f/p engraved illus., clo. (with title & Australian coat of arms in gilt on front cover), 180x130mm. KMM
The story first appeared as a serial in *The Leisure Hour* for 1854, in 26 instalments, with a b/w engraving at the beginning of each instalment; no author's name was given.
Another copy as above, but after 'Piccadilly' '/Manchester: Corporation Street. Brighton: Western Road./Sold at Railway Stations and by all Booksellers'. GK
6582 FRANK LAYTON/An Australian Story/By George E. Sargent,/Author of/"The Story of a City Arab", "The Chronicles of an Old Manor House",/"Captain Cook, His Life and Voyages",/with an introduction/by Samuel Mossman/Author of Article "Australia" in the "Encyclopaedia Britannica", etc./London:/Published at the Leisure Hour Office/56 Paternoster Row, and 164, Piccadilly
n.d. [inscribed 1866]
286pp (inc. 18pp introduction), 1p. adv., engraved frontis. & 5 f/p engravings, dec. clo., 180x130mm. Grant
6583 FRANK LAYTON/An Australian Story/by/George E. Sargent/Author of/"The Story of a City Arab", "The Chronicles of an Old Manor House"/"Captain Cook, His Life and Voyages"/London/The Religious Tract Society/56 Paternoster Row, 65 St. Paul's Churchyard/and 164 Piccadilly
n.d. [inscribed Sept. 8, 1897]
384pp, b/w frontis. & 5 f/p b/w illus., b/w chapter headings & tailpiece decorations, clo. (with all edges gilt), e/p (with adv.), 180x115mm. KP
6584 FRANK LAYTON/An Australian Story/By/George E. Sargent/Author of/"George Burley", "Hurlock Chase", etc./With illustrations by/G. E. Robertson/London/The Religious Tract Society/4 Bouverie Street & 65 St. Paul's Churchyard
n.d. [inscribed 1912]
375pp 12pp adv., part-col. t.p. (red & blue), col. frontis. & 3 b/w plates, pic. clo., 195x130mm. KMM
Another copy as previous entry, but appears to be later reprint, with different adv., and only 1 b/w illus., pic. clo., with entirely different design on front cover & spine, 185x120mm. The illustrations were redrawn for the later editions. KMM
6585 FRANK LAYTON/An Australian Story/By/George E. Sargent/Author of/"George Burley", "Hurlock Chase" Etc./With Illustrations by/G. E. Robertson/London/The Religious Tract Society/4 Bouverie Street & 65 St. Paul's Churchyard
n.d.
375pp, 12pp adv., part. col. t.p., col. frontis. & 1 f/p b/w illus., pic. clo., 185x125mm.
This copy definitely had no other illustrations when published. RM

Dutch editions
6586 FRANK LAYTON./ Eene Australische geschiedenis/ Naar het Engelsch /door/ L. van Erpecum./Overgedrukt uit het Familie. Magazjn/ [device]/Amsterdam/H.Höveker
n.d. [1856?]
iv+336pp, b/w frontis. & 25 f.p.b/w engravings, printed wrappers,205x150mm. ANL
6587 FRANK LAYTON./Avonturen/in/Australië/Door L. Vane/met 26 Platen/[device]/ Amsterdam—J. Vlieger
n.d. [186-?]
236pp, engraved frontis. & 25 f/p illus., dec. clo., 205x155mm. NSL:M
Illus. as those which first appeared in the serialized version of the book in *The Leisure Hour*.

6588 THE FRANKLINS;/or,/The Story of a Convict,/in Three Parts/By/G. E. Sargent,/author of "The Story of a City Arab", "George Burley", "Hurlock Chase"/"Without intending it", etc. etc./London:/The Religious Tract Society;/56, Paternoster Row; 65, St Paul's Churchyard;/and 164, Piccadilly.
n.d. [1886?]
413pp (inc. 2pp author's preface), engraved frontis. & 15 f/p engravings, dec. clo. with author & title in gilt panel & scene from one illus. blocked in gilt, bevelled covers, g.e., dec. e/p, 180x134mm. ANL
• Rpt from *The Leisure Hour* 1863.

SARGENT, George Hewlett [?George Etell Sargent]
6589 JOE HARMAN'S EXPERIENCES/By/George H. Sargent/Author of/"The Story of a Pocket Bible", etc./ London:/The Religious Tract Society/4 Bouverie Street and 65 St. Paul's Churchyard, E.C.4
n.d. [1884]
126pp, col. frontis. by A. Pearse, clo., 170x115mm. KP
The col. frontis. is reproduced on the cover, which also has the author's name as 'George E. Sargent'. In Chapter 10 the hero decides to go to Australia, & the next four chapters are set in Australia & on the voyage out.

SASEK, M.
6590 Greetings from/Down/Under/M. Sasek/ [drawing]/THIS/IS/AUSTRALIA/W. H. Allen
London 1970
60pp (inc. prelims), col. illus. throughout, dec. bd., 300x220mm. KMM
US edition
6590a Macmillan, New York 1970
60pp, col. illus., col. map, portrait, 31cm. Unseen: ANB 1971

SAUER, Arline
6591 [5-line dedication]/THE MAGIC GUM TREE/An Australian Musical Play/for Children/By/Arline Sauer/Copyright 1934/For all Countries and U.S.A. Price 2/-nett/W. H. Paling & Co. Ltd./Sydney/ Brisbane, Newcastle/Toowoomba, Rockhampton
24pp, unillus., wrappers, 254x180mm. KMM
Words of play, with 7 pieces of music (songs, &c.)

SAUNDERS, Guy
CAREERS IN ADVERTISING
CAREERS IN THE RETAIL TRADE
See Colwell, Max

SAVAGE, H.
6592 LARBA:/FILS DU GRAND SERPENT/Aventure chez les aborigènes/by/H. Savage, M.A., Dip.Ed./ Author of [3 lines]/First edition/William Brooks & Co Limited/The Educational Publishers of Australia/723 Elizabeth Street, Waterloo, Sydney/299 Queen Street, Brisbane
n.d.
68pp (inc. 13pp vocabulary), b/w chapter headings, pic. wrappers, 180x120mm. ANL
School French text in form of a story.
AVENTURES ET MESAVENTURES
1939
Book of extracts designed as school text. ANL

SAWER, Derek
STEEL FOR AUSTRALIA. *See* Around Australia Program

SAXBY, C. F. Argyll
6593 KOOKABURRA JACK/A Story of Australian School Life/By/C. F. Argyll Saxby, M.A., F.R.G.S./Author of/ "The Treasure of Tregudda", "The Black Lizard"/"The Fiery Totem", etc./London/The "Boy's Own Paper" Office/4 Bouverie Street, E.C.4
n.d. [first pub. 1924] Serialized in *Boy's Own Paper* 1923.
254pp, b/w frontis., clo., 190x125mm. VSL
6594 KOOKABURRA JACK/A Story of Australian School Life/By/C. F. Argyll Saxby, M.A., F.R.G.S./Author of/ "The Treasure of Tregudda", "The Black Lizard"/"The Fiery Token", etc./With six full-page illustrations/By Arthur Twidle/London/"The Boy's Own Paper" Office/4 Bouverie Street E.C.4.
n.d. [1931]
254pp, 2pp adv., b/w frontis. & 5 f/p b/w illus., pic. clo., 195x130mm. CLRC

SAXBY, Mrs
6595 BREAKERS AHEAD;/or,/Uncle Jack's Stories of/ Great Shipwrecks of recent times:/1869–1880./by/Mrs Saxby,/author of 'Rock-bound', 'Stories of Shetland'/etc.etc./[verse]/London/T. Nelson and Sons, Paternoster Row,/Edinburgh; and New York./1883
143pp & 3 pp adv., b/w frontis. & 5 f/p engravings, dec. clo., 150x120mm. CLRC
Several chapters about shipwrecks occurring on the voyage to Australia.
Another copy as above, but 1899. KMM

SAXBY, Joyce Boniwell [ed.]
6596 ONE HUNDRED POEMS/CHOSEN FOR CHILDREN/By Joyce Saxby/With illustrations by/ Astra Lacis-Dick/Angus and Robertson
Sydney 1967
148pp (inc. 6pp indexes), 1p acknowledgements & 1p publisher's note, b/w drawings throughout, clo., col. e/p, 215x135mm. KMM
• Rpt 1968, 1971. KMM

SAXTON, Patti
6597 This is the Story of/STEVIE/[drawing]/the little steam-roller/that never grew up
Pyramid Publications Pty Ltd, Sydney, n.d. [1948]
16pp, col. illus. throughout by Mollie Quick, dec. bd., 240x180mm. ANL

SAYCE, Conrad H. [pseud. 'Jim Bushman']
6598 IN THE/MUSGRAVE RANGES/By/Jim Bushman/ Illustrated by Fred Leist, R.O.I./Blackie and Son Limited/London Glasgow Bombay
n.d. [library copy acquired 1925; publishers indicate first pub. 1922]
284pp, b/w frontis. & 5 f/p b/w illus., clo., 190x125mm. ANL
6599 IN THE/MUSGRAVE RANGES/By/Jim Bushman/ Author of "The Golden Valley" etc./Illustrated by Fred Leist, R.O.I./Blackie & Son Limited/London and Glasgow
n.d.

284pp, b/w frontis. & 3 f/p b/w illus., clo., 180x125mm. ANL

6600 IN THE/MUSGRAVE RANGES/By/Jim Bushman/Author of "The Golden Valley" &c./Blackie & Son Limited/London and Glasgow
n.d.
284pp, 2pp adv., b/w frontis., clo., 180x125mm. KMM
As above but pic. bd. KMM

6601 THE GOLDEN VALLEY/By/Jim Bushman/(Conrad H. Sayce)/Author of "In the Musgrave Ranges"/Illustrated by H. Coller/Blackie and Son Limited/London Glasgow and Bombay
[1924]
256pp, b/w frontis. & 5 plates, dec. bd., 185x125mm. CLRC

6602 THE GOLDEN VALLEY/By/Jim Bushman/(Conrad H. Sayce)/Author of "In the Musgrave Ranges"/"The Valley of a Thousand Deaths"/Illustrated by H. Coller/Blackie & Son Limited/London and Glasgow
n.d.
256pp, 2pp adv., b/w frontis. & 3 f/p b/w illus., clo., 185x120mm. ANL
Life on a Central Australian cattle station.
Another copy n.d., as above, but 'Book Production War Economy Standard' (apparently a wartime reprint). KP

6603 THE VALLEY OF/A THOUSAND DEATHS/By/Jim Bushman/(Conrad H. Sayce)/Author of "In the Musgrave Ranges"/"The Golden Valley" etc./Illustrated by W. E. Wightman/Blackie & Son Limited/London and Glasgow
n.d. [1925]
256pp, 2pp adv., b/w frontis. & 3 f/p b/w illus., clo., 185x120mm. ANL
• Rpt as above with imprint 'London Glasgow and Bombay'. RM

6604 THE VALLEY OF/A THOUSAND DEATHS/By/Jim Bushman/(Conrad H. Sayce)/Author of "In the Musgrave Ranges"/"The Golden Valley" &c./Illustrated by W. E. Wightman/Blackie & Son Limited/London and Glasgow
n.d.
256pp, b/w frontis. only, clo., 180x125mm. KP

6605 THE/SPLENDID SAVAGE/A Tale of the North Coast of Australia/By/Conrad H. Sayce/[drawing]/Illustrated by Victor Cooley/Thomas Nelson & Sons Ltd./London, Edinburgh, New York, Toronto and Paris
n.d. [1927]
191pp, 1p adv., col. frontis., 6 f/p b/w illus., & text drawings, pic. bd., 210x170mm. Nelson Bumper Books. KMM

6606 Another copy as above, n.d. [1930]
280pp, & 8pp. adv., col. frontis.,1 f/p b/w illus & b/w drawings in text, pic clo., with col. illus. pasted on front cover, 185x130mm. RM

6607 THE/SPLENDID SAVAGE/A Tale of the North Coast of Australia/By/Conrad H. Sayce/[drawing]/Illustrated by Victor Cooley/Thomas Nelson & Sons Ltd./London Edinburgh New York Toronto & Paris
n.d.
280pp, b/w frontis. & b/w drawings in text, clo., 180x120mm. The 'Triumph Series'. CLRC

SCANLON, Tony
CRY ON A FOGGY NIGHT
GAYE LIZZIE
THE SNOW DROPPERS. *See* Trend Books

SCARBOROUGH, J. C.
6608 UNCLE/TOM'S/WURLEY/Rev. J. C. Scarborough
16 Miller Street, North Unley, SA, Copyright 1966. Sharples Printers Pty Ltd, 98 Hindley St, Adelaide
61pp, unillus., wrappers, 203x132mm. CLRC

SCARF, M. F.
6609 MARYANN/By/M. F. Scarf/with illustrations by/B. C. Morgan/[device]/Nihil Obstat/W. H. Hurley, S.M./1947
Printed in Australia by Hi-Tone Printing Company, Petersham, NSW
34pp, 6 f/p b/w illus., clo., 215x125mm. CLRC

SCARRY, Patricia
6610 HOP,/LITTLE KANGAROO!/[drawing]/By Patricia Scarry/Pictures by Feodor Rojankovsky/Golden Press/[device]/New York
1965
24pp, col. illus. throughout, col. pic. bd., dec. e/p, 135x100mm. Grant
Many different Australian animals illustrated.
Another copy as above, but 'Golden Press [device] Sydney' 1967, 195x155mm. CLRC

SCHAPPE, Amalia
6611 ROBINSON/IN/AUSTRALIEN./Ein Lehr—und Lesebuch/für gute Kinder/von/Amalia Schappe,/geborne Weise./Heidelberg./Verlagshandlung von Joseph Engelman/1874
244pp, 171x108mm. QSL, unseen
Ferguson Addenda 3704a gives author's name as 'Schoppe', the date of publication 1843, and details as follows:
iv+244pp, col. frontis. & 3 other col. illus., boards, 171x108mm.
No other copies of this book are known to exist in Australia.

SCHERMLE, Willy
6612 PITTY AND PATTY PENGUIN/A Children's Story Book/By/Willy Schermle/[drawing]/Clifford Series/Clifford Series *[sic]*
n.p., n.d., Printed in the Netherlands
24pp, col. & b/w illus. throughout, pic. bd., 150x145mm. KP

SCHNEIDER, H. G.
6613 MAPOON/—/Eine Millions-Erzählung/für die reifere Jugend/von/Prediger H. G. Schneider/[ornament]/Herrnhut,/Buchhandlung der Millionsanstalt der Ev. Brüderunität
n.d. [1899?]
80pp, b/w frontis. & f/p b/w map of Mapoon, Cullen Point, North Qld, b/w photograph of Melbourne, b/w photographs & engravings, pic. wrappers, 155x10mm. ANL
Describes Cape York & Thursday Island Missions.

[SCHOLEFIELD, Mrs H.]
6614 A/SHORT MEMOIR/OF/WILLIAM WIMMERA,/An Australian Boy,/who sailed from Melbourne, April 1, 1851;/died at Reading, March 10, 1852./Cambridge./MDCCCLIII
46pp, unillus., wrappers, 120x80mm. CLRC
An account of an Aboriginal boy taken to England by missionaries. He died within a year.
Also published in two issues of the *Melbourne Church of England Messenger* during 1854.

SCHONELL, Fred
See FLOWERDEW, Phyllis & SCHONELL, Fred

SCHOPPE, Amalia
See SCHAPPE, Amalia

School Magazine Stories
6615 SCHOOL MAGAZINE/STORIES/Book Two/ Sydney/Department of Education/1967
116pp, unillus., clo., 202x130mm. KP
Australian children's stories rpt. from NSW School Magazine.
See also Shelley, N. *Roundabout*

Schoolgirl Stories
6616 Schoolgirl/Stories
Colourtone Pty Ltd, Sydney for Dawfox Productions, n.d.
Collection of anonymous English girls' stories with no Australian association. TG

SCHURMANN, Edwin A.
6617 NO/TRAINS/ON/SUNDAY/by Edwin A. Schurmann/Ure Smith Sydney London
1967
144pp with numerous b/w illus., clo. bd., 196x120mm. CLRC
Victorian setting.

SCHWED, Fred
6618 WACKY/THE SMALL BOY/[drawing]/By Fred Schwed Jr./Illustrated by Gregor Duncan/Peter Huston, Publishers: Sydney 1946/Simon and Schuster, New York, U.S.A.
85pp, 5 f/p b/w illus. & b/w drawings in text, dec. bd., dec. e/p, 200x165mm. CLRC
Australian reprint of American book about a small American boy & his family whose surname is 'Wallaby': content not Australian.
Third printing 1945. KMM

SCOTT, Alan
6619 A MANUAL OF/AUSTRALIAN FOOTBALL/By Alan Scott/Illustrated by George Melrose/Lansdowne Press
Melbourne 1965
86pp, b/w illus. t.p., b/w diagrams & drawings throughout, pic. clo., 245x185mm. CLRC

6620 FOOTBALL/FOR/BOYS/[drawing]/Alan Scott/ Golden Press
Potts Point, NSW, 1971
149pp, 2pp introduction, etc., b/w photographic illus. & diagrams, pic. wrappers, 210x135mm. CLRC
An Australian Gold Pocket Guide. Based on the author's *A Manual of Australian Football.*

SCOTT, Alex
6621 COME NIGHT,/COME NINEPENCE/By Alex Scott/[drawing]/Illustrated by/Elaine Haxton/John Sands Pty. Ltd./Sydney and Melbourne
1947
106pp, line drawings, clo., 180x115mm. VSL
Verses.

SCOTT, G. Firth
6622 THE/ROMANCE OF AUSTRALIAN/ EXPLORING/By/G. Firth Scott/Author of "The Track of Midnight", Etc./With Maps and Illustrations/ London/Sampson, Low, Marston & Company/ Limited/St. Dunstan's House/Fetter Lane, Fleet Street, E.C./1899
328pp, 2pp author's preface, b/w frontis. & 7 f/p b/w illus., 9 b/w maps, clo., 190x125mm. HBM
Illustrations reproduced from *Australia Illustrated*
Popular account of Australian exploration, not intended specifically for children. HBM
6623 THE ROMANCE/OF AUSTRALIAN/ EXPLORING/By/G. Firth Scott/Author of "The Track of Midnight", etc/With maps and illustrations/ London/Sampson Low, Marston and Company/ Limited
n.d.
328pp, 2pp preface, b/w frontis. & 7 b/w illus., 9 b/w maps, clo., 180x115mm. HBM
Appears to be a cheap edition of the original edition, with reduced page size & cheap binding.

6624 THE ROMANCE OF/POLAR EXPLORATION/ Interesting Descriptions of Arctic and/Antarctic Adventure from the earliest/Time to the Voyage of the "Discovery"/By/G. Firth Scott/Author of "From Franklin to Nansen", "The Romance/of Australian Exploring", "Colonial Born" etc./With an additional chapter by R. N. Rudmose Brown, D.Sc., F.R.S.G.S./Author of "A Naturalist at the Poles", "Spitsbergen"/&c. &c./With many illustrations/ London/Seeley, Service & Co. Limited/196 Shaftesbury Avenue
n.d. [190-?]
317pp (inc. 3pp author's preface), 1p & 2pp adv., b/w frontis. & 6 f/p b/w illus., map, clo., 200x125mm. PAI
3 chapters devoted to Antarctica (34pp).

SCOTT, Ida
6625 SONGS/OF/THIS AND THAT/For the Little Ones/By/Ida Scott/Melbourne/Lothian Publishing Co. Pty. Ltd./No. 1 Fleming Place
n.d. [1933]
62pp, b/w frontis. & 7 b/w illus. in text by A. B. Lidgey, wrappers, 185x135mm. VSL

[SCOTT, Maria J.]
6626 PEARL AND WILLIE:/A Tale:/By Spray./Sydney; John Woods & Co.,/13 Bridge Street,/Printers and Publishers
n.d. [preface dated November 1880]
28pp, unillus, limp grained clo. blind stamped & gilt, 165x105mm. Grant

'SCOTT, Maxwell' [John William Staniforth]
THE SILVER DWARF. *See* Boys' Friend Library

SCOTT, Natalie
6627 FIREBRAND/PUSH YOUR HAIR OUT OF YOUR EYES/Story by Natalie Scott/Illustrated by Sandra Smith/[drawing]/Ure Smith—Sydney
First published in New Zealand & simultaneously in Australia 1968
32pp, 13 f/p col. illus., pic. clo., 275x210mm. KMM
Both the author & the artist are Australian.

6628 WINGS/ON/WEDNESDAY/written by Natalie Scott/illustrated by Sandra Smith/Paul Hamlyn/ London New York Sydney Toronto
Dee Why West, NSW, 1968
[24]pp, col. illus. t.p., col. illus. throughout, pic. bd., pic. e/p, 250x245mm. CLRC

6629 PLEASE SIT STILL/written by Natalie Scott illustrated by Sandra Smith/[col. illus.]/Paul Hamlyn/ London New York Sydney Toronto
Dee Why West, NSW, 1969
[24]pp, col. illus. t.p., col. illus. throughout, pic. bd., pic. e/p, 312x230mm. CLRC
• Rpt 1971, as above. KP

6630 HULLABALLOO/written by Natalie Scott/ illustrated by Sandra Smith/[col. illus.]/Paul Hamlyn/ London New York Sydney Toronto
Dee Why West, NSW 1969
[24]pp, col. illus. throughout, pic. bd., 250x247mm. CLRC

SCOTT, O. R.
6631 The Discover Australia Series/THE/GOVERNORS/By O. R. Scott/[contents]/Printed by Kenmure Press Pty. Ltd., Derby and Wetherill Sts., North Lidcombe, N.S.W. 2141/for the K. G. Murray Publishing Company Pty. Ltd., 142 Clarence Street Sydney, 2000/etc.
n.d. [1970]
50pp, b/w photographic reproductions of illus. from early sources, pic. wrappers, 275x200mm. KMM

Also by the same author, in the same series, uniform with the above:
6632 THE ABORIGINES
6633 THE BUSHRANGERS
6634 THE CONVICTS
6635 THE DISCOVERERS
6636 THE EXPLORERS
6637 THE GOLDSEEKERS
6638 THE SETTLERS

SCOTT, Peter & Philippa
6639 FARAWAY/LOOK/ONE/by Peter and/Philippa Scott/Cassell—London
1960
120pp, map frontis., 24pp col. photographs, b/w photographs throughout, b/w drawings & maps in text, clo., 215x160mm. KMM
A book comprising mostly photographs describing wild life in Australia, New Guinea, New Zealand & part of the South Pacific.

SCOTT, R. F.
6640 SCOTT'S/LAST EXPEDITION/Extracts from the/Personal Journals of/Capt. R. F. Scott, R.N./London John Murray
First ed. Nov 1923; rpt. 1925, 1927, 1931, 1935, 1940, 1944
188pp (inc. preface, glossary, questions &c), b/w photographic illus., clo., map e/p, 182x122mm. KP
This ed. appears to have been intended for schools.

Scouting and Guiding
6641 SCOUTING AND GUIDING/Published by Sanitarium Health Food Company
Box 9, Petersham, NSW, n.d.
12pp, part col. dec. & text with spaces for cards to be pasted in, pic. wrappers, cover title, 195x240mm. KP

SCRIVEN, Peter
6642 THE TINTOOKIES/AND/LITTLE FELLA BINDI/Written by Peter Scriven/[drawing]/illustrated by genevieve melrose [*sic*]/Lansdowne Press/Melbourne
1966
28pp, col. illus. throughout, clo., 265x185mm. CLRC
Adapted from the Marionette Theatre of Australia's production of *Little Fella Bindi.*

Sea Shells of the World
6643 Vita-Brits Album/SEA SHELLS/OF THE WORLD
Nabisco Pty Ltd, Melbourne, n.d.
16pp, text describing shells with spaces left for cards to be pasted in, pic. wrappers, cover title, 180x240mm. KP

The Search for Water
6644 THE SEARCH/FOR WATER/A Story of/Australian Exploration
Produced by Coca Cola. n.d., [197-?]. Printed at The Griffin Press, Adelaide
[8]pp (inc. 2pp 'The Story of Coca-Cola') & text printed inside both covers, col. illus. throughout, col. pic. wrappers depicting map of Australia, 236x184mm. KP

SEARCY, M. K.
6645 Imperial Edition NO. 274/RECREATION SONGS/FOR CHILDREN/Words by/M. K. Searcy/Music by/Rev. G. M. Searcy, M. A. Oxon./Precentor of St Andrew's Cathedral, Sydney./Allan & Co.,/Melbourne, Sydney, Adelaide, Bendigo
Copyright 1926
20pp, unillus., col. pic. wrappers, 250x175mm. VSL
13 songs.
Other copies seen as above but with 'price 1/6', 'price 2/-' and 'price 3/6' on cover. KP

[SEARLE, M. Lila]
6646 LITTLE RUTH'S DREAM/(A real incident)/By Eirene/[2 line quote from the New Testament]/Third Edition/Hobart Town/T. L. Hood, 60, Liverpool-Street./1880./Price 3d; for distribution, 2/6 a dozen
22pp (inc. 1p prefatory note), 1p note to the third ed., unillus., wrappers, cover title, 160x105mm. NSL:M
Also author of *Shadows*, not a children's book.

SEATON, Judith
See Lohse, Charlotte & Seaton, Judith

SEAWELL, Lawrie
BINDI-EYE
THE DARK HOUSE AND RABBIT TRAP
SOME TRANNIE THAT! *See* Trend books

The Secret Tunnel and other stories for girls
See Pedersen, Audrey & others

SEELEY, Brenda
6647 OUR TRAIN BOOK/Story by Brenda Seeley/Pictures by Hal Freedman/Published in Melbourne by Georgian House
n.d. [1950]
16pp, dec. t.p., b/w & col. lithographic illus. throughout, stiff pic. wrappers, 180x230mm. ANL

'Self-made Man, A'
6648 No. 1157 New York, December 2, 1927 Price 8 Cents/Fame and Fortune Weekly/Stories of/Boys who make Money./STRANDED IN THE GOLD FIELDS./or, The Treasure of Van Diemen's Land. By/A Self-made man./[illus. & caption]
32pp (inc. 24pp title story, 2pp serial story, 5pp miscellaneous material & 1p adv.), pic. wrappers, 230x120mm. CLRC

SELSAM, Millicent E.
6649 THE QUEST OF/CAPTAIN COOK/By Millicent E. Selsam/Illustrated by Lee J. Ames/Doubleday & Company, Inc. Garden City, New York
1962
128pp (inc. 2pp index), col. frontis. & part. col. illus. & maps throughout, clo., 235x150mm. NSL:M

SENIOR, Margaret
6650 BUSH HAVEN ANIMALS/An Australian Picture Story by Margaret Senior/Published by the House of John Sands in Australia/Sydney, Melbourne, Brisbane, Adelaide, Perth and Hobart/Registered in Australia for transmission by post as a book
n.d [1954]
20pp, dec. t.p., col. illus. throughout, pic. bd., 240x240mm. KMM

THE LOST TOY SHOP, &c. *See* Bracken, Anne & 'Piers'

The Sentry and the Shell Fairy
See [Martin, George W.]

SERVENTY, Carol & HARRIS, Alwen
6651 ROLF'S/WALKABOUT/Carol Serventy and Alwen Harris/Photography/Vincent Serventy and Rolf Harris/Rigby Ltd.
Adelaide. First publ. 1971, rpt 1971, rpt 1972

128pp, col. portrait frontis., col. photographic illus. throughout, col. pic. bd., dec. e/p, 247x184mm. KMM

SERVENTY, Vincent

6652 AUSTRALIAN/WILDLIFE/CONSERVATION/ Vincent Serventy, B.Sc., B. Ed./[drawing]
Angus and Robertson, Sydney 1968
75pp (inc. 12pp notes, etc.), 1p author's note, b/w drawings throughout, map, 3pp photographic illus. by Faye Owner, dec. wrappers, 210x135mm. BBC

6653 TURTLE BAY ADVENTURE/Vincent Serventy/ B.Sc., B.Ed./Illustrated by/Faye Owner/[device]/André Deutsch
London 1969
119pp, b/w drawings in text throughout, clo., d/w design by Seymour Fleishman, 195x125mm. KMM

6654 THE/GREAT/BARRIER/REEF/Vincent Serventy/ Golden Press Sydney
1970
60pp, col. photographic illus. throughout, pic. bd., pic. e/p, 325x240mm. KMM

6655 WILDLIFE OF/AUSTRALIA Vincent Serventy/ Nelson
Thomas Nelson (Australia) Limited, Melbourne, 1971
58pp, 2pp index, 16pp col. illus., b/w photographic illus. in text throughout, pic. bd., 280x215mm. CLRC

SETH, Ronald

6656 ROBERT/GORDON MENZIES/by/Ronald Seth/ [device]/Red Lion Lives/Cassell—London
1960
120pp, 4 f/p b/w illus., clo., 185x125mm. NSL:M

6657 LET'S VISIT/ANTARCTICA/Ronald Seth/Burke
London 1969
96pp (inc. 4pp index), extended col. photographic frontis., col. & b/w photographic illus. throughout, pic. col., 200x150mm. KMM

SEXTON, JOHN

6658 Copyright/All rights reserved/STORIES IN VERSE/FOR CHILDREN/By John Sexton, C.S.S.R./Drawings by Mary Noeline Lane/[quotation]/ Registered in Australia for transmission by post as a book
The Majellan Press, Mayfield, NSW, n.d. [1960]
88pp, line drawings, wrappers, 210x140mm. ANL

Sexton Blake in Australia

The Sexton Blake stories first appeared in weekly form in 1893 and later in the popular paper *Union Jack.* Amalgamated Press created a separate Sexton Blake Library in 1915, and this went into five numbered weekly series right up until 1970. Most of the booklets were anonymous, and so far a score or more titles have been found set in Australia or the South Pacific. Most were uniform publications with 64pp and pictorial wrappers. All but those marked 'RM' are unseen. [information from *Penny Dreadfuls and Comics*, Victoria & Albert Museum, London 1983; *The Oxford Companion to Children's Literature*, Carpenter & Prichard, Oxord UniversityPress, London 1984; *Australian Children's Books to 1980*, T. & F. O'Neill, National Library of Australia 1989.]
Format example:

6659 The/Sexton/Blake/Library/3d./Long/Complete/ Detective/Romance/THE BARRIER REEF MYSTERY/ A Strange Tale of Mystery, Detective Work, and Thrilling Adventure on the Sea, in Australia, and/at Home. Introducing Sexton Blake, Detective,/Tinker, Pedro, and John Lawless./By the Author of/"At Twelve O'clock", "The Food Profiteer". "When Greek/ meets Greek", etc. etc.
Amalgamated Press London, n.d.
No. 45, 74pp, unillus., col. pic. wrappers, cover title, 180x134mm. RM

By the same author

6660 THE BEACH-COMBER, SBL 140, 1920
6661 SEXTON BLAKE IN AUSTRALIA, Union Jack 199, 1906
6662 THE MYSTERY OF WALLAWALLA, UJ 528, 1913
6663 THE CREST OF THE FLOOD, UJ 706, 1917
6664 THE BLACK OPAL MINE, by Andrew Murray, SBL 161, 1918 RM
6665 MAROONED UJ 194 [1921]
6666 TERROR ISLAND, UJ 202 [1921]
6667 THE SECRET OF THE RED MOUNTAIN SBL 204, 1921
6668 THE PHANTOM OF THE PACIFIC, SBL 221, 1922
6669 THE CASE OF THE CULTURED PEARLS, SBL 203, 1922 [66pp] RM
6670 THE CASE OF THE COTTON BEETLE, SBL 279, 1922 RM
6671 THE CRIMSON BELT [by G. H. Teed] UJ 307 [1923]
6672 BAIL UP! UJ 1040, 1923
6673 THE GREEN ROSE [by G. H. Teed] UJ 1148, 1925
6674 THE MAN FROM AUSTRALIA, SBL 137, 1928 RM
6675 THE RIDDLE OF RURALONG BAY [by Gilbert Chester] UJ 1340, 1929
6676 THE CALL OF THE DRAGON [by A. J. Palk] UJ 1525, 1933, 24pp ANL
6677 THE SECRET OF THE LOCH [by R. Coutts Armour] SBL 400, 1933, 96pp ANL
6678 THE RED BOOMERANG, SBL 2nd series 493 [by J. G. Brandon] 1935
6679 THE MELBOURNE MYSTERY, SBL 2nd series 595 [by J. G. Brandon] 1937
6680 THE MYSTERY OF THE ENGRAVED SKULL, SBL 3rd series 309 [by Stanton Hope] 1953
6681 FLASHPOINT FOR TREASON, SBL 3rd series 379 [by Desmond Reid] 1957
6682 SHOWDOWN IN SYDNEY, SBL 3rd series 434 [by Desmond Reid] 1959

SEYMOUR, Olive

6683 BIRDS FOR/BEGINNERS/Olive Seymour/The Jacaranda Press
Milton, Queensland, 1972
96pp (inc. index, etc.), 1p foreword, 1p introduction, col. & b/w illus. throughout, clo., 255x190mm. BBC

SHACKCLOTH, Irene

TALES OF THE SHOE. *See* GUNN & TAYLOR 3178
MORE TALES OF THE SHOE. *See* GUNN & TAYLOR 3182
MRS. MATHILDA'S KITCHEN. *See* GUNN & TAYLOR 3187

6684 THE/MUDDLES OF MUGWUMPIA/By/Irene Shackcloth/Illustrated by/Armstrong/[device]/ Hallcraft Publishing Company Pty. Ltd./Melbourne/ 1951
118pp, col. frontis. & 3 f/p col. illus., 21 b/w illus. (mostly f/p), clo., 215x135mm. KMM
Humorous book intended for adults & children alike.
See also Gunn & Taylor 3196 THE WIGGLY WOGS

SHACKLETON, Ernest

6685 SHACKLETON/IN THE ANTARCTIC/Being the story of the British/Antarctic Expedition, 1907–1909/By Sir Ernest Shackleton/C.V.O./[device]/ London,/William Heinemann/MCMXI

255pp (inc. notes), b/w photograhic illus., dec. clo., b/w map e/p, 185x120mm. KP
Adapted from *The Heart of the Antarctic.*
Variant copy without map e/p, but map bound in opposite half-title and "The Hero Readers" on front cover & spine. KP

SHADWELL, Mrs Lucas
6686 NOT/HIS OWN MASTER/or/Ronald Eversley's Experiences/By/Mrs Lucas Shadwell/Author of/ "Golden Sheaves" "Only Tell Jesus"/"The Clevelands of Oaklands" "Elsie's Footprints"/Etc./The Religious Tract Society/56 Paternoster Row, 65 St Paul's Churchyard/and 164 Piccadilly
n.d., 1st publ. 1890
320pp, b/w frontis. & 3 f/p illus. & 5 drawings in text, pic. clo., 180x120mm. KP
Religious tale.
Another copy as above but with 16pp adv. KP

[SHANN, Richard Ernest Churchill]
6687 LIGHTS BURNING BRIGHT: AND/ALL'S WELL./ An Australian Idyll./By/John Curfew/Original Edition./Melbourne:/George Holroyd and Co.,/108 Elizabeth St./1894/(All rights reserved)
93pp (inc. 3pp preface), 1p verse, unillus., pic. wrappers, 135x100mm. ANL
Homily for children, beginning in London.

Shaped Books
6688 AUSTRALIA/Castell Brothers, London/Printed in Bavaria
n.d.
8pp (inc. 4pp verses (signed M.G.) & 4pp col. illus.), light card pic. wrappers, approx. 120x90mm. MAC
Book shaped as a map of Australia with two boys dressed as gold-diggers on the left-hand side of front cover.
6689 UNTITLED SHAPED BOOK
n.p., n.d. [194-?]
[16]pp, illus. throughout, light pic. bd., 375x245mm (max.) KMM
Text printed throughout in green as are line drawings, alternate pages in col., penultimate page opens out (illus. in col.). Verses & drawings relating to Australian animals; on p4 inscription 'Printed and produced in Australia'. Front & back cover identical, depicting in col. koalas on a gum tree.
6690 NAUGHTY MAGGIE
Printed in Australia n.p., n.d. [193-?]
8pp verses (signed T.A.W.) with part-col. illus. on every page, pic. col. wrappers depicting 2 magpies, 292x120mm. KP
Illus. appear to be signed 'Milgate'. Verses possibly by T. A. White, who publ. similar verses about the 1930s.
6691 THE BUSH TWINS
Printed in Australia, n.p., n.d. [193-?]
8pp, verses (signed T.A.W.) with part col. illus. on every page, stiff col. pic. wrappers, 295x120mm. KP
Verses possibly by T. A. White.
6692 UNTITLED
n.p., n.d. [193-?]
4pp printed in green & pink & red with verses about kookaburras & illus. of birds & a small boy (unsigned), 2 kookaburras on front & back covers printed in col., 300x120mm. KP
6693 A BUNCH OF HEARTSEASE
Scott & Bowne Ltd, 483 Kent St, Sydney, n.d.
12pp, illus. throughout in violet on off-white paper, col. pic. stiff paper wrappers, pansy-shaped about 160mm in diameter
Adv. for Scott's Emulsion baby's diary printed inside front cover. Possibly Australian ed. of overseas book. JC
See also the Weston Company Baby Booklets and Sunny South series

SHAPIRO, Irwin
6694 THE STORY OF YANKEE WHALING/by/the editors of/American Heritage/narrative by Irwin Shapiro/in consultation with/Edouard A. Stackpole/ Curator, Mystic Seaport,/Marine Historical Association/Mystic, Connecticut/Published by/ American Heritage/Publishing Co., Inc./New York/ Book Trade Distribution by/Golden Press, New York 1959
153pp (inc. 1p foreword & 1p index) extended t.p., col. frontis., col. & b/w illus. throughout, pic. clo., dec. e/p, 255x175mm. NSL:M

SHARLAND, Michael
TASMANIA
HOBART. *See* Around Australia Program

SHARP, Margery
6695 Margery Sharp/MISS BIANCA/IN THE/ ANTARCTIC/Illustrated by/Erik Blegvad/Heinemann: London 1970
116pp, b/w illus., bd.., 200x130mm. Grant

SHAW, Alan George Lewers
RALPH DARLING. *See* Great Australians

OUR COAL. *See* Australia at Work

SHAW, Charles
6696 THE/GREEN TOKEN/An Australian Story of Adventure and Mystery for/Boys and Girls/By/ Charles Shaw/("Old-Timer" of "The Bulletin")/Author of "Outback Occupations" and "The Warrumbungle Mare"/Sydney: Dymock's Book Arcade Ltd./1943
128pp, b/w frontis. & 3 f/p b/w illus. by H. Edgecombe, bd., 180x120mm. KMM

6697 THE TREASURE OF/THE HILLS/A Tale of Adventure and Mystery in the Bush/for Boys and Girls of all Ages/By/Charles Shaw/with which is included/ "The Green Token"/[device]/Sydney: Dymock's Book Arcade Ltd./1944
195pp, 2 b/w maps
Bound together with:
6698 THE/GREEN TOKEN/An Australian Story of Adventure and Mystery for/Boys and Girls/By/ Charles Shaw
n.d.
126pp, bd., 180x115mm.
Title on spine: 'The Treasure of the Hills'. KMM
6699 THE TREASURE OF/THE HILLS/A Tale of Adventure and Mystery in the Bush/for Boys and Girls of all ages/By/Charles Shaw/Sydney: Dymock's Book Arcade Ltd./1946
First published 1944; rpt 1946
195pp, 2 maps, clo., 180x115mm. NSL:M

'SHAW, Flora L.' [pseud. Lady Flora Louisa Lugard]
THE STORY OF AUSTRALIA
London [190-?] (The Story of the Empire series)
This is not a children's book.

SHAW, Frank H.
OUTLAWS OF THE AIR
London, 1927
Story with Antarctic references insufficient for inclusion. ANL

SHAW, John
6700 CAPTAIN STORMALONG/THE BUSHRANGER/ By/John Shaw/with illustrations by Stanley L. Wood/

London/George Routledge and Sons, Limited/ Broadway House, Ludgate Hill/1898
304pp, illus. b/w frontis., clo., 190x120mm. Dromkeen
Set in 1826 in Governor Darling's period.

SHEAD, Isobel Ann [Mrs Charles Zwar]

6701 SANDY/by/I. A. Shead/Illustrated by/Noel Syers/London/Hutchinson & Co. (Publishers) Ltd.
1st ed. September 1935; 2nd ed. October 1935
228pp, b/w frontis. & 4 f/p b/w illus., clo., 190x130mm. KMM

6702 MIKE/by/Isobel/Ann Shead/Hutchinson & Co./ (Publishers)/Ltd./London
n.d. [1936]
224pp, b/w frontis. & 4 f/p b/w illus. by Noel Syers, clo., 195x130mm. VSL

6703 CLANCY/By/Isobel Ann Shead/Hutchinson & Co./(Publishers) Ltd./London
n.d. [1937]
260pp, b/w frontis. & 4 f/p b/w illus., clo., 185x130mm. VSL
The story of a lame boy living in the Mallee.

6704 OFF/THE CHAIN/—Telling of the exciting adven—/tures that befell Beetle when he/ran away/ [drawing]/by/Isobel Ann Shead
Hutchinson & Co., London, n.d. [1938]
208pp, b/w frontis. & b/w drawings in text, clo., 200x140mm. VSL

6705 THIS WAY PLEASE!/By/Isobel Ann Shead/Author of/"Clancy", "Mike", "Sandy"/Hutchinson & Co. (Publishers) Ltd./London
n.d. [1939]
223pp, b/w frontis. & 4 f/p b/w illus., clo., 185x115mm. VSL

6706 THE/FLYING KANGAROO/By/Isobel Ann Shead/Hutchinson & Co. (Publishers) Ltd./London and Melbourne
n.d. [1940]
208pp, b/w frontis. & 2 b/w illus., clo., 185x120mm. ANL

6707 THEY SAILED BY NIGHT/by/I. A. Shead/Faber and Faber Ltd./24 Russell Square/London
1943; 2nd imp. 1943
271pp, unillus., clo., 180x115mm. KMM
The story of three English children, left homeless by an air raid, who are taken care of in Australia for the duration of the war.
3rd imp. 1944. KP
5th imp. 1948. KP

6708 TO SEE THE QUEEN/by/Ann Shead/illustrated by/Cedric Flower/[drawing]/Faber and Faber/24 Russell Square/London
1953
203pp, 5 f/p b/w illus. & b/w drawings throughout, clo., 185x115mm. NSL:M

6709 THE/JAGO/SECRET/Ann Shead/Faber and Faber/24 Russell Square London
1966
192pp, unillus., clo., d/w designed by Margaret Wolpe, 200x125mm. KMM
An Australian family on holiday in England search for the Cornish farm from which their ancestors came.
6710 THE JAGO SECRET/by Ann Shead/illustrated by Marvin Friedman/Follett Publishing Company/ Chicago [device] New York
1966
192pp, b/w frontis. only, pic. clo., 220x140mm. KP
A Merit Mystery.

KOOBORR THE KOALA *See* Barrett, Charles & Shead, Isobel Ann

Shell Project Card Albums

Format example:
6711 SHELL/PROJECT CARD ALBUM/FLOWERS AND ANIMALS
n.p., n.d. [196-?]
8pp with spaces for 60 col. cards to be inserted with printed description text, cover title, spirax binding, 232x30mm. KMM
Uniform in series, all WRT
6712 AUSTRALIAN BEETLES
6713 BIRDS
6714 BUTTERLFIES AND MOTHS
6715 SHELLS, FISH AND CORAL
6716 TRANSPORTATION
6717 PROJECT/CARD/ALBUM/SHELL—METEOROLOGY
n.p., n.d.
[4]pp text, [10]pp spaces for 60 cards & text inside back cover, wrappers, 235x210mm. WRT
6718 SHELL CITIZENSHIP/PROJECT CARD ALBUM
n.p., n.d. [inside back cover 'A. E. Keating' 1970?]
14pp (inc. 4pp text (with statistics up to Nov 1964), space for 60 cards, wrappers, 235x215mm. WRT

SHELLEY, Noreen

6719 PIGGY GRUNTER/AT THE CIRCUS/[drawing]/ Selected and Illustrated by/Noreen and Ralph Shelley/ Published by/Frank Johnson/350 George Street/ Sydney/Wholly set up and printed in Australia by the Supertone Co., 200 Chalmers Street, Sydney
n.d. [1944]
22pp, 6 col. illus. & b/w drawings in text, pic. wrappers, 220x170mm. ANL

Uniform with the above:
6720 PIGGY GRUNTER AT THE FIRE
6721 PIGGY GRUNTER'S RED UMBRELLA
6722 PIGGY GRUNTER'S NURSERY RHYMES. all ANL

6723 Mullens' Stories for Children/No. 303/ANIMALS OF THE WORLD/By Noreen Shelley/(For Ages 9 to 10)/[drawing]/Robertson & Mullens Ltd./Melbourne
n.d. [1952]
31pp, b/w frontis. & b/w drawings in text, wrappers, 180x115mm. ANL

6724 Mullens' Plays for Children/No. 4/KING OF SPAIN/And Other Plays By/Noreen Shelley/(For Ages 7 to 9)/Robertson & Mullens Ltd./Melbourne
n.d. [1953]
52pp, b/w frontis. & b/w drawings in text, wrappers, 185x120mm. ANL
Contains 5 plays.

6725 Mullens' Stories for Children/(No. 302)/THE RUNAWAY SCOOTER/By/Noreen Shelley/(For Ages 9 to 10)/[drawing]/Robertson & Mullens Ltd., Melbourne
n.d. [1953]
32pp, b/w frontis. & 2 b/w illus., wrappers, 180x115mm. ANL

6726 PIGGY GRUNTER/STORIES/[drawing]/By Noreen Shelley/Illustrated by Ralph Shelley/Angus and Robertson/Sydney London
1954
64pp, part-col. frontis., 5 f/p illus. & other drawings in text, limp clo., 170x120mm. ANL

6727 SNOW BOY/A Story by Noreen Shelley/With pictures by Margaret Senior
John Sands Pty. Ltd./Sydney Melbourne Brisbane Adelaide Perth Hobart [opposite t.p.], n.d. [1958]
24pp, col. illus. throughout, stiff pic. wrappers, dec. e/p, 180x240mm. KMM

6728 THREE CHEERS/FOR PIGGY GRUNTER!/by Noreen Shelley/[drawing]/Illustrated by Elisabeth Macintyre/Angus & Robertson
Sydney, n.d. [1959?]
46pp, part-col. illus. throughout, dec. bd., 230x150mm. BBC

6729 ROUNDABOUT/by/Noreen Shelley/Book 1/ illustrated by/Astra Dick/a Horwitz-Martin Publication
Sydney, 1967
50pp, 3 f/p & numerous other b/w drawings, pic. stiffened paper cover, 187x132mm. ANL
Stories first publ. for *NSW School Magazine.*

6730 Noreen Shelley/FAMILY AT THE LOOKOUT/ [drawing]/Illustrated by Robert Micklewright/London/ Oxford University Press/1972
153pp, b/w drawings in text, clo., 215x130mm. KMM
Winner CBCA award 1973.

THE BAKER
THE BLACK TRACKER;
THE CORRESPONDENCE SCHOOL
THE DENTIST
THE FLYING DOCTOR
THE LIFE-SAVERS
THE POSTMAN
THE SHEARER
TRAWLERS AND FISHERMEN. *See* Australian People

SHEPHERD, Catherine
6731 TASMANIAN/ADVENTURE/Catherine Shepherd/ with drawings by/Grace Huxtable/J. M. Dent and Sons Ltd/Bedford St. London WC2
n.d.
156pp, b/w frontis. & 3 f/p b/w illus., b/w drawings in text, clo., 190x120mm.
Experiences of a pioneering family who settle in Van Diemen's Land in 1825. VECD
6732 Catherine Shepherd/TASMANIAN/ADVENTURE/ with drawings by/Grace Huxtable/London/J. M. Dent & Sons Ltd.
1964
156pp, b/w frontis. & 3 f/p b/w illus., b/w drawings in text, clo., 190x120mm. KMM

SHEPPARD, Elsie
THE STORY OF THOUGHT CASTLE
EXCITEMENT ON ELF ISLAND. *See* Adventure series

'SHERE KHAN'
6733 Jacko Whacko and Greybeard Series No. 1/A JAR/ OF NUTS/A Shere Khan/Story
Shere Khan Productions, Sydney, n.d. [1945]
16pp, col. & b/w illus. by Frank Beck, pic. wrappers, cover title, 245x185mm. ANL

6734 Jacko Whacko and Greybeard Series No. 2/ RAIDING/THE/CORNFIELD/A/Shere Khan/Story
Shere Khan Productions, Sydney, n.d. [1945]
16pp, col. & b/w illus. throughout, pic. wrappers, cover title, 245x185mm. ANL

6735 THE/MAGIC CORMORANT/A/"Shere Khan"/Story
Shere Khan Productions, Sydney 1945
16pp, col. & b/w illus. throughout, pic. wrappers, cover title, 185x245mm. Sing Ting Ling series. ANL

6736 A/"SHERE KHAN" STORY/THE/RIVER DRAGON/[drawing]/Drawings by E. D. Chong "Sing Ting Ling Series"
Sydney, n.d. [194-?]
16pp, 4 f/p col. ilus., 4 b/w illus., col. pic. bd., cover title, 185x248mm. KMM
Other titles listed inside back cover 'Books of the "Sing Ting Ling" Series' and unseen, are
No 3 The Painted Duck
No 4 Stone Animals
No 5 The Hermit Crab

SHIELDS, Brenda D.
6737 TEZZA/THE CORAL TROUT/by Brenda D. Shields/illustrated by John Derrick/John F. Blair, Publisher Winston-Salem 1962 [USA]
36pp, 4 f/p col. illus. & drawings throughout (book printed in blue ink) clo., 175x245mm. ANL
Both author & illustrator are Australians.
2nd ed. 1962. KMM

Ships in Australia's History
6738 SHIPS/IN/AUSTRALIA'S/HISTORY/Presented to you by the Commonwealth Banks
n.p., n.d. [1970?]
16pp, col. illus. throughout by Graham Back, col. pic. wrappers, 244x180mm. KP

SHOBERL, Frederic
6739 THE WORLD/IN MINIATURE/Edited by/Frederic Shoberl/The Asiatic Islands/and/New Holland:/ being/a description/of the/manners, customs, characters, and/state of society/of the various tribes in which they are inhabited:/illustrated by/Twenty-six coloured Engravings/in two volumes./Vol. 1/"The Proper Study of Mankind is Man", Pope/London:/ Printed for R. Ackermann, Repository/of Arts, Strand;/and to be had of all booksellers
[1824]
2 vols bound together
xiipp, 191 & 289pp, col. frontis. & 24 col. engravings, clo. with gilt dec., 140x90mm. ANL
Vol. 1 devoted mostly to Java & Sumatra, vol. 2 has engravings of 'Man of New Holland', and 5 others of natives of NSW and VDL.

SHORE, Arnold
TOM ROBERTS. *See* Great Australians

SHORT, Bryan F.
6740 THE STORY OF/AUSTRALIAN/WOOL/ [drawing]/By Bryan F. Short, M. Ag. Sc. (New Zealand), Ph.D. (Wales)/Illustrated by Peter Chapman/Readabout Books
Readabout Publishers Pty Ltd, Crow's Nest, NSW, 1964
30pp, col. & part. col. illus. & diagrams throughout, stiff pic. wrappers, 280x210mm. KMM

A Short Memoir of William Wimmera
See [Scholefield, Mrs H.]

SHORTIS, John & SIMMONS, Brian
6741 THINGS ABOVE MY HEAD/Six Songs for Children/By John Shortis and Brian Simmons/ Illustrations by Kay Tisdell/[5 lines dedication]
Sydney, 1971
21pp, unillus., b/w illus. dec. wrappers, 277x220mm. ANL

SHORTRIDGE, C. W. (ed.)
6742 THE BOY'S/R.A.A.F. BOOK/A Tribute to the valorous deeds/of the Royal Australian Air Force; a record of the pioneers/of flying; a portfolio of aeroplanes, past and present;/a glimpse into the future

of aviation/C. W. Shortridge/Editor/Prepared in collaboration with the Directorate of Public Relations,/ Royal Australian Air Force/Planned and Published by/ The F. H. Johnston Publishing Company/Sydney
1944
104pp (inc. 3pp glossary), 24 photographic illus., plans & drawings in text, clo., 265x210mm. NSL:M

SHURTLEFF, Bertrand
6743 AWOL MUSTERS OUT/by/Bertrand Shurtleff/ [drawing of a dog]/Illustrations by Diana Thorne/The Bobbs-Merrill Company/Publishers/Indianapolis New York
1946
284pp, b/w drawings in text, clo., 200x134mm. ANL
Adventures of an American prospector for tin in North Australia with his Dobermann Pinscher dog.
Swedish edition
6744 [device]/AWOL I AUSTRALIEN/Av Bertrand Shurtleff/Roben & Sjögren—Stockholm
n.d. [1954]
173pp & 2pp adv., unillus., pic. bd., clo. spine, 187x124mm. ANL
Trans. by Ingegord Lindstrum.

SHUTTLESWORTH, Dorothy Edwards
6745 THE WILDLIFE OF/AUSTRALIA AND/NEW ZEALAND/By Dorothy E. Shuttlesworth/Illustrated by George Frederick Mason/Foreword by Fred M. Packard, International/Commission on National Parks, I.C.U.N./The Hastings House/World Wildlife Conservation Series/Hastings House Publishers New York
1967
118pp (inc. 1p bibliography, 4pp index), 2pp foreword, 1p adv., b/w drawings in text, clo., 240x165mm. ANL

SIDNEY, Neilma
BEACHES. *See* Life in Australia

SILVANUS, Eric M.
6746 [Drawing]/THE PELICAN/AND THE KANGAROO/By/Eric M. Silvanus/Illustrated by/P. B. Longson/Jonathan Cape/Thirty Bedford Square/ London
1930
222pp, b/w drawings throughout, clo., 195x125mm. VSL
• Rpt Tom Stacey London 1972, 2pp adv., b/w drawings, 215x137mm, otherwise as above. CLRC

SIMMONDS, Ralph
6747 ALL ABOUT AIRSHIPS/A Book for Boys/By/ Ralph Simmonds/Author of "The School Mystery" "For School and Country"/etc./with a Colour Frontispiece and a large/number of Illustrations from/ Photographs/Cassell and Company, Ltd./London, New York, Toronto and Melbourne
1911
xpp, 374pp, col. frontis. & 47 leaves b/w plates (of photographs or diagrams), pic. clo., 202x144mm. ANL
Written before author's arrival in Australia 1914.

6748 THE OUTLAWS/By/Ralph Simmonds/[device]/ Cassell and Company, Ltd./London, Toronto, Melbourne and Sydney
First publ. 1924, popular ed. 1929
212pp, b/w frontis. only, by H. M. Brock, pic. clo., 186x120mm. NSL:M

SIMMONS, Ida Harper
6749 LET'S FIND/KOALA BEARS/By Ida Harper Simmons/Illustrated by/Marjorie Cooper/Rand McNally/& Company/Chicago/Established 1856/Copyright 1969 [5 lines]
24pp, col. illus. t.p., col. illus. throughout, pic. bd., pic. e/p, 155x115mm. CLRC
'Start Right Elf Books' variant rpts with 25c, or 39c & blocked out price on front cover. KP

SIMONS, Marion
6750 THE/INNKEEPER'S/WIFE/By/Marion Simons/ Illustrations by/Mary P. Harris/Copyright/Rigby Limited/Publishers/16 Grenfell Street/Adelaide, South Australia
n.d. [1942]
12pp, b/w drawings, dec. wrappers, 240x180mm. KMM
Nativity story.

Simple Simon Nursery Rhymes
6751 SIMPLE/SIMON/NURSERY RHYMES
A Pyramid Production
8pp, part-col. illus. throughout, col. pic. wrappers, 125x180mm. KP

SIMPSON, Claire
6752 THE STORY OF/THE WALKING HOUSE/Written and Illustrated by/Claire Simpson/[drawing]/Angus and Robertson/Sydney London Melbourne Wellington
n.d. [1957]
25pp, col. & sepia/white illus. on alternate page openings, dec. bd., 185x245mm. BBC

SIMPSON, Helen de Guerry [Mrs J. Dennis Browne]
6753 MUMBUDGET/By/Helen Simpson/Illustrated by/ Molly McArthur/London/William Heinemann Ltd.
1928
200pp, col. frontis. & 7 f/p col. illus., clo., 195x140mm. NSL:M
Fairy stories.

6754 A WOMAN AMONG/WILD MEN/(Mary Kingsley)/by/Helen Simpson/Illustrated by/Erna Pinner/Thomas Nelson and Sons Ltd./London Edinburgh Paris Melbourne/Toronto and New York
1938
155pp, col. frontis. & 6 b/w illus., col., 210x140mm. NSL:M
6755 Helen Simpson/A WOMAN AMONG SAVAGES/ The Story of Mary Kingsley/Penguin Books/ Harmondsworth—Middlesex
First published 1938; Published in Penguin Books 1950
152pp (inc. 3pp introduction), 8pp adv., unillus., pic. wrappers, 180x110mm. KMM

SIMPSON, Kathleen M.
6756 LET'S WANDER/Stories written by/Kathleen M. Simpson/[verse]
W. J. Cryer & Co. Pty Ltd, 99 Marriott Street, Redfern, NSW, n.d. [194-?]
16pp, 6 f/p col. illus., dec. t.p., pic. wrappers, 275x215mm. KMM

Sinbad the Sailor and Ali Baba and the Forty Thieves
6757 SINBAD/THE SAILOR/AND/ALI BABA/AND THE/FORTY THIEVES/W. H. Honey Publishing Co./ 31 Cunningham Street/Sydney
n.d.
93pp, 3pp glossary & notes, dec. t.p., b/w illus. in text by Rhys Williams, dec. bd., 245x170mm. NSL:M

SINCLAIR, Dee
6758 Dee Sinclair/THE CASTLEDARE/VIGILANTES/ Illustrated by Edward Pagram/Heinemann/Castledare Books/Melbourne London
1969

129pp, b/w frontis., 18 b/w illus., clo., 195x120mm. KMM
Boys' school story set in Western Australia.

6759 Dee Sinclair/THE NIGHT THE/GHOST WALKED/Illustrated by Edward Pagram/Heinemann/Castledare Books/Melbourne London
1969
114pp, b/w frontis., 22 b/w illus., clo., 195x120mm. CLRC

SINCLAIR, Lester
See Mystery, John

SINGLETON, C. C.
AUSTRALIAN RAILWAYS. *See* Around Australia Program

SINNETT, Jane [Mrs Percy Sinnett]
6760 HUNTERS AND FISHERS:/or,/Sketches of Primitive Races in the Lands beyond the Sea./By Mrs. Percy Sinnett./London:/Chapman and Hall, 186 Strand./MDCCCXLVI
146pp, col. frontis., 3 b/w illus. in text, clo., 168x126mm. CLRC
Contains section: 'The Australians' (pp37–58).

SISTER Agnes
6761 FAIRY TALES/TOLD IN THE BUSH/By/Sister Agnes/London: Elliot Stock/62 Paternoster Row, E.C.
n.d. [inscribed by author 1912]
95pp, 1p preface, b/w frontis. & 12 f/p b/w illus., clo., 200x140mm. CLRC

SISTER Mary Winefride
6762 YOUTH/LOOKS/AHEAD/A Guide for Catholic Girls/by/Sister Mary Winefride/The Polding Press/Brisbane
1st ed. July 1962, rev. ed. June 1966
144pp (inc. 3pp index), unillus., wrappers, 205x130mm. KP

A SISTER OF MERCY
6763 THE HEIRESS OF COOLOCK HOUSE/[drawing]/By/A Sister of Mercy/Illustrations by D. Bradley
Waite & Bull, Sydney, 1951
29pp, b/w frontis., 3 f/p b/w illus. & drawings in text, 242x184mm. ANL

6764 THE LIFE OF SAINT THERESE/FOR CHILDREN/[vignette]/by/A Sister of Mercy/Illustrations adapted by D. Bradley
Printed by Waite & Bull, Sydney, n.d. [Copyright 1952]
39pp, 4 f/p col. illus., dec. wrappers, 240x180mm. NSL:M

Sister's Love
6765 SISTER'S LOVE;/or/Lost in the Bush:/An Australian Tale,/in verse,/London: Jarrold and Sons,/12, Paternoster Row./Price 2d./or in enamelled wrappers, 3d.
n.d. [1870?]
32pp (inc. 2pp preface & 1p adv.), unillus., wrappers, cover title, 160x100mm. MAC
Household Tracts for the People. Story of the Duff children. Listed as appearing in at least 4 eds

Six Australian Writers
See Great Australians series

Six Great Australians
See Great Australians series

Sixteen Explorers of Australia
See FOURTEEN EXPLORERS OF AUSTRALIA

SKILLER, Dorothy & Allan
6766 An Uncle Peter Playbook—series number one/THE/SAND-MAN/& Other Fairy Stories/By Dorothy and Allan Skiller/Illustrations by Norman T. Hope
Peter Huston Publishing Co., Sydney, n.d. [1946]
[32]pp, col. & b/w illus. throughout, dec. bd., dec. e/p, 240x185mm. ANL
Author's name spelt 'Allan' on t.p., but 'Alan' on cover.

SKINNER, Dion H.
6767 FAIR/DINKUM/AUSTRALIA/By/Dion H. Skinner/Copyright 1970 [device]
Renniks & Co Pty Ltd, Unley, SA, n.d.
80pp, b/w illus. throughout by John Chizmeysa, pic. wrappers, 195x138mm. CLRC
Factual book of events & information about Australia told in comic-strip form.

6768 Nabisco/COINS/OF AUSTRALIA/A Vita-Brits Card Series Price 2/-/Registered Trade Mark of/National Biscuit Company
Melbourne, n.d. [1966?]. Printed by The Griffin Press, Adelaide
12pp (3pp text & 9pp description of coins & spaces for cards to be collected & pasted in), pic. stiff paper covers, cover title, 238x183mm. KMM

SKINNER, Roy W.
6769 ONE HUNDRED AND FIFTY GAMES FOR CEBS/A National Publication/of the/Church of England Boys' Society/[device]/Compiled by/Roy W. Skinner/Commissioner, Formerly Branch Governor/Published by/Diocese of Perth/Approved by/National Executive, 1961
57pp & 2pp index, 1p blank, unillus., wrappers, 190x115mm. KP

SKIPPER, Mervyn Garnham
6770 THE MEETING-POOL/A Tale of Borneo/by/Mervyn Skipper/with Illustrations/by/R. W. Coulter/London/Elkin Mathews & Marrot Limited/54 Bloomsbury Street MDCCCCXXIX
124pp, dec. t.p., 11 f/p b/w drawings & b/w drawings in text throughout, pic. clo., 210x165mm. KMM
Another copy as above, 'First printing (5000 copies) Sept.1929; Second Printing Nov.1929' KMM
6771 THE MEETING-POOL/A Tale of Borneo/by/Mervyn Skipper/With illustrations/by/R. W. Coulter/Angus and Robertson Ltd./Sydney: London/1940
128pp, b/w illus. throughout, pic. bd., 240x180mm. ANL
6772 Mervyn Skipper/THE/MEETING-POOL/A Tale of Borneo/[drawing]/Illustrated by/Sheila Hawkins/Penguin Books/Melbourne London Baltimore
First published in Puffin Story Books 1954
156pp, 3pp adv., b/w drawings throughout, pic. wrappers, 180x115mm. KMM
German edition
6773 DIE WASSERSTELLE/von/Mervyn Skipper/Mit 22 Zeichnungen/von Lotte Wellnis/Kosmos, Gesellschaft der Naturfreunde/Franckh'sche Verlagshandlung, Stuttgart
n.d.
100pp & 2pp adv., b/w drawings in text, pic. bd., 193x130mm. ANL

6774 THE WHITE MAN'S GARDEN/A Tale of Borneo/By Mervyn Skipper/[drawing]/Illustrated by the Author/London/Elkin Mathews & Marrot/54 Bloomsbury Street, W.C.1/1930
118pp (inc. 2pp glossary), b/w drawings throughout, clo., 235x165mm. VSL

Morris Miller states that both these books of Skipper's have been translated into Finnish, Czech, & other European languages.

6775 THE FOOLING OF/KING ALEXANDER/By Mervyn Skipper/Illustrated by Gaynor Chapman/[coloured drawing]/Hamish Hamilton Ltd. London
First published 1930 in *The White Man's Garden*;First published in this edition 1967
32pp, col. illus. & b/w illus. on alternate page openings, pic. clo., 265x200mm. KMM

Skippy the Bush Kangaroo

6776 SKIPPY COLOURING/BOOK/[drawing]/World Distributors (Manchester) Limited.
1968
80pp, b/w illus., col. pic. wrappers, 266x194mm. KP
On front cover:
Skippy/The Bush Kangaroo/Colouring Book/Authorised edition/Based on the famous/Television Series

6777 SKIPPY/THE BUSH KANGAROO/Sticker/Fun/Book/[coloured illustration]/Push Out/Stick and/Colour/Authorised Edition/Based on the Famous/Television Series
World Distributors (Manchester) Ltd, Manchester 1968
[8]pp, line drawings, pic. wrappers, cover title, 300x260mm. KMM
With coloured illustrations to be cut out & pasted over part of the full-page drawings; there is a caption to each page.

6778 SKIPPY/THE BUSH KANGAROO/Sonny's Bush/Adventure/illustrated by/Edgar Hodges/Copyright MCMLXIX by/Norfolk International Films Limited/All rights reserved throughout the world/Published in Great Britain by World Distributors (Manchester) Limited/PO Box 111 12/14 Lever Street Manchester M60 1TS/SBN 7235 2204 9/Printed in Italy
[20]pp, col. illus. throughout, pic. bd., 253x198mm. KP

6779 SKIPPY/THE BUSH KANGAROO/in SKIPPY'S ALPINE ADVENTURE/Copyright MCMLXX by Norfolk International Films Ltd/All rights reserved throughout the world/Published in Great Britain by World Distributors (Manchester) Limited/PO Box 111, 12 Lever Street, Manchester M60 1TS/Printed in Italy/SBN 7235 2213 8
[20]pp, double-spread col. pic. t.p., col. illus. throughout, pic. bd., 257x196mm. WRT

6780 SKIPPY/THE BUSH KANGAROO/ANNUAL
Norfolk International Film Ltd., World Distributors (Manchester) Ltd, 1970
93pp, col. & part col. illus. throughout, col. pic. bd., col. pic. e/p, 267x195mm. KMM
Stories, natural history articles, games &c. Text & illus. all anonymous.

6781 SKIPPY/DAS BUSCH KÄNGURUH/Malbuch/Autorisierte Ausgabe/Nach der beliebten/Fernseh Serie
Whitman Verlag, Western Publishing GmbH, Frankfurt am Main 1970 (Printed in Italy)
[80]pp, b/w drawings throughout, pic. wrappers, cover title, 265x195mm. KMM
Colouring book with brief captions at the front of each page, based on the Australian Television serial; colour stills from the serial illustrate the wrappers.

SKOTTOWE, Elizabeth [Mrs Charles Hobson]

6782 ME/AN'/TIM/AN'/CAROLINE/Written and Illustrated/By/Elizabeth Skottowe/(Copyright)
Reliance Printery, Adelaide, n.d. [1932]
43pp, lino-cut illus., wrappers, 210x140mm. KMM
Verses.

6783 TIMOTHY RABBIT/BUILDS A HOUSE/By/Elizabeth Skottowe
Published by News of the World Ltd, London, n.d. [1950?].
26pp, col. dec. t.p., col. illus. throughout, dec. bd., dec. e/p., 205x155mm. KMM
Betterbook series

6784 Early Reader Series No. 39/THE DORMOUSE BOOK/Written & illustrated by/Elizabeth Skottowe/[picture]/Hampster Books
Paul Hamlyn, London 1958
55pp, frontis., b/w & part-col. illus. throughout, dec. bd., dec. e/p., 245x180mm. KMM
Spring Books

6785 A Gold Token Book/DILLY'S PICNIC PARTY/[col. illus.]/Elizabeth Skottowe/Young World Productions Ltd./Gold Token 2 Tokens
Gold Token Books, Young World Productions Ltd, 115, 123 Bayhan Street, London NW1
[21]pp (inc. inside back cover), col. illus. on every page, pic. bd., 160x127mm. KMM
Ensign series

Sky Stories

6786 SKY STORIES
n.p., n.d. [194-?]
8pp, col. illus. throughout, col. illus. (sgd 'Guerin') wrappers, 175x230mm. VMOU

'SLADE, Gurney' [pseud. Stephen Bartlett]

6787 PLEASURE/ISLAND/By/Gurney Slade/Ward, Lock & Co., Limited/London and Melbourne/1924
256pp, b/w frontis. & 2 b/w plates by Frances Hiley, pic. clo., 185x125mm. KMM

6788 PLEASURE/ISLAND/By/Gurney Slade/Author of "The Black Pyramid", "The Fifteen Men" etc./Ward, Lock & Co., Limited/London and Melbourne
n.d.
256pp, b/w frontis. & 2 b/w plates, clo., 185x125mm. PR

6789 THE/FIFTEEN MEN/By/Gurney Slade/Author of "Pleasure Island" etc./Ward, Lock & Co. Limited/London and Melbourne/1925
251pp, 4pp adv., b/w frontis. & 3 f/p, b/w illus., pic. clo., 190x130mm. KMM

6790 THE/FIFTEEN MEN/By Gurney Slade/Author of "Pleasure Island' etc./Ward, Lock & Co. Limited/London and Melbourne
n.d. [school prize 1939]
251pp (no adv.), b/w frontis. & 3 b/w plates by Francis E. Hiley, pic. clo., 190x130mm. KMM
The front cover design is the same as that used in the first edition though in this edition it is printed in black only, whereas in the first edition two additional colours were used.

6791 THE PEARLERS OF/LORNE/A Story for Boys/By/Gurney Slade/Thomas Nelson and Sons Ltd./London Edinburgh New York/Toronto and Paris
n.d. [Morris Miller gives first publication date as 1925, another edition 1939]
250pp, 6pp adv., b/w frontis., clo., 175x120mm. VSL

6792 THE PEARLERS OF/LORNE/A Story for Boys/By/Gurney Slade/Thomas Nelson and Sons, Ltd./London, Edinburgh, and New York
n.d.
250pp, 5pp adv., b/w frontis. & 3 f/p b/w illus. signed 'Holloway', clo., 185x120mm. CLRC
Swastika in black printed on front cover & spine.

6793 THE/BLACK PYRAMID/By/Gurney Slade/Ward, Lock & Co., Limited/London and Melbourne/1926
256pp (inc. 1p note), b/w frontis. & 3 b/w plates (W. I. Wightman), pic. clo., 185x125mm. KMM
Action set in Egypt during the withdrawal of the British forces & the Australian cavalry, after World War I.

6794 THE/BLACK PYRAMID/By/Gurney Slade/author of "The Fifteen Men", "Pleasure Island"/Ward, Lock & Co., Limited/London and Melbourne
n.d.
Details as above. KP

6795 MARLING/RANGES/by/Gurney Slade/[drawing]/Illustrated by/W. H. Holloway/Thomas Nelson and Sons Ltd./London, Edinburgh, and New York
n.d. [inscribed 1927]
293pp, 3pp adv., b/w frontis. & b/w drawings in text, dec. clo. (with col. onlay), 185x128mm. KP
Another copy n.d. as above, but with 10pp adv., clo., 175x115mm. ANL

6796 IN LAWRENCE'S/BODYGUARD/By/Gurney Slade/Author of/"The Pearlers of Lorne"/"Marling Range", &c/[device]/Frederic Warne & Co. Ltd/1–4 Bedford Court, London, W.C.2
1931
288pp (inc. 2pp preface) & 16pp adv., col. frontis. & 3 f/p b/w plates, clo., 190x127mm. ANL

6797 IN LAWRENCE'S/BODYGUARD/By/Gurney Slade/Author of/'Led by Lawrence'/'Through the Never-Never'/'The Delta Patrol', Etc./[device]/Frederick Warne & Co. Ltd./1–4, Bedford Court, London, W.C.2
n.d.
288pp & 2pp author's preface, col. frontis. only, clo., 187x124mm. KMM

6798 THE TREASURE/OF THE PASS/By/Gurney Slade/Thomas Nelson and Sons, Ltd./London, Edinburgh, New York/Toronto and Paris
n.d.
94pp, b/w frontis. only signed 'Anthony Brandt 1951', bd., 180x120mm. KMM

6799 LED BY LAWRENCE/By/Gurney Slade/[device]/Frederick Warne and Co. Ltd./London and New York
1934
288pp (inc. 2pp preface, 1p glossary), 16pp adv., col. frontis. only, clo., 190x125mm. KMM
Another copy, as above, but n.d. KMM

LAWRENCE IN THE BLUE
Unseen: Listed in *Led by Lawrence*

6800 THE DELTA PATROL/By/Gurney Slade/Author of 'In Lawrence's Bodyguard', etc./[device]/Frederick Warne and Co. Ltd./London and New York
1934
285pp (inc. 1p glossary), col. frontis. only, clo., 195x130mm. RM
A story of three young men in the AIF in Egypt during World War I

6801 THROUGH/THE NEVER-NEVER/By/Gurney Slade/Frederick Warne and Co. Ltd./London and New York
1935
288pp, col. frontis., clo., 194x130mm. KMM

6802 THROUGH/THE NEVER-NEVER/By/Gurney Slade/[device]/Frederick Warne and Co. Ltd./London and New York
n.d. [inscribed 1948]
288pp (no adv.), col. frontis., clo, 185x120mm. PR

6803 CAPTAIN QUID/By/Gurney Slade/Illustrated by/Reginald Mills, R.B.A./Frederick Warne & Co. Ltd./London and New York
1937
256pp, col. frontis. only, clo., 190x125mm. KMM

6804 QUID'S QUEST/By/Gurney Slade/[device]/Frederic Warne & Co. Ltd.,/London and New York
n.d. [1939]
252pp, col. frontis. & 3 f/p b/w illus., pic. clo., 210x145mm. Albion Library. KP

6805 QUID'S QUEST/By/Gurney Slade/[device]/Frederick Warne & Co. Ltd./London and New York
1939
252pp, b/w frontis. & b/w map of Western Australia, clo., 190x130mm. KMM

6806 GENTLEMEN O'/FORTUNE/By/Gurney Slade/Illustrated by/Victor Cooley/[drawing]/Thomas Nelson & Sons Ltd./London, Edinburgh, New York, Toronto, and Paris
n.d. [194-?]
277pp, 10pp adv., col. frontis., b/w drawings in text, clo., 185x125mm. KMM
GENTLEMEN O'/FORTUNE
Details as in the Thomas Nelson edition, but with no adv. KMM

6807 PINGOO/THE PENGUIN/by/Gurney Slade/[device—The Falcon Nature Stories]/Frederick Warne & Co. Ltd./London and New York
1948
64pp, b/w frontis., b/w drawings in text, dec. wrappers, 185x135mm. KP

6808 BAWSE/THE BADGER/by/Gurney Slade/Illustrations by/Joan Wanklyn/[device—The Falcon Nature Stories]/Frederick Warne & Co. Ltd./London and New York
1950
64pp, b/w frontis. & 9 b/w illus. in text, wrappers, 184x134mm. KMM
Listed inside back cover The Falcon Nature Stories (some by Slade).

6809 A NORTH SEA/QUEST/By/Gurney Slade/Illustrated by Ernest Ratcliff/[device]/London/Oxford University Press/Humphrey Milford
n.d. [1953]
256pp, col. frontis. & 6 b/w illus. pic. clo., 180x120mm. VSL

6810 THE LONG ARM/OF THE/CARDINAL/Gurney Slade/[drawing]/Frederick Warne & Co., Ltd./London and New York
1953
256pp, b/w frontis. only, clo., 190x125mm. KMM
Adventure story, but not specifically a children's book.

6811 THE/LEAGUE OF/GUY VARENNE/Gurney Slade/Frederick Warne & Co., Ltd./London and New York
1954
254pp, col. frontis. only, frontis. & d/w by D. C. Eyles, clo., 190x125mm. KMM
Adventure story set in 17th-century France.

SLATER, Pat

6812 AN/EAGLE FOR/PIDGIN/Pat Slater/Illustrated by Peter Slater/The Jacaranda Press
Milton, Queensland, 1970
244pp, 8 f/p b/w illus., clo., d/w by Genevieve Melrose, 215x140mm. BBC
Another copy as above, but stiff wrappers. KP

The Sleeping Beauty/Illustrated by Rhys Williams
See 'Beacon Series'

[SLESSOR, Kenneth]
6813 All Australian Picture Book Series No. 1/FUNNY/FARMYARD/[drawing]/Nursery Rhymes/and Painting Book/Line Drawings by/Syd Miller/Frank Johnson/273 Pitt Street/Sydney
n.d. [1933]
14pp, b/w illus., pic. wrappers, cover title, 295x240mm. ANL

SMALE, Fiona
6814 TALES AND RHYMES FOR TINY TOTS/by/Fiona Smale/Arthur H. Stockwell Ltd./
Elms Court—Ilfracombe/Devon
1969
19pp, b/w illus. by Cora E. M. Paterson, stiff wrappers, 195x145mm. ANL

SMART, Ralph & BORER, Mary Cathcart
6815 Ralph Smart/BUSH/CHRISTMAS/A film story retold by/Mary Cathcart Borer/[device]/London/Sir Isaac Pitman & Sons, Ltd.
First published 1947; rpt 1948
108pp, b/w photographic frontis. & 25 b/w photographic illus., clo., 185x120mm. KMM
Illustrated with stills from the film.
6816 Ralph Smart/BUSH/CHRISTMAS/A film story retold by/Mary Cathcart Borer/[publisher's device]/Melbourne/Sir Isaac Pitman & Sons Ltd.
First pub. 1947; rpt 1948, 1950, 1953, 1957
108pp, b/w frontis. & 25 b/w photographic illus., clo., 180x120mm. KMM
• Rpt Melbourne 1963, 1968 as above. KMM
Indonesian edition
6817 PAKANSI ADJAIB, Hollandia 1959, Pustaka Rakjat Translation (presumably Indonesian) of *Bush Christmas* in story & comic-strip form, 49pp, wrappers, 125x200mm. ANL

SMEATON, William Henry Oliphant
6818 THE TREASURE/CAVE OF THE/BLUE/MOUNTAINS/By Oliphant/Smeaton/Author of "By Adverse Winds"/"Allan Ramsay" "Tobias Smollett" etc./Decorated and Illustrated by/Joseph Brown/Published by/Oliphant Anderson &/Ferrier, Edinburgh and London
n.d. [1898]
312pp, 4 f/p b/w illus. & b/w drawings, clo., 200x130mm. VSL

6819 A/MYSTERY OF THE PACIFIC/By/Oliphant Smeaton/Author of "By Adverse Winds" "Our Laddie" "The Seven Ages"/"The Mystery of Grogan's Gully" &c./With eight illustrations by Wal Paget/London/Blackie & Son, Limited, 50 Old Bailey, E.C./Glasgow and Dublin/1899
[inscribed 'Christmas 1898']
335pp, 32pp adv., b/w frontis. & 7 b/w illus., pic. clo., 185x125mm. KMM
6820 A/MYSTERY OF THE PACIFIC/By/Oliphant Smeaton/Author of "By Adverse Winds" "Our Laddie" "The Seven Ages"/"The Mystery of Grogan's Gully", etc./With illustrations by Wal Paget/Blackie & Son Limited/London Glasgow Dublin Bombay
n.d. [prize 1909]
335pp, 16pp adv., col. frontis. & 3 f/p b/w illus., dec. clo., 185x125mm. KP
Another copy, prize label 1913, as above, but with slight variation in gilt title panel & on spine. KP

SMILES, Jack
6821 THE LAND/IN WHICH /WE LIVE/Universal Books Pty. Limited/Sydney/Written by: Jack Smiles, B.A., B.Ec., Dip. Ed./Educational Consultant: Allan Maclaine, B.Ed., M.A., Ph.D./Illustrated by Tuk Caldwell, A.T.D./Designed by: Neil Stevenson
Sydney 1968
96pp (inc. 6pp introduction by Sir Adrian Curlewis, glossary, etc.), double-spread col. map, col. photographic illus. & b/w drawings throughout, pic. clo., 230x155mm. BBC
Originally intended as social studies textbook, but scope widened to give more general interest.

SMILES, Samuel [ed.]
6822 A BOY'S VOYAGE/ROUND THE WORLD;/Including/A Residence in Victoria, and a Journey by Rail/Across North America./Edited/by Samuel Smiles,/Author of "Self-help"./With Illustrations./London:/John Murray, Albemarle Street./1871/The Right of Translation is reserved.
300pp, 2pp preface, 4pp index, engraved frontis., maps & engravings in text, dec. clo., 175x120mm. Grant
6823 A BOY'S VOYAGE/ROUND THE WORLD;/Including/A residence in Victoria, and a journey by rail across North America./Edited/By Samuel Smiles,/Author of "Self-help"/Fifth thousand/with illustrations/London:/John Murray, Albemarle Street./1872
304pp (inc. 4pp index), 2pp preface, engraved frontis., 12 engravings & maps in text, dec. clo., 175x115mm. CLRC
7th thousand 1872 as above, but full calf bdg & marbled e/p. RM
6824 ROUND THE WORLD;/Including/A Residence in Victoria, and a Journey by Rail/across North America./BY A BOY./Edited by Samuel Smiles,/Author of "Character", "Self-Help", "Life of the Stephensons", "The Huguenots",/etc./With illustrations./[publisher's device]/New York:/Harper & Brothers, Publishers,/Franklin Square/1872
286pp, 4pp index, 8pp adv., engraved frontis., 9 engraved illus. & 6 maps, clo., 185x120mm. CLRC
Dutch edition
6825 EINE REIS/RONDOM DE WERELD./Bladen/uit ret/Dagbeek van Een Jeugdig Reiziger./Voor de pers Bewerrt/door/Samuel Smiles./Vrij Naar 't Engelsch/door/S. J. Andriessen./Met Platen./Schoonhoven,/S. & W. N. Van Nooten
n.d. [1874?]
viii, 192pp, col. lithographed frontis. & 3 f/p col. lithographed plates, clo., 190x120mm. CLRC
6826 A BOY'S VOYAGE/ROUND THE WORLD;/Including/A Residence in Victoria, and a Journey by Rail/Across North America./Edited/By Samuel Smiles./Author of "Self-Help", "Character", "Thrift", etc./Eighth thousand/With Illustrations./London:/John Murray, Albemarle Street./1875/The right of translation is reserved.
300pp, 2pp preface, 4pp index, b/w frontis., b/w maps & engravings in text, dec. clo., 180x120mm. KMM
Another copy as above but specially bound in tooled leather as a school prize in 1877 with 'Kings College, London' emblem blocked in gilt on front cover, g.e. & spine dec. in gilt. KP
10th thousand n.d., as above. KMM
12th thousand 1884, as above. Grant
6827 A BOY'S VOYAGE/ROUND THE WORLD/including a residence &c/Popular edition/with illustrations/London:/John Murray, Albemarle Street/1897
Details as before, clo., 185x117mm. CLRC

6828 A BOY'S VOYAGE/ROUND THE WORLD/
Edited/By Samuel Smiles, LL.D./Author of "Self-Help", etc./London/John Murray, Albemarle Street/1905
xvipp, 304pp & 148pp adv., b/w frontis. & 11 b/w illus. (inc. maps), clo., 188x124mm. KMM

SMITH, B. Webster

6829 TO THE SOUTH POLE/The Story of Antarctic Exploration/By/B. Webster Smith/Author of "Some Great Adventurers"/"True Stories of Modern Explorers" &c./With Maps and Eight half-tone Plates/ Blackie & Son Limited/London and Glasgow
n.d. [1935]
224pp (inc. 2pp foreword), b/w photographic frontis. & 7 f/p photographic illus., 10 f/p b/w maps, clo., 195x135mm. KMM

6830 B. Webster Smith/SCOTT/OF THE ANTARCTIC/ [colophon]/Illustrated by Gilbert Dunlop/Blackie & Son Ltd./London and Glasgow/1955
67pp, b/w drawings, limp clo., 185x135mm. Great Endeavour series (biographical readers for secondary schools). NSL:M
• Rpt as above, 1965? BBC

6831 SCOTT/OF THE ANTARCTIC/B. Webster Smith/ [device]/Blackie: London and Glasgow
n.d. [1961?]
67pp, 1p chronological table, b/w frontis., 1 f/p b/w illus., 1 map & drawings in text, illus. by Gilbert Dunlop, decorations by Biro, clo., 185x135mm. NSL:M

6832 SIR ERNEST SHACKLETON/B. Webster Smith/ [device]/Blackie: London and Glasgow
1960
64pp, b/w frontis., 2 maps & 3 b/w illus., dec. clo., 180x135mm. KMM
Great Endeavour Books. Illus. John C. Gardner. Decoration by Biro.
Also author of *True Stories of Modern Explorers* with insufficient Australian material for inclusion, but containing 12pp chapter on Scott & Antarctic & 15pp chapter on Exploration of New Guinea.

SMITH, C. Fox

6833 THE/SHIP AGROUND/A Tale of Adventure/By/ C. Fox Smith/Illustrated by/C. Walter Hodges/ [drawing]/Geoffrey Cumberlege/Oxford University Press
1904; rpt 1941, 1942, 1946, 1947
221pp, 8 f/p b/w illus. & b/w chapter headings, clo., 214x135mm. ANL
Adventure story featuring 'Desolation Is., South Pacific' (116pp), Cook's name for Kerguelens.

SMITH, D.

See Newton, D. & Smith, D.

SMITH, E. A.

6834 12 PLAYETTES/FOR CHRISTIAN/YOUTH WORK/Prepared for Young People, intermediate/and junior age groups/by/E. A. Smith/Book 1/[3 line note on Book 2]
The author, Wollongong, NSW, n.d. [194-?]
38pp, unillus., wrappers, 205x140mm. MAC

[SMITH, Mrs Frances Lettice]'An Australian Mother'

6835 WILD ROSEBUDS/An Australian Story/For Children/By an Australian Mother/[drawing]/ Adelaide/Vardon and Prichard, Printers, Gresham Street./1889
244pp (inc. 1p preface, 1p quot. from 'The Song of Australia'), b/w tailpieces, clo., 180x120mm. KMM
Another copy as above, but bound in wrappers. VSL

SMITH, G. Barnett

6836 THE ROMANCE OF/THE SOUTH POLE/Antarctic Voyages and Explorations/By/G. Barnett Smith/ Author of "Sir John Franklin and the North-West Passage,"/"The History of the English Parliament"/&c &c/[drawing]/Thomas Nelson and Sons/London Edinburgh and New York/1902
235pp & 20pp adv. (Boys Books), dec. t.p. & additional pic. t.p., b/w frontis. (J. Williamson '95), 9 f/p plates & 1 map, dec. clo., 180x124mm. KP
Contains 2 chapters on Cook, Tasman, Dampier &c. Ross & others.
Another copy with 4pp adv. KP

SMITH, Joan Watson

6837 JINDI/THE PICCANINNY FAIRY/[col. illus.]/ Created by Bernard Tate./Written by Joan Watson Smith/Published by Southern Cross International/ Copyright 1968 by Southern Cross International Printed by United Packages Ltd for Southern Cross International [?Sydney]
18pp, col. illus. throughout, pic. bd., cover title, 280x235mm. A Jindi Book. CLRC

6838 THE/ROSELLA/AND THE RAIN CLOUD/ A/Jindi/Book/[drawing]/Created by Bernard Tate/ Written by Joan Watson Smith./Published by Southern Cross International./Copyright, 1968 By Southern Cross International [?Sydney]
[22]pp, col. illus. throughout, col. pic. bd., cover title, 280x233mm. KMM

6839 JINDI'S/AUSTRALIAN/A/B/C/Created by Bernard Tate,/Written by Joan Watson Smith/ Published by Southern Cross International/Copyright 1968 by Southern Cross International
Sydney, 1968
[22]pp (inc. front & back pastedowns), col. illus. by Bernard Tate throughout, pic. bd., cover title, 278x234mm. KMM
A rhyme & an animal for each letter. Both front & back pastedowns treated as a text page.

6840 THE/MOPOKE/AND THE NECKLACE/A Jindi Book/Created by Bernard Tate/Written by Joan Watson Smith./Published by Southern Cross International/Copyright, 1968 by Southern Cross International
22pp (text begins inside front cover), col. illus. throughout, col. pic. bd., cover title, 273x232mm. NSL:M
Note from publisher states that the original title for this book was to have been *Jindi and the Bunyip* and due to an oversight was not changed on the inside. So *Jindi and the Bunyip* and *The Mopoke and the Necklace* is in fact the same book.
JINDI AND THE BUNYIP. *See* THE MOPOKE AND THE NECKLACE

SMITH, Ida

6841 GAY AND THE/LITTLE RED MAN/[drawing]/ by/Ida Smith/Playground Publishing/Wingello House, Angel Place, Sydney/Phone BW 6119/Registered at the GPO Sydney for transmission by post as a book
n.d. [1945]
28pp, 2 f/p col. illus., col. & b/w illus. throughout by L. M. Smith, dec. bd., 235x180mm. ANL

SMITH, Jean

6842 VERSE CRAFT/A Book of Verse-making for children/By Jean Smith/Angus and Robertson/Sydney: London/1947

42pp (inc. 1p foreword), col. frontis. & b/w drawings in text, dec. wrappers, 235x185mm. NSL:M
A book for children on the construction of poetry, of more general interest than merely a school textbook.

SMITH, Keith
6843 THE PIED PIPER/KEITH SMITH'S/RIDDLE/BOOK/FOR CHILDREN
Rigby Ltd, Adelaide, n.d. [1960]
60pp (inc. 4pp 'A Word to Adults' & 2pp 'A Word to Children'), line drawings, stiff wrappers, illus. e/p, cover title, 135x105mm. KMM
Another copy bound in bd. KP
• Rpt several times with slight variations. KP

6844 Keith Smith's/RIDDLE BOOK/FROM/OUTER SPACE/Rigby Limited/Adelaide
1964
[60]pp, printed in b/w, some drawings in text, stiff wrappers, cover grey with red & black type (price in pencil 6/6), 134x102mm. MC
Another copy printed throughout in blue & red, cover red paper & stiff wrappers with moonscape & a rocket. KP
Another copy rpt 1969, printed in red & blue with moonscape design on cover. KP

6845 Keith Smith's/SHAGGY/T.V./RIDDLES/[drawing]/Rigby Limited
Adelaide 1968
[60]pp, b/w photographs inside front & back covers, line drawings, stiff paper wrappers, 135x100mm. KMM

6846 Keith Smith's/TV/COOK BOOK/FOR KIDS/Rigby/Opal/Books
Adelaide, 1972
54pp, photographic illus., illus. bd., pic. e/p, 212x142mm. CLRC

6847 Keith Smith's/T.V./JOKES/[drawing]/No. 1/FOR CHILDREN/Rigby
Sydney, n.d. [1972]
62pp, b/w drawings, stiff wrappers, 135x100mm. BBC
6848 Keith Smith's/T.V./JOKES/[drawing] 2/For Children/Rigby
Sydney, n.d. [1972]
62pp, b/w drawings, stiff wrapper, 135x100mm. BBC

Also by the same author:
6849 KEITH SMITH'S PICTURE PUZZLES No. 1.
Unseen

SMITH, Kevin R.
6850 SPACE/ADVENTURE/Kevin R. Smith/The Jacaranda Press
Milton, Queensland, 1969
100pp, 1p acknowledgements, b/w photographic frontis., b/w photographic illus. & diagrams throughout, pic. clo., dec. e/p maps, 275x100mm. KMM

SMITH, Mary
6851 FUN WITH/SEWING/by/Mary Smith/First Steps in/learning to sew/4/6
Southdown Press, Melbourne, n.d. [1960?]
32pp (inc. pic. wrappers), col. & b/w drawings & diagrams, cover title, 280x200mm. CLRC

SMITH, Minnie
6852 GRANNY SMITH'S BOOK/Verse and Legends of the Bush/Songs—Words and Music/By M. Smith/Illustrations by/Margaret Korner, Evelyn and Judith/[drawing]/[dedication]/Printed and Published by/Paterson's Printing Press Ltd./65 Murray Street, Perth/Western Australia/Price: four shillings
n.d. [1941]
59pp, b/w drawings in text, bd., 245x175mm. VSL
6853 As above but: /Second Edition/Printed and Published by/Imperial Printing Coy. Ltd./397 Hay Street, Perth/Western Australia/Copyright/Price: four shillings
n.d.
59pp (inc. 1p glossary), f/p b/w frontis. & b/w drawings in text, bd. (with col. illus. pasted on front cover), cover illus. by Judith (Mrs R. N. Grigg), 245x170mm. KMM

SMITH, Neville
6854 ANIMAL TALK/and other stories for boys and girls/Neville Smith/[vignette]/Illustrated by/Alison Forbes/F. W. Cheshire/Melbourne
1955
96pp, col. frontis. & line drawings, clo., 215x140mm. KMM

SMITH, Patsy Adam
6855 THE RAILS/GO WESTWARD/Patsy Adam Smith/Macmillan/of Australia/1969
South Melbourne
174pp, 8pp preface, etc., 16pp b/w photographic illus., clo., map e/p, 200x125mm. CLRC

SMITH, P. R.
6856 Text by P. R. Smith, M.A./THE STORY OF AUSTRALIA/Illustrations by B. Biro, M.S.I.A./Ernest Benn Limited
London 1959
64pp, extended dec. col. t.p., col. illus. & maps throughout (printed 4-colour photolithography), clo., 280x210mm. BBC

[SMITH, Sarah, pseud. 'Hesba Stretton']
6857 ENOCH RODEN'S TRAINING/By the/Author of "Fern's Hollow"/London:/The Religious Tract Society;/Instituted 1799/Depositories, 56 Paternoster Row; 65 St. Paul's Churchyard:/and 164 Piccadilly/Sold by the Booksellers.
n.d. [first pub. 1865 , this copy inscribed May,1866]
ivpp, 178pp, 10pp adv., b/w frontis. & 4 f/p b/w illus., blind-stamped clo. with title in gilt, 155x95mm. KMM
Two chapters are set in Melbourne.
6858 ENOCH RODEN'S TRAINING/By Hesba Stretton,/Author of/'Jessica's first Prayer'. 'Bede's Charity','Cobwebs and Cables'.etc/The Religious Tract Society:/56 Paternoster Row; 65, St Paul's Churchyard,/and 164 Piccadilly.
n.d.
159pp, & 16pp adv., b/w frontis. & 4 f/p b/w illus. by C. A. Ferrier, pic. clo., 182x120mm. ANL
6859 ENOCH RODEN'S/TRAINING/By/Hesba Stretton/Author of/'Carola' 'Pilgrim Street' 'Jessica's First Prayer'/'Half-Brothers', etc/London/The Religious Tract Society/4 Bouverie Street and 65 St Paul's Churchyard E.C.
n.d. [inscribed 1910]
190pp & 6pp adv., b/w frontis. & 1 f/p b/w plate, pic. clo., 182x118mm. KMM
6860 ENOCH RODEN'S/TRAINING/By/Hesba Stretton/Author of/'Jessica's First Prayer' 'Bede's Charity' 'Cobwebs and Cables'/etc/The Religious Tract Society/56 Paternoster Row; 65 St Paul's Churchyard, and 164 Piccadilly
32pp, b/w illus., wrappers, 260x175mm. CLRC

BEDE'S CHARITY, by same author, has some

references only to Australia, where the heroine's brother made a fortune.

SMITH, Sarah Elizabeth
See S., S. E.

SMITH, Thomas E. Grattan
See Grattan-Smith, Thomas E.

SMITH, Vera A. Irwin
6861 THE/STORY OF THE BABY KANGAROO/How to tell a child where the/baby came from/By Vera Irwin Smith, B.Sc./Illustrated by Olive Crane, B.A.
Published by the Australasian League of Honour, Sydney 1919
10pp & foreword (quotation from Havelock Ellis's *The Problem of Race Regeneration*); b/w drawings, wrappers, 180x140mm. NSL:M

6862 THE STORY OF OVUM AND SPERM;/and how they grew into the/Baby Kangaroo;/[drawing]/ Australasian League of Honour,/Sydney/1920
[12]pp, 2 illus., col. cover, title, wrappers, 183x144mm. VSL

SMITH, Vivian
6863 LES VIGÉS EN/AUSTRALIE/Vivian Smith, M.A. (Tas.)/Illustrated by Muriel Hilson/[device]/Longmans Croydon, Victoria, 1967
50pp, 1p preface, 8pp vocabulary, b/w drawings in text, stiff dec. wrappers, 190x125mm. BBC

SMYTH, Bene Gibson
6864 Imperial Edn. 321/TEN/EVERYDAY SONGS/FOR CHILDREN/By/Bene Gibson Smyth/Edited by/Alfred B. Lane/Price 2/- net/Copyright MCMXXXI by Allan & Co. Pty Ltd. Melbourne/Allan & Co./Melbourne Sydney Adelaide Bendigo
22pp, 1p blank, 1p adv. & inside & out back wrappers, pic. front wrapper, 251x170mm. VSL

6865 Imperial Edition No 320/SPECIAL/DAY SONGS/ Words and Music/by/Bene Gibson Smyth/Edited by/ Alfred B. Lane/Copyright./Allan & Co. Pty. Ltd./ Melbourne Sydney Adelaide Bendigo
1933
22pp, 1p blank, 1p adv., unillus., wrappers, 254x170mm. VSL

6866 Imperial Edition/No 493/TEN/NEW SONGS/ FOR/CHILDREN/Words and Music/By/Bene Gibson Smyth/Price 2/- net./Allan & Co. Pty. Ltd./ Melbourne Adelaide Bendigo/IRO.
n.d. [1944?]
22pp, unillus., adv. on both sides back wrapper, pic. cover, printed in yellow & green, 250x170mm. KP
Cover design by Ida Rentoul Outhwaite.
Another ed. as above, price 50c on cover. KP

6867 Imperial Edition No. 541/'To Children Everywhere'/FAIRY CLOCKS/and other Songs for Children/Words and Music/by/Bene Gibson Smyth/ composer of "Ten Everyday Songs" "Special Day Songs"/"Ten New Songs for Children"/[10 songs listed]/Allan & Co. Pty Ltd./Melbourne Adelaide Bendigo/Printed in Australia
1954
12pp, unillus., pic. wrappers, 247x180mm. VSL

SMYTH, Reitta
6868 Book 1/TOMMY'S PUP/TIMOTHY/By/Reitta Smyth
The Ruskin Press, Melbourne, n.d. [1946]
32pp, b/w illus. throughout, bd., cover title, 270x210mm. ANL

6869 TIMOTHY/IN/THE LAND OF STORYBOOKS/ Reitta Smyth/Illustrated/by/Lex Marshall/Geoffrey Cumberlege/Oxford University Press/Melbourne Wellington
1950
92pp, col. frontis. & b/w drawings, bd., 185x120mm. ANL

6870 TIMOTHY ON TOUR/Reitta Smyth/Illustrated/ by/Lex Marshall/Geoffrey Cumberlege/Oxford University Press/Melbourne Wellington
n.d. [1950]
93pp, col. frontis. & b/w drawings, bd., 185x120mm. ANL
Both books first published as a series of stories in *Radio Times*, Melbourne.

SNELL, F. J.
6871 THE GIRLHOOD OF/FAMOUS WOMEN/By/F. J. Snell/Author of/'Boys who became Famous' 'Garibaldi' etc/Illustrated by/Margaret W. Tarrant/ [drawing]/London/George G. Harrap & Company Ltd./2 & 3 Portsmouth Street Kingsway WC/and at Sydney
n.d. [1915]
192pp, 2pp preface, b/w frontis. & 6 f/p b/w illus., pic. clo., 190x125mm. VECD
Contains one chapter on Rosa Caroline Mackworth Prior (Mrs Campbell Praed) drawn from her book *My Australian Girlhood.*

SNOWDEN, Rita F.
Writer of moral stories not intended for children.

The Snowy Mountains Story
6872 A story in pictures and words/of Australia's/ Snowy Mountains Scheme/THE SNOWY/ MOUNTAINS/STORY/Published by the/Snowy Mountains Authority/Cooma, New South Wales/ December, 1961
36pp, 2pp pic. map, col. & b/w photographic illus., diagrams & maps, pic. bd., 270x200mm. KMM

Soldiers
6873 SOLDIERS/Educational/Cut-Out/Copyright n.p., n.d. [194-?]
4pp, 2pp of light bd. stapled together, 400x244mm. KP
Covers front & back depicting troops landing & soldiers in action in the jungle, & inner pages of soldiers with jeeps, tanks, motor bike, ambulance, gun battery &c. The whole crudely printed in pink, brown and green on a natural cardboard.

The Solvol Bird Book
6874 THE SOLVOL BIRD BOOK/54/Australian/Birds/ beautifully illustrated/in full colour by the/famous artist/Neville W. Cayley
Publ. as an adv. by J. Kitchen & Sons Pty Ltd, manufacturers of Solvol soap, n.d. Printed by John Sands Pty Ltd, Sydney
28pp (inc. 1p introduction), col. illus. throughout, pic. wrappers, 120x184mm. KMM
Introduction by S. R. Thomas, President Gould League of Bird Lovers & Director of Education NSW. Verso back wrapper adv. Each page consists of 2 col. illus. of different bird with a description. *See also* Troughton, and Whitley for others in series.

Some Australian Animals
6875 SOME/AUSTRALIAN ANIMALS/[coloured illustration]/Bank of New South Wales/Savings Bank/ Limited
Sydney 1959
17pp (inc. 1p foreword), 18 col. photographs (inc. front

cover photograph), some photographs by Dr Allen Keast, illus. wrappers, cover title, 240x160mm. NSL:M
Acknowledgement to A. H. Chisholm 'who read the text of this material and made various suggestions'. Acknowledgement also to *The Australian Encyclopaedia.*
• Rpt as above Sept. 1960, Sept. 1961, 1963, 1967, 1969, 1972. KP

Some Australian Birds

6876 SOME/AUSTRALIAN BIRDS/Bank of New South Wales/Savings Bank/Limited.
Sydney 1959
17pp (inc. 1p foreword), 16 b/w illus., wrappers (with col. illus. on front cover), cover title, 240x160mm. NSL:M
Acknowledgement to A. H. Chisholm; uniform with *Some Australian Animals.*
• Rpt 1957, 1958, 1959, 1960, 1964, 1966, 1967, 1972. KP

6877 Third edition, 1969. KMM

SOMERVILLE, Margaret

6878 [drawing of the head of a boy]/THEY/CROSSED A CONTINENT/(3,000 miles with 95 children)/by/Margaret Somerville/A Methodist Overseas Missions Publication/Wholly set up and printed by/Epworth Press, 31 Botany Street, Redfern 2016
n.d. [1967?]
48pp, map frontis. & b/w illus., pic. wrappers, 215x137mm. KP
An account of bringing Australian Aboriginal children from Croker Island in February 1942 down south to safety from the Japanese.

SOMMERLAD, Ernest Lloyd

6879 THIS/IS/MY/HOME [title printed on part-col. map]
Oswald L. Ziegler in association with Gotham (A'sia) Pty Ltd, Newcastle, NSW, [1947]
48pp, 4 f/p b/w drawings & smaller part-col. drawings, pic. wrappers, 165x150mm. NSL:M
History of Newcastle for children written to commemorate the 150th anniversary of the landing of Lt J. Shortland in 1797.

SORENSON, Edward S.

6880 FRIENDS AND FOES/IN THE/AUSTRALIAN BUSH/By/Edward S. Sorenson,/Author of "Life in the Australian Backblocks", "Quinton's/Rouseabout", &c./Illustrated by/Ernest E. Barker, R.A.O.U./[device]/London Melbourne/Christchurch, Wellington & Dunedin N.Z./Whitcombe & Tombs Limited
n.d. [1914]
226pp, part-col. frontis., 5 f/p part-col. illus., b/w drawings in text, b/w chapter headings & tailpieces, pic. clo., 220x170mm. KMM
Contents include 18 nature stories, 'Spotty, the Bower Bird', 'Quiyan, the Possum', 'Jack, the Kookaburra', etc.

6881 SPOTTY, THE BOWER BIRD/and other Nature Stories/Life Histories of Australian/Birds and Animals/By/Edward S. Sorenson/R.A.O.U./Illustrated from Line Drawings by/Ernest E. Barker, R.A.O.U./and Photographs/[device]/Melbourne/Auckland, Christchurch, Dunedin, Wellington, N.Z.,/and London/Whitcombe & Tombs Limited
n.d. [1921]
104pp (inc. 1p publisher's note), b/w photographic frontis. & 11 f/p b/w photographic illus., line drawings in text, clo., 180x115mm. KMM
Consists of 6 stories selected & adapted from *Friends and Foes in the Australian Bush.*

6882 Whitcombe's/Australian Nature Story Readers/SPOTTY/THE/BOWER BIRD/and/Other Nature Stories/Life Histories of Australian Birds and Animals/By/Edward S. Sorenson,/R.A.O.U./For Children aged 12 to 14 years/[device]/Melbourne/Auckland Christchurch Dunedin Wellington N.Z./and London/Whitcombe & Tombs Limited.
n.d. [1921]
80pp, b/w frontis. & 7 f/p b/w illus., b/w drawings in text, wrappers, 180x120mm. KMM
Includes 6 stories reprinted from *Friends and Foes in the Australian Bush.*
See McLaren 613

6883 SPOTTY, THE BOWER BIRD/And Other Nature Stories/Life Histories of Australian Birds and Animals/By/Edward S. Sorenson,/R.A.O.U./Illustrated from Line drawings/and Photographs/[device]/Whitcombe & Tombs Limited/Melbourne/Auckland, Christchurch, Dunedin, Wellington,/and London
n.d. [1921]
156pp, 4pp adv., b/w photographic frontis. & 18 f/p b/w photographic illus., 25 line drawings in text, clo., 180x120mm. KMM
Contains 9 stories. The photographic illustrations & cover appear to have been revised.

6884 Australian Nature Story Readers/KARRAWAY/THE/COCKATOO/and other Nature Stories/Life Histories of Australian Birds and Animals/By/Edward S. Sorenson, R.A.O.U./For Children aged 12 to 14 Years/[device]/Melbourne/Auckland Christchurch Dunedin Wellington/and London/Whitcombe & Tombs Limited
n.d. [192-?]
79pp, 2pp adv., b/w frontis. & 7 b/w photographic illus., b/w drawings in text, wrappers, 185x125mm. KMM
Contents include title story & 'Kojurrie the Goanna'; 'Bluey the Wren'; 'Booraby the Koala'.
See McLaren 612

SOURRY, Lois

6885 SAVING/OUR WILDFLOWERS/by/Lois Sourry/Illustrated by/John Truscott/[device]/5/Longmans
1965
Melbourne
32pp (inc. 1p bibliography), col. illus. throughout, stiff pic. wrappers, 210x150mm. KMM
Australian Nature series No. 5

SOUTER, D. H.

6886 BUSH BABS/with Pictures/by D. H. Souter/[drawing]/Published in Sydney by the Endeavour Press/252 George Street
1933
63pp, b/w illus. throughout, bd., 165x130mm. CLRC
Title on cover: 'Australian Bush-Babs'
Humorous verses.

SOUTHALL, Ivan

6887 MEET SIMON BLACK/By/Ivan Southall/Illustrations by/Frank Norton/Angus and Robertson/Sydney London
First published 1950
210pp, 4 f/p b/w illus. & b/w drawings in text, clo., 180x125mm. KMM
• Rpt 1952, 1957, /Sydney London Melbourne Wellington
204pp, b/w frontis., 3 f/p b/w illus. & other drawings, 185x165mm. KP
Norwegian edition

6888 Ivan Southall/SIMON BLACK PAJAKT/Etter Jungelfolket/Nasjonalforlaget/Oslo
1952
176pp, clo., 180x120mm. Unseen: IFA

Dutch edition
6889 Ivan Southall/DE AARDE BRANT,/SIMON BLACK/Illustraties van/W. Klerk/U.-M., "West-Friesland"/Hoorn [Holland]
n.d. [1955?]
155pp, clo., 200x150mm. Unseen: IFA

6890 SIMON BLACK IN/PERIL/By/Ivan Southall/ Author of *Meet Simon Black*/Illustrations by/I. Maher/ [vignette]/Angus and Robertson/Sydney London
1951
224pp, b/w frontis. & 2 f/p b/w illus. & b/w tailpieces, clo., 180x170mm. KP
• Rpt 1952 as above, but after *Meet Simon Black,*'Simon Black in Space'/Illustration...' KP

6891 SIMON BLACK IN/PERIL/By/Ivan Southall/ Illustrations by/I. Maher/[vignette]/Angus and Robertson/Sydney London Melbourne Wellington
First published 1951; rpt 1952, 1957
220pp, b/w frontis. & 2 f/p b/w illus., b/w drawings in text, clo., 180x120mm. KMM
Norwegian edition
6892 Ivan Southall/HEMMELIG TJENESTE/ Nasjonalforlaget/Oslo1953
144pp, clo., 180x120mm. Unseen: IFA
Dutch edition
6893 Ivan Southall/SIMON BLACK IN GEVAAR/ Illustraties van/W. Klerk/U.-M., "West-Friesland"/Hoorn [Holland]
n.d. [1957?]
155pp. LRA

6894 SIMON BLACK IN SPACE/By/Ivan Southall/ Illustrated by/I. Maher/[drawing]/Angus and Robertson/Sydney London
First published 1952
223pp, b/w frontis. & 2 f/p b/w illus., b/w drawings in text, clo., 180x120mm. KMM
• Rpt 1953 as above, bd. KP

6895 SIMON BLACK IN SPACE/By/Ivan Southall/ Illustrated by/I. Maher/[drawing]/Angus and Robertson/Sydney London Melbourne Wellington
First published 1952; rpt 1953, 1957
219pp, b/w frontis. & 2 f/p b/w illus., clo., 180x120mm. BBC

6896 Upper Primary Library/For Students Aged 11–14/SIMON BLACK IN SPACE/by Ivan Southall/ Illustrated by/I. Maher/[device]/Angus and Robertson/Sydney London Melbourne Wellington
1958
128pp, b/w frontis., 3 f/p b/w illus., limp clo., 180x120mm. KMM
• Rpt 1960, as above. KMM
Swedish edition
6897 Ivan Southall/SIMON BLACK I VARLDS-/RYMDEN/Stockholm/Albert Bonniers Forlag
1953
222pp, clo., 180x120mm. Unseen: IFA
French edition
6898 Ivan Southall/OPERATION/"SOUCOPE"/Presses de la Cité'/Paris/1954
190pp, clo., 170x110mm. Unseen: IFA
Dutch edition
6899 Ivan Southall/SIMON BLACK EN DE VLIEGENDE/SCHOTELS/Illustraties van/W. Klerk/ U.-M., "West-Friesland"/Hoorn [Holland]
n.d. [1958?]
195pp, clo., 200x150mm. Unseen: IFA
Norwegian edition
6900 Ivan Southall/SIMON BLACK I HIM MELROMMET/Nasjonalforlaget/Oslo 1964
142pp, clo., 180x120mm. Unseen: IFA

6901 SIMON BLACK IN/COASTAL COMMAND/by/ Ivan Southall/Author of *Meet Simon Black, Simon Black in Peril/Simon Black in Space*/Illustrations by/I. Maher/[drawing]/Angus and Robertson/Sydney London
1953
194pp, b/w frontis. & 2 f/p b/w illus. & tailpieces, clo., 182x122mm. KP

6902 SIMON BLACK IN/COASTAL COMMAND/By/ Ivan Southall/Illustrations by/I. Maher/[vignette]/ Angus and Robertson/Sydney London Melbourne Wellington
First published 1953; rpt 1957
188pp, b/w frontis. & 2 f/p b/w illus., b/w drawings in text, clo., 180x120mm. KMM
French edition
6903 Ivan Southall/ALLO CONTROLE, ICI RADAR!/Les Presses de la Cité/Paris/1954
190pp, clo., 170x110mm. Unseen: IFA
Dutch edition
According to the author a Dutch edition was published, but he did not receive a copy & so has no details of it.
Norwegian edition
6904 Ivan Southall/SIMON BLACK/PA UBATJAKET/ Nasjonalforlaget/Oslo 1959
140pp, clo., 180x120mm. Unseen: IFA

6905 SIMON BLACK IN CHINA/By/Ivan Southall/ [vignette]/Angus & Robertson/Sydney: London
1954
224pp, b/w frontis. & 2 f/p b/w illus., b/w tailpieces, clo., 185x120mm. KMM
Dutch edition
6906 Ivan Southall/SIMON BLACK IN CHINA/ Illustraties van/W. Klerk/U.-M., "West-Friesland"—Hoorn [Holland]
n.d. [1959?]
171pp, clo., 200x150mm. Unseen: IFA
Norwegian edition
6907 Ivan Southall/SIMON BLACK I KINA/En Marabu-bok Nasjonalforlaget, Oslo 1960
122pp, clo., 180x120mm. Unseen: IFA

6908 SIMON BLACK AND/THE SPACEMEN/By/Ivan Southall/Illustrations by/Wal Stackpool/[vignette]/ Angus and Robertson/Sydney London Melbourne Wellington
First published 1955
228pp, b/w frontis. & 1 f/p b/w illus., b/w drawings in text, clo., 180x120mm. KMM
• Rpt as above, 1958, 184x118mm. KP
Norwegian edition
6909 Ivan Southall/JAKTEN PA DET/Stjalne Romskip/ Marabu Nasjonalforlaget, Oslo 1961
122pp, clo., 180x120mm. Unseen: IFA
Dutch edition
According to the author a Dutch edition was published, but he did not receive a copy & so has no details of it.

6910 SIMON BLACK/IN THE ANTARCTIC/By/Ivan Southall/[vignette]/Angus and Robertson/Sydney London Melbourne Wellington
1956
216pp, b/w frontis. & 2 f/p b/w illus., b/w drawings in text, clo., 180x120mm. KMM
• Rpt 1958, Sydney, Angus and Robertson, as above. MK

6911 SIMON BLACK TAKES/OVER/The Strange Tale of Operation/Greenleaf/By/Ivan Southall/[vignette signed 'I.M.']/Angus and Robertson
Sydney 1959

219pp, b/w frontis. & 4 f/p b/w illus., b/w drawings in text, clo., 180x115mm. KMM

6912 SIMON BLACK AT SEA/The fateful maiden voyage of A.P.M. 1/Arion/by/Ivan Southall/Angus and Robertson
Sydney 1961
191pp, b/w frontis. & 8 b/w illus., clo., dec. e/p, 215x135mm. CLRC
Artist's name not given but d/w signed 'B. Clarke'.

6913 JOURNEY/INTO MYSTERY/A Story of the Explorers Burke and Wills/by/Ivan Southall/Illustrated by Robin Goodall/Lansdowne Press/Melbourne
1961
136pp (inc. 1p author's note), extended part-col. dec. t.p., 10 f/p b/w illus., clo., d/w by Lex Marshall, 215x130mm. KMM
Half-title reads: Heroes of Australia No. 1—Journey into Mystery.

6914 HILLS END/by/Ivan Southall/Angus and Robertson
Sydney 1962
174pp, 1p preliminary note, b/w chapter headings, clo., 215x135mm. KMM
No artist's name or initials decipherable.
• Rpt 1962. KP
• Rpt Angus and Robertson, Sydney 1963, 1966, 1967, 1969, as above. CLRC
• Rpt 1970. KP

6915 Ivan Southall/HILLS END/Illustrated by Jim Phillips/[device]/Penguin Books
Harmondsworth, Middlesex, England, Puffin Books edition 1965
223pp (inc. 1p author's note & 1p biographical note), b/w chapter headings (as in original edition), pic. wrappers, cover design by Elisabeth Grant, 180x110mm. KMM
• Rpt 1968, 1970, 1971, 1972. BBC

6916 HILLS END/by/Ivan Southall/St. Martin's Press/New York 1963
• Rpt 1964, 1965, 1966, 1967
174pp, 1p preliminary note, b/w chapter headings, illus. James Phillips, clo., 215x135mm. Unseen: IFA

Danish edition

6917 Ivan Southall/ORKAN/Pa dansk/ved Birgit Steenstrup/Gyldenal
Denmark, 1967
166pp, clo., 200x120mm. LRA

Afrikaans edition

6918 Ivan Southall/DIE ORKAAN/Tafelberg
Cape Town 1967
176pp, clo., 210x140mm. LRA

Norwegian edition

6919 BARNA I VILLMARKEN [trans. from the English by Vetle Sanden]
E. Greens Forlag, Oslo [1968]
197pp, 200mm. LRA

Swedish edition

6920 NÄR ORKANEN KOM [oversättning av Marianne Gerlaud-Ekeroth]
Raben & Sjögren, Stockholm 1970
206pp, 210mm. LRA

German edition

6921 SIEBEN WERDEN VERMISST [von] Ivan Southall
Benzigen Verlag, Zürich 1969
203pp, 210mm. LRA

LAWRENCE HARGRAVE. *See* Great Australians

6922 ROCKETS/IN THE DESERT/The Story of Woomera/by Ivan Southall/Angus and Robertson
Sydney 1964
79pp, 1p acknowledgements, 1p b/w map, b/w photographic illus. & diagrams in text throughout, clo., col. e/p, 250x185mm. BBC

6923 [drawing]/ASH ROAD/By/Ivan Southall/With Drawings by/Clem Seale/[device]/Angus and Robertson
Sydney 1965
154pp, 1p author's note, b/w chapter headings, clo., col. e/p, 215x140mm. KMM
Winner CBCA award 1966
• Rpt 1966 (twice), 1967, as above. KP
• Rpt 1969, 1971. BBC

6924 ASH ROAD/By/Ivan Southall/With Drawings by/Clem Seale/[device]/Angus and Robertson
Sydney, first school edition 1966
154pp, 1p author's preface, b/w chapter headings, limp clo., 195x125mm. BBC

US edition

6925 ASH ROAD/by/Ivan Southall/Illustrated by Clem Seale/St. Martin's Press/New York
1966
154pp, b/w chapter headings, clo., 210x135mm. CLRC
• Rpt as above, 1967, 1968, 1969. IFA

US school edition

6926 Scott, Foresman & Co., Glenview, Ill., USA, 1969
Educational Bright Horizons Edition. Unseen: IFA

6927 Ivan Southall/ASH ROAD/With drawings by Clem Seale/[drawing]/Penguin Books
First published by Angus & Robertson 1966 [*sic*]; Published in Puffin Books [England] 1967
187pp (inc. 1p author's note), b/w chapter headings throughout, pic. wrappers, cover design by Elisabeth Grant, 180x110mm. KMM
• Rpt 1969, 1970, as above. KMM

6928 [drawing]/ASH ROAD/by/Ivan Southall/With Drawings by/Clem Seale/Heinemann Educational/Books London
1972
171pp, 1p preface, b/w drawings throughout, clo., 185x120mm. The New Windmill Series. KMM

Afrikaans edition

6929 Ivan Southall/DIE BOSBRAND/Tafelberg 1967
Cape Town
167pp, clo., 210x140mm. LRA

German edition

6930 Ivan Southall/BUSCHFEUER/Signal—Verlag Hans Prevert Baden-Baden
1967
176pp, illus. by Rudiger Stoyle, clo., 210x150mm. LRA

Danish edition

6931 ILDSTORM [trans. from the English by] Birgit Steenstrup
Kobenhavn, Gyldendal [1968]
143pp, 21cm. LRA

Norwegian edition

6932 DA SKOGEN BRANT. Oversatt av Bjorn Bergh-Pedersen
E. Greens Forlag, Oslo 1969
183pp, illus., 20cm. LRA

Japanese edition

6933 MOERU ASSU RODO/Ivan Southall/Aiban Sausuoro saku; Ishii Momoko, Yamamoto Matsuyo Yaka; Nakagowa somi e.
Tokyo: Kodomo Bunko no kai, 1968. LRA
• Rpt 1969. Unseen: IFA

Finnish edition

6934 PENSASPALO
Otava, Helsinki 1970
237pp. Unseen: IFA

Italian edition
6935 L'INCENDIO DELLA FORESTA, Traduzione par Mario Riviore
Mondadori, Milan 1972
196pp. LRA
See also Howard, Peter & Levy, Wayne (eds.) AUSTRALIAN STORY SAMPLER

6936 INDONESIAN/JOURNEY/Ivan Southall/illustrated/[device]/Lansdowne
Lansdowne Press Pty Ltd, Melbourne 1965
101pp, b/w photographic frontis. & b/w photographic illus. throughout, b/w dec. chapter headings, dec. clo., map e/p, 245x175mm. CLRC
• Rpt 1966 (twice), as above. KMM

6937 INDONESIAN/JOURNEY/Ivan Southall/illustrated/[device]/Ginn and Company/Boston and Toronto
1966
Details as in the Lansdowne edition. Unseen: IFA

6938 THE FOX HOLE/Ivan Southall/Illustrated by/Ian Ribbons/Hicks Smith & Sons Pty. Ltd./Sydney Melbourne Brisbane/in association with/Methuen & Co. Ltd. London
1967
126pp, b/w frontis. & drawings in text, clo., 200x125mm. KMM
• Rpt 1968. KP
• Rpt 1970. KP
US edition

6939 THE FOX HOLE
St. Martin's Press, New York 1967
Details as above. SFU

6940 Ivan Southall/THE FOX HOLE/Cover illustration by Mark Peppé/Text illustrations by Malcolm Hargreaves/[device]/A Piccolo Book/Pan Books Ltd/London
1967
117pp, 3pp adv., 7 f/p b/w illus., b/w drawings in text, pic. wrappers, 177x112mm. KMM
• Rpt as above, 1972. KP
Dutch edition

6941 HET/VOSSEHOL
Van Holkema & Warendorf, Bussum 1970
88pp. Unseen: LRA
Italian edition

6942 LA/BUCA/DELLA/VOLPE
Bompiani, Milan 1971
115pp. Unseen: LRA
German edition

6943 DIE FALLE AM DESMOND [von] Ivan Southall
Ueberreuter, Heidelberg, West Germany 1970
126pp, illus., 210mm. Unseen: LRA
Polish edition

6944 LISIA/JAMA
Nasza Ksiegarnia, Warsaw 1971
113pp. Unseen: LRA
Swedish edition

6945 RAVINENS/HEMLIGHET
Raben & Sjögren, Stockholm 1971
94pp. Unseen: LRA

6946 THE SWORD/OF ESAU/Bible Stories retold by/Ivan Southall/Illustrated by/Joan Kiddell-Monroe/[drawing]/Angus and Robertson
Sydney 1967
116pp (inc. 1p note), extended t.p., 9 b/w illus., clo., col. e/p, 215x135mm. KMM
3 Bible stories retold.
US edition

6947 St Martin's Press, New York, 1968, as above. IFA

6948 Ivan Southall/TO THE/WILD SKY/Illustrated by Jennifer Tuckwell/[device]/Angus and Robertson
Sydney 1967
184pp, 10 b/w illus. in text, clo., 215x135mm. KMM
Winner CBCA award 1967
• Rpt 1968, 1969, 1971, as above. BBC

6949 Ivan Southall/TO THE/WILD SKY/Illustrated by/Jennifer Tuckwell/[device]/Angus and Robertson
First school edition, Sydney 1968
184pp, 10 b/w illus. in text, limp clo., 215x135mm. KMM

6950 TO THE/WILD SKY/by/Ivan Southall/Illustrated by Jennifer Tuckwell/St. Martin's Press/New York
1967
Details not given, but presumably as in Angus & Robertson edition. Unseen: IFA

6951 Ivan Southall/TO THE WILD SKY/Illustrated by Jennifer Tuckwell/Penguin Books
Harmondsworth, Middlesex, England, 1971
224pp, b/w drawings in text, pic. wrappers, 180x110mm. KMM
• Rpt 1972. KMM
Finnish edition

6952 PAKKOLASKU PIMEÄÄN [Suomentannt Pirkko Talvio]
Kustannusosakeyhtiö Otava, Helsingissä 1969
223pp, 19cm. Unseen: LRA
German editions

6953 UBERLEBEN/Ivan Southall: aus dem Englischen ubersetzt von Hans-Georg Noack. Baden-Baden, West Germany: Signal Verlag Hans Frevert, 1967. Unseen: LRA

6954 Ivan Southall/ÜBERLEBEN/Benziger Taschenbücher
Zürich—Köln, n.d. [1970]
190pp, 2pp adv., unillus., pic. wrappers, 180x105mm. ANL
Dutch edition

6955 NOODLANDING/[von]/Ivan Southall
van Holkema & Warendorf, Bussum, Holland 1971
176pp, illus., 21cm. Unseen: LRA
Croatian edition

6956 DIVLJE NEBO [Preveo: Mario Susko]
Mladost, Zagreb, Yugoslavia 1970
180pp [4] 20cm. (Biblioteka jelen). Unseen: LRA

6957 BUSHFIRE!/Ivan Southall/[drawing]/Illustrated by Julie Mattox/Angus and Robertson
Sydney 1968
26pp, 1p note, 13 b/w drawings in text, stiff pic. wrappers, 210x135mm. KMM

6958 THE CURSE/OF CAIN/Bible stories retold by/Ivan Southall/Genesis I: 1 to 9: 19/Illustrated by/Joan Kiddell-Monroe/Angus and Robertson [drawing]
Sydney 1968
117pp, extended t.p., b/w drawings throughout, clo., col. e/p, 215x135mm. CLRC
US edition

6959 St. Martin's Press, New York 1968. Unseen: IFA

6960 Ivan Southall/LET THE BALLOON GO/Illustrated by/Ian Ribbons/Methuen & Co. Ltd./11 New Fetter Lane, London E.C.4/Hicks Smith & Sons Pty. Ltd./Sydney Melbourne Brisbane
1968
142pp, b/w frontis. & drawings in text, clo., 195x130mm. KMM
• Rpt 1969, as above. KP

6961 Ivan Southall/LET THE BALLOON GO/[drawing]/Penguin Books
Harmondsworth, Middlesex, England, 1972

112pp, unillus., pic. wrappers, cover design by Margery Gill, 180x110mm. Puffin Books. KMM
US edition
6962 St. Martin's Press, New York 1968; rpt 1969, 1970, 1971
141pp, illus. Unseen: IFA
Dutch edition
6963 DE GOMBOON
Van Holkema & Warendorf, Bussum 1970. Unseen: LRA
Finnish edition
6964 PÄÄSTÄ PALLO LENTOON
Otava, Helsinki 1971. Unseen: LRA
Afrikaans edition
6965 LAAT LOS DIE BALLOON
John Malherbe, Kaapstad 1972. Unseen: LRA

6966 SLY OLD WARDROBE/Written by Ivan Southall/drawn by Ted Greenwood/Cheshire
Melbourne 1968; rpt 1969
[39]pp, col. & part-col. illus. throughout, clo., 280x210mm. KMM
US edition
6967 SLY OLD WARDROBE, Drawn by Ted Greenwood
St. Martin's Press, New York 1969
[39?] pp col. illus., 29cm. Unseen: ANB 1970

6968 Ivan Southall/FINN'S FOLLY/Angus and Robertson
Sydney 1969
158pp, unillus., clo., d/w by C. R. Evans, 215x137mm. KP
• Rpt as above 1971 but different lettering on grey clo. in gilt on spine; variant d/w. KP
US edition
6969 St. Martin's Press, New York 1969
158pp, 22cm. Unseen: ANB 1970
6970 Ivan Southall/FINN'S FOLLY/Penguin Books
Harmondsworth, Middlesex, England, 1972
158pp, 1p biographical note, 1p adv., unillus., pic. wrappers, cover design by Don Black, 180x110mm. Puffin Books. KMM
German edition
6971 KURVE IM NEBEL/[von]/Ivan Southall
Signal Verlag, Baden-Baden 1970
125pp, 22cm. Unseen: LRA
Dutch edition
6972 Van Holkema & Warendorf, Bussum, n.d.
Unseen: IFA

6973 Ivan Southall/BREAD AND/HONEY/Angus and Robertson
Sydney 1970
118pp, unillus., clo., d/w designed by Wolfgang Grasse, 210x135mm. KMM
• Rpt 1971, as above, but pic. laminated bd. KP
German edition
6974 Ivan Southall/TAG/DER/HELDEN/[device]/Signal Verlag Hans Frevert Baden-Baden
1971
128pp, unillus., clo., 206x140mm. CLRC
US edition
6975 WALK A MILE AND GET NOWHERE/by Ivan Southall
Bradbury Press, Engleood Cliffs, N.J., 1970
118pp, 22cm. Unseen: ANB 1972
6976 Ivan Southall/BREAD AND HONEY/Penguin Books
Harmondsworth, Middlesex, England, 1972
118pp, 1p biographical note, 3pp adv., unillus., pic. wrappers, cover design by Cos Aslanis, 180x110mm. Puffin Books. KMM

6977 Ivan Southall/BREAD AND HONEY/Penguin Books/in association with H. J. Ashton, Auckland & Sydney
Sydney 1972
Details as in Penguin 1972 ed. KMM
Danish edition
6978 Palbe (publisher)
Details not known. Unseen: IFA

6979 Ivan Southall/CHINAMAN'S REEF/IS OURS/Angus and Robertson
Sydney 1970
160pp, unillus., clo., d/w by Russell Drysdale, 215x140mm. KMM
US edition
6980 St. Martin's Press, New York 1970
160pp, 22cm. Unseen: ANB 1970
German edition
6981 DIE/STADT/GEHÖRT/UNS
Signal Verlag, Baden Baden 1971
183pp. Unseen: LRA

6982 Ivan Southall/JOSH/[device]/Angus and Robertson
Sydney 1971
179pp, unillus., clo., d/w by Astra Lacis Dick, 215x135mm. KMM
Carnegie Medal 1972.
• Rpt 1972, as above. BBC
German edition
6983 Ivan Southall/TIM/[device]/Signal Verlag Baden-Baden
1972
176pp, unillus., clo., 206x140mm. CLRC
US edition
6984 St. Martin's Press, New York 1972
179pp. Unseen: IFA

6985 HEAD IN CLOUDS/Ivan Southall/Angus and Robertson
Sydney 1972
108pp, b/w drawings throughout, extended illus. t.p., illus. by Richard Kennedy, clo., 195x185mm. KMM
German edition
6986 Published by Benziger, Zurich
Details not known. Unseen: IFA

6987 Ivan Southall/OVER THE TOP/Illustrated by/Ian Ribbons/Methuen London/Hicks Smith/Sydney Melbourne Brisbane
1972
126pp, b/w frontis. & 7 b/w illus., clo., 195x125mm. KMM
Dutch edition
6988 NACHTWERK/Ivan Southall; Vertaling Alet Schouten: Omslag en illustraties Henk Kneepkens. Bussum, Netherlands: Van Holkema & Warendorf, 1972. Unseen: LRA

SOUTHERN, Lois
6989 PETER COMES/TO STAY/by Lois Southern/Illustrated by Wally Jex/Ure Smith—Sydney
1966
96pp, 5 f/p b/w illus. & drawings in text, clo., 190x120mm. KMM
A shorter version of this story first appeared in the NSW *School Magazine.*

SPAULL, George Thomas
6990 WHERE THE STARS/ARE BORN/by/George Spaull/William Brooks & Co. Limited/Sydney, N.S.W., Australia
1942

200pp (inc. 1p 'Pronunciations'), unillus., bd., d/w by Mahdi McCrae, 180x115mm. CLRC
The experiences of three children in the imaginary land of Kurania.

6991 POOK-A-NOO/[drawing]/Stories by/George Spaull/Pictures by/June Mendoza
The author, Sydney, n.d. [1948]
106pp, col. frontis. & 5 f/p col. illus., b/w drawings in text, pic. bd., pic. e/p, 240x185mm. VSL

6992 SONGS OF/CHILDHOOD/Poems for Third Grade/(8–9 years)/Selected & arranged by/G. T. Spaull, M.A./William Brooks & Co. Ltd. Sydney n.d. [1957]
64pp, b/w drawings in text, dec. wrappers (with adv. inside front & back covers), 210x135mm. ANL
A school anthology, with a section of 8 Australian poems.

Speed
6993 SPEED/Every Boy's Book/of Trains/Aeroplanes/and Ships/Story and Pictures of/The Fastest of their Kind on Land, Sea and in the Air
Pantheon Publications, Melbourne, n.d. [195-?]
16pp, col. illus. throughout with text, pic. wrappers, 270x210mm. KP

SPENCE, Eleanor
6994 Eleanor Spence/PATTERSON'S TRACK/[vignette]/Illustrated by/Alison Forbes/Melbourne/Oxford University Press/London Wellington New York/1958
165pp, b/w drawings in text, clo., 220x140mm. KMM
6995 Eleanor Spence/PATTERSON'S TRACK/[vignette]/Illustrated by/Alison Forbes/Melbourne/Oxford University Press/London Wellington New York
163pp, b/w chapter headings throughout, clo., 215x135mm. BBC
• Rpt 1967. KP
Dutch edition
6996 Eleanor Spence/HET SPOOR DOOR WILDERNIS/[drawing]/Prisma-Boeken/Utrecht-Antwerpen
1962
189pp, 1p contents, 2pp adv., pic. wrappers, 180x107mm. LRA

6997 Eleanor Spence/THE SUMMER/IN/BETWEEN/Illustrated by Marcia Lane-Foster/London/Oxford University Press/1959
179pp, b/w drawings throughout, clo., 215x135mm. CLRC
6998 Eleanor Spence/THE SUMMER/IN/BETWEEN/Illustrated by Marcia Lane-Foster/London/Oxford University Press.
First pub. 1959; rpt 1960
Details as above. KMM
• Rpt 1966. KP
German edition
6999 Eleanor Spence/MACH WIEDER MIT ANNE!/Die Geschichte Einer Mädchenfreundschaft/und des Klubs der Acht/Hermann Schaffstein Verlag
Köln 1961
183pp, b/w drawings throughout, illus. by Irene Schreiber, paper bd. (clo. spine), 205x140mm. Unseen: IFA

7000 Eleanor Spence/LILLIPILLY HILL/Illustrated by/Susan Einzig/London/Oxford University Press/1960
176pp, b/w drawings in text, clo., 210x135mm. KMM
• Rpt 1963 as above. BBC
Portuguese edition
7001 NA QUINTA DAS MAGNOLIAS/Traduçao de Maria Isabel Morna Braga/Revista par Mário Braga/Illustraçoes de Susan Einzig/Livraria Civilizaçao—Editora/Rua Alberto Aires de Gouveia 27—Porto 1961
195pp, b/w drawings throughout, paper bd., 180x115mm. Unseen: IFA
7002 Eleanor Spence/THE GREEN LAUREL/[drawing]/Illustrated by/Geraldine Spence/London/Oxford University Press/1963
181pp, line drawings in text throughout, clo., 215x140mm. KMM
Won CBCA award 1964.
• Rpt 1964. KP
US edition
7003 THE GREEN LAUREL, New York, Roy [1965] v, 181p. illus. 23cm. Unseen: ANB May 1965
German edition
7004 Eleanor Spence/HAUS DER TRÄUME/Verlag Carl Ueberreuter/Wien—Heidelberg
1966
175pp, b/w drawings throughout (as in original edition), clo., 205x115mm. Unseen: IFA
Portuguese edition
7005 Eleanor Spence/UMA CASA COM RAIZES/Traducao de Maria Amelia Franqueira/Livraria Civilizacao—Editora/Rua de Alberto Aires de Gouveia 27—Porto
1965
245pp, b/w drawings throughout, paper bd., 180x115mm. Unseen: IFA

7006 THE YEAR/OF THE CURRAWONG/Eleanor Spence/[drawing]/Illustrated by Gareth Floyd/London/Oxford University Press/1965
170pp, b/w drawings throughout, clo., 215x135mm. KMM
• Rpt 1966, as above. BBC
7007 THE YEAR OF THE CURRAWONG, Illustrated by Gareth Floyd. New York, Roy [1965]
170pp, illus. 23cm. Unseen: ANB 1966

7008 THE/SWITHERBY PILGRIMS/Eleanor Spence/Illustrated by Corinna Gray/[drawing]/London/Oxford University Press/1967
170pp, 1p author's note, b/w drawings in text, clo., 215x135mm. KMM
French edition
7009 Eleanor Spence/Traduit de l'anglais par Jean La Gravière/Illustrations de Jean Reschofsky/LES PIONNIERS/DU BOUT DU MONDE/[device]/Éditions G.P./Département des Presses de la Cité/©1969 Eleanor Spence/©1970 Edition G.P.
186pp, 1p contents, 1p adv., col. & b/w illus. throughout, pic. bd., 202x140mm. LRA

7010 Eleanor Spence/JAMBEROO ROAD/[drawing]/Illustrated by Doreen Roberts/London/Oxford University Press/1969
162pp, b/w drawings in text, clo., 215x135mm. KMM
Sequel to *The Switherby Pilgrims.*

A SCHOOLMASTER;
A CEDAR-CUTTER. *See* Early Australians

7011 Eleanor Spence/THE NOTHING-PLACE/Illustrated by Geraldine Spence/[drawing]/London/Oxford University Press/1972
137pp, 15 line drawings in text, clo., 215x135mm. CLRC
See also Howard and Levy AUSTRALIAN STORY SAMPLER

SPENCER, Pat

7012 HUSTLER'S GOLD/Pat Spencer/Illustrated by/ Rachel Tonkin/Lansdowne
Melbourne 1969
126pp (inc. 1p foreword), b/w frontis. & 7 f/p b/w illus., double-spread plan, clo., d/w designed by Genevieve Melrose, dec. e/p, 215x135mm. CLRC
Story set in the Bendigo goldfields in the 1890s.

SPERRY, Armstrong

7013 DANGER TO/WINDWARD/[drawing]/written and illustrated by/Armstrong Sperry/[device]/The Bodley Head London
1952
1p verse, 241pp & 3pp adv., b/w drawings throughout, clo., 200x130mm. KP

7014 DANGER TO/WINDWARD/[drawing]/written and illustrated by/Armstrong Sperry/The Bodley Head/ London
First publ. 1952, rpt 1961
241pp & 3pp adv., b/w illus. throughout, clo., 200x130mm. KP

7015 CAPTAIN COOK/EXPLORES/THE SOUTH SEAS/(World Landmark Books)/Written and Illustrated by/Armstrong Sperry/Random House New York
1955
184pp (inc. 6pp index), 2pp adv., b/w & part-col. illus. throughout, clo., dec. e/p, 210x135mm. NSL:M
French edition

7016 Armstrong Sperry/LE CAPITAINE COOK/ EXPLORE/LE PACIFIQUE/Adapté par/Jean Petrus/ Fernand Nathan
Paris 1965
157pp, b/w portrait frontis., b/w illus. & maps in text, pic. bd., 180x155mm. HBM

7017 [drawing] Allabout/books/ALL ABOUT/THE ARCTIC AND/ANTARCTIC/written and illustrated/ by/Armstrong Sperry/[drawing] Random House/New York
1957
146pp (inc. 6pp index) & 1p list of other Allabout books, part-col. map frontis., 8 f/p part-col. illus. & numerous others in text, clo., pic. e/p, 230x170mm. KP
Another copy:

7018 ALL ABOUT/THE ARCTIC/AND ANTARCTIC/ written and illustrated by Armstrong Sperry/Random House New York [device Allabout/books]
1957
146pp, part-col. frontis. Details as above but bound in col. pic. clo. bdg. KP

7019 ALL ABOUT/CAPTAIN COOK/By/Armstrong Sperry/[publisher's device: 'Allabout Books']/W. H. Allen/London, 1960
Published in the United States by Random House 1959; First British edition revised 1960
147pp (inc. 5pp index), 9 f/p part-col. illus., 2pp part-col. map, b/w & part-col. illus., clo., 220x140mm. HBM
No artist's name shown.

Spike's Bike Book

7020 SPIKE'S/BIKE/BOOK/For Parents of Little Kids/ (Under 9)
Produced for the NSW State Bicycle Advisory Committee by the Traffic Authority of NSW, n.d.
16pp, b/w illus., pic. wrappers, 210x135mm. KP

Also uniform with above:
7021 SPIKE'S BIKE BOOK For Medium Kids (9–12). KP
7022 SPIKE'S THE BIKE BOOK/For Big Kids (13–104). KP

Spitfire and Bomber Squadron

7023 SPITFIRE AND BOMBER/SQUADRON/Cut Out, Model Builder 6 sheets, no glueing necessary
n.p., n.d., ACE Made in Australia
12pp, col. outlines, light card, cover title, 254x420mm. MAC

SPOLTON, Lewis

7024 Johnston's Bookshelf/FROM/SLEDGE-DOG/TO/ SNO-CAT/[drawing]/The Exploration of/Antarctica/ Lewis Spolton/W. & A. K. Johnston & G. W. Bacon Ltd.
Edinburgh & London, 1959
64pp, b/w photographic illus. & diagrams, dec. bd., 220x140mm
Johnsons Reference Library. Copy lacks t.p., cover transcribed. KP

Spotty at the Circus

7025 SPOTTY AT/THE CIRCUS/Registered in Australia for transmission by post as a book/Copyright/Wholly set up and printed in Australia by Supertone Company, 200 Chalmers St.,/Sydney, for the Publishers, B.B.F. Art Advertising & Publishing Company, Adams/ Chambers, 195 Elizabeth Street, Sydney.
n.d. [194-?]
32pp, part-col. illus. throughout, stiff pic. wrappers, 235x175mm. ANL
Story in prose. Other titles in series advertised on back cover as below and unseen:
7026 CHRISTMAS TALES. [Beverley Longworth Lee, 56pp, illus. Brad & Jack]
7027 PETER'S PUZZLE BOOK No. 1
7028 PETER'S PUZZLE BOOK No. 2
7029 SPOTTY ON THE FARM.
7030 THE STORY OF TIDDLES

7031 SPOTTY SEES/THE ZOO/Registered in Australia for transmission by post as a book/Copyright/Wholly set up and printed in Australia for the B.B.F. Art/ Advertising & Publishing Company, Adams' Chambers, Elizabeth/Street, Sydney, by the Longlea Printery Pty. Ltd., 433 Kent Street,/Sydney
n.d. [1943?]
32pp, b/w illus., wrappers, 235x180mm. ANL

SPOWERS, E. L.

7032 CUTHBERT/AND THE/DOGS By E. L. Spowers/ Digest Juvenile Productions (Regd.)/ Melbourne—Australia/Registered at the G.P.O. Melbourne, for transmission by post as a book
n.d. [1948]
[28]pp, dec. t.p., 14 f/p col. illus., 2 f/p b/w illus. & b/w drawings, dec. bd., 190x275mm. Grant

SPRATT, Mrs Dora E. W.

7033 THROUGH THE BUSH;/or/New South Wales of Fifty Years Ago/By/Mrs. Dora E. W. Spratt/Author of "Daylight"/Philadelphia:/American Baptist Publication Society,/1420 Chestnut Street
n.d. [1892?]
320pp, b/w frontis. & 9 f/p engravings, 2 maps, engravings in text, clo., 180x115mm. ANL
A story about the travels of an American family through Australia with much factual information about Australian wild life, living conditions &c.

'SPRAY'

See [Scott, Maria J.]

STABELL, W. W.

7034 MOT UKJENTE KYSTER: sagaen om Kaptein Cook/W. W. Stabell
Oslo H Aschehoug, 1950

182pp, [7] leaves of plates, illus. map e/p, 190mm. ANL

7035 W. W. Stabell/MOT OKÄNDA KUSTER/Kapten Cooks/Upptäckter och Aventyr/Översattning fran Norskan av/Gösta Aldener/Gummessons Bokförlag/Stockholm
1950/51
133pp, unillus., 1 f/p map, col. pic. bd., clo. backstrip, 185x125mm. RM

STABLES, William Gordon

7036 FROM POLE TO POLE/A Tale of the Sea./By/Gordon Stables, C.M., M.D., R.N.,/Author of "The Cruise of the Snowbird" "Wild Adventures round the Pole"/"Stanley Grahame" etc./With twelve illustrations./Fourth thousand/London:/Hodder and Stoughton,/27 Paternoster Row,/MDCCCXCI
[First publ. 1886]
388pp & 4pp adv., b/w frontis. & 11 f/p b/w plates, pic. clo., 185x120mm. CLRC
• Rpt 8th thousand, MCMI, as above. KP

7037 Another copy as above, but
/New Edition/Illustrated in Colour by Archibald Webb/London/Henry Frowde/Hodder and Stoughton
[1910]
388pp, col. frontis. & 5 col. plates, clo. with col. onlay on front cover & on spine, 185x120mm. KP

7038 Another ed. as above but no 'new edition' then Illustrated in Colour by Archibald Webb/Humphrey Milford/Oxford University Press/London, Edinburgh, Glasgow/Toronto, Melbourne, Cape Town, Bombay
n.d. [inscribed 1920]
388pp & 32pp adv., col. frontis. & 5 plates, clo. with col. onlay on front cover & spine, 185x120mm. KP
Different illus. used for the 2 onlays from those in earlier ed.

7039 FROM/POLE/TO/POLE/Gordon Stables/Humphrey/Milford/Oxford/University/Press—London
• Rpt 1924
388pp, col. frontis. (Archibald Webb) only, dec. clo., 165x107mm. KP

7040 WILD ADVENTURES/IN/WILD PLACES./By/Gordon Stables M.D., R.N./Author of "Jungle, Pool and Plain," &c &c. Cassell, Petter, Galpin & Co./London, Paris & New York./[All Rights Reserved]
n.d. [1881]
176pp, b/w frontis. & engravings throughout, pic. bd. quarter clo., 240x175mm VMOU
Pp141–51 Australia with 5 engravings.

7041 FROM/SQUIRE/TO/SQUATTER/A Tale of the Old Land and the New/by Gordon Stables, C.M., M.D., R.N./Author of/"The Dashing Days of Old"; "The Cruise of the Snowbird";/"From Pole to Pole"; "Born to Wander";/Etc. Etc./London:/John F. Shaw and Co.,/48 Paternoster Row, E.C.
n.d. [1888]
384pp, 24pp adv., b/w frontis. & 7 f/p b/w illus., pic. clo., 185x130mm. CLRC

7042 FROM/SQUIRE/TO/SQUATTER/A Tale of the Old Land and the New/By/Gordon Stables, C.M., M.D., R.N./Author of "In the Dashing Days of Old"; "Exiles of Fortune";/"For England, Home and Beauty";/etc. etc./New Edition/London:/John F. Shaw and Co.,/48 Paternoster Row, E.C./All rights reserved
n.d.
384pp, 1p adv. (preceding text), unillus., clo., 180x120mm. NSL:M

7043 IN SEARCH/OF FORTUNE/A Tale of the Old Land and the New/By/Gordon Stables, M.D., C.M./(Surgeon Royal Navy),/Author of "In the Dashing Days of Old"; "Exiles of Fortune";/"For England, Home and Beauty";/Etc. etc./New edition/London:/John F. Shaw and Co.,/48 Paternoster Row, E.C.
n.d. [1894]
384pp, 1p adv. (preceding text & headed 'The Hearts of Oak' Series), b/w frontis. & 7 f/p b/w illus. (copy seen re-bound), 190x130mm. CLRC
Text and illus. same as *From Squire to Squatter*.

7044 BY SEA AND LAND./A Tale of the Blue and the Scarlet./by/Gordon Stables, M.D., R.N.,/Author of/"The Cruise of the Snow-Bird", "From Pole to Pole",/"O'er many Lands, on many Seas", Etc./With original illustrations by W. S. Stacey./[device]/London and New York;/Frederick Warne and Co./1890./(All rights reserved.)
352pp, b/w frontis. & 7 b/w plates, pic. clo., 190x130mm. RM
Two chapters (35pp) are devoted to a visit to Australia, & then to New Zealand & the South Pacific; there is a description of Melbourne & the Dandenongs, & also of Tasmania.

7045 COURAGE, TRUE HEARTS/Sailing in Search of Fortune/By/Gordon Stables/Author of "The Naval Cadet" "For Life and Liberty"/"To Greenland and the Pole" &c./[4-line quotation]/Blackie & Son Limited/London and Glasgow
n.d. [1st publ. 1899]
288pp, b/w frontis. only, clo., 182x120mm. NSL:M
The Peak Library.

7046 THE ISLAND OF GOLD/A Sailor's Yarn/By/Gordon Stables, M.D., C.M./Surgeon Royal Navy/Author of "Every Inch a Sailor," "How Jack Mackenzie won His Epaulettes,"/"As we sweep through the Deep,"/etc. etc./with six illustrations by Allan Stewart/Thomas Nelson and Sons/London Edinburgh and New York/1900
vi, 344pp, b/w frontis. & additional dec. t.p. with vignette & 4 f/p b/w plates, pic. clo., dec. with gilt on front & spine, 188x125mm. KP

7047 IN THE/GREAT WHITE LAND/A Tale of the Antarctic Ocean/By/Dr. Gordon Stables, R.N./Author of "The Naval Cadet", "In Far Bolivia" "To Greenland and the Pole"/With six illustrations by Ambrose de Walton/And a Map/Blackie and Son, Limited/London, Glasgow, and Dublin
n.d. [1903]
288pp, 16pp adv., b/w frontis. & 5 b/w plates, 1 b/w map, pic. clo., 185x120mm. KMM

7048 IN THE/GREAT WHITE LAND...as above to "The Naval Cadet", then ' "Crusoes of the Frozen North" &c./Illustrated/Blackie & Son Limited/London and Glasgow,'
n.d.
288pp, 2 pp adv., col. frontis. & 3 b/w plates by de Walton, pic. clo., 176x115 mm. KP
• Rpt as above 1925, KMM

7049 THE SAUCIEST BOY/IN THE SERVICE/A Story of Pluck and/Perseverance/By/W. Gordon Stables M.D., C.M./(Surgeon Royal Navy)/Author of "In Regions of Perpetual Snow" "The Cruise of the Great Snow Bear"/"In a Great White Land", etc. etc./Coloured Illustrations by Henry Austin/London/Ward Lock & Co. Limited/1905
320pp, col. frontis. & 3 col. plates, pic. clo., 195x130mm. KMM
Four chapters are set in New Guinea & Australia.

• Rpt as above 1911 (with variation in titles quoted), blind-stamped clo. CLRC

7050 THE SAUCIEST BOY/IN THE SERVICE/A Story of Pluck and/Perseverance/By/W. Gordon Stables M.D., C.M./(Surgeon Royal Navy)/Author of "In Regions of Perpetual Snow," "The Ivory Hunters,"/"In a Great White Land," &c &c/Ward, Lock & Co., Limited/London and Melbourne
n.d.
320pp, b/w frontis. only, bd. with clo. spine, 182x120mm. KP

7051 FRANK HARDINGE/From Torrid Zones to Regions/of Perpetual Snow/by/Gordon Stables, M.D., C.M., R.N./New Edition/with Illustrations in Colour/ London/Henry Frowde/Hodder and Stoughton/1908
352pp, 8pp adv., col. frontis. & 5 f/p col. illus., pic. clo., 180x120mm. Grant
The setting for half the book is Queensland & then the action takes place in the Antarctic.
Another copy 1909, as above with 16pp adv. RM

STACK, Peter

7052 A NIGHT IN CAVERNLAND/By/Peter Stack/ Cover design by Unk White/Illustrations by Roderick Shaw/The College Press/38 Carrington St./Sydney
n.d. [1940]
67pp, line drawings in text, clo. (with illus. pasted on front cover), 230x160mm. ANL
Another copy as above but dec. wrapper. Grant

STACY, Marilyn

7053 AUSTRALIAN/CHILDREN'S/DICTIONARY/by/ Marilyn Stacy/Illustrated by Peter Chapman/and Graham Black/Collins' Book Depot/Melbourne
1964
168pp (inc. 2pp preface), col. illus. throughout, pic. clo., 240x155mm. CLRC
Issued uniformly with Carisbrooke's *The Illustrated Encyclopaedia of Australia.*

7054 THE AUSTRALIAN/CHILDREN'S/DICTIONARY/ by Marilyn Stacy/Illustrated by/Peter Chapman and/ Graham Black/Southern Cross International/Sydney
1968
168pp (inc. 2pp preface, etc.), col. drawings in text, stiff dec. wrappers, 225x150mm. ANL

7055 THE AUSTRALIAN/CHILDREN'S/DICTIONARY/ by Marilyn Stacey [*sic*] Illustrated by/Peter Chapman and/Graham Black/[device]/Universal Books Pty Limited/Sydney
1968
168pp (inc. 1p preface signed Marilyn Stacy [*sic*]), col. illus. throughout, col. pic. bd. with d/w, 235x160mm. KP
Appears to be sheets of above bound in different covers with new t.p.

STADLER, Hans

7056 REISEBILDER/AUS/AUSTRALIEN UND/ OZEANIEN teils nach Originalberichten,/teils neu erzählt von/Hans Stadler/Bilden von/Roland Strasser/ und originalauf nahmen/[device]/Wien-Leipzig/ Deutscher Verlag für Jugend und Volk/Gesellschaft M.B.H.
134pp (inc. 5pp index), 2 folding maps, 9 f/p b/w illus., photographic illus. in text, pic. wrappers, 180x125mm. NSL:M
Includes 2 chapters on James Cook, 1 on NZ, and a general chapter on Australia

STAFFORD, Harry

See Lack, Clem

STAFFORD, Mrs Stella (Mrs James)

7057 THE PATH OF LIFE/By Mrs James Stafford/[quote from Psalms]/Third Edition
Arbuckle Waddell Pty Ltd, Melbourne, 1936
62pp (inc. 1p foreword by H. P. Smith), unillus., clo. bd., 182x125mm. KP
Religious writing intended for young people.
4th ed. 1936; 8th ed. Keswick Book Depot, Melbourne, 1939; 12th imp. 1940; 13th imp. Evangelical Pub. Coy, 1941; 15th imp. 1942; 18th imp. S. John Bacon, 1942; 19th imp. 1942; 25th imp. Postal Sunday School Movement, Sydney, 1951; 29th imp. 1957, 34th imp. Christian Literature Crusade, 1962; 40th imp. 1967 (367000). KP

7058 THE GREATEST GIFT/True Stories for Boys and Girls/by Mrs. Stella Stafford/Author of:/"The Path of Life"/"Gleams of Light"/"Child Evangelism"/"Best for All"./[5 line quotation]/Illustrated by Gwen Bryce [*sic*]/Registered at the General Post Office, Sydney/for transmission by post as a book—1948/Wholly set up and printed in Australia by/Jno. Evans & Son Printing Co./
486–488 Kent Street, Sydney/N.S.W. Australia
The author
40pp, line drawings in text, wrappers, 180x120mm. KMM
Evangelical stories.
2nd imp. completing 20 000, 1949. KP
3rd imp. completing 30 000, 1955. KP

7059 THE BEST FOR ALL/Stories for Young and Old/ By/Mrs James Stafford/Author of *"The Path of Life"*/1st Edition
n.d. Printed by Arbuckle, Waddell Pty Ltd.
32pp, unillus., wrappers, 183x120mm. KP

7060 THE BEST FOR ALL/Stories for Young and Old/ by/Mrs Stella Stafford/Author of "The Path of Life"/"Gleams of Light from/the Word of Life"/"The Greatest Gift"./Illustrated by Gwen Brice./4th Edition (Completing 45,000)/Postal Sunday School Movement,/Headquarters: 841 George Street Sydney
1950
40pp, line drawings in text, wrappers, 185x120mm. Grant
6th ed. (completing 70 000 copies) as above, n.d. KP

7061 GLEAMS OF LIGHT/from/The Word of Life./ Selected Scripture Readings for/daily use, compiled by/Mrs Stella Stafford./3rd edition, 1956 (completing 20,000)
70pp, unillus., wrappers, 140x100mm. KP

7062 MY CHOICE/A Selection of Old and New/ Testament Stories Told/in Interesting/Form/Author of/"The Path of Life"/"The Greatest Gift"/"The Best for All"/"Gleams of Light/from the Word of Life"/"Child Evangelism"/Illustrated by Gwen Brice/ Wholly set up and printed in Australia by/Jno. Evans & Son Printing Coy Pty Ltd.,/486–488 Kent Street, Sydney,/NSW. Australia
n.d.
48pp, line drawings, dec. wrappers, 185x122mm. KP

7063 WITH GLADNESS/Stories for Young and Old/By/ Mrs Stella Stafford/Author of "The Path of Life"/[4 titles follow]/Illustrated by Gwen Brice/Registered at the GPO Sydney &c 1957/Wholly set up and printed in Australia by/Jno. Evans & Son Printing Coy. Pty. Ltd./486-488 Kent Street Sydney/NSW Australia
60pp, b/w headings, tailpieces &c, wrappers, 182x120mm. KP

Stamina Clothing Co. Pty Ltd

See AUSTRALIAN MEN OF STAMINA

STAMP, C. E.
DAVID'S SEASIDE HOLIDAY. *See* Joy series

JONATHAN AND HIS BILLY-GOAT CART. *See* Joy series

'STANDBY'
See PORTEOUS, Richard Sydney

STANFORD, Jan
7064 THE LITTLE FERRY BOAT/Story by Jan Stanford/ Illustrated by Aart Van Ewijk/Angus and Robertson Sydney 1965
[32]pp, dec. t.p., col. illus. throughout, dec. clo., dec. e/p, 180x250mm. KMM

STARR, Joyce Owen
7065 HUM/OF THE FOREST/By/Joyce Owen Starr/ [vignette]/Commonwealth of Australia:/Edward A. Vidler/Melbourne/Registered at G.P.O., Melbourne for transmission through the Post as a book
1931
56pp, 5 b/w illus., dec. bd., 245x185mm. KMM
Contains verse inside front cover not repeated elsewhere in book.

STEAD, David G.
7066 Shakespeare Head Australian Nature Books./ General Editor: [Publisher's device] David G. Stead/ No. 2/THE TREE BOOK/[photograph]/By David G. Stead,/Past President of the Australian Forest League (N.S.W.)...[5 lines]/Sydney:/The Shakespeare Head Press Ltd./1933
108pp (inc. 1p quotation, 1p general foreword, 1p editorial note & 1p bibliography), b/w photographic illus. & diagrams throughout, wrappers, 180x110mm. ANL

7067 Shakespeare Head Australian Nature Books/ General Editor: [Publisher's device] David G. Stead/ GIANTS AND PIGMIES/OF THE DEEP/A Story of Australian Sea Denizens/[photograph] By David G. Stead,/Author of 'Fishes of Australia", "Edible Fishes of New South Wales", "Fisheries of British Malaya", "Eggs and Breeding/Habits of Fishes", "The Great Whales of Australia and/Antarctica", etc. etc./ Sydney:/The Shakespeare Head Press Ltd.,/1933
108pp (inc. 1p general foreword &1p editorial note), b/w photographic illus. & diagrams throughout, wrappers, 180x115mm. ANL

STEAD, Richard
7068 ADVENTURES/ON/THE HIGH SEAS/Romantic incidents & Perils of/Travel, Sport, and Exploration/ throughout the world/By/Richard Stead, B.A., F.R.Hist.S./Author of 'Adventures on the Great Rivers'/'Adventures on the High Mountains'/'Will of the Dales' &c &c/with sixteen illustrations/London/ Seeley and Co. Limited/38 Great Russell Street/1909
345pp & 6pp adv., f/p b/w frontis. & 15 plates, dec. clo., 195x130mm. HBM
Illus. John F. Campbell. Bligh & the Bounty pp29–39; Vancouver pp147–56; Hurricane in Samoa in 1889; 229–39; Captain Wilkes & the Antarctic Expedition of 1836 pp311–22.

7069 ADVENTURES/IN/SOUTHERN SEAS/Stirring Stories of Adventure/among savages, wild beasts,/& the forces of Nature/By/Richard Stead B.A., F.R.Hist.S./Author of 'Adventures on the High Seas', &c &c./with seventeen illustrations/London/Seeley, Service & Co. Limited/38 Great Russell Street/1913
318pp & 3pp adv. preceding t.p. & 2pp at end, b/w frontis. & 16 b/w plates, dec. clo., 194x126mm. ANL
Illus. mostly by John F. Campbell. Includes: Fights with Fijians; Captain Dillon; Discovery of Tahiti; Bishop Patteson; The Erebus & the Terror.

STEBBING, Grace
7070 EDWARD BERTRAM/or/The Emigrant Heir/By/ Grace Stebbing/Author of "Peyton Phelps; or, Adventures among the Italian Carbonari",/"Brave Geordie", &c. &c./[vignette]/With illustrations by C. O. Murray/London:/Marcus Ward & Co., 67 & 68 Chandos Street/and at Belfast and New York/1882
284pp, 4pp adv., b/w frontis. & 5 f/p b/w illus., b/w chapter headings & tailpieces, pic. clo., 180x125mm. RM
The adventures of an English stowaway on an emigrant ship bound for Australia, cast away on a desert island with a girl passenger following a shipwreck; the pair eventually manage to reach Australia which is the setting for their future happiness.

7071 FAITHFUL GEORGIE/A Tale of Australian Adventure./By/Grace Stebbing./[vignette]/With Illustrations./London:/Ward, Lock & Co., Warwick House,/Salisbury Square, E.C./New York: 10, Bond Street
n.d. [1882]
164pp (inc. 1p preface), 28pp adv., b/w frontis., 13 plates & b/w illus. in text inc. head & tailpieces, dec. clo. (with 2 col. illus. pasted on front cover), 150x100mm. CLRC

STEDMAN, Jeanette Claire
DAY DREAM SERIES
7072 PAMELA ANNE/IN/SHADOWLAND/by/Jeanette C. Stedman
7073 PAMELA ANNE'S/MAGICAL/SHOES/ [&c.]
7074 PETER AND THE/CHINAMAN/AH CHOO/ [&c.]
7075 PETER AND PAMELA IN/JUNGLE LANE/ [&c.]
7076 PETER AND PAMELA'S/PATCHWORK/ CASTLE/ [&c.]

7077 PETER ON/CANDY-ROCK/ISLE/ [&c.]
Uniform booklets published by Hollander & Govett, Sydney 1945–46
20pp, 10 part. col. illus., wrappers, 235x185mm. all ANL

7078 THE/STORYTIME PEDLAR/Registered in Australia for transmission by post as a book/[8 lines verse]/To .../From .../By/Jeanette C. Stedman [col. illus.]
Printed by Hollander & Govett Pty Ltd, Sydney
[32]pp, 16pp with col. illus., col. pic. bd., 244x234mm. KP

7079 THE/TINKERMAN'S TALES/Registered in Australia for Transmission by Post as a Book/[verse]/ By/Jeanette C. Stedman
n.d. Printed by Hollander & Govett Pty Ltd, Sydney
[36]pp, 18pp col. illus., col. pic. bd., 240x232mm. TG
Fairy stories, one with an Aboriginal background.

STEELE, J. A.
7080 Imperial Edition No. 456./THREE AUSTRALIAN/ SKETCHES/For Piano/by/J. A. Steele/Allan & Co., Pty. Ltd./Melbourne Sydney Adelaide Bendigo/Price 1/6 net/(2/- in N.Z.)
n.d. (copyright MCMXL)
8pp, unillus., pic. wrappers, cover title, 310x235mm. KP
Cover design by Ida Rentoul Outhwaite, adv. on back of front cover. Contents include 'The Possums' Dance'; 'The Wattle Fairy' and 'Rabbits'.
Another copy with 3/- on front cover. KP

Another copy with 35c on front cover. Grey wrappers with cover design printed in green. KP

[STEELE, John V.]

7081 THE KANGAROO
No imprint, n.d. [193-?]
12pp, col. illus. throughout signed 'John V. Steele', stiff pic. wrappers, cover title, 320x265mm. CLRC
Picture book with accompanying verses.

7082 THE/BUSH PETS' PARTY
No imprint, n.d.
12pp, col. illus. throughout signed 'John V. Steele', stiff pic. wrappers, cover title, 320x265mm. KMM
Picture book with accompanying verses; appears to be a companion volume to the same illustrator's *The Kangaroo.*

7083 TEN LITTLE NIGGER BOYS
n.p., n.d. [? cover missing]
[12]pp, col. illus. each page, stiff paper, 314x266mm. KP
Uniform with *Our Pets' Picture Book; The Bush Pets' Party; The Kangaroo.*

STEINBERG, A.

7084 ADMIRAL/RICHARD E. BYRD/by Alfred Steinberg/Illustrated by Charles Beck/G. P. Putnam's Sons/New York
1960
128pp, b/w chapter headings, clo., 205x130mm. NSL:M

STEPHENS, J. Brunton

7085 MARSUPIAL BILL:/or/The Bad Boy, The Good Dog, and the Old Man Kangaroo/By/J. Brunton Stephens,/Illustrated by J. A. Clarke,/Reprinted from "The Queenslander"/Brisbane:/Gordon and Gotch./
1879
38pp, 17 b/w illus. including head & tailpieces, pic. bd. (with adv. on verso front cover, verso/recto back cover, & e/p), 215x135mm. Grant

STEVEN, Margaret

ARTHUR PHILLIP
JOHN MACARTHUR. *See* Great Australians

STEVENS, Bertram (ed.)

7086 THE/CHILDREN'S TREASURY/OF AUSTRALIAN VERSE/Edited by Bertram Stevens/and George Mackaness, M.A./Sydney/Angus & Robertson Ltd./89 Castlereagh Street
n.d. [1913]
128pp (inc. 3pp preface, 4pp notes), unillus., limp linen covers, 180x120mm. CLRC
A school anthology.

7087 A BOOK OF/AUSTRALIAN VERSE/FOR BOYS AND GIRLS/Edited by/Bertram Stevens/With Portraits/London/Angus & Robertson Ltd.
n.d. [1915]
293pp, 4pp preface, 31pp adv. (dated July 1914), portrait frontis. & 15 f/p b/w portraits, clo., 180x120mm. CLRC

STEVENS, Fae Hewston

7088 KORONGLEA COBBERS/Fae Hewston Stevens/Illustrated by Ian Nimmo Forrest/Ward Lock & Co. Limited/London, Melbourne and Johannesburg
n.d. [1961]
192pp, extended dec. t.p., b/w chapter headings, clo., 200x125mm. CLRC

7089 [drawing]/KORONGLEA COBBERS/Fae Hewston Stevens/Illustrated by Ian Nimmo Forrest/Ward Lock & Co. Limited/London, Melbourne and Cape Town.
Second imp. 1962
Details as above. KP

7090 KORONGLEA PONIES/Fae Hewston Stevens/Illustrated by Ian Nimmo Forrest/Ward Lock & Co. Limited/London, Melbourne and Cape Town
1962
206pp, extended dec. t.p., b/w chapter headings, clo., 200x130mm. CLRC

7091 Fae Hewston Stevens/KORONGLEA HOLIDAYS/[drawing]/Illustrated by/Ian Nimmo Forrest/Ward Lock & Co. Limited/London, Melbourne and Cape Town
1963
221pp, 1p adv., extended dec. t.p., 30 b/w chapter headings, clo., 200x130mm. CLRC

7092 KORONGLEA/ADVENTURES/Fae/Hewston/Stevens/Illustrated by/Ian Nimmo Forrest/Ward Lock & Co. Limited/London and Melbourne
1965
192pp, b/w extended frontis., b/w drawings in text, clo., 200x130mm. WRT

7093 KORONGLEA TWINS/Fae/Hewston/Stevens/Illustrated by/Ian Nimmo Forrest/Ward Lock & Co. Limited/London and Melbourne
1967
192pp, extended b/w frontis., b/w chapter headings, clo., 190x120mm. CLRC

STEVENS, Lyla V.

7094 THE ADVENTURES OF/BONNIE & BONZA
Modern Printing Co., Melbourne, n.d. [1946]
16pp, col. & b/w illus. throughout by 'Bunty Lou' (Jean Elder), wrappers, cover title, 300x230mm. KMM
Verses.

7095 BONNIE & BONZA/AT THE/CONCERT/by/Lyla Stevens
Modern Printing Co., Melbourne, n.d. [1946]
16pp, col. & part-col. illus. throughout by Jean Elder, dec. wrappers, cover title, 300x220mm. KMM

7096 AROUND THE CORNER/and other/bits and pieces/of/Verse and Prose/Printed by/Arthur L. Edgerton, 15 Patrick St./Melbourne C.1.
n.d. [1943]
30pp, 7 part-col. illus. by Jean Elder, pic. wrappers (with black cat on front cover), 170x115mm. KMM

7097 AROUND THE CORNER/and other/bits and pieces/of/Verse and Prose/by/Lyla V. Stevens/Photo-lithographed by/Modern Printing Co. Pty Ltd/Melbourne/All rights reserved
n.d. [1951?]
48pp, 17 part col. illus. (Jean Elder), pic. stiff wrappers with cover drawing of a dog, 180x120mm. KMM

7098 "BUSH MAGIC"/and/Other Verses/by/Lyla Stevens/All rights reserved
Photo-Lithographed by Modern Printing Co Pty Ltd, Melbourne, n.d.
16pp, 7pp col. illus. (Jean Elder) & col. pic. wrappers, 110x84mm. KMM
Verses not specifically for children.

7099 BIRDS OF AUSTRALIA/IN COLOUR/by/Lyla Stevens/[drawing]/Illustrated by/Anne Lissenden/Whitcombe & Tombs Pty. Ltd./Melbourne, Sydney, Perth, Geelong
n.d. [195-?]
61pp (inc. 1p author's foreword), 28 f/p col. & part-col. illus., drawings in text, dec. bd., 245x180mm. KMM

7100 THE LAND/WHERE/[drawing]/THE/KANGAROO/LIVES/By Lyla Stevens/Pictures by/Jean Elder/1960/Sampson Low, Marston/& Co., Ltd./This book may only be exported for sale in the

following territories by the appointed sole agents:/ Australia—Ponsford, Newman & Benson Ltd., New Zealand—Whitcombe & Tombs, Ltd./Africa—Purnell & Sons (S.A.) (Pty.) Ltd.
21pp, dec. t.p., b/w drawings throughout, dec. bd., 255x235mm. CLRC
Contains descriptions & illustrations of various Australian animals.

7101 THE LAND/WHERE/THE/PANDA LIVES/by Lyla Stevens/Pictures by Jean Elder/1960 Sampson Low, Marston & Co., Ltd. ['This book may be exported...&c.']
[London]
No proper t.p.; above printed amid decorations inside front cover
[21]pp, b/w drawings in text throughout, dec. bd., 255x240mm. KMM

7102 THE LAND/WHERE THE/BEAVER LIVES/by Lyla Stevens/Pictures by Stanley Smith/1960 Sampson Low Marston & Co. Ltd./[3 lines relating to agents]
[22]pp, b/w drawings throughout, col. pic. bd., 257x238mm. KP
Title printed on front pastedown with illus. & 2 paragraphs of information about beavers.

7103 THE LAND WHERE/THE/[drawing & some text]/ ELEPHANT LIVES/by Lyla Stevens/Pictures by Jean Elder/1960 Sampson Low, Marston & Co. Ltd. [3 lines]
London
[20]pp & text printed inside front & back covers (t.p. inside front cover), b/w illus. on every page, pic. bd., 257x237mm. CLRC

7104 ANIMALS OF AUSTRALIA/IN COLOUR/by/Lyla Stevens/[drawing]/Illustrated by Deidre East/ Whitcombe & Tombs Pty. Ltd./Melbourne, Sydney, Perth, Geelong
n.d. [1963?]
62pp (inc. 1p foreword by C. W. Brazenor, Assistant Director, National Museum of Victoria), 28 f/p col. & part. col. illus., b/w drawings in text, dec. bd., 245x180mm. CLRC

STEVENSON, Barbara
7105 ADVENTURES/OF SNUB CAT/by/Barbara Stevenson/Illustrations by/Lex Marshall/[device]/ Geoffrey Cumberlege/Oxford University Press/ Leighton House Melbourne
1947
116pp, col. frontis., b/w drawings in text, bd., 185x120mm. MK
• Rpt 1950, details as above. KMM

7106 A LITTLE/RED PRINCESS/by/Barbara Stevenson/Illustrations by/Lex Marshall/Geoffrey Cumberlege/Oxford University Press/Leighton House Melbourne
1948
104pp, col. frontis. & b/w drawings in text, bd., 180x120mm. VSL

7107 MORE ADVENTURES/OF/SNUB CAT/Barbara Stevenson/Illustrated by/Lex Marshall/Geoffrey Cumberlege/Oxford University Press/Melbourne Wellington
1950
90pp, col. frontis. & b/w drawings in text, bd., 180x120mm. VSL

STEVENSON, Ronald (ed.)
THE YOUNG PIANIST'S GRAINGER,
Schott & Co.,London 1966
Mostly music

STEWART, Athol Frederick Ferguson
7108 AUSTRALIA'S/GRACE DARLING/By/A. F. Ferguson Stewart/[vignette]/[device]/Printed and Published by/Paterson Printing Press Ltd./65 Murray Street, Perth, Western Australia
n.d. [1946?]
32pp, b/w frontis., wrappers, 214x137mm. KMM

STEWART, Christine & YAGER, Julie
7109 SIX/HORSES/AND/A/CARAVAN/by/Christine Stewart and/Julie Yager/Illustrated by/Roseanne Fuller/Ure Smith Sydney
1964
156pp, 4 f/p part. col. illus., clo., col. e/p, book designed by Sally Keep, 220x135mm. CLRC

STEWART, D. Macrae
7110 THE/LAST/LIKENESS;/and other Addresses/to Children/by/D. Macrae Stewart/Chaplain, Australian Imperial Force/Morgan & Scott Ltd./12, Paternoster Buildings/London, E.C. MCMXVI
258pp, unillus., clo., 195x125mm. CLRC

STEWART, Dorothy
7111 TEDDY KOALA'S BOOK/Songs and Stories about the adorable/[drawing]/The Koala: Australia's National Pet/by/Dorothy Stewart/The Boston Music Co. Boston, Mass., 1943
44pp, 1p introduction, b/w photographic illus. & 3 drawings in text, pic. bd., 300x230mm. MAC
The drawings are by Ida Rentoul Outhwaite, smudgily reproduced & only on one are the initial decipherable.

STEWART, Henry
7112 THE OCEAN WAVE:/Narratives/of some of/The Greatest Voyages, Seamen, Discoveries,/Shipwrecks, and Mutinies/of the World./by/Henry Stewart/Author of "Our Redcoats and Bluejackets" etc./with illustrations./London:/John Hogg, Paternoster Row./ 1883
384pp, 16pp adv., b/w frontis. & 7 f/p b/w illus., pic. clo., 170x115mm. CLRC
Contents include: 'Captain Cook's Voyages' (37pp); 'The Mutiny of the *Bounty*' (13pp).

STINGL, Miloslav
7113 UKRADENY TOTEM (Stolen Totem—Four Stories about children)
Svoboda, Prague 1972
113pp. Unseen: SLCSR

STODART, Eleanor Mary
7114 SNAILS/Eleanor Stodart/Photographs by Ederic Slater/[illustration]/Angus and Robertson
Sydney 1971
[32]pp, b/w photographic illus. throughout, clo., 165x210mm. CLRC
Both author & photographer are Australian.

STODDARD, William O.
7115 THE WHITE CAVE/By/William O. Stoddard/ Author of "Crowded Out o' Crofield" etc/[device]/ New York/The Century Co./1893
Copyright 1892, 1893
254pp, b/w frontis., 20 f/p b/w illus., dec. clo. 188x125mm. KMM
The experiences of an English baronet, recently become squatter, & his family on their property in the Grampians.

STOKES, J. P. [ed.]
7116 LORD FORREST/Centenary/Booklet/1847–1947 [Coat of arms]/FORREST/Baron Forrest of Bunbury/

and of/Forret in Fife/A tribute to a great explorer and statesman from the scholars of/Western Australian schools
Wholly set up and printed in Western Australia by S. H. Lamb Printing House, Perth and Fremantle, n.d. [1948?]
48pp (inc. 1p introduction, 1p foreword), b/w map & b/w illus. (mostly photographic), pic. wrappers, 215x140mm. KMM
Contributions by children in Western Australian schools commemorating the life & exploits of John Forrest.

STOMANN, Giulietta
7117 AUSTRALIAN ANIMALS/illustrated by Giulietta Stomann/[drawing]/Paul Hamlyn/London New York Sydney Toronto/Published by Paul Hamlyn Pty Ltd, 176 South Creek Road,/Dee Why West, New South Wales 2099/Copyright Paul Hamlyn Pty Ltd 1969/First published 1969/Printed in Hong Kong
32pp, b/w drawings with captions, pic. covers, 298x215mm. KMM
A Wombat colouring book.

STONE, Douglas M.
See Bawden, Sharman N. & Stone, Douglas M.

STONES, Carolyn R.
AUSTRALIAN EXPLORERS. *See* Golden Stamp Books

STONES, William
7118 MY FIRST VOYAGE./A Book for Youth/By/William Stones./Illustrated by E. Roffe./[quote—Bacon]/London:/Simpkin, Marshall & Co./1858
239pp & 1p & double-spread col. map, 1 f/p col. map, 1 b/w map, 2 f/p b/w plates & engravings & diagrams in text, blind-stamped clo., title & dec. in gilt, errata slip, 185x125mm. KMM
Second ed., London 1860. Unseen

7119 WHAT I LEARNED AT SEA;/or,/My First Voyage:/A Book for Youth/[vignette of an octopus]/By William Stones,/Illustrated by E. Roffe./London/Ward, Lock & Tyler, Paternoster Row
n.d. [1870]
239pp & 1p & 32pp adv., engravings in text, dec. clo., g.e., 182x120mm. ANL
This ed. does not include the maps or f/p plates.

STORER, H. C.
7120 THE BOY SETTLER/or/The Adventures of Sydney Bartlett/By/H. C. Storer/with illustrations by J. Finnemore, R.I./London/The Religious Tract Society/4 Bouverie Street and 65 St. Paul's Churchyard E.C.
n.d. [1907]
331pp, 4pp adv., col. frontis. & 2 f/p col. illus., pic. clo., 200x130mm. KMM
Concerns the adventures of an English boy who migrates to New Zealand; some of the action takes place in Australia.
7121 Another copy as above, n.d. [prize 1907]
B/w frontis. & 3 b/w plates, pic. clo., title & author in gilt on front cover & spine, 197x130mm
The Boy's Library of Adventure and Heroism Illustrated. KP
7122 THE BOY SETTLER/Or/The Adventures of Sydney Bartlett/By/H. C. Storer/London/The Religious Tract Society/4 Bouverie Street and 65 St. Paul's Churchyard E.C.4/Printed in Great Britain
n.d. [inscribed 1925]
331pp, 4pp adv., col. frontis. only, 2-col. t.p. (printed in blue & red), dec. clo., 185x125mm. Schoolboys' Library. RM

Stories for Boys
7123 STORIES/FOR BOYS
n.p., n.d.
32pp, part-col. illus., col. pic. wrappers, cover title, 244x164mm. KP
Illus. signed 'Lois Anderson' but no apparent Australian content.

Stories for Boys
7124 STORIES/FOR BOYS
W. H. Honey Publishing Co., Sydney, n.d. [copyright 1944]
[48]pp, 7 col. illus., b/w drawings throughout, stiff wrappers, cover title, 245x170mm. NSL:M
Contents include 'Aladdin' & other traditional stories.

Stories for Girls
7125 STORIES/FOR/GIRLS
W. H. Honey Publishing Co., Sydney, n.d. [copyright 1944]
[48]pp, 6 col. illus., b/w drawings throughout, stiff wrappers, cover title, 245x170mm.
Contents include 'The Sleeping Beauty' & other traditional stories. NSL:M

Stories for Little People
7126 STORIES FOR/LITTLE PEOPLE
W. H. Honey Publishing Company, 31 Cunningham St, Sydney, n.d.
[inscribed Xmas1944]
[48]pp, illus., wrappers, cover title, 245x185mm. Grant
Contents include: 'The Story of Hanky-Panky' (illus. Rufus Morris); 'Noah's Ark Nonsense' (poem of 18 verses with illus. sgd 'Gilly'); 'Pigs Won't Get over Stile' (illus. 'Gilly').

Stories for the Littlest Ones
7127 STORIES/FOR THE/LITTLEST ONES/Published/by the/Board of Religious Education, 241 Flinders Lane, Melbourne C.1
n.d. [194-?]
24 numbered leaflets publ. by The Church of England for parents & teachers to read to young children. EAch leaflet 4pp with b/w cover illus., 190x140mm. ANL

Stories from Fairyland
7128 STORIES/FROM FAIRYLAND
W. H. Honey Publishing Co., Sydney, n.d. [copyright 1943]
[96]pp, b/w illus. throughout, dec. bd., cover title, 245x175mm. NSL:M
Traditional stories.

Stories of Historical Diamonds
7129 STORIES/OF/HISTORICAL/DIAMONDS
n.d.[194-?]
[24]pp (last blank), 11 f/p sepia illus. & small dec. drawings, 185x205mm. KP
Printed in brown on beige, with col. panels on each page by G. C. Benson. On front cover: 'Prepared for 3LO/by courtesy of Dunklings/Diamond Experts/and Jewellers/294–296 Collins Street./Melbourne/[9 lines]/3LO Melbourne'.

The Story of a Star
7130 THE STORY OF A STAR
Renbar Pty Limited, 3 Rawson Place, Sydney, n.d.
20pp, 11 f/p b/w illus., wrappers, cover title, 210x170mm. Grant
The story of Christmas told in extracts from the Bible, with b/w illustrations for children to colour.

The Story of Aladdin & his Wonderful Lamp
7131 THE STORY OF/ALADDIN/& HIS WONDERFUL LAMP

Georgian House, Melbourne, n.d. [194-?]
16pp, 8 f/p col. illus., b/w drawings throughout by J. Hughes, illus. wrappers, cover title, 250x190mm. NSL:M

The Story of Aladdin and his Wonderful Lamp
7132 THE STORY OF/ALADDIN/AND HIS/ WONDERFUL/LAMP/Picture/Story/Book/The "Sandman" Series
Series 2 No. 3, n.d. Printed in Australia by John Sands Pty Ltd, Sydney, n.d.
14pp, col. & part-col. illus. throughout, col. pic. bd. covers, cover title, 305x250mm. KMM
Illus. initialled 'JV' or 'JW'.

The Story of Apinja [Mrs MacDougall]
7133 THE/STORY OF APINJA [drawing of Aboriginal boy & lizard]
Board of Religious Education, Presbyterian Church of Australia, Room 451, T & G Building, 147 Collins St, Melbourne C.1, n.d. [1954?]
16pp, 12 strips of 3 frames each, illus. wrappers, cover title, 106x137mm. ANL
Preface states: 'Apinja is an imaginary boy, but some of the things shown in this little book actually happened to an aboriginal boy in north western Australia. Mrs Macdougall wrote about them when she was helping at the Mission Station at Kunmunya'. The pictures and also the cover drawing were done by Miss D. G. Beacham of North Fitzroy, Victoria. Price 6d.

The Story of the Australian-England Telegraph Link
7134 THE STORY OF THE/AUSTRALIAN-ENGLAND/ TELEGRAPH LINK Australia's Overseas Telecommunications Centenary Nov 20 1871–1971 THE WONDER-/WORKING WIRE
Sydney, 1971
OTC Information Broadsheet (folded with 16pp), part col. illus. & dec., 240x175mm. KP

The Story of Cinderella
7135 THE STORY/OF/CINDERELLA/As Related in the Pantomime/"Cinderella"/Xmas and New Year/ [coloured drawing]
Printed by Victory Publicity Pty Ltd, 262 Queen Street, Melbourne, n.d.
31pp, col. & b/w illus. throughout, pic. wrappers, 245x185mm. MD

The Story of Currency in Australia
7136 From [illustration of coin] George III/To [illustration of coin]/Elizabeth II/THE/STORY OF CURRENCY/ IN/AUSTRALIA/Bank of New South Wales
Sydney, April 1954; rpt November 1954, 1956, 1957, 1958, 1959, 1961
18pp, b/w photographic illus. & b/w drawings throughout, wrappers, cover title, 245x155mm. KP
Acknowledgement to Mr O. C. Fleming, a former president of the Australian Numismatic Society, & Professor S. J. Butlin, Professor of Economics University of Sydney.
7137 THE/STORY OF CURRENCY/IN/AUSTRALIA/ Bank of New South Wales
Fifth edition, Sydney 1969
20pp, b/w photographic illus. & drawings, wrappers, cover title, 240x160mm. KMM
Contains an additional two pages on decimal currency.
• Rpt 1961, 1964, 1967, 1969, 1971. KP

The Story of Electricity
7138 THE STORY OF/ELECTRICITY/An Educational Booklet for Boys and Girls from 1st year up
Sydney County Council Electricity Undertaking, n.d. [195-?]
24pp (inc. covers), b/w & part col. illus. & diagrams, pic. wrappers, 180x240mm. ANL

The Story of Electricity
7139 THE STORY OF/ELECTRICITY/An Education Booklet for Boys and Girls from 1st year up
Electricity Trust of South Australia, n.d. [1971]
25pp, b/w diagrams, dec. wrappers, cover title, map on back wrapper, 170x232mm. ANL

The Story of Gold
7140 THE STORY OF/GOLD
Issued with the compliments of the Commonwealth Savings Bank, n.d. [1962]. Printed by Simmons Ltd, Sydney
16pp, part-col. illus. throughout, col. illus. wrappers, cover title, 240x185mm. KP
7141 THE STORY OF/GOLD/Presented by the Commonwealth Savings Bank/in its Golden Jubilee Year—1962
Details as above, but some col. illus. & some illus. rev. & updated. KP
7142 THE STORY OF/GOLD/Presented by the Commonwealth Savings Bank/in its Golden Jubilee Year—1962
16pp, col. & part col. illus. throughout, pic. wrappers, cover title, 240x180mm. KP
7143 THE STORY OF/GOLD/Presented to you by/The Commonwealth Banks
n.p. [Sydney], n.d. [1968?]. New ed.
16pp, col. illus. throughout, col. pic. wrappers, cover title, 240x180mm. KP

The Story of the Good Ship Bounty
7144 THE STORY/OF THE/GOOD SHIP BOUNTY/ And her Mutineers/and/Mutinies in Highland Regiments/Edinburgh:/W. P. Nimmo, Hay & Mitchell n.d. [prize 1899]
160pp (94 + 66), b/w frontis. to first book & b/w frontis. to 2nd, dec. clo., 184x122mm. KP
Another copy as above, but
Mutinies in Highland Regiments/William P. Nimmo & Co.,/Edinburgh/1880
Bound with The Story of the Indian Mutiny
160 + 240pp, b/w frontis. to each section, dec. clo. with onlay of Sir Colin Campbell on front cover, 184x116mm. KP

The Story of Joseph
See Greenberg, Joe

The Story of 'Little Emma' the Embryo
7145 THE STORY OF/"LITTLE EMMA"/THE EMBRYO/[photograph]/[text]/Vacuum Oil Company Pty Ltd
Melbourne, n.d. [193-?]
16pp, photographic illus. throughout, pic. wrappers, 230x165mm. KP
Advertising booklet.

The Story of Man-Made Light
7146 THE STORY OF MAN-MADE/LIGHT/(from the caveman's crude torch/to modern electric illumination)
Philips Electrics, Sydney, n.d. [197-?]
24pp, b/w illus. & diagrams, wrappers, cover title, 180x115mm. KP

The Story of the Manufacture of the World's Best Woollens and Worsteds
7147 THE STORY/OF/THE MANUFACTURE OF/THE WORLD'S BEST/WOOLLENS AND WORSTEDS/[6 lines text]/Associated Woollen and Worsted Textile Manufacturers of Australia
n.d. [194-?]

Board booklet folded in 3 & printed on all 6 sides with text & illus., 240x180mm. KP

The Story of Medicine in Early Australia
7148 THE STORY OF/MEDICINE/IN EARLY/AUSTRALIA
Voluntary Health Insurance Council of Australia, Sydney, n.d. [1953?]
12pp (inc. covers), col. illus. throughout, pic. wrappers, cover title, 190x227mm. KP

The Story of Oil
7149 THE/STORY/OF OIL
Shell Publication, n.d. [1947?]. Printed by A. E. Keating & Co., Melbourne
32pp, blue/white photographic illus. & drawings throughout, wrappers, cover title, 180x246mm. KP

The Story of our Flags
7150 THE STORY OF/OUR FLAGS/Girl Guides Association, Victoria/1960
McKellar Press, Malvern
24pp, 4pp col. illus. of flags, dec. wrappers, 183x123mm. KP

The Story of the Pacific
7151 Sanitarium/THE STORY/OF THE/PACIFIC/[drawing]/Volume 7 of the Sanitarium Children's Library
Sanitarium Health Food Co., Sydney, n.d. [195-?]
32pp, b/w map & b/w drawings in text (with spaces for 60 col. pictures to be collected & pasted in), dec. wrappers, 280x210mm. KMM
Brief history of the Pacific divided into different geographic areas.

The Story of Pete and Pop
7152 THE STORY OF PETE AND POP
Cresta Printing Co Pty Ltd for Assoc. Gen. Publications Pty Ltd, Sydney, n.d.
16pp, b/w & part-col. illus. throughout, pic. wrappers, 242x184mm. KMM
Title on cover reads: 'The Pete and Pop Book for Boys and Girls'.

The Story of Silver
7153 THE STORY OF/SILVER/Presented with the Compliments of the Commonwealth Savings Bank
n.d. [1960?]. Printed by Simmons Ltd, Parramatta Road, Glebe, Sydney
16pp, col. illus. throughout, col. illus. wrappers, cover title, 240x184mm. KP

The Story of TAA
7154 THE STORY OF TAA/[photograph]/Service to the Nation/Third Anniversary
Melbourne, n.d. [1949?]
16pp, b/w & part col. photographic illus., 200x278mm. ANL
Trans Australia Airlines.

The Story of Tiddles
See SPOTTY AT THE CIRCUS

The Story of/Transport
7154a THE STORY OF TRANSPORT
Allied Enterprises, Sydney, n.d. [1948?]
[12]pp [printed inside front cover], 6 f/p col. illus., smaller col. illus. in text, f/p col. illus. both sides back cover, wrapper, cover title, 270x215mm. Grant

The Story of Woofles Wombat & Bertram Bunny
7155 THE STORY OF/WOOFLES WOMBAT/&/BERTRAM BUNNY
Wee Folks Productions, Melbourne, n.d. [194-?]. Printed by Truth & Sportsman
12pp (inc. 4pp printed in col. & inc. pic. covers), b/w drawings in text, cover title, printed throughout on light bd., 237x237mm. ANL

Storytime
7156 STORYTIME/by various writers for the Australian Broadcasting/Commission Kindergarten of the Air/[part-col. drawing]/Lansdowne Press/Melbourne
1965
95pp (inc. 2pp foreword), b/w & part-col. drawings by Genevieve Melrose, pic. bd., 250x180mm. KMM
Stories & verse.

Storytime for Boys and Girls
See Gunn & Taylor

STOW, Catherine Somerville [née Field]
See Parker, Mrs K. Langloh

STOW, Randolph
7157 MIDNITE/The Story of a Wild Colonial Boy/Randolph Stow/Illustrated by Ralph Steadman/F. W. Cheshire/Melbourne Canberra Sydney
1967
140pp, b/w drawing (preceding text), & 6 f/p b/w illus., clo., 195x125mm. KMM
• Rpt 1968, as above. BBC
7158 MIDNITE/The Story of a Wild Colonial Boy/Randolph Stow/Illustrated by Ralph Steadman/Macdonald: London
1967
140pp, b/w f/p illus. precedes text & 6 f/p b/w illus., clo., 192x130mm. KMM
7159 MIDNITE/The Story of a Wild Colonial Boy/Randolph Stow/Illustrated by Joan Sandin/Prentice-Hall, Inc./Englewood Cliffs, N.J.
1968
120pp, b/w frontis. & 10 b/w illus., clo., col. e/p, 210x140mm. ANL
Joan Sandin is an American artist.
7160 Randolph Stow/MIDNITE/The Story of a Wild/Colonial Boy/Illustrated by/Ralph Steadman/Penguin Books
Harmondsworth, Middlesex, England, 1969
121pp, 7pp adv., 6 f/p b/w illus., b/w illus. t.p., pic. wrappers, 180x110mm. KMM
• Rpt 1972. KP
Japanese edition
7161 JOD HEIKA NO SANZOKUDAN/R. Suto Saku: Jinga Taruo Yaku. Tokyo: Kaiseisha, Showa 45 [1970]
208pp, illus. (Sekai no kodomo no honizo). ANL
Danish edition
7162 KAPTAJN MIDNITE og hansbande/Randolph Stow, p Dansk ved Birte Svensson: tegninger ap Ralph Steadman
[Copenhagen] Gyldendale, 1971
115pp, illus. ANL
German edition
7163 KÄPT'N MITTERNACHT/[von] Randolph Stow Aus dem Englischen übertragen van Sybil Gräfen Schonfeldt, Bilder von Isolde Schmitt-Menzel
Signal Verlag, Baden-Bden, W. Germany 1972
175pp, illus., 22cm. Unseen: ANB 1974
See also Howard, Peter & Levy, Wayne (eds) AUSTRALIAN STORY SAMPLER

STRACHAN, Michael J.
7164 A LETTER FROM/AUSTRALIA/by/Michael J. Strachan/A. H. & A. W. Reed/Sydney Wellington Auckland
[1965]

24pp, 11pp b/w photographic illus., stiff pic. wrappers, 215x140mm. KMM
The Outdoor series

STRAHAN, Lynne

7165 George Dreyfus/REFLECTIONS IN A GLASS-HOUSE,/An Image of Captain James Cook/for speaker, children's chorus and orchestra/Text Lynne Strahan/Allans Music
Melbourne, 1972
53pp, unillus., wrappers, 210x168mm. ANL

'STRANG, Herbert' [ed.] [pseud. George Herbert Ely & Charles James L'Estrange]

7166 ROUND/THE/WORLD/IN/SEVEN/DAYS/Herbert/Strang/Humphrey Milford/Oxford University/Press/London
Publ. 1910, rpt 1912, 1914, 1916, 1917, 1919, 1924, 1929 [inscribed 1932]
295pp, col. frontis., clo., 184x117mm. KP
Boys New Library
Other copies seen 1919 & 1924 with variant frontis. KP

7167 ROUND THE WORLD/IN SEVEN DAYS/By/Herbert Strang/[colophon]/Humphrey Milford/Oxford University Press/London Edinburgh Glasgow/Toronto Melbourne Cape Town Bombay
Publ. 1910, rpt 1912, 1916, 1917, 1919, 1924, 1927, 1933 (twice)
295pp, col. frontis., folding b/w map, clo., 186x120mm. TG
Australia, New Guinea & the Solomons are visited on pp. 100-42.
Swedish edition

7168 C .W. K. Gleerups Ungdomsböker N:o 27./JORDEN BUNT/PÅ/SJU DAGAR/Äventyrsskildring/Av/Herbert Strang/(Förf till "Kobo", "Jack Brown", "Samba", "Luftens Konung"/Och "Havens Herre")/Auktoriserad översättning av Karen Jensen, född lidforss/[publisher's device]/Lund/C. W. Gleerups förlag
1911
184pp (inc. 5pp preface &c), double-spread b/w map, otherwise unillus., pic. bd. with clo. spine, adv. verso back cover, 202x140mm. RM

7169 The Romance/of the World/Edited by Herbert Strang/PIONEERS/IN/AUSTRALIA/Stories of/Exploration/and/Adventure/London/Henry Frowde &/Hodder & Stoughton
n.d. [first ed. 1911]
320pp, col. frontis. & 7 f/p col. illus., 2 b/w maps, clo. (with col. onlay on front cover & another on spine), dec. e/p, 190x130mm. KMM
Contents divided into 'Across the Island Continent' & 'Adventures in the Bush'.
• Rpt 1924, as above but 'Humphrey Milford/Oxford University Press/London'
The Pioneer series. Grant
• Rpt 1934, details as above. KP

7170 The Romance/of the World/Edited by Herbert Strang/EARLY DAYS/IN/AUSTRALIA/Stories of/Discovery/and/Settlement/London/Henry Frowde &/Hodder & Stoughton
n.d. [prize label 1911]
320pp, col. frontis. & 7 f/p col. illus., 2 b/w maps, illus. W. R. S. Stott, pic. clo. (with col. onlay), pic. e/p, 195x130mm. KP
• Rpt as above 1924 but, Humphrey Milford/Oxford University Press/London. KP
• Rpt as above, 1934. KMM

7171 The Romance/of the World/Edited by Herbert Strang/IN SEARCH/OF THE/SOUTHLAND/Australia's Story/London/Henry Frowde &/Hodder & Stoughton
n.d. [1911]
160pp, 16pp adv., col. frontis. 3 f/p col. illus., by W R. S. Stott, b/w map, clo. (with col. onlay on front cover & on spine), dec. t.p., dec. e/p, 187x130mm. KP

7172 The Romance/of the World/Edited by Herbert Strang/IN SEARCH/OF THE/SOUTHLAND/Australia's Story/Humphrey Milford/Oxford University Press/London
• Rpt 1928
Details as above. VMOU
• Rpt as above, 1934. HBM

7173 The Romance/of the World/edited by Herbert Strang/THE EARLY SETTLERS/Australia's Story/London/Henry Frowde &/Hodder & Stoughton
n.d. [First published 1916]
160pp, b/w map frontis., col. frontis. & 3 f/p col. illus. by W. R. S. Stott, clo. (with col. onlay), 190x130mm. KMM
• Rpt 1934 as above but, Humphrey Milford/Oxford University Press. ANL

7174 The Romance/of the World/Edited by Herbert Strang/ACROSS/THE ISLAND/CONTINENT/Australia's/Story/London/Henry Frowde &/Hodder & Stoughton
n.d. [1911, inscribed July 1912]
160pp, 16pp adv., col. frontis. & 3 f/p col. illus. by W. R. S. Scott, b/w map, clo. (with col. onlay on front cover & on spine), dec. e/p, 190x130mm. KP
Another copy as above, but
No adv., dec. red clo. with printed on front cover: Romance of the World/II Australia's Story/ACROSS THE ISLAND CONTINENT. KP

7175 The Romance of the World/edited by Herbert Strang/ACROSS/THE ISLAND/CONTINENT/Australia's Story/Humphrey Milford/Oxford University Press/London
• Rpt 1927, 1929
Details as above; col. pic. onlays on cover & spine. KP
• Rpt as above 1937, variant bdg. KP

7176 The Romance/of the World/Edited by Herbert Strang/ADVENTURES/IN THE BUSH/Australia's Story/London/Henry Frowde &/Hodder & Stoughton
n.d. [library label1915]
160pp, 16pp adv., col. frontis. & 3 f/p col. illus. by W. R. E. Stott, f/p b/w map, clo. (with medallion of one col. illus. reproduced on front cover), 190x130mm. KMM
Contains extracts from: Finney Eldershaw's *Australia as it is*, E. W. Landor's *The Bushman*, or *Life in a New Country*; John Henderson's *Excursions & Adventures in N.S.W.*; F. de B. Cooper's *Wild Adventures in Australia*; G. H. Wathen's *The Golden Colony*; and *Adventures Ashore and Afloat* [Anon]

7177 The Romance/of the World/Edited by Herbert Strang/ADVENTURES/IN THE BUSH/Australia's Story/Humphrey Milford/Oxford University Press/London
1931, rpt 1935
160pp, col. frontis. & 3 col. illus., b/w map, clo., 190x135mm. ANL

7178 The Romance/of the World/Edited by Herbert Strang/THE/ROMANCE OF/AUSTRALIA/Its Discovery/and Colonisation/Adventures of/Its Explorers/and/Settlers/London/Henry Frowde &/Hodder & Stoughton
n.d. [1911]

640pp, 2pp preface, col. frontis. & 15 f/p col. illus., 4 f/p b/w maps, pic. clo., 210x145mm. RM
Compilation containing: 'In Search of the Southland', 'The Early Settlers'; 'Across the Island Continent' ; 'Adventures in the Bush'. The illustrations & the decorative title page & endpapers are by W. R. S. Stott. Neither the illustration on the front cover nor that on the spine is reproduced elsewhere in the book.

7179 THE AIR SCOUT/A Story/of National Defence/ By/Herbert Strang/Illustrated in Colour/by W. R. S. Stott/London/Henry Frowde/Hodder and Stoughton/ 1912
431pp (inc. 4pp preface), col. frontis. & 7 f/p b/w illus., 2 f/p b/w maps, pic. clo., 210x140mm. RM

7180 THE AIR SCOUT/A Story/of National Defence/ By/Herbert Strang/Illustrated in colour/By W. R. S. Stott/Humphrey Milford/Oxford University Press/ London, Edinburgh, Glasgow/Toronto, Melbourne, Cape Town, Bombay
• Rpt 1918
431pp & 4pp preface & 'Note to the present Edition,' col. frontis., 3 col. plates, 2 f/p b/w maps, pic. clo., 185x123mm. KMM

7181 TRUE/TO THE FLAG/Edited by Herbert Strang/ [drawing]/London/Humphrey Milford Oxford University Press
• Rpt 1919
[97]pp, col. frontis. & 2 f/p col. illus., b/w illus. in text, dec. bd., clo. spine (with oval pic. medallion on front cover), 225x175mm. KMM
Contents include: 'A Canoe Voyage in the South Seas', from *Palm Tree Island,* by Herbert Strang (21pp), & 'A Thousand-mile Journey', by Henry Kingsley, reprinted from *The Romance of Australia* (Eyre's journey; 22pp).

7182 Herbert Strang's Library/CAPTAIN COOK'S VOYAGES/London/Henry Frowde/Hodder & Stoughton
n.d. [192-?]
256pp, 3pp editorial introduction, 2pp adv., col. frontis. & 3 f/p col. illus. by Arch. Webb, clo., 190x135mm. PAI

7183 Herbert Strang's/Library/CAPTAIN/COOK'S/ VOYAGES/Humphrey Milford/Oxford University/ Press/London
1923
256pp & 3pp introduction, col. frontis. only (Archibald Webb), clo., dec. e/p, 174x108mm. KP
Herbert Strang's Empire Library
Numerous copies seen with slight variations. KP

7184 THE/BROWN BOOK/FOR BOYS/Edited by Herbert Strang/[drawing]/London:/Henry Frowde and Hodder & Stoughton
n.d. [1914]
[291]pp, dec. t.p., col. frontis. & 11 f/p col. illus., b/w drawings in text, illus. by various artists, dec. clo. (with one col. illus. reproduced in oval panel on front cover), 220x170mm. KMM
Contents include: 'The Discovery of New South Wales', from *Captain Cook's Voyages* (15pp); 'Two-Handed Dick', by Samuel Sidney from *Gallops and Gossips in the Bush* (13pp); 'Out and Home, The Story of an Aeroplane Race', by Herbert Strang, from *The Air Scout* (An Air Race from Port Darwin, or Palmerston, as it is here designated, to Pine Creek, & back) (16pp).

7185 THE BUGLE/CALL/Edited by Herbert Strang/ [drawing]/London:Henry Frowde and Hodder & Stoughton
• Rpt 1917
[146]pp, col. frontis. (W. R. S. Stott) & 3 f/p col. plates, b/w drawings by Francis Hiley, dec. bd., with col. onlay, 222x170mm. VMOU
Contents include: 'The Discovery of New South Wales' 15pp (from *Captain Cook's Voyages*); 'Two-Handed Dick' by Samuel Sidney 13pp (from *Gallops and Gossips in the Bush*).

7186 ON THE TRAIL/Edited by Herbert Strang/ [drawing]/London—Humphrey Milford/Oxford University Press
1922
[98]pp, col. frontis. & 1 f/p col. illus., b/w text drawings by C. E. Brock, Lionel Edwards & others, pic. bd., 230x175mm. KMM
Short stories, etc., which include an anonymous article on William Dampier entitled 'The First Englishman in Australia' (12pp).

7187 Herbert Strang's Library/GATEWAY TO/ ADVENTURE/Stories for Boys/Edited by/Herbert Strang/[publisher's device]/Oxford University Press/ London New York Toronto
1939
256pp (inc. 1p prefatory note), col. frontis. & b/w chapter headings, clo., 180x115mm. KMM
Contents include Philip Lindsay's 'Black and White' (10pp), a story about Queensland black trackers, & Humphrey Jordan's 'A Square Deal' (22pp), a story about South Australian station life.

Strange Peoples of the World

7188 STRANGE PEOPLES/OF THE WORLD/Vita-Brits Album
n.p., n.d.
[14]pp (inc. inside covers), b/w map of world & drawings in text, spaces for 36 col. cards to be pasted in, col. pic. wrappers, cover title, 210x270mm. KMM
Illus. signed J. Mason. 2pp describing native inhabitants of Australia & SW Pacific.

Strange Tales of Peril and Adventure

7189 STRANGE TALES/OF/PERIL AND ADVENTURE/[vignette]/London/The Religious Tract Society/56 Paternoster Row, 65 St. Paul's Churchyard/ and 164 Piccadilly
n.d. [school prize 1891]
384pp (inc. 1p prefatory note), engraved frontis. & 6 f/p engravings, engraved head & tailpieces to each chapter, dec. clo., 180x120mm. CLRC
Prefatory note states: 'This is the second volume of the series of books issued by the Committee of the Religious Tract Society to take the place of the old "Leisure Hour Library..."

7190 STRANGE TALES OF PERIL/AND ADVENTURE/ [drawing]/With Twenty-three full-page Illustrations/ London/The Religious Tract Society/4 Bouverie Street and 65 St. Paul's Churchyard
n.d. [1900]
332pp, b/w frontis. & 22 f/p b/w illus., pic. clo., 200x130mm. KMM
Contains one chapter (18pp) 'Early Australian Explorers'.

7191 STRANGE TALES/OF/PERIL AND ADVENTURE/With Coloured and other Illustrations/ London/The Religious Tract Society/4 Bouverie Street & 65 St. Paul's Churchyard
n.d.
332pp, dec. col. t.p., col. frontis. & 9 f/p b/w illus., pic. clo., 195x130mm. RM

7192 STRANGE TALES/OF/PERIL & ADVENTURE/ London/The Religious Tract Society/4 Bouverie Street and 65 St Paul's Churchyard EC4

332pp, b/w frontis. & 7 f/p b/w plates, pic. clo., 195x134mm. CLRC

STREDDER, Eleanor

7193 ARCHIE'S FIND/A Story of Australian Life/By/Eleanor Stredder/Author of "Jack and his Ostrich"/&c. &c./[quotation]/Thomas Nelson and Sons/London Edinburgh and New York/1890
160pp, additional engraved t.p., unillus., pic. clo., 180x115mm. NSL:M

7194 ARCHIE'S FIND/A Story of Australian Life/By/Eleanor Stredder/Author of "Jack and his Ostrich"/&c. &c./[quotation]/Thomas Nelson and Sons/London Edinburgh and New York/1895
160pp, b/w frontis., additional engraved t.p., pic. clo., dec. e/p, 180x120mm. RM
• Rpt as above, 1900. KMM

'STRETTON, Hesba'

See [Smith, Sarah]

STRONELL, Lynne

7195 EXPLORING/THE WORLD/Edited by/Lynne Stronell/Contents [18 lines]/Purnell/Copyright MCMLXVI Purnell and Sons Ltd./Printed in Great Britain by Purnell and Sons, Ltd., Paulton (Somerset) and London/Library of Congress Catalog Number 66–23307/Distributed in USA by Ginn and Co., Boston
77pp, col. illus. on every page of text, bd., pic. e/p, 275x215mm. ANL
AUSTRALIAN PLANES. *See* Golden Stamp Books
AUSTRALIAN SHIPS. *See* Golden Stamp Books
AUSTRALIAN CARS. *See* Golden Stamp Books

STRONG, Charles S.

7196 WE WERE THERE/WITH/BYRD/AT THE SOUTH POLE/By Charles S. Strong/Historical Consultant/Colonel Bernt Balchen/Illustrated by/Graham Kaye/Published by/Grossett & Dunlap/New York
1956
176pp, b/w frontis. & 13 f/p b/w illus., b/w drawings in text, dec. clo., dec. map e/p, 230x150mm. NSL:M

7197 THE REAL BOOK ABOUT/THE ANTARCTIC/by Charles Strong/Illustrated by Albert Orbaan/[drawing]/Garden City Books/Garden City, New York
1959
216pp (inc. 13pp index), b/w frontis., 12 f/p & numerous other b/w illus., clo., pic. e/p with map, 210x138mm. KMM

STUART, Donald

7198 ILBARANA/Donald Stuart/J. M. Dent & Sons Limited London
1972
111pp & 4pp glossary, b/w drawings throughout, bd., 185x120mm. KP

STUART, Esmé

7199 NIECEN/FRA AUSTRALIEN/af/Esmé Stuart/ved/Ingeborg Vollquartz/[device]/Forlagt af H. Aschehoug & Co./København MCMXXII
191pp, unillus., clo., 188x123mm. ANL

STUART, Isla

See YOU CAN DRAW A KANGAROO

SUBRT, Josef

7200 VLAJKY NAD SVETEM. Asie, Australie (Flags over the World—Asia, Australia)
Vol. 1: Prague 1962; Vol. 2: Prague 1965. Unseen: SLCSR
Slovak edition

7201 Vol. 1: Bratislava 1965; Vol. 2: Bratislava 1966. Unseen: SLCSR

SULEAU, V. J.

7202 LE ROI DES KOALAS/By/V. J. Suleau, B.ès. L./Assistant Master, North Sydney Boys' High School/Australia/Angus & Robertson Limited/89 Castlereagh Street, Sydney/1932
99pp (inc. 8pp notes & 1p vocabulary), 2pp adv., 6 b/w illus. by Edgar A. Holloway, wrappers, 185x120mm. KMM
School text.

SULLIVAN, Pat

7203 Pat Sullivan's/FELIX/The Cat no. 20/12c
Page Pubs Pty Ltd, Surry Hills, NSW
24pp, b/w illus. throughout, col. pic. wrappers, 250x175mm. KP

7204 KOKEY/KOALA/and his Magic Button/in/Hypnotic-Isle/No 35
Felix the Cat Enterprises, Sydney, n.d.
24pp, b/w comic-strip illus., pic. wrappers, 197x270mm. KMM

7205 FELIX/THE CAT/STAR-BUSTER No. 45
Copyright Felix the Cat Enterprises, Sydney, n.d.
46pp, b/w comic-strip illus., pic. wrappers, 200x279mm. KP
The author was Australian by birth but the many books were produced by commercial studios & come outside the scope of this bibliography. Still some uncertainty & controversy about Pat Sullivan's actual role in the creation of Felix the Cat although his name does appear on the t.p. of numerous English, American & foreign 'Felix' publications.

SULLIVAN, Walter

7206 THE POLAR REGIONS/The Geography, Climate, and Life/of the Arctic and Antarctic,/And the Explorers and Scientists/who discovered them/[3 colour photographs]/by Walter Sullivan/illustrated with photographs/drawings by Ray Pioch/Golden Press New York
1962
54pp (inc. 1p index), extended t.p., col. & b/w photographs throughout, pic. bd., 230x160mm. NSL:M

SULMAN, Florence

7207 FLORENCE SULMAN PAINTING BOOK/Compiled from the Popular Guides to/The Wild Flowers of New South Wales/By/Florence Sulman/28 outline drawings/by/Eirene Mort/Australia/Angus & Robertson Ltd./89 Castlereagh Street, Sydney/1932
32pp, b/w outlines of plants & descriptive text, pic. wrappers, 180x245mm. MAC

Sunken Gold

7208 SUNKEN GOLD/and other stories of/Adventure and school/life/London/The Epworth Press/25–35 City Road, E.C.1
1932
192pp, col. frontis., 1 col. plate & 4 b/w plates, pic. bd., 206x138mm. CLRC
Title story only (pp5–103) of Australian interest.

Sunlight Australian ABC

7209 One shilling/SUNLIGHT/AUSTRALIAN/A.B.C./[illus. of packet Sunlight Soap]
Lever Brothers Limited, Sydney, n.d. [192-?]
32pp, col. illus. throughout, pic. wrappers, cover title, 186x126mm. KMM
An ABC of Australian animals & birds.
Acknowledgements to W. W. Froggatt, Leach, Gillies, Hall, Lucas & Le Soeuf & the Sydney Museum. Adv. brochure; illus. A. H. Moginie.

An adv. in *The Children's Newspaper*, Sydney, 1900, by Lever Brothers Limited lists various books and pictures available free in exchange for wrappers of their various soap products. The above ABC is not listed.

Sunlight Painting Book of Animals
7210 SUNLIGHT PAINTING BOOK/OF ANIMALS/ Lever/Lever Brothers Limited/Sydney
1924
30pp (inc. inside cover), 13 f/p col. illus. of animals with outline to col., col. pic. wrappers with col. adv. on back cover, cover title, 184x124mm. MAC
Details of Sunlight Competition inside front cover; illus. A. H. Moginie.

Sunny South Series
SUNNY SOUTH SERIES/Printed and Published by/ John Sands Ltd. Sydney/[device]/Gordon and Gotch (Australasia) Ltd./Sole Distributors
4 untitled shaped booklets in series, n.d. [copyright 1931]
7211 1. With Kangaroos on cover, 8pp, verses with part-col. illus. on each page; verses signed 'T.A.W.'
7212 2. With Rosella on cover, as above.
7213 3. With Kookaburras on cover, as above, but not signed.
7214 4. With Koalas on cover, as above, but not signed.
Each booklet bound in stiff dec. wrappers, 290x120mm. NSL:M

The Sunshine Book
7215 THE/SUNSHINE/BOOK/[drawing]/with pictures to Color/No. 67 An Australian Production by/Gunn & Taylor Pty Ltd Melbourne/Distributors for N.S.W. and Queensland, Hamson & Leonard 101 York Street Sydney
n.d.
16pp, 2 f/p b/w illus. & b/w illus. in text, col. pic. wrappers, 268x210mm. KMM

A Surprise for Shirley
See Joy series

SURREY, George S.
7216 ADRIFT IN THE/SOUTH SEAS/by/George S. Surrey/Illustrated by John De Walton/[device]/ Humphrey Milford/Oxford University Press/London Edinburgh Glasgow New York/Toronto Melbourne Bombay Cape Town
1923
319pp, col. frontis. & 4 f/p b/w illus., pic. clo., 190x125mm. KP
Setting for part of the story is North Queensland.
7217 ADRIFT IN THE/SOUTH SEAS/by/George S. Surrey/[device]/Oxford University Press/London: Humphrey Milford
• Rpt 1940
319pp, col. frontis. only, clo., 190x125mm. KMM
• Rpt 1940, as above, but b/w frontis. only. KP

SURREY, Lionel
7218 LOST IN THE PACIFIC/by/Lionel Surrey/ Illustrated by/Ellis Silas/George G. Harrap & Co. Ltd./ London Toronto Bombay Sydney
First published July 1934; rpt Sept. 1937
255pp, col. frontis., 4 f/p b/w drawings, b/w sketch map in text, clo., 195x135mm. Grant

7219 POLAR PERIL/Lionel Surrey/[drawing]/Illustrated by A. S. Forrest/Thomas Nelson and Sons Ltd./ London Edinburgh Paris Melbourne/Toronto and New York
n.d. [1939]
285pp, 1p foreword, col. frontis., b/w map of Antarctica, 28 b/w drawings in text etc., clo., 185x120mm. KMM
The *Queen of Antarctica* sails from Hobart with the Captain's 15-year-old son & two of his friends on board.
• Rpt [1954] 'New Era' series, as above, 188x125mm. KP

SUTHERLAND, George
7220 SIXTEEN STORIES/OF/AUSTRALIAN EXPLORATION/AND SETTLEMENT/By/George Sutherland, M.A./Price Sixpence/Sixth Edition/ Publishers James Ingram & Son/227 Little Collins Street, Melbourne
[inscribed 24/7/08]
68pp, col. frontis., 1 f/p b/w map, 3 f/p & several small b/w illus., limp clo., 180x124mm. KP
7221 SIXTEEN STORIES/OF/AUSTRALIAN EXPLORATION/AND SETTLEMENT/by/George Sutherland, M.A./Price/Sixpence/Seventh Edition./ Publishers:/James Ingram & Son/227 Little Collins Street, Melbourne
n.d. [1901?]
68pp, col. frontis., b/w map & 6 b/w photographic illus., wrappers, 180x120mm. Grant
The photographs depict Their Royal Highnesses the Prince and Princess of Wales, & the last story is entitled 'The Travels of a Prince. Australia 1901'.

7222 EASY STORIES/FOR AUSTRALIAN CHILDREN/ A Junior Reader of Australian History/Correlated with Geography/by George Sutherland, M.A./[device]/ Publishers/James Ingram and Son/227 Little Collins Street, Melbourne
n.d.
99pp (inc. 1p preface, 5pp index), b/w photographic frontis. & 12 b/w photographic illus., 3 b/w maps, wrappers, 180x120mm. Grant
7223 EASY STORIES/FOR/AUSTRALIAN CHILDREN/ A Junior Reader of Australian History/Correlated with Geography/By George Sutherland, M.A./Wholly set up and printed by the/publishers/Spicers & Detmold Ltd./377–381 Lonsdale St., Melbourne/ 1927/Registered by the Postmaster General for/ transmission through the Post as a Book
99pp (inc. 1p preface, 5pp index), b/w photographic frontis. & 12 b/w photographic illus., 2 b/w maps, wrappers, 180x120mm. Grant

SUTHERLAND, Wendy
CAROLINE CHISHOLM. *See* Great Australians

SUTTON, Ann & Myron
7224 THE/ENDLESS/QUEST/The Life of John Franklin/Explorer/By/Ann and Myron Sutton/ Illustrated with photographs/and maps/Constable Young Books Ltd. London
Published in USA by Rand McNally & Co. under title *Journey into Ice* copyright 1965; first English edition 1966
London published by Constable Young Books Ltd.; Australia & NZ T.C. Lothian Pty. Ltd.
244pp (inc. 2pp introduction, 10pp index & 1p bibliography), 55 b/w illus., 6 b/w maps, clo., 215x135m. KMM

SUTTON, George
7225 MR/MUGGLEY/WUMP/Written by George Sutton/Illustrated by Bryan Membrey
Printed & publ. by Storytime Publications, 333 City Rd, South Melbourne, n.d.
12pp, b/w drawings throughout, stiff pic. wrappers, 162x114mm. KP

7226 MR./MUGGLEYWUMP/And stories about his friends/a book for/Mothers and Fathers/and/Uncles and Aunts/to read aloud/to children/or/for the bigger children/to read themselves/Dedicated to Damian/All Copyright reserved 1969
Coolibah Publishers
20pp, b/w & part-col. illus. by Bryan Membrey, stiff pic. wrappers, 280x205mm. ANL
Verses with 4 sheets of drawings to be coloured.

SUTTON, Mrs Margaret

7227 A/SHEPHERD BOY/OF AUSTRALIA/By/ Margaret Sutton/Photographic Illustrations/Grossett & Dunlap/Publishers New York
1941
191pp, b/w photographic frontis. & b/w photographic illus. throughout, pic. bd., map e/p, 215x160mm. ANL
Story of a young American girl accompanying her father who comes to Australia to take over a sheep station.

SWENSON, Eric

7228 THE SOUTH SEA/SHILLING/Voyages of Captain Cook, R.N./by Eric Swenson/[drawing]/Illustrated by Charles Michael Daugherty/New York—The Viking Press MCMLII
224pp (inc. 6pp index), 7 f/p b/w illus., line drawings in text, double-spread b/w map, clo., dec. map e/p, 235x150mm. ANL

7229 THE SOUTH SEA/SHILLING/Voyages of Captain Cook, R.N./by Eric Swenson/[drawing]/Illustrated by Charles Michael Daugherty/Angus and Robertson
224pp (inc. 6pp index), 7 f/p b/w illus., line drawings in text, double-spread b/w map, clo., dec. map e/p, 235x150mm. KMM

SWINBURNE, Mrs George [Ethel, née Hamer]

7230 BUZZIWIG/By Mrs. George Swinburne/with illustrations by Elma H. Kilgour
Lothian Publishing Co., Melbourne, 1931
79pp, 13pp b/w illus. printed on one side of paper only, b/w illus. throughout, wrappers, cover title, 135x205mm. ANL

SYLVESTER, David W.

7231 Then and there series/General Editor/Marjorie Reeves, M.A., Ph.D./CAPTAIN COOK/AND THE PACIFIC/David W. Sylvester/Illustrated from contemporary sources/[device]/Longman
London 1971
92pp (inc. 3pp glossary, 1p 'Things to do'), 1p author's note, b/w illus. in text, stiff pic. wrappers, 195x130mm. ANL
A background book for schools but of some general interest.

'SYLVANUS' [pseud. L. G. Irby]

7232 ALAN DALE/By/Sylvanus/Illustrated by George Soper/[coloured vignette]/R.T.S., 4 Bouverie Street, London, E.C.4
n.d. [1921]
309pp, 10pp adv., unillus., clo. (copy seen re-bound), 195x130mm. TSL
The story of a child convict transported to Point Puer (Van Diemen's Land). A review, reprinted from *The World*, 3 January 1921, is attached to this copy. The author's name is given as L. G. Irby.

SYME, N. R. [Ronald]

7233 THAT MUST/BE JULIAN/By N. R. Syme/with illustrations/by William Stobbs/Peter Lunn/London
1947
205pp, 1p dedication, b/w frontis. & 5 f/p b/w illus., b/w drawing in text, clo:, 180x120mm. MK
An earlier book about the same characters as *Julian's River War.*
Swedish edition

7233a DET MÅSTE VARA PETER/Av N. R. Syme/ Rabén & Sjögrem
Stockholm 1951
181pp, b/w illus. in text, pic. bd., 192x124mm. ANL
Trans. by Stina Hergin.

7234 JULIAN'S RIVER WAR/by/Ronald Syme/Author of "That must be Julian"/Illustrated by/John Harris/ William Heinemann Ltd./Melbourne London Toronto
1949
182pp, b/w frontis. & 5 b/w illus., clo., 185x120mm. ANL
The story of an inventive boy living on a farm near Melbourne.

7235 BEN OF THE/BARRIER/by/N. R. Syme/ Illustrations by/J. Nicholson/Evans Brothers Limited. London
1949
208pp & 1p author's note, b/w frontis. 4 b/w drawings in text, clo., 184x120mm. KMM
Story set in area around Thursday Island.

7236 THE/BUCCANEER/EXPLORER/by/Ronald Syme/Illustrated by/William Stobbs/Hodder & Stoughton
London, n.d. [1960]
126pp, dec. half t.p., b/w frontis. & 6 f/p b/w illus., clo., map e/p, 180x115mm. HBM
Fictional biography of William Dampier.

7237 CAPTAIN COOK/Pacific Explorer/[drawing of Cook]/By Ronald Syme/Illustrated by William Stobbs/ William Morrow and Company/New York
1960
96pp, 31 b/w illus. & 1 b/w extended map, clo., 215x155mm. ANL

7238 ICE FIGHTER/Ronald Syme/[drawing]/Illustrated by William Stobbs/Hodder and Stoughton
London 1956
159pp, b/w drawings in text, clo., 185x120mm. CLRC
The life of Sir John Franklin.

SYMONS, C. T.

7239 A/BABY IS BORN/The story of/How a baby begins to live/and is born/Told to Children Eight to Fourteen Years/By/C. T. Symon
Adelaide, n.d.
vipp, 38pp (last 3pp blank), b/w photographic frontis. & 8 photographic illus. & diagrams, wrappers, 178x120mm. SSL

7240 SPLIT SECONDS/COUNT!/A Book for Boys and Girls about/the Dangers of Alcohol in Drinks/By/Rev. C. T. Symons, M.A., B.D./Director, Methodist Young People's Department/in South Australia/Published by the/Joint Board of Graded Lessons of Australia/and New Zealand,/147 Collins Street, Melbourne
n.d. [195-?]
32pp, b/w drawings, stiff pic. wrappers, 153x102mm. SSL

SYNGE, M. B.

7241 COOK'S VOYAGES/With Introduction and Notes/ By/M. B. Synge/London/Percival & Co./1892
xpp & 106pp & 4pp adv. & adv. inside front e/p & on fly, 2 b/w maps, limp clo., 172x116mm. BL
5pp Life of Cook by editor precedes text & 6pp notes follow text (inc. in pagination)
One of a series 'English Classics for Schools'.

SYRED, Celia M.
7242 COCKY'S/CASTLE/[drawing]/Celia/M. Syred/ Illustrated by Astra Lacis Dick/Angus and Robertson Sydney 1966
192pp, b/w drawings in text, clo., 215x140mm. BBC
• Rpt 1967 (twice). KP

7243 BAKER'S DOZEN/[drawing]/Celia M./Syred/ Illustrated by Astra Lacis Dick/Angus and Robertson Sydney 1969
138pp, b/w drawings in text, clo., 215x135mm. CLRC
AN INNKEEPER
A PRINTER. *See* Early Australians

T., O.F.
See Timins, O. F.

'TAGG, Teresa'
See Burke, Alfred

'TAGG, Timothy'
See Burke, Alfred

TAINSH, Douglas
COLE'S NOISY PICTURE BOOK. *See* Cole, E. W.

TAKUMA, J.
7244 KOOKABURRA/(The Laughing Jackass)/AND THE BLACK SNAKE./By J. Takuma./Geo. Robertson & Co., Publishers,/Melbourne, Sydney, Brisbane, Adelaide,/ London
n.d. [inscribed 'Xmas '97']
19pp, 4 part. col. illus. (text printed throughout in green ink), pic. wrappers, oval-shaped booklet, 95x140mm. NSL:M
Jonaski Takuma, a Japanese artist living in Sydney, carved emu eggs & drew designs for postcards.

TALBOT, Ethel
7245 THAT WILD AUSTRALIAN/SCHOOL-GIRL/By/ Ethel Talbot/Author of "Peggy's Last Term", "Betty at St. Benedict's"/"The Luck of the School", "The School on the Moor"/etc. etc./With four full page illustrations/By/G. P. Micklewright/Robert South, Ltd./London E.C.
n.d. [1925]
279pp, b/w frontis., 3 b/w plates, clo., 190x130mm. KMM

7246 THAT WILD AUSTRALIAN/SCHOOL-GIRL/By/ Ethel Talbot/Author of "Peggy's Last Term", "Betty at St. Benedict's"/"The Luck of the School", "The School on the Moor"/etc. etc./With four full page illustrations/by G. P. Micklewright/Robert South, Ltd.,/61/2, Chancery Lane, London, W.C.2
n.d. [192-?]
318pp, b/w frontis., 3 b/w plates, clo., 200x130mm. KMM
Another copy with variant binding of dark green clo. with 'Robert South Ltd' blocked in orange on front cover. KP

7247 JEAN'S/TWO SCHOOLS/by/Ethel Talbot/ [drawing with caption]/Illustrated by E. Brier/T. Nelson & Sons Ltd./London, Edinburgh, New York, Toronto and Paris.
n.d. [first pub. 1930]
324pp, col. frontis., 27 b/w illus. in text, clo., 185x130mm. JMcG
Girls' school story set partly in Sydney

Tales of Fairy Folk
7248 TALES/OF FAIRY/FOLK
No imprint, n.d. [copyright 1945]
12pp, 4 f/p col. illus., b/w drawings throughout signed 'Guerin', pic. bd., cover title, 235x175mm. NSL:M
Contents include 2 verses as well as stories.

Tales of the Flying Fox
7249 The Lansdowne Readers/TALES OF THE/FLYING FOX/Grade Two/Book 1
Melbourne 1960
32pp (inc. 1p glossary), part. col. drawings throughout, illus. by Marjorie Howden, stiff printed wrappers, cover title, 200x130mm. KMM
Two Australian children's stories intended as school text.
Book two, uniform with above. KP

Tales of the Outback
7250 TALES OF THE /OUTBACK/A/Supplementary Reader/for/Upper Primary/Classes/[drawing]
A Western Australian Education Department Publication
n.d. [1960?] Perth
62pp, b/w drawings, dec. wrappers, 240x150mm. KP

Tales of Magic and Might
7251 TALES OF/MAGIC AND MIGHT/Edited for Victorian Schools/Illustrations by Percy Leason/E. W. Cole/Book Arcade, Melbourne/Sydney and Adelaide
n.d. [192-?]
95pp, b/w frontis & 4 f.p. b/w ills., wrappers 180x115mm. NSL:M
Contents not Australian.

The Talking Fish
7252 THE TALKING/FISH
n.p., n.d. [194-?]
61pp, b/w illus. (sgd A. Osborne), stiff pic. wrappers, 350x235mm. KP

[TANDY, Sophia]
7253 THE/CHILDREN IN THE SCRUB./A Story of Tasmania/By the author of/"Bertie's Birthday Present", etc./[vignette]/London:/The Religious Tract Society,/56 Paternoster Row; 65, St Paul's Churchyard,/and 164, Piccadilly.
n.d. [1878]
157pp & 18pp adv., engraved frontis., 3 f/p engravings & others in text, dec. clo., 180x124mm. KMM
Said to be based on the Duff children lost in Western Victoria.

TANNER, June
7254 [illustration]/LET'S MAKE A MOSAIC/June Tanner/Angus and Robertson
Sydney 1968
54pp., extended t.p., b/w & col. photographic illus., bd., 220x180mm. KP

7255 MAKING/MOSAICS/June Tanner
Rigby Ltd, Adelaide 1969 (Rigby Instant Library)
64pp., b/w photographic illus., pic. bd., 215x145mm. KP
First pub. in Rigby Instant Books 1969; published in the Instant Library series in 1971.

TAPLIN, Beth
7256 THE CAROUSEL HORSE/by Beth Taplin
Published for The Yooralla Hospital School for Crippled Children; printed by Osboldstone & Co. Pty Ltd, Richmond, Victoria, 1969
[19]pp, line drawings throughout, bd., 190x150mm. KMM
• Rpt 1970, as above. KP

7257 BIRD OF PARADISE/by Beth Taplin
Osboldstone & Co. Pty Ltd, Richmond, Victoria, 1970
20pp (last blank) 9 f/p illus., dec. bd., 190x150mm. KMM

7258 THE BRIDGE/by Beth Taplin
As above, but 18pp, 8 illus. KMM

7259 MAKE A WISH/by Beth Taplin
As above, but 20pp, 9 illus. KMM

7260 THE SONGMAN/by Beth Taplin
As above, but 18pp, 7 illus. KMM

TAPSELL, Florence A.
7261 LITTLE /PEOPLE/IN FAR-OFF/LANDS
OUR ISLAND COUSINS/(Australia New Zealand and Ceylon)/by/Florence A. Tapsell/E.J.Arnold & Son Ltd/Educational Publishers/Leeds/Glasgow and Belfast
n.d. [1914] second edition
32pp, b/w illus., wrappers, 185x135mm. Grant
(Intended for use in upper classes of Infant Schools and in lower classes of Junior Schools)

'TASMAN'
7262 A LITTLE AVERSION/By/Tasman/With coloured illustrations by J. A. Symington/London/The Religious Tract Society/4 Bouverie Street and 65 St. Paul's Churchyard E.C.
n.d. [1910]
256pp (inc. 2pp preface), col. frontis., col. dec. t.p., 2 f/p col. illus., pic. clo., 195x130mm. NSL:M
Another copy as above but 16 pp adv. and no 'E.C.' after 'St Paul's Churchyard'. KMM

TATE, J. E.
CONVICTS. 1970;
BOOM AND DEPRESSION. 1971. Discovering Australian History series. *See* Gilbert, P. F.

TAVON, O. W.
NO. 12 THE WILD RIDERS OF TEXAS. *See* Australian Boys' Adventure Library series

TAYLOR, Bronnie
7263 Imperial /edition no. 477/THE MAGIC BASKET/A Juvenile Operetta/(duration; about 45 minutes)/Words by/Bronnie Taylor/Music By/Alfred Wheeler/Musical Contents/[14 songs listed]/copyright 1940 price 2/6/Allan & Co. Pty Ltd/Melbourne Adelaide Bendigo
28pp, unillus, pic. wrappers (sgd 'J.E.'), 250 x 177mm. CLRC

7264 Imperial Edition No. 490/SONGS FOR YOUNG/AUSTRALIANS/Words by/Bronnie Taylor/Music by/Edith Harrhy/Index [list of contents of 12 songs]/Allan & Co. Pty. Ltd./Melbourne Adelaide Bendigo/Copyright MCMXLI
40pp, 12 b/w headpieces, wrappers (with col. illus. on front cover), 245x180mm. Grant
Illustrations signed 'I.R.O.' (Ida Rentoul Outhwaite).
Another copy as above, but n.d. and price 3/- on front cover. KP
Another copy as above, but n.d. & price 4/6, 45c on cover. KP

7265 Imperial Edition No. 521/THE PUDDIN' AND/THE PIXIE/12 songs for children/Words by/Bronnie Taylor/Music by/Ina Mornement/[12 song titles listed]/2/6/Allan & Co. Pty. Ltd./Melbourne Adelaide Bendigo/Copyright MCMXLIX by Allan & Co. Pty. Ltd. 276 Collins St., Melbourne/Printed in Australia
20pp, unillus., col. dec. wrappers (with adv. on outside back wrapper), cover design by Ida Rentoul Outhwaite, 245x175mm. KMM

7266 Imperial Edition No. 864/THE WALLABY MAIL/and Other Songs/Ten Songs for Children/Words by/Bronnie Taylor/Music by/Arthur S. Loam/[list of song titles]/Allans Music (Australia) Pty Ltd./Printed in Australia
[Melbourne] 1963
28pp, unillus., dec. wrappers (with adv. outside back cover), 245x180mm. Grant

TAYLOR, Geoff
7267 Geoff Taylor/BLUEBERG/Illustrated by/D. G. Valentine/[publisher's device]/Heinemann/London Melbourne Toronto
1960
93pp, b/w frontis. & b/w drawings throughout, clo., dec. e/p, 190x120mm. BBC
The story of an iceberg (as stated on an e/p: 'Blueberg—being the narrative of his adventure on a tropic shore with the whale Blowhard').

TAYLOR, Geoffrey H.
7268 AUSTRALIAN/ORES AND/MINERALS/By/Geoffrey H. Taylor M.Sc. (Adelaide) Dr. rer. nat. (Bonn)/Illustrated by/Peter Chapman/[3 colour illustrations]/Readabout Books
Readabout Publishers Pty Ltd, Crow's Nest, NSW, 1964
32pp, col. illus. & diagrams throughout, stiff pic. wrappers, 280x210mm. BBC

TAYLOR, Griffith
DOUGLAS MAWSON. *See* Great Australians

TAYLOR, Helen
7269 [music]/BLESS THIS HOUSE/Song/The Words by/Helen Taylor/The Music by/May H. Brahe/Price 2/6 net/Published also as an organ solo 1/6 net/Boosey & Co./Limited/[Addresses, London, Sydney &c.]
n.d.
6pp (back cover adv.), music & words, unillus., wrappers, 285x220mm. NSL:M

7270 A PAGEANT OF SUMMER/Song Cycle/for Four Voices/Lyrics by/Helen Taylor/Music by/May H. Brahe/[7 songs listed]/Copyright/MCMXXII/by Enoch & Sons. Price 4/6 net/London/Enoch & Sons/Enoch House,58 Great Marlborough Street,W.1/New York/Enoch & Sons [&c. Toronto & Paris]
48pp, unillus., music & words (? wrappers, copy seen re-bound), 303x235mm. NSL:M

7271 To my little daughter Marita/FROM THE NURSERY WINDOW/Six songs/The Lyrics by/Helen Taylor/The Music by/May H. Brahe/[silhouettes by L. Hummel]/Contents [6 song titles listed]/Copyright/MXMXXV/by Enoch & Sons Ltd Price 2/6 net/London/Enoch & Sons Ltd/Enoch House 58 Great Marlborough Street, W.1/Melbourne/Allan & Co./[3 lines addresses, &c.]
20pp, unillus., dec.wrappers (silhouette on front cover & at head of each song), adv. both sides back wrapper, 280 x 217mm. NSL:M

7272 THE PIPER FROM/OVER THE WAY/Song/The Lyric by/Helen Taylor/The Music by/May H. Brahe/price 3/- net/[device]/Allan & Co. Prop. Ltd./Melbourne Sydney Adelaide Bendigo/A.V Broadhurst/60 Berners Street, London W.1
n.d. [copyright 1933]
6pp, unillus., wrappers, 310x236mm. NSL:M
Doubtful children's.

TAYLOR, Jeannie
See Gunn, Jeannie, Mrs Aeneas

TAYLOR, Katherine [Kay, née Glasson, pseud. Daniel Hamline]
7273 GINGER FOR/PLUCK/By/Daniel Hamline/Australia:/Cornstalk Publishing Company/89 Castlereagh Street, Sydney/1929
245pp, unillus., clo., 185x120mm. NSL:M

7274 PICK AND THE/DUFFERS/By/Kay Glasson Taylor/Australia:/Angus & Robertson Limited/89 Castlereagh Street, Sydney/1930
274pp, 30pp adv., b/w photographic frontis. & 4pp b/w photographic illus., clo., 185x120mm. ANL

7275 BIM/By/Kay Glasson Taylor/Published by/Currawong Publishing Co. Pty. Ltd./3 Castlereagh Street, Sydney
First published in book form 1947 [published in 1946 as a serial in the *Sydney Morning Herald*]
204pp, unillus., clo., 185x115mm. ANL
The story of a girl on a Queensland cattle station.

TAYLOR, Richard
See Riley, Quintin & Taylor, Richard

TEAGUE, Violet
NIGHT FALL IN THE TI-TREE
Melbourne 1906
This handprinted book is a collection of woodcuts by the author and Geraldine Rede with slight text, and was not intended as a children's book.

TEALE, Ruth
THOMAS BRISBANE. *See* Great Australians

TEED (George) Hamilton, THE DIGGER TEC.
See The 'Boys' Friend Library'

THE CRIMSON BELT. *See* Sexton Blake in Australia
THE GREEN ROSE " " " " "

TELFER, Phyllis and GOODMAN, Hermea
7276 A POCKET FULL OF RHYMES/Verses for the very young/by/Phyllis Telfer & Hermea Goodman Horwitz-Martin Pty. Ltd., Sydney 1967
26pp (front cover inc. in pagination) some line drawings, stiffened pic. wrappers, 172x117mm. KMM

Temperance for Schools
7277 TEMPERANCE /FOR/SCHOOLS/Independent Order of Rechabites/Victorian District No. 82/Registered Office: 518 Elizabeth Street, Melbourne, Victoria
n.d. [pref. dated 1945]
48 pp (inc. p1 preface), unillus., limp clo., 185x120mm. KP

TEMPLE, Frances
7278 SHOPPING/IN/CREEPYVILLE/[drawing]/Verses by F. Temple/Illustrated by M. Corrigan/Georgian House/Melbourne
1946
25pp, dec. t.p., 11 f/p col. illus., b/w drawings, dec. bd. (clo. spine), dec. e/p, 240x180mm. ANL

TEMPLE, Ralph & Chandos
7279 THE/TEMPLE ANECDOTES./Enterprise and Adventure./by/Ralph and Chandos Temple./[quotation]/Illustrated/London/Groombridge and Sons,/Paternoster Row,/MDCCCLXV
442pp (inc. 4pp index), b/w frontis. & 13 f/p b/w illus., clo., 170x105mm. CLRC
Contents include: 'Adventurers Matthew Flinders and George Bass' (9pp); 'Major Mitchell and the Bushranger' (5pp); 'Sturt in Australia' (7.5pp); 'Strzelecki and his companions in the Bush' (4.5pp); 'Governor Grey's Explorations' (6pp); 'Grey's Second Journey' (6pp); 'An Adventure in the Bush' (4pp); 'The Martyrs of Australian Discovery' (8pp).

7280 ENTERPRISE AND ADVENTURE/A Collection/of/Interesting Anecdotes./By/Ralph and Chandos Temple./Illustrated/London:/Groombridge and Sons,/Paternoster Row
n.d. [1870]
256pp, b/w frontis. & 7 f/p b/w illus., pic. clo., 165x110mm. KMM
Contents include the first 6 items listed in *The Temple Anecdotes* & also 'The Voyage of the Astrolabe' (7pp).

TENNANT, Kylie [Mrs Lewis Charles Rodd]
7281 LONG JOHN SILVER/The Story of the Film adapted by/Kylie Tennant/from the Motion Picture Screenplay by/Martin Rackin/Associated General Publications/Sydney, Australia
1954
207pp, 4 f/p col. illus. & b/w illus. throughout (some photographic stills from film, & b/w drawings), clo., dec. e/p, 220x140mm. GI

7282 Modern Plays for Schools/15/THE BELLS OF THE CITY/and other Plays/By/Kylie Tennant/The Bells of the City/The Magic Fat Baby/The Prince who met a dragon/The Ghost tiger/Hamaguchi Goh ei/London/Macmillan and Co. Ltd./New York St. Martin's Press/1955
61pp, unillus., wrappers, 180x130mm. NSL:M

7283 Modern Plays for Schools/3/JOHN O'THE FOREST/and other Plays/by/Kylie Tennant/John o'the Forest/Lady Dorothy and the Pirates/The Willow Pattern Plate/The Laughing Girl/Christmas at the Old Shamrock Hotel/London/Macmillan and Co. Ltd./New York St. Martin's Press/1955
61pp, unillus., wrappers, 180x130mm. NSL:M

7284 THE BUSHRANGERS'/CHRISTMAS EVE/And Other Plays/By/Kylie Tennant/The Bushrangers' Christmas Eve/The Tribe of the Honey Tree/The Ladies of the Guard/A Nativity Play/The Play of the Younger Son/The Emperor and the Nightingale/Melbourne/Macmillan & Co. Ltd./New York—St. Martin's Press/1959
66pp, unillus., wrappers, 180x130mm. KMM
The first two plays only have an Australian setting.

7285 ALL THE/PROUD TRIBESMEN/By/Kylie Tennant/Illustrated by/Clem Seale/London/Macmillan & Co. Ltd./New York—St. Martin's Press/1959
159pp, b/w frontis., 5 f/p b/w illus. & map, b/w drawings in text, clo., 195x130mm. KMM
Tale of a Torres Strait Islander.
Winner CBCA award 1960.
Another copy as above, on verso of t.p.: First published 1959; rpt (twice) 1960
Details as before. CLRC
- Rpt as above 1960 (twice), 1964 (twice), rpt 1965 TG
- Rpt 1972, as above KP

7286 ALL THE/PROUD TRIBESMEN/By/Kylie Tennant/Illustrated by/Clem Seale/Melbourne/Macmillan & Co. Ltd.1961/(Head Office:London)
Special edition for Education Department, NSW 1961
159pp, b/w frontis. & b/w drawings throughout, limp clo., 162x120mm. KMM
Swedish edition
7287 DE ONDA MAKTERNAS Ö
Stockholm, Tidens, [1962]
166pp, illus., 20cm. Unseen: ANB 1963
7288 ALL THE PROUD/TRIBESMEN/Kylie Tennant/Illustrated by Clem Seale/A Piccolo Book/Pan Books Ltd./London
1971
128pp, b/w drawings throughout, pic. wrappers, 175x110mm. KMM

7289 TRAIL BLAZERS/OF THE AIR/by/Kylie Tennant/Macmillan/Melbourne London Toronto/St. Martin's Press/New York
1965
131pp (inc. 5pp notes, 3pp editor's note), 4pp foreword, part. col. frontis. & 5 f/p part. col. illus. (inc. maps), part. col. drawings & maps in text, illus. by Roderick Shaw, clo. (with illus. on front cover), dec. e/p, 220x135mm. BBC

TENNANT, Kylie, contributor

7290 OVER THE HORIZON/or/Round the World in Fifteen Stories/by/William Mayne Kylie Tennant/Grace Hogarth Conon Fraser/Terence de Vere White/Anne Sinclair Mehdevl/James McNamee Naomi Mitchison/Mark Oliver Ruskin Bond/Juliet Piggott Monica Stirling/Daphne Rooke Yrjö Kokko/Alexander Cordell/Illustrated by/Richard Kennedy/London/Victor Gollancz Ltd./1960
192pp, 15 b/w drawings, clo., 195x130mm. KMM
Includes 'Such a long way Home' by Kylie Tennant (13pp).
3rd imp. 1961. BBC

TESTRO, Ron

7291 AUSTRALIAN TRAINS AND/RAILWAYS/Ron Testro/Lansdowne Press
Melbourne 1972
39pp, b/w photographs throughout, and 8pp col. photographs, pic. bd., dec. e/p. 190x255mm. KP

THEEK, Peter

7292 TIMS FAHRT/INS LAND/DER KÄNGURUHS/Illustratioen von/Ernst Jazdzewski/Der Kinderbuchverlag Berlin
n.d. [1961?]
180pp, 2pp adv., b/w drawings throughout, dec. bd., 210x145mm. IMcG
English translation of title: 'Tim's Journey to the Land of the Kangaroos'
The author visited Australia in the late 1950s & met many Germans who had settled here.

THERRY, John Joseph

7293 HYMNS/FOR CHILDREN/&c. &c./By the Rev. J. J. Therry./Melbourne:/W. Clarke, Printer, Herald Office,/1846
8pp, unillus., wrappers, 380x260mm. NSL:M

THIELE, Colin

7294 THE SUN/ON THE STUBBLE/Colin Thiele/[device]/Rigby Limited/Adelaide
First published 1961
172pp, unillus., clo., 180x120mm. BBC
Humorous sketches of life in a German farming community in South Australia; not originally published as a children's book, but soon adopted by them.
• Rpt April 1962 as above, but limp clo. & also clo. KMM

7295 THE SUN/ON THE STUBBLE/Colin Thiele/[device]/Rigby Limited
Adelaide, 1st imp. 1961; 2nd imp. 1962; 3rd imp. 1963; 4th imp. 1963; 5th imp. 1964; 6th imp. 1965; 7th imp. 1966; 8th imp. 1967
172pp, 1p prologue, unillus., stiff pic. wrappers, 180x115mm. KMM
• Rpt as above 9th imp. 1969
• Rpt as above 10th imp. 1970. Both KP

7296 THE SUN/ON THE STUBBLE/Colin Thiele/[device]/Seal Books/Rigby
First printed 1961; 2nd imp. 1962; 3rd imp. 1963; 4th imp. 1963; 5th imp. 1964; 6th imp. 1965; 7th imp. 1966; 8th imp. 1967; 9th imp. 1969; first published in Seal Books, Adelaide 1972
172pp, 1p prologue, unillus., pic. wrappers, 180x115mm. CLRC

German edition

7297 Colin Thiele/SCHAFDIEBE/IN/DER/NACHT/Bubenjahre auf einer/australischen Farm/1964/Rascher Verlag/Zurich und Stuttgart
181pp, unillus., clo., 205x135mm. CLRC

7298 GLOOP/THE GLOOMY BUNYIP/by Colin Thiele/Illustrated by John Bailey [sic]/The Jacaranda Press
Brisbane 1962
[46]pp, col. & part-col. illus. throughout, pic. clo., 245x185mm. KMM
Humorous story told in verse. KMM

7299 GLOOP THE/BUNYIP/Colin Thiele/[drawing]/illustrated by/Helen Sallis
Rigby Limited, Adelaide 1970
[64]pp, part. col. illus. throughout, pic. clo., 250x185mm. KMM
The first part of this book was published under the title *Gloop the Gloomy Bunyip* in 1962, & is included in this book in a revised form. The second part, concerning 'Gloop the Happy Bunyip', had not been previously published.

7300 STORM BOY/Colin Thiele/Illustrated by John Baily/[drawing]/Rigby Limited
Adelaide 1963
51pp, part-col. frontis. & part-col. drawings throughout, clo., 215x135mm. KMM
Story of a boy & his pelican, set near the Murray mouth, Goolwa, South Australia.
• Rpt 1966, as above. KP

UK edition

7301 Angus & Robertson (U.K:) Ltd, London 1964 [Rigby Ltd state that Angus & Robertson 'purchased folded and collated sets from us with their own imprint'].
Unseen: Information from Rigby Ltd

US editions

7302 STORM BOY/by Colin Thiele/Illustrated by/John Baily/Rand McNally & Company/Chicago New York San Francisco
1966
62pp, line drawings throughout, clo., 210x145mm. KW

7303 STORM/BOY/By Colin Thiele/Illustrated by/John Baily/[drawing]/Rand McNally & Company
Illinois, USA, 1966; rpt 1967
62pp, part-col. t.p., part-col. illus. throughout, clo., 200x136mm. KMM
This edition has a different d/w from Australian edition, with design by Lorence Bjorklund.

Afrikaans edition

7304 Colin Thiele/STORMSEUN/[drawing]/Human & Rousseau/Kaapstad en Pretoria 1965
56pp, b/w frontis. & b/w drawings in text, illus. by John Baily, clo., 210x135mm. KMM

7305 STORM BOY/Colin Thiele/Illustrated by John Baily/Rigby Limited
First published Adelaide 1963; rpt 1966, 1969, 1971, 1972
51pp, part-col. frontis. & part-col. drawings throughout, clo. (with d/w design of col. photograph), 210x130mm. BBC

7306 STORM BOY/Colin Thiele/Illustrated by John Baily/[drawing]/Rigby Limited
Adelaide 1970
51pp, b/w frontis. & b/w illus. throughout, pic. wrappers, 180x110mm. Seal Books. KMM

7307 FEBRUARY DRAGON/Colin Thiele/[device]/Rigby Limited/Adelaide
1965
174pp, unillus., clo. (with d/w photograph printed in white on black clo. binding), 190x125mm. KMM

7308 FEBRUARY DRAGON/Colin Thiele/[device]/Rigby Limited Adelaide
1966
Details as in first edition. BBC

US edition

7309 FEBRUARY/DRAGON/by Colin Thiele/Harper & Row, Publishers/New York, Hagerstown, San Francisco, London
n.d.
162pp, unillus., pic. sim. clo., 202x134mm. LRA

7310 FEBRUARY DRAGON/Colin Thiele/[device]/Rigby Limited
First published Adelaide 1966 [*sic*], rpt 1967; published in Seal Books 1970
174pp, unillus., pic. wrappers, 180x115mm. Seal Pups Edition. KMM
• Rpt 1971. KMM

7311 FEBRUARY DRAGON/Colin Thiele/[device]/Rigby Limited
First published Adelaide 1965, rpt 1966; school edition 1967
174pp, unillus., limp pic. clo., 180x120mm. KMM

7312 FEBRUARY DRAGON, published in Seal Books, as above, 1970, pic. wrappers, 180x115mm. CLRC

7313 MRS. MUNCH/AND/PUFFING BILLY/Colin Thiele/Illustrated by Nyorie Bungey/[device]/Rigby Ltd./[drawing]
Adelaide, 1967
32pp, part-col. illus. throughout, pic. clo., 235x180mm. KMM

7314 MRS. MUNCH AND/PUFFING BILLY/Colin Thiele/Illustrated by/Nyorie Bungey/Seal Books/Rigby Ltd
Adelaide 1970
32pp, part-col. drawings throughout, pic. wrappers, 195x150mm. KMM

7315 Colin Thiele/THE RIM OF THE MORNING/Six Stories/[quotation]/[device]/Rigby Limited
First published Adelaide 1966
178pp, unillus., bd., 180x120mm. CLRC
Contains six stories.
• Rpt as above 1967. KMM
• Rpt as above 1969 (twice). KP

7316 Colin/Thiele/BLUE FIN/[drawing]/Illustrated by/Roger Haldane/Rigby Limited
Adelaide 1969
188pp, b/w drawings thoughout, clo., 210x130mm. KMM

7317 Colin/Thiele/BLUE FIN/[drawing]/Illustrated by/Roger Haldane/[device]/Seal Books/Rigby Limited
First published Adelaide 1969, rpt 1970 (twice), 1971; published in Seal Books 1971
188pp, b/w illus. in text, col. photograph on front wrapper, 180x115mm. KMM

7318 YELLOW/JACKET/JOCK/Story by Colin Thiele/Illustrations by Clifton Pugh/F. W. Cheshire Melbourne Canberra Sydney
1969
[38]pp, 9 double-spread col. illus., t.p. printed in yellow, clo., dec. e/p, 275x210mm. KMM

7319 FLASH FLOOD/Colin Thiele/[drawing]/Illustrated by Jean Elder/Rigby
Adelaide 1970
32pp, part-col. drawings throughout, clo., 250x185mm. KMM

7320 FLIP-FLOP/AND THE TIGER SNAKE/Colin Thiele/[drawing]/illustrated by/Jean Elder/Rigby
Adelaide 1970
[32]pp, part-col. illus. throughout, pic. clo., 250x135mm. KMM

THIELE, Colin & MUDIE, Ian (eds.)

7321 AUSTRALIAN POETS/SPEAK/Edited by/Colin Thiele/Ian Mudie/[device]/Rigby Limited/Adelaide
first publ. Sept.1961; 2nd imp. Dec 1961
xii, 165pp, & 1p index, unillus., limp clo., 182x120 mm. CLRC

THIELE, Colin and BRANSON, Greg (eds)

7322 PLAYS/FOR/YOUNG/PLAYERS/Colin Thiele/and/Greg Branson/Illustrated by/Helen Newell/Rigby Limited
Adelaide 1970
96pp, 4 f/p. b/w illus., stiffened wrappers, 212x135 mm. CLRC
See also HOWARD & LEVY, Australian Story Sampler

Things I See

7323 THINGS I SEE/Playjoy Books
Published by Waterman Company Pty Ltd., Sydney
1968
12pp col. photographic illus., cover title, wrappers, 177x177 mm. CLRC
Col. photographs of simple objects for young children; no captions.
Books 2, 3 & 4, uniform with above. CLRC

This Australia Series

series of social studies for Primary School children.
Format example:

7324 This Australia Series/THE FRUIT INDUSTRY/by A. McLaughlin, B.A., E.Ed./A D. L. Marks Publication/Distributed by A. R. Pittock & Co./57 Elizabeth Stteet, Melbourne/Phone 62.1807 [part-col. photograph]
n.d. [1967]
16 pp, b/w diagrams, pic. wrappers, 174x162 mm. KP
Titles include: Iron and Steel; Sugar; Beef Cattle; Wheat; Rice; Brown Coal and Electricity; The Aborigines; The Murray River; Gold; Wool; Minerals in Modern Industry, Cotton.

This is the Hut That Jack Built in Australia

See Calvert, W.

This is the Story Told by Walt which tells you all about Salt

7325 THIS IS THE STORY/TOLD BY WALT/WHICH TELLS YOU/ALL ABOUT SALT/So we call it the story of Walt the Salt
Printed at the Griffin Press, Adelaide for Salpak Pty Ltd (The Table salt manufacturers of Australia)
Melbourne, n.d.
16pp (inc. covers) col. illus. throughout (sgd 'Jane') pic. wrappers, cover title, 206x264mm. CLRC

THOMAS, Harry

7326 WHO MADE/THE CAKE?/And Other Stories/By Harry Thomas/London: The C. W. Daniel Company/Grahame House, Tudor Street, E.C.4
1925
128pp (inc. 2pp foreword), unillus., clo., 180x120mm. VSL
Essays for children on nature & other abstract subjects.

THOMAS, Henry

7327 Lives to Remember/SISTER/KENNY/By/Henry

Thomas/Illustrated by Polly Bolian/Adam & Charles Black/London
First published 1958
95pp, b/w drawings throughout, clo., 210x130mm. KMM
Appears to be of American origin.

THOMAS, James F

7328 No.348 Allans/Part Songs/Price 4d/THE BLUE WREN/Two-part song/for children's voices/Words by/James Thomas/Music by/Cora Hosking
Melbourne 1937
6pp, unillus., wrappers, 255x173mm. VSL

THOMAS, Mary

7329 PAPER COLLAR/GULLY/By/Mary/Thomas
Albany, the author [1968]
[32]pp, b/w illus. t.p. & b/w illus. (by F .H. Thomas) throughout, illus. green paper wrappers, 260x200 mm. WJSB
Story based on the animals on Australian decimal coins.

THOMAS, May

7330 GUNDY/By/May Thomas/Illustrated by the author/Blocks cut in linoleum by S. H. Fisher/[drawing]/(Copyright)/Printed by Imperial Printing Company Limited/397 Hay Street, Perth, W.A./Sole Distributors/Gordon and Gotch (Aust.) Ltd.
n.d. [1944]
28pp, col. lino-cut illus. thoughout, bd., 260x195mm. NSL:M
Story of an Aboriginal child & native animals.

7331 WARRANINNI/By/May Thomas/Illustrated by the Author/Blocks cut in linoleum by S. H. Fisher/[linocut illustration]/(Copyright)/Wholly set up and printed in Australia/By/Imperial Printing Co. Ltd., 397 Hay Street, Perth, W.A./1945/Sole Distributors:/Gordon and Gotch (Aust.) Ltd./Registered at the/General Post Office, Perth,/For transmission through/the Post as a book
29pp, 14 f/p col. lino-cut illus., bd., 260x205mm. ANL
Story of two piccaninnies, sequel to *Gundy*.

7332 WANDI/By May Thomas/Author of Gundy & Warraninni/[drawing]/Illustrated by the Author/Copyright: All rights reserved
W. A. Newspapers Ltd, Perth 1968
31pp, sepia/white drawings on alternate pages, stiff pic. wrappers, 280x200mm. ANL
Verses.

THOMAS, 'W. E.' [William Joseph]

7333 SOME/MYTHS AND LEGENDS/OF THE/AUSTRALIAN ABORIGINES/By/W. E. Thomas/Whitcombe & Tombs Limited/Melbourne Auckland Christchurch Dunedin Wellington/and London/1923
75pp, 1p adv., b/w frontis. & 5 f/p b/w illus. by R. Wenban, pic. wrappers, 175x120mm. CLRC
See McLaren 610

THOMPSON, Brian (ed.)

7334 ONCE AROUND THE SUN/An Anthology of Poetry/by Australian Children/Collected and Edited by/Brian Thompson/Melbourne/Oxford University Press/London Wellington New York
1966
80pp (inc. 4pp preface by Judith Wright & 4pp editorial note), unillus., stiff paper wrappers, 210x140mm. CLRC
• Rpt 1967, 1968, 1970, as above. BBC

THOMPSON, Charles Kenneth

7335 KING OF THE RANGES/The Saga of a/Grey Kangaroo/By/C. K. Thompson/Sydney/Dymock's Book Arcade, Ltd./1945
107pp, 1p dedication, 2 b/w illus., clo., 185x120mm. KMM

7336 KING OF THE RANGES/The Saga of a/Grey Kangaroo/By/C. K. Thompson/Dymock's Book Arcade, Ltd./Sydney London/1950
First pub. 1945; rpt 1946, 1950, as above. BBC
Also 1950 ed. in plain wrappers. KP
• Rpt as above, 1958. BBC

7337 MONARCH OF THE/WESTERN SKIES/The Story of a Wedge-tailed Eagle/By/C. K. Thompson/Author of "Kings of the Ranges" etc./Illustrated by R. Madden/Sydney/Dymock's Book Arcade Ltd./1946
118pp, 2pp foreword by Will Lawson, 4 f/p b/w illus., clo., 185x115mm. ANL

7338 Another copy, as above, but bd. & on front cover: 'Australian Books for/Boys and Girls', 180x120mm. KMM

7339 WARRIGAL THE WARRIOR/by/C. K. Thompson/(Author of "Kings of the Ranges" "Monarch of the/Western Skies" etc./Sydney: Dymock's Book Arcade Ltd./1948
130pp, 3pp dedication, 4 f/p b/w illus., bd., 175x110mm. ANL
Artist not named.

7340 MAGGIE/THE/MAGNIFICENT/By C. K. Thompson/(Author of "Kings of the Ranges" "Monarch of the/Western Skies" "Warrigal the Warrior" &c.)/With introduction by A. H. Chisholm F.R.Z.S. (President of the Royal Aust. Ornithologists' Union, President of the Field Naturalists Club/of Victoria, Advisor to the Queensland Government on Fauna Protection &c.)/Illustrated by Ron Madden/Errata/[slip]/Sydney/Dymock's Book Arcade Ltd./1949
116pp, b/w frontis. & 3 f/p b/w illus., clo., 180x120mm. ANL

7341 OLD BOB'S BIRDS/By C. K. Thompson/(Author of "Kings of the Ranges" etc.)/Illustrated by Ron Madden/Sydney/Dymock's Book Arcade Ltd./1950
121pp, 1p dedication, 1p foreword, 4 f/p b/w illus., bd., 180x120mm. ANL

7342 RED EMPEROR/By C. K. Thompson/Illustrated by Ron Madden/Dymock's Book Arcade Ltd./Sydney London/1950
118pp, 3pp author's foreword, 4 f/p b/w illus., bd., 180x120mm. KMM

7343 BLACKIE/THE BRUMBY/By/C. K. Thompson/Sydney/Dymock's Book Arcade Ltd./1951
93pp, 2pp foreword, 2 b/w illus. by Carl Lyon, bd., 180x115mm. KMM

7344 TIGER CAT/By/C. K. Thompson, R.A.O.U., J.P./(Member of the Royal Zoological Society of N.S.W./and the Royal Australasian Ornithologists' Union)/Dymock's Book Arcade Limited/Sydney/1952
93pp (inc. 3pp author's note), unillus., clo., 180x120mm. KMM

7345 WOMBAT/by/C. K. Thompson, R.A.O.B. [*sic*] J.P./(Member of the Royal Zoological Society of N.S.W. and/the Royal Australasian Ornithologists' Union)/Illustrations by/Alan Rigby
Sydney, n.d. [1953] [Book bears no publisher's imprint, though jacket has 'Dymocks'; on verso of t.p.: 'Printed by Bridge Printery Ltd., 117 Reservoir St. Sydney]'
110pp (inc. 2pp author's note), b/w drawings throughout, clo., 180x120mm. KMM

7346 THUNDERBOLT/THE/FALCON/By/C. K. Thompson, R.A.O.U., J.P./(Member of the Royal Australasian Ornithologists'/Union and the Royal Zoological Society/of N.S.W./Illustrations by Frank Hodgkinson/Dymock's Book Arcade Ltd./Sydney
n.d. [1954]
112pp (inc. 2pp author's note), b/w drawings, bd., 185x115mm. ANL

7347 WILD CANARY/By/C. K. Thompson, R.A.O.U., J.P./(Member of the Royal Australasian Ornithologists' Union)/Dymock's Book Arcade Ltd./Sydney
n.d. [1956]
124pp (inc. 1p foreword), unillus., clo., dec. e/p, 185x120mm. KMM

7348 WILLY WAGTAIL/By/C. K. Thompson, R.A.O.U., J.P./(Member of the Royal Australasian/Ornithologists' Union)/Dymock's Book Arcade Ltd./Sydney
n.d. [1957]
128pp (inc. 2pp foreword), b/w drawings in text, clo., 180x115mm. BBC

THOMPSON, D. Lindsay
7349 BLUE BRANDER/A Story of Adventure/and/ Australian School Life/By/D. Lindsay Thompson/ Ward Lock & Co. Limited/London and Melbourne/
1927
313pp, 6pp adv., b/w frontis. & 3 f/p b/w illus. by W. F. Wightman, clo., 180x120mm. ANL
Boys' school story; author was the son of Lilian Turner.
7350 BLUE BRANDER/A Story of Adventure/and/ Australian School Life/By/D. Lindsay Thompson/ Author of "The Gang on Wheels"/Ward, Lock & Co., Limited/London and Melbourne
n.d.
313pp, b/w frontis. & 3 f/p b/w illus., pic. clo., 185x130mm. RM

7351 THE GANG ON/WHEELS/By/D. Lindsay Thompson/Author of "Blue Brander"/Ward, Lock & Co., Limited/London and Melbourne/1930
269pp, b/w frontis. & 3 f/p b/w illus. by W. E. Wigtall, clo., 180x120mm. ANL
Boys' school & adventure story.
• Rpt n.d., as above. KP

THOMPSON, Mrs F. Lindsay
See Turner, Lilian Irene

THOMPSON, Nita O.
7352 EMU FAIRY BOOK/by/Nita O. Thompson/(By Kind Permission of the "Saturday Journal")/Illustrations by Lyall Lush/Published by/ Lush Studios, Box 738 F, G.P.O. Adelaide./Printed by Shipping Newspaper (S.A.) Limited, Adelaide
n.d.
40pp, 7 b/w illus., col. pic. wrappers, 235x180mm. Grant

THOMPSON, Patricia
7353 OUR/NORTHERN/TREASURE HOUSE/By/ Patricia Thompson/A Background of Australia Book/ [device]/Shakespeare Head Press/Sydney
n.d. [1954?]
127pp, b/w illus. in text, pic. bd., 210x130mm. KMM
Background reading on N.W. Australia and Queensland.

THOMPSON, Phyllis
7354 GINGER/The Story of a Chinese Kitten/By Phyllis Thompson/[drawing]/Illustrated by Wilfred Douglas/ China Inland Mission/64 Elizabeth Street/Melbourne
n.d.
24pp, b/w drawings in text, wrappers, 240x180mm. MK
Although the setting is China the book is written for Australian children.

THOMSON, A. K. (ed.)
7355 MEN AND EVENTS/Edited by/A. K. Thomson/ The Jacaranda Press/Brisbane
1964
188pp, 1p foreword, unillus., dec. bd., 180x120mm. BBC
Anthology intended for schools, of extracts from Australian books.

THOMSON, Jim
THE GREAT BARRIER REEF. *See* Around Australia Program

THOMSON, K. Graham
7356 PEOPLE OF THE/SOUTH POLE/by/K. Graham Thomson/F.R.G.S./Lutterworth Press/London and Redhill
First published 1941; second impression 1942
187pp, 4pp adv., b/w frontis. only, clo., 185x120mm. KMM

THORNE, Carina
7357 LEAVES/FROM THE/AUSTRALIAN/BUSH/A Little Collection of/odd verses, dedicated/to Australian Girls/Young and Old./By/Carina Thorne/The Heart/ [8-line stanza]/Brisbane/H. J. Diddams & Co., Printers, Adelaide Street/1912
22pp, 2 headpieces, tied wrappers, 205x95mm. ANL

THORNYCROFT, David
7358 THE FIRST BOOK OF/HEROES/Written by David Thornycroft/Illustrated by R. S. Embleton Designed by D. McLoughlin/[contents] Dean & Son Ltd./41/43 Ludgate Hill London E.C.4...[3 lines]
1958
124pp, col. & b/w illus. throughout, clo., dec. e/p, 240x180mm. KMM
Contents include: 'Scott's Expedition to the South Pole', & 'Bert Hinkler's Flights to Australia' (each 8pp).

THORP, Clara J.
7359 FAIRY FABLE/RHYMES/By Clara J. Thorp/ Drawings by W. Halls/Melbourne: /Brown, Prior & Co. Pty. Ltd/1931
[16]pp, 4 line drawings in text, pic. wrappers, 185x120mm. KMM
7360 FAIRY FABLE/RHYMES/By Clara J. Thorp/ Melbourne:/Brown, Prior, Anderson, Pty. Ltd./1946
32pp, unillus., pic. wrappers, 180x120mm. KMM
Front cover design resembles the work of Ida Rentoul Outhwaite, but is unsigned. Title on front cover reads: Fairy/Fable/Rhymes and other/verses/for/Little Folk. The second edition is unillustrated. but the covers on both books are identical.

THORPE, Joyce
See Nicholson, Joyce

THORS, Mande A.
7361 PLAYFUL/PETS/Stories and Pictures/of animal pets for/Little children/Written by M. A. Thors, Offset Offset Printing Co., Sydney, n.d. [1945]
16pp, 7 f/p col. illus. by 'T.M.R.', dec. wrappers, 175x240mm. ANL

7362 "ANGELO! WHERE ARE YOU?"/by/Mande Thors/Arthur H. Stockwell, Ltd./Ilfracombe Devon United Kingdom, n.d.
110pp, unillus., clo., 190x125mm. CLRC

7363 P.K./(the High School boy detective)/in/THE LOST PAY/ENVELOPE/by/Mande Thors/Arthur H. Stockwell Ltd./Ilfracombe Devon [England]
1960
72pp, unillus., clo., 180x120mm. ANL
Cover reads: 'The Lost Pay Envelope'. Story set in the Woy Woy district of NSW.

7364 BACK GATE OF THE/SHOWGROUND/by/Mande Thors/Author of/The Lost Pay Envelope—/the first book featuring P.K., the High School boy detective/Arthur H. Stockwell Ltd/Ilfracombe Devon
n.d.[1963]
96pp, unillus, clo., 180x120mm. NSL:M

7365 Meet again/P.K. (the High School Boy Detective)/in/SOMETHING FISHY/by/Mande Thors/Author of/"The Lost Pay Envelope" and/"Back Gate of the Showground"/Arthur H. Stockwell Ltd./Ilfracombe—Devon
1964
96pp, unillus, clo., 180x122mm. LRA

THOULET. MON PREMIER VOYAGE EN MER
See Melville, Harden S.

The Three Young Pioneers The British Empire Library 2
See LEFT ASHORE, OR LIFE AT CORAL CREEK

Through the Great White Wilderness
7366 THROUGH THE/GREAT WHITE/WILDERNESS/Scott's /Last Journey/to the/Pole/[Portrait & caption] Charles H. Kelly, London, n.d.
8pp, photographic illus. throughout, t.p. printed in red & black with crossed flags in two colours. 260x200mm. CLRC
Pathfinders of Empire series
'The Adventures of a Famous Navigator' (James Cook) listed in same series. Unseen

THURBER, Robert Bruce
7367 THE/STORY OF DANIEL/By/Robert Bruce Thurber/Signs Publishing Company/(A.C.A. Ltd., Props.)/Warburton, Victoria, Australia
n.d. [copyright 1926]
64pp, b/w drawings throughout, wrappers, 210x125mm. KMM
Biblical story retold with present-day religious implications. Not known whether author is Australian, or whether the book is an Australian reprint of an overseas book.

THURIAN, Aldus
7368 THE INSECT SCHOOL/By/Aldus Thurian/[drawing]/1/The Arcadian series,
The Hawthorn Press, Melbourne, n.d.
32 pp, b/w drawings throughout, pic. wrappers, 245x180mm. NSL:M

THURSTAN, E. Paget
7369 THE ADVENTURERS/OF PEARLY BAY./By E. Paget Thurstan,/B.S., M.D./London:/Arthur H. Stockwell,/29 Ludgate Hill, E.C.4
n.d. [1923]
96pp, brown clo., 216x140mm. PH
Stories set in Shark Bay, WA

THWAITES, Donald L.
7370 BLUE/PETER:/A Tale of the Forest, a/little boy and his pine/cone goblin friends/written and illustrated by/D. L. Thwaites; revised by/B. J. Thwaites/Wholly set up and printed in Australia by Harman & Jacka Ltd, 20–22 Wyatt Street, Adelaide/for the Publisher Southern Press, Box 877 G/1945/Registered in Australia for transmission by post as a book
1st ed. 1944; 2nd ed. 1945
29pp, dec. t.p., col. & b/w illus. throughout, dec. bd., 215x185mm. ANL

"Thy Kingdom Come"
See [Mathews, Julia A.]

THYNNE, Robert
7371 THE STORY/OF/AUSTRALIAN EXPLORATION/By/R. Thynne/with illustrations and a map/London/T. Fisher Unwin/1894
277pp, b/w frontis. & 10 f/p b/w illus. by various artists (inc. Hume Nisbet), 1 folding map, pic. clo., 180x120mm. HBM
On front cover: 'Australian Exploration/A Boys' Adventure Book', frontispiece reproduced in colour on front cover & kangaroo in gilt on spine.
7372 Another copy, as above, but190x120mm. & plain brown clo. binding with kangaroo only in gilt on front cover, & gilt lettering only on spine. HBM

7373 MATTHEW FLINDERS/or/How we have Australia/Being the true Story of/Captain Flinders' Explorations,/and Adventures/By/Robert Thynne/Author of "The Story of Australian Exploration"/[device]/With nine illustrations and a chart/London/John Hogg, 13 Paternoster Row/(All rights reserved)
n.d. [1896]
352pp, 6pp introduction, 32pp adv., b/w frontis. & 7 f/p b/w illus. signed 'J. Ayton Syminton '96', one b/w reproduction of drawing by Wm. Westall & chart, pic. clo., 180x120mm. HBM
7374 Another copy as above but without adv. Title on front cover printed in black ink instead of gilt, reads: 'Captain Flinders' Exploration and Adventures', and on spine the same; bevelled edges, KMM
Another copy dated September 1904, as above, but with 16 pp adv. KP

The Tichborne Trial
7375 THE TICHBORNE TRIAL/As told to our Grandchildren/J. F. Nash Co.[print]/N. G. Clarke & Co. 2 Garrick Street, Covent Garden
n.d. Clarke's Parlour Games, London [adv.]
16pp folding pp, printed with b/w illus. & 4-6 line verse on one side of paper only, yellow paper wrappers, cover title (title and sub-title printed diagonally across cover with figures from court scenes depicted in silhouettes in two segments), 147x110mm. CLRC
Verse written in the form of 'The House that Jack Built'

TILBROOK, J. R.
7376 BUILDERS/OF A NATION/J. R. Tilbrook/Book One/Phillip to Macquarie/1788–1820
Viking Press Pty Ltd, Curl Curl NSW, n.d. [1971]
58pp, b/w drawings in text, bd., 215x140mm. KP
Brief biographies of people distinguished in Australian history.
7377 Second volume as above: Book two/Wentworth to Maconochie/1820–1840
70pp, as above. KP

TILTMAN, H. Hessell
See Bridges, Thomas Charles & Tiltman, H. Hessell

[TIMINS, Octavius Frederic]
7378 LITTLE BEN,/THE SHEPHERD./A Tale of Australian Life in the Present Day./[quotation]/

Published under the direction of/the committee of/general literature and education/appointed by the Society for Promoting Christian Knowledge/London:/Society for Promoting Christian Knowledge;/Sold at the Depositories:/77 Great Queen Street, Lincoln's Inn Fields;/4, Royal Exchange; 48, Piccadilly;/and by all Booksellers.
n.d. [1864]
103pp & 4pp adv., engraved frontis., 2 b/w engravings, blind-stamped clo., 145x100mm. CLRC

7379 STATION DANGEROUS/and other/Tales for the Young/By/O. F. T. Author of "Little Ben, the Shepherd" etc./London/James Nisbet and Co., 21 Berners Street/MDCCCLXVII
263pp, 4pp adv., b/w frontis. only, clo., 170x110mm. VSL
Includes title story set in Central Australia; 'Orphan Willie—A Boy's Adventures in North America'; 'Tom of the Diggings'; set in Ballarat.
The author, a retired captain in the 82nd Regiment of Foot, resided in Victoria as private secretary to the Governor from 1856 till 1863, & was also the author of *First Steps in Geography,* 1886. His initials are printed in what appears to be old English lettering on the t.p. of the above book as 'D.F.T.' & the BMC lists it & also *First Steps in Geography* under 'D.F.T.'.

TIMMS, Edward Vivian

7380 THE VALLEY/OF ADVENTURE/A Story for Boys/By/Edward Vivian Timms/With Illustrations by Edgar A. Holloway/Australia:/Cornstalk Publishing Company/89 Castlereagh Street, Sydney/1926
259pp, b/w frontis. & 2 f/p b/w illus., map, clo., 185x120mm. KMM
A note states that 'the title of this book had to be altered after the inside sheets were printed as it was found that the title "Sanctuary Island" had already been used'. Throughout the book left-hand pages bear the heading 'Sanctuary Island'.

7381 THE VALLEY OF/ADVENTURE/A Story for Boys/By/E. V. Timms/Angus and Robertson Ltd./Sydney: London/1941
238pp, b/w frontis. & map, clo., 185x120mm. CLRC
• Rpt as above, 1948. GI

7382 RED MASK/A Story of the early Victorian/Goldfields/By Edward Vivian Timms/Author of 'The Hills of Hate', 'The Valley of Adventure'/'James! Don't be a Fool' etc./Australia/Cornstalk Publishing Company/89 Castlereagh Street, Sydney/1927
272pp, unillus., clo., 185x120mm. ANL
• Rpt as above 1929, but170x105mm. Grant

7383 THE CITIES/UNDER THE SEA/By/E. V. Timms/Angus and Robertson/Sydney: London/1948
242pp, unillus., clo., 185x120mm. ANL

Timothy the Cat Painting Book

7384 TIMOTHY THE CAT/PAINTING BOOK
Alex Fryda Pty Ltd.,Sydney n.d. [1950?]
Printed in Denmark by J. Chr. Sorensen & Co.A/S
[16]pp, b/w illus., no text, col. pic. light board covers, cover title, 234x183mm. KMM
Col. illus. of each page are printed on flaps inside covers for child's guidance; others in series: Bruin the Bear Painting Book, The Cowboy ditto, the Indian ditto, all by Vil. H. Hansen; presumably only distributed in Australia.

[TIMPERLEY, W. H.]

7385 HARRY TREVERTON/His Tramps and Troubles/Told by Himself/Edited by Lady Broome/[vignette]/With Twenty-five illustrations/London/George Routledge and Sons Limited/Broadway, Ludgate Hill/Glasgow and New York/1889
311pp, b/w frontis. & 24 b/w illus. by Alfred Pearse, clo., 200x130mm. CLRC
Preface states that this book was first published in the *Boy's Own Paper,* & was actually written by Mr W. H. Timperley, Superintendent of Rottnest Island, & edited by Lady Broome. (At the time of publication of this book her husband, Sir Frederick Broome, was Governor of the colony of Western Australia.). *Boy's Own Annual,* Vol. X, 1887 October–December.
Another edition as above but undated, with 8 pp adv. and dec. clo., dec. e/ps (adv. include a Kate Greenway almanac for 1889). RM

7386 The Boy's Own Bookshelf [decorative heading]/BUSH LUCK/An Australian Story/By/W. H. Timperley/London/The Religious Tract Society/56, Paternoster Row; 65 St. Paul's Churchyard/and 164 Piccadilly
n.d. [1892]
256pp, b/w frontis. & 5 b/w plates by W. S. Stacey, pic. clo., figure of a horseman & title in gilt on front cover, 190x130mm. KMM
Serialized in *Boy's Own Paper* December 1889–June 1890.

7387 BUSH LUCK/An Australian Story/by/W. H. Timperley/with coloured illustrations/London/The Religious Tract Society/4 Bouverie Street and 65 St. Paul's Churchyard, E.C.
250pp, 8pp adv., col. frontis., 1 col. plate & 1 b/w illus. in text signed Ernest Prater, dec. clo. (with col. onlay), 190x130mm. CLRC

7388 BUSH LUCK/An Australian Story/by/W. H. Timperley/The Office of "The Boy's Own Paper"/4 Bouverie Street, London, E.C.4
n.d. [school prize 1911]
Details as above. Cover drawing of a boy on a stile reading, with hat & a sleeping dog on the ground. From p243 to the end of the book a different type is used. Col. frontis. by Ernest Prater. 180x120mm. KMM

TINDALE, Norman B. & LINDSAY, Harold Arthur

7389 THE FIRST WALKABOUT/By/Norman B. Tindale, B.Sc./Ethnologist, South Australian Museum/and/H. A. Lindsay/Illustrated by Madeleine Boyce/[drawing]/Longmans Green & Co./London Melbourne New York
First published 1954
129pp (inc. 13pp glossary), 3pp authors' preface, b/w frontis. & b/w drawings in text throughout, clo., 215x135mm. KMM
Winner CBCA award 1955.
• Rpt 1956 & 1965, as above. KP

7390 A Polynesian Saga/RANGATIRA/(The High-born)/by/Norman B. Tindale/and/Harold A. Lindsay/Illustrated by/Douglas F. Maxted/Rigby Limited/Adelaide
First published 1959
208pp (inc. 12pp notes &c.), b/w drawings throughout, clo., 210x135mm. KMM
A story of the migration of the Polynesians to New Zealand in approximately the twelfth century.

7391 As above but imprint: 'George G. Harrap & Co Ltd./London Toronto Wellington Sydney also with A. H. & A. W. Reed, Wellington, New Zealand. CLRC

7392 A Polynesian Saga/RANGATIRA/(The High-born) Franklin Watts, New York 1959
The details of this edition are the same as those of the Harrap & Rigby edition. 'Harrap, London, arranged for the printing of the full 17,000 copies to be done in Britain, and each of the other three publishers, i.e.

Franklin Watts, Rigby Ltd, Adelaide, and A. H. & A. W. Reed, Wellington, New Zealand, took a share bearing their imprint'. Unseen: IFA
• Rpt school edition as above, but limp clo., 180x120mm. Rigby Adelaide 1959, rpt 1963. KMM

7393 ABORIGINAL AUSTRALIANS/Norman B. Tindale/and/H. A. Lindsay/The Jacaranda Press Brisbane 1963
139pp (inc. 2pp foreword), 8pp index & bibliography, 28pp b/w photographic illus., diagrams in text, clo., dec. e/p, 210x140mm. KMM

7394 Another edition as above, but published simultaneously by Jacaranda for the Children's Library Guild of Australia.
See also Howard and Levy, Australian Story Sampler

TINDALE, Norman B. & GEORGE, Beryl
7395 THE/AUSTRALIAN/ABORIGINES/Norman B. Tindale and Beryl George/Golden Press Sydney 1971
62pp (with errata slip), col. & b/w photographic illus. throughout, pic. bd. (with illus. & index inside front & back covers), 325x240mm. CLRC

[TINDALE, Will] pseud. 'Moan Bambi'
7396 LILI-ILLA/By/Moan Bambi/A Romance of the/Australian Aborigines/Sydney 1923/Printed by the Associated Printing and Publishing Company/Crystal Palace Chambers, 590 George Street
307pp, 2pp glossary, unillus., clo., 185x130mm. CLRC

Tiny People's Painting Book
See Kenny, J. P. & Co.

Tiny's Air Adventures RAAF Sky Stories
7397 TINY'S AIR/ADVENTURES/RAAF/SKY/STORIES
n.d., n.p.
8pp, b/w illus. (by J. H. Guerin) & models of planes, pic. wrappers, cover title, 240x170mm. KP
Another copy as above, but,
14pp, part col. & b/w ills throughout, pic. bd., cover title, 230x173mm. KP

Tip Top Book of Rhymes
7398 TIP TOP/BOOK OF RHYMES
n.p., n.d.
8pp, col. illus. throughout, pic. wrappers, 175x230mm. VMOU

7399 Another copy as above, but 8pp b/w illus. (sgd 'Guerin'), col. pic. wrappers, 227x180mm. KP
Verses; the first 2pp have verses with illus. about a kangaroo & a koala.

TISDALL, Constance
7400 AUSTRALIAN/NATURE STORIES/for/Children/By Constance Tisdall, B.A./Publishers/James Ingram & Son/227 Little Collins Street, Melbourne
n.d. [school prize 1903]
99pp, b/w frontis. & b/w photographs in text, limp pic. clo., 180x125mm. ANL
Another copy as above, clo. t.e.g.,180x115mm. KP

Toddler's ABC
7401 TODDLER'S/ABC
George Jaboor, Melbourne, n.d. [194-?]
8pp (inc. 4pp printed in colour), pic. wrappers, 240x183mm. KP

TOLL, Eileen
See Birtles, Dora/Eileen

TOMBS, John
7402 APPLE COTTAGE/AND THE/LOST KEY/[drawing/Printed by Morris & Walker, Melbourne/for the Publishers Offset Printing Co. Pty Ltd.Sydney
n.d. [194-?] Sunshine series E 169
16pp, part-col. illus. throughout, pic.wrappers, 240x180mm. CLRC

7403 JOLLY GAMES/TO PLAY/Collected and Prepared/for the Entertainment of/Children of All Ages/by/John Tombs/Printed and Published by Offset Printing Co. Pty/Limited. 169 Phillip Street, Waterloo, Sydney./(All Rights Reserved).
n.d. [194-?]
32pp, b/w drawings in text, dec. wrappers, 180x120mm. KP
Cover title: '38 Jolly Games for Children'.

7404 PETER'S PUZZLE/BOOK/Jolly Puzzles/Mazes, Stories &/Questions to Answer/By John Tombs/Registered in Australia for transmission by post as a book/copyright/[4 lines]
B.B.F.Art Advertising & Publishing Coy, Sydney, n.d.
32pp, b/w illus. in text, pic. wrappers, 242x184mm. KP

7405 BUMPER BOOK/OF 80 PICTORIAL CROSSWORD/PUZZLES AND STORIES/By John Tombs/With pictures that can be coloured/with paints and crayons/Angus & Robertson Limited/89 Castlereagh Street/Sydney
1940
172pp, b/w drawings, bd., 240x185mm. ANL
Contains stories, crosswords, pictures for colouring, &c.

7406 THE BANDIT OF PICK'S GULLY/and other stories/by/John Tombs
Playground Publishing, Rozelle, NSW, n.d. [1945]
99pp, 2 f/p col. illus. & 8 f/p b/w illus. signed L. M. Smith, bd., 175x115mm. ANL

7407 THE SECRET OF/THE GREY HOUSE/AND/MULBERRIES—AND MYSTERY!/Quick Capture!/The Dragon at the Circus/The Missing Locket/A Pair of Roosters/Nick to the Rescue/by/John Tombs/[publisher's device]/Published by Playground Publishing, Wingello House, Angel Place, Sydney/Printed by The Standard Publishing House, 69 Nelson Street, Rozelle./(All rights reserved)
[Sydney 1945]
47pp, b/w drawings in text, wrappers, 235x180mm. ANL

THE ZOO GARDEN MYSTERY. *See* Adventure series

7408 LITTLE/PASTIME/TALES/by John Tombs/[drawing]/Printed in Sydney, Australia, by Offset Printing Coy. Pty. Ltd. and published by O.P.C. Distributors Pty. Ltd.
n.d. [1952]
16pp, 7 f/p col. illus., wrappers, 280x210mm. ANL

TOMPKINS, Jane
7409 THE/PENGUIN TWINS/by/Jane Tompkins/Author of "The Polar Bear Twins"/and "Moo-wee, the Musk-Ox"/Illustrated/by/Kurt Wiese/Frederick Warne & Company, Limited,/London./1948
116pp, b/w frontis. & 9 f/p b/w plates, 12 half page b/w illus. in text, clo., dec. e/p, 205x150mm. KMM

Toppan's Foto Books Series
See Macpherson, June

The Tortoise and the Hare
7410 THE TORTOISE/AND THE HARE
Printed by Wilke & Co. Pty. Ltd., Melbourne for the Golden Bough Pub. Co., n.d. [194-?]
16pp, b/w illus. (by Lois Anderson), pic. wrappers, cover title, 244x150mm. KP
Traditional story retold in Melbourne

Toymaker ABC
7411 TOYMAKER/ABC/An Alphabet of Toys/For small Girls & Boys/Sandman Series
John Sands Pty Ltd, Sydney, n.d. [195-?]
24pp, col. illus. throughout, pic. card wrappers, 185x218mm. KMM

Toy-making with Match Boxes
7412 TOY-MAKING/WITH/MATCH BOXES/With compliments of/Bryant & May Pty Ltd./Melbourne
n.d. [1928?]
16pp (inc. 8pp with col. illus.), b/w illus. throughout, wrappers, 250x185mm. MAC
See also 1177

TOYNE, A. H.
7413 WHAT IS FIRST AID//By A. H. Toyne C. St. J., M.B., B.S., F.R.C.S./Illustrated by Weg/Cartoonist, Herald and Weekly Times, Melbourne/A Publication of the St John Ambulance Association/of the Order of St. John of the Priory in Australia.
1972
77pp, instructions with amusing drawings, pic. wrappers, 202x215mm. KMM
WEG's real name was W. E. Green.

Tracings of Maritime Discovery
7414 TRACINGS/OF/MARITIME DISCOVERY/By the author of/"Leaves of Knowledge for the Young"/Illustrated with engravings after designs by/William Davison, Esq./London:/Darton and Clark, Holborn Hill,/and/Henry John Dixon, Bishopwearmouth.
n.d. [inscribed '46, preface dated 1841]
xii, 168pp + 18pp notes &c.,engraved frontis., additional engraved t.p. and 2 f/p. engravings, dec. clo.,135x107mm. CLRC
History of maritime discovery told in dialogue form for children; includes pages on New Holland, Cook, Tasman and Dampier, Bligh, Bass and Flinders, &c.

TRACY, Mona
7415 MARTIN THORN—/ADVENTURER/By/Mona Tracy/Illustrated by Terence Cuneo/[device]/Whitcombe & Tombs, Ltd./Auckland, Christchurch Dunedin/Wellington, N.Z.; Melbourne, Sydney/London
1930
279pp, col. frontis. & 4 b/w plates, dec. clo., 180x122mm. ANL
Historical story for boys set mostly in NSW.

Transport by Air, Land & Sea
7416 TRANSPORT/BY/AIR, LAND & SEA/Robur Tea School Series No. 3
Melbourne n.d. [193-?]
12pp, b/w photographic illus. throughout, pic. wrappers, 185x120mm. KP

Travel and Adventure in Many Lands
7417 TRAVEL AND ADVENTURE/IN MANY LANDS./An Illustrated Reading-Book,./By many writers./Suitable for the Upper Classes of National Schools./And also for use in Night Schools./Published under the Direction of the Committee of/General Literature and Education/Appointed by the Society for Promoting Christian Knowledge./London:/Society for Promoting Christian Knowledge;/sold at the Depositories:/77 Great Queen Street, Lincoln's Inn Fields;/4, Royal Exchange; 48 Piccadilly;/and by all booksellers.
n.d. [1870]
204pp, 53 b/w engravings, dec. clo., 180x115mm. CLRC
Includes 5 chapters on the Australian Colonies.

Travelling On
7418 TRAVELLING ON/[col. illus.] /Department of Education/New South Wales/Compiled by the Infants Reading Committee/Illustrated by Katherine Morris/ Printed by the authority of/[edge of page cut off]
n.d. [195-?]
109pp, col. illus., dec. bd., 197x140mm. LRA
Reading material for primary grades.

TRAVERS, Pamela L.
Though Pamela Travers was born & brought up in Australia she has spent most of her life in Europe & all *Mary Poppins* books are in every way English. The production of the Walt Disney film in 1964 based on these stories resulted in many translations & different versions of the books but they are not part of Australian children's literature.

The Tree of Empire
7419 Arnold's Literary Reading Books/THE/TREE OF EMPIRE/A Book of Readings in Prose and Verse/ illustrative of the History and Development/of the British Empire./[4-line quote]/London/Edward Arnold/41 & 43 Maddox Street, Bond Street, W./(All Rights Reserved)
n.d.
256pp & 8pp adv., b/w frontis. & 10 f/p.b/w illus., clo., 180x118mm. KP
Contains Australian section pp80—137 (quotes from Kingsley's 'Tales of Old Travel', 'Captain Cook's Voyages' &c.) .

Trend Books
A series of readers for slow adolescent readers, mostly written by Bettina Bird, sometimes in collaboration with Ian Falk, and also under various pseudonyms, such as 'Lawrie Seawall', 'Terry Nash', 'Rob Noske', 'Scud Morgan', 'Kurt Hogan' &c. Format example:
7420 COFFEE AT CHARLIE's/Bettina Bird/Illustrations by John Boucher/Cheshire
Melbourne 1968
80pp, b/w illus. throughout, stiff pic. wrappers, 182x110mm. KMM
• Rpt 1971. KMM
Other titles in series, in uniform format except for number of pages & illus.:
7421 BINDI-EYE by 'Lawrie Seawall', 1969 rpt 1970, 1971, 88pp, illus. Judy Duncan. KMM
7422 COLD AT FIVE by 'Scud Morgan', 1970, rpt 1971, 73pp, illus. photographs R. Caton & R. Cushan. KMM
7423 CRASH LANDING by Bettina Bird, 1968, 98pp, illus. John Adam. KMM
7424 CRY ON A FOGGY NIGHT by Tony Scanlon, 1969, rpt 1971, 1972, 79pp, illus 'Weg' [W .E. Green]. KMM
7425 DANGER RIDE by Bettina Bird & Ian Falk, 1971, rpt 1972, 75 pp, illus. J. Howell. KP
7426 THE DARK HOUSE AND THE RABBIT TRAP by 'Lawrie Seawall', 1968, 60pp, illus. Heather Mason. KMM
7427 A FABULOUS DAY IN THE LIFE OF PROFESSOR MORTIMER G. MUGWUMP by Bettina Bird and Tony Scanlon, 1969, 88pp, illus. Hans Haëm. KMM
7428 GAYE LIZZIE by Tony Scanlon, 1969, rpt 1971, 74pp, illus. Elizabeth Howell. KP
7429 HEY, THAT'S MY BIKE! by Bettina Bird and Ian Falk, 1971, rpt 1972, 65pp, illus. Reg Buckland. KMM
7430 IT HAPPENED ON SATURDAY by 'Kurt Hogan', 1970, 54pp, illus. Dick Evans. CLRC
7431 ODD ONE OUT by Bettina Bird and Ian Falk, 1970, rpt 1971,1972, 93pp. illus. Elizabeth Howell. CLRC

7432 OLD BOOTLEG by 'Rob Noske', 1969, 72pp, illus. Elizabeth Howell. KMM
7433 A REAL CITY KID, by Bettina Bird and Ian Falk, 1971, rpt 1972, 75pp, illus. Dick Evans. KP
7434 A REAL HERO by Bettina Bird, 1969, 67pp, illus. Heather Mason. KMM
7435 RED HOT MOUNTAIN by Bettina Bird and Ian Falk, 1971, 71pp, illus. Abigail Thompson. KP
7436 ROBBIE by Bettina Bird, 1968, rpt 1971, 68pp, illus. J. Howell. KP
7437 SHARK IN THE SURF by Lexie Cannon, 1969, rpt 1971, 69pp, illus. Heather Mason. KMM
7438 SNOW AT TATARU by Talbot Crameri, 1969, rpt 1970, 102pp, illus. Jenny Tuckwell. KMM
7439 THE SNOWDROPPERS by Tony Scanlon, 1969, rpt 1971, 1972, 79pp, illus. 'Weg'. KMM
7440 SOME TRANNIE THAT by 'Lawrie Seawall', 1968, rpt 1970, 69pp, illus. Elizabeth Howell. KMM
7441 SUDDEN DEATH by Bettina Bird and Ian Falk, 1971, rpt 1972, 79pp, illus J. and Liz Howell. KMM
7442 WATCHER ON THE WHARF by 'Terry Nash', 1969, rpt 1970, 1971, 60pp, illus. J. Howell. KMM
7443 WHY PENNY KISSED ME by 'Rob Noske', 1970, rpt 1971, 71pp, illus Judy Duncan. KMM
7444 WILD DOG by Bettina Bird and Ian Falk, 1971, 65pp, illus. Dick Evans. KW

TREVOR, Elleston
WUMPUS. 1945
The only Australian reference is that one character is a koala.

TRICE, Edward
7445 STORM NELSON/AND THE SEA LEOPARD/An Eagle Novel/By/Edward Trice/HultonPress/London
1957
159pp, b/w frontis., clo., 196x130mm. KP
Set in Antarctica.

Trouble in Toyland
See Joy series

TROUGHTON, Ellis
7446 THE SOLVOL ANIMAL BOOK/55 Australian Animals /by Ellis Troughton/Illustrated in full colour/ by Neville W. Cayley
28pp, 13 col. plates, pic. wrappers, cover title, 120x185mm. ANL
Includes an introduction and descriptive notes by author

TROUT, Elizabeth M.
7447 FOLLOW/THE/ABC/Puzzle Rhyme/Easy Drawing Book/Elizabeth M. Trout, B.A./Copyright No. 36223/(All rights reserved)
Offset Printing Co., Sydney, n.d. [1945]
29pp, part. col. drawings throughout, illus. wrappers, cover title, 245x180mm. ANL
Each page has a 4-line rhyme & a puzzle picture illustrating one letter of the alphabet.

TRUDINGER, R. M. & FORBES, Alison
AUSTRALIAN ABORIGINES. *See* Life in Australia

True Australian Series
See Macpherson, Bruce & June

True Stories of Adventure in Field Flood and Forest
7448 TRUE STORIES/OF/ADVENTURE IN FIELD/ FLOOD AND FOREST/London/Blackie & Son, Limited, 50 Old Bailey, E.C./Glasgow Dublin and Bombay
n.d. (prize 1907)
256pp, & 8pp adv. (Blackie's list of Famous Books precedes text), b/w frontis. (sgd. Frank Feller). CLRC
Contents appear to be the same as those in 'Adventures in Field, Flood and Forest' & title on front cover reads: 'Adventures in Field and Flood'

TRUMBLE, Mabel C.
MICHELINE ET DIDI
Melbourne, Macmillan, 1935
School text

TUBIANA, Josiane & BICHONNIER, Henriette
7449 BABY ANIMALS/OF AUSTRALASIA/Text by Josiane Tubiana and Henriette Bichonnier/Illustrations by Nemo/Translated by Charles A. Pemberton/Golden Press Sydney
1972
[66]pp, col. illus. t.p., col. illus. throughout, pic. bd., pic. e/p, 310x240mm. KP

TUCKEY, Bill
7450 PICTORIAL BOOK OF/RACE CARS/Australia New Zealand and the World/Written by Bill Tuckey/Illustrated by Bob Arnold/[col.illus.]
Paul Hamlyn Pty Ltd, Dee Why West, NSW 1972
77pp, 30 f/p col. illus. & illus. in text, pic. bd., 270x200mm. CLRC

Tuckfields Australian Animals
7451 [col. illus]/TUCKFIELDS/AUSTRALIAN/ ANIMALS
Published by Tuckfields' Ty-nee Tips Tea
n.d., n.p.
32pp (inc. 13 pp information on Australian animals & space for 32 cards to be pasted in,) cover title, 203x150mm. KP
Uniform with above:
7452 TUCKFIELDS/DOGS/. AND THEIR CARE. KP
7453 TUCKFIELDS/CATS/AND THEIR CARE. KP

Turban Tim says win big prizes with this Kornies Painting Book
7454 TURBAN TIM SAYS/WIN BIG PRIZES/WITH THIS KORNIES/PAINTING BOOK/[verse]
Kornie Food Company, Carlton,Vic., n.d. [195-?]
16pp, b/w illus. stiff wrappers, cover title, 240x180mm. KP

TURLEY, Charles
7455 THE VOYAGES OF/CAPTAIN SCOTT/Retold from "The Voyage of the Discovery"/and "Scott's Last Expedition",/"A Band of Brothers", etc./With an Introduction/by Sir J. M. Barrie, Bart./With a portrait frontispiece in photogravure/4 coloured plates, 28 pages of half-tone illustrations/(Mostly from photographs taken by members of the 'Terranova' expedition), facsimile and map/London/John Murray, Albemarle Street, W.1./1914
240pp (inc. 8pp index), 4 col. illus., 28 b/w illus., pic. clo., 200x130mm. MK
The introduction indicates that the book was intended for children.

TURNBULL, Clive
ESSINGTON LEWIS. *See* Great Australians

TURNER, C. E. Sutton
7456 "QUICK MARCH"/The Story of England's Great War/A Book for Australian Boys and Girls/By C. E. Sutton Turner/Author of/I. Why Australia helps the Empire/II. The "Sydney"—"Emden" Fight/III The Landing in the Dardanelles/Illustrated/The net proceeds from the Sale of this book/will be donated to the Red Cross Fund for/Wounded Soldiers/Published by/Turner & Sons Sydney and Melbourne/ Copyright—all rights reserved
n.d. [1915]
32pp, 2pp adv. (preceding t.p.), col. frontis., b/w

photographic illus., map, line drawings, bd., 240x180mm. NSL:M

TURNER, Ethel Sybil [Mrs H. R. Curlewis]

7457 SEVEN/LITTLE AUSTRALIANS./By/Ethel S. Turner./Illustrated by A. J. Johnson./[vignette—The Death of Judy]/London:/Ward, Lock & Bowden, Limited,/Warwick House, Salisbury Square, E.C./New York and Melbourne./1894/(All rights reserved.)
240pp, 16pp adv., b/w frontis. & 2 f/p b/w illus., 23 b/w chapter headings (inc. vignette on t.p.), dec. clo., 180x120mm. CLRC
'Ethel S. Turner' on front cover & spine.
Note: The name of one of the children, 'Bunty' is mis-spelt 'Bunby' in the first three editions, being corrected in the fourth (1896) & subsequent editions.

7458 SEVEN/LITTLE AUSTRALIANS./By/Ethel S. Turner./Illustrated by A. J. Johnson./Second Edition/[vignette—as in first edition, but no caption (The Death of Judy)]/London:/Ward, Lock & Bowden, Limited,/Warwick House, Salisbury Square, E.C./New York and Melbourne./1894/(All rights reserved. [no concluding bracket]
240pp, 32pp adv., b/w frontis. & 2 f/p b/w illus., 23 b/w drawings in text, dec. clo., 180x120mm. CLRC
'Ethel S. Turner' on front cover & spine.
Second edition, another copy as above, but 30pp adv. KMM
SEVEN/LITTLE AUSTRALIANS./By/Ethel Turner./Illustrated by A. J. Johnson./Third Edition/[vignette as previous editions, no caption]/
Imprint 1895 but as before & details as before. CLRC
SEVEN/LITTLE AUSTRALIANS/By/Ethel Turner/Author of/"The Family at Misrule", "The Story of a Baby", etc./Illustrated by A. J. Johnson./Fourth edition/[vignette]/London:/Ward, Lock & Bowden, Limited,/Warwick House, Salisbury Square, E.C./New York and Melbourne./1896/(All rights reserved)
240pp & 16pp adv., details as before. CLRC
Fifth ed. 1896, as above. CLRC

7459 SEVEN/LITTLE AUSTRALIANS/By/Ethel S. Turner/(Mrs. Curlewis)/Author of/"The Family at Misrule", "The Little Larrikin", etc./Illustrated by A. J. Johnson./London/Ward, Lock and Co., Limited/New York and Melbourne.
n.d. [1900? Latest of author's books listed in adv.: *Three Little Maids* 1900]
236pp, 20pp adv., b/w frontis. & 2 f/p b/w illus., b/w chapter headings, dec. clo., 185x120mm. KMM
Author's name on front cover & spine appears as 'Ethel Turner'.

7460 SEVEN LITTLE/AUSTRALIANS/By/Ethel Turner/(Mrs. Curlewis)/Author of "The Family at Misrule", "The/Little Larrikin", etc./Illustrated by J. Macfarlane/Ward, Lock & Co., Limited/London, Melbourne and Toronto/1912
[Author's note dated 1912, to 'This sixteenth edition of any first book']
256pp (inc. 1p author's note), 16pp adv., b/w frontis. & 7 b/w plates, clo. (with gilt design on front cover & spine differing from earlier ed.), 185x120mm. KMM
SEVEN LITTLE AUSTRALIANS
Imprint as 1912 ed.
n.d. [1919? Foreword dated Feb. 1912 reads: 'My publishers have asked me to add a preface to this sixteenth edition of my first book.' Presumably foreword included in various reprintings of book, for advertised in this copy are books by the author up to *Brigid and the Cub*, published 1919, so probably this edition appeared 1919 or 1920]
Details as in 1912 edition. KMM

7461 SEVEN LITTLE/AUSTRALIANS/By/Ethel Turner/(Mrs. Curlewis)/Author of "The Family at Misrule", "The/Little Larrikin", etc./Ward, Lock & Co., Limited/London and Melbourne
n.d. [1934.?] Author's note reads: 'My publishers have asked me to add a Preface to this twenty-seventh edition of my first book'
256pp (inc. 1p author's note & 1p publisher's note), frontis. & 7 b/w plates by J. Macfarlane, clo., 190x125mm. KMM

7462 SEVEN LITTLE AUSTRALIANS (as before)
1944 [Same notes as appeared in 16th ed., but altered to read: '...a preface to this twenty-seventh edition of my first book'. Publisher's note also lists editions from first publication to August 1944]
Details as in 1934 ed. but only 1 plate & frontis. KMM

7463 SEVEN LITTLE/AUSTRALIANS/By/Ethel Turner/Ward, Lock & Co., Limited/London and Melbourne.
1951
192pp, b/w frontis. only by J. F. Campbell, clo., 185x120mm. CLRC
• Rpt 1954, 1956, 1959, 1962, 1966 as in 1951 edition (imprint slightly varies to include Cape Town &c.) CLRC

7464 SEVEN/LITTLE AUSTRALIANS/By/Ethel Turner/(Mrs Curlewis)/Author of "Miss Bobbie" "Three Little Maids". Etc./Illustrated by A. J. Johnson/[device, "Girls Own Library"]/Philadelphia/David McKay, Publisher/610 South Washington Square
1904
243pp & 8pp adv, b/w frontis. & 1 b/w plate, b/w text drawings, pic. clo., 184x120mm. KMM

Swedish editions

7465 SJU SYSKON/(Seven Little Australians)/Af/Ethel S. Turner/Öfversättning af Mathilda Langlet/[device]/Stockholm/Fahlcrantz & C:o
1895
187pp, unillus., pic. bd. with clo. spine, adv. verso back cover, 185x122mm. RM
• Same, Sthlm. Fahlcrantz & C:o 1909
179s. , Omsl.: Fahlcrantz & C:o. 1 Kronasböcker N:0 2
• Same, 1910 Omsl.: Fahlcrantz & C:o. 1 Kronasböcker N:0 2
• Same, 1915 Omsl.: Fahlcrantz & C:o. 1 Kronasböcker N:0 2 Information from Kungliga Biblioteket, Stockholm

7466 SJU SYSKON/(Seven Little Australians)/Av/Ethel S. Turner/Översättning av Matilda [*sic*] Langlet/[device]/Femte Svenska Upplagan/Stockholm/Fahlcrantz & C:o.
1919
179pp, unillus., col. pic. bd. with clo. spine, adv. verso back cover, 180x120mm. RM
• SJU SYSKON—Övers. av Matilda [*sic*] Langlet Sthlm. Fahlcrantz 1924
175s., Omsl. Fahlcrantz & C:os. ungdomsböcker
• SJU SYSKON. SJU RUSTIBUSSAR I AUSTRALIEN. Berättelse för Flickor. Övers. fran engelskan av Ragnar Stigen
Sthlm. B. Wahlström 1928; 153, (1) s + omsl. B. Wählstroms Flickböcker (ungdomsböcke) 107
Same, 1933 157, (1) s. & omsl.
B. Wählstroms flickböcker (ungdomsböcker) 107

7467 Ethel Turner/SJU SYSKON/SJU RUSTIBUSSAR I AUSTRALIEN/Berättelse för flickor/Översättning/frän engelska av/Ragnar Stigen/Tredje Upplagan/[device]/B. Wahlströms Bokförlag
1944
137pp & 1p & 5pp adv., unillus., pic. wrappers, 170x120mm. LRA

7468 SJU SYSKON. Fran engelskan av Viveka Starfelt. Illustr. av Georg Lagerstedt.
Sthlm. Alb. Bonnier 1937
201, (1) s, 5 pl.—bl. & omsl.—Omsl: S. Ryggsida: De Odödliga Ungdomsböckerna, 3.
• SJU SYSKON
Sthlm., J. Hasselgren; tr. Louisa, Östra Nylands tidn. & tryck. a.-b. 1943—176 s.

7469 SJU SYSKON/Av/Ethel Turner/Fran Engelskan av/Viveka Starfelt/Illustrationer av/Georg Lagenstedt/[AB device]/Stockholm/Albert Bonniers Forlag
1945
201pp & 1p contents, 6 f/p b/w illus., bd., 206x140mm. LRA
SJU SYSKON—Sthlm. Harrier; tr. Örebro, Tryckcentralen 1949, 118 s. & omsl.
Same, Sthlm. Harrier; tr. Lund, Skänska Centraltr. 1955, 118 s.
Same, 1952, 201, (1) s. 5 pl.—bl. & pärm.

7470 SJU SYSKON. Övers. fran engelskan av Ingrid Rääf—Verso—Orig:s titel: Seven Little Australians
Uppsala, J. A. Lindblad: tr. Mariestad, Tidn. för Skaraborgs Iän 1954—189 s. & omsl.
Omsl: De klassiska ungdomsböckerna

7471 SJU SYSKON/Av/Ethel Turner/Från Engelskan av/Viveka Starfelt/Illustrationer av/Georg Lagerstedt/AB/Stockholm/Albert Bonniers Förlag
1952
201pp & 1p contents, 6 b/w illus., pic. bd., 214x144mm. LRA

7472 Another copy as above but with no 'AB' device on t.p., 1962
201pp, 4pp adv. LRA

Swedish edition published in Finland

7473 Ethel S. Turner; SJU SYSKON, Översättning av [translated into Swedish by] Matilda Langlet; Sjunde svenska upplagan (7th ed.) Published in Helsingors by Söderström & C:o Förlagsaktiebolag Printed in Lovisa 1943 by Östra Nylands Tidnings- & Tryckeri A.B., 176pp, unillus., not bound, 195x130mm. Unseen: Information from the University Library, Helsinki

Finnish editions

7474 Ethel S. Turner; SEITSEMÄN SISARUSTA; Suomensi [translated into Finnish by] Antti R. (ytkönen), Published in Porvoo by Werner Söderström, Printed in Wiipuri, 1896 by Wiipurin Uusi Kirjapaino ja Sanomalehtien Osake-Yhtiön Kirjapaino, Series: Uusi Valikoima Ulkomaan Kaunokirjallisuutta III
212pp, unillus., not bound, 165x115mm.

7475 Ethel S. Turner; SEITSEMÄN SISARUSTA; Suomentanut [translated into Finnish by] Laila Järvinen; Published in Porvoo & Helsinki by Werner Söderström Osakeyhtiö, Printed in Helsinki 1954 by Kauppalehden Kirjapaino; Series—Nuorten Toivekirjasto No. 28
170pp (+ 1), 1 illus., half clo., 190x125mm.
2nd ed. 1957, as above. Unseen: Information from the University Library, Helsinki

Czech edition

7476 E. Turnerová—P. Moudrá/SEDM RARASKU/Ilustroval Fr. Hornik/[device]/Nakladatelstvi Vojtech/Seba/Knihkupectvi/V. Praze
Prague 1938
142pp. Unseen: Information & photostat of t.p. supplied by Statni Knihovna, Prague

Danish editions

7477 SYV SØSKENDE/Fortaelling fra Australien/af/Ethel S. Turner Oversat af Sofie Horten/[device]/København/Lehmann & Stages Forlag/Triers Bogtrykker/(H. J. Schou)/1895
208pp
Second edition, published by the same firm 1903
Third edition, 1910 (publisher unknown)
Fourth edition, 1921, published by P. Haase & Sons, Forlag, Copenhagen
Fifth edition, 1943, published also by P. Haase & Sons
Unseen: Information from Det Kongelige Bibliotek, Copenhagen

German editions

7478 Französische und Englische/Schulbibliothek/Herausgegeben von Otto E. A. Dickmann/und E. Pariselle/Reihe A/Band 179/Two Tales for/Beginners/SEVEN LITTLE AUSTRALIANS/THE FAMILY AT MISRULE/By/Ethel Turner/Für den Schulgebrauch ausgewahlt und erklärt/von/Maria A. Hackenberg/Leipzig 1915/Rengersche Buchhandlung
93pp (a school edition of the two books considerably abridged)
Another edition, as above 1919

7479 TWO TALES FOR BEGINNERS. Seven Little Australians. The Family at Misrule. Neudr. Leipzig 1926, Bielefeld, Rengersche Buchhandling, 1926
93pp
These editions all: unillus., clo., 190x125mm. Unseen: Information from the Deutsche Bücherei, Leipzig

Norwegian editions

7480 Ethel Turner/SYV SMA AUSTRALIERE/Oversatt av/Ebba Sparre Nilson/[device]/Oslo/Forlagt av. H. Aschehoug & Co. (W. Nygaard)/1930
136pp, unillus., bdg unknown, 195x125mm.

7481 Ethel Turner/SJU VILLSTYRINGAR/(Seven Little Australians)/Pa Norsk av/Inger Hagerup/Norsk Barneblads Forlag/Oslo
1931
141pp, unillus., bdg unknown, 200x135mm.
Translated by Inger Hagerup

7482 Ethel S. Turner/SYV SØSKEN/Norsk Utgave ved/Eugenie Winther/[device]/N. W. Damm & Søn—Oslo
1938
122pp, unillus., bdg unknown, 185x125mm.
All unseen: Information & photostats of t.p. supplied by Universitets-biblioteket, Oslo

Dutch edition

7483 Ethel Turner/ZEVEN KLEINE AUSTRALIERS/Naar den zen druk uit het Engelsch Bewerkt/door/Marie ten Brink/Geillustreerd door A. J. Johnson/[vignette]/Gouda/G. B. van Goor Zohen
n.d. [1896]
xiv (inc. 4pp translator's foreword) 310pp, b/w frontis., 2 plates & chapter headings, clo. with illus., title, author &c. on front cover & spine bevelled edges, 190x125mm. LRA

Italian edition

7484 Ethel Turner/SETTE PICCOLI/AUSTRALIANI/Traduzione di Bice Pareto-Magliano/G. B. Paravia & C.
First edition, Torino 1955
133pp, 12 f/p col. illus. & b/w drawings in text, illus. by Albino Tovagliari, clo., 230x180mm.
Collana 'Le gemme d'oro'. ANL
• Rpt as above, 1962. RM

7485 THE FAMILY AT MISRULE/By/Ethel Turner/Author of/"Seven Little Australians", "The Story of a Baby" etc./[2 quotations]/With Illustrations by A. J. Johnson./London:/Ward Lock & Bowden, Limited,/Warwick House, Salisbury Square, E.C./New York and Melbourne./1895./All rights reserved
282pp, 6pp adv., dec. t.p. with vignette (preceding t.p. proper), b/w frontis., 2 f/p b/w illus., 25 line drawings in text, dec. clo., 180x120mm. CLRC
Second edition 1895, as above, except for 'Second edition' on t.p. CLRC

Third edition, 1896, as above. CLRC
Imprint as above but: Fourth Edition/London:/Ward, Lock & Co. Limited...
n.d.
As earlier editions. KMM
Another copy as fourth edition, but n.d. & no additional t.p. KMM

7486 THE/FAMILY AT MISRULE/By/Ethel Turner/ Author of/"Seven Little Australians", "The Story of a Baby",etc./[2 quotes]/Ward, Lock & Co., Limited/ London Melbourne and Toronto
n.d. [1914?]
255pp &16 pp adv. col. frontis. only, clo. (dark blue 'peacock' design, title & author in gilt)
The col. unsigned frontispiece shows parents and two boys at a tea table at a dramatic moment. 180x120mm. CLRC
Another copy as above, n.d. (inscribed 1917) light blue clo. J.McG.
Another copy as above n.d. (inscribed 1919) clo. (grey, peacock design). CLRC

7487 THE FAMILY AT MISRULE/By/Ethel Turner/ Author of/"Seven Little Australians", "The Story of a Baby" etc./[2 quotations]/Ward, Lock & Co., Limited/ London, Melbourne and Toronto
n.d. [includes publisher's note to new edition]
255pp, b/w frontis. & 2 f/p b/w illus. by A. J. Johnson, clo., 185x120mm. KMM
• THE FAMILY AT MISRULE
Imprint as above
n.d. [publisher's note states that 17 editions of *Seven Little Australians* had now been published, which would date this edition c.1914]
255pp, b/w frontis. & 2 f/p b/w illus. by A. J. Johnson, clo., 185x125mm. KMM
• Another copy as above but publisher's note states that 28 editions of *Seven Little Australians* had now been published.

7488 THE/FAMILY AT MISRULE/Further Adventures of the famous/"Seven Little Australians"/By/Ethel Turner/[2 quotations]/Ward, Lock & Co., Limited/ London and Melbourne
n.d. [195-?]
192pp, b/w frontis. only by J. F. Campbell, clo., 185x120mm. KMM

Swedish editions

7489 STORA SYSTER. Övers af Mathilda Langlet, Sthlm., Fahlcrantz & C:o; tr. I. Haggström, 1896
(4), 202 s.
Same—Sthlm. Fahlcrantz & C:o, 1910
189s., Omsl. Fahlcrantz & C:o's 1 Kronasböcker N:0 15
Same—1910—as above
Same 1918, omsl. Fahlcrantz & C:os. ungsdomsböcker
Same 1922, omsl. Fahlcrantz & C:os. ungsdomsböcker

7490 FAMILJEN pa "VILLERVALLAN". Berättelse för flickor. övers. fran engelskan av Ragnar Stigen, Sthlm. B. Wahlström 1928
173, (1) s + omsl.
Same 1933, 158s. & omsl., B. Wählstroms flickböcker (ungdomsböcker) 123
Same 1945, 138 (1) & parm., B. Wählstroms flickböcker (ungdomsböcker) 123

7491 STORA SYSTER. Fran engelskan av Viveka Starfelt. Illustr. av Georg Lagerstedt, (Verso: Orig.s titel: The Family at Misrule), Sthlm. A. B. Bonnier, 1938
243 s, 5 pl.—bl. & omsl., Omsl. De odödliga ungdomsböckerna

7492 STORA SYSTER/av/Ethel S. Turner/Fört. till "Sju Syskon"/oversattning av Mathilda Langlet/Sjatte Upplagan/Stockholm/A. B. Hasselgrens Förlagsbokhandel
1944
210pp, unillus., clo., 174x114mm. LRA

7493 STORA SYSTER/av/Ethel Turner/Från engelskan av/Vivcka Starfelt/Illustrationer av/Georg Lagenstedt/[AB device]/Stockholm/Albert Bonniers Forlag
1954
242pp & 1p contents, 5 f/p b/w illus., clo., 212x140mm. LRA
Same 1952, 201, (1) s. 5 pl.—bl. & pärm.

Swedish edition published in Finland

7494 Ethel S. Turner; Förf. till "Sju Syskon" m.m.; STORA SYSTER; Översättning av [translated into Swedish by]/Mathilda Langlet; Sjätte upplagan [6th ed.] Published in Helsingfors by Söderström & C:o Förlagsaktiebolag; Printed in Lovisa 1944 by Östra Nylands Tidnings—& Tryckeri A.B.
210pp, unillus., not bound, 195x130mm. Unseen: Information from the University Library, Helsinki

Finnish editions

7495 Ethel S. Turner; SISARUSTEN VARTTUESSA; Suomensi [translated into Finnish by] Antti R. (ytkönen), Published in Porvoo by Werner Söderström, Printed in Wiipuri, 1897 by Wiipurin Uusi Kirjapaino ja Sanomalehtien Osake-Yhtiön Kirjapaino; Series: Uusi Valikoima Ulkomaan Kaunokirjallisuutta IV
244pp, unillus., not bound, 165x115mm. Info. from University of Helskink

7496 Ethel S. Turner; SISARUSTEN VARTTUESSA, Suomentanut [translated into Finnish by] Laila Järvinen; Published in Porvoo & Helsinki by Werner Söderström Osakeyhtiö; Printed in Kuopio 1954 by Kirjapaino Osakeyhtiö Savo; Series—Nuorten Toivekirjasto No. 47
168pp, unillus., half clo., 190x125mm. Unseen: Information from the University Library, Helsinki

Danish editions

7497 FAMILIEN/PAA "UROLIGHEDEN"/Fortaelling fra australien/af/Ethel S. Turner/Forf. af. "Syv Søskende"/Oversat af Sofie Horten/[device]/ København/Lehmann & Stages Forlag/Friers Bogtrykkeri (F. L. Lind & Numa Fraenkel)/1896
239pp. Info. from Det Kongelige Bibliotek, Copenhagen

7498 FAMILIEN PAA/"UROLIGHEDEN"/Fortaelling fra Australien/af/Ethel S. Turner/(Mrs H. R. Curlewis)/Autoriseret oversaetrelse for Danmark og Norge/ved/Sofie Horten/Anden Udgave/[device]/ København/Lehmann & Stages Forlag/1905
240pp (inc. 1p contents), unillus., three-quarter leather, 180x120mm. LRA

7499 Third edition, 1913 (? the same publisher)
Fourth edition, 1922, published by P. Haase & Søns, Forlag, Copenhagen
Fifth edition, 1944, also published by P. Haase & Søns Forlag, Copenhagen
Unseen: Information from Det Kongelige Bibliotek, Copenhagen

Norwegian edition

7500 Ethel S. Turner/DE SYV SØSKEN/PA ELVEGARDEN/Norsk utgave ved/Eugenie Winther/ [device]/N. W. Damm & Søn—Oslo
1939 [Library states that the original title is not indicated, but this translation is the continuation of the different editions of *Seven Little Australians* & was probably *The Family at Misrule*]
118pp, unillus., bdg. unknown, 190x125mm.
Unseen: Information & photostat of t.p. supplied by Universitets-biblioteket, Oslo

German edition

See Seven Little Australians—Two Tales for Beginners

Dutch edition

7501 Ethel Turner/DE BEWONERS VAN MISRULE/uit het Engelsch Bewerkt/door/Marie ten Brink/

Geillustreerd door A. J. Johnson/[vignette]/Gouda/G. B. van goor zohen
n.d.
363pp, b/w frontis., 2 b/w plates & drawings in text, pic. clo. blocked in gilt on front cover & spine, bevelled edges, 192x124mm. LRA

7502 THE LITTLE LARRIKIN,/By/Ethel Turner,/Author of/"Seven Little Australians". "The Family at Misrule",/"The Story of a Baby", Etc./[quotation]/with illustrations by A. J. Johnson/London:/Ward, Lock & Co., Limited,/Warwick House, Salisbury Square, E.C./ New York and Melbourne.
n.d. [inscribed 1896, first edition]
343pp. (inc. 2 pp dedication), 8 pp adv., b/w frontis. & 3f/p b/w illus., 21 b/w drawings in text, pic. clo., 180x120mm. CLRC

7503 THE LITTLE LARRIKIN./By/Ethel Turner,/Author of/"Seven Little Australians", "The Family at Misrule",/"The Story of a Baby", etc./[quotation]/With illustrations by A. J. Johnson./Second Edition./ London:/Ward, Lock & Co., Limited,/Warwick House, Salisbury Square, E.C./New York and Melbourne./ 1896
Details as before. KMM

7504 THE/LITTLE LARRIKIN./By/Ethel Turner/(Mrs. H. R. Curlewis)/Author of/"Seven Little Australians", "The Family at Misrule",/"Miss Bobbie", "Three Little Maids", etc./[quotation]/With illustrations by A. J. Johnson./London:/Ward, Lock & Co., Limited,/New York and Melbourne.
n.d. [1900?]
Details as above but 190x125mm. KMM

7505 THE/LITTLE LARRIKIN/By/Ethel Turner/(Mrs. H. R. Curlewis)/Author of "Seven Little Australians", "The Family at/Misrule", "Three Little Maids", etc./ [quotation]/Ward, Lock & Co., Limited,/London and Melbourne/1920
255pp (inc. 2pp dedication), b/w frontis. & 2 b/w illus. by J. Macfarlane, clo., 185x120mm. BBC

7506 THE/LITTLE LARRIKIN/By/Ethel Turner/ [quotation]/Ward, Lock & Co., Limited/London and Melbourne
n.d. [1950?]
255pp (inc. dedication), b/w frontis. only, clo., 185x120mm. K&NI
Frontispiece ('Lol was leading the downward rush') unsigned.

Swedish editions

7507 "EN LITEN SLARFVER"—Öfvers af. Mathilda Langlet, Sthlm., Fahlcrantz & C:o; tr. I. Haeggström, 1897 (2) 242 s.
• EN LITEN SLARVER/(The Little Larrikin)/Av/Ethel S. Turner/Förf. Till "Sju Syskon" och "Stora Syster"/översättning av Mathilda Langlet./[device]/ Andra Upplagen/Stockholm/Fahlcrantz & C:o
1912
238pp, unillus., col. pic. wrappers with adv., 195x130mm. RM
• Same, 1918, Omsl: Fahlcrantz & C:os. ungsdomsböcker

7508 EN LITEN SLARVER as before but: Fjärde Upplagen/Stockholm/A. B. J. Hasselgrens Forlags bokhandel
1946
254pp, unillus., bd., 176x120mm. LRA

Swedish edition published in Finland

7509 Ethel S. Turner; Förf. Till "Sju Syskon" och "Stora Syster" M. FL., EN LITEN SLARVER; Översättning av [translated into Swedish by] Mathilda Langlet; Fjärde upplagan [4th ed.] Published in Helsingfors by Söderström & C:o Förlagsaktiebolag; Printed in Lovisa 1946 by Östra Nylands Tidnings—& Tryckeri A.B.
254pp, unillus., not bound, 195x130mm. Unseen: Information from the University Library, Helsinki

Finnish edition

7510 Ethel S. Turner; PIKKU VEITIKKA; Suomennos [Anonym. trans. into Finnish] Published in Jyväskylä by K. J. Gummerus O.Y., Printed in Jyväskylä 1925 by the publisher, Series: Gummeruksen Nuorten Kirjasto No. 16
263pp, unillus., clo., 185x125mm. Unseen: Information from the University Library, Helsinki

Danish edition

7511 EN LILLE VILDKAT/af/Ethel S. Turner/(Mrs H. R. Curlewis)/Autoriseret oversaettelse for Danmark og Norge/ved/Sofie Horten/[device]/København/ Lehmann & Stages Forlag/1905
240pp. Unseen: Information & photostat of t.p. from the Royal Library, Copenhagen

Norwegian edition

7512 Ethel Turner/DEN VESLE SKØIEREN/Fortaelling fra Australien/Den Forkortede oversaettelse gjennemseet/Cammermeyers Boghandel/1903
Abridged translation by Marie Jørstad (Library states that the original title is not indicated but is probably *The Little Larrikin*)
119pp, unillus., bdg. unknown, 200x125mm. Unseen: Information & photostat of t.p. supplied by Universitets-biblioteket, Oslo

German edition

7513 LOL/Australischer Roman von/E. Turner/[device]/ Verlag und Druk von J. P. Bachem in Köln
1922
242pp, unillus., half cloth, 180x120mm. Unseen: Information & photostat of t.p. supplied by Deutsche Bücherei, Leipzig

Dutch edition

7514 Ethel Turner/BROER/uit het Engelsch bewerkt/ Door/Meurouw G. Willeumier/Geillustreerd door A. J. Johnson/[device]/Gouda/G. B. Van Goor Zonen
n.d. [189-?]
344pp (last blank), illus. (as in English edition), clo., 195x125mm. NSL:M

7515 MISS BOBBIE/By/Ethel Turner/(Mrs. H. R. Curlewis)/Author of "Seven Little Australians", "The Little Larrikin", etc./Illustrated by Harold Copping/ Ward, Lock & Co., Limited/London, Melbourne and New York/1897
316pp (inc. 1p dedication & 1p note), 4pp adv., b/w frontis. & 7 f/p b/w illus., 25 line drawings in text, dec. clo., 185x120mm. KMM
Some of the chapters of this story appeared in the *Illustrated Sydney News*.

7516 MISS BOBBIE/By/Ethel Turner/(Mrs. H. R. Curlewis)/Author of/"Seven Little Australians", "The Little Larrikin"/"In the Mist of the Mountains", etc./ Illustrated by Harold Copping/London:/Ward, Lock & Co., Limited
316pp (inc. 1p dedication,1p note), 4pp adv., b/w frontis. & 7 b/w plates, 25 line drawings, clo., 185x120mm. KMM
Several copies undated & as above but different titles by same author listed.

7517 MISS BOBBIE/By/Ethel Turner/(Mrs. H. R. Curlewis)/Author of "Seven Little Australians",/"The Little Larrikin", "The Family at Misrule", etc./ Illustrated by Harold Copping/Ward, Lock & Co., Limited/London and Melbourne
n.d. [1915?]
Details as above but frontis. & 5 b/w plates. KMM

7518 Grade IV Price Sevenpence/MISS BOBBIE/By Ethel Turner/Author of "Seven Little Australians" & etc./[vignette]/Abridged by Lillian M. Pyke/Author of

"Max the Sport", "Jack of St. Virgils" & etc./E. W. Cole Book Arcade/Melbourne & Sydney
n.d. [1917? other books advertised appearing up to, but not beyond 1916]
128pp (inc. 1p introduction & 2pp notes), 2pp adv., 4 f/p b/w illus., wrappers (with adv. inside & outside back wrapper), cover title, 180x115mm. KMM
Illustrations signed 'W.S.' (redrawn from Harold Copping's original drawings)
• Another Ward, Lock ed., imprint as 1915 ed. but dated 1923
256pp (inc. 1p dedication, 1p note), b/w frontis. & 7 b/w plates, b/w drawings in text, dec. clo., 180x125mm. MK

7519 MISS BOBBIE/By/Ethel Turner/Ward, Lock & Co. Limited/London and Melbourne
n.d. [193-?]
256pp, b/w frontis. only by Harold Copping, clo., cover design reproducing drawing from earlier editions, 180x120mm. BBC
• Rpt as above (imprint includes Cape Town) but frontis. by Rene Cloke. K&NI

Swedish editions

7520 EN LITEN YRHATTA (Miss Bobbie) Öfvers. af. Mathilda Langlet Sthlm. Fahlcrantz & C:o; tr. I. Haggström, 1899 (2) 193 s.
Same, tr. A. B. Fahlcrantz & boktr. 1913 185 s Omsl. Fahlcrantz C:os 1 kronasböcker 27
Same, 1917, 175 s. Omsl: Fahlcrantz & C:o ungsdomsböcker

7521 EN LITEN YRHÄTTA/(Miss Bobbie)/av.,/Ethel S. Turner/Förf. till "Sju Syskon" "Stora Syster" m.fl./ översättning av Mathilda Langlet/[device]/Fjarde Upplagen/Stockholm/Fahlcrantz & C:o
1921
175pp, unillus., pic. bd., clo. spine, 185x120mm. LRA

7522 BOBBIE. Berättelse för flickor. Övers. fran engelska av Kerstin Wenström. Sthlm. B. Wahlström, 1935
159 s. & omsl. (B.Wahlströms flickböcker—ungsdomsböcker)

7523 Another copy as above but: Femte Upplagan/ Stockholm/A. B. J. Hasselgrens förlägsbokhandel
1945
202pp, unillus., pic. bd., clo. spine, 183x123mm. LRA

7524 BOBBIE. Berättelse för flickor. Övers. fran engelska av Kerstin Wenström. Sthlm. B. Wahlström, 1950
159, (1) s. & pärm. (B.Wahlströms flickböcker—ungsdomsböcker)
Unseen: Information from catalogue cards of Kungliga Biblioteket, Stockholm

Swedish edition published in Finland

7525 Ethel S. Turner; Forf. till "Sju Syskon", "Stora Syster" M. FL., EN LITEN YRHATTA; Översättning av (translated into Swedish by) Matilda Langlet; Femte upplagan [5th ed.] Published in Helsingfors by Söderström & C:o Förlagsaktiebolag; Printed in Lovisa 1945 by Östra Nylands Tidnings—& Tryckeri A.B.
202pp, unillus., not bound, 195x130mm. Unseen: Information from the University Library, Helsinki

Finnish edition

7526 Ethel Turner; BOBBIE KOULITAAN POJAKSI; Suomentanut [translated into Finnish by] Aune Ståhlberg; Published in Helsinki by Kustannusosakeyhitiö Otava, Printed in Helsinki 1936 by the publishers; Series—Tuttöjen kirjasto No. 14
195pp, unillus., half clo., 170x120mm. Unseen: Information from the University Library, Helsinki

Norwegian edition

7527 Ethel Turner/LILLE FRØKEN BOBBIE/En Fortaelling for Piker og/Gutter fra syv til fjorten aar/ Oversat/av/Aagot Holst/[device]/Kristiania/Forlagt av. H. Aschehoug & Co. (W. Nygaard)/1916
152pp, unillus., bdg. unknown, 190x120mm.
Translated by Aagot Holst. Unseen: Information & photostat of t.p. supplied by Universitets-biblioteket, Oslo

Dutch edition

7528 BOBBIE
Published by Uitgeverij Kluitman, Alkmaar, Holland, n.d.
Unseen: Information supplied by Bureau Boek en Jeugd der C.V., The Hague, Holland

Czech edition

7529 Ethel Turnerová:/DANUSKA/A/VESELY CTYRLISTEK/Ilustroval akademicky malif/J. Wowk./ [device]/Knihkypectvi Vojtech Seba Nakladatelstvi/ Praha—St. Strasnice
Translation of title reads: 'Danuska and the Happy Foursome'. It is known for certain that this is a translation of *Miss Bobbie,* but no other details are known. Unseen: Information & photostat of t.p. supplied by Statni Knihovna, Prague

7530 THE CAMP AT/WANDINONG/By Ethel Turner/ (Mrs. Curlewis)/Author of "Seven Little Austra-/lians" "The Family at Misrule"/"Miss Bobbie" etc. etc./ Illustrated by Frances/Ewan and Others/London/ Ward, Lock and Co Limited/New York and Melbourne
n.d. [First published 1898]
286pp (inc. 2pp dedicatory letter), 2pp adv., b/w frontis. & 19 b/w plates, clo., dec., 185x125mm. KMM
Frontispiece & some illustrations by Frances Ewan; other illustrations by various artists.
Contains title story & 10 other stories, including 'The Child of the Children' later reprinted separately.
Another copy, n.d., as above, but: Ward, Lock & Co., Limited/London, Melbourne and Toronto
KMM
Another copy, n.d., as above, but: Warwick House Salisbury Square E.C./New York and Melbourne. MK

Swedish edition

7531 GULDGRAVARLAGRET och Andra Berättelser. Övers. av. H. Flygare
Sthlm. Fahlcrantz & Co:o 1915
170 (1) s.
Omsl.: Fahlcrantz & Co's. en-kronasböcker
Unseen: Information from photostat of catalogue cards of Kungliga Biblioteket, Stockholm, & of first page of Swedish text

7532 THREE LITTLE MAIDS/By/Ethel Turner/(Mrs. H. R. Curlewis)/Author of "Seven Little Australians", "The Little Larrikin",/"The Camp at Wandinong", etc./[quotation]/London/Ward, Lock & Co., Limited/ Warwick House, Salisbury Square, E.C./New York and Melbourne/1900
315pp, 1p dedicatory verse, 4pp adv., b/w frontis. & 3 b/w plates, 21 b/w drawings in text, illus. A. J. Johnson, dec. clo., 190x120mm. KMM
Another copy as above but undated & without 'New York and Melbourne'. KP
Another undated copy as above but imprint: Ward Lock & Co, Limited/London Melbourne and Toronto. KP

7533 THREE LITTLE/MAIDS/By/Ethel Turner/(Mrs. H. R. Curlewis)/Author of "Seven Little Australians", "The Little Larrikin",/"The Camp at Wandinong", etc./[quotation]/Ward, Lock & Co., Limited/London and Melbourne
n.d.
315pp, 4pp adv., b/w frontis. & 3 b/w plates, b/w drawings in text, clo., 185x120mm. KMM

Frontispiece & 3 plates by Margaret Tarrant; drawings in text by A. J. Johnson.
7534 Another copy as above but frontis. & 1 plate only. KMM
7535 THREE LITTLE/MAIDS/By/Ethel Turner/ [quotation]/Ward, Lock & Co., Limited/London and Melbourne
315pp, 4pp adv., b/w frontis. only, line drawings in text, clo., 185x120mm.
Frontispiece by Margaret Tarrant; line drawings by A. J. Johnson. K&NI
7536 As above n.d. [1950?]
224pp (inc. dedicatory verse), b/w frontis. only by Margaret Tarrant, clo., 180x120mm. KMM
Swedish editions
7537 TRE SMA FLICKOR. Övers. af. H. Flygare, Sthlm. Fahlcrantz & C:o tr. Centraltr. 1901
232pp
7538 DEN DAR FLICKAN. Bemynd. Övers. fran engelskan av H. Flygare, Sthlm. Fahlcrantz, 1911
268pp
7539 TRE SMA FLICKOR. Öfvers. af. H. Flygare, Sthlm. Fahlcrantz & C:o trn Centraltr. 1916
209pp
Unseen: Information from photostat of catalogue cards of Kungliga Biblioteket, Stockholm
7540 TRE SMA FLICKOR/av/Ethel S. Turner/Förf till "Sju Syskon", "Stora Syster"M. Fl./[device]/Tredje Upplagen/Stockholm/Fahlcrantz & Co.
1919
208pp, unillus., pic. wrappers, 190x125mm. CLRC
7541 Ethel Turner/DET NYA HEMMET/Berättelse för flickor/översättning/från Engelska av/Einar Ekstrand/ [device B.W]/B. Wahlströms Bokförlag
1931
158pp (inc. 2pp contents), 2pp adv., unillus., pic. bd., 170x120mm. LRA
Dutch edition
7542 DRIE JONGE MEISJES
Published by Uitgeverij Kluitman, Alkmaar, Holland, n.d.
Unseen: Information from Bureau Boek en Jeugd der C.V., The Hague, Holland

7543 GUM/LEAVES/By Ethel/Turner/With Oddme-/nts by Others/Pictures by/D. H. Souter/ William Brooks & Co./Sydney & Brisbane
n.d. [1900]
221pp, 8pp adv., b/w drawings throughout, pic. bd. (clo. spine), 250x140mm. KMM
Contains 'An Ogre Up to Date' & other stories, poems, & letters for children. Publisher's note states that 'some of the matter contained in these pages appeared in The *Town and Country Journal*". Also contains imaginary reports from the South African War.
7544 Another edition as above but varying slightly on pp67–8, 115, 116, 162, 220. A few verses have been replaced in the second edition with mock reports from the South African War. NSL:M

7545 THE/WONDER-CHILD/An Australian Story/By/ Ethel Turner/(Mrs H. R. Curlewis)/Author of 'Seven Little Aus-/tralians', 'The Camp at Wan-/dinong', 'The Story of a Baby'/'Three Little Maids' etc./[quotation]/ With illustrations/by Gordon Browne/London/The Religious Tract Society/56 Paternoster Row and/65 St Paul's Churchyard
n.d. [prize 1901]
320pp & 8pp adv., b/w frontis. & 6 b/w plates, dec. clo., 182x122mm. CLRC
2nd and 3rd eds, as above, n.d.
• Rpt as above but imprint: Fourth impression/ London/The Religious Tract Society/4 Bouverie Street and 65 St Paul's Churchyard, E.C., NSL:M
5th imp., as above, n.d. KMM
7546 Another copy fifth ed. as above except that plate opp. p78 is coloured, & the blue clo. bdg. has a coloured onlay on front cover & black not white lettering. KMM
7547 THE/WONDER-CHILD/By/Ethel Turner/Angus and Robertson Ltd./Sydney:/London/1941
234pp, b/w frontis. only, clo., 180x120mm. KMM
Swedish edition
7548 UNDERBARNET. Övers. af. H. Flygare., Sthlm., Fahlcrantz & C:o; tr. Centraltr. 1902
236 s. Unseen: Information from catalogue card of Kungliga Biblioteket, Stockholm
Finnish edition
7549 Ethel Turner: IHMELAPSI AUSTRALIALAINEN TARINA; Suomentanut (translated into Finnish by) Aune Krohn; Published in Porvoo by Werner Söderström Osakeyhtiö; Printed in Porvoo 1921 by Werner Söderström Osakeyhtiön Kirjapaino
222pp, unillus., not bound, 180x125mm. Unseen: Information from the University Library, Helsinki
Dutch edition
7550 HET WONDERKIND/Een Australisch Verhaal/ door Ethel S. Turner/Schrijtster van: Zeven Kleine Austra-/liërs, De Bewoners van Misrule, enz./Uit het Engelsch Bewekert/door/G. W. Elberts/geillustreerd door Gordon Browne./Tweede Druk/[device]/Utrecht A.W. Bruna & Zoon
n.d.
306pp & 2pp biographical note, b/w frontis. & 6 b/w plates, dec. clo., 190x126mm. LRA

7551 LITTLE MOTHER MEG/By/Ethel Turner/(Mrs. H. R. Curlewis)/Author of/"Seven Little Australians", "The Family at Misrule",/"The Little Larrikin", etc./ [quotation]/Illustrated/London/Ward, Lock & Co., Limited/New York and Melbourne/1902
266pp, 6pp adv., b/w frontis. & 3 b/w plates, b/w drawings in text throughout by A. J. Johnson, dec. clo., 190x120mm. CLRC
Another copy as above but 'The Little Larrikin' omitted. CLRC
7552 LITTLE MOTHER MEG/By/Ethel Turner/(Mrs. H. R. Curlewis)/Author of/"Seven Little Australians", "The Family at Misrule",/"The Little Larrikin", etc./ [quotation]/Illustrated/Ward, Lock & Co., Limited/ London, Melbourne and Toronto/1910
Details as above. BBC
7553 Another copy as above, n.d., but frontis. by J. Macfarlane & 1 b/w plate, text drawings by A. J. Johnson. CLRC
7554 Another copy inscribed 1930, 266pp, b/w frontis. & 3 plates by J. Macfarlane, text drawings by A. J. Johnson. CLRC
7555 LITTLE MOTHER MEG/By/Ethel Turner/ [quotation]/Ward, Lock & Co., Limited/London and Melbourne
n.d. [school prize 1953]
222pp, 2pp adv., unsgd. b/w frontis. only, clo., 180x120mm. KMM
Another copy as above but with: London, Melbourne and Cape Town. KMM
7556 LITTLE MOTHER MEG/By/Ethel Turner/(Mrs H. R. Curlewis)/Author of "Seven Little Australians","The Family at Misrule" "Miss Bobbie" etc./Illustrated/[device—Girls Own Library]/ Philadelphia/David McKay, Publisher/610 South Washington Square

n.d. [inscribed1915], 266pp, & 5pp, adv. b/w drawings in text, pic. clo., 183x123mm. NU

Swedish editions

7557 STORA SYSTER SOM GIFT/Samt/Mera Om Ungherrskapet På/Oroligheten/Av/Ethel S. Turner/ Förf. "Sju Syskon" "Stora Syster" M.M./Översättning av C. Christiansson/[device]/Stockholm/Fahlcrantz & C:o.
1914
185pp, unillus., col. pic. bd. with clo. spine, adv. verso back cover, 185x120mm. RM
Same, 1917, 185 s. + Omsl., Omsl. Fahlcrantz & cos. 1 kronasböcker 29

7558 STORA SYSTER SOM GIFT/samt/Mera om ungherrskapet på oroligheten/av/Ethel S. Turner/Förf till Sju Syskon Stora Syster M fl./oversattning av C. Christiansson/[device]/Tredje upplagen/Stockholm/ Fahlcrantz & C:o.
1922
185pp, unillus., pic. bd., clo. spine, 182x120mm. LRA

7559 STORA SYSTER/SOM GIFT/av/Ethel Turner/Från Engelskan av/Viveka Starfelt/Illustrationer av/Georg Lagerstedt/[AB device]/Stockholm/Albert Bonniers Forlag
1939
218pp & 1p contents, 5 f/p b/w illus., pic. bd., clo. spine, 214x146mm. LRA
• Rpt as 1922 edition but: Fjärde upplagan/Stockholm/ A.B. J. Hasselgrens Forlagsbokhandel
1944
198pp, unillus., pic. bd., clo. spine, 184x120mm. LRA
• Rpt as 1939 edition but 1957, plain bd., 202x127mm. LRA

Swedish edition printed in Finland

7560 Förf. till "Sju Syskon", "Stora Syster" M. Fl., STORA SYSTER SOM GIFT samt mera om ungherrskapet pa Oroligheten; Översättning av (translated into Swedish by) C. Christiansson, Fjärde upplagan [fourth ed.] Published in Helsingfors by Söderström & C:o Förlagsaktiebolag, Printed in Lovisa 1944 by Östra Nylands Tidnings & Tryckeri A.B.
198pp, unillus., not bound, 195x130mm. Unseen: Information from the University Library, Helsinki

Czech edition

7561 Ethel Turnerová—P. Moudrá/MARCELCINO/ STESTI—Ilustroval Fr. Mornik/[device]/Nakladatelstvi Vojtéch Seba Knihkypectvi/V. Praze
Prague 1938
150pp. Unseen: Information from Statni Knihovna, Prague

Danish editions

7562 LILLE MO'R MEG/Fortaelling fra Australien/af/ Ethel S. Turner/(Mrs. H. R. Curlewis)/Autoriseret oversaettelse for Danmark og Norge/ved/Sofie Horten/[device]/København/Lehmann & Stages Forlag/1903
239pp
Second edition, 1911
Third edition, 1922, published by P. Haase & Søns, Forlag, København
Fourth edition, 1945, published by P. Haase & Søns, Forlag, København
Unseen: Information & photostat of t.p. of first edition from Det Kongelige Bibliotek, Copenhagen

Dutch edition

7563 MOEDERJE MEG
Published by Uitgeverij Kluitman, Alkmaar, Holland, n.d. [Second edition 1913]
Unseen: Information from Bureau Boek en Jeugd der C.V.

7564 BETTY & CO./By/Ethel Turner/(Mrs. H. R. Curlewis)/Author of "Seven Little Australians", "The Family at Misrule",/"The Little Larrikin", "Miss Bobbie" etc./Illustrated/London/Ward, Lock & Co. Limited/New York and Melbourne/1903
309pp, 10pp adv., b/w frontis. & 23 b/w plates, dec. clo., 190x120mm. NSL:M
Illustrated by various artists, including Arthur Buckland [?], F. Ewan, J. Macfarlane, A. J. Johnson, E. Lance, A. Pearse, &c.
Contains title story & 11 short stories some reprinted from the *Windsor, Leisure Hour, Gentlewoman, Bulletin,* &c.
• Rpt as above 1908. KMM
• Rpt as above 1910. KMM

Swedish editions

7565 BETTY & CO., med. flera berättelser. Ofvers. af H. Flygare Sthlm., Fahlcrantz & Co., tr. Centrltr. 190r
136 s.
Same, Tr. A.-B. Fahlcrantz, 1918
Unseen: Information from photostats of catalogue cards of Kungliga Biblioteket, Stockholm

7566 MOTHER'S LITTLE GIRL/By Ethel Turner/(Mrs. H. R. Curlewis)/Author of "Seven Little Australians", "The/Family at Misrule", "The Little Larrikin",/etc. etc./Illustrations by A. J. Johnson/London/Ward, Lock & Co. Limited/1904
255pp, 1p dedication, 2pp adv., b/w frontis. & 7 b/w plates, dec. clo., 185x120mm. KMM
Another edition as above, 1906, no adv. BBC

7567 MOTHER'S/LITTLE GIRL/By Ethel Turner/(Mrs. H. R. Curlewis)/Author of "Seven Little Australians", "The/Family at Misrule", "The Little Larrikin",/etc. etc./Ward, Lock & Co. Limited/London and Melbourne
n.d.
255pp, b/w frontis. & 3 b/w plates, illus. by J. Macfarlane, clo., 185x120mm. KMM

Swedish editions

7568 Ethel Turner/MORS LILLA/FLICKA/(Mother's Little Girl)/Berättelse för flickor/översättning/från Engelska av/Kerstin Wenström/[device B.W]/B. Wahlströms Bokförlag
1939
156pp, 4pp adv., unillus., bd. LRA
Same, 1942—156 s. & pärm. (B. Wählstroms flickböcker—ungdomsböcker, 280)

Dutch edition

7569 MOEDERS JONGSTE LIEVELING
Published by Uitgeverij Kluitman, Alkmaar, Holland, n.d.
Unseen: IFP

7570 A/WHITE ROOF-TREE/By/Ethel Turner/(Mrs. H. R. Curlewis)/Author of "Seven Little Australians", "The/Family at Misrule",/"The Little Larrikin", etc./ With sixteen full-page illustrations/London/Ward, Lock & Co. Limited/1905
342pp, 10pp adv., b/w frontis. & 15 b/w plates, dec. clo., 190x120mm. BBC
Illustrated by A. J. Johnson, Grenville Manton, Bertha Newcombe, &c.
Contents include title story (109pp), & 8 other stories.
Another copy as above but n.d. &: Ward, Lock & Co., Limited/London and Melbourne. KMM

7571 IN THE MIST OF/THE MOUNTAINS/By/Ethel Turner/(Mrs. H. R. Curlewis)/Author of "Seven Little Australians", "The Little Larrikin",/"Miss Bobbie", etc. etc./Illustrations by J. Macfarlane/London/Ward, Lock & Co. Limited/1906
267pp, 4pp adv., b/w frontis. & 7 b/w plates, dec. clo., 185x125mm. KMM

• Rpt as above, n.d. Imprint: Ward Lock & Co. Limited/London, Melbourne and Toronto. KMM

Danish edition

7572 DOMMERENS BØRN/af/Ethel S. Turner/(Mrs. H. R. Curlewis)/Autoriseret oversaettelse for Danmark og Norge/ved/Sofie Horten/[device]/København/ Lehmann & Stages Forlag/1907
251pp. Unseen: Information from Det Kongelige Bibliotek, Copenhagen

Dutch edition

7573 IN DE BERGEN
Published by Uitgeverij Kluitman, Alkmaar, Holland, n.d.
Unseen: IFP

7574 THE STOLEN VOYAGE/By/Ethel Turner/Author of "Seven Little Australians", "The/Little Larrikin", etc./Illustrated by R. Hawcridge, J. Macfarlane, etc./ London/Ward, Lock & Co. Limited/1907
316pp, 2pp adv., b/w frontis. & 19 b/w plates, dec. clo., 190x120mm. KMM
Includes title story & 10 other short stories; illustrators include Clara Almstead as well as those named on t.p.
• Rpt as above, 1908. KMM
• Rpt n.d. but imprint: Ward, Lock & Co., Limited/ London Melbourne and Toronto. PR

7575 HAPPY HEARTS/A Picture Book for Boys and Girls/Including/"The Raft in the Bush" and "Chronicles of the Court"/By/Ethel Turner/[verse]/ London/Ward, Lock & Co. Limited/1908
176pp, col. frontis. & 8 b/w plates, b/w drawings in text throughout, pic. bd. (clo. spine), dec. e/p, 270x215mm. KMM
Frontispiece by H. G. Hewitt; f/p illustrations by D. H. Souter; drawings in text by various artists
Stories & verses by Ethel Turner, verses by Reginald Rigby & others. Included are the stories 'The Raft in the Bush', & 'Chronicles of the Court'. The coloured illustration on the front cover is unsigned & not reproduced elsewhere in the book. It depicts children skipping & the lettering reads: 'Happy Hearts/by Ethel Turner [in red ink]' & below: 'A Picture Book for Boys & Girls [in black ink]'.

7576 Another copy, dated 1908 on t.p. but has an inscription dated 19/11/07
As above, but with variation in binding. The illustration on the front cover is a reproduction of one on page 25 of the book, 'Their Majesties go Shopping' by D. H. Souter. Grant
Ward Lock issued other vols entitled 'Happy Hearts' for several years, with quite different contents, very little Australian.

7577 THAT GIRL By/Ethel Turner, Author/of "In the Mist of the Moun-/tains", "Three Little Maids", Etc./ With 25 illustrations/By Frances Ewan/Colonial Edition/(For Circulation in the British Colonies and India only.)/London: T. Fisher Unwin/Adelphi Terrace. MCMVIII
296pp, 1p adv. (facing t.p.), b/w frontis. & 24 b/w plates, b/w plan, dec. clo., 185x120mm. CLRC

7578 THAT GIRL By/Ethel Turner (Mrs./Curlewis), Author of "In the Mist/of the Mountains", "Three Little/Maids", Etc./With 25 illustrations/By Frances Ewan/Colonial Edition/(For Circulation in the British Colonies and India only)/London: T. Fisher Unwin/ Adelphi Terrace. MCMIX
Details as in first edition. KMM

7579 THAT GIRL/By/Ethel Turner/(Mrs. H. R. Curlewis)/Author of.../With 25 illustrations/By Frances Ewan/Ward, Lock & Co. Limited/London, Melbourne and Toronto/1912
296pp, 16pp adv., b/w frontis. & 24 b/w plates, b/w plan, pic. clo., 185x120mm. KMM

7580 THAT GIRL/By/Ethel Turner/(Mrs. Curlewis)/Author of.../With 16 illustrations/By Frances Ewan/Ward, Lock & Co. Limited/London Melbourne and Toronto
n.d.
296pp (no adv.), frontis. & 15 b/w plates, clo., 180x120mm. CLRC

7581 Another copy as above
n.d. [1942? inscribed 1943]
256pp, (no adv.), b/w frontis. & plan only, clo., 185x125mm. KMM

Swedish edition

7582 MARIE. Berättelse för Flickor. Övers. fran engelska av H. Svensen
Sthlm. B. Wahlström 1934
157, (1) s & omsl.—B. Wählstroms flickböcker
Unseen: Information from photostat of catalogue card of Kungliga Biblioteket, Stockholm & of first page of Swedish text

Danish edition

7583 Ethel Turner/HANS LILLE KAMMERAT/(That Girl)/Autoriseret Oversaettelse/af/Carla Hoff-Selden/ Steen Hasselbalchs Forlag/MCMXXVII
156pp
Unseen: Information & photostat of t.p. from Det Kongelige Bibliotek, Copenhagen

Czech edition

7584 Ethel Turnerová/UTRPENIM KE SLAVE/(That Girl)/Divci Pribeh/Z. angliciny prelozila/Paula Moudrá/Ilustroval akademicky malif/A. L. Salac/ [device]/Nakladatelstvi Vojtech Seba Knihkypectvi/V. Praze St.—Strajnicich
Prague, n.d.
224pp. Unseen: Information from Statni Knihovna, Prague

7585 ETHEL TURNER/BIRTHDAY BOOK/A selection of passages from the books of/Ethel Turner/(Mrs. H. R. Curlewis)/Arranged by L. T. T. With foreword by/ Coulson Kernahan/Ward, Lock & Co. Limited/London Melbourne and Toronto/1909
190pp, 2pp foreword, b/w portrait frontis., 7 b/w plates, suede binding, 120x90mm. NSL:M
Prose & verse. Illustrations reproduced from different Ethel Turner books.

7586 FUGITIVES FROM/FORTUNE/By Ethel Turner/ Author of "Seven Little Australians", "Miss Bobbie" etc./Illustrated by J. Macfarlane/Ward, Lock & Co. Limited/London, Melbourne, & Toronto/1909
253pp, 2pp+2pp adv., col. frontis. & 6 b/w plates, dec. clo., 185x125mm. KMM
This is a doubtful children's book, but like some other Ethel Turner titles, it is a borderline case & would certainly have been read by many older girls.

Dutch edition

7587 DE FAMILIE JARVIE
Uitgeverij Kluitman, Alkmaar, Nederland, n.d.
Unseen

7588 FAIR INES/By Ethel Turner/(Mrs. H. R. Curlewis)/Author of/"That Girl", "The Family at Misrule", "Three Little Maids",/etc./[quotation]/ Hodder and Stoughton/London MCMX
279pp, col. frontis. & 2 col. plates by Frank Dadd, clo., 185x120mm. KMM
Again, not considered a children's book, but certain to have been read by older girls.

7589 Rpt as above but: Ward, Lock & Co., Limited/ London and Melbourne
n.d.
Details as above. CLRC
• Rpt as above, but Ward, Lock & Co.,Limited/London, Melbourne and Toronto,
n.d.
279pp, col. frontis. & 2 col. plates, clo., with col. onlay on front cover,187x124mm. TG

7590 FAIR INES/By/Ethel Turner/(Mrs. H. R. Curlewis)/Author of "Seven Little Australians", etc./ [quotation]/Ward, Lock & Co., Limited/London and Melbourne
n.d. [copy inscribed 1943]
279pp, b/w frontis. & 1 b/w illus. in text by Norman Sutcliffe, dec. clo.,185x125mm. PR

7591 THE RAFT/IN THE BUSH/By/Ethel Turner/ Author of "Seven Little Australians", "Miss Bobbie",/"Fugitives from Fortune", etc./With 16 Illustrations by/H. C. Sandy and D. H. Souter/Ward, Lock & Co., Limited/London, Melbourne and Toronto/ 1910
235pp, 4pp & 20pp adv., b/w frontis. & 15 b/w plates, dec. clo., 185x120mm. KMM
Contains 'The Raft in the Bush', & 'Chronicles of the Court', reprinted from *Happy Hearts.*
Another edition as above, but n.d., 4pp adv. only. CLRC

7592 THE TINY/HOUSE/And Other Verses/By/Ethel Turner/Ward, Lock & Co., Limited/London, Melbourne and Toronto/1911
96pp, unillus., suede, 100x65mm. CLRC
Verses for, and about children

7593 Another ed., as above, n.d.
96pp, unillus., suede, 100x65mm. VSL

7594 FIFTEEN/AND FAIR/By/Ethel Turner/Author of/ "The Secret of the Sea"/Hodder & Stoughton/London New York Toronto
n.d. [1911]
46pp, unillus., suede, 90x65mm. NSL:M
Verses, apparently not written for children.

7595 THE APPLE OF/HAPPINESS/By/Ethel Turner/ (Mrs. H. R. Curlewis)/Author of "Fair Ines" "That Girl" etc./Illustrated/Hodder and Stoughton/London New York Toronto
n.d. [First published 1911]
275pp, 4pp adv., col. frontis. & 3 col. plates, illus. by A. N. Gough, dec. clo. (with frontis. reproduced on front cover), 185x120mm. KMM

7596 THE APPLE OF/HAPPINESS/By/Ethel Turner/ (Mrs. H. R. Curlewis)/Author of "Seven Little Australians" etc./Illustrated/Ward, Lock & Co., Limited/London and Melbourne
n.d.
275pp, 4pp adv., col. frontis. & 3 col. plates, clo. (with frontis. reproduced in col. medallion on front cover), 180x120mm. CLRC
Copy as above but title 'Flower o' the Pine' & onlay from that book on front cover. CLRC
Swedish edition

7597 LYCKOÄPPLET/Av/Ethel S. Turner/Bemyndigad Översättning av/H. Flygare/[device]/Stockholm/ Fahlcrantz & C:o
1919
172pp, unillus., col. pic. bd. with clo. spine, adv. verso back cover, 180x120mm. LRA

7598 AN OGRE/UP-TO-DATE/By/Ethel Turner/Author of "Seven Little Australians", "The Family at Misrule", "Miss Bobbie", etc./Illustrated/Ward, Lock & Co., Limited/London, Melbourne and Toronto/1911
224pp (inc. 1p publisher's note & 1p acknowledgement), 4pp & 24pp adv., col. frontis. & 7 col. plates by H. C. Sandy, b/w drawings throughout by D. H. Souter, dec. clo., 190x120mm. KMM
Short stories & verses. Acknowledgement states that 'Some of the matter contained in these pages appeared in the *Town and Country Journal'.* Much of the content of the book, including the title story, is reprinted from *Gum Leaves.*

PORT AND HAPPY HAVENS, London, Hodder & Stoughton. 1912
Travel book, not children's. NSL:M

7599 THE SECRET OF/THE SEA/By/Ethel Turner/ (Mrs. H. R. Curlewis)/Author of/"Ports and Happy Havens", "Fair Ines"/"The Apple of Happiness", "That Girl",/"Seven Little Australians", etc./ [quotation]/Illustrated/Hodder and Stoughton/London New York Toronto
n.d. [First edition 1913]
288pp, col. frontis. & 3 col. plates, dec. clo. (col. onlay on front cover), 190x120mm. KMM
Illustrator M. V. Wheelhouse.

7600 THE SECRET OF/THE SEA/By/Ethel Turner/ (Mrs. H. R. Curlewis)/Author of "Seven Little Australians", "Miss Bobbie",/"The Family at Misrule", etc./[quotation]/Ward, Lock & Co., Limited/London, Melbourne and Toronto
n.d.
288pp, col. frontis. & 3 col. plates, clo. (with vignette in colour on front cover), 180x120mm. KMM
• Rpt as above but b/w illus., 190x120mm. BBC

7601 THE SECRET OF/THE SEA/By/Ethel Turner/ Angus and Robertson Ltd./Sydney: London/1941
247pp, b/w frontis. only (re-drawn from col. illus. in first edition), clo., 180x120mm. KMM
Dutch edition

7602 HET GEHEIM VAN DE ZEE
Published by Uitgeverij Kluitman, Alkmaar, Holland, n.d.
Unseen: IFP

OH, BOYS IN BROWN, Sydney 1914
A war poem (4pp), not a children's book.

7603 FLOWER O'THE/PINE/By/Ethel Turner/(Mrs. H. R. Curlewis)/Author of/"Seven Little Australians", "The Wonder-child",/"That Girl", "Ports and Happy Havens" etc./[quotation]/Hodder and Stoughton/ London New York Toronto
First published 1914
280pp (inc. 1p dedication), col. frontis. & 3 col. plates, illus. by J. J. Hartley, clo. (with col. illus. reproduced from frontis. pasted on front cover), 190x120mm. NSL:M

7604 FLOWER O'/THE PINE/By/Ethel Turner/(Mrs. H. R. Curlewis)/Author of "Seven Little Australians", etc./[quotation]/Ward, Lock & Co., Limited/London, Melbourne and Toronto
n.d.
Details as above. KMM

7605 FLOWER/O' THE/PINE/By/Ethel Turner/ [quotation]/Angus and Robertson Ltd./Sydney: London/1942
246pp, b/w frontis. only (re-drawn after original frontis.) clo., 180x120mm. KMM

Swedish editions

7606 Ethel Turner/LILLA KUSINEN/Berättelse för flickor/Bemyndigad översättning/av/Kerstin Wenström/[BW device] Stockholm 1923/B. Wahlströms Förlag
1923
160pp, unillus., clo., 162x114mm. LRA
Same, 1928, 159, (1) s & pärm.
B. Wählstroms flickböcker (ungdomsböcker)
Same,1941, 159 s. & pärm.
B. Wählstroms flickböcker (ungdomsböcker)
Unseen: Information from photostat of catalogue card of Kungliga Biblioteket, Stockholm & of first page of Swedish text

Finnish edition

7607 PIKKU SERKKU—Suomennos (Anonymous translation into Finnish) Published in Helsinki by Kustannus Oy. Mantere Printed in Porvoo 1946 by Oy. Uusimaan Kirjapaino
191pp, unillus., half clo., 180x130mm.
Finnish title translated into English means 'The Second Cousin' or 'The Little Cousin' but text is that of *Flower of the Pine*
Unseen: Information from the University Library, Helsinki

Norwegian edition

7608 Ethel Turner/FLOWER/(The Flower of the Pine)/Oversat av/Aagot Holst/[device]/Kristiania/ Forlagt av H. Aschehoug & Co. (W. Nygaard)/1922
174pp, unillus., bdg unknown, 195x130mm.
Unseen: Information & photostat of t.p. supplied by Universitets-biblioteket, Oslo

Dutch edition

7609 SPARREBLOESEM
Published by Uitgeverij Kluitman, Alkmaar, Holland, n.d.
Unseen: IFP

7610 THE CUB/Six Months in his Life/A Story in War-time/By/Ethel Turner/(Mrs. H. R. Curlewis)/Author of/"Seven Little Australians", "That Girl", "The Wonder Girl",/"Flower o' the Pine", "Fugitives from Fortune", etc./[quotation]/Ward, Lock and Co., Limited/London, Melbourne and Toronto/ 1915
255pp (inc. 1p quotation), 2pp & 16pp adv., b/w frontis. & 7 b/w plates, illus. Harold Copping, dec. clo. (with col. onlay), 190x120mm. KMM
Another copy as above, but n.d. GI

7611 THE CUB/Six Months in his Life/By/Ethel Turner/(Mrs. H. R. Curlewis)/Author of/"Seven Little Australians", "That Girl", "The Wonder Girl",/"Flower o' the Pine", "Fugitives from Fortune" etc./[quotation]/Ward, Lock and Co., Limited/London and Melbourne
n.d.
255pp, 2pp adv. only, b/w frontis. & 7 b/w plates, clo., 185x120mm. CLRC

7612 THE CUB/By/Ethel Turner/[quotation]/Ward, Lock & Co., Limited/London, Melbourne and Cape Town
n.d. [195-?]
190pp, 1p adv., b/w frontis. only, clo., 185x120mm. CLRC
Artist's name indecipherable.

Swedish edition

7613 CUB/KAPTEN CUBS FORHISTORIA/Av/Ethel Turner/Översättning Från Engelskan/Av/H. Flygare/ [device]/Stockholm/Fahlcrantz & C:o.
1920
183pp, unillus., pic. bd. with clo. spine, adv. verso back cover, 180x120mm. RM

Dutch edition

7614 DE BENGEL
Published by Uitgeverij Kluitman, Alkmaar, Holland, n.d. [1919]
Unseen: Information from Bureau Boek en Jeugd der C.V., The Hague, Holland

7615 JOHN/OF GAUNT/By/Ethel Turner/(Mrs. H. R. Curlewis)/Author of "Seven Little Australians", etc. etc./Ward, Lock & Co., Limited/London, Melbourne and Toronto/1916
256pp, 16pp adv., b/w frontis. & 7 b/w plates, illus. by Harold Copping, dec. clo. (with col. onlay on front cover), 190x120mm. CLRC

7616 JOHN OF GAUNT/By/Ethel Turner/(Mrs H.R.Curlewis)/Author of "Seven Little Australians", etc. etc./Ward Lock & Co.,Limited/London and Melbourne
n.d. [1922?]
256pp (no adv.), b/w frontis. & 6 b/w plates by Harold Copping, dec. clo. with b/w onlay on front cover, 190x125mm. JMcG.

7617 CAPTAIN CUB/By/Ethel Turner/(Mrs. H. R. Curlewis)/Author of/"Seven Little Australians", "The Cub", "The Family at Misrule", "Miss Bobbie", etc./ [verse]/Ward, Lock & Co., Limited/London, Melbourne and Toronto/1917
255pp (inc. 1p quotation), 16pp adv., b/w frontis. & 5 b/w plates, illus. by Harold Copping, dec. clo. (with frontis. reproduced in col. medallion on front cover), 190x120mm. CLRC
• Rpt as above, but n.d. CLRC

Swedish edition

7618 KAPTEN CUB/av/Ethel S. Turner/Bemyndigad översättning fran engelskan/av/H. Flygare/[device]/ Stockholm/Fahlcrantz & C:o
1918
157pp, unillus., pic. bd., clo. spine, 184x120mm. LRA

7619 ST. TOM AND/THE DRAGON/By/Ethel Turner/ (Mrs. H. R. Curlewis)/Author of "Seven Little Australians", "Flower o'the Pine",/"The Cub", etc./ [quotation]/Ward, Lock & Co., Limited/London, Melbourne and Toronto/1918
250pp, 6pp adv., b/w frontis. & 5 b/w plates, illus. by Harold Copping, clo., 180x120mm. KMM
• Rpt as above, but n.d. CLRC

Dutch edition

7620 SINT TOM EN DE DRAAK
Published by Uitgeverij Kluitman, Alkmaar, Holland, 1919
Unseen: Information from Bureau Boek en Jeugd der C.V., The Hague, Holland

7621 BRIGID AND/THE CUB/By/Ethel Turner/ (Mrs. H. R. Curlewis)/Author of "Seven Little Australians", "The Cub",/"Captain Cub", etc./[verse]/ Ward, Lock & Co. Limited/London, Melbourne and Toronto/1919
252pp, 4pp adv., b/w frontis. & 5 b/w plates, illus. Harold Copping, clo. (b/w onlay on cover), 185x120mm. KMM

Dutch editions

7622 BRIGID EN DE BENGEL/Door/Ethel Turner/ [device]/Utrecht A. W. Bruna & Zoons Uitgevers—Mij n.d.
267pp, b/w frontis. & 5 f/p b/w illus., dec. clo., 190x130mm. RM

7623 BRIGID EN DE BENGEL
Published by Uitgeverij Kluitman, Alkmaar, Holland, n.d.
Unseen: IFP

Swedish edition
7624 BRIGID OCH CUB/Av/Ethel Turner/Översättning Från Engelskan/Av/H. Flygare/[device]/Stockholm/ Fahlcrantz & C:o
1920
219pp, unillus., col. pic. bd. with clo. spine, adv. verso back cover, 180x120mm. RM

7625 LAUGHING/WATER/By/Ethel Turner/(Mrs. H. R. Curlewis)/[quotation]/Ward, Lock & Co., Limited/ London and Melbourne/1920
256pp, b/w frontis. & 4 b/w plates, illus. by Harold Copping, clo. (with b/w onlay on front cover), 185x120mm. KMM
• Rpt as above, 1922. CLRC
Danish edition
7626 Ethel Turner/VILLA SOLSKIN/(Laughing Water)/Forf. til syv søskende og/Familien paa uroligheden/autoriseret over saettelse/af/Emmy Carstensen/Steen Hassellbalchs Forlag
1923
140pp, unillus., dec. clo., pic. e/p, 197x132mm. LRA

7627 KING ANNE/By/Ethel Turner/(Mrs. H. R. Curlewis)/Author of "Seven Little Australians", "The Cub",/"Laughing Water", etc./[quotation]/Ward, Lock & Co., Limited/London and Melbourne/1921
250pp, 6pp adv., b/w frontis. & 4 b/w plates, illus. Harold Copping, dec. clo., 185x125mm. KMM
• Rpt as above, but n.d. BBC
7628 KING ANNE/By/Ethel Turner/Ward, Lock & Co., Limited/London and Melbourne
n.d. [195-?]
250pp, 1p quotation, b/w frontis. (unsgd. modern illus. differing entirely from illus. in previous editions), clo., 185x120mm. CLRC
Swedish edition
7629 KING ANNE/av/Ethel S. Turner/översättning från engelskan av/H. Flygare/[device]/Stockholm/ Fahlcrantz & C:o
1922
147pp, unillus., pic. bd. with clo. spine, 183x122mm. LRA
Danish edition
7630 KONG ANNE/af/Ethel Turner/oversat af Else Heise/Illustreret af Harold Copping/Gyldendalske Boghandel Nordisk/Forlag Kjøbenhavn Kristiania/ London Berlin MDCCCCXXIV
171pp & 4pp adv., b/w frontis. & 4 b/w plates, pic. clo., pic. e/p, 190x130mm. LRA

7631 JENNIFER, J./By/Ethel Turner/(Mrs. H. R. Curlewis)/Author of "Seven Little Australians", "Miss Bobbie",/"The Cub", "Laughing Water", etc./ [quotation]/Ward, Lock & Co., Limited/London and Melbourne/1922
249pp, 6pp adv., b/w frontis. & 4 b/w plates, illus. by Harold Copping, dec. clo., 185x125mm. KMM
Second ed. 1922, as above but with 'Second Edition' on t.p. KMM
7632 JENNIFER, J./By/Ethel Turner/[quotation]/Ward, Lock & Co., Limited/London and Melbourne
n.d.
249pp (no adv.) b/w frontis. only by Harold Copping, clo., 185x120mm. TI
7633 JENNIFER, J./By/Ethel Turner/[quotation]/Angus and Robertson Ltd./Sydney: London/1942
235pp, b/w frontis. only by Harold Copping, clo., 185x125mm. KMM
Czech editions
7634 HANICKA VSUDYBYLKA. Dìvčí přibeh. Napsaly. E. Turnerová—P. Moudrá. Ilustroval F. Hornik, Praha, Vojtech Seba s.d.
220pp
HANICKA VSUDYBYLKA. Z angličtiny preložila Paula Moudrá. Ilustroval J. Konsul. V. Praze. Vojtech Seba, 1933
230pp
Another edition, V. Praze, Vojtech Seba, 1939—P 230
Unseen: Information from Statni Knihovna, Prague
Dutch edition
7635 JENNIFER DZJINN
Uitgeverij Kluitman, Alkmaar, Holland, 1933
Unseen: Information from Bureau Boek en Jeugd der C.V., The Hague, Holland

7636 NICOLA SILVER/By/Ethel Turner/(Mrs. H. R. Curlewis)/Author of "Seven Little Australians", "The Cub",/"Laughing Water", "Jennifer J." etc./ [quotation]/Ward, Lock & Co., Limited/London and Melbourne/1924
254pp, 2pp adv., b/w frontis. & 3 b/w plates, illus. by Harold Copping, dec. clo., 185x125mm. KMM
Swedish edition
7637 FLICKAN PÅ BERGET/Av/Ethel Turner/ Bemyndigad översättning/Av/Karin Jensen/P. Lidforss/[device]/Stockholm/Fahlcrantz & C:o
1924
184pp, unillus., col. pic. bd. with clo. spine, adv. verso back cover, 185x120mm. LRA
Dutch edition
7638 NICO SILVER
Uitgeverij Kluitman, Alkmaar, Holland [1926]
Unseen: Information from Bureau Boek en Jeugd der C.V., The Hague, Holland
Danish edition
7639 Ethel Turner/NICOLA SILVER/oversat af M. John-Hansen/Illustrationer af Harold Copping/ Gyldendalske Boghandel—Nordisk/Forlag Kjøbenhavn MDCCCCXXV
169pp & 6pp adv., b/w frontis. & 4 b/w plates, dec. clo., pic. e/p, 185x127mm. LRA
Norwegian edition
7640 Ethel Turner/NICOLA SILVER/Gyldendal/Norsk Forlag/Oslo MCMXXVI
117pp, unillus., 200x130mm.
Translated by S. Grieg.
Unseen: Information & photostat of t.p. from Universitetsbiblioteket, Oslo
Czech edition
7641 E. Turnerová/HORSKA/PRINCEZNICKA/Dívc"í Roman/Prelozila/Paula Moudra'/Ilustroval Sked. Maliz/J. Konsal/[device]/Nakladatelstvi Vojte"ch Seba/Knihkupectvi/V. Praze—St. Strasnicich
1933
214pp. Unseen: Information & photostat of t.p. supplied by Statni Knihovna, Prague

7642 FUNNY/By/Ethel Turner/(Mrs. H. R. Curlewis)/Ward, Lock & Co., Limited/London and Melbourne/1926
253pp, 2pp adv., b/w frontis. & 3 b/w plates, illus. by W. E. Wightman, pic. clo., 185x125mm. KMM
Boy's story set in England.
Swedish edition
7643 SNURREN/Av/Ethel Turner/[device]/Stockholm/ Fahlcrantz & Co
1926
192pp, unillus., col. pic. bd. with clo. spine, adv. verso back cover, 185x120mm. RM

7644 JUDY AND PUNCH/By/Ethel Turner/(Mrs. H. R. Curlewis)/Author of "Seven Little Australians",

"Jennifer J."/"King Anne", "Nicola Silver", "Funny" etc./Ward, Lock & Co., Limited/London and Melbourne/1928
256pp (no adv.), b/w frontis. & 3 b/w plates, illus. by Harold Copping, dec. clo., 180x120mm. KMM
A further story about the Woolcot family of *Seven Little Australians.*
• Rpt as above but other titles quoted & n.d.
255pp, unillus., clo., 180x115mm. CLRC
Czech edition

7645 E. Turnerová/DIBLIK/(Judy and Punch)/Divci Pribeh [Girls' Story]/Z. anglietiny prelozila/Paula Moudra'/Ilustroval akademicky malif/A. L. Salac/[device]/Nakladatelstvi Vojtech seba Knihkupectvi/V. Praze, S. T. Strasnicich
Translated by Paula Moudra'; illustrated by A. L. Salac
Date of publication &c. not known
Unseen: Information & photostat of t.p. supplied by Statni Knihovna, Prague

7646 THE CHILD/OF THE/CHILDREN/by Ethel Turner/with the original Victorian illustrations by/Frances Ewan/and an introduction by J. B. Wright/Ward, Lock & Co., Limited/London, Melbourne and Cape Town
'Ward, Lock & Co., Limited, 1897, First published in volume form in 1959'
31pp (inc. 3pp introduction & 1p biographical note), 1p adv., b/w frontis. & 4 b/w illus. (inc. reproduction of frontis.), stiff illus. wrappers, 205x135mm. KMM
The publishers state that *The Child of the Children* appeared in an issue of the *Windsor Magazine* for 1897, & that G. B. Shaw possibly used the plot for *Pygmalion,* first performed in London in 1914; they claim that various similarities substantiate this theory, & present *The Child of the Children* as the first 'Fair Lady'. The story was included in *The Camp at Wandinong* 1898.

THE STORY OF A BABY, London, Ward, Lock & Bowden, 1895 (The Nautilus Series), Reprinted (The Nautilus Series) 1896, Reprinted in enlarged edition, 190-?, 1910, 1912

THE LITTLE DUCHESS, London, Ward Lock & Bowden, 1896 (The Nautilus Series) (Included also in the enlarged reprints of *The Story of a Baby*)
These two collections of short stories were definitely not intended for children.

THE UNGARDENERS, Ward Lock & Co., Limited, London and Melbourne 1925
This simple novel again was not intended for children.

TURNER, Ethel & CURLEWIS, Jean

7647 THE SUNSHINE FAMILY/A Book of Nonsense/For Girls and Boys/By/Ethel Turner & Jean Curlewis/[drawing]/with over 150 illustrations by/D. H. Souter and H. Bancks/and others/Ward Lock & Co. Limited/London and Melbourne
n.d. [1923]
192pp, b/w frontis. & b/w illus. throughout, pic. bd., 245x180mm. VSL
The stories first appeared in *Sunbeams* , the supplement of the Sun Newspapers Coy. Jean Curlewis was the daughter of Ethel Turner. The second illustrator was actually J. C. Bancks, creator of 'Ginger Meggs', his name appearing incorrectly here.

TURNER, Frank R.

7648 No.45 Sept 2nd 1910 5 cents/ALL AROUND/THE/GOLDEN SKULL/By Frank R. Turner/[col. illus. with caption]/Weekly/Frank Tousey/Publisher/24 Union Square/New York
1910
32pp, adv. back wrapper, unillus., col. pic. wrappers, cover title, 280x203mm. RM
Grizzly bears and Indians feature as part of the local colour in this Australian setting.

[TURNER, Gladys Macaulay]

7649 JUST BEAR/STORIES
No publisher's imprint, n.d. [192-?]
10pp, 2pp col. illus. & b/w drawings throughout, dec. wrappers, cover title, 270x215mm. CLRC
Prose & verse. According to an undated newspaper cutting from a Brisbane paper the author/artist was born in South Australia, though living in Brisbane at the time of the publication of these booklets. There were four books in the series, the fourth being *The Sweetest Pet of All.*

7650 BEARGARDEN/NO NOT KINDERGARTEN
No publisher's imprint, n.d.
10pp, 2pp col. illus. & b/w drawings throughout, dec. wrappers, cover title, 275x220mm. CLRC

7651 HONEY BUN/MY/LITTLE BEAR
No publisher's imprint, n.d.
10pp, 2pp col. illus. & b/w drawings throughout, dec. wrappers, cover title, 275x220mm. CLRC

7652 THE SWEETEST PET OF ALL
listed as being in same series as above; unseen

[TURNER, Helen]

7653 Whitcombe's Historical Story Books/UNDER COOK'S/FLAG/For ages 10 to 12 years/[illustrations]/[coat of arms granted to Cook's family by King George III]/Whitcombe and Tombs Limited/Auckland, Wellington, Christchurch, Dunedin, Invercargill, N.Z./London Melbourne and Sydney
n.d.
148pp (inc. 6pp chronology, index, & double-spread map), b/w portrait frontis., b/w drawings in text throughout, stiff dec. wrappers, 185x120mm. KMM
See McLaren 533

TURNER, Lilian Irene [Mrs F. Lindsay Thompson]

7654 THE/LIGHTS OF SYDNEY/or/No Past is Dead/By/Lilian Turner/with eight full-page illustrations/by/W. H. Margetson/Cassell and Company, Limited/London, Paris & Melbourne/1896/All rights reserved
272pp, 8pp adv., b/w frontis. & 7 b/w plates, clo., 190x130mm. KMM
Not really a children's book, but written for older girls.

7655 YOUNG LOVE/By/Lilian Turner/(Mrs. F. Lindsay Thompson)/Author of "The Lights of Sydney", etc./With Frontispiece by J. Macfarlane/London:/Ward, Lock & Co., Limited/New York and Melbourne./1902
312pp, 8pp adv., b/w frontis., wrappers, 195x125mm. KMM
Not a children's book, but, like a number of this author's books, written for older girls.

7656 AN AUSTRALIAN/LASSIE/by/Lilian Turner/Author of "The Lights of Sydney"/Illustrations by A. J. Johnson/London/Ward, Lock & Co. Limited/New York and Melbourne
1903
253pp, 2pp adv., b/w frontis. & 7 b/w plates, clo., 190x125mm. Grant

7657 AN AUSTRALIAN/LASSIE/By/Lilian Turner/Author of "The Perry Girls", etc./Illustrations by A. J. Johnson/Ward, Lock & Co., Limited/London, Melbourne and Toronto
n.d. [1909?]
Details as above. KMM

• Rpt as above n.d. with b/w frontis. & 3 plates, bound in clo. printed in black with 'fern' pattern. MK

7658 BETTY THE SCRIBE/By/Lilian Turner./Author of/ "An Australian Lassie", "The Lights of Sydney."/Illustrations by A. J. Johnson/London:/ Ward, Lock & Co., Limited/1906
320pp, 1p & 2pp adv., b/w frontis. & 6 b/w plates, dec. clo., 190x125mm. KMM

7659 BETTY THE SCRIBE/By/Lilian Turner/Author of/ "An Australian Lassie", "The Perry Girls", etc./ Illustrations by A. J. Johnson/Ward, Lock & Co., Limited/London, Melbourne and Toronto
n.d.
320pp (no adv.), b/w frontis. & 6 b/w plates, dec. clo., 190x125mm. VSL

7660 BETTY THE SCRIBE/By/Lilian Turner/Author of/ "An Australian Lassie", "The Perry Girls", etc./Ward, Lock & Co., Limited/London and Melbourne
n.d.
320pp, b/w frontis. & 3 b/w plates by Saville Lumley, clo., 185x130mm. MD

US editions

7661 BETTY THE SCRIBE/By/Lilian Turner/Illustrated by/Katharine Hayward Greenland/The Saalfield Publishing Co./New York, Akron, Ohio Chicago
1907
329pp, 10pp adv., b/w frontis. only, dec. clo., 185x125mm. Grant

7662 BETTY, THE SCRIBE/By/Lilian Turner/Illustrated/ Made in U.S.A./The Saalfield Publishing Co./New York Akron Ohio Chicago
1927
324pp (no adv.), b/w frontis. only, dec. clo., 185x120mm. KMM
Title on front cover & spine: 'Betty'.

Swedish edition

7663 TVA SYSTRAR/Berättelse för unga flickor/av/ Lilian Turner/Bemyndigad översättning av E. Silfverstolpe/Stockholm/C.E. Fritzes Bokförlags Aktiebolag
1907
222pp & 1p 'contents', b/w frontis. & pic. bds by J. Macfarlane, 165x105mm. ANL

7664 PARADISE AND THE/PERRYS/By/Lilian Turner/ (Mrs. F. Lindsay Thompson)/Author of "Australian Lassie", [sic] "Betty the Scribe", etc./Illustrated by J. Macfarlane/London/Ward, Lock & Co Ltd/1908
256pp, 2pp adv. (preceding t.p.), b/w frontis. & 7 b/w plates, dec. clo., 190x125mm. KMM
• Rpt as above, 1910. BBC
• Rpt as above n.d. but: Ward Lock & Co., Limited/ London, Melbourne and Toronto VSL

Swedish edition

7665 PARADISET/Berättelse för unga flickor/av/Lilian Turner/Bemyndigad översättning från Engelska originalet/av/Elisabeth Lilljebjörn/[device]/ Stockholm/C. E. Fritzes, Bokförlags Aktieboleg
1911
225pp &1p contents, b/w frontis. only, pic. bd., 165x110mm. ANL
J. Macfarlane's illus. from original English ed.

7666 THE PERRY GIRLS/By Lilian Turner/(Mrs. F. Lindsay Thompson)/Author of/"Paradise and the Perrys", "Betty the Scribe", etc./Illustrated by J. Macfarlane/Ward, Lock & Co., Limited/London, Melbourne, and Toronto/1909
256pp (inc. 2pp dedicatory letter), col. frontis. & 8 b/w plates, dec. clo., 190x120mm. CLRC
• Rpt as above, but n.d., b/w frontis. & 8 b/w plates. CLRC

Swedish edition

7667 FLICKORNA PERRY/Berättelse för unga flickor/ av/Lilian Turner/Bemyndigad översättning frän Engelskan/av/H. Flygare/Andra upplagan/[device]/ Stockholm/C.E.Fritzes Bokförlags Aktiebolag
1923
234pp & 1p 'contents', b/w frontis. & illus. reproduced on front cover (both by J. Macfarlane), bd., 165x110mm. ANL

7668 THREE/NEW CHUM GIRLS/By Lilian Turner/ (Mrs. F. Lindsay Thompson)/Author of "The Perry Girls", "Paradise and the Perrys",/Etc./Illustrated by J. Macfarlane/Ward, Lock & Co., Limited/London/ Melbourne and Toronto/1910
256pp (inc. 1p explanatory note), 1p adv. (preceding t.p.), b/w frontis. & 7 b/w plates, dec. clo., 190x125mm. KMM
• Rpt as above, 1911. VSL
• Rpt as above n.d. & with only frontis. & 5 plates. PR

7669 APRIL GIRLS/By/Lilian Turner/(Mrs. F. Lindsay Thompson)/Author of "Three New Chum Girls", "The/Perry Girls", etc./Illustrated by J. Macfarlane/ Ward, Lock & Co., Limited/London, Melbourne and Toronto/1911
254pp, 1p adv. (preceding t.p.), b/w frontis. & 7 b/w plates, dec. clo., 190x120mm. KMM

7670 WRITTEN DOWN/By/Lilian Turner/(Mrs. F. Lindsay Thompson)/Author of "Three New Chum Girls", "Betty the Scribe"/"Paradise and the Perrys", etc./Ward Lock & Co., Limited/London, Melbourne and Toronto/1912
255pp, 16pp adv., b/w frontis. by J. Macfarlane, clo., 190x130mm. KMM

7671 STAIRWAYS/TO THE STARS/By/Lilian Turner/ (Mrs. F. Lindsay Thompson)/Author of "An Australian Lassie", "Paradise and the Perrys",/"The Perry Girls", etc./Ward, Lock & Co., Limited/London, Melbourne and Toronto/1913
286pp, 1p & 2pp adv., b/w frontis. & 5 b/w plates, by J. Macfarlane, dec. clo., 190x120mm. KMM

French edition

7672 VERS LES ÉTOILES. Roman. Traduit par Eve Paul-Marguerite, Paris, Editions de la Mode nationale, 1930. In8°
128pp
Unseen: Information from the Bibliothèque Nationale, Paris, who stated that this is the only translation into French of the works of either Lilian or Ethel Turner.

7673 THE GIRL FROM/THE BACK-BLOCKS/By/Lilian Turner/F. Lindsay Thompson)/Author of/"Stairways to the Stars", "Three New Chum Girls",/Etc./Ward, Lock & Co., Limited/London, Melbourne and Toronto/ 1914
256pp (no adv.), b/w frontis. & 7 b/w plates, illus. by J. Macfarlane, dec. clo., 190x125mm. KMM
• Rpt as above n.d., imprint: London and Melbourne PR

7674 WAR'S/HEART THROBS/By/Lilian Turner/(Mrs. F. Lindsay Thompson)/Author of/"Stairways to the Stars", "The Girl from the Back Blocks", etc./Ward, Lock & Co., Limited/London, Melbourne and Toronto/ 1915
252pp, 1p & 16pp adv., b/w frontis. & 7 b/w plates, illus. by J. Macfarlane, clo., 190x120mm. KMM

7675 THE NOUGHTS/AND CROSSES/By/Lilian

Turner/(Mrs. F. Lindsay Thompson)/Author of/"An Australian Lassie", "Three New Chum Girls",/"The Girl from the Back Blocks", etc./Ward, Lock & Co., Limited/London, Melbourne and Toronto/1917
252pp, 20pp adv., b/w frontis. & 3 b/w plates, illus. by Stanley Davis, pic. clo., 190x120mm. KMM

7676 PEGGY THE/PILOT/By/Lilian Turner/(Mrs. F. Lindsay Thompson)/Author of/"An Australian Lassie", "The Girl from the Back Blocks", etc./Ward, Lock & Co., Limited/London and Melbourne/1922
239pp, 16pp adv., b/w frontis. & 3 b/w plates, illus. by F. Dewar Mills, pic. clo., 185x125mm. KMM
• Rpt as above, 1923. KMM

7677 JILL OF THE/FOURTH FORM/By/Lilian Turner/(Mrs. F. Lindsay Thompson)/Author of "The Girl from the Back Blocks"/"Peggy the Pilot", etc./Ward, Lock & Co., Limited/London and Melbourne/1924
256pp (no adv.), b/w frontis. & 3 b/w plates, illus. by F. Dewar Mills, dec. clo., 185x125mm. KMM

7678 THE/HAPPY HERIOTS/By/Lilian Turner/(Mrs. F. Lindsay Thompson)/Author of "The Perry Girls', "The Girl from the/Back-blocks" "Jill of the Fourth Form", etc./Ward, Lock & Co., Limited/London and Melbourne/1926
256pp (no adv.), b/w frontis. & 3 b/w plates, illus. by F. Dewar Mills, dec. clo., 185x125mm. KMM

7679 RACHEL/by/Lilian Turner/(Mrs F. Lindsay Thompson)/Author of "The Girl from the Backblocks",/"The Noughts and Crosses", etc./Books Limited/Crosshall Buildings/Liverpool
[1920]
Printed in England by C. Tinling & Co. Ltd.,/53, Victoria Street, Liverpool,/and 187, Fleet Street, London
254pp, unillus., clo., 154x120mm. ANL
A romantic novel.

7680 NINA COMES HOME/By/Lilian Turner/(Mrs. F. Lindsay Thompson)/Ward, Lock & Co., Limited/London and Melbourne/1927
255pp (no adv.), b/w frontis. & 3 b/w plates by Norman Sutcliffe, pic. clo., 180x125mm. KMM

7681 ANN CHOOSES GLORY/By/Lilian Turner/(Mrs. F. Lindsay Thompson)/Ward, Lock & Co., Limited/London and Melbourne/1928
256pp, b/w frontis. & 3 b/w plates by Norman Sutcliffe, clo., 185x125mm. ANL

7682 LADY BILLIE/By/Lilian Turner/(Mrs. F. Lindsay Thompson)/Ward, Lock & Co., Limited/London and Melbourne/1929
256pp, b/w frontis. & 3 b/w plates by F. Dewar Mills, clo., 185x120mm. ANL

7683 THERE CAME/A CALL/By/Lilian Turner/(Mrs. F. Lindsay Thompson)/Author of "Ann chooses Glory", "Lady Billie", etc./Ward, Lock & Co., Limited/London and Melbourne/1930
256pp, b/w frontis. & 3 b/w plates by J. Dewar Mills, clo., 185x120mm. ANL

7684 TWO TAKE THE ROAD/By/Lilian Turner/Author of/"There came a call" etc./Illustrated/Ward, Lock & Co., Limited/London and Melbourne/1931
256pp, b/w frontis. & 3 b/w plates by Norman Sutcliffe, clo., 185x120mm. ANL

TURNER, Robert
7685 REAL/AUSTRALIAN/JUNGLE STORIES/Legends of the Aborigines/by/Robert Turner, F.R.A.I./Member of the Anthropological Society of N.S.W.,/Author of "Aboriginal Signs and Symbols"./1936/Published by/Northwood Press, Camperdown [N.S.W.]
64pp, 1p preface, b/w drawings in text, dec. wrappers, 215x125mm. ANL

7686 Scout Shop Service Library/No. 3/AUSTRALIAN/JUNGLE STORIES/Legends of the Aborigines/Book No. 1/by/Robert Turner, F.R.A.I./G.S.M. 1st. Surry Hills Troop./Author of "Aboriginal Signs and Symbols"/Published by/The Boy Scouts' Association/1944
27pp, 1p adv., b/w drawings in text, wrappers, 180x120mm. NSL:M

TURNER, Robert & BOYCE, Milton J.
7687 AUSTRALIAN/ABORIGINAL SIGNS/AND SYMBOLS/For the Use of Boy Scouts/By/Robert Turner/Fellow of the Royal Anthropological Institute of Great Britain,/&c. [2 lines]/and/Milton J. Boyce/Baden-Powell Rovers, Pennant Hills./With a Foreword by/Col. J. M. Maughan, D.S.O., V.D./Chief Commissioner for N.S.W. Scouts/Sydney/P. R. Stephensen & Co. Ltd./24 Bond Street
Sydney 1934
62pp (inc. 1p foreword & 2pp introduction), b/w drawings throughout, limp clo., 180x110mm. ANL

TURNLEY, Beris
7688 JOURNEY INTO CHINA/Beris Turnley/Lansdowne
Melbourne 1971
102pp, b/w photographic illus., line drawings, clo., map e/p, 240x180mm. LRA
• Rpt as above, 1971. ANL

TURNLEY, Jean E.
COLE'S NURSERY RHYME STORIES. *See* Cole, E. W.

TWAMLEY, Louisa Anne
See Meredith, Louisa Anne [Mrs Charles, née Twamley]

The Twelve Days of Christmas
See Blue Wren Books

Twenty-Six Adventure Stories for Boys
7689 TWENTY-SIX/ADVENTURE STORIES/FOR BOYS/Illustrated by Leading Artists/London/"The Boy's Own Paper" Office/4 Bouverie Street, E.C.4
n.d. [192-?]
288pp, col. frontis. & 8 b/w plates, clo., 215x140mm. KMM
Includes: J. G .Rowe, *The Cave Under the Sea* (14pp, New Guinea), V. M. Methley, *Andromeda* (5pp. Sydney); "Southern Cross", *The Stick-up at Jordans* (13pp), E. C. Adams, *On the Trail of the Smugglers* (13pp).

Twenty-Six Good Stories for Boys
7690 TWENTY-SIX/GOOD STORIES/FOR/BOYS/By Well-known Writers/Illustrated by Leading Artists/London/"The Boy's Own Paper" Office/Bouverie Street and 65 St Paul's Churchyard, E.C.4
n.d. [192-?]
288pp col. frontis. & 8 b/w plates, clo., 215x140mm. WRT
Contains 'Some Australian Bush Yarns' by Edward Roper, 10pp.

The Twins' Dream
7691 THE TWINS' DREAM
Associated General Publications, Sydney, n.d. [1946]
18pp, b/w drawings, stiff dec. wrappers, cover title, 245x180mm. ANL
Verse.

TWISS, F. E.
7692 THE HIGHWAYMAN/A Historical Play for/Children, suitable for/Schools and Colleges/By Miss F. E. Twiss/Christ Church School/North Adelaide, S.A./Printed and Published by the Sydney Partrige Press, 104 Parade, Norwood,/South Australia—October, 1908
39pp (inc. 1p synopsis), unillus., wrappers, 135x100mm. CLRC
Play set in England in the time of James II.

Two Kookaburras. An anonymous untitled book
See Shaped Books

TYSON, Ida Anne
7693 KIKI, TOMMY/AND THEIR FIRST TALE/Story and Illustrations/By/Ida Anne Tyson
Vardon Price, Adelaide 1963
Cover reads: Tyson's Tales—Kiki, Tommy/and/The Slippery Dip
32pp, b/w drawings throughout, dec. wrappers, 220x140mm. CLRC

'UNCLE GEORGE'
7694 VESSELS AND VOYAGES/A Book for Boys/By Uncle George/with twenty illustrations/[verse]/London:/James Blackwood & Co. 8 Lovell's Court/Paternoster Row
n.d.
155pp, 4pp adv., 6pp adv. preceding text, b/w frontis. & 14 f/p b/w illus., clo., 180x140mm. PR
Pp96–137 describe a whaling trip to Antarctica, being marooned for a year, & then travelling on to the South Seas & Tahiti.

4QG Uncle Ben's Book-o'-Fun
7695 4QG/UNCLE BEN'S/BOOK-O'-FUN/for Boys and Girls/(Copyright)/Price 3/- copy/Sole Distributors for Australasia/The Standard Press/Box 1421 T GPO, Brisbane/Published by/The Read Press Ltd, Brisbane
n.d.[1926]
60pp (inc. 2pp adv., & adv. inside both covers) & 1 p Foreword by J. W. Robinson, Director Queensland Radio Service, Brisbane, b/w illus. in text (by E. S. Watson), stiff col. pic. wrappers, 245x185mm. ANL
Jokes, stories &c.

'UNCLE LEE'
See DORE, L. M.

Uncle Philip's Conversations about the Whale Fishery and Polar Seas
See [HAWKS, Francis Lister]

'UNCLE TED'
See KAYE, E. W.

Under Cook's Flag
See Turner, Helen

UNSTEAD, R. J. & HENDERSON, W. F.
7696 HOMES IN AUSTRALIA/R. J. Unstead W. F. Henderson/A. and C. Black Ltd. London
1969
64pp, extended illus. t.p., b/w illus. throughout, pic. clo., 230x185mm. Black's Australian Scoial Studies. CLRC
• Rpt 1971. KP

Uniform with the above:
7697 TRANSPORT IN AUSTRALIA. 1970. 80pp. CLRC

7698 PIONEER HOME LIFE IN AUSTRALIA. 1971. 96pp. CLRC

UNWIN, M. J. [pseud. Maurice John Hinton]
7699 BOORAN/A Tale/of Early Australia/By/M. J. Unwin/Jacaranda Press/Brisbane
1958
193pp, b/w drawings throughout, illus. by Elizabeth Austin, clo., 210x135mm. CLRC
• Rpt 1958, 1960, as above. BBC
• Rpt school ed. 1958 as above but stiff linen wrapper, 185x115mm. CLRC
• Rpt 1960 (twice). CLRC

7700 PUPIL'S COMPANION/TO/BOORAN/M. J. Unwin/The Author of "Booran"/Jacaranda Press/1959
36pp, wrappers, 210x135mm. BBC

English edition
7701 CORROBOREE/A Tale/of Early Australia/by/M. J. Unwin/Anthony Blond
1959 [First published in Great Britain]
193pp, b/w drawings, illus. by Elizabeth Austin, clo., 215x135mm. ANL

UPFIELD, Arthur
7702 Arthur Upfield/BONY AND THE MOUSE/Illustrated by Bill Morden/[device]/Heinemann Educational Books/London
first pub. 1959; 1st pub in The New Windmill Series 1961; rpt 1963, 1965, 1966, 1970
249pp & 1p adv., b/w frontis., pic. bd., 185x117mm. KP
This edition published for use in schools

URBAN, A. J.
7703 PRITEL DOMORODCU (As a Friend of the Aborigines)
S.N.D.K., Prague 1954
173pp. Unseen: SLCSR

7704 NA KONCI SVETA JE DOMOV (At the end of the World is Home) A Story of Australia
Prague 1955
219pp. Unseen: SLCSR

7705 LOD V NEBEZPECI (A Ship in Danger)
Prague 1956
172pp. Unseen: SLCSR

UREN, Malcolm
EDWARD JOHN EYRE. *See* Australian Explorers

'U.S. DETECTIVE, A.'
7706 The New York/Detective Library/Price Ten Cents/Entered according to the Act of Congress.[2 lines]/No.480 (Complete) Frank Tousey, Publisher 34 & 36 North Moore Street N.Y./New York, February 6,1892. Issued every Saturday. Price 10 cents. Vol.1/The Subscription price[2 lines]/NED KELLY AND HIS BUSHMEN./A Story of Robber Life in Australia/By A U.S. Detective/[illustration & caption]
29pp & 3pp adv., unillus., pic. wrappers, 320x225mm. CLRC

VALENTIN, F.
VOYAGES ET AVENTURES DE LA PÉROUSE. *See* Lebrun, Henri, VOYAGES ET AVENTURES DE CAPITAINE COOK

VALENTIN, F.
7707 VOYAGES ET AVENTURES/DE/LA PÉROUSE/Par F. Valentin/Auteur de l'Histoire des Croisades, etc./Quatrième Édition/[device]/Tours/Ad. Mame et Cie, Imprimeurs—Libraires/1844 [first pub. 1839]
286pp (inc. 8pp introduction, 24pp 'supplément au voyage', 4pp appendix), 4pp adv. preceding t.p., engraved frontis., additional engraved dec. t.p., 2 f/p b/w engravings, embossed clo. (with design on front cover in gilt), 170x105mm. RM

The advertisement lists The Mame Library for Christian Young which includes the present book. La Pérouse's visit to Botany Bay is described on pp203–17; the appendix relates to the search for La Pérouse by Labillardière, Dillon & d'Urville.

VANACEK, Arnost
7708 ZLATO NA LABUTI RECE (Gold on Swan River)
S.N.D.K., Prague 1967
99pp. Unseen: SLCSR

VAN HOMRIGH, C. M. B.
7709 INTRODUCTION/TO/ART AND CRAFT/by/ C. M. B. Van Homrigh/Senior Lecturer in Art,/Kelvin Grove Teachers' College, Brisbane/[device]/Angus and Robertson
1965
119pp (inc. 2pp intro.), b/w frontis. & 8 f/p col. illus., b/w photographic illus. in text, dec. bd., dec. e/p, 240x180mm. CLRC

VARDEN, Dorothy
7710 THE/MAGIC SHELL/Story by Dorothy Varden/ Illustrated by Roma Thompson
Printed and Published by Vardon & Sons Limited, for Consolidated Merchandising Co. 325 Bourke Street, Melbourne, 204 Clarence Street, Sydney, n.d. [194-?]
18pp, 5 f/p col. illus. & drawings in text, pic. bd., dec. e/p, 235x185mm. KMM

VARDON, Mollie
7711 POTTERY/FOR BEGINNERS/Mollie Vardon
Rigby Ltd., Adelaide, first pub. in Instant Books 1970; pub. in the Instant Library series 1972
64pp, b/w drawings, pic. bd., 215x145mm. KP

VATTEMARE, H.
7712 Bibliothèque des Écoles et des Familles/A TRAVERS L'AUSTRALIE/récits de découvertes/ d'explorations, d'impressions de voyage/abrégés par H. Vattemare/Paris/Librairie Hachette et Cie/79, Boulevard Saint Germain,79/1880/Droits de propriété et de traduction réservés.
224pp (inc. 4pp contents &c.) b/w map frontis., 49 b/w illus. & 3 b/w maps, dec. clo., 215x132mm. SSL
References to Burke & Wills, McDouall Stuart, Egerton Warburton, &c.

VAUGHAN, Sam
7713 WHOEVER/HEARD/OF/KANGAROO/EGGS/By Sam Vaughan/Pictures by/Leonard Weisgard/ Doubleday & Company Inc., Garden City, N.Y.
1957
58pp, extended dec. t.p., col. illus. throughout, dec. bd., 255x180mm. NSL:M
7714 Another copy, as above but published in Great Britain as a World's Work Children's Book in 1965. KP

VAUTIER, Dorothea
7715 THE STORY OF/TEDDY KOALA/Stories and Verse by Dorothea Vautier/Monotones by Courtesy of/Noel Burnet, Koala Park/[vignette]/W. H. Honey Publishing Co./Sydney/Wholly set up and Printed in Australia by/Pratten Bros. Ltd., Sydney
n.d. [1931?]
14pp, col. frontis. & 3 f/p col. illus., b/w photographic illus., col. illus. wrappers, 280x225mm. KMM

'VEDETTE'
See Fitchett, Rev. William Henry

VENNARD, Alexander Vindex
See 'Reid, Frank'

'VERA'
7716 TEDDY/DER KLEINE BEUTELBÄR/Eine Geschichte von lustigen Leben/der Koalas und Känguruhs in Australien/mit Versen von Vera/und 60 Photos geduldiger Kamerajager/[device]/ Zwei-bären-Verlag der VDB Bern
1967
65pp, & 2pp adv., b/w photographs on every page of Australian animals with verses, photographic pic. bd., 175x130mm. NSL:M

VÉRITÉ, Marcelle
ANIMALS OF THE WILD, Rigby Ltd., Adelaide
English translation of the French *Maisons et Métiers des Animaux*, Paris 1959, marketed in Australia; not considered an Australian publication. BBC

VERNE, Jules
7717 DÉCOUVERTE DE LA TERRE/LES PREMIERS EXPLORATEURS/par Jules Verne/59 Dessins par L. Benett, et P. Philippoteaux/58 fac-similes (d'après les documents anciens) et Cartes/par Dubail et Matthis/ [vignette]/Bibliothèque/d'Education et de Récréation/ J. Hetzel et Cie, 18, Rue Jacob/Paris/Tous droits de traduction et de reproduction réservés
n.d. [1870–73]
464(i.e. vi, 458 + 6pp contents &c.), engraved frontis., maps &c, engravings throughout, bd., half leather, 268x174mm. SUA
Vol. 1 of Histoire des Grands Voyages et Grands Voyageurs, Hetzel, Paris.

7718 Histoire Générale/Des Grands Voyages et des Grands Voyageurs/LES GRAND NAVIGATEURS/du XVIIIc Siècle/par/Jules Verne/51 Dessins par P.Philippoteaux/66 fac-similes (d'après les documents anciens) et cartes/par Matthis et Morieu/[vignette]/ Bibliothèque [as before]
vii,464, engraved frontis. & engravings throughout, as previous volume. SUA

7719 Découverte de la Terre/LES VOYAGEURS/du XIX SIECLE/par Jules Verne/51 Dessins par Léon Benett/ 57 fac-similes/d'après les documents anciens/et cartes/ par Matthis et Morieu/[vignette]/Bibliothèque/ d'Education et de Recréation/J. Hetzel et Cie, 18, Rue Jacob/Paris
vi, 428pp, engraved frontis. & throughout as before. SUA

7720 Celebrated Travels and Travellers/THE EXPLORATION/OF THE WORLD./By Jules Verne./ with 59 illustrations by L. Benett and P. Philippoteaux,/and 50 Fac-similes of ancient drawings./[vignette] Translated from the French./ London:/Sampson, Low, Marston, Searle & Rivington,/Crown Buildings, 188 Fleet Street./ 1879/[All rights reserved]
xixpp, 432pp, 23pp and 28 maps & illustrations from original sources, 59 f/p illus., three-quarter leather (copy seen re-bound), 205x132mm. SSL
(The first of 3 vols)

7721 Celebrated Travels and Travellers/THE GREAT NAVIGATORS/OF THE/EIGHTEENTH CENTURY./ By Jules Verne/with 96 illustrations by Philippoteaux, Benett and Matthis,/and 20 maps by Matthis and Morieu./[vignette]/translated from the French./ London:/Sampson, Low, Marston, Searle and Rivington,/Crown Buildings, 188 Fleet Street./ 1880/[All rights reserved]
Publisher's note: 'This volume forms the second of three volumes under the general title of Celebrated Travels and Travellers. The first volume, already published, is entitled "The Exploration of the World" '.

xvipp, 409pp (& 1 p list of works by J. Verne), b/w illus. throughout, clo., 215x140mm. NSL:M

7722 Celebrated Travels and Travellers/THE GREAT EXPLORERS/OF THE/NINETEENTH CENTURY,/By Jules Verne/Translated by N. D'Anvers,/Author of "Heroes of North African Discovery", "Heroes of South African Discovery", etc./with 51 original drawings by Léon Benett, and 57 fac-similes from early mss and maps by Matthis and Morieu./[vignette]/London:/Sampson, Low, Marston, Searle & Rivington,/Crown Buildings, 188 Fleet Street./1881/[all rights reserved]
xvi, 378pp, b/w illus. throughout, clo., 207x130mm. NSL:M

Italian translation

7723 Giulio Verne/I GRANDI NAVIGATORI/DEL/SECOLO XVIII/Parte Prima/Illustrato con 52 inc., e 9 carte geogr./[device]/Milano/Tipografia Editrice Lombardo/di F. Menozzi e Comp./10 via Andre Appiani 10
Part 1, 1880
232pp, pic. wrappers, 268x175mm. NSL:M
Part 2, 1881, 242pp, and as above. NSL:M

Dutch translation

7724 HET BOEK/der/REIZEN/EN ONTDEKKINGEN./Vrij Bewerkt Naar/Jules Verne's/HISTOIRE DES GRANDS VOYAGES ET DES GRANDS VOYAGEURS/door/Dr. G. J. Dozy/Met ongeveer 300 houtgravures naar oorspronkelijke teckeningen,/1e Deal/[engraving]/Rotterdam- Uitgevers maatschappij "Elsevier"
6 vols uniform with above, preface dated 1880
iv, 240pp, engravings & maps throughout, wrappers, 275x170mm. NSL:M

Portuguese translation

7725 as grandes viagens/Julio Verne/OS EXPLORADORES DO SECOLO XIX/Traduccao/de/Manuel Pinheiro Chagas/1/[device]/Lisboa/Typographia das Horas Romanticas/40 Rua da Atalaya, 52/1882
271pp & 4pp adv., b/w illus. throughout, pic. wrappers, 216x140mm. NSL:M
vol. 2 uniform with above, 337pp. NSL:M

7726 Voyages Extraordinaires/couronnés par l'Académie française./LES ENFANTS/DU/CAPITAINE GRANT/Voyage/Autour du Monde/par Jules Verne/Illustrés de 172 Vignettes par Riou/Gravées par Pannemaker/[vignette]/Bibliothèque/D'Éducation et de Recréation/J. Hetzel et Cie, 18, Rue Jacob/Paris/Tous droits de traduction et de reproduction réservés.
n.d. [1867–68]
624pp, engraved frontis. with title, etc. repeated, 173 engravings in text, 3 maps, clo. (with morocco backstrip), 265x170mm. Grant

7727 Another copy as above to 'Jules Verne', then '172 Illustrations par Riou, gravées par Pannemaker/[vignette]/Collection Hetzel/Paris,18, Rue Jacob/Tous droits' &c....
n.d. [1868?]
620pp, engraved frontis. with title, 3 maps, 170 engravings in text, bound in red cloth elaborately decorated in colour & gilt with author's name, title and 'Voyages Extraordinaires/Collection Hetzel' printed on front cover & spine, 270x170mm. KMM

7728 Ouvrage couronné par L'Académie Francaise/LES ENFANTS/DU/CAPITAINE GRANT/Voyage/Autour du Monde/Par/Jules Verne/Neuviéme Édition/Deuxiéme Partie/Australie [within the outline of a map of Australia]/Bibliothèque d'éducation et de recréation/Paris—J. Hetzel et cie, Rue Jacob,18/Tous droits...&c.
n.d. [1889?]
328pp (inc. 2pp contents), unillus., marbled bd. and one quarter calf, with title in gilt on spine, 175x120mm. RM
(Vol. 1, South America, uniform) RM
Third volume 'Ocean Pacifique' (within a map of the Pacific) and 288pp, as above. RM

7729 Collection Hetzel/Les Voyages Extraordinaires/Couronnés Par L'Académie Française/LES ENFANTS/DU/CAPITAINE GRANT/Voyage/Autour du Monde/Par/Jules Verne/Illustrations par Riou, Gravées par Pannemaker/[vignette]/Paris/Librairie Hachette/79, Boulevard Saint-Germain, 79/1919
620pp, engraved frontis., 167 engravings in text, 3 f/p maps, dec. clo., 270x170mm. RM

7730 Voyages Extraordinaires/couronnés par l'Académie française./LES ENFANTS/DU/CAPITAINE GRANT/Voyage/Autour du Monde/Tome 1/par/Jules Verne/Illustrés de 172 vignettes par Riou/Gravées par Pannemaker/[vignette]/Bibliothèque/d'Éducation et de recréation/J. Hetzel et Cie, 18, Rue Jacob/Paris/Tous droits...&c
Hachette, Paris 1966, 2 vols, 441 and 450-871, and ppv & xii (biography of author, &c.), b/w illus. throughout, col. pic. wrappers, 166x110mm. SUA

7731 A VOYAGE ROUND THE WORLD/By Jules Verne/Author of "The English at the North Pole"/"The Field of Ice" etc. etc./AUSTRALIA/[vignette]/With 48 illustrations by Riou/London and New York/George Routledge and Sons/1877
284pp, b/w engraved frontis. & engravings thoughout, clo., g.e., 190x120mm. ANL

7732 ON THE TRACK/By/Jules Verne/Author of "A Journey into the Interior of the Earth"/"The English at the North Pole" etc. etc./London:/Ward, Lock & Co., Limited/Warwick House, Salisbury Square, E.C./New York and Melbourne
n.d. [inscribed 1905]
179pp, 12pp adv., b/w frontis. by Henry Austin, dec. clo. with sea serpents on front cover, e/p adv., 185x115mm. KMM
"Jules Verne" series. The second part of *A Voyage round the World.*

Dutch edition

7733 Jules Verne/DE KINDEREN VAN/KAPITEIN GRANT/(Australie)/Opnieuw Vertaald/Door J. Feitsma/Geillustreerd door F. S. Baljon/[device]/Hollandsch Uitgeversfonds, Amsterdam/1929
240pp, 14 f/p b/w illus., dec. clo., 175x120mm. RM

Italian edition

7734 Giulio Verne/I FIGLI/DEL/CAPITANO/GRANT/[illustration]/Piero Dami Editore
Milano 1972
30pp (inc. front cover, pagination begins at p5), col. illus., pic. bd., 310x240mm. RM
Illustrated by Piero Cattaneo; abridged and adapted by Mary Menichetti

Czech editions

7735 DETI KAPITANA GRANTA Divy Svetu Znamych a Neznamych./Vybor Romanu Jul. Vernea./IV/DETI KAPITANA GRANTA/Prelozil/Rs/V.Praze./Nakladem Knihtiskarny Aloise R. Lauermanna/1883
3 vols, 233, 232, 213pp, unillus. SLCSR
Prague 1883, 1902 (3 vols), 1907 (3 vols), 1914 (3 vols), 1920, 1923, 1926, 1931, 1940, 1947, 1950, 1954, 1955, 1958, 1964, 1971

Slovak edition

7735a 3 vols 1922–23; Bratislava 1948, 1952, 1954, 1960, 1970
Unseen: SLCSR

German editions

7736 Jules Verne's Werke, Vol.16/DIE/KINDER DES KAPITÄNS GRANT/von/Jules Verne./Bollstandige Ausgabe mit Einleitung und Erläuterungen/Neu übersezt von/Walter Heichen./Titelzeichnung und Illustration von J. Schlattmann./Erster Weltheater:SUD-AMERIKA/[device]/Berlin N.o.43/Druck und Verlag von A. Weichert./Neue Konigstrasse 9.
n.d. [1905?]
220pp, b/w frontis., pic. clo., dec. e/p, 180x123mm. ANL
As above, vol. 2 AUSTRALIEN, 224pp. ANL
" " vol. 3 OZEANIEN, 191pp. ANL

7737 Jules Verne./DE KINDEREN/VAN KAPITEIN GRANT./AUSTRALIE./[device]/Amsterdam/ Uitgevers—Maatschappij "Elsevier"/1920
111pp, unillus. pic. wrappers, adv. inside front & both sides back wrapper, 220x140mm. ANL

7738 A VOYAGE ROUND THE WORLD/By Jules Verne/Author of "The English at the North Pole",/"The Field of Ice", etc./AUSTRALIA/ [vignette]/London/George Routledge and Sons/ Broadway, Ludgate Hill/New York: 9 La Fayette Place
n.d. [inscribed 1885]
284pp, engraved frontis. & 47 engravings, pic. clo., 185x130mm. RM

7739 As above, but part 3 'NEW ZEALAND', 264pp &16pp adv., unillus., dec. clo., 'Jules Verne Library', 170x110mm. KP

7740 As above, but part 1 THE/MYSTERIOUS DOCUMENT,/by/Jules Verne,/Author of 'The English at the North Pole', 'The Ice Desert',/'Five Weeks in a Balloon', 'Among the Cannibals',/Etc., Etc./London/ Ward, Lock and Co., Limited/Warwick House, Salisbury Square, E.C./New York and Melbourne
n.d.
179pp, 12pp adv., b/w frontis. by Henry A. Austin, pic. clo. (with adv. inside both covers & on e/p), 190x120mm.
Part one. Grant
(Part two. 'The Children of Captain Grant' was also published as 'A Voyage Round the World', the three parts being sometimes published separately as 'The Mysterious Document', 'On the Track' and 'Among the Cannibals')

7741 ON THE TRACK/By/Jules Verne,/Author of 'A Journey into the interior of the earth',/'The English at the North Pole'. etc. etc. [device]/London:/Ward, Lock & Co., Warwick House,/Dorset Buildings, Salisbury Square, E.C.
n.d. [inscribed 1882]
179pp & 12pp adv., & 2pp preceding text, col. frontis. only, dec. clo., 180x117mm. CLRC

7742 ON THE TRACK/By/Jules Verne/Author of 'A Journey into the interior of the earth',/'The English at the North Pole', etc etc./Ward, Lock, Bowden and Co.,/London:Warwick House, Salisbury Square, E.C./New York: Bond Street/Melbourne: St. Jame's Street [*sic*]. Sydney, York Street/1892
179pp, & 40pp adv., unillus., pic. clo. (title in gilt on front cover), 194x120mm. GK

7743 ON THE TRACK/A Sequel to/"The Mysterious Document"/By/Jules Verne/Author of "A Journey into the Interior of the Earth"/"The English at the North Pole"/etc etc/London, E.C./Richard Butterworth & Co./16-17 Devonshire Square
n.d.
192pp, unillus., clo., 180x115mm. KP

7744 ON THE TRACK/By/Jules Verne/Author of "The Mysterious Document", "Among the Cannibals", etc./ Ward, Lock & Co., Limited/London and Melbourne
n.d. [inscribed 1943]
189pp, 2pp adv., b/w frontis. only by Henry Austin, clo., 170x120mm. The Royal Series. KMM

7745 AMONG/THE CANNIBALS./Containing/"The Mysterious Document",/"On the Track",/and/ "Among the Cannibals"./By/Jules Verne./Author of "Twenty Thousand Leagues under the Sea",/"Five Weeks in a Balloon", etc. etc./Illustrated by Henry Austin./Ward, Lock & Co., Limited,/London and Melbourne
n.d.
179, 179, 188pp, 4pp adv., b/w frontis. & 2 b/w plates (frontis. to each of the 3 vols), pic. clo., 190x120mm. NSL:M
Other copies seen as above, but with slightly varying imprints

7746 AMONG THE CANNIBALS/By/Jules Verne,/ Author of "A Journey to the Interior of the Earth",/"The English at the North Pole", etc. etc./ Ward, Lock and Co./London: Warwick House, Salisbury Square, E.C./New York: 10, Bond Street
n.d.
188pp, 4pp adv., col. frontis., dec. clo., 180x110mm. NSL:M
Another copy as above, but with slightly different imprint, and title in gilt panel of front cover and spine, and 'Jules Verne Library' blocked in panel. KP

7747 AMONG THE CANNIBALS/By/Jules Verne/ Author of/'The English at the North Pole' 'The Ice Desert'/'Five Weeks in a Balloon' 'The Mysterious Document'/etc./Illustrated/Ward,Lock & Co., Limited/ London, Melbourne and Toronto
n.d.
188pp, & 4pp adv., b/w frontis. only, clo., 190x125mm. SUA
Another copy as above but with slightly different imprint. KP

7748 AMONG THE CANNIBALS/A Sequel/to/ 'The Mysterious Document' and 'On the Track'/By/ Jules Verne/Author of 'The English at the North Pole', 'The Ice Desert'/'Five Weeks in a Balloon','The Mysterious Document'[*sic*] etc./London, E.C./Richard Butterworth & Co./16-17 Devonshire Square
n.d.
192pp, unillus, clo., 175x115mm. KP

7749 AMONG/THE CANNIBALS/By/Jules Verne/ Ward, Lock & Co. Limited/London and Melbourne
n.d. [193-?]
192pp, b/w frontis. only, clo., 170x110mm. The Royal series. KMM
Reprint of the last section (relating to New Zealand) of *A Voyage round the World.*

7750 Jules Verne/AMONG THE CANNIBALS/Including also the second part of/ON THE TRACK/Part II of/ Captain Grant's Children/Edited by/I. O. Evans/ F.R.G.S./London/Arco Publications/1964
188pp (inc. 3pp editorial introduction), unillus., clo., 195x125mm. The Fitzroy Edition of Jules Verne. BBC

7751 Les Voyages Extraordinaires/Couronnés par l'Académie française/MISTRESS BRANICAN/par/ Jules Verne/83 dessins de L. Benett/12 Grandes Gravures en chromotypographie/2 grandes cartes en chromolithographie/[vignette]/Bibliothèque/ d'education et du recréation/J. Hetzel et Cie,18, Rue Jacob/Paris/Tous droits de traduction et de reproduction réservés
n.d. [1882, first pub. 2 vols 1881]

440pp (inc. 2pp contents) engraved frontis. with title, b/w engravings throughout, 12 f/p col. lithographic illus,. 2 f/p col. maps, red clo. elaborately decorated binding uniform with *Les Enfants du Capitaine Grant*. KMM

7752 MISTRESS BRANICAN/By/Jules Verne/Author of 'Caesar Cascabel', 'Michael Strogoff, the Courier of/the Czar' etc./translated from the French by A. Estroclet/[rule]/Illustrated by/L. Benett/[rule]/New York/Cassell Publishing Company 104 & 106 Fourth Avenue
n.d. [1891]
377pp, b/w frontis. & 81 f/p illus., pic. clo., 205x135mm. Grant

7753 THE MYSTERY/OF THE FRANKLIN/MISTRESS BRANICAN/By/Jules Verne/Author of'The Lottery Ticket' 'Five Weeks in a Balloon',/'Round the World in Eighty Days' etc.etc./London/Sampson Low, Marston & Co. Ltd.
n.d.
360pp & 20pp notes, 40pp adv., b/w frontis., clo., 182x120mm. ANL

7754 MISTRESS/BRANICAN/by/Jules Verne/Author of 'The Lottery Ticket'. 'Five Weeks in a Balloon'/'A Trip to the Moon', '20,000 Leagues under the Sea'/'A Voyage to the Centre of the Earth'/'Around the World in Eighty Days' etc./[vignette]/Sun Books/Melbourne
First published 1891 [*sic*] Published in Sun Books 1970
282pp, unillus, pic. wrappers, 180x115mm. KMM

Jules Verne was fascinated with the Southern Hemisphere and particularly the South Pacific and set a number of books in the area. It is beyond the scope of this bibliography to do more than merely mention them as follows:
TWENTY THOUSAND LEAGUES UNDER THE SEA, published in 1870 as *Vingt Mille Lieues sous les Mers* (some of the action takes place in the Antarctic & in the seas near Australia)
THE MYSTERIOUS ISLAND, published in 1875 as *L'Ile Mystérieuse*, and in English in three volumes, *Dropped from the Clouds, Abandoned*, and *The Secret of the Island.*
THE MUTINEERS OF THE BOUNTY, published in 1879 as *Les Révoltés de la Bounty*, a short story. published together with THE BEGUM'S FORTUNE.
ADRIFT IN THE PACIFIC published in 1888 in two volumes as *Deux Ans de Vacances ou Un Pensionnat de Robinsons*, and of New Zealand interest.
FLOATING ISLAND, or The Pearl of the Pacific, published in 1895 as *L'Ile à hélice.*
THEIR ISLAND HOME, published in 1900 in two vols as *Seconde Patrie*, the second volume being translated as CASTAWAYS OF THE FLAG: the Final Adventures of the Swiss Family Robinson.
AN ANTARCTIC MYSTERY, published in 1897 in two volumes as *Le Sphinx des Glaces*, this being the first volume.
THE KIP BROTHERS, published in 1902 in two vols. as *Les Frères Kip* of some Australian interest.

7755 PREMIER VOYAGE DU/CAPITAINE COOK/ Edited by/H. Wilshire, M.A./Scholar and Medallist, Sydney University; Senior/Modern Language Master of Sydney Grammar School/Jules Verne
1926
74pp (inc. 1p preface & 25pp vocab. & appendix) unillus, clo., 184x125mm. ANL
Preface explains that the text is drawn from Verne's *Les Grand Navigateurs du Dix-Huitième Siècle.*

7756 V. PUSTINACH AUSTRALSKYCH (In the Australian Wilderness)
J. R. Vilimek, Prague 1930
383pp. Unseen: SLCSR

VERON, Donald Norwood
See 'Norwood, John'

VERREAUX, Jules et Edouard

7757 L'OCÉANIE EN ESTAMPES,/ou/Description Géographique et Historique/des toutes les îles du grand océan et du continent de la Nouvelle Hollande./ Notasie, Polynésie, Australie,/Contenant les anecdotes intéressantes qui se rattachment à chaque localité. L'exposition des croyances, des gouvernements,/de l'agriculture, des arts, de commerce, des caractères, des usages et des costumes de leurs habitans./Ouvrage destiné à l'instruction et à l'amusement de la jeunesse./ Orné d'une Carte et de Cent-huit Gravures, dont plusiers d'après des Dessins inédits,/et rédigé d'après les documents tant anciens que récents, et notices inédites de voyageurs français et d'étrangers. Mm Lesson./Sainson, Ellis, Marsden, etc./Par Jules et Edouard Verreaux./Membres de la Société d'histoire naturelle de Cap Bonne-Esperance./Paris Librairie Nepreu, Passage des Panorames No26;/London—Published by Ch.Tilt, 86 Fleet Street./MDCCCXXXII
xvi+437pp, b/w engravings, pic. bd., 126x 200mm. NSL:M

VESELOVSKY, Zdenek

7758 VYLET DO TRETIHOR. Cesta zoologa po Australii (Quest to the Three Mountains—Journey of a Zoologist in Australia)
Prague 1969
255pp. Unseen: SLCSR

VEVERS, G.M.

7759 THE LIFE STORY/OF THE/KING PENGUIN/By/ G. M. Vevers/F.R.C.S./Superintendent of the Zoological Gardens, London./Illustrated by Erna Pinner/Noel Carrington/Transatlantic Arts Co. Ltd./29 Percy Street, London, W.1/and at New York
n.d.
32pp, 15 f/p col. illus. & b/w drawings, pic. bd., map e/p, 144x115mm. KP

The Victorian Schoolboys' Story Book

7760 THE VICTORIAN/SCHOOLBOYS'/STORY BOOK/Authors/Harold Avery/R. A. H. Goodyear/ Herbert Hayens. . . Published expressly for/The Myer Emporium Ltd.,/Melbourne
n.d. [school prize 1929]
Title repeated on front cover with 'Myers—Melbourne and Adelaide'. KP
No Australian content. Several variant editions but with no Australian content

The Victorian Schoolgirls' Story Book
Similar to above; several variant editions but with no Australian content

The Victory Book
See [MacLean, A. S.]

VIDLER, Edward A.

7761 WONDER ANIMALS/OF AUSTRALIA/By/ Edward A. Vidler/Author of "Our Own Trees" "Our Own Birds"/"Wonder Birds of Australia" etc./ Commonwealth of Australia/W. A. Hamer Pty. Ltd./ Printers and Publishers, 205–217 Peel Street, North Melbourne N.1./Wholly set up and Printed in Australia/1931/Registered at the G.P.O. Melbourne for Transmission through the Post as a Book
20pp, b/w photographic illus. throughout, bd., 250x120mm. CLRC

7762 WONDER BIRDS/OF AUSTRALIA/By Edward A.

Vidler/Author of "Wonder Animals of Australia", "Our Own Trees"/"Our Own Birds", etc./[drawing]/ Commonwealth of Australia;/W. A. Hamer Pty. Ltd./ Printers and Publishers, 205–217 Peel Street, North Melbourne, N.1./Wholly written, illustrated and Printed in Australia/1931/Registered at the G.P.O. Melbourne for transmission through the Post as a Book
18pp, b/w photographic illus. throughout, bd., 250x120mm. CLRC

7763 OUR OWN TREES/A First Book/on the Australian Forest/By/Edward A. Vidler/[verse]/Written, Illustrated and Printed in Australia/W. A. Hamer, Printer and Publisher, 205-217 Peel Street,/North Melbourne/First printed in January 1930...
64pp, b/w photographic frontis. & photographic illus. throughout, col. pic. wrappers (front cover illus. reproduced from a painting by F .G .Reynolds), 217x175mm. CLRC

7764 OUR OWN BIRDS/OF AUSTRALIA/By Edward A. Vidler/Author of 'Our Own Trees' etc./With Foreword by Arthur H. E. Mattingley, CMZS, CFAOU/ [photograph—male lyrebird]/Commonwealth of Australia/W. A. Hamer Pty Ltd./205-217 Peel Street, North Melbourne, N.1/Written, Illustrated Wholly set-up and printed in Australia/1931
96pp, b/w photographic illus. throughout, pic. wrappers, 247x180mm. KP

7765 OUR OWN BIRDS/OF AUSTRALIA/A First Book for Bird Lovers/By Edward A. Vidler/Author of 'Our Own Trees' etc./with foreword [etc as above, but front cover has photograph of two kookaburras pasted on front, and price 3s] paper wrappers, with cloth backstrip, cover title reads: 'Our Own Birds/of Australia/A First Book for Bird Lovers', 249x170mm. KP

The Village Beech-Tree

7766 THE/VILLAGE BEECH-TREE;/or,/Work and Trust./Published under the direction of/The Committee of General Literature and Education/ Appointed by the Society for Promoting Christian Knowledge/London:/SPCK;/Sold at the depositories:/ 77 Great Queen Street, Lincoln's Inn Fields; 4 Royal Exchange; 48 Piccadilly;/and by all booksellers
n.d. [inscribed 1872]
264pp & 4 pp adv., engraved frontis. & 3 f/p engravings, dec. clo., 180x120mm. ANL
pp122-185 set in Australia

VILLIERS, Alan J.

7767 WHALERS OF THE/MIDNIGHT SUN/By/A. J. Villiers/Author of "Falmouth for Orders" etc./ Illustrated with woodcuts by/Charles Pont/Geoffrey Bles/Two Manchester Square/London
First published 1934
x+285pp, 10 b/w illus., clo., dec. e/p, 215x140mm. NSL:M

7768 WHALERS OF THE/MIDNIGHT SUN/A Story of Modern Whaling/in the Antarctic/By/Alan Villiers/ Author of "Grain Race"/Illustrated with woodcuts by/ Charles Pont/[drawing of a whale]/Charles Scribner's Sons/New York. London/1934
x+285pp, b/w frontis. & 9pp of woodcut illus, clo., dec. map e/p, 215x144mm. KMM

7769 WHALERS OF THE/MIDNIGHT SUN/A Story of Modern Whaling/in the Antarctic/By/Alan Villiers/ Illustrated with woodcuts by/Charles Pont/[device]/ Angus and Robertson/Sydney/London
1949 [first Australian edition]
248pp, dec., extended map, b/w frontis. & 7 f/p b/w illus., 3pp diagrams, clo., map e/p, 195x130mm. KMM
Winner CBCA Award 1949
• Rpt 1964. KMM
Also French edition. Unseen: IFA

7770 STORMALONG/The Story of a boy's voyage around/the world in a full-rigged ship/By/Alan Villiers/[drawing]/Illustrated with drawings by James Fuller (Hardcase)/and photographs by the author/New York/Charles Scribner's Sons/1937
189pp, b/w photographic frontis., 20 photographs, 6 drawings & plan of ship, pic. clo., dec. e/p, 218x144mm. KMM

7771 STORMALONG/The Story of a Boy's voyage round/the World in a full-rigged ship/by/Alan Villiers/[drawing]/Illustrated with drawings by James Fuller (Hardcase)/and photographs by the author/ London/George Routledge & Sons Ltd./Broadway House: Carter Lane, E.C.
1938
225pp, 1p plan, 24 b/w photographic & other illus., clo., 180x120mm. NSL:M

7772 STORMALONG/The Story of a boy's voyage round/the world in a full-rigged ship/by/Alan Villiers/[drawing]/Routledge & Kegan Paul Ltd./ Broadway House, 68–74 Carter Lane/London, E.C.4
1958
225pp, 1p plan, 16 b/w photographic illus., b/w drawings in text, illus. by James Fuller, clo., 185x120mm. ANL

7773 STORMALONG/The story of a Boys' [*sic*] Voyage/ Round the World/in a Full-rigged ship/By/Alan Villiers/[device]/Published by Penguin Books/ Harmondsworth Middlesex England/245 Fifth Avenue New York USA
1946
184pp, unillus. apart from b/w plan of ship, col. pic. wrappers (cover design by Wm Grimmond), 179x110mm. WRT
Also Polish edition. Unseen: IFP

7774 JOEY/GOES TO SEA/by/Alan Villiers/[drawing]/ Illustrated by/Victor J. Dowling/New York/Charles Scribner's Sons/1939
66pp, col. frontis. & b/w drawings throughout, clo., 205x165mm. ANL
The life of a ginger kitten on board the ship *Joseph Conrad.*

7775 PILOT/PETE/by Alan Villiers/Illustrations by/H. T. Cauldwell/London: Museum Press Limited
1953
64pp, part-col. dec. t.p., part-col. illus. throughout, clo., dec. e/p, 220x140mm. KMM
A story based on Pelorus Jack, the pilot porpoise of New Zealand.
US edition

7776 PILOT/PETE/by Alan Villiers/Illustrations by/ H. T. Cauldwell/Charles Scribner's Sons, New York
n.d.
Details as above. ANL

7777 [drawing] PILOT/PETE/by Alan Villiers/ Illustrations by/H. T. Cauldwell/[device]/Angus and Robertson
• Rpt Sydney 1963
[64]pp, dec. t.p., &c. as above. CLRC

7778 AND/NOT TO YIELD/A Story of the Outward Bound/By/Alan Villiers/London/Hodder and Stoughton
1953
160pp (inc. 2pp preface), b/w photographic frontis. & 14 f/p b/w illus., clo., 190x130mm. NSL:M

7779 [drawing]/AND NOT TO YIELD/A Story of the Outward Bound School/of Adventure by Alan Villiers/ Illustrated by Jean Main and David Cobb/Charles Scribner's Sons New York
1953
viii,183pp, 12 f/p b/w illus. & map and diagram, clo., 203x137mm. SSL

7780 THE CRUISE/OF THE "CONRAD"/Alan Villiers/ Abridged with the approval of the author/University of London Press Ltd./Warwick Square, London, E.C.4
First printed in this form 1955; Australian edition distributed by Robertson & Mullens Ltd, Melbourne
187pp (inc. 2pp introduction), double-spread b/w map, 1 diagram, limp clo., 180x120mm. KMM
Appears to have been designed as a school reader.
• Rpt 1963 as above, unseen.

7781 THE NEW/MAYFLOWER/By her Captain/Alan Villiers/Illustrated with photographs by the author and others/[photograph]/Brockhampton Press, Leicester/ First published in Great Britain in 1959/Made and printed in Great Britain by Jarrold and Sons Ltd./ Norwich/Copyright 1958 by Alan Villiers
48pp, mostly b/w photographs, pic. bd., 255x190mm. CLRC
Also clo. KMM
US edition

7782 American Edition—THE MAYFLOWER—The Building and Voyage of the Replica Mayflower II from England to U.S.A. 1957, by her Captain. Charles Scribner's Sons, N.Y. 1959
Unseen: IFA

7783 THE WINDJAMMER STORY/with School of the Sea and Sailing a Square Rigger/By Captain Alan Villiers/[vignette]/Scholastic [device] Book Services/ Published by Scholastic Book Services, a division of Scholastic Magazines, Inc., New York, N.Y.
copyright 1959; 5th printing June 1966
64pp (inc. biographical note & portrait of author) part-col. illus., diagrams & sketches & b/w photographs, pic. wrappers, 205x150mm. KMM
Based on the Louis de Rochemont Cinemiracle Production distributed by National Theatres Inc.

7784 THE BATTLE OF/TRAFALGAR/Lord Nelson Sweeps the Sea/By Alan Villiers/The Macmillan Company, New York/Collier-Macmillan Limited London
First pub. 1965, second printing 1966
96pp, illus. throughout with b/w reproductions of famous paintings & plan of the *Victory*, blue & white frontis. extending to t.p., clo., 234x156. WRT

VILLIERS, Alan (ed.)

7785 OF SHIPS AND MEN/A Personal Anthology/ Compiled by/Alan Villiers/Newnes: London
first pub. 1962; second impression 1963
202 pp & 4pp acknowledgements, 32pp b/w photographic illus., bd., pic. e/p, 246x150mm. KMM
The anthology seems intended for young people.

7786 MY FAVOURITE/SEA STORIES/edited by/Alan Villiers/with drawings by/Mark Myers/[device]/ Lutterworth Press/Guildford and London
1972
160pp, 11 b/w chapter headings, clo., 215x133mm. WRT

VINCENT, Jean

7787 LET'S JOIN IN/Songs and Rhythms/for young children/by/Jean Vincent/(Certificate Dalcroze Eurhythmics—London)/As used in the A.B.C. Session/ "Let's Join In"/Price 3/-/Boosey & Hawkes
Sydney 1955
20pp, unillus., col. dec. wrappers, 280x220mm. ANL

'VINES, Freda' [Freda Bussell Calder]

7788 "RUSTY" THE FOAL/THAT WANTED TO BE A WILD HORSE!/Story by Freda Vines/Illustrated by Jayar Studios/Published by Ayers & James Pty. Ltd./ Branches in all states
Sydney, n.d. [1950]
16pp, b/w illus. throughout, dec. wrappers, shaped picture book, approx. 300x230mm. NSL:M

7789 "BUSTER"/THE PUPPY WHO WANTED TO BE BRAVE!/Story by Freda Vines/Illustrated by Jayar Studios/Published by/Ayers & James Pty. Ltd./ Branches in all states
Sydney, n.d. [1950]
16pp, b/w illus. throughout, dec. wrappers, shaped picture book, approx. 300x225mm. NSL:M

Von BARFUS, E.

7790 TILL SJÖSS./Berättelse för Ungdom/Av/E. von Barfus/övdersättningen från Tyskan/Stockholm/Biejers Bekfölagsaktielbelag
Stockholm 1915
204pp unillus, col. pic. bd. with clo. spine, dec. e/p, 194x140mm. RM
An anonymous Swedish translation of a German children's book set in Australia and the Pacific

VONDRA, J. Gert

7791 TIMOR JOURNEY/J. Gert Vondra/Lansdowne
Melbourne 1968
105pp, b/w photographic illus. throughout, map, dec. chapter headings, clo., extended dec. t.p., 240x180mm. CLRC

7792 HONG KONG CITY WITHOUT A COUNTRY/J. Gert Vondra/Lansdowne
Melbourne 1970
105pp, b/w photographic illus., b/w frontis. & title on two pages, clo., 240x180mm. LRA
Pacific Journeys no. 8.

7793 THE/OTHER CHINA/Discovering Taiwan/J. Gert Vondra/Lansdowne
Melbourne 1970
98pp, b/w photographic illus, b/w frontis. extends on to t.p., clo., 240x180mm. CLRC

A Voyage through the Islands of the Pacific Ocean

7794 A VOYAGE/THROUGH THE/ISLANDS/OF THE/PACIFIC OCEAN./Compiled from the/most authentic and recent authorities./[vignette of a kangaroo]/London:/Printed for C. J. G. & F. Rivington./Booksellers to the Society for Promoting Christian Knowledge./St. Paul's Churchyard, and Waterloo-Place/1831
vi,162, & 1p adv., engraved frontis. & 2 f/p engravings, calf, 138x90mm. NSL:M
Advertisement reads: 'This work, originally prepared & published by the Society for Promoting the Education of the Poor in Ireland, held in Kildare Place, Dublin has been reprinted by their permission and illustrated with new cuts, for the use of the Society for Promoting Christian Knowledge'.

The Voyages of Captain Cook

7795 THE/VOYAGES/OF/CAPTAIN/COOK/ [drawing]/Collins/London and Glasgow
copyright 1971 by Mulder & Zoon, Amsterdam; 1972 in the British Commonwealth by William Collins

[42]pp, col. illus. throughout, col. pic. bd., col. pic. e/p, 265x194mm. KP

Voyages of Discovery
7796 The Brodie Books/VOYAGES OF/DISCOVERY/ Selected from the Journal of/Captain James Cook/ James Brodie Ltd./Denmark Place/W.C.2/London
n.d. [192-?]The Brodie Books no. 6
64pp, b/w portrait frontis., dec. wrappers, 184x110mm. KP

Voyages through the Northern Pacific Ocean, Indian Ocean, and Chinese Sea
7797 VOYAGES/THROUGH THE/NORTHERN PACIFIC OCEAN,/INDIAN OCEAN, and CHINESE SEA./[vignette]/London:/Printed for C. J. G. & F. Rivington,/Booksellers to the Society for Promoting Christian Knowledge;/St. Paul's Churchyard, and Waterloo-Place/1831
156pp, engraved frontis. & 2 f/p engravings, marbled bd. with leather backstrip, 135x85mm. HBM
Advertisement states that 'this work, originally prepared and published by the "Society for Promoting Education of the Poor in Ireland, held in Kildare Place, Dublin" has been reprinted by their permission and illustrated with new cuts, for the use of the Society for Promoting Christian Knowledge'.
Describes a voyage from Port Jackson, through the Indonesian islands, into the China Sea & Pacific Ocean & back to Port Jackson before returning to England via the Cape of Good Hope.

Voyages to the Southern Hemisphere
7798 VOYAGES/TO THE/SOUTHERN HEMISPHERE;/or,/Nature Explored./Being/an accurate and faithful account/of the/Voyages to the Great South Seas/Undertaken by Order of the King,/ And performed on His Majesty's Ships the/Dolphin, Swallow and Endeavour./containing the/Various Important Discoveries/that were made by/The Hon. Commodore Byron,/Dr Solander, Mr Banks/and by the Captains Wallis, Carteret,/and Cook./London:/ Printed for R. Snagg, no.29 Pater-noster Row.
n.d. [1774 or 1775]
ii, 187pp, engraved frontis., wrappers, 168x105mm. ANL
Lt Cook's Voyage occupies pp77-187. Book written in form of questions and answers. The 2-page introduction does not specify that the book was intended for children, but this is suggested by the style of the text. The publisher, R. Snagg, is said to have dealt in books for children (Quaritch, Cat 105, item 20). This seems the earliest book for children relating to Australia.

[VSHIVKINA, Tatiana Vasilievna]
7799 SHOOMO THE/MAGICIAN/By/T. V. Vee/ Chinese Legends and Fairy Tales—Series No. 2/Vee Press
Canberra 1971
47pp, b/w illus. in text, wrappers, cover title, 200x150mm. ANL

W, A. E.-[WARBURTON, A. Egerton-]
See Egerton-Warburton, A.

W., E.
7800 THE UNSPEAKABLE GIFT;/or, the/Story of Benjamin and Ruth/by E.W./London:/G. Morrish, 20 Paternoster Square./1897
124pp, & 4pp adv., b/w frontis. & 4 f/p. b/w illus. by V. Allanson Cull, pic. clo, 170x110mm. KP
Story of a Jewish family, divided because of religious differences & of one son who migrates to Melbourne

W, T. A.
THE BUSH TWINS. *See* [White, T. A.]

WADE, Mary Hazelton [Mrs, née Blanchard]
7801 THE BOY WHO/LOVED THE SEA/The Story of Captain James Cook/by/Mary Hazelton Wade/ [device]/Illustrated by/Alex A. Blum/D. Appleton and Company/New York: 1931 London
248pp, b/w frontis., 3 f/p b/w illus., clo., 185x125mm. Grant

WADDY, Ethelred [née Spittal, Mrs P. Stacy]
7802 PRINCESS CINTRA/By/Mrs Stacy Waddy./ Published under the direction of the general literature/ Committtee/London:/Society for Promoting Christian Knowledge,/Northumberland Avenue,W.C../ 43 Queen Victoria Street, E.C./Brighton: 129 North Street./ New York: E. & J. B. Young and Co.
n.d. [1903]
80pp, & 16 pp adv., b/w frontis., dec. clo., 170x116mm. ANL
Story tells of a young girl, survivor of the wrecked *Cintra*, who is rescued and adopted by a passenger on a voyage to Adelaide.

7803 THE CAMERONS OF/NIDDRY/N.S.W./By/Mrs Stacy Waddy/Author of "Princess Cintra"/Published under the direction of the Tract Committee/London:/ Society for Promoting Christian Knowledge./ Northumberland Avenue, E.C.; 47 Queen Victoria Street, E.C./Brighton: 129 North Street,/New York: E. S. Gorham
n.d. [1904]
128 pp, & 16 pp adv., b/w frontis. only, pic. clo., dec. e/p, 182x120mm. ANL

WADDY, Percival Stacy
7804 JOHN THE JACK/A Story for Children/Adapted from the greatest of French Novels,/Victor Hugo's "Les Misérables",/by/Stacy Waddy,/Headmaster of The King's School, Parramatta, N.S.W./Author of "Come for Strength", "The Great Moghul", etc./Parramatta:/ The Cumberland Argus, Ltd., Printers and Publishers.1915
104pp, one page verse precedes t.p., unillus., wrappers, adv. on both wrappers, 210x125mm. ANL
Published in aid of Red Cross

WAGNER, Jenny
7805 THE WEREWOLF KNIGHT/Story by Jenny Wagner/Pictures by Karl Homes/Macmillan
South Melbourne, Victoria, 1972
[26]pp, col. dec. t.p., col. illus. throughout, pic. boards, 245x185mm. CLRC

WAKEFIELD, Edward S.
7806 NED WILLOUGHBY:/A Tale of Love & Adventure/By/Edward S. Wakefield/Third Edition/ [quotation]/Melbourne:/J. T. Picken, Printer/244–250 Little Lonsdale Street/1904
152pp (inc. introduction), unillus., wrappers, 160x95mm. VSL
A pirate story, including some original verse, written when the author was a boy of sixteen.

WAKEFIELD, S. A.
7807 BOTTERSNIKES/AND/GUMBLES/by/S. A. Wakefield/[drawing]/drawings by/Desmond Digby/ Collins/Sydney London
1967
80pp, 1 f/p b/w illus. & b/w drawings throughout, clo., 230x165mm. KMM
7808 BOTTERSNIKES/AND/GUMBLES/by/S. A.

Wakefield/[drawing]/drawings by/Desmond Digby/Collins/Sydney—London
First published 1967; second edition 1969
80pp, col. frontis., b/w drawings throughout, clo., 235x165mm. BBC

7809 S. A. Wakefield/BOTTERSNIKES AND/GUMBLES/by/[drawing]/Drawings by/Desmond Digby/Penguin Books
Harmondsworth, Middlesex, England, 1972
87pp, 6pp adv., b/w frontis. & b/w drawings in text throughout, pic. wrappers, 180x110mm. KMM

The 'Wales' Bird Colouring Book

7810 THE 'WALES'/BIRD COLOURING /BOOK
Bank of NSW Savings Bank Ltd, Sydney 1962
[12]pp b/w drawings of Australian birds, col. pic. wrappers, cover title, 230x180mm. KP

WALINCOURT, Eug de

7811 VOYAGE/A/BOTANY BAY/Par/Le Vicomte Eug. de Walincourt/Suivi d'autres épisodes/[monogram 'E.A.T'] Limoges/Eugène Ardant et C. Thibaut,/Imprimeurs-Libraires-Éditeurs.
n.d. [1865]
94pp, bound together with a separate story 'Le dévouement d'un fils' (24pp), engraved frontis, dec. clo. with col. onlay, 205x122mm. ANL

WALKER, Edith G.

See Dane, Jeanie G. & Walker, Edith G.

WALKER, Frank B.

7812 TALES OF/THE SEA/by/Lieut. Frank B. Walker/R.A.N.V.R./Illustrated by B. E. Pike
New Century Press Pty Ltd, 3 North York St, Sydney, n.d. [194-?]
45pp, part-col. frontis., part-col. f/p illus. on alternate pages, pic. boards, 240x190mm. KMM
Contains 6 stories about the Second World War.

WALKER, 'Bonnie' [Grace Bonar]

7813 PIXIE PIE/By Bonnie Walker/[drawing]/A Book of/Verses for Young/Children
Imperial Printing Co. Ltd, Perth, n.d. [1933]
40pp, b/w drawings throughout, dec. wrappers, 205x130mm. ANL

7814 Another edition, Robertson & Mullens, Melbourne 1935. Unseen

7815 "Social Studies" Reader/and Activity Book/Upper Infants./THE BOBTAIL FAMILY/by/Bonnie Walker/Lessons on/Health, Good Manners,/and Safety First/Carroll's Ltd., Printers and Publishers./566 Hay Street, Perth./Copyright. 48
n.d. [1936]
36pp, 6 f/p b/w illus., stiff wrappers, cover title, 185x120mm. KMM

7816 BENNY,/BILLY AND/BETTY—More About the/Bob-Tail Family/By Bonnie Walker/Book One/Lessons on/Needs of the/Family, Health, Safety First and/Good Manners/Carroll's Pty. Ltd./566 Hay Street/Perth, W.A.
n.d. [1954]
24pp, 6 f/p b/w illus., illus. wrappers, cover title, 245x195mm. KP
A Social Studies Reader

7817 Book One/"Social Studies" Reader and activity book/BENNY, BILLY/AND/BETTY/(More about the bob-tail family)/by/Bonnie Walker/Wholly set up and printed in Australia by/Carroll's Pty Ltd/Printers and Publishers/566 Hay Street, Perth/Registered at the General Post Office, Perth, for/transmission through the post as a book/Copyright 51/Lessons on/Needs of the Family,/Health, Safety First/and Good Manners
n.d. [1951]
• Rpt with same contents but different cover. KP

WALKER, H. K. McG.

MATT, JEUNE AUSTRALIAN, Melbourne, Macmillan 1924.
Primarily a school textbook

WALKER, Kath [Oodgeroo Noonucca]

7818 STRADBROKE/DREAMTIME/Kath Walker/Illustrated by Dennis Schapel/Angus and Robertson
Sydney 1972
120pp, 25 f/p b/w illus., pic. clo., col. e/p, 105x205mm. KMM
D/w illustration by a 14-year-old Aboriginal girl.

WALKER, Marjorie [pseud. Marjory Rose Casson]

7819 JAIMIE/Written by Marjorie Walker/Illustrated by Paul Rigby/Acacia Press
Melbourne 1972
28pp, b/w drawings throughout, pic. boards, 170x220mm. BBC
Verses

WALKER, Rowland

7820 PHANTOM ISLAND/a modern Crusoe Story/by/Rowland Walker/Author of "The Rival Schools",/"By Airship to the Tropics"/"The Lost Expedition" etc./Ward, Lock & Co., Limited/London and Melbourne
n.d. [1925]
256pp, col. frontis., b/w map, boards, 185x120mm. Grant
Story of two Australian schoolboys offered a trip to Europe in a flying ship. After flying round Australia they leave Fremantle, but the flying ship crashes off N.W. Cape, & the boys are eventually rescued from a nearby island by an Australian destroyer, & return to Melbourne.
Another copy as above, n.d., clo. with b/w frontis. KMM

WALKER, W. N. [ed.]

7821 OLD AUSTRALIAN/BALLADS/An Anthology/by W. N. Walker/School Projects Pty. Ltd.
Sydney 1967
47pp (inc. 1p preface & acknowledgements, & 1p introduction), illus. t.p., b/w drawings throughout, illus. by Anne Pickering, stiff dec. wrappers, 210x130mm. BBC
Australian Scene series

WALKER, William Sylvester [pseud. 'Cooee']

7822 AT POSSUM CREEK/By/William Sylvester Walker/(Coo-ee)/Author of "Native Born", "Virgin Gold", "When the Mopoke Calls",/"In the Blood", "From the Land of the Wombat",/"Zealandia's Guerdon", "What Lay Beneath",/"Blair's Ken", "Silver Queen", etc./London/J & J. Bennett Ltd./(The Century Press)/8 Henrietta Street, W.C./All rights reserved
n.d. [1915]
274pp (inc. 3pp introductory verses & 2pp envoi verse), 3pp adv., unillus., clo. (with col. illus. pasted on front cover), 180x120mm. NSL:M

WALKER, Thea Campbell

See Campbell-Walker, Thea

WALL, Dorothy

7823 TOMMY BEAR/AND/THE ZOOKIES/[drawing]/Story and Illustrations/by Dorothy Wall
Triumph Printers, Sydney, n.d. [1920]
16pp, col. & b/w illus. throughout, wrappers, 235x180mm. ANL

7824 BLINKY BILL/The Quaint Little Australian/Story and Decorations/By/Dorothy Wall/Angus & Robertson Limited/89 Castlereagh Street/Sydney/1933
72pp (inc. 1p note), col. frontis. & 14 plates, line drawings throughout, printed in sepia, dec. boards, 240x185mm. VSL
• Rpt 1935, 1936, 1937. Unseen
• Rpt as above 1938, 237x180mm. KMM
• Rpt as above 1941, 86pp, col. frontis. & 14 f/p b/w illus. (inc. in pagination), drawings in text (printed in b/w) col. pic. boards, 240x185mm. KMM

7825 BLINKY BILL GROWS UP/Story and Decorations/by/Dorothy Wall/[drawing]/Angus & Robertson Limited/89 Castlereagh Street/Sydney/1934
vi, 84pp, 16 sepia/white plates & drawings in text, plain boards with green lettering & decoration, 240x180mm. KMM
• Rpt 1935 as above, printed in b/w. KP
• Rpt 1938 as above, printed in b/w. KP

7826 BLINKY BILL GROWS UP/Story and decorations/by/Dorothy Wall/[drawing]/Angus & Robertson Limited/89 Castlereagh Street/Sydney/1941
100pp (i.e. 98pp numbered & 2 illus. pp), 20 f/p b/w illus. on text paper (& inc. in pagination), pic. boards, 240x180mm. KP

7827 THE TALE OF/BRIDGET/AND THE/BEES/Written & Illustrated/by/Dorothy Wall/[drawing]/Methuen & Co. Ltd. 36 Essex Street W.C. London
First published 1934
56pp, col. frontis. & 8 f/p col. illus., b/w drawings in text throughout, pic. boards, 210x165mm. ANL

7828 THE TALE OF/BRIDGET/AND THE/BEES/Written & illustrated/by/Dorothy Wall/Authorized Edition/Artists and Writers Guild, Inc./Poughkeepsie, New York/Printed in U.S.A.
1935
45pp, 4 f/p col. plates, some b/w drawings, boards with col. illus. pasted on front cover (drawing of one gnome & alongside, in a line, 3 bees), 205x165mm. ANL
One page foreword signed Edith Kovar

7829 BROWNIE/The Story of a naughty little Rabbit/Story and Decorations/By/Dorothy Wall/Angus & Robertson Limited/89 Castlereagh Street/Sydney/1935
56pp, col. front., 16 b/w plates (not in pagination), b/w drawings throughout, boards, 240x185mm. VSL
• Rpt 1940. Unseen
• Rpt 1941 as above but 73pp, col. frontis. & 16 f/p sepia/white illus. (on text paper & inc. in pagination), pic. boards, adv. on back cover, 238x182mm. KP
• Rpt as above 1942. Unseen

7830 STOUT FELLOWS/Chum, Angelina Wallaby, Um-Pig/and Flip/Story and Illustrations/By Dorothy Wall/[4 lines verse]/Angus and Robertson Ltd./89 Castlereagh St./Sydney 1936
52pp, col. frontis., 10 b/w plates (one printed on both sides making 11 illustrations), line drawings throughout, boards, 240x185mm. KMM
• Rpt as above 1940. Unseen

7831 BLINKY BILL AND NUTSY/Two little Australians/[drawing]/Story and Illustrations/by Dorothy Wall/Angus & Robertson Ltd./89 Castlereagh St./Sydney 1937
viii, 115pp, 22 f/p b/w illus. on text paper, b/w drawings throughout, pic. boards, dec. e/p, 240x185mm. ANL
• Rpt 1940 as above. KMM

7832 THE COMPLETE ADVENTURES OF/BLINKY BILL/Containing:/Blinky Bill/Blinky Bill Grows up/Blinky Bill and Nutsy/Told & Illustrated by/Dorothy Wall/Angus & Robertson Limited/89 Castlereagh Street/Sydney
1939
85, 99, 115pp & (2pp, 1p note, 1p illus), col. frontis. & drawings printed in sepia throughout, col. pic. boards (e/p drawing of BB & Nutsy at Mrs Koala's Guest House, printed in green) 215x170mm. ANL
• Rpt in b/w as above (note printed on p115, drawing on foll. page), 1940. KP
• Rpt 1942 as above, col. frontis. & 15, 18 & 22 f/p drawings printed on text paper in b/w, plain e/p, col. pic. bds as 1st ed. KMM

7833 THE COMPLETE ADVENTURES OF/BLINKY BILL/Containing/Blinky Bill/Blinky Bill Grows up/Blinky Bill and Nutsy/Told & Illustrated by/Dorothy Wall/Angus & Robertson/89 Castlereagh St./Sydney/1946
305pp, 1p note, 1p illus.,(continuous pagination) col. frontis. & 4 col. plates, drawings throughout, pic. boards (clo. spine), dec. e/p, 240x180mm. KMM
Text printed in black, and ills., inc. e/p, and page headings, in sepia. Contains col. plates not in previous eds. The cover has only a small illus. quite different from previous editions.
• Rpt 1947 as above. CLRC
• Rpt 1952, 1954, 1956 as above, printed in sepia, bound in col. pic. boards, 236x180mm. CLRC
• Rpt 1962 as above. KMM
• Rpt 1964 (twice), 1965. KP
• Rpt 1966, 1968 as above, bound in sim. clo. KP
• Rpt 1969 as above, but pic. boards, 238x184mm. KP
• Rpt 1972, 21st imp, as above. KMM

7834 BLINKY BILL/JOINS THE ARMY/Story and Decorations/by/Dorothy Wall/[drawing]/Angus & Robertson Limited/89 Castlereagh Street/Sydney/1940
130pp, col. frontis. & 11 f/p b/w illus. (on text paper), pic. boards, 240x185mm. ANL
• Rpt 1942. Unseen.
• Rpt 1943 as above but plain light card wrappers with col. pic. d/w attached to spine (frontis. reproduced on d/w), otherwise as above. CLRC

7835 BLINKY BILL'S/ABC BOOK/By Dorothy Wall
Offset Printing Co., Sydney, n.d. [1947]
16pp, col. illus. throughout, pic. wrappers, cover title, 270x215mm. KMM

7836 A TINY STORY OF/BLINKY BILL/[drawing]/Written and illustrated by/Dorothy Wall/Printed and Published by Offset Printing Coy. Pty. Ltd. [OPC] 169 Philip Street, Waterloo, Sydney (All Rights Reserved) n.d. [1942?]
46pp, 8 f/p col. illus., dec. border round each page of text, wrappers, 230x180mm. Grant

7837 BLINKY BILL/Dress-up Book/by/Dorothy Wall/[drawing & cutting-out instructions]
Offset Printing Coy. Pty Ltd, Sydney, n.d. [1942]
16pp, alternate pp printed in col. with instructions on back, printed on light board, col. pic. boards, cover title, 280x215mm. MAC

7838 NUTSY/Dress-up Book/by/Dorothy Wall
[1942]
Uniform with *Blinky-Bill Dress-up Book*, above. MAC

7839 FUN WITH/BLINKY BILL/[drawing]/Adapted from the Stories of/Dorothy Wall
Angus and Robertson Ltd, Sydney, n.d. [1953]
30pp, 8 col. illus. & b/w drawings throughout, pic. wrappers, cover title, 155x115mm. ANL

7840 [drawing]/BLINKY BILL
Thumb-print (Aust.) Co. [Angus & Robertson Pty Ltd], Sydney, n.d.
[6]pp, col. illus. throughout, pic. clo., cover title, 150x175mm. MAC
Rag book.

7841 THE/RAINY DAY/GIFT BOOK/of the/ Commonwealth Savings Bank of Australia
Printed by Simmons Ltd, Sydney, n.d. [1925?]
[16]pp (printed inside front & back covers), 30 part-col. illus. by Dorothy Wall, pic. wrappers, cover title, 200x125mm. Grant

7842 THE/RAINY DAY/GIFT BOOK/of the/ Commonwealth Savings Bank of Australia
Printed by Patterson & Beck Pty Ltd [Syd.], n.d.
18pp, part. col. & b/w illus., pic. wrappers, 215x140mm. KMM

7843 Another copy printed by John Sands Pty Ltd, Sydney, n.d.
As above but back cover (printed in b/w & green) has a different illustration from that on copy above which is printed in b/w & sepia. KP

7844 KNOWLEDGE/FOR/BOYS/AND/GIRLS/issued by the/Commonwealth/Savings/Bank/of/Australia
Printed by Patterson & Beck Ltd, Sydney, n.d. [internal evidence suggests 1932]
36pp, b/w photographic illus. & some anonymous drawings, part-col. pic. wrappers, cover title, 165x125mm. KMM
Factual book promoting the Savings Bank. The front & back wrappers designed by Dorothy Wall.

7845 BLINKY BILL/"Magic Action" [drawing]/Book
Whitman Publishing Co., Racine, Wisconsin, n.d. [1935]
28pp, b/w & part-col. illus., col. pic. board cover, 196x183mm. CLRC
Three double page moveable (pop-up) pictures. Pirated work not attributed to Dorothy Wall.

WALL, Dorothy & ODELL, Carol

7846 LET'S CALL HIM/BLINKY BILL/Based on The Complete Adventures of Blinky Bill/by Dorothy Wall/ Adapted by Carol Odell/Illustrated by Wal Stackpool/ Angus and Robertson/(C) Angus & Robertson 1970 [7 lines]/Printed in Australia by Halstead Press, Sydney
[26]pp, col. illus. throughout, pic. boards, dec. e/p, 290x235mm. Young Australia Series. BBC
• Rpt 1971. KMM

7847 BLINKY BILL/AND THE RABBIT'S BIRTHDAY PARTY/Based on The Complete Adventures/of Blinky Bill/by Dorothy Wall/Adapted by Carol Odell/ Illustrated by Wal Stackpool/Angus and Robertson Sydney 1971
[25]pp, col. illus. throughout, pic. boards, dec. e/p, 285x215mm. KMM

7848 BLINKY BILL/AND NUTSY/Based on/The Complete Adventures of Blinky Bill/by Dorothy Wall/ Adapted by Carol Odell/Illustrated by Patricia Mullins/Angus and Robertson/First published in 1972 by Angus & Robertson (Publishers) Pty Ltd/Sydney Melbourne Brisbane London and Singapore/[9 lines]
[26]pp, col. illus. throughout, pic. boards, dec. e/p, 285x215mm. KMM

WALLACE, Helen E.

7849 MAGIC CASEMENTS/By/Helen E. Wallace/With three Plates from Watercolours by/Blamire Young/ Brown, Prior & Co. Pty. Ltd./Printcraft House, Melbourne/1926
Limited de luxe edition of 1000 copies, the first 150 being signed by author & artist
104pp, 3 f/p col. illus., clo., 240x185mm. VSL

7850 SO LITTLE/by/Helen E. Wallace/The Arts & Crafts/Publishing Company Ltd.,/34, Bloomsbury Street, London, W.C.1
n.d. [1929]
51pp, unillus., dec. boards, 195x120mm. ANL
Children's verses.

WALLACE, J. T. Gilmour

7851 WHERE FAIRIES DWELL/(Specially prepared for Elementary Schools)/Tales from many lands/Selected and retold for/Young children/By/J. T. Gilmour Wallace/With Four Original Illustrations by Louis McCubbin/[device]/Melbourne/Thomas C. Lothian/ Publisher
n.d. [1914?]
90pp &5pp notes, 1p adv., 4 f/p b/w illus., pic. wrappers, 182x120mm. KP
Traditional stories, inc. a Maori myth and two Aboriginal tales.

WALLACE-CRABBE, Kenneth

7852 THE STORY OF/OTTO/[drawing]/Or How they Fissioned/The Atom/By/K. Wallace-Crabbe, O.B.E./Illustrated by Wally Driscoll/Melbourne/The Hawthorn Press
n.d.
34pp, b/w drawings in text throughout, boards, dec. e/p, 215x150mm. KMM

WALLER, Leslie

7853 EXPLORERS/Leslie Waller/Illustrated by Gil Miret/[drawing]/Oliver & Boyd
Edinburgh, n.d. [1963]
48pp, part-col. t.p., part-col. illus. throughout, dec. clo., 210x180mm. KP
The Open Gate Library 1

WALLER, Olga D. A.

See ERNST, Olga Dorothea Agnes

WALPOLE, Andrew H.

7854 THE BLACK STAR/A School Story for Boys/By/ Andrew H. Walpole/Australia:/Cornstalk Publishing Company/Arnold Place, Sydney/1925
226pp, b/w frontis. only, clo., 185x120mm. ANL
2nd ed. Nov. 1925. Unseen

WALTER, L. Edna

7855 "Men of Courage" Series—Book Two/CAPTAIN COOK/by/L. Edna Walter/O.B.E., B.Sc./Illustrated by A. W. Knott/[device]/London/Newnes Educational Publishing Co., Ltd./Tower House, Southampton Street, Strand, W.C.2
First published 1952
48pp, b/w map, 4 f/p b/w illus. & 6 small b/w illus., dec. limp clo., 185x120mm. KP
Advertisement inside back cover lists six titles in this series by the same author, including:
No. 4, *Ferdinand Magellan;* No. 5,*William Dampier;* No. 6, *John Franklin.* No. 12, *Captain Scott,*

'WALTERS, Hugh' [pseud. Walter Hughes]

7856 BLAST OFF AT/WOOMERA/Hugh Walters/Faber and Faber Ltd./24 Russell Square/London
1957
202pp, unillus., clo., 205x125mm. BBC
Adventure story about rockets; the author is not Australian & the book, though partly set at Woomera, has only a slight Australian background.

7857 BLAST OFF AT/WOOMERA/Hugh Walters/Faber and Faber Ltd./24 Russell Square/London

First published 1957; first published in this edition 1965
202pp, unillus., pic. wrappers, 185x120mm. KMM

7858 THE DOMES/OF PICO/Hugh Walters/Faber and Faber Ltd./24 Russell Square/London
1958
196pp, unillus., clo., 200x120mm. BBC
Sequel to *Blast off at Woomera;* some of the action takes place in Australia.

WALSH, Amanda
7859 EGRIN AND/THE PAINTED/WIZARD/Amanda Walsh/[drawing]/Penguin Books
Ringwood, Victoria, 1972
[36]pp, col. & b/w illus. throughout, pic. wrappers, 235x215mm. KMM

WALTON, Brenda Alice Margaret
7860 "SNUFFLE"/THE PIG WHO WOULD/WEAR A GREEN COAT/Story by/Margaret Walton/Illustrated by Margery Luth
Ramsay Ware, Printers, Melbourne, n.d. [1945]
16pp, part-col. illus. throughout, cover title, wrappers, 265x210mm. ANL

The Wanderer
7861 THE WANDERER./Published under the direction of The Committee of General Literature and Education/Appointed by the Society for Promoting/ Christian Knowledge/London./Society for Promoting Christian Knowledge,/Northumberland Avenue, Charing Cross, W.C.;/48 Queen Victoria Street, E.C.;/ Brighton: 135, North Street/New York; E. & J. B. Young & Co.
n.d. [189-?]
224pp, 8pp adv., b/w frontis. & 2 f/p b/w illus., clo. (with one illus. blocked in brown, on front cover), 180x120mm. KMM
Set partly in the Victorian gold diggings.

WANE, Aldea
7862 SULKS/GRIZZLEGRUMPS/By/Aldea Wane/ Illustrations by/Dorothy Fry/The Aldea Wane/Fairy Stories/No. 1 Copyright
Printed by W. C. Penfold & Co. Ltd, Sydney, n.d. [foreword dated 1917, library copy acquired 1918]
20pp (inc. 3pp foreword by James Peddle), 3 b/w drawings, wrappers, 180x120mm. NSL:M

WARBURTON, Margaret
7863 FENNEL-/SEED/By/Margaret/Warburton/ Illustrated/by/John Emery
Roneod booklet, no place of imprint, n.d. [illustrations dated 1935]
26pp, b/w illus., wrappers, 195x150mm. KMM
Fairy stories with occasional reference to Australia.

WARD, Frederick
7864 JUNGLE GOLD/By/Frederick Ward/Copyright/ Published by W. J. Nesbit/124 Liverpool Street,/ Sydney
n.d.
128pp, b/w frontis & 3 f/p b/w illus., pic. wrappers, 100x135mm. KMM
Cover reads 'Breath-taking/Adventures in/Queer/ Places'. Story set in Australia and New Guinea

WARD, Raymond
7865 True Adventure Series/TALES OF/FAMOUS/ CRICKETERS/Raymond Ward,/Headmaster, Blairtummock Primary/School, Glasgow./illustrated by/Trevor Stubley/ Blackie & Son Limited. London Glasgow
1971
26pp, b/w frontis. & text drawings, stiff pic. wrappers, 185x140mm. VMOU
Includes 'The Boy from Bowral' (Don Bradman) 9pp

WARNER, Oliver
7866 GREAT SEAMEN/by/Oliver Warner/London/G. Bell and Sons, Ltd./1961
226pp (inc. 1p introduction, 1p epilogue, 2pp bibliography & 6pp index), 8 f/p b/w portrait illus., clo., 200x130mm. HBM
Lives of 10 great seamen, including Anson, Cook, Captain Kane at Samoa, Shackleton, &c.

7867 [publisher's device]/A Cassell Caravel Book/ CAPTAIN COOK/AND THE SOUTH PACIFIC/By the Editors of/Horizon Magazine/Author/Oliver Warner/ In consultation with/Dr. J. C. Beaglehole/Victoria University of Wellington, New Zealand/Illustrated with Paintings, Drawings,/and Maps of the Period/ [illustration]/Cassell—London/©1963 by American Heritage Publishing Co., Inc. 551 Fifth Avenue, New York 17./New York. All rights reserved under Berne and Pan-American Copyright Conventions./First published in Great Britain 1964.
153pp (inc. 1p foreword, 1p acknowledgements, 1p bibliography & 2pp index), 41 col. illus. & b/w illus. throughout, pic. clo., dec. maps e/p, 250x175mm. HBM

WARSZAWSKI, B.
7868 THE LOST PRINCESS/A Fairy Tale/By B. Warszawski/Printed by York Press Pty. Ltd./ 198–202 Faraday Street, Carlton,/Melbourne, Australia
n.d. [1944]
126pp, unillus., wrappers, 205x130mm. VSL
Text in Yiddish with additional t.p. translated into English as above.

Water Conservation in Australia
7869 WATER CONSERVATION/IN AUSTRALIA/ Drink/Coca-Cola
Printed by the Griffin Press, Adelaide, n.d.
12pp (inc. covers), pic. illus. throughout & pic. wrappers, cover title, 240x180mm. KP
Advertising booklet, includes 2pp 'The Story of Coco-Cola'

WATERWORTH, Alfred G.
7870 THE STORY OF/ANZAC DAY/Told for/Boys and Girls/By/Alfred G. Waterworth/Head Teacher, Glen Dhu State School,/Launceston./With a foreword by/ Major-General Sir John Gellibrand/K.C.B., C.B., D.S.O./Copyright by the Returned Sailors and Soldiers Imperial/League, Launceston Sub-Branch/With the approval of the Tasmanian Education Department./ Tasmania;/"The Examiner" and "Weekly Courier" office./73–75 Patterson St., Launceston, Tas.
On cover: 1920, Published by Gordon & Gotch (A/sia) Ltd.
63pp (inc. 1p foreword), b/w portrait frontis. & 6 f/p b/w photographic illus., wrappers, 185x120mm. KMM
'Contents' lists a map of Gallipoli not included in copy examined which does not appear to have any pages missing.

WATKINS, Allan
7871 DANGER ISLAND/by/Allan Watkins/Golden Press/Sydney
1972
195pp, 3 f/p b/w illus. by Hal English, pic. clo., pic. e/p, 210x135mm. KMM

7872 PILLARS OF CRYSTAL/by/Allan Watkins/Golden Press/Sydney
1972

185pp, 3 f/p b/w illus. by Hal English, pic. clo., pic. e/p, 209x134mm. KMM

WATSON, Ina

7873 SILVERTAIL/The Story of a Lyrebird/by/Ina Watson/[device]/Illustrations by/Walter Cunningham/ John Sands/Pty. Ltd./Sydney Melbourne/1946
42pp (inc. 1p foreword), 6 f/p col. illus. & 2 col. illus. on e/p, b/w drawings throughout, plain boards with col. pic. wrappers, 245x177mm. KMM
• Rpt n.d. as above, with front & back wrapper design printed direct on to board covers. KMM

7874 LARRY/The Story of an Australian Seagull/by Ina Watson/Illustrated by Margaret Senior/[drawing]/ Published by John Sands Pty. Ltd./Sydney Melbourne Brisbane Adelaide/Perth Hobart
Sydney, n.d. [1961]
42pp, dec. t.p., 10 col. illus. & part. col. & b/w drawings throughout, dec. boards, dec. e/p, 250x180mm. KMM
• Rpt n.d. [1967] as above. BBC

WATSON, Elspeth J. Boog

7875 Great Exploits/SHACKLETON IN/THE ANTARCTIC/By/E. J. Boog Watson/[device]/Oxford University Press/London New York Toronto
1943
39pp, b/w frontis & 1 f/p b/w illus, sgd 'G.M.', 1 f/p map, dec. wrappers, 184x123mm. WJSB

WEATHERLY, Marjorie

7876 AUSTRALIA'S CHILD/A Story of Station Life from/a Child's Point of View/By/Marjorie Weatherly/ (Mrs. Carter)/Author of/Contrast, Voices from My Garden, Key of Heaven, Fragments, etc./F. W. Cheshire/Melbourne
1951
71pp, b/w drawings throughout, clo., 190x120mm. VSL

WEBB, Robert

7877 CHALLENGE/OF ICE/by/Robert N. Webb/ illustrations by/Arnie Kohn/Whitman Publishing Company/Racine, Wisconsin
1963
212pp, drawings throughout printed in blue ink, pic. boards, pic. e/p, 185x140mm. ANL
'Real life stories of Polar explorers'

WEBB, Z. V.

7878 FLUFFY'S/ADVENTURE/By/Z. V. Webb/The Story of a Little Rabbit
Offset Printing Co., Sydney, n.d. [1947]
16pp, 8 f/p col. illus., b/w illus. throughout, dec. boards, cover title, 275x220mm. ANL

7879 THE SHARED DOG/By Z. V. Webb/Georgian House [device]/Melbourne
n.d. [195-?]
21pp, drawings in text printed in blue, wrappers, 118x144mm. KP

WEBSDALE, Charles D.

7880 SEAFARERS/Charles D. Websdale/Sydney:/The States Publishing Co.,/1905
279pp (inc. 4pp prologue), 5pp adv., b/w frontis. & 4 f/p b/w illus. by J. Muir Auld, clo., 185x120mm. ANL

WEBSTER, F. A. M.

THE IVORY TALISMAN
CARRUTHERS OF COLHURST
WHERE STRANGE DRUMS SOUND
Sydney [194-?]
Not Australian, but rpt of overseas books (first published by Warne)

The Weekly Times Puzzle Book

7881 THE/WEEKLY/TIMES/PUZZLE BOOK/1/- Printed & Published by Edgar H. Baillie of 185 Balaclava Road Caulfield for The Herald and Weekly Times Ltd., n.d. [195-?]
62pp, b/w diagrams, wrappers, 270x200mm. KP

WEEKS, R. G.

7882 BE PREPARED!/[b/w photograph with caption]/A Story for Every Boy/By/R. G.Weeks
Adelaide [Hunken Ellis & King], n.d. [1943]
12pp, unillus., wrappers, cover title, 168x105mm. SSL
Religious story, first published 1940

7883 CLIMBING UP/[b/w photograph]/A Story for Schoolboys/By/R. G. Weeks
Murray Bridge, S. A., n.d.
[12]pp, 4 b/w photographic illus., wrappers, cover title, 183x108mm. SSL

7884 "JOIN US"/[b/w photograph] SENDING A MESSAGE/A Story for Schoolboys/By/R. G.Weeks
Adelaide, n.d. [1948]
16pp, 6 b/w photographic illus., wrappers, cover title 170x105mm. SSL

7885 WHAT'S THIS!/[b/w photograph]/A Story for Schoolboys/By/R. G.Weeks
Murray Bridge, SA [1948]
10pp, b/w photographic illus., wrappers, 184x110mm. ANL
Religious tract

WEIGALL-CHASE, Cedric & Sylvia

7886 HOOKUM'S GANG/or/The Story of Jimmie/and His Elephant/By Cedric and Sylvia Weigall-Chase/ 1940/New Century Press Pty. Ltd./3 North York Street/Sydney
187pp, 3pp adv., b/w drawings, clo., 185x125mm. ANL

WEIR, Isobel

LEGENDS OF THE ABORIGINES: A Series of Infant Readers, written by Isobel Weir, illustrated by Jann Hood
Titles in series:
7887 BROLGA THE DANCER
7888 HOW THE ANIMALS CAME TO AUSTRALIA
7889 THE KANGAROO AND THE WOMBAT
7890 TARA THE DUCK
7891 WAYAMBA THE TORTOISE

7892 WHY THE CROW IS BLACK
A. H. & A. W. Reed, Sydney, n.d. [1967]
16pp, illus. throughout, stiff dec. wrappers, cover title, 200x125mm. CLRC
others in series as above and all KMM:
7893 THE BABY ECHIDNA
7894 A BOY AND A GIRL
7895 THE/KANGAROO/DANCE
7896 THE MAN AND THE SPIRIT
7897 THE PROUD EMU
7898 THE SNAKE AND THE LIZARD

WEIR, Rosemary

7899 Rosemary Weir/THE REAL GAME/Illustrated by Aedwin Darroll/Brockhampton Press
Leicester, England 1965
128pp, b/w frontis., line drawings in text, clo., 215x135mm. NSL:M
Set partly on a Queensland sugar farm

[WELCH, Sarah]
See 'Europa'

WELLS, Ann E.
7900 TALES/FROM/ARNHEM LAND/by Ann E. Wells/Illustrated by Margaret Paice/Angus and Robertson
Sydney 1959
98pp, 1p preface, extended part-col. frontis., 3 part-col. illus. (after the style of Aboriginal bark paintings) & part-col. drawings throughout, clo., dec. e/p, 230x150mm. KMM
Preface states that the stories were told to Ann Wells by the Wurungu Aborigines of Milingimbi, one of the Crocodile Islands off the coast of Arnhem Land.

7901 RAIN/IN/ARNHEM LAND/Further adventures of three aboriginal children/on the far north coast of Australia, and some/of the stories of their people/by/Ann E. Wells/[drawing]/Illustrated by Margaret Paice/Angus and Robertson
Sydney 1961
87pp, 1p preface, 5 f/p part-col. illus. (after the style of Aboriginal bark paintings), b/w & part-col. drawings in text, dec. boards, dec. e/p, 235x155mm. KMM
Author states that of the five stories in the volume, three are simple outlines of the great myths of the Arnhem Land people, & the other two are more like folk stories belonging to the totems of different groups of people.
7902 Another copy, Supplementary reader edition 1963
90pp & 1p preface, 3 f/p. b/w illus. & drawings in text, limp pic. clo., 185x120mm. KMM

7903 [decoration] SKIES/OF/ARNHEM LAND/by/Ann E. Wells/illustrated by/Margaret Paice/Angus and Robertson
Sydney 1964
97pp, 1p acknowledgements, part-col. t.p., 1 f/p part-col. illus., part-col. & b/w drawings throughout, clo., 235x155mm. CLRC

WELLS, Augusta J.
7904 "WE THREE",/and/THE OGRE'S STORY/(A Sequel to "We Three".)/By/A. J. Wells./[device]/Melbourne:/A. H. Massina & Co., Printers and Publishers,/Howey Street, off Little Collins Street/1892
16pp, unillus., wrappers, cover title, 217x140mm. ANL

WELLS, Louisa Clarke
7905 THE/RED/PEN/By/Mrs. Clarke Wells/Author of/"Cause and Sufferings of Fallen Women"/[printer's device]/Published by/Mrs. Wells, at Sturt Street,/Adelaide/1887
32pp, unillus., wrappers, on front wrapper: 'A Story for the Young', 190x130mm. CLRC
Moral tale about a family of geese

WELLS, E. Gambier
7906 THE/CHILD PILGRIM/(An Eastern Legend in Verse)/Written for the Young/and dedicated with Uncle Harry's approval to the/Members of the/Children's "Sunbeam" Society/of South Australia/By/E. Gambier Wells/Adelaide:/Vardon & Pritchard, Printers, Gresham Street./1897/(Copyright)
26pp, unillus., wrappers, 140x100mm. CLRC
Religious tale in verse, written for the author's niece

WELLS, Ernest
7907 THE/BUBBLE GALLEON/A/Holiday Pantomime/by/Ernest Wells/Set to Pictures by R. W. Coulter/[drawing]/Australia/Angus & Robertson Limited/89 Castlereagh Street, Sydney/1934
111pp, b/w illus. throughout, pic. boards, 245x185mm. VSL

7908 MASTER DAVY'S LOCKER/A Story of Adventure in the Under Sea/By/Ernest Wells/Author of "The Bubble Galleon"/Illustrations by/R. W. Coulter/[drawing]/Australia/Angus & Robertson Limited/89 Castlereagh Street, Sydney/1935
131pp, b/w drawings throughout, pic. boards, 245x185mm. VSL

WELSH, Alexander Carl
7909 NANCY/IN THE BUSH/and other Australian Rimes/for children/by/Alex C. Welsh/Illustrations/By/Minnie I. Rowe/With a Prefatory Note by John Smyth, M.A., Ph.D.,/Professor of Education, Melbourne University/[quotation]/Commonwealth of Australia/Sydney J. Endacott/Melbourne/1923
39pp (inc. 1p introduction), 1p adv., b/w drawings throughout, clo., 210x160mm. ANL
One of a special edition of 25 copies signed by the author.
Also bound in wrappers. KMM

WELSH, Jean Mary
7910 Mullens' Stories for Children/No. 301/THE WREN'S NEST/by/J. M. Welsh/(For Ages 9–10)/Robertson & Mullens Ltd./Melbourne. n.d. [1952]
47pp, b/w frontis. & 4 f/p b/w drawings signed 'Rolland', wrappers, 180x115mm. ANL
Contains five stories about Australian animals & birds.

'WENDY' [Mrs Eva Rose Berney]
7911 DOZER/DISOBEYS/Story by/Wendy/pictures by/Kem
Consolidated Press, Sydney, n.d. [1946]
32pp, col. & b/w illus. throughout, dec. boards, dec. e/p, 240x185mm. ANL
A story about a bomb

Wendy's Day Round the Clock
7912 WENDY'S DAY/ROUND THE CLOCK
Offset Printing Co., Sydney 1947
12pp, col. illus. throughout by Diana Martin, wrappers, cover title, 270x220mm. ANL
Picture book with 2 lines rhyming text on each page

[WERNER, Alice] 'A. W.'
THE KING OF THE SILVER CITY & other Poems, by A. W. (1882)
Not a children's book

WESLEY-SMITH, Peter
7913 THE OMBLEY-GOMBLEY/Peter Wesley-Smith/[drawing]/Drawings by David Fielding/Angus and Robertson
Sydney 1969
[46]pp, part-col. illus. throughout, 2-col. t.p., clo., col. e/p, 230x180mm. KMM
Humorous verses
• Rpt as above 1970, 1972. KP

WEST, Francis
HUBERT MURRAY. *See* Great Australians

WEST, Katharine
THE AUSTRALIAN LIBERAL PARTY. *See* Australian Landmark series

WEST, R. V.
7914 THE LUCIFLINS/AND/THE DUCK THAT LAID/EASTER EGGS/by/R. V. West/Illustrated by/Chas. H. Crampton/Whitcombe & Tombs Pty. Ltd./Melbourne, Sydney, Perth/Wholly set up and printed in Australia for Whitcombe & Tombs Pty. Ltd./by Modern Printing

Co. Pty. Ltd./Registered at the G.P.O., Melbourne, for transmission through the Post as a book
n.d. [1945]
32pp, 8 part-col. illus., illus. wrappers, 240x170mm. ANL

WESTBURY, Atha

7915 AUSTRALIAN FAIRY TALES./By/Atha Westbury./Illustrated by A. J. Johnson./London:/Ward, Lock & Co., Limited,/Warwick House, Salisbury Square, E.C./New York and Melbourne./1897/All rights reserved
357pp, 2pp adv., b/w frontis. & 3 f/p b/w illus., 21 b/w drawings in text, dec. clo., 190x125mm. KMM
Another copy as above but variant binding; dark green cloth, & the face of the woman at the head of the decoration is not gilded & the publisher's imprint at base of spine is slightly different. KP

WESTERMAN, J. F. C.

7916 THE ANTARCTIC/TREASURE/By/J. F. C. Westerman/Illustrated by/Victor Cooley/[device]/ Oxford University Press/London: Humphrey Milford First printed 1929
232pp, 7pp adv., col. frontis. & 7 f/p b/w illus., clo., 185x120mm. KMM
• Rpt as above 1932. KP

7917 THE ANTARCTIC/TREASURE/By/J. F. C. Westerman/Illustrated by/Victor Cooley/Geoffrey Cumberlege/Oxford University Press/Leighton House Melbourne
1948
190pp, 8 f/p b/w illus., boards, 180x120mm. KMM

7918 THE/LOOTED GOLD/By/John F. C. Westerman/ Author of/"Bringing down the air pirate"/"Peter Garner, Cadet" etc./Ward, Lock & Co., Limited/ London and Melbourne
1932
256pp, b/w frontis. sgd W. Edward Wigfull & 3 b/w plates, pic. clo., 187x130mm. KP
Another copy as above but col. frontis. only, 183x120mm. 'The Sentinel Series', KP

7919 John F. C. Westerman/THE/LOOTED GOLD/ Ward, Lock/and Company Limited/London, Melbourne & Johannesburg 1960
182pp, 1p adv., b/w frontis. & 5 f/p b/w illus., clo., 185x120mm. Grant

7920 THE/AERO CONTRACT/By/John F .C. Westerman/Illustrated by/A. Mason Trotter/[device]/ Oxford University Press/London: Humphrey Milford
1935
255pp, col. frontis. & 6 b/w plates, clo., 180x120mm. ANL
Includes an account of the London–Sydney air race.

7921 John F. C. Westerman/THE SECRET/ISLAND/ Ward Lock/and Company Limited/London Melbourne and Cape Town
n.d.
184pp, unillus, boards, 185x120mm. KP

WESTERMAN, Percy F.

7922 CAPTAIN STARLIGHT/By/Percy F. Westerman/ Author of "On the Wings of the Wind", "Captain Blundell's Treasure"/"The Fight for the *Golden Dawn*" &c./Illustrated by W. E. Wigfull/Blackie & Son Limited/London and Glasgow
n.d. [1929]
224pp, b/w frontis. & 3 f/p b/w illus., pic. clo., 180x120mm. CLRC
Adventure story about an airship, set partly in Queensland, the Pacific & Sydney.
• Rpt [1945] as above but 'war economy standard', b/w frontis. & 2 plates. KP
Norwegian edition

7923 Percy F. Westerman/DEN SORTE KOMET/Pa Norsk ved/Johan Saastad/5 Helsides/Illustrajoner/ [device]/Windju Simonsens Forlag/Oslo
1935
156pp, 5 f/p b/w illus., col. pic. boards, clo. spine. 182x127mm. ANL

7924 THE LAST OF /THE BUCCANEERS/By/Percy F. Westerman/Author of "Captain Swing"&c./Illustrated by John de Walton/Blackie & Son Limited/London and Glasgow
1937
223pp, b/w frontis. & 2 b/w plates, clo., 184x120mm. KP
The hero sails with Anson as a midshipman on a voyage round the world.

WESTERN AUSTRALIAN EDUCATION DEPARTMENT

This department has published a large number of supplementary readers for primary & secondary students which are not considered as coming within the range of this bibliography.

WESTFALL, Fran

7925 A Storybook Knitting Book/WILLIE 50 cents/ WOMBAT/AND HIS FRIENDS/Willie and his eight pals/come to life as you read/Their adventures in the/ village of Gundy goo.../You simply knit them. Southdown Press Pty Ltd, Melbourne, n.d.
26pp, col. & part-col. & b/w illus., wrappers, 290x200mm. KP
Storybook with instructions for knitting 12 toys of Australian animals

WESTFIELD, Robert

7926 TIM/AND HIS DOG/A Thrilling story of how a dog saved his/young master's life/by/Robert Westfield/Illustrated by/Walter Cunningham/ [drawing]/An Alpha Book/Published by/ Commonwealth/Trades Alphabet/142 Phillip Street, Sydney/(Copyright)
n.d. [1945]
32pp, part. col. illus., pic. wrappers, 190x180mm. ANL

7927 AUSTRALIA/ON PARADE/By/Rob Westfield/ Drawings by Stuart Reid/Commonwealth Trades Alphabet/Sixth Floor/149 Castlereagh Street/Sydney n.d. [foreword dated June 1956]
32pp (inc. 1p foreword by A. H. Chisholm, 1p verse, & 2pp explanatory notes), 27pp b/w illus., boards, 275x210mm. NSL:M

7928 AUSTRALIA/ON PARADE/A Story in Song/and Picture/of Australia's/Wonder Fauna/by/Rob/ Westfield
the author, Sydney, n.d.
32pp, b/w illus. throughout, col. pic. wrappers, 267x214mm. KP
Includes song with 4pp of original music & 2pp explanatory notes about the animals depicted.

WESTMORELANDE, Lesley

7929 MUFFIN/THE LAZY MOUSE/Written by/Lesley Westmorelande/Illustrated by/Bill Davies/[coloured drawing]/John Sands Pty. Ltd./Sydney Melbourne Brisbane Adelaide Perth and Hobart
Sydney, n.d. [1956]
32pp, col. illus. throughout, dec. boards, dec. e/p, 175x155mm. BBC

[WESTON, Harry J.]
THE WESTON CUT-OUT NURSERY RHYME BOOKLETS, [or, Weston Company Baby Booklets]
The Weston Co.Ltd., Sydney, 1918
A series of 5 shaped booklets, each of 6 leaves of light card with col. pic. cover, secured by eyelet at top of booklet, and verse and b/w illus. printed on one side of leaf only, approx 180x115mm. NSL:M
Appear to have been illustrated by Harry J. Weston.
Titles:
7930 LITLE BETTY BLUE
7931 LITTLE BO-PEEP
7932 LITTLE MISS MUFFET
7933 MARY HAD A LITTLE LAMB
7934 RED RIDING HOOD

WESTON, Mary
7935 CHRISTINE,/AIR HOSTESS/by/Mary Weston/Hutchinson & Co. (Publishers) Ltd./Hutchinson House/London, W.1
n.d.
216pp, unillus., sim. clo., 184x120mm. Chestnut Library. KP
7936 CHRISTINE/AIR HOSTESS/Breath-taking/action & excitement/Hutchinsons Books for Young People
n.d. [1950?]
216pp, unillus., clo., 190x130mm. VMOU

What Susan Likes
7937 WHAT SUSAN LIKES: Pictures by Dorothy Ayers & James Pty Ltd, Sydney, n.d. [1950]
16pp, col. illus. throughout, pic. wrappers, cover title, 275x210mm. NSL:M

WHEELER, Alfred
THE ROSE OF JOY. *See* Rentoul, Annie Rattray & Wheeler, Alfred

7938 Imperial Edition No. 61/SOOT AND THE FAIRIES./An Amusing Cantata./suitable for schools, &c./By/Rev. Alfred Wheeler, M.A./(Precentor of St Paul's Cathedral)/Allan & Co. Pty Ltd.
Melbourne, n.d. [190- ?(adv. in *Argus* 29/11/1913, price 9d.)]
23pp, 1p adv. unillus., dec. wrappers, 254x 172mm. VSL
Another copy as above, but after 'Cathedral' '[device]/Allan & Co., Pty.Ltd./Melbourne Sydney Adelaide Bendigo.'
n..d [195-?]
23pp, 1 p blank, adv. on back cover; price 2/6 on front cover with illus. of a fairy, 250x180mm. KP

WHEELER, Harold F. B.
7939 MAKERS OF/THE BRITISH EMPIRE/By/Harold F. B. Wheeler/M.I.E.I., F.R.Hist.S./Editor of "Cassell's Book of Knowledge"/Author of "The Story of the British Navy",. etc./With sixteen illustrations/by/R. Caton Woodville/[device]/George G. Harrap & Co.Ltd/London Bombay Sydney
1927
256pp & 5 pp author's foreword, 16 b/w plates, clo., 195x142mm. HBM

WHEELER, John
7940 First Set/FIVE/AUSTRALIAN/CHRISTMAS/CAROLS/Words by/John Wheeler. Music by/William G. James/Chappell & Co. Ltd./London Sydney Price 3/- net.
1948
11pp., unillus., dec. wrappers, 280x220mm. VSL

7941 Second Set/FIVE/AUSTRALIAN/CHRISTMAS/CAROLS/Words by/John Wheeler/Music by/William G. James/Chappell & Co. Ltd./London Sydney. Price 3/- net/made in England
n.d. [copyright 1954]
20pp (inc. covers), unillus, dec. wrappers, 277x212mm. ANL

7942 Third Set/FIVE/AUSTRALIAN/CHRISTMAS/CAROLS/Words by/John Wheeler/Music by/William G. James/[Titles of 5 songs]/Published by/Chappell & Co. Ltd.,/50 New Bond Street/London, W.1 & Sydney
n.d. [copyright 1961]
16pp & covers (adv. on back cover), unillus., 275x216mm. ANL

7943 FIVE AUSTRALIAN/EASTER SONGS/(For Young Singers)/Words by/John Wheeler/Music by/William G. James/[titles of songs]/Price 3/- net/Published by/Chappell & Co. Ltd./50 New Bond Street/London W.1 & Sydney/Made in England
Copyright 1962
23pp & 1 p adv., unillus., dec. wrappers, 280x216mm. NSL:M

7944 THE TEN FAMOUS/AUSTRALIAN/CHRISTMAS CAROLS/Words with melodies/words by/John Wheeler/Music by/William G. James/Chappell & Co. Ltd./Sydney 1/- net/copyright
n.d. [1954?]
16pp (inc. covers,) unillus., pic. wrappers, cover title, 120x175mm. ANL

7945 Imperial edition 663/NINE AUSTRALIAN/CHILDREN'S SONGS/Words by/John Wheeler/Music by/Robin Wood/[9 songs listed]/2/6/copyright 1951 by Allan & Co. Pty Ltd. 276 Collins St., Melbourne/Allan & Co. Pty Ltd./Melbourne Adelaide Bendigo
20 pp, unillus., wrappers, 250x176mm. VSL

7946 UNDER THE/COOLIBAH TREE/Songs for Young Australians/Words by John Wheeler/Music by Werner Baer/Contents [7 songs]/W. H. Paling & Co. Ltd./Sydney Brisbane/and established throughout NSW and Q'ld.
n.d. [copyright 1955]
16pp, unillus., pic. wrappers, 248x183mm. ANL

Adv. on back wrapper: THE WHITE SHIP, Poem by John Wheeler, music by Mirrie Hill (copyright 1943) 4pp, and

THE SONG OF YOUTH, words by John Wheeler, music William G. James (copyright 1946) 4pp.

THE THREE DROVERS. *See* Jill Lyons

WHEELHOUSE, Frances
HUGH VICTOR McKAY. *See* Australia Past and Present

WHIPPLE, Amy
7947 THE CHILDREN OF/THE CRAG/By/Amy Whipple/Author of "Kiddie", "Sea Baby" etc./The Pilgrim Press/16 Pilgrim Street, London, E.C.4
n.d. [1914]
290pp &2pp adv., b/w frontis., clo., 195x120mm. KMM
Story of mixed-up identity of two boys, the first chapter only being set in Australia

Whitcombe's Numberland Fun
7948 WHITCOMBE'S/NUMBERLAND FUN/A picture book with a purpose/progressive number series Book 1
Whitcombe & Tombs Pty Ltd., Melbourne, Sydney, Perth n.d.
16pp, col. illus. throughout, stiff pic. wrappers, 180x240mm. KP

A number book for schools & also possibly entertainment.

Whitcombe's Pictorial Story of Australia

7949 WHITCOMBE'S/PICTORIAL STORY/OF AUSTRALIA/Drawings/For Young Australians/No. 444/10d.
No imprint [?Whitcombe & Tombs, Melbourne], n.d. [1927?]
32pp, b/w drawings throughout, pic. wrappers, cover title, 210x165mm. Grant
• Rpt as above, revised ed. n.d. [194-?]
Contains some references to World War II. VMOU

WHITE, Beryl

7950 Imperial Edition no., 942/TWELVE MUSICAL/MIMES FOR YOUNG/CHILDREN/Words by/Beryl White/Music by/June Epstein/Allans Music(Australia) Pty.Ltd./Melbourne Adelaide Bendigo Launceston Hobart/Printed in Australia
1964
44pp (last blank), unillus., pic. wrappers, 245x182mm. KP

WHITE , David

7951 KANDY/IN BUNNY-BABE LAND/By /David White/Pictures by Mary Brooks/Contents/[6 lines]/[col. border & illus.]/Copyright/Sampson Low, Marston & Co., Ltd./1958
77pp, col. illus. throughout, col. pic. boards & e/p, 202x164mm. KP
Story about toy kangaroos & koalas

WHITE, J. M.

7952 BASIC SOCCER FOR JUNIORS/J .M. White/with an introduction by M. A. Jones,/Director of Coaching for NSW/Australian Soccer Coaches Federation/Line drawings by Peter Harrigan/Angus and Robertson Sydney 1971
100pp (last blank), b/w photographic frontis., b/w illus. in text, pic. wrappers, 125x200mm. CLRC

WHITE, John

7953 JOHN WHITES/RESA/TILL/NYA HOLLAND,/Aren 1787 och 1788./I Sammandrag/af/Samuel Ödmann./[emblem]/Upsala,/Tryckt hos dir. J. Edmansenka, 1793
xii, 147pp, 4 f/p engravings & some engravings in text, boards, half leather, 166x95mm. ANL (First section relates to Port Jackson; the remainder to James Cook.)

[WHITE, J. H.]

7954 FORTUNATUS/A Romance/With Seven original illustrations by/Phil Ebbutt/[quotation]/Melville & Mullen/London and Melbourne/1903
295pp, b/w frontis. & 6 b/w illus., clo., 180x120mm. VSL
The story of a Jersey boy who migrates to the Victorian gold fields in the 1860s

WHITE, Paul

A New South Wales doctor who achieved fame with his many 'Jungle Doctor' books, based on his life as a missionary doctor in Africa. These books have been translated into many languages and have achieved very high sales in different forms but are not considered relevant to Australian children's literature. Some of his other books do relate to Australia and are recorded as follows:

WHITE, Paul and BRITTEN, David

7955 RUCTIONS AT/RANFORD/By/Paul White/and David Britten/The Paternoster Press/London
1961
156pp, unillus., clo., 184x120mm. ANL

7956 THE RANFORD/MYSTERY MILER/By/Paul White/and David Britten/London/The Paternoster Press
1960
158pp, unillus., sim. clo., 185x120mm. NSL:M

7957 RANFORD IN/FLAMES/By/Paul White/and David Britten/The Paternoster Press/Gospel Supplies/Convention Avenue./Belgrave Heights, Vic.
1965
159pp, unillus., clo., 185x120mm. VMOU
Also author of *Ranford goes Fishing* [1962] unseen

WHITE, Rubina

7958 PATHWAYS IN THE SUN/by/Rubina White/(Copyright)/Paterson Brokenshaw Pty. Ltd./65 Murray St., Perth
n.d. [1961]
94pp, clo. PH

[WHITE, T. A.]

7959 THE BUSH TWINS [no t.p.]
Printed in Australia, n.p., n.d. [192-?]
8pp, col. illus. signed 'J. Milgate', col. pic. wrappers, 300x120mm. Grant
Verses with initials 'T.A.W.' at end of last verse

WHITE, T. A.

7960 Whitcombe's Nature Story Books/YAPPY DINGO/An Australian Fairy Tale/By/T. A. White/Inspector of Schools Cooma/For ages 9 to 10 years/Whitcombe & Tombs Limited/Sydney and Melbourne/Auckland, Christchurch, Dunedin, Wellington, N.Z./and London
1934
24pp, b/w drawings in text, pic. wrappers, 180x120mm. ANL
No. 439 in series.
See McLaren 439 & *see also* 'Sunny South' series

'WHITE, Unk' [pseud. Cecil John White]

7961 BEAR FOLK
7962 BLUEY AND JACKY
7963 THE PENGUIN PARTY
Uniform booklets published by Frank Johnson, 350 George Street, Sydney, n.d. [1941]
16pp, col. illus. throughout, wrappers, 240x180mm. NSL:M
See also Miller, Sydney, for books in same series

7964 THE AUSSIES ARE HERE
Frank Johnson, Sydney 1943
12pp, col. illus. throughout, dec. wrappers, cover title, 280x220mm. NSL:M
Verse

7965 TWINKLE TWINKLE SOUTHERN CROSS
Frank Johnson, Sydney 1943
12pp, col. illus. throughout, dec. wrappers, cover title, 280x180mm. NSL:M
Verse

7966 UNK WHITE'S BOAT BOOK FOR LITTLE JACK TARS
Frank Johnson, Sydney 1943
8pp, 7 f/p b/w illus. (to be coloured), dec. wrappers, cover title, 310x250mm. NSL:M
Magpie Picture Books. Colouring book with caption & directions beneath each picture.

WHITE, Zita

7967 THE ONE-DAY PONIES/by/Zita White/Illustrated by/Sheila Rose/Lutterworth Press/London
1958
160pp, b/w frontis., 3 f/p b/w illus. & b/w drawings in text, clo., 195x130mm. KMM

7968 RIDE ACROSS THE OCEAN/by/Zita White/Illustrated by/Sheila Rose/Lutterworth Press/London 1959
154pp, b/w frontis. & b/w drawings in text throughout, clo., 195x130mm. KMM
A horse story about an English girl who emigrates to Brisbane.

WHITE, Zita [ed.]
7969 A RACE OF/HORSEMEN/Arranged by/Zita White/The Jacaranda Press
Brisbane 1962
176pp (inc. 16pp editorial introduction), 81 b/w photographic illus., clo., 210x135mm. CLRC
Practical book on horsemanship for young riders by various authorities

The White Guard
7970 THE WHITE GUARD
Whithall Pharmacal [*sic*] Co. (Inc. in U.S.A.) 44 Bridge Street Sydney, n.d. [195-?]
[32pp] col. illus. on every page (anon. & in the style of Disney), pic. wrappers (illus. and text printed inside covers), cover title, 140x87mm. CLRC
Brochure in the form of a fairy story encouraging tooth care & advertising Kolynos toothpaste.[?Australian]

WHITFELD, Adeline J.
7971 THE/TWILIGHT HOUR/By/Adeline J. Whitfeld/Tasmania:/Printed at The Examiner Office/Launceston/1900
189pp, 6 f/p b/w illus. by W. O. Bowman, boards, 200x140mm. VSL
Short tales about animals.

WHITFELD, Jessie Mary [Mrs Owen Harris]
7972 THE SPIRIT/OF THE BUSH FIRE/and other Australian Fairy Tales/By/J. M. Whitfeld/With 32 illustrations by G. W. Lambert/Sydney/Angus & Robertson/89 Castlereagh Street/1898
313pp, 16pp adv. (dated December 1897), b/w frontis. & 19 f/p b/w illus., b/w drawings in text, pic. clo., 180x120mm. KMM
Note states that 'Ladies' first appeared in the *Sydney Mail.*
Other copies seen, as above, with adv. dated November 1900, & also April 1901

7973 THE SPIRIT/OF/THE BUSH FIRE/SERIES/Part I./By/J. M. Whitfeld/With Illustrations by G. W. Lambert/Sydney/William Brooks & Company Limited/17 Castlereagh Street
n.d.
101pp, 5 f/p b/w illus. & b/w drawings in text, boards, 185x115mm. KMM
Contains the first three & one other story from the complete volume.
7974 THE SPIRIT OF THE BUSH FIRE Series Part I
Details as above, but variant label on front cover. The title is printed in black, with 'Part 1' in red, & a decorative border of leaves & flames printed in red surrounds the title. CLRC

7975 THE SPIRIT/OF/THE BUSH FIRE/SERIES/Part II./By/J. M. Whitfeld/With illustrations by G. W. Lambert/Sydney/William Brooks & Company Limited/17 Castlereagh Street
n.d.
94pp, 3 f/p b/w illus. & b/w drawings in text, boards, 180x110mm. CLRC

7976 THE SPIRIT/OF/THE BUSH FIRE/SERIES/Part III/By/J. M. Whitfeld/With Illustrations by G. W. Lambert/Sydney/William Brooks & Company Limited/17 Castlereagh Street
n.d.
93pp, 5 f/p b/w illus., boards, 180x120mm. VSL
George Lambert's initials are printed as 'C' in the above 3 books.[i.e. 'C. W. Lambert']

7977 THE SPIRIT/OF/THE BUSH FIRE/Book IV/by/J. M. Whitfeld/Author of "Tom Who was Rachel", "The Colters"/"Gladys and Jack"/With three illustrations by G. W. Lambert./Edward Lee & Co., 14 Carrington Street, Sydney./1916
n.d.
94pp, 3 f/p b/w illus. & b/w drawings in text, boards, 180x110mm. KMM

7978 TOM WHO WAS/RACHEL/By/J. M. Whitfeld/Illustrated in colour by N. Tenison/London/Henry Frowde/Hodder and Stoughton/1911
317pp, col. frontis. & 5 f/p col. illus., pic. clo. (with col. medallion on front cover & small one on spine), 185x120mm. ANL
7979 TOM/WHO WAS/RACHEL/J. M./Whitfeld/London/Henry Frowde/Hodder & Stoughton
n.d. [prize1915]
317pp, dec. t.p., col. frontis. only, clo., dec. e/p, 185x120mm. KMM
7980 TOM/WHO WAS/RACHEL/J. M. Whitfeld/Humphrey Milford/Oxford University/Press/London
• Rpt 1923
317pp, col. frontis. only, clo., dec. e/p, 170x115mm. KMM

7981 THE COLTERS/An Australian Story/For Girls/By/J. M. Whitfeld/Author of "Tom who was Rachel"/Illustrated in Colour by George Soper/London/Henry Frowde/Hodder and Stoughton/1912
320pp, 16pp adv., col. frontis. & 5 f/p col. illus., pic. clo., 190x125mm. KMM
THE COLTERS
Variant 1912 copy with one of the coloured illustrations reproduced in an oblong medallion on front cover, & another reproduced in an oval medallion on spine, 190x130mm. KMM
7982 THE/COLTERS/J. M. Whitfeld/Humphrey Milford/Oxford University/Press/London
• Rpt 1917
318pp, col. frontis. only, clo., dec. e/p, 185x120mm. KMM
7983 THE COLTERS/An Australian Story/for Girls/By/J. M. Whitfeld/Author of "Tom who was Rachel"/Illustrated in Colour by George Soper/London/Henry Frowde/Hodder and Stoughton
n.d.
320pp, col. frontis. & 5 col. plates, clo., with col. patriotic design, 186x120mm. KP
The Clarion Series for Girls
Publisher's name on spine reads 'Milford' indicating the binding later than the title page, as Milford succeeded Frowde as publisher to Oxford University Press.
7984 THE /COLTERS/J. M./Whitfeld/Humphrey Milford/Oxford University/Press/London
rpt 1923
320pp, col. frontis. (George Soper), dec. border surrounds lettering on t.p., clo., dec. e/p, 186x120mm. KMM
• Rpt 1930. Unseen

7985 GLADYS AND JACK/By/J. M. Whitfeld/Author of/"The Spirit of the Bush Fire", "Tom who was Rachel",/"The Colters", etc. etc./Illustrated in Colour

by N. Tenison/London/Henry Frowde/Hodder and Stoughton/1914
318pp, 16pp adv., col. frontis. & 5 f/p col. illus., clo. (with one col. illus. reproduced on front cover), 190x130mm. NSL:M

7986 Another copy as above until 'N. Tenison', then Humphrey Milford/Oxford University Press/London, Edinburgh, Glasgow/Toronto, Melbourne, Cape Town, Bombay
• Rpt 1919
318pp & 32pp adv. (& 2pp note on author & her two previous books), col. frontis. & 5 col. plates, pic. clo, with patriotic cover design, 188x120mm. KP

7987 GLADYS/AND/JACK/J. M. Whitfeld/Humphrey Milford/Oxford University/Press/London
• Rpt 1921
318pp, 2pp adv., col. frontis., boards, 180x120mm. Grant

WHITING, Mary Bradford

7988 JOSÉE/An Australian Story./By/Mary Bradford Whiting/Published under the direction of the General Literature/Committee/London:/Society for Promoting Christian Knowledge./Northumberland Avenue, W.C.;/43, Queen Victoria Street, E.C./Brighton: 129, North Street./New York: E. & J. B. Young and Co.
n.d. [1890?]
96pp & 16pp adv., b./w frontis. only, pic. clo., 170x115mm. CLRC

7989 WALLABY HILL/By/Mary Bradford Whiting/The Religious Tract Society/4 Bouverie Street and 65 St. Paul's Churchyard,/London
n.d. [1895]
122pp, 8pp adv., col. dec. t.p., col. frontis, illus. by F. E. Hiley, clo., 185x125mm. ANL

7990 WALLABY HILL/By/Mary Bradford Whiting/The Religious Tract Society/56 Paternoster Row and 65 St. Paul's Churchyard
n.d.
128pp, b/w frontis. & 3 f/p b/w illus., pic. clo., 180x120mm. KMM
The b/w frontispiece is entirely different from that in the edition previously noted. The illustrations are all initialled 'C.W.'. The binding in green cloth with the title in gilt is quite different also, though both copies reproduce the same illustration.
As above n.d., prize 1900, & 1909, both KP

7991 A DAUGHTER OF/THE EMPIRE/By/Mary Bradford Whiting/Illustrated by John Campbell/ Humphrey Milford/Oxford University Press/London, Edinburgh, Glasgow/Toronto, Melbourne, Cape Town, Bombay/1919
288pp, col. frontis. & 3 f/p col. illus., pic. clo., 190x120mm. NSL:M

7992 PEGGY AND PAT/A Tale of the Australian Bush/ by/Mary Bradford Whiting/Frontispiece by/D. Eyles/ London/The Sheldon Press/Northumberland Avenue, W.C.2
n.d. [1931]
159pp, 16pp adv., col. frontis., pic. clo., 190x125mm. KP
THE TREASURE HOUSE. 1920
Not a children's book

[WHITLEY, Gilbert P.]

7993 SOLVOL FISH BOOK/The Life and Habits of 80 Australian Fishes described by Gilbert P. Whitley: illustrated by Mary E. Soady
Boylan & Co. Pty. Ltd., Printers Sydney, n.d. [1956?]
20pp (inc. 1p intro. & 1p index), col frontis. & 12 f/p col. plates, sev. diagrams, col. pic. wrappers, cover title (adv. inside back cover), 118x178mm. NSL:M

WHITLOCK, Judith

7994 THE/GREEN BUNYIP/by/Judith Whitlock/ illustrated by/Leslie Green/[drawing]/London/Dennis Dobson
1962
88pp (inc. 1p introduction), b/w & part. col. drawings throughout, clo., dec. e/p, 195x125mm. CLRC

Uniform with above:

7995 BUNYIP AT THE SEASIDE. 1962. CLRC

7996 BUNYIP/AND THE/BROLGA BIRD. 1963. CLRC

7997 BUNYIP/AND THE BUSHFIRE. 1964. CLRC

7998 BUNYIP/AND THE/TIGER CATS. 1965. BBC

'WHITLY, Reid" [R. Coutts Armour]

See Aldine Adventure Library, Aldine War Stories, &c.
RALSTON'S PENNY CRUISER. *See* Aldine War Stories

BEYOND THE DESERT. *See* The Boys' Friend Library

7999 THE BOY CHIEF/Reid Whitly/Thomas Nelson and Sons Ltd./London Edinburgh Paris Melbourne/ Toronto and New York
n.d. [194-? first pub. 1928]
95pp, b/w frontis., clo., 180 x120mm. ANL
Story with African background

8000 SWORDS ACROSS THE SEA/A Story of Buccaneering Days/By/Reid Whitly/Author of "Special Services".etc./The Aldine Publishing Co./ Goodship House, Farringdon Avenue, E.C.4
n.d. [1931]
192pp, col frontis., pic. clo., 184x118mm. ANL

WHITMARSH, H. Phelps

8001 THE /YOUNG PEARL DIVERS/A Story of Australian Adventure/by Land and Sea/By/Lieut. H. Phelps Whitmarsh/Author of/"The Mysterious Voyage of the Daphne", etc./London/John F. Shaw and Co./ 48 Paternoster Row.
n.d. [first published Boston 1896, London 1901]
256pp, b/w frontis. & 1 b/w plate by H. Burgess, dec. clo., 180x125mm. KMM

WHITMORE, G. E.

8002 The Little Ones' Library/A LITTLE BOOK OF/ THE/ISLAND CONTINENT/By/G. E.Whitmore/With Pictures in Colour/[device]/Cassell and Company, Ltd/London, New York, Toronto and Melbourne
n.d. [192-?]
48pp, 1 col. and 3 part-col. illus., & b/w photographic illus., pic. wrappers, 175x128mm. CLRC

'WICKHAM, Anna'

See Harper, Edith Alice Mary

WIESE, Kurt

8003 KAROO,/THE KANGAROO/Written and Illustrated by/Kurt Wiese/Coward-McCann, Inc./1929 New York
[36]pp, 15 f/p col. lithographed illus., b/w illus. in text, clo. (with col. illus. pasted on front cover), dec. e/p, 240x175mm. VSL
The kangaroo meets a kiwi in the Australian bush! And some of the other indigenous animals depicted seem rather large in proportion to the kangaroo.

WIGGINS, Arch. R.

8004 KNIGHTS OF THE/BLIZZARD/A Tale of Heroism and Good Scouting in the Great/White Silence of the South/by/Arch R. Wiggins/Foreword by/Admiral Lord Mountevans, KCB/[device]/Salvationist

Publishing and Supplies Ltd./Judd Street, King's Cross, London, W.C.1/1949
108pp, 1p foreword, col. frontis. (unsigned), clo., 185x120mm. KMM
Adventure story set in Antarctica

Wiggins Teape Ltd.
8005 CAPTAIN COOK ON ORBIT ROUND THE WORLD 1768–1968
Wiggins Teape, London 1968
A collection of coloured facsimile documents in a folder, with a printed description of the facsimiles reproduced. Issued to commemorate the bicentenary of Cook's first voyage. 365x230mm. ANL
Advertisement for a paper-making company

WIGHTON, Rosemary (ed.)
8006 KANGAROO TALES/A Collection of Australian Stories/for Children/Selected by/Rosemary Wighton/ Illustrated by/Donald Friend/Penguin Books
Harmondsworth, Middlesex, England & Mitcham, Victoria, 1963
215pp (inc. 2p acknowledgements & 2pp introduction), 8pp adv., 34 b/w drawings in text throughout, pic. wrappers, 180x110mm. KMM
Another copy as above, 1963, wrappers printed in b/w with pink band top & bottom and price 4/- . KP
Another copy as above, rpt. 1965, with pink & yellow sections top and bottom, and price 6/6. KP
Another copy as above but with price 95 cents (decimal currency introduced 1966). KP
8007 KANGAROO TALES/A Collection of Australian Stories/for Children/Selected by/Rosemary Wighton/ Illustrated by/Donald Friend/Lansdowne Press
Melbourne 1964
215pp (inc. 2pp acknowledgements & 2pp introduction), 34 b/w drawings in text throughout, clo., 215x135mm. KMM

WILCKEN, Mrs Beatrice
8008 FAIRY TALES,/FABLES/and/LEGENDS/By/Mrs Beatrice Wilcken./All Rights Reserved.
Hobart, Calder, Bowden & Co., pr. [1890]
24pp (inc. 1p. preface), 11 sepia photographs, each 40x50mm laid down with a ruled border, stiff dec. wrappers, 195x163mm. ANL
Not listed in R. Holden, *The Mechanical Eye and the Illustrated Book,* and perhaps the only item of nineteenth-century children's literature so illustrated.
8009 FAIRY TALES,/FABLES,/AND/LEGENDS,/ Second revised edition/All rights reserved./Hobart/ Calder, Bowden & Co.,/Liverpool Street./MDCCCXCI
59pp, unillus., stiff wrappers, 175x125mm. NSL:M
Stories about the Jenolan Caves, Blue Mountains

Wild Rosebuds by 'An Australian Mother'
See SMITH, Frances Lettice

Wildflowers of Australia
8010 WILDFLOWERS/OF AUSTRALIA/Issued by Sanitarium Health Food Company
Sydney, n.d. [1961?]
12pp (with spaces for 25 col. pictures to be collected & pasted in), wrappers, cover title, 240x165mm. KMM
Variant copy, Petersham NSW, n.d., 10pp, as before. KP

'WILGA'
See Lord, Florence E.

WILKIE, A. A. W. & OSBORN, Mrs A. R.
8011 ALMOST HUMAN/Reminiscences from the/ Melbourne Zoo/Told by/A. A. W. Wilkie/Overseer, Melbourne Zoological Gardens/Written by/Mrs. A. R. Osborn/(Annie O'Neill)/Author of "Fresh Scenes from Clerical Life", etc./Whitcombe & Tombs Limited/ Melbourne/Auckland, Christchurch, Dunedin and Wellington, N.Z./and London
n.d. [192-?]
237pp (inc. 1p introduction & 1p preface), portrait frontis. & b/w photographic illus. throughout, clo., 240x180mm. ANL
Introduction by Henry Short, Editor of the *Leader*, for the children's page of which the articles were first written.

WILKINS, Frances
8012 The Conquerors Series/UNKNOWN/LANDS/ Frances Wilkins/Macdonald Educational
London 1969
135pp, b/w maps, 8pp b/w photographic illus., clo., 198x128mm. KP
Includes: James Cook, the Man who changed maps (25pp) and
Vivian Fuchs, the Man who crossed Antarctica. (25pp)

WILKINS, Susan
AUSTRALIAN TRAINS. *See* Golden Stamp Books

WILKINSON, Irene
8013 DAHLIA SLUG/By/Irene Wilkinson/Pictures by/ Edith Grieve/[publisher's device]/Georgian House/ Melbourne
1944
27pp, col. frontis. & 11 col. illus., dec. boards, 100x100mm. ANL

Uniform with above
8014 ADA CICADA. 1945. 20pp, 10 col. illus. BBC

8015 MRS MOSQUITO. 1945. 25pp, 10 col. illus. KMM

8016 WALTER WORM. 1945. 28pp, 10 col. illus. ANL

WILLEY, Keith
8017 STRANGE SEEKER/The Story of/Ludwig Leichhardt/by/Keith Willey/[drawing]/Illustrated by/ William Mahony/Macmillan/Melbourne London Toronto/St. Martin's Press/New York/1966
131pp (inc. 2pp editor's note & bibliography), 1p foreword, 14 part. col. illus., clo., dec. e/p, 215x135mm. HBM

WILLIAMS, Archibald
8018 THE ROMANCE OF/MODERN EXPLORATION/ With descriptions of curious/customs, thrilling adventures/and interesting discoveries of/explorers in all parts/of the world/by/Archibald Williams, F.R.G.S./author of/"The Romance of Modern Invention"/etc./with twenty-six illustrations/London/ Seeley and Co. Limited/38 Great Russell Street/1905
384pp, 3pp introduction & 1p prefatory note, 16pp adv., b/w frontis. & b/w illus., pic. clo., 190x125mm. KMM
Contents include: 'In the Heart of the Southern Ice Continent' (Ross, Scott, Shackleton in Antarctic: 17pp); 'How the Murray was Found' (Sturt: 9pp); 'An Australian Tragedy' (Burke and Wills: 11pp).

WILLIAMS, Gerald
THE DROVER. *See* Australian People

THE FORESTER. *See* Australian People

WILLIAMS, Gomer
8019 THE BANDICOOT/AND FRIENDS/ (Illustrated)/Words by/Gomer Williams/Music by/J. Maynard Grover/Drawings by N. MacKnight/ Figurehead [colophon] Adelphi/18 Adam Street, London, W.C.2
1933

27pp & 1 p adv., 6 b/w illus., pic. clo., 277x215mm. KMM
Title song & illus. refer to a bandicoot (illus. repeated on cover) and another song, 'Teddy and the Bees' illustrated with drawing of a koala.

WILLIAMS, John
8020 GALLIPOLI/The Dardanelles Campaign/John Williams/Illustrated by/F. D. Phillips/Lutterworth Press London
1969
80pp, line drawings in text, clo., 195x147mm. CLRC

WILLIAMS, Kathleen M.
8021 THEY CALL/ME BUNTY/by/Kathleen Williams/ Illustrations by/Lex Marshall/Geoffrey Cumberlege/ Oxford University Press/Leighton House Melbourne
n.d. [1948]
90pp, col. frontis. & b/w drawings in text, boards, 185x120mm. ANL
Story of a dog

WILLIAMS, Mary
8022 THE BLUE GAZINTA/by/Mary Williams
The Author, Adelaide 1944
19pp, unillus., wrappers, 215x135mm. CLRC
Poems for children, some reprinted from *A Comment* & from *Meanjin Papers*.

WILLIAMS, N. J.
8023 OLD/JONAS/N. J. Williams/Illustrated by Ann Culvenor/[drawing]/Nelson
1969
126pp, b/w drawings in text, map, dec. wrappers, 180x120mm. CLRC
Pacemakers series. Story set in the South-west Pacific.

WILLIAMS, Rhys [illustrator]
8024 Rhys Williams/BOYS AND GIRLS/ADVENTURE/ BOOK/W. H. Honey Publishing Co.—Sydney
n.d. [1946]
64pp, 12 f/p b/w illus. & b/w drawings in text, dec. boards, cover title, 245x180mm. ANL
Contains Ali Baba & Robin Hood.

8025 HOW THE/KOOKABURRA/LEARNED/TO LAUGH. An Aboriginal Legend/[drawing]/By/Rhys Williams.
Frank Johnson, 350 George St, Sydney, n.d. [194-?]
8pp, col. illus. throughout, pic. wrappers, cover title, 278x220mm. KMM

WILLIAMS, Rhys & Ruth C.
8026 THE ADVENTURES OF/GEORGIE GRUB/By/ Rhys Williams/Verse by/Ruth C. Williams
Frank Johnson, Sydney, n.d. [1946]
16pp, col. illus. throughout, dec. wrappers, cover title, 245x175mm. ANL

8027 MORE ADVENTURES OF/GEORGIE GRUB
As above. ANL

WILLIAMS, Ruth C.
8028 OUR FRIEND RODNEY/by/Ruth C. Williams/ Illustrated by/Rhys Williams/[drawing]/The W. H. Honey Publishing/Company/Sydney
1945
60pp, 3 f/p col. illus. & b/w drawings throughout, dec. boards, 230x175mm. ANL

8029 PIRATES' GOLD/By/Ruth C. Williams/Illustrated by/Rhys Williams/[drawing]/The W. H. Honey Publishing/Company Sydney
n.d. [1945]
103pp, dec. t.p., 12 f/p col. illus. & b/w drawings throughout, boards, 275x200mm. CLRC

8030 TIMOTHY TATTERS/by/Ruth C. Williams/ Illustrated by/Rhys Williams/W. H. Honey Publishing Co./31 Cunningham Street, Sydney/N.S.W., Australia
n.d. [1947]
238pp, col. frontis. & 22 b/w drawings throughout, clo., 180x115mm. ANL

8031 VERITY OF/SYDNEY TOWN/By/Ruth C. Williams/Illustrated by/Rhys Williams/[medallion]/ Angus and Robertson/Sydney London
1950
145pp, 13 b/w drawings & chapter headings, clo., dec. e/p, 230x145mm. KMM
Story of life in NSW in Macquarie's regime.
Winner CBCA award 1951.
• Rpt 1952, as above. KMM
8032 VERITY/OF/SYDNEY/TOWN/Written by Ruth C. Williams/Illustrated by Rhys Williams/[medallion]/ Paul Hamlyn/London New York Sydney Toronto
1970
145pp, b/w drawings throughout, clo., dec. e/p, 235x150mm. BBC
8033 Upper Primary Library/For Students Aged 11–14/VERITY OF/SYDNEY TOWN/By Ruth C. Williams/Illustrated by Rhys Williams/Angus and Robertson/Sydney London
First school edition 1954
128pp, b/w frontis. & 5 f/p b/w illus., b/w drawings in text, pic. limp clo., 180x120mm. Grant

8034 THE/ABORIGINAL/STORY/by Ruth C. Williams/ [decoration] Illustrated by Rhys Williams/[device]/ Shakespeare Head Press/Sydney/1955
46pp (inc. 1p glossary), b/w drawings throughout, dec. boards, dec. e/p, 230x175mm. NSL:M
• Rpt as above 1957, 1959, 1962, 1963 (twice), 1965, 1967, 1970. KP

WILLIAMS, William Lloyd
8035 ROUND THE WORLD/WITH/BILLY BEAR/ Sketches by/Dick Ovenden/Jingles by/W. L. Williams/and/J. R. Lyall/[drawing]/Melbourne/ Robertson & Mullens Limited.
n.d. [1937-?]
39pp (inc. 1p introduction by J. S. Seitz, Director of Education, Melbourne), illus. throughout, pic. wrappers, 230x170mm. Grant
Each page consists of a series of strip pictures with rhymes below.

8036 RED GUM BEND/Stories of the River Murray/by/ W. L. Williams/Illustrated by/R. A. Ovenden/ Consolidated Press Limited/Sydney/1945
91pp, b/w drawings in text, boards, 185x125mm. NSL:M

8037 THE SILVER BONE/by/W. Lloyd Williams/ Illustrations by Dick Ovenden/[drawing]/Whitcombe & Tombs Pty. Ltd./Melbourne Sydney Perth
1948
165pp, b/w frontis. & b/w drawings in text, suede, 185x125mm. ANL
The quest of a poetical dog in check pants in the Victorian bush

8038 Mullen's Plays for Children/No. 1/FIRST FLIGHTS/Drama for Junior Grades/by/W. Lloyd Williams, M.A., Dip. Ed./Robertson & Mullens Ltd./ Melbourne
n.d. [1952]
40pp, 1p introduction, b/w frontis., wrappers, 185x120mm. ANL
Includes seven plays.

Willie Wombat and his Friends
8039 A Storybook Knitting Book/WILLIE/50 cents WOMBAT/AND HIS FRIENDS/Willie and his eight pals/come to life as you read/their adventures in the/village of Gundygoo/you simply/knit them! [printed on an illus. of the toys in a bushland setting]
Southdown Press Pty Ltd., 32 Walsh St., Melbourne n.d. [197-?]
26pp, col. & part-col. illus. throughout, cover title, pic. wrappers, 280x292mm. KP

WILLIS, Blanche
8040 WARE/AND/TARE/Story of the Twin Rabbits/by/Blanche Willis/illustrated by/Gordon Richards
Crusader Publishers, Auburn, Victoria, n.d. [Copyright 3/12/57]
46pp, 7 f/p col. illus. & b/w illus. throughout, pic. boards, dec. e/p, cover title, 260x195mm. VSL

'WILLO & BILLO' [pseud. William Haynes & William H. Williamson]
8041 WONGABILLA/AND HIS BABY WALLABY/by/Willo and Billo/Angus and Robertson Limited/89 Castlereagh Street, Sydney/1943
77pp, col. frontis., 10 f/p b/w illus. & b/w drawings in text, dec. boards, 235x180mm. ANL
Stories & some verse about a native boy found by Australian soldiers in Papua.

8042 FURTHER ADVENTURES/OF/WONGABILLA/AND HIS BABY WALLABY/By/Willo and Billo/Supertone Coy./Publishers/200 Chalmers Street, Sydney
n.d. [1945?]
[67]pp (inc. author's preface), 2 f/p col. illus., b/w drawings throughout, dec. boards, 245x195mm. CLRC
Story about a little Papuan boy & his friends in the services

8043 SCOUT CHIEF/WONGABILLA/AND HIS PAL DIGGER
Printed by Hollander & Govett, Sydney, n.d. [1945]
[12]pp, part-col. illus. throughout, stiff wrappers, cover title, 350x240mm. ANL
Story in verse

WILLS, Vec [Viola Ethel]
8044 ALBINGO/An Old World Fable in an Australian setting/By/Vec Wills/Illustrated by/Ian McBain
Wholly set up & printed in Australia by Frearson's Printing House, Adam Street, Hindmarsh, SA, 1948
16pp, 6 f/p part-col. illus. & marginal drawings, dec. boards, dec. e/p, 240x180mm. KMM

Willys Äventyrliga Australienfärd
8045 WILLYS/ÄVENTYRLIGA/AUSTRALIENFÄRD,/Pris Kr.1:60
n.d. [1946?]
[31]pp & 1p.adv., & adv. verso back wrapper, col. illus. throughout, col. pic. wrappers, cover title, 168x255mm. RM
A Swedish story told in comic-strip form with col. illus. of a boy's adventures getting to Australia; no author or illustrator's name given, and no publisher's imprint.

WILMOT, Frank
See 'Maurice, Furnley'

WILSON, Barbara Ker
8046 Barbara Ker Wilson/BELOVED/OF THE GODS/Constable Young Books Ltd./Longmans Canada Ltd. 1965
140pp, unillus, clo., 197x127mm. LRA

8047 A FAMILY/LIKENESS/[drawing]/Barbara/Ker/Wilson/Illustrated by Astra Lacis Dick/London: Constable Young Books Ltd./Sydney: Angus and Robertson Ltd./Toronto: Longmans Canada Ltd.
1967
206pp, line drawings throughout, clo., 195x125mm. KMM
8048 THE/BISCUIT-TIN/FAMILY/Barbara Ker Wilson/Illustrated by Astra Lacis Dick/The World Publishing Company/Cleveland and New York
1968
190pp & 1p biography, b/w frontis. & text drawings, clo., 202x135mm. KP
U.S. edition of *A Family Likeness*

8049 HICCUPS AND OTHER STORIES/Thirty Tales for little/children/Barbara Ker Wilson/[drawing]/With drawings by/Richard Kennedy/Garnet Miller/London n.d. [1972]
124pp, b/w drawings in text, dec. clo., 215x140mm. KMM

8050 AUSTRALIAN/KALEIDOSCOPE/Edited by Barbara Ker Wilson/Illustrated by Margery Gill/[drawing, extended from frontispiece]/Collins/London & Sydney 1968
256pp (inc. 5pp introduction, 8pp notes about authors), b/w drawings throughout, clo., 220x150mm. KMM
An anthology of prose & verse.
US edition
8051 Meredith Press, New York 1969
Details as above. Unseen: ANL Catalogue

8052 AUSTRALIA/Wonderland Down Under/Barbara Ker Wilson/Author of "Australian Kaleidoscope"/Illustrated with photographs/Dodd, Mead & Company, New York
1969
80pp, b/w photographs throughout, clo., 225x160mm. CLRC

WILSON, Cecily
8053 PENNY WOCK'S AND DONALD DUCK'S/ADVENTURES IN JUNGLELAND/By Cecily Wilson/[drawing]/Illustrated by Jean Moreton
n.d. [1921 or 1922] n.p.[the author] Geelong, Victoria
16pp, col. frontis., 3 f/p & 2 smaller b/w illus., pic. wrappers, 250x182mm. VMOU
Dec. cover, with title printed in colour and oval section cut-out showing part of the col. illus. on first page.

WILSON, Erle
8054 THE GREEN FROG/and other Far-away stories/By/Erle Wilson/22 illustrations by/Ernest Aris, F.Z.S./W. R. Chambers, Ltd./38 Soho Square, London, W.1; and Edinburgh
1939
191pp (inc. 2 pp glossary), b/w frontis., 6 f/p & other smaller illus., clo., 202x142mm. VMOU
Collection of folk tales from Australia, the Pacific, Nth America, & others
8055 CHURINGA TALES/Stories of Alchuringa—The Dream Time/of the Australian Aborigines/by/Erle Wilson/Illustrated by/Sally Medworth/Australasian Publishing Company/Sydney/Wellington London
First published 1950
94pp, b/w drawings throughout, dec. boards, 185x135mm. The York Series. NSL:M

8056 COORINNA/A Novel of/The Tasmanian Uplands/By/Erle Wilson/André Deutsch
London, First published September 1953; 2nd imp. Dec. 1953
160pp, unillus., clo., 185x120mm. KMM

8057 COORINNA/A Novel of/The Tasmanian Uplands/By/Erle Wilson/Illustrated by/Pamela Lindsay/Longmans, Green and Co./London New York Toronto
First published in *The Heritage of Literature Series* 1955, by kind permission of André Deutsch Ltd
152pp, b/w frontis. & 5 f/p b/w illus., clo., 170x105mm . BBC
An edition published for use in schools.
• Rpt as above 1959 2nd imp. BBC
• Rpt " " 1962 4th " KMM
US edition
8058 [drawing] COORINNA/A Novel of the Tasmanian Uplands/by Erle Wilson/Random House/New York
First published in USA 1954
181pp, extended t.p., unillus., clo., 205x205mm. ANL
8059 COORINNA/A Novel of the/Tasmanian Uplands/Erle Wilson/Drawings by/Alison Forbes/Melbourne University Press
First pub. 1953; 2nd imp. Dec. 1953; Melbourne Paperback edition 1963
124pp, 6 b/w tailpieces, stiff wrappers, 185x110mm. KMM
8060 COORINNA/The Story of a Marsupial Wolf/condensed from the Book by/Erle Wilson/Title page and colour illustration by/Walter Stackpool/Additional illustrations by/Will Mahony/First published by Deutsch, London
The Readers Digest Assoc. Pty Ltd, Surry Hills, NSW, 1971
542pp, col. frontis. & 1 double-spread col. illus., 8 part-col. drawings in text, clo., 185x130mm. KMM
Coorinna (66pp) is the first book in this collection of 5 condensed books; there is also an accompanying biographical note on the author (1p).
Swedish edition
8061 Erle Wilson/COORINNA—Pungvargen/Stockholm/Natur och Kultur
Stockholm 1956
140pp, unillus., printed wrappers, 200x125mm. NSL:M

8062 FAR-AWAY TALES/Nature Myths of Sea and Shore/by/Erle Wilson/illustrated by/Mary Loveless/Australasian Publishing Company/Sydney Wellington London/in association with/George G. Harrap & Co. Ltd.
First published 1954
88pp (inc. 1p glossary), b/w illus. throughout, dec. boards, 185x135mm. CLRC The York Series.
Contents include myths from the Australian Aborigines, New Zealand, India, Fiji, New Guinea, The Marquesas, China &c.
Also author of *Minado, the Devil Dog: A Novel of the Quebec Woods* (Deutsch 1955) which is not a children's book.

WILSON, Hardy
8063 "YIN-YANG"/By/Hardy Wilson/[decoration]/Published by the author at/Flowerdale, Tasmania
n.d. [preface dated 1934]
213pp, unillus., clo., 180x115mm. HBM
Preface states that 'The stories are selected from a series told to a small boy at bed time', though the book does not seem designed or intended for children.

WILSON, Helen Helga [Mrs Edward Lionel, née Mayne]
8064 THE LETTERS OF/HUANG HU/Told by H. H. Wilson/and illustrated by Gordon [i.e. Clive Gordon]
West Australian Newspapers Ltd, Perth, n.d. [1946]
24pp, b/w drawings throughout, wrappers, cover title, 320x230mm. ANL
Verse from a dog to a small boy

WILSON, James & RANDLES, Tony
8065 THE/ENDEAVOUR/The authentic story of Captain/Cook's epic voyage of discovery/from which Australia sprang/[map, illus., &c.]/illustrated with reproductions/of original pictures and charts.
Southdown Press Pty Ltd., Melbourne, n.d. [197-?]
48pp, b/w & part col. illus. throughout, double-spread map, pic. wrappers, cover title, 273x202mm. WRT

WILSON, Keane
8066 PIP OF PYNALONG/By/Keane Wilson/Geoffrey Cumberlege/Oxford University Press/Leighton House Melbourne
1949
112pp, unillus., boards, 180x115mm. ANL

8067 PIP AND ANDREW—/SCHOOLMATES/By/Keane Wilson/Geoffrey Cumberlege/Oxford University Press/Leighton House Melbourne
1949
110pp, unillus., boards, 180x120mm. ANL

8068 PIP AND ANDREW/IN DANGER/Keane Wilson/Geoffrey Cumberlege/Oxford University Press/Melbourne Wellington
1950
111pp, unillus., clo., 180x120mm. KMM

8069 NICKY AT/TUMBARINGA/Keane Wilson/Geoffrey Cumberlege/Oxford University Press/Melbourne Wellington
1950
111pp, unillus., clo., 180x120mm. KMM

8070 LOOK AFTER ARTHUR/By/Keane Wilson/London: The Epworth Press
1955
170pp, unillus., clo., 185x125mm. KMM

WILSON, Lloyd Arnold
8071 CHARLIE CHEESECAKE RIDES A BIKE
Adelaide Cycle Manufacturers' Association, 1955
32pp, illus., cover title. Unseen: Annual Catalogue of Australian Publications 1955

THE ADVENTURES OF CHARLIE CHEESECAKE. *See* Hann, Marjorie & Wilson, Lloyd Arnold

WILSON, Marion
8072 Foreword/[4 lines]/WHEN I GROW UP/Seven action Songs for Infants/Words and Music by/Marion Wilson/Contents[7 titles listed]/Copyright/W. H. Paling Pty. Limited/
Sydney—Brisbane/and established throughout N.S.W. and Queensland
n.d. [copyright 1959]
8pp, unillus., pic. wrappers, 246x182mm. ANL

8073 NINE SONGS FOR/SPECIAL DAYS/IN AUSTRALIA/Marion Wilson/[song titles listed]/[drawing]/J.Albert & Son Pty Ltd./Copyright
Sydney 1969
10pp, unillus, wrappers, 273x220mm. NSL:M

WILSON, Noel
8074 IF I/WERE/AN/ATOM/Written by Noel Wilson/Graphics and production by Raymond Smith/For Danita & Christopher
Hutchinson of Australia, Melbourne 1970
[46]pp, col. illus. throughout, pic. boards, dec. e/p, 240x180mm. Headstart Science Series. KMM

Uniform with above, all 1970 and KMM
8075 IF I/MET/A/MOLECULE
8076 IF I/WERE/AN/ELECTRON

8077 IF I/WERE ENERGY [rpt 1972 as above KP]
8078 IF I/WERE/RADIOACTIVE

WILSON, Philip St. J.
8079 THE PIONEERS/OF PORT PHILLIP/The Story of Early Melbourne/for boys and girls/By/Phillip St. J. Wilson, M.A./History Master at Grimwade House,/ Melbourne Grammar School/Copyright
The author, Melbourne, n.d. [pencilled date 1928]
[Printed by Fraser & Morphet, 3 & 5 Eastbourne Street, Windsor, Melbourne]
84pp (inc. 1p author's preface), b/w frontis. & 10 b/w drawings in text, 7 b/w maps & 1 plan, wrappers, 185x107mm. KMM
Author's preface states that works of Bonwick, 'Garryowen', Ruden, Selby & Scott have furnished the material for the story.
8080 Second ed. as above but: 'with appendix'
1930
103pp as above. KMM
8081 THE PIONEERS/OF PORT PHILLIP/The Story of Early Melbourne/for Boys and Girls/By/P. St. J. Wilson/1934/Robertson & Mullens Ltd./Melbourne
102pp, & 1p preface, b/w frontis., maps & line drawings in text, 4 f/p b/w illus., wrappers, 180x120mm. KMM
Illustrations include 3 reproductions of drawings by S. T. Gill.
• Rpt 1945, as above. KMM

8082 THE OPEN EYE/A series of Essays for/Senior boys and girls/Edited by/the Rev. P. St. J. Wilson, M.A./Chaplain, Melbourne Church of England Grammar School/Number One/Melbourne/Ramsay, Ware Publishing Pty. Ltd/129 King Street/1941
70pp, unillus., wrappers, 177x115mm. ANL
Contains 5 essays by different writers on moral and religious matters.
8083 Volumes 2 and 3 also published in 1941, uniform with the above. ANL

WILSON, Rev. Theodore Percival
8084 [vignette]/FRANK OLDFIELD;/or,/Lost and Found./A Tale/By the Rev. T. P. Wilson, M.A.,/Rector of Smethcote/[1 line quotation]/T. Nelson & Sons, London, Edinburgh and New York:/W. Tweedie, 337 Strand, London:/and at/The Office of the United Kingdom Band of Hope Union,/5 Red Lion Square, London/1870
408pp (inc. 2pp preface), & 6pp adv., b/w frontis. & 4 f/p b/w illus., dec. clo., 175x120mm. KP
Title & subtitle in gilt on front cover, also a medallion with a biblical quotation printed in gilt; on spine, title & subtitle and 'A Temperance Prize Tale'
8085 FRANK OLDFIELD;/or,/Lost and Found/A Tale/ by the/Rev. T. P. Wilson, M.A.,/Rector of Smethcote/ [quot.]/T. Nelson & Sons, London, Edinburgh, and New York:/W. Tweedie, 377 Strand, London:/and at/ The Office of the United Kingdom Band of Hope Union/5 Red Lion Square, London/1873
408pp & 6pp adv., b/w frontis. & 4 f/p b/w illus., dec. clo., 175x115mm. NSL:M
8086 FRANK OLDFIELD;/or,/Lost and Found./A Tale/ By the/Rev. T. P. Wilson, M.A.,/Rector of Smethcote/ [quotation]/T. Nelson & Sons, London, Edinburgh, and New York:/and at/The United Kingdom Band of Hope Union,/4 Ludgate Hill, London, E.C./1883
408pp, 2pp preface, 4pp adv., b/w frontis. & 4 f/p b/w illus., dec. clo., 175x120mm. KMM
8087 One hundred Pounds Prize Tale/FRANK OLDFIELD/or, Lost and Found/By/Rev. T. P. Wilson, M.A./Rector of Smethcote/[quote]/T. Nelson and Sons, London and Edinburgh/and/The United Kingdom Band of Hope Union/60 Old Bailey, London E.C./1897
408pp (no preface, but publisher's note, listing seven other prize tales) & 6pp adv., b/w frontis. & 4 f/p b/w illus., dec. clo., 190x124mm. KMM
8088 Another copy as above, but 1900, 4pp adv., b/w frontis. only, dec. clo., 185x125mm. NSL:M
8089 FRANK OLDFIELD/or/Lost and Found/By/T. P. Wilson, M.A./T. Nelson and Sons, London and Edinburgh/and/The United Kingdom Band of Hope Union/60 Old Bailey.
n.d. [190-?]
408pp. & 6pp adv., col. frontis. & 3 col. plates by P. B. Hickling, t.p. printed in 2 cols, dec. clo., 189x126mm. KMM
Nelson's 'Red Rose' Library
NEARLY LOST BUT DEARLY WON; temperance tale containing one Australian anecdote, and not of sufficient interest for detailed entry CLRC

AIMING HIGHER
A TRUE HERO
WORKING IN THE SHADE
None of these titles has Australian references. NSL:M

WILSON, Thomas H.
DOUBLE QUICK THE KING HARPOONER. *See* PLUCK AND LUCK

WILTON, Elizabeth M.
Uniform booklets published by Rigby Ltd, Adelaide 1967
8090 THE/FOOLISH FAIRY
8091 THE LITTLE/SEA-DRAGON
8092 THE/LOST BANGLE
8093 PRETTY FOOT
8094 THE TWINS/AND THE/CHRISTMAS TREE
8095 THE TWINS/AND THE "TORTLE"
Each 24pp, b/w & part-col. illus. by Virginia Brown, stiff dec. wrappers, cover title, 200x150mm. KMM
A series of supplementary readers for beginners

8096 A RIDICULOUS IDEA/Elizabeth M. Wilton/Angus and Robertson
Sydney 1967
155pp, 1p author's note, 12 b/w drawings in text (one reproduced as frontis.), by Sandra Hargrave, clo., 215x135mm. KMM
Danish edition
8097 EN TOSSET IDÉ/Tegningen af Bernhard Petersen/ På dansk ved Nina Juul/Gyldendal/Printed in Denmark 1971
156pp, b/w illus., clo., 205x130mm. Unseen: IFA
German edition
8098 EIN LÄCHERLICHER EINFALL/Signal Verlag Hans Frevert
Baden Baden 1970
160pp, clo., 205x140mm. Unseen: IFA

8099 Elizabeth M. Wilton/RIVERBOAT FAMILY/ [drawing]/Illustrated by Sandra Hargrave/Angus and Robertson
Sydney 1967
196pp, 1p author's note, b/w drawings in text, clo., 195x125mm. KMM
US editions
8100 Farrar, Straus & Giroux, New York 1969
214pp, clo., 200x135mm.
An Ariel book: designed by Sheila Lynch. Unseen: IFA

Junior Literary Guild edition
8101 Category A—details as in Farrar, Straus edition. Unseen: IFA
German edition
8102 DAS FLUSSBOOTS/Signal Verlag Hans Frevert Baden Baden 1969
185pp, b/w illus. by Sandra Hargrave, clo., 205x140mm. Unseen: IFA

8103 ADVENTURE AHOY!/Elizabeth Wilton/A story of Bass and Flinders
Rigby Ltd, Adelaide 1969
20pp, 8 b/w & part-col. illus. by Vic. Hatcher, pic. wrappers, cover title, 200x150mm. KMM

Uniform with above, all KMM:
8104 A REMARKABLE OBSTACLE/Elizabeth Wilton/A story of Lawson and Blaxland
8105 LAND OF HIS DREAMS/Elizabeth Wilton/A story of Dirck Hartog
8106 ON THE BANKS OF THE YARRA/Elizabeth Wilton/A story of William Buckley and John Batman
8107 THE UNKNOWN LAND/Elizabeth Wilton/A story of Captain Phillip and Bennelong
All KMM

8108 RED/RIBBONS/AND/MR. ANDERS/Elizabeth Wilton/Illustrated by Richard Kennedy/[drawing]/Angus and Robertson/Sydney London Melbourne Singapore/First published in 1970/Text (C) Elizabeth Wilton 1970/ISBN 0 207 95400 3
[32]pp, b/w & part. col. illus. throughout, pic. boards, 240x180mm. CLRC

8109 Elizabeth Wilton/RIVERVIEW/KIDS/[drawing]/Illustrated by Deborah and Kilmeny Niland/Angus and Robertson
Sydney 1971
200pp, b/w drawings in text, map e/p, clo., d/w design by Astra Lacis Dick, 195x120mm. KMM

[WINCHCOMBE, D. M.]
8110 HOLLYMAN/Benagarna/Printed and Published by the Santal Mission Press/1923
103pp, unillus., wrappers, 230x145mm. MAC

WINER, Yvonne
8111 FINGER PLAYS/AND/ACTION RHYMES/by Yvonne Winer/Angus and Robertson
Sydney 1970
49pp, 2pp introduction, b/w drawings in text by Frank Knight, pic. wrappers, 225x150mm. ANL
Verses, with suggested accompanying actions
• Rpt 1972. KP

Wings across the World
8112 WINGS ACROSS THE WORLD/The fascinating story of flight/[drawing]/Approved by the New South Wales Department of Education for distribution to schools
Qantas, Sydney, n.d. [1958]
[52]pp (inc. covers), col. drawings in text, pic. wrappers, 174x256mm. KMM
On recto of back cover: 'A message from the Chairman of Qantas' signed 'Hudson Fysh'

WINTER, Winifred
BROWNIE POKO. *See* Gunn & Taylor no. 92, Junior Library no. 2

WINTERFELD, Henry
8113 CASTAWAYS/IN LILLIPUT/Henry Winterfeld/Translated by Kyrill Schabert/Illustrated by Regina Ackermann-Ophuls/[drawing]/Lutterworth Press London
First British edition 1961 [Originally published by Lothar Blanvalet Verlag, Berlin, under the title *Telegramm aus Liliput*, 1958; American edition published by Harcourt, Brace & Company Inc. 1960, English translation by Henry Winterfeld]
188pp, b/w drawings in text throughout, clo., 200x125mm. CLRC
A story of three Australian children castaways on Lilliput

WISE, Joan
8114 TRAPPED/ON/TASMAN/Joan Wise/Illustrated by Helen Sallis/Rigby Limited
Adelaide 1971
123pp, 10 f/p b/w illus., clo., 210x135mm. KMM
Story of a lighthouse-keeper's son living on Tasman Island
UK edition
John Gifford Ltd, 1972 as above. KMM

WISE, William
8115 THE AMAZING/ANIMALS OF/AUSTRALIA/by William Wise/Illustrated by Joseph Sibal/[device—A See & Read beginning to Read Book]/G. P. Putnam's Sons New York/[drawing]
1970
61pp & 2pp biographical notes on author & artist, b/w frontis., b/w & part-col. illus. throughout, pic. bd., 210x145mm. ANL

WISHART, William
8116 UNCLE WILL'S/DOG STORIES/[drawing & caption]/Interestingly written by Mr. William Wishart/for boys and girls, and based upon actual facts/Illustrated by Mr. V. Brun/Printed by Arbuckle, Waddell Pty. Ltd., McKillop Street, Melbourne/Published by/Gordon & Gotch Pty. Ltd., Queen Street, Melbourne/And at Sydney, Brisbane, New Zealand and New York
n.d. [1918]
30pp, 4 col. illus. & b/w drawings in text, dec. boards, dec. e/p, 240x185mm. ANL

WITCOMBE, Eleanor
8117 PIRATES AT/THE BARN/by/Eleanor Witcombe/[drawing]/Illustrated by Les Tanner/Ure Smith—Sydney 1963
64pp (inc. 1p foreword by N. Hutchinson, Retiring Executive Director, Australian Elizabethan Theatre Trust, 2pp author's preface & 1p notes), b/w frontis. (inside front cover), 4 b/w drawings, stiff dec. wrappers (with plan inside back cover), 180x125mm. CLRC
Children's play, with notes on production & plans of stage setting

WITTBER, C. A.
8118 "PLEASANT HOURS"/READER/Illustrated By/C. A. Wittber/Head Teacher, Rose Park School./Adelaide/Gurney Road Dulwich
1906. Bound by F. Binns & Co.
216pp, dec. t.p., b/w photographic frontis., photographic illus. in text, clo., 180x120mm. KP
School reader. Includes original Australian material & excerpts of Capt Cook, Bounty mutineers, Buckley the Wild White Man, The Duff Children & others.

WITH, Cläre
8119 LÄNDER UND VÖLKER/Ein Bilderatlas in Einzelheften/von/Cläre With/AUSTRALIEN/Müller & J. Kiepenheuer/Gm. Verlag/Potsdam
[1930]

24pp, b/w illus. on every page, pic. wrappers, 190x238mm. KMM
History of Australia told in brief text & amusing illus. & maps

'WOLKOWSKY, Marea' [Prerauer, Maria]
8120 THE ENCHANTED/PANCAKES/[illustration]/A Fairy Tale for Children...By Marea Wolkowsky
Offset Printing Co., Sydney, n.d. [1946]
16pp, col. illus. on alternate pages, b/w illus. by W. H. Davies, wrappers, cover title, 240x180mm. KMM

8121 Marea Wolkowsky/PERILOUS/JOURNEY/A Story of Adventure in Elizabethan Times/The Shakespeare Head/London New York Sydney Paris Durban/1947
146pp, unillus., clo., d/w by Raymond Johns, 210x130mm. ANL

8122 AUSTRALIAN ADVENTURE/by/Maria [*sic*] Wolkowsky/London/Victor Gollancz Ltd./1965
First published in German under the title *Australisches Abenteuer*, by K. Thienemanns Verlag, Stuttgart 1961
126pp, 1p biographical note, unillus., clo., 195x125mm. KMM
D/w designed by Richard Kennedy. Author's name spelt 'Maria' throughout in this book.
8123 AUSTRALIAN/ADVENTURE/Maria [*sic*] Wolkowsky/Cover Illustration/by Mary Gernat/[device]
Atlantic Book Publishing Co. Ltd, London 1968
125pp, 3pp adv., col. pic. wrappers, 180x105mm. CLRC
Dutch edition
8124 Maria [*sic*] Wolkowsky/AVONTUUR/IN AUSTRALIE/G. F. Callenbach N.V.—Uitgever Nijkerk n.d.
150pp (inc. 2pp glossary), unillus., clo., 215x145mm. CLRC

WOLLASTON, Tullie C.
8125 THE SPIRIT OF/THE CHILD/By/Tullie C. Wollaston/[quotation]/Thomas C. Lothian/Melbourne and Sydney/1914/Printed in England
First edition May 1914
227pp (inc. 4pp preface), 12pp adv., col. frontis. & 6pp col. illus., 5 f/p b/w illus., dec. clo., 205x145mm. KMM
Comprises travel letters written to children, & natural history studies; includes some verse. Although addressed to children, the letters are philosophical & reminiscent & the result is not a children's book.

The Wonder Annual
8126 THE/WONDER/ANNUAL
Ed. Vera Francis, Colorgravure, Melbourne 1950
308pp, 16pp col. illus. & b/w illus. throughout, clo., dec. e/p, 270x195mm. ANL
Much of the book is not Australian in content; includes articles by Charles Barrett; G. B. Portus, 'The First White Foot to be set on New South Wales—The Story of Isaac Smith'; Garth Raymond, 'Castaways in Arnhem Land'; 'Butterflies of Australia', &c.

The Wonder Book of General Knowledge
8127 THE/WONDER BOOK/OF/GENERAL/KNOWLEDGE/Volume/5/of the/Sanitarium Children's Library
Sanitarium Health Food Co., P.O. Box 9, Petersham, N.S.W., n.d. [195-?]
[Wholly set up & printed in Australia by Compress Printing Limited 168 Castlereagh Street Sydney]
72pp, line drawings (with spaces for 60 col. cards to be collected & pasted in), pic. wrappers, 270x210mm. KMM
Contains 72 factual articles, only two—on Captain Cook & W. M. Hughes—dealing with Australian subject matter.

Wonder Book of Modern Aircraft
8128 Weeties/Vita-Brits/Crispies/WONDER BOOK/OF/MODERN AIRCRAFT
Purina Grain Foods (SA) Pty Ltd, 90 Ann St, Stepney, Adelaide, n.d. [1941?]. Printed by McLaren's, Melbourne
24pp, b/w illus. throughout with spaces left for 48 photographic cards to be collected & pasted in, pic. wrappers, 276x215mm. KMM
Adv. inside front & back covers.
Another copy, as above, but also with Purina Grain Foods Sydney & Melbourne addresses. KP

The Wonder Book of Working Models
8129 THE WONDER BOOK OF WORKING MODELS
The Sun News Pictorial, Melbourne, n.d. [1937?]
Prov. Patent 30544/37
26pp, press-out models printed on light bd., pic. covers, 270x380mm.
Antique Toy Museum, Ballarat

The Wonderful History of Thomas Hickathrift
8130 THE/WONDERFUL HISTORY/OF/THOMAS HICKATHRIFT,/of Notable Memory,/Showing/The extraordinary Feats of Valour atchieved [*sic*] by him in/the various Battles he had with Giants, Highwaymen,/Lions, Wolves, &c. and of his surprising great Strength./To which is added,/THE SAILOR BOY,/A Very interesting Tale./London./Printed and Sold by J. Bailey, 116, Chancery Lane,/and may be had of most Book sellers./Price Sixpence
n.d. [180-?]
36pp, hand-coloured engraved frontis., wrappers, 138x880mm. CLRC
The Sailor Boy consists of 5pp of text relating the adventures of the young hero on a voyage to New Holland (mentioned once in the text).

The Wonderful Story of Milo
8131 THE WONDERFUL/STORY OF MILO
Nestlés Australia, n.d. [195-?]
16pp (inc. 14pp comic strip 'Milo's Wonderful Journey', 1p safety quiz &c), pic. wrappers, cover title, 240x180mm. KP
Advertising brochure for Nestlés products printed throughout in red & black; illus. signed 'John L. Curtis'(?). Story based on Roman hero that ends in Australia.

Wonders of the World
8132 WONDERS/OF THE/WORLD/[introduction &c]/Issued by/Nestlé and Anglo-Swiss Condensed Milk Co. (Australasia) Ltd./[address & telephone nos of 7 major branches listed]
Printed by W. C. Penfold, Sydney, n.d.
16pp (inc. 12pp printed with numbers for cards to be pasted on), pic. wrappers, 260x206mm
Album printed on thick grey paper. KMM
8133 Nestlé's Picture Stamp Album/WONDERS OF THE WORLD
17 Foveaux St, Sydney, n.d.
16pp (inc. 4pp text) & 12pp with spaces for different series of cards to be pasted in, pic. wrappers, 260x208mm. KP

Woobinda
8134 WOOBINDA/(Der Busch-Doktor)/Malbuch/

[drawing]/Western Publishing GmbH/Frankfurt/Main, Feuerbachstrasse 31
Copyright 1970 by Franz Schneider Verlag, Munich, in conjunction with Talbot Television Ltd
[80]pp, b/w drawings throughout, pic. wrappers, cover title, 265x195mm. KMM
Colouring book with brief captions at the foot of each page based on the Australian television serial; colour stills from the serial illustrate the wrappers.

WOOD, [Captain] A.
8135 TRUE BLUE/by/Captain A. Wood/[drawing]/ Illustrated by A. S. Forrest/T. Nelson & Sons Ltd./ London & Edinburgh
n.d. [1926]
249pp & 6pp adv., b/w frontis. & 23 b/w drawings, clo. (with col. onlay on front cover), 187x121mm. KMM
Story begins with 3 convicts who escape from Sydney & stow away on a ship bound for England.

WOOD, Andrew
8136 Sea Story Readers by Andrew Wood/4/STREET PAVED/WITH WATER/[drawing]/Melbourne/ Macmillan & Co. Ltd./(Head Office: London)
First published 1958; Australian edition 1959
63pp, 1p exercises, b/w map & drawings throughout, limp clo., 180x115mm. ANL
School text describing the experiences of an Australian girl & others on a Thames barge on London river.

8137 Longacre Series—12/THE BUSHRANGERS/By/ Andrew Wood/Illustrated by Pat Williams/[device]/ Odhams Press Limited/Long Acre, London
1961
62pp & 2pp exercises, b/w drawings in text, dec. wrappers, 200x140mm. VMOU

WOOD, David
8138 COOK/THE EXPLORER/by David Wood/ Illustrated by/John Worsley/With four maps by/Eric Saunders/Peter Lunn/London/1947
218pp, b/w frontis. & 6 f/p b/w illus., clo., 180x115mm. NSL:M

'WOOD, Eric' [pseud. F. Knowles Campling]
8139 THE BOY'S BOOK OF/ADVENTURE/By/Eric Wood/Author of "Famous Voyages of the Great Discoverers"/With four colour plates and twelve full-page/black-and-white illustrations/Cassell and Company, Ltd./London, New York, Toronto and Melbourne/1912
308pp, col. frontis. & 3 f/p col. illus., 12 f/p b/w illus. by various artists, pic. clo., 205x145mm. KMM
Contents include: 'The End of Michael Howe—Hunting a Bushranger in Van Diemen's Land' (4pp); 'Attacked by Aborigines' (Sir George Grey; 5pp); 'The Mutiny of the *Bounty*' (18pp).
• Rpt n.d. [1922], lettering on pic. clo. bdg in black instead of gilt. KMM
Second imp., as above. KMM

8140 THE BOY'S BOOK OF/BATTLES/By/Eric Wood/ Author of "The Boy's Book of Adventure", "Famous Voyages/of the Great Discoverers", etc./with four colour plates and twelve full-page/black-and-white illustrations/Cassell and Company, Ltd/London, New York, Toronto and Melbourne/1913
315pp, col. frontis. & 3 col. plates, 12 b/w plates, pic. clo., 200x140mm. KMM
Contains 'The Battle at the Eureka Stockade', 7pp.

8141 EVERY BOY'S BOOK/OF HEROES/By/Eric Wood/Author of "The Boys Scouts' Roll of Honour," "The Boy's Book of Battles,"/"The Boy's Book of Adventures"/with four colour plates and twelve full-page/Black and white illustrations/Cassell and Company, Ltd./London, New York, Toronto and Melbourne/1914
311pp, col. frontis. & col. & b/w plates, pic. clo. with title in gilt, 205x140mm. KP
Only Australian content 'The Pioneer as Hero; the story of Eyre's Journey' (20pp)

8142 THE BOY'S BOOK OF/THE SEA/By/Eric Wood/ Author of "The Boy's Book of Heroes", "The Boy Scouts' Roll of Honour",/etc. etc./With four colour plates and twelve/Illustrations in black-and-white/ Cassell and Company, Ltd./London, New York, Toronto and Melbourne
n.d. [1915?]
312pp, col. frontis. & 3 f/p col. illus., 12 f/p b/w illus., pic. clo., 205x145mm. KMM
Contents include 'The Wreck of the *Batavia*' (10pp) & 'Scott in the Antarctic' (13pp), the battle of the *Sydney* & the *Emden* in World War I.
8143 Another edition as above entitled *Every Boy's Book of the Sea.* Grant

8144 THE BOY'S BOOK OF/PIONEERS/by/Eric Wood/ With four colour plates and four/full-page black-and-white illustrations/Cassell and Company, Ltd./London, New York, Toronto and Melbourne
n.d. [inscribed 1917]
308pp, illus., pic. clo., 205x140mm. KMM
Contents include: 'Opening Up the Great Rivers of Australia' (12pp); 'The Tragedy of Burke and Wills' (11pp); 'The Discovery of the Poles' (17pp); 'El Dorado—How the Seekers of Gold have pioneered for Civilization' (4pp relate to the Australian gold discoveries).

8145 THE BOY'S BOOK OF/BUCCANEERS/By/Eric Wood/With four colour plates/and three maps/Cassell and Company, Ltd./London, New York, Toronto and Melbourne
n.d.
312pp, col. frontis. & 3 col. plates & 3 maps, pic. clo., title & author's name blocked in col., 205x145mm. KP
Includes 'The Voyage of Capt John Cook', describing Dampier's voyage (16pp).

8146 DISCOVERERS OF THE/WORLD/By/Eric Wood/ With four Coloured Plates/Cassell and Company, Ltd./London, New York, Toronto and Melbourne
London, n.d. [192-?]
96pp, col. frontis. & 3 f/p col. illus., limp pic. clo., 170x130mm. HBM
Cassell's Continuous Readers
Contains chapters on Magellan (6pp), Eyre (12pp) & Capt. Scott (11pp).

8147 UNDER THE/SOUTHERN CROSS/by/Eric Wood/Author of/"Winged Mountie" "Rebel Skies" etc./London/The Ace Publishing Co.
n.d. [1938]
224pp, f/p b/w frontis. & 3 b/w illus., clo., 185x125mm. KMM
Adventure story

WOOD, George Arnold
8148 THE VOYAGE OF THE/ENDEAVOUR/By/G. Arnold Wood, M.A./Professor of History in the University of Sydney/Illustrated/Melbourne:/ Macmillan & Co. Limited/Head Office: London/1926
116pp, 2pp preface, b/w frontis. & 7 f/p b/w illus. (inc. 2 maps), clo., 180x120mm. HBM

Author states in preface that the book was primarily intended for boys & girls.
• Rpt 1929, 1933. Unseen

8149 Australian Pocket Library Edition April 1944, as above.
Preface same as in first edition, but first sentence stating that: 'In this little book I try to tell the story of Cook's Voyage in the Endeavour in a way that will make it interesting to boys & girls...&c.' has been omitted. HBM

8150 THE VOYAGE OF THE/ENDEAVOUR/G. Arnold Wood, M.A./late Professor of History/University of Sydney/Foreword by/Allan E. Bax/President/Royal Australian Historical Society/Royal Australian Historical Society/Macmillan of Australia/1970
116pp, 2pp foreword, photographic frontis., 7 b/w illus. (inc. 2 maps), pic. wrappers, 175x115mm. BBC

WOOD, O'Hara [John James O'Hara Wood]

8151 CUP WEEK/and Other Verse/Together with two short Fairy Tales and/Two illustrations by Alek Sass/ and an end-piece by by [*sic*] A. H. O'Hara Wood/By/ O'Hara Wood/Writer of "Mortgaged Years"/"The Opal Necklace" etc./1912/The Specialty Press Pty. Ltd./Melbourne
94pp, 2 b/w illus., wrappers, 180x120mm. BBC
Book of adult verse with two very slight animal & Aboriginal fables for children. BBC

WOODBERRY, Joan

8152 RAFFERTY/TAKES TO/FISHING/Written & illustrated by/Joan Woodberry/[drawing]/Max Parrish—London
1959
185pp, b/w drawings in text, clo., d/w designed by Shirley Farrow, 185x120mm. BBC

8153 FLOODTIDE/FOR RAFFERTY/written & illustrated by/Joan Woodberry/[drawing]/Max Parrish—London
1960
183pp, b/w drawings in text throughout, clo., 180x115mm. BBC

8154 RAFFERTY/RIDES/A WINNER/Written and illustrated by/Joan Woodberry/[drawing]/Max Parrish—London
1961
187pp, b/w chapter headings & tailpieces, clo., d/w designed by Dick Hart, 185x120mm. KMM
Joint winner CBCA award 1962.
Second ed. (re-set) 1962, as above BBC
Second imp. 1962 as above, but 195x125mm. CLRC

8155 RAFFERTY/MAKES/A LANDFALL/written and illustrated by/Joan Woodberry/[drawing]/Max Parrish—London
1962
156pp, b/w chapter headings & tailpieces, clo., d/w designed by Shirley Farrow, 195x125mm. KMM

8156 ASH TUESDAY/by/Joan Woodberry/With illustrations by Max Angus/[drawing]/Macmillan of Australia/1968
Melbourne
46pp, part-col. illus. throughout, col. dec. t.p., dec. boards, col. e/p, 265x205mm. KMM

8157 'Special ed. 1970' as above, pic. wrappers. KW

8158 Joan Woodberry/COME BACK/PETER/[drawing]/ Illustrated by George Tetlow/Rigby Limited
Adelaide 1968
103pp, 9 f/p b/w illus., b/w drawings in text, clo., 210x130mm. KMM
• Rpt Sept. 1969, as above. KP

8159 THE CIDER DUCK/by/Joan Woodberry/With illustrations by Molly Stephens/[drawing]/Macmillan of Australia/1969
[29]pp, part. col. illus. throughout, pic. boards, 270x205mm. KMM

8160 A GARLAND/OF GANNETS/Joan Woodberry/ Illustrated by Elizabeth Lord/[drawing]/Nelson
Thomas Nelson (Australia) Limited, Melbourne 1969
69pp, b/w map frontis., b/w drawings throughout, pic. wrappers, 180x120mm. Pacemakers series. KMM

8161 LITTLE BLACK/SWAN/Joan Woodberry/ Illustrated by/Carol Lawson/Macmillan
London 1970
39pp, 16 b/w illus., clo., 195x125mm. KMM

WOODFULL, Howard Thomas Colin

AGRICULTURAL SHOWS. *See* Life in Australia

WOODGATE, Fred

8162 JACKAROO IN AUSTRALIA/by/Fred Woodgate/ Tamworth N.S.W./1958
Printed by Davies & Cannington Pty Ltd, 137–139 King Street, Newcastle
32pp (and also printed on both front & back e/p), 21 b/w photographs & brief text, bd., 240x183mm. KMM

WOODHALL, Edwin T.

8163 THE KELLY GANG/By/Edwin T. Woodhall/ Author of/Jack Sheppard, Jonathan Wild, Claude Duval,/Jack the Ripper, Colonel Blood, Captain Kidd, Etc/[3 lines]/Mellifont Press, Limited/38 Furnival St. London, E.C.4
n.d. [1930?]
96pp, unillus. col. pic. wrappers, adv. on back cover, 214x136mm. CLRC
No 25 of the Mellifont Celebrated Crime Series. 2pp breakdown on location & characters true & fictional.

WOOD JONES, Frederic

See Jones, Frederic Wood

WOODLEY, Bruce

8164 Bruce Woodley/of the/Seekers/Presents/FRIDAY STREET/FANTASY/and Other Stories/Paul Hamlyn/ London New York Sydney Toronto
Dee Why West, NSW, 1969
A Paul Hamlyn/Pennywheel Production
[16]pp, illus. bd. with record, 190x190mm. CLRC
Designed by Paul Corley, illus. Jeannette Spencer. Songs

WOODS, Barbara

8165 TALES/FOR TINIES/by/Barbara Woods/ Illustrated by/Donald Gunn/Printed and Published by/J. Roy Stevens/1–7 Knox Place, Melbourne C.1
n.d. [194-?]
64pp (last blank), col. frontis. & 13 half-page col. illus., 8 half-page & 10 small b/w illus., pic. boards, 240x180mm. KMM

8166 TALES/FOR TINIES/By/Barbara Woods/ Illustrated by Donald Gunn/Printed and Published by/ Boylan & Co. Pty. Limited/31 Cunningham Street, Sydney/1943
Contents appear to be the same as above though rearranged & some illus. printed in different col.; also 244x174mm, thicker paper. KP

8167 THE ADVENTUROUS KOALAS/[coloured illustration]/by Barbara Woods/Illustrations by B. E. Pike
Printed by J. T. Picken & Sons, Melbourne, n.d. [library copy acquired 1944]
44pp, 21 col. illus., dec. wrappers, 180x120mm. NSL:M

8168 THE PIG/WITH THE/STRAIGHT TAIL/by Barbara Woods/[coloured illustration]/Illustrations by/ B. E. Pike
Printed by J. T. Picken & Sons, Melbourne, n.d. [library copy acquired 1944]
46pp, 21 col. illus., dec. wrappers, 180x120mm. NSL:M

8169 THE RINGTAIL/FAMILY/by Barbara/Woods/ Illustrated by/Betty Pike.
n.d. [Printed in Australia for the publishers by Boylan & Co. Pty. Limited, 31 Cunningham Street, Sydney] [inscribed 1944]
31pp, col. t.p. & 7 col. illus., pic. boards, 240x170mm. KP

8170 THE/APPLE/ELVES/by/Barbara Woods/ illustrated by/Betty Pike
New Century Press Pty Ltd, Sydney, n.d. [194-?]
[16]pp, col. dec. t.p., col. illus. on every page, pic. wrappers, 203x167mm. KMM

WOODS, Renee
8171 THE CROOKED TREE/and other Stories/by/ Renee Woods/Arura Writers/Melbourne
n.d. [1944]
40pp, 6 f/p col. illus., & b/w drawings in text, dec. boards, 240x180mm. ANL
Fairy stories of the Australian bush

WORDLEY, Dick (ed.)
8172 HOW TO PLAY/AUSSIE RULES/Edited by Dick Wordley/of Applied Journalism/Photographs selected by Bob Buchanan/Lansdowne Press/Melbourne
1960
118pp, 1p acknowledgements, 2pp foreword, 1p index, b/w photographic frontis. & b/w photographic illus. throughout, clo., 235x180mm. BBC
Book on Australian Rules Football, with contributions by various players
8173 HOW TO PLAY/AUSSIE RULES/Edited by Dick Wordley/Photographs selected by Bob Buchanan/ Lansdowne Press/Melbourne
First publ. July 1960; rev. & enlarged ed. April 1963
viiipp, 118pp, b/w photographic frontis. & b/w illus. throughout, ?bd. (copy seen re-bound), 227x175mm. CLRC

WÖRISHÖFFER, S.
8174 EIN/WIEDERSEHEN IN AUSTRALIEN./Von/S. Wörishöffer./Verfasser von "Robert de Schiffsjunge", "Das Naturfurscherschiff","Auf dem Kriegspfade"/[2 lines titles]/Mit 16 Bollbildern/[device]/Bielefeld und Leipzig./Verlag von Velhagen & Klasing./1888
562pp & 2pp adv., b/w frontis. & 15 f/p b/w illus., pic. clo., 215x145mm. CLRC
8175 As above, but after titles
Sechste Auflage/Mit 4 farbigen Einschaltbildern von Fritz Ahlers/und 16 Bollbildern von Joh. Gehrts'[device]/ Beilefeld und Leipzig 1930/Verlag von Velhagen & Klasing
352pp, illus. as before but with an additional 4 col. plates (copy re-bound), 215x15mm. ANL

8176 DAS NATURFORSCHERSCHIFF/oder/FAHRT DER JUNGEN HAMBURGER MIT DER "HAMMONIA"/nach den Besitzungen ihres Vaters in der Sudsee./von/S. Wörishöffer/
[author of—3 lines]/Kleine Ausgabe/Mit 20 Vóllbildern/[device]/Bielefeld und Leipzig 1922/Verlag von Velhagen & Klasing
230pp, b/w frontis. & 19 b/w plates, pic. clo., 213x142mm. ANL

The World of Tennis
8177 THE WORLD OF TENNIS/Published by the Nestlé Co (Aust.) Ltd., Makers of MILO
n.p., n.d. [196-?]
24pp, b/w photographs, stiff wrappers, 135x207mm. KP
Includes hints, photographs & careers of champions, &c.

'WOTHERSPOON, John' [pseud. Rylah, Ann Flora Flashman]
8178 THE/AUSTRALIAN/PET BOOK/John Wotherspoon/with Photographs by A. F. Flashman, B. V. Sc./Lansdowne Press/Melbourne
1962
111pp (inc. 2pp index), b/w photographic frontis. & b/w photographic illus. throughout, clo., 235x175mm. CLRC
Practical handbook on choice & care of pets for children

WREN, Patricia
8179 Part 1/LIVING WONDERS/OF/AUSTRALIA/by Patricia Wren/School Projects Pty. Limited
Sydney 1966
40pp, illus. t.p., line drawings in text, b/w map, illus. by author, stiff dec. wrappers, 210x130mm. Australian Scene series. BBC

WRIGHT, C. H.
8180 The Story of the Exploration/and Settlement of Australia/CONQUERING THE CONTINENT/C. H. Wright, B. Com., Dip. Ed./illustrated by Jack Newnham/F. W. Cheshire Melbourne
1960
96pp, part-col. frontis. & part-col. illus. throughout, dec. boards 235x150mm. CLRC

WRIGHT, Judith
8181 Judith Wright/KINGS OF THE DINGOES/Illustrated by/Barbara Albiston/[vignette]/Melbourne/Oxford University Press/London Wellington New York/1958
94pp, b/w chapter headings, clo., 215x135mm. KMM

8182 THE DAY/THE MOUNTAINS/PLAYED/by/ Judith Wright/Illustrated by/Annette Wright/[coloured illustration]/Brisbane/The Jacaranda Press/1960
48pp, col. & b/w illus. throughout, dec. clo., 240x180mm. CLRC
Illustrated by the author's sister.
• Rpt 1963, 1970 as above. BBC

8183 RANGE THE/MOUNTAINS/HIGH/Judith Wright/Lansdowne Press/Melbourne
1962
142pp (inc. 1p preface), 8 f/p b/w illus. by I. Waloff, clo., 215x135mm. KMM
Second imp. 1963, as above. KMM
• Rpt as above, 1967. KP
8184 RANGE THE/MOUNTAINS HIGH/Judith Wright/ Lansdowne Press/Melbourne
Revised [third] edition, Milton, Queensland, 1971
142pp (inc. 1p preface), b/w frontis. & 8 f/p b/w illus., clo., d/w designed by Genevieve Melrose, dec. e/p, 210x135mm. CLRC

8185 BIRDS/Poems/by/Judith Wright/[device]/Angus and Robertson
Sydney 1962
34pp, unillus., clo., 215x130mm. KMM
8186 BIRDS/poems by/Judith Wright/Illustrated by/ Annette Macarthur-Onslow/Angus and Robertson
Sydney, First published 1962; 2nd ed. 1967
42pp, b/w & part-col. drawings throughout, clo., dec. e/p, 215x135mm. CLRC
• Rpt 1968, as above. KMM

COUNTRY TOWNS. *See* Life in Australia

8187 THE RIVER AND/THE ROAD/Judith Wright/ Lansdowne Press/Melbourne
1966

139pp, 12 f/p b/w drawings, clo., 210x130mm. KMM
Illustrations anonymous.

8188 THE RIVER AND THE ROAD/Judith Wright/illustrated by/Rachel Tonkin/Lansdowne Press
First published 1966; revised edition Melbourne 1971
139pp, 12 f/p b/w drawings, clo., 210x135mm. KMM

HENRY LAWSON. *See* Great Australians

See also Howard & Levy. AUSTRALIAN STORY SAMPLER

WRIGHT, Sid

8189 [drawing]/THE WAY OF THE DINGO/Sid Wright/Angus and Robertson
Sydney, 1968
153pp (inc. 6pp preface), b/w drawings, clo., 196x127mm. KP

WRIGHTSON, Alice Patricia

8190 THE/CROOKED/SNAKE/by/Patricia/Wrightson/[decorative device]/Illustrated by/Margaret/Horder/Angus and Robertson/Sydney London Melbourne Wellington
First published 1955
153pp, b/w drawings throughout, clo., dec. e/p, 200x125mm. KMM
Winner CBCA Award 1956.
• Rpt 1956, 1957, as above. KMM

German edition

8191 Patricia Wrightson/DIE KRUMME SCHLANGE/Jugendroman/[device]/Verlag Ludwig Auer Cassianeum/Donauworth
1964
280pp, b/w illus. throughout by Lieselotte Mende, clo., 205x130mm. IFA

8192 Patricia/Wrightson/THE BUNYIP/HOLE/[drawing]/Illustrated by Margaret Horder/Angus and Robertson/Sydney London Melbourne Wellington
1957
150pp, b/w frontis. & b/w drawings throughout, clo., dec. e/p, 200x125mm. KMM

8193 Patricia Wrightson/THE/ROCKS/OF HONEY/[drawing]/Illustrated by/Margaret Horder/Angus and Robertson
First published Sydney 1960
184pp, b/w drawings throughout, clo., dec. e/p, 210x135mm. KMM

8194 Patricia Wrightson/THE ROCKS OF HONEY/[drawing]/Illustrated by Margaret Horder/Penguin Books
Puffin Book edition, Middlesex, England, 1966
176pp, line drawings throughout, dec. wrappers, cover design by Susan Einzig, 180x110mm. KMM
Re-issued 1972, as above but cover design by Jack Newnham. KMM

8195 Patricia Wrightson/THE/FEATHER STAR/Illustrated by Noela Young/[drawing]/Hutchinson of London
1962
180pp, b/w chapter headings, tailpieces & line drawings in text throughout, dec. e/p (with reproductions of two of drawings in text), clo., 195x125mm. KMM

8196 THE FEATHER STAR/Patricia Wrightson/[drawing]/Illustrated by Noela Young/Harcourt, Brace & World, Inc., New York
1963
160pp, b/w drawings throughout, clo., 205x140mm. Unseen: IFA

German edition

8197 Patricia Wrightson/DER GEFIEDERTE STERN/Lindys Geheimnis/Rex-Verlag Luzern/Munchen
1968
170pp & 1p adv., unillus., clo., 205x135mm. LRA

8198 Patricia Wrightson/DOWN TO EARTH/Illustrated by/Margaret Horder/[extended frontispiece illustration]/[device]/Hutchinson/of/London
1965
192pp, inc. 1p author's note, b/w drawings in text, clo., 195x120mm. KMM

8199 DOWN TO EARTH/Patricia Wrightson/Illustrated by Margaret Horder/[extended frontispiece illustration]/Harcourt, Brace & World, Inc., New York
1965
222pp, b/w drawings throughout, clo., 205x140mm. Unseen: IFA

Japanese edition

8200 Hakusai Kara Kita shonen/Patorishia Raitoson saku: Kume minoru yaku: Sugimoto Kazufumi e Tokyo: Akana Shobo 1971
253pp, illus. ANL

8201 Patricia Wrightson/DOWN TO EARTH/Illustrated by/Margaret Horder/Penguin Books
Harmondsworth, Middlesex, England; first published in Puffin Books 1972
192pp, b/w extended frontis., b/w drawings throughout, pic. wrappers, cover design by Jack Newnham, 180x110mm. KMM

8202 Patricia Wrightson/"I OWN THE RACECOURSE!"/[drawing]/Hutchinson of London
Hutchinson Junior Books Ltd, 1968
159pp, b/w drawings, illus. by Margaret Horder, clo., 195x120mm. KMM
Second imp. February 1969; third imp. August 1969
Details as above. BBC

8203 Patricia Wrightson/"I OWN THE RACECOURSE!"/[drawing]/Illustrated by Margaret Horder/Penguin Books
Harmondsworth, Middlesex, England; first published in Puffin Books 1971
155pp, 4pp adv., b/w drawings in text, pic. wrappers, cover design by Richard Kennedy, 180x110mm. KMM

8204 Patricia Wrightson/"I OWN THE/RACECOURSE!"/[device]/Hutchinson Educational
London 1972
159pp, 12 b/w chapter headings, by Margaret Horder, pic. boards, 185x120mm. KMM

US edition

8205 A RACECOURSE/FOR ANDY/Patricia Wrightson/[drawing]/Illustrated by Margaret Horder/Harcourt, Brace & World, Inc. New York
1968
156pp, b/w illus. throughout, extended t.p., clo., 202x132mm. LRA

Danish edition

8206 Patricia Wrightson/BANEN ER MIN!/Oversat of Inger Bang/[device]/Jespersen og Pios Forlag/København 1969
118pp, unillus., pic. bd., 205x130mm. LRA

Italian edition

8207 PATRICIA WRIGHTSON/L'IPRODROMO/E MIO/Prefazione di Adriano Ossieini/a cura de Gaetano Sansone/Bompieni Editore
1972
180pp (inc. 2pp preface & 1p introduction), 1p contents, unillus., wrappers, 205x115mm. LRA

Japanese edition

8208 P. RAITOSON/INOKUMA/YOKO/YAKU/M. HODA/c./[illus.]
BOKU WA SHISUJO NO MOCHINUSHIDA
P. Raitoson—Inokuma Hyoronsha, 1972. ANL

8209 Patricia Wrightson/AN OLDER KIND OF MAGIC/ Illustrated by Noela Young/[drawing]/Hutchinson of Australia
Richmond, Victoria, 1972
152pp, extended b/w frontis., 12 b/w chapter headings, clo., 195x125mm. KMM
US edition
8210 AN/OLDER/KIND/OF/MAGIC/Patricia Wrightson/Illustrated by Noela Young/Harcourt Brace Jovanovich,/Inc./New York/[device]
1972
186pp (inc. 4pp epilogue), 12 b/w illus., clo., 202x130mm. KP
See also Howard, Peter & Levy, Wayne (eds). AUSTRALIAN STORY SAMPLER

WRIGHTSON, Alice Patricia (ed.)
8211 BENEATH/THE SUN/an Australian collection for/ children chosen and edited by/Patricia Wrightson/ Collins/Sydney London
1972
256pp (inc. 2pp acknowledgements), col. frontis. & 12pp col. illus., 18pp half-tone b/w photographic illus., b/w drawings in text, clo., 235x150mm. KMM
Illustrated by various artists; stories by Hesba Brinsmead, Richard Parker, Ella McFadyen, Lilith Norman, Dennis Hall, Max Fatchen, Eve Pownall, etc. Also verse & articles.

Wrigley's Rimes
8212 WRIGLEY'S/RIMES/[drawing]/"Emusing [*sic*] and/Refreshing/like/Wrigley's P.K.
Wrigley's (Aust) Ltd, Rosebery, Sydney, n.d. [192-?]
16pp, printed in col. throughout, pic. wrappers, 155x104mm. KP

WYMER, Norman
8213 Lives of Great Men and Women/Series II/GREAT/ EXPLORERS/by/Norman Wymer/Oxford University Press
First published London 1956; rpt 1962
256pp, b/w photographic illus. & maps, clo., 185x120mm. KMM
Includes Magellan, Cook, Sir John Franklin, Captain Scott, Sir John Hunt.

8214 Lives of Great Men and Women/CAPTAIN JAMES COOK/by Norman Wymer/Oxford University Press
London, n.d.
32pp, b/w frontis., 9 b/w illus. & map, limp clo., cover title, 185x125mm. HBM

Uniform with above, all KP
8215 CAPTAIN SCOTT
8216 FERDINAND MAGELLAN
8217 SIR JOHN FRANKLIN

YAGER, Julie
See Stewart, Christine & Yager, Julie

YARDLEY, Lynette
THE PIXIE O. HARRIS FAIRY BOOK. *See* Harris, P. O. & others

YARWOOD, A. T.
SAMUEL MARSDEN. *See* Great Australians

YATES, Matthew Thompson (ed.)
8218 The Graphic Story Books/GRAPHIC STORIES/ OF/OTHER LANDS./Edited by/M. T. Yates, LL.D./Editor of "Collins' Object Readers", "Nelson's New Royal Readers",/"Royal Star Readers", etc./ Coloured Illustrations./[device]/London and Glasgow:/ William Collins, Sons, & Co. Ltd./Collins' Clear-Type Press
n.d. [189-?]
256p, 16pp adv., part-col. frontis., 2 col., 5 part-col. & 19 f/p b/w illus., smaller b/w illus. in text, dec. clo., 190x130mm. KMM
Frontis., relating to Flinders, is reproduced much reduced on front cover; another b/w illus. depicts the 'Natives of Australia'. Contents include: 'Australian Natives' (6pp); 'A Gold Mine' (Victoria; 3pp); 'Caroline Islanders' (3pp); 'A Visit to New Guinea' (10pp); 'New Guinea Village' (4pp).
Another copy as above n.d. [prize label 1903], bevelled bd. KMM
8219 GRAPHIC STORIES OF/OTHER LANDS/With/ Illustrations in Colour and Black and White/London and Glasgow/Collins' Clear-type Press
n.d. [inscribed Xmas 1912]
256pp, sepia/white frontis. (G. C. Hindley) & 7 sepia plates, numerous b/w illus., dec. clo., 190x125mm. KP
8220 GRAPHIC STORIES/OF SAILORS/With Illustrations in Colour and Black and White/London and Glasgow/Collins' Clear-type Press
n.d. [prize label 1911]
256pp, sepia frontis. & 3 sepia plates & numerous b/w illus., pic. clo., bevelled edges, 190x125mm. KP
Magellan on the Pacific (10pp); Vasco da Gama (17pp); Anson's Voyage round the World (8pp); Sir Francis Drake (20pp); Captain Cook (9pp); Sir John Franklin (17pp).

A Year at Sunbury College
See The Australian Boys' Adventure Library

YENCKEN, H. B.
8221 THE SICK CHILD'S RHYME BOOK/By H. B. Yencken/An Echo of the Great/War which is/ constantly waged/against pain in all hospitals/ Published by Alexander McCubbin/One-five two Elizabeth Street
Melbourne, n.d. [1921]
38pp, unillus., t.p. & poem titles printed in two col., wrappers, 190x125mm. ANL
Verse. Based on recollections of years spent as a child in St Thomas's Hospital, London.

Yooralla Colouring Rhyme Alphabet Book
8222 YOORALLA/COLOURING/RHYME/ALPHABET/ BOOK[inset: Hundreds of/Prizes/for children of all ages/See inside for details]/[col. illus.]/1/- Entire/ Proceeds/to the Yooralla/Hospital School/for Crippled Children
n.d. [194-?]. Printed by Jorker Printing Pty Ltd, 127 Dorcas Street, South Melbourne
[12]pp, b/w illus. throughout, pic. wrappers, cover title, 327x216mm. Grant
Front wrapper only in col. Each illus., with accompanying rhyme, advertises some domestic product.

You & the Law
8223 YOU &/THE/LAW/[illus.]/PLUS/YOUR HOBBY GUIDE!
Victoria Police Dept, Sydney, 1972
64pp, b/w illus. & diagrams, pic. wrappers, cover title, 210x130mm. KP
Second half of book devoted to hobbies.

You can draw a Kangaroo
8224 YOU CAN DRAW A/KANGAROO/The Poems tell you what to do
Australian News and Information Bureau, Canberra ACT, n.d. [196-?]
[48]pp, b/w drawings of Australian animals & birds, wrappers, 210x200mm. MD

Verses by Ronald McCuaig & Isla Stuart; drawings by Joan Morrison. Rpt as a supplement to the *Australian Women's Weekly*, December 30, 1964.
Rev. & rpt 1965, 1966. KP

Young Adventurers
8225 YOUNG ADVENTURERS/Being Sixteen Tales/of Young Heroes/[4 line quote/vignette]/W. H. White & Co. Ltd/Edinburgh and London
n.d. [prize label 1907]
Sixteen stories with separate pagination bound together, each story contains 32pp
58 f/p b/w illus. (various artists), pic. clo., 185x120mm. KMM
Australian contents include: 'Left Ashore: or life at Coral Creek' by Robert Savage; 'The Three Young Pioneers' by Robert Savage. Pacific contents include: 'Among the Islands' by Joseph Milne; 'The Treasures of Shark Island' by W. T. Fyfe.

Young Adventurers Story Book
8226 YOUNG/ADVENTURERS/STORY BOOK/The Brave Tin Soldier/The Brave Little Tailor/Rip van Winkle/Dick Whittington/Tom Thumb/Aladdin/ Published by/W. H. Honey Publishing Co./31 Cunningham Street, Sydney
n.d. [copyright 1943]
64pp, b/w drawings throughout, dec. bd., 245x175mm. NSL:M

The Young Australia A.B.C.
8227 THE YOUNG/AUSTRALIA/A.B.C./Produced in Australia. Copyright
n.p., n.d. [purchased Jan. 1921 from W. Geo Smith, New & Secondhand Bookseller & Stationer, 12 Queen Victoria Buildings, George St, Sydney]
16pp, col. illus. throughout, col. pic. bd., 182x240mm. NSL:M
8228 Another copy as above, but
'Printed and Published in Australia and copyright by A. E. Weaver & Co. and C. H. Taylor, Melbourne'
n.d. [acquired 14 April 1923]
16pp, col. illus. throughout, col. pic. bd., cover title, 176x237mm. BL
Cover shows an Aborigine throwing a boomerang, and a map of Australia, inside which 2 children are dancing hand in hand with kangaroos. Black swans & wattle dec. the cover.
A is for Anzac, B for Boomerang &c.

Young Australia Speaks
8229 YOUNG/AUSTRALIA/SPEAKS/Prize-winning and Commended Poems/Young People's Poets' Competition, 1955/Arranged by/Poetry—Poets—People
Available from Miss Grace Stafford, 139 Queen St, Woollahra, Sydney, n.d.
24pp, unillus., wrappers, 210x136mm. CLRC

Young Australia's Painting Book
8230 YOUNG AUSTRALIA'S PAINTING BOOK
'On each page are one or two coloured illustrations, quite little works of art. Kate Greenaway sketches, familiar nursery figures &c and below are the outlines of the same ready for painting.' Reviewed, *Parthenon* 1899. Unseen

The Young Australian's Alphabet
See Calvert, William

The Young Emigrants
See Emigrant Tracts

Young Folks Stories
8231 YOUNG FOLKS/STORIES
No publisher's name or imprint ['W. H. Honey Publishing Co., Sydney' appears at end of one of the stories], n.d. [copyright 1944]
48pp, 6 col. illus. & b/w drawings, dec. wrappers. 246x185mm. NSL:M
Three booklets bound together: *The Golden Goose* (illustrated by L. G. Jordan); *Jack and the Beanstalk; Puss in Boots*

YOUNG, Irwin
8232 Australian Scene/THE/BLIGH/SAGA/Irwin Young/School Projects/Pty. Limited/Sydney
1966
40pp, line drawings in text, stiff dec. wrappers, 210x130mm. BBC
Brief account of career of William Bligh, the mutiny on the *Bounty*, & his governorship in New South Wales.

8233 Australian Scene/THE DAYS OF COBB & CO./ Irwin Young, M.Ed./School Projects Pty. Ltd. Sydney 1965
40pp, extended illus. t.p., line drawings in text, b/w map, stiff dec. wrappers, cover design by Lenore Andrews, 210x130mm. BBC

YOUNG, I. S. Hunter
8234 VICTORIAN/GEOGRAPHICAL AND BIOGRAPHICAL/CHARADES/Intended as/A Pastime for Winter Evenings/Combining/Amusement with Instruction./by/I. S. Hunter Young/Melbourne./ Stillwell and Knight, Collins Street East./MDCCCLXX
100pp, clo., 210x165mm. CLRC

YOUNG, Noela
8235 FLIP THE FLYING POSSUM/Story and Pictures by Noela Young/Methuen & Co. Ltd.—36 Essex Street—London—W.C.2.
1963
28pp, part-col. illus. throughout, clo., 175x240mm. BBC
• Rpt as above ,1964. KP
8236 FLIP, THE FLYING POSSUM
F. Watts, New York [1963]
Unseen

8237 MRS PADEMELON'S JOEY/Story and pictures by Noela Young/Hicks Smith & Sons Pty. Ltd. Sydney Melbourne Brisbane/in association with/Methuen & Co. Ltd. London
1967
[31]pp, part-col. illus. throughout, pic. bd., 175x235mm. BBC
8238 MRS PADEMELON'S JOEY/Story and pictures by Noela Young/Methuen & Co. Ltd 11 New Fetter Lane London EC4
Details as above. WRT

Your Friend the Postman
8239 YOUR FRIEND THE POSTMAN
P.O. Australia, 1969. Printed by The Dominion Press, North Blackburn
42pp, b/w drawings & photographic illus., pic. wrappers, 245x165mm. KP
• Rpt 1972. KMM

The Zoo Book
8240 Produced in Australia/by John Sands Pty Ltd/ THE/ZOO/BOOK/Merry go Round/A World of Education and Fun (The Book that becomes a merry-go-round)
n.d. [1942]
16pp (inc. covers on light bd., together with frame), col. illus. throughout, 180x350mm. MAC
Partly shaped book which converts into a merry-go-round. Cover title with col. pictures of different zoo animals.

A Select Bibliography of the South West Pacific Area

ABEL, Charles W.
8241 SAVAGE LIFE IN/ NEW GUINEA/The Papuan in many moods/By/Charles W. Abel/(of Kwato, New Guinea)/with seventy illustrations/London/London Missionary Society/14 Blomfield Street, E.C./Trade Agents,/Messrs Simpkin, Marshall, Hamilton, Kent & Co., Ltd.
1902
221pp, & 2 pp adv., b/w frontis. & 69 b/w photographic illus., pic. clo., 210x165mm. KP
Front cover reads 'with 64 illustrations'.
Another copy as above but 'London./London Missionary Society/16, New Bridge Street, E.C.'
n.d. [prize label 1910] KP

ABEL, Mary K.
8242 CHARLES W. ABEL/Papuan Pioneer/by/Mary K. Abel/[device]/Oliphants Ltd./London Edinburgh
1957
96pp, col. frontis. only, clo., 185x120mm. AJH

ABBOTT, J. H. M.
8243 Peeps at Many Lands/THE/ SOUTH SEAS/ (Melanesia)/By/J. H. M. Abbott/Author of/ "Tommy Cornstalk" etc./with twelve full page illustrations/in colour/by/Norman Hardy,F.R.G.S./London/Adam and Charles Black/1908
viii,83pp, & 4pp adv., col. frontis. & 7 col. plates, b/w map, clo. with col. onlay, 190x130mm. KMM
• Rpt as above, 1910. KMM
Second edition revised by Frank Fox, with 8 col. plates. Imprint: 'A. &. C. Black, Ltd./4,5 & 6 Soho Square' 1926; details as above. KMM

ADAM, R. S.
8244 Pacific Heritage Series/HEROES FROM FIJI/by/R. S. Adam/In Association with the/South Pacific Commission Literature Bureau/Macmillan & Co. Ltd./ St. Martin's Street, London/1956
47pp (inc. 1p author's preface), b/w photographic frontis. & 9 f/p b/w photographic illus., wrappers, 185x130mm. NSL:M

Adventures in the South Pacific
8245 ADVENTURES IN THE/SOUTH PACIFIC/By/ One who was born there/with illustrations by/ Lancelot Speed/London/The Religious Tract Society/4 Bouverie Street and 65 St. Paul's Churchyard
n.d. [1900?]
228pp, 1 b/w illus., clo., 185x120mm. ANL
8246 Another copy as above, n.d. [prize1919], but col. frontis., t.p. printed in red and blue, 5 b/w plates, pic. clo. with lettering on front cover & spine in gilt, g.e., 194x130mm. KP
Another copy as above but with col. frontis. & 2 b/w plates. Grant
8247 ADVENTURES IN THE/SOUTH PACIFIC/By one who was born there/with six illustrations by Lancelot Speed/Third Edition/London/The Religious Tract Society/4 Bouverie Street and 65 St. Paul's Churchyard E.C.
n.d.
228pp, 8pp adv., b/w frontis. & 5 f/p b/w illus., pic. clo., 195x130mm. KMM
In the advertisements the book is listed by the author of *Annie Carr* (*see* Australian section).
Another copy as above, but '4 Bouverie Street, E.C.4' & col. frontis. only, 'The Crown Library' [prize 1936] KMM

The Adventures of Madiboo
8248 THE/ADVENTURES/OF/MADIBOO/A Native/of the Pellew Islands/London/Printed for T. & R. Hughes, 35 Ludgate Street/1809
138pp, engraved frontis., quarter leather, 135x85mm. ANL
Sequel to *The Interesting and Affecting History of Prince Lee Boo* (Anon).

Aleck, the Last of the Mutineers
See [FISKE, Nathan Welley]

Aleck and the Mutineers of the Bounty
See [FISKE, Nathan Welley]

ALLEN, James T.
8249 THE/ STORY OF A NOBLE LIFE./JOHN G. PATON:/His Early Days and his work in the New Hebrides./By James T. Allen, Author of "Real Heroes", "Life of C. H. Spurgeon," Etc./ [illustration]/"They had built their house on the Shore"/Contents[9 chapter headings]/A.Keir Murray, Agent National Bible Society of Scotland,/62 Sutherland Street, Paddington; 108 Pitt Street Sydney, New South Wales./Price One Penny
n.d. [190-?]
16pp, b/w illus., wrappers, cover title (adv. inside front & on both sides back wrapper), 270x185mm. ANL

8250 Memoirs of Mighty Men/JOHN G. PATON/The Hero of the Wonderful/work in the New Hebrides/by James T. Allen/Author of "Real Heroes"/[device]/ Pickering & Inglis/14 Paternoster Row, London/229 Bothwell Street, Glasgow
1929
63pp, b/w photographic frontis. & 3 plates, illus. on each side, col. pic. boards, 176x117mm. ANL
Also included in *Dauntless & Daring, Mighty Missionary Heroes* [1929]

AMOS, Rev. Arthur Wesley
See 'Talatala'

ANGER, Martin
8251 DIE MEUTERER/DER BOUNTY/Eine dramatische Verkettung/von schicksalhaften Ereignissen/Von/ Martin Anger/Neuer Hanover Neuer Jugendschriften-Verlag
1969
192pp (inc. 4pp notes, Crew of the Bounty, &c.), part-col. map of route of *Bounty*, part-col. illus. in text, col. pic. boards, 208x140mm. KMM

Annie and Mital of Goroka
8252 ANNIE AND MITAL OF GOROKA/ R. H. Smith
Thomas Nelson (Australia) Ltd, 507 Little Collins St., Melbourne
1965
16pp, b/w photographs throughout, pic. wrappers, 150x180mm. KP

ARBLASTER, P. A.
THE TOLAIS. *See* Peoples of the Pacific

'ARCHER, Richard'
THE ISLAND HOME. *See* Bowman, James

AWDRY, Frances
8253 THE STORY/OF A/FELLOW-SOLDIER/By/ Frances Awdry./Second Edition./London:/ Macmillan and Co./1875/(The right of translation and reproduction is reserved)
222pp & 32pp adv., engraved frontis. & 5 f/p engravings, pic. clo., 166x112mm. ANL
Life of Bishop Patteson narrated for the young
8254 New edition, as above 1883 (with preface by Charlotte M. Yonge). RC
• Rpt 1895. Unseen

BAKER, Eleanor Zuckerman
8255 Eleanor Z. Baker/NEW GUINEA:/A Journey into Yesterday/Steck-Vaughn Company/Austin, Texas
1968
38pp, 1p introduction, part. col. map & b/w photographic illus. throughout, clo., 230x185mm. NSL:M

BALLANTYNE, Robert Michael
THE CORAL ISLAND: A Tale of the Pacific Ocean. Nelson, London 1858
The most famous of all desert island books for boys is not included in this bibliography. Though set in the South Pacific, it belongs to a wider sphere than this bibliography covers & is regarded as one of the great classic boys' books.

8256 [Decoration]/ MAN ON THE OCEAN./A Book for Boys./By R. M. Ballantyne,/Author of "The Young Fur Traders", "The Gorilla Hunters". Etc. Etc./London :/ T. Nelson and Sons, Paternoster Row;/Edinburgh; and New York./1863
viii + 408pp., col. frontis. & 7 f/p col. illus., b/w engravings, dec. clo., 175x115mm. GK
Includes The Mutiny on the Bounty, Bligh's Boat Voyage, the Wreck of the Pandora; Captain Cook; and John Williams.
8257 [Decoration'/MAN ON THE OCEAN/A Book about Boats and Ships/By/R. M. Ballantyne,/Author of 'Young Fur-Traders". "The Gorilla Hunters",/Etc. Etc./ London:/T. Nelson and Sons, Paternoster Row;/Edinburgh; and New York./1874
2pp preface & 368pp, additional engraved t.p. (with vignette 'Ancient war galleys'), engraved frontis., both printed in sepia, & 5 sepia/white engraved plates, 10 b/w engravings & others in text, clo., 167x110mm. CLRC
Plates vary and text abridged slightly from first edition.
8258 MAN ON THE OCEAN./A Book about Boats and Ships./Pictorial and Descriptive./By/R. M. Ballantyne,/and R. Richardson./with sixty-eight illustrations/London:/T. Nelson and Sons, Paternoster Row./Edinburgh; and New York./1883
278pp & 10pp adv., engraved frontis. & 13 f/p engravings, dec. clo., 175x105mm. CLRC

8259 FIGHTING THE WHALES;/or/Doings and Dangers/on a/Fishing Cruise./Vol 1/of/Ballantyne's Miscellany/with four coloured illustrations/London:/ James Nisbet & Co., 21 Berners Street./1863
124pp (inc. 1p note 'plan of this miscellany'), col. frontis. & 3 col. plates (by the author), clo. (copy seen re-bound, but others of same date in same series have 'Ballantyne's Miscellany' and title blocked in gilt in a circular decoration on front cover), 134x92mm. CLRC
8260 FIGHTING THE WHALES/or/Doings and Dangers/on a/Fishing Cruise/By R. M. Ballantyne/ Author of "The Lifeboat" "The Lighthouse" "The Iron/Horse" Under the Waves" "Rivers of Ice"/"Shifting Winds" etc. etc./London/James Nisbet & Co.,/21 Berners Street.
n.d. [1890?]
126pp, 18pp adv., b/w frontis. & 2 f/p b/w illus., pic. clo., 170x120mm. CLRC
8261 FIGHTING/THE/WHALES/By/R. M. Ballantyne/ Blackie & Son Ltd./London and Glasgow
n.d.
124pp, col. frontis. & 3 col. plates, clo. with col. onlay on front cover, dec. e/p, 178x120mm. KP
Title printed in sepia inside a dec. green border. 'Stories Old and New series'

8262 GASCOYNE,/The Sandalwood Trader;/A Tale of the Pacific/By/R. M. Ballantyne/Author of "The Young Fur Traders", "The Wild Man of the West",/Etc. etc. etc./With illustrations/London:/James Nisbet and Co., 21 Berners Street,/MDCCCLXIV
[First published December 1863]
440pp, 14pp adv., frontis. & 7 other tinted engraved illus., clo., 170x110mm. ANL
8263 GASCOYNE/THE SANDALWOOD TRADER;/A Tale of the Pacific/By R. M. Ballantyne,/Author of [6 lines of titles]/Etc. Etc./With Illustrations./London: James Nisbet & Co. Limited/21 Berners Street/(All rights reserved)
440pp, 32pp adv., b/w frontis. & 3 b/w plates, illus. by Matt B. Hewerdine, dec. clo., gilt edges, 200x140mm. GK
Numerous rpts as above with frontis. & 4, or 3 f/p b/w illus., pic. clo. KP
• Rpt 12th thousand as above. KP
• Rpt 18th thousand as above. n.d. [prize 1900], dec. clo. with gilt edges, 'The Boy's Holiday Library' with a variant b/w frontis. KP
8264 GASCOYNE/The Sandal-wood Trader/A Tale of the Pacific/By/R. M. Ballantyne/Author of 'The Coral Island' [3 more titles]/[device]/London: 38 Soho Square, W./W. & R. Chambers, Limited/Edinburgh: 339 High Street.
n.d.
329pp, b/w frontis. by W. S. Stacey, clo., 184x122mm. KP
8265 GASCOYNE/The Sandal-wood Trader/A Tale of the Pacific/By/R. M. Ballantyne/[device]/ Blackie and Son Limited/London Glasgow and Bombay
n.d.
252pp (inc.1p biographical note), 2pp adv., col. frontis. by Jas. F. Sloane, clo., 180x120mm. KP

8266 THE LIFEBOAT/A Tale/of/Coast Heroes/By/ R. M. Ballantyne,/Author of "Gascoyne", "The Wild Man of the West",/"The Coral Island", etc./with illustrations./Seventh Edition./London: /James Nisbet & Co., 21 Berners Street/1869
First pub. 1864
viii+392pp, engraved frontis. & additional engraved t.p. & 4 f/p engravings, clo. (copy seen re-bound), 164x110mm. CLRC.
Chapter 18 relates to the Victorian gold diggings.

8267 THE CANNIBAL ISLANDS/or/Captain Cook's Adventures in/The South Seas/By R. M. Ballantyne/ Author of "The Lifeboat:" "The Lighthouse:" "The Iron/Horse;" "Under the Waves;" "Rivers of Ice"/"Shifting Winds," etc. etc./London/James Nisbet & Co., Limited 21 Berners Street
n.d. [1869]
120pp (inc. 1p note), 8 + 8pp adv., additional engraved t.p., engraved frontis. (depicting the death of Cook), & 2 f/p engravings, pic. clo., 185x120mm. GK
As above but: James Nisbet & Co. 21 Berners Street 120pp, 25pp. adv., additional engraved t.p., frontis. (depicting NZ canoe), 2 f/p engravings, clo., 170x115mm. HBM

8268 THE CANNIBAL ISLANDS/or/Captain Cook's Adventures in/The South Seas/By R. M. Ballantyne/ Author of "The Lifeboat;" "The Lighthouse;" "The Iron/Horse;" "Under the Waves;" "Rivers of Ice"/"Shifting Winds," etc. etc./London/James Nisbet & Co., 21 Berners Street.
n.d.
116pp (inc. 1p note), 22pp adv., unillus., pic. clo., 185x120mm. KMM
Numerous rpts with minor variations in imprint, illus., bdg, &c.

8269 THE CANNIBAL ISLANDS/Captain Cook's Adventures in/the South Seas/by/R. M. Ballantyne/ London/James Nisbet & Co., Limited/22 [*sic*]/Berners Street/W 1.
n.d.
120pp, 8pp. adv., col. frontis. only, pic. clo., 190x120mm. The Pioneer Library. VSL

8270 Nisbet's Supplementary Readers/The Ballantyne Series/CAPTAIN COOK'S/ADVENTURES/An Account of his Voyages and/Discoveries in the South Seas/By/R. M. Ballantyne/School Edition/James Nisbet & Co., Limited/22 Berners Street, London, W.
n.d.
102pp, 2pp adv. (& 1p adv. preceding t.p.), limp clo., b/w frontis., 185x110mm. CLRC

8271 CAPTAIN COOK'S/ADVENTURES/An Account of his Voyage and/Discoveries/in the South Seas/by/ R. M. Ballantyne/London/Nisbet & Co., Ltd./22 Berners Street/W.1
n.d.
102pp, b/w frontis, dec. clo., 185x120mm. Grant
Nisbet's Supplementary Readers, The Ballantyne series
Swedish translation
KAPTEN COOK ÄFVENTYR PA SÖDERHAFSFÄRDER
1889 Örebro, Örebro Bokförlags-Aktiebolags Förlag. Unseen BP42

8272 SUNK AT SEA;/or/The Adventures of Wandering/ Will in the Pacific./By R. M. Ballantyne,/Author of "The Lifeboat"; "The Lighthouse"; "The Iron/Horse"; "Under the Waves"; "Rivers of Ice";/"Shifting Winds", Etc. Etc./London:/James Nisbet & Co., 21 Berners Street./1880 [first pub. 1869]
126pp, 3pp notes, etc., b/w frontis., additional b/w engraved t.p., 2 f/p b/w illus., clo. (with illus. pasted on front cover), 155x110mm. Ballantyne's Miscellany. RM
• Rpt as above, n.d. [prize 1896] but: 128pp, 2pp adv., b/w frontis. & 2 b/w illus. in text, pic. clo., 185x120mm. CLRC
• Rpt as above but: London/James Nisbet & Co., Limited/22 Berners Street, W.
n.d.
124pp, 14pp adv., b/w frontis. only, pic. clo., 185x124mm. KP

8273 TALES OF ADVENTURE/ON THE SEA/By R. M. Ballantyne/Selected from Ballantyne's Miscellany/With illustrations by the Author/London:/James Nisbet & Co., 21 Berners Street/1873
Consists of 4 books bound together with separate pagination: 124, 124, 124, 126pp & 24pp adv., b/w frontis. & 11 b/w engravings, clo., 170x115mm. HBM
Contents: *Fighting the Whales; Fast in the Ice; The Cannibal Islands & The Battle and the Breeze.*
The second & fourth stories do not relate to Australia or the Pacific.
• Rpt 1884 as above. KMM

8274 TALES OF ADVENTURE/ON THE OCEAN/by/ R. M. Ballantyne/London/James Nisbet & Co., Limited/22 Berners Street, W.
n.d.
366pp, 8pp adv., f/p b/w frontis., clo. (with col. illus. pasted on front cover & spine), 180x115mm. Grant
Three books bound together: *Fighting the Whales* (122pp); *Sunk at Sea* (124pp); *The Battle and the Breeze* (120pp).
Another copy as above with separate pagination 122, 124, 120pp & 8pp adv. GK

8275 TALES OF ADVENTURE/by/Flood, Field and Mountain./By R. M. Ballantyne./Selected from Ballantyne's Miscellany./With Illustrations by the Author./London:/James Nisbet & Co., 21 Berners Street/1881.
Consists of 4 books bound together with separate pagination: each 126pp, 16pp adv., b/w frontis. & 11 b/w engravings, clo., 170x115mm. RM
Contents: *Sunk at Sea; Lost in the Forest; Over the Rocky Mountains & Digging for Gold.*

8276 JARWIN AND CUFFY./A Tale/By/ R. M. Ballantyne./Author of 'The Silver Lake', 'The Red Eric' etc./[device]/With original illustralions/London:/ Frederick Warne and Co./Bedford Street, Covent Garden/and New York
n.d.
179pp & 6pp adv., b/w frontis. & 3 plates, pic. clo., 174x117mm. GK
First publ. as serial in *Old Merry's Annual, The Round Robin* 1872; first publ. in book form 1873

8277 JARWIN AND CUFFY/A Tale/By/R. M Ballantyne/Author of/"The Silver Lake", "The Red Eric"/Etc./[drawing]/London/Frederick Warne & Co./ and New York/(All rights reserved)
n.d. [190-?]
179pp, 6pp adv., b/w frontis., pic. clo., 180x115mm. KMM

8278 JARWIN AND CUFFY/A Tale/By R. M. Ballantyne/Author of 'Silver Lake' etc./[device]/ London/Frederick Warne & Co. Ltd./and New York.
n.d. [193-?]
179pp. & 1 p. adv., col. frontis. (J. M. R. Peacock), clo. 185x120mm. KP

8279 THE LONELY ISLAND/or/The Refuge of the Mutineers/By R. M. Ballantyne/Author of "Post Haste"[18 titles listed]/With illustrations/London:/ James Nisbet & Co., 21 Berners Street/1880/(All rights reserved)
viii, 413pp, 18 adv., frontis., 4 plates & additional illus. t.p., dec. clo. with title & illus. blocked in gilt on front, 180x115mm. CLRC
Author's preface dated 1880, describes how the book is founded on the mutiny of the *Bounty* & the subsequent colonizing of Pitcairn Island.
• Rpt as above tenth thousand. HBM
• Rpt as above, 2pp adv., n.d. [prize 1908], pic. clo. with design of seabirds flying against a gold sun. HBM

• Rpt as above [prize 1911] with illus. by Arthur Twidle & picture of an old seaman leaning on a cannon & two boys, blocked on front cover. KMM
• Rpt as above, prize 1912, front cover 'The Lonely Island' in gold panel & a palm tree & island scene vignette in black & grey. KP

8280 PHILOSOPHER JACK/A Tale of the Southern Seas/by R. M. Ballantyne,/Author of [14 titles listed]/ With illustrations/Twelfth thousand/London/James Nisbet & Co., Limited/21 Berners Street/ (All Rights Reserved)
n.d. [first pub. 1880]
246pp & 17pp adv., b/w frontis., 10 b/w illus., pic. clo., 190x125mm. VECD
• Rpt as above, 17th thousand. CLRC
• Rpt as above, 20th thousand. CLRC
• Rpt as above, 23rd thousand. KP

8281 THE ISLAND QUEEN;/or,/Dethroned by Fire and Water,/A tale of the Southern Hemisphere/By R. M. Ballantyne,/Author of [12 lines of titles]/with illustrations./London:/James Nisbet & Co., 21 Berners Street./1885/(All rights reserved)
261pp (inc. 1p preface), 16pp adv., b/w frontis. & 5 b/w f/p illus., pic. clo. with title in gilt panel, 184x120mm. CLRC

8282 THE ISLAND QUEEN/A Tale of the Southern Hemisphere/By R. M. Ballantyne/Author of "Fighting the Flames", 'The Lifeboat" etc./London/ James Nisbet & Co.,Limited/21 Berners Street
n.d.
261pp & 32pp adv., b/w frontis., & 5 f/p b/w illus., pic. clo., 186x120mm. KP
Numerous undated variant editions with 'Author of...(various titles listed)' some with 5, 6 illus. in addition to frontis,. & with variant pic. clo. binding. KP

8283 Nisbet's Supplementary Readers/The Ballantyne Series/THE ISLAND QUEEN/A Tale of/The Southern Hemisphere/By/R. M. Ballantyne/School Edition/ James Nisbet & Co. Limited/22 Berners Street, London, W.
n.d. [191-?]
237pp, 1p & 2pp adv., b/w frontis., limp clo., 185x120mm. KMM

BARBARY, James

8284 An Adventure in History/THE BOY/MUTINEER/ James Barbary/Illustrated by/Charlotte Mensforth/Max Parrish—London
1966
134pp, b/w chapter headings throughout, clo., 195x125mm. HBM
A story based on the mutiny on the *Bounty*

BARBOUR, Ralph Henry

See Holt, H. P.

BARKER, Victor

8285 INSIDE THE REEF/A Journey through the Fiji Islands/Victor Barker/Lansdowne
Melbourne 1968
113pp, b/w frontis., b/w photographic illus. throughout & dec. chapter headings (title on 2 pp.) clo., pic. e/p, 240x180mm. KMM

BARRADALE, V. A.

8286 PEARLS OF THE PACIFIC/Being Sketches of Missionary Life/and Work in Samoa and other/Islands in the South Seas/By/V. A. Barradale, M.A./(formerly of the Malua Institution, Samoa)/with Ninety-three Illustrations./London/London Missionary Society/16 New Bridge Street, E.C./Trade Agents/Messrs. Simpkin, Marshall. Hamilton, Kent & Co., Ltd./1907
192pp (inc. 1p dedication, 1p preface), b/w photographic frontis., 9 f/p b/w illus. & numerous illus. in text, 2 maps, pic. clo., 215x165mm. RM
Five of the illustrations are portraits or pen & ink sketches, the remainder are b/w photographs.
Doubtful children's book as is the author's *Pearls of the Southern Seas.*

BARROW, John

8287 THE MUTINY/OF THE 'BOUNTY'/John Barrow/ [drawing]/With illustrations by/Nigel Lambourne/ Blackie: London and Glasgow
1961
318pp (inc. 2pp biographical note on author, 2pp preface), 8 f/p b/w illus., clo., 195x130mm. Chosen Books series [this edition adapted for children] HBM
• Rpt n.d., as above, but with new d/w by Bernard Brett. HBM

BAYARD, Georges

8288 DIE FIDSCHI SINGEN/UM MITTERNACHT/ [device]/Verlag Aschendorff—Münster Westfalen
1964
168pp, 4pp adv., unillus., map front e/p, clo., 200x125mm. NSL:M
Book has a South Pacific setting; a German translation by Magret Borgmann of *Les Fidji Chantent à Minuit,* Paris 1960.

BERESFORD, C. E. (compiler)

8289 LEGENDS OF MANUS/collected by/C. E. Beresford/District Inspector of Schools,/New Ireland District,/Territory of Papua and New Guinea/Cover and text illustrations by/Alan Stephens/[device]/ Longmans 1965
Longmans Green, Croydon, Victoria
38pp, map frontis., 17 b/w drawings, pic. wrappers, 185x150mm. BBC

BERKELEY, Reginald & DIXON, James

8290 THE/OILSKIN PACKET/A Tale of/the Southern Seas/By/Reginald Berkeley/and/James Dixon/with illustrations by/Arch Webb/London/Duckworth & Co./3 Henrietta Street, Covent Garden, W.C.
first pub. 1917; 2nd imp. 1918
337pp & 22pp adv., col. frontis. & 4 b/w plates, clo., 183x120mm. NSL:M

BERRY, W. Grinton

8291 JAMES CHALMERS/OF NEW GUINEA/Prepared by/ W. Grinton Berry, M.A./London/The Religious Tract Society/4 Bouverie Street and 65 St. Paul's Churchyard.
n.d. [1908]
32pp, b/w illus., map, wrappers with photographic portrait, 190x125mm. ANL
Short sketch based on R. Lovett's 'James Chalmers, his Autobiography' [Price one penny, on front cover]

8292 MEN OF/FAITH AND DARING/Edited by W. Grinton Berry, M.A,/High character and heroic action are the/dominating notes of the careers/described in this volume/London/The "Boy's Own Paper" Office/4 Bouverie Street E.C.
n.d.[1910]
221pp, & 2pp adv., col. frontis., col. t.p., 2 col. plates (by Stanley Wood), pic. clo., 190x125mm. KMM
Contents include 'Tamate: and his Stirring Adventures in New Guinea' (33pp)

BINGLEY, Thomas

8293 TALES/OF/SHIPWRECKS/AND OTHER/ DISASTERS AT SEA./By Thomas Bingley/Author of 'Stories about Dogs'. 'Tales about Travellers', etc./sixth

edition/London:/W. Kent & Co., Paternoster Row/ MDCCCLXI
[first published 1839]
xvi,191pp, engraved frontis. & 7 other f/p engravings, dec. clo., 134x105mm. KMM
Eleven narratives for children including *The Mutiny of the Bounty*

BISHOP, Gilbert

8294 THE/BEACHCOMBERS;/or, Slave Trading under the Union Jack/By/Gilbert Bishop./With seven illustrations by Hume Nisbet; and a map./[quotation]/ London:/Ward & Downey,/12 York Street, Covent Garden/1889
310pp, 3pp preface, 2pp adv., b/w frontis. & 6 f/p b/w illus., pic. clo., dec. e/p, 190x125mm. NSL:M
Adventure story & a borderline children's book.

8295 THE BEACHCOMBERS/or,/Slave-trading under the Union Jack/By/Gilbert Bishop/[quotation]/ Illustrated by Hume Nisbet/London/Ward, Lock & Co., Limited/New York and Melbourne
n.d. [prize label 1904]
ix (inc. 3pp preface) 307pp, 3pp appendix & 10pp adv., b/w frontis, map, & 2 plates, clo., 190x120mm. KP

BOURNE, Lawrence R.

8296 CAPTAIN COPPERNOB/The Story of a Sailing Voyage/by/Lawrence R. Bourne/[drawing of a four-master]/Humphrey Milford Oxford University Press
1929
158pp, col. frontis. & b/w text drawings (by Savile Lumley), dec. boards, 205x155mm. NSL:M

8297 THE RADIUM CASKET/By/Lawrence R. Bourne/ [device]/Humphrey Milford/Oxford University Press London 1929
192pp col. frontis. (by Ellis Silas) & 4 f/p b/w illus., clo., 185x 120mm. NSL:M

8298 THE/FOURTH ENGINEER/By/Lawrence R. Bourne/Illustrated by Rowland Hilder/[device]/ Oxford University Press/London: Humphrey Milford
1934
287pp, col. frontis. & 6 f/p b/w illus., clo., 188x124mm. NSL:M.
Shipwreck on a Pacific island

8299 RADIUM ISLAND/By/Lawrence R. Bourne/ Illustrated by/W. Edward Wigfull/[device]/Oxford University Press/London: Humphrey Milford
1936
288pp, col. frontis. & 7 b/w plates, clo., 187x125mm. NSL:M
Adventures in the Pacific ending in Sydney; sequel to *The Radium Casket.*

[BOWMAN, James]

8300 THE ISLAND HOME; or, The Young Cast-aways; ed. by Christopher Romaunt, Boston, D. Lothrop Comp. n.d. [1851?]
xviii, 461pp, Unseen NUC
• Rpt Boston, Gould and Lincoln, 1852, 1864, Unseen NUC

8301 THE/ISLAND HOME;/or/The Young Cast-aways./Edited by Christopher Romaunt, Esq./ [quotation]/London:/T. Nelson and Sons, Paternoster Row;/and Edinburgh/MDCCCLII
333pp, additional engraved t.p., engraved frontis. & 4 other engravings, clo., 165x95mm. NSL:M
Mitchell Library note: 'The British Museum gives C. Romaunt's real name as J. F. Bowman and says he is the author, not merely the editor...The story tells of the life of an imaginary party of boys shipwrecked in the Kingsmill Is. in 1841'. The book was first published by D. Lothrop & Company in 1851. The author was a Californian journalist, and the English edition of this book provided R. M. Ballantyne with a direct inspiration for *Coral Island,* as shown by Eric Quayle in his *Ballantyne the Brave* (Hart-Davis, London, 1967).

8302 Rpt T. Nelson and Sons as above MDCCCLIV
xvi, 333pp & 16pp adv., additional engraved t.p., 4 f/p engravings, clo. with gilt decorations on front cover and spine, 170x104mm. SUA
Later Nelson editions were published anonymously, and Routledge also published a number of editions under the name of 'Richard Archer'.

8303 THE ISLAND HOME/or/The Young Castaways/A Story of Adventure in the Southern Seas/[quotation]/ Thomas Nelson and Sons/London, Edinburgh, and New York/1889
381pp (& 4pp Preface), 2pp adv., additional engraved t.p., engraved frontis. & 6 f/p engravings, pic. clo., 183x120mm. KMM
Five chapters (20–23 & 30) are omitted & different illus. have been used.
• Rpt 1898 as above. WRT

'ARCHER, Richard'

8304 THE/ISLAND HOME/or,/The Adventures/of/Six Young Crusoes/By/Richard Archer/[quotation] /Fourth Thousand./London/George Routledge and Co./Farringdon Street./1854
383pp, engraved frontis., 7 engraved plates, pic. clo. with title in gilt, 180x120mm. RM
As above, new edition 1858. Grant

8305 THE/ ISLAND HOME/or,/The Adventures/of/Six Young Crusoes/By/Richard Archer/[quote] /London/George Routledge and Sons/The Broadway, Ludgate
n.d. [1873?]
383pp, b/w frontis. & 7 engraved plates, pic. clo, with title in gilt, 180x120mm. CLRC

8306 THE ISLAND HOME; or The Young Castaways. A Story of Adventure in the Southern Seas, 1877
288pp. BMC, unseen

BOYD, Edward

8307 WANDERLUST/GOES SOUTH/By/Edward Boyd/ Drawings by Duncan/[device]/Collins/London Glasgow
Copyright 1948
256pp, b/w chapter headings, clo., 180x120mm. KMM
Boys' adventure story in the South Seas.
• Rpt as above 1949. KP
• Rpt as above 1953, Sea Gull Library. KMM
• Rpt as above n.d. [prize 1956], col. frontis. (sgd W.G.S.), cheap edition. KP

[BRETT, E. J.]

8308 DICK & HIS FRIEND DUKE;/A Tale of/Adventure in the Fiji Islands./Beautifully illustrated./Office: Harkaway House, West Harding Street, Fetter Lane,/ London, E.C.
n.d.
138pp, 10 f/p b/w illus., pic. wrappers, 255x180mm. NSL:M

8309 Complete Price Sixpence/DICK AND HIS/FRIEND DUKE/A Tale of Adventure/in the Fiji Islands/[tinted illus.]/Edwin J. Brett, Limited,/Harkaway House, 6 West Harding Street, London E.C./and all booksellers
n.d.
Details as before. CLRC

BREWSTER, H. C.

8310 PEARLS OF PAPUA/By/H. C. Brewster/ Commander, R.D.; RNR./Illustrated by G. K.

Townsend/The Endeavour Press/252 George Street, Sydney/1934
323pp, dec. t.p., b/w chapter headings, clo., dec. map e/p, 205x130mm. CLRC

BRICE, A. Montefiore
author of HEROES WHO HAVE WON THEIR CROWN; DAVID LIVINGSTONE. non-Australian, bound together with ELLIS, James J., JOHN WILLIAMS, The Martyr Missionary of Polynesia. *See* ELLIS, James J.

BROOKS, Edwy Searles
8311 THE/CANNIBAL/INVADERS!/By/Edwy Searles Brooks/[coloured illustration]/Schoolboys' Own/3.8.39 Library No. 381 4d.
Amalgamated Press, London
96pp (inc. 1p extraneous material), 2 b/w drawings, col. pic. wrappers (with adv. verso front cover, verso/recto back cover), cover title, 175x140mm. RM
The boys of St Frank's marooned on a lonely island in the South Seas.

Also by same author:
8312 THE ISLAND OF TERROR

8313 THE SCHOOLBOY CRUSOES! both RM
These two books are stories of schoolboy adventures on uncharted islands somewhere in the 'South Seas'; they are both roughly uniform with *The Cannibal Invaders.*

BROWN, Anne
8314 THE/GRASS SKIRT/By/Anne Brown/Pictures by/H. A. Brown/London/[device]/The Livingstone Press/42 Broadway S.W.1
1951
23pp, 7 col. & 1 b/w illus., dec. boards, 170x120mm. KMM
Simple missionary story of Papuan girl.

BROWN, Bill
8315 PEOPLE OF THE/MANY ISLANDS/The Challenge of the Polynesians/by Bill Brown/Maps and Diagrams by/Wes McKeown/1963 Chatto and Windus London
first pub. in 1957 by Coward-McCann Inc.
94pp, b/w photographic frontis., maps, diagrams & b/w photographic illus. throughout, clo., 209x136mm. CLRC

BROWN, Robert
8316 JACK'S YARN;/or,/Perils in the Pacific./By/Robert Brown, A.B./Author of "Spunyarn and Spindrift", etc./with thirty-two illustrations, by R. T. Prichett/[device]/London:/Griffith, Farran, Okeden & Welsh,/Successors to Newbery and Harris,/West Corner of St. Paul's Churchyard./E. P. Dutton & Co., New York./1888
345pp, b/w frontis. & 8 f/p b/w illus., b/w drawings in text, pic. clo., dec. e/p, 180x120mm. NSL:M
8317 JACK'S YARN/or/Perils in the Pacific/By/Robert Brown, A.B./Illustrated by R. T. Pritchett/London/Griffith Farran Browne & Co. Ltd/39 Charing Cross Road
n.d. [1896 re-issue?]
viii, 344pp & 32pp adv., other details as before 'Boys' Own Favourite Library'. WRT

Budge and Betty in the Pacific, [and] in the East, &c.
See [PROTHEROE, Ernest]

BULLEN, Frank T. A.
8318 A/BOUNTY BOY/Being some Adventures of a Christian/Barbarian on an unpremeditated Trip/Round the World/By/Frank T. Bullen, F.R.G.S./Author of "The Cruise of the Cachalot",/"With Christ at Sea" etc./London/Holden & Hardingham/Adelphi 1912
361 pp & 1 p pref., b/w frontis., by Harold C. Earnshaw, pic. clo., 190x123mm. HBM

BURGESS, Constance & Andrew
8319 EKUM/A Little Boy of New Guinea/By Constance Burgess/and Andrew Burgess/Illustrations by/Paul Konsterlie/Copyright 1957/Augsburg Publishing House, Minneapolis 15, Minnesota
31pp (inc. 1p suggestions to parents & teachers), 14 f/p part-col. illus., dec. wrappers, 135x100mm. ANL

BURTON, Rev. J. W.
8320 CHILDREN OF PAPUA/By/Rev. J. W. Burton, M.A./Second Edition/The Methodist Missionary Society of Australasia/139 Castlereagh Street/Sydney/1927
68pp, b/w photographic illus. throughout, dec. wrappers, 210x130mm. ANL
Didactic book about missionary work in Papua

BUTMAN, Harry R.
8321 FAR ISLANDS/being the true story of the adventures/of David Snow/by Harry R. Butman/Illustrations by Rafal Tajpowski/[drawing]/London Missionary Society/Westminster, S.W.1
First published by 'Venture', Philadelphia 1954; Published by the Livingstone Press 1956
95pp, b/w frontis. & 12 f/p b/w illus., clo., 180x120mm. KMM
The story of an American boy who goes to sea in a whaler, & during the voyage is influenced by the tale of John Williams, missionary of Erromanga, to become a missionary himself.

BYRUM, Bessie L.
8322 JOHN G. PATON/Hero of the/South Seas/By/Bessie L. Byrum/Instructor in the History of Missions/Anderson Bible School and Seminary/Gospel Trumpet Company/Anderson, Indiana
1924
127pp, b/w photographic portrait frontis., 5 f/p b/w drawings [? by author], dec. clo., 183x120mm. NSL:M

CALDWELL, John C.
8323 LET'S VISIT THE/SOUTH PACIFIC/John C. Caldwell/The John Day Company, New York
1963
96pp (inc. 1p index, 1p biographical note), b/w photographic illus. throughout, clo., 200x150mm. NSL:M

CALLOW, D. M.
8324 TOBY IN/THE SOUTH SEAS/A Story of Adventure/By/D. M. Callow/London/Sampson Low, Marston & Co., Ltd.
n.d. [192-?]
218pp & 32pp adv., b/w frontis. & 1 b/w plate, clo., 184x120mm. KMM
8325 TOBY IN THE SOUTH/SEAS/A Story of Adventure/by/D. M. Callow/Purnell
1961
176pp, b/w frontis., clo., 195x125mm. KMM

CAPPER, W. A.
THE TROBRIAND ISLANDERS. *See* Peoples of the Pacific

CAMERON, Verney Lovett
8326 THREE SAILOR BOYS/or/Adrift in the Pacific/By/Verney Lovett Cameron, C.B., D.C.L./Commander Royal Navy/Author of "Jack Hooper"."Among the Turks"/"In Savage Africa"/&c.

&c./[device]/Thomas Nelson and Sons/London Edinburgh, and New York/1903
149pp & 10pp adv., b/w frontis. & 3 plates, pic. clo., 180x117mm. KP
• Rpt as above, n.d. [1926 pencilled on fly], col. frontis. only. KP
• Rpt as above, n.d. [1933, pencilled date], no adv. KP

CAMPBELL, A. B.
8327 GREAT MOMENTS AT/SEA/Commander/A. B. Campbell, R.D./Illustrated/by Bruce Cornwell/ School Edition/J. M. Dent & Sons Ltd./10–13 Bedford St., London,W.C.2
First pub. 1957, this ed. 1961
128pp, b/w drawings in text, sim. clo., 182x120mm. KP
'Life and Enterprise' series; anthology with some Pacific episodes

CAREW, Jack
8328 THE SILVER IDOL/By/Jack Carew/Frontispiece by/V. Cooley/London/The Sheldon Press/ Northumberland Avenue, W.C.2
n.d.
160pp, 16pp adv., col. frontis., dec. clo., 190x130mm. RM
Story set in New Guinea

CARPENTER, Frances
8329 THE PACIFIC;/Its Lands/and Peoples/By/Frances Carpenter/F.R.G.S./American Book Company/New York Cincinnati Chicago Boston Atlanta Dallas San Francisco
1944
ix+502pp (inc. 17pp statistics & index), b/w photographic frontis. & illus. throughout, pic. e/p, dec. clo., 200x136mm. CLRC
An educational background book

CARRICK, Noel
8330 LET'S VISIT/NEW GUINEA/Noel Carrick/Burke London 1969
96pp, extended col. pic. frontis., col. & b/w photographic illus. throughout, b/w maps, pic. clo., 200x150mm. CLRC

CATO, Helen D.
8331 CHILDREN/OF/FIJI/By/Helen D. Cato, B.A./Methodist Overseas Missions/139 Castlereagh Street, Sydney/1955
53pp, 1p foreword by Arnold D. Hunt, 1 map, 25 b/w photographic illus., pic. wrappers, 210x140mm. KMM

CAVANNA, Betty
8332 The Around the World Today Books/TAVI/OF THE SOUTH SEAS/A Boy in Bora Bora/By Betty Cavanna/Photographs by George Russell Harrison/ Chatto & Windus, London
1965
68pp, pic. frontis. & f/p map, b/w illus. on every page, clo., pic. e/p, 225x152mm. CLRC

8333 A FIRST BOOK/FIJI/by Betty Cavanna/illustrated with photographs/Franklin Watts/London and New York
1969, This edition 1972
66pp (inc. 3pp index), f/p b/w map, b/w photographic illus., clo., 215x180mm. KMM

CHAMPION, Ivan
8334 ACROSS/NEW GUINEA/by/Ivan Champion/ Simplified and abridged by/E. P. W. Marriott/ Illustrated by/Pamela Lindsay/In association with the South Pacific/Commission Literature Bureau/ Longmans Green and Co./London Melbourne New York
1955
24pp, map frontis. & b/w illus. throughout, wrappers, 180x125mm. NSL:M
Bonito Series. Abridged from *Across New Guinea from the Fly to the Sepik.*

CHASE, Owen
8335 THE WRECK OF THE/WHALESHIP ESSEX/A Narrative Account by/Owen Chase, first mate/ Edited, and with a Prologue and Epilogue, by/Iola Haverstick/ and/Betty Shepard/Illustrated with reproductions of prints/and a map by Kathleen Voute/Constable Young Books Ltd/London
1968
128pp & 4pp glossary, portrait frontis., double-spread b/w map & contemporary engravings throughout, clo., 203x129mm. KMM

CHATTERTON, Rev. P.
THE MOTUANS. *See* Peoples of the Pacific

CLARKE, Arthur C.
8336 Arthur C. Clarke/DOLPHIN ISLAND/A Story of the People of the Sea/Victor Gollancz Limited/London
1966
First published August 1963; second impression 1966
186pp, unillus., clo., 195x125mm. KMM
A science fiction story set in the South Pacific.

CLAYTON, W.
8337 Little/People/in Far-off/Lands/SUNNY ISLANDS OF THE SOUTH SEAS/SAMOA AND FIJI/
W. Clayton B.A. No. 17
E. J. Arnold, Leeds, n.d.
32pp, b/w photographic illus. wrappers, 182x140mm. SUA

COCHRANE, Jeanie Douglas
8338 THE GOSPEL IN/THE TROPICS/Jeanie Douglas Cochrane/[col. vignette]/With Frontispiece in Colour/ [device]/London & Glasgow/Collins' Clear Type Press
n.d.
64pp, col. frontis. & t.p., boards with col. illus. on front cover, 185x117mm. KP
Last 22pp on James Calvert in Fiji

8339 MISSIONARY PIONEERS/By Jeanie Douglas Cochrane/Author of "Peerless Women" "All Aboard for Storyland".etc./Four Illustrations/Collins' Clear Type Press/London and Glasgow
n.d
240pp, adv. 16pp & 16pp, b/w frontis. & 3 b/w plates by Jas. Elder, dec. clo., 183x115mm. KP.
Contains 'John Williams', pp84–106, 'James Calvert', pp137–158; 'John C. Patteson', pp180–211.

COCHRANE, Percy Norman
8340 VAGI AND VARO/Children of Papua/Percy Cochrane/Melbourne/Oxford University Press/London Wellington New York
1961
56pp, 10 b/w chapter headings, wrappers, 195x150mm. CLRC

In same series, details as above, all CLRC
8341 CANOES by Percy Cochrane
8342 TAPA CLOTH by Peter Livingstone
8343 THE STORY OF FIJI by Kingsley Roth
8344 UNDER THE MANGO TREE by Dinah Frank

COCHRANE, Renata
8345 Life in the Pacific/HOUSES/Renata Cochrane/

Melbourne/Oxford University Press/London
Wellington New York
1961
28pp, 6 b/w drawings, stiff dec. wrappers, 185x125mm. BBC
Illustrations of houses in Papua, The Trobriand Islands, Fiji, The Gilbert Islands, The Cook Islands, Samoa, with descriptions of each

8346 Life in the Pacific/DRESS/Renata Cochrane/ Melbourne/Oxford University Press/London Wellington New York
1966
30pp, 8 b/w drawings, illus. by Anne Lissenden, dec. wrappers, 185x125mm. KMM

8347 Stories of our People: NEGODE/OF/ NABWAGETA/Renata Cochrane/Melbourne/Oxford University Press/London Wellington New York
1966
22pp, b/w photographic illus., dec. wrappers, 184x122mm. SUA

'COLLINGWOOD, Harry' [pseud. William Joseph Cosens Lancaster]

8348 THE/MISSING MERCHANTMAN,/By/Harry Collingwood/Author of "The Pirate Island" [& 2 other titles]/With Six Page Illustrations/By W. H. Overend./ [device]/London/Blackie & Son, Limited, 50 Old Bailey, E.C./Glasgow and Dublin
n.d. [prize label 1901, first published 1889]
352pp & 32pp adv., b/w frontis. & 5 b/w plates, pic. clo., 180x126mm. CLRC
Action takes place partly aboard an Australian clipper, & also at sea between the Celebes, New Guinea and Australia. This boys' adventure story writer was not an Australian.
• Rpt as above, but 'New and Cheaper edition/ London:/Blackie & Son, Limited, 49 Old Bailey, E.C./Glasgow, Edinburgh and Dublin/1893'
Details as before. ANL

8349 THE/MISSING MERCHANTMAN/By/Harry Collingwood/Author of [3 titles]/With a Frontispiece by W. H. Overend/Blackie & Son Limited/London and Glasgow
n.d. [re-issue 1939]
352pp, b/w frontis. only, dec clo., 180x120mm. RM

8350 THE PIRATE ISLAND:/A Story of/the South Pacific./By/Harry Collingwood,/Author of...&c./with eight full-page illustrations by C. J. Staniland and/J. R. Wells./[publisher's device]/London:/Blackie & Son, 49 & 50 Old Bailey, E.C.1/Glasgow, Edinburgh, and Dublin./1885
339pp, 8 f/p black & tinted plates., clo., 185x118mm. QSL

8351 THE PIRATE ISLAND;/A Story of/The South Pacific./By/ Harry Collingwood,/Author of "The Log of the Flying Fish" "The Rover's Secret"/The Missing Merchantman",&c./With eight full-page illustrations by C. J. Staniland and/J. R. Wells./[device]/London:/ Blackie & Son, Limited,49 Old Bailey, E.C./Glasgow, Edinburgh and Dublin.
n.d. [1893?]
339pp +32pp adv., engraved frontis. & 7 f/p engravings, pic. clo. with one illus. repro. in gilt on front cover & another on spine with title in gilt, 185x120mm. ANL

8352 THE PIRATE ISLAND/A Story of/the Pacific/By/ Harry Collingwood/Author of "The Log of the Flying Fish", "The Rover's Secret", "The Missing/ Merchantman", "The Log of a Privateersman" &c./With six page illustrations by C. J. Staniland and J. R. Wells./New edition/Blackie and Son Limited/ London Glasgow and Dublin/1902
[prize label Xmas 1901]
339pp, 32pp adv., b/w frontis. & 5 f/p b/w illus., pic. clo., 190x120mm. RM
Another copy as above, n.d., no 'new edition'. KP

8353 THE PIRATE ISLAND/A Story of the South Pacific/By/Harry Collingwood/Author of "The Log of the Flying Fish", "The Missing Merchantman",/"The Strange Adventures of Eric Blackburn", &c./Illustrated by/C. J. Staniland and J. R. Wells./Blackie and Son Limited/London Glasgow and Bombay
n.d.
339pp, b/w frontis. & 5 f/p b/w illus., pic. clo., 185x125mm. RM
• Rpt as above n.d. [193-?] Zenith Library
318pp, b/w frontis. & 2 b/w plates, clo., 184x120mm. KP

8354 FOR TREASURE/BOUND/By/Harry Collingwood/Author of/"The Log of a Privateersman"etc./[vignette]/Griffith Farran Browne & Co.,Limited/35 Bow Street, Covent Garden/London
n.d.[? first ed. 1897]
395pp, b/w frontis. & 7 b/w plates (some sgd 'Acme') pic. clo., g.e., 197x130mm. KP

8355 FOR TREASURE/BOUND/By/Harry Collingwood/Author of "A Pirate of the Caribees" etc. etc./[drawing]/Griffith Farran Browne & Co. Limited/ 35 Bow Street, Covent Garden/London
n.d. [school prize 1912]
395pp, b/w frontis. & 3 f/p b/w illus., dec. clo., 190x130mm. KMM
• Rpt as above but illus. printed in blue; clo., with title in gilt, & vignette of ship in gilt, g.e. KP
• Rpt as above, but frontis. only, & variant cover design. KP

8356 THE CASTAWAYS/An Ocean Romance/By/Harry Collingwood/Author of "An Ocean Chase" "The Log of the 'Flying Fish'"/"For Treasure Bound" "Jack Beresford's Yarn"/Etc. Etc./Illustrated by Percy F. S. Spence/Griffith Farran Browne, & Co. Limited/35 Bow Street, Covent Garden/London
n.d. [189-?]
320pp, b/w frontis. & 7 f/p b/w illus., dec. clo., 190x130mm. KMM
An adventure story, part of the action of which takes place in the South Pacific.
• Rpt as above [prize label 1900], pic. clo. elaborately dec. in gilt on front cover & spine, bevelled boards, g.e. KP

8357 THE/CASTAWAYS/by/Harry Collingwood/ Humphrey Milford/Oxford University/Press—London
n.d.
320pp, dec. t.p., col. frontis. only, clo., dec. e/p, 165x110mm. KMM
The Boy's Pocket Library series

8358 THE WRECK OF/THE ANDROMEDA/by/Harry Collingwood/Author of/"In Search of Eldorado", "The Cruise of the Flying-Fish",/"Under a Meteor Flag"/London/Sampson Low, Marston & Co., Ltd.
n.d. [inscribed 1932]
288pp, 32pp adv., b/w frontis. & 7 b/w illus. in text, boards, 180x120mm. Grant
Adventure story of the wreck of a ship bound from America to Australia in 1914 just after war had been declared, & of the survivors' experiences on a Pacific island.
• Rpt as above but different frontis. and 1 plate only. KP

8359 THE FIRST MATE/The Story of a Strange Cruise/ By/ Harry Collingwood/Author of /"The Missing Merchantman" "The Pirate Island" &c.&c./Illustrated by E. S. Hodgson/Blackie & Son Limited/London and Glasgow
n.d. [1st pub. 1914, this edition 193-? Zenith Library]
288pp, b/w frontis. & 2 b/w plates, clo., 180x120mm. KP

8360 A STRANGE CRUISE/A Tale of Piracy on the/ High Seas/By/Harry Collingwood/Author of "Two Gallant Sons of Devon"/"A Middy of the King" [&c. 2 more titles]/Illustrated by Archibald Webb/Blackie and Son Limited/London Glasgow and Bombay
n..d. [1912?]
296pp, sepia/white frontis. & 5 plates, pic. clo., 185x120mm. KP
Adventure, shipwreck & marooning of young hero on a south Pacific island west of Samoa

8361 OVERDUE/ Or, The Strange Story of a Missing Ship/By/ Harry Collingwood/Author of [5 titles]/ Illustrated by W. H. Holloway/Blackie and Son Limited/London Glasgow and Bombay/1911
[first edition]
287pp, b/w frontis. & 5 b/w plates, pic. clo., 185x125mm. KMM
Adventures on a voyage from Liverpool to Sydney

8362 OVERDUE/The Story of a Missing Ship/By/ Harry Collingwood/Author of [3 titles]/ Blackie & Son Limited/London and Glasgow
n.d. [194-?]
287pp b/w frontis. only, clo., 180x120mm. KP

8363 THE/STRANGE ADVENTURES/OF ERIC BLACKBURN/By/ Harry Collingwood/Author of "The Log of the Flying Fish"/"A Chinese Command"/&c./Illustrated by C. M. Padday, R.O.I./Blackie & Son Limited/ London and Glasgow
n.d. [prize label 1933]
317pp & 2pp adv., b/w frontis, 2 b/w plates & 1 b/w map, pic. clo., 180x120mm. KP
Hero shipwrecked between Cape Town and Melbourne, eventually arriving in Sydney

8364 TURNED ADRIFT/An Adventurous Voyage/By/ Harry Collingwood/Author of [4 titles listed]/ Illustrated by Edward S. Hodgson/Blackie and Son Limited/London Glasgow and Bombay
n.d. [prize label 1914]
295pp, sepia frontis. & 5 sepia plates, pic. clo., 182x125mm. ANL
Mutiny, the hazards of being turned adrift and landing on a South Pacific island

COOK, Boris & JOHNSON, Patricia

8365 Boris Cook and Patricia Johnson/MAIA/GOES TO SCHOOL/The Story of a litle girl in New Guinea/ Angus and Robertson
Sydney 1968
30pp (inc. 1p biographical note), b/w photographic illus. throughout with slight text, pic. clo., col. e/p, 245x180mm. BBC
Note by Sylvia Lawson on Boris Cook who provided the illustrations.

COOMBE, Florence

8366 SCHOOL-DAYS/IN NORFOLK ISLAND/By/ Florence Coombe/Illustrated from photographs/By Beattie, Hobart/Published under the direction of the tract/committee for the Melanesian Mission/London/ Society for Promoting Christian Knowledge/ Northumberland Avenue, W.C.; 43 Queen Victoria Street, E.C./Brighton: 129 North Street/New York: E. S. Gorham/1909
63pp, b/w frontis. & 4 f/p b/w photographs, clo., 168x118mm. KMM

CORBIN, Iris

8367 KUMA OF THE/SOUTH SEAS/By/Iris Corbin, B.A./Author of "Wong the Patriot"/London: The R.T.S. Office/4 Bouverie Street, E.C.4
n.d.
95pp, b/w frontis., clo., 185x120mm. NSL:M
The story is set in New Guinea.

8368 ALL ABOARD! A Voyage in the Children's Missionary steamship *John Williams IV* described in a series of letters. By/I. A. Corbin, B.A./London Missionary Society/43 Broadway, Westminster, S.W.1/1931
155pp, b/w photographic portrait frontis., 30 b/w photographic illus. & drawings & map in text, boards, pic. e/ps, 184x114mm. ANL
• Rpt as above, but after author's name '[device]/ London:/The Livingstone Press,/Livingstone House, Broadway, S.W.1'
n.d.; details as before. SUA

8369 TAMATE/THE FEARLESS/By/Iris A.Corbin/ London/Independent Press, Ltd./Memorial Hall , E.C.4
1932
63pp, b/w map frontis., 2 b/w drawings in text, wrappers with portrait of James Chalmers on front cover, 178x115mm. ANL

COUSINS, George

8370 THE STORY OF THE SOUTH SEAS/Written for Young People/By/George Cousins/Editorial Secretary and Assistant Foreign Secretary of the London Missionary Society/Author of "From Island to Island in the South Seas"/with maps and many illustrations/ Special Centenary Gift and New Year Offering Edition/London/London Missionary Society/14, Blomfield Street, E.C./John Snow & Co., 2 Ivy Lane, Paternoster Row, E.C./1894
211pp, 1p preface, 4pp adv., b/w frontis. & 51 b/w illus., 5 maps, dec. clo., 210x165mm. KMM
History of the work of the Christian missionaries in the South Pacific

COWAN, James

8371 Whitcombe's Story Books [No. 426]/FAIRY TALES FROM/THE SOUTH SEAS/Little Legends of some Pacific Islands/By James Cowan/(For ages 9 to 10 years)/[drawing]/Whitcombe & Tombs Limited/ Auckland, Christchurch, Dunedin, Wellington, N.Z./Melbourne and London
n.d. [193-?]
66pp (inc. 4pp notes & questions), b/w photographic frontis. & 16 b/w illus. in text, pic. wrappers, cover design by Manie Inglis, 185x125mm. KMM
See McLaren 426

CRISP, Frank

8372 THE/HAUNTED/REEF/Frank Crisp/Illustrated by/A. K. Lee/The Bodley Head/London
First published 1950
231pp, b/w frontis., b/w chapter headings, clo., dec. e/p, 195x130mm. BBC

8373 Frank Crisp/THE HAUNTED/REEF/Illustrated by/ A. K. Lee/Penguin Books
London 1957
220pp, b/w frontis, b/w chapter headings, dec. wrappers, 180x110mm. KMM A Puffin Book
Adventure story based on diving for treasure in the South Pacific, with slight references to Australia

8374 A Dirk Rogers Adventure/THE DEMON/WRECK/ by/Frank Crisp/London/Hodder and Stoughton
1958
160pp, col. frontis. only, clo., 185x120mm. KMM
Action takes place on an island in eastern Indonesia.

8375 Frank Crisp/THE CORAL WRECK/A Dirk Rogers Adventure/Jonathan Cape/Thirty Bedford Square/ London
1964
187pp, b/w frontis. & 9 b/w illus. by Pat Williams, clo., 180x120mm. KMM
Adventure story set in the Philippines & Celebes

8376 THE SANGUMAN/by/Frank Crisp/A Dirk Rogers' Adventure/Illustrated by/Patrick Williams/Jonathan Cape/Thirty Bedford Square/London
1965
160pp, 5 f/p b/w illus. & b/w drawings, clo., 180x120mm. KMM
Adventure story set on an island off the north New Guinea coast

CROCKER, Rev. Henry (ed.)
8377 ADVENTURES IN NEW GUINEA/The narrative of Louis Trégance/A French Sailor/Nine Years in captivity among the Orangwoks/a tribe in the interior of New Guinea/Edited, and with an introduction by/ The Rev. Henry Crocker/incumbent of St. Anne's, Weremai, N.Z./London:/Sampson Low, Marston, Searle & Rivington/Crown Buildings, 188 Fleet Street./ 1876/All rights reserved)
viii, 238pp (inc. 6pp introduction, etc.), 32pp adv., b/w frontis. & 3 b/w plates, b/w map, pic. clo., 180x120mm. ANL
• Rpt as above, but 'New and cheaper edition/London/ Sampson Low, Marston, Searle & Rivington/Limited/ St. Dunstan's House/Fetter Lane, Fleet Street, E.C./1888/(All rights reserved)
Details as above. KMM
• Rpt as above 1892. KP

CROCOMBE, Marjorie
THE COOK ISLANDERS. *See* Peoples of the Pacific

CROMBIE, Isabel
8378 My Home No.11/MY HOME IN/FIJI/[drawing]/ Isabel Crombie
Longmans Green & Co. Ltd., London and Harlow, first pub. 1959; 5th imp. 1968
18pp, col. illus. throughout, col. pic. boards, cover title, 150x122mm. CLRC

CRUTWELL, N. E. G.
8379 PETER POSARO/A Papuan's Progress/by/N. E. G. Cruttwell/Illustrated by Jennifer Murray
Published by the Australian Board of Missions 1959
63pp (inc. 2pp preface), b/w illus., stiff pic. wrappers, 180x115mm. ANL

CURTIS, Nancy
8380 LITTLE CHIMBU:/[col. drawing]/story and drawings by/Nancy Curtis/Pacific Publications/ Sydney
1966
32pp, col. & b/w drawings, pic. boards, 254x195mm. KMM
• Rpt 1968 as above. KP
• Rpt 1970 as above. KP
• Rpt 1972 as above. KP

8381 FIJI/JOHNNY/story and drawings by/Nancy Curtis/Pacific Publications
Sydney 1967
[38]pp, part-col. illus. t.p., b/w & part. col. illus. throughout, pic. boards, 250x195mm. ANL

8382 another Little Chimbu adventure story/LITTLE BALUS/story and drawings by/Nancy Curtis/Pacific Publications/Sydney, N.S.W.
1969
38pp, col. & b/w drawings throughout, col. illus. t.p., pic. boards, 250x195mm. ANL
The author, a New Zealander, has lived in New Guinea since 1966.

CULLEN, A. H.
8383 BLAZING THE TRAIL/ Some L.M.S. Pioneers of 1816/By/A. H. Cullen/of Heaton Mersey, Manchester/with thirty-four illustrations (four coloured)/and four maps/London/London Missionary Society/16 New Bridge Street/1916
192pp (inc. 2pp preface, 4pp index), col. illus. by Ernest Prater, others b/w & photographic, map e/p, dec. clo., 196x126mm. KP

DANIEL, Elizabeth
8384 Stories of our People/MOLU OF MENDI/Elizabeth Daniel/Melbourne/Oxford University Press/London Wellington New York
1961
16pp, 5 b/w illus., dec. wrappers, 185x120mm. KMM
The story of a child of the Mendi tribe of Papuans.

DANIELSSON, Bengt
8385 Bengt Danielsson/VILLERVALLES OKENAVENTYR/[drawing]/Stockholm. Saxon & Lindströms Förlag.
1958
223pp, 9 f/p b/w drawings & text drawings throughout by Pierre Heyman, pic. boards, pic. map e/p, 200x130mm ANL

8386 Bengt Danielsson/TERRY IN/THE SOUTH SEAS/ Translated from the Swedish/By Reginald Spink/ Illustrations by/Pierre Heyman/Ruskin House/George Allen & Unwin Ltd./Museum Street London
First published in Great Britain in 1959
216pp, 10 f/p b/w illus. & b/w drawings in text, clo., 215x140mm. BBC
US edition
8387 Chicago, Reilly & Lee 1959. Unseen

8388 Bengt Danielsson/TERRY'S KON-TIKI ADVENTURE/Translated from the Swedish/By Roy Duffel/Illustrated by/Liliane and Paul Risch/London/ George Allen & Unwin Ltd./Ruskin House Museum Street
1965
192pp, 9 f/p b/w drawings, boards, 210x135mm. KMM

DARLING, Lois and Louis
8389 CORAL REEFS/Written and Illustrated by/Lois and Louis Darling/London/Methuen & Co. Ltd.
1965
80pp, double-spread illus. t.p., b/w drawings by authors throughout, clo., 230x155mm. KMM

DAVID, Mrs Edgeworth [Margaret Harriette, née Thomson]
8390 FUNAFUTI/or Three Months on a Coral/Island: An Unscientific Account of a Scientific/Expedition/by Mrs. Edgeworth David/With Portraits, Map, and Illustrations/(School Edition; Abridged)/Sir Isaac Pitman & Sons, Ltd./London. Bath. New York/1913
150pp, 2pp introduction, 2pp glossary, b/w photographic portrait frontis., 5 b/w photographic illus. in text, b/w map, clo., 180x120mm. Grant

DAUNCEY, H. M.
8391 PAPUAN PICTURES/By/H. M. Dauncey/(Of Delena, Papua)/With sixty-three illustrations from/ photographs by the author/London/London Missionary Society/16, New Bridge Street/1913
184pp, col. frontis. & 3 f/p col. illus., 59 b/w photographic illus., clo. (with col. illus. pasted on front cover), (includes presentation page from LMS), 195x130mm. KMM
Another copy with gilt lettering and bevelled boards. KP

DAVIDSON, Norman J.
8392 PATTESON/OF THE/SOUTH SEA ISLANDS/the story of the first bishop of Melanesia and his /heroic work amongst the cannibal islanders & his /Tragic death, told for boys and girls/by /N. J. Davidson, B.A./Author of/"Pennell of the Indian Frontier". "Moffat of Africa". "Modern Travel" &c. &c./With illustrations/London/Seeley, Service & Co. Limited/196 Shaftesbury Avenue/1931
64pp, b/w frontis. & 3 f/p illus., col. pic. boards, 197x125mm. ANL

DAVIS, Charles M.
8393 SOUTH/SEA/ISLANDS/by Dr. Charles M. Davis/ University of Michigan/[drawing]/Nelson Doubleday Inc. Garden City, N.Y.
copyright 1957, 1962
63pp (inc. 2pp geographical list & biography of author), part col. illus., b/w photographic illus. & 2 maps, 25 col. photographic illus. pasted in, col. pic. wrappers, 210x135mm. KMM
American Geographical Society, Around the World Program

DAY, A. Grove
8394 THEY PEOPLED THE PACIFIC/by A. Grove Day/ [drawing]/Illustrated by George Wilson /Duell,Sloan and Pearce/New York
1964
180pp, b/w illus., map e/p, clo., 202x137mm. SUA

8395 EXPLORERS OF THE PACIFIC/by/A. Grove Day/ Duell,Sloan and Pearce/New York
1966
x+180pp, b/w text illus. throughout, maps, & dec. map e/p, boards, with clo. spine, 200x135mm. NSL:M

8396 ADVENTURERS/OF THE/PACIFIC/by A. Grove Day/Foreword by/James A. Michener/ Meredith Press New York
1969
xvi, 303pp (inc. 11pp index, 4pp bibliography), unillus., clo., 295x140mm. SUA
Not specifically written for children; includes chapters on Ned Kelly, Bushrangers of Van Diemen's Land, Dampier, John Macarthur, &c.

The Dayspring for the New Hebrides
8397 THE/DAYSPRING/FOR/THE NEW HEBRIDES./A Little Ship to wait on Him, Mark iii, 9,/Tongariki and Adjacent islands. New Hebrides./ London: and Derby
n.d.[1895]
16pp, 2 pp map of New Hebrides, text illus., stiff dec. wrappers, cover title, 185x120mm. ANL
A history of the first & second missionary vessels each named *Day Spring.* A large portion of the money required for the building of these ships was raised in Australia, particularly from the Sunday School children. For threepence a year the children were made shareholders in the mission ship.

Deadwood Dick Afloat
8398 The Boys' First-Rate Pocket Library./ DEADWOOD/DICK AFLOAT/[coloured illustration]/ or/The Prisoner/of the/Weird Isles./No. 91 [caption] 1d./Aldine Publishing Co., 9 Red Lion Court, Fleet Street, London, E.C.
n.d.
32pp, unillus., col. pic. wrappers, cover title, 215x140mm. RM
Adventure story set in the Pacific, arising from the discovery of a message in a bottle found floating in Auckland harbour

DEANE, Rev. W.
8399 THE STRANGE/ADVENTURES/OF A WHALE'S/TOOTH/A Missionary Story of Fiji for/ young people and/others/by/Rev. W. Deane, M.A., B.D./obtainable at/The Methodist Book Depot/381 George St. Sydney
1919
169pp (inc. 1p foreword & 1p author's note), 3pp adv., b/w frontis., 14 b/w photographic illus., clo., 180x120mm. NSL:M

DEANE, Wallace
8400 THREE COMRADES IN FIJI/by/Wallace Deane/ London/R. T. S.—Lutterworth Press/4 Bouverie Street, E.C.4
1939
256pp, col. frontis. only, clo., 185x115mm. CLRC

DEBENHAM, Mary H.
8401 PATTESON OF/THE ISLES/ By/ Mary H. Debenham/ with four illustrations by/ T. H. Robinson/and other pictures and map/Humphrey Milford/Oxford UniversityPress/London Edinburgh Glasgow Copenhagen/New York Toronto Melbourne Cape Town/Bombay Calcutta Madras Shanghai Peking/1921
160pp b/w frontis., 8 f/p b/w illus. & 1 map, clo., 183x120mm. KMM

DECK, Catherine M. A.
8402 A SON OF THE SOLOMONS/By/Catherine M. A. Deck/of the/South Sea Evangelical Mission/ [device]/ S. John Bacon/(Marshall, Morgan & Scott Ltd.). Southern Cross Chambers, 217 Collins Street./ Melbourne
1944
32pp, b/w frontis. & 5 f/p b/w photographic illus., stiff pic. wrappers, 178x114mm. ANL

DÉNÉNÉ, Judith B.
THE PEOPLE OF NEW CALEDONIA. *See* Peoples of the Pacific

DICKER, Gordon
8403 CHILDREN/ OF TIMOR/By/Gordon Dicker/ Drawings by/Beverley Dunphy/Published by/the Committee for Promotion and Literature/Head Office:/ Methodist Overseas Missions/139 Castlereagh Street/ Sydney
1960
64pp, b/w drawings, dec. wrappers, 215x140mm. KP

DIXON, James
THE OILSKIN PACKET. *See* Berkeley, Reginald & Dixon, James

DOWNS, Evelyn A.
8404 DAUGHTERS OF THE/ISLANDS/by/Evelyn A. Downs/Author of *The Bible as Drama,* etc./Foreword/ by Dr. Basil Yeaxlee, C.C., M.A., B.Litt./[device]/ London/The Livingstone Press, 42 Broadway, Westminster,S.W.1
n.d. [foreword dated 1944]

78pp, col. frontis. & 1 col. illus., b/w photographic illus. throughout, boards, with clo. spine, 240x175mm. CLRC
The cover design is an exact facsimile of part of a piece of bark cloth designed & made by a schoolgirl of Papauta
8405 Another copy as above but, The Religious Education Press, Limited/Wellington Surrey. KP

DUNN, J. Allan
8406 JIM MORSE/SOUTH SEA TRADER/By/J. Allan Dunn/Illustrated/ [device]/Boston/Small, Maynard & Company/Publishers
1919
239pp, b/w frontis. only, clo., 185x125mm. RM
8407 JIM MORSE/South Sea Trader/By J. Allan Dunn/ Thomas Nelson and Sons, Ltd./London, Edinburgh, New York,/Toronto and Paris
n.d. [inscribed Christmas 1929]
viii, 234pp (inc. 1p dedication), b/w frontis. & 3 b/w plates, dec. clo., 180x120mm. KP
8408 JIM MORSE/SOUTH SEA TRADER/By/J. Allan Dunn/Thomas Nelson and Sons, Ltd./London, Edinburgh, New York/Toronto and Paris
n.d.
viii, 239pp, 9pp adv., b/w frontis. & 3 b/w plates, pic. clo., 180x120mm. RM
The Triumph series
Another copy as above, prize 1938. KP

DWIGHT, E. W.
8409 MEMOIR/OF/HENRY OBOOKIAH./A native of the/Sandwich Islands,/who died at Cornwall, Connecticut,/ February 17, 1818, aged 26./Revised Edition/By Rev. E. W. Dwight,/First Instructor of the "Foreign Mission School"/Published by/The American Tract Society./150 Nassau-Street, New-York/
D. Fanshaw, Printer.
n.d.
124pp, engraved portrait frontis., marbled boards with leather spine, 148x90mm. SUA

DWYER, James Francis
8410 The International/Adventure Library/[device]/The Three Owls Edition/THE/WHITE WATERFALL/An Adventure Story/By/James Francis Dwyer/W. R. Caldwell & Co./New York
1912
288pp, 3pp preface, b/w frontis. & 2 f/p b/w illus., b/w illus. in text, clo., 185x125mm. ANL
Adventure story with a Pacific setting

EADY, K. M.
8411 THE SECRET/OF/THE FIRE MOUNTAIN/A Tale of the Solomon Islands/by/K. M. Eady/Author of/"A Long Chase" "The Heir of Sandyscombe"/"The Lifting of the Shadow" Etc./With Illustrations by A. Pearse/ London:/Andrew Melrose/16 Pilgrim Street, E.C.
n.d. [inscribed 1897]
304pp, 6pp adv., b/w frontis. & 8 f/p b/w illus., pic. clo., 185x130mm. Grant
8412 Second edition, as above. KMM

Eagle Omnibus
8413 EAGLE OMNIBUS/Number One/Edinburgh House Press/2 Eaton Gate, London, S.W.1
4th imp. 1956
184pp, unillus., clo., 184x120mm. KP
On front cover, 'Unarmed among Outlaws' & other true stories
Includes: Basil Mathews, 'If I had a ship' & Cecil Northcott, 'My Friends the Cannibals'.
8414 EAGLE OMNIBUS/Number Three/[device]/ London/The Livingstone Press/Livingstone House/ Broadway, Westminster S.W.1/1945
184pp, unillus., boards, 180x120mm. KMM
Contains: 'The Bricklayer and the King', the life of Henry Nott of the London Missionary Society's mission to Tahiti (30pp).
8415 EAGLE/OMNIBUS/Number Seven/London/ Edinburgh House Press/2 Eaton Gate, S.W.1/1948
184pp, unillus., boards, 180x120mm. KMM
Contains an abridgement of *Send me Among Savages*, by Cecil Northcott, concerning James Chalmers of New Guinea (29pp).

EASTMAN, G. H.
8416 CORAL ISLAND FOLK/Stories and Pictures/From the South Sea Islands/By/G. H. Eastman/of the London Missionary Society/Gilbert Islands, Central Pacific/1925/London Missionary Society/48 Broadway, Westminster, S.W.1.
153pp (inc. 1p author's foreword & 3pp list (principal ships of the London Missionary Society), 2pp adv., b/w frontis., 3 b/w maps & 26 b/w illus., dec. clo., 185x120mm. KP

8417 VOYAGES ALL!/The Story of the Ships/of the/ London Missionary Society/By/G. H. Eastman/of the Gilbert Islands/The London Missionary Society,/250, Pitt Street, Sydney, N.S.W./1947
64pp, b/w frontis. & b/w drawings in text, clo., 185x120mm. KMM
Another copy as above, but '/the Livingstone Press,/ Livingstone House,/42 Broadway, Westminster, S.W.1/1947'. KP

EDEN, Charles H.
8418 RALPH SOMERVILLE/or/A Midshipman's Adventures in the/Pacific Ocean/By/Charles H. Eden/ Author of "The Twin Brothers of Elfredale" "Australia's/ Heroes" "The Fortunes of the Fletchers,"etc./[device]/London:/Marcus Ward & Co., 67 Chandos Street/and Royal Ulster Works, Belfast/ 1876
316pp & 14pp adv., col. frontis. & additional col. dec. t.p., & 4 f/p b/w engravings, pic. clo., 180x120mm. CLRC

EDMONDS, I. G.
8419 THE/BOUNTY'S BOY/I. G. Edmonds/Illustrated by Gil Walker/[drawing]/The Bobbs-Merrill Company, Inc./a subsidiary of Howard W. Sams & Co., Inc./ Publishers Indianapolis New York
1962
189pp (inc. 5pp foreword), double-spread b/w map (repeated on e/p) & 8 double-spread b/w illus., b/w drawings in text, boards (clo. spine), 210x135mm. HBM
A tale based on the experiences of a boy aboard H.M.S. *Bounty* under the command of Lieutenant Bligh
8420 THE/BOUNTY'S BOY/I. G. Edmonds/Illustrated by Gil Walker/[drawing]/London/Dennis Dobson
Copyright 1962; first published in Great Britain 1964
189pp (inc. 5pp foreword), b/w frontis., double-spread b/w map & double-spread b/w illus., b/w drawings in text, clo., 205x130mm. HBM

EDWARDS, E. D.
8421 TIM PILI/THE GECKO/A Story from the South Seas/By/E. D. Edwards/London/[device]/The Livingstone Press/42 Broadway, Westminster, S.W.1
n.d. [194-?]
31pp, 13 b/w illus. in text signed 'J.C.', pic. wrappers, 155x100mm. KMM
Story of a Samoan gecko

ELIAS, Frank
8422 A/BOY'S ADVENTURES/IN THE/SOUTH SEAS/

or/With Williams to Erromanga/By/Frank Elias/Author of/"First Voyages retold from Hakluyt",/"Heaven and the Sea", Etc./London/The Religious Tract Society/4 Bouverie Street and 65 St Paul's Churchyard
n.d.
270pp, 2pp adv., col. frontis. & 1 f/p col. illus., 8 b/w plates, pic. clo., 195x130mm. RM
2nd edition as above, illus. by Ernest Prater. KMM

ELIOTT, Lydia S.
8423 THE/COCONUT ISLAND TWINS/by/Lydia S. Eliott/[device]/Lutterworth Press/London
1956
96pp, col. frontis. only, clo., 180x120mm. KMM
• Rpt as above, 2nd imp. 1958, 3rd 1962, 4th 1967. All KP

CANOES AND COCONUTS
Unseen: Advertisement in Downie's *Skip of the Islands*

ELLIS, Edward S.
8424 LOST IN SAMOA:/A Tale of Adventure in the/Navigator Islands./By/E. S. Ellis/Author of "Boys Pioneer Series", "Great River Series"/Etc. Etc. Etc./With eight original illustrations by Gordon Browne/Cassell & Company, Limited:/London, Paris & Melbourne/1890/All rights reserved.
248pp (inc. 3pp introduction), 16pp adv., b/w frontis. & 7 b/w plates, pic. clo., 185x120mm. KMM
The author explains in the introduction that the story is based on the experiences of many escaped convicts & ticket-of-leave men from Australia who came to settle various Pacific islands during the nineteenth century. The author was an American writer whose books became very popular in English editions also.
• Rpt 1903 as above but with only 4 plates. KP
8425 LOST IN SAMOA/A Tale of Adventure in the/Navigator Islands/By/Edward S. Ellis/Author of "From the Throttle to the President's Chair", "Tad;/or Getting even with Him", "Lost in the Wilds", "Up the/Tapjos", "Down the Mississippi", Etc./With Illustrations/New York/The Mershon Company/Publishers.
1891
248pp (inc. 3pp introduction), b/w frontis. & 6 f/p b/w illus., pic. clo., 190x125mm. RM
8426 LOST IN SAMOA/A Tale of Adventure in/the Navigator Islands/By/Edward S. Ellis/Author of "River and Jungle", "The Hunt of the White Elephant",/"Fire, Snow and Water", etc./With four illustrations by/Gordon Browne/Eleventh thousand/Cassell and Company, Ltd./London, New York, Toronto and Melbourne/1909
248pp, 8pp adv., b/w frontis. & 3 f/p b/w illus., pic. clo., 185x115mm. KMM
Twelfth thousand n.d. as above, but: Author of "The Mountain Star", "A Hunt on Snow-Shoes"/"The Forest Messengers" etc. etc....
Copy has a new cover design blocked in several colours, of two boys propelling a craft down river. KP
8427 Fourteenth thousand n.d. as the twelfth but with a col. frontis. & 4 b/w plates. KMM

8428 ADRIFT ON THE PACIFIC/A Boy's Story of the Sea and its Perils/by Edward S. Ellis/Author of/ "The Young Pioneers" "Fighting to Win" "Adrift in the/Wilds" "The Boy Patriot" Etc./ [device]/A. L. Burt Company, Publishers/New York
1911
273pp & 12pp adv., unillus (? frontis. missing), pic. clo., 185x125mm. SUA

ELLIS, James J.
8429 JOHN WILLIAMS/The Martyr Missionary of Polynesia/By/ Rev. James J. Ellis./[3 line quot.] London/S. W. Partridge & Co./9 Paternoster Row [1st published 1890]
xii+160pp, 16pp adv., b/w frontis., 6 f/p b/w illus., 1 f/p map & text engravings, pic. clo., dec.e/p. Front. illus. repro. on front cover & medallion portrait on gilt star background & title in gilt, 180x116mm. KMM.
Third edition, thirteenth thousand, as above. KMM
8429a HEROES WHO HAVE WON THEIR CROWN as above, but 'Partridge 8 & 9 Paternoster Row'
n.d., 160pp & 32pp adv., col. frontis., 6 f/p engravings, &c. as above, and bound together with:
A MONTEFIORE BRICE, *David Livingstone.* KP
• Rpt as above, but after quote' Fully illustrated/Kilmarnock, Scotland/John Ritchie, Publisher of Christian Literature/and through all booksellers.
160pp, b/w frontis., clo., 180x120mm. KP

EMMETT, Ian
8430 ALL ABOUT SANGIN/The Garoland/Painting Book/by/Ian Emmett/The Australian Baptist Foreign Mission/(Incorporated)/486 Albert Street, Melbourne, C.1.
n.d. [1951]
37pp, 1p adv., 16 f/p b/w illus. (to be coloured), dec. wrappers, 185x245mm. ANL
See also THE NEW GUINEA HIGHLANDS PAINTING BOOK

ESCOTT-INMAN, H.
8431 THE CASTAWAYS OF/DISAPPOINTMENT/ISLAND/Being an account of their sufferings/By Rev. H. Escott-Inman/From the description supplied to him by Mr Charles Eyre/of Dulwich, London, one of the survivors/with six illustrations by Ernest Prater/London/S.W.Partridge & Co., Ltd
n.d. [first pub. 1911]
319pp & 32pp adv., b/w frontis. & 5 f/p b/w illus., pic. clo., title in gilt on cover & spine, 190x130mm. KMM
• Rpt n.d. [prize label 1917] as above, but with col. frontis. only, 185x120mm. KP
8432 Whitcombe's Story Books/THE CASTAWAYS OF/DISAPPOINTMENT ISLAND/A True Story/abridged and adapted from the book/by the Rev. H. Escott-Inman/For ages 10 to 12 years/[vignette]/Whitcombe and Tombs Limited/Christchurch, Auckland, Wellington, Dunedin, Invercargill, N.Z./London, Melbourne and Sydney
n.d.
95pp (inc. 8pp notes, etc.), b/w frontis., 2 f/p b/w photographic illus., smaller illus. in text, 2 maps (printed on one page), pic. wrappers, 185x120mm. KMM
See McLaren 547
8433 The Cheapest Book on the Market/THE/CASTAWAYS OF/DISAPPOINTMENT/ISLAND/[illustration]/'This is a true story/related by Charles Eyre/one of the Survivors/No. 13—"Sunday Companion" Library—Threepence'
Amalgamated Press London n.d.
120pp (inc. 1p author's note), unillus., pic. wrapper printed in black & red, cover title (advs verso front wrapper & both sides back wrapper), 180x130mm. KMM

EVERARD, Maurice
CRUSOE ISLAND. *See* The Boys' Friend Library

EVISON, B.

8434 [coloured drawing]/THE/LITTLE PEARL-FISHER/ English text by B. Evison/Illustrated by M. B. Cooper Danny Books, Montreal; Litor Publishers Ltd, Brighton; printed by Helsingborgs Litografiska A.B., Sweden, n.d. [inscribed 1963]
[23]pp, 10 f/p col. illus., stiff pic. wrappers, 180x130mm. KMM
Story relates to a 'South Sea Island'.
Another copy, boards. KP

FAIRHALL, Constance

8435 SOME SHAPE/OF/BEAUTY/Constance Fairhall/ Pictures by Milein Cosman/London Missionary Society/11, Carteret Street, Westminster/London, S.W.1 1960
63pp, b/w illus. throughout, pic. wrappers, 180x110mm. KP
Author was a missionary nurse in Papua from 1932; not specifically a children's book

Famous Discoveries by Land and Sea

8436 FAMOUS DISCOVERIES/BY/LAND AND SEA/ With four full-page illustrations/London:/Blackie & Son, 49 & 50 Old Bailey, E.C.;/Glasgow, Edinburgh, and Dublin/1886
256pp, 40pp adv., b/w frontis. & 3 f/p b/w illus., dec. clo., 175x120mm. BBC
Contents include one chapter on Bougainville at Tahiti (14pp).

8437 FAMOUS DISCOVERIES/BY/SEA AND LAND/ Blackie and Son Limited/London Glasgow Bombay n.d. [1914?]
256pp, 16pp adv., b/w frontis. only, dec. clo., 185x120mm. KMM

FARMER, Sarah S.

8438 TONGA/AND THE FRIENDLY ISLANDS;/With/ A Sketch of their Mission/History./Written for Young People./By Sarah S. Farmer/London:/Hamilton, Adams, & Co., Paternoster Row./MDCCCLV
427pp, engraved frontis., 7 f/p engravings & 2 maps, clo., 180x120mm. ANL
Includes a chapter on Captain Cook's visits, &c.

FENN, G. Manville

8439 NAT THE NATURALIST/or/a Boy's Adventure in the/Eastern Seas/by/Geo. Manville Fenn/Author of "In the King's Name", "Off to the Wilds", "The Vicar's/People", etc. etc./Illustrated/[device]/London:/ Blackie & Son, 49 & 50 Old Bailey, E.C./Glasgow, Edinburgh and Dublin/1883
320pp, 32pp adv., b/w & sepia frontis. & 7 b/w & sepia plates by Gordon Browne, pic. clo., 185x125mm. KP
Cover design in gilt panel of a man pointing a gun surrounded by foliage.
Set partly in Papua & New Guinea
• Another copy as above but 'Author of [6 titles listed]/ With Eight Fullpage Illustrations by Gordon Browne./ [device]/London/ Blackie...&c.'
n.d.
Details as before, but illus. b/w. RM
• Rpt as above, but 'New edition/Blackie and Son Limited/London Glasgow and Dublin/1905'
Details as before, but front cover illus. shows a boy with a rifle holding up his trophy of a dead bird. KP

8440 As above but 'Illustrated by Gordon/Browne/ Blackie and Son Limited/London Glasgow and Bombay'
n.d.
320 pp, col. frontis. & 6 b/w plates, clo., 190x130mm. KP
The b/w illus. are by Gordon Browne with an anonymous col. frontis. repeated as a col. onlay on front cover in a dec. panel with title & author's name in gilt.
• Rpt as above, with 320pp, & b/w frontis. & 5 b/w plates, pic. clo. 184x124mm. KP
The illus. appear to have been copied from Gordon Browne's original illus. The front cover shows native canoes arriving at a tropical beach. The Boys Library

8441 NAT/THE NATURALIST/Or, A Boy's Adventures/in the Eastern Seas/By/George Manville Fenn/Blackie and Son Limited/London Glasgow and Bombay
n.d. [1911] Blackie's Crown Library
256pp &18pp adv., col. frontis. & 3 col. plates, dec. clo., 180x118mm. KP

8442 FIRE ISLAND/Being the Adventures of Uncertain/ Naturalists in an unknown Track/By /George Manville Fenn/Author of "Nat the Naturalist", "Dick o' the Fens".."Off to the Wilds"./etc. etc./with illustrations/New and Cheaper Edition/ London/Sampson Low, Marston & Company /Limited/St Dunstan's House/FetterLane, Fleet Street, E.C.
n.d. [1894]
334pp, b/w frontis. & 7 b/w plates (by F. W. Boyington), pic. clo., title & author's name in gilt on front & spine, 180x120mm. KP
Action takes place on an island off the coast of Papua.

8443 FIRE ISLAND/Being the Adventures...[up to etc.etc. device]/New and cheaper edition/London/Sampson, Low Marston & Company Limited.
1919
334pp & 4pp adv., unillus., clo., 180x117mm. KP

FERRIS, Norman A.

8444 THE STORY OF/PITCAIRN ISLAND/[illus.]/By Norman A. Ferris/Illustrations by Stanley Dunlap, Jr./ Review and Herald Publishing Assn./Washington, D.C. copyright 1957,1958
12pp, (inc. 2pp preface by A. S. M. Richards), 10 part-col. illus., pic. clo., 170x90mm. KP

FIELD, Claud

8445 HEROES OF/MISSIONARY ENTERPRISE/True Stories of the Intrepid Bravery and/Stirring Adventures of Missionaries with/Uncivilised man, wild beasts, and the/Forces of Nature in all parts of/the world/By/ Claud Field, M.A. Cantab./Sometime C.M.S. Missionary in the Punjab/with twenty-four illustrations/London/Seeley and Co. Limited/38 Great Russell Street/1908
335pp & 16pp adv., b/w frontis. & 23 plates mostly by J. F. Campbell & Ernest Prater, dec. clo., 190x130mm. KP

FINLAY, Roger T.

8446 ADVENTURES ON/STRANGE ISLANDS/By/ Roger T. Finlay/Illustrated/[device]/The Goldsmith Publishing Company/Chicago New York
n.d. [192-?]
242pp, b/w drawings in text, clo., 183x122mm. ANL

8447 THE CASTAWAYS/By/Roger T. Finlay/ Illustrated/[device]/Goldsmith Publishing Company /Chicago New York
n.d. [192-?]
238pp (inc. 6pp glossary), b/w diagrams & text drawings, clo., 196x130mmm. ANL

FINNEY, R. C.

8448 Eagle Books No. 70/I'LL HAVE A/HURRICANE/

(John Coleridge Patteson)/By/R. C. Finney/London/ Edinburgh House Press/2 Eaton Gate, S.W.1
1955
24pp, wrappers, 180x115mm. NSL:M
The story of J. C. Patteson (1827–71), missionary bishop in New Zealand & South Pacific islands

[FISKE, Nathan Welley]
8449 THE STORY OF ALECK,/or/PITCAIRN'S ISLAND./Being a True Account of a Very Singular/ and Interesting Colony./Amherst., Mass./Published by J. S. & C. Adams.1829
54pp, unillus., wrappers with 'Story of Aleck/ or/ Pitcairn's Island.'/—/ 'Don't you know Aleck?' on front cover, 140x90mm ANL
'NUC pre-1956 imprints' has the foll. note: 'Aleck, i.e. John Adams alias Aleck or Alexander Smith. 200 copies printed. A 2nd edition, enlarged with the title altered was printed from stereotype and published in Amherst in 1845.* From the same plates the 3rd ed. Boston 1848 was printed. There were also Boston 1854 & 1860 eds.'
[* *see* next entry]
8450 ALECK;/THE/LAST OF THE MUTINEERS;/or/ The History/of/Pitcairn's Island./with illustrations./ Third edition/Philadelphia./Published by E. C. Biddle,/6 South Fifth Street./1845
vi, 162pp, 8 f/p engravings, clo., 160x95mm. HBM
'Story of Aleck' on spine

8451 ALECK,/AND THE/MUTINEERS OF THE BOUNTY;/or,/Thrilling Incidents/of/Life on the Ocean./Being the/History of Pitcairn's Island./with illustrations/New Edition, Revised and Enlarged./ Boston:/Published by John P. Jewett & Company./ Cleveland, Ohio/Jewett, Proctor & Worthington./1854
161pp & 2pp preface, 8 f/p b/w engravings, dec. clo., 154x90mm. CLRC

8452 ALECK,/AND THE/MUTINEERS OF THE BOUNTY;/or,/Thrilling Incidents/of/Life on the Ocean./ Being the/History of Pitcairn's Island/and a remarkable illustration of/The Influence of the Bible./ New edition, Revised and Enlarged./Boston:/Published by John P. Jewett & Company./Cleveland, Ohio:/ Jewett, Proctor & Worthington/1855
176pp (inc. 2pp preface & 15pp appendix), engraved frontis. & 8 f/p engravings & smaller text engravings, blind-stamped clo with ship blocked in gilt on front cover & spine in gilt, 174x110mm. NSL:M
Title on spine: 'Mutineers of the Bounty or the Influence of the Bible at Pitcairn's Island'.
8453 ALECK,/AND THE/MUTINEERS OF THE BOUNTY./A remarkable illustration of/The Influence of the Bible./Approved by the Committee of Publications./New Edition/Boston:/Massachusetts Sabbath School Society./Depository, No.13 Cornhill 1855
176pp, no frontis. but otherwise contents appear the same as the Jewett revised ed. of 1855. Both appear to be identical in the printing apart from the t.p. and frontis. Blind-stamped clo. with 'Mutineers of the Bounty' on spine; 'Mass. Sabbath School Society 40' at base, 175x110mm. NSL:M

FOX, Frank
8454 Peeps at Many Lands/OCEANIA/By/Frank Fox/ Author of [3 lines]/Containing Thirty-two Full-page Illustrations in Colour/By/Norman H. Hardy, F. & W. Wright/and Percy F. S. Spence/London/Adam and Charles Black/1911
204pp, col. frontis. & 30 col. plates, fold-out map, pic. clo. with col. onlay, 205 x 140mm. RM
An omnibus volume of 3 of the Peeps at Many Lands series, including *The Blessed Isles of the Pacific, Australia,* and *New Zealand*
8455 Peeps at Many Lands/OCEANIA/By/ Frank Fox/ Author of[3 lines]/containing thirty-one full-page/ illustrations in colour/by/Norman H. Hardy, F. & W. Wright/and Percy F. S. Spence/London/Adam and Charles Black/1912/This edition is specially printed for/the Salvation Army, Australasia.
n.d.
204pp, folding map, col. frontis. & 30 col. plates, clo. with gilt Salvation Army emblems & title, and col. onlay on front cover, 210x136mm. KP
Salvation Army coat of arms printed twice on front cover and once on spine.
8456 OCEANIA/By/Frank Fox/Author of [3 lines]/ Containing thirty-two full-page/illustrations in colour/ by/Norman H. Hardy, F. & W. Wright/and Percy F. S. Spence/London/Adam and Charles Black/1913
Details as above. KP
• Rpt as above 1919. KP

FRANCIS, B.
8457 THE/ISLES OF THE PACIFIC;/or,/Sketches from the South Seas./By/B. Francis/[vignette]/Cassell, Petter, Galpin & Co./London, Paris & New York./(All rights reserved)/1882
224pp (inc. 2pp introduction), b/w frontis. & 29 f/p illus., b/w illus. in text & 2 maps, dec. clo., 180x115mm. HBM
The first hundred pages relate to New Zealand; other chapters on New Caledonia, The Loyalty & Fiji Islands, The Island of Tahiti, The Sandwich Islands, Pitcairn's Island & the Marquesas. The book is written for children.
Another copy as above, but 32pp adv. headed 'A List of Books suitable for Young People/And the Little Ones'. KP
8458 • Rpt as above but: Twelfth Thousand/Cassell and Company, Limited/London, Paris & Melbourne/all rights reserved
n.d. [school prize 1896]
Contents the same, cover design of two natives armed with rifles doing a war dance, with heading 'The/ World in Pictures', completely different from cover of 1882 edition. HBM

FRANK, Dinah
UNDER THE MANGO TREES. *See* Stories of our People

FRAZAR, Douglas
8459 PERSEVERANCE ISLAND:/or,/The Robinson Crusoe of the/Nineteenth Century/By/Douglas Frazar,/Author of"Practical Boat-Sailing," &c./Illustrated/ London:/Blackie & Son, 49 & 50 Old Bailey, E.C./Glasgow, Edinburgh and Dublin/1887
x+374pp & 48pp adv., b/w frontis. & 11 f/p b/w illus. by F. J. Merrill, pic. clo., 186x122mm. KP
Story tells of a crew of a ship marooned on an island in the S. Pacific 1500 miles west of Straits of Magellan.
• As above, but 'with six page illustrations./New and cheaper Edition./London:/ Blackie & Son, Limited,49 Old Bailey, E.C./ Glasgow Edinburgh and Dublin'.
n.d.
details as before, but 32pp adv., b/w frontis & 5 f/p illus., pic. clo., with variant cover illus., 180x120mm. KP
Later variant copies seen, undated, one, school prize 1916, with col. frontis. & 3 b/w plates. KP

FREMONT, Isabelle
8460 Oxford Story Readers for the Pacific/WHY COCKS

CROW/and other stories/by Isabelle Fremont/ Illustrated by/Barbara Albiston/Melbourne/Oxford University Press/London Wellington New York
1958
48pp, 15 b/w illus., pic. wrappers, 184x123mm. KMM

The Friends
8461 THE/FRIENDS,/or, The/History/of Billy Freeman/and Tommy Truelove/Proper to be imitated/ by all those who desire to, be Good/and Great./ London/Printed and Sold by John Marshall and Co. at/No 17 Queen-Street, Cheapside; and No. 4 Aldermary Churchyard, Bow-Lane, Printers to/the Society of Lilliputians, and Booksel-/lers in ordinary to the Good children of/Great Britain and Ireland./[Price three-pence, Bound and Gilt.]
76pp + 3pp adv., woodcut frontis. & 29 woodcut illus., calf, 124x75mm. CLRC
The adventures include a brief visit (clearly inspired by Captain Cook) to the Solomon Islands, and a shipwreck, slavery, and capture by Red Indians in North America.

Friday Christian
8462 FRIDAY CHRISTIAN;/Or the/First-Born on Pitcairn's Island./By/A Poor "Member of Christ"./[2-line quotation]/ New-York./D. Appleton & Co., 200 Broadway./Philadelphia:/G .S. Appleton, 164 Chestnut Street/MDCCCXLIX
138pp (inc. 4pp intro.), & 4pp adv., unillus., clo., 175x120mm. NSL:M

GALLYON, R. N.
8463 STORIES/FROM PAPUA/Retold by/R. N. Gallyon/Illustrated by Nina Murphy/In association with the/South Pacific Commission Literature Bureau/ Macmillan & Co. Limited/St. Martin's Street London/ 1959
40pp, 19 b/w drawings, dec. wrappers, 190x135mm. NSL:M

GAMMON, David
8464 PACIFIC PLUNDER/by/David Gammon/ Illustrated by Douglas Relf/Thomas Nelson and Sons Ltd./London Edinburgh Paris Melbourne Johannesburg/Toronto and New York
1959
218pp, col. frontis. & 6 f/p b/w illus., clo., 185x120mm. BBC
Boys' adventure story set in the Celebes.
• Rpt 1964, as above but b/w frontis. & 6 b/w illus. KP

GAUNT, L. H.
8465 SCHOOL-MATES/Pictures of School-time/and Play-time in the Mission Field/By/Lewis Herman Gaunt/L.M.S. Editor with eighty-two illustrations/ London/London Missionary Society/16 New Bridge Street, E.C./Trade Agent/Messrs Simpkin Marshall, Hamilton, Kent & Co. Ltd./1906
191pp & 1p 'The story of our ships', b/w frontis., 82 text illus., dec. clo., bevelled edges, gilt decorations, 210x160mm. KP
Another copy as above but without gilt lettering. KP

GEIS, Darlene (ed.)
8466 LET'S TRAVEL IN THE/SOUTH/SEAS/Edited by Darlene Geis/[device]/Prepared for Odhams Books Limited, London/A Travel Press Book
New ed. pub. by The Children's Press Inc., Chicago,1965
85pp, 32 f/p col. plates & b/w & part-col. illus. & dec. maps, pic. clo. 277x205mm. KP
Another copy, third printing, 1965 as above. CLRC

GERSTAECKER, Frederick
8467 FRANK WILDMAN'S/ADVENTURES ON LAND & WATER/By Frederick Gerstaecker/Translated and Revised by/Lascelles Wraxall/With tinted illustrations/ By Harrison Weir/London:/Geo. Routledge & Co. Farringdon Street/New York: 18, Beekman Street/1858
296pp, 2pp translator's preface (dated 1855), tinted front. & 3 f/p tinted illus., blind stamped clo. with title & dec. in gilt, 170x100mm. KMM
Much of the action takes place in Java & Sumatra, some in Tonga, none in Australia.
8468 FRANK WILDMAN'S/ADVENTURES/ON LAND AND WATER/By/Frederick Gerstaecker/With Illustrations by Harrison Weir/London/George Routledge and Sons/Broadway, Ludgate Hill/New York: 9, La fayette Place/1883
296pp, 2pp translator's preface, b/w frontis. & 5 b/w illus., dec. clo., 170x110mm. NSL:M

8469 THE/YOUNG WHALER;/or,/The Adventures of Charles Hollberg./By Frederick Gerstäcker./Author of "Wild Sports of the West",/"Frank Wildman's Adventures" etc etc./A New Edition./Illustrated by Harrison Weir/London:/G. Routledge & Co., Farringdon Street./New York: 18 Beekman Street./ 1858/(Printed under the International Copyright law.)
n.d.
viii+343pp, engraved frontis. & 7 f/p engravings, blind-stamped clo. with gilt dec. & title, 167x102mm. CLRC
The setting for part of the book is the South Seas Islands, Hawaii, &c.
8470 THE/YOUNG WHALER/Or the/Adventures of Charles Hollberg/By/Frederick Gerstaecker/Illustrated by Harrison Weir/London: George Routledge and Sons/Broadway, Ludgate Hill/New York: 416 Broome Street
n.d.
343pp, b/w frontis. & 3 b/w engravings, dec. clo., 170x110mm. ANL
Another copy as above, but 8 engravings. KMM
Gerstaecker's *The Young Gold-Digger* (Routledge 1860) has a Californian, not Australian background. *See also* Australian section for other titles.

GIBBINGS, Robert
8471 COCONUT/ISLAND/or/The Adventures of Two Children/in the South Seas/written/and illustrated by/Robert Gibbings/[decoration]/Faber and Faber Limited/24 Russell Square/London
1936
283pp, b/w frontis. & b/w woodcuts throughout, clo., 240x130mm. HBM
8472 COCONUT ISLAND/or/The Adventures of Two children/in the South Seas/Written and Illustrated by/ Robert Gibbings/[decorative device]/Letchworth/J. M. Dent & Sons Ltd.
First published 1936; first published in this edition 1949
245pp, b/w frontis. & woodcut illus. throughout, clo., map e/p, 185x115mm. BBC
• Rpt as above London 1953, 1958. Both KP
8473 COCONUT ISLAND/or/The Adventures of Two children/in the South Seas/written/and illustrated by/ Robert Gibbings/[device]/Penguin Books/ Harmondsworth Middlesex England/245 Fifth Avenue New York USA
First published November 1936; published in Puffin Story Books 1945
192pp, b/w illus. throughout, pic. wrappers, 180x110mm. KMM

GILSON, Charles

8474 THE PIRATE YACHT/A Tale of the Southern Seas/Captain Charles Gilson/Author of/"Submarine U 93", "A Motor Scout in Flanders", "The Sword of Freedom", Etc./Coloured Illustrations and Photographs/London and Glasgow/Collins' Clear-Type Press
n.d. [inscribed Xmas 1921]
228pp, col. frontis. & 3 f/p col. illus., 6 b/w photographic illus., pic. clo., 250x185mm. RM
The photographs are of naval ships of the First World War.

8475 THE/LOST/ISLAND/Humphrey/Milford/Oxford/University/Press [within dec. border]
• Rpt 1923 [1st pub. 1919]
x+288pp, col. frontis. by Cyrus Cuneo, dec. e/p., clo., 163x110mm. ANL
Adventure story set in the Pacific, and a Tibetan mystery

8476 MYSTERY ISLAND/by/Major Charles Gilson/Author of/"The Lost Island"/"The Land of Shame"/"Jack-without-a-roof" "Treasure of Kings"/etc. etc./Eleventh thousand/S. W. Partridge & Co./(A. & C. Black Ltd., Proprietors.) 4, 5 & 6 Soho Square London W1
First pub. 1928; rpt 1930; this impression issued 1933
128pp, unillus., boards, 180x120mm. Grant
Boys' adventure story of the survivors of a ship, with a cargo of wool bound from Sydney to Vancouver, which founders near Fiji.

SOUTH SEAS GOLD. *See* The Boys' Friend Library

GITTINS, Anne

8477 TALES FROM/THE/SOUTH SEAS/Collected and Adapted by/Anne Gittins/Government Press, Suva
1st imp. 1952
88pp, b/w frontis. & 10 b/w illus. by J. K. Payne and Miss O. Reeve, illus. wrappers, 210x165mm. KP
A collection of 36 island legends written especially for children
Second impression as above 1954. NSL:M
• Rpt 1965, 1969, as above. KP

GLENCROSS, Barbara

8478 Eagle Books No. 58/NEW GUINEA? NOT ME!/By/Barbara Glencross/London:/Edinburgh House Press/The Book Depot/Melbourne:/288 Little Collins Street, C.1/1949
24pp, unillus., wrappers, 180x120mm. KMM
The Story of Copland King (1863–1918).

GOMES, Edwin H.

8479 CHILDREN OF BORNEO/By/Edwin H. Gomes, M.A./Author of/"Seventeen Years among the Sea Dyaks of Borneo"/with eight coloured illustrations/Edinburgh and London/Oliphant, Anderson & Ferrier/1912
93pp, 16pp adv., 8 col. illus., clo. with col. illus. on front cover, 190x120mm. NSL:M

The Great Dance

8480 The Pacific Series/THE GREAT DANCE/and other Stories/Standard Three/Melbourne/ Oxford University Press/London Wellington New York
1969
88pp, col. & part-col. illus. throughout by Barbara Taylor, pic. wrappers, 215x140mm. KP

GREY, Estelle

8481 JULIE GORDON/AND THE NEW GUINEA SMUGGLERS/by/estelle grey/Golden Pres/Sydney
1972
233pp, 3 f/p bw illus. pic. clo., dec. e/p. 210x 134mm. ANL

GREY, Eve

8482 CHILDREN'S LEGENDS OF THE SOUTH SEAS/Book Three/Text by Eve Grey/Illustrations by Tambi Larsen/Copyright 1954/Island Import Co./Honolulu, Hawaii/Printed by/Fisher Corp. Ltd./Honolulu, Hawaii
n.d.
32pp, part-col. illus. throughout, pic. wrappers, 256x185mm. KP
Four other books in series, unseen

GRIERSON, E.

8483 JOHN COLERIDGE/PATTESON/Söderhavsöarnas Biskop/en hjältesaga/berättad för de unga/av/E. Grierson/översatt av/Aline Cronhielm/[device]/Stockholm/Svenska Kyrkans diakonistyrelses Bokförlag
1927
168pp, unillus., pic. wrappers, 200x130mm. NSL:M

8484 BISHOP PATTESON/OF THE/CANNIBAL ISLANDS/A record of the life of the first Bishop of Melanesia/His Heroic work amongst the treacherous/islanders & his tragic death/told for boys & girls/By/E. Grierson/Author of "The Story of St. Francis of Assisi", "Things seen in Florence"/"Things seen in Edinburgh", &c., &c./with illustrations/London/Seeley, Service & Co. Limited/196 Shaftsbury Avenue/1927
182pp, 10pp adv., 5pp adv. preceding text, col. frontis., 7 f/p b/w illus., dec. clo., 195x130mm. AJH
• Rpt 1965 illus. by various artists. KP

GRIMBLE, Arthur

8485 Arthur Grimble/A PATTERN/OF ISLANDS/Junior Edition/John Murray/Albemarle Street, London, W.1
1st pub. 1952, Junior ed. first pub. Feb.1955, Rpt July 1955, Rpt Dec. 1957, Rpt March1960
154pp. f/p b/w frontis. & headpieces by Shirley Hughes, other illus. & map e/p. by Tom Pomfret, clo., 184x124mm. KP
Thirteenth printing 1969 as above. KP

GROSS, Alma Southwell

8486 SAMANI/OF KUM KUM ISLAND/By Alma Southwell Gross/With illustrations by/Dorothy M. Potter/Whitcombe and Tombs Pty. Ltd./Melbourne, Sydney, Perth, Geelong
n.d. [1955]
84pp, b/w map frontis. & 5 b/w illus., pic. wrappers, 180x120mm. ANL
See McLaren 575

GUILLOT, René

8487 René Guillot/MOUNTAIN/WITH A SECRET/Translated by John Marshall/Illustrated by B. L. Driscoll/Collins/St. James's Place, London/1963
192pp, 8 f/p b/w illus., clo., 215x135mm. BBC
Originally published under the title *Le Chef au Masque d'or,* Librairie Hachette, Paris 1958 (Copyright 1961, in US).
Boys' adventure story set in New Guinea, with references to Cook, &c.

GWYTHER-JONES, Roy, *et al.*

8488 TODAY'S STORIES/FROM/NEW GUINEA/By/Roy Gwyther-Jones/Neville Threlfall/Worike Narewe./Published by Kristen Press Inc./Madang, New Guinea/1969
First ed. 4000 copies

44pp, b/w drawings in text, pic. wrappers, 210x138mm. KMM

HACK, Maria Barton

8489 WINTER EVENINGS;/or,/Tales of Travellers./By Maria Hack/[quotation]/London:/Printed for Darton, Harvey and Darton/No. 55, Gracechurch Street./1818
4 vols (Vols 1 & 3 1818, Vol. 2 1819, Vol. 4 1820), Vol. 1: 219pp, 7pp preface, engraved frontis. only, boards, 140x85mm. NSL:M
Vol. 2: 226pp, as Vol. 1.
Vol. 3: 211pp, as Vol. 1.
Vol. 4: 248pp (inc. 4pp concluding verse), as Vol. 1.
Volume 4 includes 'The Escape of Captain Bligh' from Bligh's *Voyage to the South Seas* (70pp), & 'Pitcairn's Island' from the *Quarterly Review*, July 1815 (32pp).

8490 WINTER EVENINGS;/or,/Tales of Travellers./By Maria Hack/[quotation]/in four volumes/Vol. 1/Third edition/London:/Printed for Harvey and Darton/ Gracechurch Street 1823
As above, engraved frontis. to each vol., marbled boards, 136x85mm. CLRC
Vol. 4 Bligh & Pitcairn's Island as before.

8491 WINTER EVENINGS/Or, Tales of Travellers/By Maria Hack/with eight illustrations by Gilbert and Harvey/[publisher's device]/Strahan & Co., Publishers/56 Ludgate Hill, London/1872
463pp, 4pp author's preface, b/w engraved frontis. & 7 f/p engravings, dec. clo., 165x110mm. HBM
Contents as in first edition.

8492 ADVENTURES/BY/LAND AND SEA/By Maria Hack/With Twelve Full-Page Illustrations /[vignette]/London/George Routledge and Sons/ Broadway, Ludgate Hill, New York: 416 Broome Street
n.d. [inscribed1891]
185pp & 1 p adv., b/w frontis. & 11 f/p b/w illus. & tailpieces &c., pic. clo., g.e.,163x103mm. RM
'Every Boy's Library', a selection from 'Winter Evenings'

HACKFORTH-JONES, Gilbert

8493 GREEN SAILORS/IN THE/SOUTH SEAS/by/ Gilbert Hackforth-Jones/Illustrated by/Jean Main and David Cobb, R.O.I./Hodder and Stoughton
London 1961
192pp, 8 b/w illus., clo., dec. e/p, 190x130mm. BBC
Adventures of a group of people on a ketch washed up by a tidal wave on an island near the Galapagos.

HALE, E. E.

8494 STORIES OF THE SEA/Told by Sailors/By E. E. Hale/[device]/Boston/Robert Brothers/1880
300pp (inc. 2pp preface), 1p adv., engraved frontis, dec. clo., 165x110mm. NSL:M
Contents include one chapter on 'Pitcairn's Island' (43pp).

Half Hours in the Far South

8494a The Half Hour Library/of Travel, Nature and Science/For Young Readers/HALF HOURS IN THE/ FAR SOUTH/The People and Scenery of the Tropics/ with numerous illustrations/London/James Nisbet & Co., Limited/21 Berners Street/1901
342pp & 16 pp adv., engraved frontis., 26 f/p engravings & text illus., pic. clo., 184x120mm. KMM
Includes New Guinea, pp103-147; Fiji, 235-254.

HALL, J. N.

See Nordhoff, C. B. & Hall, J. N.

HAMES, Inez

See Reed, Alexander Wyclif & Hames, Inez

HAMILTON, Bruce

8495 FOLK TALES/OF THE/FUZZY WUZZIES/Seven/ Folk Lore Stories/from Papua/By/Bruce Hamilton/ Illustrations by/Sheila Farquharson/Ayers & James Pty. Ltd./Sydney/Price:/Two shillings and sixpence
1945
99pp (inc. 3pp author's note), b/w frontis. & text decorations, pic. wrappers, 208x104mm. KMM
Not specifically for children.

HAMILTON, Charles

CHUMS OF THE ISLANDS. *See* The Boys' Friend Library, and for following titles
GALLEONS GOLD
THE HAUNTED ISLAND
KING OF THE ISLANDS
PALS OF THE PACIFIC
SOUTH SEAS TREASURE

HAMMOND, Ralph

COCOS GOLD
West Indies, not Cocos Island, north of Australia

HARDY, Arthur S.

SHIPWRECK KELLY. *See* The Boys' Friend Library

HARRISSON, Tom

8496 LIVING/AMONG CANNIBALS/by/Tom Harrisson/Illustrated by/Ellis Silas/[publisher's device]/George G. Harrap & Co. Ltd./London Toronto Bombay Sydney
1943
120pp (inc. 1p prefatory note), col. frontis., b/w map, 4 f/p b/w illus. & b/w drawings in text, clo., 180x120mm. NSL:M
An account of two years the author spent on the island of Malekula in the New Hebrides.
• Rpt 1948. KP

HARRY, Robert R.

8497 By Robert R. Harry, Sr./ISLAND BOY/A story of Ancient Hawaii/Illustrated by Reisie Lonette/New York, N.Y./Lothrop, Lee & Shepard Co. Inc.
1956
212pp (inc. 2pp glossary), b/w illus. throughout, clo., 208x138mm. SUA
Weekly Reader Children's Book Club Edition, 1957

HARTMAN, Tom

8498 Star [device] Book/MAN IN/THE PACIFIC/By Tom Hartman/Pictures by George Craig/Hamish Hamilton/London
1967
32pp (inc. 1p index), b/w & part. col. drawings throughout, pic. boards, 200x145mm. KMM

[HAWKS, Francis Lister]

8499 UNCLE PHILIP'S/CONVERSATIONS/ABOUT THE/WHALE FISHERY/AND POLAR SEAS. /[vignette]/London:/Felfe and Fletcher, Cornhill;/Harper, Brothers, New-York./1836
xii+379pp, engraved frontis. & engravings in text, clo., 126x100mm. CLRC
Includes chapters on whaling in the Pacific, mentioning the Galapagos, Society Islands, Easter Island, &c.

HAYENS, Herbert

8500 BESET/BY SAVAGES/By/Herbert Hayens/ London/James Nisbet & Co.,Limited/22 Berners Street, W. 1910
336pp, & 32pp adv., b/w frontis & 3 f/p b/w illus. by Arthur Twidle, pic. clo., 195x130mm. RM
Story of shipwreck of the schooner *Southern Cross* on a voyage from South America to Sydney

HAYES, Courtenay

8501 ON THE FRINGE/OF THE CYCLONE/A Tale for Adventurous Youth/by/Courtenay Hayes/Author of/ "Seamew and Co.," "Witchery o'the Moor"/etc./ [device]/London/Frederick Warne & Co., Ltd./and New York/(All rights reserved)
n.d.
244pp, col. frontis, 1 map & 2 charts, clo., 185x130mm. Grant

HAYES, Ernest H.

8502 WILIAMU-/Mariner-Missionary/The Story of John Williams/By/Ernest H. Hayes/Author of/"The Concise Guides" "The Child in the Midst" etc./ Foreword by/Edward Shillito, M.A./London:/The Livingstone Press/48 Broadway, Westminster, SW1
n.d. [1922]
111pp (inc. 2pp foreword & 1 p. author's preface) b/w map & 4 sepia plates, text drawings, dec. clo., 184x120mm. SUA

8503 The Pioneer Series, No.1/WILIAMU/ Mariner–Missionary/The Story of John Williams...as above, but The Religious Education Press, Ltd/Manor Road, Wallington Surrey
8th ed. 1946, details as above. KP

8504 CHALMERS/OF/PAPUA/By/Ernest Hayes/ Author of/"The Concise Guides" "The Child in the Midst"/etc etc/London:/"Teacher and Taught" Office/ 4, Fleet Lane, E.C.4
First pub. Jan.1930
128pp, b/w drawings in text, dec. clo., 184x120mm. KP
• Rpt 1932, 1939, 1943, 1945, 1946, as above. SUA

HEADLAND, A. R.

8505 ADVENTURES AFLOAT/IN MISSIONARY SHIPS/by/A. R. Headland, B.A./Illustrated by Wal Paget/The London Missionary Society/Livingstone House, Broadway, Westminster, S.W.1/1929
155pp, b/w frontis. & 14 f/p b/w illus., clo., 180x120mm. KMM
Chapters include: 'The *Duff* and her Captain', 'John Williams builds a Ship', 'Morgan of the *Camden*', 'A Trip with Bully Hayes', 'Butcher and the *Tamate*, (Papua), 'John Williams the Fourth'.

HEIGHWAY, Dorothy

8506 SANCTIFIED COMMONSENSE/A story of missionary adventure with Christ./by/Dorothy Heighway/Illustrated by Rosslyn Oliver/[drawing]/A Methodist Overseas Missions Publication
n.d.
32pp (& epilogue printed inside back cover), b/w illus. in text, stiff pic. wrappers, 214x140mm. KMM
Story of Mary Woolnough, missionary to New Britain 1914-47(?)

[HERBERT, David]

8507 THE STORY/OF THE/GOOD SHIP BOUNTY/and her Mutineers/and/Mutinies in Highland Regiments/ William P. Nimmo/London and Edinburgh/1878
160pp, b/w frontis., dec. clo., 185x120mm. HBM
'The Bounty and her Mutineers' to p94, then 'Mutinies in Highland Regiments' follow. Printed in double column. On front cover: 'Nimmo's Library of History, Travel & Adventure'
Copy seen bears prize label for the State School, Carlton, 1880, awarded to Louisa Koster as 5th prize in 3rd class. Although in appearance not intended for children, it was reprinted many times at the end of last century, and often awarded to children as a prize.

Heroes of the Cross

8508 HEROES OF THE CROSS/John Williams: James Chalmers/Abel of Kwato/[drawing]/Marshall, Morgan & Scott, Ltd./London—Edinburgh
First published March 1933; 2nd imp. Dec. 1933
96pp, col. frontis, 4 b/w photographic illus., b/w drawings in text by John F. Campbell, dec. clo., dec. e/p, 180x120mm. KMM
Describes missionary enterprises in Polynesia & Papua.
• Rpt 1936 as above. KP

HEROES WHO HAVE WON THEIR CROWN

See ELLIS, James J.

HIGGINSON, John Andrew

8509 THE/STRANGE ADVENTURES/OF A YOUNG SAILOR/By/John Andrew Higginson/Author of/'A Boy's Adventures Round the World'/'A Mystery of the Sea' 'The Adventures of Norman Pawle'/etc.etc./with coloured illustrations/London/The Religious Tract Society/4 Bouverie Street and 65 St Paul's Churchyard
n.d. [1908]
222pp & 2pp adv. (copy appears to have 1 col. plate only), clo., with col. onlay on front cover, 190x120mm. ANL

HIOB, Frank

THE CHIMBUS. *See* People of the Pacific

The History of Prince Lee Boo

8510 THE/HISTORY/OF/PRINCE LEE BOO/a Native of the Pelew Islands./brought to England/by Capt. Wilson./a new edition/[engraving]/London/Printed for E. Newbery/The Corner of/St Paul's Churchyard
n.d.[first pub. 1789]
viii, 178pp, 5 engravings, boards, 130x84mm. CLRC

8511 THE/HISTORY/OF/PRINCE LEE BOO,/a Native/ of the/Pelew Islands./Seventeenth Edition./London:/ Printed for John Harris./Corner of St. Paul's/1827
144pp, engraved frontis., half calf, marbled bds, 140x85mm. Grant
Neither *The History of Prince Lee Boo* nor *The Adventures of Madiboo* is strictly eligible for entry in this Bibliography as the Pelew Islands are in the Northern Hemisphere and not in the region adjacent to Australia.

HOLBERG, Ruth Langland

8512 THE/WONDERFUL VOYAGE/By Ruth Langland Holberg/Illustrated by Phyllis Coté/[drawing]/Junior Books/Doubleday, Doran & Company Inc./Garden City, New York
1945
208pp (inc. 1p acknowledgement), 10 f/p b/w illus. & b/w drawings throughout, clo., dec. map e/p, 230x145mm. NSL:M
Story of two children who accompany their father on a whaling voyage in the 1850s from the East Coast of North America, round Cape Horn & into the South Pacific, but not touching Australia.

HOLDING, James

8513 THE SKY-EATER/and other South Sea Tales/ [drawing]/by James Holding/Illustrated by Charles Keeping/Abelard Schuman/London New York Toronto
1st pub. in Great Britain in 1966
124pp, b/w & part-col. frontis. & 27pp part-col. illus., b/w text drawings, clo., pic. e/p, 203x153mm. KP

8514 Abelard-Schuman Library edition 1966, details as above, but e/p illus. reproduced before t.p. & plain e/p, reinforced binding & jacket illus. printed on front & back covers. KP

8515 POKO/AND THE/GOLDEN DEMON/[drawing]/ By James Holding/illustrated by Charles Keeping/ Abelard-Schuman/London New York Toronto

First published in the US 1967; this edition London 1968
123pp, 1p biographical note on author & illustrator, 22pp part. col. illus., b/w drawings in text, clo., dec. e/p, 210x155mm. KMM
Story of a Polynesian boy

HOLT, H. P. & BARBOUR, Ralph Henry
8516 LOST ISLAND/By/H. P. Holt/and Ralph Henry Barbour/Illustrated by/Charles M. Relyes & Percy Tarrant/[drawing]/London/George G. Harrap & Co. Ltd./2 & 3 Portsmouth Street, Kingsway, W.C./ MCMXIX
256pp, col. frontis. & 8 b/w plates, clo., 195x135mm. KP
Boys' sea story set in the South Pacific. The first illustrator's name is spelt as above in the first edition but as 'Relya' in the second & third editions
• Rpt 1923 as above, but after [drawing]/George G. Harrap & Co. Ltd/London Calcutta Sydney. Details as above. CLRC

The Home of the Mutineers
8517 THE/HOME/OF THE/MUTINEERS/ Philadelphia:/American Sunday School Union,/No. 316 Chestnut Street./New York: No.147 Nassau St. Boston: No.9 Cornhill/Louisville: No.103 Fourth St. 1854
342pp,engraved frontis. portrait of John Adams, & 8 f/p engravings, dec. clo., 150x90mm. ANL

HOOK, S. Clarke
VOLCANO ISLAND! *See* The Boys' Friend Library

HORNBY, John
8518 Far and Wide Stories/1/THE BEACHCOMBERS' BELL/By/John Hornby/[drawing]/Illustrated by Eric Wade/Macmillan/London Melbourne Toronto/St. Martin's Press/New York/1968
First ed. 1951, rpt 1955, 1956, 1958, 1965, 1968
64pp, b/w illus. in text, double-spread map of world, pic. wrappers, 188x135mm. KMM
A background reader set in S. Pacific

HORSLEY, Reginald
8519 HUNTED/THROUGH FIJI/or/'Twixt Convict and Cannibal/by/Reginald Horsley/Author of/'The Yellow God','Blue Balloon', 'Stonewall's Scout' etc/with six illustrations/ by J. Ayton Symington/ London: 38 Soho Square,W./W. & R. Chambers, Limited/ Edinburgh: 339 High Street
First published 1897
viii+316pp, b/w frontis. & 5 plates, head & tailpieces, pic. clo., 185x130mm. KP
Part of an illus. from the book, of a native in the prow of a canoe, repro. in col. on front cover.
8520 Another edition, but after 'Symington'/'W. & R. Chambers Limited/London and Edinburgh'
prize label 1904, and with 34pp adv. KMM
8521 Another copy as above, but after 'Symington'/London: 38 Soho Square, W.1/W. & R. Chambers, Limited/ Edinburgh: 339 High Street
n.d. [prize label 1929]
316 pp & 2pp author's note, b/w frontis. & 2 plates (? some missing), pic. clo., 180x120mm. KP
8522 HUNTED/THROUGH FIJI/or/Twixt Convict and Cannibal/By/Reginald Horsley/Author of [as before]/ With six Illustrations/By/J. Ayton Symington/ Philadelphia/J. B. Lippincott Company.
n.d.
Details as in English first edition but with 2pp adv. RM
Swedish edition
8523 BLAND VILDAR/Af/Reginald Horsley/Förf. till "Till Sjöss Ochlands" M. Fl./Öfversättning/fran Engelskan/Af/H. Nordenadler./med sex illustrationer./Stockholm./Adolf Johnsons Förlag. 1903
320pp, 2pp foreword, b/w frontis. & 6 b/w illus., dec. chapter headings & tailpieces, col. pic. boards (with adv. verso back cover), clo. spine, 200x140mm. RM
Front cover illus. signed 'G. L. Fürth'; others 'J. Ayton Symington'.

HOWARD, Vernon Linwood
8524 JOHN G. PATON/Apostle to the South Seas/Story by/Vernon Howard/Pictures by/J. L. Craig/Book 6/Children's Missionary Library
The Fleming H. Revell Company, New York 1950
30pp, col. illus. on alternate pages, dec. boards, cover title, 135x210mm. ANL

HUGHES, Brenda
8525 NEW GUINEA FOLK TALES/by/Brenda Hughes/ illustrated by/Michael Brett/[device]/George G. Harrap & Co. Ltd./London Toronto Wellington Sydney 1959
80pp, b/w map frontis., b/w drawings throughout, clo., 181x120mm. CLRC
Author acknowledges her indebtedness to the volume on Papuan folk tales by Dr Gunnar Landtman.

8526 KING AMONG/CANNIBALS/The Story of James Chalmers/By/Brenda Hughes/Published by/ Lutterworth Press/for/the London Missionary Society/ 42 Broadway, London, S.W.1
1959
95pp, col. frontis. (unsigned) & 1 b/w map, clo., 180x120mm. KMM
Life & work of the well-known missionary to New Guinea.
• Variant first edition with front. illus. blocked in black & yellow on front cover (? in lieu of d/w) and presentation page from The London Missionary Society. KP
• Second imp. 1961 as above but after author's name, [device]/Lutterworth Press/ London KP
• Rpt 1965. KP
8527 KING AMONG/CANNIBALS/The Story of James Chalmers/by/Brenda Hughes/[device]/Lutterworth Press/London
First published 1959; second impression 1961, third impression 1965
95pp, col. frontis., 1 f/p b/w map, clo., 180x120mm. KMM

HUTCHESON, John C.
8528 THE/ WRECK OF THE NANCY BELL/or/Cast Away on Kerguelen Land./By/John C. Hutcheson/ Author of "Afloat at Last". "Picked up at Sea". "The White Squall" &c./Illustrated/[device]/ London:/ Blackie & Son, Limited, 49 Old Bailey, E.C./Glasgow, Edinburgh, and Dublin/
288pp & 32pp adv., tinted frontis. & 5 tinted plates, pic. clo. (boys on a raft, title & background panel in gilt), 177x117mm. KP
The story of a New Zealand-bound clipper wrecked on Kerguelen Land
8529 THE/WRECK OF THE NANCY BELL/Or/Cast Away on Kerguelen Land./By/John C. Hutcheson/ Author of "Afloat at Last", "Picked up at Sea". "The White Squall", &c./Illustrated/ [device]/ New and cheaper edition/London:/Blackie & Son, Limited, 49 Old Bailey, E.C./Glasgow, Edinburgh, and Dublin/ 1893
288pp & 32 pp adv.., b/w frontis. & 2 f/p b/w illus., pic. clo., 177x117 mm. CLRC

8530 THE/WRECK OF THE NANCY BELL/Or/Cast Away on Kerguelen Land/By/John C. Hutcheson/ Author of "Afloat at Last" "Picked up at Sea" "The White Squall" &c./Illustrated/Blackie and Son Limited/London Glasgow and Dublin
n.d. [prize 1904]
288pp, 32pp adv., b/w frontis. & 2 b/w illus. by W. S. Stacey, pic. clo., 180x120mm. KMM

8531 THE/WRECK OF THE NANCY BELL/Or/Cast Away on Kerguelen Land/By/John C. Hutcheson/ Author of 'Picked up at Sea' &c. &c./with six full-page illustrations/London:/Blackie & Son, 49 & 50 Old Bailey, E.C.;/Glasgow, Edinburgh and Dublin
n.d. [192-?]
288pp, 32pp adv., b/w frontis. & 5 f/p b/w illus. by Frank Feller, pic. clo., 185x120mm. KMM

HYNE, C. J.

8532 SANDY CARMICHAEL/ By/ C. J. Hyne/author of/"Four Red Night Caps" "Stimson's Reef...[& 3 titles]/London/Sampson Low, Marston & Company Ltd./1907
xii, 308pp, col. frontis. & 7 b/w plates, pic. clo., 210x152mm. NSL:M

8533 SANDY CARMICHAEL/By/Cutcliffe J. Hyne/ Author of/"Adventures of Captain Kettle", "Further/ Adventures of Captain Kettle"/etc/[device]/London/ Sampson Low, Marston & Co., Ltd.
n.d. [inscribed Xmas 1926]
xii, 308pp, b/w frontis. & 5 b/w plates sgd A. Hitchcock, pic. clo., 180x120mm. KP

INGLIS, E. R.

8534 Mullens' Stories for Children/(No. 401)/TIKIUS/A Tale of New Guinea/by/E. R. Inglis/(For Ages 10 to 12)/[drawing]/Robertson & Mullens Ltd./Melbourne
n.d. [1951]
95pp, b/w frontis. & 1 f/p b/w illus., b/w drawings in text, pic. wrappers, 180x100mm. ANL

IREMONGER, Lucille

8535 THE YOUNG TRAVELLER IN THE/SOUTH SEAS/by/Lucille Iremonger/Phoenix House London 1952
158pp (inc. glossary & index), b/w frontis. & map, 16pp b/w photographic illus., clo., 180x115mm. NSL:M

8536 THE YOUNG TRAVELLER IN THE/SOUTH SEAS/Lucille Iremonger/with a map, 25 photographs/ and a frontispiece/[device]/Phoenix House/London
Second Imp. 1959
158pp (inc. 5pp index &c.), col. frontis., double-spread b/w map, b/w photographic illus., clo., 185x120mm. SUA

JENNISON, John W.

8537 THUNDERBIRDS/LOST WORLD/by/John J. Jennison/Published by/World Distributors (Manchester)/Limited/London. Manchester/England
1966
205pp, unillus., boards, 187x120mm. ANL
New Guinea setting

JOHNS, William Earl

8538 BIGGLES IN/ THE SOUTH SEAS/By Captain W. E. Johns/Illustrated by/Norman Howard /[device]/Oxford University Press/London New York Toronto
1940
255pp, col. frontis. & 6 f/p b/w illus., clo., 185x125mm. GK

8539 Another copy as above, both printed at the University Press Oxford by John Johnson, but 2nd copy printed on less bulky paper. Both bound in green cloth, but bulky copy is blocked on front cover with a design in darker green of a plane flying over an island, and on spine a design of seaweed & shells, while the slimmer vol. shows a plane flying over the Pyramids. GK
• Rpt as above 1943, 1946, 1947, 1950, 1951. KP

8540 BIGGLES IN/THE SOUTH SEAS/Captain W. E. Johns/Illustrated by/Norman Howard/Geoffrey Cumberlege/Oxford University Press.
London, 1st pub. 1940; Rpt 1943, 1946, 1947, 1950, 1952
245pp & 1p preface & 1p note, 6 f/p b/w illus., clo., 185x120mm. SUA

8541 BIGGLES IN/THE SOUTH SEAS/Capt. W. E. Johns/Brockhampton Press/Leicester
First printed 1940, sixth imp. 1952, this edition first published 1962
184pp (inc. 3 pp note) unillus., clo., 184x118mm. KP

8542 Captain W. E. Johns/BIGGLES IN THE/SOUTH SEAS/Cover illustration/by Peter Archer;/Text illustrations/by Norman Howard/[device]/Armada/ Paperbacks/for Boys and Girls
1965
159pp (inc. 1p summary on the South Sea Islands), 1p adv., 5 f/p b/w illus., pic. wrappers, 180x110mm. RM

8543 Another copy as above but with different cover illus. and copyright note reads: 'The estate of the late W.E. Johns' indicating date of publication late 1968 or later. KP

8544 BIGGLES IN/THE SOUTH SEAS/By/Captain W. E. Johns/Illustrated by/Norman Howard/Geoffrey Cumberlege/Oxford University Press/Leighton House, Melbourne
n.d. [1946. First published in Great Britain 1940]
222pp, 6 f/p b/w illus., clo., 185x125mm. KMM
• Rpt as above [1946]. GK
• Rpt as above 1950. KP

German edition

8545 BIGGELS [*sic*] FLIEGT IN DIE SÜDSEE
Berne, Hallwag, n.d.
256pp, marbled bds & leather spine. Unseen

8546 WORRALS/OF THE ISLANDS/A Story of the/ War in the Pacific/by/Captain/W. E. Johns/[map]/ Pictures by Stead/Hodder & Stoughton Ltd./London
1945
192pp, b/w frontis. & 12 b/w illus. (6 plates printed on each side), clo., 185x120mm. GK
• Rpt as above, January 1948. GK
Third imp. April 1950 as above, 185x117mm. KP

8547 WORRALS/INVESTIGATES/A further adventure in the career of Joan Worralson and her friend 'Frecks'/Lovell, one time of the W.A.A.F. by/Captain W. E. Johns/[device]/Lutterworth Press/London/1950
173pp, col. frontis. & 4 f/p col. illus., clo., 185x120mm. Grant
Story has a South Pacific setting.
See also Australian section for other Biggles and Worrals titles.

JOHNSON, Patricia

See Cook, Boris & Johnson, Patricia

JOYCE, Roger

NEW GUINEA. *See* Australian Explorers

JOVOPA, Mackenzie

OROKAIVA. *See* Stories of our People

JUDD, Alfred

8548 AT SCHOOL ON/THE OCEAN/By/Alfred Judd/ Thomas Nelson and Sons, Ltd./London Edinburgh New York/Toronto and Paris
First published 1928

95pp, b/w frontis., col. pic. bds, 180x120mm. KMM
The Captain series
A boy's attempt to solve the mystery of his father's ship, missing off the New Guinea coast.
New edition [1952] as above, but clo. CLRC
Also various undated rpts (195-?) 'The Peerless Series'. KP

KABELL, Margaret
8549 PROPHET OF THE/PACIFIC/The Story of John G. Paton/by/Margaret Kabell/[device]/ Lutterworth Press/London
1969
95pp, unillus., clo., 184x120mm. VSL

KÄSTNER, Erich
8550 THE 35th OF MAY/or/CONRAD'S RIDE TO THE/SOUTH SEAS/Erich Kästner/Illustrated by /Walter Trier/English version by/Cyrus Brooks/ [device]/The New English Library
First pub. in Great Britain by Jonathan Cape in 1933; Rpt 1939, 1958, 1966
125pp, 1p adv, b/w text drawings, stiff col. pic. wrappers, 190x134mm. ANL
8551 THE 35th OF MAY/OR/CONRAD'S RIDE/TO THE SOUTH SEAS/by/Erich Kästner/[device]/ Illustrated by Walter Trier/English Version by/Cyrus Brooks/Jonathan Cape/Thirty Bedford Square London
• Rpt 1966, 1971
192pp, 21 b/w drawings, clo., 195x134mm. KMM

KELLERMAN, Annette
8552 FAIRY TALES OF THE/SOUTH SEAS/and/other Stories/by/Annette Kellerman/Illustrations by/ Marcelle Wooster/London/Sampson Low, Marston & Co. Ltd.
n.d. [1933]
318pp, 16 f/p b/w illus. in text, clo., 185x120mm. KP
Stories of the South Seas
Another copy inscribed 1944. KP

KELMAN, Janet H.
8553 THE STORY OF/CHALMERS OF/NEW GUINEA/ By/Janet Harvey Kelman/With pictures by/W. Heath Robinson/London: T. C. & E. C. Jack/New York: E. P. Dutton & Co.
n.d.
120pp, 1p introduction, col. frontis. & 7 f/p col. illus. signed 'Will Bennett Robinson', clo. (with col. illus. pasted on front cover), 145x110mm. NSL:M
The Children's Heroes series

KENDALL, K.
8554 SOUTH FROM/'FRISCO/A Sea Story/by/ K. Kendall/[device]/Collins/London and Glasgow
1965
188pp, unillus., clo., 180x120mm. KMM
A story of the South Seas
• Rpt 1970, sim. clo. with previous d/w illus. printed on front cover. KP

KENNEDY, Dorothy M.
8555 A Pan-Pacific Book/CHILDREN OF/THE PACIFIC ISLANDS/by Dorothy M. Kennedy/line illustrations/ by T. Plaisted/Reed Education
Wellington N.Z. 1972
48pp, b/w photographic illus. & drawings, stiff pic. wrappers, 250x185mm. KP

KENT, Louise Andrews
8556 HE WENT WITH/MAGELLAN/By/Louise Andrews Kent/Author of "He Went with Marco Polo" etc./Illustrated by/Paul Quinn/[illus.]/George G. Harrap & Co.Ltd./London Toronto Wellington Sydney
First published in Great Britain 1945, rpt 1948, 1952, 1954, 1956, 1959, 1963
200pp, b/w frontis. & 7 f/p b/w illus., chapter headings, dec. e/p, clo., 195x130mm. KP

KER, Annie
8557 PAPUAN/FAIRY TALES/By/Annie Ker/With illustrations/Macmillan and Co., Limited/St. Martin's Street, London/1910
149pp, 3pp introduction, 2pp adv., b/w photographic frontis. & 12 f/p b/w photographic illus., clo., 205x135mm. CLRC

KER, David
8558 IN QUEST OF THE UPAS/A Tale of Adventure in New Guinea/By/David Ker/Author of/'A Wave-Worn Rock'. 'Cossack and Czar'/'Marooned on Mystery Isle', etc./Illustrated by/John Mackay/W. & R. Chambers, Limited/38 Soho Square, London, W.1; and Edinburgh
1934
264pp, b/w frontis., & 3 b/w plates, clo., 184x126mm. KMM

KEYSSER, Missionar Christian
8559 AJO!/ Ein Missionsbuch für deutsche Jügend/Von Missionar Christian Keysser/Früher in Deutsch-Neuguinea,/[device]/Zugleich Nr.64 der Neuendettelsayer Missions schriften/Glocken-Verlag Nürnberg
1926
240pp & 1 p. adv., col. frontis, & 12 leaves, b/w photographic plates, boards with clo. spine, 202x140mm. NSL:M

KINGSTON, William H. G.
8560 THE/OCEAN QUEEN/and/THE SPIRIT OF THE STORM/A New Fairy Tale of the Southern Seas/By/ William H. G. Kingston Esq./Author of "The Albatross", "Peter the Whaler", etc. etc./With illustrations/by/F. Königstadt Esq./London/T. Bosworth 215 Regent Street/1851
91pp, 2pp introduction, b/w frontis. & 3 b/w illus., clo., 170x130mm. ANL
8561 THE/OCEAN QUEEN/and/The Spirit of the Storm/A New Fairy Tale of the Southern Seas/By/ William H. G. Kingston Esq./Author of "The Albatross", "Peter the Whaler" etc. etc./With Illustrations/by/F. Königstadt Esq./Second Edition/ London:/Thomas Bosworth 215 Regent Street/1854
91pp, 2pp introduction, col. frontis. & 3 col. illus., clo., 180x130mm. ANL

8562 THE EARLY LIFE OF OLD JACK: a Sea Tale, by William H. G. Kingston...London [etc.] T. Nelson & Sons, 1859
303pp, 17x10.6cm. Cover title & caption 'Old Jack'
Unseen: Osborne Bibliography.
8562a [decoration]/OLD JACK;/A Tale for Boys./By/ W. H. G. Kingston,/Author of 'A Voyage round the World'. 'My First Voyage/to Southern Seas', &c./ London:/T. Nelson and Sons, Paternoster Row:/ Edinburgh; and New York./1869
vii+507+4 pp adv., engraved frontis., & engravings in text throughout, gilt dec. clo., 190x124mm. KMM

8563 OLD JACK/A Tale for Boys/By/W. H. G. Kingston/Author of "A Voyage round the World", "My First Voyage to/Southern Seas" &c./With upwards of sixty engravings/London:/T. Nelson and Sons,/Paternoster Row./Edinburgh; and New York./ 1881
507pp, 1p preface, engraved frontis. & engravings

throughout, pic. clo., gilt lettering & vignette, 185x124mm.
Includes 3 chapters relating to whaling in the South Seas. KP
• Rpt as above 1886. KMM

8564 OLD JACK/A Tale for Boys/By/W. H. G. Kingston/Author of/'Peter the Whaler' 'The Three Midshipmen' 'From/Powder-Monkey to Admiral' etc/ Illustrated by Henry Austin/London/Ward, Lock & Co., Limited/New York and Melbourne/1903
433pp & 14pp adv., b/w frontis., 3 b/w plates, clo., 187x123mm. CLRC

8565 OLD JACK/By/W. H. G. Kingston/Thomas Nelson and Sons/London, Edinburgh, Dublin/and New York
n.d. [prize label 1912]
472pp & 8pp adv., col. frontis. & 4 col. plates by W. S. Stacey, pic. clo. with gilt panel on spine, 185x125mm. KP
• Rpt as above, all edges gilt, KP

8566 OLD JACK/by/W. H. G. Kingston/[coloured illustration]/Illustrated by/Arthur H. Buckland/Collins Clear-type Press/London & Glasgow
n.d. [inscribed 1919]
380pp, 4pp adv., col. frontis. & 3 f/p col. illus, 2-col. t.p. (printed in red & blue), clo. (with illus. pasted on front cover & spine), 200x135mm. Grant
Copies of this edition seen inscribed 1909, 1912, 1920, some with col. pic. t.p. & one copy (inscribed 1919) with col. onlays on front cover & spine. KP

8567 BOYS' SEA STORY/OMNIBUS/*Mr Midshipman Easy*/Captain Marryat/*Two Years before the Mast*/R. H. Dana/*Old Jack*/W. H. G. Kingston/[device]/London and Glasgow/Collins Clear-type Press
n.d. [1934]
Separate pagination 362, 304, 380pp, unillus., clo., 193x124mm. KP

8568 A VOYAGE/ROUND THE WORLD/A Book for Boys/By/W. H. G. Kingston/Author of "My First Voyage to Southern Seas", "Old Jack", etc./London/ T. Nelson and Sons, Paternoster Row;/Edinburgh; and New York/1872
[BMC Lists: Round the World; a tale for Boys, Lond. 1859]
460pp, engraved frontis. & engravings throughout, clo., 185x120mm. NSL:M
Part of action takes place in South Pacific.
• Another copy as above but: [decoration] at top of t.p. & dated 1873
460pp, 4pp adv., b/w frontis., 12 f/p engravings & smaller ones in text, dec. clo. with medallion in gilt on front cover, bevelled boards, 185x124mm. GK

8569 A VOYAGE/ROUND THE WORLD./A Book for Boys./by/W. H. G. Kingston,/Author of "My First Voyage to Southern Seas", "Old Jack",/&c. &c./With Forty Engravings./London:/T. Nelson and Sons, Paternoster Row./Edinburgh; and New York./1880
460pp, 4pp adv., b/w engraved frontis. & b/w engravings throughout, pic. clo., 185x125mm. KP
• Rpt as above 'The Kingston Library' 1888. KP
• Rpt as above 'The Kingston Library' 1900. CLRC

8570 A VOYAGE ROUND/THE WORLD/By/W. H. G. Kingston/Thomas Nelson and Sons/London, Edinburgh, Dublin/and New York
n.d. [prize label 1909]
415pp, col. frontis. & additional pic. t.p. in two cols, 4 col. plates, pic. clo., gilt panel on front cover & spine, 185x130mm. KP
• Rpt as above 1908, 1910. KP
• Rpt as above, n.d. [193-?] KMM

French edition

8571 W. H. G. Kingston/UNE/CROISIERE/AUTOUR DU MONDE/ouvrage/Imité de l'Anglais avec l'autorisation de l'auteur/Par/J. Belin de Launay/E. E./Illustré de 44 gravures sur bois/Par Riou/[device]/ Paris/Librairie Hachette et Cie/79, Boulevard Saint Germain, 79/1876/Droits de traduction et de reproduction réservés.
279pp, 34 f/p illus. & smaller ones in text, dec. clo., gilt edges, 250x155mm. NSL:M

8572 LITTLE BEN HADDEN,/or,/Do Right, whatever comes of it./By/W. H. G. Kingston./[vignette]/ London:/The Religious Tract Society,/56, Paternoster Row; 65, St Paul's Churchyard:/and, 164 Piccadilly
n.d. [inscribed 1877; first pub. 1870]
viii, 206pp, 2pp adv., engraved frontis. & 4 f/p b/w engravings, & in text, pic. clo., 160x100mm. GK
Set in the South West Pacific
• Rpt as above, but additional line on t.p.: Manchester: Corporation Street. Brighton: Western Road
Details as before. KMM

8573 LITTLE BEN HADDEN;/or,/Do Right whatever comes of it./By/W. H. G. Kingston,/Author of "Captain Cook: His Life, Voyages, and Discoveries",/Etc./[vignette]/The Religious Tract Society,/56 Paternoster Row, 65 St. Paul's Churchyard,/and 164 Piccadilly
n.d. [inscribed 1884]
206pp, 18pp adv., b/w frontis & 4 b/w illus., b/w head & tailpieces, etc., dec. clo., 180x120mm. RM

8574 BEN HADDEN/or/Do Right, whatever comes of it/By/W. H. G. Kingston/Author of/"Captain Cook; His Life, Voyages & Discoveries", etc./[vignette]/ London/The Religious Tract Society/56 Paternoster Row, 65 St. Paul's Churchyard/and 164 Piccadilly.
n.d.
160pp, 16pp adv., engraved frontis., tailpieces & small engravings throughout, clo., 185x120mm. KMM
• Rpt as above but also author of: "The Golden Grasshopper", "The Cruise of the 'Mary Rose'"/etc. etc./[vignette]/London/The Religious Tract Society/4 Bouverie Street and 65 St Paul's Churchyard. KP
• Rpt as above but 4pp adv., pic. clo., 180x110mm. KMM

8575 BEN HADDEN/or/Do Right, Whatever Comes of it/By/W. H. G. Kingston/Author of 'Captain Cook', 'The Cruise of the Mary Rose'/London/The Religious Tract Society/4 Bouverie Street and 65 St Paul's Churchyard E.C.
n.d.
189pp, 2pp adv., col. frontis, 1 f/p b/w illus., 2 colour t.p. (printed in red & blue), pic. clo., 180x120mm. KMM

8576 IN THE EASTERN SEAS:/or,/The Regions of/The Bird of Paradise./A Tale for Boys./By/W. H. G. Kingston,/author of "Round the World", "My First Voyage", "Old Jack", etc./London:/T. Nelson and Sons, Paternoster Row;/Edinburgh; and New York/ 1874
[First published 1871]
608pp, engraved frontis. & folding map, b/w engravings throughout (copy seen re-bound in leather), 180x115mm. NSL:M
Several chapters relate to New Guinea & the Pacific islands.
Another copy as above but green clo. dec. in gilt. GK

8577 IN THE/EASTERN SEAS;/or/The Regions of the Bird of Paradise/A Tale for Boys./by the late/W. H. G. Kingston./Author of "Round the World", "My First Voyage", "Old Jack"/etc. etc./with one hundred and eleven engravings/London:/T. Nelson and Sons,

Paternoster Row/Edinburgh; and New York/1881/(All rights reserved)
608pp, engraved frontis., 19 f/p engravings & others in text, dec. clo., 185x120mm. KP
• Rpt 1884 as above. KP
• Rpt 1889 as above. CLRC

8578 IN THE/EASTERN SEAS/By/W. H. G. Kingston/Thomas Nelson and Sons/London, Edinburgh, Dublin/and New York
n.d.
510pp, 2pp adv., col. frontis. & 4 f/p col. illus., clo., 185x120mm. KMM
• Rpt as above but t.p. printed in red & black, col. frontis., additional pic. t.p. & 4 col. plates, pic. clo. with title in gilt panel on front cover & spine, 186x126mm. KP
Other copies as above, n.d. [prize labels 1909, 1910] with different col. clo. bindings. KP
Another copy as above [prize 1915] but has no pic. t.p. KP

8579 [decoration]/MARY LIDDIARD; or, the Missionary's Daughter. A Tale of the Pacific,/By/William H. G. Kingston/Gall & Inglis./Edinburgh:/Bernard Terrace/London:/25 Paternoster Sqr./(The right of translation is reserved.)
[1873]
128pp, col. frontis., dec. clo., title in gilt on spine & on black panel on front cover, 160x100mm. KMM
• Rpt as above but: Gall & Inglis/London: Edinburgh:/30 Paternoster Row. 6 George Street./(the right of translation is reserved)
n.d.
As above but caption under frontis. printed in red, 157x98mm. GK
• Rpt as above but: Gall & Inglis./London: Edinburgh:/25 Paternoster Sqr/6 George Street
RM

8580 Another copy: MARY LIDDIARD/The Missionary's Daughter/By/W. H. G. Kingston,/Author of "The Cruise of the Frolic" "The Fire Ships",/"Uncle Boz", etc./London:/Gall and Inglis, 25 Paternoster Square:/and Edinburgh.
Details as before but pic. clo., 180x115mm. WRT

8581 THE VOYAGE OF THE "STEADFAST";/or the/Young Missionaries in the Pacific/by/William H. G. Kingston,/author of/"Captain Cook", "Little Peter the ship Boy" etc./[vignette]/London:/The Religious Tract Society,/56, Paternoster Row; 65 St. Paul's Churchyard;/and 164 Piccadilly
n.d. [prize 1889; first pub. 1877, BMC]
128pp, 16pp adv., engraved frontis. & 2 f/p engravings, dec. clo. with title in gilt panel on front cover, pic. e/p, 170x110mm. GK

8582 THE VOYAGE/OF THE "STEADFAST"/By/W. H. G. Kingston/Author of "From Powder/Monkey to Admiral", etc./This book is condensed from the longer work by/this justly popular writer of stories of adventure/London/4 Bouverie Street and 65 St. Paul's Churchyard.
n.d.
95pp (inc. 3pp notes), 1p biographical note, b/w frontis. & 5 b/w f/p illus., clo., 185x120mm. KMM

8583 THE/MATE OF THE "LILY";/or/Notes from Harry Musgrave's Log Book./by/W. H. G. Kingston,/Author of "Owen Hartley", "The Settlers",/&c. &c./Published under the direction of/The Committee of General Literature and Education,/Appointed by the Society for Promoting/Christian Knowledge./Society for Promoting Christian Knowledge;/Sold at the Depositories:/London: 77 Great Queen Street, Lincoln's Inn Fields;/4 Royal Exchange; 48 Piccadilly;/and by all Booksellers./New York: Pott Young & Co.
n.d. [first edition; advertisements dated 1878]
160pp, 4pp adv., b/w frontis. & 2 f/p b/w illus., dec. clo., 180x120mm. RM
Setting Singapore, New Guinea &c.

8584 Another copy as above but: Northumberland Avenue, Charing Cross, W.C.:/43 Queen Victoria Street, E.C./Brighton: 135 North Street/New York: E. & J. B. Young & Co.
KMM

8585 As above but: Brighton: 129 North Street/New York: Edwin S. Gorham
n.d. [school prize 1913]. CLRC

8586 KIDNAPPING IN THE/PACIFIC/or/The Adventures of Boas Ringdon/A Long Yarn in Four Lengths/By. W. H. G. Kingston/With twenty-three illustrations/London/George Routledge and Sons, Limited/Broadway, Ludgate Hill/Manchester and New York
n.d. [1878]
173pp, 12pp adv., b/w illus., pic. clo., 180x120mm. KMM
Another copy 'Every Boy's Library' with a dec. non-pictorial cover design. KMM

8587 Another copy as above but: George Routledge and Sons/Broadway, Ludgate Hill/New York: 9 Lafayette Place.
n.d.
173pp, 10pp adv., col. frontis., 22 f/p b/w illus., pic. clo., 184x120mm. NSL:M

8588 THE TWO WHALERS;/or,/Adventures in the Pacific./by/William H. G. Kingston,/Author of "Ned Garth", "Owen Hartley", &c. &c./Published under the Direction of/The Committee of General Literature and Education,/Appointed by the Society for Promoting/Christian Knowledge./London./Society for Promoting/Christian Knowledge;/Northumberland Avenue, Charing Cross;/4, Royal Exchange; 48 Piccadilly./New York: Pott, Young & Co.
n.d. [advertisements dated 1879]
128pp, 4pp adv., b/w frontis. & chapter headings, pic. clo., 165x115mm. RM

8589 As above but: 43 Queen Victoria Street, E.C./Brighton: 135, North Street,/New York: E. & J. B. Young & Co.
128pp, 8pp adv., b/w frontis. & 1 vignette in text, pic. clo., dec. e/p, 167x114mm. CLRC

8590 THE/SOUTH SEA WHALER./A Story of the Loss of the "Champion" and/the adventures of her crew./By/W. H. G. Kingston/Author of "Old Jack", "In the Eastern Seas", "On the Banks/of the Amazon" "In the Wilds of Africa", etc/With thirty-one engravings./London T. Nelson and Sons, Paternoster Row./Edinburgh; and New York./1882
363pp, engraved frontis. & add. engraved t.p., 29 f/p engravings, dec. clo., 185x120mm. ANL
A whaling party in the South Pacific are wrecked & finally settle in NSW.
• Rpt 1885 as above. GK
• Rpt 1892 as above. RM

8591 THE SOUTH SEA/WHALER/By/W. H. G. Kingston/Thomas Nelson and Sons/London, Edinburgh, Dublin/and New York
n.d. [prize 1907]
304pp, col. illus. prelim. title, col. frontis. & t.p. printed in 2 cols, 4 col. plates (by W. H. C. Groome), pic. clo., 187x128mm. KP

Another copy as above but without prelim. t.p. KP
Another copy as above n.d. [prize 1911]. KP
Another copy, e/p designed with 'T. N. & S.' monogram. KP
Another copy as above, n.d. [prize 1930]. CLRC

8592 THE/CRUISE OF THE "DAINTY",/or/Rovings in the Pacific,/By/William H. G. Kingston,/Author of/"Owen Hartley", "Ned Garth", "Mate of the Lily" etc./Published under the Direction of the Committee/of General Literature and Education appointed by the/Society for Promoting Christian Knowledge/London:/Society for Promoting Christian Knowledge;/Northumberland Avenue, Charing Cross;/43 Queen Victoria Street; and 48, Piccadilly./New York: Pott, Young and Co.
n.d. [1880, copy inscribed 1881 & adv. dated 1/10/80]
192pp, 4pp adv., b/w frontis. & 2 f/p b/w illus., dec. clo., 178x117mm. GK
Story of a Pacific voyage begins & ends in Brisbane.
8593 Another copy as above but 'By the late W. H. G. Kingston' [Kingston died 1880] & slightly different publisher's imprint [Brighton 129 North Street/New York: E. S. Gorham], tinted frontis. & 2 f/p tinted illus., 190x125mm. RM
8594 Another copy with again variant imprint [Brighton: 135 North Street/New York: E. & J. B. Young and Co.]
n.d. [inscribed 1891]
Pic. clo., 180x120mm. KMM

8595 [decoration]/THE TWO VOYAGES:/or,/MIDNIGHT AND DAYLIGHT./By/William H. G. Kingston,/Author of/"Captain Cook, his Voyages and Discoveries", "The Golden Grasshopper", etc./[drawing]/London:/The Religious Tract Society./56 Paternoster Row: 65, St. Paul's Churchyard;/and 164 Piccadilly
n.d. [1881? Copy seen inscribed 1884. Note in pencil states: 'This was first published as a serial in the "Sunday at Home" 1865']
315pp, 4pp adv., b/w frontis., 20 f/p b/w illus., map, small engravings, pic. clo., 180x130mm. NSL:M
Story of missionary enterprise in the South West Pacific; also published as *The Cruise of the Mary Rose.*
Another copy as above with 16pp adv. GK

8596 THE CRUISE OF THE/'MARY ROSE'/Or, Here and There in the Pacific/by William H. G. Kingston./Author of "Captain Cook, his Voyages/and Discoveries"/"The Golden/Grasshopper" "Little Peter/the Ship Boy", etc./London, The Religious Tract Society/56 Paternoster Row and 65 St. Paul's Churchyard
n.d. [copy inscribed 1901]
269pp, 6pp adv., b/w frontis. & 16 b/w illus., pic. clo., 195x135mm. Grant
8597 THE CRUISE OF THE/"MARY ROSE"/or Here and There in the Pacific/by William H. G. Kingston/Author of "Captain Cook, his Voyages/and Discoveries" "The Golden/Grasshopper" "Little Peter/The Ship Boy" etc./New edition/London The Religious Tract Society/56 Paternoster Row and 65 St. Paul's Churchyard
n.d.
269pp, 6pp adv., b/w frontis. & 16 b/w illus., pic. clo., 195x135mm. KMM
Another copy 'New edition' but address given as '4 Bouverie Street and 65 St Paul's Churchyard E.C.', details the same. KMM
8598 THE CRUISE OF THE 'MARY ROSE'/or/Here and there in the Pacific/By/William H. G. Kingston/Author of/'Captain Cook, his Voyages and Discoveries', etc. etc./With Coloured Illustrations by/Alfred Pearse/London/The Religious Tract Society/4 Bouverie Street and 65 St Paul's churchyard.
n.d.
269pp, 6pp adv., col. frontis. & 2 col. plates & b/w drawings, pic. clo., 205x135mm. VECD

8599 PETER TRAWL;/or/The Adventures of a Whaler./By/W. H. G. Kingston/Author of "The Three Midshipmen", "Clara Maynard"/"Hendriks the Hunter", etc. etc./Illustrated/Fourth thousand/London:/Hodder and Stoughton,/27, Paternoster Row./MDCCCLXXXII
iv, 350pp & 2pp adv., b/w frontis. & 2 plates, pic. clo., gilt edges, title on front cover & spine in gilt, 184x120mm. GK
Part of the action takes place in the Pacific, Philippines & New Guinea.
8600 PETER TRAWL;/or,/The Adventures of a Whaler;/by/W. H. G. Kingston/Author of "From Powder Monkey to Admiral", "James Braithwaite",/"Hendriks the Hunter"/With eight full page illustrations/sixth thousand/London:/Hodder and Stoughton/27 Paternoster Row./MDCCCXC
350pp, 2pp adv., b/w frontis. & 7 b/w plates, pic. clo., 185x120mm. CLRC
8601 Another copy as above to: "Hendriks the Hunter", etc/New Edition/Illustrated in Colour by James Durden/London/Henry Frowde/Hodder and Stoughton/1910
350pp & 18pp adv., col. frontis. & 3 col. plates, clo. with col. onlay on front cover, 185x120mm. KMM
8602 PETER TRAWL/The Adventures of a Whaler/By/W. H. G. Kingston/Illustrated in Colour by James Durden/[device]/Humphrey Milford/Oxford University Press/London, Edinburgh, Glasgow/Toronto, Melbourne, Cape Town, Bombay
1924
350pp, col. frontis. & 3 f/p col. illus., clo., 190x125mm. KMM

8603 JAMES BRAITHWAITE/The Supercargo/The Story of His Adventures Ashore and Afloat./by/W. H. G. Kingston/author of/"Peter Trawl; or, The Adventures of a Whaler"/"Hendricks the Hunter", "Jovinian", etc./with eight full page illustrations/London:/Hodder and Stoughton,/27, Paternoster Row./MDCCCLXXXII
xii, 266pp, 26pp adv., 5pp introduction, engraved frontis. & 7 f/p engravings, dec. clo., 185x120mm. CLRC
Another copy as above but 'third thousand'. GK
Another copy as above but 'eighth thousand' 1892. KMM
8604 Another copy as above but: London/Henry Frowde/Hodder and Stoughton/1909
xii, 266pp, 16pp adv., col. frontis. & 3 col. plates, clo. with col. onlay (T. C. Dugdale), 185x120mm. KMM
8605 Another copy as above but: Illustrated in Colour by T. C. Dugdale/[device]/Humphrey Milford/Oxford University Press/London Edinburgh Glasgow/Toronto Melbourne Cape Town Bombay
1924
Details as in 1909 ed. but 190x120mm. CLRC

8606 HAPPY JACK/and other/Tales of the Sea./By/W. H. G. Kingston./Author of "Ronald Morton" "The Cruise of the Frolic"/"The African Trades" etc/London:/Gall and Inglis, 25 Paternoster Square,/and Edinburgh.
n.d. [1889?]
124pp, engraved frontis. & 3 f/p b/w illus., pic. clo., 174x120mm. KMM
Most of the action in the title story occurs in the Pacific.

8607 THE/RIVAL CRUSOES/By/W. H. G. Kingston/[drawing]/Griffith Farran Browne & Co. Limited/35 Bow Street, Covent Garden/London
n.d. [1st published 1879]
378pp, 1p preface, b/w engraved frontis. & 7 f/p engraved illus., dec. clo., 190x135mm. GK
Some of the action takes place in the Indian & South Pacific oceans; the author states that the book is based on a short story by Agnes Strickland.

KNIGHT, Arthur Lee
8608 THE MIDS/OF/THE "RATTLESNAKE";/or,/Thrilling Adventures with Illanun Pirates./and/Ned Burton's Adventures in the/Fiji Islands./By/Arthur Lee Knight/Author of "Adventures of a Midshipmite", "Ronald Hallifax; or He would be a Sailor", "The Cruise of the Theseus", Etc. Etc./Illustrated by Walter S. Stacey./London/Ward, Lock & Co., Limited./Warwick House, Salisbury Square, E.C.,/New York and Melbourne
n.d.
227pp, 28pp adv., b/w frontis. & 3 b/w plates, pic. clo., 195x125mm. RM
Title story takes place off the coast of Borneo.
Another copy as above but dated 1889. WRT
Second edition 1891 as above. ANL

KNIGHT, F. E.
8609 THE ISLAND/OF/RADIANT PEARLS/By/F. E. Knight/Illustrated by/Stephen Russ/London/Hollis & Carter.
1950
206pp, b/w frontis. & 3 f/p b/w illus., clo., 184x120mm. ANL

The Knight and the Sailor
8610 An all colour picture book/THE KNIGHT/AND THE SAILOR/[extended col. frontispiece]/Ward Lock & Co Limited 1964—Made in England—Ward, Lock & Co.Limited London & Melbourne
[44]pp, col. illus. throughout, col. pic. boards & e/p. 276x217mm. KP
The last 23pp tell the story of the Mutiny on the *Bounty*.

LACRE, Michel & SABATIE, Louis
8611 HEROES OF/EXPLORATION/by Michel Lacre and Louis Sabatie/Illustrations by/J. C. Forest, G. Fouille/P. Leroy Marcellin/J. Mora, R. Peron/Translated by Cmdr. H. Emmet/[coloured illustration]
Golden Pleasure Books London, 1962, by arrangement with Grosset and Dunlap Inc. New York (copyright 1961)
128pp, col. illus. throughout, pic. boards, dec. map e/p, 275x205mm. BBC
Includes one chapter (12pp) on the exploration of the Pacific & Oceania.

LAMBERT, John C.
8612 THE ROMANCE OF/MISSIONARY HEROISM/True Stories of the Intrepid bravery/and stirring adventures of Mission-/aries with uncivilized man, wild beasts/and the forces of nature in all parts of the world./By/ John C. Lambert, M.A., D.D./Author of/"The Omnipotent Cross", "Three Fishing Boats", etc./with thirty-nine illustrations/London/Seeley and Co. Limited/38 Great Russell Street1907
346pp & 16pp adv., b/w frontis. & 34 b/w plates, dec. clo., 195x130mm. KP

8613 MISSIONARY HEROES/IN OCEANIA/True Stories of the intrepid bravery/and stirring adventures of missionaries/with uncivilized man, wild beasts and/the forces of nature/by/John C. Lambert, M.A., D.D./Author of/"The Omnipotent Cross", "Three Fishing Boats"/&c. &c./with eight illustrations/London/Seeley and Co. Limited/38 Great Russell Street/1910
163pp (inc. 1p prefatory note, 4pp introduction), 28pp adv. (2pp adv. precede text), b/w frontis. & 7 f/p b/w illus., dec. clo. (front cover has vignette in gilt of native), 195x125mm. KMM
Contents include: Bishop Selwyn of Melanesia; Father Damien of Milokai; Rev. James Calvert in Fiji; John Williams and John G. Paton in the New Hebrides; Opukahaia & the American Mission to Hawaii.
• Rpt as above but 'with ten illustrations/London/Seeley, Service & Co., Limited/196 Shaftsebury Avenue'.
1925, details as before. KP

LAMPEN, C. Dudley
8614 THE/QUEEN OF THE EXTINCT VOLCANO./A Story of Adventure./By/C. Dudley Lampen./Author of "The Dead Prior", etc./Illustrated by Leonard Linsdell./Published under the direction of the general/literature committee./London:/Society for Promoting Christian Knowledge,/Northumberland Avenue, W.C.;/41, Queen Victoria Street, E.C./Brighton: 129 North Street./New York: E. & J. B. Young and Co.
n.d. [inscribed 1900]
224pp, 32pp adv., b/w frontis & 2 f/p b/w illus., map in text, pic. clo., 180x120mm. RM
Boys' adventure story set on an island near 'Feejee'

[LANCASTER, W. J. C.]
See 'Collingwood, Harry'

LANSDOWN, G. N.
8615 HOW/THE CROCODILE/GOT HIS TEETH/and other stories/[drawing]/G. N. Lansdown
Macmillan & Co.Ltd., London 1959
32pp, b/w illus. throughout, stiff pic. wrappers, 185x135mm. NSL:M
Pub. by the Dept. of Education in assoc. with the South Pacific Commission Literature Bureau. NSL:M

LAVILLE, Jean and BERKOWITZ, J.
8616 PACIFIC ISLAND/ LEGENDS/Life and Legends in the South Pacific Islands/by Jean Laville /and/Captain Joseph Berkowitz/Medical Corps, United States Army/Librairie Pentecost /Noumea, New Caledonia
1944
xviii, 164pp & 2pp index, 1 map, b/w illus. throughout by T .F. Wildes, clo., 195x135mm. SUA

LEA, Beverley
THE ABELAM PEOPLE. *See* Peoples of the Pacific

LEDERER, CHLOE
8617 Chloe Lederer/DOWN THE HILL/OF THE SEA
Lothrop, Lee & Shepard Co., New York 1971
96pp, b/w extended frontis. & b/w illus. throughout by Ati Forberg, clo., 228 x150mm. KP
Story tells of a Pacific island whose inhabitants are forced to move when the island is chosen to be a weapon testing site.

LEGGATT, T. Watt and ALEXANDER, W. M. M.
8618 JOHN G. PATON, D.D./Missionary to the New Hebrides/A Memorial life for our children/[photograph] By Rev. T. Watt Leggatt./J. Clerk New Hebrides Synod/and Rev. W. M. M. Alexander./J. Clerk S.A. of Victoria/issued by the State Assembly of Victoria./Price One Penny/Arbuckle, Waddell & Fawckner, Printers, 20 McKillop St., Melbourne
n.d. [1907?]

16pp b/w photographs & map of the New Hebrides on back wrapper, wrappers, cover title, 207x139mm. ANL

LEHR, Hans

8619 Hans Lehr/SAMBIO/Unter deen Kopfjägern/von Neu Guinea/Ensslin & Laiblin Verlag Reutlinger
n.d. [1952?]
80pp, b/w text illus. by Willi Widmann, pic. wrappers, 180x120mm. KP

LEIGHTON, Robert

8620 THE KIDNAPPING OF/PETER CRAY/A Story of the South Seas/By/Robert Leighton/London:/John F. Shaw & Co. Ltd., 3 Pilgrim Street,/Ludgate Hill, E.C.
n.d. [first pub. Grant Richards, 1903]
viii, 324pp., col. frontis. & 3 f/p col. plates & 1 b/w map, clo., 185x124mm.
Title on cover & spine 'Peter Cray'. KMM

8621 PETER CRAY/A Story of the South Seas/by/Robert Leighton/John F. Shaw (1928) & Co., Ltd./Publishers/3 Pilgrim Street, London, E.C.
n.d.
324pp, col. frontis. & 3 f/p b/ illus., b/w map in text, clo., 185x120mm. KMM

8621a PETER CRAY/A Story of the South Seas/by/Robert Leighton/John F. Shaw & Co. Ltd./4 & 5 Friar Street, Carter Lane,/London, E.C.4
n.d. [inscribed 1945]
324pp, b/w frontis. & 2 f/p b/w illus., b/w map in text, clo., 185x120mm. KMM

8622 SEA SCOUT AND/SAVAGE/Adventures among the Cannibals of the/Solomon Islands/By/Robert Leighton/Author of "The White Man's Trail" etc./Ward, Lock & Co., Limited/London and Melbourne
n.d. [1923]
256pp, b/w frontis., pic. clo., 185x120mm. CLRC

8623 Another copy as above, but with t.p. reading: '...Melbourne/1923', & 2 f/p b/w illus. KMM

Swedish edition

8624 MALAITAS HEMLIGHET/En Sjöscouts Äventyr I/Stilla Havet/Av/Robert Leighton/ Översättning Fran Engelsan/Av/Styrbjörn Melander/[device]/C. E. Fritzes Bokförlags Aktiebolag
Stockholm 1925
164pp, unillus., col. pic. boards with clo. spine, 185x120mm. RM

8625 COO-EE!/A Story of Peril and Adventure/in the South Seas/By/Robert Leighton/Author of /"Kiddie of the Camp". "The Pilots of Pomona"/etc. etc./Philadelphia: J. B. Lippincott Coy./London: C. Arthur Pearson Ltd 1910
256pp, b/w frontis. & 7 b/w plates, clo., 196x125mm. KP

8626 COO-EE!/A Story of Peril and Adventure/in the South Seas/By/Robert Leighton/Author of "Kiddie of the Camp", "The Pilots of Pomona"/etc.etc./London/C. Arthur Pearson Ltd./Henrietta Street/1911
256pp, & 3 pp adv. preceding t.p., b/w frontis. & 7 f/p b/w illus. (printed on text paper), clo., 196x125mm. KP
The Scout Library No. 10

8627 COO-EE!/A Story of Peril and Adventure/in the South Seas/By/Robert Leighton/Illustrated by E.P.Kinsella/London/C. Arthur Pearson Ltd./Henrietta Street
First published 1910, Rpt 1922
Details as above, but pic. clo., 195x125mm. KP

Swedish edition

8628 COO-EE!/En Boyscoutberättelse Fran/Soderhavsöarna/Av/Robert Leighton/[device]/ Ahlen & Äkerlunds Förlag/Goteborg 1912
190pp, unillus., col. pic. wrappers, adv. verso back wrapper, 195x130mm. ANL

LELIE, Frans

8629 KAPERS OF/NIEUW-GUINEA/Door Frans Lelie/Geïllustreerd door Van Looy/Leeftud 12–16 Jaar/[vignette]/Amsterdam/Van Holkema & Warendorf N.V.
n.d.
198pp, 2pp adv., b/w frontis. & 3 f/p b/w illus., b/w drawings throughout, pic. clo., 225x145mm. RM

Let's go to Papua

8630 LET'S GO TO PAPUA/[drawing]/Australian Board of Missions/242 Pitt Street, Sydney./First Edition/Wholly set up and printed in Australia by D. S. Ford, 44–50 Reservoir Street, Sydney.
n.d. [195-?]
33pp (inc. 1p foreword), b/w frontis., b/w drawings & photographic illus. throughout, map, wrappers, 210x130mm. ANL
Another copy, Australian Board of Missions/14 Spring Street, Sydney/Wholly set up and printed in Australia by Luxton & Hooper, 336 Kent St. Sydney
n.d., details as before. KMM

LEWIS, David

THE KARKAR ISLANDERS. *See* Peoples of the Pacific

Life on Desolate Islands

8631 LIFE ON DESOLATE ISLANDS;/ or/Real Robinson Crusoes./By the Author of/"Tales of the Northern Seas" etc./[decoration]/London:/The Religious Tract Society:/56 Paternoster Row; 65 St Paul's Churchyard:/ and 164 Piccadilly
n.d. [school prize 1879]
127pp, engraved frontis. & 8 f/p & smaller engravings, clo., 156x98mm. HBM
Contains 'The Pitcairn Islanders' pp31-60.

LINDGREN, Astrid

8632 PIPPI/IN THE SOUTH SEAS/[drawing]/Astrid Lindgren/London/Oxford University Press/1957
Originally published 1955 by Raben & Sjogren, Stockholm, under the title *Pippi Langstrump Isoderhavet*
117pp, b/w drawings throughout, illus. by Richard Kennedy, clo., 195x145mm. NSL:M
Translated by Marianne Turner.
• Rpt 1963, 1965. KP

8633 Astrid Lindgren/PIPPI IN THE SOUTH SEAS/translated by Marianne Turner/Illustrated by /Richard Kennedy/London/Oxford University Press/1971
88pp, b/w illus., pic. wrappers (cover by Victor G. Ambrus), 195x125mm. KP

LINGGOOD, E.

8634 NEW/BRITAIN/Three Missionary/Studies/Dedicated to the memory of the/men who lost their lives on the/"Montevideo Maru"/Mrs. E. Linggood/This littlebook was originally prepared /for Victorian Y.W.M.M.[Young Womens Methodist Mission]
n.d. [194-?]
32pp (last 2pp blank, and inc. map frontis. & bibliography), b/w photographic illus., pic. wrappers, 182x122mm. KP

LINGGOOD, Rev. W. L. I.

8635 CHILDREN/OF/NEW BRITAIN/By/Rev. W. L. I. Linggood/The Methodist Missionary Society of Australia/139 Castlereagh Street/Sydney/1935
64pp, b/w photographic illus. throughout, dec. wrappers (adv. inside & map outside back wrapper), 210x130mm. ANL
Describes the work of the missions.

LIVINGSTON, Peter
8636 Pacific Heritage Series/HEROES FROM PAPUA/ AND NEW GUINEA/by/Peter Livingston/Illustrations by/Elizabeth Halls/In association with the/South Pacific Commission Literature Bureau/Macmillan & Co. Ltd./St. Martin's Street London/1959
47pp (inc. 1p author's preface), b/w map frontis. & 9 f/p illus., wrappers, 185x130mm. KMM
• Rpt 1965. KP

LOVETT, RICHARD
8637 TAMATE/The Life and Adventures/of a Christian Hero/By/Richard Lovett, M.A./Author of /"James Chalmers: His Autobiography/and Letters"./Etc. Etc./with 15 illustrations by James Finnemore/and two maps/London/The Religious Tract Society/4 Bouverie St. & 65 St Paul's Churchyard, E.C./1904
320pp, b/w frontis. & 14 f/p b/w illus., 2 b/w maps, pic. clo. with medallion portrait in gilt on front cover & repro. of one illus., 195x130mm. KP
Second ed. 1904 as above. RM
Third imp. 1907 " ", but lettering on front cover in colour not gilt. KP
• Rpt as above, but after 'Autobiography and Letters/ Etc. Etc./', 'London/The Religious Tract Society/4 Bouverie Street and 64 St Paul's Churchyard, E.C.4'
n.d.
320pp, col. frontis. & map, clo., 180x125mm. KP
• Rpt as above, but 'The Leisure Hour' Library Office/4 Bouverie Street London, n.d.
192pp, b/w frontis., 3 plates & 2 maps, clo., 210x137mm. KP
• Rpt as above, but 'R.T.S., 4 Bouverie Street, London, E.C.4'
n.d. [inscribed 1924]
320pp, col. frontis., & t.p. printed in red and blue, 1 b/w map only, pic. clo., 184x122mm. KP.
Missionary Pioneer series

LUCKER, Sydney C. (ed.)
8638 MISSIONARY HEROES/IN/MANY LANDS/ Stories of Adventure, High Endeavour, and Great Enterprise/Edited by Sydney C. Lucker/The National Sunday School Union./104/5 Newgate Street, London E.C.1
n.d. [1946]
256pp., b/w drawings in text, clo., 178x120mm. NSL:M
Includes James Calvert of the Fiji Isles (pp67-88) & John Williams of the South Seas (pp151-78).

LYONS, R. S.
8639 THE SCHOOL IN/THE SKIES/by/R. S. Lyons/ The Children's Press/London and Glasgow
n.d.
190pp, b/w frontis., clo., 180x120mm. KP

McCULLAGH, S. K.
8640 Sea Hawk Library Book 4/[col. drawing]/MUTINY AT SEA/S. K. McCullagh, M.A./Illustrated by A. E. Harris/E. J. Arnold & Son Limited/Leeds
1965
32pp, col. & part-col. illus. on each alternate page opening, clo., dec. map e/p, 200x145mm. HBM
Story of the mutiny of the *Bounty* told for school children.

MACKAY, Margaret
8641 Margaret Mackay/Illustrated by Peggy Fortnum/ DOLPHIN BOY/A Story of Hawaii/Sydney /Australasian Publishing Company/in association with/George G. Harrap & Co. Ltd./London
n.d.
96pp, b/w frontis., & extended t.p., b/w drawings in text, limp dec. clo., 184x120mm. LRA

8642 ISLAND BOY/Robert Louis Stevenson/and/ His step-grandson/in Samoa/by/Margaret Mackay/author of/"Dolphin Boy"/Illustrated by/John Lewis/[device]/ George G. Harrap & Co. Ltd./London Toronto Wellington Sydney
1969
95pp, b/w frontis., & b/w drawings throughout, clo., 196x132mm. NSL:M

McKENZIE, Fred A
8643 JOHN WILLIAMS,/The/Martyr of Erromanga./By/ Fred A. McKenzie,/Author of "David Livingstone", "H. M. Stanley". etc, etc,/London:/James B. Knapp, 6 Sutton St., Commercial Road, E.;/and/26 Paternoster Row, E.C.
n.d. [prize label 1902]
60pp & 4pp adv., b/w frontis. & 3 f/p b/w illus., chapter headings & tailpieces, pic clo., 165x100mm. RM

MACPHERSON, June
8644 CANOE TO SCHOOL/Discovering New Guinea with Kari and Kateo/June Macpherson/Ure Smith—Sydney
1971
32pp, col. photographic illus. throughout, clo., map e/p, 285x210mm. BBC
Photographs by the author

MADDOX, Marie
8645 CHILDREN OF/SAMOA/A True story of the children of/Western Samoa/By/Marie Maddox /Drawings by/Beverley Dunphy/Published by/The Committee for Promotion and Literature/ Head Office:/Methodist Overseas Missions/139 Castlereagh Street/Sydney
1959
64pp, b/w drawings in text, dec. wrappers, 213x130mmm. KMM
• Rpt 1964 as above. KP

MARCHANT, Bessie
8646 ISLAND BORN/A Tale of Hawaii/By/Bessie Marchant/With Frontispiece by Leo Bates /Blackie & Son Limited/London and Glasgow
n.d.
256pp, b/w frontis. only, clo., 180x120mm. The Peak Library. SUA

MARRIOTT, E. P. W.
8647 PAPUA & NEW GUINEA/IN PICTURES/A Book of Elementary Social Studies/by/E. P. W. Marriott/In Association with the/South Pacific Commission Literature Bureau/Macmillan and Co. Limited/St. Martin Street, London/1961
First published 1956; rpt 1961
95pp (inc. 1p author's preface & 1p foreword by W. C. Groves, Director of Education, Territory of Papua & New Guinea), b/w photographic illus. throughout, dec. wrappers, 210x165mm. NSL:M

MARRYAT, Frederick
MASTERMAN READY;/or, The Wreck of the Pacific./ Written for Young People/By/Captain Marryat/ London:/Longman, Orme, Brown, Green, & Longmans/Paternoster Row/1841
Often considered the first adventure story for boys.

Belongs to the wider sphere of world children's literature & so not included here.

MARSH, David
THE MEKEOS. *See* Peoples of the Pacific

MARTIN, R. G. & REASON, J.
8648 TREASURE/ON THE DEEP/Adventures of the Bible on Ocean/and River round the world/By/R. G. Martin and J. Reason/With introduction by John A. Patten/[quotation]/The London Missionary Society/42 Broadway, Westminster,/London, S.W.I
1938
141pp (inc. 1p foreword), col. frontis., 9 f/p b/w illus., 1 b/w map, clo., 185x120mm. HBM
Contents include: The Mutiny on the *Bounty* (9pp); The Voyage of the *Duff* (15pp); Papuan Waterways, etc. (11pp).

MATANE, Paulias Nguna
8649 Stories of our People/KUM TUMUN/OF MINJ/ Paulias Matane/Melbourne/Oxford University Press/ London Wellington New York
1966
14pp, 5 b/w photographic illus., pic. wrappers, 180x120mm. CLRC

8650 MY CHILDHOOD IN/NEW GUINEA/Paulias Matane/Oxford University Press/1972
112pp, b/w photographic illus., clo., 215x137mm. ANL

MATHEWS, Basil
8651 YARNS OF/SOUTH SEA/PIONEERS/By/Basil Mathews, M.A./Editor of "The Fascinated Child" /Author of "The Splendid Quest" and/"Livingstone the Pathfinder"/With Notes and/Suggestions by/ F. Deaville Walker/Author of "The Call of the Dark Continent"/"China, A Nation in the Making".etc./A Book for Workers/among boys and girls./London Missionary Society/16 New Bridge Street, E.C.
n.d. [1st ed. July 1913?]
96pp, brown pic. wrappers (price 6d on front cover), b/w drawings in text, 245x97mm. KP
Stories for children with notes for teachers.
8652 YARNS OF/SOUTH SEA PIONEERS/To be told to Boys/By/Basil Mathews, M.A..&c. as above, London/ Edinburgh House Press/2 Eaton Gate S.W.1/1928
80pp, brown paper wrappers, 185x124mm. KP
• Rpt 1933 as above. KMM
• Rpt 1949 as above, but 'London/The Cargate Press/ Holborn Hall, E.C.1/1949'. RM
First pub. July 1913, rpt 1914, 1917, 1918, 1920, 1924, 1926, 1928 (twice), 1930, 1933, 1937, 14th imp. 1949

8653 JOHN WILLIAMS/THE SHIPBUILDER/By/Basil Mathews/with thirty-three illustrations/eighteen by/ Ernest Prater/Humphrey Milford/Oxford University Press/London New York Toronto Melbourne Bombay/ 1915
298pp (inc. 6pp index), col. frontis. & 3 f/p col. illus., 24 f/p sepia/white illus., 4 maps, dec. clo. (with col. onlay), dec. e/p, 185x120mm. CLRC
The e/p are illus. with drawings of ships named for John Williams & paid for by the children of Great Britain in his memory; the page preceding the frontis. was printed with a space left for a name & amount of money to be filled in, as this edition was designed to be presented to those children who collected sums of money to support the mission ships, a list of which, and also where they were based, is given.
8654 Another copy as above but: second impression/ (twenty-seventh thousand)/London/The Livingstone Press/48 Broadway Westminister, S.W.1/1922/Printed in England
298pp, b/w frontis, 4 sepia plates (printed on both sides), drawings, maps, clo., 180x120mm. KP
8655 Another copy as above but: fourth impression/ (thirty-first thousand)
With 15 illus., seven by Ernest Prater. KP
Fifth imp. 33rd thousand, 1927. KP
Seventh imp. 36th thousand, 1935. KMM
8656 JOHN WILLIAMS/THE SHIPBUILDER/By/Basil Mathews/With ten illustrations/by/Ernest Prater/ London/[device]/Published by the Livingstone Press/ 42 Broadway: Westminster, S.W.I
Revised & reprinted 1947
204pp, 10 b/w plates, clo., 185x120mm. KMM
This edition contains no index nor maps.
Second ed. as above. KMM

8657 THE SHIPS OF PEACE/By/Basil Mathews/London Missionary Society/16 New Bridge Street, London, E.C.4/1919
136pp (inc. double-spread map & 4pp list of principal ships & voyages), b/w frontis. & 5 b/w plates & other b/w drawings, limp clo., 182x120mm. KP
8658 THE SHIPS OF PEACE/ by/ Basil Mathews/ (Revised and Edited by Joyce Reason)/ London/ [device] /Livingstone Press 42 Broadway S.W.1/1947
94pp (inc. 3pp list of principal ships, &c.), b/w frontis. & 6 f/p b/w illus., clo., 186x120mm. KMM

8659 Friends of/all the world/HEROES IN/ FRIENDSHIP/By/Basil/Mathews, M.A./London /Humphrey Milford/Oxford University Press
1925
183pp, b/w illus. throughout, dec. t.p., pic. clo., 184x120mm. KP
Includes Bishop Patteson, Tamate & other South Seas missionaries.
• Rpt 1936, as above. KMM

8660 THERE/GO THE SHIPS/By/Basil Mathews/ Author of The Splendid Quest, Paul the Dauntless/A Life of Jesus, etc. etc./with eight illustrations in black and white/and frontispiece in colour by/Ernest Prater/ S. W. Partridge & Co.,/4, 5 & 6 Soho Square, London, W.I.
1935
236pp, 5pp prologue, col. frontis. & 8 f/p b/w illus., clo., 200x140mm. KMM
Includes chapters on James Cook, John Williams of Rarotonga, Elikana the South Sea Islander, Alexander Duff, & Bishop Patteson.

8661 Eagle Books, No. I/IF ONLY/I HAD A SHIP/(John Williams of the South Seas) By/Basil Mathews/First published 1937/Ninth impression, 1954/London/ Edinburgh House Press/2 Eaton Gate, S.W.I/1954
32pp, unillus., pic. wrappers, 180x120mm. Grant
2nd Australian ed. 1946. unseen

MATHEWS, Basil & SOUTHON, Arthur E.
8662 YARNS ON/HEROES OF THE DEEP/By/Basil Mathews/Author of "Yarns of South Sea Pioneers", "John Williams the Shipbuilder"/"Paul the Dauntless" etc./and/Arthur E. Southon/Author of/"A Yellow Napoleon/London/Edinburgh House Press/2 Eaton Gate, S.W.I/1927
First pub. June 1922; 2nd ed. Jan. 1924; 3rd ed. July 1926; 4th ed. June 1927
64pp (inc. 2pp authors' preface & 5pp notes), unillus., stiff dec. wrappers (with map on back cover), 185x120mm. KMM
Missionary tales including: 'John Williams' (8pp); 'The Twins of Star Island' (8pp, Bishop Patteson and the

Southern Cross); 'Adrift on a Raft (Elikana from the Northern Cook Islands, 8pp).

MATTHEWMAN, Phyllis
8663 JOHN WILLIAMS/by/Phyllis Matthewman/[device]/Oliphants Ltd./London Edinburgh
First pub. 1954, rpt 1955
95pp (inc. 1p foreword), col. frontis. sgd 'Jarvis', dec. clo., 154x120mm. KMM

MAYNE, William
8664 THE OLD ZION/William Mayne/Illustrated by Margery Gill/Hamish Hamilton—London
1966
64pp, part-col. illus. on every page & extended part-col.. frontis., clo., 243x180mm. KMM
South Sea island setting

MAZIERE, Francis
8665 TEIVA/His Life in the Pacific Isles/Written and Photographed by/Francis Maziere/Chatto & Windus/London
n.d.
48pp, b/w photographs throughout, clo., 260x215mm. KP

'METCALFE, William Charles' [pseud. C. Lawrence]
8666 UNDAUNTED./A Story of the Solomon Islands./By/W. Charles Metcalfe,/Author of/"Honours divided; or, Rescued from Rogue's Island: A Story of/the China Seas", "Steady your Helm";/etc. etc./New Edition/London:/John F. Shaw and Co.,/48, Paternoster Row, E.C.
First published 1895; this edition n.d. [inscribed 1918]
288pp, 10pp adv., b/w frontis. & 5 f/p b/w illus., pic. clo., 185x120mm. KMM
See also Australian section for other titles.

MIALL, Derwent
8667 Enlarged to 64 pages/The Nugget Library/of School and Adventure Tales Id./WRECKED IN THE PACIFIC/A Story of the stirring adventures of three boys on a desert island/[coloured illustration]
James Henderson & Sons, Red Lion House, London, n.d.
64pp, 3 f/p b/w illus., 1 b/w diagram, col. pic. wrappers (with adv. verso front cover, verso/recto back cover), cover title, 180x140mm. RM

MICHAEL, Charles D. (ed.)
8668 MISSIONARY/HEROES/Stories of/Heroism on the Mission Field/Edited by Charles D. Michael/Author of 'Heroes all!" "Deeds of Daring", "Heroines" etc./[quote.]/with eight illustrations/London/S. W. Partridge & Co./8 & 9 Paternoster Row
n.d. [1905]
viii+176pp & 32pp adv., b/w frontis. & 7 b/w plates by Lancelot Speed & others, pic. clo., 185x122mm. KP

8669 JOHN GIBSON PATON, D.D./The Missionary Hero/of the New Hebrides/By/Charles D. Michael /Author of "James Harrington, Bishop and Martyr"/Heroes All", &c./with eleven illustrations /London:/S. W. Partridge & Co.
n.d. [1912]
160pp (inc. 2 pp preface) &32pp catalogue of books. portrait frontis. & 10 b/w plates (? by J. Finnemore), pic. clo. with title in gilt, 190x127mm. KP
Another copy as above but London:/S. W. Partridge & Co., Ltd./Old Bailey
160pp, no adv., title in black, 190x120mm. KP
• Rpt as above, 'London:/S. W. Partridge & Co., Ltd./E.C.4', n.d. [prize label 1924]
160pp, b/w portrait frontis. & 10 b/w illus., clo., 184x122mm. KP
• Rpt as above, but 'Kilmarnock, Scotland/John Ritchie, Publisher of Christian Literature/and through all Booksellers/[pasted on to page]/ Pickering & Inglis/London and Glasgow'
n.d.
Details as before. KP

MILLER, Charles
8670 LIFE AMONG/THE CANNIBALS/by/Charles Miller/illustrated/Robert Hale Limited/63 Old Brompton Road London S.W.7
1958
158pp, 8 f/p b/w photographic illus., clo., 183x123mm. KP

MILLER, F. B.
8671 TALES OF TRAVEL:/Consisting of/Narratives of Various Journeys/ through/Some of the Most interesting parts /of the World/By F. B. Miller/Author of "Domestic Pleasures" &c. &c./London:/Printed for Harvey Darton,/Gracechurch-Street/1833
198pp, 2pp adv., engraved frontis. & 3pp b/w engravings, clo., 170x100mm. NSL:M
A mother relates to her children what she has read of various places. Pp86–167 relate to the Polynesian Isles; pp168–72 relate to Pitcairn Islands.

MILLER, Warren H.
8672 The Boy Explorers Series/THE BOY EXPLORERS/IN/DARKEST/NEW GUINEA/By/Warren H. Miller/With illustrations by/Frank Spradling/[device]/Harper & Brothers Publishers/New York and London
1921
236pp & 4pp adv., b/w frontis. &3 f/p b/w illus. dec. clo., 185x125mm. ANL

Missionary Present about the Children in Fiji
8673 MISSIONARY PRESENT/ABOUT THE CHILDREN IN/FIJI/Wesleyan Methodist/Missionary Society printed by W. M. Watts 80 Grays Inn Road [London]
n.d.
32pp, engraved dec. t.p., 4 f/p engravings & some in text, col. dec. wrappers printed by J. M .Kronheim, 160x120mm. CLRC

Missionary Voyages among the South Sea Islands
8674 MISSIONARY VOYAGES/AMONG THE/SOUTH SEA ISLANDS/[engraving]/With engravings from original designs/Boston:/Published by Clapp & Broaders/1834
viii, 200pp (inc. 2pp pref.), 9 f/p engravings, clo., 138x102mm. SUA
Missionary voyages from August 1796 when Captain Wilson in the *Duff* weighed anchor.

[MOGRIDGE, George]
8675 THE/OLD SEA CAPTAIN/[engraving of a ship]/London:/The Religious Tract Society: /Instituted 1799./Sold at the depository, 56 Paternoster Row,/and 65 St Paul's Churchyard; and/by the Booksellers./1842
xii, 324pp, engraved frontis., chapter headings, endpieces & engravings in text, clo. with vignette of ship & native canoes on front cover, 148x110mm. ANL
8676 THE/OLD SEA CAPTAIN/[engraving of a ship]/London:/The Religious Tract Society;/56 Paternoster Row; 65 St Paul's Churchyard;/and 164 Piccadilly;/and sold by the booksellers
n.d.
xii,324pp, engraved frontis. & engravings in text, clo. gilt dec., 132x104mm. CLRC

MOORE, F. Frankfort
8677 MATE OF THE JESSICA/a Story of the South Pacific/by/F. Frankfort Moore/Author of "Where the Rail runs now", "Told by the Sea" etc./with Twelve Full-page illustrations/[device]/London:/Marcus Ward & Co., 67–68 Chandos Street/and at Belfast and New York/(All rights reserved)
First published in 2 vols, Marcus Ward, London [BMC 1879] this edition n.d.
423pp, 2pp adv. (preceding t.p.), b/w engravings, dec. clo., 170x120mm. CLRC

8678 THE FATE/OF/THE "BLACK SWAN"/A Tale of New Guinea/By/F. Frankfort Moore/Author of "The Mutiny on the Albatross" etc./Illustrated by W. H. Overend/Published under the direction of the committee/of general literature and education appointed by the/Society for Promoting Christian Knowledge/London:/Society for Promoting Christian Knowledge,/Northumberland Avenue, Charing Cross, W.C./43 Queen Victoria Street, E.C.;/26 St. George's Place, Hyde Park Corner, S.W./Brighton: 135, North Street./New York: E. & J. B. Young and Co.
n.d. [school prize 1887]
320pp, 4pp adv., b/w frontis. & 3 f/p b/w illus., pic. clo., 180x120mm. ANL

8679 CORAL AND COCOA-NUT/The Cruise of the Yacht 'Fire-Fly'/to Samoa/by/F. Frankfort Moore, /Author of 'Fireflies and Mosquitoes','Will's Voyages'/ 'Tre, Pol, and Pen' etc./Illustrated by W. H. Overend./ Published under the direction of the Committee/of general literature and education appointed by the/ Society for Promoting Christian Knowledge/London:/ Society for Promoting Christian Knowledge,/ Northumberland Avenue, Charing Cross, W.C.;/97 Westbourne Grove, W.; 43 Queen Victoria Street, E.C./Brighton: 135 North Street./New York: E. & J. B. Young & Co./1890
vi, 379pp & 4pp adv., b/w frontis. & 3 f/p b/w illus., pic. clo., 180x120mm. NSL: M
Appears to be a sequel to FIRE-FLIES AND MOSQUITOES, which, being set in Formosa, is not included here
Also author of:
WILL'S VOYAGES [a story] London C.K.S. [1886] unseen
TWO IN THE BUSH, and others elsewhere, London A. D. Innes, 1895.
Not children's.

MOORE, W. G.
8680 This is Their Life/FAMILY IN SAMOA/by/W. G. Moore/[device]/Hulton Educational Publications London 1961
82pp (inc. 2 maps & 1p glossary), 1p author's note, 41 b/w photographic illus. & b/w drawings, dec. clo., 185x120mm. NSL:M

[MORTIMER, Favell Lee, née Bevan]
8681 THE/ NIGHT OF TOIL,/or,/A Familiar Account of the Labours of/the first Missionaries in the South/Sea Islands./By the Author of the "Peep of Day"/[vignette and quotation]/London:/J. Hatchard and Son, 137 Piccadilly:/John Harris, St. Paul's Church-Yard./1838
xvi, 438pp & 23 appendices, &1p adv., engraved frontis., 6 small engravings and 1 map, clo., 172x108mm. SUA
This history includes a chroonology of mission activities in Tahiti 1796–1837 and a description of Tahiti and the neighbouring islands.

MUDDOCK, Joyce Emmerson
8682 THE GOLDEN IDOL/A Story of Adventure By/ Sea and Land/By/Joyce Emmerson Muddock /Author of/'Basile the Jester'. 'The Dead Man's Secret'...[& 5 more titles]/[device]/ London/Chatto & Windus/1899
314pp & 8pp preface, 36 pp adv., unillus, pic. clo., 190x125mm. KMM
The first 80pp are set in the Victorian & NSW gold diggings, & the remainder in New Guinea and also partly in New Britain.

MURCHIE Jr, Guy & others
8683 Classic Romances of Literature/THE/MUTINY/OF THE/BOUNTY/And Other Sea Stories/[device]/The Spencer Press
Copyrighted 1937 by Consolidated Book Publishers Inc., USA
309pp, 1p foreword, b/w frontis., b/w map, clo., 200x140mm. HBM
Contains 'The Mutiny of the *Bounty*' (pp1–137), & 'Idylls of the Sea', by Frank Bullen (pp235–309), which partly relates to Australia & the Pacific region.

The Mutiny of the Bounty and Life of a Sailor Boy
8684 THE/MUTINY OF THE BOUNTY/AND/LIFE OF A SAILOR BOY/W. & R. Chambers, Limited/London and Edinburgh
n.d.
139pp, b/w frontis., pic. clo. (frontis. reproduced on front cover), 180x115mm. HBM
'Life of a Sailor Boy' (pp71–139) abridged with some alterations from a small work entitled 'Thirty Years from Home, or a Voice from the Main Deck, being the experiences of Samuel Leech' (Boston 1843). This story has no connection with Australia.
Many variant editions dated from 1892. HBM
8685 Whitcombe's Story Books/THE MUTINY OF THE/ "BOUNTY"/(For ages 10 to 12 years)/[drawing]/ Whitcombe & Tombs Limited/Auckland, Christchurch, Dunedin, Wellington/Melbourne and London.
n.d. [192-?]
96pp (inc. 2pp notes), b/w photographic frontis. & 4 f/p b/w photographic illus., 1 f/p b/w map, 1 f/p b/w drawing & b/w drawings in text, illus. by J. M. Thomasson, stiff pic. wrappers (with adv. inside front cover & on both sides of back cover), 175x115mm. HBM
See McLaren 527
8686 THE MUTINY OF THE *BOUNTY*; or, The Marvellous Adventures of Christian and his Comrades [1832?] 'London: Published at the 'Cheerful Visitor' Office, 10, Red Lion Court, Fleet Street; Price one penny per volume'. 128pp. Unseen BP 888
8687 A Sapphire Picture Book/MUTINY ON THE/ BOUNTY/[extended col. illus.]/Ward, Lock & Co., Limited—London & Melbourne.
1964
20pp, col. illus. throughout, pic. boards, 275x210mm. HBM

Mutiny on the Bounty
8688 MUTINY/ ON THE/BOUNTY
Metro-Goldwyn-Mayer presents an Arcola Production Printed in the USA, n.d.
16pp, decorations in text, wrappers, 190x140mm. KP
Printed throughout in blue; promotional material for film

NACKINGTON, M.
8689 WITH BLIGH OF/THE BOUNTY/or/From Tofoa to Timor/By/M. Nackington/with three illustrations/ London:/The Sheldon Press/Northumberland Avenue, W.C.2/New York and Toronto: the Macmillan Company
n.d. [first published 1924]

128pp & 8pp adv., b/w frontis, 1 b/w illus., &1 b/w map, pic. clo., 184x118mm. KMM

NAIRNE, W. P.

8690 GREATHEART OF/PAPUA/(James Chalmers)/By/ W. P. Nairne, M.A./with a map, four illustrations in colour/and twenty-two in half-tone, chiefly from/ drawings by/Ernest Prater/Humphrey Milford/Oxford University Press/London New York Toronto Melbourne Bombay/1913
229pp, col. frontis. & 3 f/p col. illus., 22 b/w illus. (inc. 9 photographic illus.), 1 b/w map, dec. clo. (with col. onlay), gilt edges, 185x120mm. RM

8691 GREATHEART OF/PAPUA/(James Chalmers)/By/ W. P. Nairne/with a map, one illustration in colour/ and eight in half-tone, chiefly from/drawings by/ Ernest Prater/Humphrey Milford/Oxford University Press/London New York Toronto Melbourne Bombay/ 1920
229pp, col. frontis. & 8 f/p b/w illus., map e/p, clo., 185x120mm. KMM

8692 3rd impression, The Livingstone Press, 42 Broadway S.W.1 London 1937, b/w frontis., 6 plates. KP
Another copy n.d. [inscribed 1943] as above with new pic. map. KP

8693 JAMES CHALMERS/Greatheart of Papua/By/ W. P. Nairne/Illustrated from drawings by/Ernest Prater/London/Livingstone Press/42 Broadway SW1/1948
160pp, b/w frontis. & 9 b/w plates, clo., 182x120mm. CLRC

Welsh edition

8694 DEWRGALON PAPUA (James Chalmers) Humphrey Milford, London 1915
206pp, frontis, 26 plates, clo.
Text includes list of Welsh missionaries. Unseen, info. from RM

NEVILL, E. Mildred

8695 LITTLE/BROWN ISLANDERS,/Talks and Stories about Papuan Children for the/use of Teachers or Children 6–8 years of age,/together with Training Class Notes for/the Primary Department/By/E. Mildred Nevill/London:/The Sunday School Union,/ 57 and 59 Ludgate Hill, E.C.4
n.d.
32pp, b/w frontis., wrappers, 180x122mm. KP

New Guinea Animal Picture Book

8696 NEW GUINEA ANIMAL PICTURE BOOK
Illustrated by Naoka Kikkawa/Robert Brown and Associates Pty Ltd./The Jacaranda Press
Port Moresby TPNG and Milton, Queensland, 1970
[62]pp, 30pp col. illus., col. frontis., pic. boards, 190x250mm. CLRC

The New Guinea Highlands Painting Book

8697 THE NEW GUINEA/HIGHLANDS/PAINTING BOOK
Published by The Australian Baptist Foreign Mission, 486 Albert Street, Melbourne, n.d. [195-?]
32pp (inc. 1p introduction), 12 f/p b/w illus., pic. wrappers, cover title, 185x245mm. KMM
Introductory note mentions this to be the third in a series, *The India Painting Book* & *All About Sangin* being the others. Acknowledgement is made to various people, & 'the art work was done by Miss Jean Storie'.

NODAWAY, Max

8698 A Romance: Thrilling, Instructive, Entertaining./ ROLLO IN HAWAII/By/Max Nodaway/A Tale of Thrilling Adventure, amid Volcanoes, Fire/Fountains and Tropical Wonderlands; into which/is woven a vivid description of those Mystic/Isles, where Fire and Water have built up a Delirium of Chaos and Beauty./ Profusely Illustrated/Chicago/Thompson & Thomas/ 1908
300pp, b/w frontis., 24 b/w illus. (some photographs), pic. clo., 194x134mm. NSL:M

NORDHOFF, Charles Bernard

8699 THE/PEARL LAGOON/By/Charles Nordhoff/ Illustrated by/Anton Otto Fischer/Boston/Little, Brown and Company/1939
[Copyright 1924]
224pp, 1p preface (dated 1924), b/w frontis. & 3 b/w illus., 205x135mm. NSL:M
South West Pacific background to the book

NORDHOFF, Charles Bernard & HALL, James Norman

8700 The Laurel and Gold Series/MUTINY ON/THE BOUNTY/by/Charles Nordhoff/and/James Norman Hall/(Abridged)/Illustrated by Logan McFarland/ Collins Clear-Type Press
Collins, Glasgow, Third impression 1960
295pp (inc. 7pp notes & questions), 1 f/p & 17 b/w illus. in text, clo., 155x100mm. HBM
An abridged edition for schools of the well-known novel

8701 Charles Nordhoff & James Hall/MUTINY/ON THE BOUNTY/with illustrations by/Phil Gascoine/Collins/ London and Glasgow
First published in this series 1964
256pp (inc. 4pp notes), b/w frontis. & 13 b/w illus., clo., 190x120mm. HBM
Collins Abridged Classics No. 1

8702 MUTINY ON THE/BOUNTY/Charles Nordhoff and James Norman Hall/ Brockhampton Press
Abridged edition first published Leicester, England, 1971
251pp, 1p publisher's note, b/w double-spread map only, clo., d/w designed by Val Biro, 204x133mm. HBM
Edited by Dorothy Ward.
Second imp. as above 1972. KP

8703 MUTINY ON THE/BOUNTY/Charles Nordhoff and James Norman Hall/Knight Books/the paperback division of Brockhampton Press
Revised edition Leicester, England, 1972
251pp, 1p publisher's note, unillus., pic. wrappers, 180x110mm. HBM

8704 MEN/AGAINST THE SEA/Charles Nordhoff/ &/James Norman Hall/With illustrations by/Nigel Lambourne/Blackie: London and Glasgow
n.d. [1971?]
206pp (inc. 1p introductory note), 6 f/p b/w illus., clo., 195x130mm. HBM
'Chosen Books' series

NORTHCOTT, Cecil

8705 Eagle Books, No. 5/MY FRIENDS/THE CANNIBALS/(John H. Holmes of Papua)/By/Cecil Northcott/First published 1937/First Australian Edition October 1943/Second Australian Edition, April 1944/London:/Edinburgh House Press/Melbourne:/ The Book Depot/288 Little Collins Street, C.1./1944
32pp, unillus., wrappers, 180x120mm. KMM

8706 SOUTHWARD HO!/An adventure and an Enterprise/in the South Pacific Ocean/by/Cecil Northcott, M.A./[6 line quotation]/[device]/London/ Livingstone Press
n.d. [1938]

98pp, b/w photographic frontis. & 6 f/p b/w illus., pic. wrappers, map e/p, 185x120mm. NSL:M
Story of opening of the South Pacific to Christian Missions

8707 JOHN WILLIAMS/SAILS ON/by Cecil Northcott/[portrait]/London/Hodder and Stoughton
1939
255pp, part-col. frontis. & 5 part-col. illus., clo., 180x115mm. Grant

8708 JOHN WILLIAMS/SAILS ON/By/Cecil Northcott/London/[device]/The Livingstone Press/42 Broadway [*sic*], S.W.1
First published 1938; revised edition 1948
160pp, b/w drawings in text, clo., dec. map e/p, 180x120mm. AJH

8709 Eagle Books, No. 38/SEND ME AMONG/SAVAGES/By/Cecil Northcott, Author of/My Friends the Cannibals, Hero of the Hottentots,/All God's Chillun/First published July 1941/Second impression November 1941/First Australian Edition, October 1943/London:/Edinburgh House Press/Melbourne:/The Book Depot/288 Little Collins Street, C.1./1943
32pp, unillus., wrappers, 180x120mm. KMM
The story of James Chalmers (1841–1901) of Papua.
• Another copy as above, but: Second Australian Edition April 1944, London. KMM
• Rpt London, Livingstone Press, 42 Broadway, 1951, pic. wrappers. KMM

8710 THIRTY HEROES/From the 150 years of Story of the/London Missionary Society/1795–1945/Chosen by/Cecil Northcott/and illustrated by/Joyce Reason/London Missionary Society/250, Pitt Street, Sydney, N.S.W./1944
64pp (inc. 1p author's preface), b/w drawings, pic. boards, 185x120mm. KMM
Contains 2-page biographies of various missionaries including some who worked in Papua & the S.W. Pacific region.

8711 Merlin Books/General Editor: J. Compton, M.A./VENTURERS OF FAITH/by/Cecil Northcott/[device]/London/Edward Arnold & Co.
1950
174pp & 1p adv., b/w illus., dec. boards,180x112mm. KP
Includes 'Give me a Ship' (John Williams)
• Rpt 1952,1955,1957, as above NSL:M

8712 THE SOUTH SEAS/SAILOR/The Story of John Williams and his Ships/by/Cecil Northcott/[device]/Lutterworth Press/London
1965
95pp, col. frontis., b/w map, clo., 185x120mm. KMM

Ol Meri Bilong Mamayang

8713 Territory of/Papua and New Guinea/OL MERI BILONG MAMAYANG/Wanpela Stori bilong ol meri/Illustrated by/Lois Nial/Produced by/Department of Native Affairs, Port Moresby and/South Pacific Commission Literature/Bureau in association
n.d.
22pp, b/w drawings, pic. wrappers, 210x150mm. CLRC

Old Sefanaia

8714 OLD SEFANAIA/The Fijian Herald/By/An old friend of his/London/Charles H. Kelly/25-35 City Road, and 26 Paternoster Row, E. C.
n.d. [188-?]
64pp, b/w frontis., & b/w text engavings, pic. clo., 160x110mm. KP
Missionary tale apparently intended for children

Over the Seas with a Brush

8715 OVER THE SEAS/WITH A BRUSH./A Painting Book/for Children/Part I./The London Missionary Society,/16 New Bridge Street, London, E.C.
n.d.
[23]pp, 12pp illus., pic. wrappers, 230x170mm. KMM
Contains one page of text on the S.S. *John Williams*, the South Seas missionary ship, & a coloured & sepia/white illustration of the vessel.

OWEN, Jean Allen [later, Visgar]

8716 OUR HONOLULU BOYS./A Story of/Child Life in the Sandwich Islands./By Mrs. J. A. Owen/[vignette of a boy]/The Religious Tract Society,/56,Paternoster Row; 65, St. Paul's Churchyard;/and 164, Piccadilly.
n.d. [first published 1881]
128pp, b/w frontis. 2 f/p b/w illus. chapter headings & tailpieces, dec. clo., 164x100mm. KMM

OXLEY, J. Macdonald

8717 IN THE SWING OF/THE SEA/By/J. Macdonald Oxley/Author of/'On the World's Roof' [& 3 more titles]/Illustrations by W. B. Lance/London/James Nisbet & Co.,Limited/21 Berners Street
n.d.[1897]
296pp, & 8pp adv., b./w frontis., & 3 f/p b/w illus., dec. clo with gilt panels & title on front & spine, t.e.g.,194x127mm. KP 'Boy's Holiday Library'
A whaling story set in the South Pacific by a Canadian writer.

8718 IN THE SWING OF/THE SEA/By/J. Macdonald Oxley/London/James Nisbet & Co.,Limited/22 Berners Street.W.
n.d. [prize label 1910]
296pp, & 32pp adv., col. frontis. & 3 col. plates, dec. clo., 193x128mm. KP

The Pacific Islands Today

8719 THE PACIFIC ISLANDS TODAY/People and Places/Prepared by the Staff of the/South Pacific Commission/Literature Bureau/South Pacific Commission/Noumea, New Caledonia/1962
72pp (inc. 1p foreword & 4 pp intro.), b/w photographic illus., diagrams & maps throughout, stiff dec. wrappers, 210x165mm. NSL:M

The Pacific Ocean Colouring Book

8720 THE/PACIFIC/OCEAN/COLOURING BOOK
H. E. C. Robinson Pty Ltd, 221–3 George Street, Sydney, n.d.
16pp, b/w illus. throughout, stiff dec. col. covers (with folding flap), cover title, 185x245mm. CLRC
The two sides of the flap contain reduced coloured reproductions of all the inner b/w pages as a painting guide.

PAGE, Jesse

8721 BISHOP PATTESON/The/Martyr of Melanesia/By/Jesse Page/[verse]/London/S. W. Partridge and Co./9 Paternoster Row
n.d.
160pp &16pp adv., b/w frontis. & numerous b/w illus., pic. clo. with gilt lettering & medallion of the bishop in a boat being rowed, blocked in gilt on front cover, 180x120mm. KP
Second edition, 10th thousand as above. KP
4th edition,19th thousand (inscribed Xmas 1895) as above. KP
27th thousand as above but on thicker paper, entirely different clo. bdg. KP
28th thousand (prize 1921) similar to 27th thousand but title &c. blocked in black instead of gilt. KP

PAGET, Elma K.
8722 THE STORY OF/BISHOP/PATTESON/By Elma K. Paget/With pictures by S. T. Dodd/device] /London : T. C. & E. C. Jack/New York: E. P. Dutton & Co.
n.d.[1906]
viii, 120pp., col. frontis. & 7 f/p col. plates, clo., col. onlay on front cover, 145x115mm. SUA
The Children's Heroes series, ed. by John Lang.

Papua and New Guinea
8723 PAPUA/AND/NEW GUINEA/Australia's Trust Territory/[col. illus. of a Bird of Paradise]
Published by British Commonwealth Youth Sunday Council of Victoria, Melbourne, Specialty Press, n.d. [195-?]
16pp, double-spread col. dec. t.p., map, numerous b/w photographic illus., pic. wrappers, 208x188mm. KP
In same series, uniform with above, *Malaya, our Commonwealth Neighbour* 1960. KP

Papua and New Guinea
8724 PAPUA AND/NEW GUINEA/A new series of 25 picture plates/issued by Sanitarium Health Food Company
Sydney n.d. [195-]
12pp, text, sketches & spaces left for pasting 25 cards, pic. wrappers, 235x165mm. KP

PARKMAN, Sydney
8725 THE/REEF PEARLERS/By/Sydney Parkman/with Illustrations/by C. J. Ambler/University of London Press, Ltd./War-time address:/St. Hugh's School, Bickley, Kent
n.d. [1937]
144pp (inc. 5pp questions) b/w frontis., & 11 f/p b/w illus., & others in text, limp pic. clo., 180x135mm. KP
'The Signal Books' supplementary readers; (re-issued 1942 in *The Sea Story Omnibus*; and in 1951 in Warwick Adventure Library)

PARR, Charles McKew
8726 SO NOBLE/A CAPTAIN/The Life and Voyages of/Ferdinand Magellan/by/Charles McKew Parr/ Robert Hale Limited/63 Old Brompton Road London S.W.7
First published 1955; First published in this abridged edition 1958
156pp, 14 b/w illus., col., 185x120mm. HBM
World Adventure series
Illus. consist of reproductions from early editions of Magellan's Voyages.

PASCOE, L.
THE SEPIK RIVER PEOPLE. *See* Peoples of the Pacific

PATEMAN, E. M.
8727 THE STORY/OF NABETARI/By/E. M. Pateman/ Illustrated by/Nancy Parker/In association with the South Pacific/Commission Literature Bureau/ Longmans
Melbourne 1959
24pp, b/w illus. in text, map, wrappers, 185x125mm. ANL
Bonito series The story of a Gilbert Island boy.

PEARCE, Winifred M.
8728 JOHN G. PATON/by/Winifred M. Pearce/ [device]/Oliphants Ltd./London Edinburgh
1954
96pp, unillus., pic. wrappers, 185x120mm. KP
• Rpt 1957, as above, but col. frontis. (sgd 'Jarvis'), clo., 185x120mm. SUA
• Rpt 1962. NSL:M

Pearls and Gold [Mona Tracy]
8729 Whitcombe's Story Books/PEARLS AND GOLD/For Ages 12–14 years/[drawing with caption]/ Whitcombe and Tombs Limited/Auckland, Christchurch, Dunedin and Wellington, N.Z./Melbourne and London
n.d. [193-?]
142pp (inc. 4pp glossary & 5pp questions), b/w frontis. signed 'H.C.' & 2 b/w illus., stiff illus. wrappers, 180x115mm. KMM
Most of the action takes place in the New Hebrides. Anonymous author appears to be Mona Tracy.
See McLaren 636

PEASE, Howard
8730 Howard Pease/SCHIFFBRUCH IN DER SÜDSEE
Werna Hörnemman Verlags, Bonn 1970
192pp, unillus, clo., 186x115mm. ANL
First published as *Shipwreck*, Doubleday & Co., New York, unseen

PENNY, Alfred
8731 THE HEAD-HUNTERS/OF/CHRISTABEL/A Tale of Adventure in the South Seas/By/Alfred Penny/ Author of "Ten Years in Melanesia"/Illustrated by Harold Piffard/Published under the direction of the general/literature committee/London:/Society for Promoting Christian Knowledge,/Northumberland Avenue, W.C.; 43, Queen Victoria Street E.C./Brighton: 129, North Street./New York: E. & J. B. Young & Co.
n.d. [1903]
301pp, 16pp adv., b/w frontis. & 3 f/p b/w illus., col. e/p, pic. clo., 190x125mm. KP
A story about the capture of Kanaka workers for the Queensland sugar plantations, set in the Solomon Islands & New Guinea.
8732 THE HEAD-HUNTERS/OF/CHRISTABEL/[as before to publisher's imprint]/London/The Sheldon Press/Northumberland Avenue W.C.2
n.d.
Details as before, but no adv., 183x120mm. KP

PILKINGTON, Roger
8733 THE GREAT SOUTH SEA/Roger Pilkington/ Illustrated by/G. Burgess Sharrocks/London Missionary Society/42 Broadway London/Macmillan and Co. Limited/St. Martin's Street London/1957
120pp, b/w drawings & diagrams, dec. clo., 185x125mm. KMM
Another copy as above without London Missionary Society imprint. BBC

PINCHOT, Gifford Bryce
8734 GIFF AND STIFF IN/THE SOUTH SEAS/By/ Gifford Bryce Pinchot/[engraving]/Illustrated with Photographs/and Wood Engravings/The John C. Winston Company/Chicago Philadelphia Toronto
1933
241pp, b/w photographic frontis. & 62pp b/w photographic illus. & engravings in text, dec. clo., map e/p, 215x145mm. NSL:M

PINFOLD, F. M.
THE MAORIS OF NEW ZEALAND. *See* Peoples of the Pacific

POLLARD, Eliza F.
8735 THE WRECK OF THE/'PROVIDENCE'./By/Eliza F. Pollard,/Author of "Roger the Ranger" "A Hero King" "The Green Mountain Boys",etc./with ten illustrations by W. Hatherall/London: /S. W. Partridge & Co.,/8 & 9 Paternoster Row
n.d. [190-?]

288pp, 26pp adv., 10 b/w plates, clo., 182x120mm. KMM
Borderline children's book about a wreck on a voyage from Hong Kong to the Victorian gold diggings and set partly in N. Australia

POOLE, Michael
8736 THE/REAL THING/A Story for Boys/By/Michael Poole/Thomas Nelson and Sons, Ltd/London, Edinburgh, New York/Toronto, and Paris
n.d. [195- ?] first published 1930
92pp, b/w frontis. only, clo., 180x120mm. NSL:M
Set in the South Pacific

POND, Seymour Gates
8737 FERDINAND/MAGELLAN/Master Mariner/ [device: World Landmark Books]/By Seymour Gates Pond/Illustrated by Jack Coggins/Random House—New York
1957
174pp, 6pp index, b/w chapter headings, b/w & part. col. drawings in text, map, dec. clo., dec. e/p, 205x140mm. HBM
Young Readers of America Selection

PONTING, Clarence
8738 THE BLUE/ISLAND TREASURE/An Adventure by Aeroplane in the South Seas/By/Clarence Ponting/ London/The Epworth Press/Edgar C. Barton
First published 1926; this edition n.d. [1935]
127pp, col. frontis. sgd 'Ogle', clo., 180x120mm. MK

POPPINS, J. E. (ed.)
8739 FALLING IN LOVE WITH/COLOURS/and/Other Missionary Stories of Many Lands/Prepared for the Use of All Lovers of Children/Arranged by J. E. Poppins/[device]/All profits to Overseas Missions/ Melbourne:/Young Methodist Missionary League,/ 134a Little Collins Street./288 Little Collins Street
n.d. [1945]
16pp, unillus, pic. wrappers, 214x135mm. ANL

8740 SAVED FROM THE/HEAD-HUNTERS/and/Other Missionary Stories of Many Lands/Prepared for the Use of All Lovers of Children/Arranged by J. E. Poppins/Fairfield, Victoria/First Volume in this Series/ "Falling in Love with Colours"/Melbourne:/Wyatt & Watts Pty. Ltd.
[1947]
16pp, unillus, pic. wrappers, 215x140mm. ANL

PRICE, Willard
8741 SOUTH SEA/ADVENTURE/by/Willard Price/ [drawing]/Illustrated from drawings by/Pat Marriott/ Jonathan Cape/Thirty Bedford Square London
1952
221pp, col. frontis. & 24 b/w illus. in text, clo., 200x130mm. NSL:M
Adventure story set in the South Pacific.
• Rpt 1954, 1956, 1959, 1971 as above. KMM
8742 Willard Price/SOUTH SEA ADVENTURE/ Illustrated from drawings by Pat Marriott/[device] /Knight Books/the paperback division of Brockhampton Press
5th imp. 1963
190pp & 2pp adv., b/w text illus., pic. wrappers, 180x110mm. KP
German edition
8743 Willard Price/ABENTEUER/IN DER SÜDSEE/ [drawing]/Benziger Verlag Einsiedeln Zürich Köln
1953
180 pp, b/w drawings in text by Kurt Stieger, clo., 200x130mm. ANL

8744 UNDERWATER/ADVENTURE/by/Willard Price/ [drawing]/Illustrated from drawings by/Pat Marriott/ Jonathan Cape/Thirty Bedford Square London
1955, Rpt 1955, 1958, 1963, 1967
204pp, & 1p illus. & note, col. frontis. & b/w drawings in text, clo., 196x134mm. KP

8745 VOLCANO/ADVENTURE/By Willard Price/ [drawing]/Illustrated from drawings by/Pat Marriott/ Jonathan Cape/Thirty Bedford Square London
1956
190pp, col. frontis. & b/w illus. in text, clo., 200x130mm. MK
• Rpt 1963, 1967. KMM

8746 Willard Price/WHALE/ADVENTURE/The John Day Company/New York
1960
191pp, unillus. apart from col. illus. e/p., clo., 203x130mm. NSL:M

PRIEST, Elizabeth
8747 CHILDREN OF/THE/MENDI VALLEY/A true story of the children of the/mountains of Papua New Guinea/by/Elizabeth Priest/Published by/The Secretary for Promotion and Literature/Head Office:/ Methodist Overseas Missions/139 Castlereagh Street/ Sydney
First edition 1957; rpt 1958
72pp, b/w map, b/w drawings throughout, stiff dec. wrappers, 210x120mm. CLRC
8748 CHILDREN/OF THE/MENDI/VALLEY/Story by/ Elizabeth Priest/drawings by/Dorothy Dunphy/ Published by the Committee for Promotion and Literature/Methodist Overseas Missions, 139 Castlereagh Street, Sydney
1961
64pp, b/w map & b/w marginal drawings, pic. wrappers, 217x140mm. KP

[PROTHEROE, Ernest]
8749 BUDGE AND BETTY/IN THE PACIFIC/ [drawing]/Published Renwick of Otley/180, Fleet Street/London, E.C.4
n.d. [inscribed 1932]
[97]pp, col. frontis., 2 f/p col. illus., b/w illus. throughout, pic. boards, 190x130mm. CLRC

BUDGE AND BETTY IN THE EAST
Uniform with above, contains half page text & one b/w illus. relating to Australia KMM

8750 THE SISTER CRUSOES/By/Ernest Protheroe/ Author of/'The Redemption of the Duffer' [& 2 other titles] with six full-page illustrations/London/Robert Culley/25-35 City Road, and 26 Paternoster Row, E.C.
1909
336pp. b/w frontis. & 5 b/w plates, by Leonard Skeats, pic. clo. with gilt lettering,187x124mm KP
• Rpt as above, but London/The Epworth Press/ J. Alfred Sharp
n.d. [school prize 1930]
336pp, col. frontis. & 3 b/w plates, clo., 186x120mm. KP

RANKIN, R. F.
THE SAMOANS. *See* Peoples of the Pacific

REASON, Joyce
8751 Eagle Books No. 16/THE BRICKLAYER/AND THE KING/(Henry Nott of the South Seas)/By/J. Reason/ Author of/The Man who disappeared; Storm over Madagascar./First published July 1938/second impression January 1940/First Australian Edition

January 1947/London:/Edinburgh House Press/2 Eaton Gate, S.W.1/Melbourne:/The Book Depot/288 Little Collins Street, C.1/1947
32pp, unillus., wrappers, 182x122mm. KMM

8752 TALES/FROM CHALMERS/By Joyce Reason/ Illustrated by S. E. Iredale/Colour Plates by K. M. Waterson/[device]/The Livingstone Press/42, Broadway, Westminster/London, S.W.1
First pub. 1942; 2nd imp. 1944; 3rd imp. 1947
96pp, 3 f/p col. illus. & b/w drawings in text, pic. boards (clo. spine), 210x165mm. KMM
Stories of James Chalmers, missionary to Raratonga & Papua.

8753 TALES FROM THE/L.M.S./By. J. Reason/ Illustrated by R. W. Ford/[device]/London/The Livingstone Press/42, Broadway, Westminster, S.W.1
1945
88pp, col. frontis. & 2 f/p col. illus., b/w drawings, pic. boards (with col. illus. pasted on front cover & clo. spine), 205x160mm. KMM
Includes: 'A. W. Murray, missionary to Samoa 1835–1872' (7pp); 'Raratonga and Samoa' (5pp); 'W. E. Goward in the Gilbert Islands' (7pp).

8754 FETCH FILIMONI/A Story of Papua/By/Joyce Reason/Author of 'Hunt for a Hero' etc./Illustrated by/Kathleen M. Waterson/[drawing]/London/ Edinburgh House Press/2 Eaton Gate S.W.1/1946
90pp, b/w frontis. & 3 f/p b/w illus., b/w drawings in text, dec. boards, 215x135mm. NSL:M

8755 L. M. S./OMNIBUS/Edited by/Joyce Reason/ London/[device]/Published by The Livingstone Press/ for the London Missionary Society/42 Broadway— Westminister, S.W.1
1951
96pp, b/w drawings & diagrams, pic. boards, 180x120mm. KMM
Includes several articles on Papua.

8756 Eagle Books No.53/TAKE MY LIFE/(Ruatoka of Papua)/By/J. Reason/Author of...[3 lines]/London/ Edinburgh House Press/2 Eaton Gate, S.W.1
Second impression 1957
24pp, unillus., pic. wrappers, 182x122mm. KP

8757 THE MAGIC SCREEN/by/Joyce Reason/ Illustrations/by/James Moss/Published by/The London Missionary Society/42 Broadway, London, S.W.1
1958
110pp, 10 f/p b/w illus., dec. initials at beginnings of chapters, dec. clo., 185x125mm. KMM
Contains chapter on James Chalmers & Rarotonga, & John Williams & Erromanga.

REED, Alexander Wyclif

8758 GEORGE AUGUSTUS SELWYN/Pioneer Bishop of New Zealand/A. W. Reed/[device]/London/Pickering & Inglis Ltd.
First published 1939; rpt 1947 & issued in conjunction with A. H. & A. W. Reed, New Zealand
96pp, b/w frontis. & 5 b/w drawings in text, clo., 180x120mm. KMM
Memoirs of Mighty Men and Women series

8759 Pageant of the Pacific/ISLANDS OF/ THE PACIFIC/Written by/A. W. Reed/Illustrated by /Conrad Frieboe/[drawing]/[device]/A. H. & A. W. Reed/Wellington Auckland Sydney
first pub.1958, rpt 1961
24pp, index inside back cover, b/w illus. throughout, stiff pic. wrappers (printed in black & blue), 248x188mm. KP
Uniform with the above *The Story of the Pacific*, KP

8760 FAIRY TALES/FROM THE PACIFIC ISLANDS/ Retold by/A. W. Reed/Illustrated by/Stewart Irwin/ [device]/A. H. & A. W. Reed/Wellington Auckland Sydney Melbourne
1969
136pp, b/w frontis., f/p b/w illus., b/w drawings in text, clo., 215x145mm. KMM

REED, Alexander Wyclif & HAMES, Inez

8761 MYTHS AND LEGENDS OF/FIJI/AND ROTUMA/by/A. W. Reed and Inez Hames/illustrated by Roger Hart/A. H. & A. W. Reed/Wellington Auckland Sydney
1967
251pp (inc. 2pp preface), 16 f/p b/w illus., clo., map e/p, 200x130mm. KMM

REED, A. H.

8762 SAMUEL MARSDEN/Greatheart of Maoriland/ A. H. Reed/[device]/London/Pickering & Inglis Ltd
first published 1939, rpt 1947
95pp, b/w frontis., b/w text drawings, clo., 182x122mm. SUA

'RICHARDS, Frank' [pseud. Charles Hamilton]

8763 BILLY BUNTER/AMONG THE/CANNIBALS/By/ Frank Richards/Illustrated by/R. J. Macdonald/Charles Skilton Ltd./London
First published 1950
236pp, 4pp adv., col. frontis., 5 f/p b/w illus., clo., 185x120mm. RM
• Rpt 1953 as above, 183x117mm. KP

8764 BIG CHIEF/BUNTER/By/Frank Richards/ Illustrations by/C. H. Chapman/[device]/Cassell London
First published 1963
216pp, col. frontis & 4 f/p b/w illus., clo., 180x120mm. RM

RITCHIE, John

8765 AMONG THE CANNIBALS;/Peeps at the South Sea Islands and their Savage/inhabitants...with Life Stories of their/Missionary Heroes and Martyrs/[b/w photograph]
/Profusely illustrated/John Ritchie, Publisher, Kilmarnock, Scotland./And through all Booksellers
n.d.
104pp (inc. 2pp intro), b/w frontis., photographic illus. throughout, pic. clo., 180x120mm. KP
Includes, John Williams, Voyage of the *Duff*, James Chalmers, &c.

8766 New and Revised edition, as above, but 'John Ritchie, Ltd; Publishers of Christian Literature. /and through all Booksellers', n.d.
Details as above, but with 16pp adv., KP

ROBSON, William

8767 JAMES CHALMERS/Missionary and Explorer/of Rarotonga and New Guinea/by/William Robson/ Kilmarnock, Scotland:/John Ritchie/Publisher of Christian Literature/and through all Booksellers
n.d. [first published 1887]
176pp, b/w frontis., & illus. throughout, clo., 180x120mm. KP

8768 JAMES CHALMERS/Missionary and Explorer/of Rarotonga and New Guinea/By/William Robson/new edition/London/S. W. Partridge & Co./8 & 9 Paternoster Row
n.d. [stamp on fly, Nov. 1902]

176pp & 28pp adv., portrait frontis., map & b/w drawings throughout, 8 f/p engravings, clo. with portrait in gilt of missionary, & vignette in black of him greeting natives, 185x120mm. KP
Last chapter written by Frank Broad.

8769 JAMES CHALMERS/Missionary and Explorer/of/Rarotonga and New Guinea/By/William Robson/New Edition/London/S. W. Partridge & Co. Ltd./Old Bailey n.d.
176pp (inc. 2pp preface), 1 f/p b/w map, 8 f/p b/w illus., b/w illus. in text, dec. clo., 185x120mm. KP
Other copies seen with minor variations, undated & with prize labels, 1914, 1947 &c. KP

8770 JAMES CHALMERS/Missionary and Explorer/of/Rarotonga and New Guinea/By/William Robson/of the London Missionary Society/Fourth edition. Fourteen thousand/London
/S. W. Partridge & Co./9 Paternoster Row
160pp, 2pp preface & 16pp adv., b/w frontis. & text illus., map, pic. clo., dec. e/p., 183x120mm. KP

8771 JAMES CHALMERS/OF NEW GUINEA/By/William Robson/Bright Biographies/[device]
/Pickering & Inglis/London Glasgow Edinburgh
n.d. [inscribed1943, this edition first pub. 1933]
191pp, & 2pp preface, 1p adv., portrait frontis. & 3 b/w plates, clo., 180x120mm. KP

ROGERS, R. W.
THE GOGODALAS. *See* Peoples of the Pacific

ROMAUNT, Christopher (ed.)
THE ISLAND HOME. *See* [Bowman, James F.]

ROOS, Ann
8772 MAN OF MOLOKAI/The Life of Father Damien/by Ann Roos/Illustrated by Raymond Lufkin
/J. B. Lippincott Company/Philadelphia Chicago New York/London
1943
254pp, part col. portrait frontis., b/w chapter headings, clo., pic. e/p, 204x138mm. SUA

ROSE, Lyndon Margaret
8773 Lyndon Rose/THE PARTING OF/THE MIST/[dec.]/The Jacaranda Press
Brisbane 1963
191pp, 3 f/p b/w illus., b/w chapter headings, illus. by Richard Ressom, clo., 210x135mm. KMM

8774 THE PARTING OF THE MIST, Brisbane [Jacaranda for] Children's Library Guild of Australia [1963]
Details as above.

8775 Lyndon Rose/TUNGI/OF THE BIG REEF/[drawing]/The Jacaranda Press
Brisbane 1964
102pp, 10 b/w drawings in text, dec. clo., 215x135mm. Illustrator not named. Background of this book is Samoa. KMM

ROSE, Ronald
8776 INOKE SAILS THE/SOUTH SEAS/by Ronald Rose/Collins, St. James's Place, London/1966
[46]pp, col. illus. throughout, dec. boards (clo. spine), 290x210mm. KMM

8777 INOKE SAILS THE/SOUTH SEAS/by Ronald Rose/Harcourt, Brace & World, Inc./New York
/Ronald Rose 1966, All rights reserved, First American edition/Printed in the Netherlands by Joh. Enschede en Zonen, Haarlem
Details as above. KP

ROSS, Betty
8778 TRUE/ADVENTURES/Great Explorers told me/Betty Ross/with 24 photographs/and 4 maps/[publisher's device]/Phoenix House/London 1959
144pp (inc. 4pp index), b/w frontis. & 14pp b/w photographic illus., b/w maps in text, clo., 205x125mm. NSL:M
Includes 'Thor Heyerdahl, He braved the Pacific on a Raft' (17pp).

Round the World
8779 ROUND THE WORLD/and/other Stories/containing/Round the World/The Prophet and the Lost City./The Ship and the Island/Illustrated/London:/Groombridge and Sons,/5, Paternoster Row.
n.d. [prize label 1877]
[148]pp, & 8 pp adv., b/w frontis. & 2 f/p engravings & small text engravings, dec. clo., 180x120mm. HBM
The third story tells of the mutiny on the *Bounty*. *See also* THE SHIP AND THE ISLAND

ROWE, John G.
8780 BLUEJACKET AND/CORSAIR/A Story of/Adventure in Southern Seas/By/John G. Rowe
/Author of/"The Boy Detective"/&c./London/The Epworth Press/J. Alfred Sharp
1932
190pp, b/w frontis. (sgd 'D.W.A.'), clo., 180x120mm. KP
Another copy seen as above, but entirely different front (?Leopold Mills). KP

ROY, Bernard
8781 Bernard Roy/DANS LE SILLAGE/DE LA PÉROUSE/[device]/La Technique du Livre/29 bis, rue du Moulin-Vert Paris 14
1946
95pp, unillus., dec. wrappers, 185x115mm. NSL:M

RUSSELL, W. Clark
8782 THE/EMIGRANT SHIP/by/W. Clark Russell/Author of "List, Ye Landsmen", "The Romance of a/Transport", "The Wreck of the 'Grosvenor'",/"An Ocean Tragedy", "The Frozen/Pirate", etc. etc./New York/The Cassell Publishing Co./104 and 106 Fourth Avenue 1893
348pp, unillus., clo., 180x120mm. Grant
This adventure story reads like a boys' book.

8783 JACK'S COURTSHIP/A Sailor's Yarn of Love and Shipwreck/by/W. Clark Russell/Author of "The Wreck of the Grosvenor"/"A Sea Queen" etc./London/Sampson Low, Marston & Co., Ltd.
n.d.
474pp, 4pp adv., unillus., boards, 180x120mm. Grant
An adventure story for older boys telling of the shipwreck of a liner on which Jack & his girl friend are bound for Australia.

RUST, Doris
8784 A MELON FOR ROBERT/and other South Sea Tales/by/Doris Rust/illustrated by/Cecil Elgee/[drawing]/Faber and Faber Ltd./24 Russell Square/London
1963
62pp, b/w drawings throughout, clo., 210x150mm. CLRC

8785 Doris Rust/TALES FROM THE PACIFIC/illustrated by/Cecil Elgee/Faber and Faber/24 Russell Square/London
1965
63pp, 7 f/p b/w illus., 5 b/w drawings, clo., 205x150mm. KMM
Adapted from ancient Maori myths, & legends of Fiji & Samoa

RUTLEY, C. Bernard

8786 EXPLOSION ISLAND/By/C. Bernard Rutley/Author of "The Golden Mirage" "The Box of St Bidolph's" &c./with frontispiece by John de Walton/Blackie & Son Limited/London and Glasgow
n.d. [first published 1983]
224pp, b/w frontis., clo., 184x120mm. KP
• Rpt in the 'Tower Library', as above, n.d. with col. d/w by J. de Walton. KP

8787 The A. L. Bright Story Readers, No. 631/THE AIR STOWAWAYS/By/C. Bernard Rutley/Melbourne/Macmillan & Co. Limited/1941
63pp, 1p questions, 4 f/p b/w illus., wrappers, 185x135mm. ANL
Action takes place on a Pacific Island near New Guinea.

8788 THE CAVE OF/WINDS/by/C. Bernard Rutley/[device]/Frederick Warne and Co. Ltd./London and New York
n.d. [1946?]
256pp, col. frontis. only, clo., 183x118mm. ANL
Adventure story on a fantasy island in the Southern Ocean

ST. JOHNSTON, Alfred

8789 CHARLIE ASGARDE/The Story of a Friendship/By/Alfred St. Johnston/London/Macmillan and Co/1884
viii, 265pp. & 2pp adv., b/w frontis. & 11 f/p b/w illus., by Hugh Thomson, clo. with frontis. illus. blocked in black on front cover, 182x120mm. SFU
Adventures of two young survivors of a shipwreck on one of the 'Feejee' islands

ST. LEGER, Hugh

8790 SKELETON REEF/or/THE ADVENTURES OF JACK ROLLOCK/by Hugh St. Leger/Author of/"Sou'wester and Sword", "Hallowe'en Ahoy",/"An Ocean Outlaw", etc./Frontispiece by Lancelot Speed/London/S. W. Partridge & Co./8 and 9 Paternoster Row
n.d. [1897]
320pp, 32pp adv., b/w frontis., pic. clo., 190x125mm. Grant
Adventure story set in the S.W. Pacific

8791 JACK ROLLOCK'S/ADVENTURES/or/Skeleton Reef/By/ Hugh St. Leger/Author of "Sou'wester and Sword" "Hallowe'em Ahoy"/"An Ocean Outlaw",etc./Illustrated by Ernest Prater/London /S. W. Partridge & Co. Ltd./Old Bailey
n.d. [1913?]
320pp, b/w frontis. & 4 b/w plates, pic. clo., 185x125mm. KMM
Hallowe'en Ahoy, Lost on the Crozet islands is set in the Indian Ocean, and not included here.

SALTER-MATHIESON, N.

8792 LITTLE/CHIEF/MISCHIEF/From/Tales of the Menehune/Written by/N. Salter-Mathieson/Illustrated by/Chuck Gruen/An Astor Book. Ivan Obolensky, Inc. New York 1962
45pp, col. dec. t.p., col. illus. throughout, clo., dec. e/p, 250x170mm. NSL:M
Picture book story about an imaginary Pacific people

SANDERLIN, George

8793 George Sanderlin/FIRST/AROUND/THE/WORLD/A Journal of Magellan's Voyage/Hamish Hamilton
London 1966
188pp (inc. 4pp chronological table & 4pp index), 1p author's note, 1p acknowledgements, 4pp introduction, b/w frontis. & 12 b/w illus., maps, pic. clo., 200x150mm. KMM
Illustrations from contemporary sources

SARGENT, George E.

8794 THE/YOUNG PRINCE,/By G. E. Sargent/[engraving with caption]/London:/Groombridge and Sons,/Paternoster Row
n.d. [185-?]
32pp, engraved frontis. (presumably wrappers, but bound with a number of others in a volume of *Buds and Blossoms*),127x88mm. CLRC
The story of Prince Lee Boo told in chap-book form.
See also Australian section for other titles by this author

SAVILLE, Ray

8795 THE BOY SCOUT/CRUSOES/The Chums of Fellsgate in Search of/Treasure/2d./Coloured illustration/Boys'/Pocket/Library/No. 7
Aldine Publishing Company, London, n.d.
64pp, unillus., 1 f/p b/w map, col. pic. wrappers (with adv. verso front cover, verso/recto back cover), cover title, 155x105mm. RM
Story set in South Pacific; author's name given with title above Chapter 1

SCHOLES, S. E.

8796 FIJI/AND/THE FRIENDLY ISLES:/Sketches of/Their Scenery and People./By/S. E. Scholes/Author of 'Peeps into the Far North'./London: T. Woolmer, 2 Castle Street, City-Road, E.C.;/and 66, Paternoster Row, E.C.
n.d. [1882]
96pp, 2pp preface, engraved frontis. & 14 engravings, pic. clo., 150x120mm. NSL:M

8797 Another copy as above, but London: / C. H. Kelly, 2, Castle-Street, City-Road, E.C.;/and 66, Paternoster Row, E.C.
Details as above but 146x108mm. CLRC

SCHUBERT, E.

8798 THE PITCAIRN/ISLAND STORY/by/E. Schubert/In association with the South Pacific Commission Literature Bureau/Longmans
Melbourne 1961
36pp, b/w frontis. & 4pp b/w photographic illus., double-spread map, wrappers, 185x120mm. HBM
Bonito series

SCHUBERT, Ernest (ed.)

Peoples of the Pacific series, format example:

8799 Peoples/of the/Pacific/Ernest Schubert Editor—Rod Fowler Artist/[col. illus.]/1. THE TROBRIAND/ISLANDERS/[device]
Longmans Green, Croydon, Victoria 1964
16pp, part-col. illus. & maps, pic. wrappers, cover title, 180x116mm. KMM
Others in series:

8800 2 THE MOTUANS, 1964, rpt 1967, 1969. KMM
8801 3 THE TOLAIS, 1964. BBC
8802 4 THE SEPIK RIVER PEOPLE, 1964. BBC
8803 5 THE GOGODALAS, 1964. BBC
8804 6 THE CHIMBUS, 1964, rpt 1967, 1969. BBC
8805 7 THE MEKEOS, 1965. BBC
8806 8 THE KARKAR ISLANDERS, 1965. BBC
8807 9 THE ABELAN PEOPLE, 1966, rpt 1969. BBC
8808 10 THE BUKAS, n.d. KMM
8809 11 THE SAMOANS, 1966. BBC
8810 12 THE MAORIS OF NEW ZEALAND, 1966. BBC
8811 13 THE PEOPLE OF NEW CALEDONIA, 1967. KP
8812 14 THE PEOPLE OF FIJI, n.d. KP
8813 15 THE GILBERT ISLANDERS, 1967. KP
8814 16 THE COOK ISLANDERS, 1967. KP

8815 17 THE HULI PEOPLE, 1967. KP
8816 18 THE OROKAIVA, 1967. KP

SCOTT, Winifred
8817 GIRL CASTAWAYS/Winifred Scott/[device]/ London/Pickering & Inglis Ltd.
first pub. 1954, rpt 1956
95pp, col. frontis., clo., 132x124mm. KP

SERRAILLIER, Ian
8818 THEY/RACED FOR TREASURE/A Novel for Children/by/Ian Serrailier/[device]/Jonathan Cape/ Thirty Bedford Square/London
first published Oct. 1946, rpt 1947, 1949, 1955, 1962
237pp., b/w map, b/w drawings by C. Walter Hodges, clo., 196x135mm. KP
8819 THE BALLAD OF/KON-TIKI/and other Verses/ Ian Serraillier/[vignette]/Illustrated by Severin/ Geoffrey Cumberlege/Oxford University Press/1952
72pp, 14 b/w illus., pic. boards, 195x120mm. Grant

SETON, Walter
8820 CHALMERS/OF/NEW GUINEA/The Martyr Missionary/By/Walter Seton/with portrait and illustrations/Published at 57 and 59 Ludgate Hill, E.C./By the Sunday School Union, London
n.d. [first pub. 1909]
122pp, & 14pp adv., portrait frontis. & 13 b/w illus., dec. clo., 180x120mm. KP
'Splendid Lives' series
Second edition as above but 8pp adv., n.d. [prize label 1916] KP
Third edition as above n.d. [prize label 1921]. SUA
Fourth edition as above, n.d. KP

SHAW, Frank H.
8821 TREASURE TROVE OF/THE SOUTHERN SEAS/ By/Captain Frank H. Shaw/Author of "Keepers of the Sea", "When Beatty/kept the Seas", etc. etc./With Four Coloured Plates/Cassell and Company, Ltd./ London, New York, Toronto and Melbourne
1919
312pp, col. frontis. & 3 f/p col. illus., pic. clo., 205x140mm. KMM
Boys' adventure story, part of the action taking place in the South Seas

SHERIDAN, R. J.
8822 THE BRAVE JOURNEY/OF PHILIP CARTERET/ by/R. J. Sheridan/Illustrated by/Nancy Parker/In Association with the South Pacific Commission Literature Bureau/Longmans
Melbourne 1961
23pp, 8 b/w illus., wrappers, 185x120mm. Bonito series. BBC

The Ship and the Island
8823 THE/SHIP AND THE ISLAND/[engraving 'The attack at Tofa' page 13]/London:/Groombridge and Sons, Paternoster Row.
n.d.
48pp, engraved frontis. & 3 engravings in text, 137x94mm. CLRC
Bound in with 'Stories for Summer Days and Winter Nights', Second series, first volume. Also published in 'Round the World'.

SHORT, H. J. [Harold James Edward, Rev.]
8824 Missionary stories, printed by the Raukele Press, Papua [single page leaflets only]
Souvenir/THE/ CHILDRENS'/SHIP/By the Rev. Harold Short/of the/London Missionary Society. /Printed by/The "Papuan Courier" Ltd./Port Moresby, Papua
n.d. [copy acquired 1935]
8pp, unillus., wrappers, cover title, 194x105mm. NSL:M
An account of missionary ships in the Pacific & the Sunday schools' collection for the *John Williams*, &c.

8825 WHY VAITA VANISHED/A Story of Brown Children on/Mountains, Rivers and Sea/By /H. J. E. Short/(of Papua)/The London Missionary Society/42 Broadway, Westminister/London, S.W.1
1940
144pp, b/w frontis. & 10 f/p b/w illus. (sgd. 'J.C.'), pic. clo., 185x124mm. ANL

SINKER, William
8826 BY REEF AND SHOAL/Being an account of a Voyage amongst/the islands in the south-/western Pacific/by/William Sinker, R.N.R./Commander of the Melanesian Mission's steamer "Southern Cross"/Published under the Direction of the Tract Committee/for the Melanesian Mission/Third Edition/ Society for Promoting Christian Knowledge,/London: Northumberland Avenue, E.C.;/43 Queen Victoria Street, E.C./Brighton:129, North Street,/New York: Edwin S. Gorham/1905
64pp, & 2pp preface, b/w frontis. & 6 b/w drawings, clo., 165x11cmm. KP
• Rpt 1906 [9th thousand] as above, first published 1904. KP

SMALL, Alexander
8827 CHALMERS OF/NEW GUINEA/By/Alexander Small, R.L./Hodder and Stoughton/Limited London
n.d. [1923]
ix, 176pp, b/w photographic frontis. & 3 b/w plates by Leo Bates, clo., 185x120mm. KP
Master Missionary series

SMITH, R. A.
8828 ANNIE AND MITAL OF GOROKA/R. A. Smith Thomas Nelson (Australia) Ltd., Melbourne, 1965
16pp, b/w photographic illus. on every page, sepia/ white pic. wrappers, 152x184mm. KP

SONDERGAARD, Arensa
8829 MY FIRST/GEOGRAPHY/OF THE/PACIFIC/by Arensa Sondergaard/Illustrations by Cornelis/Little, Brown and Company/Boston 1944
56pp, dec. col. t.p., col. & b/w illus. throughout, clo., dec. e/p, 320x245mm. NSL:M

SOMERVILLE, Ena
8830 OUR FRIENDS THE/PAPUANS/Compiled by/Ena Somerville/Australian Board of Missions/14 Spring Street, Sydney./1945
186pp, 1p adv., sepia & white illus. (photographs & drawings), pic. boards, clo. spine, 217x134mm. KP

SOUTHON, Arthur E.
See Mathews, Basil & Southon, Arthur

SPERRY, Armstrong
8831 CALL IT/COURAGE/Armstrong Sperry/ Illustrations by the author/The Macmillan Company /New York 1945
95pp, 10 f/p illus. & other drawings in text, dec. clo., dec e/p., 230x172mm. WRT
Illus. printed in blue ink.

8832 THE/BOY WHO/WAS AFRAID/by/Armstrong/ Sperry/illustrated by the author/John Lane the Bodley Head—London
First published in Great Britain 1942 [copyright in USA under the title *Call it Courage*, first published in USA 1940]

95pp, b/w illus. throughout, clo., dec. e/p, 205x155mm. NSL:M
• Rpt 1950 as above. KMM
• Rpt 1957 as above, but 186x120mm. KP

8833 THE/BOY WHO/WAS AFRAID/by/Armstrong Sperry/illustrated by the author /[device]/William Heinemann Ltd./ Melbourne London Toronto
1952 (first New Windmill series edition)
95pp., illus., throughout, clo., 186x120mm. KP
• Rpt in this edition 1955, 1957, 1959, 1960, 1961, 1964 (twice), 1965, 1966, 1968 (twice). KP

8834 THE/BOY WHO/WAS AFRAID/by/Armstrong/ Sperry/Illustrated by the Author/William Heinemann Ltd./Melbourne: London: Toronto: 1956
First published in Australia 1956
95pp, 10 f/p b/w illus. & b/w drawings in text, clo., 185x125mm. The New Windmill series. Grant

8835 THE BOY/WHO WAS AFRAID/Armstrong Sperry/Newbery Award Winner/Illustrated by/ William Stobbs/[device]/The Bodley Head/London
First published in Great Britain 1942; 6th imp. 1957; This edition 1963
92pp, 7 f/p b/w illus. & b/w drawings in text, clo., 195x130mm. BBC
• Rpt 1968 as above, but 'London Sydney Toronto'. KMM

8836 Armstrong Sperry/THE BOY/WHO WAS/ AFRAID/Illustrated by William Stobbs/Knight Books Leicester England 1967
95pp, b/w illus., pic. wrappers, 177x110mm. CLRC

8837 Armstrong Sperry/THE BOY WHO/WAS AFRAID/Illustrated by Graham Chiswell/[device] /Heinemann
Heinemann Essar Series, adapted & designed to help children with difficulties in learning to read English, 1972
34pp & 1p illus., 4pp adv., 7 f/p b/w illus. & text illus., col. pic. wrappers, 190x125mm. KP

8838 LOST/LAGOON/A Pacific Adventure/by/ Armstrong Sperry/with illustrations/by the author/ London/John Lane The Bodley Head
First published in Great Britain 1943; rpt 1950, 1953
160pp (inc. 1p preface), b/w drawings in text throughout, clo., 205x160mm. BBC

8839 BAMBOO/THE GRASS TREE/ Story and Pictures [illus. printed in red] by/Armstrong Sperry /Copyright 1942, The Macmillan Company/The Macmillan Company/New York 1944
47pp, t.p. in red and black, illus. printed throughout in red, clo., pic. e/p, 210x157mm. KP

8840 BAMBOO/THE GRASS TREE/Story and Pictures by/Armstrong Sperry/[drawing]/Printed in Great Britain by Lowe and Brydone Printers Ltd./for/John Lane, the Bodley Head/1946
Details as above. KP

8841 COCONUT/THE WONDER TREE/Story & Pictures by/Armstrong Sperry/Printed in Great Britain by Lowe and Brydone Printers Ltd, for/John Lane, The Bodley Head, 1946
[46]pp, drawings throughout printed in blue, pic. boards, pic. e/p, 204x154mm. CLRC
Uniform with *Bamboo*

8842 HULL-DOWN/FOR ACTION/[drawing]/written and illustrated by/Armstrong Sperry/The Bodley Head London
1948
159pp, b/w chapter headings, clo., col. pic. e/p, 210x164mm. KP

8843 THE RAIN FOREST/written and illustrated by/ Armstrong Sperry/The Bodley Head London
1950
191pp, b/w frontis. & b/w illus. throughout, part-col. pic. e/p, clo., 200x130mm. KP
New Guinea Setting

Swedish edition

8844 REGNSKOGEN, Stockholm 1949, 212pp, illus., printed wrappers. Unseen

8845 PACIFIC/ISLANDS/SPEAKING/The Macmillan Company/New York, 1955
viii, 220pp, b/w drawings & maps, dec. map e/p., clo., 208x135mm. KMM

STABLES, William Gordon

8846 THE ISLAND OF GOLD/A Sailor's Yarn/Gordon Stables, M.D./Author of "Every Inch a Sailor", "As we Sweep/Through the Deep", etc. etc./Thomas Nelson and Sons, Ltd./London Edinburgh New York/Toronto, and Paris
First published 1898; this edition n.d. [194-?]
344pp, 10pp adv., b/w frontis. & 3 f/p b/w illus. by Allan Stewart, clo., 185x120mm. KMM
Setting of part of the story is a volcanic isle in the South Pacific.

8847 KIDNAPPED BY CANNIBALS/By/Gordon Stables, M.D., C.M./Surgeon, Royal Navy./Author of "The Naval Cadet" [& 2 other titles]/with six illustrations by J. Finnemore, R.B.A./Blackie and Son Limited/ London Glasgow and Dublin 1900
287pp & 32pp adv., b/w frontis. & 5 b/w plates, pic. clo. with gilt dec. design & lettering, 185x120mm. KP
Story of blackbirding in the Pacific

8848 KIDNAPPED/BY CANNIBALS/By/Dr. Gordon Stables, R.N./Author of "The Naval Cadet" "For Life and Liberty"/"Courage, True Hearts" &c./Blackie and Son Limited/London Glasgow and Bombay
n.d. [inscribed 1925]
287pp, col. frontis. only, clo., 170x110mm. CLRC

8849 YOUNG PEGGY McQUEEN/by Gordon Stables, M.D., R.N./Author of "A Fight for Freedom", "Honour/not Honours". etc. etc./Four Coloured/ Illustrations./Collins'/Clear-type Press/ London and Glasgow
n.d.
152pp, col. frontis. & 3 col. plates by Warwick Goble, pic. clo., 185 x120mm. KP
Action takes place partly in South Seas.

STEER, Gary

8850 LIFE IN PAPUA AND NEW GUINEA/Gary Steer/ Assisted by John Davis
Viking Press, Dee Why NSW [1970]
61pp, b/w photographic illus. on t.p. & throughout, e/p maps, pic. boards, 210x137mm. CLRC

STEVENSON, P. M.

8851 JAMES CHALMERS/by/P. M. Stevenson/[device]/ Oliphants Ltd/London Edinburgh
First published 1953; rpt 1954, 1957
95pp, col. frontis. sgd 'Jarvis', dec. clo., 180x120mm. KMM

STONE, William S.

8852 TERI TARO/FROM BORA BORA/William S. Stone/with illustrations by Armstrong Sperry /New York. A. Knopf./1940
134pp, b/w frontis. & dec. t.p., 8 f/p part-col. illus. & b/w chapter headings, dec. clo., pic. e/p, 220x152mm. SUA

8853 THUNDER/ISLAND/by William S. Stone/New York Alfred A. Knopf—Illustrated by Mordvinoff
First edition 1942

195pp (inc. 3pp glossary), extended col. t.p., 8 f/p col. illus. & b/w drawings, clo., 205x150mm. NSL:M
Story about native life on a South Pacific island

8854 THUNDER ISLAND/By/William S. Stone/[drawing]/London/George G. Harrap & Co. Ltd./Sydney Toronto Bombay Stockholm
1946
140pp (inc. 2pp glossary), 7 f/p col. illus. & 1 f/p b/w illus., b/w drawings in text, clo., 200x135mm. PAI

Stories of our People series
Format example:

8855 Stories of our People/UNDER THE MANGO/TREE/Dinah Frank/Melbourne/Oxford University Press/London Wellington New York
first published 1958; rpt 1960, 1964
16pp, b/w photographic illus., dec. wrappers, 185x122mm. SUA

Others in series:

8856 MOLU OF MENDI, by Elizabeth Daniel, 1961. KMM

8857 OROKAIVA by Mackenzie Jovopa, 1967. CLRC

Stories of the Sea in Former Days

8858 STORIES/OF/THE SEA IN FORMER DAYS/Narratives of Wreck and Rescue./Illustrated./[device]/London/Blackie & Son, Limited, 50 Old Bailey, E.C./Glasgow and Dublin
n.d. [1900?]
256pp, 32pp adv., b/w frontis. & 3 f/p b/w illus. sgd 'Frank Feller', pic. clo., 180x120mm. HBM
Contents include: 'Life and Melancholy Fate of La Pérouse' (30pp); 'The "Antelope" of Pelew Islands' (25pp); 'The Mutiny of the "Bounty"'(34pp).

8859 STORIES OF THE SEA/IN FORMER DAYS/Narratives of Wreck and Rescue/With Frontispiece in Colour/Blackie & Son Limited/London and Glasgow
n.d. [194-?]
256pp, col. frontis. only, clo., 185x120mm. HBM
Details as in previous edition

The Story of Aleck, Or Pitcairn's Island
See [FISKE, Nathan Welley]

The Story of the Pacific
See [TRACY, Mona]

The Story of Two New Guinea Boys

8860 Missionary/Stories No. 17/THE/STORY/OF/TWO/NEW/GUINEA/BOYS/[photographic illus. of 'Peter']
London n.d. [191-?]
16pp, & adv. inside back wrapper, b/w photographic illus. throughout, stiff wrappers, cover title, 184x126mm. ANL

STRANG, Herbert' [pseud., George Herbert Ely & Charles James L'Estrange]

8861 PALM TREE ISLAND/Being the narrative of Harry Brent/showing how he in the company with/William Bobbin of Limehouse was/left on an island in the Southern/Hemisphere, and the accidents and/adventures that sprang therefrom,/the whole faithfully set forth/By/Herbert Strang/With illustrations by/Archibald Webb and Alan Wright/London/Henry Frowde/Hodder and Stoughton/1910
443pp, 4pp adv., col. frontis & 7 f/p col. illus., 29 pen & ink sketches, by Alan Wright, 1 f/p b/w map (folding), pic. clo., 190x135mm. RM
New edition as above 1915 but no adv., 187x125mm. RM

8862 New edition as above n.d. but: Humphrey Milford/Oxford University Press/London Edinburgh Glasgow/Toronto Melbourne, Cape Town Bombay
As above col frontis. & 4 b/w plates, 29 b/w drawings, double-page map, clo. with col. onlay, 185x120mm. KP

8863 PALM TREE/ISLAND/Herbert Strang/Humphrey Milford/Oxford/University/Press/London
• Rpt 1923
443pp, col. frontis. & some small b/w drawings, dec. t.p., clo., 185x120mm. CLRC
Another copy 1923 as above but different col. plate used as frontis. RM

8864 PALM TREE ISLAND/A Story of Perseverance/under difficulties/By/Herbert Streng/[device printed in green]/Humphrey Milford/Oxford University Press/London, Edinburgh, Glasgow/Toronto, Melbourne, Cape Town, Bombay
1934 b/w drawings in text, clo., 195x130mm. KMM

8865 ROUND/THE/WORLD/IN/SEVEN/DAYS/Herbert/Strang/London/Henry Frowde/Hodder & Stoughton
Copyright by the G. H. Doran Company in the United States of America, n.d. [copy inscribed 1914]
295pp, col. frontis. only, clo., 165x110mm. KMM
Contents include: 'Australian Hospitality' (18pp), a story based on a shipwreck in the Solomons & the search party which came out by air from England.

8866 THE BLUE RAIDER/A Tale of Adventure/In the Southern Seas/By/Herbert Strang/Illustrated by/C. E. Brock/Humphrey Milford/Oxford University Press/London, Edinburgh, Glasgow/Toronto, Melbourne, Capetown, Bombay/1920
First printed 1919, rpt 1920
288pp, col. frontis., 4 f/p b/w illus. & 14 smaller b/w illus., pic. clo., 190x125mm. RM

8867 THE BLUE/RAIDER/Herbert/Strang/Humphrey Milford/Oxford University Press/London
First published 1919; rpt 1920, 1925, 1929
288pp, dec. t.p., col. frontis., b/w drawings in text throughout, clo., 185x120mm. KMM
Adventure story set in New Guinea

8868 LORD/OF THE/SEAS/Herbert/Strang/Humphrey/Milford/Oxford/University/Press London
First published 1909, rpt 1918
vi, 238pp, unillus. clo., dec. e/p, 184x120mm. NSL:M
First edition published with col. frontis. & 4 col. plates by C. Fleming Williams

'STRANG, Mrs Herbert'

8869 THE GIRL CRUSOES/A Story of the South Seas/By/Mrs Herbert Strang/Illustrated in Colour by N. Tenison/London/Henry Frowde/Hodder and Stoughton/1912
312pp, 24pp adv., col. frontis. & 5 f/p col. illus., pic. clo., 190x125mm. RM
Another copy as above, but n.d. WRT

8870 THE/GIRL/CRUSOES/Mrs. Herbert/Strang/Humphrey Milford/Oxford University/Press/London 1921
312pp, col. frontis., dec. e/p, clo., 185x120mm. Grant
Many reprints, inc. 1918 (The Clarion Series) KP; The Girls New Library ed. 1921, KP; 1925, KP; 1939 with some minor variations, KP

8871 THE GIRL/CRUSOES/by/Mrs. Herbert Strang/[device]/London: Humphrey Milford/Oxford University Press 1935
312pp, col. frontis., pic. clo., 185x120mm. KP

8872 THE GIRL CRUSOES/A Story of the South Seas/By/Mrs. Herbert Strang/Illustrated in colour by N. Tenison/Humphrey Milford/Oxford University Press/

London, Edinburgh, Glasgow/Toronto, Melbourne, Cape Town, Bombay
n.d. [prize 1936]
312pp, col. frontis. & 3 f/p col. illus., clo. (with col. medallion on front cover), 185x120mm. KMM
See also Australian section for other titles by this author

STRATEMEYER, Edward
8873 Dave Porter Series/DAVE PORTER IN THE SOUTH SEAS/or/The Strange Cruise of the Stormy Petrel/By/Edward Stratemeyer/Author of[5 lines]/ Illustrated by I. B. Hazelton/[device] /Boston/Lothrop, Lee & Shepard Co.
1906
286pp, & 2pp adv. & 2pp preface, b/w frontis. & 7 b/w plates, pic. clo, 185x120mm. NSL:M

SUGGS, Robert C.
8874 LORDS OF THE/BLUE PACIFIC/by Robert C. Suggs/Drawings by Catherine Scholtz/Maps by Leonard Darwin/[Device]/Cassell—London
New York Graphic Society 1962; First published in Great Britain 1963
151pp (inc. 7pp prologue), b/w drawings & maps in text, clo., 195x315mm. BBC
Written to give young people a true picture of Polynesian pre-history.

SULLIVAN, Violet M.
8875 CHOCOLATE/PICCANNINIES [*sic*]/By/Violet M. Sullivan/of the/South Sea Evangelical Mission/Author of/"Bible Teaching made Easy"/S. John Bacon/ (Marshall, Morgan & Scott Ltd.)/Southern Cross Chambers/317 Collins St., Melbourne
n.d. [1944]
31pp, 12 b/w photographic illus., wrappers, 205x140mm. ANL
Cover bears subtitle: 'Children's Stories from the Solomon Islands'.

SURREY, Lionel
8876 LOST IN THE PACIFIC/By/Lionel Surrey/ Illustrated by/Ellis Silas/[device]/George G. Harrap & Co. Ltd./London Toronto Bombay Sydney
First pub. July 1934, rpt 1937
255pp, col. frontis., 4 f/p b/w plates & 1 map, dec. clo., 198 x 135mm. KP

SWEENEY, T. V.
8877 Tales from Papua and New Guinea/THE CRANES/Collected by T. V. Sweeney/Illustrated by J. Hall/[drawing]/Thomas Nelson (Australia) Ltd/ Melbourne/Sydney
1967
32pp (last blank), b/w & part col. illus., pic. wrappers, 190x170mm. CLRC

Others in uniform series:
8878 THE CROCODILE.
8879 THE DWARF OF BUA
8880 HIGH TIDE AND LOW TIDE all CLRC

SYME, Ronald
8881 THEY CAME TO/AN ISLAND/By/Ronald Syme/ Illustrated by/William Stobbs/London/Hodder and Stoughton
1955
157pp (inc. 2pp author's foreword), col. frontis., b/w chapter headings, tailpieces, clo., 185x120mm. KMM
Boys' adventure story set on South Pacific island

8882 THE/AMATEUR COMPANY/By/Ronald Syme/ [drawing]/Hodder & Stoughton
London 1957
158pp, 5 f/p b/w illus. by William Stobbs, clo., 214x135mm. CLRC

8883 THE GREAT CANOE/Ronald Syme/London/ Hodder and Stoughton
1957
160pp, b/w frontis. & 7 f/p b/w illus. by Wm Stobbs, clo., 225x137mm. SUA

8884 THE GREAT CANOE/Ronald Syme/Illustrated by William Stobbs/Brockhampton Press/Leicester [England]
n.d. [1962]
185pp (inc. 2pp author's foreword), b/w frontis. & 7 f/p b/w illus., clo., 185x120mm. KMM

8885 THE/MOUNTAINY MEN/by/Ronald Syme/ Illustrated by/Richard Payne/London/Hodder and Stoughton
1961
159pp, 9 f/p b/w illus., clo., 215x135mm. CLRC
Set on the Pacific island of Tuku Tuku

8886 NOSE-CAP/ASTRAY/By/Ronald Syme/Illustrated by Roger Payne/London/Hodder and Stoughton
1962
144pp, b/w frontis. & 7 f/p b/w illus., 1 col. illus., clo., 215x140mm. KMM
Adventure story set in Polynesia

8887 THE SAVING OF THE/FAIR EAST WIND/Ronald Syme/with illustrations by/A. R.Whitear/London: J. M. Dent & Sons Ltd.
1967
176pp (inc. 2 pp foreword), b/w drawings in text, clo., 185x125mm. ANL
Adventures of a 15-year-old boy left with only a steward on an abandoned cargo ship foundering in the South Pacific, and of the attempts made to salvage the vessel

TACEY, Charles
8888 MUTINY ON THE/ BOUNTY/By/Charles A. Tacey/[device—Epic readers]/Edited for/School use by/Charles Dealtry/Frederick Warne and Co., Ltd./ London and New York
1939
48pp, b/w frontis. & 7 f/p b/w illus. (? by Robert Gibbings), pic. wrappers, 180x122mm. ANL

'TALATALA' [pseud. Rev. Arthur Wesley Amos]
8889 TOA/The Life Story of/JOELI BULU/Told by Toa, his Club/Published by the/Young Methodist Missionary League/134a Little Collins Street,/ Melbourne/All Profits to Overseas Missions
n.d. [1949]
12pp, b/w portrait frontis., wrappers, 220x140mm. ANL
Foreword by Jocelyn McCallum, Children's Librarian, Prahran, Victoria
On front cover: 'by Talatala (Rev. A. W. Amos)'
Story of a Tongan Christian who became a missionary in Fiji

TESSADRI, Elena S.
8890 LEGENDS/FROM THE/SOUTH SEAS/by Elena S. Tessadri/Rylee Ltd/Pageant Book
1969, London
83pp, col. illus. throughout, boards, pic. e/p, 320x227mm. KP
Illustrated by Colombi Studio Brambilla, Milan, translated by Susan Cannat

THOMPSON, Harlan
8891 OUTCAST/Stallion of Hawaii/by/Harlan

Thompson/Doubleday & Company Inc./Garden City, New York/1957
191pp, unillus., clo., 205x135mm. SUA

THOMPSON, R. Wardlaw
8892 MY TRIP IN THE/"JOHN WILLIAMS'/By/R. Wardlaw Thompson/With sixty-two illustrations /London/London Missionary Society/14 Blomfield Street, E.C./1900
208pp & 4pp adv., b/w photographic frontis., b/w illus. throughout, pic. clo., title in gold, 210x165mm. KP
Another copy as above, but title printed in black. KP

THOMSON, D. P.
8893 GOODWIN SANDS TO/SOLOMON ISLANDS/ More Stories of the Ships of Christ/Maritime Missionary Adventure/throughout the World/D. P. Thomson, M.A./with 12 Black and White Illustrations/ by Robert Marshall/[device]/London/Pickering & Inglis Ltd./1948
95 pp (inc. 2pp preface & 2pp bibliography), b/w illus., clo., 182x120mm. ANL

Three Boy Crusoes
8894 THREE/BOY CRUSOES;/or,/Perseverance & Indolence./Beautifully Illustrated./Complete./ London:/Harkaway House, 6, West Harding Street,/ Fetter Lane, Fleet Street, E.C.,/and all booksellers
n.d.
106pp (inc. part page adv.), b/w frontis. & 9 f/p b/w illus., col. pic. wrappers, 245x175mm. RM
Edwin J. Brett's 'Boys of England' edition
Experiences of three boys in various South Pacific islands, & their eventual rescue & arrival in British Samoa
Another copy, as above, but with 8 pp adv., & slight variation in colour & wording of part of front wrapper. RM

THUM, Marcella
8895 ANNE OF THE/SANDWICH ISLANDS/Marcella Thum/Dodd, Mead & Company/New York
1967
244pp & 1p biography of author, unillus, clo., 202x135mm. NSL:M
The story of the chief's Children's School 1839-50 established by American missionaries

TITCOMB, Margaret
8896 Winner of Dodd, Mead Librarian and Teacher Prize Competition/THE VOYAGE OF/THE FLYING BIRD/ By Margaret Titcomb/[drawing]/ Illustrated by Joseph Feher/Dodd, Mead & Company/New York
1963
236pp, 2pp biographies of author & artist, 8 f/p b/w illus. & numerous text drawings, clo., 227x150mm. SUA
Exploration of the Pacific by the Polynesians before the coming of the Europeans to the Pacific

To the Town
8897 The Pacific Series/TO THE TOWN/Standard Two/ Melbourne/Oxford University Press/London Wellington New York
1966
79pp & 2pp word list, col. illus. throughout by Barbara Taylor, pic. wrappers, 215x135mm. CLRC
Reader written for Papua New Guineans

TRACY, Mona
8898 THE /STORY OF THE PACIFIC/Revised and enlarged edition/[drawing]/Whitcombe and Tombs Limited/Auckland Christchurch Dunedin Wellington/ Melbourne Sydney London/Simpkin, Marshall Limited, London E.C.
n.d. [1932?]
153pp (inc 5pp chronology, 3pp index), 12 b/w plates, pic. clo., 195x120mm. SUA
See McLaren 633, also item 8669

TRÉGANCE, Louis
See Crocker, Rev. Henry

TUFUI, Jean
8899 Tales of the South Pacific/DOLFINI/Written by Jean Tufui/Illustrated by Murray Zanoni/[drawing]/ Paul Hamlyn/London Sydney New York Toronto
1971
[26]pp, col. illus. throughout, pic. boards, pic. e/p, 310x230mm. KMM
8900 Ngaaha Talanoa'o e Pasifiki Tongs/TOLOFINI/ Fa'u'e Jean Tufui/Fai e Ta Fakatata 'e Murray Zanoni/ Paul Hamlyn/London Sydney New York Toronto
1971
Translation of *Tales of the South Pacific.* Details as above, CLRC

TURNER, Frederick
8901 MARTIN/OF MANIKULU/A Story of Adventure in the/South Seas/By/Frederick Turner/S. W. Partridge & Co./4, 5 & 6 Soho Square, London, W.I
1937
247pp, 2pp adv., col. frontis. only, clo., 185x120mm. Boys' Empire series. KMM

Uncle Haro's/New Guinea Stories
See Endeavour Books

Uncle John's Adventures and Travels
8902 UNCLE JOHN'S/ADVENTURES/AND/ TRAVELS/with illustrations/[device]/Frederick Warne and Co.,/Bedford Street, Strand.
n.d. [inscribed 1885]
120pp &4 pp adv., col. frontis., b/w f/p map of New Guinea, dec. clo., 163x110mm. CLRC
Contents include 'Uncle John's Shipwreck' (22pp) 'on a whaling voyage to the South Seas', the castaways being picked up by an English merchant vessel bound from Sydney for India.
8903 UNCLE JOHN'S/ADVENTURES AND/TRAVELS/ with illustrations/[device]/Frederick Warne and Co.,/Bedford Street, Strand/New York: Scribner Walford and Armstrong.
n.d. [inscribed 188?]
120pp & 4pp adv., col. frontis., b/w f/p map of New Guinea, dec. clo., 155x110mm. KMM

Uncle Pippin's Tales For Boys
8904 UNCLE PIPPIN'S/TALES/FOR/BOYS./"Persevere and Prosper"./London:/Thomas Brooks, Publisher./8, Baker Street, Portman Square./Cumming, Dublin; Menzies, Edinburgh./1845
316pp, engraved frontis, numerous b/w engravings in text, clo., 165x100mm. Grant
The Pacific Ocean & Juan Fernandez Island are mentioned in one story only.

VAN LOON. Hendrik Willem
8905 Hendrik Willem Van Loon/THE STORY OF THE/ PACIFIC/[drawing]/George G. Harrap & Co.Ltd./ London Toronto Bombay Sydney
First published Nov. 1940, rpt Nov. 1940
315pp (inc. 3pp index), b/w illus. throughout, clo., pic. e/p, 214x136mm. KP
There were many reprints of this prize-winning book.

VENIS, Winifred
8906 CHILDREN/OF THE/SOLOMON/ISLANDS/

Story by/ Winifred Venis/Drawings by/Dorothy Dunphy/Published by the Overseas Missions Department of the/Methodist Church of New Zealand, 378 Queen Street Auckland
1963
40pp, 9 f/p b/w illus., & text drawings, dec. wrappers, 217x132mm. WRT

VERNE, Jules
See Australian section for this author's books

VERNON, R.
8907 JAMES CALVERT;/or, From Dark to Dawn in Fiji/ By R. Vernon/[device]/London/S.W.Partridge & Co./ 9 Paternoster Row
n.d. [1890]
160pp, & 16pp adv., b/w frontis. & numerous engravings, pic. clo., dec. e/p, 195x124mm. KP

VISIAK, E. H.
8908 THE HAUNTED ISLAND./Being the History of an Adventure to an Island in/the Remote South Sea. Of a Wizard there. Of his/Pirate Gang; His Treasure; His combustible; His/Skeleton Antic Lad. Of his Wisdom; Of his Poesy;/His Barbarous Cruelty; His Mighty Power. Of a/Volcano on the Island. And of the Ghostly Terror/[vignette]/By E. H. Visiak/Illustrated by Jack Matthew/Peter Lunn/London 1946
164pp, part-col. frontis. & 7 f/p part-col. illus., some b/w chapter headings, clo., 175x120mm. CLRC

VOORHOEVE, R.
8909 R. Voorhoeve/JÄGARNA FRAN/TAMIFLODEN/ Stockholm/Ählèn & Söners Förlag
1937
121pp, 6 f/p b/w illus., pic. boards, clo. backstrip, 170x120mm. RM
Story set entirely in Papua & New Guinea. Swedish trans. by Petrus Bogners of *Tili Auw Desawai.*

8910 R. Voorhoeve/MEDICINMANNENS/HAMND/ Stockholm/Ählèn & Söners Förlag/
1937
164pp (inc. 1p foreword), 8 f/p b/w illus., pic. boards, clo. backstrip, 170x120mm. RM
Story set in Papua & New Guinea. Swedish trans. of Dutch book *De Jagers Van De Tami River.* Illus Fred Ockerse.

WALKDEN-BROWN, Bruce
8911 CHILDREN OF/PAPUA/A true story of the children of the/coast and islands of South-East Papua/ By/Bruce Walkden-Brown/Drawings by/ Beverley Dunphy/Published by/The Committee for Promotion and Literature/Head Office:/Methodist Overseas Missions/139/Castlereagh Street/Sydney
1959
62pp (inc. 1p dedication, 1p map), b/w drawings throughout, dec. wrappers, 220x140mm. KP
• Rpt as above 1964. WRT

WARD, R. G.
8912 How People Live in/ISLANDS OF THE SOUTH PACIFIC/R. Gerard Ward M.A. Lecturer in Geography/University of Auckland/[device]/The Educational Supply Association Ltd. London
1961
104pp (inc. 3pp index & 1p bibliography), maps, diagrams & b/w photographic illus., throughout, dec. clo., 210x160mm. NSL:M
Produced as a school textbook

WARREN, Jane S.
8913 THE MORNING STAR;/History of/The Children's Missionary Vessel,/and of the/Marquesan and Micronesian Missions./By/Mrs Jane S. Warren/ Published by the/American Tract Society,/28 Cornhill, Boston
1860
309pp (inc. 2pp preface) & 6pp adv., frontis. (copy of 'Certificate of stock in the Morning Star' with date 1856), text engravings & maps, clo. with embossed design & ship in full sail in gilt on front cover, 166x104mm. SUA
bound together with
'Account of Henry Obookiah and the building of the Mission ship and its voyages'

WATERHOUSE, Joseph
8914 VAH-TA-AH,/THE FEEJEEAN PRINCESS:/with occasional/allusions to Feejeean customs;/and/ illustrations of Feejeean life./By the/Rev. Joseph Waterhouse./[quotation]/London:/Hamilton, Adams, and Co.:/sold by John Mason, 66, Paternoster-Row./ MDCCCLVII
164pp (inc. 1p dedication, 2pp preface, 14pp introduction by Rev. Elijah Hoole & 18pp appendices), 14pp adv., col. portrait frontis. of Vah-Ta-ah by Baxter, dec. clo., 140x90mm. KMM
Missionary tale, 'published for the benefit of the young' of the life, conversion, & death of the Fijian princess
8915 Another copy, as above, but bound together with:
8916 THE/NATIVE MINISTER;/A Biographical Sketch/ of/Abraham Navukitu,/of Fiji./By the Rev. Joseph Waterhouse./[quotation]/London:/Published by J. Mason,14/City-Road,/sold at 66 Paternoster Row/283
n.d., printed by H. T. & J. Roche, 25, Hoxton Square, London (author's preface dated Sept. 14th 1857 from 'Lythville, Rewa, Fiji')
34pp, & 1p. verse sgd 'Sutton'. KMM
Title on front cover reads:'The/Feejeean Princess/A Memoir/of/Vah-ta/ah/[in dec. scroll]/The Native Minister'
Preface to 'The Native Minister' reads: 'During the time of awaiting the "John Wesley"' which is to call at Rewa for the writer and his family, to convey them to the Australian colonies, the following sketch of a lamented colleague has been written; and it is sent forth with the hope that it will interest the children connected with the Wesleyan Methodist Sunday schools generally, and those of Australasia in particular'.
8917 VA-TA-AH,/THE FEEJEEAN PRINCESS etc.
Second edition 1857
Details as in first edition. KMM
8918 Third edition 1857
Details as in first edition, but 12pp adv., 145x90mm. RM

WATSON, Anthony
8919 ISLAND OF MYSTERY/by/Anthony Watson/ Publishers Distributing Co./Sydney
n.d. [library copy acquired 1950]
178pp, b/w frontis. by C. W. Barnes, clo., 175x120mm. ANL
Adventure story set on Bougainville Island

8920 ISLAND TREASURE HUNT/by/Anthony Watson/ Publishers Distributing Co./Sydney
n.d. [copyright 1950]
205pp, b/w frontis. by C. W. Barnes, clo., 180x120mm. ANL
Adventure story set in the Pacific

8921 THE SECRET OF THE/ISLAND/By/Anthony Watson/Publishers Distributing Co./Sydney
n.d. [1951]

212pp, b/w frontis. by C. W. Barnes, clo., 180x115mm. ANL
Adventure story set in the Pacific

WATTS, H. J.
THE BUKAS. *See* Peoples of the Pacific

WEBB, CHRISTOPHER
8922 Christopher Webb/QUEST OF THE *OTTER*/ Illustrated by William Stobbs/Macdonald: London 1965
Copyright 1963 Funk & Wagnalls Inc.
156pp, b/w extended frontis, 2 b/w illus., clo., 197x132mm. WRT
Story of a mid-nineteenth-century whaling voyage in the South Seas

8923 THE/ANN AND HOPE/MUTINY/Christopher Webb/Illustrated by William Stobbs/Macdonald: London
first published in Great Britain 1967
168pp, b/w extended frontis. & 2 b/w drawings, clo., 198x130mm. WRT
Set in Fiji

WEDGWOOD, Camilla Hildegarde
8924 THE HIRI/by/Camilla Wedgwood/Illustrated by/ Pamela Lindsay/In Association with the South Pacific/ Commission Literature Bureau/Longmans Green and Co./London Melbourne New York
Melbourne 1955
24pp (inc. 1p glossary), b/w illus. & map, wrappers, 180x115mm. Bonito series. NSL:M

WELCH, Clifford A.
8925 OUR NEIGHBOURS/OF THE PACIFIC/By Clifford A. Welch/Illustrated by George Armstrong/ Beckley-Cardy Company Chicago
1955
192pp (inc. 4pp index & 1p acknowledgements), dec. t.p., b/w frontis. & b/w photographic illus. throughout, b/w drawings in text & 9 maps, dec. clo., dec. e/p, 200x140mm. NSL:M

WEST, Rev, Thomas
8926 HAFOKA:/A Missionary Tale/of the/South Sea Islands./By the/Rev. Thomas West/London:/ Published at the Wesleyan Mission House/Bishopsgate Street Within/And sold by John Mason, 66 Paternoster Row/1860
117pp, 2pp adv., col. engraved frontis., clo., 140x90mm. VSL
Simple tale of missionary enterprise

WESTERMAN, Percy F.
8927 THE NAMELESS/ISLAND/A Story of some Modern/Robinson Crusoes/By/Percy F. Westerman/ Author of "The Young Cavalier", etc./London/C. Arthur Pearson Ltd./Henrietta Street/1915
252pp, 4pp adv., b/w frontis. & 7 f/p b/w illus. by E. S. Hodgson, pic. clo., 195x130mm. RM
Boys' adventure story on an island in the South Pacific between New Zealand & Panama
Second impression 1920, as above. KMM

8928 A CADET OF THE/MERCANTILE MARINE/By/ Percy F. Westerman/Author of "The Wireless Officer", "Clipped Wings" &c./Illustrated by W. Edward Wigfull/Blackie & Son Limited/London and Glasgow
n.d. [1923]
256pp, b/w frontis. & 3 f/p b/w illus., clo., 285x120mm. KMM
Like many of the books of writers of boys' adventure stories this book barely qualifies for inclusion, being an account of a voyage from England to Sydney round the Horn & return via Cape Town. Three chapters only deal with the Pacific or Australian regions.

8929 THE TREASURE OF/THE "SAN PHILIPO"/By/ Percy F. Westerman/Author of/"A Lad of Grit" etc. etc./London/"The Boy's Own Paper" Office/4 Bouverie Street, E.C.
n.d.
248pp, 8pp adv., b/w frontis. only, clo., 185x115mm. KMM
Search for treasure in the Truk Islands, in the Caroline Group

8930 KING OF KILBA/By/Percy F. Westerman/Author of "Nameless Island". "Winning his Wings"./"Mystery Ship", etc. etc./Ward, Lock & Co.,Limited/London and Melbourne/1926'
256pp, b/w frontis. & 3 b/w plates, by W. Edward Wigfull, dec. clo., 184x126mm. KP
• Rpt as above, n.d., col. frontis. only, patterned clo., KP
• Rpt as above n.d. [school prize 1949] , b/w frontis. only, boards, clo. spine. KP

8931 Percy F. Westerman/KING OF/KILBA/Ward, Lock/and Company Limited/London, Melbourne & Cape Town
1959
183pp, b/w frontis. & 5 f/p b/w illus. (on text paper), boards, 184x120mm. KMM

8932 IN THE CLUTCHES/OF THE DYAKS/By/Percy F. Westerman/Author of/"The Secret Battleplane", "To the Fore with the/Tanks", "The Airship Golden Hind", "The Mystery/of Stockmere School", etc. etc./[device]/ S. W. Partridge & Co./4, 5& 6 Soho Square, W.1
First published 1927, & frequently reprinted; this impression 1933
127pp, col. frontis. only, pic. clo., 180x120mm. CLRC

8933 MYSTERY ISLAND/By/Percy F. Westerman/ Illustrated by Savile Lumley/[device]/Humphrey Milford/Oxford University Press/London
1928
189pp, col. frontis. & 4 b/w plates, clo., 180x117mm. NSL:M
Story of survivors of a shipwrecked whaler on a nearby island being rescued and taken to Fiji.

WESTLAKE, W. E.
8934 THE 'RED STAR':/ or,/Fred and Bert in the South Seas./By/W. E. Westlake./Copyright 1895 by George Munro's Sons./New York:/George Munro's Sons, Publishers./17 to 27 Vandewater Street.
100pp & 2 pp adv., unillus., wrappers, 183x120mm. KP
Adv. for The Boys' Dashaway series on front cover

WESTPHAL, Fritz
8935 TONGA TABU/The True Story of/an English naval cadet in the South Seas/by Fritz Westphal Methuen & Co. Ltd, London 1962 [first published by Herald-Verlag Brück K.G., Stuttgart, 1958]
229pp (inc. 1p foreword), extended dec. t.p., b/w frontis. & 6 f/p b/w illus. by Nikolaus Plump, 1 b/w map, clo., 200x130mm. BBC
Translated by Ursula Lehrburger & Oliver Colburn
Based on William Mariner's recollections as given in Dr John Martin's *An Account of the Natives of the Tonga Islands* (London 1817)

WHISHAW, Fred
8936 MYSTERY ISLAND/A Tale of the Pacific/by/Fred Whishaw/Author of "Harold the Norseman", "Sons of Freedom",/"Lost Sir Brian", "Boris the Bear Hunter",

etc./Illustrations by R. H. Smith/London: John F. Shaw and Co. Ltd./3, Pilgrim Street, Ludgate Hill,/E.C.
n.d. [inscribed 1920]
316pp, col. frontis., pic. clo. (with col. onlay pasted on front cover), 200x135mm. RM
Adventure story of lost treasure, etc., set in Pacific with brief visit to Sydney

WICKLOE, Peter
8937 SOUTH SEAS OF PERIL/By/Peter Wickloe/ Author of "The Yellow Ship" "Casper Clinton—China Coaster", etc./With frontispiece by Jack Matthew/ Blackie & Son Limited/London and Glasgow
n.d. [1945?]
208pp, b/w frontis. only, clo., 185x120mm. KMM
Historical adventure story set in the Pacific

[PAUL, Adrien]
WILLIS THE PILOT/A Sequel to the Swiss Family Robinson
Like *The Swiss Family Robinson* of wider interest than those included in this bibliography.

WOOD, J. Claverdon
8938 UNDER THE/SERPENT'S FANG/A Tale of Adventure in New/Guinea in the last Century/By/J. Claverdon Wood/Author of "When Nicholson Kept the Border," "The Stolen/Grand Lama", "Jeffrey of the White Wolf Trail", etc./London/"The Boy's Own Paper" Office/4, Bouverie Street, E.C.4./Printed in Great Britain
n.d. [1920?]
264pp, part-col. t.p., col. frontis. & 8 f/p b/w illus. by Stanley L. Wood, pic. clo., 200x130mm. KMM

The Wonder of the Waves
8939 THE WONDER OF THE WAVES
Aldine Publishing Company Limited, London, n.d.
A story set in the Pacific off the coast of Chile, & not qualifying for inclusion in this bibliography. RM

WRIGHT, E. Forsyth
8940 GOD'S OTHER CHILDREN/FAFOA, WHO DOES WHAT SHE LIKES/Missionary Leaflet/Price Twopence No. 6 South Seas
United Society for Christian Literature (Lutterworth Press) London
n.d.
Leaflet of 3 folding pages printed on both sides with col. illus. on cover, cover title, and illus. repeated in b/w inside, 185x120mm. KP

WRIGHT, Rob
THE PEOPLE OF FIJI. *See* Peoples of the Pacific

WYATT, H. G.
8941 THE TALE OF THE BOUNTY/Retold by H. G. Wyatt/[Part col. illus. extended from frontis.] /Hong Kong/Oxford University Press/Kuala Lumpur Singapore Jakarta Tokyo
1972
105pp & 1p adv., 3 col. illus., b/w & part-col. illus. throughout, by Wai-Kit Johnny Ng, pic. wrappers, map e/p, 216x140mm. CLRC
Oxford Progressive English Readers Grade 1; based on Sir John Barrow's 'The Mutiny of the Bounty'

WYBORN, Arthur
8942 WONDERFUL/NEW GUINEA/By/Arthur Wyborn/Whitcombe and Tombs Ltd.
1952
86pp, b/w frontis. & 10 b/w illus., pic. wrappers, 183x123mm. ANL
See McLaren 573

8943 Arthur Wyborn/THE MYSTERIOUS/VALLEYS/ [device]/Frederick Warne and Co. Ltd./London and New York
1952
255pp, col. frontis. only by Aub. Stapleton, clo., 184x120mm. KP
Warne's Crown Library for Boys; set in New Guinea

WYSS, Johann David
THE SWISS FAMILY ROBINSON
First published in German 1812 and 1813, and in English 1814 this famous work cannot be considered as part of Australian or Pacific children's literature even though the pastor and his family has set out for Otaheite. Like several other classic tales it belongs to the broader sphere of world literature for children.

YOUNG, Clarence
8944 THE MOTOR BOYS/ON THE PACIFIC/or/The Young Derelict Hunters/By/Clarence Young /Author of/"The Racer Boys Series" and "The Jack Ranger Series"/Illustrated/New York /Cupples and Leon Company
1909
244pp, b/w frontis. (sgd 'Nuttall'), pic. clo., 188x125mm. KMM

Title Index

Title Index

Illustrator Index

Illustrator Index